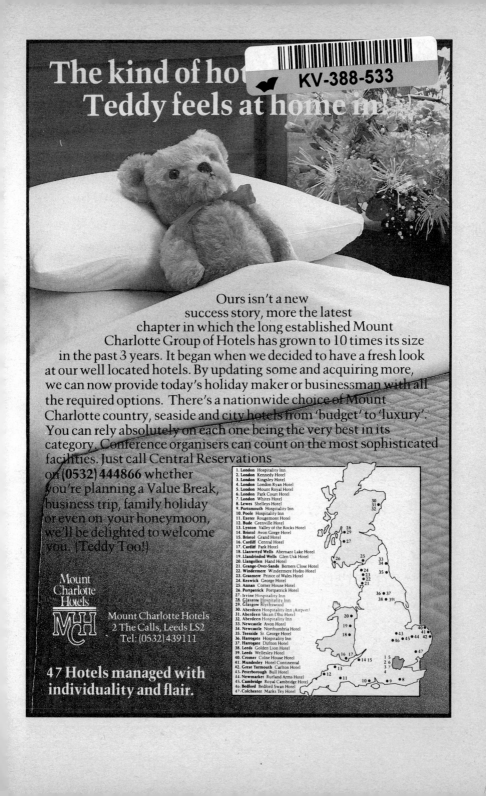

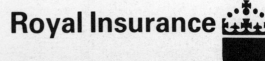

The Royal Automobile Club

HANDBOOK AND HOTEL GUIDE 1985

First published in 1904

Published for

The Royal Automobile Club

by RAC Motoring Services Limited
Croydon

Contents

*Every care has been taken to ensure the accuracy of the
particulars given in this Handbook, but no liability
can be accepted by the RAC for any error or omission.
   Copyright © The Royal Automobile Club 1985
   ISBN 0 86211 048 3
   Printed and bound in Great Britain by William Clowes
   Limited, Beccles and London*

*Cover picture: Belgrave Hotel, Torquay
Photograph: Blantern & Davies*

The Royal Automobile Club

The Royal Automobile Club

Membership of the RAC

The Royal Automobile Club founded in 1897

Patron
Her Majesty The Queen

President
H.R.H. Prince Michael of Kent

Vice-Presidents
Sir Carl D. Aarvold, O.B.E., T.D.
His Grace The Duke of Richmond and Gordon, D.L.
The Rt. Hon. Lord Nugent of Guildford, P.C.
Sidney L. Lesser

Chairman
Jeffrey Rose

Stewards
Sir Carl D. Aarvold, O.B.E., T.D.
S/Ldr. John Crampton, D.F.C., A.F.C., A.F.R.Ae.S.
The Rt. Hon. The Earl of Halsbury, F.R.S.
His Grace The Duke of Richmond and Gordon, D.L.
Jeffrey Rose
J. G. S. Sears
The Rt. Hon. Lord Shawcross of Friston, G.B.E., P.C., Q.C.
Sir Norman Skelhorn, K.B.E., Q.C.

Organisation

The Automobile Proprietary Ltd.
The Board (The Committee of the RAC)
(Chairman) Jeffrey Rose
(Directors) A. P. de Boer, C.B.E.
M. A. Bone, J.P., F.C.I.S., F.I.B.
Eric Charles, O.B.E., F.I.M.I., F.B.I.M. *(Chief Executive—RAC Motoring Services)*
R. M. Cooke
S/Ldr John Crampton, D.F.C., A.F.C., A.F.R.Ae.S.
G. B. Flewitt
A. D. Gill
J. S. F. Hogg, M.I.M.I.
T. G. Keown
M. J. Limb, F.B.I.M., M.I.M.I. *(General Secretary)*
B. K. McGivern
H. G. Mutkin, M.A., F.C.A.
J. G. S. Sears
F. L. Shaw, J.P., B. Com., F.C.A., F.C.M.A., F.C.I.S. *(Director-Finance)*
J. A. Williams, T.D., T.Eng. (C.E.I), F.I.M.I., F.R.S.A., J.P.
F. L. Shaw, J.P., B. Com., F.C.A., F.C.M.A., F.C.I.S. *(Company Secretary)*

RAC Motoring Services Ltd.
(Chairman) Jeffrey Rose
(Chief Executive) Eric Charles, O.B.E., F.I.M.I., F.B.I.M.
(Directors) M. A. Bone, J.P., F.C.I.S., F.I.B.
G. B. Flewitt
J. S. F. Hogg, M.I.M.I.
M. J. Limb, F.B.I.M., M.I.M.I.
Hugh M. Palin, M.B.E., T.D.
F. L. Shaw, J.P., B. Com., F.C.A., F.C.M.A., F.C.I.S.
J. A. Williams, T.D., T.Eng. (C.E.I.), F.I.M.I., F.R.S.A., J.P.

Divisional Directors
(Director-Accounting Services) N. V. C. Jackaman, M.A., I.C.M.A.
(Director-Administration) David Faull, F.C.A.
(Director-Computer Services) P. E. Davie, B.A., M.B.C.S.
(Director-Legal Services) David K. Johnston
(Director-Marketing and Sales) John C. F. Davies
(Director-Member Services) N. H. Austin, F.I.M.I.
(Director-Public Affairs) A. J. A. Lee
(Chief Engineer) P. J. Lovell, C.Eng., F.I.Mech.E., F.B.I.M.

Regional Directors
J. Styles, F.Inst.S.M.M. *(Birmingham)*
A. B. Andrews *(Bristol)*
W. J. F. Proud *(Croydon)*
K. P. Sheridan *(Glasgow)*
J. S. Mason *(Stockport)*

RAC Insurance Ltd
(Chairman) Jeffrey Rose
(Chief Executive) Eric Charles, O.B.E., F.I.M.I., F.B.I.M.
(Directors) M. A. Bone, J.P., F.C.I.S., F.I.B.
G. B. Flewitt
J. S. F. Hogg, M.I.M.I.
M. J. Limb, F.B.I.M., M.I.M.I.
Hugh M. Palin, M.B.E., T.D.
F. L. Shaw, J.P., B.Com., F.C.A., F.C.M.A., F.C.I.S.
J. A. Williams, T.D., T.Eng. (C.E.I.), F.I.M.I., F.R.S.A., J.P.

RAC Insurance Brokers Ltd
(Chairman) Jeffrey Rose
(Managing Director) R. A. C. White
J. M. Bozman
E. Charles
R. V. Craig
W. Foley
G. Harding
V. Royle
F. L. Shaw
J. Taylor
J. A. Williams

RAC British Motor Sports Council
(President) H.R.H. Prince Michael of Kent
(Chairman) P. G. Cooper, A.M.I.M.I.
(Vice-Chairman) K. H. Douglas, F.Inst.M., M.S.A.E., A.I.Mech.E.
(Vice-Chairman) R. M. Southcombe
P. Ashcroft
M. H. Bowler
D. Cardell
H. Dewar
G. B. Flewitt
K. W. Giles, F.R.C.S.
G. Hall
N. Jesty
P. F. Jowitt
The Hon. Gerald Lascelles
R. C. McKinney
J. G. Malcolm
Jeffrey Rose
M. J. Stephens
W. S. Troughear
J. Webb

Associate Committee

The RAC Associate Committee is a consultative Committee and is concerned with the oversight of the affairs of the Associate Section of the Club.

The RAC Associate Committee is composed of the Chairman and three Vice-Chairmen of the RAC ex-officio, six other members appointed by the Committee of the RAC, five members elected annually by the General Council by ballot from nominations previously made by the Associated Clubs, each Club being entitled to make one nomination, and five members elected annually by the General Council by ballot from the 20 members representing individual associate members on the Council.

(Chairman) G. B. Flewitt
Jeffrey Rose *(Chairman, RAC)*
A. D. Bellingham
Mrs. M. J. Benson, O.B.E., J.P.
R. Bensted-Smith, B.A.
C. C. Bigwood
M. A. Bone, J.P., F.C.I.S., F.I.B.
A. J. Burton, M.A., F.R.G.S.
B. D. Draycott
P. A. Gordon Forster
P. Hewitt
J. S. F. Hogg, M.I.M.I.
H. B. Olive
Hugh M. Palin, M.B.E., T.D.
Major A. Pownall, R.A.(Retd)
Mrs. Elwyn Reed
F. A. Snowden
J. A. Williams, T.D., T.Eng. (C.E.I.), F.I.M.I., F.R.S.A., J.P.

Legal Committee

(Chairman) C. W. Short
R. G. W. Bray
P. Geen
G. W. Stevenson

Public Policy Committee

(Chairman) J. A. Williams, T.D., T.Eng. (C.E.I.), F.I.M.I., F.R.S.A., J.P.
Dr. C. Ashley, C.B.E., B.Sc., Ph.D., C.Eng., F.I.Mech.E.
A. P. de Boer, C.B.E.
Peter Fry, M.P.
Sir John Garlick, K.C.B.
Arthur D. Gill
Roy Hughes, M.P.
P. B. Kavanagh, C.B.E., Q.P.M.
James Moorhouse, M.E.P.
Hugh M. Palin, M.B.E., T.D.
Jeffrey Rose
Allen Smith, O.B.E., B.Sc.(Eng.), F.Eng., F.I.C.E., F.I.Mun.E., F.I.H.E., M.I.W.M.
Prof. T. E. H. Williams, C.B.E., M.Sc., Ph.D., C.Eng., F.I.C.E., P.P.Inst.H.E., M.I.Struct.E., M.C.I.T.

Technical Committee

(Chairman) Dr. C. Ashley, B.Sc., Ph.D., C.Eng., F.I.Mech.E.
David Collins
Sir Kenneth Corley, Kt.
S/Ldr John Crampton, D.F.C., A.F.C., A.F.R.Ae.S.
F. E. Denmee, C.Eng., M.I.Mech.E.
John Furness, C.B., C.Eng., F.I.Mech.E.
Dr. B. C. Lindley, C.B.E., B.Sc.(Eng.), Ph.D., C.Eng., F.I.Mech.E., F.I.E.E., F.Inst.P.

Dr. G. M. Mackay, D.Sc., Ph.D., B.Sc., F.M.(M.I.T.), C.Eng., M.I.Mech.E., M.I.C.E.
Professor R. H. Macmillan, M.A., C.Eng., F.I.Mech.E.
C. A. A. D. Mitchell, B.Sc.(Eng.), C.Eng., M.I.Mech.E.
John A. Oldfield, M.Sc.
J. Owen, C.Eng., F.I.E.E., F.I.E.R.E.
J. A. Williams, T.D., T.Eng.(C.E.I.), F.I.M.I., F.R.S.A., J.P.

Motor Cycle Committee

(Chairman) Hugh M. Palin, M.B.E., T.D.
R. Bryan
N. E. Goss
H. Louis
Brig. D. B. Rendell, C.B.E., M.C.
G. Saunders
P. R. T. Sheen
K. E. Shierson
G. Wilson

RAC Pall Mall Clubhouse Ltd

(Chairman) B. K. McGivern
(Directors) J. A. Fingleton
F. R. Gordon
T. G. Keown
Jeffrey Rose
P. F. D. Trimingham
(Chief Executive) J. N. Cranfield
(Club Secretary) Capt. J. C. Judge, R.N. (Retd), C.Eng., M.I.Mech.E., F.B.I.M.

RAC Woodcote Park Clubhouse Ltd

(Chairman) B. K. McGivern
(Directors) M. A. Bone, J.P., F.C.I.S., F.I.B.
A. J. Clarke
R. M. Cooke
J. S. F. Hogg, M.I.M.I.
Jeffrey Rose
E. Whiteley
K. Wolstenholme
(Chief Executive) J. N. Cranfield
(Club Secretary) Capt. J. C. Judge, R.N. (Retd), C.Eng., M.I.Mech.E., F.B.I.M.

General Council of the RAC

The General Council is established to provide opportunities for the discussion of motoring matters of national importance to owners and users of motor cars and motor cycles, such as legislation, taxation, upkeep of roads, and to enable the RAC to obtain the views of motorists generally on all such matters.

It is composed of members of the Committee of the RAC, representatives appointed by each of the Clubs associated with the RAC, not more than 20 individual representative Associate Members, representatives of the Auto-Cycle Union and such other bodies and on such terms and conditions as the RAC may determine from time to time.

Each Club associated with the RAC is entitled to appoint a representative or representatives to the General Council on the following basis: one representative for each Club with 250 or less Associate Members; two representatives where its Associate Members exceed 250 but not 500; three representatives where its Associate Members exceed 500 but not 1,000; and four representatives where its Associate Members exceed 1,000; provided however

that only one representative from each Club shall be entitled to vote at meetings.

Individual Associate Members are represented on the General Council by not more than 20 Associate Members and they shall be selected from a panel of not less than 30 persons who have displayed interest and zeal in the welfare of private motorists. The 20 Members will be selected by the Committee of the RAC.

The Chairman of the RAC shall be the Chairman of the General Council. The General Council shall meet at least once a year, and the quorum for its meetings shall be ten. The General Council elects annually up to ten Associate Members to sit on the RAC Associate Committee, and it also elects annually the Stewards of the RAC under the rules of the RAC.

Clubhouses

Pall Mall Clubhouse,
89–91 Pall Mall,
London, SW1Y 5HS.
T 01-930 2345. *Telex:* 8813741.

Country Club,
RAC Woodcote Park,
Epsom, Surrey, KT18 7EW.
T Ashtead 76311.

The Pall Mall Clubhouse and the Country Club at Woodcote Park

New Full Members are welcome at Europe's finest Club in Pall Mall and at the Country Club at Woodcote Park, near Epsom, Surrey.

The facilities at Pall Mall include a magnificent Great Gallery Restaurant with superb cuisine and one of the best wine-cellars in London; a Members' Dining Room with good food at reasonable prices; and "pub lunches" in the new Long Bar. The Cocktail Bar is a popular meeting place, especially for lady guests.

The Sports Area includes four squash courts, solarium, a fully-equipped gymnasium, Turkish and sauna baths and one of the most splendid heated swimming pools in the world. There are also facilities for billiards and snooker, cards and chess. Five banqueting and reception rooms, including the delightful Mountbatten Room, are available for dinners,

lunches, seminars, press conferences, etc.

There are 90 bedrooms, a barber's shop, Post Office and two libraries—general and motoring.

The Country Club has two full-length golf courses, tennis courts and an open-air heated swimming pool. There is a large restaurant, bedroom accommodation and ample parking space. The Country Club too is available for receptions, seminars, weddings and private functions.

Membership of the clubhouses is available to individuals and companies and full details of both can be obtained from the membership office at 89, Pall Mall, London SW1Y 5HS. T 01–930 2345. Telex: 8813741. Direct booking for squash courts T 01–839 7246. Direct booking for Great Gallery Restaurant T 01–930 3265.

Motor sport

RAC British Motor Sports Council

The RAC Motor Sports Association Ltd
RAC/ACU British Motor Sports Training Trust
31 Belgrave Square,
London, SW1X 8QH.
T 01-235 8601. *Telex:* 27203.

Auto-Cycle Union
Millbuck House, Corporation Street, Rugby,
Warwickshire. CV21 2DN. T Rugby (0788) 70332.
Telex: 311156 ACU G.

Speedway Control Board Ltd
31 Belgrave Square, London, SW1X 8QJ. T 01-235 8601. *Telex:* 27203.

RAC Paris Office

RAC Office,
8 Place Vendôme,
75001 Paris.
T 260.62.12. *Telex:* 230723.

Divisions, Directors, Departments and Services

HEAD OFFICE
RAC House,
Lansdowne Road,
Croydon, CR9 2JA.
Telephone: 01-686 2525. Telex: 21418.

RAC Motoring Services Ltd

Chief Executive
Executive Secretariat and
Port Office Administration

Member Services
Director
Home and Overseas
Touring Services
Hotels
Member Relations
Radio Communications
Recovery
Road Services

Administration
Director
Communications
Membership
Office Services
Personnel
Property Services
Purchasing Services
Training

Computer Services
Director

Finance Division
Director—Accounting Services
Financial Accounts
Financial Information

Legal
Director
Accident Claims Recovery Services
Free Legal Representation Scheme
General Legal Enquiries

Marketing & Sales
Director
Design and Exhibitions
Marketing Operations
Market Research
Publications

LONDON
49 Pall Mall, London, SW1Y 5JG.
Telephone: 01-839 7050. Telex: 24974.
Public Affairs
Director
Press & Public Relations Information
Membership & Touring Reception

BIRMINGHAM
61a Maypole Lane, Maypole,
Birmingham, B14 5JX. Telephone: 021-430 4460.
Technical and Transport
Chief Engineer
Technical Services
Transport Service

RAC INSURANCE BROKERS Ltd
Chairman
Managing Director

LONDON OFFICE
RAC House,
Lansdowne Road,
Croydon, CR9 2JA.
Telephone: 01-686 2525. Telex: 21418.

ADMINISTRATIVE OFFICES
Hermitage Road, Hitchin,
Herts, SG5 1DH.
Telephone: 0462 57151.

Beaumont House, Beaumont Street,
Darlington, Durham, DL1 5RW.
Telephone: 0325 460721.

Area and Other Offices

Belfast, BT1 4JR
(Ulster Office)
RAC House
79 Chichester Street
T (General) Belfast (0232) 240261
(Rescue Service only) Belfast (0232) 223333
Telex: 74524

Birmingham, B14 5UH
(Midland Counties Office)
1059 Alcester Road South, Maypole
T (General) 021-430 8585
(Rescue Service only) 021-430 3232
Telex: 337471

Birmingham, B2 4XJ
(City Centre Office)
57 North Court,
Birmingham Shopping Centre
T 021-430 8585

Bournemouth, BH2 5QW
(Southern Counties Office)
9 Poole Road
T (General) Bournemouth (0202) 765328
(Rescue Service only) Bournemouth (0202) 766697
Telex: 41162

Brighton, BN1 2DW
23 Churchill Square
T Brighton (0273) 509253

Bristol, BS8 1PE
(South Western Counties Office)
4–6 Whiteladies Road
T (General) Bristol (0272) 732201
(Rescue Service only) Bristol (0272) 739311
Telex: 44137

Cardiff, CF2 1YR
(South Wales Office)
202 Newport Road
T (General) Cardiff (0222) 490959
(Rescue Service only) Cardiff (0222) 493030
Telex: 498247

Croydon, CR9 2JH
(Southern Home Counties Office)
P.O. Box 8, Marco Polo House,
3–5 Lansdowne Road
T (General) 01-686 2314
(Rescue Service only) 01-681 3611
Telex: 21418

Edinburgh, EH1 2BQ
(Scottish Eastern Counties Office)
17 Rutland Square
T 031-229 3555
Telex: 72136

Exeter, EX4 6RD
188 Sidwell Street
T Exeter (0392) 58333

Glasgow, G3 8NZ
(Scottish Western Counties Office)
RAC House, 200 Finnieston Street,
T (General) 041-248 4444
(Rescue Service only) 041-248 5474
Telex: 777801

Gloucester, GL1 1RP
Kings Square
T (General) Gloucester (0452) 20460
(Rescue Service only) Gloucester (0452) 502011

Hanley, ST1 4HL
2 Broad Street
T Stoke-on-Trent (0782) 266783

Leeds, LS2 7QL
(Yorkshire Office)
34 Regent Street
T (General) Leeds (0532) 436091
(Rescue Service only) Leeds (0532) 448556
Telex: 55145

Liverpool, L2 7NY
(Merseyside and North Wales Office)
Queen's Building, James Street
T (General) 051-227 3421
(Rescue Service only) 051-236 2521
Telex: 629282
This Office may move during 1985

London, SW1Y 5JG
49 Pall Mall
T 01-839 7050
Telex: 24974

Newcastle upon Tyne, NE2 1UB
(Northern Counties Office)
2 Granville Road, Jesmond Road
T (General) Newcastle (0632) 815714
(Rescue Service only) Newcastle (0632) 814271
Telex: 53122

Norwich, NR2 1RS
(Eastern Counties Office)
Norvic House, Chapel Field Road
T Norwich (0603) 28255
Telex: 97321

Nottingham, NG7 6NY
(North Midland Counties Office)
21 Gregory Boulevard
T (General) Nottingham (0602) 623331
(Rescue Service only) Nottingham (0602) 626200
Telex: 37513

Oxford, OX2 7DN
(South Midland Counties Office)
226 Banbury Road
T (General) Oxford (0865) 53443
(Rescue Service only) Oxford (0865) 53333
Telex: 83150

Plymouth, PL1 2SZ
(Western Counties Office)
RAC House, 15–17 Union Street
T (General) Plymouth (0752) 669301
(Rescue Service only) Plymouth (0752) 21411
Telex: 45544

Sheffield, S1 4PP
39 Hereford Street
T (General) Sheffield (0742) 737944
(Rescue Service only) Sheffield (0742) 25882

Stockport, SK1 1DS
(North Western Counties Office)
65–81 St Petersgate
T (General) 061-477 6500
(Rescue Service only) 061-477 7000
Telex: 667411

Watford, WD2 4AH
(Northern Home Counties Office)
130 St Albans Road
T (General) Watford (0923) 33543
(Rescue Service only) Watford (0923) 33555
Telex: 21576

Port Offices in the United Kingdom and the Channel Islands

The Port Offices listed below offer the full range of RAC services to members. Many of these offices are open for extended hours and the Dover Port Office is open 24 hours a day

Dover, CT16 1JA
RAC Port Office, Terminal Building, Eastern Docks, Dover Harbour
T Dover (0304) 204256 and 204153
Telex: 96120

Folkestone, CT20 1QG
RAC Port Office, West Side Terminal
Folkestone Harbour
T Folkestone (0303) 58560

Guernsey, C.I.
RAC Port Office, St. Julian's Pier, St Peter Port
T Guernsey (0481) 20822

Harwich, CO12 4SH
RAC Port Office, Parkeston Quay
T Harwich (0255) 503567

Jersey, C.I.
RAC Office, 27 The Parade, St Helier
T Jersey (0534) 23813

Newhaven, BN9 0DB
RAC Port Office, Newhaven Harbour
T Newhaven (0273) 514068

Portsmouth, PO2 8HB
RAC Port Office, Wharf Road
T Portsmouth (0705) 697713

Ramsgate, CT11 9LG
RAC Port Office, Ferry Terminal, Military Road
T Thanet (0843) 588452

Southampton, SO1 0NY
RAC Office, West Quay Road Car Park
West Quay Road,
T Southampton (0703) 24244

Allied Organisations

The Standing Joint Committee of the RAC, the AA and the RSAC

Chairman: J. A. Williams, T.D., T.Eng. (C.E.I.), F.I.M.I., F.R.S.A., J.P.
Joint Secretaries: J. T. Carr, I I. Dewar and J. B. Smeaton
Headquarters: 66 Whitcomb Street, London, WC2H 7DW.
T.A.: "Racaasac, Lesquare, London".
Scottish Office: 11 Blythswood Square, Glasgow, G2 4AG.
The Standing Joint Committee of the RAC, the AA and the RSAC was formed in 1944 to co-ordinate the views of the motoring organisations. The objective was to ensure that a united front would be presented in comment and discussion on matters of policy affecting the interests of the owners of cars and motor cycles, especially in approaches to Government Departments and local authorities.

The RAC Motor Sports Association Ltd

Headquarters and Registered Office: 31 Belgrave Square, London SW1X 8QH. T 01-235 8601. Telex 27203 Racing G.
Effective from 1st January, 1979, the above Company, by agreement with The Royal Automobile Club and the RAC British Motor Sports Council, assumed full responsibility for the control of automobile sport in the United Kingdom, and responsibility for authorising, on behalf of the Department of Transport, the holding of competitions and trials for motor vehicles on the public highway in England and Wales. The Company also organises and administers the British Grand Prix, RAC International Rally of Great Britain, RAC Tourist Trophy, British Kart Grand Prix, RAC Veteran Car Run and the British Rallycross Grand Prix.

Directors

(Chairman) R. M. Southcombe
(Deputy Chairman) P. G. Cooper, A.M.I.M.I.
M. A. Bone, J.P., F.C.I.S., F.I.B.
M. H. Bowler
D. S. Cardell
Eric Charles, O.B.E., F.I.M.I., F.B.I.M.
K. H. Douglas, F.Inst.M., M.S.A.E., A.Inst.Mech.E.
G. B. Flewitt
J. H. Kemsley
M. J. Limb, F.B.I.M., M.I.M.I.
B. K. McGivern
Jeffrey Rose
J. G. S. Sears
F. L. Shaw, J.P., B.Com., F.C.A., F.C.M.A., F.C.I.S.
M. J. Stephens
(Company Secretary) T. A. Lankshear

Auto-Cycle Union

Founded by the RAC in 1903
Patron: H.R.H. The Prince Philip, Duke of Edinburgh, K.G., P.C., K.T.
President: Sir Hector Monro, A.E., J.P., D.L., M.P.
Chairman: N. E. Goss
Secretary-General: K. E. Shierson
Headquarters: Millbuck House, Corporation Street, Rugby, Warwickshire, CV21 2DN. T Rugby (0788) 70332. Telex *311156* ACU G.
Membership through Affiliated Clubs.
The ACU is the recognised motor cycling organisation controlling the sport in Great Britain, and representing the British Commonwealth of nations, except Australia, Canada and N. Ireland, on the Federation Internationale Motocyclists. Its objects are to encourage and control the sporting side of the pastime. The ACU is governed by a Council of representatives of Affiliated Clubs and of the RAC.

Speedway Control Board Ltd

Chairman: M. J. Limb
Directors: N. E. Goss, R. Langford, K. E. Shierson
Secretary: R. W. Bracher
Manager: R. W. Bracher, 31 Belgrave Square, London, SW1X 8QJ. T 01-235 8601. TA "Speecon, London, SW1". Telex *27203.*
The body to which the RAC and ACU have delegated the control of the sport of speedway and indoor motor cycle racing in the United Kingdom. Following a reorganisation in 1965, the Board consists of two RAC and two ACU nominees. It maintains the overall control of the sport and is responsible for the organisation of major international events such as the World Championship Final and World Team Final when held in this country. The promotion of the sport is carried out by the British Speedway Promoters Association.

Roads Campaign Council

Chairman: J. A. Williams, T.D., T. Eng. (C.E.I.), F.I.M.I., F.R.S.A., J.P.
Director: A. J. A. Lee, F.I.H.T.
Secretary: Arthur Butler
Headquarters: 30 Farringdon Street, London, EC4V 4EA.

The Roads Campaign Council came into being early in 1955 as the result of discussions which were initiated by the RAC between all the principal organisations concerned with the manufacture, maintenance and use of road transport. As well as pressing for greatly increased Government and local authority expenditure on road modernisation and improved parking facilities, the Roads Campaign Council arranges activities for the Parliamentary All-Party Roads Study Group.

British Road Federation

Chairman: A. P. de Boer
Director: J. D. W. Gent
Headquarters: Cowdray House, 6 Portugal Street, London, WC2A 2HG. T 01-242 1285.
The British Road Federation is an organisation sponsored by industry and commerce, as well as motoring and road-user organisations—including the RAC. It operates in close collaboration with the Roads Campaign Council and is persistently pressing for expansion and improvement of the national road network and emphasising how this will help to achieve economic recovery, energy conservation and a better environment.

Royal Scottish Automobile Club

Chief Executive: H. Dewar
Club and Secretariat Office: 11 Blythswood Square, Glasgow, G2 4AG. T 041-221 3850.
TA "Royscotto, Glasgow".

Royal Irish Automobile Club

Secretary: Lt. Col. D. J. Healy
Competitions Director: W. J. Fitzsimmons
Competitions Manager: M. R. V. Mackay
Headquarters: 34 Dawson Street, Dublin.
T 775141, 775928, 775628.
TA "Automobile, Dublin".

Royal Motor Yacht Club

Founded by the RAC in 1905
Admiral: Admiral of the Fleet, H.R.H. The Prince Philip, Duke of Edinburgh, K.G., K.T., O.M., G.B.E.
Commodore: J. A. Rowe
Membership: 1,500. *Entrance Fee:* £83 (inc VAT). (RAC Members—no entrance fee)
Subscription: £86 (inc VAT).
Headquarters: Poole, RMYCS "Enchantress", Sandbanks, Poole, Dorset.
T Canford Cliffs (0202) 707227.

Rees Jeffreys Road Fund

Secretary: W. H. P. Davison, I.P.F.A., 35 Kirk Close, Oxford, OX2 8JL. T Oxford (0865) 54083.
The Rees Jeffreys Road Fund was established in December, 1950, by the late William Rees Jeffreys, Hon. M.T.P.I., C.I.Mech.E., to foster the improvement of the design and layout of public highways and of adjoining lands in order to secure the maximum of safety and beauty. Educational and research grants and bursaries are offered as well as some finance for roadside rests.

International Motoring Bodies

International Motoring and Touring Organisations

The RAC is a founder member of the Federation Internationale de l'Automobile (FIA), formed in 1904 as the Association Internationale des Automobile-Club Reconnus (AIACR), its new title being adopted in 1946. The RAC is also a member of the Alliance Internationale de Tourism (AIT), which was founded in 1919. These two organisations are the largest touring associations in the world.

The RAC, by virtue of its affiliation with these international bodies, offers its members the latest information on motor touring, advice and many other services. Numerous clubs and associations have reciprocal assistance agreements with the RAC which vary according to their size and development. The influence of the FIA and AIT has been recognised by the United Nations which has granted them consultative status.

The Secretariat of the FIA is in Paris and that of the AIT in Geneva.

Commonwealth Motoring Conference

President: Lord Erroll
Joint Secretaries: A. J. A. Lee, B. A. M. Pielow
Headquarters: 66 Whitcomb Street, London, WC2H 7DW. T 01-930 8686. TA: Racaasac, Lesquare, London
The Commonwealth Motoring Conference was created in 1959 at a meeting held in London at the invitation of the British motoring organisations and attended by representatives of the motoring organisations throughout the Commonwealth. There have been subsequent meetings in Ottawa at the invitation of the Canadian Automobile Association, and in Melbourne at the invitation of the Australian Automobile Association.

One of the major functions of the Conference is the organisation of arrangements for reciprocal membership facilities free of charge for members of the affiliated motoring organisations when they travel to other countries in the Commonwealth. These arrangements now apply not only to temporary visitors but also to members who emigrate to Commonwealth countries. Membership of the motoring organisation in another country can be obtained free of charge for the unexpired portion of the membership of the motoring organisation in the country from which the motorist originates, subject to a maximum period of 12 months. In the case of motorists emigrating to other countries, it is naturally expected that they will join the national motoring organisation at the end of the free service period. In that case, payment of any entrance fee which would otherwise be applicable will normally be waived.

The degree of service available in different countries in the Commonwealth varies according to the facilities of the individual organisations. Information about the affiliated organisations in each country and the services which they provide can be obtained from any RAC office. Members of the RAC wishing to take advantage of these arrangements should apply at any RAC office, prior to departure from this country, for Reciprocal Service Cards for presentation to the motoring organisations in other Commonwealth countries.

Clubs Associated with RAC

A.E.R.E. Motor Club
Sec.: J. W. Isaacs, Chemistry Division, A.E.R.E. Building 220, Harwell, Didcot, Oxon.

Alvis Owner Club
Gen. Sec.: M. J. Cummins, The Hill House, Rushock, Droitwich, Worcestershire.

B.B.C. Club
Sec.: 14A Cavendish Place, London, W1A 1AA. T 01-580 4468, ext. 35243.

Bibby Social Club
Hon. Sec.: G. T. Cope, 57 Great Howard Street, Liverpool, L3 7AW. T 051-236 6671.

Blackfriars Motor Club
Sec./Treasurer: Miss M. D. Arnfield, Unilever House, Blackfriars, London, EC4P 4BQ. T 01-822 6371.

Boots Motor Club
Hon. Sec.: J. E. Fox, Boots Co. Ltd., Merchandise Technical Services, Head Office, Nottingham, NG2 3AA.

Brighton & Hove Motor Club
Hon. Sec.: G. H. Small, 26 Mill Hill, Shoreham-by-Sea, West Sussex.

Bristol Aeroplane Company Motor Club
Hon. Treasurer: G. E. Bath, Sunnydene, Gloucester Road, Upper Swainswick, Bath, Avon, BA1 8BQ.

BAC (Stevenage) Motor Club
Sec.: B. Tremlett, 17 Maytrees, Hitchin, Herts, SG4 9LT.

Camping & Caravanning Club Ltd
Gen. Sec.: G. A. Cubitt, M.B.E., 11 Lower Grosvenor Place, London, SW1W 0EY. T 01-828 1012.

City of London Police Motor Club
Sec.: Mr Taylor, c/o Bishops Gate Police Station, 182 Bishops Gate, London EC2. T 01-601 2606.

Disabled Drivers Motor Club
Hon. Sec.: A. D. Paine, 1a Dudley Gardens Ealing, London W13 9LU. T 01-840 1515.

Dowty Motor Club
Hon. Sec.: R. C. Gough, Katia, 113 Tuffley Avenue, Gloucester, GL1 5NP. T Gloucester (0452) 712424, ext. 24. Gloucester (0452) 28825 (Home).

Edinburgh Civil Service Motoring Club
Sec.: I. C. Duguid, 17 West Craigs Crescent, Edinburgh, FH12 8NB. T 031-339 4190.

Ferranti (Bracknell) Motor Club
Hon. Sec.: M. Walde, 40 Evedon, Bracknell, Berks, RG12 4NF. T Bracknell (0344) 20611 ext. 275.

5 Motor Club
Sec.: Mr March, 56 Castle Road, Northolt, Middx, UB5 4SE.

Gate Motor Club
Sec./Treasurer: L. Singleton, 112 Hill View Road, Kimberworth, Rotherham, South Yorkshire, S61 2BN.

G.E.C. (Coventry) Motor Club
Sec.: R. D. Morris, 35 Vicarage Field, Warwick, CV34 5NJ. T Warwick (0926) 492334.

G.E.C. (Portsmouth) Motor & Motor Cycle Club
Hon. Sec.: P. R. Withenshaw, A.T.E. Division, G.E.C. Ltd., Broad Oak Works, The Airport, Portsmouth, PO3 5PQ. T Portsmouth (0705) 663211.

Glass Bulbs Auto Club
Acting Sec.: R. B. Thomas, Glass Bulbs Ltd., Harworth, Doncaster, South Yorkshire.

Guild of Lady Drivers
Gen. Sec.: Mrs N. Woolmore, 413a Brixton Road, London, SW9 7DH. T 01-733 4830. (Home—mornings only).

Halifax Motor Club
Hon. Sec.: Mrs J. Sharp-Tetley, 11 Hebble Gardens, Wheatley, Halifax, HX2 0TF. T Halifax (0422) 41358.

Ibis Motoring Club
Sec.: G. Howe, The Prudential Assurance Co. Ltd., 142 Holborn Bars, London, EC1N 2NH. T 01-405 9222, ext. 6035.

Kent Automobile Club
Hon. Sec.: B. R. Fagg, 44 Dane Crescent, Ramsgate, Kent, CT11 7JT. T Thanet (0843) 53913.

Leyland Motors Car Club
Sec.: C. Brooks, 16 Worden Lane, Leyland, Preston, Lancs, PR5 1EL.

L.E. Velo Club
Hon. Sec.: A. E. Lawrie, 68 Bingley Road, Sunbury-on-Thames, Middlesex, TW16 7RB.

Lincolnshire Louth Motor Club
Treasurer: R. Coggle, c/o Trustee Savings Bank, Eastgate, Louth, Lincs, LN11 9NB. T Louth (0507) 603174.

London Transport (CRS) Sports Association Motor Club
Hon. Sec.: J. Hanshaw, 76 Hillfoot Road, Collier Row, Romford, Essex RM5 3LL

Maidstone & Mid-Kent Motor Club
Sec.: J. A. Owen, 19 Hookers Lane, Detling, Maidstone, Kent, ME14 3JL. T Maidstone (0622) 62341.

Marjon Automobile Club
Hon. Sec.: G. R. Cannan, 47 Havers Avenue, Hersham, Walton-on-Thames, Surrey, KT12 4ND. T Walton (093 22) 21123.

MG Owners Club
The Secretary, 2–4 Station Road, Swavesey, Cambs, CB4 5QJ. T Swavesey (0954) 31125.

Middlesex County Automobile Club
Mem. Sec. & Hon Sec.: Mrs R. J. Williams, The Verne, Church Road, Lane End, High Wycombe, Bucks. HP14 3HR. T High Wycombe (0494) 881566.

Midland Automobile Club
Sec.: M. T. Joseland, 65 Coventry Street, Kidderminster, Worcs, DY10 2BS. T Kidderminster (0562) 3096.

Mid-Surrey Automobile Club
Hon. Sec.: Dave Speer, 5 Effingham Road, Surbiton, Surrey, KT6 5JZ. T 01-398 2663.

Motor Cycling Club
Gen. Sec.: M. Halliday, 74 Worcester Road, Sutton, Surrey, SM2 6QQ.

Mullard Auto Club (Simonstone)
Sec.: S. Douthwaite, Mullard Simonstone, Blackburn Road, Burnley, Lancs. T (0282) 72511, ext. 066.

National Press Automobile Association
Hon. Sec.: F. A. Snowden, 5 Folkington Corner, Woodside Park, London, N12 7BH. T 01-445 7607, 01-353 4242 Process Dept. (Office).

North Thames Gas Motor Club
Sec.: J. Garlick, North Thames House, 30 The Causeway, Staines, Middx, TW18 3BY. T Staines (0784) 51400.

Northumberland Police Motor Club
Sec.: W. A. Emmerson, 7 Hanover Walk, Chapel House Estate, West Denton, Newcastle upon Tyne, NE5 1EF. T Newcastle upon Tyne (0632) 323451, ext. 3274.

Order of the Road
Sec.: R. Bensted-Smith, The Business Centre, 14 West Street, Horsham, West Sussex, RH12 1PB. T Horsham (0403) 69691.

Overseas Drivers' Club
Sec.: S. Whittaker, Imperial Chambers Office 13, 62 Dale Street, Liverpool, L2 5SX. T 051-236 2929.

Owen Motoring Club
Membership Registrar: R. C. Southam, 5 Fitzroy Avenue, Harborne, Birmingham B17 8RL.

Oxford Motor Club
Sec.: Ms Rita Sammons, 4 Coniston Avenue, Headington, Oxfordshire, OX3 0AN. T Oxford (0865) 65657.

Pandor Motor Club
Sec.: B. E. C. Martin, 17 Parkway, Southgate, London, N14 6QU. T 01-283 8080, ext. 3931.

Perkins Sports Association Motor Club
Gen. Sec.: D. C. Ives, Eastfield Factory, Peterborough, Cambridgeshire, PE1 5NA. T Peterborough (0733) 67474.

Port of London Police Motor Club
Sec.: B. Davies, C.I. Dept., Divisional Police Station, Tilbury Dock, Essex.

Pre-War Austin Seven Club
Hon. Chairman: N. H. Barr, 41 Leopold Street, Derby, DE1 2HF. T Derby (0332) 46626.

Riley Motor Club
RAC Sec.: B. D. Draycott, 37 Gibbon Road, Acton, London, W3 7AF. T 01-903 9322 (Home) 01-743 9585.

Rose Motor Club
Hon. Sec.: P. Clark, 166 Lea Road, Gainsborough, Lincs, DN21 1AN.

Association of Scottish Motorists
Sec.: Mr Johnson, 2b Belmar Court, Linwood, Renfrewshire, PA3 3EE. T Johnstone (0505) 27970.

Shenstone & District Car Club
Gen. Sec.: M. F. Finnemore, 147 Lichfield Road, Sutton Coldfield, West Midlands, B74 2RY. T 021-308 0362.

Silver Wheel Motor Club
RAC Sec.: K. G. Salmon, 113 Blackmoor Drive, West Derby, Liverpool, Merseyside, L12 9ED.

Simon Engineering Motor Club
Gen. Sec.: R. Fleming, c/o Simon Container Machinery Ltd, Bird Hall Lane, Cheadle Hulme, Cheadle, Cheshire, SK3 0RT.

Skoda Owners' Club
RAC Sec.: Mrs M. White, 78 Montague Road, Leytonstone, London E11 3EN.

Somerset Automobile Club
Hon. Sec.: Mrs E. E. Salter, The Long House, High Hall, Compton Martin, Bristol, BS18 6JH. T West Harptree (076 122) 522.

Spring Hill Car Club
Sec.: F. Eland, 331 Willows Lane, Accrington, Lancs, BB5 0NH.

Steersafe Auto Club
Hon. Joint Gen. Sec.: P. C. Turner, 4 Wharwell Lane, Great Wyrley, Walsall, West Midlands, WS6 6ET. T Cheslyn Hay (0922) 414746

Sutton Coldfield & North Birmingham Automobile Club
Hon. Sec.: R. D. Baxter, 5 Hillmorton Road, Knowle, Solihull, W. Midlands, B93 9JL. T Knowle (056 45) 77505.

Suzuki Owners' Club
Nat. Treasurer: S. Wing, 55 Runnymede, Colliers Wood, London, SW19 2PG.

Thames Estuary Automobile Club
Gen. Sec.: T. Waite, 156 Southchurch Boulevard, Thorpe Bay, Essex, SS2 4UT.

Thames Valley Police Motor Club
Sec.: T. Franklin, 67 Beech Lane, Earley, Reading, Berkshire. T Reading (0734) 872975.

The Thomson House Motor Club
Sec.: F. Hanrahan, Withy Grove, Manchester, M60 4BJ. T 061-834 1234, ext. 71.

Times Auto Club
Hon. Sec.: P. Taylor, "Gayhurst", 140 Woodside Road, Amersham, Bucks, HP6 6NP. T Amersham (024 03) 4773.

Trailer Caravan Club
Sec.: Mrs D. M. England, 10 Lichfield Street, Burton-on-Trent, Staffs, DE14 3QZ. T Burton-on-Trent (0283) 48969.

2300 Club
Sec.: A. Breckwell, 13 Devonshire Road, Rishton, Blackburn, Lancs, BB1 4BX.

U.C.T.A. (Stockport) Motor Club
Hon. Sec.: A. K. Wilson, 26 Vernon Drive, Marple, Stockport, Cheshire, SK6 6JH. T 061-427 5128.

Membership of the RAC

Associate Members of the RAC

should take particular note of the following services:

Roadside Rescue: RAC patrols in radio equipped vans cover England, Scotland, Wales and Northern Ireland and are backed by a network of garages. More details on page 20.

'At Home' Service: This optional service is an extension of our Rescue Service. See page 21.

Recovery: This is complementary to our Roadside Service and ensures driver, car and up to three passengers are taken to the destination of their choice in the event of severe mechanical failure or accident. See page 22.

Telephone Boxes and Service Centres: These are strategically placed on main roads throughout the country and can be used to obtain assistance. See pages 23–27.

Touring and Travel: A comprehensive touring and travel service is available at any of the RAC Offices. For more details see page 27.

Legal Advice: This can be quickly obtained on request and Members can have the benefit of legal representation by a solicitor appointed by the RAC Legal Department in some instances. More information on page 29.

Technical Services: RAC Engineers will provide advice on technical matters and will arrange vehicle examination and certified trials. Details on page 31.

Insurance: A wide range of car insurance policies are available and advice from expert staff can be obtained. See page 31.

Lombard North Central Finance Plan: Offers personal loans at special rates. More details on page 33.

Public Policy: Protects the interest of the motorist and keeps a watchful eye on Legislation. See page 34.

Highways: Experts are available to deal with any road problems. See page 34.

Driving Instruction: Organised training schemes aimed at achieving higher standards of driving for motorists. See page 34.

Publications: Books, maps, touring aids and leaflets (providing a wide range of information) are produced and published by the RAC. See page 37.

BUPA Scheme: Special rebate arrangements for RAC Members. See page 37.

Associate membership

Summary of conditions

Associate Membership of the RAC is available in a number of categories:

Individual Associate Membership
Membership is available to any person owning or using a private car, three-wheeler, motor cycle, scooter or light van up to 3050 kg gross vehicle weight. There is an annual subscription and a joining fee. A free windscreen sticker badge and telephone box key are issued.

Associate Membership of the RAC is purely personal. The advantages may be enjoyed only by the individual subscriber and by his wife, to whom the benefits are extended without additional subscription. The benefits also extend to an Associate Member's personal full-time chauffeur in the course of his or her duties. Associate Membership does not include the use of the Club premises in Pall Mall or at Woodcote Park.

Benefits include the RAC Rescue service, Technical services, Legal services etc. See RAC Services beginning on page 19.

The Recovery service and "At home" service are available at an additional subscription. Full details are given on pages 22 and 21.

Vehicle Hire Membership
Membership is available to individuals or firms owning vehicles for hire (other than those licensed to ply for hire) including cars or scooters. RAC Membership is linked to the vehicles offered for hire. It is possible to cover individual vehicles or the total fleet available at any time. There are specially reduced subscription rates on a sliding scale for fleets of 12 or more vehicles. For fleets of over 200 vehicles there are further reductions, details of which can be obtained from RAC offices. There is a joining fee with a minimum payment. In all cases a free windscreen sticker badge and telephone box key are issued.

Family Associate Membership
Sons and daughters of existing members, who are under the age of 25 and living in the member's household, may enrol as individual members paying an annual subscription with the joining fee waived.

Group Membership
May be arranged by firms or organisations for their employees or members. Special terms are available. A minimum of 250 members is required.

Fleet Membership
Membership is available to fleets of private vehicles owned by firms, nominated by vehicle registration numbers. Provided more than eleven vehicles are registered, specially reduced rates are allowed on a sliding scale for fleets of 12 or more vehicles. Reduced terms for fleets of over 500 vehicles can be obtained from RAC offices. There is a joining fee with a minimum payment. In all cases a free windscreen sticker badge and telephone box key are issued. Cars, motor cycles, scooters, three-wheelers and light goods vehicles up to 3050 kg gross vehicle weight are eligible, with benefits available to authorised drivers.

Goods Vehicle Membership
Membership is available to owners of goods vehicles of more than 3050 kg gross vehicle weight. Benefits are accorded to any authorised driver but these benefits exclude the Rescue Service. There are specially reduced subscription rates on a sliding scale for 2 or more vehicles. There is a joining fee with a minimum payment. A free sticker badge and key will be issued for each vehicle. Public service vehicles and coaches are eligible in this category.

Overseas Associate Membership

Membership for motorists residing abroad and paying visits to the United Kingdom is available. Unattached motorists pay an annual subscription with a joining fee. There is a specially reduced rate for members of FIA Clubs, with no joining fee. Members of Commonwealth Affiliated Clubs—free reciprocal service up to 12 months, thereafter a reduced annual subscription unless on permanent transfer of residence. A free windscreen sticker badge is issued to every member on joining.

Invalid Tricycle Membership

Special facilities are available for disabled people driving three-wheeled vehicles only. Full details and terms of membership are obtainable on application at any RAC office.

Associated Clubs

Members of clubs associated with the RAC may subscribe through those clubs on special terms (see list on p. 15).

Full Members of the RAC

Full Members of the RAC enjoying the many amenities at the Pall Mall and Woodcote Park Clubhouses may also, by paying the appropriate fee, take advantage of the further facilities available to Associate Members.

Clubhouse and Country Club membership

The RAC Clubhouses in Pall Mall, London, and Woodcote Park, near Epsom, Surrey, welcome Full Members and provide a range of sporting and leisure activities unmatched in the United Kingdom. Full information on the facilities offered, and how to join appears on page 10. Further details and membership application forms can be obtained from the Membership Office, The Royal Automobile Club, 89, Pall Mall, London SW1Y 5HS.

RAC NAVIGATOR SERIES

Specially designed motoring maps at a scale of 1.6 miles to 1". They include town access maps and leisure maps featuring the countryside, historic houses, castles, gardens, zoos and wildlife parks, historic transport, art galleries and museums and much more. (See page 37-8)

RAC Services

As an Associate Member of the RAC you can benefit from the following services.

RAC Services

RAC Services

Rescue service

These details reflect the Rescue Service Terms and Conditions at 3rd Sept, 1984. They are the subject of continual review and may be changed without notice. The current Terms and Conditions at any time may be obtained from any RAC office.

1. The Rescue Services are arranged by RAC Motoring Services Ltd. (abbreviated as 'RAC') to give assistance to members who are STRANDED ON THE PUBLIC HIGHWAY in Great Britain, N. Ireland and Eire, throughout the year (Christmas Day in England, Wales, N. Ireland and Eire, and New Year's Day in Scotland excepted) as a result of a MECHANICAL BREAKDOWN of a private car, three-wheeler, motor cycle, scooter or light van up to 3050 kg gross vehicle weight. 'MECHANICAL BREAKDOWN' does not include items which, though legal requirements, do not render the vehicle immobile such as mirrors, horn, speedometer, etc. The RAC will not service, assemble, reassemble or otherwise reinstate the member's vehicle.

2. With a service of this nature there must be regulations and exemptions and to avoid misunderstanding they are listed below.

3. The member must be carrying his or her current membership card or valid membership receipt to obtain service.

4. This service is restricted to the member and his wife (or her husband). Other members of the family, including sons and daughters, must enrol individually and are NOT COVERED EVEN IF THE MEMBER'S CAR IS BEING USED. (Only the authorised driver of the registered vehicle is covered when Fleet/Hire Membership applies.) If your car suffers a breakdown, please ring the nearest 24-hour Emergency Control or the nearest RAC Service Centre. For telephone numbers and times of opening see p. 21. Your RAC telephone box key will open all RAC and AA telephone boxes. Give the following information:

a. Your full name, current membership number and expiry date.

b. Your home address or that of your temporary residence.

c. Make, year of manufacture and registration number of your vehicle to assist in identification later.

d. Nature of breakdown.

e. Precise location of your vehicle.

IMPORTANT
RAC staff have instructions not to deal with an unattended vehicle. Therefore, you or your representative must be present when assistance arrives.

5. The RAC will send a Patrol, subject to availability, to your assistance. If through circumstances beyond the control of the RAC it is not possible to despatch a road patrol within reasonable time, a garage breakdown vehicle will be sent to your assistance. When service is provided by RAC uniformed staff, the patrol will endeavour to repair the vehicle at the roadside. If he cannot, or the job needs special tools, spare parts which are not immediately available, or if repairs may be considered unwise or of a specialised nature (eg steering, brakes), he will, provided the vehicle displays a current tax disc, either tow the vehicle to a nearby garage or will arrange for that garage to tow your vehicle in. No warranty is given by the RAC that such a garage is competent to repair your make of car. You, the member, must give direct instructions to the garage for any repairs. Immediate workshop repairs by a garage cannot be guaranteed.

6. This Service is free within the following limitations: Where service is arranged by the RAC through a garage, the RAC will pay the garage for one journey to the scene of the breakdown and back, or, subject to the vehicle displaying a current tax disc, the towage back to the garage should this be necessary, up to a maximum round trip of 20 miles. The service includes delivery (but not cost) of petrol, oil, water or keys, if available.

7. Any garage used in connection with the Service is deemed to be the agent of the member and not of the RAC and the RAC cannot accept responsibility for any damage or loss resulting from the garage's acts or omissions.

8. In addition to the foregoing, if your car cannot be repaired for some time due to the breakdown or accident, and you wish to continue your journey, you and up to three passengers can be conveyed by taxi or hire car (NOT self-drive hire) to your home, nearest railway or omnibus station, or other agreed destination up to a maximum distance of 20 miles round trip from the hire car's base. Bus and rail fares are NOT refundable.

9. a. MEMBERS SHOULD ALWAYS BE IN POSSESSION OF A CURRENT MEMBERSHIP CARD OR VALID MEMBERSHIP RECEIPT TO SHOW TO THE PATROL OR GARAGE MECHANIC ON ARRIVAL.

b. Failure to produce a card or valid membership receipt will mean that it will be necessary for you to pay the garage representative the costs involved, although you may claim reimbursement from the RAC for the attendance of the mechanic following proof of your membership and on production of a receipted garage invoice. The official "Refund Request form" can be obtained from any RAC office and this, together with receipted VAT invoices for the amounts paid, should be sent to:

> RAC Motoring Services Ltd.,
> Rescue Accounts Department,
> P.O. Box 100, RAC House,
> Lansdowne Road,
> Croydon CR9 2JA

The refund of costs falling within the scope of the service will be made strictly in accordance with the current RAC scales issued to appointed garages. Any balance payable is your responsibility. No claim can be considered unless membership is current at the time of the breakdown.

10. Always ensure that you sign the completed Rescue Service Voucher tendered by the garage, verifying the service rendered.

11. Rescue service for trailers and trailer caravans excludes towage of the unit.

(NB. Recovery is available for those members subscribing to that service.)

12. Because we do not have any jurisdiction over the charges imposed by statute for breakdown service provided by a public authority in areas to which RAC Rescue Service vehicles have no right of access (e.g. Erskine, Forth, Tay and Severn Road Bridges, Dartford-Purfleet Tunnel, Mersey Tunnel, Clyde Tunnel, Blackwall Tunnel, Tyne Tunnel, etc.), assistance cannot be provided, nor costs incurred accepted.

13. The RAC Rescue Service does not cover:
a. The cost of petrol, oil and any materials or spare parts provided, whether from RAC stocks or by garages, the cost of collecting these parts or cost of collecting the car after repair.
b. Garage labour at the scene of the breakdown and the services of a second mechanic.
c. Repairs carried out at garage premises after the arrival of the vehicle, whether towed there or otherwise.
d. Garage charges for running in excess of 20 miles round trip and the cost of a second journey.
e. Breakdowns occurring at your residence or in the vicinity. So far as Hire, Fleet and Company Memberships are concerned 'residence' is deemed to be the home of the authorised user of the vehicle. The above limitation is necessary in order that the Rescue Service can operate as intended, i.e. to rescue members who are stranded away from home and are waiting at the roadside for assistance.
f. Cost of extricating a ditched, bogged or snowbound vehicle. Free service only covers roadside assistance.
g. Any cost of service arising as a result of an accident, or accidental damage apart from personal conveyance as mentioned in paragraph **8** (even if the accident is caused by mechanical failure).
h. Towage of the vehicle to any destination other than the assisting garage, unless the destination is on the direct route between the scene of the breakdown and the garage.
i. Second towage after the vehicle has been delivered to the assisting garage or to the alternative destination (referred to in sub-paragraph **h**).
j. Service in respect of Hackney Carriages.
k. Any hotel costs or cost of meals incurred as a result of a breakdown.
l. Any delay or loss consequential on delay howsoever arising caused as a result of your availing yourself of the service.

m. The cost of telephone calls incurred by or on behalf of the member in connection with a breakdown.
n. Any cost of service arising in connection with a breakdown occurring to vehicles engaged in or rendered unroadworthy through racing, pacemaking, speed testing, reliability trial, rally or other competitions.
o. Any costs arising from a breakdown on garage/service station premises or motorway service areas apart from those of personal conveyance as mentioned in paragraph **8**.
p. Any costs incurred through lack of a suitable spare wheel (motor cycle excepted), such as towage, personal conveyance, additional journeys. Free service only covers roadside assistance.
q. Vehicles used for demonstration or delivery by the motor trade or used under trade plates.

14. The RAC and its employees and agents will take all reasonable care and exercise all reasonable skill in respect of the towage or rescue of your vehicle, no stricter duty than this is deemed to be imposed upon them and the RAC will not accept liability of any kind whatsoever resulting from failure to exercise or comply with any stricter duty or higher standard.

15. The RAC reserves the right for its staff to insist on the signature by the member of a disclaimer in respect of any liability arising out of the provisions of some unusual service such as breaking into a car, temporary repairs and towing by tow rope.

16. The RAC reserves the right to restrict excessive use of the Rescue Service by any particular member.

17. The RAC has the power to add to, vary or amend these Terms and Conditions at any time without notice and any such addition, variation or amendment shall have immediate effect and shall bind the member forthwith.

"At Home" service

This service is available to Associate Members upon payment of an additional subscription and extends most of the benefits of Rescue Service to cover breakdowns occurring in the vicinity of the member's home. Full Terms and Conditions may be obtained from any RAC office.

Rescue service emergency controls

24-hour service.
General areas covered are shown in brackets.

LONDON
London & Home Counties
Croydon*
(London south of Thames, Kent, Surrey, East and West Sussex)
T 01-681 3611

Watford*
(London north of Thames, Bedfordshire, Essex, Hertfordshire)
T Watford (0923) 33555

Belfast
(Northern Ireland)
T Belfast (0232) 223333

Birmingham
(Hereford and Worcester, Shropshire, South Staffordshire, Warwickshire, West Midlands)
T 021-430 3232

Bournemouth
(Dorset, Hampshire, Isle of Wight)
T Bournemouth (0202) 766697

Bristol
(Avon, Gloucestershire, Somerset, Wiltshire)
T Bristol (0272) 739311

Cardiff
(South Wales)
T Cardiff (0222) 493030

Edinburgh
(Eastern Scotland)
T 031-229 3555

Exeter
(Mid and East Devon)
T Exeter (0392) 58333

Glasgow
(Western Scotland)
T 041-248 5474

Gloucester
(Gloucester)
T Gloucester (0452) 502011

Recovery Service

This is a nationwide service available to transport your vehicle together with caravan or trailer with you and up to three people to the destination of your choice on the mainland of England, Scotland, Wales and Northern Ireland in the event of severe mechanical failure or accident. Also, should you be the only driver in a car and suffer an injury or be taken ill, Recovery can be called upon to provide assistance. You must have your current membership card with you in order to obtain **Recovery** Service. The **Recovery** Service is available throughout the year, 24 hours per day.

This RAC service is a continuance of the existing Rescue Service and has been added to provide an additional benefit to members.

To obtain the benefits of the **Recovery** Service the member telephones the RAC first for normal Rescue Service. If it becomes apparent under the Rescue Service that the repairs are not possible within a reasonable time, of which the RAC shall be the sole judge, **Recovery** to the destination of the member's choice will then be arranged subject to the terms and conditions of the **Recovery** Service.

Members should apply to their local RAC office for an application form. Full details of the Recovery terms and conditions are available with the application form.

Guernsey
(Guernsey)
T Guernsey (0481) 20822

Jersey
(Jersey)
T Jersey (0534) 23813

Leeds
(North Humberside, South Cleveland, Yorkshire)
T Leeds (0532) 448556

Leicester
(Leicester)
T Leicester (0533) 536113

Liverpool
(Merseyside, North Wales, West Cheshire and Isle of Man)
T 051-236 2521

Newcastle upon Tyne
(Cumbria, Durham, North Cleveland, Northumberland, Tyne and Wear)
T Newcastle (0632) 814271

Norwich
(Cambridgeshire, Norfolk, Suffolk)
T Norwich (0603) 28255

Nottingham
(Leicestershire, Lincolnshire, Nottinghamshire, South Derbyshire, South Humberside)
T Nottingham (0602) 626200

Oxford*
(Berkshire, Buckinghamshire, Northamptonshire, Oxfordshire)
T Oxford (0865) 53333

Plymouth
(Devon, Cornwall)
T Plymouth (0752) 21411

Sheffield
(South Yorkshire)
T Sheffield (0742) 25882

Stockport
(East Cheshire, Greater Manchester, Lancashire, North Derbyshire, North Staffordshire)
T 061-477 7000

Call queueing system in operation. If ringing tone obtained, wait for an answer as calls are taken in turn.

Service centres

Hours of opening: 9 am to 7 pm daily. These hours may vary slightly according to the time of year.

ENGLAND AND WALES

Avon
GORDANO
Gordano Service Area
Junc. of A369/M5–Portbury
T Pill (027 581) 3426
PATCHWAY
Carrefour Hypermarket, Highwood Lane, Patchway, Bristol
T Bristol (0272) 792977

Berkshire
MEMBURY (M4)
Westbound Service Area, M4
T Lambourn (0488) 72602
READING
Fairfield Services, Basingstoke Rd, A33, 2½ m. S. of Reading and adj to Junc. 11 of M4 Motorway (Three Mile Cross).
T Reading (0734) 876533

Buckinghamshire
NEWPORT PAGNALL (M1)
Newport Pagnell Service Area, M1 Northbound Carriageway
T Newport Pagnell (0908) 610383

Cheshire
CHESTER BY-PASS
Gorse Stacks Car Park, Inner Ring Road
T Chester (0244) 45027
WARRINGTON
Leigh Street Multi Storey Car Park
T Warrington (0925) 38358
WIDNES
Co-op Hypermarket, Lugsdale Rd
T 051-423 4098

Cleveland
STOCKTON-ON-TEES
Bishop St
T Stockton-on-Tees (0642) 678104

Cornwall
PERRANARWORTHAL
A39 Truro-Falmouth Rd 1 m. S. of Perranarworthal
T Devoran (0872) 863453

Cumbria
CARLISLE
Car Park, Viaduct Rd
T Carlisle (0228) 26990

SOUTHWAITE
Granada Service Area, M6 Northbound Carriageway, 6 m. S. of Carlisle
T Southwaite (069 93) 505
WORKINGTON
Washington St Car Park
T Workington (0900) 5481

Derbyshire
DERBY
Cock Pitt Car Park
T Derby (0332) 362742

Devon
BARNSTAPLE
Queen St
T Barnstaple (0271) 42391
EXETER BY-PASS
Granada Service Area, M5 Exeter
T Exeter (0392) 59200
KINGSKERSWELL
A380 Aller Lay-by, Newton Rd, Kingskerswell
T Kingskerswell (080 47) 3095

Durham
DARLINGTON
Commercial St
T Darlington (0325) 485931

Dyfed
KILGETTY
Sited at the Wales Touring Board Complex,
Carmarthen/Tenby Rd A477, 200 yds, E. of junc. with A487 Tenby/Cardigan Rd
T Saundersfoot (0834) 813321

Essex
CHELMSFORD CONTROL
A12 200 yds S. of Junc. with Westway at Widford
T Chelmsford (0245) 50335
COLCHESTER
Eld Lane, Colchester Shopping Centre
T Colchester (0206) 574250
SOUTHEND-ON-SEA
Seafront—Western Esplanade
T Southend-on-Sea (0702) 345645

Gloucestershire
MICHAELWOOD
Michaelwood Service Area, M5
T Falfield (0454) 260975

Greater London
BLACK PRINCE (Kent)
Black Prince Hotel Car Park
Junc. A2/Bourne Rd, Bexley
T Crayford (0322) 527596

CHISWICK ROUNDABOUT (W4)
Junc. A4/North Circular Rd
T 01-994 6975
GALLOWS CORNER (Essex)
Junc. A12/A127, Romford
T Romford (0708) 65316
PURLEY WAY (Surrey)
A23 Car park ½ m. S. of Aerodrome Hotel
T 01-686 3691
SCRATCHWOOD
Scratchwood Service Area, M1
T 01-906 2519
TOLWORTH (Surrey)
A240 Junc. Kingston Rd/Old Kingston Lane
T 01-337 7953

Greater Manchester
ASHTON-UNDER-LYNE
Henrietta Street Car Park
T 061-339 9299
BIRCH HEYWOOD
Birch Service Area, East side of M62 Motorway
T 061-653 5964
BOLTON
Coronation Street Car Park
T Bolton (0204) 387821
OLDHAM
New Radcliffe St
T 061-620 6040

Gwent
NEWPORT
A4042 Newport/Abergavenny Rd
¾ m. Junc. 26 M4 Motorway
T Newport (0633) 855938

Hampshire
FLEET
Westbound carriageway M3—midway between Aldershot junc. 4 and Hook junc. 5
T Fleet (025 14) 22927

Hereford and Worcester
FRANKLEY (M5)
East side of Service Area Car Park
T 021-550 5477

Hertfordshire
PARK STREET
M10/A5/A405 R/Abt S. of St Albans
T Park Street (0727) 73368

Humberside
GRIMSBY
Riverhead Car Park, Baxtergate
T Grimsby (0472) 41033
HULL
Car Park, Junc. Wright St/Percy St
T Hull (0482) 25991

Come under our wing

– for the right policy at the right price

 **Eagle Star Insurance**

Kent
POLHILL
A21 Halstead, 1 m. S. of Badgers Mount
T Knockholt (0959) 34519

Lancashire
BLACKBURN
A666 Penny St
T Blackburn (0254) 60528
BLACKPOOL
Imperial Hotel
T Blackpool (0253) 293239
CHARNOCK RICHARD (M6)
Charnock Richard Service Area, M6, 10 m.
S. Preston Northbound Carriageway
T Coppull (0257) 791566

Leicestershire
LEICESTER
Free School La, Junc. with West Bond St.
T Leicester (0533) 530769

Lincolnshire
GRANTHAM
A1/A1081 Junc. North End–Grantham
By-Pass,
Gonerby Moor, nr Grantham
T Grantham (0476) 65789

Merseyside
BIRKENHEAD
Car Park, Claughton Rd/Conway St
T 051-647 8239
BURTONWOOD
M62 Service Area, Eastbound
Carriageway
T Warrington (0925) 50959
SOUTHPORT
Esplanade Car Park
T Southport (0704) 34089

Mid Glamorgan
SARN
Sarn Service Area
At Junc. M4 with A4061
(Junc. 36 M4)
T Aberkenfig (0656) 60044

Northamptonshire
WATFORD GAP (M1)
Watford Gap Service Area, M1
Northbound Carriageway
T Daventry (032 72) 3282
WESTON FAVELL
Weston Favell Centre, Northampton
T Northampton (0604) 402325

Nottinghamshire
RANBY
Junc. A1/A57/A614 North Notts
4½ m. S.W. of Retford
T Retford (0777) 703953

TROWELL
Trowell Service Area, M1 South
T Nottingham (0602) 303389

Shropshire
SHREWSBURY BY-PASS
Junc. A5/A48 at Weeping Cross
T Shrewsbury (0743) 4908

South Yorkshire
WOODALL
Woodall Service Area, Northbound M1
Harthill
T Sheffield (0742) 484080

Staffordshire
KEELE (M6)
Keele Service Area, M6 Northbound
Carriageway
T Stoke-on-Trent (0782) 626481

Surrey
OTTERSHAW
Council Car Park,
Junc. A320/A319 at Ottershaw
T Ottershaw (093 287) 3536

Tyne & Wear
SUNDERLAND
Bedford St Car Park
T Sunderland (0783) 42527

Warwickshire
CORLEY
Fortes (M6) Motorway Services,
Corley Fillongley
T Meriden (0676) 40882

West Sussex
CHICHESTER
A27 Chichester By-Pass 1 m. S. of
Chichester
T Chichester (0243) 784673
HICKSTEAD
A23 at Little Chef Restaurant, Hickstead
T Bolney (044 482) 790

West Yorkshire
HARTSHEAD MOOR
Hartshead Moor Service Area, M62
Southbound Carriageway
T Cleckheaton (0274) 877805
HUDDERSFIELD
Junc. King St/Venn St
T Huddersfield (0484) 28598

Wiltshire
SALISBURY
Central Car Park
T Salisbury (0722) 26566.
SWINDON
Queen's Drive, Coate Water
T Swindon (0793) 38442

SCOTLAND
Borders
JEDBURGH
A68 Canongate Car Park
T Jedburgh (083 56) 3280

Central
FALKIRK
Hope St. Car Park,
Grahamston B.R. Station
T Falkirk (0324) 31001

Fife
KIRKCALDY
Port Brea Car Park, Kirkcaldy Esplanade
T Kirkcaldy (0592) 266110

Grampian
ABERDEEN
Junc. Great Southern Road/Anderson
Drive, Bridge of Dee
T Aberdeen (0224) 872828

Highland
INVERNESS
Manse Place, Friars La
T Inverness (0463) 231640

Strathclyde
ABINGTON
Harvie's Filling Station
Southbound Carriageway A74
T Crawford (086 42) 483
GREENOCK
Rue End St, rear of P.O.
T Greenock (0475) 27085
HAMILTON
Brandon Street Car Park
T Hamilton (0698) 281152
KILMARNOCK
St Marnock Street Car Park
T Kilmarnock (0563) 25002
MOTHERWELL
Brandon Parade Car Park
T Motherwell (0698) 69779

Tayside
DUNDEE
Car Park, Dock St
T Dundee (0382) 22543
PERTH
Pavilion Car Park
Junc. Tay St/Shore Rd/Marshal Pl.
T Perth (0738) 23717

NORTHERN IRELAND
Co. Antrim
ABBEYCENTRE
Longwood Rd.
T Whiteabbey (0231) 60969
Co. Londonderry
COLERAINE
Stone Row
T Coleraine (0265) 55700

Road patrols

The modern day RAC Road Patrols can be easily recognised in the blue/grey uniform, patrolling the length and breadth of both major and 'B' class roads in Great Britain, manning distinctive vehicles which are divided into three main categories:
1. The fully trained Service Patrols operate radio-equipped vehicles providing assistance by day or night to members in distress and are able to supply

immediate assistance in cases of minor breakdowns etc., including first-aid help where required. Information is on hand in respect of routes, hotels, local events, garage agencies etc., either from their own knowledge or by contact with the 24 hour manned Radio Control Room in their specific area, where a close liaison is maintained between staff.
2. The Signs Officers provide a valuable service to the public in general by erecting the, by now, well known

Two quotes well worth considering.

"Guardian Royal Exchange are officially approved by us."

RAC.

"Compare the cover our policies provide, and you'll find that we offer excellent value for money."

GRE.

Guardian Royal Exchange Assurance

PRIVATE CAR INSURANCE.

blue and white temporary signs giving advance warning of diversions or adverse weather conditions etc., or directions for events in conjunction with the local authorities. Details of the cost of this service can be obtained from any RAC Office.

3. The Sales Patrols are to be found in the new white mini vans in attendance at RAC Service or Mobile Centres for the purpose of recruiting new members and offering advice in general with a view to extending the services provided by the most respected of Automobile Organisations in this country. Main events including Motor or Agricultural Shows are attended by Sales staff.

In addition to the above, there are of course Supervising Officers for each category ensuring smooth and efficient running of a service to road users unparalleled in this country.

Telephone boxes

RAC Telephone Boxes are located at carefully chosen sites on main roads throughout the United Kingdom. They are available to members at any hour of the day or night. In addition to providing the normal telephone service, all boxes list the numbers to ring in case of emergency or breakdown. RAC members also have the use of AA telephone boxes, the locks on all boxes being identical. In all, some 1,400 boxes are at the disposal of members. Their location is shown in the atlas in this Handbook.

Touring and travel services

A complete touring service is available to members.

Routes. Route information is supplied on request from the RAC Head Office at Croydon. Normally the route will be that recommended by the RAC and will be marked on one of the specially designed route maps. Special requests, for example, the quickest, or the most direct route, will receive expert consideration.

The planning of individual routes for caravan journeys, having regard to road conditions, and gradients is dealt with by specialists in this type of travel.

Some members, when on holiday, prefer to use a fixed centre as a base and booklets containing suggested motor tours in popular holiday areas may be had on request, for which no charge is made.

Road and Weather Information. All RAC offices are equipped to give information in respect of adverse road and weather conditions. During the winter months a countrywide network covering Great Britain is set up and the RAC is in a position to give information in respect of road and weather conditions anywhere on the mainland.

Caravanning and Camping. The RAC operates a caravan and camping site inspection scheme in Great Britain and Northern Ireland to establish a list of sites which can be recommended to members. Caravan sites which maintain a high standard are granted Appointment. Sites recognised by the RAC are permitted to display an official sign.

A Caravan and Camping site book covering Great Britain and Ireland is available which also contains information on the law relating to the towing of caravans and trailers, both in this country and abroad, together with many other useful items of information and general hints. This publication is free to members.

The International Camping Carnet is available to members. This provides Third Party Risks and Personal Accident insurance cover whilst camping abroad. It also enables a member to use certain sites operated by Clubs affiliated to the AIT/FIA. An application form is available from any RAC office.

Hotels. The RAC has, since early in its existence, recommended hotels to its members.

The appointment of hotels follows a full inspection by RAC officials and to ensure that the high standards required for appointment are maintained, further inspections are carried out at regular intervals. For details of the scheme, which operates in the United Kingdom, and explanation of the classification requirements, see pp. 120–124.

For details of the RAC's appointed and recommended hotels on the Continent, please refer to the RAC Continental Motoring Guide, see p. 37.

TRAVELLING IN THE ISLE OF MAN, CHANNEL ISLANDS AND IRELAND

Isle of Man. There are no Customs formalities, but there are certain conditions which refer to the provision of driving licences and insurance. Members should ask at their nearest RAC office for an information leaflet.

Channel Islands. The formalities to be observed when taking a car to Jersey or Guernsey are detailed in the special information leaflet. Members should make application for this to any RAC office. Members must produce evidence of insurance cover valid for the Channel Islands.

Ireland. For full details of the Travellers Bond Vehicle Protection for Ireland apply to any RAC office. Cover includes contributions to expenses for vehicle repatriation, car hire, spares despatch, garage labour and additional hotels.

TRAVEL

The Club is in a position to provide information and documentation for travel at home and abroad with assistance of staff at selected ports.

RAC qualified staff are able to make reservations and provide tickets for car ferries, hovercraft crossings and motorail services.

Insurance is an important item not to be overlooked by the traveller abroad. Our Travellers Bond service offers a variety of schemes for both personal and vehicle cover.

The RAC 1985 brochure on Continental Motoring gives full particulars of the various services available and may be obtained from any RAC office or on application to RAC Motoring Services Ltd., Touring Services, P.O. Box 100, Croydon CR9 2JA.

TRAVELLING ON THE CONTINENT

The RAC Travellers Bond Vehicle Protection service should always be taken by motorists intending to drive on the Continent. There is a choice of De Luxe and Standard versions.

APART FROM THE RAC, NAME ANOTHER POPULAR MOTORING ORGANISATION.

Of course we're talking about NEM Insurance, the company who have been taking the knocks for RAC members for over fifty years. And to make life easier, you can also insure your home and business with us at the same time as you insure your car through the newly formed RAC insurance brokers. Just ask your nearest NEM or RAC Office for details.

Together for over fifty years

The De Luxe service provides a comprehensive cover in the event of breakdown or accident abroad. The De Luxe service includes roadside assistance, a spares despatch service and reimbursement for some of the costs incurred for towing, garage labour, continuation of the journey and/or return home by hire car etc., and additional hotel charges. Vehicles which cannot be repaired abroad by the planned date of return home may use the repatriation service and other useful benefits. Legal Protection with a £1500 Bail Bond is also included with the service.

An added advantage of the De Luxe Scheme is the option which may be taken to double the limit of selected benefits, allowing car hire in the UK whilst a Member's own vehicle is being repatriated under the terms of the service.

The Standard scheme is principally designed to cover the expensive item in any breakdown or accident abroad, the cost of repatriating the vehicle to the UK. Roadside assistance, the spares despatch service and compensation for some towing and garage labour costs are also included. Legal Protection with a £1500 Bail Bond is also a part of the service.

RAC Emergency Control Centres in France and Spain are able to render assistance and members are able to take advantage of the service of affiliated Clubs throughout Europe.

Extra benefits provided with both schemes are Letters of Credit, Car Hire and Air Transport vouchers repayable to the RAC, but which, when used in an emergency can conserve expenditure of cash at a time when it is needed most.

Travel Insurance. It is important for all members of the party to have insurance cover as well as the vehicle and a specially designed Personal Protection policy is available under Travellers Bond. Included in the policy is cover for medical expenses, loss of deposits, personal baggage and money, personal accident, personal public liability and an emergency repatriation service enabling a member of the party who becomes seriously ill, or is injured, in certain circumstances to be flown back by air ambulance to the UK or conveyed by road ambulance without charge.

Legal Aid Insurance. Available as a separate item if required, for members hiring a vehicle abroad. A £1500 Bail Bond is included as part of the insurance.

Legal

Free Legal Representation. The recipient of a summons for a motoring offence is entitled to the benefit of legal representation by solicitor (or, at the option of the Legal Department, by counsel) appointed by the Legal Department in any court of summary jurisdiction in the United Kingdom (including the Isle of Man and the Channel Islands) or Eire on the following terms:

1. Application must be made to the Legal Department in Croydon at least 10 days before the hearing date on the RAC's printed form.
2. The date of the alleged offence must have been within the currency of membership.
3. The summons must be for a motoring offence arising out of the use or ownership of a vehicle covered by membership or of a type covered by the personal

membership of the defendant or his or her spouse. Representation is also extended to a member's personal full time chauffeur in the course of his or her duties. Taxis, minicabs and P.S.V.s are excluded.
4. The following are excluded: drink, drugs or excess alcohol offences; trade plate offences or those arising out of the use of a vehicle being tested or demonstrated or delivered by the motor trade; goods vehicle operators' licensing offences and those relating to hours of work or failure to keep records; criminal charges; illegal driving instruction offences.
5. The RAC reserves the right to refuse legal representation in cases in which the Legal Committee considers it desirable to do so.
6. Travelling expenses incurred by the solicitor are covered but not the cost of tracing or securing the attendance of witnesses, or fees of expert witnesses.
7. The RAC shall be entitled to reimbursement from the member of any costs resulting from his or her failure to keep an appointment or from the arrangement of adjournments to suit his or her convenience.
8. If a member wishes to stipulate that counsel shall be briefed, counsel's fees and any additional solicitors' fees involved must be borne by the member.
9. A member may if he or she so desires instruct his or her own solicitor. In such cases the RAC will pay an amount equal to the fee which a solicitor appointed by the Legal Department would have received if he or she had been instructed in the normal way, any balance will be the responsibility of the member. Completion of the RAC's printed application form is required for record purposes and a receipted solicitor's account must be provided. This concession applies only to representation on summonses and not to assistance with negotiations.

Manslaughter. The benefit of the Free Legal Representation Scheme extends to manslaughter charges, arising out of driving, both in the Magistrates' and Crown Courts. Experienced counsel will be briefed at the Crown Court, but it is to be understood that the conduct of the defence, including the selection of counsel, is left to the Legal Department.

S.1. Road Traffic Act, 1972. In cases of causing death by reckless driving the Free Legal Representation Scheme operates in respect of the preliminary hearing before the Magistrates but not at the Crown Court. The Legal Committee has a discretion to authorise contributions towards the cost of defence at the Crown Court.

Removal of Disqualification. The Legal Committee is prepared to consider authorising applications by solicitor for the removal of disqualifications imposed on members. Full details of the proceedings at which the disqualification was imposed, any previous convictions and reasons for requiring the return of the licence must be submitted. See p. 88 (Motor Laws).

Financial Assistance. The RAC is prepared to entertain applications for financial assistance towards the cost of legal representation in respect of cases not falling within the scope of the Free Legal Representation Scheme. Such applications are considered on their merits by the Legal Committee after full investigation of the facts.

Car Insurance

Match the quality of RAC Service with the quality of Sun Alliance Car Insurance.

- Competitive premiums
- First class cover and claims service
- Protected N.C.D. option
- Monthly instalments

Appeals. If a member suffers a conviction or sentence which appears to be a gross miscarriage of justice or wrong in law, the Legal Committee will consider the support of, or financial assistance towards, the conduct of an appeal. It is important to remember that notice of appeal may have to be lodged within 21 days of the date of conviction. In Scotland the time limit is in some cases only ten days.

Inquests. Representation either by solicitor or counsel at the discretion of the Legal Department will be provided for the member in respect of the death of his or her passenger in a traffic accident if the member is not entitled to have such representation arranged by his or her insurers. The benefit of such representation will also be given to the relatives of a member who is fatally injured while travelling in the member's private vehicle.

Free Consultation with Solicitor. Members are entitled to consult a solicitor of the Legal Department in Croydon or, by special arrangement in London, for the purpose of obtaining advice and assistance, where relevant, on any legal matter relating to the use or ownership of private motor vehicles, whether of a civil or criminal nature, free of charge. In the first instance, members should phone or write to the Legal Department in Croydon. Should a personal interview with a Solicitor subsequently be deemed necessary this may be arranged by prior appointment.

Personal Injury and Accidental Damage Claims. In civil claims for damages for personal injuries or uninsured losses arising during the currency of membership out of road traffic accidents in the United Kingdom and Eire in which members are involved as drivers or passengers in private motor vehicles, or commercial vehicles covered by membership, the RAC will, under its Claims Recovery Service, appoint a solicitor of its choice to advise and conduct negotiations up to the point at which litigation becomes inevitable. The RAC reserves the right to charge a small non-recoverable registration fee, but will otherwise bear the cost except disbursements (e.g. on police and medical reports) or such costs as are customarily recoverable from a third party or his insurers. The conduct of litigation or special enquiries is not covered.

Technical services

Advisory. Free technical advice is available to members on all aspects of motoring from RAC engineers. This includes advice on the purchase, repair, upkeep and general maintenance of cars and the cost of motoring. RAC engineers will also check estimates for repairs and negotiate with garages on behalf of members in the event of disagreement concerning charges or quality of work carried out. Similarly, negotiations with manufacturers can be undertaken in order to assist in problems associated with new vehicle warranty claims.

If you live in the area covered by the following offices, Croydon, Watford, Liverpool, Stockport, Nottingham, Bristol, Leeds, Glasgow and Oxford, please ring or contact that office for technical advice. Members living in other areas should contact the RAC National Technical Centre, 61a Maypole Lane, Maypole, Birmingham B14 5JX. T 021-430 4460.

Vehicle Examinations. Members are recommended to take advantage of the RAC Vehicle Examination Scheme if contemplating the purchase of a used vehicle. For a moderate fee, a full and comprehensive written report on the condition of a vehicle is supplied, which can be a valuable aid in deciding whether or not to purchase.

This service is also recommended prior to the expiry of the manufacturer's warranty and following completion of accident damage repairs, to ensure that all necessary repairs have been satisfactorily carried out. Written estimates should be obtained before repair work of any kind is authorised.

It is also often advantageous for a car owner to obtain expert advice and a written report on the condition of a car at periodic intervals throughout its life, so that any necessary adjustments, repairs or replacements can be carried out in good time.

Members are strongly advised to arrange for examinations to be carried out on premises where a pit or hoist is available. A satisfactory examination of the underside of a vehicle cannot be carried out without such a facility. (This does not apply to motor cycles.)

Applications for vehicle examinations should be made to the nearest RAC office, who will also advise as to the fees applicable for each class of vehicle. Fees may be subject to special negotiation should the RAC Engineer need to travel an excessive distance. Appointments can be made for any part of the United Kingdom, subject to adequate notice being given. All applications received are dealt with strictly in order of rotation, regardless of how they are submitted.

All examinations are carried out subject to the following conditions.

(a) The results of examinations are confidential to the member and may not be divulged to any other party without the permission of the RAC.

(b) Reports are based on a visual, external examination and no dismantling or repairs will be carried out. Defects only discoverable by internal examination cannot be revealed, nor can internal corrosion of body parts.

(c) Reports can only comment on the condition of the vehicle at the time of the examination. No responsibility can be accepted for latent defects in components or equipment which subsequently fail.

(d) The Chief Engineer, or his staff, cannot act as expert witnesses in cases of litigation.

RAC Certified Trials. The control and organisation of trials connected with cars and accessories is the responsibility of the Department. Official reports, whether favourable or otherwise to the article under test, can be published at the RAC's discretion.

The object of the Trials is to test the merits of a car as a whole or in part, or of an accessory, under controlled conditions. The Club reserves the right to refuse to undertake any particular Trial. RAC Certified Trials do not cover bench or similar tests of an academic nature.

Insurance

MOTOR INSURANCE

Motor insurance is an essential part of motoring and to protect members' interests the RAC has arranged a wide range of RAC Approved Motor Policies. These

policies are kept under constant review to reflect current market trends and the RAC's buying power has enabled it to obtain competitive and usually preferential rates for members.

A free, no-obligation quotation service is provided, and details and forms are available from all RAC offices or our Patrols. Advice on motor insurance may be obtained from any RAC office.

PRIVATE CARS

The long established RAC Approved Lloyd's Car Policy offers a No Claims Bonus Protection facility and the option of paying premiums by instalments.

The "RAC Shield" policy underwritten by Royal Insurance offers preferential terms to the private motorist who uses his car for social purposes and commuting. "RAC Shield 50" is designed for the motorist aged 50 or above and includes No Claims Bonus protection facility.

Other RAC Approved Car Policies include those underwritten at attractive rates by the National Employers' Mutual and the Sun Alliance Insurance Companies.

The Royal and Sun Alliance policies also allow premiums to be paid by instalments—the Royal with no extra charge and the Sun Alliance with a small charge for a twelve-month facility.

Several additional policies are being arranged with major insurance companies and details of these policies will be available shortly.

GREEN CARDS

The minimum cover available under motor policies to comply with EEC and certain non-EEC countries' insurance legislation without a Green Card does not generally include fire, theft, accidental damage, personal accident, etc. Members are strongly advised to obtain a Green Card to ensure full protection when going abroad.

MOTOR CYCLES

The Comprehensive RAC Approved Lloyd's Motor Cycle Policy has a No Claims Bonus rising to 25% after four years.

OTHER RAC INSURANCES—Travellers Bond Personal Protection

This protects members travelling abroad with or without their cars. There is medical cover up to £50,000 per person coupled with emergency repatriation on medical grounds with no limit on the sum insured. There is special provision for protection of a car's No Claims Bonus following an accident on the Continent. Other protection includes baggage, loss of deposits, cash, RAC credit vouchers and compensation for ferry or flight delay.

Details in RAC Continental and Irish Motoring Brochure.

CAUTION!

The so-called reciprocal agreements for medical treatment of certain British nationals in some European countries are in general very limited and it is most unwise to rely upon them and not take adequate insurance. They certainly do not provide for emergency repatriation or non-medical expenses such as loss of baggage, money, etc.

CARAVAN AND CAMPING

The RAC Caravan Policy allows up to 60 days Continental use without extra charge in any one year of insurance.

HOUSE CONTENTS AND BUILDING INSURANCE

Although this insurance is not directly related to motoring, RAC members recognise how essential it is to protect their homes against disasters such as fire, burglary or burst pipes. A Lloyd's policy has been negotiated by the RAC which provides very full cover at competitive rates and a special 5% discount to members. Many members have already made substantial cash savings on this essential part of every household budget, and full details and cover may now be obtained from any RAC office.

The above information is correct at the time of going to press. Full details of all RAC insurance policies are available from RAC offices and the RAC's specialist insurance brokers RACIB

RAC INSURANCE BROKERS LTD.

Hermitage Road,
Hitchin,
Herts. SG5 1DH
Tel: Hitchin (0462)
57151

Beaumont House,
Beaumont Street,
Darlington,
Durham DL1 5RW
Tel: Darlington (0325)
460721

RAC Members—Lombard North Central finance plan

Being an RAC member means you can benefit from a special arrangement between the RAC and Lombard North Central which offers loans to members at reduced rates. It's called the RAC Members' Finance Plan. What advantages does it provide?

★ A personal cheque within a few days, subject to acceptance, for any amount from £200 to £5000
★ All the freedom open to a cash buyer, of choice and better bargains
★ No need to touch your hard earned savings
★ The cost can be spread to suit your pocket
★ A personal loan facility specially negotiated for you, the RAC Member
★ A better tomorrow at today's prices.

What can a loan be used for? For almost any purpose you wish—the cheque is payable to you personally. Your loan is not limited to motoring needs and the Members' Finance Plan also offers peace of mind with Credit Protection—for just a small increase in your monthly payment, subject to some simple conditions, you can make certain that payments are made in case of sickness and accident, giving protection to your family.

RAC personal loans are available to RAC Members aged 18 or over in England, Scotland and Wales.

If you would like further written details either complete the coupon on the card insert, or contact:
Lombard North Central PLC, RAC Members' Personal Service, 320 Purley Way, Croydon CR9 9ER, Tel: 01-686 4466, or call in at any RAC or Lombard North Central office.

RAC Motorloan is a new and modern approach to car finance. Written details are available from any RAC office.

Public policy

With the rapid increase in the number of motor vehicles in Great Britain, it has become even more important to ensure that the interests of the motoring public are adequately represented in negotiations with Governmental Departments and other organisations concerning the many proposals affecting the use and ownership of motor vehicles.

All such matters are carefully considered by the Public Policy Committee of the RAC and its views are presented to the Standing Joint Committee of the Royal Automobile Club, the Automobile Association and the Royal Scottish Automobile Club by the Club's representatives. This aspect of the Club's activities is administered by the Public Policy Department which conducts negotiations, examines proposed legislation and takes appropriate action when necessary to secure the presentation of the Club's views during Parliamentary debates.

An active part has been taken in the work of the Roads Campaign Council, which was created in 1955 to co-ordinate the pressure exerted by transport interests for increased expenditure on roads. The RAC was instrumental in securing the formation of this organisation.

The Club also participates in the activities of the British Road Federation which pursues similar objectives in collaboration with the Roads Campaign Council.

Detailed information concerning the RAC's many public policy activities is provided in an illustrated publication entitled "Protecting the Interests of the Motorist", which is produced annually.

Highways

The Highways Department provides the necessary link between the road user and highway authorities, and is constantly striving for road improvement.

The Department deals with all complaints and suggestions made by members and reports of unsatisfactory road conditions are investigated. In all cases where action is considered to be justified, appropriate representations are made to the authorities concerned, which have taken action in the great majority of the cases brought before them by the RAC.

The RAC seeks to co-operate with authorities in improving road conditions and avoids putting forward non-constructive criticisms.

Proposals for the construction of new roads and the improvement of existing roads are examined, and proposed new traffic regulations and orders, including controlled parking schemes and bus lanes, are investigated.

Objection is lodged by the RAC to any such proposals which appear to be unreasonable or to affect adversely the interests of motorists.

Local authorities which are known to be contemplating parking meter schemes are urged to consider other systems which do not involve charges. These include controlled parking schemes supervised by traffic wardens, without meters, which are operating successfully in many cities and towns, and the parking disc systems which are operated with successful results in twelve towns, i.e. Birkenhead, Harrogate, Ripon, Devizes, Richmond (North Yorks),

Knaresborough, Carlisle, Malton, Northallerton, Whitehaven, Barrow in Furness and Workington.

Standard Department of Transport RAC parking signs, indicating the whereabouts of official car parks, have been supplied by the RAC to highway authorities and erected in many towns throughout the country.

The RAC initiated a traffic signs experiment in 1983 in collaboration with the Department of Transport, the BBC and IBA to advise drivers concerning the radio frequencies of local broadcasting stations (Radio Kent and Radio 210 in Berkshire) providing traffic information services.

RAC driving instruction activities

RAC Registration of Driving Instructors and Schools

In an attempt to reduce the number of road accidents, some of which are attributable to lack of proper instruction of drivers, the Royal Automobile Club instituted fifty years ago an examination and a voluntary system of certification and registration of motor vehicle driving instructors.

Driving instruction acquired a new importance with the advent of the compulsory driving test, and the RAC felt that the time was appropriate for the elevation of the status of instructors, with corresponding advantage to the pupil and an increase in general road safety.

Subsequently, in 1970, a new compulsory registration scheme for driving instructors—on similar lines to the RAC system—was introduced by the Government. It was considered appropriate, however, to continue to operate the RAC Registration Scheme which provides an incentive for instructors to achieve higher standards than the minimum required to obtain official approval.

Names and addresses of RAC Registered Driving Instructors and Driving Schools can be obtained from the Royal Automobile Club, (Register of Instructors), RAC House, Lansdowne Road, Croydon, CR9 2JA, or from any RAC office.

Driving Instructors

The object of registration is to ensure that driving instructors are properly qualified for the job, by investigating:

(a) their character; (moral and general integrity).
(b) their practical ability in the giving of motor driving tuition; (by instructing a novice, provided by the RAC, in front of the Examiner)
(c) their own driving ability and observance of the Highway Code; (by demonstration to the Examiner during the practical test).

Although the examination in connection with the registration of instructors was instituted 50 years ago, continual changes are being made to keep the methods in line with modern developments and conditions. The examination also takes into account the fact that the candidates will be giving driving tuition for gain and, therefore, special attention is paid to the assessment of their ability to teach a pupil up to the required standard in the shortest possible time.

In order that a fee-paying pupil may be in no doubt as to whether he or she is actually receiving instruction from a Registered Instructor, such Instructors have issued to them a certificate in the form of an identity

card bearing their photograph, which is affixed to the fascia panel. In addition, special RAC "L" plates are available for attachment to their cars when instruction is being given.

Driving Schools and Driver Training Centres

The RAC also registers Schools which provide driving instruction. These Schools are inspected by the RAC, and the chief conditions necessary to qualify for approval are that they should have proper office facilities, keep training records and ensure that the majority of the instructors are RAC registered. An RAC Registered Driving Training Centre has approved facilities for indoors instruction.

Registration of instructors, schools and DTC's applies for one year only, but is renewable annually without further examination. From time to time the methods of tuition employed by a Registered Instructor, DTC or School are re-examined in order to ensure that the standard is being maintained.

Statistics

Since the inauguration of the Examination, the RAC has tested over 16,000 instructors, and on 1st January, 1985, about 1,500 instructors held the current RAC certificate for instruction.
Approximately 75 Driving Schools and 8 Driver Training Centres were registered.

Motor cycle section

Motor cyclists, moped riders and owners of three-wheelers enjoy exactly the same facilities as car members. Members benefit additionally from the activities of the RAC Motor Cycle Committee—consisting of many well-known personalities in the motor cycling world—which considers matters affecting the interests of motor cyclists, moped riders and three-wheeler users.

Benefits. Associate motor cyclist members are entitled to all the advantages of Associate membership, as detailed on these pages, including the Rescue Services, and the Recovery Service (for details see p. 22) which is highly recommended for motor cyclists.

A summary of conditions for Associate membership can be found on p. 17.

Activities. The Motor Cycle Section is constantly seeking to improve motor cycling conditions and has been responsible for many legislative reforms. As recommended by the Motor Cycle Committee, representations are made to Government Departments, MPs, local authorities and other organisations about many important matters affecting the interests of motor cyclists.

Legal Representation. Many claims for compensation for personal injuries incurred by members riding motor cycles are successfully negotiated every year under the RAC's Claims Recovery Service. Cover for this risk is outside the scope of the ordinary motor cycle insurance policy and substantial sums of money are frequently involved. The RAC charges a small registration fee (at present £12 inc. VAT), for opening a file but otherwise the cost of the negotiations (except disbursements or such costs as are customarily recoverable from a third party) is borne by the RAC. Free representation in Magistrates' Courts is also available in respect of prosecutions for most motor cycling offences. The Director of Legal Services, in conjunction with the Technical Services Department, is able to give advice and assistance and to conduct negotiations with motor cycle manufacturers, traders, repairers and insurers in regard to all matters relating to the ownership and use of a motor cycle.

Motor Cycle Examinations. It is strongly advised that secondhand machines should be examined before purchase. For particulars of RAC services in this respect, see "Technical Services", p. 31.

Repairers. Much motor cycle and moped repair work is of a specialised nature and riders frequently find it difficult to obtain the assistance services required from ordinary garages. The RAC has appointed a number of Motor Cycle Scooter and Moped Repairers who are equipped to carry out this class of work. In addition, garages are listed which have agreed to assist motor cycle members under the terms of the RAC Rescue and Recovery Service.

Press and public relations

Press and Public Relations ensures that Britain's motoring public is kept constantly informed of RAC activities on its behalf.

Regular contact is maintained with more than 2,000 media outlets covering national, provincial and weekly newspapers, magazines, television and radio stations, to enable RAC views and comments to remain at the forefront of important motoring issues.

The London Press Office gathers road and weather information, reports on traffic hold-ups and handles news of home and foreign motoring services, new governmental legislation and the RAC's continuing efforts to protect the interests of road users.

A fully-equipped broadcasting studio enables the office in Pall Mall to present daily "live" traffic broadcasts to Radio London and Radio Kent. The studio can be linked quickly and easily to many other radio stations in the country and overseas.

Latest technological aids mean that the Press Office is in immediate touch with any developments relating to motoring and can, when necessary, respond without delay on behalf of the motoring public.

The Pall Mall staff also provide features on a wide range of motoring topics, from legal, technical, safety and economy subjects right through to advice on coping with winter and summer motoring in this country and abroad. This service is being constantly expanded and updated.

There is also a photographic darkroom with a library of photographs illustrating all aspects of RAC activities.

In addition to publicising the RAC as the world's leading motoring organisation, the Press Office also handles some information aspects of the RAC Motoring Sports Association, in the Club's important role as controlling body of Motor sport, and of the Clubhouses at Pall Mall and Woodcote Park.

Discover how <u>you</u> can benefit from private medicine with
this new Guide from BUPA
and save 10%* as a member of the RAC

A unique arrangement with hospitals, to keep costs down ▶

An easier way for you to have all the benefits of private medicine – plus a special discount as well ▶

Full details on how simple it is to arrange treatment as a BUPA member ▶

It's yours for the asking.

YOUR GUIDE TO PRIVATE MEDICINE AND WHAT BUPA MEANS TO YOU AND YOUR FAMILY

BUPA makes all the difference

Mobile offices

As part of the policy of bringing personal service to members, RAC Mobile Offices attend important functions, including the major agricultural shows and sporting events in all parts of the country.

Towed by Road Service transport, these Mobile Offices can be quickly moved from place to place in order to provide service and information where it is most needed. Many are equipped with radio.

Throughout the spring and summer, Mobile Offices are located at popular seaside and inland resorts and tourist centres. At any of these offices, existing members can renew their subscriptions. New members can enrol and obtain immediately all the articles of membership, such as badges, keys, membership cards, handbooks and RAC diaries. Maps, atlases, guides, touring information and details of all the services provided by the Club are also available.

RAC/BUPA group

Join the RAC/BUPA Group and get a 10% discount (15% discount if you pay by annual direct debit).

BUPACARE is a health insurance scheme for families and individuals from BUPA, Britain's largest independent health care organisation.

It offers you the advantages of independent medicine, treatment at a time to suit you, a choice of hospitals and specialist, a private room with telephone—all for a subscription you can realistically afford. And as a member of the RAC you are entitled to 10% or 15% discount off the basic rate. The discount could help towards or even cover the cost of your RAC membership.

BUPACARE offers a simple choice of cover, allowing you to tailor the scheme to suit your needs as well as your pocket. It is inflation-protected too, so if hospital accommodation charges rise during your registration year, your subscription is unaffected. And BUPA's unique arrangement with hospitals means that BUPA pays your hospital bills direct.

BUPACARE cover is immediate on joining. (You must, however, be under 65 years of age to join.)

BUPACARE has all the resources, experience and reputation of BUPA, the country's leading independent health care organisation, behind it. A non-profit-making body, BUPA today protects over three million people against the cost of private medical treatment.

BUPA pioneered preventive medicine in the UK and operates medical centres in London, Birmingham, Bristol, Cardiff, Manchester, Nottingham and Glasgow equipped with some of the most advanced diagnostic facilities in the country. The centres are open to the public, but BUPA subscribers qualify for comprehensive health checks at a special reduced rate. Subscribers can also take advantage of BUPA's Worldwide Travel Scheme. Available exclusively to members, the Scheme provides additional medical insurance while travelling abroad.

BUPA has done much to improve and expand independent surgical facilities in the UK. In 1957, it set up Nuffield Hospitals, a charity which today runs 31 modern, surgical hospitals. BUPA has its own hospitals in Bushey, Cardiff, Harpenden, Manchester, Norwich, Portsmouth and Wirral and has plans to develop others throughout the country with preferential terms for subscribers.

To find out how BUPACARE can bring the benefits of independent health care within your reach, write for the free brochure to BUPA (RAC Group), Provident House, Essex Street, London, WC2R 3AX, T 01-353 5212, or contact any BUPA or RAC office.

Publications available to RAC Members

The RAC Handbook and Hotel Guide is just one of a selection of titles published by RAC Motoring Services. These books, maps and atlases can be purchased at any RAC Office (see page 12) or by mail order from the Publications Department at Croydon. Available from the same outlets are a number of Touring Aids. A complete Publications and Touring Aids price list is available free from any RAC Office.

RAC Continental Motoring Guide 1985 This excellent value guide to driving on the Continent, which includes a directory of appointed hotels, is available from 2nd January. £2·95 for members (£3·75 inc p & p); £3·95 for non-members (£4·75 inc p & p).

RAC Motorist's London and 60 Miles Around The pocket book for the London-based motorist. £2·95 (£3·45 inc p & p).

RAC Motorist's Diary 1985 The contents this year include hints and tips for Motorway driving, bad weather driving and towing a caravan or trailer. The diary makes a perfect present for the driving enthusiast. £1·95 (£2·50 inc p & p).

RAC Guide to British and Continental Camping and Caravanning Sites. Jüri Gabriel's mammoth guide to the location and facilities of over 5,600 European sites in 31 countries. £6 (£7·80 inc p & p).

RAC Car Driving for Beginners The standard introduction to car driving. A new edition is available this year. £1·95 (£2·55 inc p & p).

The Complete Learner Driver Norman Sullivan draws on 40 years' experience of driving instruction to help you banish those "L" plates. £4·50 (£5·55 inc p & p).

RAC Motorists' Easy Guide to Car Care and Repair series. Easy-to-use information on the maintenance of the modern car: 1. *How a car works* 2. *Servicing and Care of the Car* 3. *Diagnosis and Repair of Ignition and Carburettor Faults* 4. *Servicing and Care of the Braking System* 5. *Care and Maintenance of Suspension Systems.* £2 (£2·50 inc p & p).

RAC Going Places A series of 12 regional motor tour guides covering mainland Britain. "Handy, practical and cheap"—ENGLISH TOURIST BOARD 1. *Southeast England* 2. *Scotland* 3. *West Country* 4. *Southwest England* 5. *Northwest England* 6. *Southern England* 7. *Home Counties* 8. *East Anglia and Essex* 9. *Central England* 10. *East Midlands* 11. *Wales* 12. *North-East England.* £2·95 (£3·55 inc p & p).

100 Years of Motoring—A social history of the car from its inception in the 1880s to its present position as part of our daily lives. Member's price £11·50 (£13·35 inc p & p).

Maps and Atlases

RAC Map of England and Wales Scale 10 miles to 1 inch. In 4 colours, with town plans. £2·25 (£2·75 inc p & p).

RAC Map of Scotland Scale 8 miles to 1 inch. In 4 colours, with town plans. £2·25 (£2·75 inc p & p).

RAC Map of Ireland Scale 8 miles to 1 inch. In 3 colours, with town plans. £2·25 (£2·75 inc p & p).

RAC Regional Maps In 4 colours with town plans. Scale 3 miles to 1 inch. 1. *South East* 2. *South* 3. *South West* 4. *East Anglia* 5. *Midlands* 6. *South Wales* 7. *Lancashire and North Wales* 8. *Yorkshire* 9. *The North.* Scale 4 miles to 1 inch: 10. *South Scotland* 11. *North Scotland.* £2·25 (£2·80 inc p & p).

RAC London Region Super Planner Scale 1·6 miles to 1 inch. The overall planning map for the area enclosed by the M25. £2·25 (£2·80 inc p & p).

RAC Great Britain Super Planner Scale 10 miles to 1 inch. A single reversible sheet map for route planning. £2·25 (£2·80 inc p & p).

RAC Great Britain Road Atlas Scale 4 miles to 1 inch. A new edition of this popular large format atlas for all who use Britain's roads. £3·50 (£4·50 inc p & p).

RAC London Map The definitive tourist and street map for Central London. £1·25 (£1·75 inc p & p). London.

RAC Navigators These regional atlases combine business and pleasure in the form of Leisure and route planning maps. 1. *South, South East, Thames and Chilterns, London* £5·95 (£7 inc p & p). 2. *The West Country, South Wales, Bristol and Cardiff.* 3. *East and West Midlands* 4. *Northern England, Lakes, Borders, Leeds and Manchester.* £5·50 each *(£6·55 inc p & p).*

RAC Navigator France Scale 8·7 miles to 1 inch. *The* French holiday atlas covering all of Metropolitan France and Corsica. A must for touring. £4·95 (6 inc p & p).

RAC Paris Visitor's Map Scale ¼ mile to 1 inch. A useful map of the capital of France for any visitor. £1·25 (£1·70 inc p & p).

RAC Road Atlas: Europe Completely new large format road atlas of Europe. Mainly 16 miles to 1 inch. £4·95 (£5·95 inc p & p).

Other publications available from RAC Offices
Michelin Maps 408 Netherlands; 409 Belgium; 987 Benelux–Germany–Austria; 988 Italy–Switzerland; 989 France; 990 Spain–Portugal. £1·60 each (£2·25 inc p & p).

Michelin Red Guide France. £6·40 (£7·75 inc p & p).

RAC Touring Aids

Members' price list with order form can be obtained free from RAC offices listed on p. 12, or by post from The Publications Manager, PO Box 100, RAC Motoring Services Ltd, Lansdowne Road, Croydon CR9 2JA.

RAC Advance Warning Triangle Compulsory in most European countries, equally valuable in Britain in case of breakdown or accident, the triangle is sturdily made and folds for easy stowage in your vehicle. £5·65 (£7.45 inc p & p).

PVC Suit Cover Ideal for transporting suits on hangers in cars. Strong, thick and waterproof. £1·50 (£2·15 inc p & p).

RAC Tow Belt Broken down? Need a tow? The RAC retractable tow belt is worth its weight in gold to the stranded motorist. £5·25 (£6·25 inc p & p).

Motorists' Sunglasses A choice of three anti-glare fashionable sunglasses plus clip-ons specially designed with Sunsitive or tinted lenses for motorists. Not suitable for night use. Prices range from £5–£6 (£5·50–£6·50 inc p & p); clip-ons £2·10 (£2·65 inc p & p).

Travellers' Adaptor This travellers' boon fits most types of socket world-wide. You should not be without one. £4·45 (£5 inc p & p).

Headlamp Beam Converters Essential for European motoring, "automatically" converts headlamp beam from left to right. Please quote year, model and make of car when ordering. £2·55 (£3·20 inc p & p).

RAC Key Rings Carry your spare set of ignition keys on an RAC key ring. Choice of 2 designs on leather fobs. 70p (£1·20 inc p & p).

RAC First Aid Kit In a strong plastic case, the first aid kit contains cotton wool, triangular and stretch bandages, safety pins, antiseptic tissue sachets, antiseptic cream, first aid dressings, plasters, scissors and a first aid leaflet. £9·95 (£11·45 inc p & p).

Prices valid at Oct 1984

Motoring in Great Britain

Major Motorways
Motorway Junctions with Restricted Access
See page 40
Motorway Service Areas and Operating Companies See page 41
Motorway Services Map See page 42

Vehicle Ferry Services
Channel Islands See page 44
Isle of Man See page 44
Isles of Scilly See page 44
Isle of Wight See page 44
Scottish Islands See page 45
Firth of Clyde Ferries See page 45
Local Ferries See page 46

Tolls—Bridges, Roads, Tunnels
Tolls in England and Wales See page 48
Tolls in Scotland See page 50

Motoring in London
Selected BR stations with parking places
See page 51
London parking places See page 52
Concert Halls, Theatres and cinemas
See page 54
London street maps See page 56

Planning a route
How to plan a route See page 76
Local radio See page 80
Local radio stations map See page 84
Distance tables See page 85

Major Motorways

Motorway Junctions with Restricted Access
(See Atlas section facing page 320.)

M1 Restrictions for northbound traffic
Jn 2 No exit; Access only from A1
4 No exit; Access only from A41
7 No exit; Access only from M10
17 No access from M45
19 No access from M6
44 No exit; Access only
45 No access; Exit only

M1 Restrictions for southbound traffic
Jn 2 No access; exit to A1 only
4 No access; exit to A41 only
7 No access from M10
17 No exit; access only from M45
19 No access; access only from M6
44 No access; exit only
45 No exit; access only
46 No access; exit only

M2 Restrictions for westbound traffic
Jn 1 Exit to A2 westbound lane only

M2 Restrictions for eastbound traffic
Jn 1 Access from A2 eastbound lane only

M20 Restrictions for westbound traffic
Jn 2 No exit; access only
3 No access; exit only to M20/26 spur
8 Access only from westbound lane of A20

M20 Restrictions for eastbound traffic
Jn 2 No access; exit only
3 No exit; access only from M20/26 spur
8 Exit only to eastbound lane of A20

M23 Restrictions for northbound traffic
Jn 7 Exit only to northbound lane of A23

M23 Restrictions for southbound traffic
Jn 7 Access only from southbound lane of A23

M25 Restrictions for westbound traffic
Jn 5 Access only

M25 Restrictions for eastbound traffic
Jn 5 No access from A21; exit only

M11 Restrictions for northbound traffic
Jn 4 No exit; access only
5 No access; exit only
9 No access; exit only
13 No access; exit only
14 No exit to westbound lane of A45

M11 Restrictions for southbound traffic
Jn 4 No exit to eastbound lane of A406
5 No exit; access only
9 No access; exit only
13 No exit; access only
14 No access from eastbound lane of A45

M27 Restrictions for westbound traffic
Jn 4 Access only from southbound lane of A33 spur
5 Exit only to northbound lane of A33 spur
10 No access; exit only

M27 Restrictions for eastbound traffic
Jn 4 Exit only to northbound lane of A33 spur
5 Access only from southbound lane of A33 spur
10 Access from southbound lane of A32 only

M3 Restrictions for eastbound traffic
Jn 8 Access only from eastbound lanes of A30 and A31

M4 Restrictions for westbound traffic
Jn 1 Access only from westbound lane of A4
29 No access; exit only
38 No access; exit only
39 No exit; access only
41 No exit; access only
46 No access; exit only

M4 Restrictions for eastbound traffic
Jn 1 Exit only to eastbound lane of A4
29 No exit; access only from A48(M)
39 No exit; no access
41 No access; exit only
46 No exit; access only from A48 and B4489

M40 Restrictions for westbound traffic
Jn 3 No access; exit only

M40 Restrictions for eastbound traffic
Jn 3 No exit; access only from A40
7 No exit; access only

M5 Restrictions for northbound traffic
Jn 10 No exit; access only
12 No access; exit only
29 No access; exit only

M5 Restrictions for southbound traffic
Jn 10 No access; exit only
12 No exit; access only
19 No exit; access only

M53 Restrictions for northbound traffic
Jn 11 No exit; access only from M56 westbound lane

M53 Restrictions for southbound traffic
Jn 11 No access; exit only to M56 eastbound lane

M56 Restrictions for westbound traffic
Jn 1 No exit to M63
2 No access; exit only
3 No exit; access only
4 No access; exit only
7 No access; exit only
8 No exit; access only
9 No access to M6 southbound
15 No access from M53; exit to M53 northbound only

M56 Restrictions for eastbound traffic
Jn 1 Exit to A34 northbound lane and M63 eastbound lane only
2 No exit; access only
3 No access; exit only
4 No exit; access only
8 No access; no exit
9 No access from M6 northbound
15 No exit to M53; access only from M53 southbound

M57 Restrictions for northbound traffic
Jn 3 No exit; access only

M57 Restrictions for southbound traffic
Jn 3 No access; exit only

M58 Restrictions for westbound traffic
Jn 1 No exit; access only

M58 Restrictions for eastbound traffic
Jn 1 No exit; access only

M6 Restrictions for northbound traffic
Jn 5 No access; exit only
10A No access from M54; exit only
24 No access; exit only
25 No access; exit only
30 No exit; access only from M61

M6 Restrictions for southbound traffic
Jn 5 No exit; access only
10A No exit; access only from M54
24 No access; exit only
25 No access; exit only
30 No access; exit only to M61

M61 Restrictions for northbound traffic
Jn 2 No access from eastbound lane of A580
3 No access

M61 Restrictions for southbound traffic
Jn 2 No exit to westbound lane of A580

M62 Restrictions for westbound traffic
Jn 14A No access from and no exit to A580
15 No access; exit only
23 No exit; access only

M62 Restrictions for eastbound traffic
Jn 14A No access from and no exit to A580
15 No exit; access only
23 No exit; access only

M63 Restrictions for westbound traffic
Jn 5 No access; exit only
10 No exit to northbound lane of A34; no access from M56
11 No exit

M63 Restrictions for eastbound traffic
Jn 5 No exit; access only
10 Exit only to southbound lane of A34; no exit to M56
11 No access; exit only

M65 Restrictions for westbound traffic
Jn 9 No exit; access only
11 No access; exit only

M65 Restriction for eastbound traffic
Jn 9 No access; exit only
11 No exit; access only

M66 Restrictions for northbound traffic
Jn 1 No access; exit only
M66 Restrictions for southbound traffic
Jn 1 No exit; access only

M67 Restrictions for westbound traffic
Jn 1 No exit; access only
2 No access; exit only
M67 Restrictions for eastbound traffic
Jn 1 No access; exit only
2 No exit; access only

M69 Restrictions for northbound traffic
Jn 2 No exit; access only
M69 Restrictions for southbound traffic
Jn 2 No access; exit only

M73 Restrictions for northbound traffic
Jn 2 No exit to A89; no access from A89 or M8
3 Exit only to northbound lane of A80
M73 Restrictions for southbound traffic
Jn 2 No access from A89; no exit to A89 or M8
3 Access only from southbound lane of A80

M74 Restrictions for northbound traffic
Jn 3 No exit; access only from A72
M74 Restrictions for southbound traffic
Jn 3 No access; exit only

M8 Restrictions for westbound traffic
Jn 8 Access from westbound lanes of A8, A89 and northbound lane of M73 only
9 No exit; access only
14 No exit; access only
16 No access; exit only
20 No access; exit only
21 No access; exit only
22 No access; exit only
23 No access; exit only
M8 Restrictions for eastbound traffic
Jn 9 No access; exit only
14 No access; exit only
16 No exit; access only
19 No access; exit only
20 No access; exit only
21 Neither exit nor access
22 Access only from M77
23 No exit; access only from B768

M80 Restrictions for northbound traffic
Jn 5 No access from M876; exit only
M80 Restrictions for southbound traffic
Jn 5 No access; access only from M876

M9 Restrictions for westbound traffic
Jn 1 No access; exit only to A8000 spur
2 No exit; access only
3 No access; exit only
5 No access; exit only
6 No exit; access only from A904 and A906
8 No access from M876; exit only
M9 Restrictions for eastbound traffic
Jn 1 No access; access only from A8000 spur
2 No access; exit only
3 No exit; access only
5 No exit; access only

6 No access; exit to A905 only
8 No exit to M876; access only

M90 Restrictions for northbound traffic
Jn 7 No exit; access only from A91
8 No access; exit only
10 No access from A912
M90 Restrictions for southbound traffic
Jn 7 No access; exit only
8 No exit; access only
10 No exit to A917

M180 Restrictions for westbound traffic
Jn 1 No exit; access only
M180 Restrictions for eastbound traffic
Jn 1 No access; exit only

A1(M) Restrictions for northbound traffic
Jn with A6129 No exit; access only
with A66(M) No access from A66(M)
with A69 No access; exit only
A1(M) Restrictions for southbound traffic
Jn with A69 No exit; access only
with A66(M) No exit; access only
with A6129 No access; exit to southbound lane of A1 only

A3(M) Restrictions for northbound traffic
Jn with unclassified road. No access; exit only
A3(M) Restrictions for southbound traffic
Jn with unclassified road. No exit; access only

Motorway Service Areas and Operating Companies

M1
1. **Scratchwood** (Trusthouse Forte)
2. **Toddington** (Granada)
3. **Newport Pagnell** (Trusthouse Forte)
4. **Rothersthorpe** (Blue Boar)
5. **Watford Gap** (Blue Boar)
6. **Leicester Forest East** (Motoross)
7. **Trowell** (Granada)
8. **Woodall** (Trusthouse Forte)
9. **Woolley Edge** (Granada)

A1(M)
10. **Washington-Birtley** (Granada)

M2
11. **Farthing Corner** (Rank)

M3
12. **Fleet** (Trusthouse Forte)

M4
13. **Heston** (Granada)
14. **Membury** (Motoross)
15. **Leigh Delamere** (Granada)

16. **Aust** (Rank)
17. **Tredegar Park** (Proposed site)
18. **Croyton** (Proposed site)
19. **Sarn** (Sarn Park)
20. **Pont Abraham** (Roadchef)

M5
21. **Frankley** (Granada)
22. **Strensham** (Kenning)
23. **Michael Wood** (Motoross)
24. **Gordano** (Trusthouse Forte)
25. **Taunton Deane** (Roadchef)
26. **Exeter** (Granada)

M6
27. **Corley** (Trusthouse Forte)
28. **Hilton Park** (Rank)
29. **Keele** (Trusthouse Forte)
30. **Sandbach** (Roadchef)
31. **Knutsford** (Rank)
32. **Charnock Richard** (Trusthouse Forte)
33. **Forton** (Rank)
34. **Burton West** (northbound only) (Granada)

35. **Killington Lake** (southbound only) (Roadchef)
36. **Tebay West** (northbound only) (Westmorland)
37. **Southwaite** (Granada)

M8
38. **Harthill** (Roadchef)

M27
39. **Rownhams** (Roadchef)

M61
40. **Anderton** (Kenning)

M62
41. **Burtonwood** (Trusthouse Forte)
42. **Birch** (Granada)
43. **Hartshead Moor** (Motoross)
44. **Ferrybridge** (Granada) (Opening Easter 1985)

M74
45. **Hamilton** (northbound only) (Roadchef)
46. **Bothwell** (southbound only) (Roadchef)

M90
47. **Kinross** (Granada)

See Motorway Service Areas map overleaf.

LONDON TO EDINBURGH, BRISTOL TO LEEDS AND BOURNEMOUTH TO DOWNTOWN ULLAPOOL!

As a lesson in geography, this map shows where some of our major towns and cities are, together with a few scenic places too.

As a lesson in where to find the best hotels it's more useful, because it tells you where to find Ladbroke Hotels.

And to save you counting up all our little 'L's', there are 33 of them.

Unfortunately our map isn't able to show that all our rooms have a private bathroom, colour TV, radio and tea and coffee tray. But we're working on it!

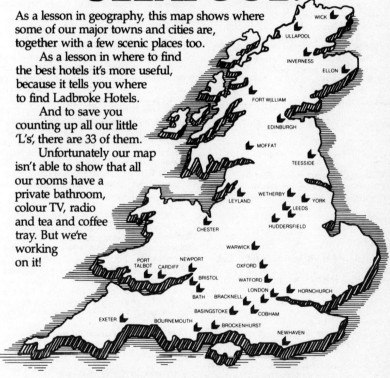

◣ Ladbroke Hotels

Central reservations: LONDON 01-734 6000 Telex 897618
LEEDS (0532) 872717 Telex 556324 EDINBURGH 031-343 3111 Telex 727979

43

Vehicle Ferry Services

Unless otherwise stated, reservations are required and should be made well in advance with the appropriate company. RAC OFFICES CAN ARRANGE RESERVATIONS FOR THE CHANNEL ISLANDS (SEALINK), ORKNEY AND SHETLAND (P&O), AND ISLE OF MAN SERVICES ONLY. Further details of any of the following services can be obtained direct from the relevant company, RAC Touring Services Information, Croydon or any RAC Area Office. Solo motorcycles and scooters usually accepted without booking. All vehicles carried at owners risk. Unless stated, all services are drive on/drive off.
* time in transit. *Compiled July 1984.*

Channel Islands (Jersey, Guernsey and Alderney)

Operator—Sealink UK Ltd

PORTSMOUTH AND WEYMOUTH TO ST PETER PORT (GUERNSEY) AND ST HELIER (JERSEY)
* between 7–11 hrs Portsmouth to Guernsey, 7¼–9½ hrs, Portsmouth to Jersey, 4½–12 hrs, Weymouth to Guernsey, 6¼–8¾ hrs Weymouth to Jersey.
Daily sailings from Portsmouth and Weymouth during summer. Advance reservation essential for all vehicles, which can be made to Sealink offices in London, Portsmouth, Weymouth or any RAC office.

Operator—Torbay Seaways
5 Beacon Quay, Torquay, Devon
T. Torquay (0803) 211974

TORQUAY TO GUERNSEY AND ALDERNEY
*6 hrs to Guernsey, 5¼ hrs to Alderney.
Sailings to Alderney and Guernsey on certain days between May and September only. Advance reservations essential due to limited number of vehicles carried on each sailing. Vehicles loaded by crane.

Isle of Man

Operator—Isle of Man Steam Packet Co. Ltd
PO Box 5, Douglas, I.O.M.
T. Douglas (0624) 3887/4564 (car reservations)
(0624) 3824 (motorcycle reservations)

LIVERPOOL TO DOUGLAS
*4 hrs. Up to 4 sailings daily during season. Also during season from Fleetwood, Ardrossan, Dublin and Belfast.
Reservations essential for all vehicles.
N.B. Towed caravans are not permitted on the island. The island has 500 miles of excellent motoring roads.

Operator—Sealink UK Ltd
Sea Terminal, Heysham, Lancs, LA3 2XF
T. (0524) 53802

HEYSHAM TO DOUGLAS
*3¾ hr. Twice daily during season including Sundays. Reservations essential for all vehicles.

Isles of Scilly

Operator—Isles of Scilly Steamship Co. Ltd
16 Quay Street, Penzance. T. Penzance (0736) 2009/4013, and Hugh Street, Hugh Town, St. Mary's. T. Scillonia (0720) 22357/8.

PENZANCE TO ST MARY'S
*Approx 2½ hr. Sailings vary according to season: twice daily between late March and early October, some Sunday sailings between mid-May and mid-September only; up to eight sailings weekly remainder of year. Advance booking essential during summer months. Reservations for vehicles essential. N.B. Motorable roads on St Mary's total approx 9 miles.

Isle of Wight

Operator—Sealink Isle of Wight Services
PO Box 59, Portsmouth, PO1 2XB.
T. Portsmouth (0705) 827744.

LYMINGTON TO YARMOUTH
*30 mins. Number of daily sailings varies according to season, however approx every 30 mins. during the day in summer. Advance reservations recommended for all sailings, but not made for motorcycles and motorscooters as they are conveyed as space permits.
Reservations should be made by post or telephone to the above address. Application for travel on any day except Fridays, Saturdays, and Sundays May–September can also be made by post or telephone to: Sealink Car Ferry Booking Office, Lymington Pier, Lymington, Hants, SO4 8ZE. T. Lymington (0590) 73301. Returns valid via Fishbourne–Portsmouth or Cowes–Southampton, subject to space available and any excess charge paid.

PORTSMOUTH TO FISHBOURNE
*Approx 35/45 mins. Number of daily sailings varies according to season, however every ½ hour or hour during summer. Advance reservations recommended for all sailings, but not made for motorcycles and motorscooters as they are conveyed as space permits. Reservations should be made by post or telephone to the Portsmouth address. Returns valid via Yarmouth–Lymington or Cowes–Southampton, subject to space available and any excess charge paid.

Operator—Red Funnel Ferries
12 Bugle Street, Southampton, SO9 4LJ.
T. Southampton (0703) 26211

SOUTHAMPTON TO COWES
*55 mins. to E. Cowes, via W. Cowes 70 mins.
During summer between 11–18 sailings daily.
Reservations required in both directions and should be made well in advance to the above address. Reservations not required for motorcycles, these are conveyed by all services when space permits. The vehicle service is primarily between Southampton and East Cowes, but limited space may be available for cars embarking at West Cowes on certain sailings.

Scottish Islands: Orkney and Shetland

Operator—P&O Ferries
PO Box 5, P&O Ferries Terminal, Jamieson's Quay, Aberdeen, AB9 8DL. T. Aberdeen (0224) 572615.

SCRABSTER TO STROMNESS (ORKNEY)
*2 hrs. 1–3 sailings Monday to Saturday throughout year. Sunday sailings July and August only. Advance reservation for vehicles recommended.

ABERDEEN TO LERWICK (SHETLAND)
*14 hrs. 3 sailings weekly throughout year. Advance reservation for vehicles recommended.

Operator—Orkney Islands Shipping Co.
4 Ayre Road, Kirkwall, Orkney. T. Kirkwall (0856) 2044

KIRKWALL TO EDAY, EGILSAY, NORTH RONALDSAY, PAPA WESTRAY, ROUSAY, SANDAY, SHAPINSAY, STRONSAY, WESTRAY, WYRE
    Certain weekdays only. Advance booking recommended due to limited capacity. Vehicles loaded by crane.

FLOTTA, HOY, FLOTTA, MAINLAND (ORKNEY)
    Certain days only. Reservations to Company's Houton office. T. Orphir (085 681) 397.

    Information on local services within Shetland Islands available from: Shetland Islands Council, Lerwick. T. Burravoe (095 782) 259 or 268.

Scottish Islands—Hebrides

Operator—Western Ferries (Argyll) Ltd
16 Woodside Crescent, Glasgow, G3 7UT
T. 041 332 9766

ISLAY–JURA
    Port Askaig (Islay)–Feolin (Jura)
*5 mins. Up to 10 sailings daily Monday to Saturday. 3–4 sailings on Sundays according to season. Advance reservations not required.

Operator—Caledonian MacBrayne Ltd
The Ferry Terminal, Gourock, PA19 1QP.
T. Gourock (0475) 33755   (General enquiries)
    Gourock (0475) 34664/6 (Car Reservations—
                        Western Isles)
    The following services are operated by the above company:—

GIGHA—Tayinloan to Gigha
*20 mins. Frequent daily sailings according to season. Vehicle reservations not required. Caravans not conveyed.

ISLAY—Kennacraig to Port Ellen or Port Askaig
*Approx 2 hrs. Daily. Vehicle reservations required.

LISMORE—Oban to Lismore
*60 mins. Certain sailings Monday–Saturday only. Vehicle reservations arranged with Caledonian MacBrayne office in Oban. T. Oban (0631) 62285. Caravans not conveyed.

COLONSAY—Oban to Colonsay
*2½ hrs. 3 sailings weekly. Not Sunday. Vehicle reservations required. Caravans not conveyed.

MULL—Oban to Craignure
*45 mins. Daily. Number of daily sailings varies according to season. Vehicle reservations required.

MULL—Fishnish to Lochaline
*15 mins. Continuous service throughout day, Monday to Saturday only. Advance reservations not required.

COLL AND TIREE—Oban to Coll to Tiree (via Lochaline and Tobermory)
*Approx 3¼–5¾ hrs. to Coll, 4–5 hrs to Tiree. 3–5 sailings weekly according to season. Vehicle reservations required.

SKYE—Mallaig to Armadale
*30 mins. 1–5 sailings daily according to season. Vehicle reservations required.

SKYE—Kyle of Lochalsh–Kyleakin
*5 mins. Frequent daily sailings—Monday to Saturday from 0600 hrs. (not Saturday) until 2315 hrs. Sunday 1015 hrs to 1745 hrs. (Summer to 2115 hrs). Advance reservations not required.

RAASAY—Raasay–Sconser (Isle of Skye)
*15 mins. 1–6 sailings daily according to season. Not Sunday. Advance reservations not required.

BARRA and SOUTH UIST—Oban to Castlebay (Barra) and Lochboisdale (South Uist)
*5½–9 hrs. to Barra, 6–9 hrs to South Uist. 3–4 sailings weekly to Barra, 3–6 sailings weekly to South Uist according to season. Vehicle reservations required.

NORTH UIST and HARRIS—Uig (Skye)–Tarbert (Harris) and/or Lochmaddy (N. Uist)
*Approx 2–4½ hrs. from Uig to Tarbert, 2–2½ hrs. from Uig to Lochmaddy, 2½ hrs from Tarbert to Lochmaddy. Daily sailings (not Sundays). Vehicle reservations required.

LEWIS—Ullapool to Stornoway
*3½ hrs. 1–2 sailings daily (not Sundays) according to season. Vehicle reservations required.

Firth of Clyde Ferries

Operator—Caledonian MacBrayne Ltd
COWAL—Gourock to Dunoon
*20 mins. 12–14 sailings daily inc. Sundays. Advance reservations not required.

BUTE—Wemyss Bay to Rothesay
*30 mins. 4–13 sailings daily according to season. Advance reservations not required.

BUTE—Colintraive to Rhubodach
*5 mins. Frequent daily service inc. Sundays. Advance reservations not required.

CUMBRAE—Largs to Cumbrae Slip
*10 mins. Frequent daily service inc. Sundays. Advance reservations not required.

ARRAN—Cloanaig (Kintyre) to Lochranza (Arran)
*30 mins. 6–8 daily sailings inc. Sunday. Service from May to September only. Advance reservations not required.

ARRAN—Ardrossan to Brodick
*1 hr. Number of daily sailings (inc. Sundays) vary according to season. Advance vehicle reservations should be made to Caledonian MacBrayne. T. Gourock (0475) 34531/3.

Operator—Western Ferries (Argyll) Ltd
16 Woodside Crescent, Glasgow G3 7UT. T. 041 332 9766.

DUNOON (HUNTERS QUAY)–GOUROCK (McINROYS POINT)
*20 mins. Frequent daily service. Advance reservations not required.

Local Ferries

In the interest of safety, members should endeavour to ensure that vehicles taken on ferries are not parked so close together as to prevent their occupants from opening the doors in case of emergency.

Ferries on Trunk Roads
Owing to the considerable volume of traffic using these ferries, delays are likely, particularly at weekends during the summer.

The times of some ferries vary according to season. Fares are levied on the following services, unless otherwise stated. Further information may be obtained from Touring Services Information, RAC, Croydon.

Care is required with low built cars and towing caravans, etc, when boarding and leaving certain ferries.
* Time in transit. Figures in brackets after time in transit show number of cars carried at each crossing.

ENGLAND

Bodinnick–Fowey Cornwall
*5 min. (6). Continuous service daily from dawn to dusk. During the summer period service operates between 7 a.m. to 8.45 p.m. Weight limit 2½ tons. Drivers should engage low gear when leaving the ferry. Approaches difficult for trailer caravan. Rec. route via Lostwithiel. T. Polruan (072 687) 232.

Bournemouth, Sandbanks–
Swanage, Shell Bay, Dorset
*5 min. (28). 1st Monday in May until 1st Sunday in October. From Sandbanks: 7 a.m. and 7.30 a.m., 8 a.m. to 9 p.m. every 20 mins.; 9 p.m. to 10 p.m. half-hourly. On Fridays, Saturdays, Sundays, Bank Holidays (except Christmas Day and New Years Day) and daily from the last Monday in May until 2nd Sunday in September at 10.30 and 11 p.m. From Shell Bay: similar frequency

only 10 mins. later, 1st Monday in October until 1st Sunday in May: from Sandbanks 7 a.m. and 7.30 a.m. (from 7.30 a.m. on Sundays), 8 a.m. to 7 p.m. every 20 mins.; 7 p.m. to 9 p.m. half-hourly. On Fridays, Saturdays, Sundays and Bank Holidays (except Christmas Day and New Years Day) from 9.30 p.m. to 11 p.m. half-hourly. From Shell Bay: similar frequency only 10 mins. later. T Studland (092 944) 203.

Bowness–Far Sawrey (Windermere Ferry), Cumbria
*5 mins. (10). Summer 6.50 a.m. to 9.50 p.m. weekdays, 9.10 a.m. to 9.50 p.m. Sundays. Winter 6.50 a.m. to 8.50 p.m. weekdays, 9.50 a.m. to 8.50 p.m. Sundays. Service normally every 20 mins., but every 15 mins. during busy periods. No service Dec. 25th and 26th; New Years Day service 10.10 a.m. to 5.30 p.m. Weight limit 10 tons laden.

Cowes East–Cowes West I. of W.
*2 min. (12–15). From East Cowes; weekdays 5.35 a.m. to 11.15 p.m. plus 12 mdnt. Sundays 7.05 a.m. to 11.15 p.m. plus 12 mdnt. From West Cowes weekdays 5.30 a.m. to 11.20 p.m. plus 12.10 a.m. Sundays 7 a.m. to 11.20 p.m. plus 12.10 a.m. At short intervals. Special bridge. After 12.15 a.m. 24-hr notice required plus £3.00 retaining fee. Weight limit 12 tons. T Cowes (0983) 293041.

Dartmouth–Kingswear Floating Bridge
Higher Ferry, Devon
*5 min. (18). 6.30 a.m. to 10.50 p.m. Sundays from 9 a.m. to 10.50 p.m. Vehicles taken at owner's risk. Weight limit 16 tons. T Dartmouth (080 43) 3351.

Dartmouth–Kingswear
Lower Ferry, Devon
*3 min. (8). Weekdays from 7 a.m., Sundays from 8 a.m. Continuous service, double track service during summer. Last ferry from Dartmouth 10.55 p.m., from Kingswear 10.45 p.m. Weight limit 10 tons. T Kingswear (080 425) 342.

Devonport Devon–**Torpoint** Cornwall
*7 min. (30) (Winter) Weekdays and Sundays. From Torpoint: hourly from 1 a.m. to 5 a.m.; half-hourly 5 a.m. to 6.30 a.m. (Mon. to Fri.); half hourly 5 a.m. to 7 a.m. (Sat. and Sun.); quarter-hourly, 6.30 a.m. to 9.30 p.m. (Mon. to Fri); quarter-hourly 7 a.m. to 9.30 p.m. (Sat. and Sun.); half-hourly 9.30 p.m. to 1 a.m. (daily). From Devonport: hourly 1.15 a.m. to 5.15 a.m.; half-hourly 5.15 a.m. to 6.45 a.m. (Mon. to Fri.); half-hourly 5.15 a.m. to 7.15 a.m. (Sat. & Sun.); quarter-hourly 6.45 a.m. to 9.45 p.m. (Mon. to Fri.); quarter-hourly 7.15 a.m. to 9.45 p.m. (Sat. and Sun.); half-hourly 9.45 p.m. to 1.15 a.m. (daily). (Summer) From 1st April to 30th Sept. 3 ferries operating.
North Ferry: Leaves Torpoint 20 mins. to and 10 mins. past the hour, and from Devonport 5 mins. to and 25 mins. past the hour.
Centre Ferry: Leaves Torpoint 10 mins. to and 20 mins. past the hour and from Devonport 5 mins. past and 35 mins. to the hour.
South Ferry: Leaves Torpoint on the hour and half-hour and from Devonport quarter to and quarter past the hour.

Weight limit normally 16 tons gross. Extreme caution to be taken for vehicles towing trailers, caravans and vehicles fitted with towbars when boarding and leaving ferries. T Plymouth (0752) 812233 (at night, Plymouth (0752) 361577).

Feock–Philleigh (King Harry Ferry) Cornwall
*5 min. (28). Weekdays from 8 a.m. to 8.15 p.m. mid-May to mid-July and during Sept.; to 9.15 p.m. from mid-July and Aug.; to 6.15 p.m. Oct. to Whitsun. Sundays April to September only, as weekdays but starting at 10 a.m. Bank Hols. and Good Friday as Sundays. No service Christmas Day and Boxing Day. Half-hourly service, from King Harry (Feock) at the hour and ½ hr., from Philleigh at the ¼ and ¾ hr. Vehicles taken at owner's risk. Max. gross weight per vehicle 16 tons. T Truro (0872) 862312 and 862298. Office, Truro (0872) 72463.

Loddon–Reedham Norfolk
*2–5 mins. (2) 8 a.m. to 10 p.m. weekdays and Sundays. In emergency, after hours, by special arrangement. Weight limit 20 tons. T Gt. Yarmouth (0493) 700429.

Woolwich Gtr London
*6 min. (50). Weekdays from 6 a.m. (6.10 a.m. N. Side), every 10 or 20 min. Last crossings 10.15 p.m. S side, 10.30 p.m. N. side. Sundays from 7.40 a.m. (7.55 a.m. N. side) approx. every 30 mins. Last crossings 9.45 p.m. S. side, 10 p.m. N. side. Limits: weight 4 tons on any one wheel, wheel base 8 ft 3 ins, height 14 ft 6 ins, width overall 12 ft 6 ins, length inc trailer and space between 70 ft. Free ferry. T 01-854 3488. (*Marine supt.*)

SCOTLAND

Corran–Ardgour Strathclyde
*6 min. (20). Summer: weekdays 7.40 a.m. to 9 p.m., Sundays 9 a.m. to 9 p.m. Winter: weekdays 7.40 a.m. to 6.30 p.m. Sundays 10 a.m. to 6.30 p.m. Weight limit 32 tons. Tides and weather conditions affect running of ferry. T Ardgour (085 55) 243.

Cuan Strathclyde, Seil-Luing
*12 min. approx. (5). Apr.–Sept. 8 a.m. to 6 p.m. March & Oct. 8 a.m. to 5 p.m. Nov. to Feb. 8 a.m. to 4 p.m. Weekdays only. Tide and weather conditions permitting. Weight limit 13 tons laden. Time-table on notice board near Kilninver Post Office.

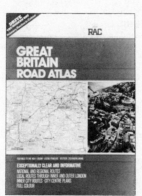

Tolls—Bridges, Roads, Tunnels

mc *motor cycle* mcs *motor cycle and sidecar*
motor scooters are normally rated as for motor cycles
tr *trailer caravan*   3w *three-wheeler*
L *lorry*   tv *trade van*   ltr *luggage trailer*

N.B. Tolls subject to alteration.

Tolls in England and Wales

Avon

BATHAMPTON BRIDGE
Car 10p: car and trailer 12p: car/caravan 15p: mc and mcs 5p.

CLIFTON SUSPENSION BRIDGE
Pedestrians, pedal cycles, invalid carriages 2p: all vehicles under 3 tons 20p: heavy lorries, coaches and trailer caravans not accepted.

KEWSTOKE WOOD ROAD Weston-super-Mare–Kewstoke
Cars and vans 30p: mcs mc 10p: tr motor caravan L tv 30p: coaches £1.

SEVERN ROAD BRIDGE
Mc 10p: car 20p: lorries, buses and coaches 40p: breakdown assistance: £15 for first ½ hour or part of, then £6 for every ensuing ¼ hour.

Berkshire

WHITCHURCH BRIDGE Pangbourne–Whitchurch
Motor vehicles: 3 wheels 3p: 4 wheels 4p: 6 or more wheels 6p: car and ltr, car and tr 2 wheels 6p: 4 wheels 6p: mcs 3p. mc 2p: pedestrians free. Weight limit 10 tons.

Cleveland

MIDDLESBROUGH TRANSPORTER BRIDGE
Middlesbrough–Port Clarence
Takes 1½ mins: max. 9 vehicles. From Middlesbrough 5 a.m. to 10.50 p.m. Mon.–Sat., 2 p.m. to 10.50 p.m. Sun. Car, 3w, motor caravan, tv 40p: tr 70p: mc, mcs 20p: lorry 95p. Coaches not allowed. Max. weight 3 tons: max. length 20 ft: max. height 10 ft.

Cornwall

TAMAR BRIDGE Saltash–Plymouth
See Devon

Devon

HOBBY DRIVE, CLOVELLY
Open 10 a.m. to 6 p.m. 7 days a week. (Easter–end Oct.). Entrance from A39 only. Commercial vehicles and mc not allowed: car £1.10: bicycles 5p: pedestrians free.

LEE ABBEY Valley of Rocks
Cars 20p each way, Parking 20p, mc mcs 10p each way: no coaches or vehicles over 7 seats.

TAMAR BRIDGE Plymouth–Saltash
All classes of vehicle 40p: except goods vehicles over 3.5 tons, 2 axles unladen 90p: 3 axles £1.35: 4 or more axles £1.80: ltr and tr same rate as towing vehicle. No charge for breakdowns. Tolls levied on vehicles leaving Cornwall only (i.e. Eastwards).

Dorset

SWANAGE, Studland–SHELL BAY
Charges only applicable to vehicles not using ferry, car & driver 20p: trailer 20p: mcs 10p: mc 5p: passenger 10p.

Dyfed

CLEDDAU BRIDGE
Cars, motor caravans, tv/caravan/tr up to 2 tons, minibuses with up to 15 seats 40p: vehicles, tr & ltr over 2 tons: coaches 80p: mc, mcs, 3w 20p.

Essex

DARTFORD–PURFLEET TUNNEL
See Kent.

Greater London

DULWICH COLLEGE ROAD Dulwich–Sydenham
Cars & mcs 5p: lorries and heavy vehicles 30p.

Greater Manchester

WARBURTON BRIDGE Warburton–Irlam
motor vehicle under 2 tons 10p: 2 to 5 tons max. 12½p: mc 5p: mcs 5p: cycles free. Weight limit 5 tons.

Gwynedd

BRIWET (Penrhyndeudraeth–Harlech) TOLL BRIDGE
Car 15p with tr 20p: tv 20p: mc, mcs 15p: weight restriction 2 tons. Toll fees apply between 7 a.m. and 9 p.m.

MARINE DRIVE Llandudno–Great Orme's Head
Car 35p: tr 10p: mc & mcs 20p: open dawn–dusk.

PENMAENPOOL BRIDGE Barmouth–Tywyn
Car 15p with ltr or tr 30p: mc 10p: mcs 10p: Landrovers, minibus 15p: L 15p (1½ tons per axle). Closed 11 p.m. to 7 a.m.

PORTHMADOG EMBANKMENT
Penrhyndeudraeth–Porthmadog
All classes of vehicle 5p except car and trailer/caravan 10p. Toll fees apply 7 a.m. to 7 p.m. (Summer) and 7 a.m. to 5 p.m. (Winter).

Hampshire

ELING BRIDGE Totton–Hythe
Mc 10p: cars and lorries 20p.

ITCHEN BRIDGE Southampton–Woolston
mc 10p: cars with or without trailer, light vans, other vehicles under 1 ton 30p (peak periods Mon.–Fri. 6.00 a.m. to 9.30 a.m. and 4.00 p.m. to 6.30 p.m.), 20p (all other times): buses, commercial vehicles 1–3 tons 40p, over 3 tons (2 axles only) £1·60, over 3 tons with 3 or more axles £15.

Hereford & Worcester

WHITNEY-ON-WYE Whitney–Hay
Car and passengers 20p: mc mcs 10p: ltr tr 5p: bicycles 5p: coaches 40p: motor caravan L tv from 20p–30p: Weight limit 10 tons.

Humberside

HUMBER BRIDGE Barton upon Humber to Hessle
Motor cycles 50p: cars and light vans £1: light commercial vehicles, mini buses and cars and light vans with trailers £2: heavy commercial vehicles: 2 axles £4·50: 3 axles £6: 4 or more axles £7·50: buses and coaches £4·50.

Isle of Wight

SALTERNS ROAD Spring Vale–Seaview
Car 10p: mc 5p: coaches per head 2p: lorries 20p.

Kent

DARTFORD–PURFLEET TUNNEL
Car 60p: mc mcs 20p: tv up to 30 cwts unladen £1: heavy goods vehicles £1·60: tr ltr same rate as towing vehicle. Breakdown assistance: first 15 min. £15, each add. 10 min. or part £5. Vehicles with less than 4 wheels, first 15 min. £5, each additional 10 min. or part £2. Where it is considered by the tunnel staff that the breakdown could have been avoided by the driver of the vehicle, i.e. shortage of petrol, an additional £25 charge is made in respect of all vehicles.

LOWER SANDGATE ROAD, FOLKESTONE
Cars 30p.

SANDWICH–SANDWICH BAY
Cars and light vans £2: mc, mcs 50p: trailers £2: coaches £10. No charge for L and tv on business. Caravans and motor caravans not admitted.

Lancashire

CARTFORD BRIDGE Great Eccleston–Nateby
Car including driver and passengers 10p: mc 5p: car and tr, van or minibus inc. driver 15p: lorry or bulk tanker, or bus or coach and driver up to 0 tons–15p, over 6 tons–30p. Weight limit 12 tons.

SHARD BRIDGE Little Singleton–Hambleton
All vehicles with two or more wheels, driver and passengers, not exceeding 2 tons, unladen weight 8p: 2 to 6 tons 15p: tr 8p: exceeding 6 tons unladen weight 30p: two wheel vehicles including driver and passengers 4p: mc sidecar or trailer including driver and passengers 4p: bus or coach 30p. Free use allowed on production of two tickets for the current day.

Vehicles must remain not less than 20 feet apart when crossing: weight limit 12 tons.

Lincolnshire

DUNHAM TOLL BRIDGE Markham Moor–Lincoln
Car 15p: 3w 10p: mc 10p: mcs 10p: car and tr 20p: L tv 20p: L 6 wheels 30p: 8 wheels 40p: 10 wheels 50p: motor coaches 30p. Width restriction 12 ft: weight limit 38 tons.

Merseyside

KINGSWAY AND QUEENSWAY TUNNELS
Vehicles not over 3 tons unladen weight 40p, over 3 tons £1: mc 20p: no charge for trailers. Breakdown assistance: due to fuel shortage and flat tyre (no spare) £27: other causes £28 per hour (minimum £7). Maximum speed limit: Queensway Tunnel 30 mph: Kingsway Tunnel 40 mph.

North Yorkshire

ALDWARK BRIDGE Little Ouseburn–Aldwark
Car 8p: mc 4p: mcs 5p: cycles 1p: pedestrians 1p: car & caravan, motor caravan 12p: Lorries 8p per ton up to 8 tons.

SELBY BRIDGE Selby–York
Car 5p: car and trailer 10p: mc 1p: L tv 5p per ton, weight unlimited.

Oxfordshire

SWINFORD BRIDGE Eynsham–Oxford
Car 2p: mc 1p: mcs 2p: car and tr 4p. Weight limit 32 tons. Vehicles over 2 tons 2p per ton.

Shropshire

KINGSLAND BRIDGE Shrewsbury–Kingsland
Mc 2p: cars 5p: cyclists 1p: pedestrians ½p. Large vehicles 10p per ton. Weight limit 3 tons.

Somerset

PORLOCK HILL PRIVATE ROAD Porlock–Lynmouth
Cars 30p: vans 50p: mc and mcs 15p: cars with caravan or trailer, motorised caravans under 3 tons and L under 3 tons 50p: L over 3 tons £1: coaches £1.

Tyne & Wear

TYNE TUNNEL Newcastle
Car 40p: mc mcs 10p: other vehicles over 30 cwt. with or without trailers 80p. Extra charge for abnormal loads, prices by special application only. Breakdown assistance: mc mcs and invalid carriages £2, all other vehicles £12 an hour with min. charge of £3. Stoppages due to fuel shortage £5 for mc and £6 for other vehicles.

West Yorkshire

GRANGE ROAD, DEWSBURY Leeds–Dewsbury Road to Bateley gasworks.
No longer a toll but road is closed New Year's Day to avoid public right of way.

Tolls in Scotland

Fife

TAY BRIDGE
Cars, 3w, goods vehicles up to 30cwt unladen weight, mcs 20p, mc 5p, goods vehicles over 30cwt unladen weight 60p. Breakdown assistance: due to fuel shortage and flat tyre (no spare) £10·00; other causes £5·00.

Lothian

FORTH ROAD BRIDGE
Cars, minibuses (up to 12 passengers), goods vehicles up to 30cwt 30p, goods vehicles over 30cwt 80p, buses (over 12 passengers) 50p, mc and mcs free. No charge for breakdown assistance except when a garage is called.

Strathclyde

CLYDE TUNNEL (West of Glasgow)
Free. Slow moving vehicles permitted only between 0600 and 0700 hrs, 0930 and 1600 hrs, 1800 and 2200 hrs. Wide loads permitted by arrangement between 1000 and 1600 hrs. Breakdown or fuel shortage: cars £5·00, mc £2·00. Recovery of HGV from £10·00. No smoking while passing through tunnel.

ERSKINE BRIDGE
Cars, trailers, goods vehicles up to 30cwt 30p, goods vehicles over 30cwt 80p, mc and mcs 10p, scheduled buses 80p. Breakdown assistance due to fuel shortage from £2·50, other causes £5·00 for first hour or part thereof, extra time at £1·00 per ¼ hour.

Motoring in London

Selected BR Stations in the London Area with Parking Facilities

Charges vary from 30p to 60p per day.
* Free

The stations listed below serve the following London termini:

C *Cannon Street*　CX *Charing Cross*
B *Broad Street*　E *Euston*
F *Fenchurch Street*　H *Holborn Viaduct*
KX *King's Cross*　L *Liverpool Street*
LB *London Bridge*　M *Marylebone*
P *Paddington*　S *St Pancras*
V *Victoria*　W *Waterloo*

The road numbers given below are the roads which are close to the station and do not necessarily infer that the station is located thereon.

Abbey Wood
(C.CX.H.L.B.W.)A206
Barnehurst
(C.CX.H.L.B.W.) A207, A220
Barnes
(W) A205, A306
Beaconsfield
(M) A40, B474
Beckenham Hill
(H) A21, A2015
Beckenham Junc.
(V) A222, A234
Berrylands
(W) A3
Bexley
(C.CX.H.L.B.W) A2,
A222, A223
Bexleyheath
(C.CX.H.L.B.W) A207
Bickley
(H.V.) A222
Brentford
(W) M4, A4, A315
Bromley North
(CX.LB.W.) A21, A222
Bushey
(E) A411
Carshalton
(LB.V.) A232
Catford Bridge
(C.CX.LB.W.) A21, A205
Cheam
(LB.V.) A217, A232
Chelsfield
(C.CX.LB.W.) A21, A224
Cheshunt
(L) A10, A1010, A121
Chessington North
(W) A243
Chingford
(L) A11, A110
Chislehurst
(C.CX.LB.W.) A222
Chiswick
(W) M4, A4, A316
Clapham Junc.
(V.W.) A3, A205
Claygate
(W) A3, A244
Clock House, Beckenham
(C.CX.LB.W) A222

Coulsdon South
(LB.V.) A23
Crayford
(C.CX.H.L.B.W.) A206
Crystal Palace
(LB.V.) A214
Dagenham Dock
(F) A13
Denham
(M) A40, A412
Elmers End
(C.CX.LB.W.) A214, A222
Eltham Well Hall
(C.CX.LB.W.) A208
Elstree
(S) A5
Esher
(W) A3
Ewell East
(LB.V.) A24, A232, A240
Ewell West
(W) A24, A240
Feltham
(W) A30, A244
Forest Hill
(LB) A205
Gerrards Cross
(M) A40, A332
Gidea Park
(L) A118
Greenwich
(C.CX.LB.W.) A2
Hackbridge
(LB.V.) A237
Hampton Court
(W) A308, A309
Hampton Wick
(W) A308, A310
Harold Wood
(L) A12, A127
Harrow & Wealdstone
(B.E.) A409
Hatch End
(B.E.) A4090
Haydons Road
(H) A218
Hayes (Kent)
(C.CX.LB.W.) B251
***Hayes & Harlington**
(P) A312
Hendon
(S) A5
Hinchley Wood
(W) A3
Kenley
(CX.LB.W.) A22
Kidbrooke
(C.CX.H.L.B.W.) A2
Lee
(C.CX.H.L.B.W.) A205
Lewisham
(C.CX.H.L.B.W.) A20, A21
Malden Manor
(W) A3, A2043, B284
Mill Hill Broadway
(S) M1, A1
Mitcham Junc.
(LB.V.) A237
Mortlake
(W) A205
Mottingham
(C.CX.H.L.B.W.) A20
New Eltham
(C.CX.H.L.B.W.) A20

Norbiton
(W) A238, A308
Norbury
(LB.V.) A23
Orpington
(C.CX.LB.W.) A21, A232
Penge West
(LB.) A234
Petts Wood
(C.CX.LB.W.) A208
Purley
(CX.LB.V.W.) A22, A23
Purley Oaks
(CX.LB.V.W.) A235
Reedham
(V.LB) A23
***Richmond**
(B.W.) A307
St Mary Cray
(H.V.) A224
Sanderstead
(C.CX.LB.V.W.) B269
Shortlands
(H.V.) A222
Sidcup
(C.CX.H.L.B.W.) A20
South Croydon
(CX.LB.V.W.) B243, B275
Stonebridge Park
(B.E.) A404, A406
Strawberry Hill
(W) A310, A311
Streatham Common
(LB.V.) A23
Sundridge Park
(CX.LB.W.) A2212
Surbiton
(W) A240, A307
Sydenham Hill
(H.V.) A2199, A205, A212
Teddington
(W) A313, A309
Tolworth
(W) A3, A240
Tottenham Hale
(L) A10
Turkey Street
(L) A10, A1010
Twickenham
(W) A310, A316
Waddon
(LB.V.) A23, A232
Wallington
(LB.V.) A232, A237
Waltham Cross
(L) A121, A1010
Walthamstow Central
(L) A112
Welling
(C.CX.H.L.B.W.) A207
Westcombe Park
(C.CX.LB.W.) A206
West Drayton
(P) M4, A408
West Ruislip
(M) A40, B466
West Wickham
(C.CX.LB.W.) A214, A232
Woldingham
(V.LB.) A22
Woolwich Arsenal
(C.CX.LB.W.) A205, A206
Worcester Park
(W) A2043

51

London Parking Places

See Maps on pages 56–75

Although there are a number of streets available for parking, these are constantly under review and changes are continually occurring. Street parking details are therefore not included.

Car Parks

Charges are made at the following car parks, details being displayed on the sites. Some of the car parks are on land scheduled for redevelopment and may therefore be closed without warning.

Parking places are shown on the maps by a number prefixed with the letter **C**. Garages offering parking facilities are shown by a number prefixed with the letter **G**.

The hours of operation at car parks controlled by National Car Parks Ltd are liable to alteration. Members are therefore advised to contact NCP (T. 01–499 7050) for up-to-date information shortly before using any of their parks.

		MAP REF.	REF.
EC1			
Aldersgate, Aldersgate St. (NCP)	Open 24 hrs, all week	6	C1
Caxton House, Cowcross St., Off Farringdon Rd. (NCP)	7.30 a.m. to 6.30 p.m. Mon–Fri	6	C2
Charterhouse Square, nr Smithfield Market (NCP)	6 a.m. to 4 p.m. Mon–Fri	6	C3
Peter's Lane, St. John St., Smithfield (NCP)	7 a.m. to 5 p.m. Mon–Fri	6	C4
Saffron Hill, Holborn (NCP)	7 a.m. to 10 p.m. Mon–Fri		
	8 a.m. to 1 p.m. Sat	6	C5
Smithfield, Hosier Lane (NCP)	7 a.m. to 6 p.m. Mon–Fri	6	C6
Smithfield, cnr. Hosier Lane/Smithfield St. (NCP)	7 a.m. to 6 p.m. Mon–Fri	6	C7
Smithfield Central Markets, West Smithfield (NCP)	Open 24 hrs, Mon–Fri		
	Closes 1 p.m. Sat.	6	C8
EC2			
Barbican Centre, Beech St. (NCP)	8 a.m. to midnight, all week	7	C9
Broad St. Station, Eldon St. (NCP)	7 a.m. to 11 p.m. Mon–Fri		
	7 a.m. to 3 p.m. Sat–Sun	7	C10
Finsbury Square (NCP)	7.30 a.m. to 8 p.m. Mon–Fri		
	Closed Sat, Sun and Bank Holidays	7	C11
London Wall (NCP)	7.30 a.m. to 7.30 p.m. Mon–Fri		
	Closed Sat, Sun and Bank Holidays	7	C12
EC3			
Houndsditch, Stoney Lane (NCP)	8 a.m. to 7 p.m. Mon–Fri		
	8 a.m. to 2 p.m. Sun	8	C13
Minories, Shorter St. (NCP)	Open 24 hrs, all week	8	C14
Tower Hill, Lower Thames St. (NCP)	7.30 a.m. to 7.30 p.m. Mon–Fri		
	7.30 a.m. to 1.30 p.m. Sat	8	C15
EC4			
Distaff Lane, Cannon St. (NCP)	8 a.m. to 7 p.m. Mon–Fri	6	C16
Hillgate House, Seacoal Lane (NCP)	Open 24 hours, all week	6	C17
International Press Centre, Shoe Lane (NCP)	8 a.m. to 8 p.m. Mon–Fri	6	C18
Paternoster Row, Ave Maria Lane (NCP)	Open 24 hrs, all week	6	C19
Queen Victoria St. (NCP)	Open 24 hrs, all week	6	C20
Shoe Lane	7 a.m. to 7.30 p.m. Mon–Fri	6	C21
Vintry, Upper Thames St./Queen St. Place (NCP)	7 a.m. to 7 p.m. Mon–Fri	7	C22
E1			
Commercial St., Spitalfields Markets (NCP)	7 a.m. to 3 p.m. Sun only	8	C23
Folgate St., Spitalfields (NCP)	7 a.m. to 3 p.m. Sun only	8	C24
Rodwell House, Strype St. off Middlesex St. (NCP)	Open 24 hrs, all week	8	C25
Royal Mint St. (NCP)	7 a.m. to 7 p.m. Mon–Fri	8	C26
Spitalfields, White's Row, off Commercial Rd. (NCP)	Open 24 hrs, all week	8	C27
Spital Square, Spitalfields (NCP)	7 a.m. to 3 p.m. Sun only	8	C28
Steward St. Spitalfields (NCP)	7 a.m. to 3 p.m. Sun only	8	C29
NW1			
Bell St. Garage	Open 24 hrs, all week	1	C30
Marylebone Road, Gloucester Place (NCP)	Open 24 hrs, all week	2	C31
NW8			
Church St. Garage, junc. Penfold St./Broadley St.	7.30 a.m. to 7.30 p.m.	1	C32

SE1

		MAP REF.	REF.
Barge House St., Upper Ground (NCP)	8 a.m. to 6.30 p.m., all week	6	C33
Coin St., Stamford St. (NCP)	6 a.m. to Midnight Mon–Fri	13	C34
Doon St. (NCP)	8 a.m. to Midnight all week	13	C35
Elephant and Castle Shopping Centre (NCP)	8 a.m. to 7 p.m. Mon–Sat (9 p.m. Fri)	14	C36
National Theatre, South Bank	8 a.m. to 2 a.m. Mon–Sat	13	C37
Royal Festival Hall complex	8 a.m. to Midnight, all week	13	C38
Skipton St. (NCP)	8 a.m. to 6.30 p.m. Mon–Fri	14	C39

SW1

		MAP REF.	REF.
Abingdon St. (NCP)	Open 24 hrs, all week	12	C40
Arlington St. (NCP)	Open 24 hrs, all week	11	C41
Berkeley Garage, Wilton Place	Open 24 hrs, all week	10	C42
Cadogan Place (NCP)	Open 24 hrs, all week	10	C43
Dolphin Sq. Garage, Grosvenor Rd. (NCP)	Open 24 hrs, all week	17	C44
Eaton Sq. Garage, Eaton Mews West	8 a.m. to 11.30 p.m., all week	16	C45
Knightsbridge Green, Raphael St. (NCP)	8 a.m. to 8 p.m. Mon–Fri		
	8 a.m. to 1 p.m. Sat	9	C46
Motcomb Garage, Kinnerton St.	Open 24 hrs, all week	10	C47
Park Towers Hotel, Knightsbridge (NCP)	Open 24 hrs, all week	10	C48
Rochester Row (NCP)	Open 24 hrs, all week	12	C49
Semley Place, nr Victoria Coach Stn. (NCP)	Open 24 hrs, all week	16	C51
Thorney St., off Millbank (NCP)	7 a.m. to 11 p.m. Mon–Fri		
	7 a.m. to 3 p.m. Sat–Sun	18	C52
Trafalgar Garage, Spring Gardens (NCP)	Open 24 hrs, all week	12	C53
Warwick Way	Open 24 hrs, all week	17	C54

SW3

		MAP REF.	REF.
Kings Road, Chelsea (NCP)	8 a.m. to 6.30 p.m. Mon–Sat	15	C55
Pavilion Rd., (NCP)	Open 24 hrs, all week	10	C56
St. Lukes, Cale St. (NCP)	8 a.m. to 6 p.m. Mon–Sat	15	C57

SW7

		MAP REF.	REF.
Kingston House Garage, Ennismore Gdns.	7.30 a.m. to 11 p.m. Sat, Sun and most Bank Holidays	9	C58

SW8

		MAP REF.	REF.
Bridgefoot, Vauxhall Stn. (NCP)	Open 24 hrs, all week	18	C59

W1

		MAP REF.	REF.
Audley Sq., Sth. Audley St. (NCP)	Open 24 hrs, all week	10	C60
Bilton Towers Garage, Gt. Cumberland Place (NCP)	Open 24 hrs, all week	2	C61
Brewer St. (NCP)	Open 24 hrs, all week	4	C62
Britannia Hotel, Adams Row (NCP)	Open 24 hrs, all week	2	C63
Broadwick Garage, Broadwick St.	Open 24 hrs, all week	3	C64
Bryanston St., Marble Arch (NCP)	Open 24 hrs, all week	2	C65
Burlington Garage, Old Burlington St. (NCP)	7.30 a.m. to Midnight Mon–Fri	3	C66
Carrington St., Shepherd Mkt. (NCP)	Open 24 hrs, all week	11	C67
Cavendish Sq., Oxford Circus (NCP)	7 a.m. to 11 p.m. Mon–Sat	3	C68
Chiltern St., off Baker St. (NCP)	Open 24 hrs, all week	2	C69
Churchill Hotel, Portman Sq. (NCP)	Open 24 hrs, all week	2	C70
Cleveland St. (NCP)	8 a.m. to 9 p.m. Mon–Fri	3	C71
Clipstone Garage, Clipstone St.	Open 24 hrs, all week	3	C72
Cramer St., off Marylebone High St. (NCP)	8 a.m. to 6.30 p.m. Mon–Fri		
	8 a.m. to 1 p.m. Sat	2	C73
Crawford St. (NCP)	8 a.m. to 6.30 p.m. Mon–Fri		
	8 a.m. to 1 p.m. Sat	1	C74
Dean St. (NCP)	8 a.m. to Midnight Mon–Sat	4	C75
Denman St., Piccadilly (NCP)	Open 24 hrs, all week	4	C76
Fountain Garage, Park Lane (NCP)	Open 24 hrs, all week	2	C77
Gt. Marlborough St. (NCP)	8 a.m. to 6 p.m. Mon–Sat	3	C78
Grosvenor Hill, Bourdon St. (NCP)	7 a.m. to 8 p.m. Mon–Fri	3	C79
Harley Garage, Chandos St.	Open 24 hrs, all week	3	C80
Inn on the Park, Hamilton Place	Open 24 hrs, all week	10	C81
Kingly St. (NCP)	8 a.m. to 7 p.m. Mon–Sat	3	C82
London Hilton Hotel, Park Lane (NCP)	Open 24 hrs, all week	10	C83

W1—*cont.*

		MAP REF.	REF.
London Marriott, off Duke St. (NCP)	7 a.m. to 8 p.m., all week	2	C84
Mamos, Grosvenor House Garage, Reeves Mews	Open 24 hrs, all week	2	C85
Old Park Lane (NCP)	8 a.m. to 8 p.m. Mon–Fri	10	C86
Park Lane Garage, Hyde Park (NCP) (entrances from Park Lane and Nth. Carriage Drive)	Open 24 hrs, all week Nth. Carriage Drive entrance closed from midnight to 7 a.m.	1 & 2	C87
Park Lane Hotel Garage, Brick St.	Open 24 hrs, all week	11	C88
Poland St. Garage	6 a.m. to Midnight Mon–Sat	3	C89
Portman Sq., Gloucester Place (NCP)	Open 24 hrs, all week	2	C90
St. Annes Court, Dean St. (NCP)	8 a.m. to 6 p.m. Mon–Fri 8 a.m. Sat to 2 a.m. Sun	4	C91
Sanderson House, Berners St.	9 a.m. to 5.30 p.m. Mon–Fri 9 a.m. to 7 p.m. Thurs.	3	C92
Selfridge Garage, Orchard St.	Open 24 hrs, all week	2	C93
Stourcliffe Close Garage, Stourcliffe St.	7 a.m. to 11 p.m. daily 8 a.m. to 11 p.m. Sun	1	C94
Wardour Garage, Wardour St.	Open 24 hrs, all week	4	C95
Welbeck St. (NCP)	8 a.m. to 8 p.m. Mon–Sat	2	C96

W2

Kendal St. (NCP)	Open 24 hrs, all week	1	C97
London Metropole Hotel, Harbet Road (NCP)	Open 24 hrs, all week	1	C98
Water Gardens, Burwood Place, Edgeware Rd. (NCP)	Open 24 hrs, all week	1	C99

WC1

Bloomsbury Sq. (NCP)	Open 24 hrs, all week	4	C100
Coptic St. (NCP)	8 a.m. to 6.30 p.m. Mon–Fri	4	C101
Holborn, Museum St. (NCP)	Open 24 hrs, all week	4	C102
Imperial Hotel, Russell Sq. (NCP)	7 a.m. to 10 p.m. Mon–Fri	4	C103
Ridgmount Place (NCP)	8 a.m. to 6.30 p.m. Mon–Fri 8 a.m. to 1 a.m. Sat	4	C104
St. Martins St. nr Trafalgar Square (NCP)	7 a.m. to 1 a.m. Mon–Sat Open Sun	4	C50
YMCA, Adeline Place, off Tottenham Court Rd (NCP)	Open 24 hrs, all week	4	C105

WC2

Bedfordbury (NCP)	7.30 a.m. to 12.30 a.m. Mon–Sat	4	C106
Drury Lane, Parker St. (NCP)	Open 24 hrs, all week	4	C107
New Compton St.	8 a.m. to Midnight Mon–Sat	4	C108
Savoy Aldephi Garage, Savoy Place	Open 24 hrs, all week	5	G1
Swiss Centre, Leicester St. (NCP)	8 a.m. to 2 a.m. Mon–Fri 8 a.m. Sat to 3 a.m. Sun	4	C109
Upper St. Martins Lane (NCP)	8 a.m. to Midnight Mon–Fri 8 a.m. to 2 a.m. Sun	4	C110
Whitcomb Garage, Whitcomb St.	Open 24 hrs, all week	4	C111

London Concert Halls, Cinemas and Theatres with Nearest Car Parks

The name of the cinema, concert hall or theatre is followed by a figure in brackets which indicates the number of the map on which it is marked by name, followed by the numbers which relate to the nearest car parks offering casual parking facilities listed on pages 52–54. Where no other information is given concerning a concert hall or theatre this denotes that it is outside the area covered by the maps.

It should be noted that there is a great demand for parking space in the West End area and accommodation cannot, therefore, be guaranteed.

CINEMAS
ABC One & Two, Shaftesbury Av., (4) C108, C110

Academy One, Two, Three, Oxford St., (3) C64, C89, C91, C95
Barbican, Barbican (7) C1, C9
Cinecenta One, Two, Three, Four, Panton St. (4) C50, C53, C109, C111
Classic One, Two, Three, Haymarket (4) C50, C76, C111
Classic One, Two, Three, Four, Five, Oxford St. (4) C91, C105, C108
Classic Royal, Charing Cross Rd. (4) C50, C106, C110
Classic, Tottenham Court Rd. (4) C105, C108
Curzon, Curzon St. (11) C60, C67, C81, C83, C88
Empire One & Two, Leicester Square, (4) C50, C75, C109, C111
Filmcenta One, Two, Three, Charing Cross Rd, (4) C75, C108, C110

Leicester Square Theatre (4) C50, C75, C109, C111
Lumiere, St Martins Lane, (4) C50, C106, C110
National Film Theatre, Waterloo Rd, (13) C34, C35, C37, C38
Odeon, Haymarket (4) C50, C76, C109, C111
Odeon, Leicester Square (4) C50, C75, C106, C109, C110, C111
Odeon, Marble Arch (2) C61, C65, C87
Plaza One, Two, Three & Four, Lower Regent St, (4) C50, C76, C109, C111
Premiere, Shaftesbury Av. (4) C62, C75, C108, C109, C110
Prince Charles, Leicester Square, (4) C75, C106, C109, C110, C111
Scene One, Two, Three, Four, Wardour St, (4) C62, C75, C76, C109, C111
Studio One, Two, Three, Four, Oxford St, (3) C64, C89, C91, C95
Warner West End One, Two, Three, Four, Leicester Square, (4) C75, C106, C109, C110, C111

CONCERT HALLS & THEATRES
Adelphi, The Strand, (4) C106, C110, G1
Albery, St Martins Lane, (4) C106, C109, C110
Aldwych, The Aldwych, (5) C107, G1
Ambassadors, West St, (4) C75, C106, C108, C110
Apollo, Shaftesbury Av, (4) C62, C75, C76, C109
Apollo Victoria, Wilton Rd, (11) C49, C51
Astoria, Charing Cross Rd, (4) C91, C95, C105, C108
Barbican, Barbican, (7) C1, C9
Cambridge, Earlham St, (4) C107, C108, C110
Coliseum, St Martins Lane, (4) C50, C106, C110, C111
Comedy, Panton St, (4) C50, C53, C109, C111
Cottesloe – See National Theatre (13)
Criterion, Piccadilly, (4) C50, C76, C109, C111
Dominion, Tottenham Court Rd, (4) C91, C105, C108
Donmar Warehouse, Earlham St, (4) C107, C108, C110
Drury Lane Theatre Royal, Drury Lane, (5) C107, C110, G1
Duchess, Catherine St, (5) C107, G1
Duke of Yorks, St Martins Lane, (4) C50, C106, C109, C110, C111
Fortune, Russell St., (5) C107, C110, G1

Garrick, Charing Cross Rd., (4) C50, C106, C109, C110, C111
Globe, Shaftesbury Av., (4) C62, C75, C76, C109
Haymarket Theatre Royal, Haymarket, (4) C50, C53, C109, C111
Her Majesty's, Haymarket, (12) C50, C53, C111
London Palladium, Argyll St., (3) C64, C89, C91, C95
Lyric Shaftesbury, Shaftesbury Av., (4) C62, C75, C76, C109
Lyttleton – See National Theatre (13)
Mayfair, Stratton St., (11) C41, C66, C67
Mermaid, Puddle Dock, (6) C19, C20
National Theatre, Upper Ground, (13) C34, C35, C37, C38
New London, Parker St., (4) C102, C107
Old Vic, Waterloo Rd., (14) C34, C35, C37, C38
Olivier – See National Theatre (13)
Palace, Shaftesbury Av., (4) C75, C108, C109, C110
Phoenix, Charing Cross Rd., (4) C91, C108, C110
Piccadilly, Denman St., (3) C62, C76, C109, C111
Prince Edward, Old Compton St., (4) C75, C91, C95, C108, C110
Prince of Wales, Coventry St., (4) C62, C76, C109, C111
Queen Elizabeth Hall, South Bank, (13) C34, C35, C37, C38
Queen's, Shaftesbury Av., (4) C62, C75, C76, C109
Royal Albert Hall, Kensington –
Royal Festival Hall, South Bank, (13) C34, C35, C37, C38
Royal Opera House, Covent Garden, (4) C106, C107, C110, G1
Royal Court, Sloane Square, (16) C43, C45, C51
Sadlers Wells, Rosebery Avenue –
St. Martins, West St., (4) C75, C106, C108, C109, C110
Savoy, The Strand, (5) C106, C107, G1
Shaftesbury, Shaftesbury Av., (4) C102, C107, C108
Shaw Theatre Euston Rd –
The Pit – See Barbican (7)
The Strand, Aldwych, (5) C107, G1
Vaudeville, The Strand (5) C106, C107, G1
Victoria Palace, Victoria St., (11) C49, C51
Westminster, Palace St., (11) C49, C51
Whitehall, Whitehall, (12) C50, C53, C111
Wyndhams, Charing Cross Rd., (4) C106, C109, C110, C111
Young Vic, The Cut, (14) C34, C35, C37, C38

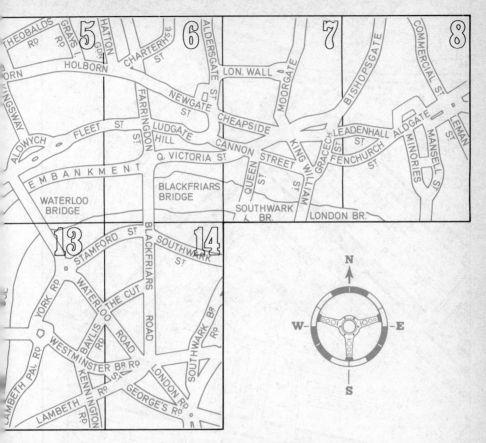

SIGNS USED IN THE LONDON STREET MAPS

⟶ **One-way Street**

⊣⌐⌐⊢ **Restricted Access/Exit**

C1 **Car Parks**

G1 **Garages**

Underground Stations

SCALE IN MILES ¼

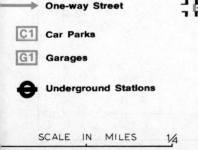

ONE-WAY STREETS

There are many experimental one-way traffic schemes operating in the London area which had not been confirmed, i.e. made permanent, at the time of going to press. Members are therefore advised to pay particular attention to the signposting of one-way streets.

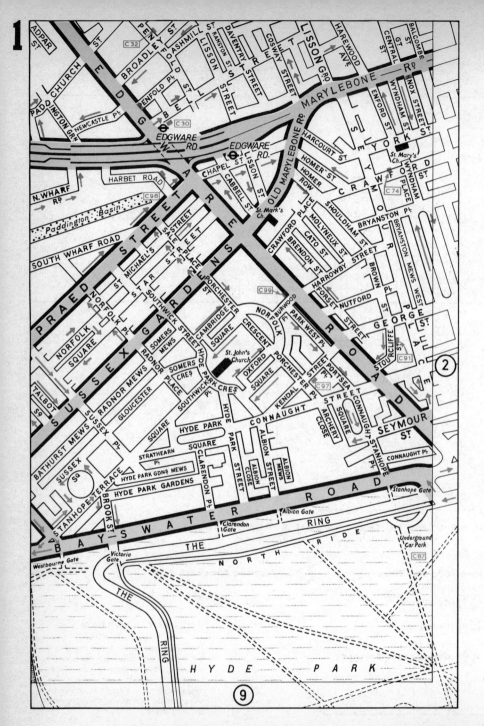

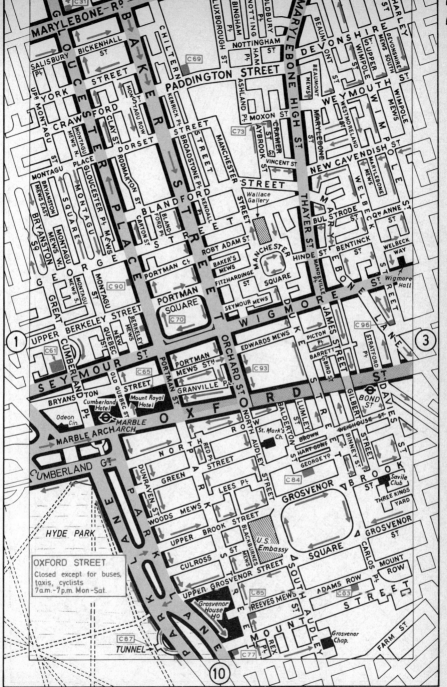

2

MARYLEBONE RD.

C31

BAKER STREET

CHILTERN STREET

PADDINGTON STREET

MARYLEBONE HIGH ST.

DEVONSHIRE STREET

HARLEY ST.

SALISBURY PL.
BICKENHALL ST.
UPP. YORK
MONTAGU ST.
CRAWFORD
DORSET
STREET
GLOUCESTER PLACE
RODMARTON ST.
CLAY ST.
MONTAGU ROW
KENRICK PL.
ASHLAND PL.
MOXON ST.
CRAMER ST.
AYBROOK ST.
VINCENT ST.
C69
C73

BRYANSTON SQ.
MONTAGU SQUARE
MONTAGU MEWS N.
MONTAGU PLACE
BLANDFORD STREET
MANCHESTER STREET
MANCHESTER STREET
Wallace Gallery
NEW CAVENDISH ST.
WELBECK ST.
WIMPOLE ST.

BRYANSTON MEWS EAST
MONTAGU MEWS W.
MONTAGU ST.
CARLTON ST.
BLAND FORD PL.
ROBT ADAM ST.
BAKER'S MEWS
FITZHARDINGE ST.
MANCHESTER SQUARE
HINDE ST.
BENTINCK ST.
BUL STRODE
WELBECK WAY
Wigmore Hall

C90
PORTMAN CT.
PORTMAN SQUARE
C70
SEYMOUR MEWS

GREAT CUMBERLAND PL.
BERKELEY STREET
QUEBEC ST.
BERKELEY MEWS
NEW
PORTMAN ST.
ORCHARD ST.
WIGMORE STREET
DUKE STREET
JAMES STREET
STRATFORD PL.
C96

UPPER BERKELEY ST.
C61
SEYMOUR
BRYANSTON PL.
Cumberland Hotel
OLD QUEBEC ST.
C65
PORTMAN MEWS STH.
GRANVILLE PL.
Mount Royal Hotel
EDWARDS MEWS
PICTON PL.
BARRETT ST.
BIRD ST.
LUMLEY ST.
GILBERT ST.
C93
OXFORD STREET
BOND ST.
DAVIES STREET

Odeon Cin.
MARBLE ARCH
MARBLE ARCH
NORTH ROW
RED PL.
NORTH AUDLEY STREET
St. Mark's Ch.
BROWN HART GDNS.
GEORGE YD.
BALDERTON ST.
WEIGHOUSE ST.
BINNEY ST.
BROOK STREET
Savile Club
THREE KINGS YARD

CUMBERLAND GT.
DUNRAVEN ST.
GREEN STREET
LEES PL.
BLACKBURNES MEWS
GROSVENOR
C84
BROOK ST.
GROSVENOR ST.

HYDE PARK
WOODS MEWS
UPPER BROOK STREET
U.S. Embassy
GROSVENOR SQUARE
CARLOS PL.
MOUNT ROW

OXFORD STREET
Closed except for buses, taxis, cyclists 7a.m.-7p.m. Mon-Sat.

CULROSS ST.
UPPER GROSVENOR STREET
GROSVENOR STREET
C85
REEVES MEWS
ADAMS ROW
SOUTH AUDLEY STREET
C63
MOUNT STREET

Grosvenor House Ho.
REX PL.
MOUNT STREET
Grosvenor Chap.
FARM ST.

C87
TUNNEL
C77

PARK LANE

CUMBERLAND GT.

PARK LANE

① ③ ⑩

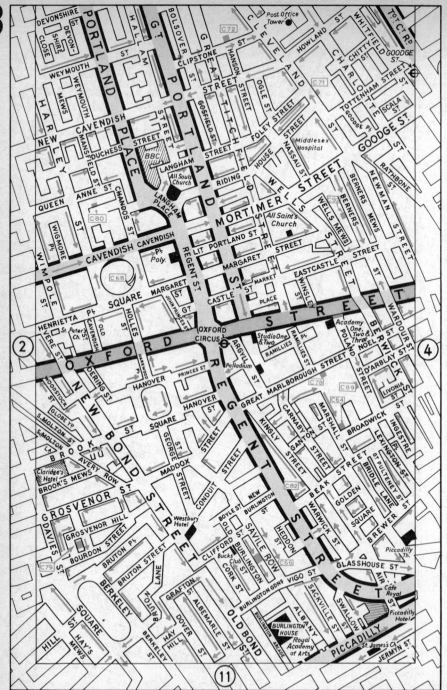

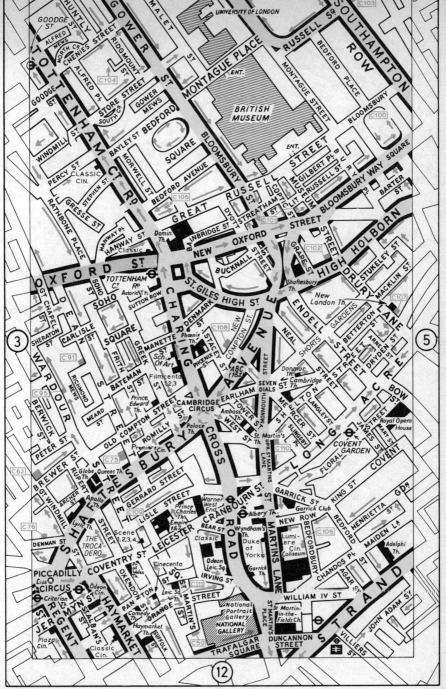

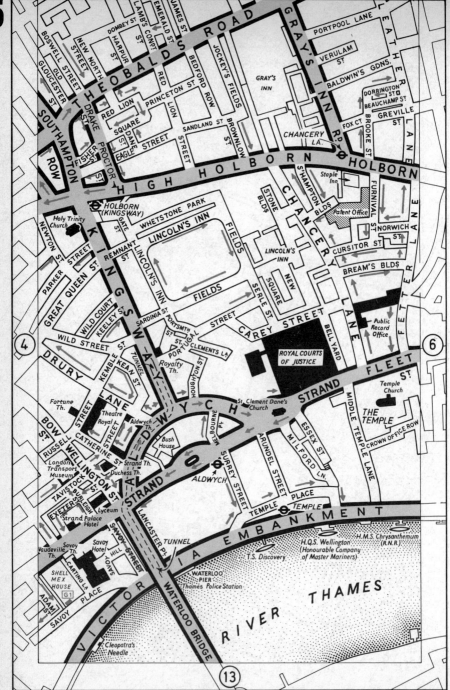

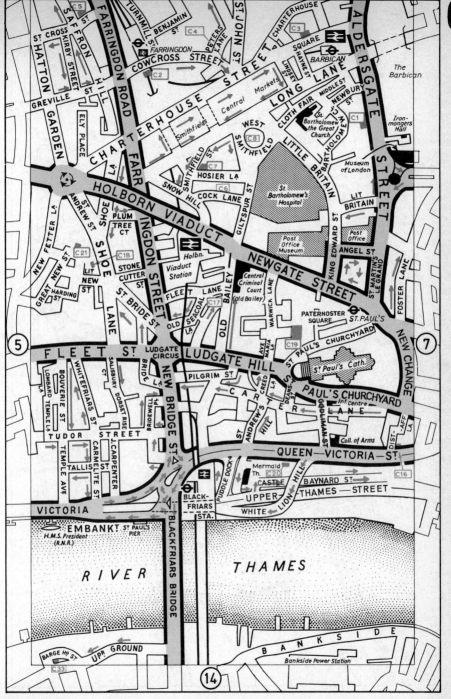

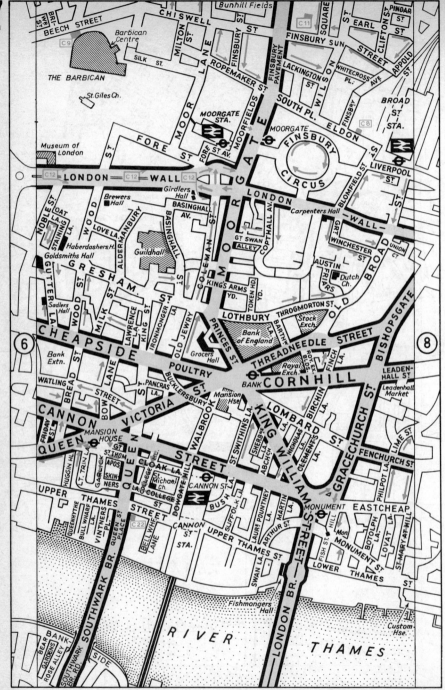

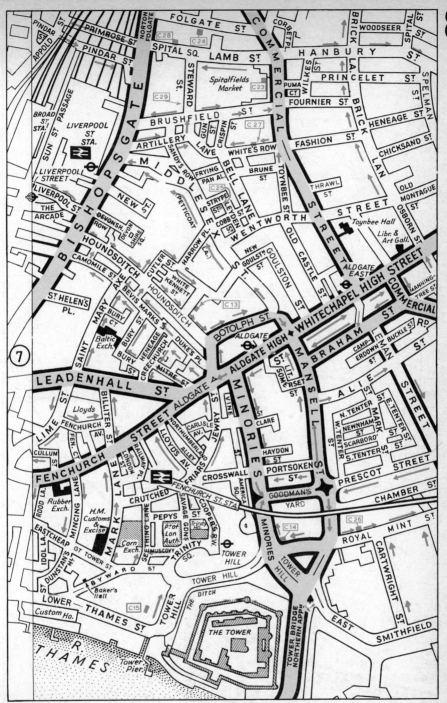

PINDAR ST.
APPOLD ST.
NORTON FOLGATE
FOLGATE ST.
CORBET PL.
WOODSEER ST.
SPITAL ST.
BRICK LA.

PRIMROSE ST.
PINDAR ST.
SPITAL SQ.
C28   C24
LAMB ST.
HANBURY ST.
WILKES ST.
PUMA CT.
PRINCELET ST.
SPELMAN ST.

BROAD ST. STA.
SUN ST. PASSAGE
STEWARD ST.
Spitalfields Market
C23
FOURNIER ST.
HENEAGE ST.
CHICKSAND ST.

LIVERPOOL ST. STA.
C29
BRUSHFIELD
CRISPIN ST.
C27
FASHION ST.
BRICK LA.
OLD MONTAGUE ST.

LIVERPOOL STREET
ARTILLERY LANE
SANDY'S ROW
GUN ST.
WHITE'S ROW
THRAWL ST.
OSBORN ST.

THE ARCADE
NEW ST.
FRYING PAN AL.
BRUNE ST.
Toynbee Hall
Libr. & Art Gall.

DEVONSH. ROW
DEVONSHIRE SQ.
PETTICOAT
STRYPE ST.
LEYDEN ST.
NEW GOULST. ST.
ALDGATE EAST

HOUNDSDITCH
HARROW PL.
COBB ST.
WENTWORTH STREET
GOULSTON ST.
OLD CASTLE ST.
MANNING-TREE ST.

CAMOMILE ST.
CUTLER ST.
WHITE KENNETT ST.
C13
ALDGATE EAST
COMMERCIAL RD.

ST. HELEN'S PL.
BEVIS MARKS
HOUNDSDITCH
BOTOLPH ST.
ALDGATE
WHITECHAPEL HIGH STREET
BRAHAM ST.
BUCKLE ST.

SAINT MARY AXE
BURY CT.
HENEAGE
DUKE'S PL.
ALDGATE HIGH ST.
MINORIES
CAMP ERDOWN ST.
LEMAN ST.

Baltic Exch.
BURY ST.
CREECHURCH
MITRE ST.
VINE ST.
LIT. SOMERSET ST.
MANSELL ST.

LEADENHALL ST.
ALDGATE
JEWRY ST.
CLARE ST.
ALIE STREET
N. TENTER ST.
E. TENTER ST.

LIME ST.
BILLITER ST.
RAILWAY PL.
CARLISLE AV.
HAYDON ST.
W. TENTER ST.
NEWNHAM ST.
SCARBORO'

Lloyds
FENCHURCH AV.
NORTHUMBERLAND ALLEY
CROSSWALL
PORTSOKEN ST.
S. TENTER ST.
PRESCOT STREET

CULLUM ST.
FEN CT.
LLOYDS AV.
FRIARS
AMERICA SQ.
GOODMAN'S YARD

FENCHURCH STREET
LONDON ST.
FENCHURCH ST. STA.
CHAMBER ST.

ROOD LA.
MINCING LANE
Rubber Exch.
CRUTCHED FRIARS
SAVAGE GDNS.
C14
C26
ROYAL MINT ST.

EASTCHEAP
MARK LANE
H.M. Customs & Excise
PEPYS ST.
Prior. Lon. Auth.
Trinity RW.
MINORIES
CARTWRIGHT ST.

IDOL LA.
GT. TOWER ST.
SEETHING LANE
MUSCOVY ST.
TRINITY SQ.
TOWER HILL

ST. DUNSTAN'S HILL
Corn Exch.
Baker's Hall
BYWARD ST.
TOWER HILL
THE DITCH

LOWER THAMES ST.
C15
TOWER HILL
TOWER BRIDGE NORTHERN APP.
EAST SMITHFIELD

Custom Ho.
THE TOWER
Tower Pier
R. THAMES

7
LEADENHALL ST.
FENCHURCH STREET

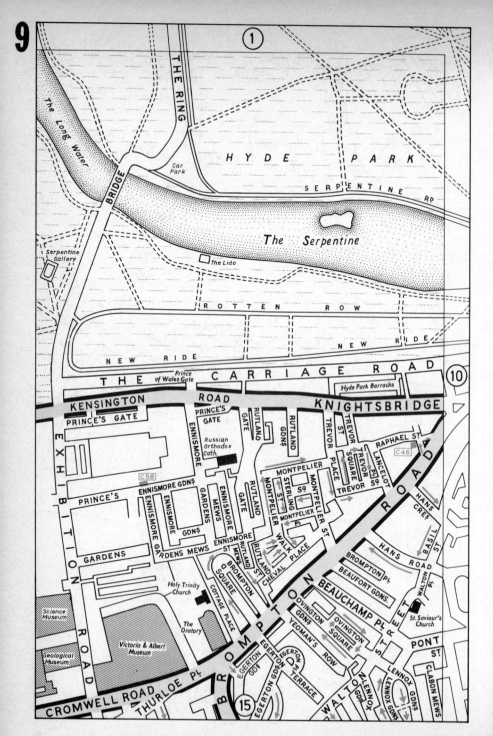

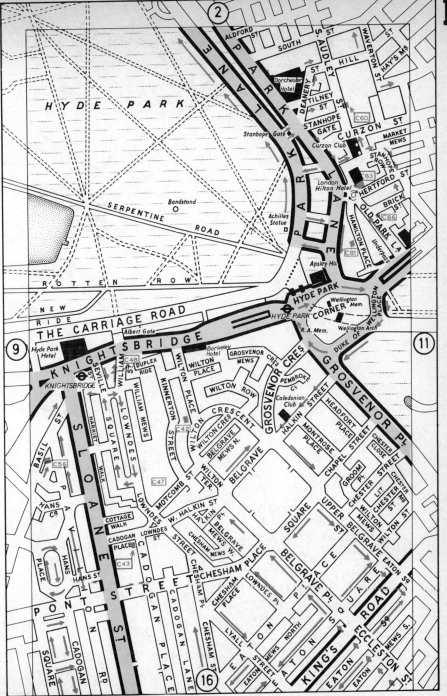

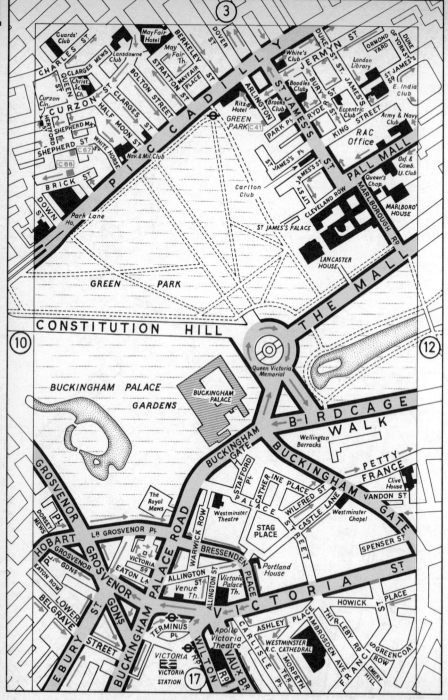

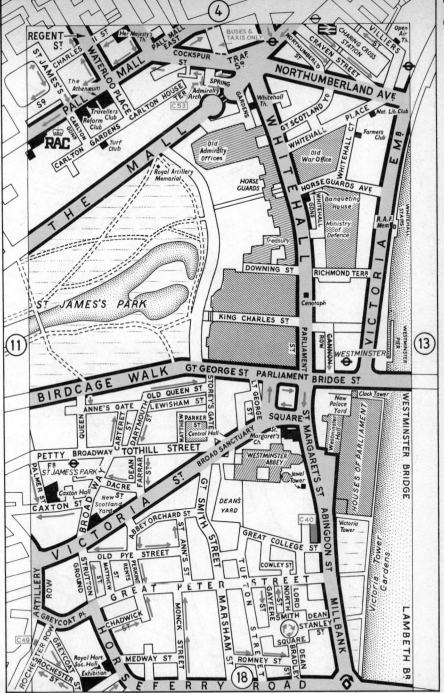

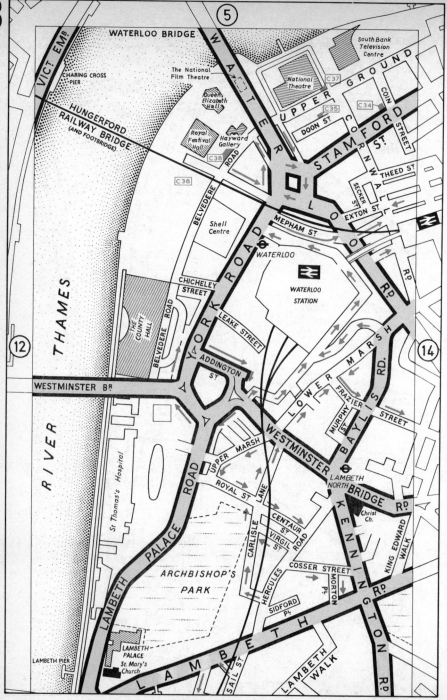

13

WATERLOO BRIDGE

VICT. EMB.

CHARING CROSS PIER

The National Film Theatre

South Bank Television Centre

National Theatre

C37

UPPER GROUND

HUNGERFORD RAILWAY BRIDGE (AND FOOTBRIDGE)

Queen Elizabeth Hall

C35   C34   COIN STREET

DOON ST

STAMFORD ST.

Royal Festival Hall   Hayward Gallery

C38

ROAD

CORNWALL

THEED ST

SECKER ST

EXTON ST

BELVEDERE

Shell Centre

MEPHAM ST

WATERLOO

Waterloo

C38

THAMES

CHICHELEY STREET

YORK ROAD

WATERLOO STATION

R.D

THE COUNTY HALL

BELVEDERE ROAD

LEAKE STREET

LOWER   MARSH

BAYLIS   RD.

⑫   ADDINGTON ST   FRAZIER STREET

⑭

WESTMINSTER B.R   MURPHY ST

RIVER

St Thomas's Hospital

WESTMINSTER   LAMBETH NORTH

UPPER MARSH

ROYAL ST

LANE   BRIDGE   RD

LAMBETH   PALACE ROAD   CENTAUR ST   Christ Ch.

CARLISLE   VIRGIL ST   ROAD

KENNINGTON

KING EDWARD WALK

ARCHBISHOP'S PARK

HERCULES   COSSER STREET

MORTON PL

SIDFORD PL

RD.

LAMBETH PIER

LAMBETH PALACE   St. Mary's Church

SAIL ST

LAMBETH   WALK

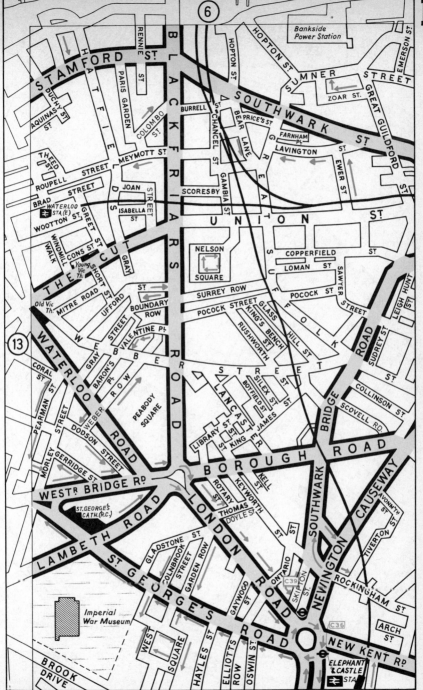

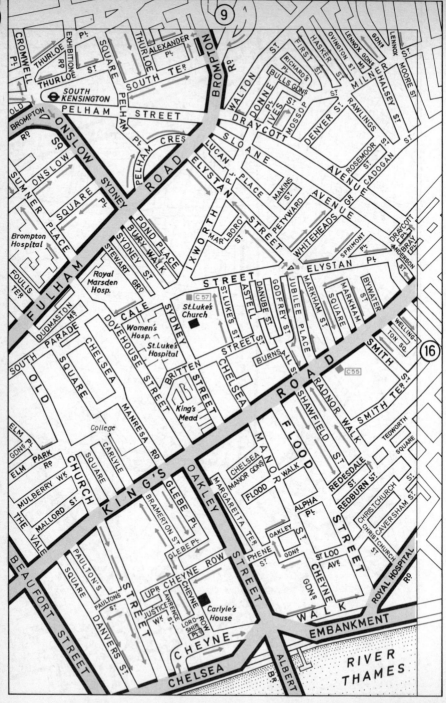

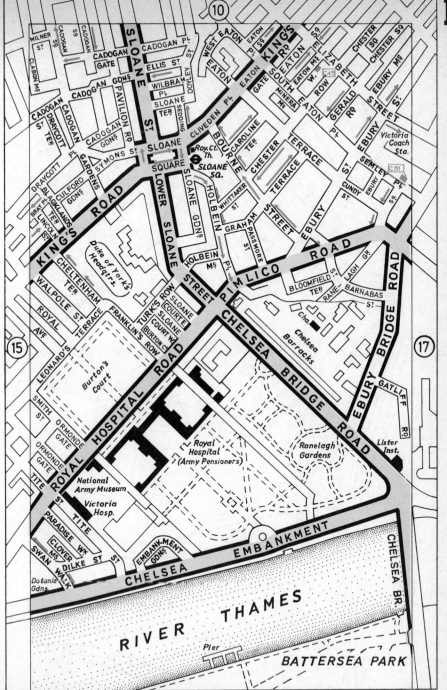

MILNER ST.
CLABON M^S

CADOGAN SQ.
CADOGAN SQ.

SLOANE

CADOGAN
GATE
CADOGAN PL.

ELLIS ST.

WILBRAM
PL.
SLOANE
TER.

CADOGAN GDNS.

PAVILION RD.

SLOANE

ST.

CADOGAN
GDNS.

SYMONS ST.

CADOGAN
PL.
DRAYCOTT
TER.

CADOGAN
GARDENS

DRAYCOTT
ST.

BRAY PL.
BLACKLANDS
TER.
CULFORD
GDNS.
LINCOLN ST.

KING'S

ROAD

CHELTENHAM
TER.

WALPOLE ST.
FRANKLIN'S ROW

ROYAL
AVE.

LEONARD'S
TERRACE

SMITH
ST.

ORMONDE
GATE

ORMONDE
GATE

TITE
ST.

PARADISE
W^K.

CLOVER
M^S.

SWAN
WALK

DILKE ST.

Botanic
Gdns.

WEST EATON

EATON
GATE

CLIVEDEN PL.

SLOANE

SQUARE

LOWER
SLOANE

SLOANE
GDNS.

STREET

ROYAL HOSPITAL ROAD

TURK'S ROW
SLOANE
COURT E.
SLOANE
COURT W.
BURTON C^T.
BURTON'S ROW

Burton's
Court

National
Army Museum

Victoria
Hosp.

EMBANKMENT
GDNS.

CHELSEA

KINGS
RD.

EATON
SQ.

W. EATON
PL.

EATON

SOUTH EATON
PL.

SLOANE

CLIVEDEN PL.

BOURNE

Roy. Ct.
Th.
SLOANE
SQ.

HOLBEIN

PL.

HOLBEIN
M^S.

STREET

PIMLICO

CHELSEA

BRIDGE

ROAD

CAROLINE
TER.

CHESTER

WHITTAKER
ST.

GRAHAM

PASSMORE
ST.

BLOOMFIELD
TER.

RANE-
LAGH
ST.

C^Hd.

Chelsea
Barracks

Royal
Hospital
(Army Pensioners)

Ranelagh
Gardens

ELIZABETH
EATON M^S.
W.
C45
MINERA
M^S.

CHESTER

TERRACE

TERRACE

CHESTER

STREET

EBURY

ROAD

BARNABAS
ST.

GERALD
RD.

EBURY
ST.

EBURY

CUNDY
ST.

ST.

EBURY
SQ.

CHESTER
SQ.

CHESTER
SQ.

EBURY M^S.

STREET

EBURY

SEMLEY
PL.

GATLIFF

RD.

Victoria
Coach
Sta.

C51

Lister
Inst.

CHELSEA
BR.

EMBANKMENT

RIVER THAMES

Pier

BATTERSEA PARK

Duke of York's
Headqtrs.

⑩

⑮

⑰

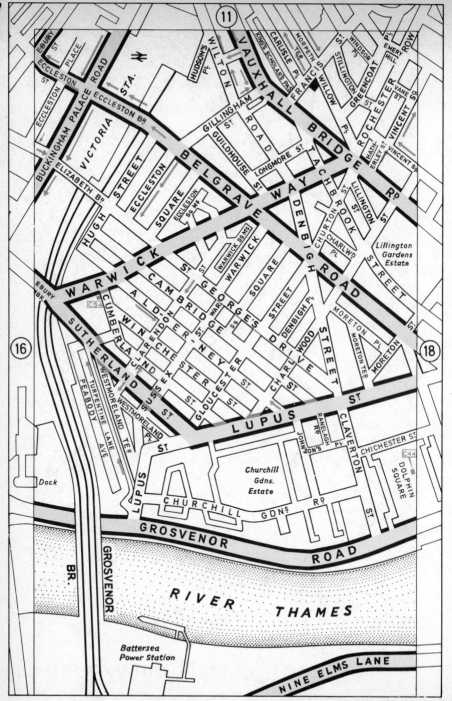

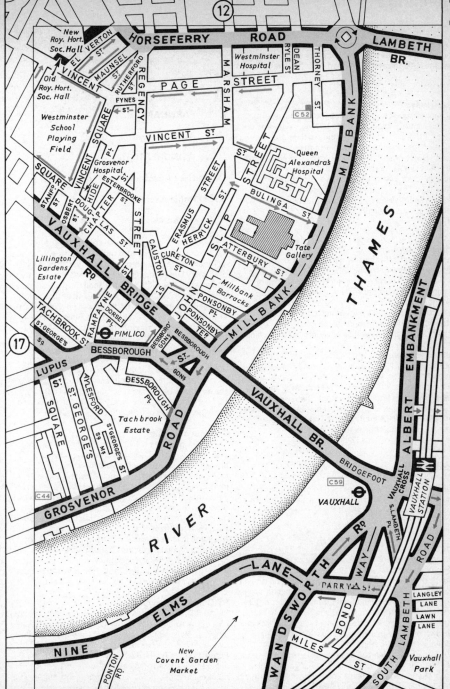

New Roy. Hort. Soc. Hall
EL VERTON ST.
Old Roy. Hort. Soc. Hall
VINCENT
MAUNSEL ST.
RUTHERFORD
REGENCY ST.
FYNES ST.
HORSEFERRY ROAD
PAGE STREET
VINCENT ST.
Westminster Hospital
MARSHAM STREET
DEAN RYLE ST.
THORNEY ST.
LAMBETH BR.
C 52
MILLBANK
Westminster School Playing Field
VINCENT SQUARE
PL.
Grosvenor Hospital
ESTERBROOKE ST.
HIDE PL.
STANF.D
OSBERT ST.
DOUGLAS ST.
ST. GEORGE'S
VINCENT
SQUARE
STREET
ST.
STREET
ST.
ERASMUS ST.
HERRICK ST.
ISLIP STREET
BULINGA ST.
Queen Alexandra's Hospital
THAMES
VAUXHALL BRIDGE ROAD
Lillington Gardens Estate
RAMPAYNE ST.
DORSET PL.
CAUSTON ST.
CURETON ST.
JOHN
ATTERBURY ST.
PONSONBY PL.
PONSONBY TER.
Tate Gallery
Millbank Barracks
ST.GEORGE'S S.R.
TACHBROOK ST.
PIMLICO
BESSBORO GDNS.
BESSBOROUGH ST.
BESSBOROUGH GDNS.
MILLBANK
BESSBOROUGH
LUPUS ST.
ST. GEORGE'S SQUARE
AYLESFORD ST.
ST.GEORGE'S ST.
ST.GEORGES SQ. M.
Tachbrook Estate
BESSBOROUGH PL.
BESSBOROUGH ROAD
VAUXHALL BR.
ALBERT EMBANKMENT
C 44
GROSVENOR
RIVER
BRIDGEFOOT
C 59
VAUXHALL
VAUXHALL CROSS
S.LAMBETH PL.
VAUXHALL STATION
ELMS
NINE
PONTON R.D
WANDSWORTH ROAD
LANE
PARRY ST.
MILES ST.
BOND WAY
SOUTH LAMBETH ROAD
LANGLEY LANE
LAWN LANE
Vauxhall Park
New Covent Garden Market

12

17

Planning a route

How to plan a route

The time to study the route is before you go; it is too late to look for clues on route. Start by studying a good map, the RAC Great Britain Road Atlas, for example.

Motorways

The route you choose will depend on your priorities. Do you want the quickest route between A and B? If so, see if there is a motorway going in the right direction for you and opt to use it to the greatest extent. Remember that many motorway intersections are not available for use for travel in certain directions. These junctions with restrictions are identified on all RAC maps. The direction in which you wish to travel may not be followed by a motorway, in which case you will probably use Primary Traffic Routes.

Primary routes

Primary Traffic Routes form a national network between important towns known as Primary Destinations. A number of major road junctions, for example Scotch Corner, have also been selected as Primary Destinations. Primary Traffic Routes and Primary Destinations are identified on all RAC maps. If you are planning a long journey, the most straightforward route will be one which goes from one Primary Destination to the next.

When you are planning a journey on Primary Traffic Routes, you still have a degree of choice. Before you opt for the shortest route connecting Primary Destinations, look to see if it passes through several major towns or a large conurbation. There may be a route of a similar or slightly longer distance which does not pass through so many towns. This longer route may provide you with a shorter journey in time.

Minor roads

If you are motoring to a destination which is off a major road, or if you have decided to take a quiet or scenic route, you have more alternatives and therefore more decisions to make about the route you take.

Route plans

Whatever the length of your journey, or the type of road you opt for, it is advisable for ease of navigation to note both the numbers of the roads you are going to use and the names of the places you will pass through. The place names you list are of two types: directional aids, which are the major places you pass through, and identification aids, which are major places that will be approached or by-passed but whose names you will follow on the traffic signs.

A simple route plan can be prepared using two columns. It is best to write road numbers on the left hand column and place names on the right. (An optional third column on the right hand side could display mileages.)

A plan for a journey between Cobham in Surrey and Itchen Abbas in Hampshire might be drawn up as follows:

A245	
A3	GUILDFORD
A31	FARNHAM
	ALTON
	(WINCHESTER)
	New Alresford
B3047	Itchen Stoke
	Itchen Abbas

As you will see from the plan above, it is not necessary to repeat road numbers. If you are following a primary route the only names you need list are those of Primary Destinations. On other roads, particularly unclassified ones, it is wise to list all the places you will pass through. You may find it helpful to enter Primary Destinations in capitals. In the specimen route plan, the Primary Destinations Guildford and Alton are shown in capitals because although they are both by-passed they will appear on the primary green signs. Winchester, another Primary Destination, is only included because it will keep you on the correct road out of Alton—you will turn off on the B3047 some way before it is reached. New Alresford is included and is the last place on the primary route you will pass through, and both places you will enter on the B road are listed for ease of navigation.

Tactical planning

Preparing a route plan is logical planning. Tactical planning can also play an important part in your preparations. For example, avoid travelling through major built-up areas at peak hours when people are journeying to and from work (7.30–9.30a.m., noon to 2.00p.m. and 4.30–6.30p.m.). If your journey will involve driving in the dark, it is better to motor entirely in the dark rather than to drive in increasing darkness as night falls. Tactical planning should alert you against travelling in the early morning in autumn and winter when fog or mist might be a hazard. When you are drawing up your route for a long journey you may also have to consider places to stay overnight and to refuel your car.

RAC touring services

The RAC will assist in route planning for Members as part of the touring service available to Members. Route information is supplied on request from the RAC Head Office in Croydon. Normally the route will be that recommended by the RAC and will be marked on a specially designed map. Special requests for the quickest or most direct route or for a route suitable for touring with a caravan will also receive expert attention.

On route

Before you set out on a long journey it is as well to check road and weather conditions. All RAC offices are equipped to give information in respect of adverse road and weather conditions. When you are on route you can find out about any major traffic hold-ups ahead by tuning in to the appropriate local radio station. (You will find a full list of local radio station frequencies starting on page 80.)

Following your route is a matter of projecting yourself forward. On a motorway your route plan is simple—you need to look out for the number of the junction at which you are going to leave the motorway. On Primary Traffic Routes, you will be thinking ahead, looking at the green traffic signs for the next Primary Destination listed on your route plan. Remember that once a named place appears on a green traffic sign you will be able to follow the same named place on all succeeding signs until that place is reached. On country roads you will be following names on sign posts rather than road numbers. If you have recorded the names of all the places you will pass through on minor roads, you can use the boundary signs as you come into each village to check that you are still on the right route.

Journey time

One question you are bound to ask about any journey you are planning is "How long will it take?" If your route is by motorway the calculation is straightforward. On average, you should travel a mile a minute on the motorways, in other words 60 miles an hour. It is more difficult to estimate the journey time if using Primary Traffic Routes, other classified roads or country lanes. There are so many incalculable factors. For instance, there might be a bottleneck you do not suspect. The traffic density could be unusually heavy. On a narrow country lane there is always the danger of being stuck behind a slow-moving farm vehicle for several miles. It is hard to make allowance for these chance conditions.

You are the best judge of how long your journey will take. You know your vehicle. Similar journeys will provide the experience on which to base your estimates.

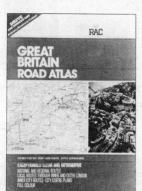

Sony don't make things just for fun.

DXC 1850 video camera.

At Sony Communication Systems we take ourselves somewhat seriously.

But not without good reason. Every machine we make has, literally, a serious job to do. In offices, factories, schools, hospitals and even outside in the open air.

Sony Communication Systems is a division of Sony whose sole aim is to make machines that make your working life easier. And to make those machines better than anyone else.

Nobody's doing more to improve office communications, for example. Sony are working overtime to see to that, with a range of viewdata terminals, dictation equipment, and our new Series 35 word processor.

In company communication, too, Sony's complete range of video programme making equipment is out on its own when it comes to performance. With the quality and durability to

Type 5 U-Matic and monitor.

cope with the demands of commercial use, indoors and out.

Portable conference system.

Series 35 word processor.

the teacher a better chance to teach.

And for students of commerce our portable conference system can provide interpretation facilities for up to sixty people.

We've even developed a compact video camera which weighs in at 4.1 ounces, needs practically no light and is not affected by vibration, shock or magnetic fields. Its uses in industry and medical research are limited only by the imagination.

Of course there's more to learn about Sony Communication Systems than we've room to mention here so contact Sarah Ash on Staines 61688 to see how we can make things better for you.

Going back to school, Sony have the widest range of language teaching aids. Giving the student a better chance to learn, and

Because even if this side of Sony doesn't make things for fun, it can certainly make the serious business of working a bit lighter.

9″ desktop colour viewdata terminal.

COMMUNICATION SYSTEMS DIVISION

SONY.

We make things better. Or not at all.

Travellab student recorder.

Local Radio

Local BBC and Commercial Local
Radio Wavelengths and Area
Coverage

BBC

	VHF Frequency (MHz)	MF Wavelength (m)	Frequency (kHz)
Bristol	95·5	194	1548
Bristol City	104·4		
Bath	102·2*		
Taunton		227	1323
Cambridgeshire	96·0	292	1026
Peterborough	103·9	207	1449
Cumbria	95·6	397	756
Whitehaven		206	1458
Cleveland	96·6	194	1548
Whitby	95·8		
Cornwall			
West	96·4	476	630
East	95·2	457	657
Isles of Scilly	97·3		
Derby		269	1116
(main)	96·5		
(relay)	94·2		
Devon	97·5*		
Barnstaple	103·9	375	801
Exeter	97·0*	303	990
Okehampton	96·2		
Plymouth		351	855
Torbay		206	1458
Furness (with Cumbria)	96·1	358	837
Guernsey		269	1116
Humberside	96·9	202	1485
Jersey		292	1026
Kent	96·7	187	
West		290	1035
East	102·6	388	774
Tunbridge Wells			1602
Lancashire	96·4	351	855
Lancaster	103·3		
Preston		193	1557
Leeds	92·4	388	774
Wharfedale	95·3		
Leicester	95·1	358	837
Lincolnshire	94·9	219	1368
London	94·9	206	1458
Manchester	95·1	206	1458
Merseyside	95·8	202	1485
Newcastle	95·4	206	1458
N. Northumberland	96·3		
Norfolk	95·1	351	855
King's Lynn	96·7*	344	873
Northampton		271	1107
South	96·6*		
North	103·3*		
Nottingham			
South	95·4	197	1521
North		189	1584
Oxford	95·2	202	1485

*not in service at date of publication

	VHF Frequency (MHz)	MF Wavelength (m)	Frequency (kHz)
Sheffield		290	1035
S. Yorkshire	97·4		
City of Sheffield	88·6		
Solent	96·1		
Fareham		300	999
Bournemouth		221	1359
Stoke-on-Trent	94·6	200	1503
Sussex	95·3		1485
Bexhill		258	1161
North	103·1		
WM (West Midlands)	95.6		
Birmingham		206	1458
Wolverhampton		362	828
York	90·2	450	666
Scarborough	97·2		1260
BBC National UK Services with Traffic Information			
Radio 1	88–90.5	285	1053
	(with R2)	275	1089
Radio 2	88–90·5	433	693
	(with R1)	330	909
Radio 4	92–95	1500	200
	(England & S. Wales only)		

*not in service at date of publication

IBA

	VHF Frequency (MHz)	MF Wavelength (m)	Frequency (kHz)
Aberdeen (North Sound)	96·9	290	1035
Ayr (with Girvan) (West Sound)		290	1035
Darvel	96·2		
Girvan	97·1		
Belfast (Downtown Radio)	96·0	293	1026
Birmingham (BRMB Radio)	94·8	261	1152
Bournemouth (2CR)	97·2	362	828
Bradford (Halifax and Huddersfield) (Pennine Radio)	96·0		
Tyersal Lane		235	1278
Vicars Lot		196	1530
Brighton (Southern Sound)	103·4	227	1323
Bristol (Radio West)	96·3	238	1260
Bury St Edmunds (Saxon Radio)	96·3	240	1251
Cardiff (CBC)	96·0	221	1359
Coventry (Mercia Sound)	95·9	220	1359
Doncaster (Radio Hallam)		302	990
Dundee/Perth (Radio Tay)			
Dundee	95·8	258	1161
Perth	96·4	189	1584
East Kent (Invicta Sound)		497	603
Dunkirk	95·1		
Dover	97·0		
Westwood	95·9		
Edinburgh (Radio Forth)	96·8	194	1548
Exeter/Torbay (DevonAir)			
Exeter	95·8	450	666
Torbay	95·1	314	954
Glasgow (Radio Clyde)	95·1	261	1152
Gloucester & Cheltenham (Severn Sound)	95·0	388	774
Great Yarmouth & Norwich (Radio Broadland)	97·6	261	1152

	VHF Frequency (MHz)	MF Wavelength (m)	Frequency (kHz)
Guildford (County Sound)	96·6	203	1476
Hereford/Worcester (Radio Wyvern)			
Hereford	95·8	314	954
Worcester	96·2	196	1530
Humberside (Viking Radio)	102·7	258	1161
Inverness (Moray Firth Radio)	95·9	271	1107
Ipswich (Radio Orwell)	97·1	257	1170
Leeds (Radio Aire)	94·6	362	828
Leicester (Leicester Sound)	97·1	238	1260
Liverpool (Radio City)	96·7	194	1548
London (Capital Radio)	95·8	194	1548
London (LBC)	97·3	261	1152
Luton/Bedford (Chiltern Radio)			
Luton	97·6	362	828
Bedford	95·5	379	792
Maidstone & Medway (Invicta Sound)	103·8	241	1242
Manchester (Piccadilly Radio)	97·0	261	1152
Newport (Gwent Broadcasting)	104	230	1305
Northampton (Hereward Radio)	102·8	193	1557
Nottingham (Radio Trent)	96·2	301	999
Peterborough (Hereward Radio)	95·7	225	1332
Plymouth (Plymouth Sound)	96·0	261	1152
Portsmouth (Radio Victory)	95·0	257	1170
Preston & Blackpool (Red Rose Radio)	97·3	300	999
Reading (Radio 210)	97·0	210	1431
Reigate & Crawley (Radio Mercury)	103·6	197	1521
Sheffield & Rotherham/Barnsley (Radio Hallam)		194	1548
Rotherham	95·9		
Tapton Hill	95·2		
Ardsley	95·6	230	1305
Southend/Chelmsford (Essex Radio)			
Southend	95·3	210	1431
Chelmsford	96·4	220	1359
Stoke (Signal Sound)	104·3	257	1170
Swansea (Swansea Sound)	95·1	257	1170
Swindon/West Wilts (Wiltshire Radio)			
Swindon	96·4	258	1161
West Wilts	97·4	320	936
Teesside (Radio Tees)	95·0	257	1170
Tyne/Wear (Metro Radio)	97·0	261	1152
Wolverhampton/Black Country (Beacon Radio)	97·2	303	990
Wrexham & Deeside (Marcher Sound/Sain-y-Gororau)	95·4	238	1260

N.B. These details reflect the conditions at July 1984. Some frequencies may change and new frequencies may be added.

For further information contact:

BBC Engineering Information Department, Broadcasting House, London W1A 1AA *or*

IBA Engineering Information Service, Crawley Court, Winchester, Hants SO21 2QA

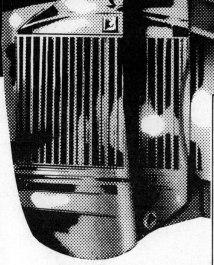

Local Radio Stations

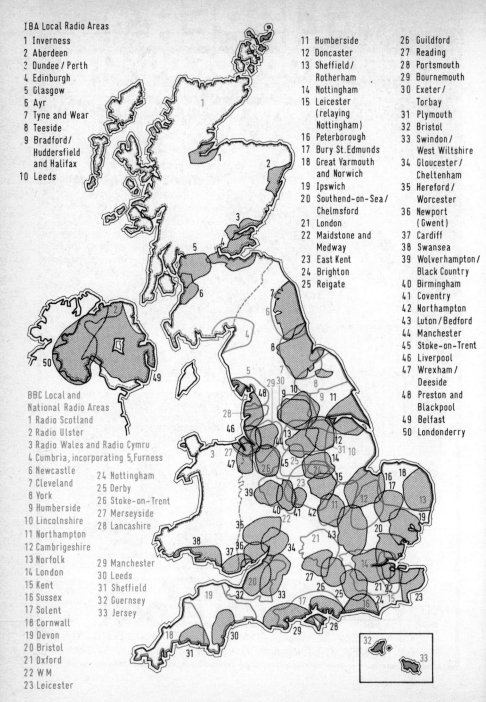

IBA Local Radio Areas

1 Inverness
2 Aberdeen
3 Dundee / Perth
4 Edinburgh
5 Glasgow
6 Ayr
7 Tyne and Wear
8 Teeside
9 Bradford / Huddersfield and Halifax
10 Leeds

11 Humberside
12 Doncaster
13 Sheffield / Rotherham
14 Nottingham
15 Leicester (relaying Nottingham)
16 Peterborough
17 Bury St. Edmunds
18 Great Yarmouth and Norwich
19 Ipswich
20 Southend-on-Sea / Chelmsford
21 London
22 Maidstone and Medway
23 East Kent
24 Brighton
25 Reigate

26 Guildford
27 Reading
28 Portsmouth
29 Bournemouth
30 Exeter / Torbay
31 Plymouth
32 Bristol
33 Swindon / West Wiltshire
34 Gloucester / Cheltenham
35 Hereford / Worcester
36 Newport (Gwent)
37 Cardiff
38 Swansea
39 Wolverhampton / Black Country
40 Birmingham
41 Coventry
42 Northampton
43 Luton / Bedford
44 Manchester
45 Stoke-on-Trent
46 Liverpool
47 Wrexham / Deeside
48 Preston and Blackpool
49 Belfast
50 Londonderry

BBC Local and National Radio Areas

1 Radio Scotland
2 Radio Ulster
3 Radio Wales and Radio Cymru
4 Cumbria, incorporating 5, Furness
6 Newcastle
7 Cleveland
8 York
9 Humberside
10 Lincolnshire
11 Northampton
12 Cambrigeshire
13 Norfolk
14 London
15 Kent
16 Sussex
17 Solent
18 Cornwall
19 Devon
20 Bristol
21 Oxford
22 WM
23 Leicester
24 Nottingham
25 Derby
26 Stoke-on-Trent
27 Merseyside
28 Lancashire
29 Manchester
30 Leeds
31 Sheffield
32 Guernsey
33 Jersey

Great Britain Distance Chart

The distance chart is a triangular matrix. Cities appear along the diagonal in the following order, each heading a column/row of mileages:

LONDON · ABERDEEN · ABERYSTWYTH · BIRMINGHAM · BLACKPOOL · BOURNEMOUTH · BRIGHTON · BRISTOL · BUXTON · CAMBRIDGE · CANTERBURY · CARDIFF · CARLISLE · DARLINGTON · DOVER · EDINBURGH · EXETER · FISHGUARD · GLASGOW · GLOUCESTER · HOLYHEAD · HULL · INVERNESS · KENDAL · LEEDS · LEICESTER · LINCOLN · LIVERPOOL · MANCHESTER · NEWCASTLE UPON TYNE · NORTHAMPTON · NORWICH · NOTTINGHAM · OBAN · OXFORD · PLYMOUTH · PORTSMOUTH · SCARBOROUGH · SHEFFIELD · SHREWSBURY · SOUTHAMPTON · STRANRAER · SWANSEA · TRURO · YORK

Mileages from LONDON to each town (first column of the chart):

Aberdeen	492
Aberystwyth	212
Birmingham	111
Blackpool	228
Bournemouth	104
Brighton	53
Bristol	116
Buxton	159
Cambridge	55
Canterbury	58
Cardiff	150
Carlisle	295
Darlington	244
Dover	74
Edinburgh	372
Exeter	170
Fishguard	261
Glasgow	389
Gloucester	105
Holyhead	261
Hull	171
Inverness	529
Kendal	257
Leeds	191
Leicester	97
Lincoln	133
Liverpool	198
Manchester	184
Newcastle upon Tyne	274
Northampton	66
Norwich	112
Nottingham	123
Oban	479
Oxford	56
Plymouth	212
Portsmouth	71
Scarborough	231
Sheffield	160
Shrewsbury	154
Southampton	77
Stranraer	395
Swansea	189
Truro	247
York	194

Ireland Distance Chart

	BELFAST	CASTLEBAR	CORK	DONEGAL	DUBLIN	DUNDALK	GALWAY	KILKENNY	KILLARNEY	LARNE	LIMERICK	LONDONDERRY	ROSCREA	ROSSLARE	SLIGO	TRALEE	WATERFORD
ATHLONE	141	81	134	114	78	91	58	78	144	162	76	142	40	130	73	140	108
BELFAST		182	263	128	103	51	199	175	271	21	203	75	167	205	129	267	205
CASTLEBAR			177	94	151	157	50	155	183	204	114	138	118	218	54	178	185
CORK				248	161	213	128	92	54	284	63	276	95	129	207	74	78
DONEGAL					154	107	127	191	260	133	191	44	153	243	41	255	221
DUBLIN						52	135	73	191	124	123	152	77	102	135	187	103
DUNDALK							148	125	220	72	152	100	116	154	107	216	155
GALWAY								106	133	220	65	171	68	169	86	129	136
KILKENNY									123	197	70	217	38	63	151	133	30
KILLARNEY										292	68	286	114	171	219	20	120
LARNE											224	72	188	226	150	288	227
LIMERICK												217	46	130	151	64	79
LONDONDERRY													181	254	85	281	247
ROSCREA														100	113	110	68
ROSSLARE															203	181	51
SLIGO																215	181
TRALEE																	130
WATERFORD																	

DISTANCE TABLES

Distances between any two selected towns can be found at
the intersection of the vertical and horizontal rows thus:
Belfast to Dundalk 51 miles
Mileages are computed by the shortest practical routes which
are not necessarily those recommended by the RAC.

Advice for the Motorist

Motor Laws

by J. K. W. Derby, M.A., Legal Department, RAC

This summary of legislation in regard to private motor vehicles is necessarily concise. Broadly speaking, it concentrates on the law concerning the use of vehicles rather than their construction, and on points most likely to be of use for reference. Members who require full information on the law summarised below and on matters not dealt with in the summary are invited to communicate with the Legal Department, RAC House, Lansdowne Road, Croydon CR9 2JA (T 01-686 2525). Amendments to the law subsequent to August 1984 have not been included.

Note. An electrically assisted pedal cycle, which is not treated in law as a motor vehicle, may be driven on a road by a person who is 14 or more years of age without the normal requirements of motoring law applying to either the rider or his machine. The cycle must (a) not exceed 40 kg kerbside weight if a bicycle, 60 kg if a tandem bicycle or tricycle, (b) be fitted with pedals by means of which it is capable of being propelled and (c) be fitted solely with an electric motor having a continuous rated output not exceeding 0·2 kw if a bicycle, 0·25 kw if a tandem bicycle or tricycle and which cannot propel the vehicle when it is travelling at more than 15 m.p.h.

Important Statutes. Vehicles (Excise) Act, 1971; Petroleum Act, 1928; Road Traffic Acts, 1960 to 1974; Road Traffic Regulation Act, 1967; Transport Acts, 1968, 1978, 1980–1982; Vehicle and Driving Licences Act, 1969; Criminal Justice Act, 1982.

Registration and payment of duty

Registration. Every motor vehicle used or kept, for however short a period, on a road repairable at the public expense must be registered and carry identification marks.

The licensing of a new vehicle is undertaken by a Local Vehicle Licensing Office on receipt of the applicant's completed form together with the appropriate duty and certificate of insurance. Details of the vehicle are recorded at the Driver and Vehicle Licensing Centre at Swansea and it is from there that the registration document is issued.

A V11 renewal reminder form is sent from the DVLC at Swansea and this form may be used for renewal in person at a licensing Post Office or by post to a listed Head Post Office, provided that the registration particulars are unaltered and that licensing is continuous. Where the V11 form is inappropriate because of a change in particulars or licensing is not continuous or the V11 reminder is not received, renewal may be effected by means of a V10 form obtainable from main Post Offices or LVLOs. The V10 form may be taken to a licensing Post Office or posted to a Head Post Office but must be taken or posted to an LVLO where the registration document cannot be produced, the vehicle taxation class is altered or the vehicle is subject to Customs concession or restriction, and, similarly, but using a V85 form, in the case of a goods vehicle exceeding 1525 kg unladen weight.

A licence applicant still in possession of an old-style registration book should make application to his nearest LVLO who will issue the licence and initiate conversion onto the central record.

It is necessary, on renewing a licence, to produce a test certificate issued within the preceding 12 months if the vehicle is of a type and age subject to compulsory inspection.

Identification Marks. Identification marks are allotted to an applicant upon the first registration of the vehicle and must be carried on the back and, except in the case of a motorcycle, on the front of the vehicle on flat rectangular plates or flat unbroken rectangular surfaces forming part of the vehicle. The lettering and figures must be in white, silver or light grey on a black background and must be of the prescribed size. The plates must be kept clean so as to be clearly distinguishable. The back number plate must be illuminated during the hours of darkness as to be easily legible in the absence of fog at a distance of 18 metres (cars) or 15 metres (motor cycles).

Alternatively, a reflective number plate may be fitted at either end of the vehicle or at both ends. This plate must be legibly marked with the relevant British Standard and the front plate must consist of black digits on a white reflective background while the back plate must be black on yellow. The other requirements for number plates remain unchanged including the necessity to illuminate the back plate.

It is obligatory that reflective number plates shall be fitted to motor vehicles first registered from 1st January, 1973. The number plate on a trailer or caravan need not be reflective.

Taxation. Licences are issued for any period of 12 months or (provided the annual rate of duty is more than £18), for any period of 6 months.

Electrically propelled vehicles are exempt from Vehicle Excise Duty. Cars and light goods vehicles first registered before 1st January, 1947, are taxed at the reduced rate of £60 per annum. Ordinary private cars are taxed at the "Private" rate under which the duty is £90 per annum. Goods and utility vehicles must be taxed at the "Goods" rate if they are used for the conveyance of goods or burden of any description for hire or reward or for or in connection with a trade or business, otherwise they may be taxed at the "Private" rate. The "Goods" rate for a vehicle not exceeding 1525 kg unladen weight is £90 p.a., that for one not exceeding 7·5 tonnes plated gross weight is £130 p.a. and for one not exceeding 12 tonnes plated gross weight is £290 p.a.

The duty for a motor cycle not exceeding 150 c.c. capacity is £9 p.a., that for one exceeding 150 c.c. but not exceeding 250 c.c. is £18 p.a. and for other motor cycles £36 p.a. The duty for tricycles not exceeding 425 kg in weight unladen is £36 p.a. Those weighing more are taxed at the "Private" or "Goods" rate according to construction and use.

Invalid carriages (defined for Excise purposes as vehicles, including cycles with an attachment for propelling the same by mechanical power, not exceeding 10 cwt in weight unladen adapted and used for invalids) are exempt from duty, though they must be registered. A vehicle used by a disabled person, who is

in receipt of mobility allowance, war pensioners' mobility supplement or who has obtained a grant for modification, is exempt from duty but must be registered.

Surrender of Licence. The holder of a licence may at any time surrender the licence disc to the Authority and obtain a rebate in respect of each *complete* month of the period of the currency of the licence which is unexpired at the date of the surrender. IMPORTANT. To obtain a rebate for a complete month it is necessary that the application for rebate and the licence surrendered shall be in the hands of the Authority on or before the last day of the preceding month or if forwarded by post it should be posted in time for the envelope to bear a post mark of the preceding month.

Registration Document. The registration document should not be kept on the vehicle. The document contains instructions as to the procedure on change of registration particulars, change of address, and transfer, destruction or permanent exportation of the vehicle.

Loss or Destruction of Registration Document or Licence Disc. If the licence disc or registration document has been lost, destroyed, defaced, or the particulars become illegible or colour faded, the owner must apply to the Authority for a duplicate licence disc or registration document. A fee of £2 is payable, but if the Authority is satisfied that there has been no neglect on the part of the licence holder causing the particulars to become illegible or colour faded, then no fee is payable. If the original licence disc or registration document is found, it must be returned to the Authority.

Driving licences

Before any person may drive a motor vehicle on a road he must hold a licence to drive, and no person shall employ a person to drive a motor vehicle unless such person is a holder of a licence. This requirement must be met except where a driver has held and is entitled to obtain a licence and his licence application has been received by the Driver and Vehicle Licensing Centre. Application for the grant of a licence is made to the DVLC, Swansea SA99 1AB, and may be received and dealt with at any time within two months before the date on which the licence is to take effect. Unless the applicant can satisfy the Authority that within the 10 years prior to the date on which the licence is to come into force he has either (1) passed the Department of Transport test or (2) held a full licence issued in Great Britain, Northern Ireland, the Isle of Man or the Channel Isles, in respect of the class of vehicle concerned, he will be granted only a provisional licence which lasts until his 70th birthday, except for motor cycles, and costs £10.

Provisional licence entitlement to ride a motor cycle, other than a moped, which must be specifically requested, is limited to a period of 2 years. Where both parts of the test applying to a solo motor cycle or the single element test for a motor cycle combination are not passed within the 2 year period an interval of 1 year must elapse before the licence may be renewed. A fee of £3 is payable on renewal of motor cycle provisional

entitlement. Subject to certain practical limitations, the 2 year "clock" may be stopped because of temporary medical factors, voluntary surrender of the licence or disqualification. The "on/off" limitation does not apply to motor cycle provisional entitlement which is automatically included within a full car, motor tricycle or moped licence.

A full licence, unless revoked or surrendered, remains in force for the period ending on the applicant's 70th birthday or for a period of 3 years, whichever is the longer, except that the Authority may limit a licence to a period of not more than 3 years and not less than 1 year where the applicant suffers from a relevant or prospective disability—(see "Declaration as to Physical Fitness"). A once-for-all licence fee of £10 is payable either on the grant of a provisional licence or first full licence.

The minimum age for obtaining a licence to drive a small passenger or small goods vehicle is 17 except that 16 applies to certain persons receiving a mobility allowance. A motor cycle (a mechanically propelled vehicle with less than four wheels not exceeding 410 kg in unladen weight) may be driven at 17. However, a moped, which is either a motor cycle not exceeding 50 c.c. equipped with pedals by means of which it is capable of being propelled and which was first used before 1st August 1977 or a motor cycle first used from 1st August 1977 which has a maximum design speed of 30 m.p.h., a kerbside weight which does not exceed 250 kg and does not exceed 50 c.c. if propelled by internal combustion engine, may be driven at 16. (See also p. 94, "Distinguishing Plates for Motor Cycles".)

In the case of a goods vehicle exceeding 3·5 but not exceeding 7·5 tonnes permissible maximum weight the minimum age is 18. The minimum age for a heavier goods vehicle or a passenger vehicle suitable to carry more than nine persons including the driver is 21, except that 18 applies in limited circumstances.

An E.E.C., Gibraltar, Australia, Kenya, New Zealand, Norway, Singapore, Spain, Sweden, Switzerland or Hong Kong driving licence may be exchanged for an equivalent British driving licence provided that at the date of application the applicant is normally resident here and is within his first year of residence. The fee is £10.

Declaration as to Physical Fitness. The applicant for a licence must declare on the form whether he is suffering from a prescribed disability (see below) or any other disability likely to cause his driving to be a source of danger to the public, such prescribed or other disability being known as a relevant disability. The applicant must also declare any other disability which at that time is not a relevant disability but which, by virtue of its intermittent or progressive nature or otherwise may become a relevant disability in course of time, such disability being referred to as a prospective disability.

The Authority may neither refuse the grant of a provisional licence to an applicant suffering from a non-progressive limb disability nor a full or provisional licence to such an applicant who has passed a relevant test at any time and whose disability has not become more acute. This disability relates solely to the absence, deformity or loss of use, including deficient movement or power, of one or more limbs or part of a limb.

A provisional licence granted to a person suffering from a relevant or prospective disability may be restricted to vehicles of a particular construction or design.

If the applicant for a licence suffers from a prescribed disability, namely, epilepsy, sudden attacks of disabling giddiness or fainting, or severe subnormality or mental deficiency, or is unable to read (with glasses, if worn) a motor car number plate with large symbols at 67 feet in good daylight, the Authority must refuse to grant a licence. In the case of epilepsy, however, if the applicant can satisfy conditions indicating freedom from any attack during the two years preceding the date the licence is effective or where he has had attacks whilst asleep during that period, he shall have had attacks only whilst asleep during at least the three years preceding the date the licence is effective and his driving is not likely to be dangerous, he may not be refused a licence. In the case of disabling giddiness or fainting caused by a heart disorder, where the applicant has a heart-regulating device implanted in his body and can satisfy the conditions that his driving is not likely to cause danger and that he has made arrangements for supervision by a cardiologist, and is conforming to those arrangements, he may not be refused a licence. The eyesight requirements are relaxed in respect of the use of mowing machines or pedestrian controlled vehicles and the provisional licence issued to an applicant whose eyesight is such will be restricted to this category of vehicle.

A licence holder must notify the Authority in writing of the onset of a relevant or prospective disability or of the worsening of a disability already disclosed, except where he has not previously suffered from the disability and he reasonably believes that it will not last for more than 3 months.

If the Authority has reasonable grounds for believing that an applicant for, or holder of, a licence is suffering from a relevant or prospective disability, the Authority may ascertain the facts by obtaining consent to seek medical information or by medical examination or driving test, the cost of which will be borne by the Authority.

Tests. The fee for a driving test is £14·40 (£17·94 in respect of a Part I manoeuvrability test required to be undertaken by a solo motor cyclist that is conducted by a licensing authority examiner). This fee will only be returned on cancellation of test where not less than three working days' notice is given before appointment date. The points on which it is necessary to satisfy the examiner are set out on the application form. Where the examiner is satisfied that the test proves ability to drive vehicles of a particular construction or design only, the driver shall not be failed because he was not tested on a vehicle of that construction or design.

A full licence permits the holder to drive vehicles not covered by the licence without his having to obtain a separate provisional licence subject to certain restrictions applying to motor cycles, but he must comply with the usual provisional licence conditions. Provisional coverage does not apply where (a) the person is under the relevant minimum age for driving the vehicle (b) the vehicle is a solo motor cycle exceeding 125 c.c., except where a driving test has been passed (c) the full licence is restricted to the driving of vehicles of a particular construction or

design, or (d) the full licence is restricted to the driving of pedestrian controlled vehicles or mowing machines. See "Declaration as to Physical Fitness" and "Provisional Licence".

A person who passes a driving test on a car with automatic transmission is only entitled to a full licence for "automatics" and will not be covered for three wheelers, However, where the test is taken on a "non-automatic" car the licence granted will include entitlement to drive "automatics" and three-wheelers.

A person subject to a test must provide a motor vehicle which is suitable for the purposes of the test and if it is fitted with a dual accelerator control this must be rendered inoperable by removal of the pedal and any other necessary parts. A person submitting himself to a test must sign the examiner's attendance record.

A person who fails the test in any one group cannot submit himself for another test in that group until a period of one month has elapsed, other than a Part I solo motor cycle test.

Provisional Licence. The holder of a provisional licence and a person using a relevant full licence as described above must, until he has passed the test, display "L" plates on the front and rear of the vehicle. He must also, until he has passed the test, be accompanied by a full licence holder whose licence authorises him to drive as a full licence holder a vehicle of the class being driven at the time, except when (a) undergoing a test or (b) driving a vehicle not being a motor car not constructed or adapted to carry more than one person or (c) driving certain electrically propelled vehicles or (d) driving certain road rollers or (e) riding a motor bicycle, with or without sidecar. (Note: In the case of a motor cycle combination it is not necessary for any passenger to be the holder of a licence) or (f) he is driving on certain remote islands. A full licence holder whose car licence is limited solely on account of leg disability may act as supervisor of a provisional licence holder driving a car within the same group.

A solo motor cyclist, until he has passed the test, may only carry as a pillion passenger a person who holds a full licence covering motor cycles. This restriction does not apply to the co-rider of a motor-assisted tandem bicycle.

A provisional licence restricts the riding of a solo motor cycle to one not exceeding 125 c.c. with a maximum power output of 9 kw. and maximum power to weight ratio of 100 kw/tonne, until the holder has passed the test. If the machine was first used before 1st January, 1982, only the 125 c.c. restriction applies.

Until he has passed the test the holder of a provisional licence may not drive a vehicle drawing a trailer except an agricultural tractor or articulated vehicle.

Signing of Licence. A person to whom a licence is granted must forthwith sign it **in ink** with his ordinary signature.

Change of Name or Address. Where these details shown on a driving licence cease to be correct the licence must be surrendered to the Authority together with the relevant new particulars and the Authority will

grant a replacement licence for the unexpired period without charge.

Appeals against Failure to pass Test. A person who fails the driving test may appeal to the Court of Summary Jurisdiction of the division in which the test took place, but the Court **only** has power to determine whether the test was properly conducted in accordance with the regulations. If it determines that it was not so conducted, the Court may order that the applicant may undergo another test without waiting for the usual period of a month to expire.

Production of Licence and Date of Birth. The licence should always be carried by the driver when driving the vehicle and must be produced on demand to a constable so that he may ascertain the name and address of the licensee, the date of issue and issuing authority. Alternatively the licence must by produced by the licensee **in person** within *five* days of the production being required at such Police Station as may be specified by him at the time when its production was required.

The constable may also require the driver to state his date of birth where he fails to produce his licence or where he produces a licence which the constable suspects is not his, was granted in error or contains an alteration made with intent to deceive or where the driver number has been altered, removed or defaced. PENALTY for failure to produce licence or to state date of birth, fine not exceeding £400.

Duplicate Licences. If the licence is lost or defaced, a duplicate may be obtained from the Authority on payment of a fee of £3. If the original licence is found it must be returned to the Authority.

Issue of New Licence Free from Endorsement. A person who has had his licence endorsed is entitled to apply for a licence free from endorsement four years from the date of commission of the offence or, where disqualification was ordered, four years from the date of conviction. If the endorsement was in respect of causing death by reckless driving or reckless driving it may be removed four years from date of conviction. If the endorsement was in respect of driving or attempting to do so while unfit through drink or drugs or with excess alcohol in breath, blood or urine or for failing, without reasonable excuse, to provide a specimen for analysis or laboratory test after driving or attempting to do so involving obligatory disqualification, it may be removed eleven years from date of conviction.

A clean licence may be obtained either on applying for the grant of a licence or, subject to payment of £3 and surrender of the subsisting licence, at any time in which case the clean licence will run for the unexpired portion of the licence surrendered. In practice time-expired endorsements are automatically removed when a new licence is issued on notification of change of name and/or address or on application for an exchange licence for which a fee of £3 is payable.

Motor Vehicles (Construction and Use) Regulations

The following are some points from the Motor Vehicles (Construction and Use) Regulations:

Liability. A person who contravenes or fails to comply with these Regulations or who uses, or causes or permits, a motor vehicle or trailer to be used which does not comply with the Regulations, is liable to a fine not exceeding £1,000.
NOTE: Where a person is convicted of an offence for which disqualification or endorsement can be ordered he can escape disqualification or endorsement if he proves that he did not know, and had no reasonable cause to suspect, that the facts of the case were such that that offence would be committed. (See p. 96, "Disqualification and Endorsement" B.12.)

General. 1. Every motor vehicle and trailer with its accessories shall at all times be in such condition, and the number of passengers carried and the manner in which they are carried, and the weight, distribution, packing and securing of the load be such that no danger or nuisance is caused or is likely to be caused to any person on the vehicle, trailer, or on a road.
2. No person driving a motor vehicle shall be in such a position that he cannot have control over the same or so that he cannot retain a full view of the road and traffic ahead.
3. No person driving a vehicle shall quit it without having stopped the engine **and** set the brake.
N.B.—The duty to stop the engine does **not** apply to gas-propelled vehicles, or vehicles being used for fire brigade, ambulance or police purposes, or to a vehicle the engine of which is being used to drive machinery in certain circumstances.
4. No person shall open or cause or permit to be opened any door of a motor vehicle or trailer on a road so as to cause injury or danger to any person.

Seat Belts and Anchorage Points. Seat belts and anchorage points must be provided for the driver and front passenger seat, or outer front passenger seat where more than one, of passenger and dual-purpose vehicles with seating for less than 13 passengers manufactured from 1st July 1964 and first registered from 1st January 1965.

A goods vehicle not exceeding 1525 kg in unladen weight manufactured from 1st September 1966 and first registered from 1st April 1967 must be similarly equipped as must also such a vehicle exceeding 1525 kg in unladen weight, but not exceeding 3500 kg maximum gross weight, manufactured from 1st October 1981 or first used from 1st April 1982.

A three-wheeled vehicle exceeding 255 kg in unladen weight manufactured from 1st March 1970 and first used from 1st September 1970 must also be so equipped.

The seat belts provided for a vehicle manufactured from 1st October 1972 and first used from 1st April 1973 must, with limited exceptions, meet improved standards of ease of use.

Subject to limited exceptions, vehicles required to be fitted with anchorages that are manufactured from 1st October 1981 or first used from 1st April 1982 must have anchorage points for seat belts on all forward-facing adult seats although only having to be provided with belts for the driver and front outboard passenger.

An obligatory seat belt, its anchorages and parts, including the load-bearing structure of the vehicle, shall be free from defect or serious corrosion likely to affect adversely the belt's performance. These

requirements do not apply on a journey during which a defect occurs or where expeditious steps have been taken to remedy the defect.

Mirrors.
1. A motor vehicle other than a motor cycle must be equipped either externally or internally with a reflecting mirror so constructed and fitted as to assist the driver, if he so desires, to become aware of traffic to the rear of the vehicle. Goods and dual-purpose vehicles must have at least two mirrors, of which one must be on the offside and the other either internal or on the nearside and so fitted as to assist the driver, if he so desires, to become aware of traffic to the rear and on both sides rearwards.

2. Internal mirrors fitted to a motor vehicle first used from 1st April, 1969, must have protective edges to reduce the risk of injury through cuts.

3. A motor vehicle manufactured from 1st December, 1977, and first used from 1st June, 1978, must, with certain exceptions, be fitted with an interior and an offside exterior rear-view mirror and also an exterior mirror on the near-side where the interior mirror does not provide an adequate view to the rear. Where an interior mirror would provide no view to the rear it need not be fitted if the vehicle is equipped with exterior mirrors on the near and off-sides. A mirror, including one voluntarily fitted to a motor cycle manufactured from 1st April, 1978 and first used from 1st October, 1978, must bear an approval mark.

Windscreen Wipers and Washers. One or more efficient automatic wipers are required where the driver cannot obtain an adequate view to the front without looking through the windscreen. The wipers shall be capable of clearing the windscreen so that the driver has an adequate view of the road to the front and in front of the near and off-side of the vehicle. Subject to certain limited exceptions, a vehicle required to be fitted with wipers must also be fitted with a windscreen washer which is capable of clearing mud or other similar deposits from the area swept by the wipers.

Latches, Hinges and Steering Mechanism. Three-wheelers, cars and dual-purpose vehicles, with certain exceptions, first used from 1st July, 1972, must be fitted with anti-burst latches and hinges to the side doors. Similarly these vehicles, and certain goods vehicles, must have a protective type of steering mechanism. Neither requirements apply to certain models manufactured before 1st January, 1974. A vehicle subject to these requirements must bear the appropriate approval marks.

Petrol Tanks. The petrol tank fitted to a motor vehicle first used from 1st July, 1973, and manufactured from 1st February, 1973, other than one bearing an approval mark, must be made of metal. The tank of a vehicle shall be reasonably secure from damage and free from leakage.

Tyres.
1. No person shall use or cause or permit to be used on a road any motor vehicle or trailer a wheel of which is fitted with a pneumatic tyre, if—(a) the tyre is unsuitable having regard to the use to which the motor vehicle or trailer is being put or to the types of tyres fitted to its other wheels; (b) the tyre is not so inflated as to make it fit for the use to which the motor vehicle or trailer is being put; (c) the tyre has a cut in excess of 25 millimetres or 10 per cent of the section width of the tyre, whichever is the greater, measured in any direction on the outside of the tyre and deep enough to reach the ply or cord; (d) the tyre has any lump, bulge or tear caused by separation or partial failure of its structure; (e) the tyre has any portion of the ply or cord exposed; (f) the base of any groove which showed in the original tread pattern of the tyre is not clearly visible; (g) either (i) the grooves of the tread pattern of the tyre do not have a depth of at least 1 millimetre throughout a continuous band measuring at least three-quarters of the breadth of the tread and round the entire outer circumference of the tyre; or (ii) in a case where the original tread pattern of the tyre did not extend beyond three-quarters of the breadth of the tread, the base of any groove which showed in the original tread pattern does not have a depth of at least 1 millimetre.
(**See also paragraph 6.**)

2. The above requirements are not infringed where a tyre is deflated or not fully inflated and which has any of the defects specified in (c), (d) or (e) above, provided that the tyre and the wheel to which it is fitted are so constructed as to make the tyre in that condition fit for the use to which the motor vehicle or trailer is being put and the outer sides of the wall of the tyre are marked so as to identify the tyre as being constructed to comply with the requirements of this paragraph.

3. Nothing in paragraph 1 applies to a land locomotive, land tractor, land implement or land implement conveyor, or to an agricultural trailer being drawn by a land tractor or to a broken down vehicle or one proceeding to a place for breaking up, provided it is being towed at not more than 20 m.p.h. Nothing in paragraph 1(g) applies to a motorcycle not exceeding 50 c.c.

4. No person shall use or cause or permit to be used on a road any motor vehicle or trailer a wheel of which is fitted with a recut pneumatic tyre if its ply or cord has been cut or exposed by the recutting process or it has been wholly or partially recut in a pattern other than the manufacturer's recut tread pattern. (This does not prevent the fitting of remould tyres.)

5. Without prejudice to paragraphs 1 and 4, all the tyres of a motor vehicle or trailer shall at all times while the vehicle or trailer is used on a road be maintained in such condition as to be fit for the use to which the vehicle or trailer is being put, and as to be free from any defect which might in any way cause damage to the surface of the road or danger to persons on or in the vehicle or to other persons using the road.

6. A cross-ply tyre may not be fitted on the same axle as a radial tyre nor may radial tyres be fitted on the front axle with cross-ply on the rear.

Silencers and Excessive Noise.
1. No person shall use or permit to be used a motor vehicle or trailer which causes excessive noise, or noise in excess of that permitted for the particular type of vehicle as measured by a prescribed apparatus. It shall be a good defence to prove that the noise was due to temporary or accidental cause and could not have been

prevented by due care on the part of the driver or owner, or in the case of proceedings against a driver who is not the owner to prove that the noise was through a defect in design or through the negligence of some other person whose duty it was to keep the vehicle in proper condition and could not have been prevented by reasonable diligence on the part of the driver.

The maximum permissible noise meter reading is dependent on whether the vehicle was first used before or since 1st November, 1970, or whether it is subject to E.E.C. Council Directive. The requirements do not apply to a motor vehicle first registered before 1931 or to a vehicle going to or from a place where, by previous arrangement, the noise level is to be measured or the vehicle is to be adjusted, modified or equipped to ensure that it complies with the requirements. The noise emitted by a vehicle includes that of any trailer drawn and any load carried. Motor vehicles first registered after 1st April, 1970, must be constructed to a separate set of noise levels according to category of vehicle.

A motor cycle or moped first used from 1st January 1985 must be fitted with its original silencer or one marked B.S.AU 193: 1983 "test 2" or with a reference to its make and type specified by the vehicle manufacturer.

2. No person shall use a motor vehicle in such a manner as to cause excessive noise which could have been prevented by the exercise of reasonable care.

3. A driver when the vehicle is stationary otherwise than through enforced stoppage owing to traffic conditions shall stop the engine so far as may be necessary for the prevention of noise. This Regulation does not apply to gas-propelled vehicles.

Pollution Prevention. A motor vehicle which is first used from 1st January, 1972, and is propelled by a spark ignition engine, other than a two-stroke, must be equipped with means within its engine for preventing the escape of vapours or gases into the atmosphere. This requirement does not apply to a motor cycle with or without sidecar.

A motor vehicle which is first used from 10th November, 1973, with certain exceptions and which is propelled by a spark ignition engine, other than one exceeding 3500 kg in laden or unladen weight or a vehicle with less than four wheels not exceeding 400 kg in laden or unladen weight, must bear the approval mark indicating that the vehicle meets requirements as to emission of gaseous pollutants by the engine.

Warning Instruments. It is an offence to sound a warning instrument on a restricted road between the hours of 11.30 p.m. and 7 a.m. or on any road at any time if the vehicle is stationary except where sounded as an anti-theft device or in an emergency. A gong, bell or siren may only be fitted to a vehicle for the prevention of theft or, as may also two-tone horns, to vehicles used for fire brigade, police, ambulance and certain other rescue purposes. Musical and multi-tone horns may not be fitted to a motor vehicle first used from 1st August, 1973.

Direction Indicators. From 1st January, 1971, these became obligatory for most motor vehicles and trailers. A motor cycle, with or without sidecar, a vehicle first

used before 1st January, 1936, and a vehicle which has no front or rear lamps are, however, exempt. Similarly, a trailer which has no front or rear lamps or one in the case of which an observer standing centrally 6 metres behind it, whether it is loaded or not, can still see the rear or side indicators on the towing vehicle, need have no indicators.

The regulations prescribe the type of indicator that shall be fitted. The older types of indicator are still permitted for vehicles first used before 1st September, 1965.

Direction indicators must be maintained in a clean condition and in good and efficient working order.

Where direction indicators can be operated simultaneously as a hazard warning, they may only be used when the vehicle is stationary on a road for the purpose of warning others of a temporary obstruction on any part of a road.

Stop Lamps. From 1st January, 1971, these became obligatory for most motor vehicles and trailers. A moped, other than one manufactured from 1st October 1983, a vehicle first used before 1st January, 1936, a vehicle or trailer which has no front or rear lamps and a trailer the towing vehicle of which has two stop lamps which can be seen in the manner described within "Direction Indicators", are, however, exempt.

A motor vehicle first used before 1st January, 1971, and a trailer manufactured before that date, must be fitted with at least one stop lamp. An eligible moped, a motor cycle, with or without sidecar, and an invalid carriage first used from 1st January, 1971, must have one stop lamp but other vehicles and trailers must have two.

Stop lamps must be red in colour and be maintained in a clean condition and in good and efficient working order.

Mascots. No mascot shall be carried by a motor vehicle first registered on or after 1st October, 1937, in any position where it is likely to strike any person with whom the vehicle may collide unless the mascot is not liable to cause injury to such person by reason of any projection thereon.

Speedometers. Every motor vehicle first used from 1st October, 1937, and that is either manufactured before 1st October 1983, or first used before 1st April, 1984, other than a motor cycle not exceeding 100 cc first used before 1st April 1984, must be equipped with an instrument to indicate speed either in miles or kilometres per hour within an accuracy of plus or minus 10 per cent. Later vehicles must be equipped with an instrument indicating speed in both miles and kilometres per hour and switched so that either indication may be replaced by the other.

Footrests. If a pillion passenger is carried astride a motor bicycle (whether a sidecar is attached or not) suitable footrests must be provided.

Width of Loads. No load other than an indivisible load (subject to certain conditions) and loose agricultural produce not baled or crated may be carried on any motor vehicle or trailer if it projects more than 305 millimetres laterally beyond the overall width of the vehicle or if its total width exceeds 2·9 metres.

Obstruction.
No person in charge of a motor vehicle or trailer shall cause or permit the motor vehicle or trailer to stand on a road so as to cause any unnecessary obstruction thereof.

On a charge of obstruction it is not necessary for the prosecution to prove that other vehicles or persons have been actually obstructed. All that is required to substantiate the charge is evidence that there has been some unreasonable use of the highway or that the vehicle has been left in such a position as to be likely to obstruct other users of the highway.

Television Sets. A television set shall not be installed in a motor vehicle if the screen is partly or wholly visible to the driver whilst in the driving seat or if the controls, other than the volume control and main switch, are within reach of the driver whilst in the driving seat.

It is an offence to use in a motor vehicle a television set which might cause distraction to drivers of other vehicles on the road.

Inspection of Brakes, etc. Any police constable in uniform, Department of the Environment certifying officer or examiner or Metropolitan Police public carriage examiner, who shall produce his authority (if required), is empowered to test brakes, silencers, steering gear, tyres, lighting equipment and reflectors on any premises subject to the consent of the owner of the premises. The power shall not be exercised unless the owner of the vehicle consents or notice of such inspection has been given to him personally 48 hours beforehand or sent to him by registered letter 72 hours before the proposed inspection. The above provisions as to notice do not apply in the case of a test and inspection made within 48 hours of an accident in which the vehicle has been involved. See also p. 99, "Inspection of Vehicles after Accidents" and p. 106, "Spot Checks".

Distinguishing Plates for Motor Cycles. A motor cycle not exceeding 150 c.c. which is first used from 1st August 1977 and before 1st January 1982 must be equipped with a plate indicating, among other details, whether it is a standard motor cycle or a moped. A motor cycle not exceeding 125 c.c. first used from 1st January 1982 must be equipped with a new-style plate providing additional information. For these purposes a moped is defined as a motor cycle with a design speed not exceeding 30 m.p.h., a kerbside weight not exceeding 250 kg. and if propelled by an internal combustion engine a cylinder capacity not exceeding 50 c.c.

Type Approval. The system of testing and approving sample models of serially produced vehicles and components is obligatory for passenger and dual-purpose vehicles, other than those categorised as such solely by reason of four-wheel drive, suitable to carry not more than eight passengers exclusive of the driver and for certain three-wheelers, which are manufactured from 1st October, 1977, and first used from 1st August, 1978. These vehicles, where manufactured from 1st October, 1979, and first used from 1st April, 1980, must be equipped with a plate indicating type approval.

Goods vehicles, dual-purpose vehicles other than those mentioned above, motor ambulances and motor caravans with three or more wheels, with exceptions, which are manufactured from 1st October 1982 and first used from 1st April 1983, and their parts, are subject to type approval.

Amateur built vehicles are exempt from type approval, provided that in the case of a goods vehicle its unladen weight does not exceed 1525 kg.

Trailers

General.
1. Not more than one trailer may be towed by a motor car at the same time. No trailer shall be used for the conveyance of passengers for hire or reward except in limited circumstances following breakdown. Passengers may not be carried in a moving caravan with four close-coupled wheels or less except when it is under test.
2. No motor cycle shall draw a trailer exceeding 254 kg in weight unladen or 1·5 metres in overall width.
3. A two-wheeled motor cycle without sidecar that exceeds 125 c.c. may tow a trailer restricted to a maximum width of 1 metre, a maximum length of 2·5 metres from the rear axle of the motor cycle to the rearmost part of the trailer and a maximum laden weight of the lesser of 150 kg or two-thirds of the motor cycle's kerbside weight. No passenger may be carried in the trailer and the motor cycle must be marked with its kerbside weight and the trailer with its unladen weight. A motor cycle may tow a broken-down motor cycle with one person riding it without engine capacity, marking or weight restrictions applying.
4. When a trailer is towed by a tow rope or chain the nearest points between the two vehicles must not exceed 4·5 metres. Where the gap between the vehicles exceeds 1·5 metres, the tow rope must be rendered clearly visible to persons on either side.
5. A trailer must display to the rear a number plate similar in dimensions to that of the towing vehicle, and bearing the same mark and numbers. See p. 88, "Identification Marks". The plate must be illuminated at night and two red rear lights and two red rear reflectors must be fitted. The reflectors must be marked AU40LIII or AU40LIIIA or with an approval mark which incorporates the Roman numeral III.
6. The towing vehicle shall be equipped either externally or internally with a reflecting mirror so fitted as to assist the driver if he so desires to become aware of the presence of traffic to the rear of the vehicle (see also p. 92, "Mirrors"). A mirror is not required if a person is carried on the trailer in a position which gives an uninterrupted view to the rear and is provided with efficient means of communicating with the driver.
7. No person in charge of a motor vehicle or trailer drawn thereby shall cause or permit such trailer to stand when detached from the drawing vehicle unless one at least of the wheels of the trailer is prevented from revolving by the setting of the brake or the use of a chain, chock or other efficient device.
8. No motor vehicle drawing a trailer shall be driven in the right-hand lane of a motorway with three or more lanes which are in use, except where this lane has to be used to pass a vehicle of exceptional width.

Brakes. Trailers exceeding 750 kg maximum gross weight, that is the weight which a trailer is designed or adapted not to exceed when in use and travelling on a road laden, must, with exceptions, be equipped with running brakes and parking brakes. On trailers not exceeding 3560 kg total laden weight (3500 kg. if manufactured from 27th February 1977) overrun brakes are permitted.

Unbraked Trailers. The laden weight of an unbraked trailer in use on a road shall not exceed its maximum gross weight. No unbraked trailer, with exceptions including one not exceeding 102 kg. in weight unladen until 1st October 1986, shall be drawn on a road by a vehicle if the kerbside weight of the drawing vehicle is less than twice the unladen weight of the trailer together with the weight of any load which the trailer is carrying. Every unbraked trailer, other than one not exceeding 102 kg in unladen weight manufactured before 1st October 1982 (until 1st October 1986), shall have its maximum gross weight, stated in kilograms, marked in a conspicuous and readily accessible position on the outside on its left or near side.

Safety Glass. The windows of a trailer caravan first used from 1st September, 1978, and every other trailer first used from 1st June, 1978, must be constructed of either specified safety glass or safety glazing. Safety glazing is a material, other than glass, that does not fragment so as to cause severe cuts. All trailers manufactured from 1st October, 1984 must, in the case of safety glass, meet more stringent standards.

Side Facing Reflectors. If a trailer exceeding 5 metres in length, excluding drawbar, is used on a road during the hours of darkness it must carry two amber side facing reflectors on each side, which must be of a prescribed type and fitted in prescribed positions. This requirement also applies to a motor vehicle exceeding 8 metres in length.

Rearguards and Sideguards. A goods trailer exceeding 1020 kg in unladen weight manufactured from 1st May 1983 and a goods vehicle exceeding 3500 kg maximum gross weight manufactured from 1st October 1983 and first used from 1st April 1984, must, with exceptions, be fitted with a rear under-run protective device and sideguards, where the distance between axles exceeds 3 metres, maintained so as to perform effectively.

Rear Markings. A trailer exceeding 3500 kg maximum gross weight and a goods vehicle exceeding 7500 kg m.g.w. must, with exceptions, be fitted with prescribed rear markings. A trailer or goods vehicle first used before 1st August 1982 not exceeding, respectively, 1000 kg or 3000 kg in unladen weight are exempted from the requirements. The type of markings required depend on the overall length of the towing combination but each must bear the specification number B.S.AU 152 and be maintained in clean and efficient condition. The markings may be fitted to a load where, if fitted to the rear of the vehicle or trailer, they would be obscured.

Direction Indicators and Stop Lamps. See p. 93.

Speed Limits. See p. 95.

Radio interference suppression

Regulations apply to vehicles sold by the manufacturers or imported for sale on or after 1st July, 1953. Under the regulations, owners of such vehicles must ensure that they continue to be fitted with the suppression equipment with which they were supplied and that it is in good order.

A motor vehicle first used from 1st April, 1974, which is propelled by a spark ignition engine, must bear the approval mark indicating that it is fitted with suppression equipment.

Offences under the Road Traffic Acts

Illegal Sale of Vehicles. It is an offence to sell or supply or to expose for sale a motor vehicle or trailer for delivery in such a condition that its use on a road would be unlawful on account of non-compliance with the law as to construction, weight, equipment, brakes, steering, tyres, or obligatory lamps and reflectors or maintenance in a safe condition. It is an offence to fit a part to a vehicle or to sell or supply a part the fitting of which would cause the use of the vehicle to contravene construction and use requirements. PENALTY. Fine not exceeding £2,000. It is a defence to the above for the person concerned to prove that the vehicle was sold for export or that he had reasonable cause to believe that it would not be used on British roads in its unlawful condition. A conviction does not affect the validity of any contract or any rights arising under a contract.

Speed Limits. The speed limit on a motorway or dual-carriageway road is 70 m.p.h. and that on other roads is 60 m.p.h. Only roads subject to a lower limit have to be marked by signs.

A general speed limit of 30 m.p.h. applies on roads having a system of street lighting provided by means of lamps placed 200 yards or less apart unless there are derestriction signs. On other roads where a speed limit of 30 m.p.h. or more applies, a motorist shall not be convicted for exceeding the speed limit unless "repeater" signs are erected at appropriate intervals.

A passenger vehicle including a car, motor caravan, car-derived van not exceeding 2 tonnes maximum laden weight, dual-purpose vehicle as defined on p. 106, motor cycle and three-wheeler is solely governed by road speed limits. These vehicles are limited to 50 m.p.h. on all types of road when towing a caravan or trailer, the earlier provisions as to weight ratio and markings affecting maximum speed are discontinued.

A passenger vehicle exceeding 3·05 tonnes unladen weight or adapted to carry more than 8 passengers is limited to 70 m.p.h. on a motorway (60 m.p.h. if exceeding 12 metres in overall length), 60 m.p.h. on a dual-carriageway road and 50 m.p.h. on other roads. A limit of 50 m.p.h. applies when towing on all types of road.

A goods vehicle not exceeding 7·5 tonnes maximum laden weight is limited to 70 m.p.h. on a motorway, 60 m.p.h. on a dual-carriageway road and 50 m.p.h. on other roads. Where a trailer is towed and the aggregate maximum laden weight does not exceed 7·5 tonnes or that weight is not exceeded in the case of an articulated goods vehicle, a speed limit of 60 m.p.h. applies on a motorway and 50 m.p.h. on other roads. A goods vehicle exceeding 7·5 tonnes maximum laden weight whether rigid, articulated or drawing a trailer is limited to 60 m.p.h. on a motorway, 50 m.p.h. on a dual-carriageway road and 40 m.p.h. on other roads.

An invalid carriage, which is not permitted on a motorway, is limited to 20 m.p.h.

PENALTY. Fine not exceeding £400, on motorways £1,000.

Evidence in Speed Limit Cases. A person shall not be convicted of exceeding a speed limit on the evidence of one witness alone to the effect that in the opinion of the witness the person charged was driving the vehicle at a speed exceeding the limit. The evidence of a policeman as to his observations of the readings of a speedometer may be accepted by the Court as sufficient to justify a conviction.

Reckless Driving. PENALTY. On summary conviction, imprisonment not exceeding six months or a fine not exceeding £2,000 or both. On conviction on indictment, imprisonment not exceeding two years or a fine or both.

Causing Death by Reckless Driving. PENALTY. On indictment, imprisonment for not exceeding five years. In Scotland, only the High Court of Justiciary may sentence for more than two years.

Careless Driving. This is defined as driving without due care and attention or without reasonable consideration for other persons using the road. PENALTY. Fine not exceeding £1,000.

Restrictions on Prosecution under the above Sections. No person shall be convicted of exceeding a speed limit or of reckless or careless driving or of failure to observe traffic directions and signs or of leaving a vehicle in a dangerous position unless: (a) He was warned at the time the offence was committed that the question of prosecuting him would be taken into consideration; or (b) within fourteen days of the commission of the offence a summons for the offence was served on him; or (c) within the said fourteen days, a notice of the intended prosecution specifying the nature of the alleged offence, and the time and place when it is alleged to have been committed, was served on him or the person registered as the owner of the vehicle at the time the offence was committed. The above requirements do not apply in relation to an offence if, at the time of the offence or immediately thereafter, an accident occurs owing to the presence on a road of the vehicle in respect of which the offence was committed. Notice is deemed to have been served if sent by registered post or recorded delivery service to last known address. This applies even if the notice is returned as undelivered or is for any other reason not received. Failure to comply with the above requirements shall not be a bar to the conviction of the

accused if the Court is satisfied that the name and address of the accused or the registered owner could not with reasonable diligence have been ascertained in time for a summons to be served or for a notice to be served or sent as aforesaid, or the accused by his own conduct contributed to the failure. These restrictions on prosecution do not apply to cases of causing death by reckless driving or driving under the influence of drink or drugs.

In the majority of cases information must be laid before a Magistrate within six months of the alleged offence and the summons can be issued at any time thereafter.

Disqualification and Endorsement. The Road Traffic Act, 1972, as amended, contains provisions the effect of which is dependent on whether conviction is for an offence under A or B:

A
1. Manslaughter (in Scotland, culpable homicide).
2. Causing death by reckless driving.
3. Reckless driving committed within three years of conviction for this offence or for causing death by reckless driving.
4. Driving or attempting to drive while unfit through drink or drugs.
5. Driving or attempting to drive with excess alcohol in breath, blood or urine.
6. Failing to provide a specimen for analysis or laboratory test after driving or attempting to drive.
7. Racing and speed trials on the highway.

B
1. Reckless driving where not committed within three years of conviction for reckless driving or causing death by reckless driving. (10).
2. Careless and inconsiderate driving. (2–5).
3. Being in charge of a motor vehicle while unfit through drink or drugs. (10).
4. Being in charge of a motor vehicle with excess alcohol in breath, blood or urine. (10).
5. Failing to provide specimen of breath for breath test. (4).
6. Failing to provide specimen for analysis or laboratory test after being in charge of a motor vehicle. (10).
7. Improper carriage of passenger on motor cycle. (1).
8. Failure to comply with a direction of a police constable or warden or with a "Stop" sign, traffic light signals, double white line markings or a sign referring to large or slow vehicles at an automatic half-barrier level crossing. (3).
9. Leaving vehicle in a dangerous position. (3).
10. Failing to stop after accident. (5–9).
11. Failing to give particulars or report accident. (4–9).
12. Using, or permitting a vehicle to be used, in contravention of construction and use regulations either (a) so as to cause danger by condition of the vehicle, parts or accessories, the number of passengers, or weight, distribution, packing or adjustment of load; or (b) for any unsuitable purpose likely to cause danger; or (c) in breach of requirements as to brakes, steering gear or tyres; or (d) by carrying a dangerously insecure or ill-positioned load. (3).
13. Driving without licence where no licence could have been granted or, where a provisional licence could

have been granted, failure to comply with the conditions applicable to provisional licence. (2).

14. Failure to comply with conditions applicable to provisional licence or full licence treated as such. (2).

15. Driving with uncorrected defective eyesight. (2).

16. Refusing to submit to test to establish eyesight requirements. (2).

17. Driving under age. (2).

18. Driving while disqualified. (6).

19. Using, or permitting to use, a motor vehicle uninsured or unsecured against third-party risks. (4–8).

20. In Scotland taking a motor vehicle without authority or knowingly driving it or allowing oneself to be carried in it. (8).

21. Contravention of motorway regulations except illegal parking on the hard shoulders. (3).

22. Contravention of pedestrian crossing regulations. (3).

23. Failure to obey sign exhibited by school crossing patrol. (3).

24. Contravention of a street playground order. (2).

25. Exceeding a speed limit. (3).

26. Taking a motor vehicle without authority or knowingly driving it or allowing oneself to be carried in it. (England and Wales). (8).

27. Going equipped for stealing or taking a motor vehicle. (England and Wales). (8).

28. Stealing or attempting to steal a motor vehicle. (8).

Effect of Conviction. The effect of conviction for an offence under the above headings will be as follows:—

A

Obligatory Disqualification for not less than twelve months unless for special reasons (which must relate to the offence and not the offender) the Court orders a shorter period or none at all. In the case of a second conviction within 10 years for driving or attempting to drive whilst unfit through drink or drugs or for having consumed excess alcohol or for failing to provide a specimen for analysis the minimum disqualification is three years.

Where a conviction is for aiding, abetting, counselling or procuring, or inciting commission of an offence under A, disqualification is as in B (below).

Driving Test. On conviction the Court may order disqualification until a driving test has been passed.

Endorsement. Obligatory if disqualification ordered. If there is no order for disqualification, the conviction must be endorsed unless the Court finds special reasons to the contrary.

B

Discretionary Disqualification for such period as Court thinks fit. (See also p. 91, "Construction and Use Regulations: Liability".)

Driving Test. May be ordered as at A.

Endorsement. As A. (See also p. 91, "Construction and Use Regulations: Liability".)

Penalty Points. Where a person is convicted of an offence involving obligatory or discretionary disqualification and the Court does not order him to be disqualified but orders particulars of the conviction to be endorsed on his licence, the endorsement shall include particulars of the offence and its date of commission and the number of penalty points. The number of penalty points or the points within a range of penalty points to be endorsed are indicated after each particular offence listed under B (above). Where a person is convicted of aiding and abetting the commission of an offence involving obligatory disqualification under A (above) he will be recorded with 10 penalty points and in any other case where obligatory disqualification is waived 4 penalty points will be recorded.

On conviction for two or more offences committed on the same occasion, only the penalty points relating to the highest rated offence will be ordered to be endorsed. An endorsement ordered before 1st November 1982 counts as 3 penalty points unless disqualification was imposed at that time or subsequently.

Where on conviction of an offence the penalty points to be endorsed at that time together with any previously endorsed, that have not been "wiped clean" by disqualification, number 12 or more the Court shall order disqualification. Penalty points are ignored that relate to an offence committed more than three years before the date of commission of another offence being counted. The minimum period of disqualification is six months but if a previous disqualification has been imposed on the offender within the three years immediately preceding the commission of the latest offence for which penalty points are taken into account the minimum disqualification is one year and if there are two or more such disqualifications the minimum disqualification is two years. A shorter period of disqualification or none at all may be ordered where the Court is satisfied that there are grounds for mitigating the normal consequences of the conviction. The Court may not take into account the gravity of the offence, hardship, other than exceptional hardship, or circumstances which within the three years immediately before the conviction have been taken into account for a similar purpose.

Removal of Disqualification. Where disqualification is imposed under Road Traffic Act, 1972, application for removal can be made after two years or half the period of disqualification, whichever is the longer; where the period is ten years or more, after five years.

Removal of Endorsement. See p. 91.

Date of Birth. If a person is convicted with endorsement or disqualification of an offence under A or B (above), the Court may order him to state his date of birth in writing. Where the plea of guilty in absence procedure is used in respect of these offences the notification to the Court must include the date of birth and sex of the accused.

Duty to Give Name and Address. If the driver of a motor vehicle is alleged to have committed an offence of reckless or dangerous driving, or careless driving, and is requested by any person having reasonable grounds for so requesting, he must give his name and address, and if he refuses or gives a false name and

address he shall be guilty of an offence. A police constable may arrest without warrant the driver of any motor vehicle who within his view commits an offence of reckless or dangerous driving or careless driving, unless that driver gives his name and address or produces his licence for examination.

Uncorrected Eyesight. Any person who drives a motor vehicle on a road while his eyesight is such (whether through a defect which cannot be or one which is not for the time being sufficiently corrected) that he cannot comply with the eyesight requirement prescribed for the driving test, commits an offence. PENALTY. Fine not exceeding £400.

A constable having reason to suspect this offence may require the person to submit to a test to ascertain whether, using no other means of correction than at the time of driving, he can comply with the eyesight requirement. PENALTY for refusal to submit to test, fine not exceeding £400.

Safety Helmets. Riders and passengers, other than those in a sidecar and other than a turbaned follower of the Sikh religion, when using motor cycles, scooters and mopeds on a road must wear a safety helmet of approved design. It is not necessary to wear a helmet when pushing a machine.

The helmet must bear the marking B.S. 2001:1956, B.S. 1869:1960, B.S. 2495:1960, B.S. 2001:1972, B.S. 5361:1976 or B.S. 2495:1977, or be of a type manufactured for motor cyclists which, by virtue of shape, material and construction, could reasonably be expected to afford similar, or greater, protection to that of a British Standard helmet. The helmet must be securely fastened by means of the straps or other fastening provided and, if a chin cup is worn, an additional strap must be provided for fastening under the jaw.

From 1st January, 1982, only helmets complying with any version of B.S. 5361:1976 or B.S. 2495:1977 may be sold and helmets manufactured from 1st April, 1981, must be marked to indicate compliance with Amendment 5 as to resistance to solvents and petrol.

Pillion Riding. Only one passenger may be carried on a solo motor cycle, and he or she must be seated astride behind the driver on a proper pillion seat securely fixed to the machine. PENALTY (for driver), fine not exceeding £400. Suitable footrests must be provided. (For restrictions on pillion riding with a provisional licence holder, see p. 90.)

Wearing of Seat Belts. A seat belt must be worn by a person both driving a vehicle or riding in the front passenger seat if the vehicle is of a category for which seat belts are a compulsory fitment (see p. 91, "Seat Belts and Anchorage Points"). Where there are two front passenger seats only the outer passenger need wear a seat belt except that if the outer seat is unoccupied a passenger using the inner seat would have to wear a seat belt. From a viewpoint of private motoring, a person is exempt from wearing a seat belt while reversing or supervising a provisional licence holder who is doing so, where his seat belt is defective or has temporarily locked or he is the holder of a valid medical exemption certificate. Only the person contravening the requirement to wear a seat belt

commits an offence. PENALTY. Fine not exceeding £100.

Wearing of Seat Belts by Children. It is an offence for a person, without reasonable excuse, to drive a motor vehicle on a road of a category for which seat belts are a compulsory fitment when there is in the front of the vehicle a child under the age of fourteen years who is not wearing a seat belt. PENALTY. Fine not exceeding £100. (See p. 91, "Seat Belts and Anchorage Points").

A child for whom a valid medical exemption certificate is held is exempt from wearing a seat belt. The requirement to be restrained does not apply to a child on an inner front passenger seat where the outer and all other seats are occupied or in respect of a seat for which no restraining device for a young person is provided and the adult seat belt is defective or has temporarily locked. A child under the age of one year must be in an approved restraining device for a young person appropriate to the child's weight while a child one year of age or older may be in any type of restraining device for a young person or an adult seat belt.

Drink or Drugs Offences. A person who drives or attempts to drive a motor vehicle on a road or public place while unfit to drive through drink or drugs commits an offence. PENALTY. On summary conviction, imprisonment not exceeding 6 months or a fine not exceeding £2,000 or both.

A person who when in charge of a motor vehicle but not driving is unfit to drive through drink or drugs is guilty of an offence. PENALTY. On summary conviction, imprisonment not exceeding 3 months or a fine not exceeding £1,000 or both. It is a defence to prove that the circumstances were such that there was no likelihood of defendant driving but in so determining a Court may disregard any injury to him and any damage to the vehicle. A person shall be taken to be "unfit to drive" if his ability to drive properly is for the time being impaired.

A constable may arrest a person without warrant on reasonable suspicion that he is or has been committing either of the above offences. For the purpose of this power of arrest a constable may enter, if necessary forcibly, any place where the person is or the constable reasonably suspects him to be.

Excess Alcohol. It is an offence to drive, attempt to drive or be in charge of a motor vehicle on a road or other public place having consumed alcohol in excess of 35 microgrammes in 100 millilitres of breath, 80 milligrammes in 100 millilitres of blood or 107 milligrammes in 100 millilitres of urine. The penalties for Excess Alcohol offences are the same as for the corresponding Drink or Drugs offences.

It is a defence to a charge of being in charge of a vehicle with excess alcohol to prove that the circumstances were such that there was no likelihood of the defendant driving whilst his alcohol level remained likely to exceed the prescribed limit but in so determining the Court may disregard any injury to him and any damage to the vehicle.

A constable in uniform may require a person driving, attempting to drive or in charge of a vehicle whom he reasonably suspects of having alcohol in his body or of

having driven etc. and still has alcohol in his body or of having committed a moving traffic offence, to submit to a breath test. Similarly where an accident occurs a constable, who need not be in uniform, may require a breath test to be undertaken which may, if he thinks fit, take place at a police station specified by him. These requirements for submission to a breath test are subject to safeguards for hospital patients. Penalty for refusal to submit to test without reasonable excuse, fine not exceeding £400.

A constable may arrest a person without warrant where the test is positive or it is refused, except a patient in hospital, and take him to a police station. For the purpose of arresting a person in these circumstances or to obtain a specimen of breath where an accident has occurred which a constable reasonably caused injury to another person he may enter, if necessary forcibly, any place where that person is or is reasonably suspected to be.

An "Excess Alcohol" or "Drink or Drugs" suspect, subject to the safeguards for a hospital patient, may be required to provide two specimens of breath for analysis by an approved device but only at a police station. Alternatively the provision of a specimen of blood or urine may be required for laboratory test either at a hospital or, if at a police station, only where the constable believes that for medical reasons a breath specimen cannot or should not be provided or a breath device is not available or in the case of a suspected "Drink or Drugs" offence the constable has been advised medically that the condition might be due to drugs, and this request may be made despite the prior provision of two breath specimens. The constable may decide whether the specimen shall be of blood or urine except where a doctor decides that urine is only appropriate; two samples of urine are required within one hour. The lower reading of two specimens of breath will be regarded but if it contains 50 or less microgrammes of alcohol in 100 millilitres of breath then the motorist may claim its replacement by a specimen of blood or urine the choice of which, as before, is made by the constable. A constable must warn a person that failure to provide a specimen may render him liable to prosecution. A person who, without reasonable excuse, fails to provide a specimen is guilty of an offence.

A person required to provide a specimen may be detained at a police station until his condition is such that he would not commit a drink or drugs driving offence except where there is no likelihood of his driving or attempting to do so and when deciding as to impairment of driving ability through drugs a doctor's advice is sought and followed.

Procedures provide for a driver categorised as a problem drinker being medically examined and only being permitted to resume driving after effective treatment and cure.

Driving while Disqualified. A constable in uniform may arrest without warrant any person driving or attempting to drive a motor vehicle on a road whom he has reasonable cause to suspect of being disqualified.

Racing on the Highway. It is an offence to promote or take part in a race or trial of speed between motor vehicles on a public highway. PENALTY. Fine not exceeding £1,000.

Trials on Footpaths and Bridleways. No person may promote or take part in a trial of any description between motor vehicles on a footpath or bridleway (i.e. ways over which the public have no vehicular rights) unless the trial has been authorised by the Local Authority, after written consent of the owner and occupier of the land over which the footpath or bridleway runs. PENALTY. Fine not exceeding £400.

Driving on Land off the Road. It is an offence, without lawful authority, to drive a motor vehicle on to or upon any land not forming part of a road or on any road being a bridleway or footway, but it is not an offence to drive a motor vehicle on any land within fifteen yards of the road for the purpose only of parking the vehicle on the land. This provision is without prejudice to the law of trespass or local byelaws or regulations. PENALTY. Fine not exceeding £400. A person shall not be convicted under this section if he proves to the satisfaction of the Court that the car was driven in contravention of this section for the purpose of saving life or extinguishing fire or meeting any other like emergency.

Duty to Stop and Report in Case of Accidents. If in any case owing to the presence of a motor vehicle on a road an accident occurs whereby damage or injury is caused to any person, vehicle, animal* or to any property contructed on, fixed to, growing in or otherwise forming part of the land on which the road in question is situated or land adjacent thereto, the driver of the motor vehicle shall stop and, if required so to do by any person having reasonable grounds for so requiring, give his name and address and also the name and address of the owner and the identification marks of the vehicle. If in the case of such accident the driver *for any reason* does not give his name and address to any such person he shall report the accident at a police station or to a police constable as soon as practicable and in any case within twenty-four hours of the occurrence. PENALTY. Fine not exceeding £2,000.

(In the case of accidents involving personal injury, see p. 101.**)**

Notification of Disease or Disability. If it appears from any proceedings that the accused may be suffering from any relevant or prospective disability the Court shall notify the Licensing Authority (see p. 89, "Driving Licences").

Inspection of Vehicles after Accidents. Any person authorised by the Secretary of State may, on production of his authority, inspect any vehicle in connection with which an accident arose, and may enter premises at any reasonable time for the purpose.

Taking Motor Vehicles without Consent. It is an offence in Scotland (*a*) to take and drive away any motor vehicle without the consent of the owner or other lawful authority or (*b*) knowing that a motor vehicle has been so taken, drives it or allows himself to be carried in or on it without such consent or authority. PENALTY. On summary conviction, imprisonment not

*For the purpose of this provision "Animal" includes horse, cattle, ass, mule, sheep, pig, goat or dog.

exceeding three months or a fine not exceeding £2,000. On indictment, imprisonment not exceeding one year or a fine or both such imprisonment and fine. Similar offences apply in England and Wales under the Theft Act, 1968. PENALTY. On indictment, imprisonment not exceeding three years.

It is an offence under the Theft Act, 1968, which applies in England and Wales, for a person to be equipped for stealing or taking a motor vehicle. PENALTY. On indictment, imprisonment not exceeding three years.

Interference with Vehicles. A person is guilty of the offence of vehicle interference if he interferes with a motor vehicle or trailer or with anything carried in or on the vehicle or trailer with the intention of theft or taking and driving away without consent by himself or another. A constable may arrest without warrant anyone who is or whom he reasonably suspects to be guilty of this offence. PENALTY. On summary conviction, imprisonment not exceeding three months or a fine not exceeding £1,000 or both.

Tampering with Motor Vehicles. If, while a motor vehicle is on a road or on a parking place provided by a Local Authority, any person without lawful authority or reasonable cause gets on to the vehicle or tampers with the brake or other part of its mechanism, he shall be guilty of an offence. PENALTY. Fine not exceeding £400.

Leaving Motor Vehicles in Dangerous Position on the Road. To leave a motor vehicle on any road in such a position or under such circumstances as to be likely to cause danger to other persons using the road is an offence. PENALTY. Fine not exceeding £400.

See p. 96 as to restrictions on prosecution.

Removal of Vehicles. Provision is made for the removal from a road of a vehicle which is broken down, parked contrary to a statutory prohibition or restriction, or in such a position, condition or circumstances as to cause obstruction or to be likely to cause danger. Further a vehicle may be removed both from a road and from any land in the open air where it appears to have been abandoned without lawful authority. PENALTY. For abandoning vehicle or part of it: on summary conviction fine not exceeding £1,000; second or subsequent conviction fine not exceeding £1,000 or imprisonment not exceeding three months or both. Where an abandoned vehicle is a "wreck" the removing authority will place a notice on it indicating that it will be removed for destruction within seven days if not taken away by the owner earlier. A vehicle which is a "runner" can be removed by the Authority immediately and if the owner is traced and does not reclaim it within 21 days, or he is not traced, it will be disposed of. Where a vehicle has been unlawfully abandoned on private land the Authority must give the occupier 15 days notice of intention to remove and if the occupier formally objects no action may be taken. Local authorities must now provide places where residents may dispose of unwanted vehicles without charge.

The charge for removal from a motorway is £47, for removal in the City of London and areas wholly in the Metropolitan Police District, £45, and elsewhere, £43.

A storage charge of £4 per day may be levied and also a disposal charge of £12.

Wheel Clamps. An experimental scheme for attaching an immobilisation device to a vehicle illegally parked is now in operation in a specified area of central London. A constable or a person under his direction may attach the device to a vehicle where he finds it or after removing the vehicle to another place. A vehicle either displaying a disabled person's badge or in a meter bay during the two hours following the end of the initial charge period is exempt from immobilisation. A notice must be affixed to the immobilised vehicle indicating that the device has been attached, warning that the vehicle should not be driven and stating the procedure for release. A constable or person under his direction may release the vehicle on payment of the charge of £19.50. On summary conviction for unauthorised removal or interference with the notice on the vehicle. PENALTY. Fine not exceeding £100. On summary conviction for unauthorised removal or attempts to remove the immobilisation device. PENALTY. Fine not exceeding £400.

Traffic Signs. Non-compliance with a "Stop" sign, traffic light signals, double white line markings or a sign referring to large or slow vehicles at an automatic half-barrier level crossing is an offence. PENALTY. Fine not exceeding £400, discretionary disqualification and endorsement. In the case of offences related to other traffic signs the maximum fine is also £400, but disqualification and endorsement do not apply (see p. 96, "Disqualification and Endorsement", p. 96, "Restrictions on Prosecution" and p. 104, "Double White Lines").

"Zebra" Pedestrian Crossings. The limits of these crossings are indicated by two lines of studs placed across the carriageway enclosing alternate black and white "zebra" stripes. Crossings are marked by two or more yellow globes illuminated by a flashing, or in certain circumstances constant, light mounted on black and white posts. The validity of a crossing is not prejudiced by failure of the lights provided that at least one globe is still illuminated. To improve safety, "zig-zag" markings are being added to both sides of crossings where the road layout permits.

A driver approaching a crossing where traffic is not being controlled by a police constable or traffic warden must accord precedence to any pedestrian who is on the crossing before the vehicle reaches it. The driver must stop at the broken give-way line, where provided, one metre from the crossing. Where there is a street refuge or reservation the crossing on each side is treated as a separate crossing.

A driver may not stop within the limits of a crossing, as described above, unless (a) he is prevented from proceeding by circumstances beyond his control or (b) it is necessary to do so to avoid an accident. A pedestrian may not loiter on a crossing.

A driver, other than of a pedal cycle or motor assisted pedal cycle without sidecar, may not stop in the zig-zag area except (a) to accord precedence to a pedestrian or (b) where he is prevented from proceeding by circumstances beyond his control or (c) where it is necessary to do so to avoid an accident or (d) for the purpose of making a left or right turn.

A driver within the zig-zag areas on the approach side of a crossing may not overtake the leading vehicle within that area or the vehicle nearest the crossing which is stationary for the purpose of according precedence to a pedestrian, except where the vehicle is stationary at the separate crossing formed by a central reservation in a one-way street. PENALTY. Fine not exceeding £400.

"Pelican" Crossings. These push-button pedestrian crossings are a simplified form of "X-Way" crossing, which they replace. The signals displayed to the driver are on a black ground and normally a steady green light will be shown which means "Proceed". When a pedestrian pushes the button a steady amber light will be shown to the driver which means "Stop" unless the vehicle is so close to the stop line or signals that it is unsafe to do so. A steady red light is then shown which indicates to the driver that he must not proceed. This is followed by a flashing amber light during which period the driver must accord precedence to any pedestrian on the crossing but if there is none he may proceed. The signal then returns to the normal green "Proceed" light.

School Crossing Patrols. A duly appointed school crossing patrol in uniform may by exhibiting a "Stop—Children" sign stop traffic between the hours of 8 a.m. and 5.30 p.m. to allow children to cross the road on their way to and from school. Drivers must stop before reaching the place where the children are crossing or seeking to cross and may not restart until the sign ceases to be exhibited. PENALTY. Fine not exceeding £400.

Compulsory Insurance

It is unlawful to use, or permit any other person to use, a vehicle on a road unless there is in force a policy (a) against liability to third parties in respect of the death of or bodily injury to any person caused by, or arising out of, the use of the vehicle on a road in Great Britain and (b) against any liability arising from the use of the motor vehicle or any trailer which is compulsorily insurable in E.E.C. countries. It has been held by the High Court that an unattended parked vehicle is nevertheless "in use". A policy is of no effect unless and until a certificate of insurance in the prescribed form has been delivered by the insurer to the insured. PENALTY. Fine not exceeding £1,000.

In respect of (a) above, the policy shall not be required to cover liability in respect of death or bodily injury sustained by a person employed by the person insured arising out of and in the course of that person's employment.

A person charged with using a vehicle uninsured shall not be convicted if he proves that the vehicle was not his or hired or lent to him, that he was using it in the course of his employment, and that he neither knew nor had reason to believe there was no insurance in force.

Car Sharing. In the case of a vehicle that is not adapted to carry more than eight passengers, other than a vehicle with less than four wheels that does not exceed 8 cwt. in unladen weight, it is permissible to accept fares from passengers. The fare or fares paid must not exceed the running costs for the journey,

which may include an appropriate amount in respect of depreciation and general wear. The arrangements for payment of fares must be made before the journey begins. It is permissible to advertise a willingness to carry passengers on a cost sharing basis.

Notification of State of Health. Where insurance is refused because of unsatisfactory state of health, or for reasons which include this ground, the insurer must notify the Licensing Authority and provide details of the person concerned.

Emergency Treatment. The Road Traffic Act, 1972, provides that where medical or surgical first-aid treatment is rendered by any registered doctor to any person whose injuries have been caused by or have arisen out of the use of a motor vehicle on a road the user of the vehicle shall pay the doctor a fee of £10·90 in respect of each person to whom emergency treatment has been rendered plus 21p for each mile or part of a mile in excess of two miles the doctor has to travel to render the treatment. The foregoing provisions are also applicable when the emergency treatment is rendered in a hospital. Claims for payment for emergency treatment must be made orally to the user of the vehicle at the time it was effected or alternatively within seven days in writing served or sent by registered letter or recorded delivery. The liabilities of the user of a motor vehicle in respect of emergency treatment must be covered by insurance.

Treatment in Hospital. The Road Traffic Act, 1972, provides in certain circumstances for payment to any hospital which has afforded treatment to a person where death or bodily injury arises out of the use of a motor vehicle on the road up to a sum of £1,525 for each person treated as an in-patient, and up to £152·50 for a person treated as an out-patient.

Production of Certificate of Insurance. Any person driving a motor vehicle shall, on being so required by a police constable, give his name and address and the name and address of the owner of the vehicle and produce his certificate or a document issued by the insurer where the vehicle is based in certain countries abroad. Failure to do so is an offence, but he shall not be convicted if it is produced (not necessarily by the driver personally) within five days at such police station as may be specified by him at the time its production was required.

The above provisions also apply to production of a test certificate. See p. 105, "Vehicle Testing".

A person who accompanies the holder of a provisional licence commits an offence if he fails to give his name and address and that of the owner of the vehicle on being so required by a police constable. PENALTY for above offences, fine not exceeding £400.

Duty to Give Information. The owner of a motor vehicle must give such information as he may be required, by or on behalf of a chief officer of police, for the purpose of determining whether the vehicle was or was not insured in accordance with the provisions of the Act. PENALTY. Fine not exceeding £1,000.

A person against whom a claim is made in respect of injury to a third party shall on demand by or on behalf of the injured person state whether he was insured and if

insured shall give the details specified in the certificate of insurance issued under such insurance. PENALTY. Fine not exceeding £1,000.

Report of Accident to Police Station. When an accident occurs involving personal injury to another person, and the driver of the vehicle does not at the time produce his certificate of insurance to a police constable or to some person who on reasonable grounds has called for its production, the driver shall report the accident at a police station or to a police constable as soon as possible, and in any case within twenty-four hours, and produce his certificate. Failure to report is an offence, but if the certificate is not available it may be produced within five days after the accident at the police station specified at the time the report was made. PENALTY. Fine not exceeding £400.

Security in Place of Policy of Insurance. Instead of effecting a policy of insurance as above stated, a security in respect of third-party risks can be given, but the private motorist is seldom likely to avail himself of this facility.

Lighting of vehicles

The law affecting lighting of vehicles has been subject to major revision at the time of writing and will be further researched and rewritten for the next edition.

The law relating to the lighting of vehicles is contained in Regulations made under powers conferred by the Road Traffic Act, 1972, as amended. The requirements of the law as to the illumination of the back number plate are contained in the Registration and Licensing Regulations. (See page 88, "Identification Marks".)
See also p. 93, "Direction Indicators" and "Stop Lamps", and p. 95, "Side Facing Reflectors".

Vehicle light bulbs sold as separate items must be "E" marked to indicate quality and performance.

Definition of "Road". The Act defines a road as any highway and any other road to which the public has access, and includes bridges over which a road passes.

Hours of Darkness. These are defined as the time between half an hour after sunset and half an hour before sunrise (all the year).

Obligatory Lights. Motor cars on a road during the hours of darkness must carry (*a*) two lamps showing to the front a white light, or a yellow light where incorporated in a headlamp only capable of emitting a yellow light, visible from a reasonable distance, (*b*) two lamps showing to the rear a red light visible from a reasonable distance, and (*c*) two red rear reflectors. Every obligatory lamp and reflector fitted to a vehicle used on the road shall be clean and in good working order with the proviso that daytime hours use of a vehicle is not precluded by a defect occurring during the progress of a journey or if arrangements for expeditious repair have been made.
Solo motor bicycles must carry one lamp showing a white light to the front, a lamp showing a red light to the rear and a red rear reflector. Motor bicycles with sidecar must carry two lamps showing a white light to

the front, two lamps showing a red light to the rear and two red rear reflectors. If a solo motor bicycle is being wheeled by a person on foot as near as possible to the left-hand edge of the carriageway no lights are required.
Invalid carriages must carry one lamp showing a white light to the front, mounted on the offside, two lamps showing a red light to the rear and two red rear reflectors.

Lights in Daytime. No lamp or reflector is required to be fitted during daytime to a vehicle which has no front or rear lamp, which includes a lamp painted over or masked so as to be incapable of immediate use or which is not provided with a system of wiring.

Headlamps. Most motor vehicles, but excluding those first used before 1st January, 1931, must carry either a single headlamp or a matched pair, in which case both lamps must operate simultaneously on either main or dipped beams. If a vehicle carries two groups of headlamps the dip switch must cut out all main beams and simultaneously switch on, or leave in operation, dipped beams on the outermost lamps. A single headlamp may emit either a white or yellow light but a pair must emit beams of the same colour.
A vehicle having four or more wheels and a three-wheeler (with the exception of a motor cycle combination), first used from 1st January, 1972, and which either exceeds 400 kg unladen or the overall width of which exceeds 1·30 metres, must carry a matched pair of headlamps. Other three-wheeled vehicles, and two-wheelers, must carry at least one headlamp.

Use of Front Lamps. In the case of the above vehicles, which are obliged to have headlamps, these must now be kept lit, as well as side lights, when the vehicle is in motion other than under tow, during the hours of darkness, except when on a road furnished with a system of street lighting with lamps 200 yards or less apart that is lit, and also in seriously reduced visibility at any time. The provisions as to the use of headlamps do not apply where a front fog lamp is lit or in the case of a motor vehicle, other than a solo motor bicycle or motor bicycle combination, that is fitted with a pair of headlamps, if a pair of front fog lamps the outermost part of the illuminated area of each of which is not more than 400 millimetres from the outer edge of the vehicle are lit.

General. No vehicle shall be readily capable of showing a red light to the front or a light to the rear other than a red light, except to illuminate the interior of the vehicle, to illuminate the number plate, for direction indication, reversing and certain other specified purposes.
No vehicle shall be fitted with a lamp or reflector capable of being swivelled or deflected while the vehicle is in motion other than a dipping, compensating or retracting headlamp or a lamp or reflector which can be deflected by the movement of the steering of the vehicle, although not necessarily through the same angle.

Projecting Loads. If a load is carried which projects more than 1 metre beyond the rear of the vehicle, an

additional rear lamp must be fitted within 1 metre of the rear of the load. If a load is carried the outermost projection of which is more than 400 millimetres beyond the front or rear lamp on that side either the front or rear lamp shall be transferred to the load or additional lamps shall be fitted. If an obligatory lamp, reflector or marking is obscured by a load it must be transferred to a position where it is not obscured or an additional one must be fitted.

Anti-Dazzle. A headlamp, front fog lamp or rear fog lamp may not be used so as to cause undue dazzle or discomfort to other persons using the road nor may such a lamp be lit when a vehicle is parked.

Rear Fog Lamps. Motor vehicles first used from 1st April, 1980, and trailers manufactured from that date, with limited exceptions, must be equipped with a minimum of one approval marked rear fog lamp and a "tell-tale" must be fitted to indicate to the driver when a lamp is lit. A vehicle first used before 1st April, 1986, need not be fitted with a rear fog lamp whilst a trailer fitted with such a lamp is attached to it. A trailer manufactured before 1st October, 1985, need not be fitted with a rear fog lamp whilst being drawn by a vehicle for which such a lamp is not an obligatory fitment.

The minimum separation distance between a rear fog lamp and a stop lamp must be 100 millimetres and a rear fog lamp may not be illuminated by the application of the vehicle's braking system.

A rear fog lamp may only be lit in conditions of seriously reduced visibility and may not be lit, save in the case of an emergency vehicle, when a vehicle is parked.

Dim-Dip Lighting Device. A motor vehicle with three or more wheels, other than a motor cycle with sidecar, that is first used from 1st April 1987 must be fitted with a dim-dip lighting device. The requirement will not affect a vehicle's lighting controls or the driver's responsibility for using dipped headlamps. However, the device will make it impossible to drive on side lights alone and should add to the level of conspicuity without causing dazzle. Side lights will only operate in isolation when the vehicle's ignition is switched off.

Parking without Lights. Passenger vehicles with seating for up to seven passengers exclusive of the driver, goods vehicles not exceeding 1525 kilograms in unladen weight, invalid carriages and motor cycles need not be lit on a road subject to a speed limit of 30 m.p.h. or less provided that it is standing in a recognised parking place or in a lay-by indicated for such a purpose or if it is standing elsewhere it is parked close to the kerb and parallel to it and no part of it is within 10 metres of a road junction on either side of the road. The nearside of the vehicle must be next to the kerb except in the case of a one-way street. The regulations do not exempt a vehicle from being lit which has a trailer attached or which carries an overhanging or projecting load requiring additional lamps (see above "Projecting Loads").

Parked vehicles which do not qualify for exemption from lighting must be fully lit; a parking lamp or offside front and rear lamps only will not suffice.

Where lights are not required a motorist is not prevented from using the vehicle's lights or, as an alternative, a parking lamp or the vehicle's offside front and rear lamps only, with a view to safety. PENALTY for lighting offences. Fine not exceeding £400.

Note. The Regulations relaxing the lighting requirements for parked vehicles do NOT relax the general law as to parking and obstruction (see below "Parking Places" and p. 94, "Obstruction").

Parking places

Local Authorities may provide suitable places where vehicles may wait and may make regulations as to their use. Motorists should enquire of the attendant the time permitted to leave the car, as this depends on the regulations for such particular place.

Parking Meters. The regulations governing the various parking meter schemes differ and it is therefore necessary to refer to the instructions indicated on the meter when parking in a metered parking bay. Once the period of parking has been selected and the meter has started operating by insertion of the appropriate coin or coins, it is an offence to come back later and "feed the meter" with further coins. No period of grace is allowed for getting change at the time of parking. Where unexpired time is shown on the meter at the time of parking this period may be used without payment. A motorist who overstays the period for which he has paid, or the "free" unexpired time, is liable to an excess charge. Subject to the liability to pay this charge, the vehicle may be left for a further period as prescribed by the relevant order. If this period is exceeded, the motorist is liable to prosecution and to have his vehicle towed away. A vehicle may not be brought back to the same parking place until an hour has elapsed. N.B. At the entry to a meter zone signs indicate the days and times when metered parking is in force.

Parking within a meter zone is restricted and is permitted only where there is a specific invitation to park as at a meter or at a resident's parking place.

It is permissible to park within the zone for the purpose of picking up or setting down a passenger or that passenger's effects for a period of time not exceeding 2 minutes (unless the passenger is disabled) or for a period of up to 20 minutes for the purpose of a continuous process of loading or unloading. These exemptions apply where there is no restriction on loading or unloading indicated by kerb markings.

A code of carriageway and kerb markings is in operation to indicate restrictions on waiting and loading and unloading. The hours of restriction are indicated on an accompanying sign.

The ticket system

The police and traffic wardens have power to issue "tickets" to drivers alleged to have committed offences relating to parking meters, no-waiting regulations, one-way streets, "U" turns, vehicle lighting and non-display of excise licence. The ticket gives the driver the opportunity of paying a fixed penalty of £10 within 21 days. Offences dealt with in this way are not recorded against the driver as convictions. The driver is under no

obligation to pay the fixed penalty, but if he fails to do so a summons is issued. The penalty which a Court may impose is not limited to £10, and a conviction on summons is recorded.

Owner Liability. Where the fixed penalty in respect of certain fixed penalty offences and excess parking charges is not paid, for the purposes of proceedings brought against any person as being the owner of the vehicle at the time of the alleged offence it is conclusively presumed that he was the driver of the vehicle. An opportunity to rebut the presumption lies, in certain circumstances, within the procedure which follows non-payment of the penalty. Where a vehicle is let under a hiring agreement liability is transferred to the hirer by his signing a statement of liability.

Functions of traffic wardens

Traffic wardens may be employed with respect to an offence (a) committed in respect of a vehicle left or parked on a road during darkness without obligatory lights or reflectors (b) committed in respect of a vehicle's obstruction, or its waiting, or being left or parked, or being loaded or unloaded, in a road or other public place (c) committed in respect of a contravention of vehicle licensing provisions, or (d) committed in connection with chargeable parking places on highways.

Wardens may regulate traffic and pedestrians on or off the highway and discharge other normal police functions in this respect.

Wardens may also act (a) as parking attendants at street parking places (b) in exercise of functions conferred by a traffic or street parking place order (c) to obtain information as to the identity of a driver (d) in respect of the custody of vehicles removed from the road or land or from a parking place, or (e) as school crossing patrols.

Nearside parking at night

Except with permission of a police constable in uniform no vehicle shall remain at rest on any road during the hours of darkness otherwise than with the nearside of the vehicle as close as possible to the edge of the carriageway.

This regulation does not apply to vehicles on a parking place where the local regulations governing the use of the parking place conflict with this regulation or to any one-way road.

VAT and Car Tax

Value Added Tax is charged at 15% on the sale price of a motor vehicle or trailer and on the cost of parts, accessories, service, repairs, petroleum and oil but not on statutory test fees. Where a person whose taxable turnover exceeds £18,700 a year undertakes the conversion of a vehicle by the fitting of side windows, the fitting of additional seats or the removal of seats, as described more fully in the next paragraph, VAT is payable. If the conversion is carried out by a private individual, or one whose level of turnover does not demand registration, VAT is not payable.

An additional 10% Car Tax, which itself is liable to VAT, is levied on the wholesale value of motor vehicles

(in the case of a motor caravan on 3/5ths of its wholesale value) either (a) constructed or adapted solely or mainly for the carriage of passengers or (b) having to the rear of the driver's seat roofed accommodation which is fitted with side windows or which is constructed or adapted for the fitting of side windows. Certain vehicles such as a one-seater with three or more wheels and vehicles suitable for carrying 12 or more persons are exempt. Among the types of conversions which give rise to liability for Car Tax are (a) the fitting of side windows, or a single window, in a van to the rear of the driver's seat (b) the reduction of the load space of a van of less than 10 cwt. carrying capacity by the installation of additional passenger seating and (c) the conversion of a vehicle suitable for carrying 12 or more persons into one to seat less than 12.

A vehicle designed or substantially adapted for the carriage of a disabled person is exempt from VAT and Car Tax.

Further information as to tax liability can be obtained from H.M. Customs and Excise, King's Beam House, Mark Lane, London EC3R 7HE, or from one of the many Customs and Excise VAT Offices.

Give way rule at roundabouts

The general advisory rule for a vehicle entering a roundabout is that it shall give way to traffic on its immediate right. As this is a general rule "Give Way" signs are not required but the points of entry to a roundabout have been marked by a single broken line at which the driver giving way should stop, if necessary. In exceptional cases, vehicles in a roundabout will have to give way to vehicles entering it. This requirement is indicated by double broken lines in the roundabout. As this marking alone has been found to be inadequate, it is being reinforced by roadside "Give Way" signs, in cases where the general rule is reversed.

Double white lines

Double white lines are applied to the carriageway at places where limited visibility makes it imperative that motorists should at all times keep to their own side of the road.

Infringement of the rules relating to double white lines is an offence. PENALTY. Fine not exceeding £400 (see p. 96, "Disqualification and Endorsement"). Failure to observe the rules may also be used as evidence in cases of careless or dangerous driving.

The Rules are as follows:
1. When the continuous white line is nearest or when both lines are continuous *you may not cross or straddle the lines* except
(a) to enter or leave a side road or the driveway of adjacent premises
(b) in an emergency (e.g. to avoid an accident)
(c) to pass a stationary vehicle
(d) for the purpose of complying with the direction of a police constable in uniform or a traffic warden.
2. When the broken line is nearest *you may cross provided it is safe to do so.*
3. On any section of the road where double white line

markings have been applied vehicles may not wait except
(a) to enable passengers to get in and out
(b) to enable goods to be loaded or unloaded
(c) in circumstances beyond the control of the motorist
(d) in order to avoid an accident
(e) with the permission of a police constable in uniform or a traffic warden.

Utility vehicles

Depending on their exact construction in each case, utility vehicles may fall into the passenger, goods, or dual-purpose vehicle class. For the definition of passenger vehicles and information as to speed limits, see p. 95. A goods vehicle is one "constructed or adapted for use and used for the conveyance of goods or burden of any description, whether in the course of trade or otherwise", and a dual-purpose vehicle is one "constructed or adapted for the carriage of both passengers and of goods or burden of any description", being a vehicle of which the unladen weight does not exceed 2040 kg and which either **(a)** satisfies the following conditions as to construction:
1. The vehicle must be permanently fitted with a rigid roof, with, or without a sliding panel.
2. The area of the vehicle to the rear of the driver's seat must satisfy the following requirements:
(i) It must be permanently fitted with at least one row of transverse seats, whether fixed or folding, for two or more passengers, and those seats must be properly sprung or cushioned and provided with upholstered backrests, attached either to the seats or to a side or the floor of the vehicle.
(ii) It must be lit on each side and at the rear by a window or windows of glass or other transparent material having an area or aggregate area of not less than 1850 sq. cm. on each side and not less than 770 sq. cm. at the rear.
3. The distance between the rearmost part of the steering wheel and the backrests of the row of transverse seats satisfying the requirements specified in sub-paragraph 2(i) above (or, if there is more than one such row of seats, the distance between the rearmost part of the steering wheel and the backrests of the rearmost such row) must, when the seats are ready for use, be not less than one-third of the distance between the rearmost part of the steering wheel and the rearmost part of the floor of the vehicle.
or **(b)** is so constructed or adapted that the driving power of the engine is, or by the appropriate use of the controls of the vehicle can be, transmitted to all the wheels of the vehicle.

Private hire cars and hackney carriages

Before a vehicle can ply in the streets for hire as a hackney carriage a licence from the Local Authority should be obtained. Enquiry should be made in the case of a **private hire** car, i.e. a vehicle which does not pick up chance passengers on the highway or in other public places, as the licensing of this type of vehicle is also controlled by the Local Authority in certain areas.

Rates of Excise Duty. Both private hire cars, and those which actually ply in the streets and are generally known as hackney carriages, can be taxed at the rate applicable to a hackney carriage because, for the purpose of taxation, a hackney carriage is defined as a mechanically propelled vehicle standing or plying for hire, and includes any mechanically propelled vehicle let for hire by a person whose trade it is to sell mechanically propelled vehicles or to let mechanically propelled vehicles for hire. A vehicle which is taxed at the hackney carriage rate must, where the rate is lower than it would be if the vehicle were taxed as a private car, either carry the hackney carriage plate issued by the Local Authority as a result of an application under the first paragraph above, or a plate of the semi-circular type, 12 in. wide and 6½ in. high, bearing the lettering in white upon black, "Hackney Carriage—4 seats" (number of seats to be altered according to circumstances).

Cars used for private purposes in addition to private hire must be taxed at the higher of the two rates.

Storage of petroleum spirit

Caution. Vapour given off by petroleum spirit at ordinary temperatures is not only capable of being ignited but is also capable, when mixed with air, of forming an explosive mixture. It is illegal to smoke near a vehicle which is being refuelled.

Storage. The storage and use of petroleum spirit in connection with motor cars is regulated by the provisions of the Petroleum Act, 1928, The Petroleum-Spirit (Motor Vehicles, etc.) Regulations, 1929, and The Petroleum-Spirit (Plastic Containers) Regulations, 1982.

The 1929 Regulations provide that a maximum of 4 gallons of petrol may be carried on a motor vehicle, in addition to the fuel in the tank of the vehicle, that is within 20 ft of a building or inflammable substance, without the complication of notice to the Local Authority. Elsewhere a maximum of 60 gallons may be kept in one storage place. In both cases the capacity of the cans, which must be made of metal, securely stoppered and indelibly marked or labelled "Petroleum Spirit—highly inflammable", may not exceed 2 gallons and a fire extinguisher or supply of sand must be provided.

The 1982 Regulations permit the keeping of petrol in not more than two plastic containers of a maximum capacity of 5 litres each in or on a motor vehicle. Additionally two plastic containers of petrol of 5 litres each may be kept in any domestic premises where it is safe to do so and in any other safe place, two places not more than 6 metres apart in the same occupation being treated as one. A plastic container must be made of suitable materials and designed to prevent loss of contents and be marked or adhesively labelled "Complies with S.I. 1982/630", "Petrol" and "Highly Flammable".

Vehicle testing

Compulsory Vehicle Test. With certain restricted exceptions motor vehicles are subject to test three years from date of first registration or, where the vehicle has been used on roads either here or abroad

before being registered, three years from date of manufacture. A passenger vehicle with more than 8 seats, excluding that of the driver, a taxi or ambulance are subject to test one year from date of first registration. The test is to ascertain that the vehicle complies with the statutory requirements for brakes, steering, lights including stop lamps and direction indicators, windscreen wipers and washers, exhaust system, horn, tyres, and road wheels in so far as they may affect the tyres, bodywork and suspension in so far as they affect braking and steering and the presence of seat belts and their condition. The test fee is £6 for a solo motorcycle and £10 for other vehicles. An appeal against refusal of test certificate must be lodged with the appropriate Area Traffic Commissioners within 14 days of notification of the refusal. See p. 114.

Spot Checks. A police constable in uniform may stop a vehicle (including a trailer) for test and examination by an authorised examiner, who must produce his authority if required, of brakes, silencer, steering gear, tyres, lighting equipment and reflectors, and as to the prevention or reduction of noise, smoke, fumes or vapour. The driver may elect to have the test deferred to a time specified by him within a 7-day period falling within the next 30 days (disregarding any day on which the vehicle is outside Great Britian) at such premises or in such area as he may specify. If the driver is not the owner, he must give the examiner the owner's name and address and the owner must specify the time and place.

The right to elect to have the test deferred does not apply if the vehicle has been involved in an accident or is, in the opinion of a police constable, so defective that it ought not to be allowed to proceed without a test being carried out. PENALTY for obstructing examiner or failing to submit to test—fine not exceeding £400.

Inspection of Vehicles and Parts. An authorised examiner, who must produce his authority if required, may enter premises where used motor vehicles or trailers are kept for sale in the course of business, at any reasonable hour, for the purpose of ascertaining that such vehicles comply with the requirements as to road-worthiness. Similar inspection of vehicles and parts may be undertaken to ensure compliance with type approval requirements and to ensure that construction and use regulations are not contravened by the fitting or sale of defective or unsuitable parts. (See also p. 95, "Illegal Sale of Vehicles".) PENALTY for obstructing examiner—fine not exceeding £400.

Control of rallies

Any person who promotes or takes part in a competition or trial involving the use of motor vehicles on a public highway commits an offence unless the competition or trial is authorised by regulations. PENALTY. Fine not exceeding £400. The following are authorised automatically:

1. An event in which the total number of vehicles driven by the competitors does not exceed 12 provided that it does not take place within 8 days of any other similar event where the promoters are the same or members of the same club.

2. An event in which no merit is attached to completing the event with the lowest mileage and in which, as respects such part of the event as is held on a public highway, there are no performance tests and no route and competitors are not timed or required to visit the same places, except that they may be required to finish at the same place by a specified time.

3. An event in which, as respects such part of the event as is held on a public highway, no merit attaches to a competitor's performance except in relation to good road behaviour and compliance with the Highway Code.

4. An event in which all the competitors are members of the armed forces of the Crown and which is designed solely for the purpose of their service training.

Authorisation for all other events must be obtained from the RAC. An explanatory leaflet is obtainable from the RAC Motor Sports Association Ltd, 31 Belgrave Square, London, SW1X 8QH.

Registration and Licensing of Vehicles

Arrangements

1. In March 1978 the local authority motor taxation offices, which had operated the vehicle registration and licensing system on behalf of the Department of Transport for over 50 years, closed their doors to the public for the last time.

2. The computerised system administration by the Driver and Vehicle Licensing Centre at Swansea and the Local Vehicle Licensing Offices (LVLOs) then wholly took over this work. All records relating to vehicles used or kept in Great Britain (ie England, Scotland and Wales but not Northern Ireland or the Isle of Man) are now held centrally at Swansea from where Vehicle Registration Documents are issued. Vehicle licences (or tax discs) are issued at licensing post offices or in certain circumstances at any LVLO (listed on p. 109).

3. Registering New Vehicles

Application to register and licence a vehicle is made on form V55 which should be taken or sent to an LVLO. Blocks of marks can be allocated by the LVLOs to motor dealers but when a dealer uses an "allocated" mark he must post or take the application to the LVLO which issued it, otherwise, application may be made either by post or in person to any LVLO, regardless of the customer's or dealer's address. The LVLO will then allocate a mark to the vehicle, issue the licence and return the insurance certificate and any other supporting documents to the vehicle keeper. The LVLO then sends the form V55 to the Driver and Vehicle Licensing Centre (DVLC) where the vehicle details are recorded and the Registration Document issued to the registered keeper.

Note As it takes up to three weeks before the keeper receives the document he should notify the LVLO at the time of registration (or arrange for the dealer to do so) if intending to take a vehicle abroad. A Certificate of Registration (V379) which covers the use of the vehicle under international circulation arrangements will then normally be issued in its place.

4. Renewing a Licence

Straightforward licence renewal is normally carried out on form V11 which is sent to the registered vehicle keeper by DVLC about 2–3 weeks before the licence expires. This can be used over the counter at any licence issuing Post Office or by post by sending it to the Head Postmaster (MVL Duty) at the nearest Head Post Office (not to DVLC, Swansea). In the London area, a person wishing to obtain a vehicle licence by post should apply to the District Postmaster at the local District Office.

5. When form V11 is not available form V10 (which is available at post offices and LVLOs) should be used. Instructions regarding the use of the V11 and V10 forms are printed on the forms themselves.

6. Registration Document and Changes of Ownership

The Registration Document, which is a "print-out" of the computer-held vehicle record, gives the name and address of the registered keeper and particulars of the vehicle. The document must be surrendered and a new one issued every time the vehicle changes hands or if changes to the details shown on the Registration Document are reported.

7. Anyone buying a vehicle for use on a public road must enter his name and address in the Changes Section of the Registration Document and send it to DVLC for the change to be recorded and a new document to be issued. If a dealer agrees to relicense a vehicle on a customer's behalf he should get the customer to put their name and address on the Registration Document and application should be made to a licensing post office. A Registration Document will be posted to the applicant from DVLC.

8. Refunds

Unexpired vehicle licences may be handed in for refund but payment is only made on complete calendar months unexpired at the date of surrender of the disc. Form V14, available at main post offices and from LVLOs, may be used for this purpose. The application and disc must either be handed in to a LVLO or posted to DVLC from where payment will be sent. Where the licence is not available, a refund can still be claimed using form V33.

9. Taking a Vehicle Abroad

For temporary visits the Registration Document may be taken abroad. If it is not available application should be made at least 2–3 weeks before leaving to any LVLO. A Certificate of Registration (V379) will then normally be issued.

10. Enquiries

Further information about vehicle registration and licensing can be obtained from the leaflet V100 (which is available at post offices and LVLOs) or DVLC, Vehicle Enquiry Unit, Swansea, SA6 7JL. T Swansea (0792) 72134.

Local Vehicle Licensing Offices
England and Wales

Bangor
1st Floor, 271 High Street, Bangor, LL57 1BX
T Bangor (0248) 351822

Birmingham
St Martin's House, 10 Bull Ring,
Birmingham, B5 5DP
T 021-643 2261/4

Bournemouth
Tregonwell Court, 118 Commercial Road,
Bournemouth, BH2 5LN
T Bournemouth (0202) 28531

Brighton
P.O. Box 357, Circus House, New England
Road, Brighton, BN1 1DH
T Brighton (0273) 692271

Bristol
Colston House, Colston Street, Bristol,
BS1 5AH
T Bristol (0272) 291371 Exts. 21/2

Cardiff
Hodge House, 1st Floor, 114 St Mary
Street, Cardiff, CF1 3LF
T Cardiff (0222) 397010 & 397017

Carlisle
23 Portland Square, Carlisle, CA1 1QH
T Carlisle (0228) 39401

Chelmsford
Globe House, New Street, Chelmsford,
CM1 1LA
T Chelmsford (0245) 81111

Chester
Norroy House, Nun's Road, Chester, CH1
2NB
T Chester (0244) 315571

Coventry
Greyfriars House, Greyfriars Lane,
Coventry, CV1 2HB
T Coventry (0203) 26091

Dudley
Churchill Precinct, Dudley, DY2 7BN
T Dudley (0384) 232585 & 233181

Exeter
Clifton Court, Southernhay East, Exeter,
EX1 1TP
T Exeter (0392) 70991

Gloucester
Elmbridge Court, Cheltenham Road,
Gloucester, GL3 1JY
T Gloucester (0452) 21421

Guildford
Cavridy House, Lady Mead, Guildford,
GU1 1BZ
T Guildford (0483) 503444

Haverfordwest
Winch Lane, Haverfordwest, SA16 1RD
T Haverfordwest (0437) 5114/5

Huddersfield
Kirklees House, Market Street,
Huddersfield, HD1 2HR
T Huddersfield (0484) 38414

Hull
Kingston House, Myton Street, Hull, HU1 2PE
T Hull (0482) 223685

Ipswich
5th Floor, St Clare House, Greyfriars,
Ipswich, IP1 1UT
T Ipswich (0473) 58451

Leeds
24A Union Street, Leeds, LS2 7JR
T Leeds (0532) 443035

Leicester
County Hall, Glenfield, Leicester, LE3 8RD
T Leicester (0533) 870831

Lincoln
Mill House, Brayford Side North, Lincoln,
LN1 1YW
T Lincoln (0522) 43681

Liverpool
Corn Exchange Building, Fenwick Street,
Liverpool, L2 7TT
T 051-236 4442/5

London Central
1 Zoar Street, London, SE1 0SY
T 01-928 3163

London North East
23 Balfour Road, Ilford, Essex, IG1 4MM
T 01-478 2231

London North West
Building No. 2, 1st Floor, Victoria Road,
South Ruislip, HA4 0NZ
T 01-845 7788

London South West
Broadway House, 112–134 The
Broadway, SW19 1RL
T 01-543 3160 & 3169

London South East
12–18 Station Road, Sidcup, DA15 7EQ
T 01-302 9331

Luton
2 Dunstable Road, Luton, LU1 1EB
T Luton (0582) 412143

Maidstone
11 Queen Ann Road, Maidstone, ME14 1XB
T Maidstone (0622) 675432

Manchester
Trafford House, Chester Road,
Manchester, M32 0SL
T 061-872 8691

Middlesbrough
Floor 9, Corporation House, 73–75 Albert
Road, Middlesbrough, TS1 2BP
T Middlesbrough (0642) 217722

Newcastle
Eagle Star House, Regent Farm Road,
Newcastle upon Tyne, NE3 3QF
T Newcastle upon Tyne (0632) 841026

Northampton
Wootton Hall Park, Northampton, NN4 9BG
T Northampton (0604) 62131

Norwich
Rouen House, Rouen Road, Norwich, NR1 1UP
T Norwich (0603) 616411

Nottingham
Lambert House, Talbot Street,
Nottingham, NG1 5NJ
T Nottingham (0602) 419581

Oxford
P.O. Box 66, 3–7 Cambridge Terrace,
Oxford, OX1 1RW
T Oxford (0865) 724056

Peterborough
88 Lincoln Road, Peterborough, PE1 2ST
T Peterborough (0733) 51671

Portsmouth
1–4 Queen Street, Portsmouth, PO1 3JD
T Portsmouth (0705) 823627/8

Preston
Buckingham House, Glovers Court,
Preston, PR1 3LS
T Preston (0772) 23911

Reading
Minster House, 52–53 Minster Street,
Reading, RG1 2JS
T Reading (0734) 598011/4

Sheffield
St Peter's House, Hartshead, Sheffield, S1 1JX
T Sheffield (0742) 22236

Shrewsbury
Shire Hall, Abbey Foregate, Shrewsbury,
SY2 6NG
T Shrewsbury (0743) 50511

Stoke-on-Trent
London House, 4th floor, Hide Street, ST4 1EL
T Stoke-on-Trent (0782) 411421

Swansea
Ty-Nant House, 180 High Street,
Swansea, SA1 1NA
T Swansea (0792) 473322

Swindon
St Mark's School, Maxwell Street,
Swindon, SN1 5DS
T Swindon (0793) 39181 & 38848

Taunton
Brendon House, High Street, Taunton, TA1 3NT
T Taunton (0823) 54404

Truro
Eagle Star House, 74 Lemon Street, Truro,
TR1 2TG
T Truro (0872) 78635

Worcester
Haswell House, St. Nicholas Street,
Worcester, WR1 1NX
T Worcester (0905) 29518

Scotland

Aberdeen
Inverlair House, 10 West North Street,
Aberdeen, AB9 1XH
T Aberdeen (0224) 648216

Dundee
Overgate House, 3rd floor, 121
Marketgait, Dundee, DD1 1QT
T Dundee (0382) 25765.

Edinburgh
Pentland House, 47 Robbs Loan,
Edinburgh, EH4 1VW
T 031-443 8661

Glasgow
107 Bothwell Street, Glasgow, G2 7EE
T 041-226 4161

Inverness
Caledonia House, 63 Academy Street,
Inverness, IV1 1RP
T Inverness (0463) 239321/2

You and Your Car

What to do if your car will not start

The main causes of a car not starting are usually associated with ignition/electrical faults or with fuel system faults. Some rudimentary checks can be carried out by the motorist based on the following symptoms:

A. If the engine will not turn over or cranks over sluggishly

The main cause of the trouble is likely to be associated with battery condition, poor battery connections or earth connections.

Corrosion is a problem, particularly a green or powdery fungus growing on the terminal. Even if the terminal may appear clean EXTERNALLY, remove the connector and thoroughly clean the mating surfaces with a wire brush or emery paper.

If after checking the battery and earth connections the engine will still not crank or is sluggish, the battery may have become severely discharged or be defective. Specialised checks are required to determine battery condition although a quick look at the fan belt might reveal a potential cause of the battery becoming discharged. If the fan belt is excessively slack (there should be no more than ½" free movement on the belt's longest run) or it is frayed or glazed on its drive faces, it could be slipping. This will allow the battery to become progressively discharged as the current drawn from the battery by each of the vehicle's electrical accessories will not be replaced. Check the fan belt and retighten it, if necessary, and arrange for the battery to be recharged and checked.

The fan belt is retightened in the following manner: release the fixing nuts and then slide the alternator away from the engine to tighten the belt, then retighten the nuts.

If the battery recharging facility is not immediately available "jump starting" from a slave battery can get you mobile.

JUMP STARTING

Some basic precautions must be carried out to prevent damage to electrical components or even a battery explosion.

If you are jump starting from a slave battery on another vehicle:

1. ENSURE THE IGNITION AND ALL OTHER ELECTRICAL COMPONENTS ARE SWITCHED OFF ON BOTH VEHICLES.

2. Ensure both batteries are of the same nominal voltage.

3. The jump start cables must be of sufficient capacity to carry starting current—use a proprietary brand NOT just any length of electrical wire.

4. Ensure the 2 vehicles are NOT TOUCHING each other, do not allow the jump lead connectors to come into contact with each other or the vehicle body work as this will cause a spark. WARNING: A SPARK AT OR NEAR THE BATTERY TERMINALS CAN CAUSE A BATTERY TO EXPLODE particularly on a fully charged battery i.e. the slave battery.

5. The jump leads must be connected positive (+ or RED) to positive, negative (− or BLACK) to negative. Connect the jump leads one at a time and ALWAYS TO THE CHARGED OR SLAVE BATTERY FIRST to avoid the risk of explosion from a gassing battery.

6. Ensure the jump lead clamps are secure and crank the engine on the immobilised vehicle using normal starting procedures. Run the engine for a short while with the leads connected to allow it to warm up.

7. Before disconnecting the jump leads, it is advisable to stop the engine. If this cannot be achieved because the discharged battery has not become sufficiently charged to restart the car, keep the engine running at tickover speed only when disconnecting the leads.

8. Disconnect the leads one at a time again ensuring no contact is made with the vehicle's body work or the jump lead terminals to each other.

B. Engine cranks over but will not fire

To check the ignition circuit for a spark, pull one of the plug leads from the spark plug and remove the plug. Re-insert the spark plug into the lead and rest the metal body of the plug on the engine. Switch on the ignition and crank the engine—you may need an assistant and look for a blue spark across the plug electrodes.

If there is no spark carry out the following checks to find the source of the fault.

Remove the plug from the lead being tested and test the lead for a spark by placing it $\frac{1}{16}$" from the engine block and repeat the previous test. Some plug leads are shrouded so *either* pull back the cover *or* alternatively insert a screwdriver into the cap to provide an earth. If a spark occurs when cranking the engine the plugs may be faulty and need replacing.

If there is no spark check all HT cable connections including the centre one from the coil to the distributor cap at both ends to ensure they are clean, dry, free from corrosion and secure. Check the 2 low tension connections from the coil.

Again, if there is no spark remove the distributor cap and crank the engine. The contact points should open and close and a blue spark occur at the points just as the points open. If there is still no spark, the contact points may require cleaning or replacing and the gap resetting.

To check and adjust the contact point gap, it is necessary to rotate the engine until one of the lobes on the distributor cam has pushed the moving arm of the points to its fullest open position. The gap varies from one model to another, so check your vehicle handbook for the setting. Using the correct feeler gauge, make any adjustment by slackening the contact base plate retaining screws and move the position of the contact relative to the distributor base plate. This can usually be best achieved by placing a screwdriver between the adjustment notches and turning. Adjust the contact gap until the feeler gauge becomes a nice sliding fit between the points. Lock the retaining screws and recheck the gap as sometimes the gap can alter when the screw is tightened.

Tip. A strip torn off a cigaratte packet or a visiting card can provide an approximate points gap setting in an emergency. Dirty or pitted points can be cleaned sufficiently to get an engine running using an emery board (the type used to file finger nails) or the striking board cut from a match box.

If after checking the ignition system for a spark to the plugs, you find that all is in order, a check might be

necessary to determine if the spark is occurring at the correct time, referred to as the Ignition Timing. Specific knowledge of the vehicle timing setting will need to be known as will the location of the timing marks. These are usually on the crank pulley/front cover or flywheel/bell housing.

Ignition timing is usually expressed in terms of degrees of crankshaft movement before a piston (usually no. 1) reaches its Top Dead Centre position on the compression stroke hence the term 5° B.T.D.C. (or Before Top Dead Centre). When the timing marks are aligned by turning the crankshaft in its normal direction of rotation, the contact points should just commence opening and the spark occur across them. This can be checked manually to achieve or confirm a setting close enough to allow the engine to start but will require specialist equipment to set accurately.

Ignition timing rarely goes out of adjustment sufficiently to prevent a car from starting unless the distributor has worked loose or somebody has been tampering with the timing, provided, of course, it was set *correctly* in the first place.

C. If the engine cranks over, the plugs spark but the engine does not fire

After eliminating faults on the ignition system, the fuel system should be checked next, if the engine will turn and there is a spark.

First ensure there is adequate fuel in the tank—do not rely on the gauge as it may be inaccurate. Shake the car from side to side and listen by the fuel filler neck with the cap removed. If in doubt, add a gallon of fuel from an emergency can.

A simple check to determine if fuel is getting through to the carburettor is to detatch the inlet pipe from the carburettor. If possible, place the detached pipe into a container to catch any fuel and BEWARE THAT FUEL DOES NOT BECOME EJECTED OVER A HOT EXHAUST MANIFOLD OR NEAR THE IGNITION SYSTEM, AS A SPARK COULD CAUSE AN EXPLOSION. Be on the safe side and disconnect the low tension lead from the coil to the distributor.

On cars fitted with an electric fuel pump, simply switch on the ignition switch, for manual pumps, it is necessary to crank the engine over. Fuel should start spurting out of the pipe.

If it does not, you will have to check back along the fuel system for the fault. Check for:
a. Blocked or restricted fuel line.
b. Fuel filter blockage.
c. Electrical feed to electric pumps.
d. Manual operation of manual pumps.
e. Fuel cap venting or blocked fuel tank breathing pipes.
f. Poor fuel pipe connections—may be drawing in air.

D. If fuel being pumped to carburettor but engine will not fire

If fuel is being pumped to the carburettor the restriction may be in the carburettor itself. There is a small fuel shut-off valve located in the top of the fuel/float chamber which is actuated by a rising float in the fuel. If the valve or float was stuck in the closed position, fuel will be prevented from entering. It can sometimes be "shocked" free by a tap on the carburettor body if you are not familiar with dismantling the carburettor. Preferably remove the

float chamber lid to check for the presence of fuel and attend to the valve if necessary.

How to change a wheel

Ideally the vehicle should be on a level firm surface. If it is not, and this is unavoidable, additional precautions may have to be taken such as placing a chock behind a road wheel not being changed and placing a suitable platform or block beneath the jack to spread the load and avoid sinkage into the ground. Apply the handbrake firmly.

Before jacking the vehicle, remove the wheel trim or centre cap (where fitted) and slacken each wheel nut by turning anti-clockwise approximately half a turn.

Place the car jack beneath or into the vehicle jacking point. As jacking point locations and vehicle jacks vary from one manufacturer to another refer to the vehicle owners handbook for details.

Raise the vehicle until the punctured wheel is well clear of the ground, making allowances for re-fitting a fully inflated wheel/tyre assembly.

Undo the road wheel nuts and remove the punctured wheel/tyre assembly. Fit the replacement wheel/tyre assembly to the hub and replace the wheel nuts, tightening them moderately in a diagonally opposed sequence so they are evenly tightened.

Lower the vehicle to the ground and remove the jack. Retighten each wheel nut securely, again in a diagonally opposed sequence and refit wheel trim or centre cap.

WARNING: NEVER WORK UNDER A VEHICLE THAT IS ONLY SUPPORTED BY A WHEEL CHANGING JACK—ALWAYS USE ADDITIONAL MEANS OF SUPPORT.

Tip: If difficulty is experienced undoing the road wheel nuts, additional leverage can be obtained by sliding a tubular steel extension over the standard wheel nut spanner supplied with the vehicle. Do not, however, use this method for re-tightening as it is possible to over-tighten the nuts, damage the threads or shear the road wheel studs.

Coping with a broken windscreen

A windscreen can shatter unexpectedly, although you can avoid this happening by not following too closely behind vehicles on surfaces freshly laid with chippings.

Many vehicles are fitted with a toughened glass screen and when this shatters be alert to the effect of the glass crazing because your forward vision will be restricted. Pull over to the side of the road as quickly and safely as possible.

If you are only a short distance from your destination, it is possible to push an area of the broken glass out to give visibility. Place a car rug or blanket over the dash and facia panel to prevent broken glass dropping down in unaccessible places such as the demist vents.

Cover your hand with an old blanket or car mat and push the glass outwards. Ideally carry a proprietary emergency screen which can be placed over the screen aperture as a "get-you-home" measure.

Most windscreen specialists will do a roadside replacement of a windscreen but this can depend on the type fitted. Some vehicles have bonded screens which require special workshop facilities to fit.

General Information

Half-barrier level crossings

Advice concerning the use of half-barrier crossings is provided in the Highway Code. The following advice is given by the Department of Transport.

These crossings have automatic barriers across the left side of the road. The trains work the barriers, which fall just before the train reaches the crossing. Amber lights and bells followed by flashing red stop lights warn you when the barriers are about to come down. DO NOT MOVE ON TO THE RAILWAY ONCE THESE SIGNALS HAVE STARTED—THE TRAIN CANNOT STOP and will be at the crossing very soon. Wait at the "Stop" line. If you are on foot, wait at the barrier, or the broken white line on the road or footpath, or by the wicket gate. NEVER ZIG-ZAG ROUND THE BARRIERS—you may be killed and endanger other lives. If one train has gone by, but the barriers stay down and the red lights continue to flash, you must wait. A sign under the traffic light signal on your right saying "ANOTHER TRAIN COMING" will flash and another train will arrive soon. If you are already crossing when the amber lights and bells start, KEEP GOING.

If the barriers stay down at any time for more than three minutes without a train arriving, use a telephone at the crossing and ask the signalman's advice. If you are driving a large, or slow-moving vehicle, you must first phone the signalman, as instructed by the sign before the crossing, to ask him to let you cross. There is a special railway telephone at that sign. If you are herding animals, you must also phone for permission to cross. If you have phoned the signalman before crossing, phone him again to let him know you are over.

If your vehicle stalls, or breaks down, or if you have an accident on the crossing:

FIRST: get your passengers out of the vehicle and clear of the crossing; then use the telephone at the crossing immediately to tell the signalman.

SECOND: if there is time, move the vehicle clear of the crossing.

If the amber lights and bells start, stand well clear of the crossing.

Traffic area offices

Enquiries concerning the Vehicle Testing Scheme should be addressed to any of twelve Traffic Area Offices listed below. They are also able to supply the names and addresses of local Testing Stations and garages authorised to carry out vehicle testing.

No. 1 Area Office
Northern
Westgate House, Westgate Road
Newcastle upon Tyne, NE1 1TW
T Newcastle upon Tyne (0632) 610031

No. 2 Area Office
Yorkshire
Hillcrest House, 386 Harehills Lane
Leeds LS9 6NF
T Leeds (0532) 495661

No. 3 Area Office
North Western
Arkwright House, Parsonage Gardens
Deansgate, Manchester, M60 9AN
T 061-832 8644

No. 4 Area Office
West Midland
Cumberland House, 200 Broad Street
Birmingham, B15 1TD
T 021-643 5011

No. 5 Area Office
East Midland
Birkbeck House, 14–16 Trinity Square
Nottingham, NG1 4BA
T Nottingham (0602) 45511

No. 6 Area Office
Eastern
Terrington House, 13–15 Hills Road
Cambridge, CB2 1NP
T Cambridge (0223) 358922

No. 7 Area Office
South Wales
Caradog House, 1–6 St Andrews Place
Cardiff, CF1 3PW
T Cardiff (0222) 24801

No. 8 Area Office
Western
The Gaunts House, Denmark Street
Bristol, BS1 5DR
T Bristol (0272) 297221

No. 9 Area Office
South Eastern
Ivy House, 3–5 Ivy Terrace
Eastbourne, BN21 4QT
T Eastbourne (0323) 21471

No. 10 Area Office
Metropolitan
P.O. Box 643, Government Buildings
Bromyard Avenue, Acton, London, W3 7AY
T 01-743 5566

No. 11 Area Office
Scottish
83 Princes Street, Edinburgh, EH2 2ER
T 031-225 5494

No. 12 Area Office
Scottish (Sub-Office)
Greyfriars House, Gallowgate, Aberdeen, AB9 2ZS
T Aberdeen (0224) 636411

Disabled persons

For any motorist a breakdown inevitably means inconvenience and extra expense. For the many thousands of drivers who are disabled the problem can be far more serious, since it may be dangerous or simply physically impossible for them to leave their vehicle and call for help. Now that the familiar blue invalid tricycle is becoming less common and more and more disabled people are driving standard production models, with adapted controls where necesary, a disabled driver in distress is less apparent to fellow motorists. There have been cases of disabled drivers stranded for many hours by the roadside at night and in the depth of winter.

All of us who are motorists have a responsibility to prevent situations like these. So please bear these points in mind when you are out on the road:

If you see a stationary car displaying a pennant at right angles to the driver's window bearing the word HELP and probably the well-known wheel-chair symbol, it means that a disabled driver is in need of assistance. You should stop your car, if it is safe to do so, find out the nature of the problem and offer to pass on a message to someone who could help—on a motorway this would just mean using one of the (free) emergency telephones.

DO NOT attempt to carry out roadside repairs; you could be putting yourself and the disabled motorist at risk.

All it takes is a little extra vigilance and a few moments of your time. Please be ready to help a fellow motorist.

111

White canes for the blind

Supplied by The Royal National Institute for the Blind

RNIB reminds all motorists of the significance of the white canes sometimes carried by pedestrians. These are now recognized in many countries as an indication that the carriers are blind or suffer from severely restricted vision; their use has the full approval of the Department of the Environment and the Royal Society for the Prevention of Accidents. White canes with two broad red bands (reflectorised) indicate that their carriers are deaf as well as blind.

Responsible blind welfare organisations strongly recommend all blind people to carry a white cane, both for their own protection and for that of sighted pedestrians and motorists who might, without this warning, fail to take the extra care necessary to avoid accidents. Unfortunately, white canes no longer look white in the yellow light from sodium street lamps, and this apparent change of colour cannot easily be overcome. Motorists are therefore particularly requested to be on their guard.

The Royal National Institute for the Blind, 224 Great Portland Street, London, W1N 6AA, will supply white canes to registered blind people, and they can also be obtained through Social Services Departments of local authorities.

Guide dogs for the blind

Supplied by The Guide Dogs for The Blind Association

A blind person being guided by a guide dog does not normally use the white cane referred to in the previous paragraph, but some guide dog owners use a short white baton when crossing a road.

There are over 3,000 guide dog owners in the United Kingdom. most of whom are out and about in the streets daily carrying out their normal business and social engagements, irrespective of traffic conditions. In the Greater London area alone there are about 200 guide dog owners.

These dogs and their owners have been especially trained by The Guide Dogs for the Blind Association and the dog is relied on by the blind person to guide its owner across roads. Guide dogs are taught to stop at down kerbs and wait while the blind person listens for traffic movement. A guide dog should only obey a command to cross the road if it is safe to do so.

The RAC appeals to motorists and other road users to pay particular attention to guide dog owners with their dogs and grant them the courtesy expected by users of the highways and streets.

Guide dog owners are easily recognised by the white harness worn by the dog and the fact that in nearly every case the dog proceeds on the left-hand side of its owner. Pieces of reflective material are incorporated in the harness handle, which show up clearly in headlights.

The deaf child

Supplied by The National Deaf Children's Society (Avon)

A blind person's white cane, or the distress of a thirsty animal in a hot car, are readily understood causes for concern. A deaf child, wearing a well-hidden hearing aid, looks normal—yet has special needs in traffic that are rarely understood. The child may not hear, and as a result misses danger signals that most of us recognise and benefit from—the changing engine note of an approaching vehicle, the sound of a horn or the squeal of brakes. We would appeal to motorists, therefore, NEVER to assume that a child pedestrian or cyclist has heard their horn. Rather that drivers should BRAKE EARLY when seeing children in a possibly dangerous situation ahead. Further, that drivers should never wait until they are close to a child, before sounding a particular stringent horn note since this could be the first warning detected by the deaf child of your approach. The child could then be frightened into making an error of judgement rather than simply being warned to take normal avoiding action.

NOTE: If you see a young cyclist with a "cancelled ear" sign—a black outline ear with a red bar diagonally across it—he or she *is* deaf and will definitely need extra consideration.

Dogs in cars

Supplied by The Royal Society for the Prevention of Cruelty to Animals

Great suffering can be caused to a dog by leaving him shut up in a car with insufficient air. This is the case even on a cool dry day. In hot weather, no dog should ever be left unless absolutely unavoidable.

Dogs are extremely sensitive to heat and heat stroke can occur in a very short time, especially in older dogs.

If you must leave your dog in a car, even for short periods, make sure you do the following:
1. Always park in the shade.
2. Open at least two windows to allow ventilation. Wire mesh window panels are available to allow windows to be left open without the dog getting out.
3. The dog should be allowed out of the car on a lead to relieve itself before being left.
4. On return to the car, give your dog some water.

But in hot weather it is always best to leave the dog at home.

Boarding kennels

The RAC receives many enquiries from pet owners who seek boarding facilities for their dogs, cats and other domestic pets (e.g. rabbits, guinea pigs, hamsters, cage-birds) whilst they themselves are on holiday.

The Pet's Boarding Advisory Service (PBAS) offers free advice and addresses.

Specific enquiries should be directed to the Publicity Officer, c/o Blue Grass Animal Hotel, Little Leigh, nr. Northwich, Cheshire CW8 4RJ; telephone (0606) 891303 during office hours. Please enclose a SAE if writing.

Those selecting boarding establishments from Yellow Pages and other directories are advised by the PBAS to "look before you book".

Motor Racing Circuits and Hill Climb Courses

Motor racing circuits

Listed below are leading permanent circuits. Motor sport also takes place from time to time at other suitable venues. In the majority of cases, the near approaches to all circuits are signposted by the RAC on race days.

Brands Hatch Kent
Lies within the area bounded by Farningham, Gravesend and Wrotham.
A2 to M25/M20 Junc. to Swanley and then A20 to circuit.

Cadwell Park Lincolnshire.
5 m S of Louth, adjacent to A153.

Castle Combe Wiltshire
5 m NW of Chippenham on B4039. From Chippenham on A420 for 2½ m then right on B4039.

Croft North Yorkshire
7 m S of Darlington. Approached from Darlington by A167 then via track to Croft.

Donington Leicestershire
8 m from Derby, 12 m from Nottingham, 20 m from Leicester on A453.

Ingliston Edinburgh, Lothian
Highland Show Ground 6½ m W of Edinburgh. By A8 from Edinburgh or Newbridge.

Knockhill Fife
Approx. 4 m N of Dunfermline approached on the A823.

Lydden Kent
6 m NW of Dover. Approached by A2 from Dover or Canterbury, then by unclassified road to Wootton 2 m NW of Lydden village.

Oulton Park Cheshire
Lies between Tarporley, Northwich and Nantwich, 2½ m NE of the first named. Reached from Cote Brook on A49; take Little Budworth road, turn S 1½ m from the main road.

Silverstone Northamptonshire
Lies within the area bounded by Towcester, Buckingham, Brackley and Stony Stratford.
Reached from A43, just S of Silverstone village, by an unclassified road towards Buckingham.

Snetterton Norfolk
Near A11, between Thetford and Attleborough.

Thruxton Hampshire
4 m W of Andover on the A303.

Hill climb courses

Some of the following courses are used for the qualifying rounds of the British Hill Climb Championship

Barbon Cumbria
2¾ m NE of Kirkby Lonsdale. Reached by A683.

Bouley Bay Jersey
On NE coast of Jersey.

Craigantlet Co. Down
8 m E of Belfast. Approached by A20 to Dundonald and unclassified road to Craigantlet.

Doune Central
1¼ m W of Doune on the Callander Road.

Fintray
8½ m NW of Aberdeen. Approached by B977 from Dyce or Kintore and the B979 from Blackburn.

Gurston Down Wiltshire
6 m W of Salisbury. Reached by leaving A354 at Coombe Bissett, 1 m W of Broadchalke.

Harewood West Yorkshire
7½ m ENE of Leeds. Reached from Leeds by A61 to Harewood village, then A659 to Harewood.

Loton Park Shropshire
8½ m W of Shrewsbury. Approached from Shrewsbury via A458 then B4393.

Prescott Gloucestershire
5 m NNE of Cheltenham. Approached by A435 from Cheltenham.

Ramsey Road Hillberry, Isle of Man
2½ m from Douglas.

Shelsley Walsh Hereford & Worcester
10 m NW of Worcester. Approached by B4204 from Worcester.

Val des Terres Guernsey
Starts on the front at St Peter Port.

Wiscombe Park Devon
6 m S of Honiton. 12 m W of Lyme Regis. Approached by A375 from Honiton, then by unclassified road.

Streets ahead the length and breadth of Britain.

With the largest number of hotels around the country, Trusthouse Forte assures you of variety, hospitality and charm, be you staying at one of our historic inns, country, seaside or city centre hotels.

Wherever you choose to go, on business or pleasure, you can be certain that our managers and staff will never forget they are there to look after your every need.

What's more, no other hotel group offers better value-for-money. Compare our standards and prices with the competition and judge for yourself.

Trusthouse Forte Hotels

For your free holiday brochures and U.K. map tariff.
Telephone: London 01-567 3444. Manchester 061-969 6111.
Leeds (0532) 431261.
Edinburgh 031-226 4346. Cardiff (0222) 371889.

GLASGOW Albany Hotel

LEEDS Post House Hotel

HARROGATE Majestic Hotel

SOUTHAMPTON Polygon Hotel

CHELTENHAM Queens Hotel

SHEFFIELD Grosvenor House Hotel

NOTTINGHAM Albany Hotel

CAMBRIDGE Post House Hotel

LONDON Grosvenor House

LONDON Waldorf Hotel

COVENTRY Post House Hotel

MANCHESTER Post House Hotel

SWANSEA The Dragon Hotel

Directories

Explanatory Notes to Directory
Hotels See page 116
Hotel Bookings See page 120
Appointed repairers and rescue service
See page 120
General notes See page 120

Explanatory Notes to Directory

Hotels

Appointment of Hotels. The RAC appointment of hotels is made following an unannounced overnight stay by one of the Club's inspectors and a full inspection of the premises.

Classification. The following definitions give a summary of the requirements for classification and are intended to indicate the type of hotel rather than the degree of merit. The range of menus and the standard and hours of service are appropriate to the classification. The requirements of the lower classifications are included in the higher.

A change in the classification of an hotel from that held in previous years does not necessarily indicate a lowering of standards at the establishment.

This may well be the result of changes from time to time in the basic standards required by the RAC for the various classifications and which in turn reflects the requirements of members.

★Simple in furnishing, or menus, or service. May well be managed by the proprietor personally, with few employed senior staff. Usually few if any private bathrooms. Generally a more personal atmosphere than hotels with more stars.

★★Formal reception arrangements and more employed senior staff. More accommodation usually of a higher standard. Greater provision for non-resident diners, including separate toilet arrangements. Lounge service available to residents.

★★★Small luxury hotels, or larger well-appointed hotels offering a high degree of comfort. Some room service. Telephones/intercoms in bedrooms. A good proportion of bedrooms with private bathrooms. Full meal facilities for residents and non-residents, including chance callers, on every day of the week.

★★★★Large hotels with a full brigade of professional staff. Reception, porterage and room service at all hours. Post Office telephones in all bedrooms. A high proportion of private bathrooms. Some bedrooms with private lounges; conference and/or banqueting facilities; or recreational facilities.

★★★★★Large luxury hotels offering the highest standard of accommodation, service and comfort.

Ap. Recommended hotels which do not conform to the minimum classification requirement in respect of porterage, reception facilities and choice of dishes; facilities for non-residents often limited.

M Modern hotels. These establishments sometimes called Motels, Motor Hotels, Motor Inns, etc., will sometimes be found more suitable for overnight stops than for long visits. They must conform to the same basic requirements as hotels, although the type of facilities they offer may differ slightly. For instance, lounge accommodation and porterage will often be rather limited and full room service may not be provided. On the other hand ample parking space, extended meal hours and a higher proportion of private bathrooms to bedrooms than will sometimes be found in hotels of similar classification, will provide facilities

of great value to the touring motorist. For a complete, easy reference list see p. 463.

Country House Hotels. ♨ Hotels, set in secluded rural surroundings which have many of the characteristics of a country house. Reception and service facilities may differ from those at hotels of similar classification. For a complete, easy reference list see p. 466.

Restricted Meals. ▣ Hotels which, judged by their classification, do not provide meals to the extent, or with the type of service or variety of menu normally expected, at all times of the year when they are shown as being fully open. It also covers City Centre hotels where full restaurant services applicable to the classification are not always available at weekends. **The symbol does not indicate that the quality of food is below standard.**

Small Hotels, Guest Houses, etc. These establishments which have been inspected and are recommended by the Club, are also included in the Directory. As some establishments in this category do not provide lunch or dinner the weekly terms shown should be verified at the time of making a booking.

Unclassified Hotels. Certain hotels, which were under construction at the time of going to press. For obvious reasons these hotels have not been inspected and, therefore, are included for the convenience of Members.

Other Hotels not Appointed. Members are reminded that at some country and seaside resorts there are many estimable hotels which for certain reasons are not appointed. Information about them can usually be obtained from local Information Centres, the addresses of which are shown in the Directory and are indicated thus ⓘ

Layout of the Hotel Entry
In order to clarify the information which is included in each hotel entry, the following symbols have been used and therefore segregate the various types of information:

⇄	Bedroom/bathroom facilities
✕	Meals details
ⓟ	Hotel facilities
£	Pricing structure

Hotel Annexes. Only where it has been found, following inspection, that annexe accommodation is generally up to the standard of the hotel in question is the word annexe (followed by the number of bedrooms) included in the details against the hotel entry. It should be noted that hotel annexes, often used only during the season, may lack some of the facilities available in the main hotel and it is desirable, therefore, that full details of the accommodation offered and the charges involved should be obtained before reservations are confirmed.

Restricted Services in Hotels. During certain periods of the year, particularly in areas which rely to a large extent on tourist trade, certain establishments do not provide full facilities, for example lunch and dinner on every day of the week. Periods when full service are not available are shown as follows: RS Oct-March. Members are advised to check in advance the type of restriction in operation.

Hotels Suitable for Disabled Persons. Where an hotel has available ground floor bedrooms together with bath and toilet facilities on the same floor, the information regarding the number of ground floor bedrooms shown under the hotel entry is followed by the letter "f". Additional information which will be of use to those guests who have difficulty in negotiating steps is also included, for example 4BGf 2st. Where the hotel offers all the following facilities the abbreviation Dis will be found in the entry:
    Maximum of 1 step to hotel entrance.
    Ground floor bedroom(s) with adjacent bath and toilet facilities, restaurant and lounge on ground floor or lift. Car park.

Conferences at Hotels. A number of the larger hotels cater for conferences and special functions. At such times, guests may find that some of the normal services and amenities are restricted, although hoteliers are requested to inform intending visitors of conference arrangements and take steps at all times to ensure that private guests are disturbed as little as possible.

Children. At most hotels, reductions are made for children when they do not occupy rooms which otherwise would be available for adults. Care should be exercised when making reservations to avoid any misunderstanding as to the facilities available and the prices to be charged. The abbreviation C indicates that children are accommodated. If followed by a figure, this denotes the minimum age at which they will be accepted. The abbreviation CF indicates that the hotel offers one or more, but not necessarily all, of the following facilities:
    Baby watching service; baby listening inter-communication service; laundry facilities; cots; high chairs; special meals (baby foods); a playroom, playground or playing area.

Non-Smoking Hotels. Those establishments where the proprietor bans smoking throughout the hotel are indicated in the hotel entry by the abbreviation **NS**.

Non-Smoking Areas. In certain hotels a number of bedrooms/areas are set aside for non-smokers. This is indicated in the hotel entry by the abbreviation ns.

Dogs. The abbreviation Dgs is used to indicate that dogs are allowed (a) in public rooms, not necessarily including dining rooms or restaurants, and (b) in bedrooms. *The accommodation of dogs in hotels is always at the manager's discretion.* There may be some restriction on size, and, to avoid disappointment, members are advised to confirm the conditions under which dogs are accepted.

Charges and Payment. Proprietors of establishments may find the need to increase their forecasted tariffs for 1985, therefore as much of the tariff information in this book is, of necessity, compiled well in advance of publication, varying conditions may have brought about increases in published charges.

Bank Holiday periods, special local occasions, such as shows or sporting events, conferences, exhibitions and the like, change of ownership of an hotel, may justify extra charges.

Special Weekend Terms. Establishments which operate special terms for weekends at certain times of the year, "Bargain Breaks" etc., are indicated by the abbreviation WB. Details of the terms should be obtained direct from the hotel or owning company concerned.

Deposits. Some hoteliers require a deposit on arrival. Where a deposit is required one of the following abbreviations appears under the hotel entry:
Dep. Deposit always required
Dep. a having booked by post or telephone
Dep. b without a prior booking.

Credit Cards. Because of the increasing number of hotels which now accept payment by credit card, details have been included in the relevant directory entries. (See inside back cover.)

Value Added Tax. Value Added Tax applies to the total cost of the service bought, including service charge.
VAT is not payable in the Channel Islands.

Service Charge and VAT. To indicate whether prices include service charge and Value Added Tax where applicable, the following code has been used:
① Price includes service charge and VAT.
② Price includes VAT but not service charge.

Hotel Entries without Tariff. A number of hotels failed to provide tariff information for 1985. In such cases only the classification, name, address and telephone number appear in the entry.

Cancellation of Reservations. Should it become necessary to cancel reserved accommodation, members are advised to telephone at once to the hotel.
If rooms which are reserved and not occupied cannot be re-let, the hotel proprietor may suffer loss and members may be held legally responsible for part of the cost.

Table Reservations. Members are advised always to make table reservations at hotels and restaurants to avoid disappointment.

Licences. All hotels listed in the Directory serve alcoholic liquor during permitted hours unless they are shown as un-licensed or are subject to any of the following limitations:
Club Licence. A licence granted to establishments at which it is necessary to become a member of a club in order to obtain alcoholic refreshment. To comply with the law, a period of 48 hours after joining should elapse before such club membership can take effect.

When we decide to take a break, Crest is always part of it.

And, as Crest just happen to have 50 hotels around the country, we stand a very good chance of being **"It wouldn't** able to stay with them wherever we're going. **be the same**

Which suits us because, whether we take the children or not, we can normally get a great package deal. **without a Crest hotel."**

They greet you as though you've stayed there dozens of times before. And nothing ever seems to be too much trouble.

It shows in the genuinely friendly service. There's even tea, coffee and biscuits in your room.

All in all, a Crest hotel puts you in exactly the right frame of mind when you just want to relax and enjoy yourself.

Crest Hotels International

Nobody works harder to make your stay better.

Restaurant or Table Licence. A licence whereby the sale of alcoholic liquor is restricted to customers taking meals.

Residential Licence. A licence whereby the sale of alcoholic liquor is restricted to residents at an hotel, guesthouse, etc., and their private bona fide friends entertained by them at the residents' expense.

Residential and Restaurant Licence. A combination of both of the above licences granted for instance to private hotels that also have a public restaurant.

Supper Licence. A licence whereby the licensing hours for the premises are extended by one hour for the supply of alcohol for persons taking table meals.

Maintenance of Standards. All hotels listed in the Directory are inspected periodically. Nevertheless the Club welcomes reports from members on the standards being maintained and are invited to comment on such visits to RAC appointed hotels. Additionally, reports in respect of establishments visited by members, which are not appointed by the Club, are useful and may enable the number of appointments to be increased, with consequent benefit to members. *In cases of dissatisfaction or dispute, members will usually find that criticisms voiced personally to the management at the time will allow the matter to be settled quickly, amicably and to the benefit of all concerned.* The Club will investigate any matter if this personal approach fails.

Location of Hotels. The Directories of England, Scotland and Wales are designed to be used in conjunction with the atlas of Great Britain in the centre of the book. All towns and villages in which there are RAC Appointed Hotels, Small Hotels, Guest Houses etc., are indicated on the maps in the atlas section by a blue circle. Having first located the town or village required, reference should then be made to the Directory where full particulars of the hotels, etc., will be found under the appropriate place name.

Vegetarian Hotels. Information concerning these can be obtained from the Vegetarian Society of London, 53 Marloes Road, London, W8 6LA. T 01-937 7739.

Hotel bookings

Hotel Bookings Service Ltd
Cashmere House, 13–14 Golden Square, London, W1R 3AG.
London Reservations: T 01-437 5052
Country Reservations: T 01-437 3213
Telex: 262892 Reshot G
Monday–Friday 9.30–5.30

Hotelguide
Faraday House, 8 Charing Cross Road, London, WC2H 0HG
T 01-836 7677
Telex: 22650 Hotelg G
Monday–Friday 9.00–5.00.
No charge for reservations.

Room Centre UK Ltd
(incorporating **H.B.I.—Hotac**)
Kingsgate House,
Kingsgate Place,
London NW6 4HG
T 01–328 1790
Monday–Friday 9.30–5.30.
No charge for reservations.
Also HBI–Hotac in arrivals terminals at Heathrow Airport and Gatwick Airport.

Appointed repairers and rescue service

Appointed Repairers. The RAC appointment is granted only to those firms which possess the necessary staff, tools and equipment to carry out major repair work. It is also a condition of appointment that in addition to the employment of suitably qualified mechanics, there should be at least one who is knowledgeable in the repair and maintenance of electrical equipment.

Most RAC Appointed Repairers undertake to operate the Club's Rescue Service.

Members will find it in their own interest to employ RAC appointed repairers wherever possible and to mention that they do so because of the appointment. Where the RAC sign is displayed this particular appointment is indicated by the word "Repairer".

Rescue Service. In order to ensure the efficient working of the Rescue Service, RAC Appointed Rescue Agents located throughout the country are able and willing to render assistance under this scheme in case of breakdown or accident. Where the RAC sign is displayed this particular appointment will be indicated by the words "Rescue Service". The repairing qualifications of such appointment holders are not examined. Full particulars of the Rescue Service are given on p. 20.

Appointed Specialists. A limited number of firms which specialise in certain types of repair work have been granted RAC Appointment, and these are listed under the appropriate headings. Their qualifications and equipment are examined in exactly the same way as in the case of the Repairer Appointment.

Vehicle Testing Station. In view of the number of changes which may take place during the currency of the Handbook, no attempt has been made to indicate in the Directory those garages which are authorised to carry out vehicle testing. On p. 111, however, there is a list of the twelve Traffic Area Offices which, between them, cover the whole of Great Britain. These offices are able to advise on local Testing Stations.

General notes

The RAC Guide and Handbook is not a gazetteer and the Directory lists only those towns and villages in which there are RAC Appointed Hotels, Small Hotels, Guest Houses and Appointed Repairers and Rescue Service. Every entry includes the appropriate map reference or map area.

All the establishments named in the Directory are either "appointed", or "recommended" by the RAC. It should be noted, however, that the publication of an announcement in the advertisement section does not necessarily indicate, *except in the case of hotels*, that the advertiser has been granted RAC Appointment or Recommendation nor does it in itself confer the right to exhibit the RAC sign or to an entry in the Directory.

While the RAC takes every care to ensure the accuracy of the particulars given in the Directory at the time of going to press, no liability can be accepted for any error or omission which may occur.

Mileages. The mileages shown are computed by the shortest practical routes, which are not necessarily those recommended by the RAC. The town which precedes London in each entry is the nearest town in the direction of London.

Early Closing Days. By the Shops (Early Closing Days) Act, 1965, each individual shopkeeper has the right to fix the day he will close his shop early. Most shops in any one town, however, close early on the same day. Early Closing Days are indicated in the Directory by the abbreviation **EC**, but members are warned that these may be subject to variation.

Local Government Act 1972. Under this Act, changes were made to many administrative areas which had the effect, as from 1st April 1974, of altering certain county boundaries and forming a number of new counties and administrative areas in England and Wales. English and Welsh entries are therefore listed under the new county names.

The Post Office has decided that in general the new county names should be used when addressing mail in England and Wales. All town headings in the Directories of England and Wales show the respective county name. In those cases where the postal county differs from the geographical location this is followed by the old county name, which should be used for postal purposes only.
e.g. BOLTON, Gtr. Manchester (Lancs).

Local Government Scotland Act 1973. The changes in administrative areas in Scotland took effect on 16th May 1975: the Scottish entries are therefore shown under the new regions.

The Scottish Postal Board has announced that, despite the introduction of new regions in Scotland, postal addresses will retain the old county names. Consequently, all town headings in the Directory of Scotland show the respective regional name followed by the old county name, which should be used for postal purposes only.
e.g. GIRVAN, Strathclyde (Ayrshire).

Tourist Information centres. These are indicated by the symbol 🛈.

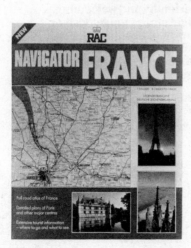

Farnham, Bush

Crowthorne, Waterloo

Alton, Swan

Staines, Thames Lodge

Traditional Hospitality Throughout Britain

Wherever you're driving in Britain, there's likely to be an Anchor Hotel within easy reach. Hotels of great charm and character, friendly and welcoming, whether you plan an overnight stop, a longer visit or are simply looking for somewhere to enjoy a good lunch. The cuisine at our excellent restaurants is typical of our high standards. Stop by at an Anchor Hotel soon and see for yourself.

Write or telephone for further details. Central Reservations Office, Queen's Hotel, Lynchford Road, Farnborough, Hants, GU14 6AZ. Tel: (0252) 517517.

Alton, Swan (0420) 83777
Andover, White Hart (0264) 52266/7
Basingstoke, Red Lion (0256) 28525
Bawtry, Crown (0302) 710341
Boston, New England (0205) 65255
Bristol, St. Vincent Rocks (0272) 739251
Crowthorne, Waterloo (0344) 777711
Croydon, Aerodrome (01) 688 5185
Doncaster, Earl of Doncaster (0302) 61371
Dorking, Punch Bowl (0306) 889335

Farnborough, Queens (0252) 545051
Farnham, Bush (0252) 715237
Harlow, Green Man (0279) 442521
Leamington Spa, Manor House (0926) 23251
Leeds, Selby Fork (0977) 682711
Maidstone, Larkfield (0732) 846858
Melton Mowbray, Harboro' (0664) 60121
Newark, Robin Hood (0636) 703858
Newport, Queens (0633) 62992
Oundle, Talbot (0832) 73621

Oxford, Eastgate (0865) 248244
Parkgate, Ship (051 336) 3931
Portsmouth, Keppel's Head (0705) 833231
Reading, Ship (0734) 583455
Scunthorpe, Royal (0724) 868181
Southwell, Saracen's Head (0636) 812701
Staines, Thames Lodge (0784) 54221
Stroud, Bear of Rodborough (045 387) 3522
Swindon, Goddard Arms (0793) 692313

 ANCHOR HOTELS

Directory–England

Directory of appointed hotels, small hotels, guest houses, etc., repairers and agents in England. See separate sections for Scotland, Wales, The Channel Islands and Northern Ireland.

National Tourist Board:
English Tourist Board
4 Grosvenor Gardens, London SW1W 0DU
📞 01-730 3400

For explanatory notes to Directory see page 116
For abbreviations see inside back cover

You're Welcome

...at over 500 Tourist Information Centres in England where you can get advice and details about what's on, where to go, what to see and do and where to stay.

Remember, Tourist Information Centres can be used by local residents just as much as by visitors for the provision of information about local events and attractions.

Many can book a room for you; look for the Local Bed Booking Service sign:

Wherever you go throughout England, look for the Tourist Information Centre sign:

A free Directory of Tourist Information Centres is published annually and is available from:
Dept. D(R), English Tourist Board,
4 Grosvenor Gardens, London SW1W 0DU.
or from your nearest Tourist Information Centre.

ABBERLEY Hereford & Worcester
(Worcestershire) Map 13B
Pop 547. Worcester 12, London 126,
Kidderminster 8, Ludlow 18, Bromyard 12.
See Clock Tower, Good views Abberley
Hill.

⚲★★★**Elms**, *WR6 6AT.* ✆ Gt Witley
(029 921) 666. C ⛟ 18 bedrs, 16 bp, 2
bps, TV, ✗ a l c, mc, at, LD 9. ⓓ N, CH, CP
100, Ac, tc, con 50, CF. £ BB £41–£43, DB
£62–£68, WB. ⬜, Bk £4·50, L £9·50, D
£15·50, cc 1 2 3 4 5 6, Dep b.

ABINGDON Oxfordshire. Map 14F
Pop 21,966, Henley-on-Thames 21,
London 56, Aylesbury 27, Burford 21,
Faringdon 14, High Wycombe 29,
Newbury 19, Oxford 6½, Reading 25,
Swindon 25, Wallingford 10, Wantage 10.
EC Thur. **MD** Mon. **Golf** Frilford Heath
18h. **See** County Hall, 1677, containing
Museum, 15th-18th cent Guildhall
(portraits and plate), 14th cent Abbey
ruins, Almshouses, 13th-15th cent St
Helen's Church, St Nicholas' Church,
Milton Manor House, 5m SE Ruskin
Nature Reserve.
ⓘ 8 Market Pl. ✆ Abingdon (0235) 22711.

★★ **M Upper Reaches** (TH), *Thames St,
OX14 3TA.* ✆ (0235) 22311. C. ⛟ 20
bedrs, 20 bp, TV, Dgs. ✗ a l c, mc, LD 10.
ⓓ CH, Dgs, CP 90, Ac, con 140, CF, 1 BGf,
0 st, Dis. £ BB£47, DB £64, WB, ⬜, cc 1 2 3
4 5 6, Dep (Xmas).

Repairer: Hartwells of Abingdon Ltd,
Drayton Rd. ✆ (0235) 22822.
Rescue Service: Lodge Hill Garage, Lodge
Hill, Oxford Rd. ✆ Oxford (0865) 735447.

ACCRINGTON Lancashire. Map 27B
Pop 35,891. Bury 13, London 205,
Blackburn 5, Bolton 16, Burnley 8,
Rochdale 14, Todmorden 14, Whalley 6.
EC Wed. **MD** Tue, Fri, Sat. **Golf**
Accrington 18h, Baxenden 9h, Green
Haworth 9h. **See** Hamworth Art Gallery,
Parish Church.

Waverley, PH, z (RI) *1 Brunswick Terr.
BB5 1QJ.* ✆ (0254) 32338.

Repairer: Southern Bros (Accrington)
Ltd, Clock Garage, Whalley Rd.
✆ (0254) 395511.

ADDINGTON Kent. M Area 10C
Pop 600. 2 m NE of Wrotham Heath.
Swanley 12, London 30, M20 Motorway
2½, Canterbury 34, Maidstone 8,
Sevenoaks 9.
MD Wed. **Golf** West Malling 18h.

Rescue Service: Addington Motors,
London Rd. ✆ West Malling
(0732) 841839.

ADDLESTONE Surrey. Map 7A
Pop 15,472. Weybridge 1½, London 19,
Bagshot 10, Leatherhead 14, Reading 25,
Ripley 7, Staines 5½, Woking 5½.
EC Wed. **Golf** Foxhills, Chertsey 18h,
Wentworth (2) 18h, (1) 9h.

Rescue Service: Surrey Brake & Exhaust
Service Ltd, 29 Brighton Rd. ✆ Weybridge
(0932) 52991 & 41267.

ADLINGTON Lancashire. Maps 20C and
27D
Pop 5,700. Wigan 6½, London 201, Bolton
8½, Preston 12.
EC Wed. **Golf** Duxbury Park 18h.

★ **Gladmar,** (R), *Railway Rd, Chorley PR6
9RH.* ✆ (0257) 480398. Closed Dec 24,
25 & 31 & Jan 1. C. ⛟ 13 bedrs, 9 bps, 2
ba, TV, ✗ a l c, mc, at, LD 8.30. ⓓ CH, TV,
CP 24, con 24, CF 3 BGf, 2 st. £ BB £20–
£22, DB £28, WT £150, DT £32, ⬜, Bk
£2·50, L £6·50, D £6·50, Dep b.

AINSDALE Merseyside. Map 20E
Pop 10,798. Ormskirk 7½, London 210,
Liverpool 15, Southport 4.
EC Wed. **Golf** Southport and Ainsdale
18h.

Rescue Service: Thacker Autos, Central
Plant Hire Buildings, Stevenson Way,
Formby Industrial Estate, Altcar Rd,
Formby. ✆ Formby (070 48) 70893.

ALCESTER Warwickshire. Map 14C
Pop 5,287. Stratford-upon-Avon 7½,
London 100, Birmingham 19, Bromsgrove
13, Droitwich 13, Evesham 9½,
Wolverhampton 30, Worcester 17.
EC Thur. **Golf** Stratford-upon-Avon 18h.
See No. 1 Malt Mill La (Shakespeare
assns), Coughton Court 2 m N, Ragley Hall
1½ m SW.

★★ **M Cherrytrees**, *Stratford Rd, B49
6LN.* ✆ (0789) 762505. Closed Xmas C.
⛟ 22 bedrs, 18 bp, 4 bps, TV, Dgs. ✗ a l c,
mc, at, LD 9.30 (8.30 Sun). ⓓ CP
22, Ac, con 30, CF, 12 BGf, 1 st, Dis. £ BB
£20·25, DB £30·50, WB, ⬜, Bk £3, L £4·15,
D £5·75, cc 1 3, Dep.

ALCONBURY WESTON
Cambridgeshire. Map 15B
Pop 1,175. Biggleswade 23, London 68,
Bedford 23, Huntingdon 6½, Peterborough
14, Stamford 23.
Golf Ramsey 18h, St Ives 9h. **See** Old
Bridge, Church.

Rescue Service: Bridge Garage, Great
North Rd. ✆ Huntingdon (0480) 890260

ALDBOURNE Wiltshire Map 6A
Hungerford 7, London 70, Oxford 39,
Salisbury 39, Swindon 9½.

Rescue Service: West Street Motors
(Aldbourne) Ltd, West St. ✆ Marlborough
(0672) 40729.

ALDBURY Hertfordshire. Map 15F
Pop 733. Watford 16, London 32,
Aylesbury 10, Denham 22, Dunstable 8½,
High Wycombe 19, Slough 25, St Albans
16.
EC Wed. **Golf** Ashridge 18h. **See** Stocks
and Whipping Post, Pendley Chapel,
Chantry Well and Bakehouse, 13th–14th
cent Church, 16th–17th cent half
timbered cottages.

Rescue Service: Aldbury Garage, Trooper
Rd. ✆ Aldbury Common (044 285) 255.

ALDEBURGH ON SEA Suffolk. Map
17A
Pop 2,911. Ipswich 24, London 98,
Lowestoft 27, Norwich 41, Saxmundham
7, Stowmarket 31.
EC Wed. **Golf** Aldeburgh 18h. **See**
Memorial to George Crabbe, poet, in Perp
Church, 16th cent Moot Hall, Festival of
Music and the Arts at Snape Maltings.
ⓘ Festival Office, High St. ✆ Aldeburgh
(072 885) 3637.

★★★ **Brudenell** (TH), *The Parade, IP15
5BU.* ✆ (072 885) 2071. C. ⛟ 47 bedrs,
47 bp, TV, Dgs. ✗ a l c, mc, at, LD 9. ⓓ Lt,
N, CH, Dgs, CP 14, G 6, Ac, con 100, CF, 5

st. £ BB £33·50, DB £50, WB, ⬜,
cc 1 2 3 4 5 6, Dep (Xmas).

★★ **White Lion**, *Market Pl, IP15 5BJ.*
✆ (072 885) 2720. C. ⛟ 34 bedrs, 28 bp,
2 bps, 4 sh, 3 ba, TV, Dgs. ✗ a l c, mc, at,
LD 8.45. ⓓ Lt, N, CH, TV, CP 12, Ac, con
60, CF, 6 st. £ BB £23–£28, DB £46·20–
£51·70, DBB £31·90–£35·50, WB, ⬜, 10%,
Bk £3·75, L £6, D £8·25, cc 1 2 3 5 6,
Dep a.

Rescue Service: Ward & Son (Aldeburgh)
Ltd, High St, ✆ (072 885) 2721.

ALDERLEY EDGE Cheshire. Map 20B
Pop 4,262. Congleton 11, London 172,
Altrincham 9, Knutsford 6½, Macclesfield
6, Manchester 14, Middlewich 14,
Sandbach 15, Stockport 9½.
EC Wed. **Golf** Alderley Edge 9h. **See** The
Edge (views), Chorley Hall, Alderley Old
Mill 1½ m S (Nat Trust).

★★★ **De Trafford Arms**, *Congleton Rd,
SK9 7AA.* ✆ (0625) 583881. C. ⛟ 37
bedrs, 37 bp, TV, Dgs. ✗ a l c, mc, at, LD
10. ⓓ Lt, N, CH, CP 60, Ac, con 20, CF, 1
st. £ BB fr £34·50, DB £44, WB, ⬜, Bk £4, L
£1·50, D £8, cc 1 2 3 5 6.

Repairers: Central Garage, London Rd.
✆ (0625) 582218.
Tower Garage Ltd, Wilmslow Rd.
✆ (0625) 582222.

ALDERSHOT Hampshire. Map 6D
Pop 80,300. Bagshot 9½, London 36,
Basingstoke 16, Farnham 3½, Guildford 9½,
Henley-on-Thames 24, Reading 19,
Woking 12.
EC Wed. **MD** Thur. **Golf** Aldershot 18h.
See Heroes' Shrine, Churches, Lido,
Rowhill Copse Nature Reserve, West End
Centre.

Repairer: Wadhams Stringer (Aldershot)
Ltd, 39 Station Rd, ✆ (0252) 20581.
Rescue Service: McDiarmids Garage,
Halimote Rd. ✆ (0252) 22047.

ALDRIDGE West Midlands. Map 21C
Pop 20,000. Coventry 25, London 119,
Birmingham 10, Lichfield 7, Stafford 19,
Sutton Coldfield 5½, Walsall 3½, Wellington
29.
EC Thur. **Golf** Aldridge 18h. **See** Barr
Beacon, 14th cent Church, Manor Hse.

★★★ **Fairlawns**, *Little Aston Rd,
WS9 0NU.* ✆ (0922) 55122. C. ⛟ 30
bedrs, 19 bp, 11 bps, TV. ✗ a l c, mc, at, LD
9.30. ⓓ N, CH, TV, CP 60, Ac, con 50, CF, 3
BGf, 0 st, Dis. £ BB £32, DB £40, WT £315,
DT £45, WB, ⬜, Bk £3·50, L £5·50, D £7·50,
cc 1 2 3 5, Dep b.

Repairer: Aldridge Garage, Walsall Rd.
✆ (0922) 52103.
Rescue Service: Bunn, W H, Aldridge
Garage. ✆ (0922) 52103.

ALFORD Lincolnshire. Map 23B
Pop 2,596. Boston 25, London 142,
Horncastle 17, Louth 13, Skegness 14.
EC Thur. **MD** Tue, Fri. **Golf** Sandilands,
Sutton-on-Sea 18h.
See St Wilfred's Parish Church, 1350,
restored 1867, old working Windmill,
Manor House. Well Vale Nature Trail.

Repairer: Fletcher's Garage Ltd, South St.
✆ (052 12) 3209.

ALFRETON Derbyshire. Map 22D
Pop 8,359. M1 Motorway 4, London 138,
Ashbourne 16, Chesterfield 10, Derby 13,

Loughborough 29, Mansfield 10, Matlock 8½, Nottingham 16.
EC Wed. **MD** Tue, Fri, Sat. **Golf** Alfreton 9h. **See** Old Lock-up (King St), Alfreton Hall, Park and Lido.
🛈 County Library, Severn Sq. ✆ Alfreton (0773) 833199.

Repairer: Parkin & Jones (Motors) Ltd, Nottingham Rd. ✆ (0773) 832572.

ALFRISTON East Sussex. Map 7F
Pop 712. Uckfield 16, London 60, Eastbourne 9½, Hastings 22, Hurst Green 24, Lewes 10, Newhaven 7½, Tunbridge Wells 28.
EC Wed. **Golf** Seaford Head 18h. **See** 14th cent Clergy House (Nat Trust), 16th cent Star Inn, Market Cross House, Church, George Inn, Charleston Manor 1½ m S, Drusillas (at Berwick—zoo, gardens, rly), High and Over (viewpoint S of the village), Litlington Church.

★★★ **Star Inn** (TH), *High St, BN26 5TA.*
✆ (0323) 870495. C. ➡ 32 bedrs, 32 bp, TV, Dgs. ✗ a l c, mc, at, LD 9. ⓓ CH, Dgs, CP 36, Ac, con 20, CF, 9 BGf, 1 st, Dis. £ BB £37·50, DB £57, WB, ①, cc 1 2 3 4 5 6, Dep (Xmas).

★★ **Dean's Place** *Seaford Rd, BN26 5TW.* ✆ (0323) 870248. Closed Jan. C. ➡ 44 bedrs, 44 bp, ns, Dgs. ✗ mc, at, LD 8.15. ⓓ CH, TV, CP 80, sp, tc, pf, con 200, CF, 4 BGf. £ BB £20–£22, DB £36–£40, WT (b) £147–£151, DT £25·50–£27·50, WB, ②, Bk £4, L £4·50, D £7·50.

★★ **George Inn,** *High St, BN26 5SY.*
✆ (0323) 870319. C. ➡ 8 bedrs, 3 bp, 2 ba, TV. ✗ a l c, mc, LD 9. ⓓ CH, Dgs, Ac, 1 st. £ BB £15–£20, DB £25–£32, DBB £22·75–£27·75, ②, 10%, Bk £4, L £5·50, D £7·75, cc 2 3 5.

Rescue Service: Alfriston Motors, Star La. ✆ (0323) 870202.

ALLENDALE Northumberland. Maps 26A and 31E
Pop 650. Middleton-in-Teesdale 26, London 284, Alston 13, Bellingham 25, Brampton 28, Hexham 10.
EC Wed. **Golf** Allendale 9h. **See** Church.

◼★**Riding,** *NE47 9EE.* ✆ (043 483) 237.

Rescue Service: Beaumonts of Allendale, Market Pl, ✆ (043 483) 570

ALLENHEADS Northumberland. Maps 26A and 31E
Pop 250. West Auckland 30, London 278, Alston 12, Bellingham 30, Durham 35, Hexham 17, Middleton-in-Teesdale 24.
EC Sat. **Golf** Hexham 18h, Allendale 9h. **See** Church.

★ **Allenheads Inn,** *NE47 9HJ.*
✆ (043 485) 200.

ALNMOUTH Northumberland. Map 31D
Pop 543. Alnwick 4½, London 309, Corbridge 45, Newcastle upon Tyne 35.
EC Wed. **Golf** Alnmouth 18h, Alnmouth Village 9h. **See** Alnmouth Bay, Alnwick Castle and Church (4½ m NW).

Marine House, PH, x (RI), *1 Marine Rd, NE66 2RW.* ✆ Alnwick (0665) 830349. Open Feb–Nov. C. ➡ 8 bedrs, 2 bps, 2 sh, 2 ba, Dgs. ⓓ CH, TV, Dgs, CP 8, CF. £ BB £13–£15, DB £22–£26, WT (b) £116–£130, DT (b) £17·50–£19·50, ①, Bk £2·75, D £6·50.▲

ALNWICK Northumberland. Map 31C
Pop 6,972. Newcastle upon Tyne 34, London 307, Berwick-upon-Tweed 30, Coldstream 32, Hexham 44.
EC Wed. **MD** Sat. **Golf** Alnwick 9h. **See** Castle, Church of SS Mary and Michael, Howick Hall Gardens 4½ m NE, Dustanburgh Castle ruins 6½ m NE, Warkworth Castle and Hermitage 7 m SE, Cragside Grounds 11 m SW. 15th cent Bondgate Tower, Hulne Priory, 13th cent Carmelite Hse.
🛈 The Shambles, Northumberland Hall. ✆ Alnwick (0665) 603120.

★★★ **White Swan,** *Bondgate Within, NE66 1TD.* ✆ (0665) 602109. C. ➡ 41 bedrs, 40 bp, 1 ba, TV, Dgs. ✗ a l c, mc, at, LD 9. ⓓ N, CH, TV, Dgs, CP 30, Ac, con 180, CF, 6 BGf, 1 st. £ BB £38–£45·90, WT £182–£196, WB, ①, Bk £5·50, L £4·80, D £7·50, cc 1 2 3 5 6, Dep b.

◼★★ **Hotspur,** *Bondgate Without, NE66 1PR.* ✆ (0665) 602924. C. ➡ 28 bedrs, 17 bp, 1 bps, 4 ba, Dgs. ✗ a l c, LD 9. ⓓ CH, TV, CP 22, Ac, con 30, CF, 6 BGf. £ BB fr £17·50, DB fr £32, WB, ①, Bk £3·50, L £4·50, D £8. cc 1 3.

Aln House, PH, x, (RI), *South Rd, NE66 2NZ.* ✆ (0665) 602565. Closed Xmas. C. ➡ 8 bedrs, 2 bp, 1 ba, TV. ⓓ CH, TV, CP 7, CF, 3 st. £ BB £8–£8·50, DB £16–£22, WT (c) £50–£55, DT (b) £12·50–£13·50, ①, D £4·50.

Aydon House, PH, x (R), *South Rd, NE66 2NT.* ✆ (0665) 602218. C. ➡ 10 bedrs, 3 ba, Dgs. ⓓ CH, TV, CP 10, CF, 4 st. £ BB £7·50–£8·50, DB £15–£17, DT (b) £12–£14, ①, Bk £2, L £3, D £4·50, cc 1 2 3 4 5 6.

Bondgate House, PH, z, (Rt), *20 Bondgate Without, NE66 1PN.*
✆ (0665) 602265.
Farm House, F, x, y, (Unl) *West Ditchburn, NE66 2UE.* ✆ Powburn (066 578) 337. Open Apr–Oct. C. ➡ 4 bedrs, 1 ba, TV, Dgs. ⓓ CH, TV, CP 10.
Hope Rise, G, z (Unl), *The Dunterns, NE66 1AL.* ✆ (0665) 602930. C5. ➡ 7 bedrs, 2 ba. ⓓ CH, TV, CP 12, 3 st. £ BB £8–£8·50, DB £16–£17, WT (c) £56–£58, DT (b) £15–£16, ①.

Rescue Service: Brownieside Service Station, A1 Road, Chathill. ✆ Charlton Mires (066 579) 280.
Jennings, 3 Lta, Central Garage. ✆ (066 578) 602294.

ALPERTON Greater London. Map 8
1 m S of Wembley, London 9, Brentford and Chiswick 4½, Denham 10, Ealing 3, Uxbridge 10.
EC Wed. **Golf** Sudbury 18h.

Rescue Service: Wembley Auto Ltd, 199 Ealing Rd. ✆ 01-902 9595.

ALSTON Cumbria. Map 26A
Pop 1,985. Middleton-in-Teesdale 22, London 280, Bellingham 34, Brampton 19, Hexham 21, Penrith 19, West Auckland 38.
EC Tue. **MD** Sat. **Golf** Alston 9h. **See** Open-sided Market Cross, 19th cent Church, Pennine Walk.
🛈 Railway Station. ✆ Alston (0498) 81696.

♨ ★★ **Lovelady Shield** (R), *CA9 3LF.* ✆ (0498) 81203. Open Mar–Oct. C. ➡ 11 bedrs, 7 bp, 4 bps, Dgs. ✗ mc, at, LD 8.

ⓓ CH, TV, CP 20, tc, CF, 3 st. £ BB fr £17, DB fr £34, DBB fr £25, WB, ②, L £5, D £10·50, cc 2 5.

◼★★ **Lowbyer Manor** (R), *CA9 3JX,* ✆ (0498) 81230. Open May–Oct. C. ➡ 7 bedrs, 3 bp, 1 bps, 2 ba. ✗ a l c. ⓓ CH, TV, Dgs, CP 12. £ BB £19, DB £28–£31·50, ①, Bk £3·50, D £8.
★ **Hillcrest,** *Town Foot, CA9 3RN.*
✆ (0498) 81251.
★ **Victoria,** *Front St.* ✆ (0498) 81269.

Rescue Service: Henderson, J H & Sons Ltd, The Garage. ✆ (0498) 81204 and (0498) 81265.
Moredun Garage, Station Rd.
✆ (0498) 81318.

ALTON Hampshire. Map 6D
Pop 15,000. Farnham 9½, London 48, Basingstoke 12, Fareham 24, Haslemere 16, Hindhead 13, Midhurst 18, Petersfield 12, Reading 23, Winchester 17.
EC Wed. **MD** Tue. **Golf** Alton 9h. **See** 15th cent Church, Curtis Museum, Jane Austen's Home at Chawton ½ m S. Watercress Steam Railway ¾ m W, Allen Gallery.

★★★ **Swan,** *High St, GU34 1AT.*
✆ (0420) 83777. C. ➡ 38 bedrs, 33 bp, 5 bps, TV, Dgs. ✗ a l c, mc, at, LD 10. ⓓ N, CH, Dgs, CP 50, Ac, con 50, CF, 0 st. £ BB fr £34·50, DB £45, WB, ②, Bk £3·40, L £6·95, D £6·95, cc 1 2 3 5 6, Dep b.
★★ **Grange,** (R) *London Rd, GU34 4EG.* ✆ (0420) 86565.
★ **Alton House** (Rt & CI), *Normandy St, GU34 1DW.* ✆ (0420) 82369. Closed 2 weeks Xmas. C. ➡ 24 bedrs, 9 bp, 4 ba, TV, Dgs. ✗ a l c, mc, at, LD 8.30. ⓓ TV, Dgs, CP 70, Ac, sp, tc, cor 　). CF, 6 BGf, 2 st. £ BB £15–£24, DB £24–£36, WT £120–£150, ②, Bk £3, L £4, D £3.

ALTRINCHAM Gtr Manchester (Cheshire), Map 20B.
Pop 39,641. Knutsford 7½, London 180, M56 Motorway 2½, Congleton 20, Macclesfield 15, Manchester 8, Middlewich 16, Northwich 13, Sandbach 19, Stockport 8½, Walkden 12, Warrington 11.
EC Wed. **MD** Tue, Fri, Sat. **Golf** Municipal 18h, Dunham Forest 18h. **See** Dunham Park, St George's Church, Wythenshawe Hall 3 m NE.

★★★ **Bowdon** (R), *Langham Rd, Bowdon, WA14 2HT.* ✆ 061-928 7121. C. ➡ 42 bedrs, TV, Dgs. ✗ a l c, mc, at, LD 10. ⓓ N, CH, TV, CP 168, Ac, con 270, CF, 5 st. £ BB £20–£30, DB £30–£44, WT £200, DT £29–£39, WB, ①, Bk £4·60, L £7, D £7, cc 1 2 3 5, Dep b.
◼ ★★★ **Cresta Court,** *Church St, WA14 4DP.* ✆ 061-928 8017. C. ➡ 139 bedrs, 139 bp, TV, Dgs. ✗ a l c, mc, at, LD 10.30. ⓓ Lt, N, CH, Dgs, CP 250, Ac, con 350, CF. £ BB £17·50–£31·50, DB £32–£42·50, DBB £24–£38, WB, ①, L £5·50, D £6·50, cc 1 2 3 5, Dep b.
★★ **George & Dragon,** *Manchester Rd, WA14 4PH.* ✆ 061-928 9933. Closed last wk Dec & 1st wk Jan. C. ➡ 48 bedrs, 47 bp, 1 ba, TV, Dgs. ✗ a l c, mc, LD 10. ⓓ Lt, N, CH, Dgs, CP 100, Ac, CF. £ BB fr £35, DB £44, WB, ①, Bk £4, L £3, D £8·10, cc 1 2 3 5, Dep b.
◼ ★★**M Pelican,** *Manchester Rd, WA14 5NH.* ✆ 061-962 7414. C. ➡ 50 bedrs, 50 bps, ns, TV, Dgs. ✗ a l c, mc, at, LD 9. ⓓ N,

CH, Dgs, ns, CP 150, Ac, con 40, CF, 25
BGf, 2 st. **£** BB fr £34, DB fr £42, WB, Bk
£4·50, L £4·60, D £6·75, cc 1 2 3 4 5 6,
Dep b.
Bollin, PH, z (Unl), *58 Manchester Rd,*
WA14 4PJ. **☎** 061-928 2390. C. **☎** 10
bedrs, 2 ba, Dgs. ⊞ ch, TV, Dgs, CP 12, CF,
4 st.**£** BB £12·65, DB £21·85, ②, Bk £2·50.

Repairers: Altrincham Service Station,
Dunham Rd. **☎** 061-928 2118.
Arden & Bull Ltd, Old Market Pl. **☎** 061-
928 3333.
Quick, H & J Ltd, Hale Rd, **☎** 061-928
2275.
Rescue Service: Timberley Service
Station Ltd, 280 Stockport Rd. **☎** 061-
980 3212.

ALVECHURCH Hereford & Worcester
(Worcestershire) Map 14A
Pop 6,300. Redditch 3½, London 112,
Birmingham 10, Bromsgrove 5, Coventry
24. **Golf** Blackwell 18h.

Rescue Service: Tanyard Garage, Tanyard
La. **☎** 021-445 1752

ALVELEY Shropshire. Map 13B
Pop 2,167. Kidderminster 7, London 130,
Bridgnorth 7

Mill, PH, y, *WV15 6NG.* **☎** Quatt
(0746) 780437. C. **☎** 3 bedrs, 2 bps, 1 sh,
1 ba, ns, TV, Dgs. ✘ a l c, mc, at. ⊞ CH, CP 150,
CF, 4 st.**£** BBc £15–£20, DBc £25–£30,
DT £30, ①, L £4·50, D £5·50, cc 1 2 3 5.

ALVESTON Avon. Maps 5A and 13E
Pop 2,611. Chippenham 24, London 115,
M5 Motorway 4, Bristol 10, Chepstow 9½,
Gloucester 24, Tetbury 20.
EC Wed **Golf** Filton, Bristol 18h. **See**
British Encampment, Tumuli, Church of St
Helen (Norman font).

★★★M Post House (TH), *Thornbury Rd,*
BS12 2LL. **☎** Thornbury (0454) 412521.
C. **☎** 75 bedrs, 75 bp, TV, Dgs. ✘ a l c, mc,
at, LD 10.15. ⊞ N, CH, TV, Dgs, CP 200,
Ac, sp, con 150, CF, 38 BGf, 2 st.**£** BB
£44·50, DB £57·50, WB, ①, cc 1 2 3 4 5 6,
Dep (Xmas).
★★Alveston House, *BS12 2LJ.*
☎ Thornbury (0454) 415050. C. **☎** 15
bedrs, 6 bp, 9 bps, TV, Dgs. ✘ a l c, mc, at,
LD 9.30. ⊞ CH, TV, CP 50, Ac, con 75, 1
BGf, 2 st.**£** BB £28·50, DB £36·50, DBB
£37·45, WB, ①, Bk £3·25, L £5·50, D £6·50,
cc 1 3, Dep b.

Repairer: Hawkins (Berkeley Vale
Motors) Ltd. **☎** Thornbury (0454) 412207
and (0454) 413681.

AMBERGATE Derbyshire. Map 22D
Derby 11, London 137, Ashbourne 14,
Buxton 26, Chesterfield 15, Mansfield 15,
Matlock 7½, Nottingham 18.

★Hurt Arms, *Derby Rd, DE5 2EJ.*
☎ (077 385) 2000. C. **☎** 0 bedrs, 1 ba.
✘ a l c, mc, LD 8. ⊞ CH, TV, Dgs, CP 100,
Ac, 2 st.**£** BB £12, DB £20, DBB fr £16·60,
①, Bk £3·50, L £4·50, D £4·60, Dep a.

AMBERLEY Gloucester. Map 13F
Pop 680. Stroud 2½, London 100, Bath 25,
Bristol 27, Cheltenham 17, Chepstow 28,
Cirencester 12, Gloucester 12, Stow-on-
the-Wold 30, Tetbury 7½.
Golf Minchinhampton 18h. **See** Old
Houses, Church.

★★Amberley Inn, *GL5 5AF.*
☎ (045 387) 2565. C. **☎** 10 bedrs, 7 bp, 2

ba, TV, Dgs. ✘ a l c, mc, LD 9.30. ⊞ CH,
Dgs, CP 18, CF, 1 BGf. **£** BB £20–£34, DB
£34–£42, DBB £25·75–£36·75, WB, ①, Bk
£4, L £4·50, D £8·75, cc 1 2 3 6.

AMBLESIDE Cumbria. Map 26D
See also RYDAL
Pop 2,562. M6 Motorway 25, London 269,
Broughton-in-Furness 16, Kendal 13,
Keswick 16, Lancaster 33, Penrith 22,
Ulverston 21.
EC Thur. **MD** Wed. **Golf** Windermere 18h.
See House on the Bridge, Stock Ghyll
Force, Lake Windermere, Jenkin Crag
(viewpoint), Borrans Field (remains of
Roman Camp), Rush Bearing ceremony
July, White Craggs Rock Garden 1 m W.
🛈 Old Courthouse, Church St.
☎ Ambleside (096 63) 3084.

★★★★ M Pillar (R), *Langdale Estate, Gt*
Langdale, LA22 9JB. (5 m NW B5343).
☎ Langdale (096 67) 302. C. **☎** 36 bedrs,
36 bp, TV. ✘ a l c, mc, at, LD 10. ⊞ N, CH,
CP 120, Ac, sp, pf, sc, sb, sol, gym, con 70,
CF, 17 BGf, 1 st, Dis.**£** BB £50–£65, DB
£50–£75, DBB £60–£90, WB, ①, Bk £4·50,
L £6, D £12, cc 1 2 3 5 6, Dep b.▲
■★★★Langdales, *Gt Langdale, LA22*
9JF. (5 m NW B5343). **☎** Langdale
(096 67) 253. RS Jan. C. **☎** 20 bedrs, 12
bp, 4 bps, 2 ba. ✘ a l c, mc, at, LD 8.15.
⊞ CH, TV, Dgs, CP 50, pf, CF, 3 st.**£** BB fr
£19, DB fr £38, WT fr £196, DT fr £30, ②,
Bk £4, L £5, D £10.
■★★★Rothay Manor (R), *Rothay*
Bridge, LA22 0EH. **☎** (0966) 33605.
Closed Jan. C. **☎** 14 bedrs, 14 bp, TV.
✘ a l c, mc, at, LD 9. ⊞ CH, ns, CP 40, con
10, CF, 1 BGf, 1 st, Dis.**£** BB £40–£42, DB
£58–£64, DBB £43–£46, WB, ②, Bk £5, L
£5, D £15, cc 1 3, Dep a.
■★★★Waterhead, *Waterhead, LA22*
0ER. **☎** (0966) 32566. C. **☎** 30 bedrs, 14
bp, 16 bps, TV, Dgs. ✘ a l c, mc, at, LD
8.45. ⊞ CH, Dgs, CP 60, Ac, con, CF, 3 BGf,
2 st.**£** BB £18·30–£24·25, DB £36·60–
£48·50, WT £118–£223, DT £31·85–
£37·80, WB, ①, Bk £4, L £4, D £9·95,
cc 1 2 3 5, Dep.
■★★Britannia Inn, *Elterwater.*
☎ Langdale (096 67) 210. Closed Xmas.
C. **☎** 10 bedrs, 3 ba, Dgs. ✘ a l c, mc, LD
7. ⊞ Dgs, CP 10, CF. **£** BB £14·50–£15·90,
DB £29–£31·80, ②, Bk £4·50, L £3, D
£8·75, Dep a.
■✦★★Eltermere (R), *Elterwater, LA22*
9HY. (4 m W B5343). **☎** Langdale
(096 67) 207.
■★★Fisherbeck, *Lake Rd, LA22 0DH.*
☎ (0966) 3215. Open Feb–Dec. RS Feb. C.
☎ 16 bedrs, 12 bps, 2 ba, TV. ✘ mc, LD 7.
⊞ CH, TV, CP 24, con 20, CF.**£** BB £14–
£18, DB £24–£32, WB, ②, Bk £3, L £3·25, D
£7·25, cc 1 3, Dep.
■✦★★Kirkstone Foot (R), *LA22 9EH.*
☎ (0966) 32232. Closed mid Nov–mid
Feb. C. **☎** 12 bedrs, 10 bp, 2 bps, TV.
✘ mc, LD 8. ⊞ CH, CP 30, CF.**£** DBB £24–
£28, WB, ①, Bk £3·25, D £10·50,
cc 1 2 3 5 6, Dep a.
■✦★★Nanny Brow (R), *Clappersgate,*
LA23 9NF. **☎** (0966) 32036. C. **☎** 12
bedrs, 10 bp, 2 bps, TV, Dgs. ✘ a l c, LD
7.45. ⊞ CH, ns, CP 15, pf, con 12, CF, 2
BGf, 3 st.**£** BB £15·50–£19, DB £31–£38,
WT £155–£180, WB, ①, D £8·50, cc 1 3.
■★★Regent (R), *Waterhead, LA22 0ES.*
(1 m S A591). **☎** (0966) 32254. Closed
Jan. C. **☎** 11 bedrs, 5 bp, 4 bps, 1 ba, TV,
Dgs. ✘ a l c, mc, at, LD 10. ⊞ CH, CP 20,

sp, CF.**£** BB £28–£38, DB £39–£48, WT
£160–£185, DBB £22–£30, WB, ①, Bk £3,
L £2, D £8·50, cc 1 2 3 4 5 6, Dep b.
■★★Riverside Hotel & Lodge (R), *nr*
Rothay Bridge, Under Loughrigg, LA22
9LJ. **☎** (0966) 32395. C5. **☎** 10 bedrs, 4
bp, 3 bps, 2 ba, TV. ✘ a l c, mc, at, LD 7.45.
⊞ CH, TV, CP 15, pf, con 20.**£** DBB £20–
£26, WB (winter), ②, D £9·50, cc 1 3,
Dep a.▲
★★Royal Yachtsman, *Lake Rd,*
LA22 9BX. **☎** (0966) 2244.
■★★Skelwith Bridge, *Skelwith Bridge,*
LA22 9NJ. (2½ m W A593).
☎ (0966) 32115. C. **☎** 19 bedrs, 10 bp, 4
ba, Dgs. ✘ mc, LD 8.45. ⊞ CH, TV, Dgs,
CP 60, con 20, CF.**£** BB £13·50–£22·50,
DB £27–£43, DBB £18·50–£29, WB, ①, Bk
£4·50, L £4·95, D £9·50, cc 1 3, Dep a.
■★★Vale View (R). *Lake Rd, LA 22 0BH.*
☎ (0966) 33192. Open Mar–Oct. C. **☎** 20
bedrs, 11 bp, 9 bps, 2 ba. ✘ a l c, mc, LD 8.
⊞ CH, TV, CP 10, Ac, CF, 3 st.**£** BB
£11·75–£16·50, DB £21·60–£28, WB, ①,
Bk £2·25, D £6·50, cc 1 3, Dep a.
■★★Wateredge (Rl), *Waterhead, LA22*
0EP. **☎** (0966) 2332.
■★Elder Grove (R), *Lake Rd, LA22 0DB.*
☎ (0966) 32504. Open Mar–Nov. C. **☎** 9
bedrs, 9 bp, annexe 5 bedrs, 2 ba, TV, Dgs.
✘ LD 7.30. ⊞ CH, TV, CP 14, CF.**£** BB fr
£12·50, DB fr £25, DBB fr £20, WB, ②, D
£8, cc 1 3, Dep a.
■★Romney, (R), *Waterhead, LA22 0HD,*
(1 m S A591). **☎** (0966) 32219. Closed
Nov–Feb. C. **☎** 9 bedrs, 3 bps. ✘ mc, ac,
at, LD 7. ⊞ ch, TV, CP 20, U 3, CF, 2 st.
£ BB fr £12, DB fr £24, DT fr £18, ①, Bk
£3·50, D £8, cc 3, Dep a.
■★Three Shires Inn, *Little Langdale, LA*
22 9NZ. **☎** Langdale (096 67) 215.
★White Lion, *Market Pl, LA22 9DB.*
☎ (0966) 3140.
Borrans Park, PH, y (R), *Borrans Rd,*
LA22 0EN. **☎** (0966) 33454. Open Feb–
Nov. C. **☎** 9 bedrs, 2 bp, 5 bps, 1 ba, TV.
⊞ CH, CP 20, CF, 1 BGf, 9 st, Dis.**£** BB
£13·50–£16, DB £27–32, WT (b) £138–
£158, DT (b) £21·50–£24, ①, Bk £4·50, D
£8, cc 1 3.
Chapel House, H, x (R), *Kirkstone Rd,*
LA22 9DZ. **☎** (0966) 33143. C. **☎** 9
bedrs, 2 ba. ⊞ CH, CF.**£** WT (b) £105, DT
(b) £15·40–£16·50, ①, Bk £4, D £8.
Gables, PH, x (Rl) *Church Walk, LA22*
9DJ. **☎** (0966) 33272. Open Mar–Oct. C.
☎ 15 bedrs, 1 bp, 1 bps, 1 ba, Dgs. ✘ mc.
⊞ CH, TV, Dgs, CP 8, CF, 1 BGf, 5 st.**£** BB
£9–£10, DB £17–£20, WT (b) fr £94·50, DT
(b) £13·50–£14, ②.▲
High Green Gate, G, x (Unl), *Near*
Sawrey, LA22 0LF. **☎** Hawkshead
(096 66) 296.
Hillsdale, PH, z (Unl), *Church St, LA22*
0BT. **☎** (0966) 3174.
Horseshoe, G, z (Unl) *Rothay Rd, LA22*
0EE. **☎** (0966) 32000. Closed Jan–Feb. C.
☎ 12 bedrs, b bps, 2 ba, Dgs. ⊞ ch, TV, ns,
CP 11.**£** BB fr £11·50, DB £19–£23, WT
(c) £65, ①.▲
Lattendale, H, (Rt) *Compston Rd, LA22*
9DJ. **☎** (0966) 32368. C. **☎** 8 bedrs, 2 bp,
1 sh, 1 ba, TV, Dgs. ⊞ CH, TV, Dgs, CF, 1
BGf, 2 st.**£** BB £7–£9, DB £14–£21, WT (b)
£80–£95, DT (b) £12·50–£15·50, ①, Bk
£1·75, L £3·25, D £5·50.
New Dungeon Ghyll, H, x, y, *Great*
Langdale, LA22 9JX. **☎** Langdale
(096 67) 213. Open Mar–Oct. C. **☎** 19
bedrs, 4 ba, Dgs. ✘ a l c. ⊞ ch, TV, Dgs, CP

20, CF. 1 st. **£** BB £10·95–£12·95, DB
£21·90–£25·90, WT £76·65–£90·65, ⊡, Bk
£3, L £2·50, D £7.
Rothay Garth, H, x, y (R), *Rothay Rd,
LA22 OEE.* **✆** (0966) 32217. C. ⊷ 15
bedrs, 4 bp, 6 bps, 2 ba, TV, Dgs. ✘ a l c.
⊡ CH, TV, CP 13, G 1, CF, 3 BGf, 2 st. **£** BB
£16·50–£20·50, DB £33–£41, WT (b)
£127–£168, DT (b) £19–£26, ⊡, Bk £4·50,
L £1·75, D £8·50, cc 1 2 3 5.
Rysdale Hotel, PH, x (R). *Kelsick Rd,
LA22 OEE.* **✆** (0966) 32140. Closed Xmas,
C3. ⊷ 9 bedrs, 2 ba, TV. ⊡ CH, 3 st. **£** BB
£8·50–£9·50, DB £17–£19, WT (b) £90–
£95, DT (b) £13·50–£14·50, ⊡.

Rescue Service: Bell's Kelsick Garages
Ltd, Knott St. **✆** (0966) 3273.
Oak Bank Garage, Broadgate, **✆** Grasmere
(096 65) 423.
Pinfold Garage, The Green.
✆ (0966) 2864.
Scott, E & M (Ambleside) Ltd, Millans
Park Garage. **✆** (0966) 3033.
Young Motors, Knott St. **✆** (0966) 2322.

AMERSHAM Buckinghamshire. Map
15E
Pop 17,517. Denham 9½, London 26,
Aylesbury 15, Dunstable 19, High
Wycombe 7½, Rickmansworth 8, St Albans
17, Slough 12.
EC Thur. **MD** Tue. **Golf** Harewood Downs
18h. **See** Parish Church (brasses), 17th
cent Almhouses, Market Hall (1682), 17th
cent Bury Farm (Penn assns), Protestant
Martyr's Memorial, Milton's Cottage 3 m
S, Little Missenden Church (7th cent
Saxon, 13th cent mural St Christopher), 2
m W.

★★Crown (TH), *High St, HP7 0DH.*
✆ (024 03) 21541. C. ⊷ 19 bedrs, 6 bp, 3
ba, TV, Dgs. ✘ a l c, mc, at, LD 10. ⊡ CH,
Dgs, CP 51, Ac, con 110, CF, 4 st. **£** BB
£34·50–£41, DB £50·50–£57, WB, ⊡, cc
1 2 3 4 5 6, Dep (Xmas).
★Ken House (R), *Long Park, North Rd, off
A416, HP6 5JX.* **✆** (024 03) 6368. RS
Xmas. C. ⊷ 24 bedrs, 4 bp, 6 ba, TV, Dgs.
✘ a l c, LD 8.30. ⊡ CH, TV, CP 28, U 4, Ac,
con 45, CF, 1 st. **£** BB £14·83–£21·73, DB
£26·33–£30·93, ⊡, Bk £2·75, L £4·48, D
£4·48, cc 1 2 3 5 6, Dep b.

Repairer: Merritts of Amersham, 44
London Rd. **✆** (024 03) 5911.

AMESBURY Wiltshire. Map 6C
Pop 5,499. Andover 14, London 79,
Devizes 18, Pewsey 13, Salisbury 8,
Shaftesbury 26, Wantage 37, Warminster
19, Wincanton 30.
EC Mon. **Golf** High Post, Salisbury 18h,
Salisbury and S Wilts 18h. **See** Fine Parish
Church (formerly Abbey Church),
Stonehenge 2½ m W, Woodhenge 2 m N.
🛈 Redworth House, Flower La.
✆ Amesbury (0980) 23255.

★★Antrobus Arms, *Church St, SP4 7EY.*
✆ (0980) 23163. RS Xmas. C. ⊷ 20 bedrs,
12 bp, 8 bps, 4 ba, TV, Dgs. ✘ a l c, mc, at,
LD 10. ⊡ CH, Dgs, CP 60, G 2, Ac, CF, 4 st.
£ BB fr £21, DB fr £33, WB, ⊡, 10%, Bk
£3·50, D £8, cc 1 2 3 4 5 6, Dep a.
Druids Motel, y, *2 Countess Rd, SP4
7DW.* **✆** (0980) 22800. C. ⊷ 17 bedrs, 17
bps, TV, Dgs. ✘ a l c. ⊡ CH, CP 100, CF, 8
st. **£** BB £13·50, DB £19·50, ⊡, cc 1 3.
Fairlawns, H, x (Rt). *High St, SP4 7DJ.*
✆ (0980) 22103.

ANCASTER Lincolnshire. Map 23C
Pop 1,100. Stamford 26, London 117,
Grantham 8, Lincoln 19, Newark 17,
Sleaford 6.
Golf Belton Park, Grantham 18h. **See** St
Martin's Church, Site of Roman town, AD
43 (excavations).

Repairer: A C Williams (Ancaster) Ltd.
✆ Loveden (0400) 30491.
Rescue Service: Gilberts of Ancaster, 65
Ermine St. **✆** Loveden (0400) 30463.

ANDOVER Hampshire. Map 6C
Pop 31,590. Basingstoke 19, London 65,
Amesbury 14, Devizes 27, Marlborough
21, Newbury 16, Pewsey 18, Romsey 17,
Salisbury 18, Winchester 14.
EC Wed. **MD** Thur, Sat. **Golf** Andover 9h.
See Guildhall, 19th cent Church.

★★White Hart, *12 Bridge St, SP10 1BH.*
✆ (0264) 52266. C. ⊷ 21 bedrs, 21 bp,
TV, Dgs. ✘ a l c, mc, LD 9.30. ⊡ CH, TV, CP
21, Ac, con 40, CF. **£** BB fr £34·50, DB fr
£45, WT fr £249·80, DT fr £26, WB, ⊡, Bk
£3, L £7·95, D £7·95, cc 1 2 3 5, Dep b.

Repairer: Monro's of Andover, Newbury
Rd. **✆** (0264) 4233.
Rescue Service: G. Potter, Unit 1, Alfs
Garden Centre, Picket Piece.
✆ (0264) 54108.

ANGMERING-ON-SEA West Sussex.
Map 7E
Horsham 21, London 47, Arundel 5,
Haywards Heath 24, Littlehampton 4,
Worthing 6.
EC Wed. **Golf** Littlehampton 18h.

★★South Strand, *BN16 1NY.*
✆ Rustington (090 62) 5086. C. ⊷ 14
bedrs, 3 bp, 3 ba, Dgs. ✘ a l c, mc, at.
⊡ CH, TV, Dgs, CP 25, CF, 1 st. **£** BB £15–
£19, DB £30–£34, WT fr £224, ⊡, Bk £3·50,
L £7, D £7, Dep.
Three Crowns, H, y, *Sea Rd, BN16 1LS.*
✆ Rustington (090 62) 4074.

Rescue Service: Manor Road Garage,
Manor Rd. **✆** Rustington (090 62) 4232.

ANNFIELD PLAIN Durham. Map 32E
Pop 7,850. West Auckland 21, London
248, Corbridge 17, Durham 11, Hexham
19, Newcastle upon Tyne 11, Sunderland
17.
EC Wed. **Golf** South Moor 18h, Municipal
18h. **See** Cathgate, Museum.

Rescue Service: Morrison Road Garage.
✆ Stanley (0207) 34021.

APPLEBY Cumbria. Map 26D
Pop 2,438. Brough 8, London 272, Alston
26, Hawes 26, Kendal 24, Kirkby Lonsdale
30, Penrith 13.
EC Thur. **MD** Sat. **Golf** Appleby 18h. **See**
Castle (not open), St Lawrence's Church,
St. Michael's Church, Grammar School,
High Cross, 16th cent Moot Hall, Bull Ring,
Old organ.
🛈 Moot Hall, Boroughgate. **✆** Appleby
(0930) 51177.

★★Appleby Manor, *Roman Rd, CA16
6JD.* **✆** (0930) 51571. C. ⊷ 12 bedrs, 7
bp, 3 ba, annexe 7 bedrs, TV, Dgs (annexe).
✘ a l c, mc, at, LD 9. ⊡ CH, TV, CP 40, G 7,
Ac, con 60, CF, 4 BGf, 0 st, Dis. **£** BB
£17·50–£26·50, DB £27–£40, WB, ⊡, Bk
£3·65, L £8·25, D £8·25, cc 1 2 3 5 6,
Dep b.

★★Tufton Arms, *Boroughgate, CA16
6XA.* **✆** (0930) 51593. C. ⊷ 19 bedrs, 15
bp, 3 ba, TV, Dgs. ✘ a l c, mc, at, LD 9.30 (9
winter). ⊡ CH, TV, Dgs, CP 30, G 5, Ac,
con 100, CF, 1 st. **£** BB £13·50–£15, DB
£25–£28, WT £148–£157·50, DT £23·50–
£25, WB, ⊡, Bk £2·50, L £4, D £6·50,
cc 1 3 5, Dep.
▣★Courtfield (R), *Bongate, CA16 6UP.*
✆ (0930) 51394. C. ⊷ 6 bedrs, 2 ba,
annexe 6 bedrs, 1 ba, Dgs. ✘ mc, at, LD
7.45. ⊡ CH, TV, Dgs, ns, CP 30, U 2, G 2,
CF, 6 BGf, 0 st, Dis. **£** BB £11–£12, DB
£22–£24, WT £120–£140, DT £23·50–
£24·50, ⊡, Bk £3·50, L £5, D £7·50, cc 1 3.
★White Hart (R) *Boroughgate, CA16
6XB.* **✆** (0930) 51598. C. ⊷ 8 bedrs, 2 ba,
Dgs. ✘ a l c, mc, at, LD 9.30. ⊡ CH, TV,
Dgs, CP 6, Ac, CF, 1 st. **£** BB £10·50–
£11·50, DB £21–£23, DBB £15–£20, WB,
⊡, Bk £2·50, L £6, D £7·50, Dep.
Bongate, G, xy (R). *CA16 6UE.*
✆ (0930) 51245. C. ⊷ 7 bedrs, 1 bp, 3
bps, 1 ba, Dgs. ⊡ CH, TV, Dgs, CP 6, G 2,
CF. **£** BB £8·50–£9·50, DB £17–£19, WT
(b) £78, (c) £51, DT (b) £13, ⊡, D £4·50.
Howgill, G, x, (Unl), *CA16 6UW.*
✆ (0930) 51574. Open Apr–Oct. C. ⊷ 6
bedrs, 1 ba. ⊡ TV, ns CP 6, CF. **£** BB fr £8,
DB fr £14, ⊡.

Rescue Service: Spooner, R Ltd, The
Sands. **✆** (0930) 51133.

APPLEDORE Devon. Map 4C
Pop 2,500. Bideford 3½, London 205, Bude
28.
EC Wed. **Golf** Royal North Devon,
Westward Ho! 18h. **See** Hubba Stone
near Quay, landing place of Danish
invader, (892), Docton House.

▣★★Seagate, *The Quay, EX39 1QS.*
✆ Bideford (023 72) 2589. C. ⊷ 9 bedrs,
2 bp, 3 ba, TV, Dgs. ✘ a l c, mc, LD 9.30.
⊡ CH, TV, Dgs, CP 60, Ac, con 40, CF, 1 st.
£ BB £15–£20, DB £30–£45, ⊡, cc 1 5.

APPLEDORE Kent. Map 10E
Pop 650. Tenterden 5½, London 60,
Ashford 10, Folkestone 19, Rye 6.
Golf Tenterden 18h. **See** Horne's Place
Chapel, Royal Military Canal.

▣★Swan, *The Street, TN26 2BU.*
✆ (023 383) 329.

APPLETON LE MOORS North
Yorkshire. Map 24D
Pickering 7, London 220, Thirsk 23, York
33.

⬙★★Dweldapilton Hall, *YO6 6TE.*
✆ (075 15) 227.

ARCLID Cheshire. Map 19D
Pop 238. Newcastle-under-Lyme 11,
London 161, Congleton 5, Knutsford 11,
Manchester 27, Northwich 12, Sandbach
2½, Stockport 23, Warrington 20.
Golf Sandbach 9h, Malkins Bank 9h.

Rescue Service: Pace Arclid Ltd, Old
Smithy Garage, **✆** Smallwood
(047 75) 334.

ARDINGLY West Sussex. Map 7D
Pop 2,000. East Grinstead 7, London 37,
Crawley 9, Haywards Heath 4, Horsham
18.
EC Sat. **Golf** Haywards Heath 18h. **See**
14th cent Church, Botanical Gardens,
Reservoir, annual agricultural show.

Greyhound, H, x, *Street Lane, RH17 6UA.* ✆ (0444) 892214.

ARMATHWAITE Cumbria. Map 26C
Pop 431. Penrith 11, London 287, Brampton 11, Carlisle 9½.
Golf Penrith 18h. **See** Castle.

▩★**Duke Head Inn,** *Front St, CA4 9PB.* ✆ (069 92) 226.

ARNOLD Nottinghamshire. Map 22D
Pop 37,390. Nottingham 4, London 127, Grantham 25, Mansfield 11, Matlock 25, Newark 18, Ollerton 16.
EC Wed, **MD** Fri, Sat. **Golf** Mapperley 18h.
See Church, Country Park.

Specialist Body Repairer: John Rann Coachbuilder, Arnot Hill Rd.
✆ Nottingham (0602) 266046.

ARNSIDE Cumbria. Map 27C
Pop 1,865. M6 Motorway 7, London 249, Ambleside 22, Broughton-in-Furness 31, Kendal 13, Kirkby Lonsdale 13, Lancaster 14, Ulverston 25.
EC Thur. **Golf** Silverdale 9h, Grange-over-Sands 18h. **See** Arnside Knott (viewpoint), ruins of Arnside and Hazelslack pele towers.

Willowfield, PH, x (Rt), *The Promenade, LA5 0AD.* ✆ (0524) 761354. Open Mar–Oct, C.4. ⇔ 9 bedrs, 2 ba, Dgs. ◫ ch, TV, ns, CP 7. **£** BB fr £7·75, DB fr £15·50, WT (b) fr £92·75, DT fr £13·25, ②, D £5·50.

Rescue Service: Norman Hodgson, Station Garage, Station Rd.
✆ (0524) 761398.

ARRINGTON Cambridgeshire. Map 15D
Pop 360. Royston 6, London 47, Bedford 20, Biggleswade 12, Cambridge 11, Huntingdon 15.
Golf Royston 18h. **See** Wimpole Hall N.T.

Rescue Service: Hardwicke Arms Garage, 98 Ermine Way. ✆ Cambridge (0223) 207302.

ARUNDEL West Sussex. Map 7E
Pop 2,162. Pulborough 9, London 56, Bognor Regis 9½, Brighton 20, Chichester 11, Haywards Heath 29, Littlehampton 4, Petworth 11, Worthing 10.
EC Wed. **Golf** Goodwood 18h, Littlehampton 18h. **See** Castle, Maison Dieu ruins, Swanbourne Lake, 14th cent St Nicholas Church, R.C. Cathedral of Our Lady and St Philip Howard, Museums, Wildfowl Trust.
🛈 61 High St. ✆ Arundel (0903) 882268.

★★★**Norfolk Arms,** *High St, BN18 9AB.* ✆ (0903) 882101. C. ⇔ 22 bedrs, 19 bp, 3 ba, TV, Dgs. ✕ a l c, mc, at, LD 10. ◫ CH, Dgs, CP 16, G 12, Ac, con 20, CF,8 BGf, 0 st, Dis. **£** BB fr £19·50–£27·50, DB £26–£40, DBB £25–£30, WB, ①, Bk £3·25, L £4·95, D £8·95, cc 1 2 3 5, Dep b.

▩★**Bridge,** *Queens St, BN18 9JG.* ✆ (0903) 882242. C. ⇔ 13 bedrs, 1 bp, 4 sh, 3 ba. ✕ a l c, mc, at. ◫ CH, TV, Dgs, CP 15, Ac. **£** BB fr £16–£18, DB £22–£26, WT fr £185, DT £29, WB, ①, Bk £1·50, L £5·50, D £6·50, cc 1 2 3 4 5.

ASCOT Berkshire. Map 7A
Pop 7,100. Staines 8, London 25, Bagshot 4½, Henley-on-Thames 16, High Wycombe 20, Reading 14, Windsor 6½.
EC Wed. **Golf** Wentworth 18h, Sunningdale and R Berkshire 18h.

See Racecourse founded 1711 by Queen Anne, Royal Meeting in June.

★★★**Berystede** (TH), *Bagshot Rd, Sunninghill SL5 9JA.* ✆ (0990) 23311. C. ⇔ 90 bedrs, 85 bp, 5 bps, TV, Dgs. ✕ a l c, mc, at, LD 10. ◫ Lt, N, CH, Dgs, CP 140, G 6, Ac, sp, con 120, CF, 10 BGf, 4 st. **£** BB £47·50, DB £61·50, WB, ①, cc 1 2 3 4 5 6, Dep (Xmas).

Highclere House, H, x (Rl), *Kings Rd, SL5 9AD.* ✆ (0990) 25220. C. ⇔ 12 bedrs, 5 bps, 3 ba, TV, Dgs. ◫ CH, TV, Dgs, CP 14, G 2, CF, 2 BGf, 1 st, Dis. **£** BB £12–£16, DB £24–£28, ①.

Repairers: May, H (Ascot) Ltd, Ascot Motor Works, Winkfield Rd.
✆ (0990) 20324.
Royal Ascot Garage, Raygar House, 71 High St. ✆ (0990) 21481.

ASCOTT UNDER WYCHWOOD Oxfordshire. Map 14F
Oxford 20, London 76, Banbury 20, Burford 6, Stow on the Wold 10, Witney 8.

Wychwood Arms, H, xy, *London Lane, OX7 6JA.* ✆ Shipton under Wychwood (0993) 830271. C10. ⇔ 6 bedrs, 6 bp, TV. ◫ CH, Dgs, CP 30, 1 st. **£** BB £21, DB £31·50, ②, Bk £4·75, D £7·35, cc 1 3 5.

ASHBOURNE Derbyshire. Map 22C
Pop 5,960. Derby 13, London 139, Burton-upon-Trent 19, Buxton 20, Leek 15, Lichfield 26, Mansfield 29, Matlock 13, Sheffield 33, Stoke-on-Trent 22, Stone 23, Tamworth 32, Uttoxeter 12.
EC Wed. **MD** Thur, Sat. **Golf** Clifton 9h. **See** 13th cent Church with 212ft spire, curious double transepts and fine monuments. Shrovetide football game in main street on Shrove Tue and Ash Wed. Manifold Valley 3 m NW, Dovedale 4 m NW, Alton Tower 9 m W.
🛈 13 Market Pl. ✆ Ashbourne (0335) 43666.

Brookfields, H, z *Station Rd, DE6 1AA.* ✆ (0335) 43330. C. ⇔ 11 bedrs, 2 ba. ✕ a l c. ◫ CH, TV, Dgs, CP 24, 0 st. **£** BB £13·50–£14·50, DB £23–£25, ①, Bk £2·75, L £4·50, D £7·50, cc 1 2 5.

Rescue Service: Preston's Garage, Derby Rd. ✆ (0335) 43179.

ASHBURTON Devon. Map 3D
Pop 3,750. Honiton 35, London 187, Axminster 45, Exeter 19, Lyme Regis 47, Newton Abbot 7½, Okehampton 27, Plymouth 24, Saltash 27, Tavistock 20, Totnes 8.
EC Wed. **Golf** Newton Abbot (Stover) 18h. **See** Remains of Chapel of St Lawrence, Ashburton Museum in 'The Little House', St Andrew's Church, Buckfast Abbey 3 m SSW, Dean Prior 5 m SSW, where Herrick was Rector, Dartmoor.

★★**M Dartmoor,** *Pear Tree Cross, TQ13 7JW.* ✆ (0364) 52232. RS Xmas. C. ⇔ 8 bedrs, 6 bp, 2 bps, annexe 14 bedrs, 14 bp, TV, Dgs. ✕ a l c, mc, at, LD 9.30. ◫ CH, CP 32, U 2, Ac, con 70, CF, 7 BGf, 1 st, Dis. **£** BB £20·85–£27, DB £28·85–£38, WT £160–£182, WB, ②, Bk £3·50, L £4, D £4·50, cc 1 2 3 5.

★★**Golden Lion,** *East St, TQ13 7AX.* ✆ (0364) 52205. C. ⇔ 12 bedrs, 4 bp, 2 bps, 2 ba, TV, Dgs. ✕ a l c, mc, at, LD 10. ◫ CH, TV, Dgs, CP 100, Ac, sol, gym, con

100, CF, 0 st. **£** BB fr £14, DB fr £20, ①, Bk £2·50, L £3·50, D £5, cc 1 2 3 5.

₽★★**Holme Chase** (R), *TQ13 7NS.* ✆ Poundsgate (036 43) 471. C. ⇔ 12 bedrs, 5 bp, 4 bps, 2 ba, TV, Dgs. ✕ mc, at, LD 8.30. ◫ CH, TV, CP, U 2, G 4, con 40, CF, 1 BGf, 1 st, Dis. **£** BB fr £18·40, DB fr £34, WT £153, DBB fr £27, WB, ②, 15%, Bk £5, L £6·50, D £8·50, cc 1 2 3 5 6, Dep a.

★**Tugela House,** *68–70 East St, TQ13 7AX.* ✆ (0364) 52206. C. ⇔ 6 bedrs, 2 bp, 2 sh, 2 ba, TV, Dgs. ✕ a l c, mc, at, LD 9.30. ◫ CH, TV, Dgs, G 4, CF, 1 st. **£** BB £11–£12·50, DB £22–£25, DT fr £19, WB, ①, Bk £2·95, L £6·95, D £7·95.

Gages Mill, G, x, y (R), *Buckfastleigh Rd, TQ13 7JW.* ✆ (0364) 52391. Closed Xmas. C5. ⇔ 7 bedrs, 2 bps, 4 sh, 1 ba. ◫ ch, TV, CP 7. **£** DB £18–£21, WT (b) £88–£93, DT (b) £15–£16, ①.

Repairer: Eastern Garage, Eastern Rd. ✆ (0364) 52216.
Rescue Service: Ashburton Motor Works, East St. ✆ (0364) 52215.
Churley Road Garage, Churley Rd.
✆ (0364) 52670.
D R Aucock Ltd, Great Bridge Garage, North St. ✆ (0364) 52588.

ASHBURY Oxfordshire. Maps 6A & 14F
Wantage 9½, London 70, Hungerford 14, Lechlade 12, Swindon 8. **See** White horse (Chalk Hill figure), Castle

★**Rose & Crown,** *Ashbury, Swindon, Wilts, SN6 8NA.* ✆ (0793 71) 222. C. ⇔ 10 bedrs, 2 bp, 2 bps, 1 sh, 3 ba, TV, Dgs. ✕ a l c, mc, at, LD 10.30. ◫ N, CH, TV, Dgs, CP 70, Ac, pf, con 40, CF, 1 st. **£** BB fr £15, DB fr £25, WT £200, DT £30, WB, ②, 10%, Bk £3, L £2, D £2, cc 1 2 3 4 5 6, Dep b.

ASHBY-DE-LA-ZOUCH Leicestershire. Map 22F
Pop 11,500. Hinckley 16, London 113, Atherstone 13, Burton-upon-Trent 9, Derby 14, Leicester 20, Loughborough 12, Nottingham 21, Nuneaton 17, Tamworth 13.
EC Wed. **MD** Sat. **Golf** Willesley Park 18h. **See** Castle ruins (Scott's "Ivanhoe"), Church, 14th cent Bulls Head (oldest hse in Ashby), RC Church.

★★★**Royal Crest,** *Station Rd, LE6 5GP.* ✆ (0530) 412833. C. ⇔ 31 bedrs, 25 bp, 6 bps, ns, TV, Dgs. ✕ a l c, mc, LD 9.15. ◫ N, CH, TV, Dgs, CP 250, Ac, con 60, CF, 3 st. **£** BB fr £43·25, DB £58·50, WB, ①, Bk £5·25, L £5·60, D £9·25, cc 1 2 3 4 5 6, Dep.

Rescue Service: Allsop, C W & Sons, Tamworth Rd. ✆ (0530) 412141.

ASHFORD Kent. Map 10C
Pop 47,000. Maidstone 19, London 56, Canterbury 14, Folkestone 16, Rochester 27, Tenterden 12, Tunbridge Wells 32.
EC Wed. **MD** Tue, Sat. **Golf** Ashford 18h. **See** St Mary the Virgin Church, 120 ft tower, Windmill, Godinton Park 1½ m NW, Old Houses, Memorial Gdns.
🛈 Lower High St. ✆ Ashford (0233) 37311.

₽★★★★★**Eastwell Manor,** *Eastwell Park, TN25 4HR.* ✆ (0233) 35751. C (7 in restaurant). ⇔ 24 bedrs, 24 bp, TV. ✕ a l c, mc, at. ◫ Lt, N, CH, TV, CP 100, G 25, Ac, tc, pf, con 75, CF, 3 BGf, 0 st, Dis. **£** BB £48–£90, DB £63–£108, WT

£511–£805, DT £73–£115, ①, Bk £5·50, L
£9, D £20, cc 1 2 3 5, Dep a.
★★★**Spearpoint** (R), *Canterbury Rd,
Kennington, TN24 9QR.* ✆ (0233) 36863.
C. ⊷ 37 bedrs, 30 bp, 4 bps, 1 ba, TV, Dgs.
✗ a l c, mc, LD 9.45. ⌂ N, CH, CP 60, Ac,
con 80, CF, 8 BGf, 1 st, Dis. £ BB fr £20–
£31, DB £41, WB, ①, Bk £2·50, L £6·50, D
£8·50, cc 1 2 3 5.
★★**George,** *High St, TN24 8TB.*
✆ (0233) 25512.
Croft H, x (R), *Canterbury Rd,
Kennington, TN25 4DU.* ✆ (0233) 22140.
Closed Xmas. C. ⊷ 28 bedrs, 9 bp, 14 bps,
TV. ⌂ CH, TV, CP 36, CF, 6 BGf, 6 st. £ BB
£15·50–£24, DB £24–£34, ①, Bk £3, D
£7·50, cc 3.
Downsview H, x (Rl), *Willesborough Rd,
Kennington.* ✆ (0233) 21953. C. ⊷ 16
bedrs, 3 bps, 2 sh, 3 ba, TV, Dgs. ✗ a l c.
⌂ CH, TV, CP 20, CF, 1 BGf, 0 st, Dis. £ BB
£15·10–£20·70, DB £24·60–£28·25, WT
(b) £114·70, DT (b) fr £20·45, ①, D £6·30,
cc 1 3.

Rescue Service: East Stour Service
Station, Hythe Rd. ✆ (0233) 21977.

ASHFORD Surrey. (Middx) Map 7A
Pop 26,806. Brentford and Chiswick 8½,
London 15, Kingston upon Thames 7½,
Richmond-upon-Thames 8, Staines 3,
Uxbridge 12, Weybridge 6, Woking 10.
EC Wed. **Golf** Ashford Manor 18h. **See**
Churches.

Rescue Service: Ashmans Garage Ltd,
286 Kingston Rd. ✆ (078 42) 52763.
White House Garage, Kingston Rd.
✆ (078 42) 53290 and (078 42) 58061.

ASHINGTON Northumberland. Map 31D
Pop 27,786. Newcastle upon Tyne 17,
London 291, Alnwick 22, Coldstream 50,
Corbridge 30.
EC Wed. **MD** Fri, Sat. **Golf** Newbiggin-by-
the-Sea 18h, Bedlingtonshire 18h. **See**
Bothal Castle and Church, Wansbeck
Riverside Park.

Rescue Service: Universal Garage,
Woodhorn Rd. ✆ (0670) 813113.

ASHTON Cornwall. Map 3C
Callington 1½, London 215, Launceston
12, Liskeard 10, Plymouth 13.

Rescue Service: Double S Service Station.
✆ Germoe (073 676) 3204.

ASHTON-UNDER-LYNE Gtr
Manchester (Lancashire). Maps 22A and
27B
Pop 44,725. Buxton 22, London 181,
Barnsley 30, Glossop 7½, Huddersfield 20,
Manchester 6½, Oldham 4, Stockport 7½.
EC Tue. **MD** Daily (exc Tue). **Golf** Hyde
18h. **See** Restored Parish Church of St
Michael, Stamford Park.

★★**York House** (R), *York Pl, OL6 7TT.*
✆ 061-330 5899. C. ⊷ 26 bedrs, 8 bp, 3
bps, 6 sh, 3 ba, TV, Dgs. ✗ a l c, LD 9.30.
⌂ N, CH, CP 26, Ac, con 65, CF, 1 st. £ BB
£16·90–£23·70, DB £30–£33, ①, Bk £4·65,
L £5·61, D £5·61, cc 1 2 3 5, Dep b.

Repairers: Grahams of Ashton Ltd,
Katherine St. ✆ 061-330 1817.
H & J Quick Ltd, Manchester Rd. ✆ 061-
330 4556.

ASHURST Hampshire. Map 6E
Pop 2,200. Winchester 16, London 81,
Lyndhurst 3, Romsey 9, Salisbury 19,
Southampton 6½.
EC Wed. **Golf** New Forest, Lyndhurst
18h.

⧫★★**Busketts Lawn** (R), *174
Woodlands Rd, Woodlands, SO4 2GL.*
✆ (042 129) 2272. ▲
▣⧫★★**Woodlands Lodge,** (R) *Bartley
Rd, SO4 2GN.* ✆ (042 129) 2257. Closed
Xmas. C. ⊷ 11 bedrs, 7 bp, 1 bps, 1 ba, TV.
✗ a l c, mc, at, LD 8. ⌂ CH, TV, CP 40, con.
£ BB £14–£19, DB £28–£38, DBB £16·95–
£26·75, WB, ①, Bk £4, L £3, D £8, cc 1 3,
Dep a.

ASHWELL Hertfordshire. Map 15D
A1 (M) Motorway 3, Baldock 4½, London
43, Bedford 15, Cambridge 18, Hitchin 10.

Three Tuns, H, x, *High St. SG7 5NL.*
✆ (046 274) 2387.

ASKAM-IN-FURNESS Cumbria. Map
27E
M6 Motorway 30, London 276, Ambleside
25, Broughton-in-Furness 8, Kendal 30,
Lancaster 40, Penrith 47.

Rescue Service: Furness Cars &
Commercials, Unit 1, Station Approach.
✆ Dalton-in-Furness (0229) 65336.

ASTON CLINTON Buckinghamshire
Map 15E
Pop 3,167. Watford 19, London 36,
Aylesbury 4½, Denham 22, Dunstable 11,
High Wycombe 15, St Albans 19.
Golf Ellesborough, Wendover 18h. **See**
Roman remains, Parish Church.

★★★**Bell Inn,** *London Rd, HP22 5HP.*
✆ Aylesbury (0296) 630252. C. ⊷ 6
bedrs, 6 bp, annexe 16 bedrs, 15 bp, TV,
Dgs. ✗ a l c, mc. ⌂ CH, Dgs, ns, CP 200,
Ac, con, CF, 7 BGf, 1 st, Dis. £ BBc fr £46,
DBc fr £62, ①, Bk £5, L £20, D £28, cc 1 3,
Dep (overseas).

Repairer: Madge Garages Ltd, London
Rd. ✆ Aylesbury (0296) 630214.
Rescue Service: Aston Clinton Motors,
Aylesbury Rd. ✆ Aylesbury (0296)
630271.

ATHERSTONE Warwickshire. Map 21A
Pop 7,429. M1 Motorway 24, London 104,
Ashby-de-la-Zouch 13, Birmingham 19,
Burton-upon-Trent 19, Hinckley 8½,
Lichfield 14, Market Harborough 31,
Newport 40, Northampton 39, Nuneaton
5½, Rugby 22, Sutton Coldfield 14,
Tamworth 8, Towcester 40, Walsall 20,
Wellington 43.
EC Thur. **MD** Tue, Fri. **Golf** Athestone 9h.
See Church, Shrove Tue Football in Main
St, Milestone, Roman Roads.

★**Old Red Lion,** *Long St, CV9 1BB.*
✆ (082 77) 3156. RS Xmas. C. ⊷ 10
bedrs, 4 bps, 2 ba, TV, Dgs. ✗ a l c, mc, LD
9.45. ⌂ CH, TV, Dgs, CP 20, U 2, G 3, CF, 1
st. £ BB £15·50–£21·50, DB £24–£31, ②,
Bk £2·75, L £7, D £7, cc 1 2 3 5.
Three Tuns H, x, *95 Long St.*
✆ (082 77) 3161. C. ⊷ 14 bedrs, 5 bp, 5
bps, 4 ba, ns, TV. ⌂ CH, TV, Dgs, CP 20, CF,
0 st. £ BB £12·50–£18·50, DB £25–£36·50,
DT (b) £15·50, ①, cc 2 3 5.

ATHERTON Gtr Manchester
(Lancashire). Map 20A

Pop 21,837. M6 Motorway 8, London 193,
Altrincham 15, Bolton 5, Chorley 13,
Liverpool 26, Manchester 12, St Helens
13, Warrington 12, Wigan 6½.
EC Wed. **MD** Fri. **Golf** Leigh 9h,
Westhoughton Municipal 9h. **See** Parish
Church, Chowbent Chapel, Alder Ho.

Rescue Service: Peter Thompson, Taylors
Yard, Leigh Rd. ✆ (0942) 3980.

ATTLEBOROUGH Norfolk. Map 16D
Pop 6,000. Thetford 14, London 96, East
Dereham 14, Lowestoft 36, Norwich 15,
Scole 14, Stowmarket 26, Swaffham 19.
EC Wed. **MD** Thur. **Golf** Thetford 18h.
See Norm and Perp Parish Church of St
Mary, Attleborough Hall, Earthworks.

Rescue Service: Attleborough Motor
Works Ltd, High St. ✆ (0953) 452274.

AUDENSHAW Gtr Manchester
(Lancashire). Map 19B
Pop 11,929, Stockport 7, London 186,
Barnsley 32, Glossop 9, Manchester 5½,
Oldham 5½. **Golf** Hyde 9h.

★**Trough House** (Rl), *103 Manchester
Rd. M34 5PY.* ✆ 061-370 1574. RS Sat. C.
⊷ 10 bedrs, 2 ba, annexe 16 bedrs, 1 bp, 2
sh, 2 ba, Dgs. ✗ a l c, mc, at, LD 9. ⌂ CH,
TV, Dgs, CP 80, Ac, con 100, CF, 6 BGf, 1
st, Dis. £ BB £11·50–£13·65, DB £18·40–
£24, ①, Bk £2·58, L £3, D £4, cc 1 3.

AUDLEM Cheshire. Map 19D
Pop 1,293. Stone 18, London 159,
Nantwich 7, Newcastle-under-Lyme 13,
Newport 18, Shrewsbury 32, Stafford 24,
Wellington 25, Whitchurch 8.
EC Wed. **Golf** Whitchurch 18h. **See**
Parish Church, old Market Cross. 17th
cent Moss Hall.

Rescue Service: J & W Motors (Audlem)
Ltd, Chapel End Garage.
✆ (0270) 811458.

AUSTWICK North Yorkshire. Map 27A
Pop 250. Settle 4, London 233, Hawes 21,
Kirkby Lonsdale 12, Lancaster 21.
Golf Bentham 9h.

⧫★**Traddock** (R), *LA2 8BY.* ✆ Clapham
(046 85) 224. Open Apr–Oct. C. ⊷ 12
bedrs, 2 bp, 8 bps, 1 ba, Dgs. ✗ LD 7.
⌂ CH, TV, ns, CP 30, con 20, CF, 1 st. £ BB
fr £12·50, DB fr £23, DBB fr £19, WB, ②, D
£8.

AVETON GIFFORD Devon. Map 3F
Pop 551. Ashburton 17, London 204,
Dartmouth 16, Kingsbridge 4, Plymouth
16, Tavistock 26, Totnes 14.
Golf Bigbury-on-Sea 18h. **See** St
Andrew's Course.

Rescue Service: Robertson, R M, Avon
Bridge Garage. ✆ Loddiswell
(054 855) 248.

AVON Hants. M. Area 6E
Christchurch 4, London 98, Bournemouth
9½, Lymington 16, Ringwood 4¾,
Southampton 23

⧫★★**Tyrrells Ford** *BH23 7BH,*
✆ Bransgore (0425) 72646. C. ⊷ 15
bedrs, 6 bp, 9 bps, 1 ba, TV. ✗ a l c, mc, at,
LD 10. ⌂ CH, TV, CP, Ac, con, CF, 2 st.
£ BB fr £20, DB fr £40, DBB fr £25, WB, ②,
L £5·95, D £8·95, cc 1 2 3 5.

AVONWICK Devon. Map 3D
Pop 300. Ashburton 9, London 196,
Dartmouth 14, Kingsbridge 11, Plymouth
16, Saltash 20, Tavistock 20, Totnes 6.
Golf Wrangaton 9h.

Rescue Service: Cousins Bros, Avon
Garage. ✆ South Brent (036 47) 3152.

AXBRIDGE Somerset. Map 5A
Pop 1,525. Wells 10, London 132, Bath 27,
Bridgwater 16, Bristol 17, Glastonbury 14,
Radstock 21, Weston-super-Mare 10.
Golf Burnham & Berrow 18h. **See**
Ambleside Watergardens and Aviaries,
King John's Hunting Lodge (Museum),
14th cent Church, Manor House, ancient
buildings in High St.

Rescue Service: Axbridge Motors,
Cheddar Rd. ✆ (0934) 732400.

★★★Koppers *Kilmington EX13 7RJ.*
✆ (0297) 32074.
★★Cedars, *Silver St, EX13 5DP.*
✆ (0297) 32775. C. 🛏 18 bedrs, 1 bp, 2
sh, 4 ba, TV. ✗ a l c, mc, at. 🅟 CH, TV, Ac,
CF. £ BB fr £10, DB fr £18, WB, 🄻, Bk
£2·50, L £5·75, D £7·85, cc 1 3 6.
★★George, *Trinity Sq, EX13 5DW.*
✆ (0297) 32209. C. 🛏 10 bedrs, 3 bp, 2
bps, 2 ba, TV, Dgs. ✗ a l c, mc, at, LD 8.30.
🅟 ch, TV, CP 20, Ac, con 60, CF, 2 st. £ BB
£10—£15, DB £20—£25, DT fr £18, 🄻, Bk
£2·90, L £2·95, D £4·20, cc 1 3 6, Dep b.
🌂★★Woodbury Park, *Woodbury Cross,*
EX13 5TL. ✆ (0297) 33010. C. 🛏 8 bedrs,
4 bp, 1 bps, 2 ba, Dgs. ✗ a l c, mc, at, LD
9.15. 🅟 CH, TV, Dgs, CP 50, sp, con 20, CF,
4 st. £ BB £11—£21, DB £22—£32, DBB
£15·50—£25·50, WB, 🄻, Bk £2·75, L £4·50,
D £4·50, cc 1 2 3 5, Dep a.
Elford F, x (Rt), *Dalwood, EX13 7HB.*
✆ (0297) 32415. Open Mar—Oct. C. 🛏 7
bedrs, 2 bp, 1 ba. 🅟 CH, TV, CP 7, CF, 1 st.
£ BB £8·50—£9, DB £16—£20, WT (b)
£73·85—£79·85, DT (b) £11·50—£12, 🄻.

Rescue Service: Early's Garage,
Chardstock. ✆ South Chard
(0460) 20337.
Hunters Lodge Garage, Charmouth Rd.
✆ (0297) 32737.
Masters Garage, Charmouth Rd.
✆ (0297) 32100.
Webster's (Axminster) Ltd, West St.
✆ (0297) 32220.
West End Motors, West St.
✆ (0297) 32143.

AYLESBURY Buckinghamshire. Map
15E
Pop 46,149. Watford 23, London 40,
Bedford 29, Bicester 16, Bletchley 16,
Buckingham 16, Denham 24, Dunstable
15, Henley-on-Thames 27, High Wycombe
16, Northampton 27, Oxford 22, Reading
32, St Albans 23, Wallingford 25.
EC Thur. **MD** Wed, Fri, Sat. **Golf** West
Turville 18h. **See** 15th cent EE Church of
St Mary, King's Head Hotel, Statue of
John Hampden, Bucks County Museum,

Prebendal House (home of John Wilkes),
Waddesdon Manor 5½ m NW.
🄸 County Hall, Walton St. ✆ Aylesbury
(0296) 5000.

★★Bell (TH), *Market Sq, HP20 1TX.*
✆ (0296) 82141. C. 🛏 17 bedrs, 16 bp, 1
bps, TV, Dgs. ✗ a l c, mc, LD 9.30. 🅟 ch,
Dgs, Ac, CF, 0 st. £ BB £37·50, DB £50·50,
WB, 🄻, cc 1 2 3 4 5 6, Dep (Xmas).

Repairers: Keith Garages Ltd, Bicester
Rd. ✆ (0296) 28001.
Perry's, 54 Walton St. ✆ (0296) 84864.
Shaw & Kilburn Ltd, 143 Cambridge St.
✆ (0296) 82321.
Specialist Radiator Repairer: Serck
Radiator Services Ltd, Southend Rd.
✆ (0296) 82581.
Rescue Service: Dutton-Forshaw (Bucks)
Ltd, Buckingham Rd. ✆ (0296) 82711.

AYLSHAM Norfolk. Map 16A
Pop 4,800. Norwich 13, London 124,
Cromer 10, East Dereham 18, Fakenham
19, Great Yarmouth 27, King's Lynn 39,
Swaffham 29.
EC Wed. **MD** Mon, Fri. **Golf** Royal Cromer
18h. **See** Perp Church (grave of Humphrey
Repton, famous landscape gardener),
Blickling Hall 1½ m NW (Nat Trust).

Rescue Service: Watt Bros, Norwich Rd
Garage. ✆ (026 373) 2134.

AYSGARTH North Yorkshire. Map 26B
Pop 170. Leyburn 7½, London 241, Hawes
8½, Leeds 39, Skipton 27.
EC Wed. **Golf** Catterick 18h. **See**
Aysgarth Falls triple waterfall, Carriage
Museum.

Rescue Service: HBS Motors (Aysgarth)
Ltd. ✆ (096 93) 209

BABBACOMBE Devon
See listing after TORQUAY

BAGBY North Yorkshire. Map 25E
Pop 390. Boroughbridge 14, London 222,
Helmsley 13, Thirsk 3½, York 22.
Golf Thirsk & Northallerton 9h.

Rescue Service: Bagby Service Station.
✆ Thirsk (0845) 597342.

BAGSHOT Surrey. Map 7A
Pop 4,000. Staines 10, London 27, M3
Motorway 1, Basingstoke 20, Farnham 12,
Guildford 11, Henley-on-Thames 19,
Reading 16, Weybridge 11, Windsor 10,
Woking 7½.
EC Wed. **Golf** Sunningdale 18h (2),
Camberley Heath 18h, Wentworth 18h.
See Parish Church of St Anne.

🌂★★★Pennyhill Park, *College Ride,*
GU19 5ET. ✆ (0276) 71774. C. 🛏 17
bedrs, 17 bp, TV. ✗ a l c, mc, at, LD 10.30.
🅟 N, TV, Dgs, CP 250, Ac, sp, gc, tc, pf, rf,
sb, sol, con 70, CF, 0 st. £ BB £48—£64, DB
£70—£74, WB, 🄻, Bk £3·95, L £11·95, D
£16, cc 1 2 3 4 5 6, Dep b.
🌂 🌂The Cricketers, *London Rd, GU19*
5HR. ✆ (0276) 73196.

Repairers: Brandon Service Station Ltd,
Guildford Rd, Lightwater.
✆ (0276) 73060.
Fina Garage, By-pass Rd. ✆ (0276) 71696.

BAINBRIDGE North Yorkshire. Map 26B
Pop 360. Leyburn 12, London 245, Hawes
4, Leeds 54, Skipton 31.
EC Wed. **Golf** Catterick 18h. **See** Old Inn,
Waterfalls, Semerwater Lake (water ski-
ing and yachting) 1 m W, Stocks on Green.

◨★★Rose & Crown, *Village Green, DL8*
3EE. ✆ Wensleydale (0969) 50225. C.
🛏 13 bedrs, 3 bp, 8 bps, 2 sh, 1 ba, TV,
Dgs. ✗ a l c, mc, LD 9. 🅟 CH, CP 60, Ac, pf,
con, CF, 0 st. £ BB £15·50—£18, DB £31—
£36, 🄻, L £3·50, D £7·50, cc 1 3 6, Dep a.
Riverdale, G, x (RI), *DL8 3EW.*
✆ Wensleydale (0969) 50311.

BAKEWELL Derbyshire. Map 22C
See also HASSOP.
Pop 3,946. Matlock 8, London 153,
Ashbourne 17, Buxton 12, Chapel-en-le-
Frith 15, Chesterfield 12, Leek 19,
Sheffield 16.
EC Thur. **MD** Mon. **Golf** Bakewell 9h. **See**
Church (Vernon monuments), Saxon
Cross in Churchyard, Old Bridge, Grammar
School, Almshouses, Holme Hall, Old
House Museum, Haddon Hall 2 m SE,
Chatsworth House, Garden and Theatre
Gallery, 3 m NE.

★★Rutland Arms, *The Square, DE4 1BT.*
✆ (062 981) 2812. C. 🛏 18 bedrs, 18 bp,
TV, Dgs. ✗ mc, at, LD 9.15. 🅟 CH, Dgs, CP
35, Ac, con 80, CF, 7 BGf, 4 st. £ BB fr
£32·25, DB fr £47·50, WB, 🄻, Bk £4·25, L
£5·50, D £9·50, cc 1 2 3 4 5 6, Dep b.
★Milford House, (R), *Mill St, DE4*
1DA. ✆ (062 981) 2130. Closed Xmas &
Jan, RS Feb, Nov, Dec. C8. 🛏 11 bedrs, 5
bp, 3 ba, TV. ✗ mc, at, LD 7.30. 🅟 CH, TV,
CP 10, U 2, G 7. £ BB fr £14·38, DB fr
£27·60, WT fr £170, DT fr £26·50, 🄻, Bk
£3·50, L £6·60, D £7, Dep a.
Castle Cliff, PH, xy (Rt), *Monsal Head,*
DE4 1NL. ✆ Gt Longstone (062 987) 258.
Merlin House, PH, x (R), *Ashford Lane,*
Monsal Head, DE4 1NL. ✆ Great
Longstone (062 987) 475. Open Mar—
Nov, C5. 🛏 7 bedrs, 2 bps, 2 ba, Dgs.
🅟 CH, TV, CP 8, 1 st. £ BB £9—£14, DB
£18—£32, WT £112—£133, DT £16—£22, 🄻,
D £8.

Repairer: Bakewell Garage Ltd, Haddon
Rd, ✆ (062 981) 2711.

BALDOCK Hertfordshire. Map 15D
Pop 6,679. Hatfield 17, London 38,
Bedford 17, Biggleswade 7½, Bishop's
Stortford 20, Bletchley 26, Hoddesdon 21,
Luton 13, Royston 8½, St Albans 20.
EC Thur. **MD** Wed. **Golf** Letchworth 18h.
See Mainly 14th cent Church of St Mary.

MC Repairer: Larry Langshaw (Motor
Cycles), 27B Butlers Yard, Whitehorse St.
✆ (0462) 893201.
Sctr Repairer: Larry Langshaw (Motor
Cycles), 27B Butlers Yard, Whitehorse St.
✆ (0462) 893201.
Rescue Service: D P Developments,
Odsey Service Station, Baldock Rd,
✆ Ashwell (046 274) 2252.
Rusbridge L & J, Football Close.
✆ (0462) 893249.

BAMBER BRIDGE Lancashire. Map
27D
M6 Motorway 2, London 208, Blackburn
9½, Chorley 5½, Ormskirk 19, Preston 4,
Southport 15, Whalley 15, Wigan 14.
EC Wed. **Golf** Pentwortham, Preston 18h.
See Ye Old Hob Inn.

Rescue Service: Brindle Rd Service
Station. ✆ Preston (0772) 35121.

BAMBURGH Northumberland. Map 31A
Pop 458. Alnwick 16, London 324,
Berwick-upon-Tweed 20, Coldstream 26,

EC Wed. **Golf** Bamburgh Castle 18h. **See** Castle, St Aidan's Church, Grace Darling Museum and boathouse, Farne Islands (Bird sanctuary).

★★Lord Crewe Arms, *Front St, NE69 7BL.* ✆ (066 84) 243. Open Apr-Oct, C5. ⊨ 26 bedrs, 12 bp, 4 ba, TV, Dgs. ✗ mc, at, LD 8.30. ⌂ ch, TV, CP 45, 5 BGf, 3 st. **£** BB £17·50–£24·50, DB £29–£36, WB, ②, Bk £3·50, L £3, D £7·95.▲

⊞★★Victoria, *Front St, NE69 7BP.* ✆ (066 84) 431. RS Nov–March. C. ⊨ 22 bedrs, 14 bp, 1 bps, 3 ba, TV, Dgs. ✗ a l c, mc, LD 8. ⌂ CH, TV, CP 6, con 50, CF. **£** BB £13·20–£18·70, DB £24·20–£35·20, DBB £19·30–£25·50, WB, ①, Bk £3·50, L £4, D £7·50, cc 1 2 3 5.

★Mizen Head, *NE69 7BS.* ✆ (066 84) 254.

Sunningdale, H, x (R), *Lucker Rd, NE69 7BS.* ✆ (066 84) 334. Open Mar-Oct. C. ⊨ 18 bedrs, 6 bp, 4 ba, Dgs. ✗ a l c. ⌂ CH, TV, CP 16, CF, 3 st. **£** BB £10– £17·25, DB £20–£28·75, WT (b) £96·60– £126·50, DT (b) £16·10–£23, ②, Bk £3·45, D £6·90.

Rescue Service: A J K Thompson, The Ranch. ✆ (066 84) 221.

BAMPTON Devon. Maps 3B and 4D
Pop 1,440. Taunton 20, London 163, Dunster 19, Lynmouth 27, South Molton 17, Tiverton 7½.
EC Thur. **Golf** Tiverton 18h. **See** Exmoor Pony Fair (last Thur in Oct), 13th cent Church, The Mount (castle site), 19th cent Town Hall.
🅿 Station Rd Car Park. ✆ Bampton (0398) 31854

Bridge House, PH, x (R), *24 Luke St, EX16 9NF.* ✆ (0398) 31298. C. ⊨ 6 bedrs, 2 bp, 1 bps, 1 ba, Dgs. ✗ a l c. ⌂ CH, TV, Dgs, 2 st. **£** BB £8·50, DB fr £17·55, WT (b) £80, ①, Bk £2, L £2·50, D £3·50, cc 1 3.

BAMPTON Oxfordshire. Map 14F
Pop 1,800. Faringdon 6½, London 76, Burford 9, Lechlade 8, Oxford 17, Witney 5½.
EC Wed. **MD** Sat, **Golf** Burford 18h. **See** Church, Town Hall.

Rescue Service: Rumshall Ltd, Market Square Garage. ✆ Bampton Castle (0993) 850366.

BANBURY Oxfordshire. Map 14D
See also WROXTON
Pop 38,176. Bicester 15, London 72, Buckingham 17, Chipping Norton 13, Coventry 27, Daventry 16, Evesham 30, Moreton-in-Marsh 19, Northampton 24, Oxford 23, Rugby 25, Stratford-upon-Avon 20, Towcester 17, Warwick 20.
EC Tue. **MD** Thur, Sat. **Golf** Cherwell Edge 9h. **See** 19th cent Cross in Horse Fair, 16th cent Calthorpe Manor House, 18th cent Church, Sulgrave Manor (ancestral home of Washington) 7½ m NE, Broughton Castle 2½ m SW, Aynhoe Park Mansion 6 m SE, Farnborough Hall 6 m N, Upton House 6½ m NW, Compton Wynyates 11 m W.
🅿 8 Horsefair. ✆ Banbury (0295) 59855.

★★★★Whately Hall (TH), *Banbury Cross, OX16 0AN.* ✆ (0295) 3451. C. ⊨ 72 bedrs, 63 bp, 9 bps, TV, Dgs. ✗ a l c, mc, at, LD 9.15. ⌂ Lt, N, CH, Dgs, CP 80, Ac, con 160, CF, 2 BGf, 1 st, Dis. **£** BB

£41·50, DB £54·50, WB, ①, cc 1 2 3 4 5 6, Dep (Xmas).

★★★Banbury Moat House, *Oxford Rd, OX16 9AH.* ✆ (0295) 837537. C. RS Dec 26–Jan 2. ⊨ 30 bedrs, 30 bp, TV, Dgs. ✗ a l c, mc, LD 10. ⌂ N, CH, Dgs, CP 25, Ac, con 180, CF, 6 st. **£** BB £25–£36, DB £35–£45, DBB £32–£42·50, WB, ①, Bk £4·50 L £7·50, D £8·50, cc 1 2 3 5 6, Dep b.

Kelvedon, G, z (Unl), *11 Broughton Rd, OX16 9QB.* ✆ (0295) 3028. Closed Xmas. C. ⊨ 4 bedrs, 1 ba, Dgs. ⌂ CH, TV, 4 st. **£** DB £16, WT £56, ①.

Lismore, PH, z (R), *61 Oxford Rd, OX16 9AJ.* ✆ (0295) 62105. C. ⊨ 14 bedrs, 7 bp, 1 bps, 2 ba, TV, Dgs. ✗ a l c. ⌂ CH, CP 6, CF, 1 BGf, 2 st. **£** BB £12–£23, DB £18– £32, ①, Bk £3, D £4·50, cc 1 3.

Tredis, G, z (Unl), *15 Broughton Rd, PL11 3ER.* ✆ (0295) 4632. C. ⊨ 6 bedrs, 2 ba, ns, TV, Dgs. ⌂ CH, TV, Dgs, CF, 1 st. **£** BB £9, DB £16, ①.

Rescue Service: Antelope Garage Ltd, Main Rd, Middleton Cheney.
✆ (0295) 710233.
Castle Garage, Castle St. ✆ (0295) 51192
Hartwell's of Banbury Ltd, Southam Rd.
✆ (0295) 51551.
Righton Garage, Lower Brailes. ✆ Brailes (060 885) 239.
Warmington Hill Garage, A41.
✆ Farnborough (029 589) 234.

BANSTEAD Surrey. Map 7A
Pop 43,048. Mitcham 6, London 14, Croydon 6, Epsom 3½, Kingston upon Thames 8½, Purley 4, Reigate 7.
EC Wed. **Golf** Banstead Heath 18h. **See** Early Norman Church, Banstead Wood, Epsom Downs nearby.

Rescue Service: McVee Motors Ltd, Nork Motor Engineering, Nork Gdns. ✆ Burgh Heath (073 73) 57636.

BARCOMBE East Sussex. M. Area 7F
Pop 1,425. East Grinstead 17, London 48, Hastings 29, Haywards Heath 10, Hurst Green (Sussex) 25, Lewes 4½, Uckfield 7½.
EC Sat. **Golf** Lewes 18h. **See** Church.

Rescue Service: Brook & Churches Bros Ltd, Barcombe Eng Works. ✆ (0273) 221.

BARFORD ST. MARTIN Wiltshire.
Maps 6C and 5D
Salisbury 6, London 89, Devizes 25, Shaftesbury 15, Warminster 17, Wincanton 24.
EC Tue. **See** Stone cottages.

Bakehouse, PH, x *SP3 4AJ.* ✆ Salisbury (0722) 742029. C. ⊨ 5 bedrs, 1 bp, 1 bps, 1 ba, Dgs. ✗ a l c. ⌂ CH, TV, CP 20, CF, 1 BGf, 0 st, Dis. **£** BB £9, DB £18–£30, WT (c) £55, ①, D £12.

BARHAM Kent. Map 10D
Pop 4,238. Canterbury 6, London 64, Dover 9, Folkestone 10, Margate 18.
EC Wed. **Golf** Canterbury 18h. **See** St John the Baptist Church, remains of Roman Camp on Downs, Broom Park, once home of Lord Kitchener (now Country Club).

★Old Coach House, *A2 Trunk Rd, Dover Rd, CT4 6SA.* ✆ Canterbury (0227) 831218. C. ⊨ 9 bedrs, 3 ba. ✗ a l c, mc, at. ⌂ CH, Dgs, ns, CP 60, Ac, con 60, CF. **£** BB £12·50–£13, DB £24–

£25, WT £120, DT £18, WB, ①, Bk £2·50, L £4, D £4·50, cc 1 2 3 5 6, Dep.

Rescue Service: Arter Bros Ltd, Eagle Motor Works, Dover Rd. ✆ Canterbury (0227) 831356.

BARLEY Hertfordshire. Map 15D
Pop 548. Hoddesdon 20, London 40, Bishop's Stortford 15, Braintree 30, Cambridge 14, Dunmow 23, Haverhill 21, Newmarket 23, Royston 3½, Sudbury 35.
Golf Royston 18h. **See** Church, with Norman tower, Old Lock-up, Tudor Town House.

Repairer: Richmond Coaches & Garage, The Priors. ✆ Barkway (076 384) 226.

BARMBY MOOR Humberside. Map 25C
Market Weighton 9, London 204, Bridlington 29, York 12.

Rescue Service: Hewson & Robinson, York Road Garage. ✆ Pocklington (075 92) 3172.

BARNARD CASTLE Durham. Map 26B
Pop 6,050. Boroughbridge 41, London 248, Brough 18, Darlington 16, Leyburn 27, Middleton-in-Teesdale 10, Northallerton 29, West Auckland 15.
EC Thur. **MD** Wed. **Golf** Barnard Castle 18h. **See** Castle ruins, Bowes Museum, St Mary's Church, Old Houses, Raby Castle 6 m NE, Egglestone Abbey, scenic Teesdale (10 m NW).
🅿 43 Galgate. ✆ Teesdale (0833) 38481 (37913 summer weekends).

★Montalbo, *Montalbo Rd, DL12 8BP.* ✆ Teesdale (0833) 37342. C. ⊨ 7 bedrs, 1 bp, 2 sh, 2 ba, TV, Dgs. ✗ a l c, mc, at, LD 9. ⌂ CH, CP 4, Ac, con 40, CF, 2 BGf, 2 st.

Bowes Moor, *Bowes Moor, DL12 9RH.* ✆ Teesdale (0833) 28331.

Rescue Service: Jacksons Garage, 42 Galgate. ✆ Teesdale (0833) 38154.
Town End Garage. ✆ Middleton-in-Teesdale (083 34) 525.

BARNBY MOOR Nottinghamshire. Map 22B
Pop 260. Newark 23, London 150, A1 (M) Motorway 3½, Doncaster 14, Gainsborough 14, Lincoln 26, Ollerton 13, Rotherham 17, Sheffield 22, Thorne 19, Worksop 9.
Golf Retford 9h. **See** Old Posting House.

★★★Ye Olde Bell (TH), *Gt North Rd, DN22 8QS.* ✆ Retford (0777) 705121. C. ⊨ 55 bedrs, 44 bp, Dgs. ✗ a l c, mc, at, LD 9.30. ⌂ N, CH, Dgs, CP 250, Ac, con 250, CF. **£** BB £33·50–£36, DB £45·50– £50, WB, ①, cc 1 2 3 4 5 6, Dep Xmas.

BARNET Greater London (Herts). Map 15F
See also HADLEY WOOD
Pop 27,846. London 11, Brentford and Chiswick 14, Enfield 6, Hatfield 9, Hoddesdon 14, St Albans 9½, Watford 10, Woodford 12.
EC Thur. **MD** Wed, Sat. **Golf** Hadley Wood 18h, Old Ford Manor 18h. **See** Museum, Hadley Highstone (monument to the Battle of Barnet 1471), St Mary's Church.

Rescue Service: Park Garage (Barnet) Ltd, Wood St. ✆ 01-449 0907.

BARNETBY Humberside (South Humberside).
M. Areas 23A and 25B.

Pop 1,457. Lincoln 28, London 161, Gainsborough 24, Grimsby 18, Hull 17, Louth 27, Market Rasen 16, Scunthorpe 12.
Golf Holme Hall 18h. **See** St Mary's Church, Melton Gallows.

Rescue Service: Gallows Wood Service Station, A18. ✆ (0652) 688259.

BARNOLDSWICK Lancashire. Map 27A
Pop 10,276. Burnley 10, London 216, Blackburn 19, Bradford 23, Halifax 23, Settle 15, Skipton 8, Whalley 15.
EC Tue. **Golf** Ghyll 18h. **See** 12th cent Church.

Rescue Service: Gott's Garage Ltd, Gisburn Rd Garage. ✆ (0282) 812109.

BARNSDALE BAR South Yorkshire. Map 25D
Doncaster 8, London 171, A1 (M) Motorway 3, Barnsley 12, Boroughbridge 36, Goole 21, Harrogate 32, Pontefract 6½, Selby 15, Wakefield 13, York 29.
Golf Pontefract & District 18h.

■★★★M TraveLodge (TH), *Gt North Rd, WF8 3JB.* ✆ Pontefract (0977) 620711. C. ⇄ 72 bedrs, 72 bp, TV, Dgs. ✗ mc. ☎ N, CH, Dgs, CP 350, con 25, CF, 36 BGf, 1 st. £ BB £26, DB £35·50, WB, ①, cc 1 2 3 4 5 6. Meals are served in the adjacent Motorway Service Area Restaurant.

BARNSLEY South Yorkshire. Maps 22B and 25E and 33D
Pop 224,000 (Metropolitan Borough).
Rotherham 11, London 172, M1 Motorway 1½, Doncaster 15, Glossop 24, Huddersfield 17, Manchester 36, Oldham 29, Pontefract 14, Sheffield 14, Stockport 33, Wakefield 9½.
MD Mon, Wed, Fri, Sat. **Golf** Silkstone 18h. **See** Parish Church of St Mary, Town Hall, College of Technology, Cooper Art Gallery, Locke Park, Tower, Monk Bretton Priory, Cannon Hall Park and Museum, Quaker burial grounds.
🛈 Civic Hall, Eldon St. ✆ Barnsley (0226) 6757.

★★**Queens,** *Regent St, S70 2HQ.*
✆ (0226) 84192.
★**Royal,** *11 Church St, S70 2AD.*
✆ (0226) 203658. C. ⇄ 17 bedrs, 1 bp, 3 ba, TV, Dgs. ✗ mc, at, LD 9.30. ☎ CH, TV, Dgs, U 1, G 5, Ac, con 100, CF, 0 st. £ BB £21–£28·50, DB £31–£35, WB, ①, Bk £2·90, L £3·75, D £6·20, cc 1 2 5 6, Dep b.

Repairers: Grimes, Leonard V & Sons (Barnsley) Ltd, Foundry St.
✆ (0226) 81227.
Rescue Service: H. Hepworth, Manor Flint Service Station, Wombwell La.
✆ (0226) 6424 and (0226) 5024.

BARNSTAPLE Devon. Map 4C
Pop 11,000. South Molton 11, London 193, Bideford 12, Crediton 33, Dunster 34, Holsworthy 26, Ilfracombe 11, Lynmouth 19, Okehampton 28.
EC Wed. **MD** Tue, Fri. **Golf** Saunton 18h (2). **See** St Peter's Church, 13th cent Arched Bridge, Norm Castle, Almshouses, Queen Anne's Walk, St Anne's Chapel, Museum, New Civic Centre, Barnstaple Fair (Sept), Arlington Court 7 m NE.
🛈 20 Holland St. ✆ Barnstaple (0271) 72742.

★★★**M Barnstaple,** *Braunton Rd, EX31 1LE.* ✆ (0271) 76221. C. ⇄ 60 bedrs, 60 bp, 1 ba, TV, Dgs. ✗ a l c, mc, at, LD 10. ☎ N, CH, TV, CP 132, G 35, Ac, sp, sol, con 250, CF, 17 BGf, 1 st, Dis. £ BB £20·50, DB £31, DBB £26·50, WB, ②, L £3, D £6, cc 1 2 3 5 6.▲

★★★**Imperial** (TH), *Taw Vale Par, EX32 8NB.* ✆ (0271) 45861. C. ⇄ 56 bedrs, 55 bp, TV, Dgs. ✗ a l c, mc, at, LD 9.15. ☎ Lt, N, CH, Dgs, CP 80, Ac, con 60, CF, 1 st. £ BB £34·50, DB £50, WB, ①, cc 1 2 3 4 5 6.

★★★**M North Devon,** *New Rd, EX32 9AE.* ✆ (0271) 72166. C. ⇄ 26 bedrs, 24 bp, 2 bps, TV, Dgs. ✗ mc, at, LD 9.30 (9 winter). ☎ N, CH, CP 60, G 8, Ac, con 160, CF, 1 st. £ BB £17–£21, DB £26–£31, DBB fr £26·50, WB, ①, Bk £3·45, L £4·25, D £6·90, cc 1 2 3 5 6, Dep b.▲

■≋★★★**Roborough House** (R), *EX31 4JG.* ✆ (0271) 72354.
★★**Royal & Fortescue,** *Boutport St, EX31 3HG.* ✆ (0271) 42289. C. ⇄ 61 bedrs, 32 bp, 9 ba, TV, Dgs. ✗ a l c, mc, at, LD 9.30 (8.30 Sun). ☎ Lt, N, CH, TV, CP 30, G 6, Ac, con 30, CF, 5 BGf, 0 st, Dis. £ BB £14·50–£18·50, DB £24–£29, WT £132, DT £23·25, WB, ②, Bk £1·95, L £3·90, D £5·75, cc 1 2 3 5 6.

Northcliff, H, z (RI), *8 Rhododendron Av, Hele Manor, EX31 2DL.*
✆ (0271) 2524.
Yeo Dale, H, z (RI), *Pilton Bridge, EX31 1PG.* ✆ (0271) 42954. C. ⇄ 12 bedrs, 2 ba. ☎ CH, TV, CF, 1 st. £ BB £9·50, DB £19, WT (b) £90, DT (b) £14, ①.

Repairer: County Garage, Boutport St.
✆ (0271) 73232.
Rescue Service: Chivenor Motors, Chivenor. ✆ Braunton (0271) 815404.

BARRASFORD Northumberland. Map 31E
Pop 200. Corbridge 10, London 287, Alnwick 38, Alston 27, Bellingham 10, Brampton 29, Hawick 44, Hexham 7½, Jedburgh 41, Newcastle upon Tyne 24.
Golf Hexham 18h. **See** Haughton Castle, 13th cent Tower House, Hadrian's Wall (2 m S), scenic N. Tyne Valley.

■**Ap. Barrasford Arms,** *Main Rd, NE48 4AA.* ✆ Humshaugh (043 481) 237.

BARROW IN FURNESS Cumbria. Map 27E
Pop 72,635. Ulverston 8½, London 280, Broughton-in-Furness 14.
EC Thur. **MD** Wed, Fri, Sat. **Golf** Barrow 18h, Furness 18h. **See** Parish Churches, Ruins of Furness Abbey, Piel Island and Castle, Two Nature Reserves on Walney Island, Biggar Village.
🛈 Civic Hall, Duke St. ✆ Barrow in Furness (0229) 25795.

★★★**Victoria Park,** *Victoria Rd, LA14 5JX.* ✆ (0229) 21159. Closed between Xmas & New Year. C. ⇄ 44 bedrs, 23 bp, 5 ba, TV. ✗ a l c, mc, at, LD 9.30. ☎ N, CH, TV, CP 60, Ac, con 50, CF, 1 st. £ BB £35–£40, DB £45–£50, ①, Bk £4·50, L £5·50, D £8·50, cc 1 2 3 5, Dep b.
★★**White House,** *Abbey Rd, LA13 9AE.* ✆ (0229) 27303. C. ⇄ 29 bedrs, 2 bp, 6 ba, TV, Dgs. ✗ a l c, mc, at. ☎ N, ch, Dgs, CP 60, G 20, Ac, con 20, CF. £ BB £23–£28, DB £30–£36, ①, Bk £3, L £4, D £6·95, cc 1 2 3 5, Dep b.

Barrie House Hotel, PH, z *179 Abbey Rd, LA14 5JP.* ✆ (0229) 25507. C. ⇄ 10 bedrs, 3 bps, 3 ba, TV. ☎ CH, TV, CF, 5 st. £ BB £17·50–£22·50, DB £25–£35, WT (b) £115, ②, Bk £3·50, L fr £3·50, D fr £4·50, cc 1 2 3 5.

Specialist Body Repairer: County Coachbuilders (Barrow) Ltd, Duke St. ✆ (0229) 20742.

Rescue Service: Crellin St Autos, 88 Crellin St. ✆ (0229) 21715.
Dutton Forshaw North West, Abbey Rd. ✆ (0229) 20595.
Holker Ford Motor Co Ltd, Holker St. ✆ (0229) 23310 and (0229) 22213.

BARTON-LE-CLAY Bedfordshire. Map 15C
Luton 6, London 37, Bedford 12, Hitchin 7, Ampthill 7½.

Repairer: Hacfield Ltd, 71 Bedford Rd.
✆ Luton (0582) 881254.

BARTON MILLS Suffolk. Map 16F
Pop 840. Newmarket 9, London 71, Bury St Edmunds 12, Ely 15, King's Lynn 35, Thetford 11.
Golf Royal Worlington and Newmarket 9h. **See** 13th cent Parish Church.

★★**Bull Inn,** *IP28 6AF.* ✆ Mildenhall (0638) 712181.

Rescue Service: Ponsford, W & Sons Ltd, Five Ways Garage. ✆ Mildenhall (0638) 712292.

BARTON-ON-HUMBER Humberside (South Humberside). Map 25B
Pop 8,243. Lincoln 34, London 168, Grimsby 24, Hull 9½, Louth 34, Market Rasen 26, Scunthorpe 15.
EC Thur. **Golf** Elsham 18h. **See** Suspension Bridge, Churches, Museum, Country Park.
🛈 Humber Bridge Viewing Area, Waterside Rd. ✆ Barton-on-Humber (0652) 52441.

Rescue Service: Norman Cox Ltd, Ferriby Rd. ✆ (0652) 33331.

BARTON ON SEA Hampshire. Map 6E
Pop 3,600. Lyndhurst 13, London 97, Blandford Forum 26, Bournemouth 11, Lymington 7, Ringwood 12.
EC Wed. **Golf** Barton on Sea 18h.

■★★★**Red House,** *Barton Court Av, BH25 7HJ.* ✆ New Milton (0425) 610119. C. ⇄ 45 bedrs, 36 bp, 9 sh, 6 ba, TV, Dgs. ✗ a l c, mc, at, LD 9. ☎ Lt, CH, TV, Dgs, CP 80, Ac, con 45, CF, 5 BGf, 0 st, Dis. £ BB £23–£27, DB £32–£38, DBB £31–£35, WB, ①, Bk £3, L £6, D £8, cc 1 2 3 5 6, Dep b.
Cliff House, H, z (R), *Marine Dr West, BH25 7QL.* ✆ New Milton (0425) 619333.
Gainsborough, H, z (RI), *39 Marine Dr East, BH26 7DX.* ✆ New Milton (0425) 610541. C8. ⇄ 10 bedrs, 4 bp, 3 ba, TV, Dgs. ☎ CH, TV, CP 20, U 2, 2 BGf, 2 st. £ BB £12·50–£14, DB £25–£31, WT (b) £114–£130, DT (b) £18–£20, ①.
Old Coastguard, H, x (R), *53 Marine Dr East, BH25 7DX.* ✆ New Milton (0425) 612987. C 12. ⇄ 8 bedrs, 1 bps, 2 ba, Dgs. ☎ CH, TV, Dgs, CP 15, 4 BGf, 1 st, Dis. £ BB £10·50–£12·50, DB £21–£25, WT £105–£110, DT £14·50–£17·50, ①.
Ventana, PH, x. *Marine Dr,* ✆ New Milton (0425) 610309.

BASILDON Essex. Maps 10A and 17F
Pop 101,200. Romford 13, London 30,
Brentwood 9, Chelmsford 13, Dartford-
Purfleet Tunnel 14, Southend 12.
MD Mon, Tue, Thur, Fri, Sat. **Golf** Basildon
18h. **See** St Martin's Church ('Basildon
Christ' sculpture by T Huxley-Jones),
Gloucester Park—355 acres, Town Gate
Theatre & Art Centre, Fairytale Clock.

★★★**M Crest.** *Cranes Farm Rd, SS14
3DG.* ✆ (0268) 3955. C. 🛏 116 bedrs, 116
bp, ns, TV, Dgs. ✗ a l c, mc, at LD 10. 🅿 Lt,
N, CH, Dgs, Ac, con 300, CF, 6 BGf, 0 st.
£ B fr £42, BD fr £48, WB, 🔟, Bk £4·75, L
£3, D £9·25, cc 1 2 3 4 5, Dep b.

Rescue Service: Southend Motor & Aero
Co Ltd, Southernhay. ✆ (0268) 22661.

BASINGSTOKE Hampshire. Map 6D
Pop 78,000. Bagshot 20, London 47, M3
Motorway 1½, Alton 12, Andover 19,
Farnham 15, Guildford 25, Newbury 16,
Reading 16, Salisbury 36, Wallington 28,
Winchester 18.
EC Thurs. **MD** Wed, Sat. **Golf**
Basingstoke 18h. **See** 15th cent Church,
Museum, War Memorial Park, The Vyne—
early 16th cent house (Nat Trust) 3 m N.

★★★**M Ladbroke,** *Aldermaston
Roundabout, RG24 9NU.* ✆ (0256) 20212.
C. 🛏 108 bedrs, 108 bp, 2 ba, ns, TV, Dgs.
✗ a l c, mc, at, LD 10. 🅿 Lt, N, CH, CP, Ac,
con, CF, 1 st. £ B fr £42, BD fr £48, WB, 🔟,
Bk £5·50, L £6·50, D £9·50, cc 1 2 3 5 6,
Dep b.

■★★★**M Crest,** *Grove Rd, RG21 3EE.*
✆ (0256) 68181. C. 🛏 86 bedrs, 86 bp, ns,
TV, Dgs. ✗ a l c, mc, LD 9.45. 🅿 N, CH,
Dgs, CP 140, Ac, con 200, CF. £ B fr
£47·75, BD fr £54·50, WB, 🔟, Bk £4·75, L
£3, D £11·50, cc 1 2 3 4 5 6.

★★**Red Lion,** *London St, RG21 1NY.*
✆ (0256) 28525. C. 🛏 63 bedrs, 31 bp, 32
bps, TV, Dgs. ✗ a l c, mc, LD 10. 🅿 Lt, N,
CH, CP 60, con 35, CF, 1 st. £ BB £22–£44,
DB £39–£52, WB, 🔟, Bk £3, L £8·65, D
£8·65, cc 1 2 3 5 6, Dep b.

Repairer: Jackson's (Basingstoke) Ltd,
Lower Wote St. ✆ (0256) 3561.
MC Repairer: Gifford, H J Ltd, New St.
✆ (0256) 65266.
Rescue Service: A.W.J. Ltd, 36B Vyne Rd.
✆ (0256) 797101.
Clover Leaf Cars Ltd, Byfleet Garage,
Basing. ✆ (0256) 3896.
Gibson Bros, The Garage, Charter Alley,
Ramsdell. ✆ (0256) 850157.
Smith, H C & Sons (Baughurst) Ltd,
Baughurst. ✆ Tadley (073 56) 3731.
Wheatsheaf Service Station, North
Waltham. ✆ Dummer (025 675) 254.

BASLOW Derbyshire. Map 22C
Pop 1,204. Matlock 9, London 154,
Ashbourne 21, Buxton 14, Chapel-en-le-
Frith 15, Chesterfield 9, Leek 22, Sheffield
12.
Golf Bakewell 9h. **See** St Anne's Church,
17th cent bridge, Chatsworth (House,
Garden and Theatre Gallery) 1½ m S,
Haddon Hall 5 m SW.

★★★**Cavendish,** *DE4 1SP.*
✆ (024 688) 2311. C. 🛏 23 bedrs, 23 bp,
TV. ✗ a l c, mc, at LD 10. 🅿 CH, CP 50,
Ac, pf, con 10, CF, 2 BGf, 6 st. £ BB £42·10,
DB £56·70, WB, 🄸, Bk £2·80, L £12, D £12,
cc 2 3 5.

BASSENTHWAITE Cumbria. Map 26E
Pop 400. Keswick 7, London 292, Carlisle
21, Cockermouth 8, Penrith 23.
Golf Embleton, Cockermouth 18h. **See**
Old Church by Lake.

★★★**Castle Inn,** *Carlisle Rd, CA12 4RG.*
✆ Bassenthwaite Lake (059 681) 401.
Closed Nov & Xmas. C. 🛏 20 bedrs, 20 bp,
TV, Dgs. ✗ mc, at, LD 8.30. 🅿 CH, CP 100,
Ac, sp, tc, sb, sol, con 120, CF, 1 BGf, 1 st.
Dis. £ BB fr £27, DB fr £36, WB, 🔟, Bk £5, L
£6, D £9, cc 1 2 3 4 5 6, Dep a.

■🈟★★★**Overwater Hall** (R), *Ireby, CA5
1HH.* ✆ Bassenthwaite Lake
(059 681) 566. Open Mar–Dec. C. 🛏 13
bedrs, 9 bp, 2 ba, TV, Dgs. ✗ mc, at, LD
8.30. 🅿 CH, CP 26, CF, 6 st. £ BB fr £18,
DB fr £26, DBB fr £22, WB, 🄸, D £9·50,
cc 1 3.

★★**Pheasant Inn,** *Bassenthwaite Lake,
CA13 9YE.* ✆ Bassenthwaite Lake
(059 681) 234. Closed Xmas Day. C.
🛏 17 bedrs, 11 bp, 1 bps, 3 ba. ✗ a l c, mc,
at, LD 8.15. 🅿 CH, Dgs, CP 80, con 20, CF,
3 BGf, 0 st, Dis. £ BB fr £21, DB fr £41, 🔟,
Bk £3·75, L £5, D £9·50.

■**Ap. Ravenstone** (Rl), *CA12 4QG.*
✆ Bassenthwaite Lake (059 681) 240.
Open Apr-Oct. C. 🛏 12 bedrs, 1 sh, 3 ba,
Dgs. ✗ mc, at, LD 6.30. 🅿 CH, CP 12, CF.
£ BB £11–£12, DB £22–£24, DBB £15–
£16, 🄸, Bk £2, L £4, D £6, Dep a.

Link House, H, x, (R), *CA13 9YD.*
✆ Bassenthwaite Lake (059 681) 291.
Open Mar–Nov. C. 🛏 7 bedrs, 6 bps, 1 ba,
TV. 🅿 CH, CP 8, CF. £ BB fr £10, DB fr £23,
WT fr £112, DT (b) £18·50, 🄸, D £7.

Rescue Service: Skiddaw Service Station
Ltd, Bothel Rd. ✆ Bassenthwaite Lake
(059 681) 218.

BATH Avon. Map 5B
Pop 80,000. Chippenham 13, London 104,
M4 Motorway 9, Bristol 12, Cheltenham
42, Chepstow 25, Devizes 19, Frome 13,
Gloucester 38, Radstock 8½, Tetbury 23,
Warminster 16, Wells 19, Weston-super-
Mare 31.
See Plan p. 135.
MD Mon, Wed. **P** See Plan. **Golf** Sham
Castle 18h, Lansdown 18h. **See** Abbey
Church, 18th cent Pump Room and Hot
Springs, Roman Baths, Assembly Rooms
and Museum of Costume, Victoria Art
Gallery, Prior Park College, Royal
Crescent (No 1 viewable), Pulteney
Bridge, Holbourne of Menstrie Museum,
Bath Festival in summer, The American
Museum in Britain (Claverton Manor) 2 m
E, Farleigh Castle 5½ m SE, Dyrham Park 7
m N. Herschel House & Museum.
🄸 8 Abbey Churchyard. ✆ Bath (0225)
62831.

★★★★**Ladbroke Beaufort,** *Walcott St,
BA1 5BJ.* ✆ (0225) 63411. C. 🛏 123
bedrs, 119 bp, 4 bps, TV, Dgs. ✗ a l c, mc,
at, LD 9.30. 🅿 Lt, N, CH, Dgs, Ac, con 120,
CF, 0 st. £ WB, Bk £5·50, L £4, D £9,
cc 1 2 3 5 6, Dep b.

★★★★**Royal Crescent,** *Royal Cres. BA1
2LS.* ✆ (0225) 319090. C. 🛏 28 bedrs, 28
bp, TV. ✗ a l c, mc, at LD 12. 🅿 Lt, N, CH,
CP 8, U 4, G 4, con 25, CF, 1 st. £ BB £50–
£62, DB £82–£264, 🔟, Bk £7, L £8·50, D
£22·50, cc 1 2 3 4 5 6.

★★★**Francis** (TH), *Queen Sq, BA1 2HH.*
✆ (0225) 24257. C. 🛏 90 bedrs, 90 bp,
TV, Dgs. ✗ a l c, mc, at, LD 9.30. 🅿 Lt, N,
CH, Dgs, CP 72, Ac, con 100, CF, 0 st. £ BB

£47·50, DB £63·50, WB, 🔟, cc 1 2 3 4 5 6,
Dep (Xmas).

★★★**Landsdown Grove,** *Lansdown Rd,
BA1 5EH.* ✆ (0225) 315891. C. 🛏 41
bedrs, 38 bp, 3 bps, TV, Dgs. ✗ mc, at, LD
9.30 (9 Sun). 🅿 Lt, N, CH, Dgs, CP 30, G 4,
Ac, con 100, CF, 1 st. £ BB £33–£36, DB
£47–£52, WB, 🄸, Bk £3·50, L £5, D £8·50,
cc 1 2 3 5 6.

★★★**Pratt's,** *South Parade, BA2 2AB.*
✆ (0225) 60441. C. 🛏 46 bedrs, 46 bp, 3
ba, TV, Dgs. ✗ a l c, mc, at, LD 10. 🅿 Lt, N,
CH, Dgs, Ac, con 50, CF, 2 st. £ BB £27–
£32, DB £38–£42, WB, 🔟, Bk £3·75, L
£1·50, D £8·95, cc 1 2 3 5 6.

★★★**Priory,** (R), *Weston Rd, BA2 2XT.*
✆ (0225) 331922. C10. 🛏 15 bedrs. 14
bp, 1 bps, TV. ✗ a l c, mc, at LD 9.15.
🅿 CH, CP 20, G 2, sp, con 25, 1 st. £ BB
£40·25–£44·25, DB £74·25–£82·50, WB,
🔟, Bk £3·80, L £7·45, D £17·25,
cc 1 2 3 4 6.

★★★**Redcar,** *Henrietta St, BA2 6LR.*
✆ (0225) 65432. C. 🛏 31 bedrs, 22 bp, 4
sh, 1 ba, TV, Dgs. ✗ a l c, mc, at LD 9.30.
🅿 N, CH, CP 16, Ac, con 80, CF, 4 st. £ BB
£28–£35, DB £41–£49·50, WB, 🔟, Bk £4, L
£7·50, D £7·50, cc 1 2 3 5, Dep b.

★★★**Royal York,** *York Buildings, George
St, BA1 2DH.* ✆ (0225) 61541. C. 🛏 53
bedrs, 42 bp, 6 ba, TV, Dgs. ✗ a l c, mc, at,
LD 9.30. 🅿 Lt, N, CH, Dgs, U 2, G 5, Ac,
con 80, CF, 3 BGf, 2 st. £ BB £20·50–£32,
DB £32·50–£48, WB, 🔟, Bk £4·25, L £5·25,
D £8, cc 1 2 3 5, Dep b.

■★★**Fernley,** *North Parade, BA1 1LG.*
✆ (0225) 61603. C. 🛏 47 bedrs, 21 bp, 6
bps, 6 sh, 7 ba, TV. ✗ a l c, mc, at, LD 10. ·
🅿 Lt, CH, Ac, con 70, CF, 0 st. £ BB £21–
£31, DB £33–£42, WB, 🄸, Bk £3·50, L £1, D
£6·95, cc 1 3, Dep b.

★★**Old Mill,** *Toll Bridge Rd, Batheaston,
BA1 7DE* (3 m NE A4). ✆ (0225) 858476.
C. 🛏 9 bedrs, 2 bp, 3 bps, 4 sh, 2 ba, Dgs.
✗ a l c, mc, at, LD 9. 🅿 CH, TV, CP 35, Ac,
pf, con 20, CF, 4 st. £ BB £16·50–£20·50,
DB £28–£36, WB, 🄸, 10%, Bk £3·75, L
£6·15, D £8, cc 1 2 3, Dep.

★**Ashley Villa,** *26 Newbridge Rd, BA1
3TZ.* ✆ (0225) 21683. Closed Xmas. C.
🛏 15 bedrs, 3 bp, 6 bps, 3 ba, TV, Dgs.
✗ a l c, LD 9. 🅿 CH, TV, Dgs, CP 10, sp,
CF, 1 BGf, 2 st. £ BB £20–£25, DB £25–
£30, DBB £26–£37, L £5, Bk £4, cc 1 3.

Arden, PH, z (Rl) *73 Gt Pulteney St, BA2
4DL.* ✆ (0225) 66601. Closed Dec. C6.
🛏 12 bedrs, 1 bp, 3 bps, 4 ba. 🅿 CH, TV, G
2, 3, st. £ BB £15–£17, DB £28–£34, 🔟.

Avon, H, z (Rl), *Bathwick St, BA2 6NX.*
✆ (0225) 65469. C. 🛏 15 bedrs, 13 bp, 2
bps, 3 ba, TV, Dgs. ✗ a l c. 🅿 CH, TV, ns,
CP 20, CF, 3 BGf, 2 st. £ BB £12·50–£29,
DB £20–£33, 🄸, Bk £2·87, D £5, cc 1 2 5.

County, H, y, *18 Pulteney Rd, BA2 4DN.*
✆ (0225) 66493. C. 🛏 24 bedrs, 2 bp, 5
bps, 3 ba, TV, Dgs. ✗ a l c. 🅿 CH, TV, Dgs,
CP 75, CF, 3 st. £ BB £16·50–£32·50, DB
£28·50–£45, 🄸, Bk £3·75, L £3·50, D
£3·50.▲

Edgar, H, z, *64 Gt Pulteney St, BA2 4DN.*
✆ (0255) 20619. Closed 3 weeks Xmas. C.
🛏 11 bedrs, 4 bps, 2 ba. 🅿 CH, TV, 4 st.
£ BB £13–£15, DB £22–£32, 🔟, Bk £2·50.

Gainsborough, H, y, (R), *Weston Lane,
BA1 4AB.* ✆ (0255) 311380. Closed Xmas
& first 2 weeks Jan. C. 🛏 15 bedrs, 15 bp,
TV. ✗ a l c. 🅿 CH, CP 18, CF. £ BB £19–
£20, DB £36–£38, 🄸, Bk £3, cc 1 2 3.▲

Georgian, G, z (Unl), *34 Henrietta St,
BA2 6LR.* ✆ (0255) 24103. C. 🛏 10 bedrs,

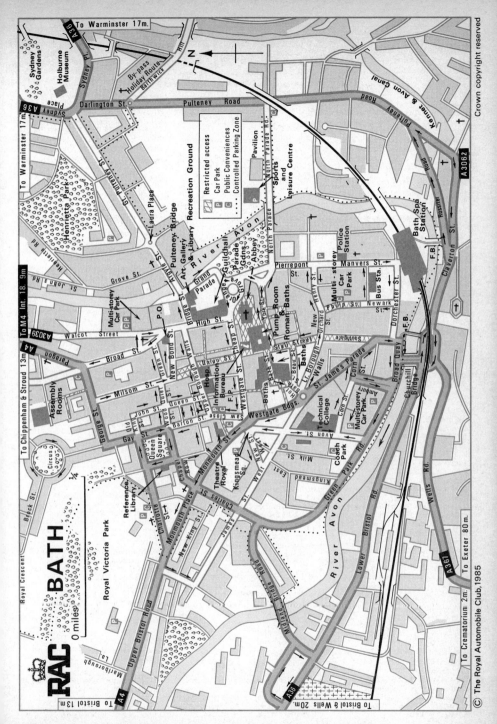

© The Royal Automobile Club, 1985

2 ba, TV, Dgs. 🅿 Dgs, U 2. £ BB fr £8, DB fr £16, cc 3.

Glenbeigh, G, z (RI), *1 Upper Oldfield Park, BA2 3JX.* ✆ (0225) 26336. Closed Jan. C. 🛏 12 bedrs, 3 bps, 3 ba, Dgs. 🅿 CH, TV, CP 7, G 3, CF. £ BB fr £12, DB £19–£24, WT (c) £60–£76, DT (b) fr £12, 🆃

Grove Lodge, G, z (RI), *11 Lambridge (London Rd), BA1 6BJ.* ✆ (0225) 310860. C. 🛏 8 bedrs, 2 ba, TV, Dgs. 🅿 ch, CF, 4 st. £ BB fr £9, DB fr £18, 🆃

Highways House, G, z (Unl), *143 Wells Rd, BA2 3AL.* ✆ (0225) 21238. 🛏 5 bedrs, 1 bp, 2 bps, 1 sh, 1 ba, Dgs. 🅿 CH, TV, Dgs, CP 6, 2 st. £ BB fr £11, DB £20–£22, 🆃

Hotel St Clair, PH, z (R), *1 Crescent Gardens, Upper Bristol Rd, BA1 2NA.* ✆ (0225) 25543. C. 🛏 10 bedrs, 2 bps, 2 ba, TV, Dgs. X a l c. 🅿 CH. £ BB £12–£32, DB £24–£45, 🆃, Bk £2·50, D £4.▲

Jane's, *7–11 Manver St, BA1 1JQ.* ✆ (0225) 65966.

Kennard, PH, z (Unl), *11, Henrietta St, BA2 6LL.* ✆ (0225) 310472. Closed Dec 24–Jan 1. C. 🛏 12 bedrs, 6 bps, 1 sh, 3 ba, TV, Dgs. 🅿 CH, TV, CF. £ BB £15–£16·50, DB £24–£30, 🆃

Leighton House, G, y, z (Unl) *139 Wells Rd, BA2 4QE.* ✆ (0225) 314769. Closed Dec. C5. 🛏 7 bedrs, 2 bp, 2 bps, 1 sh, 1 ba, TV, Dgs. 🅿 CH, TV, CP 7, U 2, 2 BGf, 5 st. £ BB £10–£14, DB £18–£26, 🆃

Lynwood, G, z (Unl), *6 Pulteney Gdns, BA2 4HG.* ✆ (0225) 26410. C3. 🛏 14 bedrs, 14 sh, 1 ba, TV, Dgs. 🅿 CH, TV, CP 3, CF. £ BB £13–£14, DB £21·50–£27, 🆃, cc 1 2 3 5.

Millers, PH, z (RI), *69 Gt Pulteney St, BA2 4DL.* ✆ (0225) 65798. Closed Xmas. C. 🛏 12 bedrs, 2 bp, 3 ba. 🅿 CH, TV, CP 3, CF, 3 st. £ BB £14, DB £23–£30, 🆃, Bk £2·50.

Oxford, PH, z (Unl), *5 Oxford Row, Lansdown Rd, BA1 2QN.* ✆ (0225) 314039. C. 🛏 8 bedrs, 3 bps, 2 ba. 🅿 TV. £ BB £9·50–£15, DB £16·50–£20, 🆃, cc 1 2 3 5.

Tacoma, G, z (Unl), *159 Newbridge Hill, BA1 3PX.* ✆ (0225) 310197. C. 🛏 8 bedrs, 2 ba. 🅿 CH, TV, CP 5, CF. £2·50.

Tasburgh, G, *Warminster Rd, Bathampton, BA2 6SH.* ✆ (0225) 25096.▲

Villa Magdala, PH, z (Unl), *Henrietta Rd, BA2 6LX.* ✆ (0225) 66329. Closed Jan, C5. 🛏 17 bedrs, 10 bp, 7 bps, TV. X a l c. 🅿 CH, CP 16. £ BB fr £18, DB £30–£32, 🆃

Wentworth House, PH, z (R), *106 Bloomfield Rd, BA2 2AP.* ✆ (0225) 310460. C. 🛏 20 bedrs, 10 bp, 3 ba, TV, Dgs. 🅿 CH, TV, CP 15, CF. £ BB £13–£20, DB £20–£30, WT £82·90–£94·50, DT £19–£21·50, 🆃, Bk £3, D £6·50, cc 1 3 5.

Repairer: Richardson, A & Sons Ltd, Bathwick Hill. ✆ (0225) 66286.
Rescue Service: Bees, D H R & Sons, Piccadilly Garage, Kensington. ✆ (0225) 310103.
Bodywork Ltd, 54 St John's Rd, Bathwick. ✆ (0225) 63322.
Lansdown Auto Services, The High St, Weston Village. ✆ (0225) 25784.
Millmead Garage, 49 Millmead Rd. ✆ (0225) 22875.
Morning Star Motors Ltd, St John's Rd. ✆ (0225) 65884.

Swainswick Garage, Gloucester Rd. ✆ (0225) 858252.
Wychwood Garage, Hinton Charterhouse. ✆ Limpley Stoke (022 122) 3174.

BATLEY West Yorkshire. Map 25F/33B
Pop 41,373. M62 Motorway 2, Dewsbury 2, London 189, Bradford 7½, Halifax 11, Huddersfield 9, Leeds 7.
EC Tue. **MD** Fri, Sat. **Golf** Howley 18h. **See** Ancient Church, Oakwell Hall, Bagshaw Museum.

Alder House, PH, y (R), *Towngate Rd, WF17 7HR.* ✆ (0924) 475540. C. 🛏 13 bedrs, 4 bp, 7 bps, 3 ba, TV. X a l c. 🅿 CH, TV, Dgs, CP 23, U 2, G 3, CF, 1 st, Dis. £ BB £18–£24, DB £31–£34, WT £150–£200, DT £26–£32, 🆃, Bk £2·50, L £3, D £7·50, cc 1 3.

BATTLE East Sussex. Map 10E
Pop 5,000. Hurst Green 7½, London 57, Eastbourne 15, Hastings 6½, Lewes 24, Tenterden 18, Uckfield 20.
EC Wed. **MD** Fri, Sat. **Golf** Beauport Park 9h. **See** Abbey ruins, 15th cent Pilgrim's Rest, St Mary's Church, The Deanery, Bullring, Windmill, Langton House Museum, Bodiam Castle 6½ m NE.
🆃 88 High Street. ✆ Battle (042 46) 3721.

★★**George,** *High St, TN33 0EA.* ✆ (042 46) 4466. C. 🛏 22 bedrs, 20 bp, 2 ba, TV, Dgs. X a l c, mc, at, LD 9.30. 🅿 CH, Dgs, CP 40, U 1, G 5, Ac, con 24, CF. £ BB £21·70, DB £32·40, WT £175, DT £28·40, WB, 🆃, L £5·95, D £5·95, cc 1 2 3 5, Dep b.

Repairer: Vicarys of Battle Ltd, 32 High St. ✆ (042 46) 2425.
Rescue Service: Stiles Garage (Battle) Ltd, 2 Upper Lake. ✆ (042 46) 3155.

BAWTRY South Yorkshire. Map 22B
Pop 2,820. Newark 28, London 155, A1(M) Motorway 3½, Doncaster 9, Gainsborough 12, Ollerton 17, Rotherham 15, Thorne 13, Worksop 10.
EC Thur. **Golf** Doncaster 18h. **See** Georgian shops, old coaching inns.

★★★**Crown,** *Market Pl, DN10 6JW.* ✆ Doncaster (0302) 710341. C. 🛏 14 bedrs, 14 bp, 1 ba, TV, Dgs. X a l c, mc, at, LD 9.45. 🅿 N, CH, TV, CP 32, Ac, con 150, CF, 2 BGf, 0 st, Dis. £ BB fr £38·50, DB fr £46·50, WB, 🆃, Bk £3·50, L £6·50, D £7·50, cc 1 2 3 5 6, Dep b.

MC Repairer: Brindley Motor Cycles, Church St. ✆ Doncaster (0302) 710603.
Rescue Service: J H Anderson Autobodies, Regent Garage, Everton. ✆ Retford (0777) 817460.

BAY HORSE Lancashire. Map 27C
Preston 16, London 229, M6 Motorway 1, Blackpool 19, Lancaster 5½.
Golf Lancaster 18h.

Rescue Service: J. Boardman (Garages) Ltd, Forton Services M6. ✆ Forton (0524) 791666.

BEACONSFIELD Buckinghamshire.
Maps 7A and 15E
Pop 11,300. Denham 7½, London 24, M40 Motorway 1, Aylesbury 20, Dunstable 64, Henley-on-Thames 16, High Wycombe 6, Reading 21, Slough 7½.
EC Wed. **Golf** Beaconsfield 18h. **See** Church, 16th cent, The Old Rectory, Bekonscot Model Village.

★★★**M Bell House,** *Oxford Rd, HP9 2XE.* ✆ Gerrards Cross (0753) 887211. C. 🛏 126 bedrs, 126 bp, TV, Dgs. X a l c, mc, LD 10. 🅿 Lt, N, CH, CP 405, Ac, con 400, CF, 1 st. £ BB fr £48·50, DB fr £59, DBB fr £56·75, WB, 🆃, Bk £4·50, L £7·75, D £8·25, cc 1 2 3 4 5, Dep b.
🅱★★**Crest,** *Aylesbury End, HP9 1LW.* ✆ (049 46) 71211. C. 🛏 41 bedrs, 28 bp, 3 ba, ns, TV, Dgs. X a l c, mc, LD 9.30. 🅿 N, CH, CP 100, Ac, con 100, CF, 9 BGf, 1 st, Dis. £ BB fr £30, DB fr £37·50, WB, 🆃, Bk £4·95, L £3·90, D £6·30, cc 1 2 3 4 5 6, Dep.

Repairer: Hughes of Beaconsfield Ltd, 53 Station Rd. ✆ (049 46) 2141.
Specialist Body Repairer: G & G Motors (Beaconsfield), 38 London Rd. ✆ (049 46) 5211 and (049 46) 2411.

BEAFORD Devon. Maps 3A and 4C
Pop 365. South Molton 18, London 199, Barnstaple 16, Bideford 12, Crediton 22, Okehampton 14.
EC Wed. **Golf** Torrington 9h. **See** Arts Centre, Green Warren House (Dartington Trust).

Repairer: White, S A, Beaford Garage. ✆ (080 53) 212.

BEAL Northumberland. Map 31A
Alnwick 21, London 329, Berwick-upon-Tweed 9½, Coldstream 16.
Golf Goswick 18h. **See** Holy Island (Lindisfarne Castle).

Rescue Service: Beal Garage, Gt North Rd. ✆ Berwick (0289) 81253.

BEAMINSTER Dorset. Map 5E
Pop 2,369. Sherborne 19, London 139, Axminster 14, Crewkerne 7, Dorchester 17, Lyme Regis 15, Weymouth 24.
Golf Bridport and West Bay 18h. **See** 15th cent Church, Mapperton House.

★★**White Hart,** *Hogshill St. DT8 3AE.* ✆ (0308) 862779.

Rescue Service: Tunnel Road Garage, Crewkerne Rd. ✆ (0308) 862247.

BEAULIEU Hampshire. Map 6E
Pop 910. Winchester 22, London 86, Lymington 6½, Lyndhurst 7½, Ringwood 17, Romsey 14, Southampton 13.
Golf Bramshott Hill 18h. **See** Beaulieu Abbey, Palace House and National Motor Museum, old Church, Exbury Gardens 3 m SE, Maritime Museum at Bucklers Hard.
🆃 John Montagu Building. ✆ Beaulieu (0590) 612345.

★★★**Montagu Arms,** *Palace Lane, SO4 7ZL.* ✆ (0590) 612344. C. 🛏 26 bedrs, 26 bp, TV, Dgs. X a l c, mc, LD 10. 🅿 N, CH, CP 60, G 8, con 30, CF, 2 st. £ BB fr £33·50, DB fr £46·50, WB, 🆃, Bk £5·50, L £8·45, D £14·95, cc 1 2 3 5 6.▲
★★**Master Builder's House,** *Bucklers Hard, SO4 7XB.* ✆ Bucklers Hard (059 063) 253.

Repairer: Beaulieu Garages Ltd, The Garage. ✆ (0590) 612446.
Rescue Service: Martin (East Boldre) Ltd, East Boldre Garage. ✆ (0590) 612259.

BEBINGTON Merseyside. Map 20F
2 m S of Birkenhead. Pop 34,080. Chester 13, London 195, Northwich 28, Queensferry 12.
EC Thur. **Golf** Brackenwood 9h, Bromborough 18h. **See** Garden village of

Port Sunlight, Lady Lever Art Gallery,
Stork Margarine Works, Bromborough (by
appmt), Norman Church.

Repairers: Cheshire Bros Ltd, 129 Mount
Rd. ✆ 051-608 2323.
James Edwards (Chester) Ltd, 151 Old
Chester Rd. ✆ 051-645 5401.
T. Gowan & Son, Bebington Service
Station, Kings Rd. ✆ 051-608 6273.

BEBSIDE Northumberland. Map 32A
Newcastle upon Tyne 12, London 285,
Alnwick 26, Blyth 3, Coldstream 53,
Hexham 31, Sunderland 20.

Rescue Service: Bebside Motors Ltd.
Front St. ✆ Bedlington (0670) 823030.

BECCLES Suffolk. Map 16B
Pop 8,903. Ipswich 40, London 114,
Aldeburgh 23, Great Yarmouth 14,
Lowestoft 9½, Norwich 17, Scole 20.
EC Wed. **MD** Fri. **Golf** Beccles 9h. **See**
Fine Perp Church with detached tower,
Roos Hall (by appmt).

★★**Waveney House,** *Puddingmoor,*
NR34 9PL. ✆ (0502) 712270. C. ⊷ 13
bedrs, 7 bp, 4 bps, 1 ba, TV, Dgs. ✗ a l c,
mc, at, LD 9.15. ⊕ CH, Dgs, CP 70, Ac, pf,
con, CF, 0 st. **£** BB £22–£25, DB £38–
£41·50, WB, ☑, Bk £4·50, L £7, D £7, cc
1 2 3 5, Dep b.

Rescue Service: Ingate Garage Ltd,
Lowestoft Rd. ✆ (0502) 712513.

BECKENHAM Greater London (Kent).
M. Area 7B
Pop 62,074. London 9½, Bromley 2,
Croydon 4.
EC Wed. **Golf** Langley Park 18h,
Beckenham Place Park 18h. **See** St
George's Church (18th cent milestone
and Almshouses adj), RC Church.

Repairer: Masters of Beckenham Ltd, 150
Upper Elmers End Rd. ✆ 01-650 9151.
Park Langley Garage (Beckenham) Ltd,
Wickham Rd. ✆ 01-650 3466.

BECKERMET Cumbria. Map 26F
Pop 2,180. Broughton-in-Furness 28,
London 305, Egremont 3.
Golf Seascale 18h. **See** St Bridget's
Church.

◼★★**Blackbeck Inn,** *Blackbeck, CA22*
2NY. ✆ (0946 84) 661. ⊷ 22 bedrs, 20 bp,
2 bps, TV, Dgs. ✗ a l c, mc, LD 9.30. ⊕ CH,
TV, CP 100, Ac, con 15, CF, 6 BGf, 3 st.
£ BB £27·50–£29·50, DB £40–£45, WB, ☑,
Bk £3·50, L £3, D £5, cc 1 2 3 5 6, Dep a.
Royal Oak, H, x, *CA21 2XB.*
✆ (0946 84) 551. C. ⊷ 8 bedrs, 8 bp, TV,
Dgs. ✗ a l c. ⊕ CH, Dgs, CP 25, CF, 4 BGf,
2 st. **£** BB fr £17, DB fr £36, Bk £3·50, L £4,
D £6·50.

Rescue Service: J W Jacques, Beckermet
Service Garage. ✆ (0946 84) 200.

BEDALE North Yorkshire. Map 24F
Pop 2,420. Boroughbridge 16, London
224, Brough 41, Darlington 20, Harrogate
23, Leyburn 10, Middleton-in-Teesdale 36,
Northallerton 8, Thirsk 13, West Auckland
25.
EC Thur. **MD** Tue, Thur. **Golf** Bedale 18h.
See St Gregory's Church, Bedale Hall,
14th cent Market Cross, Oddfellows
Arms.

★★★**M Leeming,** *DL8 1DT.*
✆ (0677) 22112. Closed Xmas. ⊷ 40
bedrs, 40 bp. ✗ mc, at, LD 9.45. ⊕ N, CH,

Ac, con, CF, 20 BGf, 0 st, Dis. **£** BB £21, DB
£30, WB, ☑, Bk £2, L £3·50, D £7,
cc 1 2 3 5 6.

Repairer: Bedale Garage Ltd, Market Pl.
✆ (0677) 22492.

BEDFORD Bedfordshire. Map 15C
Pop 75,000. Luton 19, London 50, M1
Motorway 10, Alconbury 22, Aylesbury
30, Baldock 17, Biggleswade 11,
Bletchley 16, Buckingham 27, Cambridge
30, Dunstable 19, Hatfield 31, Huntingdon
21, Kettering 25, Northampton 22,
Towcester 28.
EC Thur. **MD** Wed, Sat. **Golf** Bedfordshire
18h, Bedford and County 18h. **See**
Higgins Art Gallery, Museum, Bedford
School, Churches, Bunyan Museum at rear
of meeting house, Statue of John Bunyan,
Elstow Moot (Bunyan Museum) 1½ m S,
Stagsden Bird Zoo 4 m W.
[i] St Paul's Sq. ✆ Bedford (0234) 215226.

★★★**Bedford Moat House,** *St Mary's St,*
MK42 0AR. ✆ (0234) 55131. C. ⊷ 117
bedrs, 117 bp, TV. ✗ a l c, mc, at. ⊕ Lt, N,
CH, TV, CP 80, Ac, sb, gym, con 300, CF.
£ BB fr £35, DB £50, WB, ☑, Bk £4·50, L
£6, D £9, cc 1 2 3 5 6, Dep b.
◼★★★**Woodland Manor,** *Green La,*
Clapham, MK41 6EP. ✆ (0234) 63281.
Closed first 2 weeks Aug & 2 weeks at
Xmas. C7. ⊷ 18 bedrs, 10 bp, 8 bps, TV.
✗ a l c, mc, at, LD 9.45. ⊕ N, CH, CP 60,
con 25, 3 BGf, 2 st. **£** BB fr £44, DB fr £57,
WB, ☑, Bk £6·75, L £12·50, D £12·50,
cc 1 2 3 5, Dep.
★★**Bedford Swan,** *The Embankment,*
MK40 1RW. ✆ (0234) 46565. C. ⊷ 102
bedrs, 84 bp, 4 ba, TV, Dgs. ✗ a l c, mc, at,
LD 9. ⊕ N, CH, TV, CP 100, con 120, CF, 0
st. **£** BB fr £32·50, DB fr £42, WB, ☑, Bk
£3·45, L £5·95, D £5·95, cc 1 2 3 5.
★★**De Parys,** *De Parys Av, MK40 2UA.*
✆ (0234) 52121. Closed Dec, RS Xmas
week. C. ⊷ 34 bedrs, 6 bp, 16 bps, 2 ba,
TV, Dgs. ✗ a l c, mc, at. LD 9. ⊕ CH, CP 23,
Ac, con 60, CF, 1 BGf, 1 st. **£** Bk £3, L
£1·90, D £7, cc 1 2 3 5 6, Dep a.
★**Shakespeare** *Shakespeare Rd,*
MK40 2DX. ✆ (0234) 213147.
Hurst House, PH, z (R), *178 Hurst*
Grove, MK40 4DS. ✆ (0234) 40791. C.
⊷ 6 bedrs, 2 ba, TV, Dgs. ✗ a l c. ⊕ CH,
TV, CP 5, CF, 2 BGf. **£** BB fr £12, DB fr
£21·75, WT (b) fr £99·50, DT (b) fr £15·50,
☑, Bk £2·65, L £3·15, D £3·70,
cc 1 2 3 5.
Kimbolton, H, y (R), *78 Clapham Rd,*
MK41 7PN. ✆ (0234) 54854. Closed
week after Xmas. C. ⊷ 16 bedrs, 6 bps, 6
sh, 3 ba, TV. ⊕ CH, TV, CP 23, 1 st. **£** BB
£21–£23, DB £30–£34, WT (b) fr £147–
£203, DT (b) fr £22–£30, ☑, Bk £3·50, D
£7·50.

Repairer: Marshalls (Cambridge) Ltd, 120
Goldington Rd. ✆ (0234) 53343.
Rescue Service: Arlington Motor Co Ltd,
Barkers La. ✆ (0234) 50011.
Ouse Valley Motors, 9 Kingsway.
✆ (0234) 64491.

BEDLINGTON Northumberland. Map
32A
Pop 14,785. Newcastle upon Tyne 13,
London 286, Alnwick 24, Coldstream 51,
Corbridge 26, Sunderland 22.
EC Wed. **Golf** Bedlingtonshire 18h. **See**
Parish Church.

Rescue Service: Lion Garage (Bedlington)
Ltd, Front St. ✆ (0670) 823244.

BEER Devon. Map 4F
Pop 1,500. Axminster 8½, London 155,
Exeter 22, Honiton 11, Lyme Regis 9½.
EC Thur. **See** Old quarries, Open brook in
main street, Miniature Railway, Home of
"Honiton Lace".

◼★★**Dolphin,** *Fore St. EX12 3EQ.*
✆ Seaton (0297) 20068. C. ⊷ 21 bedrs, 5
bp, 16 sh, 4 ba, TV, Dgs. ✗ a l c, mc, at, LD
10.30 (9 winter). ⊕ ch, TV, Dgs, CP 30, G
2, Ac, con 130, CF, 0 st. **£** BB £9·50–
£13·50, DB £19–£27, WT £123–£143, DT
£18·50–£21·50, WB, ☑, Bk £2·50, L £2·65,
D £7·50, cc 1 3 5 6, Dep a.

Repairer: Good, C R & Sons Ltd, Pioneer
Garages. ✆ Seaton (0297) 20034.
Rescue Service: Townsend Garage,
Townsend. ✆ Seaton (0297) 20759.

BEESTON Cheshire. Map 19D
Pop 200. Nantwich 11, London 173,
Chester 13, Middlewich 14, Northwich
13, Warrington 20, Whitchurch 9,
Wrexham 17.
Golf Hill Valley 18h. **See** Castle ruins.

★★★**M Wild Boar,** *CW6 9NW.*
✆ Bunbury (0829) 260309. RS Dec 27–
31. C. ⊷ 30 bedrs, 30 bp, TV, Dgs. ✗ a l c,
mc, at, LD 9.45. ⊕ CH, TV, Dgs, CP 100,
Ac, con 50, CF, 30 BGf, 3 st. **£** BB fr
£29·25, DB fr £40·50, WB, ☑, Bk £4·50, L
£8·80, cc 1 2 3 4 5 6, Dep b.

BEESTON Nottinghamshire. Map 22D
Pop 41,935. Long Eaton 3, London 124,
M1 Motorway 5, Ilkeston 5½, Nottingham
4.
MD Fri, Sat. **Golf** Beeston Fields 18h,
Chilwell Manor 18h. **See** St John's
Church, War Memorial, Bramcote
Hemlock Stone.

Brackley House, PH, y, *31 Elm Av.*
✆ Nottingham (0602) 256739. C. ⊷ 14
bedrs, 3 bp, 2 bps, 1 sh, 2 ba, TV, Dgs.
✗ a l c. ⊕ CH, TV, Dgs, CP 20, CF, 0 st.
£ BB £17·50–£19·50, DB £25–£28, ☑, D
£7·95, cc 1 2 3▲

MC Repairer: Downtown Motor Cycles,
48 Lilac Crescent. ✆ Nottingham
(0602) 256641.

BEETHAM Cumbria. Map 27C
Pop 1,657. London 247, M6 Motorway 5½,
Ambleside 20, Kendal 8½, Kirkby Lonsdale
8½, Lancaster 12, Ulverston 23.
EC Sat. **Golf** Silverdale 9h. **See** Norman
and EE Church, 14th–17th cent Beetham
Hall (now farmhouse), Fairy Steps
(wooded ravine).

★**Wheatsheaf,** *A6 Road, LA7 7AL.*
✆ Milnthorpe (044 82) 2123. C. ⊷ 8
bedrs, 2 bp, 2 ba, TV, Dgs. ✗ mc, LD 8.15.
⊕ CH, TV, Dgs, U 4, CF, 0 st. **£** BB £16·50–
£18·50, DB £24·50–£28·50, Bk £4, L
£4·75, D £7·50, Dep a.

BEETLEY Norfolk. Map 16C
Pop 1,050. East Dereham 4, London 109,
Cromer 25, Fakenham 9½.
EC Wed. **Golf** Dereham 9h. **See** Church.

Rescue Service: Green & Son, Two Oaks
Garage. ✆ Dereham (0362) 860219.

BELBROUGHTON Hereford &
Worcester (Worcestershire) Map 21F

Bromsgrove 6½, London 119, Birmingham 14, Bridgnorth 20, Kidderminster 8, Wolverhampton 15, Worcester 19.

Rescue Service: The Bell Service Station, Bromsgrove Rd. ✆ (0562) 730796.

BELFORD Northumberland. Map 31A
Pop 460. Alnwick 16, London 322, Berwick-upon-Tweed 15, Coldstream 20.
EC Thur. **Golf** Bamburgh Castle 18h. **See** St Mary's Church, Bamburgh Castle 5 m E.

★★**Blue Bell,** *Market Pl, NE70 7NE.*
✆ (066 83) 543. C. ⊷ 15 bedrs, 8 bp, 2 ba, TV, Dgs. ✗ a l c, mc, at, LD 9. ⓓ CH, TV, Dgs, CP 26, U 2, Ac, con 100, CF, 0 st.
£ BB fr £25, DB fr £38, WT fr £210, DBB fr £23·50, WB, ①, Bk £5·50, L £4·50, D £7·95, cc 1 2 3 5 6, Dep b.

Rescue Service: R Renner & Son Ltd, West St. ✆ (066 83) 212.

BELLINGHAM Northumberland. Map 31C
Pop 800. Corbridge 18, London 295, Alnwick 35, Alston 35, Brampton 33, Hawick 38, Newcastle upon Tyne 32.
EC Tue, Sat. **Golf** Bellingham 9h. **See** Manmade Forest (largest in Europe), Kielder Water (largest reservoir in Britain).

Rescue Service: L & C Motors, The Foundry. ✆ (0660) 20555.

BELPER Derbyshire. Map 22D
Pop 16,453. M1 Motorway 2, Derby 7½, London 134, Alfreton 7½, Ashbourne 12, Matlock 10.
EC Wed. **MD** Sat. **Golf** Chevin 18h. **See** Church.

Shottle Hall Farm, G, xy (R), *Shottle, DE5 2EB.* ✆ Cowers Lane (077 389) 276.
Closed Dec. C. ⊷ 9 bedrs, 2 ba, ns, Dgs.
ⓓ CH, TV, CP 30, CF, 3 st. £ BB £12·75–£14, DB £25·50–£28, ②, D £6.

BEMBRIDGE Isle of Wight. Map 6F
Pop 3,366. Portsmouth (Fy) 9, London 80, Newport 11, Ryde 6, Sandown 7.
EC Thur. **Golf** Ryde 9h, Shanklin and Sandown 18h. **See** Ruskin Art Gallery and Museum at Bembridge School (by appmt), Old Windmill (Nat Trust), Pottery.

★★**Birdham,** *1 Steyne Rd, PO35 5UH.*
✆ Isle of Wight (0983) 872875. RS Xmas.
C. ⊷ 14 bedrs, 12 bp, 1 sph, 1 sh, 2 ba, TV, Dgs. ✗ a l c, mc, LD 10. ⓓ N, CH, TV, Dgs, ns, CP 120, Ac, con 30, CF, 0 st. £ BB £11·50–£14·37, DB £23–£28·75, DT fr £15, ①, Bk £3·75, L £4·50, D £7·50, cc 2, Dep a.

★★**Elms Country** (R), *Swaines Rd, PO35 5XS.* ✆ Isle of Wight
(0983) 872248. Open Mar–Oct. C.
⊷ 12 bedrs, 10 bp, 2 bps, TV, Dgs. ✗ a l c, mc, at, LD 7.30. ⓓ CH, CP 60, con 24, CF, 2 BGf, 1 st, Dis. £ DB fr £32, WT fr £196, DT fr £28, ①, Bk £2·50, L £6, D £8, Dep a.

★★**Highbury** (R), *Lane End, PO35 5SU.*
✆ Isle of Wight (0983) 2838.

MC Repairer: Bembridge Motor Services Ltd, Embankment Rd. ✆ Isle of Wight (0983) 873744.

BENSON-ON-THAMES Oxfordshire. Map 14F
Pop 4,700. Henley-on-Thames 12, London 47, Aylesbury 22, Basingstoke 28, Faringdon 23, High Wycombe 18, Oxford 12, Reading 14, Wantage 6½.

EC Wed. **Golf** Huntercombe 18h. **See** Church of St Mary (Chaucer family assns), Grammar School and Almshouse (founded 1437) all at Ewelme.

White Hart, *Castle Square, OX9 6SD.*
✆ Wallingford (0491) 35244.

Rescue Service: Atalanta Garages Ltd, Old London Rd. ✆ Wallingford (0491) 35656.

BENTHAM North Yorkshire. Map 27C
Pop 2,900. Settle 11, London 241, Hawes 20, Kirkby Lonsdale 20, Lancaster 14.
EC Thurs. **MD** Wed. **Golf** Bentham 9h.
See Big Stone of Fourstones, St John the Baptist Church.
ⓘ Station Rd. ✆ Bentham (0468) 61043.

Rescue Service: Fred Crossley (Garages) Ltd. ✆ (0468) 61551.
Taylor's Garage, Crow Trees Garage, Low Bentham. ✆ (0468) 61306.

BERE ALSTON Devon. M. Area 3C
Pop 2,000. Tavistock 6½, London 209, Launceston 17, Liskeard 19.
EC Thur. **Golf** Tavistock 18h. **See** 12th cent St. Andrew's Church.

Rescue Service: Hillson, P W, Bedford Garage, Bedford St. ✆ Tavistock (0822) 840225.
Sleep, H & A, Station Hill. ✆ Tavistock (0822) 840244.

BERE FERRERS Devon Map 3C
Tavistock 8, London 210, Liskeard 21, Plymouth 15.

Lanterna, PH, x, (R), *PL20 7JL.*
✆ Tavistock (0822) 840380. C. ⊷ 5 bedrs, 2 bps, 1 ba. ✗ a l c. ⓓ CH, TV, CP 8, CF, 1 st. £ BB £8–£11, DB £16–£22, WT (b) £84–£90, DT (b) £12–£15, ①, Bk £1, L £2, D £4, cc 1 3.

BERKELEY Gloucestershire. Map 13F
See also NEWPORT.
Pop 1,424. Tetbury 15, London 113, M5 Motorway 4, Bath 27, Bristol 20, Chepstow 18, Chippenham 28, Gloucester 16.
EC Wed. **Golf** Stinchcombe Hill 18h. **See** EE Parish Church (grave of Dr Jenner), Castle, Wildfowl Trust, Slimbridge 6 m NE.

The Elms, G, y (RI), *Stone, GL13 9JX.*
✆ Falfield (0454) 260279. C. ⊷ 10 bedrs, 3 ba, Dgs. ⓓ CH, TV, CP 15, CF. £ BB £11–£20, DB £20, ①.

BERKELEY ROAD Gloucestershire. M. Area 13F.
2 m E of Berkeley. Tetbury 13, London 111, M5 Motorway 2.

★★**Prince of Wales,** *GL13 9HD.*
✆ Dursley (0453) 810474. C. ⊷ 9 bedrs, 7 bp, 1 ba, TV, Dgs. ✗ a l c, mc, at, LD 9.30. ⓓ CH, Dgs, CP 120, Ac, con 20, CF, 0 st. £ BB £20·35–£26·29, DB £24·15–£34·10, WB, ①, Bk £4·50, L £5·50, D £6·75, cc 1 2 3 5 6.

BERKHAMSTED Hertfordshire. Map 15E
Pop 16,963. Watford 11, London 27, Aylesbury 12, Denham 17, Dunstable 11, High Wycombe 15, Rickmansworth 14, Slough 20, St Albans 11.
EC Wed, Sat. **MD** Sat. **Golf** Berkhamsted 18h. **See** Castle ruins, St Peter's Church (Saxon doorway), 17th cent Almshouses, 15th cent house of Dean Incent (founder

of Berkhamsted School), 16th cent Court House, Kings Arms.
ⓘ County Library, Kings Rd.
✆ Berkhamsted (044 27) 74545.

★**Swan Inn,** *129 High St, HP4 3HH.*
✆ (044 27) 71451. C. ⊷ 13 bedrs, 5 bp, 2 bps, 2 ba, annexe 3 bedrs, TV, Dgs. ✗ a l c, mc, at, LD 10. ⓓ CH, TV, Dgs, CP 12, U 1, CF, 1 st. £ BB £22–£25, DB £33–£38, DBB fr £28, WB, ①, Bk £3·75, L £6, D £7·50, cc 1 3.

Rescue Service: Berkhamsted Motor Co Ltd, 33 High St. ✆ (044 27) 71171.
Underhill & Young Ltd, High St.
✆ (044 27) 2371.

BERRYNARBOR Devon. Map 4C
Pop 700. Lynmouth 13, London 197, Barnstaple 10, Ilfracombe 3, South Molton 20.
EC Wed. **Golf** Ilfracombe 18h. **See** Caves, EE Church, 95ft tower.

⊷★★**Sandy Cove,** *EX34 9SR.* ✆ Combe Martin (027 188) 2243. C. ⊷ 31 bedrs, 14 bp, 1 bps, 4 ba, annexe 2 bedrs, 2 bp, TV, Dgs. ✗ a l c, mc, at, LD 9.30. ⓓ TV, CP 50, Ac, sp, pf, sb, sol, gym, con 100, CF, 3 BGf, 1 st, Dis. £ BB £12·65–£18·69, DB £25·30–£48·88, WT £112·58–£180·48, WB, ②, Bk £3·45, D £9·78.▲

Rescue Service: On-A-Hill. ✆ Combe Martin (027 188) 2308.

BERWICK-UPON-TWEED Northumberland. Map 37F
Pop 11,647. Alnwick 30, London 337, Coldstream 14, Haddington 39, Lauder 32.
EC Thur. **MD** Wed, Fri, Sat. **Golf** Berwick-on-Tweed 18h, Magdolene Fields 18h.
See Elizabethan Ramparts, 18th cent Georgian Walls, Castle remains, 17th cent Jacobean Bridge and modern Royal Border and Royal Tweed Bridges, Museum and Art Gallery, 18th cent Town Hall, Holy Trinity Church, Bell Tower, Norham Castle 6 m SW.
ⓘ Castlegate Car Park. ✆ Berwick-upon-Tweed (0289) 307187.

★★**King's Arms,** *Hide Hill, TD15 1EJ.*
✆ (0289) 307454. C. ⊷ 32 bedrs, 27 bp, 5 bps, TV, Dgs. ✗ a l c, mc, at, LD 10. ⓓ N, CH, TV, Dgs, Ac, con 40, CF, 0 st. £ BB £26, DB £43, WT £215, DT £36, WB, ①, Bk £3·50, L £5, D £9·50, cc 1 2 3 5 6, Dep b.
★★**Ravensholme,** *32 Ravensdowne, TD15 1DQ.* ✆ (0289) 307170.
★**Queen's Head** (R), *Sandgate, TD15 1EP.* ✆ (0289) 307852. C. ⊷ 6 bedrs, 1 ba, Dgs. ✗ a l c, mc, LD 9. ⓓ CH, TV, Dgs, Ac, CF, 1 st. £ BB £13–£14, DB £26–£28, WT £150, DT £25, ①, Bk £3·50, L £6, D £7, cc 2 3 5.

MC Repairer: Darling & Swinney, Scremerston Garage, Scremerston.
✆ (0289) 6570.
Rescue Service: Blackburn & Price Ltd, 12 Silver St. ✆ (0289) 7436.
McBain, John & Son Ltd, Castle Garage.
✆ (0289) 7459.
Peter Spellman Ltd, 3 Main St, Spittal.
✆ (0289) 7214.
Simpson, R A & Son, Colliery Yard Garage, Scremerston. ✆ (0289) 6717.

BETCHTON Cheshire. M Area 19D
Pop 950. 3 m SE of Sandbach. Newcastle-under-Lyme 11, London 160.

Golf Sandbach 9h, Alsager 18h. **See** Two 17th cent Farmhouses, Betchton Hall.

Rescue Service: A & T Hassall, Betchton Motors, Newcastle Rd. ✆ Smallwood (047 75) 205.

BEVERLEY Humberside (North Humberside). Map 25A
Pop 17,180. Lincoln 46, London 179, Bridlington 22, Hull 8½, Malton 27, Market Weighton 10, Scarborough 33.
MD Wed, Sat. **Golf** Beverley and East Riding 18h. **See** Minster, 15th cent North Bar, Art Gallery and Museum, Market Cross, St Mary's Church, Guildhall, Skidby Windmill.
🛈 30 Market Pl. ✆ Hull (0482) 867430.

★★★Beverley Arms (TH), *North Bar Within, HU17 8DD.* ✆ Hull (0482) 869241. C. ⌘ 61 bedrs, 61 bp, TV, Dgs. ✗ a l c, mc, at, LD 9.15. ⓓ CH, N, CH, Dgs, CP 70, Ac, CF, 1 st. £ BB £40·50, DB £56, WB, 🛈, cc 1 2 3 4 5 6, Dep (Xmas).

⋕★★★Tickton Grange, *HU17 9SH.* ✆ Leven (0401) 43666. RS Xmas. C. ⌘ 12 bedrs, 5 bp, 7 bps, TV, Dgs. ✗ a l c, mc, at, LD 9.30. ⓓ CH, CP 65, Ac, con 50, CF, 1 BGf, 2 st. £ BB £39, DB £53, WB, 🛈, Bk £4·25, L £8, D £9, cc 1 2 3.

★★Lairgate (R), *30 Lairgate, HU17 8EP.* ✆ Hull (0482) 882141. C. ⌘ 24 bedrs, 10 bp, 8 bps, 3 ba, TV, Dgs. ✗ a l c, mc, at, LD 9.30. ⓓ CH, TV, Dgs, CP 22, Ac, con 40, CF, 0 st. £ BB £31–£34, WT £231, DT £33, WB, ②, Bk £4, L £5, D £8, cc 1 3 6, Dep b.

★King's Head, *38 Market Pl, HU17 9AH.* ✆ Hull (0482) 868103.

Rescue Service: Hull Bridge Garage Ltd, Hull Bridge. ✆ Hull (0482) 869155.

BEWDLEY Hereford & Worcester (Worcestershire). Map 13B
Pop 9,927. Kidderminster 3, London 126, Bridgnorth 15, Bromyard 19, Droitwich 13, Leominster 24, Ludlow 19, Worcester 15.
EC Wed. **MD** Tue, Sat. **Golf** Kidderminster 18h. **See** Forest of Wyre, St Anne's Church, old Tudor houses and inns, Georgian houses, fine bridge (1797, by Telford), Severn Valley Rly (steam engines) to Bridgnorth.
🛈 Library, Load St. ✆ (0299) 403303.

★★Black Boy, *14 Kidderminster Rd, DY11 1AG.* ✆ (0299) 402119. Closed Xmas Day. C. ⌘ 18 bedrs, 5 bp, 13 sh, 9 ba, annexe 7 bedrs, TV, Dgs. ✗ a l c, mc, at, LD 9.15. ⓓ ch, TV, Dgs, CP 30, CF, 3 BGf, 2 st. £ BB £14·50–£27, DB £27·50–£36, DT £24·75–£37·25, WB, 🛈, Bk £4, L £4·95, D £7·25, cc 1 2 3.

BEXHILL-ON-SEA East Sussex. Map 10E
See also COODEN BEACH
Pop 35,000. Hurst Green 14, London 64, Eastbourne 12, Hastings 5½, Lewes 23, Uckfield 24.
EC Wed. **Golf** Cooden Beach 18h. **See** St Peter's Church (1070), De La Warr Pavilion, Manor House Gardens (Old Town).
🛈 De La Warr Pavilion, Marina. ✆ Bexhill-on-Sea (0424) 212023.

★★Granville, *Sea Rd, TN40 1EE.* ✆ (0424) 215437.

★Southlands Court (R), *Hastings Rd, TN40 2HJ.* ✆ (0424) 210628.

Leahyrst, Private Hotel for Non-Smokers, PH, z (R), *9 Bedford Av, TN40 1ND.* ✆ (0424) 219906. C, NS. ⌘ 8 bedrs, 2 bp, 1 ba, ns, TV, Dgs. ⓓ Lt, CH, TV, Dgs, ns, CF, 1 BGf, 0 st, Dis. £ DB £10–£12, DB £18–£24, WT (b) £86–£105, DT (b) £14–£16, 🛈.

Moorings, H, z, *23 Hastings Rd, TN40 2AF.* ✆ (0424) 213668.

Park Lodge, H, z (R), *16 Egerton Rd, TN39 3HH.* ✆ (0424) 216547.

Victoria, H, y (Rl), *1 Middlesex Rd, TN40 1LP.* ✆ (0424) 210382. Open Mar–Oct. C. ⌘ 11 bedrs, 4 bps, 2 ba, TV, Dgs. ⓓ CH, TV, CP 7, CF, 1 BGf, 0 st, Dis. £ BB £10·75–£12, DB £21·50–£28·50, WT (b) £85–£99, DT £14·75–£16·50, 🛈.

Repairers: Skinners (Bexhill) Ltd, 57 London Rd. ✆ (0424) 212000.
Rescue Service: Smith & Humphrey, 75 Ninfield Rd. ✆ (0424) 210746.

BEXLEY Greater London (Kent). Map 7B. London 15, Dartford 3½, Sidcup 2½.

★★★M. Crest, *Southwold Rd, DA5 1ND.* ✆ Crayford (0322) 526900. C. ⌘ 78 bedrs, 78 bp, ns, TV, Dgs. ✗ a l c, mc, LD 9.30. ⓓ Lt, N, CH, Dgs, CP 130, Ac, con 70, CF, 26 BGf. £ BB fr £42, BD fr £52·50, WB, 🛈, Bk £5·25, D £9·60, cc 1 2 3 4 5 6, Dep b.

BEXLEYHEATH Greater London (Kent). Map 7B
1½ m N of Bexley. London 13, Dartford 3, Sidcup 3½.
EC Wed. **Golf** Bexleyheath 9h, Barnehurst 9h. **See** Hall Place and Gardens.

Rescue Service: Lex Motor Co (Bexleyheath) Ltd, 74 Broadway. ✆ 01-303 6363.

BIBURY Gloucestershire. Map 14E
Pop 568. Faringdon 14, London 84, Burford 10, Cirencester 7, Cheltenham 17, Stow-on-the-Wold 14.
EC Wed. **Golf** Cirencester 18h. **See** Interesting Church, Arlington Row (15th cent cottages), Arlington Mill Museum, picturesque old cottages, Jacobean Bibury Court (now hotel), Wildfowl Reserve (Nat Trust), Trout Hatchery.

★★★Swan, *GL7 5NW.* ✆ (028 574) 204. C. ⌘ 23 bedrs, 22 bp, 1 bps, TV, Dgs. ✗ mc, at, LD 8.30. ⓓ CH, CP 20, G 4, pf, con 20, CF, 0 st. £ BB fr £27·50, DB fr £47·50, DBB fr £32·50, WB, ②, Bk £4·50, L £8·75, D £12·50, cc 1 3 6.

⋕★★Bibury Court, *GL7 5NT.* ✆ (028 574) 337. Closed Xmas week. C. ⌘ 16 bedrs, 15 bp, 1 ba, Dgs. ✗ a l c, mc, at, LD 9. ⓓ CH, TV, Dgs, CP 100, con 16, CF, 3 st. £ BB £20–£23, DB £40–£48, DBB £29–£34, WB, 🛈, Bk £3, L £1·50, D £9, cc 1 2 3 5 6.

BICESTER Oxfordshire. Map 14F
Pop 17,156. Aylesbury 16, London 57, Banbury 15, Buckingham 11, Brackley 10, Chipping Norton 19, Henley-on-Thames 34, High Wycombe 31, Oxford 12, Towcester 22.
EC Thur. **MD** Mon, Fri. **Golf** Chesterton Country Golf Club 18h. **See** St Edburg's Church, old houses, Garth Park, Wootton House 7½ m SE.

★★King's Arms, *Market Sq, OX6 7AH.* ✆ (086 92) 2015.

Repairer: Booth & Phipps Garages Ltd, Buckingham Rd. ✆ (086 92) 2606.
Rescue Service: Bicester Motor Co Ltd, Banbury Rd. ✆ (086 92) 42369.
Jubilee Garage (R Hewison & Sons), London Rd. ✆ (086 92) 44000.

BICKINGTON Devon. Map 3D
Pop 300. M5 Motorway 14, London 183, Ashburton 3, Newton Abbot 5, Totnes 11.
EC Sat. **Golf** Stover 18h. **See** Church tower with illuminated cross.

Privet Cottage, G, x (Unl), *TQ12 6JT.* ✆ (062 682) 319. Closed May–Sep. C. ⌘ 4 bedrs, 1 ba, Dgs. ⓓ TV, Dgs, CP 4, CF.

BICKLEIGH Devon. Maps 3B and 4F
Pop 208. Tiverton 4, London 169, Crediton 9, Exeter 10, Honiton 17.
Golf Tiverton 18h. **See** Bickleigh Castle (open to visitors).

★★Fisherman's Cot, *EX16 8RW.* ✆ (088 45) 237. C. ⌘ 11 bedrs, 8 bp, 1 ba, TV, Dgs. ✗ a l c, mc, LD 9.30. ⓓ N, CH, Dgs, CP 80, Ac, pf, con 20, CF, 0 st. £ WB, D £7, cc 1 3 4 6.

BIDEFORD Devon. Map 4C
Pop 12,210. Barnstaple 9, London 202, Bude 25, Crediton 34, Holsworthy 18, Okehampton 26.
EC Wed. **MD** Tue. **Golf** Royal North Devon 18h. **See** Royal Hotel (assoc. with Kingsley), Kingsley Statue, Chudleigh Fort, Burton Art Gallery, St Mary's Church, Victoria Park (Armada guns), Tapeley Park Gardens, Instow, 2½ m NE.
🛈 The Quay. ✆ Bideford (023 72) 77676.

★★★Durrant House, *Heywood Rd, Northam, EX39 3QB.* ✆ (023 72) 2361. C. ⌘ 58 bedrs, 54 bp, 4 bps, 1 ba, TV, Dgs. ✗ mc, at, LD 9.30. ⓓ N, CH, TV, CP 180, Ac, sp, sb, sol, con 120, CF, 6 BGf, 4 st. £ BB £20–£27·50, DB £35–£39·50, DBB fr £29·50, WB, ②, Bk £4·80, L £2, D £8·25, cc 1 2 3 5 6, Dep.

⋕★★★Portledge, *Fairy Cross, EX39 5BX.* (3½m W A39). ✆ Horns Cross (023 75) 262. Open Apr–Oct. C 5. ⌘ 33 bedrs, 22 bp, 9 bps, TV, Dgs. ✗ at, LD 8.45. ⓓ CH, TV, CP 40, sp, s, con 20, CF, 2 st. £ BB £20–£25, DB £40–£57, DBB £50–£68, ②, Bk £2·50, L £12·50, D £9·50, cc 3.

⚫★★★Riversford (R), *Limers Lane, EX39 2RG,* ✆ (023 72) 74239. Open Feb–Nov. C. ⌘ 17 bedrs, 16 bp, 1 bps, 2 ba, TV, Dgs. ✗ mc, at, LD 8. ⓓ N, CH, TV, Dgs, CP 20, U 1, G 2, Ac, sol, con 25, CF, 1 st. £ BB £13·70–£19·70, DB £27·40–£37·80, DBB £21·30–£26·50, WB, ②, Bk £3·30, L £4·70, D £7·60, cc 2 3 5, Dep a.

★★Royal, *Barnstaple St, EX39 4AE.* ✆ (023 72) 78181. C. ⌘ 33 bedrs, 13 bp, 7 ba, TV, Dgs. ✗ mc, at, LD 8.30. ⓓ CH, CP 30, G 4, Ac, con 150, CF, Ost. £ BB fr £17·25, DB fr £29·90, WB, ②, Bk 3, D £6 03, oo 1 2 3 5, Dep b.

⚫★★Yeoldon House (R), *Durrant La, EX39 2RL.* ✆ (023 72) 4400. Closed Xmas–New Year. C. ⌘ 10 bedrs, 8 bp, 2 bps, TV. ✗ a l c, mc, at, LD 8.30. ⓓ CH, CP 20, CF, 1 st. £ BB £27·75–£29·75, DB £22·50–£24·25, DBB £22·50–£33·75, WB, 🛈, Bk £3·50, D £9·50, cc 1 2 3 5 6, Dep a.

★Rosskerry (R), *Orchard Hill, EX39 2QY.* ✆ (023 72) 2872. Closed Jan–Feb, RS Nov–Dec. C. ⌘ 10 bedrs, 4 bp, 2 ba. ✗ mc, LD 7.30. ⓓ CH, TV, CP 10, CF 2, BGf, 3 st. £ BB £9·25–£11·25, DB £18·50–

£22·50, DBB £14·25–£16·25, ⓘ, Bk £3, D
£5, cc 1 2 3, Dep a.
Edelweiss, H, z (R), *2 Buttgarden St,
EX39 2AU.* ✆ (023 72) 2676. Closed Dec
(except Xmas). C5. ⍫ 8 bedrs, 2 sh, 2 ba,
Dgs. ⓐ CH, TV, CF. £ BB £7·50–£10, DB
£14–£19, WT (b) £80·50–£98, DT (b) £13–
£15·50, ②, Bk £2·75, L £2·95, D £6,
cc 1 2 3 5.

Repairer: Elliott & Sons (Motors) Ltd,
Kingsley Rd. ✆ (023 72) 2456.
Rescue Service: Boards Garage,
Torrington La. ✆ (023 72) 2292.
Piper, C & Son, Newport Garage, Wolsery
Village. ✆ Clovelly (023 73) 217.
Raleigh Garage (Bideford) Ltd, Northam
Rd. ✆ (023 72) 2384.
Warmington, L, C, Warmington's Garage, 7
Bridgeland St. ✆ (023 72) 2016.

BIDFORD-ON-AVON Warwickshire.
Map 14C
Pop 3,196. Stratford-upon-Avon 7½,
London 102, Birmingham 24, Bromsgrove
17, Droitwich 17, Evesham 7½.
Golf Stratford 18h. **See** 15th cent Bridge,
13th cent Church, Elizabethan house.

★★**White Lion,** *B50 4BQ.*
✆ (0789) 773309. C. ⍫ 16 bedrs, 1 bp, 7
bps, 2 ba, TV, Dgs. ✘ mc, at, LD 9. ⓐ CH,
TV, Dgs, CP 20, Ac, pf, con 20, 3 st. £ BBc
£17–£26, DBc £30–£32, DBB £21·50–
£24·50, WB, ②, Bk £3, L £4·60, D £8·50,
cc 1 2 6.

Rescue Service: Bidford Garages Ltd,
High St. ✆ (0789) 773363.

BIGBURY-ON-SEA Devon. Map 3F
Pop 532. Ashburton 21, London 209,
Kingsbridge 9, Plymouth 18, Tavistock 29,
Totnes 18.
Golf Bigbury 18h. **See** Clematon Hill (Nat
Trust), Burgh Island, Church spire.

★**Henley** (R) *Folly Hill, TQ7 4AR.* ✆ (054
881) 240. Open May–Sep and Easter. C3.
⍫ 9 bedrs, 4 bp, 1bps, 1 ba, Dgs. ✘ a l c,
mc, LD 7.30, ⓐ CH, TV, Dgs, CP 8, 1 BGf, 1
st. £ BB £11–£13, DB £22–£30, DBB £16–
£18, ⓘ, Bk £2, L £2, D £7.

BIGGLESWADE Bedfordshire. Map 15D
Pop 11,295. Baldock 7½, London 45,
A1(M) Motorway 6, Alconbury 22,
Bedford 11, Bletchley 24, Cambridge 22,
Huntingdon 20, Luton 19, Royston 16, St
Albans 27.
EC Thur. **MD** Sat. **Golf** John o'Gaunt 18h.
See 15th cent Church, Market House,
Shuttleworth Collection—planes, cars,
etc, at Old Warden Aerodrome, 4 m (off
A1)
◨★**Crown,** *High St, SG18 0JE.*
✆ (0767) 312228. RS Xmas. C. ⍫ 17
bedrs, 5 sh, 3 ba, TV, Dgs. ✘ a l c, mc, at,
LD 8.30. ⓐ CH, TV, Dgs, CP 21, Ac, CF, 1
st. £ BB £16·10–£18·40, DB £23·15–
£26·45, DBB £24·15–£26·45, ⓘ, Bk £3, D
£8, cc 1 6.

BILLESLEY Warwickshire. Map 14C
Stratford-upon-Avon 4, London 97,
Birmingham 24, Bromsgrove 17,
Worcester 22.

⇲★★★★**Billesley Manor,** *Stratford-upon-
Avon, B49 6NF.* ✆ Stratford-upon-Avon
(0789) 763737. C. ⍫ 28 bedrs, 28 bp, TV.
✘ a l c, mc, at, LD 9.30. ⓐ N, CH, CP 150,
G 6, sp, tc, sb, con 50, CF, 0 st. £ BB £41–

£49, DB £55·80–£88, WB, ⓘ, Bk £4, L £9, D
£16, cc 1 2 3 5 6, Dep b.

BILLINGE Merseyside. Map 20C
Pop 5,791. M6 Motorway 6, London 195,
Liverpool 14, Wigan 4½.

Rescue Service: Fleming Motor Repairs,
Newton Rd. ✆ (0744) 892165.

BILLINGHAM Teeside, Cleveland. Map
24F
Pop 34,000. Stockton-on-Tees 2½, London
346, Darlington 13, Durham 20,
Middlesbrough 4, Sunderland 23, West
Auckland 22.
MD Mon. **Golf** Billingham 18h. **See** St
Cuthbert's Church, Art Gallery.

★★★**Billingham Arms Thistle,** *The
Causeway, TS23 2LH.* ✆ Stockton-on-
Tees(0642) 553661. C. ⍫ 64 bedrs, 43
bp, 12 bps, ns, TV, Dgs. ✘ a l c, mc, LD
9.30. ⓐ Lt, N, CH, TV, Dgs, CP 100, G 2,
con 400, CF, 0 st. £ BB £33·75–£42·75, DB
£47·50–£57·50, WB, ②, Bk £4·75,
cc 1 2 3 4 5 6, Dep b.

Rescue Service: Billingham Auto Repairs,
Frederick Ter, Haverton Hill. ✆ Stockton-
on-Tees (0642) 563528.
Teeside Cars Ltd, 23 The Green.
✆ Stockton-on-Tees (0642) 554901.

BILLINGHURST West Sussex. Map 7C
Pop 5,570. Dorking 18, London 41,
Guildford 18, Haywards Heath 18,
Horsham 7, Petworth 8½, Pulborough 5½,
Worthing 17.
EC Wed. **Golf** Pulborough 18h. **See** Old
Church (15th cent wooden ceiling),
Unitarian Church.

Repairers: Hillview Garage Ltd, 107 High
St. ✆ (040 381) 2537.
Southern Counties Garages
(Billinghurst) Ltd, 62 High St.
✆ (040 381) 2022.
Specialist Body Repairer **Poplar Garage,**
Horsham Rd, Five Oaks.
✆ (040 381) 2075.
Rescue Service: Poplar Garage, Horsham
Rd, Five Oaks. ✆ (040 381) 2075.

BILSTON West Midlands. Map 21E
Pop 33,067. Birmingham 10, London 122,
Bromsgrove 17, Kidderminster 17, Walsall
4½, Wolverhampton 2½.
EC Thur. **MD** Mon, Fri, Sat. **See** Ancient
'Greyhound and Punchbowl' Inn, Museum,
St Leonard's Church.

Rescue Service: M F J Garage (Bilston)
Ltd, Millfield Service Station, 5 Millfields
Rd. ✆ (0902) 42116.

BINFIELD Berkshire. Map 6B
Pop 3,215. Staines 14, London 30,
Bagshot 7½, Basingstoke 20, Farnham 18,
Henley-on-Thames 10, Reading 8½,
Windsor 9½.
Golf Downshire Municipal 18h. **See**
Parish Church, Manor House.

Rescue Service: Cody Garage (Motor
Engineers) Ltd, London Rd. ✆ Bracknell
(0344) 21189.

BINGLEY West Yorkshire. Map 25E
Pop 13,300. Bradford 6, London 202,
Halifax 12, Leeds 14, Skipton 13,
Todmorden 18.
EC Tue. **MD** Wed, Fri, Sat. **Golf** Bingley
(St Ives) 18h. **See** Stocks, Cross and
Market House re-erected in Prince of
Wales Park, All Saints' Church.

★★★**Bankfield,** *Bradford Rd, BD16 1TU.*
✆ (0274) 567123. C. ⍫ 69 bedrs, 69 bp,
TV, Dgs. ✘ a l c, mc, at, LD 9.15. ⓐ N, CH,
Dgs, CP 250, Ac, con 200, CF, 3 st. £ BB fr
£37·25, DB fr £49·50, WB, ⓘ, Bk £4·25, L
£7·50, D £7·50, cc 1 2 3 4 5 6, Dep b.
Hall Bank, PH, y (Unl) *Beck Lane, BD16
4DD.* ✆ Bradford (0274) 565296. Closed
Xmas. C 2. ⍫ 10 bedrs, 2 bp, 1 bps, 2 sh, 2
ba. ✘ a l c. ⓐ CH, TV, ns, CP 20, CF, 1 BGf,
2 st. £ BB £10·35–£15, DB £20·12–£25·50,
ⓘ, Bk £2·30, D £5·17, cc 6.

BIRCHINGTON ON SEA Kent. Map
10D
Pop 7,923. Rochester 39, London 70,
Canterbury 12, Dover 20, Margate 3½,
Folkestone 23.
EC Wed. **Golf** Westgate and Birchington
18h. **See** All Saints' Church with Celtic
cross marking grave of D G Rossetti, Quex
Park, Powell Cotton Big Game Museum.

★★**Bungalow,** *Lyell Rd, CT7 9HX.*
✆ Thanet (0843) 41276.

Rescue Service: Jenners Garages Ltd,
214 Canterbury Rd, ✆ Thanet
(0843) 41241.

BIRDLIP Gloucestershire. M Areas 13F
and 14E
Pop 282. Andoversford 7½, London 98,
Cheltenham 6, Cirencester 10, Gloucester
7, Stroud 8½.
Golf Cotswold Hills 18h. **See** 13th cent
Parish Church.

Repairer: Birdlip Garage, Cirencester Rd.
✆ Witcombe (045 282) 2513.

BIRKENHEAD Merseyside. Maps 19A
and 20F
See also WALLASEY.
Pop 110,055. Chester 15, London 197,
M53 Motorway 3, Liverpool 2,
Queensferry 14.
EC Thur. **MD** Daily. **P** Disc Parking is in
operation on weekdays from 8 am to 6 pm.
Sundays and Bank Holidays are exempt.
PARKING IS FREE where indicated on the
carriageway by L-shaped white markings
at the termination points of the parking
places which will be connected by broken
white lines. PARKING DISCS must be
displayed on the nearside front of the
vehicle and can be obtained from the
Council's Parking Attendants, Municipal
Offices, hotels, shops, garages and police
stations. PARKING MUST NOT TAKE
PLACE WHERE THERE ARE YELLOW
LINES ALONG THE ROAD. **Golf** Arrowe
Park 18h. **See** Priory ruins, Town Hall,
Williamson Art Gallery, Queen Victoria
Memorial (styled in form of an Eleanor
Cross), Docks, Birkenhead Park, Bidston
Hill.
🛈 Central Library, Borough Rd.
✆ 051-652 6106.

★★★**M Bowler Hat,** *2 Talbot Rd, Oxton,
L43 2HH.* ✆ 051-652 4931. C. ⍫ 29
bedrs, 29 bp, TV, Dgs. ✘ a l c, mc, at, LD
10. ⓐ N, CH, Dgs, ns, CP 40, Ac, con 100,
CF, 2 st. £ BB £38·50–£40·42, DB £49–
£51·45, WT £210–£231, DT £54·40–
£58·12, WB, ⓘ, Bk £5·55, L £6·95, D £8·95,
cc 1 2 3 5 6, Dep a.
◨★★**Riverhill** (R), *Talbot Rd, Oxton, L43
2HJ.* ✆ 051-652 4847. C. ⍫ 17 bedrs, 5
bp, 2 bps, 4 ba, TV. ✘ a l c, mc, at, LD 10.
ⓐ CH, CP 25, Ac, CF, 7 BGf, 1 st, Dis. £ BB
£16·50–£22, DB £28–£33, WT £150, DT

£26, ②, Bk £1·50, L £3·50, D £5·95,
cc 1 2 3 5 6, Dep b.

■★★**Woodside,** Woodside, L41 5DG.
✆ 051-647 4121. C. ⊷ 27 bedrs, 5 bp, 6
bps, 5 ba. ✗ a l c, LD 9.15. ⓓ N, CH, TV, CP
75, Ac, CF, 3 st. £ BB £12·25–£15·12, DB
£22·80–£26·40, ②, 10%, Bk £3·20, L £5·50,
D £5·50, cc 1 2 3.

BIRMINGHAM West Midlands. Map
21D
See also SOLIHULL and SUTTON
COLDFIELD.
RAC Office, 1059 Alcester Road South,
Maypole, Birmingham, B14 5UH.
✆ (General) 021-430 8585. (Rescue
Service only) 021-430 3232.
RAC Office, 57 North Court, Birmingham
Shopping Centre, Birmingham B2 4XJ.
✆ 021-430 8585.
RAC Technical & Transport Services,
Technical Centre, 61A Maypole Lane,
Maypole, Birmingham, B14 5JX.
✆ 021-430 4460.
Pop 1,006,948. Coventry 18, London 111,
A38(M) Motorway 1½, Atherstone 19,
Bridgnorth 25, Bromsgrove 13, Droitwich
19, Evesham 30, Kidderminster 17,
Lichfield 15, Nuneaton 21, Stratford-
upon-Avon 23, Sutton Coldfield 7, Walsall
8½, Warwick 21, Wolverhampton 13.
See Plan, p. 142.
EC Wed (suburbs). **MD** Daily. **P** See Plan.
Golf Eight public courses and numerous
others. **See** University Buildings at
Edgbaston and Gosta Green, Cathedral
Church of St Philip (Burne-Jones
windows), Hall of Memory and Civic
Centre, RC Cathedral of St Chad, St
Martin's Church, Art Gallery and Museum,
Town Hall, Museum of Science and
Industry, Engineering and Building Centre,
Botanical Gardens, Midlands Art Centre,
Edgbaston New Repertory Theatre, BBC
Radio and TV Centre (Pebble Mill),
Sarehole Mill, Aston Hall (Jacobean), 16th
cent Blakesley Hall (Yardley), Weoley
castle (site).
ⓘ National Exhibition Centre, ✆ 021-780
4141.

★★★★**Albany** (TH), Smallbrook,
Queensway, B5 4EW. ✆ 021-643 8171. C.
⊷ 254 bedrs, 254 bp, TV, Dgs. ✗ a l c, mc,
at, LD 11. ⓓ Lt, N, CH, Ac, sp, sc, sb,
con 630, CF, 0 st. £ BB £48·50, DB
£63·50, WB, ①, cc 1 2 3 4 5 6.

★★★★**M Holiday Inn,** Holliday St, B1
1HH. ✆ 021-643 2766. C. ⊷ 304 bedrs,
304 bp, 2 ba, TV, Dgs. ✗ a l c, mc, at, LD
10.30. ⓓ Lt, N, CH, Dgs, Ac, sp, sb, sol,
gym, con 200, CF, 0 st. £ BB £38, DB £43,
WB, ②, Bk £4·25, L £7·45, D £7·95, Dep b.

★★★★**Midland,** New St, B2 4JT.
✆ 021-643 2601. C. ⊷ 114 bedrs, 100 bp,
9 bps, 5 sh, 4 ba, TV, Dgs. ✗ a l c, mc, at,
LD 10.30. ⓓ Lt, N, CH, Ac, com 200, CF.
£ BB £19·50–£45, DB £26·05–£55, DBB
£22–£30, ①, Bk £2·75, L £10·50, D £12·50,
cc 1 2 3 5 6, Dep b.

★★★★**Plough & Harrow,** Hagley Rd,
B16 8LS. ✆ 021-454 4111. C. ⊷ 44 bedrs,
44 bp, ns, TV, Dgs. ✗ a l c, mc, at. ⓓ Lt, N,
CH, ns, sb, con 90, CF, 11 BGf. £ B fr
£60·50, BD fr £71·50, WB, ①, Bk £6, L
£14·80, D £14·80, cc 1 2 3 4 5 6, Dep b.

■★★★★**M Strathallan Thistle,** Hagley
Rd, B16 9RY. ✆ 021-455 9777. C. ⊷ 170
bedrs, 170 bp, ns, TV, Dgs. ✗ a l c, mc, at,
LD 9.45. ⓓ Lt, N, CH, Dgs, CP 150, G 93,
Ac, sol, con, CF, 2 st. £ BB £43·95–£49·95,

DB £54·90–£58·40, WB, ②, Bk £4·95, L
£6·65, D £9, cc 1 2 3 4 5 6, Dep b.

★★★**M Apollo,** (R) Hagley Rd,
Edgbaston, B16 9RA. ✆ 021-455 0271. C.
⊷ 130 bedrs, 130 bp, TV, Dgs. ✗ a l c, mc,
at, LD 10.30. ⓓ Lt, N, CH, TV, Dgs, CP 130,
Ac, con 120, CF, 38 BGf, 0 st, Dis. £ BB
£38·70–£44·75, DB £49·25–£55·85, DBB
fr £57·50, WB, ①, Bk £4·50, L £7·50, D
£7·95, cc 1 2 3 4 5 6, Dep b.▲

★★★**Barr,** Newton Rd, Gt Barr, B43 6HS.
✆ 021-357 1141. RS Xmas and some
Bank Holidays. C. ⊷ . 111 bedrs, 111 bp,
TV. ✗ a l c, mc, at, LD 9.45 (exc. Fri and
Sun). ⓓ N, CH, CP 250, Ac, con 120, CF, 3
st. £ BB fr £35, DB £44, WB, ①, Bk £3·50, L
£5·50, D £6, cc 1 2 3 5, Dep.

■★★★**Birmingham International,**
New St, B2 4RX, ✆ 021-643 2747. Closed
Xmas. C. ⊷ 198 bedrs, 198 bp, TV, Dgs.
✗ a l c, mc, at, LD 9.45. ⓓ Lt, N, CH, Dgs,
Ac, con 200, CF, 1 st. £ BBc fr £29·50, DBc
fr £38·50, WB, Bk £3·25, L £5·15, D £7·95,
cc 1 2 3 4 5 6, Dep b.

★★★**Grand,** Colmore Row, B3 20A.
✆ 021-236 7951. Closed 4 dys Xmas. C.
⊷ 184 bedrs, 184 bp, TV, Dgs. ✗ a l c, mc,
at, LD 10. ⓓ Lt, N, CH, Dgs, Ac, con 500,
CF, 0 st. £ BB £39, DB £48, WB, ①, Bk
£4·25, L £7·20, B £7·20, cc 1 2 3 5, Dep b.

★★★**M Post House** (TH), Chapel La. Gt
Barr, B43 7BG. ✆ 021-357 7444. C.
⊷ 204 bedrs, 204 bp, TV, Dgs. ✗ a l c, mc,
at, LD 10. ⓓ N, CH, Dgs, CP 280, Ac, sp,
con 140, CF, 68 BGf, 0 st, Dis. £ BB
£39·50, DB £52, WB, ①, cc 1 2 3 4 5 6.

★★★**Royal Angus Thistle,** St Chads,
Queensway, B4 6HY. ✆ 021-236 4211. RS
Dec 26–29. C. ⊷ 140 bedrs, 140 bp, ns,
TV. ✗ a l c, mc, at, LD 10.30. ⓓ Lt, N, CH, CP
600, Ac, con 200, CF, 1 st. £ BB fr £41·75,
WB, ①, Bk £4·75, L £7·95, D £8·75,
cc 1 2 3 4 5 6, Dep b.

★★**Annabelle** (RI) 19 Sandon Rd, B17
8DP. ✆ 021-429 1182.

★★**Bailey House,** 21 Sandon Rd,
Edgbaston, B17 8DR. ✆ 021-429 1929.
Closed Xmas. C. ⊷ 16 bedrs, 1 bp, 6 bps, 9
sh, 2 ba, TV. ✗ a l c, mc, at, LD 8.30. ⓓ CH,
TV, CP 16, Ac, con 40, CF, 3 BGf, 2 st. £ BB
£18·37–£23·46, DB £27–£33, WB, ①, Bk
£3·50, L £2·50, D £7, cc 1 2 3 5 6, Dep b.

★★**Cobden** (Unl), 166 Hagley Rd, B16
9NZ. ✆ 021-454 6621. Closed Xmas. C.
⊷ 210 bedrs, 25 bp, 112 bps, 18 ba, TV,
Dgs. ✗ a l c, mc, at, LD 8.45 (7.45
weekends). ⓓ Lt, N, CH, TV, CP 130, Ac,
con 100, CF, 7 BGf, 0 st, Dis. £ BB £14–
£27, DB £28–£38, WB, ①, Bk £4, L £3, D
£6·50, cc 1 2 3, Dep b.

★★**Norfolk** (Unl), Hagley Rd, B16 9NA.
✆ 021-454 8071. Closed Xmas. C. ⊷ 175
bedrs, 32 bp, 56 bps, 37 ba, TV, Dgs.
✗ a l c, mc, at, LD 8.45 (7.45 weekends).
ⓓ Lt, N, CH, TV, CP 130, Ac, con 100, CF,
20 BGf, 0 st, Dis. £ BB £14–£27, DB £28–
£30, WB, ①, Bk £4, L £3, D £6·50, cc 1 2 3,
Dep b.

■★★**M Robin Hood,** Stratford Rd, Hall
Green. ✆ 021-745 9900. C. ⊷ 29 bedrs,
29 bp, TV. ✗ a l c, LD 10.30. ⓓ N, CH, CF,
14 BGf, 1 st, Dis. £ BB fr £24·75, DB fr £33,
WB, ②, Bk £4·50, L £3·20, D £5, cc 1 2 3 6,
Dep.

Alexander, G, x (RI), 44 Bunbury Rd,
Northfield, B31 2DW. ✆ 021-475 4341. C.
⊷ 12 bedrs, 2 ba, Dgs. ⓓ ch, TV, CP 12,
CF, 1 st. £ BB fr £11·50, DB fr £20, WT (b)
fr £80, DT fr £17·50, ①.

Bridge House, PH, z (RI), 49 Sherbourne
Rd, Acocks Green, B27 9DQ. ✆ 021-706
5900.

Bristol Court, H, yz, (Rt), 250 Bristol Rd,
Edgbaston, B5 7SL. ✆ 021-472 0413. C.
⊷ 32 bedrs, 9 bp, 6 bps, 4 ba, TV, Dgs.
✗ a l c. ⓓ CH, TV, Dgs, CP 25, G 6, CF, 2
BGf, 3 st. £ BB £18·90–£21·60, DB £30–
£33·40, WT £147, ①, Bk £2·75, L £3·50, D
£6·50, cc 1 2 3 5.

Hurstwood, H, z (RI) 775, Chester Rd,
B24 0BY. ✆ 021-373 8212.

Kerry House, PH, z (RI), 946 Warwick
Rd, Acocks Green, B27 6QC. ✆ 021-707
0316. C 3. ⊷ 23 bedrs, 3 bps, 17 sh, 2 ba,
TV, Dgs. ⓓ CH, TV, CP 23, 3 st. £ BB £16,
DB £22, ①, Bk £3·50, D £6·50.

Lyndhurst, H, z. (RI), 135 Kingsbury
Rd, Erdington, B24 8QT. ✆ 021-373 5695.
C. ⊷ 15 bedrs, 1 bp, 3 sh, 4 ba, TV. ✗ a l c.
ⓓ CH, TV, CP 15, CF, 5 BGf, 2 st. £ BB
£12·08–£16·10, DB £20·70–£21·85, WT
£70–£80·50, DT £16·68–£17·83, ①, Bk £3,
D £4·60, cc 1 2 3 5.▲

Rollason Wood, PH, z (RI), Woodend
Rd, Erdington, B24 2BJ. ✆ 021-373 1230.
C. ⊷ 33 bedrs, 5 bp, 5 bps, 1 sh, 6 ba, Dgs.
ⓓ CH, TV, Dgs, CP 40, CF, 3 BGf, 2 st.
£ BB £8–£13·75, DB £13·50–£24, WT (c)
£43·50–£75, ①, D £2·20, cc 1 2 3 4 5 6.

Tri-Star, Coventry Rd, Elmdon, B26 3QR.
✆ 021-799 2233.

Warwick, H, z (RI), 419–421 Hagley Rd.
✆ 021-429 1663. C. ⊷ 17 bedrs, 4 bps, 7
sh, 2 ba, TV, Dgs. ✗ a l c. ⓓ CH, TV, Dgs,
CP 22, CF, 3 st. £ BB £14·95–£18·90, DB
£25·50–£27·50, WT (b) £90–£120, DT (b)
£19·90, ①, Bk £3·50, L £4·50, D £4·95,
cc 3.

Welcome House, G, z (Unl), 1641
Coventry Rd, B26 1DD. ✆ 021-707 3232.
Closed Xmas week. C 5. ⊷ 7 bedrs, 1 sh, 1
ba, TV. ⓓ CH, CP 6. £ BB £10, DB £20, WT
(c) £70, ①, cc 3.

Wentsbury, PH, y (Unl), 21 Serpentine
Rd, Selly Park, B29 7HU. ✆ 021-4721258.
C. ⊷ 9 bedrs, 3 sh, 2 ba. ⓓ CH, TV,
Dgs, CP 10, U 1, CF, 4 st. £ BB £12·50, DB
£20, WT £110, DT (b) £17·50, ①, Bk £2, L
£4, D £5·50.

Wentworth, H, x (RI), 103 Wentworth
Rd, Harborne, B17 9SU. ✆ 021-427 2839,
Closed Xmas week. C. ⊷ 21 bedrs, 2 bp, 5
sh, 3 ba, ns. ✗ a l c. ⓓ CH, TV, Dgs, CP 14,
U 2, CF, 1 BGf, 2 st. £ BB fr £12·08, DB fr
£23, DT (a) £22, (b) £17·50, ①, Bk £3·50, L
£4, D £6.

Westley Arms, H, z, Westley Rd, B27
7UJ. ✆ 021-706 4312.

Willow Tree, H, z (Unl), 759 Chester Rd,
B24 0BY. ✆ 021-373 6388. C. ⊷ 5 bedrs,
3 sh, 1 ba, TV. ✗ a l c. ⓓ CH, TV, CP 5, CF.
£ BB £14–£16, DB £24, ①.

Repairers: Bellamy & Co (Birmingham)
Ltd, 37 Clement St. ✆ 021-233-3542.
Hanger Motor Co (Birmingham) Ltd,
Kingsbury Rd. ✆ 021-373 8121 and at
Sheepcote St. ✆ 021-643 7131.
Patrick Motors Ltd, 479 Bristol Rd,
Bournbrook. ✆ 021-472 1331.
Renault U.K. Ltd, 75 High St, Bordesley.
✆ 021-773 8251.
Ryland Vehicles Ltd, Ryland House,
Ryland St. ✆ 021-455 7171.
Tessall Garage Ltd, 1306 Bristol Rd
South. ✆ 021-475 5241.
Yardley Wood Service Station, Yardley
Wood Rd. ✆ 021-474 4972.

BIRMINGHAM

To M6 Int 5
A47
A4540

To M6 Int 6
A38(M)

To Lichfield 16m.
A38

To Walsall 9 m.
A34

To Crematorium 3m.
To M6 Int.7

To Wednesbury 7 m.
A34

To M5 Int.1
A41

To Dudley 8m.
A457

To Kidderminster 17m.
A456
To M5 Int 3

To M5 Int. 2
(A4123) Wolverhampton 17m.

A38
To M5 Int.4

To Crematorium 4m.
To Bromsgrove 18 m.

To Stratford 24m.
A34
To Crematorium 3½m.

Net chells Parkway

Lawley St.
Dartmouth St.
Canal
Howe St.
Prospect Row
Woodcock St.
Corporation St.
Aston Road
Birmingham Polytechnic
University of Aston
University of Aston
Aston St.
James Watt Queensway
Lancaster St.
West Midlands County Hall
St. Chad's Queensway
Lower Loveday St.
Lister St.
Summer Lane
St. Chad's Cathedral (R.C.)
St. Chad's Circus
Constitution Hill
Snow Hill
Colmore Row
Ringway
Law Courts
Steelhouse Lane
Police H.Q.
Police Sta.
Priory
Ringway
Dale End
Albert St.
Fazeley St.
Moor St. Station
Bull Ring Centre
St. Martin's Church
Birmingham Shopping Centre
Curzon St.
Goods Station
Cattle Market
Canal
New St.
Fazeley St.
Bordesley St.
Digbeth
Meriden
Moor St. Queensway
Masshouse Circus
Masshouse Ringway
High St.
St. Martin's Circus
Bull Ring
Multi-storey Car Park
Ped. Precinct
Corporation St.
St. Philip's Cath.
Council House
Waterloo St.
New St.
Bull St.
Union St.
Cherry St.
Temple Row
Needless Alley
Bennett's Hill
New St.
Navigation St.
New Street Station
Multi-storey Car Parks
Smallbrook Queensway
John Bright St.
Hill St.
P.O.
Hinckley St.
Art Gallery & Museum
Council H.Q.
Information Centre
Victoria Sq.
Paradise St.
Great Charles St. Queensway
Livery St.
Ludgate Hill
Snow Hill
Lionel St.
Canal
Newhall St.
Charlotte St.
George St.
St. Paul's Sq.
Summer Row
Fleet St.
Cambridge St.
Newhall Hill
Sand Pits Parade
Vyse St.
Warstone Lane
Central Library
Paradise Circus
Civic Centre (Baskerville House)
Town Hall
Central T.V.
New Repertory Theatre
Bingley Hall
Multi-storey Car Park
Birmingham Multi-storey Car Park
Suffolk Street Queensway
Underpass
Broad St.
Canal
Cattle Heath
Mill St.
High St.
Digbeth
Deritend

RAC Midland Counties Office
1059 Alcester Road South

RAC Birmingham City Centre Office
57 North Court
Birmingham Shopping Centre

0 miles 5

P Car Park
C Public Conveniences
··· Parking Meter Zone

142

Specialist Body Repairers: Ashley Repairs Ltd, Hay Rd, Hay Mills. ✆ 021-722 5364.
California Garage, Barnes Hill, Weoley Castle. ✆ 021-427 5231.
Davies & Gibberson Ltd, Railway Arches, Floodgate St. ✆ 021-643 5493.
Hanger Motor Co (Birmingham) Ltd, 187 Broad St. ✆ 021-373 8121.
Harborne Garage Ltd, 78 Station Rd. ✆ 021-427 1218
Henry Martyn Car Body Repairs, 40 Knights Rd, Tyseley. ✆ 021-706 8639.
W H Perry Ltd, 32 Bartholomew St. ✆ 021-643 1419.
Renault U.K. Ltd, 75 High St, Bordesley ✆ 021-773 8251
Tessall Garage Ltd, 1306 Bristol Rd South. ✆ 021-475 5241.
Yenton Motor Co Ltd, 103 Goosemore La, Erdington. ✆ 021-373 4360.
MC Repairers: Forumburn Ltd, T/As Midland Motor Cycles, 529 Coventry Rd, Small Heath, ✆ 021-772 1733.
Chas Mann, The Green, Kings Norton. ✆ 021-458-3074.
Moto-Continental, 661 Bristol Rd, Selly Oak. ✆ 021-472 7760.
Rescue Service: Albany Garage (Stechford), 11 Albert Rd, Stechford. ✆ 021-783 4572.
Ashley Repairs Ltd, Hay Rd, Hay Mills. ✆ 021-722 5364.
Beeches 24 hour Rescue/Recovery Service, Beeches Service Station, Aldridge Rd, Great Barr. ✆ 021-360 2218 and 9192.
Birches Garage (Hall Green) Ltd, Stratford Rd, Hall Green. ✆ 021-777 1131.
California Garage, Barnes Hill, 29. ✆ 021-427 4321.
Check Point Garage, 160 Handsworth New Rd, Winson Green. ✆ 021-523 9200.
Clark's Motor Services (Rednal) Ltd, Rednal Garage, 472 Lickey Rd, Rednal. ✆ 021-453 3117
Coles of Birmingham, 32 Coventry Rd, Bordesley. ✆ 01-772 5916
George Heath Motors (Prop. Talbot Motor Co Ltd), P.O. Box 263, Coventry Rd, Small Heath. ✆ 021-772 4388.
Harborne Garage Ltd, 78 Station Rd, Harborne. ✆ 021-449 3738.
Jameson A F (B'ham) Ltd, 27 Summer Lane, Newtown. ✆ 021-359 7991.
Maypole Garage Ltd, 1057 Alcester Rd South, Hollywood. ✆ 021-430 5161.
Motor Safe Auto's, 518 Alum Rock Rd, Alum Rock, ✆ 021-327 1838.
Murco Service Station, Turnhouse Rd, Castle Vale. ✆ 021-747 6326.
Ridgeacre Service Station, Ridgeacre Rd, Quinton. ✆ 021-421 3978.
Rottner & Rudge Ltd, T/As Pershore Road Service Station, 582 Pershore Rd. ✆ 021-472 0244.
Stockfield Motor Repairs Ltd, Stockfield Rd, South Yardley. ✆ 021-707 8140 & 021-706 0734.
Stonehouse Motors Ltd, Barnes Hill, California. ✆ 021-427 6201.
Swan Motors, Coventry Rd. ✆ 021-706 1688 and 1680.
Tame Service Station, 230 Birmingham Rd, Great Barr. ✆ 021-357 7960 & 021-358 5986.
Transdart Ltd, Frankley Service Area, M5 Motorway, Illey La. ✆ 021-550 5197.
Witherford Motor Garage, Bristol Rd, Selly Oak. ✆ 021-475 1614.

Yardley Wood Service Station, Yardley Wood Rd. ✆ 021-474 4972.
Yenton Motor Co Ltd, 103 Goosemoor La, Erdington. ✆ 021-373 4360.

BIRMINGHAM AIRPORT West Midlands. Map 21D
Coventry 11, London 105, Atherstone 15, Birmingham 7, Bromsgrove 19, Evesham 30, Nuneaton 18, Stratford-upon-Avon 22, Sutton Coldfield 11, Tamworth 15.

★★★★**Excelsior** (TH), *Coventry Rd, B26 3QW.* ✆ 021-743 8141. C. 🛏 141 bedrs, 141 bp, TV, Dgs. ✗ a l c, mc, LD 10.15. 🅿 N, CH, Dgs, CP 200, Ac, con 170, CF, 47 BGf, 0 st. £ BB £41·50, DB £56, WB, 🅣, cc 1 2 3 4 5 6.

BIRSTALL West Yorkshire. Map 25F/33A
Dewsbury 3, London 190, Bradford 6, Huddersfield 8, Leeds 7.

Rescue Service: Highway Recovery (Northern) Ltd, Gelderd Rd. ✆ Batley (0924) 477474.

BIRTLEY Tyne & Wear. Maps 32C, 24E, 31F
Pop 8,724. A1 1¼m, Chester-le-Street 3, London 268, Consett 14, Gateshead 3, South Shields 10, Sunderland 10.
EC Wed. **MD** Sun. **Golf** Birtley 9h. **See** Bowes Railway—only rope-hauled railway in preservation.

Rescue Service: Durham Road Service Station, Durham Road. ✆ (0632) 403485.

BISHOP AUCKLAND Durham. Map 24E
Pop 15,839. West Auckland 3, London 251, Alston 36, Corbridge 29, Darlington 11, Durham 11, Hexham 32, Middleton-in-Teesdale 19, Stockton-on-Tees 19.
EC Wed. **MD** Thur, Sat. **Golf** Bishop Auckland 18h. **See** 12th cent Castle, Roman Heating Chamber at Vinovium (Binchester), Saxon Church (Escomb), Auckland Castle, residence of the Bishops of Durham since 12th cent (Chapel viewable by arr).

★★**Binchester Hall,** *DL14 8DJ.* ✆ (0388) 604646. C. 🛏 21 bedrs, 3 bp, 7 bps, 4 sh, 1 ba, TV, Dgs. ✗ a l c, mc, LD 10. 🅿 CH, TV, Dgs, CP 150, Ac, pf, con 100, CF, 1 st. £ BB £10–£16, DB £18–£21, WB, 🅕, Bk £1·30, L £2, D £5.

★★**Queens Head,** *Market Place, DL14 7NX.* ✆ (0388) 603477. 🛏 10 bedrs, 4 bp, 1 bps, 3 sh. 1 ba, TV, Dgs. ✗ mc, at, LD 9.15. 🅿 CH, Dgs, CP 30, Ac, pf, con 200, CF. £ BB fr £15·25, DB fr £23·50, DBB fr £21·65, 🅣, L £4·50, D £6·40, cc 1 2 3 5 6.

BISHOP MIDDLEHAM Durham. M. Area 24E
Sedgefield 3, A1 (M) 4, London 255, Bishop Auckland 9½ Darlington 14, Durham 8½, Hartlepool 14, Stockton-on-Tees 11.

Rescue Service: Bishop Middleham Garage, High St. ✆ Ferryhill (0740) 51587.

BISHOP'S CAUNDLE Dorset. Map 5F
Pop 350. Sturminster Newton 6½, London 118, Blandford Forum 14, Dorchester 16, Shaftesbury 15, Yeovil 10.
Golf Sherborne 18h. **See** Church.

Rescue Service: Caundle Service Station, Main Street ✆ (096 323) 81328.

BISHOPS FROME Hereford & Worcester (Herefordshire) Map 13D
Pop 651. Worcester 14, London 127, Bromyard 4½, Hereford 12, Ledbury 8, Leominster 16, Ross-on-Wye 19.
Golf Herefordshire 18h. **See** Church.

Rescue Service: Partridge, B C, The Garage. ✆ Munderfield (088 53) 235.

BISHOP'S LYDEARD Somerset. Map 4D
Pop 2,280. Taunton 5, London 148, Bridgwater 11, Dunster 17, Exeter 31, Minehead 18, South Molton 33, Tiverton 20.
Golf Taunton 18h. **See** 15th cent Church (14th cent cross in churchyard), 17th cent almshouses, West Somerset Rly (Steam Engines).

Rescue Service: Brendon Motors, ✆ (0823) 208 and (0823) 250.

BISHOP'S STORTFORD Hertfordshire. Map 17F
Pop 24,000. Epping 13, London 31, M11 Motorway 1½, Baldock 20, Brentwood 23, Cambridge 27, Chelmsford 18, Dunmow 9, Hoddesdon 14, Hatfield 22, Haverhill 24, Newmarket 32, Royston 19.
EC Wed. **MD** Thur. **Golf** Bishop's Stortford 18h. **See** Cecil Rhodes birthplace, Rhodes Memorial Museum, St Michael's Church, old inns.
🅸 The Causeway. ✆ Bishop's Stortford (0279) 55261.

★★★**Foxley** (R), *Foxley Dr. Stanstead Rd, CM23 2EB.* ✆ (0279) 53977. Closed 1 week after Xmas. C. 🛏 12 bedrs, 12 bp, 2 ba, annexe 2 bedrs, TV, Dgs. ✗ a l c, mc, at, LD 9.30. 🅿 CH, TV, Dgs, CP 20, con 20, CF. £ cc 1 3 6.

Brook House, H, y (R). *29 Northgate End, CM23 2LD.* ✆ (0279) 57892. C. 🛏 24 bedrs, 10 bp, 12 bps, 1 ba, TV. ✗ a l c, mc, LD 9.15. 🅿 CH, TV, CP 26, CF, 8 st. £ BB £19·50–£24, DB £27–£29, 🅣, Bk £3·75, L £7, D £7.

Repairers: Bradford, J R & Co, The Garage, Dunmow Rd. ✆ (0279) 54335.
Chantry Garage (Northgate) Ltd, Northgate End. ✆ (0279) 53127.
Rescue Service: Franklin's Garage Ltd, The Causeway. ✆ (0279) 52305.
Whalley, John Ltd, London Rd. ✆ (0279) 54181.

BISHOPSTEIGNTON Devon. Map 3D
Pop 1,900. Exeter 13, London 181, Newton Abbot 4, Torquay 9.
EC Thur. **Golf** Teignmouth 18h. **See** Old walls of 11th cent. Bishop of Exeter's Palace, Church.

Rescue Service: Central Garage, 35 Fore St. ✆ Teignmouth (062 67) 5253.

BITTON Avon. Map 5B
2 m NE of Keynsham. Chippenham 16, London 107, Bath 6, Bristol 7, Shepton Mallet 21.

MC Repairer: Pillion Motor Cycles, Bath Rd. ✆ (027 588) 6655.

BLABY Leicestershire. Map 14B
Pop 6,997. Northampton 28, London 95, Ashby-de-la-Zouch 19, Coventry 21, Daventry 23, Hinckley 11, Leicester 4½, Market Harborough 14, Rugby 15, Towcester 34.
EC Wed. **Golf** Cosby Leicester 18h.

Repairer: Blaby Garage Ltd, 21 Leicester Rd. ✆ Leicester (0533) 773322.

BLACKBURN Lancashire. Map 27D
Pop 89,313. Bolton 13, London 208, Burnley 11, Bury 15, Chorley 10, Preston 10, Rochdale 18, Skipton 28, Todmorden 19, Whalley 7.
EC Thur. **MD** Wed, Fri, Sat. **Golf** Blackburn 18h. **See** Cathedral, Museum and Art Gallery, Lewis Textile Museum, Nature Trail (Witton Park), Ribchester Museum of Roman Antiquities 5 m NW.
🛈 Town Hall. ✆ Blackburn (0254) 55201 Ext 214.

★★★M Blackburn Moat House,
Preston New Rd, BB2 7BE.
✆ (0254) 64441. C. ⋈ 98 bedrs, 98 bp, TV, Dgs. ✗ a l c, mc, at, LD 10.30. 🖪 Lt, N, CH, Dgs, CP 400, Ac, sp, con 350, CF, 15 BGf, 0 st, Dis. £ BB £33, DB £43, WB, 🗓, Bk £3·75, L £6, D £7, cc 1 2 3 4 5 6, Dep b.

Repairers: Cliff Holden (Blackburn) Ltd, West End Garage, Preston New Rd.
✆ (0254) 52662.
Cuerden Motors Ltd, King St.
✆ (0254) 52981.
Rescue Service: Beardsworth, G & Sons Ltd, Stancliffe St Garage.
✆ (0254) 54480.

BLACKCROSS Cornwall. Map 2D
Bodmin 13, London 246, Newquay 7, Penzance 37, Truro 13, Wadebridge 10.

Home Stake Farm, F, x (Unl), *nr Newquay TR8 4LU.* ✆ St Austell (0726) 860423. Open Apr–Oct. C. ⋈ 8 bedrs, 2 ba, Dgs. 🖪 ch, TV, Dgs, CP 12, CF, 2 BGf, 0 st, Dis. £ BB £6·50–£7, DB £13–£14, WT (b) £56–£59·50, DT (b) £8·50–£9, 🗓.

BLACKPOOL Lancashire. Map 27F
See also THORNTON CLEVELEYS.
Pop 147,200. Preston 16, London 228, M55 Motorway 4, Lancaster 24.
See Plan, p. 145.
EC Wed. **P** See Plan. **Golf** Blackpool Park 18h, North Shore 18h. **See** Tower (518ft), Winter Gardens, International Circus, Zoo Park, Model Village (Stanley Park), Tussaud's Waxworks, Art Gallery, Autumn Illuminations, Last electric trams in Britain.
🛈 1 Clifton St. ✆ Blackpool (0253) 21623.

★★★★Imperial, *North Promenade, FY1 2HB.* ✆ (0253) 23971. C. ⋈ 159 bedrs, 159 bp, TV, Dgs. ✗ a l c, mc, at, LD 10.30. 🖪 Lt, N, CH, CP 200, Ac, sp, sb, sol, con 350, CF, 5 st. £ BB £36, DB £51, WT £288·75, WB, 🗓, Bk £4·50, L £7·50, D £7·50, cc 1 2 3 4 5, Dep b.

★★★★Pembroke, *North Promenade, FY1 2JQ.* ✆ (0253) 23434. C. ⋈ 201 bedrs, 201 bp, TV, Dgs. ✗ a l c, mc, at, LD 10.30 (11 Sat). 🖪 Lt, N, CH, TV, CP 300, Ac, sp, con 650, CF, 0 st. £ BB £37–£39·75, DB £52–£56·75, DBB fr £25·50, WB, 🗓, Bk £5·50, L £6·50, D £7·50, cc 1 2 3 4 5, Dep.

★★★Savoy, *Queen's Promenade, FY2 9SJ.* ✆ (0253) 52561. C. ⋈ 126 bedrs, 116 bp, 10 ba, TV, Dgs. ✗ a l c, mc, at, LD 11.45 (8.30 Sun). 🖪 Lt, N, CH, TV, CP 40, Ac, con 300, CF, 4 st. £ BB £17–£21, DB £34–£42, DBB £24–£28, WB, 🗓, Bk £2·50, L £4·25, D £7·50, cc 1 2 3 4 5 6, Dep.

★★Carlton, *North Promenade, FY1 2EZ.* ✆ (0253) 28966. C. ⋈ 58 bedrs, 31 bp, 8

bps, 6 ba, TV, Dgs. ✗ a l c, mc, at, LD 8.45. 🖪 Lt, N, CH, CP 50, Ac, con 80, CF, 0 st. £ BB £18–£26, DB £29–£40, WT £143–£163, DT £20·50–£25·50, WB, 🗓, Bk £3, L £2·95, D £5·50, cc 1 2 3 5, Dep b.

★★Chequers (RI), *24 Queens Promenade, FY2 9RN.* ✆ (0253) 56431. RS First 2 weeks Jan. C. ⋈ 46 bedrs, 41 bp, 5 bps, TV, Dgs. ✗ a l c, mc, at, LD 7.45. 🖪 Lt, N, CH, CP 27, G 3, Ac, CF, 5 st. £ BB £25–£26, DB £32–£43·50, WT £126–£150, DBB £22·50–£32·50, WB, 🗓, Bk £3, L £3·25, D £6·50, cc 1 2 3 5 6, Dep b.

★★Claremont, *270 North Promenade, FY1 1SA.* ✆ (0253) 293122. C. ⋈ 143 bedrs, 143 bp, TV, Dgs. ✗ mc, at, LD 8.30. 🖪 Lt, N, CH, TV, Dgs, CP 100, Ac, con 300, CF, 10 BGf. £ BB £14·75–£41, DB £29·50–£44, DBB £21·75–£29·50, WB, 🗓, Bk £3, L £3·95, D £7, cc 1 2 3, Dep b.▲

🔳 **★★Cliffs,** *Queen's Promenade, FY2 9SG.* ✆ (0253) 52388. C. ⋈ 160 bedrs, 120 bp, 20 ba, TV, Dgs. ✗ a l c, at, LD 9. 🖪 Lt, N, CH, TV, CP 70, Ac, con 400, CF, 0 st. £ BB £12–£41·50, DB £20–£41·50, DBB £19–£28·25, WB, 🗓, Bk £3, L £4·75, D £7, cc 1 2 3, Dep b.▲

★★Gables Balmoral (R), *Balmoral Rd, FY4 1HP.* ✆ (0253) 45432. C. ⋈ 70 bedrs, 64 bp, 6 bps, TV, Dgs. ✗ a l c, mc, at, LD 9.30. 🖪 N, CH, TV, Dgs, CP 4, Ac, con 500, CF, 1 BGf, 4 st. £ BB £22–£30, DB £36–£42, DBB £28–£36, WB, 🗓, Bk £3·50, L £4·50, D £6, cc 1 2 3 5 6, Dep b.

★★Headlands (RI), *New South Promenade, FY4 1NJ.* ✆ (0253) 41179.

★★Kimberley (RI), *New South Promenade, FY4 1NQ.* ✆ (0253) 41184. Closed Jan 2–15. C. ⋈ 52 bedrs, 30 bp, 8 ba, TV, Dgs. ✗ mc, at, LD 7.30. 🖪 Lt, N, TV, CP 24, con 120, CF, 2 BGf, 4 st. £ BB £11·25–£14.45, DB £22·50–£26·50, WT £124·60–£133·35, DT £16·75–£19·05, 🗓, Bk £3, L £3·65, D £4·50, cc 1 3, Dep a.▲

🔳 **★★Warwick,** *603 New South Promenade, FY4 1NG.* ✆ (0253) 42192. RS first 2 weeks Jan and first 2 weeks Nov. C. ⋈ 52 bedrs, 47 bp, 5 bps, TV, Dgs. ✗ mc, at, LD 8. 🖪 N, CH, TV, Dgs, CP 40, Ac, sp, sol, con 80, CF, 6 st. £ BB £14–£24, DB £32–£40, DBB £22–£26, WB, 🗓, Bk £4, D £8, cc 1 2 3 5 6, Dep b.

★Revill's (RI), *1924 North Promenade, FY1 1RJ.* ✆ (0253) 25768. C. ⋈ 53 bedrs, 9 bp, 1 bps, 9 ba, ns, TV. ✗ mc, at. 🖪 Lt, N, CH, TV, CP 21, Ac, con 50, CF, 10 st. £ BB £11–£14, DB £22–£28, DBB £15·50–£18·50, WB, 🗓, Bk £3, L £3·50, D £5, cc 1 2 3, Dep a.

Arandora Star, PH, z (R), *559 New South Promenade, FY4 1NF.*
✆ (0253) 41528. Closed 30 Oct–20 Dec. C. ⋈ 18 bedrs, 3 ba, Dgs. 🖪 CH, CP 12, G 4, CF, 1 st. £ BB fr £7·48, DB fr £15·96, DT (b) £9·78, 🗓, cc 3.▲

Arosa, PH, z (RI), *18 Empress Dr, FY2 9SD.* ✆ (0253) 52555. Open May–Oct & Xmas. C. ⋈ 21 bedrs, 2 bp, 7 bps, 3 ba, Dgs. 🖪 CH, TV, CP 6, CF, 2 st. £ BB £10–£14, DB £20–£28, WT (b) fr £70, 🗓.

Ashcroft, PH, z (RI), *42 King Edward Av, FY2 9TA.* ✆ (0253) 51538. Open Apr–Oct. C. ⋈ 11 bedrs, 2 ba, TV, Dgs. 🖪 CH, TV, CP 4, CF, 1 st. £ BB £7·25–£9·50, DB £14·50–£19, WT (b) £59–£79, DT (b) £8·95–£11·95, 🗓.

Beauclif, PH, z (Unl), *22 Holmfield Rd, North Shore, FY2 9TB.* ✆ (0253) 51663. Open Apr–Oct. C. 4. ⋈ 12 bedrs, 2 ba. 🖪 ch, TV, CP 10, 2 st. £ BB £9–£10, DB

£16–£17, DT (b) £9·25–£10·25, 🗓, Bk £2·75, D £3·75.

Berwick, PH, z (RI), *23 King Edward Ave, FY2 9TA.* ✆ (0253) 51496. C. 3. ⋈ 8 bedrs, 1 sh, 2 ba. 🖪 CH, TV, 0 st. £ BB £7–£9·50, DB £14–£20·50, WT (b) £59·50–£80, DT (b) £8·50–£12, 🗓, cc 1.

Brabyns, PH, z (R), *1–3 Shaftesbury Ave, FY2 9QQ.* ✆ (0253) 52163.

Bromley, PH, z (Unl), *306 North Promenade, FY1 2EH.* ✆ (0253) 24171. C. ⋈ 14 bedrs, 2 bp, 12 bps, TV, Dgs. 🖪 CH, Dgs, CP 10, 7 st. £ BB £11–£14, DB £18–£20, WT (c) £45–£55, 🗓, cc 13.

Burlees, PH, z (Unl), *40 Knowle Ave, North Shore, FY2 9TQ.* ✆ (0253) 54535. Open Mar–Oct. C. ⋈ 10 bedrs, 2 ba, Dgs. 🖪 ch, TV, Dgs, ns, CP 5, G 1, CF, 1 st. £ BB fr £8·50, DB fr £16, WT fr £77, DT fr £11·50, 🗓, Bk £2, L £4.

Cliftonville, PH, z (RI), *14 Empress Dr, FY2 9SE.* ✆ (0253) 51052. Open Apr–Oct & Xmas & New Year. C. ⋈ 20 bedrs, 18 bps, 3 ba. 🖪 CH, TV, CP 4, CF, 0 st. £ BB £7·50–£15, DB £16–£31, WT (b) £75–£104, DT £11–£17, 🗓, Bk £1·25, D £2·50.

Denely, PH, z (Unl), *15 King Edward Av, FY2 9TA.* ✆ (0253) 52757. C. ⋈ 9 bedrs, 1 bps, 2 sh. 🖪 CH, TV, CP 5, CF, 5 st. £ BB £8–£9, DB £16–£19, WT (b) £70–£73·50, DT (b) £10–£10·50, 🗓.

Derwent, PH, z (RI), *8 Gynn Ave, FY1 2LD.* ✆ (0253) 55194. C 3. ⋈ 12 bedrs, 4 bps, Dgs. 🖪 CH, TV, Dgs, CP 4, U 1, CF, 1 st. £ BB £9·50–£11·50, DB £18–£22, WT (b) £70–£77, DT (b) £11–£12, 🗓, Bk £2, D £3·50.

Hartshead, PH, z (RI), *17 King Edward Av, FY2 9TA.* ✆ (0253) 53133. Closed Xmas. C 3. ⋈ 8 bedrs, 1 sh, 2 ba, Dgs. 🖪 CH, TV, CP 5, CF. £ BB £7·50–£8·50, DB £15–£17, WT £63–£68·25, DT £9–£9·75, 🗓.

Holm Lea, PH, z (Unl), *22 Lowther Av. FY2 9PE.* ✆ (0253) 52136. C. ⋈ 5 bedrs, 1 ba. 🖪 CH, TV. £ BB fr £8, DB fr £15, 🗓.

Knowsley, H, z (RI), *68 Dean St, FY4 1BP.* ✆ (0253) 43414. C. ⋈ 14 bedrs, 4 bps, 2 ba, Dgs. 🖪 CH, TV, Dgs, CP 4, CF. £ BB £10·50–£13·50, DB £20–£26, WT (b) £78–£92·50, 🗓, Bk £2·50, L £3·50, D £4·50

Lyndale, *13 Northumberland Av, FY2 9SB.* ✆ (0253) 54033.

Lynstead, PH, z (RI), *40 King Edward Av. FY2 9TA.* ✆ (0253) 51050.

New Heathcot, PH, z (RI), *270 Queens Prom, FY2 9HD.* ✆ (0253) 52083. C. ⋈ 9 bedrs, 2 ba, Dgs. 🖪 CH, TV, CP 6, CF. £ BB £8–£8·50, DB £16–£17, WT (b) £66·50–£70, DT (b) £9·50–£10, 🗓.

North Mount, PH, z (R), *King Edward Av. FY2 9TD.* ✆ (0253) 55937. C. ⋈ 8 bedrs, 3 ba, Dgs. 🖪 CH, TV, Dgs, CP 1, CF, 1 st.

Sunny Cliff, PH, z (RI), *98 Queens Promenade, FY2 9NS.* ✆ (0253) 51155. Open Apr–Oct & Xmas. C. ⋈ 12 bedrs, 2 ba, Dgs. 🖪 ch, TV, CP 10, CF. £ BB £8–£9, DB £16–£18, WT £70–£73, DT £10–£11·50, 🗓, D £5.

Sunray, G, z (Unl). *42 Knowle Av, North Shore, FY2 9TQ.* ✆ (0253) 51937. Closed Xmas. C. ⋈ 8 bedrs, 1 bp, 7 bps, 1 ba, TV, Dgs. 🖪 CH, TV, Dgs, CP 6, CF, 1 st. £ BB £9·80–£12, DB £17·85–£22·05, WT (b) £95·13–£107·10, DT (b) £15–£17, 🗓, Bk £2·25, D £5·25.

Surrey House, PH, z (Unl), *9 Northumberland Av, FY2 9SB.*
✆ (0253) 51743. Open Mar–part Nov. C 3

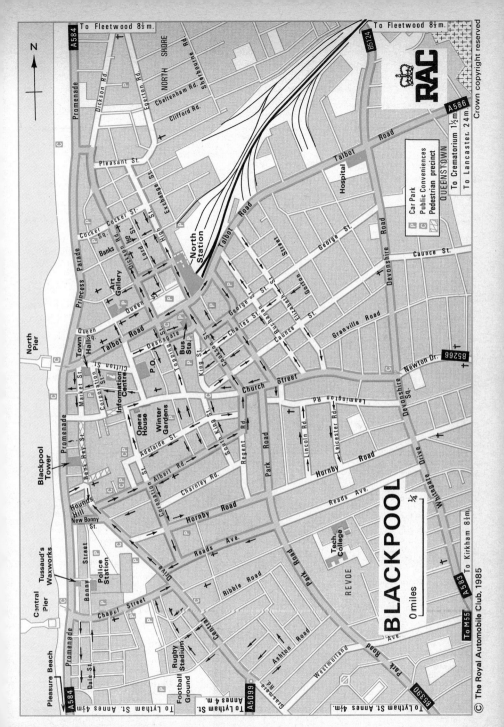

BLACKPOOL

0 miles ¼

months. ⊷ 12 bedrs, 2 bp, 7 bps, 2 ba, ns, Dgs. ☎ CH, TV, Dgs, CP 6, G 1, CF, 1 st. £ BB £6·75–£9·75, DB £13·50–£19·50, WT (c) £47·25–£68·25, DT (b) £8·95–£11·95, ①, Bk £2·50, L £2·50, D £3·50.

Repairers: Dutton Forshaw (Blackpool) Ltd, Vicarage La. ✆ (0253) 67811.
Fylde Spares Garage, 351 Waterloo Rd. ✆ (0253) 41357.
Woodheads Garage (Blackpool) Ltd, Squires Gate La. ✆ (0253) 45544.
Rescue Service: Ingham & Wicks Ltd, 7 Princess St. ✆ (0253) 24467.
Stephenson, H L, Dover Rd Garage. ✆ (0253) 63026.

BLACKWATER Cornwall. Map 2E
Pop 600. Fraddon 14, London 259, Camborne 7, Falmouth 11, Newquay 12, Penzance 20, Redruth 3½, Truro 6.
See Birthplace of Passmore Edwards (philanthropist).

Rescue Service: Chapel Garage. ✆ Truro (0872) 560333.

BLAGDON Avon. Map 5A
Pop 1,186. Bath 19, London 123, Bridgwater 23, Bristol 13, Radstock 15, Wells 10, Weston-super-Mare 12.
Golf Weston 18h. **See** Church, Chew Valley Reservoir.

★★★**Mendip,** *Street End, BS18 6TS.*
✆ (0761) 62688. Closed Xmas week. C. ⊷ 36 bedrs, 36 bp, ns, TV, Dgs. ✗ a l c, mc, at, LD 10. ☎ N, CH, TV, Dgs, ns, CP 300, Ac, con 300, CF, 3 BGf, 4 st. £ BB fr £25, DB fr £44, WB, ②, Bk £4·30, L £7·50, D £9·95, cc 1 2 3 5 6.▲

BLAKENEY Norfolk. Map 16C
Pop 834. Fakenham 13, London 125, Cromer 12, East Dereham 22, Norwich 27.
EC Wed. **Golf** Sheringham 18h. **See** 15th cent Guildhall, 14th cent Church, with two towers, Bird Sanctuary (Blakeney Point, Nat Trust).

▣★★★**Blakeney,** *The Quay, NR25 7NE.*
✆ Cley (0263) 740797. C. ⊷ 54 bedrs, 37 bp, 2 bps, 4 ba, annexe 13 bedrs, 12 bp, TV, Dgs. ✗ a l c, mc, at, LD 9.30. ☎ N, CH, TV, CP 100, Ac, sp, sb, sol, con, CF, 10 BGf, 1 st, Dis. £ BB £20–£34, DB £36–£60, WB, ②, Bk £3·80, L £7, D £9, cc 1 2 3 5, Dep.

▣★★**Manor,** *The Quay, NR25 7ND.*
✆ Cley (0263) 740376. Closed Dec. C. ⊷ 8 bedrs, 8 bp, annexe 14 bedrs, 12 bp, 2 bps, TV, Dgs. ✗ a l c, mc, at, LD 8.45. ☎ CH, CP 60, CF, 10 BGf, 0 st, Dis. £ BB £20·24–£23·40, DB £40·48–£55·66, WB, ①, Bk £4, L £5, D £7, Dep a.

BLANCHLAND Northumberland. Map 31E
Pop 150. West Auckland 27, London 276, Corbridge 11, Durham 24, Hexham 10, Middleton-in-Teesdale 24, Newcastle upon Tyne 24.
Golf Hexham 18h. **See** Abbey Church (1165), Derwent Reservoir 3 m NE, Historic Inn.

▣★★**Lord Crewe Arms,** *DH8 9SP.*
✆ (043 475) 251. Open Mar–Dec. RS Jan–Feb. C. ⊷ 8 bedrs, 6 bp, 2 bps, Dgs. ✗ a l c, mc, at, LD 9.15. ☎ ch, TV, Dgs, CP 15, Ac, sb, con 30–40, CF, 2 BGf. £ BB £27–£32, DB £37–£44, WB, ①, Bk £3·50, L £6·50, D £9·50, cc 1 2 3 5 6.

BLANDFORD FORUM Dorset. Map 5F
Pop 7,309. Salisbury 23, London 106, Bournemouth 17, Dorchester 16, Ringwood 19, Shaftesbury 11, Sherborne 20, Wareham 14.
EC Wed. **MD** Thur, Sat. **Golf** Ashley Wood 9h. **See** Parish Church, old houses, Milton Abbey 6 m SW.
[T] Church of St Peter and St Paul, Market Pl. ✆ Blandford (0258) 51989.

★★★**Crown,** *West St, DT11 7AJ.*
✆ (0258) 56626. C. ⊷ 28 bedrs, 27 bp, 1 bps, TV, Dgs. ✗ a l c, mc, at, LD 9. ☎ CH, TV, Dgs, CP 60, Ac, con 35, CF. £ BB £26–£36, DB £38–£45, WB, ①, Bk £4, L £6·50, D £6·50, cc 1 2 3 5, Dep b.

★★**Anvil** (R), *Anvil Rd, DT11 8UQ* (2 m NE on A354). ✆ Blandford (0258) 53431.
Badger, H, z *Salisbury Rd, DT11 7QH.*
✆ Blandford (0258) 52166.

Rescue Service: Ashleywood Service Station, Tarrant Keyneston. ✆ Blandford (0258) 52595.

BLAYDON-ON-TYNE Tyne & Wear. Map 32C
Pop 9,942. Durham 18, London 278, Corbridge 14, Hexham 16, Newcastle upon Tyne 4, Sunderland 16.
EC Wed. **Golf** Garesfield 18h, Whickham 18h. **See** Gibside Chapel at Rowlands Gill, Summerhill, Derwent Walk (Country Park), Winlaton Forge (Museum of Chain Making).

Repairer: Humble, A H Ltd, Bridge St Garage. ✆ (0632) 443247.

BLEADON Avon. Map 5A
Pop 823. M5 Motorway 6, Bath 31, London 135, Bridgwater 14, Bristol 20, Cheddar 9.
Golf Uphill Road, Weston-super-Mare 18h. **See** Parish Church of SS Peter & Paul.

Rescue Service: Bridge Garage, A370. ✆ (0934) 812206.
Fork Service Station Co Ltd. ✆ (0934) 812244.

BLETCHLEY Buckinghamshire. Map 15C
See also MILTON KEYNES
Pop 42,450. Dunstable 12, London 46, Aylesbury 16, Baldock 26, Bedford 16, Biggleswade 24, Buckingham 11, Kettering 30, Northampton 21, Towcester 15.
EC Wed. **MD** Thur, Sat. **Golf** Bletchley 18h. **See** 13–15th cent St Mary's Church, St Martin's Church, Roman site.

Repairer: Bletchley Motors, 32 Aylesbury St. ✆ Milton Keynes (0908) 72211.
MC Repairer: Mayle, A W, 13 Victoria Rd. ✆ Milton Keynes (0908) 72211.
Rescue Service: APM Coachworks, 16 Watling St, Fenny Stratford. ✆ Milton Keynes (0908) 70108.

BLOCKLEY Gloucestershire. Map 14C
Pop 1,718. Moreton-in-Marsh 4, London 87, Banbury 22, Cheltenham 20, Daventry 36, Evesham 11, Rugby 36, Stow-on-the-Wold 6½, Stratford-upon-Avon 15, Tewkesbury 20, Warwick 23.
Golf Broadway 18h. **See** 12th cent Parish Church, 17th cent Porch House, Rock Cottage (home of Joanna Southcott the 19th cent prophetess).

★★**Lower Brook House,** *Lower St, GL56 9DS.* ✆ (0386) 700286. Closed Jan. C.

⊷ 8 bedrs, 7 bp, 1 bps, TV, Dgs. ✗ mc, LD 9.30.☎ CH, CP 12, con 10, CF. £ BB £25–£33, DB £50–£67, WB, ①, Bk £4, L £4, D £13, cc 1.

Rescue Service: Stuart-Turner, Central Garage. ✆ (0386) 700306.

BLOFIELD Norfolk. Map 16A.
Norwich 6½, London 118, Great Yarmouth 12.

Globe, H, x, *Yarmouth Rd, NR13 4JS.*
✆ Norwich (0603) 712545. C 5. ⊷ 7 bedrs, 7 bps, 1 ba, TV, Dgs. ☎ CH, TV, Dgs, CP 150, CF, 1 st. £ BB £15, DB £25, ②, Bk £4·50, L £5·45, D £5·45, cc 1 3.

BLOXHAM Oxfordshire. Map 14D
Pop 3,000. Bicester 15, London 72, Banbury 3½, Buckingham 18, Chipping Norton 9½, Evesham 28, Moreton-in-Marsh 16, Oxford 20.
EC Wed. **Golf** Tadmarton Heath 18h. **See** 14th cent Church. Museum.

★★**Olde School,** *Church St, Nr Banbury, OX15 4ET.* ✆ Banbury (0295) 720369.

BLOXWICH West Midlands. Map 21E
Pop 30,000. Walsall 3, London 123, Atherstone 22, Lichfield 8, Newport 22, Stafford 15, Tamworth 15, Wellington 24, Wolverhampton 6½.
EC Thur. **MD** Sat. **Golf** Bloxwich 18h. **See** Church Cross, Library Theatre, Memorial Park, Nature Trail.

Rescue Service: Newtown Service Station Ltd, Stafford Rd, Newtown. ✆ (0922) 76366.

BLUE ANCHOR Somerset. Map 4D
Bridgwater 21, London 162, Dunster 3, Minehead 4, Taunton 20.
See West Somerset Rly (steam engines).

Camelot, G, x (Unl), *TA24 6LB.*
✆ Dunster (064 382) 348. Open Apr–Oct. C 16.⊷ 5 bedrs, 1 ba. ☎ CH, TV, CP 6, 2 st. £ BB £6·50–£7, DB £13–£14, WT (b) £65–£70, DT (b) £10·50–£11, ①.
Newlands, G, x (Rl), *TA24 6LB.*
✆ Dunster (064 382) 354. C. ⊷ 5 bedrs, 1 ba, Dgs. ☎ CH, TV, ns, CP5, CF. £ BB £7–£8·50, DB £14–£17, WT (b) £69–£78, (c) £45·50–£55·50, DT (b) £11·50–£13, ①.

BLYTH Northumberland. Map 32B
Pop 36,000. Newcastle upon Tyne 13, London 287, Alnwick 29, Coldstream 55, Corbridge 29, Sunderland 21.
EC Wed. **MD** Fri, Sat. **Golf** Blyth 18h. **See** Seaton Delaval Hall 3½ m S.

Rescue Service: Blyth Motor Co, Plessey Rd and Ridley St. ✆ (067 06) 2272.

BLYTH Nottinghamshire. Map 22B
Pop 1,179. Newark 26, London 153, A1(M) Motorway ½, Gainsborough 14, Lincoln 29, Rotherham 14, Worksop 6.
EC Wed. **See** Churches.

Rescue Service: Holmgarth Motor Co, Bawtry Rd. ✆ (090 976) 273.

BODIAM East Sussex. Map 10E
Hawkhurst 3½, London 54, Battle 8, Hastings 13, Heathfield 15, Maidstone 22.
See Castle (N.T.).

Justins, PH, xy (R) *Sandhurst Rd, TN32 5UJ.* ✆ Staplecross (058 083) 372.
Closed Dec. C 3. ⊷ 4 bedrs, 2 bp, 2 sh, 1 ba, Dgs. ☎ CH, TV, CP 12, 1 st. £ BB £16·10–£17·10, DB £32·20–£34·20,

WT (b) £138·25, DT (b) £22·43, ⊠, D £7, cc 1 3.

BODINNICK Cornwall. Map 2D
Pop 200. Liskeard 15, London 229, Bodmin 13, Looe 10, St Austell 16 (Fy) 8. **Golf** Looe Bin Down 18h. **See** Old Chapel and cottages.

◨★**Old Ferry Inn**, *PL23 1LX.* ✆ Polruan (072 687) 237. Open Mar-Oct. RS Nov-Feb. C. ⋈ 13 bedrs, 5 bp, 8 bps, 3 ba. ✗ a l c, mc, at, LD 8.30. ⌂ CH, TV, Dgs, CP 10, G 4, CF. £ BB £15·50–£17, DB £31–£34. DBB £25–£26·50, ☐, Bk £3, D £9·60, Dep a.

BODMIN Cornwall. Map 2D
Pop 14,000. Launceston 22, London 233, Camelford 13, Fowey 9, Liskeard 13, Looe 13, Newquay 19, Redruth 30, St Austell 11, Truro 24, Wadebridge 7.
EC Wed. **MD** Sat. **Golf** St Enodoc Rock 18h. **See** Parish Church of St Petroc, 14th cent chantry chapel ruins in churchyard, Guildhall, Respryn Bridge, DCLI Regimental Museum, Bodmin Beacon (obelisk), Lanhydrock House 2 m SE (Nat Trust).
🛈 Peverell Cross. ✆ Cardinham (020 882) 233.

♨★★★**Tredethy** (R). *Helland Bridge, PL30 4QS.* ✆ St Mabyn 262. Closed Xmas. C 12. ⋈ 11 bedrs, 9 bp, 2 bps, TV. ✗ a l c, LD 8.30. ⌂ CH, TV, CP 30, sp, sol. £ BB £17, DB £30, WT £125–£170, DT £29, WB, ⊠, Bk £3·50, L £5·50, D £7.

◨★★**Allegro** (R), *50 Higher Bore St. PL31 1JW.* ✆ (0208) 3480. C. ⋈ 12 bedrs, 2 bp, 1 bps, 7 sh, 2 ba. ✗ a l c, mc, at, LD 10 (9 winter). ⌂ ch, TV, CP 30, con 12, CF, 1 st. £ BB £13–£19, DB £23–£28·50, DT £19, WB, ⊠, Bk £2·50, L £4·10, D £4, cc 1 2 3.

◨★★**Westberry**, *Rhind St, PL31 2EL.* ✆ (0208) 2772.
The Whitehouse, H, y, z (R), *Castle Hill, PL31 2EF.* ✆ (0208) 2310. C 12. ⋈ 5 bedrs, 2 ba, Dgs. ✗ a l c. ⌂ CH, TV, Dgs, CP 12. £ BB £10·50–£12, DB £21–£24, WT (b) £105–£120, DT (b) £16–£18, ⊠, Bk £3, L £4·50.

Specialist Body Repairer: Paul Miller & Son, Flaxmoor Works, Berrycombe Rd. ✆ (0208) 2885.
Rescue Service: Allen Valley Garage, St Teath. ✆ (0208) 850270.
Cornish Garage, Westheath Av. ✆ (0208) 2870.
Darcroft Garage, Four Winds. ✆ Cardinham (020 882) 453.
Kinsman, H G & Son Ltd, Russell Garage. ✆ (0208) 2669.
Phil Ugalde, Auto & Towing Services, 10 Normandy Way. ✆ (0208) 4983 & (0208) 2218.
R & R Motors, 5 Wood's Browning Industrial Estate. ✆ (0208) 2273.

BOGNOR REGIS West Sussex. Map 7E
Pop 36,960. Pulborough 16, London 63, Arundel 9½, Chichester 6½, Haywards Heath 35, Littlehampton 7, Petworth 16.
EC Wed. **MD** Fri. **Golf** Bognor 18h. **See** Hotham Park (Arboretum, Mansion and Children's Zoo), RC Church, Dome House.
🛈 Place St Maur des Fosses, Belmont St. ✆ Bognor Regis (0243) 823140.

★★★**Royal Norfolk**, *Esplanade, PO21 1LH.* ✆ (0243) 826222. C. ⋈ 52 bedrs, 39 bp, 1 bps, 12 sh, 5 ba, TV, Dgs. ✗ a l c, mc, at, LD 9.30. ⌂ Lt, N, CH, Dgs, CP 150, Ac,

sp, con 100, CF, 2 BGf. £ BB £23–£35.75, DB £34·50–£47·95, WT £172·90–£233·45, DT £28·45–£36·35, WB, ☐, Bk £3·85, L £6·95, D £8·50, cc 1 2 3 5, Dep b.

★★**Clarehaven**, *Wessex Av, PO21 2QW.* ✆ (0243) 823265. C. ⋈ 28 bedrs, 4 bp, 2 bps, 5 ba, Dgs. ✗ a l c, mc, at, LD 8. ⌂ CH, TV, Dgs, CP 12, Ac, con 150, CF, 2 BGf, 2 st. £ BB £15–£26, DB £30–£42, WT £129–£155, DT £22·50–£28, WB, ☐, Bk £3, L £4·50, D £5·50, cc 1 2 3 6.

★★**Royal**, *Esplanade, PO21 1SZ.* ✆ (0243) 864665. C. ⋈ 30 bedrs, 2 bp, 4 bps, 8 sh, 6 ba, TV. ✗ a l c, mc, at, LD 9.45. ⌂ N, CH, TV, Dgs, CP 6 Ac, sol, con 40, CF, 5 st. £ BB £11·50–£21·50, DB £23–£45, WT £114·50–£164·50, DT £19·25–£28, WB, ☐, Bk £2·50, L £3·25, D £4·50, cc 1 2 3 5, Dep.

★**Black Mill House** (R), *Princess Av, PO21 2QU.* ✆ (0243) 821945. C. ⋈ 22 bedrs, 7 bp, 2 bps, 5 ba, annexe 4 bedrs, 1 ba, Dgs. ✗ mc, at, LD 7.45. ⌂ CH, TV, Dgs, CP 12, CF, 0 st. £ BB £14–£25·75, DB £28–£41·50, DT £20·50–£26·75, Bk £3, L £4, D £5, cc 1 2 3 6, Dep b.

★**Lyndhurst** (Rt), *Selsey Av, PO21 2QZ.* ✆ (0243) 822308. C. ⋈ 8 bedrs, 1 bp, 2 ba, TV. ✗ mc, at, LD 7. ⌂ CH, TV, CP 2, CF. £ BB £10·50–£16·50, DB £21–£33, WT £98–£118, DT £17–£20·50, WB, ☐, Bk £2·50, L £3·45, D £4.

Alancourt, H, z (R), *Marine Drive West, PO21 2QA.* ✆ (0243) 864844. C. ⋈ 12 bedrs, 1 bp, 1 sh, 2 ba, TV, Dgs. ✗ a l c, ⌂ ch, Dgs, CF, 1 st. £ BB £10–£25, DB £23–£40, WT (b) £91–£185·50, DT £14–£29, ☐, Bk £2·50, L £4, D £4, cc 1 2 3 5.

Homestead, PH, z, *90 Aldwick Rd, PO21 2PD.* ✆ (0243) 823443. C. ⋈ 9 bedrs, 2 bps, 1 ba. ⌂ ch, TV, Dgs, CP 12, CF, 2 BGf, 1 st, Dis. £ BB £7·50–£8, DB £15–£16, WT fr £60, DT £10–£10·50, ☐, D £2·50, cc 1 3 6.

Repairers: Central Garage (Felpham) Ltd, 96 Felpham Rd. ✆ (0243) 864221.
Jones, W & Sons (Motor Engineers) Ltd, Lennox St. ✆ (0243) 864641.
Wilmott's Garage, 65 Aldwick Rd. ✆ (0243) 864041.
Rescue Service: Aldwick Motors, Aldwick St. ✆ (0243) 823693.
Anton Motors, Shripney Rd. ✆ (0243) 823408.

BOLDON COLLIERY Tyne & Wear. M. Areas 24E, 31F & 32D
Pop 10,500 (Inc W. Boldon). Durham 16, A1(M) 3, London 276, Gateshead 7, Jarrow 3½, Sunderland 6, Washington 5½.
EC Wed. **Golf** Boldon 18h.

Rescue Service: Auto Centre, North Rd. ✆ Boldon (0783) 36854.

BOLLINGTON Cheshire. Map 22A
Pop 7,000. Macclesfield 3½, London 171, Altrincham 15, Buxton 13, Chapel-en-le-Frith 10, Glossop 17, Knutsford 14, Stockport 10.
EC Wed. **Golf** Macclesfield 18h. **See** The "Nab Side" (viewpoint).

★★★**Belgrade**, *Jackson La, SK10 5BG.* ✆ (0625) 73246.

BOLNEY West Sussex. Map 7C
Pop 1,200. Crawley 9½, London 40, Arundel 24, Brighton 13, East Grinstead 16, Haslemere 26, Haywards Heath 5½, Horsham 10, Lewes 15, Littlehampton 24,

Petworth 21, Pulborough 15, Worthing 18.
EC Sat. **Golf** Mannings Heath 18h. **See** Parish Church.

Bolney Grange, H, xy, (Rl), *RH17 5PA.* ✆ Burgess Hill (044 46) 45164.

Repairer: G & W Motors, Bolney Motor Works, London Rd, ✆ (044 482) 273.

BOLTON Gtr Manchester (Lancashire), Map 20A
Pop 148,000. Manchester 11, London 195, M61 Motorway 3, Blackburn 13, Burnley 19, Bury 6, Chorley 11, Liverpool 28, Oldham 16, Preston 19, Walkden 4½, Warrington 17, Wigan 10.
EC Wed. **MD** Tue, Thur, Sat. **Golf** Bolton 18h, Bolton Municipal 18h. **See** 15th cent Hall i'th' Wood Museum, Civic Centre, Art Gallery, Aquarium and Museum, Smithills Hall, St Peter's Church, Turton Tower 3½ m N.
🛈 Town Hall. ✆ Bolton (0204) 22311 ext 211 or 485.

★★★**M Crest**, *Beaumont Rd, BL3 4TA.* ✆ (0204) 651511. C. ⋈ 100 bedrs, 100 bp, ns, TV, Dgs. ✗ a l c, mc, LD 10. ⌂ N, CH, Dgs, CP 153, Ac, con 90, CF, 50 BGf. £ B fr £42, BD fr £53, WB, ☐, Bk £5·25, D £9·25, cc 1 2 3 4 5 6, Dep b.

♨★★**Egerton House** (Rl), *Blackburn Rd, BL7 9PL.* ✆ (0204) 57171. RS Xmas week. C. ⋈ 25 bedrs, 25 ba, TV, Dgs. ✗ a l c, mc, at, LD 9.30. ⌂ CH, CP 50, con 25, CF, 5 st. £ BB fr £38, DB fr £48, WB, ☐, L £5·40, D £14·50, cc 1 2 5, Dep b.▲

★★★**M Last Drop Village**, *Hospital Rd, BL7 9PZ.* ✆ (0204) 591131. C. ⋈ 80 bedrs, 80 bp, TV, Dgs. ✗ a l c, mc, at, LD 10.30. ⌂ N, CH, Dgs, CP 400, Ac, sp, sh, sol, gym, con 230, CF, 4 st. £ BB £20–£38, DB £32–£48, WB, ☐, Bk £4·50, D £6·50, cc 1 2 3 5 6, Dep b.▲

★★★**Pack Horse**, *60 Bradshawgate, BL1 1DP.* ✆ (0204) 27261. RS Dec 24 to Jan 2. C. ⋈ 78 bedrs, 76 bp, 2 bps, 3 ba, TV, Dgs. ✗ mc, at, LD 10. ⌂ Lt, N, CH, CP 250, Ac, con 200, CF, 4 BGf, 1 st, Dis. £ BB fr £35, DB fr £46·50, WB, ☐, Bk £3·50, L £7, D £8, cc 1 2 3 5 6, Dep b.

Repairers: Kennings Motor Group Ltd, Anderton, M61 Motorway Service Area. ✆ Horwich (0204) 68641.
Knowles, W & Sons (Garages) Ltd, Moor La. ✆ (0204) 27593.
Lex Cockshoot Ltd, Manchester Rd. ✆ (0204) 32241.
Parkers (Manchester and Bolton) Ltd, Bradshawgate. ✆ (0204) 31323.
Rescue Service: Holland Street Motors, 134 Holland St. ✆ (0204) 52886.
I G W Services Ltd, Northway Service Station, Belmont Rd, Astley Bridge. ✆ (0204) 591786.
J. Boardman (Garages) Ltd, Lucy St, off Chorley Old Rd. ✆ (0204) 42468.
Radcliffe Road Garage, Radcliffe Rd. ✆ (0204) 382234.

BOLTON ABBEY N. Yorks. Map 27A
Leeds 23, London 214. Harrogate 17, Keighley 11, Skipton 6.

★★★**Devonshire Arms**, *BD21 6AH,* ✆ (075 671) 441. C. ⋈ 38 bedrs, 38 bp, TV, Dgs. ✗ a l c, mc, at, LD 9.30. ⌂ N, CH, TV, CP 60, Ac, pf, con 100, CF, 2 BGf, 0 st, Dis. £ BB £43·50–£48·50, DB £52–£62,

WB, 🅟, Bk £4·50, L £5·75, D £15,
cc 1 2 3 6, Dep b.▲

Rescue Service: Forge Garage, Bolton
Bridge. ✆ (075 671) 221.

BOOTLE Merseyside. Map 20E
Pop 69,500. Liverpool 3, London 200,
Ormskirk 10, St Helens 11, Southport 16.
EC Wed. **Golf** Bootle Municipal 18h. **See**
Nos 1–3 Merton Rd (1773) (former
hunting lodge of the Earls of Derby), St
Benet's Church (1743) (Netherton
Village).

Repairer: Ryder's Autoservice, 215
Knowsley Rd. ✆ 051-922 7585.

BORDON Hampshire. Map 6D
Pop 9,731. Farnham 8, London 46, Alton
7½, Haslemere 9, Hindhead 6½, Midhurst
12, Petersfield 8½, Winchester 23.
EC Wed. **Golf** Blackmoor 18h.

Repairers: Broxhead Motors Ltd,
Lindford. ✆ (042 03) 2484.
Lindford Garage, Lindford Village, nr
Bordon. ✆ (042 03) 2828.
MC Repairer: Southern Motorcyle
Supplies (SMS), Farnham Rd.
✆ (042 03) 2266.

BOREHAM STREET East Sussex. Map
10E
Pop 442. Tunbridge Wells 27, London 59,
Eastbourne 9, Hastings 11, Hurst Green
13, Lewes 18, Newhaven 20, Uckfield 17.
EC Wed. **Golf** Highwoods (Bexhill) 18h.
See Smugglers Farm, Royal Observatory.

★★★White Friars (R), *BN27 4SE.*
✆ Herstmonceux (0323) 832355. Closed
Jan. C. ⋈ 12 bedrs, 8 bp, 2 ba, TV, Dgs.
✗ a l c, mc, LD 9.15, CH, Dgs, CP 50, Ac,
con 20–40, 6 BGf, 2 st. £ BB £19–£23, DB
£33–£39, DBB £42–£56, WB, 🅟, Bk £4, L
£7, D £10, cc 1 2 3 5.

BOREHAMWOOD Hertfordshire. Map
15F
Pop 26,990. London 12, Barnet 4,
Brentford and Chiswick 14, Harrow 7½,
Hatfield 10, St Albans 8, Watford 6½.
EC Thur. **Golf** Dyrham Park 18h. **See** Film
and TV Studios.
🅘 Civic Offices, Elstree Way. ✆ 01-207
2277.

★★★M Elstree Moat House, *Barnet By-
Pass, WD6 5PU.* ✆ 01-953 1622. C. ⋈ 60
bedrs, 60 bp, TV, Dgs. ✗ a l c, mc, LD 9.45.
🅝 N, CH, Dgs, CP 350, sp, con 200, CF, 29
BGf, 4 st. £ BB fr £38·50, DB fr £50, WB, 🅟,
Bk £4·50, L £7·50, D £7·50, cc 1 2 3 5 6,
Dep b.
Grosvenor, *148 Shenley Rd, WD6 1EQ.*
✆ 01-953 3175. Closed Xmas. C. ⋈ 17
bedrs, 9 sh, 4 ba, Dgs. ✗ a l c. 🅝 CH, TV,
CP 24, G 2, 2 BGf, 0 st. £ BB £18–£21, DB
£27–£30, DT (b) £27–£30, 🿂, Bk £3·50, L
£9, D £9, cc 1 2 3 5.

Rescue Service: Borehamwood Motor
Centre Ltd, Stirling Way. ✆ 01-953 6022.

BOROUGHBRIDGE North Yorkshire.
Map 25E
Pop 2,500. Doncaster 44, London 208,
Brough 57, Darlington 36, Durham 53,
Harrogate 10, Leeds 25, Leyburn 26,
Middleton-in-Teesdale 43, Northallerton
19, Pontefract 31, Thirsk 12, Wakefield 34,
West Auckland 43, York 17.
EC Thur, **MD** Mon. **Golf** Knaresborough
18h. **See** "Devil's Arrows", millstone-grit

monoliths ½ m from bridge, Roman
Museum at Aldborough.
🅘 St James Sq. ✆ Boroughbridge
(090 12) 2876.

★★★Crown, *Horsefair, Scotch Corner,
YO5 9LB.* ✆ (090 12) 2328. RS Xmas. C.
⋈ 43 bedrs, 42 bp, 1 bps, TV, Dgs. ✗ a l c,
mc, at, LD 9.30. 🅝 Lt, N, CH, CP 45, Ac, sb,
sol, con 40, CF, 7 BGf, 0 st, Dis. £ BB
£29·75, DB £39·75, WT £305·90, DT
£45·95, WB, 🿂, Bk £5, L £6·95, D £9·25,
cc 1 2 3 5 6.

⚑★★★Three Arrows, *Horsefair, YO5
9LL.* ✆ (090 12) 2245. C. ⋈ 17 bedrs, 16
bp, 1 bps, TV, Dgs. ✗ a l c, mc, at, LD 9.
🅝 CH, Dgs, CP 100, G 8, Ac, con 60, CF, 2
st. £ BB fr £29, DB fr £39, WB, 🿂, Bk £4·25,
L £6·25, D £8·50, cc 1 2 3 4 5 6, Dep b.

Rescue Service: Crown Motors
(Boroughbridge) Ltd, Horsefair.
✆ (090 12) 2327 & (090 12) 2305.

BORROWDALE Cumbria. Map 26F
See also GRANGE IN BORROWDALE and
KESWICK
Pop 736. Keswick 6½, London 286,
Cockermouth 16, Egremont 24.
Golf Embleton 18h, Cockermouth 18h.
See Bowder Stone, Lodore Falls.

★★★Borrowdale (R), *Borrowdale Rd,
CA12 5UV.* ✆ (059 684) 224. Closed Jan.
C. ⋈ 35 bedrs, 32 bp, 3 bps, TV, Dgs.
✗ mc, LD 8.15. 🅝 CH, Dgs, CP 100, CF,
1 st. cc 1.
★★★Mary Mount (R), *CA12 5UX.*
✆ (059 684) 223.

BOSCASTLE Cornwall. Map 2B
Pop 750. Launceston 18, London 229,
Bude 14, Camelford 5.
Golf St Enodoc Rock 18h. **See** Harbour,
Willapark Point, Museum of Witchcraft.

■★Bottreaux House (R), *PL35 0BG.*
✆ (084 05) 231.
St Christophers, PH, x (R), *High St,
PL35 0BD.* ✆ (084 05) 412. Open Mar–
Oct. C. ⋈ 6 bedrs, 1 bps, 2 ba, Dgs. 🅝 CH,
TV, CF, 5 st. £ BB £9–£12, DB £18–£24,
WT (b) £93–£107·50, DT (b) £15–£16, 🿂,
D £6.

BOSHAM West Sussex. Map 6F
Pop 3,825. Chichester 4, London 65,
Cosham 11, Petersfield 16.
Golf Goodwood 18h. **See** Interesting old
Church, Old water mill, Fishbourne Roman
Palace and Museum.

★★Millstream (R), *Bosham La, PO18
8HL.* ✆ (0243) 573234. C. ⋈ 22 bedrs, 22
bp, TV, Dgs. 🅝 N, CH, TV, CP 40, con 30,
CF, 3 BGf, 0 st, Dis. £ BB £30, DB £48, WT
£155–£205, WB, 🿂, Bk £5, L £6, D £10,
cc 1 2 3 5.

BOSTON Lincolnshire. Map 23D
Pop 52,000. Spalding 16, London 117,
Grantham 30, Horncastle 18, King's Lynn
34, Lincoln 33, Louth 30, Skegness 21,
Sleaford 17, Wisbech 29.
EC Thur. **MD** Wed, Sat. **Golf** Boston 18h,
Sleaford South Rauceby 18h. **See** 14th
cent St Botolph's Church with 272 ft
tower—"Boston Stump", 15th cent
Guildhall with Museum, Maud Foster
Windmill, 18th cent Fydell House, Hussey
Tower, Shodfriars' Hall, 13th cent
Dominican Friary (incorp Arts Centre and
Blackfriars Theatre), Docks.

🅘 Assembly Rooms, Market Pl. ✆ Boston
(0205) 62354.

★★Burton House, *Wainfleet Rd,
PE21 9RW.* ✆ (0205) 62307. C.⋈ 6
bedrs, 2 bp, 1 ba, TV, Dgs. ✗ a l c, mc, LD
9.30. 🅝 CH, TV, Dgs, CP 150, Ac, CF, 6 st.
£ BB fr £20, DB fr £28, 🿂, Bk £3, L £4.75, D
£5.25, cc 3.
★★New England, *Wide Bargate, PE21
6SH.* ✆ (0205) 65255. C. ⋈ 25 bedrs, 25
bp, TV. ✗ a l c, mc, LD 10. 🅝 N, CH, Ac,
con 35, CF, 0 st. £ BB fr £33, DB fr £44,
WB, 🿂, Bk £4·50, L £6·95, D £6·95,
cc 1 2 3 4 5 6, Dep b.

Repairers: Bargate Motors (Boston) Ltd,
6 Horncastle Rd. ✆ (0205) 64708.
Holland Bros Ltd, Bargate and Tawney St.
✆ (0205) 64892.
Specialist Body Repairer: E C Stanwell &
Sons Ltd, Main Ridge. ✆ (0205) 63867.
Rescue Services: Hill Engineering
Services, Main Rd, Sibsey.
✆ (0205) 750376.
King's Garage, Main Rd, Stickney.
✆ Stickney (020 578) 227.

BOTLEY Hampshire. Map 6F
Pop 3,454. Alton 23, London 71, M27
Motorway 2½, Cosham 11, Fareham 8,
Petersfield 20, Romsey 12, Southampton
6½, Winchester 11.
EC Wed. **Golf** Southampton Municipal
18h and 9h. **See** 12th cent Church,
Cobbett Memorial.

⚑★★★Botleigh Grange, *Grange Rd,
Hedge End, SO3 2GA.* ✆ (048 92) 5611.
C. ⋈ 21 bedrs, 10 bp, 4 ba, TV, Dgs.
✗ a l c, mc, at, LD 9.30. 🅝 N, CH, TV, CP
300, Ac, pf, con 200, CF. £ BB £28·50–
£31·50, DB £38–£42, 🿂, WB, Bk £4·60, L
£7, D £7, cc 1 3.

Repairer: Michael J. Sparshatt Ltd,
Sharpshatts of Botley, Southampton Rd.
✆ (048 92) 5111.

BOTTISHAM Cambridgeshire. Map 17E
Pop 1,750. Saffron Walden 16, London 59,
Cambridge 7, Ely 18, Newmarket 13.
EC Wed. **Golf** Newmarket 18h. **See**
Church, Bottisham Hall.
Rescue Service: Rank Bros, 56 High St.
✆ Cambridge (0223) 811122.
Tunbridge Lane Motors, Tunbridge La.
✆ Cambridge (0223) 811849.

BOTTLESFORD Wiltshire. Map 6A
Newbury 57, London 79, Amesbury 12,
Andover 21, Devizes 9, Marlborough 9,
Wantage 31.

Rescue Service: Space Engineering.
✆ Woodborough (067 285) 360.

BOUGHTON Kent. Map 10D
Pop 1,827. 3 m SE of Faversham.
Rochester 20, London 52, Ashford 15,
Canterbury 6, Maidstone 21.
EC Thur. **Golf** Faversham 18h.

Rescue Service: Wood's Garage, 49 The
Street. ✆ Canterbury (0227) 751307.

BOUGHTON MONCHELSEA Kent.
Map 10C
Maidstone 3½, London 39, Ashford 20,
Tenterden 16, Tonbridge 15.

Rescue Service: Wood's Garage, 49 The
Street. ✆ Canterbury (0227) 751307.

BOURNE Lincolnshire. Map 23E
Pop 8,218. Peterborough 15, London 98,
Boston 26, Grantham 18, Melton

Mowbray 25, Sleaford 18, Spalding 11, Stamford 11, Wisbech 31.

EC Wed. **MD** Thur, **Golf** Stoke Rochford 18h, Stamford 18h. **See** Church (Abbey remains), School (1678), Elizabethan Red Hall and pleasure grounds, Roman Carr Dyke.

Angel, H, z. *Market Place, PE10 9AC.* ✆ (0778) 422346. C. ⊷ 10 bedrs, 5 bp, 5 bps, TV, Dgs. ✘ a l c. ⊡ CH, Dgs, 0 st. £ BB £15–£19, DB £25–£28, Bk £2·50, L £4, D £6, cc 1 3.

Beaufort House, PH, z (R). *30 West St. PE10 9NE.* ✆ (0778) 422609.

BOURNEMOUTH and BOSCOMBE

Dorset. Map 6E

See also POOLE.

RAC Office, *9 Poole Road, Bournemouth, BH2 5QW.* ✆ (General) Bournemouth (0202) 765328. (Rescue Service only) Bournemouth (0202) 766697.

Pop 144,800. Lyndhurst 20, London 104, Blandford Forum 17, Dorchester 27, Lymington 17, Ringwood 12, Sandbanks Ferry 5, Wareham 13.

See Plan, p. 150.

P See Plan. **Golf** Two 18h Municipal Courses—Queen's Park and Meyrick Park, over which several clubs play. **See** Russell-Cotes Art Gallery and Museum, Rothesay Museum, Winter Gardens, Pine Woods, Chines, St Peter's Church, Pavilion Entertainment Centre, Compton Acres Gardens 2 m SW, Christchurch Priory 5 m E.

🛈 Westover Rd. ✆ Bournemouth (0202) 291715.

★★★★★**Carlton,** *East Overcliff, BH1 3DN.* ✆ (0202) 22011. C. ⊷ 55 bedrs, 55 bp, 2 ba, TV, Dgs. ✘ a l c, mc, at, LD 11. ⊡ Lt, N, CH, Dgs, CP 175, U 10, G 20, Ac, sp, sb, sol, gym, con 180, CF, 3 st. £ BB £48·50–£59·50, DB £76–£87, WB, ②, Bk £6, L £9, D £12·50, cc 1 2 3 4 5 6, Dep b.▲

★★★★★**Royal Bath,** *Bath Rd, BH1 2EW.* ✆ (0202) 25555. C. ⊷ 135 bedrs, 135 bp, TV. ✘ a l c, mc, at, LD 10.30. ⊡ Lt, N, CH, G 120, Ac, sp, sb, sol, gym, con 550, CF, 20 BGf, 1 st, Dis. £ BB £47·50, DB £81, WB, ②, Bk £6, L £8·50, D £15, cc 1 2 3 4 5 6, Dep b.

★★★★**East Cliff Court,** *East Overcliff Dr, BH1 3AN.* ✆ (0202) 24545. C. ⊷ 72 bedrs, 58 bp, 14 bps, TV, Dgs. ✘ a l c, mc, at, LD 9. ⊡ Lt, N, CH, CP 130, Ac, sb, sol, con 250, CF, 2 BGf, 4 st. £ BB £23–£32·50, DB £46–£64, DT £53·50–£45, WB, ②, Bk £4·50, L £6·95, D £8·95, cc 1 2 3 6, Dep.

★★★★**Highcliff,** *105 St Michael's Rd, BH2 5DU.* ✆ (0202) 27702. C. ⊷ 96 bedrs, 96 bp, TV, Dgs. ✘ a l c, mc, at, LD 9 (9.30 Fri–Sat). ⊡ Lt, N, CH, CP 80, Ac, tc, sb, sol, con 180, CF, 2 st. £ BB £30–£38, DB £60–£80, DBB £40–£45, WB, ①, Bk £1·60, L £6·60, D £0·60, cc 1 2 3 4 5, Dep.

★★★★**Marsham Court,** *Russell Cotes Rd, BH1 3AB.* ✆ (0202) 22111. C. ⊷ 80 bedrs, 72 bp, 8 bps, 7 ba, TV. ✘ a l c, mc, at, LD 9.30. ⊡ Lt, N, CH, CP 40, U 3, G 36, Ac, sp, con 200, CF, 0 st. £ BB £30–£33, DB £50–£56, WT £242–£262, DT £44·50–£47·50, WB, ②, Bk £4·50, L £6·75, D £8, cc 1 2 3 4 5 6, Dep b.

★★★★**Palace Court,** *Westover Rd, BH1 3BZ.* ✆ (0202) 27681. C. ⊷ 108 bedrs, 108 bp, TV, Dgs. ✘ a l c, mc, at, LD 10.45. ⊡ Lt, N, CH, TV, G 200, sb, sol, gym, con 200, CF, 4 st. £ WB, ②, cc 1 2 3 5, Dep b.

★★★**Anglo-Swiss,** *16 Gervis Rd, BH1 3EQ.* ✆ (0202) 24794. C. ⊷ 63 bedrs, 44 bp, 1 bps, 6 ba, TV, Dgs. ✘ mc, at, LD 8.30. ⊡ Lt, N, CH, CP 65, Ac, con 120, CF, 4 BGf, 6 st. £ BB £15–£24, DB £30–£48, DBB £20–£29, WB, ①, Bk £4, L £7, D £8, cc 1 2 3.

★★★**Angus** (R). *Bath Rd, BH1 2NN.* ✆ (0202) 26420.

▣★★★**Burley Court** (RI). *Bath Rd, BH1 2BP.* ✆ (0202) 22824. Closed Jan. C. ⊷ 41 bedrs, 31 bp, 1 bps, 4 ba, TV, Dgs. ✘ a l c, mc, at, LD 8.30. ⊡ Lt, N, CH, TV, CP 35, sp, CF, 3 BGf, 0 st, Dis. £ BB £16·50–£26, DB £32–£45, DBB £19·50–£29, WB, ①, Bk £4, L £5, D £6·50, cc 1 3, Dep b.▲

★★★**Cecil,** *Parsonage Rd, Bath Hill, BH1 2HJ.* ✆ (0202) 293336. C. ⊷ 28 bedrs, 28 bp, TV, Dgs. ✘ a l c, mc, at, LD 9.30. ⊡ Lt, CH, CP 25, Ac, CF, 0 st. £ BB £16–£23, DB £32–£46, DBB £22–£29, WB, ①, Bk £4, L £4·75, D £7·50, cc 1 2 3 4 5, Dep.

★★★**Chesterwood** (R). *East Overcliffe Dr, BH1 3AR.* ✆ (0202) 28057. Closed Jan–Feb. C. ⊷ 51 bedrs, 33 bp, 9 bps, 4 ba, TV, Dgs. ✘ mc, at, LD 8. ⊡ Lt, N, ch, Dgs, CP 30, G 8, Ac, sp, con 40, CF, 2 st. £ BB £15–£21·80, DB £29–£43·60, WT £119–£156, DBB £22–£28·30, WB, ①, Bk £3, L £5, D £6·50, cc 1 3, Dep.

★★★**Chine,** *25 Boscombe Spa Rd, BH5 1AX* (Boscombe) ✆ (0202) 36234. C. ⊷ 108 bedrs, 73 bp, 1 bps, 8 ba, ns, TV. ✘ mc, at, LD 8.30. ⊡ Lt, N, CH, CP 100, U 5, Ac, sp, sb, sol, con 200, CF, 2 BGf, 4 st. £ BB £15·50–£21, DB £31–£42, WT £140–£185, DT £22·50–£28, WB, ①, Bk £3, L £5·50, D £6·50, cc 1 3, Dep b.

★★★**Cliff End** (RI). *Manor Rd, BH1 3EX.* ✆ (0202) 309711. C. ⊷ 40 bedrs, 35 bp, 5 bps, TV, Dgs. ✘ mc, at, LD 8.30. ⊡ Lt, N, CH, CP 40, Ac, sp, tc, sol, con 80, CF, 2 st. £ BB £22·40–£24·50, DB £45–£49, DBB £28·50–£30·50, WB, ①, Bk £2·50, L £5·75, D £7·25, Dep.

★★★**Cliffeside** (R). *East Overcliff Dr, BH1 3AQ.* ✆ (0202) 25724. C. ⊷ 64 bedrs, 43 bp, 10 bps, 4 ba, TV, Dgs. ✘ a l c, mc, at, con 150, CF, 12 st. £ BB £16–£30·50, DB £30–£48, WT £120–£199·50, DT £19–£28·50, WB, ②, Bk £3·50, L £5·50, D £6·50, cc 1 3 6, Dep b.

★★★**Cotford Hall,** *Knyveton Rd, BH1 3QT.* ✆ (0202) 33332. C. ⊷ 51 bedrs, 23 bp, 9 bps, 5 ba, TV, Dgs. ✘ a l c, mc, at, LD 9. ⊡ N, CH, TV, CP 40, Ac, sp, con 200, CF, 1 BGf, 0 st, Dis. £ BB £15·58–£24·15, DB £31·16–£48·30, WT £121–£178·02, DT £20·41–£29·90, WB, ②, Bk £3·15, L £4·90, D £6·60.

★★★**Courtlands,** *16 Boscombe Spa Rd, BH5 1BB.* ✆ (0202) 302442. C. ⊷ 46 bedrs, 40 bp, 6 bps, TV, Dgs. ✘ a l c, mc, at, LD 8.30. ⊡ Lt, N, CH, CP 50, Ac, sp, con 100, CF, 1 BGf, 1 st, Dis. £ DB £10 £23, DB £36–£46, WT £160–£200, DT £27–£32, WB, ①, Bk £3·25, L £5·25, D £7·25, cc 1 2 3 5, Dep.

★★★**M Crest,** *The Lansdowne, BH1 2PR.* ✆ (0202) 23262. C. ⊷ 102 bedrs, 102 bp, ns, TV, Dgs. ✘ a l c, mc, at, LD 9.45. ⊡ Lt, N, CH, CP 55, Ac, G 78, Ac, con 120, CF. £ B fr £36·50, BD fr £54·50, WB, ①, Bk £5·25, D £8·95, cc 1 2 3 4 5 6, Dep b.

★★★**Durley Dean,** *West Cliff Rd, BH2 5HE.* ✆ (0202) 27711. C 3. ⊷ 110 bedrs, 86 bp, 4 bps, 5 ba, TV, Dgs. ✘ a l c, mc, at, LD 10. ⊡ Lt, N, CH, TV, CP 35, Ac, sp, con

150, CF, 8 st. £ BB £17–£21·50, DB £34–£43, WT £193, DT £28·50–£30·50, WB, ②, BK £4, L £5·50, D £6·50, cc 1 2 3 5, Dep.▲

★★★**Durley Hall,** *Durley Chine Rd, BH2 5JS.* ✆ (0202) 766886. C. ⊷ 72 bedrs, 48 bp, 5 bps, 11 ba, annexe 10 bedrs, 8 bp, 1 bps, 1 ba, TV, Dgs. ✘ mc, at, LD 8.45. ⊡ Lt, N, CH, CP 250, Ac, sp, sol, con 200, CF, 1 st. £ BB £14–£24, DB £28–£48, WT £157–£185, DT £25–£29, WB, ①, Bk £3·50, L £5, D £6·50, cc 1 2 3 5 6, Dep.

★★★**Durlston Court,** *Gervis Rd, BH1 3DD.* ✆ (0202) 291488. C. ⊷ 56 bedrs, 45 bp, 4 ba, TV, Dgs. ✘ mc, at, LD 8.30. ⊡ Lt, N, CH, TV, Dgs, CP 50, Ac, sp, con 200, CF, 0 st. £ BB £15–£24, DB £30–£48, DBB £20·50–£30, WB, ①, Bk £4·25, L £6·25, D £8, cc 1 2 3 5, Dep b.

★★★**East Anglia,** *6 Poole Rd, BH2 5QX.* ✆ (0202) 765163. C. ⊷ 49 bedrs, 40 bp, 9 bps, annexe 22 bedrs, 14 bp, 1 bps, 2 ba, TV. ✘ mc, at, LD 8.30. ⊡ Lt, N, CH, CP 60, Ac, sp, sb, sol, con 150, CF, 8 BGf, 1 st. £ BB £20–£25, DB £30–£50, DBB £20–£30, WB, ②, Bk £3·75, L £5, D £8, cc 1 2 3 5 6, Dep.

▣★★★**Embassy** (R). *Meyrick Rd, BH1 3DW.* ✆ (0202) 20751. C. ⊷ 40 bedrs, 37 bp, 1 bps, 2 sh, 2 ba, TV, Dgs. ✘ mc, at, LD 8.15. ⊡ Lt, N, CH, TV, Dgs, CP 60, Ac, sp, con 70, CF, 2 st. £ BB £15–£22, DB £30–£44, DBB £21·50–£28·50, WB, ②, Bk £3, L £2, D £6·50, cc 1 2 3 5 6, Dep b.

▣★★★**Grosvenor** (R). *Bath Rd, BH1 2EX.* ✆ (0202) 28858. C. ⊷ 37 bedrs, 29 bp, 3 bps, 3 ba, TV, Dgs. ✘ mc, at, LD 8.30. ⊡ Lt, N, CH, TV, ns, Ac, sb, sol, CP 44, CF, 1 st, Dis. £ BB £18–£22, DB £36–£44, WT £133–£150·50, DT £24–£25, WB, ②, Bk £3, L £3·25, D £6·25, cc 1 2 3 6, Dep.

★★★**Hazelwood** (R). *43 Christchurch Rd, BH1 3NZ.* ✆ (0202) 21367. C. ⊷ 58 bedrs, 29 bp, 10 bps, 7 sh, 8 ba, TV, Dgs. ✘ mc, at, LD 10.30. ⊡ Lt, N, CH, TV, CP 40, Ac, sp, sol, con 85, CF, 1 BGf, 0 st, Dis. £ BB fr £16·10, DB fr £32·20, WT fr £154·10, DT fr £31·05, WB, ②, Bk £4·60, L £5·75, D £9·20, cc 1 2 3 5 6, Dep.

★★★**Heathlands,** *12 Grove Rd, BH1 3AY.* ✆ (0202) 23336. C. ⊷ 120 bedrs, 100 bp, 1 bps, 7 ba, TV, Dgs. ✘ a l c, mc, at, LD 10. ⊡ Lt, N, CH, CP 80, Ac, sp, con 350, CF, 13 BGf, 0 st, Dis. £ BB £20–£28, DB £40–£56, DBB £25–£35, WB, ①, Bk £3, L £6·50, D £8·50, cc 1 2 3 5 6, Dep b.

★★★**Ladbroke Savoy,** *West Hill Rd, BH2 5EJ.* ✆ (0202) 294241. C. ⊷ 88 bedrs, 80 bp, 8 ba, TV, Dgs. ✘ mc, at, LD 9. ⊡ Lt, N, CH, Dgs, CP 60, U 8, Ac, sp, con 150, CF, 10 BGf, 0 st, Dis. £ BB £28–£48–£50, DBB £22–£30, WB, ①, Bk £5, L £6, D £8·50, cc 1 2 3 5, Dep b.

▣★★★**Langtry Manor** (R). *26 Derby Rd, BH1 3QB.* ✆ (0202) 23887. C 2. ⊷ 18 bedrs, 14 bp, 4 bps, TV, Dgs. ✘ a l c, mc, at, LD 8.30. ⊡ CH, CP 30, con 80, 3 BGf, 1 st, Dis. £ DD £25 £20, DB £42 £40, DDD £24–£27, WB, ②, Bk £3·50, L £5·50, D £7·75, cc 1 2 3 5, Dep a.

★★★**Melford Hall** (R). *St Peter's Rd, BH1 2LS.* ✆ (0202) 21516. C. ⊷ 60 bedrs, 54 bp, 1 bps, 5 ba. ✘ a l c, mc, at, LD 8. ⊡ Lt, N, CP 55, Ac, CF, 12 BGf, 1 st, Dis. £ WB, 10%, Bk £4, L £5·70, D £7·60, Dep.

★★★**Miramar** (R). *19 Grove Rd, BH1 3AL.* ✆ (0202) 26581. C. ⊷ 42 bedrs, 34 bp, 5 bps, 1 ba, TV, Dgs. ✘ a l c, mc, at, LD 8. ⊡ Lt, N, CH, TV, CP 40, U 6, Ac, con 10, CF, 1 st. £ BB £17·25–£25·50, DB £35·66–£48·30, WT £217·35–£249·55, DT

BOURNEMOUTH

0 miles   ¼   ½

P Car Park   C Public Conveniences
☒ Pedestrian precinct

Closed to vehicular traffic during Summer Season, Apr-Sept (inc.)

Queens Park Golf Course
Queen's Pk. South Drive
Club Entrance

To Crematorium 1½ m.

To Ringwood 12 m.

To Ringwood 7m.

A3062
A347
A35

St. John's Rd.
Owls Road
Boscombe Pier
BOSCOMBE
Walpole Rd.
Drummond Rd.
Manor Rd.
Manor Rd.
East Overcliff Drive
East Cliff
Curzon Rd.
St. Clement's Rd.
Windham Rd.
Holdenhurst Rd.
Cleveland Rd.
Southcote Road
Derby Rd.
Knyveton Rd.
Christchurch Road
Wessex Way
Richmond Park Road
Library
St. Leonard's Rd.
Capstone Rd.
Lowther Road
Malmesbury Park Rd.
Portchester Road
SPRINGBOURNE
Richmond Road
Alma Road
Baths Rd.
Heron Court Rd.
Charminster Rd.
Wellington Rd.
Lansdowne Rd.
St. Paul's Rd.
Police Sta.
Holdenhurst Rd.
Library
Meyrick Rd.
Gervis Rd. E.
Gervis Rd. W.
Russel Cotes Rd.
Undercliff Drive
Art Gallery & Museum
Ice Skating Rink
Cemetery
Stourwood Road
Dean Park Road
Cavendish Rd.
Dean Park
Wimborne Road
Wessex Way
Horseshoe Common
Dean Park
County Cricket Ground
P.O.
Madeira Rd.
Christchurch Rd.
St. Peter's Rd.
St. Peter's Church
St. Stephen's Rd.
Hinton Rd.
Gervis Place
Bath Rd.
Exeter Rd.
Bus Station
The Pavilion
Baths
The Pier
The Pier Theatre
Conference Centre
West Cliff Promenade

RAC Southern Counties Office
9 Poole Road

Wimborne Rd.
Stourwood Road
Dunkeld Road
East Avenue
Glenferness Avenue
Cambridge Rd.
Durlls Road
Meyrick Park
Central Drive
Durrant Rd.
Bourne Av.
Town Hall
Central Gardens
Poole Hill
The Triangle
The Square
Commercial Rd.
Richmond Hill
Priory Rd.
Winter Gardens
Tregonwell Rd.
WEST HILL
Durley Chine Rd.
West Cliff Road
Undercliff Drive
Durley Chine
Middle Chine
Alum Chine

Golf Links
Leven Av.
Surrey Rd.
Queen's Rd.
Wood Road
Upper Terrace Rd.
Cambridge Rd.
Clarendon Rd.
Coach & (Cars)
E.N.T. Hospital
WESTBOURNE
Grosvenor Rd.
West Cliff Road
West Overcliff Drive
Alumhurst Rd.

R.A.C. Office

Pug's Hole
Branksome Wood Road
Prince of Wales Rd.
The Bourne
Wessex Way
Poole Road
Seamoor Rd.
Library
Post Office
West Overcliff Drive
Alum Chine
Alum Promenade
Tower Rd.
The Avenue
Western Avenue

Dublin Road

To Poole 7m.

RAC

N

For abbreviations see inside back cover—RAC

£25·90–£35·65, WB, ②, Bk £4·60, L £5·20, D £8·90, cc 1 2 3.

★★★**New Normandie,**Manor Rd, East Cliff, BH1 3HL. ✆ (0202) 22246. C. ⇔ 62 bedrs, 62 bp, TV. ✗ a l c, mc, at, LD 9. ⓕ Lt, M, CH, ns, CP 36, Ac, sp, sb, sol, con 100, CF, 0 st. £ BBc fr £29·50, DBc fr £39·50, WB, ①, Bk £4·50, L £5·75, D £5·75, cc 1 2 3 4 5 6, Dep b.

★★★**Pavilion** (R), Bath Rd, BH1 2NS. ✆ (0202) 291266. C. ⇔ 47 bedrs, 33 bp, 6 bps, 4 ba, TV, Dgs. ✗ a l c, mc, at, LD 8.30. ⓕ Lt, N, CH, TV, Dgs, CP 30, Ac, con 60, CF, 2 BGf. £ BB £18–£24·50, DB £29–£41·50, WT £130–£195, DT £25·50–£29·50, WB, ①, Bk £4·50, L £5·50, D £8·50, cc 1 2 3 5 6, Dep b.

★★★**Queen's** (R), Meyrick Rd, East Cliff, BH1 3DL. ✆ (0202) 24415. C. ⇔ 103 bedrs, 77 bp, 7 ba, TV. ✗ a l c, mc, at, LD 8.30. ⓕ Lt, N, CH, CP 50, G 10, con 200, CF, 7 st. £ BB £15·50–£25·50, DB £31–£51, WT, £168–£213·50, DT £27–£33·50, WB, ②, Bk £3·50, L £4·95, D £6·95, cc 1 3 6.

★★★**Trouville** (R), 5 Priory Rd, BH2 5DH. ✆ (0202) 22262. Open Mar–Dec. C. ⇔ 80 bedrs, 70 bp, 3 ba, TV, Dgs. ✗ a l c, mc, at, LD 8.30. ⓕ Lt, N, CH, CP 70, U 5, CF. £ BB £18–£29, DB £36–£44, WT £147–£175, DT £23–£27, WB, ②, Bk £3·50, L £5·50, D £8·50, cc 1 2 3 5 6, Dep b.

★★★**Wessex,** 11 West Cliff Rd, BH2 5JN. ✆ (0202) 21911. C. ⇔ 96 bedrs, 78 bp, 18 bps, TV, Dgs. ✗ a l c, mc, at, LD 10.30. ⓕ Lt, N, CH, CP 300, sp, con 300, CF, 9 BGf, 0 st. £ BB fr £25, DB fr £40, WB, ①, Bk £3·95, L £5·95, D £7·95, cc 1 2 3 5, Dep b.

★★★**White Hermitage** (RI), Exeter Rd, BH2 5AH. ✆ (0202) 27363. C. ⇔ 67 bedrs, 56 bp, 7 bps, 2 ba, TV, Dgs. ✗ a l c, mc, at, LD 8.30. ⓕ Lt, N, CH, ns, CP 60, sb, sol, con 150, CF, 2 BGf, 0 st, Dis. £ BB £16–£30·50, DB £29–£54, WT £189–£255·50, WB, ①, Bk £4, L £5·95, D £7·50, cc 1 2 3 5, Dep b.▲

★★**Albany** (R), Warren Edge Rd, Southbourne, BH6 4AU. ✆ (0202) 428151. C 3. ⇔ 19 bedrs, 17 bp, 2 bps, TV. ✗ mc, at, LD 8. ⓕ Lt, CH, TV, Dgs, CP 19, con 20, 5 BGf, 4 st. £ BB £14·08–£19·03, DB £25·96–£35·86, DBB £16·50–£22·88, WB, ①, Bk £2·75, L £3·95, D £7·95, cc 1 2 3 5 6, Dep b.▲

★★**Avonmore** (R), Foxholes Rd, BH6 3AT. ✆ (0202) 428639. C. ⇔ 15 bedrs, 4 bp, 3 ba. ✗ a l c, mc, at, LD 8. ⓕ Lt, CH, TV, CP 10, Ac, con 25, CF, 1 st. £ BB £6–£20, DB £12–£28, WT £74–£124, DT £10–£22, WB, ①, Bk £2, L £3, D £6, cc 1 2 3, Dep.

■★★**Belvedere,** Bath Rd, BH1 2EU. ✆ (0202) 21080. C. ⇔ 29 bedrs, 16 bp, 3 bps, 4 ba, TV, Dgs. ✗ a l c, mc, at, LD 8. ⓕ Lt, CH, TV, CP 22, Ac, con 25, CF, 0 st. £ BB £15–£21, DD £27–£39, WD, ①, Bk £3, L £3·50, D £6·45, cc 1 2 3 5, Dep.

★★**Bournemouth Moat House,** Knyveton Rd, BH1 3QQ. ✆ (0202) 293311. C. ⇔ 113 bedrs, 107 bp, 6 bps, TV, Dgs. ✗ a l c, mc, at, LD 9.30. ⓕ Lt, N, CH, CP 120, Ac, sp, con 1500, CF, 6 BGf, 0 st, Dis. £ BB £27, DB £41, WT £210, DT £41, WB, ①, Bk £4·25, L £6, D £8, cc 1 2 3 5 6, Dep b.

★★**Brummell's** (R), 2 Boscombe Spa Rd, BH5 1AT. ✆ (0202) 33252. C. ⇔ 23 bedrs, 3 bp, 10 bps, 2 sh, 6 ba, ns, Dgs. ✗ a l c, mc, at, LD 8. ⓕ N, CH, TV, CP 25,

---

Ac, con 50, CF. £ BB £10–£15, DB £20–£30, WT £86–£106, DT £15–£19, WB, ①, Bk £2·50, L £5, D £5·50, Dep a.

■★★**Cadogan** (R), 8 Poole Rd, BH2 5QU. ✆ (0202) 763006. C. ⇔ 50 bedrs, 18 bp, 7 bps, 7 ba, TV, Dgs. ✗ mc, at, LD 5. ⓕ Lt, CH, TV, Dgs, CP 60, Ac, con 130, CF. £ BB fr £11, ①, cc 1 3 6.

★★**Chinehurst** (R), Studland Rd, Westbourne, BH4 8JA. ✆ (0202) 764583. C 3. ⇔ 30 bedrs, 19 bp, 5 bps, 3 ba, TV, Dgs. ✗ a l c, mc, at, LD 8. ⓕ CH, TV, CP 22, G 2, Ac, con, CF. £ BB £13–£20, DB £21–£35, WT £122–£150, DT £17·50–£21·50, WB, ①, Bk £3·25, L £3·95, D £6·50, cc 1 2 3 5, Dep.

■★★**Commodore,** Overcliff Dr, Southbourne, BH6 3SJ. ✆ (0202) 423150. Open Apr–Sep. C. ⇔ 19 bedrs, 7 sh, 5 ba. ✗ mc, LD 8.30. ⓕ Lt, CH, TV, CP 12, CF, 6 st. £ BB fr £17·50, DB fr £32, ②, Bk £4, D £6·50, cc 1 2 3, Dep.

★★**County** (R), Westover Rd, BH1 2BT. ✆ (0202) 22385. C. ⇔ 53 bedrs, 31 bp, 3 bps, 7 ba, TV, Dgs. ✗ mc, at, LD 7.45. ⓕ Lt, N, CH, CF, 0 st. £ BB £16–£18, DB £28–£38, WT £120–£146, DT £20–£24, WB, ①, Bk £3·50, L £5·50, D £7, cc 1 2 3, Dep.

★★**Elstead** (R), 12 Knyveton Rd, BH1 3QP. ✆ (0202) 22829.

■★★**Fircroft** (R), Owls Rd, BH5 1AE. ✆ (0202) 309771. C. ⇔ 49 bedrs, 44 bp, 5 bps, TV, Dgs. ✗ mc, at, LD 8. ⓕ N, CH, TV, CP 50, Ac, con 40, CF, 12 BGf, 8 st. £ BB £14·50–£18, DB £29–£36, DBB £105–£147, WB, ①, Bk £3, L £2·50, D £5·50, cc 1 3, Dep b.

★★**Grange,** Overcliff Dr, Southbourne, BH6 3NL. ✆ (0202) 424228. C. ⇔ 29 bedrs, 14 bp, 1 bps, 4 sh, 4 ba, TV, Dgs. ✗ a l c, mc, at, LD 7.15. ⓕ Lt, ch, TV, Dgs, CP 55, Ac, CF, 1 st. £ BB £12–£17. DB £20–£26, WT £75–£130, DT £14–£20, WB, ①, Bk £2, L £1·50, D £5.

★★**Hinton Firs,** Manor Rd, BH1 3HB. ✆ (0202) 25409. C. ⇔ 50 bedrs, 28 bp, 5 ba, annexe 6 bedrs, 6 bp, TV, Dgs. ✗ mc, at, LD 8. ⓕ N, CH, TV, CP 40, Ac, sp, sol, con 40, CF, 5 BGf, 0 st, Dis. £ BB fr £13·70, DB fr £25, WT £122–£182, DT £17·50–£30·30, WB, ①, Bk £3·30, L £5·25, D £6.25, Dep a.

★★**Hotel Riviera** (RI), West Cliff Gdns, BH2 5HL. ✆ (0202) 22845. Open Apr–Oct. C. ⇔ 35 bedrs, 25 bp, 4 bps, 6 sh, 4 ba, TV, Dgs. ✗ mc, at, LD 7.30. ⓕ Lt, N, ch, CP 24, sol, CF, 4 BGf, 6 st. £ BB £10·50–£15·50, DB £21–£31, WT £105–£125, DT £16·50–£18·50, ①, Bk £3·50, L £3·50, D £6·50, cc 1 2 3, Dep.

★★**Manor House** (R), Manor Rd, East Cliff, BH1 3EZ. ✆ (0202) 36669. Closed Jan. C. ⇔ 27 bedrs, 9 bp, 6 bps, 1 sh, ba, ns, TV, Dgs. ✗ mc, at, LD 8.30. ⓕ CH, TV, ns, CP 40, con 70, CF. £ BB £9·50–£15·50, DB £19–£31, WT £74–£128, DT £12·50–£18·50, ①, Bk £3·50, L £3·50, D £6·50, cc 1 2, Dep.

★★**New Somerset** (R), Bath Rd, BH1 2NW. ✆ (0202) 21983. C. ⇔ 38 bedrs, 7 bp, 1 bps, 6 ba, TV, Dgs. ✗ mc, at, LD 8. ⓕ Lt, N, CH, TV, CP 20, Ac, con 50, CF, 1 st. £ BB £11·50–£16, DB £23–£32, WT £118–£160, DT £17·50–£23, WB, ②, Bk £3, L £1, D £5.75, cc 1 3, Dep a.

★★**Pinehurst** (R), West Cliff Gardens, BH2 5HR. ✆ (0202) 26218. Closed Jan–Feb. C. ⇔ 75 bedrs, 32 bp, 21 bps, 12 ba, TV, Dgs. ✗ mc, at, LD 8.30. ⓕ Lt, N, CH, TV, Dgs, CP 46, Ac, sol, con 150, CF, 3 BGf, 0 st, Dis. £ BB £13·50–£17·25, DB £25–

£32·50, DBB £16·25–£21·50, WB, ②, Bk £3·50, L £4, D £5·95, cc 1 6, Dep a.

★★**Riviera** (R), Burnaby Rd, Alum Chine, BH4 8JF. ✆ (0202) 763653. Closed Jan. C. ⇔ 65 bedrs, 51 bp, 1 bps, 3 ba, TV, Dgs. ✗ mc, at, LD 8. ⓕ Lt, CH, CP 64, Ac, sp, sb, sol, CF. £ BB £16·50–£20, DB £19–£43, WT £135–£195, DT £22·75–£30·75, WB, ①, Bk £3·95, L £6·50, D £8·50, Dep b.

★★**St George** (RI), West Cliff Gardens, BH2 5HL. ✆ (0202) 26075. Open Mar–Nov. C 5. ⇔ 21 bedrs, 13 bp, 7 bps, 1 sh, TV, Dgs. ✗ mc, at, LD 7.30. ⓕ Lt, CH, CP 5, 4 BGf, 8 st. £ BB £10·50–£17, DB £24–£36, WT £100–£150, DT £15–£22·50, WB, ②, Bk £2·50, L £3·50, D £4·85, cc 1 2 3 5, Dep a.

■★★**Studland Dene,** Studland Rd, Alum Chine, BH4 8JA. ✆ (0202) 765445. Closed Jan. C. ⇔ 32 bedrs, 10 bp, 6 bps, 3 ba, TV, Dgs. ✗ mc, at, LD 10. ⓕ CH, Dgs, CP 25, CF, 1 BGf, 1 st, Dis. £ BB £12–£20, DB £24–£40, DBB £17·50–£25, WB, ①, Bk £4, L £4, D £4·50.

★★**Sun Court** (R), West Hill Rd, BH2 5PH. ✆ (0202) 21343. C. ⇔ 36 bedrs, 15 bp, 16 bps, 2 ba, TV, Dgs. ✗ a l c, mc, at, LD 8. ⓕ Lt, N, CH, TV, CP 26, Ac, con 30, CF, 1 st. £ BB £12–£20·50, DB £24–£42, WT £87–£148, DT £19–£25, ①, Bk £3·50, L £4·50, D £6·50, cc 1 2 3 5 6, Dep b.

★★**Tralee** (R), West Hill Rd, BH2 5EQ. ✆ (0202) 26246. C. ⇔ 86 bedrs, 45 bp, 4 bps, 3 sh, 10 ba, TV, Dgs. ✗ mc, at, LD 8. ⓕ Lt, N, CH, TV, CP 40, Ac, sp, sb, sol, con 200, CF, 0 st. £ BB £16·50–£25, DB £33–£50, WT £109–£161·50, DT £21·50–£27·50, WB, ①, Bk £3·50, L £3·95, D £4·95, cc 1 2 3 4 5 6, Dep b.▲

■★★**West Cliff Hall**(R), Priory Rd, BH2 5DN. ✆ (0202) 22669.

★★**Whitehall** (R), Exeter Park Rd, BH2 5AX. ✆ (0202) 24682. Open Mar–Oct. C. ⇔ 47 bedrs, 15 bp, 8 bps, 6 ba, TV, Dgs. ✗ mc, at, LD 8. ⓕ Lt, CH, TV, CP 25, Ac, con 40, CF, 1 st. £ BB £14–£19·50, DB £28–£39, DT £24–£28, WB, ①, Bk £3, L £4, D £6, cc 1 2 3 5, Dep a.

■★★**Winterbourne** (R), 4 Priory Rd, BH2 5DJ. ✆ (0202) 24927. C. ⇔ 41 bedrs, 34 bp, 7 bps. ✗ mc, at, LD 8. ⓕ Lt, CH, CP 32, G 2, Ac, sp, con, CF, 1 BGf, 2 st. £ BB £15–£22·50, DB £26·25–£43, WT £130–£180, WB, ①, Bk £3, D £6·75, cc 1 3, Dep a.

★★**Winter Gardens** (Unl), 32 Tregonwell Rd, BH2 5NJ. ✆ (0202) 25769. Closed Jan–Feb. C. ⇔ 39 bedrs, 18 bp, 1 bps, 6 ba, TV, Dgs. ✗ a l c, mc, at, LD 8. ⓕ Lt, N, CH, TV, CP 24, G 2, Ac, con 60, CF. £ BB £11·90–£17·90, DB £23·80–£35·80, WT £115–£150, DT £17·25–£25, WB, ①, Bk £3·50, L £4, D £5·50, cc 1 2 3 4 5 6, Dep b.

★★**Woodcroft Tower** (R), 49 Gervis Rd, BH1 3DE. ✆ (0202) 28202. C. ⇔ 43 bedrs, 19 bp, 7 bps, 5 ba, TV, Dgs. ✗ mc, at, LD 8. ⓕ Lt, N, CH, Dgs, CP 30, U 6, con 100, CF. £ BB £13·80–£18·40, DB £27·60–£36·80, WT £103·50–£143·75, DT £19·55–£24·15, WB, ②, Bk £3, L £4, D £5·50, cc 1 2.

■★★**Abbey Mount** (R), Priory Rd, BH2 5DL. ✆ (0202) 21888. RS Oct–Mar. C. ⇔ 36 bedrs, 9 bp, 5 ba, TV, Dgs. ✗ a l c, mc, at, LD 7.30. ⓕ TV, Dgs, CP 25, U 1, sp, con 25, CF, 2 st. £ BB £9–£17, DB £18–£34, DBB £13–£21·50, WB, ①, Bk £3·50, D £5, cc 1 2 3, Dep a.

◪★**Cliff Court,** 15 West Cliff Rd, BH2 5EX. ☏ (0202) 25994. Closed Jan. C. ⊨ 43 bedrs, 20 bp, 14 bps, 9 sh, 3 ba, TV, Dgs. ✗ mc, at, ⓓ Lt, CH, TV, CP 33, Ac, CF, 6 st. £ BB £10–£15·50, DB £20–£30, WB, ⊡, Bk £3, D £5·25, Dep b.

◪★**Glencairn** (R), Manor Rd, East Cliff, BH1 3PZ. ☏ (0202) 36054. Closed Jan. C 3. ⊨ 30 bedrs, 4 bp, 7 bps, 19 sh, 4 ba, TV, Dgs. ✗ mc, at, LD 7.30. ⓓ CH, TV, CP 36, con 50, CF. £ BB £9·75–£14·50, DB £19·50–£33·60, WB, ⊡, Bk £3, D £4·95, cc 1 2 3 5, Dep a.

◪★**Tree Tops** (R), 52 Christchurch Rd, BH1 3PE. ☏ (0202) 23157. C. ⊨ 58 bedrs, 25 bp, 2 bps, 10 sh, 5 ba, TV, Dgs. ✗ mc, at, LD 7. ⓓ Lt, N, CH, TV, Dgs, CP 28, Ac, con 100, CF, 2 BGf, 1 st, Dis. £ BB £12–£18, DB £24–£32·50, DBB £17·50–£24·50, ⊡, Bk £3, D £6, cc 1.

★**Ullswater** (R), West Cliff Gdns, BH2 5HW. ☏ (0202) 25181. Closed Dec–Feb, open Xmas. C. ⊨ 46 bedrs, 4 bp, 4 bps, 6 ba, TV, Dgs. ✗ mc, at, LD 6.45. ⓓ Lt, CH, TV, CP 20, Ac, CF, 2 BGf, 10 st. £ BB £12–£18·50, DB £24–£37, DBB £15–£21·50, ②, Bk £3·45, L £4·60, D £5·75, Dep.

★**Wellington** (R), 10 Poole Rd, BH2 5QU. ☏ (0202) 768407. Closed Jan–Feb & Nov. C. ⊨ 27 bedrs, 3 bp, 7 bps, 5 ba, TV, Dgs. ✗ mc, at, LD 7. ⓓ Lt, ch, Dgs, CP 25, Ac, CF, 1 BGf, 6 st. £ BB £11–£16, DB £22–£32, WT £68–£108, DT £16–£18, WB, ⊡, Bk £2, L £2·50, D £4·50, cc 1 3, Dep.

Alum Bay, H, z (RI), 19 Burnaby Rd, Alum Chine, BH4 8JF. ☏ (0202) 761034. C. ⊨ 12 bedrs, 1 bps, Dgs. ⓓ TV, Dgs, ns, CP 12, CF. £ BB £8·05–£10·35, DB £16·10–£20·70, WT (b) £69–£92, DT (b) £11·50–£13·80, ②.

Anfield, PH, z (RI), 12 Bradburne Rd, BH2 5ST. ☏ (0202) 290749. C 5. ⊨ 16 bedrs, 4 ba, ns. ⓓ ch, TV, CP 4, BGf, 2 st. £ BB £8·62–£11·50, DB £17·24–£23, WT (b) £69–£98, DT £12·07–£14·30, ⊡, cc 1 2.

Arlington, H, z (RI), Exeter Park Rd, BH2 5RD. ☏ (0202) 22879. Open Mar–Nov & Xmas. C. ⊨ 30 bedrs, 2 bp, 6 bps, 4 ba, Dgs. ⓓ CH, TV, CP 21, CF, 6 BGf, 0 st, Dis. £ BB £10·50–£16·50, DB £21–£33, WT (b) £86–£120, DT (b) £13–£17·50, ⊡, Bk £2·20, L £3·30, D £4·60.

Avon Royal, PH, z (RI), 45 Christchurch Rd, BH1 3PA. ☏ (0202) 292800. Closed Jan. C. ⊨ 21 bedrs, 7 bp, 2 bps, 4 ba, TV. ⓓ CH, TV, CP 25, CF, 4 BGf, 1 st, Dis. £ BB £11–£15·50, DB £22–£30, WT (b) £80–£122, DT (b) £16–£19, ⊡, Bk £2·75, D £5.

Beechwood, H, z (RI), 14 Studlands, BH4 8JA. ☏ (0202) 767015.

Blinkbonnie Heights, PH, x (RI), 26 Clifton Rd, Southbourne, BH6 3PA. ☏ (0202) 426512. Open Apr–Nov. C. ⊨ 12 bedrs, 1 bp, 2 ba. ⓓ CH, TV, CP 12, CF, 3 BGf, 1 st, Dis. £ BB £8–£10·75, DB £18–£24, WT (b) £70–£90, DT (b) £11–£14, ⊡.

Blue Cedars, PH, z (RI), Portchester Place, BH8 8JS. ☏ (0202) 26893. C. ⊨ 12 bedrs, 2 sh, 2 ba. ⓓ CH, TV, CP 9, CF. £ BB £6·50–£8, DB £13–£18, WT (b) £49–£73, DT (b) £10–£11·50, ⊡.

Borodale, PH, z, 10 St John's Rd, BH5 1EL. ☏ (0202) 35285. C 6. ⊨ 16 bedrs, 1 bp, 2 bps, 3 sh, 3 ba, Dgs. ⓓ CH, TV, Dgs, CP 20, CF. £ BB £8·50–£10·50, DB £17–£24, WT £70–£92, DT £11·50–£14·50, ⊡.

Bracken Lodge, PH, z, (R), 5 Bracken Rd, Southbourne, BH6 3TB. ☏ (0202) 428777. Open Mar–Oct. C 5. ⊨ 12 bedrs, 2 bp, 2 sh, TV. ⓓ CH, TV, ns, CP 14. £ BB £8·05–£23, DB £16·10–£23, WT £69–£97·75, DT £13·80–£17·25, ⊡.

Braemar, PH, z, (RI), 30 Glen Rd, BH5 1HS. ☏ (0202) 36054. Open Apr–Oct & Xmas & Easter. C. ⊨ 11 bedrs, 2 bp, 2 ba. ⓓ CH, TV, CP 7, CF. £ BB £8–£12, DB £16–£24, WT (b) £60–£85, DT (b) £9–£12, ⊡.

Britannia, H, y (Unl), 40 Christchurch Rd, BH1 3PE. ☏ (0202) 26700. C 5. ⊨ 28 bedrs, 2 bp, 2 sh, 5 ba, Dgs. ⓓ CH, TV, CP 60, 1 st. £ BB £8·05–£9·20, DB £16·10–£19·50, WT (b) £69–£79·25, DT (b) £10·75–£12·50, ⊡.

Brun-Lea, H, z (RI), 94 Southbourne Rd, BH6 3QQ. ☏ (0202) 425956. C 8. ⊨ 15 bedrs, 3 bps, 2 ba. ✗ a l c. ⓓ CH, TV, CP 11, 2 st. £ BB £8–£10, DB £16–£22·30, WT £60–£80, DT £11·50–£13·50, ⊡, Bk £1·50, L £2, D £3·50.

Bursledon, H, z (Unl), 34 Gervis Rd, East Cliff, BH1 3DF. ☏ (0202) 24062. C 3. ⊨ 23 bedrs, 2 bp, 7 bps, 4 ba, Dgs. ⓓ ch, TV, CP 14, U 5, 3 BGf, 3 st. £ BB £10·35–£16·15, DB £20·70–£32·30, WT (a) £96·60–£140·30, DT (a) £14·95–£21·85, ⊡, Bk £2·30, L £4·60, D £5·75, cc 3.

Canonbury, PH, z (RI), 23 Beaulieu Rd, T (0202) 761338. C. ⊨ 9 bedrs, 2 ba, ns, Dgs. ⓓ CH, TV, Dgs, ns, CP 4, CF. £ BB £9–£10, DB £17–£19, WT (b) £69–£82, ⊡, cc 1 2 3 4 5 6.

Charles Taylor, H, z (RI), 40 Frances Rd, BH1 3SA. ☏ (0202) 22695. Open Mar–Oct. C 3. ⊨ 28 bedrs, 11 bp, 6 ba. ⓓ CH, TV, CP 12, CF, 2 BGf, 2 st. £ BB £8–£14, DB £16–£28, WT (b) £70–£94, DT (b) £12–£15, ②, Bk £2·75, D £4.

Chequers, H, z (Rt), 17 West Cliff Rd, BH2 5EX. ☏ (0202) 23900. Open Mar–Oct. C. ⊨ 28 bedrs, 17 bp, 11 bps, 3 ba, TV. ⓓ CH, TV, CP 25, CF, 2 BGf, 12 st. £ BB £10–£18, DB £20–£36, WT (b) £95–£125, ⊡, Bk £3·50, D £5·50.

Chilterns, H, z (RI), 44 Westby Rd (Boscombe), BH5 1HD. ☏ (0202) 36539. Open Apr–Oct. C. ⊨ 19 bedrs, 3 ba, Dgs. ⓓ ch, TV, CP 17, G 2, CF, 2 BGf, 1 st, Dis. £ BB £7·50–£10, DB £15–£20, WT (b) £70–£90, DT £11–£13·50, ⊡, L £4, D £4.

Chineside, PH, y (Unl), 15 Studland Rd, BH4 8HZ. ☏ (0202) 761206. Open Apr–Oct. C 4. ⊨ 13 bedrs, 3 bps, 3 ba. ⓓ CH, TV, CP 30, 6 st. £ BB £7·50–£11·25, DB £15–£22·50, WT (b) £73–£93, DT (b) £10·50–£15, ⊡.

Christina, H, z (RI), 6 Westbourne Park Rd, BH4 8HG. ☏ (0202) 763510.

Cleasby Grange, PH, z (Unl), 8 Wollstonecroft Rd. (Boscombe), BH5 1JQ. ☏ (0202) 33960. Open Apr–Sept. ⊨ 13 bedrs, 2 ba. ⓓ TV, ns, CP 10, G 2, 1 BGf. £ BB £8·05–£9·20, DB £14·95–£17·25, WT £75–£80·05, DT £11·50–£13·25, ⊡, Bk £2, D £4.

Clifton Court, PH, z, 30 Clifton Rd, Southbourne, BH6 3PA. ☏ (0202) 427753. C. ⊨ 12 bedrs, 2 bp, 4 ba, Dgs. ⓓ CH, TV, CP 10, CF, 2 st. £ BB fr £7·50–£10·50, DB £15–£23·50, WT (c) £45–£63, DT (b) £10–£15, ⊡, Bk £2, D £3·50.▲

Collindale Lodge, H, z (RI), 154 Richmond Park Rd, BH8 8TW. ☏ (0202) 514528. C 4. ⊨ 20 bedrs, 3 bps,

12 sh, 5 ba, TV, Dgs. ✗ a l c. ⓓ ch, TV, ns, CP 16.

Cransley, PH, z (RI), 11 Knyveton Rd, BH1 3QG. ☏ (0202) 290067. Open Apr–Oct. C. ⊨ 12 bedrs, 4 bp, 3 bps, 2 ba, TV, Dgs. ⓓ ch, TV, CP 10, CF. £ BB £7·50–£13, DB £15–£26, WT (b) £55–£85, DT (b) £10·50–£14·50, ⊡, cc 1 3.

Crescent Grange, PH, z (RI), 6 Crescent Rd, BH2 5SS. ☏ (0202) 26959. Open Mar–Oct & Xmas. C 3. ⊨ 21 bedrs, 8 bp, 1 bps, 4 ba, Dgs. ⓓ CH, TV, Dgs, ns, CP 24, 0 st. £ BB £9–£11·50, DB £18–£26·40, WT (b) £80–£105, DT (b) £13–£15·50, ⊡, D £4, cc 1 3.

Cresta Court, H, z (RI), 3 Crescent Rd, BH2 5SS. ☏ (0202) 25217. C 4. ⊨ 20 bedrs, 3 bp, 5 ba, TV, Dgs. ⓓ CH, TV, CP 17, CF, 1 BGf. £ BB £9·50–£12·50, DB £19–£29, WT (b) £95–£115, ⊡, Bk £2·50, D £4·50, cc 1 3.

Croham Hurst, H, z (RI), 9 Durley Rd, BH2 5JH. ☏ (0202) 22353.

Cromford House Hotel, PH (RI), 59 Alumhurst Rd, Alum Chine, BH4 8EW. ☏ (0202) 764147. Open Apr–Oct. C. ⊨ 9 bedrs, 1 bps, 3 sh, 2 ba, Dgs. ⓓ CH, TV, Dgs, CP 9, CF. £ BB £7·60–£8·85, DB £15·20–£17·70, WT (b) £74–£83, DT (b) £10·50–£11·85, ⊡.

Denbry, PH, z (RI), 179 Holdenhurst Rd, BH8 8DG. ☏ (0202) 28700.

Derwent House, PH, z (RI), 36 Hamilton Rd, BH1 4EH. ☏ (0202) 309102. C. ⊨ 10 bedrs, 2 sh, 2 ba. ⓓ CH, TV, CP 14, CF, 1 st. £ BB fr £10·85, DB fr £22, WT (b) £80·50–£114·55, DT (b) £15·53–£18·40, ②, cc 2 3 5.

Dorset Westbury, H, y (RI), 62 Lansdowne Rd, BH1 1RS. ☏ (0202) 21811. Closed Dec. C. ⊨ 17 bedrs, 3 bp, 2 bps, 1 sh, 3 ba, Dgs. ✗ a l c. ⓓ CH, TV, CP 20, CF. £ BB £8·05–£12·07. DB £16·10–£26·78, WT (b) £82·80–£110·97, DT (b) £12·45–£16·47.

Earlham Lodge, H, z (RI), 91 Alumhurst Rd, Alum Chine, BH4 8HR. ☏ (0202) 761943. Open Feb–Nov & Xmas. C. ⊨ 14 bedrs, 6 bps, 4 ba. ⓓ CH, TV, CP 9, CF, 4 st. £ BB £8·50–£13, DB £16–£24, WT (b) £85–£99, DT (b) £12–£15, ②, cc 1 2 3.

East Cliff Cottage, PH, z (Unl), 57 Grove Rd, BH1 3AT. ☏ (0202) 22788. C. ⊨ 10 bedrs, 4 bp, 6 sh, 2 ba, TV, Dgs. ✗ a l c. ⓓ CH, TV, CP 10, CF, 1 st. £ BB £8–£12·50, DB £16–£25, WT (b) £84–£114, ⊡, Bk £2·50, L £4·50, D £5·50.

Egerton House, PH, z (RI), 385 Holdenhurst Rd, BH8 9AN. ☏ (0202) 34024. C. ⊨ 8 bedrs, 2 ba. ⓓ CH, TV, CP 8, CF, 1 st. £ BB £7·50–£8·50, DB £15–£17, WT (c) £46·50–£55, DT (c) £11·50–£12·50, ⊡.

Eglan Court, PH, z (RI), 7 Knyveton Rd, BH1 3QF. ☏ (0202) 290093.

Farlow, PH, z (Unl), 13 Walpole Rd, BH1 4HB. ☏ (0202) 35865. C 5. ⊨ 12 bedrs, 2 ba. ⓓ ch, TV, CP 15, 0 st. £ BB £7–£8, DB £14–£16, WT (b) £70–£77, (c) £47–£54, DT (b) £10·50–£11·50, ⊡, cc 1.

Fieldon Court, PH, z (RI), 20 Southern Rd, BH6 3SR. ☏ (0202) 427459. C. ⊨ 10 bedrs, 2 sh, 2 ba, TV, Dgs. ⓓ CH, TV, CP 8, CF, 1 st. £ BB £5–£8, DB £10–£16, WT (b) £50–£85, DT (b) £7·50–£12, ⊡.

Florida, H, z, 33–35 Boscombe Spa Rd, BH5 1AS. ☏ (0202) 34537.

Freshfields, PH, z (RI), 55 Christchurch Rd, BH1 3PA. ☏ (0202) 34023. C. ⊨ 11

bedrs, 3 bp, 2 bps, 2 ba. ⌂ CH, TV, CP 9,
CF, 3 BGf, 12 st. £ BB £7·50–£17, DB £15–
£34, WT (c) £52–£70, ⒒, B £2·40, L £1·10,
D £4·50.

Gervis Court, H, z (RI), *38 Gervis Rd,
BH1 3DH.* ✆ (0202) 26871. Open Apr–
Oct. C. ⊨ 19 bedrs, 3 bp, 3 bps, 4 ba, Dgs.
✗ a l c. ⌂ ch, TV, CP 15, G 2, CF. £ BB
£11·25–£13·25, DB £19·50–£26·50, WT
£69–£105, DT £14·25–£16, ⒒, B £2, L
£2·50, D £5.

Glen, PH, z (RI), *12 Rosemount Rd, BH4
8HB.* ✆ (0202) 763795. Closed Nov. C.
⊨ 12 bedrs, 1 sh, 2 ba, Dgs. ⌂ ch, TV, CP
5, CF, 1 BGf, 2 st. £ BB £7·50–£11, DB
£15–£23, WT (b) £60–£85, DT (b) £10–
£15, ⒒, Bk £3, D £4.

Golden Sands Hotel, PH, z, *83
Alumhurst Rd, BH4 8HR.*
✆ (0202) 763832. Open Apr–Oct. C. ⊨ 14
bedrs, 2 bps, 3 ba, TV. ⌂ ch, TV, CP 9, 1
BGf. £ BB £9·25–£11·50, DB £18·50–£24,
WT (b) £82·50–£97·75, DT £13–£15·50,
⒒.

Hamilton Hall, PH, z (RI), *1 Carysfort
Rd, Boscombe, BH1 4EJ.* ✆ (0202) 35758.
Open Feb–Nov. C 5. ⊨ 11 bedrs, 2 bp, 2
bps, 6 sh, 1 ba, Dgs. ⌂ CH, TV, CP 9. £ BB
£5·75–£9·10, DB £11·50–£25, WT (b)
£60–£85, DT (b) £8–£11·60, ⒒, Bk £2, D
£3.

Hawaiian, PH, z, *4 Glen Rd, Boscombe,
BH5 1BR.* ✆ (0202) 33234. Open Apr–Oct.
C 4. ⊨ 13 bedrs, 5 bp, 1 bps, 2 ba, ns.
⌂ CH, TV, CP 9, 1 BGf, 2 st. £ BB £7·48–
£10·35, DB £14·96–£20·70, WT £64·40–
£78·20, DT (b) £9·20–£11·20, ⒒, cc 3.

Heathcote, PH, z (R), *2 Heathcote Rd,
Boscombe, BH5 1EZ.* ✆ (0202) 36185. C.
⊨ 16 bedrs, 2 bp, 2 ba. ⌂ ch, TV,
CP 14, CF, 2 BGf, 1 st. £ BB £7·50–£9, DB
£15–£21·30, WT (b) fr £69, DT (b) fr £11.
⒒

Highlin, PH, z (RI), *Knole Rd, BH1 4DQ.*
✆ (0202) 33758.

Holmcroft, PH, y (RI), *Earle Rd, Alum
Chine, Westbourne, BH4 8JQ.*
✆ (0202) 761289. Open Apr–Oct. C 3.
⊨ 21 bedrs, 1 bp, 7 bps, 2 ba, TV, Dgs.
⌂ ch, TV, CP 17. £ BB £10·50–£14·50, DB
£21–£32, WT (b) £85–£106, DT (b)
£14·50–£17·50, ⒒.

Holme Lacy, PH, z (R), *32 Florence Rd,
Boscombe, BH5 1HQ.* ✆ (0202) 36933.

Holmwood, PH, z (RI), *4 Westbourne
Park Rd, BH4 8HG.* ✆ (0202) 761106. C.
⊨ 10 bedrs, 1 bps, 2 sh, 2 ba, ns, Dgs.
⌂ CH, TV, Dgs, ns, CP 6, CF, 1 BGf, 1 st.
£ BB £9–£14·50, DB £18–£29, WT £70–
£90, DT £11–£13, ⒓.

Hotel Cavendish, PH, z (Unl), *20 Durley
Chine Rd, West Cliff, BH2 5LF.*
✆ (0202) 290489. C 5. ⊨ 18 bedrs, 5 bp,
3 ba, TV. ⌂ ch, TV, CP 14, CF, 10 st. £ BB
£9·20–£12·50, DB £18·40–£30, WT £69–
£98·44, DT £12·65–£16·61, ⒒.

Hotel Sorrento, PH, z (Rt), *16 Owls Rd,
Boscombe, BH5 1AG.* ✆ (0202) 34019.
Open Apr–Oct. C. ⊨ 19 bedrs, 3 bp, 3 sh,
4 ba, Dgs. ⌂ ch, CP 16, CF, 1 st. £ BB
£8·62–£13, DB £17·24–£26, WT (b) £69–
£110, DT (b) £11·50–£17, ⒒.

Kenton House, H, z (Unl), *9 Irving Rd,
BH6 5BG.* ✆ (0202) 427387. Closed
Xmas. ⊨ 8 bedrs, 3 sh, 2 ba, Dgs. ⌂ CH,
TV, CP 6, CF, 0 st. £ BB £7·50–£8, DB £15–
£16, WT (b) £82–£92, DT (b) £12–£14,
⒒▲

Kings Barton, H, z, *22 Hawkwood Rd,
Boscombe, BH5 1DW.* ✆ (0202) 37794. C.

⊨ 15 bedrs, 2 bp, 1 bps, 12 sh, 3 ba, ns.
⌂ CH, TV, CP 15, CF. £ BB £7·50–£8·50,
DB £15–£18, WT £73–£83, DT £11–£12,
⒒

Langton Hall, PH, z (R), *8 Durley Chine
Rd, BH2 5JY.* ✆ (0202) 25025. C. ⊨ 22
bedrs, 8 bp, 1 bps, 3 ba, TV. ✗ a l c. ⌂ CH,
TV, CP 20, CF. £ BB £8–£14, DB £16–
£31·40, WT £65–£105, DT (b) £10·50–
£17, ⒓, Bk £2, L £2, D £3·50, cc 1 2 3.

Linwood House, PH, z (RI), *11 Wilfred
Rd, Boscombe, BH5 1ND.*
✆ (0202) 37818. Open Mar–Oct. C 3.
⊨ 10 bedrs, 3 bps, 2 sh, 2 ba, TV, Dgs.
⌂ CH, TV, CP 7, CF, 1 BGf, 1 st, Dis. £ BB
£7–£12, DB £14–£24, WT (b) £65–£83,
DT (b) £10·50–£14, ⒒.

Mae Mar, PH, z (RI), *91 West Hill Rd,
BH2 5PQ.* ✆ (0202) 23167. C. ⊨ 29
bedrs, 5 ba, Dgs. ⌂ Lt, CH, TV, CF, 4 BGf,
10 st. £ BB £9·20–£10·35, DB £18·40–
£20·70, WT (b) £63·25–£92, DT £10·35–
£13·80, ⒒.

Mariners, PH, y (Unl), *22 Clifton Rd,
Southbourne, BH6 3PA.*
✆ (0202) 420851. Open Mar–Oct. C.
⊨ 15 bedrs, 3 ba, Dgs. ⌂ CH, TV, ns, CP
20, CF, 1 st. £ BB £7·50–£10, DB £15–£20,
WT (b) £66–£85, DT (b) £11–£15, ⒒, Bk
£2, L £2·50, D £3·50.

Monreith, H, y (RI). ✆ (0202) 290344.
Open Apr–Oct & Xmas. C 4. ⊨ 30 bedrs, 6
ba. ⌂ ch, TV, CP 22. £ BB £10–£13, DB
£20–£26, WT (b) £86–£110, DT (b) £14–
£17, ⒒.

Moorings, PH, y (RI), *66 Lansdowne Rd
North, BH1 1RS.* ✆ (0202) 22705.

Mount Stuart, H, z (RI) *31 Tregonwell
Rd, BH2 5NT.* ✆ (0202) 24639. Closed
Jan–Mar. C. ⊨ 17 bedrs, 1 bp, 8 bps, 2 ba,
TV. ⌂ CH, TV, CP 17, CF, 2 BGf, 8 st. £ BB
£12–£17·50, DB £19–£29, WT (b) £75–
£104, DT £13·50–£16·50, Bk £2, D £4·50,
cc 1 2 3.

Myrtle House, PH, z (RI), *41 Hawkwood
Rd, Boscombe, BH5 1DS.*
✆ (0202) 36579. C. ⊨ 10 bedrs, 3 ba,
Dgs. ⌂ CH, TV, CP 8, CF, 1 BGf, 1 st, Dis.
£ BB £6·50–£11, DB £13–£22, WT (b)
£55–£92, DT (b) £8–£14, ⒒, cc 1.

Naseby-Nye, PH, z (RI), *Byron Rd,
Boscombe Overcliff, BH5 1JD.*
✆ (0202) 34079.

Northover, PH, z (RI), *10 Earle Rd, Alum
Chine, BH4 8JQ.* ✆ (0202) 767349. C.
⊨ 12 bedrs, 5 bps, 2 ba, TV, Dgs. ⌂ CH,
TV, CP 10, CF, 0 st. £ BB £7·95–£11·95,
DB £16–£24, WT (b) £70–£99, DT (b)
£12–£15, ⒒.

Overdale, PH, z (RI), *63 Alumhurst Rd,
BH4 8EW.* ✆ (0202) 763001.

Parklands, PH, z (R), *4 Rushton Cres, BH3
7AF.* ✆ (0202) 22529. Closed Oct–Nov,
RS Xmas. C 8. ⊨ 10 bedrs, 2 bp, 3 bps, 2
ba, TV, CP 7, 3 BGf, 0 st, Dis.
£ BB £10·15–£15·35, DB £20·30–£27·70,
WT (b) £68·46–£125, DT (b) £11·30–
£18·70, ⒒, Bk £2·50, D £6·25.

Penmone, H, z (RI), *17 Carysfort Rd,
Boscombe, BH1 4LJ.* ✆ (0202) 35903. C.
⊨ 9 bedrs, 3 ba. ⌂ ch, TV, Dgs, CP 12, CF,
0 st. £ BB £6–£7, DB £12–£14, WT (b)
£59–£75, DT (b) £8–£10·50, cc 2 3.

Pigalle, PH, z (Unl), *24 Campbell Rd,
Boscombe, BH1 4EP.* ✆ (0202) 34067. C.
⊨ 9 bedrs, 2 ba, Dgs. ⌂ CH, TV, Dgs, CP 4,
CF, 8 BGf. £ BB £7, DB £14, WT (b) £60–
£64, DT (b) £8·57–£9·14, ⒒.

Pine Beach, PH, z (RI), *31 Boscombe
Spa Rd, Boscombe, BH5 1AS.*
✆ (0202) 305902.

Pine Tree, PH, z (RI) *Rosemount Rd,
Alum Chine, BH4 8HB.* ✆ (0202) 763685.
Open Apr–Oct & Xmas. C. ⊨ 14 bedrs, 2
sh, 2 ba, ns, Dgs. ⌂ ch, TV, Dgs, CP 6, CF, 1
BGf, 0 st, Dis. £ BB £9–£11, DB £18–£22,
WT (b) £85–£96, (c) £57–£70, DT (b)
£13–£15, ⒒, Bk £3, D £4.

Ravenhead, PH, z (RI), *9 Rushton Cres,
BH3 7AF.* ✆ (0202) 290417.

Restormel, H, z (R), *Upper Terrace Rd,
BH2 5NW.* ✆ (0202) 25070. C. ⊨ 18
bedrs, 2 bp, 4 ba, TV, Dgs. ✗ a l c. ⌂ CH,
TV, CP 8, CF, 2 BGf, 1 st, Dis. £ BB £7·50–
£12·50, DB £15–£30, WT (b) £84–£119,
DT (b) £12–£17, ⒒, Bk £2, D £4·50.

St. Johns Lodge, PH, z (RI), *10 St.
Swithun's Rd, BH1 3RQ.* ✆ (0202) 20677.

St. Ronan's, PH, z (RI), *64 Frances Rd,
BH1 3SA.* ✆ (0202) 23535. Closed Nov. C.
⊨ 14 bedrs, 3 ba, TV, Dgs. ⌂ CH, TV, CP 8,
CF, 2 st. £ BB fr £7·28–£11·66, DB £14–
£23, WT (b) £71·52–£99, DT (b) £10·20–
£14·58, ⒒.

St. Wilfreds, PH, z (Unl), *15 Walpole Rd,
Boscombe, BH1 4HB.* ✆ (0202) 36189.

Sandelheath, H, z (R), *1 Knyveton Rd,
East Cliff, BH1 3QF.* ✆ (0202) 25428. C.
⊨ 15 bedrs, 3 ba. ✗ a l c. ⌂ CH, TV, CP
12, CF, 2 st. £ BB £8·75–£10·75, DB
£17·50–£20, WT (b) £60–£75, DT (b)
£12·50–£15·50, ⒒, Bk £3·50, L £4·50, D
£5·75.

Sea Dene, PH, z (RI), *10 Burnaby Rd,
Alum Chine, BH4 8JF.* ✆ (0202) 761372.
Open Mar–Oct. C 5. ⊨ 7 bedrs, 4 bps, 1
ba, Dgs. ⌂ CH, TV, Dgs, CP 4, G 1. £ BB
£8–£12, DB £16–£24, WT (b) £100–£120,
DT (b) £13–£18, ⒒.

Sea Shells, G, z, (Unl), *201 Holdenhurst
Rd, BH8 8DE.* ✆ (0202) 292542. Closed
Xmas & Jan. C. ⊨ 20 bedrs, 3 ba, TV, Dgs.
⌂ ch, TV, CP 25, CF, 2 st. £ BB £9–£10, DB
£17·25–£19·50, ⒒, Bk £2, cc 1 3.

Seastrole, PH, z (RI), *12 Campbell Place,
Boscombe, BH1 4EP.* ✆ (0202) 36996. C.
⊨ 9 bedrs, 2 ba, Dgs. ⌂ ch, TV, CP 10, CF,
2 st. £ BB £6·25–£8·75, DB £12·50–
£17·50, WT (b) £55–£75, DT (b) £8·50–
£11, ⒒.

Sea View Court, PH, y (RI), *14
Boscombe Spa Rd, BH5 1AZ.*
✆ (0202) 37197. Closed Jan, Feb & Nov.
C. ⊨ 20 bedrs, 8 bp, 8 bps, 3 ba, Dgs.
⌂ CH, TV, CP 25, CF, 4 BGf, 4 st. £ BB
£7·50–£9·50, DB £15–£21·30, WT (b)
£65–£82, DT (b) £12–£13·50, ⒒.

Seaway, G, z (RI), *22 Westby Rd,
Boscombe, BH5 1HD.* ✆ (0202) 35002. C.
⊨ 9 bedrs, 3 ba, Dgs. ⌂ ch, TV, Dgs, CP 6,
CF. £ BB £6·90–£10·35, DB £13·80–
£20·70, WT (b) £57·50–£75·90, DT (b)
£9·20–£12·65, ⒒▲

Seaway, PH, z (Unl), *30 St. Catherines
Rd, Southbourne, BH6 4AB.*
✆ (0202) 423636. Closed Dec. C. ⊨ 8
bedrs, 2 bps, 2 ba, Dgs. ⌂ ch, TV, CP 8, CF.
£ BB £7·50–£8, WT £79·50–£83, ⒒

Sherbourne, *6 Walpole Rd, Boscombe.*
✆ (0202) 36222. C. ⊨ 10 bedrs, 2 ba.
✗ a l c. ⌂ ch, TV, CP 10, CF. £ BB £6–
£10·50, DB £12–£21, WT (a) fr £79, DT (a)
fr £9, ⒒, Bk £3·50, L £2·50, D £4·50, cc 1 3.

Silver Trees, PH, yz (Unl), *57 Wimborne
Rd, BH3 7AL.* ✆ (0202) 26040. C 5. ⊨ 9
bedrs, 4 bps, 1 ba, TV, Dgs. ⌂ CH, CP 12,
1 st. £ BB £12·50–£19, DB £21–£26,
WT (b) £80–£110, DT (b) £15·50–£18, ⒒,
D £5, cc 1 2 3 5.

Springdale, PH, z (Unl), *25 Southern Rd,
BH6 3SR.* ✆ (0202) 426301.

Stonecroft, H, z (RI), *6 Wollstonecraft Rd, BH5 1JQ.* ✆ (0202) 309390. Open Mar–Oct & Xmas. C. ⋈ 8 bedrs, 8 bps, Dgs. 🏠 ch, TV, CP 6, CF, 2 st. £ BB £8–£9, DB £16–£18, WT (b) £72–£85, DT (b) £11–£13, ①, D £3·50.

Stratford, H, z (RI), *20 Grand Av, Southbourne, BH6 3SY.* ✆ (0202) 424726. C. ⋈ 13 bedrs, 5 bps, 3 ba, ns, Dgs. 🏠 CH, TV, CP 8, CF. £ BB £7·50–£13, DB £15–£24·50, WT (b) £55–£89, DT (b) £9–£14, ①.

Sunnyside Court, PH, z (RI), *26 Florence Rd, Boscombe, BH5 1HF.* ✆ (0202) 37875.

Tree Tops, PH, z (RI), *16 Grand Ave, BH6 3SY.* ✆ (0202) 426933. Open Apr–Sept. C. ⋈ 14 bedrs, 3 sh, 2 ba, TV, Dgs. 🏠 ch, TV, CP 12, CF, 1 st. £ BB £8–£10·50, DB £16–£21, WT (b) £74·75–£98, DT (b) £10·68–£14, ②, col 3.

Tregonholme, H, z, (RI), *33 Tregonwell Rd, (Sea end), West Cliff, BH3 5NT.* ✆ (0202) 27117. C. ⋈ 13 bedrs, 1 sh, 3 ba, TV, Dgs. 🏠 ch, TV, CP 14, CF, 1 BGf, 2 st. £ BB £8·50–£11, DB £17–£22, WT (b) £64–£93, (c) £59–£75, DT (b) £11·50–£14, ①.

Trent, PH, z (RI), *12 Studland Rd, BH4 8JA.* ✆ (0202) 761088. Open Apr–Oct. C. 4. ⋈ 12 bedrs, 5 bps, 1 sh, 1 ba. 🏠 ch, TV, CP 9. £ BB £9–£10·50, DB £18–£28, DT (b) £13·50–£15, ①.

Tudor Grange, H, y (RI), *31 Gervis Rd, BH1 3EE.* ✆ (0202) 291472. C. ⋈ 12 bedrs, 1 bp, 2 ba, Dgs. 🏠 CH, TV, CP 8, CF, 2 BGf, 1 st, Dis. £ BB £10–£14, DB £20–£30, WT (b) £86–£110, DT (b) £14–£18, ①.

Upton Hall, PH, y (RI), *15 Rosemount Rd, Alum Chine, BH4 8HB.* ✆ (0202) 761304. Closed Jan–Feb. C. ⋈ 15 bedrs, 3 bp, 7 bps, 1 ba, TV, Dgs. ✗ a l c. 🏠 CH, TV, Dgs, ns, CP 10, CF, 2 BGf, 2 st. £ BB £7·50–£12·50, DB £15–£25, WT (c) £59·50–£89·50, ①.

Valberg, PH, z (Unl), *1a Wollstonecraft Rd, BH5 1JQ.* ✆ (0202) 34644. C. 5. ⋈ 10 bedrs, 10 bps. 🏠 CH, TV, CP 8, CF. £ BB £8·50–£11, DB £13–£18, WT (c) £39–£57, ①.

Vine, PH, z (RI), *22 Southern Rd, Southbourne, BH6 3SR.* ✆ (0202) 428309. Closed New Year. C. ⋈ 8 bedrs, 6 bps, 1 sh, 1 ba, Dgs. 🏠 CH, TV, Dgs, CP 8, CF, 1 st. £ BB £8–£11, DB £16–£24, WT (b) £70–£85, DT (b) £12–£15, ②.

Waldale, H, z (R), *37–39 Boscombe Spa Rd, BH5 1AS.* ✆ (0202) 37744. Open Mar–Oct & Xmas. C. 7. ⋈ 19 bedrs, 8 bp, 2 ba, Dgs. 🏠 CH, TV, CP 17, G 9. £ BB £11–£13, DB £21–£27, WT (b) £129–£147, DT (b) £14–£17, ①, Bk £2·50, D £4.

Wenmaur House, H, z (RI), *14 Carysfort Rd, Boscombe, BH1 4EJ.* ✆ (0202) 35081. C. ⋈ 12 bedrs, 2 ba. 🏠 CH, TV, CP 10, CF. £ BB £7–£8·50, DB £14–£17, WT (b) £65–£80, DT £10·50–£12, ①.

West Bay, G, z (Unl), *West Cliff Gdns, BH2 5HL.* ✆ (0202) 22261. Open May–Sep. C. ⋈ 13 bedrs, 2 ba, Dgs. 🏠 ch, TV, CF, 9 st. £ BB £8–£10, DB £16–£20, WT £70–£87·50, DT £11·50–£13·50, ②, Bk £2·50, D £5·50.

West Dene, PH, z (RI), *117 Alumhurst Rd, BH4 8HS.* ✆ (0202) 764843. Open Feb–Nov & Xmas. C. ⋈ 17 bedrs, 4 bp, 7 bps, 3 ba. 🏠 CH, TV, CP 17, CF, 2 st. £ BB £12–£16·50, DB £24–£33, WT (b) £95–

£113·50, DT (b) £15–£17·50, ②, cc 1 2 3 5.

West Leigh, H, y, (R), *26 West Hill Rd, BH2 5PG.* ✆ (0202) 292195. C. ⋈ 31 bedrs, 19 bp, 10 bps, 2 ba, TV, Dgs. 🏠 Lt, ch, TV, CP 40, CF. £ BB £9–£14, DB £18–£28, WT (b) £90–£140, DT £12–£20, ①.

Whitley Court, PH, z (RI), *West Cliff Gdns, West Cliff, BH2 5HL.* ✆ (0202) 21302. Closed Nov. C 3. ⋈ 15 bedrs, 2 bps, 3 sh, 2 ba, Dgs. 🏠 ch, TV, Dgs, CP 12, 6 st. £ BB £9–£11·50, DB £18–£29, WT (b) £65–£95, DT (b) £13–£15·50, ①, Bk £1·50, D £4.

Windsor Court, H, x (RI), *34 Bodorgan Rd, BH2 6NJ.* ✆ (0202) 24637.

Wood Lodge, PH, y (RI), *10 Manor Rd, East Cliff, BH1 3EY.* ✆ (0202) 290891.

Woodside, PH, z (RI), *29 Southern Rd, Southbourne, BH6 3SR.* ✆ (0202) 427213. Open Apr–Oct. ⋈ 11 bedrs, 5 sh, 1 ba. 🏠 CH, TV, CP 5. £ BB £7–£8·50, DB £14–£17, WT (b) £70–£85, DT (b) £10·50–£12·50, ①, ▲

Repairers: Auto Service Garage (Bournemouth) Ltd, 35 R L Stevenson Av. ✆ (0202) 763344.
Butlers Garage, 24 Seabourne Rd, Pokesdown. ✆ (0202) 48202.
English, F Ltd, Poole Rd. ✆ (0202) 762442.
Hendy-Lennox (Bournemouth) Ltd, Palmerston Rd. Boscombe. ✆ (0202) 34262.
Wadham Stringer (Bournemouth) Ltd, 573 Wallisdown Rd. ✆ (0202) 519191.
Specialist Body Repairer English, F Ltd, Poole Rd, Parkstone. ✆ (0202) 762442.
Specialist Car Lighting and Ignition Repairer Auto Service Garage (Bournemouth) Ltd, 33 R L Stevenson Av. ✆ (0202) 763344.
Rescue Service: Barton Car Sales, 970 Wimborne Rd. ✆ (0202) 529705.
Carbery Garage, 14 Carbery Row, Southbourne. ✆ (0202) 37130.
Gloucester Road Service Station, 1A Gloucester Rd, Boscombe. ✆ (0202) 35271.
H P Transport, 21 Elliot Rd. ✆ (0202) 511801.
St Christopher's Garage, Colin B Johnson (Boscombe) Ltd, 1191 Christchurch Rd. ✆ (0202) 424381.
Scientific Motors (Bournemouth) Ltd, Exeter Rd. ✆ (0202) 23254.
Southbourne Park Garage, 78 Tuckton Rd, Southbourne. ✆ (0202) 428787.

BOURTON-ON-THE-WATER Glos. Map 14E
Pop 2,711. Burford 9½, London 84, Cheltenham 16, Cirencester 16, Gloucester 24, Stow-on-the-Wold 4, Tewkesbury 22.
EC Sat. **Golf** Burford 18h. **See** Model Village, Aquarium, Birdland.

★★★**Old Manse**, *Victoria St, GL54 2BX.* ✆ Cotswold (0451) 20642. Closed 2nd & 3rd week Jan. C 6. ⋈ 9 bedrs, 9 bp, TV. ✗ mc, at, LD 8.30 (9.30 Fri & Sat). 🏠 CH, TV, CP 15, con 12, 2 st. £ BB £20·50, DB £36, WB, ②, 10%, L £5·50, D £6·85, cc 1 3 6, Dep a.

★★**M Chester House,** (R), *GL54 2BS.* ✆ Cotswold (0451) 20286. Open Feb–Nov. C. ⋈ 12 bedrs, 2 bp, 5 bps, 2 ba, TV, Dgs. ✗ a l c, LD 8.45. 🏠 CH, CP 22, Ac,

CF, 7 BGf, 1 st, Dis. £ WB, cc 1 2 3 4 5 6, Dep a.

★★**Old New Inn,** *High St, GL54 2AF.* ✆ Cotswold (0451) 20467. Closed Xmas. C. ⋈ 18 bedrs, 5 ba, annexe 6 bedrs, 1 bp, 2 ba, Dgs. ✗ mc, LD 8.15. 🏠 ch, TV, Dgs, CP 24, U 8, CF, 0 st. £ BB fr £15·90, DB fr £31·80, WT fr £172·50, DT fr £28·70, WB, ①, Bk £3, L £4, D £8·80, cc 1 3.

Southlands, PH, z (RI), *Rissington Rd, GL54 2AY.* ✆ Cotswold (0451) 20724. Closed Xmas. C 5. ⋈ 7 bedrs, 3 bp, 1 bps, 1 ba, TV. 🏠 CH, TV, CP 8. £ BB £10, DB £20–£25, WT (b) £108·50, DT (b) £15·50, ①.

The Ridge, G, x (Unl), *Whiteshoots, GL54 2LE.* ✆ Cotswold (0451) 20660. Closed Xmas. C 4. ⋈ 6 bedrs, 2 ba, ch, TV, CP 10. £ BB £8, DB £16, ①, Bk £3.

Rescue Service: F H Burgess (Three Counties) Ltd, Broadlands. ✆ (0202) 20407.

BOVEY TRACEY Devon. Map 14F
Pop 5,000. Exeter 14, London 181, Ashburton 8, Crediton 16, Newton Abbot 6, Okehampton 18, Tavistock 26.
EC Wed. **Golf** Newton Abbot (Stover) 18h. **See** Church, Hay Tor.
ℹ️ Lower Car Park. ✆ Bovey Tracey (0626) 832047.

★★**Blenheim** (Rt), *Brimley La, TQ13 9DH.* ✆ (0626) 832422. C. ⋈ 8 bedrs, 1 bps, 5 sh, 1 ba, Dgs. ✗ at, LD 8. 🏠 CH, TV, Dgs, CP 8, U 1, CF, 2 st. £ BB £10·50–£12·50, DB £21–£23, DBB £17·50–£19·25, WB, ①, Bk £3, D £7, Dep a.

★★**Coombe Cross** (Rt), *Coombe La, TQ13 9EY.* ✆ (0626) 832476. Closed Xmas & Jan. C. ⋈ 23 bedrs, 17 bp, 1 sh, 2 ba, TV. ✗ mc, at, LD 8. 🏠 CH, TV, CP 20, Ac, con 50, CF, 2 BGf, 1 st, Dis. £ BB £13·75–£18, DB £27·50–£36, WT £168–£182, DT £25–£29, WB, ②, Bk £3·50. L £3·50, D £7·50, cc 2 3 6.

■★★**Edgemoor,** *Haytor Rd, TQ13 9LE.* ✆ (0626) 832466. C. ⋈ 18 bedrs, 10 bp, 1 sh, 3 ba, Dgs. ✗ mc, at, LD 8.30. 🏠 CH, TV, CP 45, U 2, Ac, con 150, CF, 2 BGf, 3 st. £ BB £16·25, DB £29·50–£35, DBB £18·80–£24, WB, ①, Bk £3·50, L £1·50, D £8·50, cc 1 2 3 5 6.

■♣★★**Prestbury Country House** (R), *Brimley La, TQ13 9JS.* ✆ (0626) 833246. Open Mar–Oct. C 12. ⋈ 9 bedrs, 5 bp, 2 bps, 1 ba, ns. ✗ mc, at, LD 8. 🏠 CH, TV, ns, CP 12. £ BB £17–£20, DB £34–£40, ①, Bk £3·50, D £9, cc 1 2 3 5, Dep a.

Rescue Service: Dartmoor Garages, Station Rd. ✆ (0626) 832432.

BOVINGDON Hertfordshire. Map 15E
Pop 4,200. Watford 8½, London 25, Aylesbury 16, Bletchley 25, Dunstable 15, High Wycombe 15, Luton 14, Rickmansworth 8½, St Albans 10.
EC Wed. **Golf** Little Hay 18h. **See** St Lawrence Church.

Rescue Service: Gilbert Motors, Leyhill Rd. ✆ Hemel Hempstead (0442) 833264.

BOWBURN Durham. Map 32F
Pop 5,174. Darlington 16, London 260, Durham 4, Bishop Auckland 8.
EC Wed. **Golf** Brancepeth Castle 18h.

Rescue Service: Bowburn Filling & Service Station. ✆ Durham (0385) 3821.

BOWDON Greater Manchester (Cheshire).
See ALTRINCHAM.

BOWES Durham. Map 26B
Pop 450. Boroughbridge 43, London 251, Brough 13, Darlington 21, Leyburn 29, Middleton-in-Teesdale 13, Northallerton 31, West Auckland 16.
Golf Barnard Castle 18h. **See** Castle Keep. Roman Camp. "The Villa", reputed original "Dotheboys Hall", Bowes Museum at Barnard Castle.

Rescue Service: Tallentire, J W, Town End Garage. ☎ Teesdale (0833) 28222.

BOWNESS ON WINDERMERE Cumbria.
See WINDERMERE.

BRACKLEY Northamptonshire. Map 14D
Pop 6,621. Buckingham 8, London 64, Banbury 10, Bicester 11, Chipping Norton 21, Oxford 22, Towcester 11.
EC Wed. **MD** Fri. **Golf** Buckingham 18h. **See** St Peter's Church (EE Tower), Magdalen College School, Town Hall.

Repairer: Brackley Motors, 71 High St. ☎ (0280) 702227.
Specialist Body Repairer: Burwell Hill Garages Ltd, Burwell Hill. ☎ (0280) 702268.
Rescue Service: Burwell Hill Garages Ltd, Burwell Hill. ☎ (0280) 702268.
Reeve & Barney, Hinton Road Garage, Hinton Rd. ☎ (0280) 703561.

BRACKNELL Berkshire. Map 7A
Pop 52,905. Staines 11, London 28, Alton 24, Bagshot 5½, Basingstoke 21, Henley-on-Thames 13, High Wycombe 18, Reading 11, Weybridge 14, Windsor 9.
EC Wed. **MD** Fri, Sat. **Golf** Downshire 18h. **See** Met. Office HQ.
[i] Central Library, Town Sq. ☎ Bracknell (0344) 23149.

★★★★**M Ladbroke,** *Bagshot Rd, RG12 3QJ.* ☎ (0344) 424801. RS Xmas–New Year. C. 🛏 115 bedrs, 114 bp, 1 bps, TV, Dgs. ✕ a l c, mc, at, LD 10 (9 Sun). 🏠 Lt, N, CH, Dgs, CP 250, Ac, con 180, CF, 1 BGf. £ BB fr £51·50, DB fr £67, WB, [1], Bk £5·50, L £10, D £10, cc 1 2 3 5 6, Dep b.

Repairer: Strachan Motors Ltd, Downshire Way. ☎ (0344) 22100.
Rescue Service: Priestwood Motors Ltd, Unit No 1, Longshot Lane, Western Industrial Estate. ☎ (0344) 56450.

BRADFORD West Yorkshire. Map 25F and 33A
See also BINGLEY.
Pop 288,800. Wakefield 14, London 196, M606 Motorway 2, Barnsley 23, Burnley 25, Halifax 8, Harrogate 18, Huddersfield 10, Leeds 9, Pontefract 22, Skipton 19.
EC Wed. **MD** All week (not Wed). **Golf** West Bowling 18h, Bradford Moor 9h, South Bradford 9h, West Bradford 18h. **See** Cathedral, City Hall, Cartwright Hall (Museum and Art Gallery), 15th cent Bolling Hall (Museum), Wool Exchange, Industrial Museum (Moorside Mills, Eccleshill), Charlotte Brontë's birthplace at Thornton 4 m W.
[i] City Hall. ☎ Bradford (0274) 729577.

★★★★**Stakis Norfolk Gardens,** *Hall Ings, BD1 5SH.* ☎ (0274) 734734. C. 🛏 126 bedrs, 126 bp, 4 ba, TV, Dgs. ✕ a l c, mc, at, LD 10.15. 🏠 Lt, N, CH, TV, Ac, con 700, CF, 3 st. £ WB, Bk £4·50, L £5·95, D £8·50, cc 1 2 3 5 6, Dep b.
★★★**M Novotel,** *Merrydale Rd, BD4 6SA.* ☎ (0274) 683683. C. 🛏 136 bedrs, 136 bp, TV, Dgs. ✕ a l c, mc, at, LD 12. 🏠 Lt, N, CH, Dgs, CP 140, Ac, sp, con 300, CF, 2 BGf, 1 st, Dis. £ BB £33·50–£36, DB £42·50–£45·50, WB, [1], Bk £4·50, L £7·50, D £7·50, cc 1 2 3 5 6, Dep b.
★★★**Victoria** (TH), *Bridge St, BD1 1JX.* ☎ (0274) 728706. C. 🛏 59 bedrs, 22 bp, 6 bps, TV, Dgs. ✕ a l c, mc, LD. 🏠 Lt, N, CH, Dgs, CP 40, Ac, con 200, CF, 6 st. £ BB £31·50–£38, DB £43–£52, WB, [1], cc 1 2 3 4 5 6.
Belvedere, H, z (R), *19 North Park Rd, BD9 4NT.* ☎ (0274) 492559. C 5. 🛏 13 bedrs, 3 sh, 3 ba, TV, Dgs. 🏠 CH, TV, CP 10. £ BB £15–£16·50, DB £23·20–£25, DT (b) £22, [1], Bk £2·50, D £7.
Pollard House, Commercial, H, *54 Pollard La, BD2 4RW.* ☎ (0274) 636208.

Repairers: Bramall, C D (Bradford) Ltd, 146 Tong St. ☎ (0274) 681601.
Harrison Automobile Co (Bradford) Ltd, 103 City Rd. ☎ (0274) 24144.
Polar Motor Co (Bradford) Ltd, 113 & 117 Manningham La. ☎ (0274) 305941.
Lookersthornton Engineering Ltd, 150 Manningham La. ☎ (0274) 27181.
Specialist Radiator Repairer: Northern Radiators (Bradford) Ltd, 134 Dirkhill Rd. ☎ (0274) 74609.
Rescue Service: John Wilkinson & Sons (Greengates) Ltd, Harrogate Rd, Greengates. ☎ (0274) 612266.
Park Motor Engineering Co, Mansfield Rd. ☎ (0274) 41676.
Sandy Lane Garage, Wilsden Rd, Allerton. ☎ (0274) 42848.
Turf Motors of Frizinghall Ltd, Frizinghall. ☎ (0274) 41337.

BRADFORD-ON-AVON Wiltshire. Map 5B.
Marlborough 26, London 99, Bath 8, Chepstow 32, Chippenham 11, Devizes 13, Frome 9½, Radstock 12, Warminster 12, Wells 23.
[i] 1 Church St. ☎ Bradford-on-Avon (022 16) 2224.

Rescue Service: Saxon Garage, Woolley St. ☎ (022 16) 2352.

BRADWELL Derbyshire. Map 22A
Pop 1,456. 2 m S of Hope. Matlock 17, London 162, Buxton 13, Chapel-en-le-Frith 10, Chesterfield 18, Sheffield 16.
Golf Chapel-en-le-Frith 18h. **See** Bagshawe Cavern, Hazelbadge Hall, Samuel Fox Cottage.

Rescue Service: Bradwell Auto Ltd, Main Rd. ☎ Hope Valley (0433) 20482.

BRAINTREE Essex. Map 17E
Pop 30,515. Chelmsford 11, London 44, Cambridge 32, Colchester 15, Dunmow 8½, Haverhill 18, Royston 33, Sudbury 14.
EC Thur. **MD** Wed, Sat. **Golf** Braintree and District 18h. **See** Old Church, Bocking Windmill, Paycocke's (Nat Trust) 5½ m E Old Post Mill, Old Houses.

▣★★**White Hart,** *Bocking End, CM7 6AB.* ☎ (0376) 21401. C. 🛏 35 bedrs, 28 bp, 2 ba, TV, Dgs. ✕ a l c, mc, at. 🏠 N, CH, CP 15, G 10, con 30, CF, 2 st. £ BB £25–£32, DB £44, WB, [2], Bk £3, L £7, D £7, cc 1 2 3 5 6.
Bensons, H, z, *Rayne Rd, CM7 8RD.* ☎ (0376) 26251. C. 🛏 36 bedrs, 36 bps, TV, Dgs. ✕ a l c. 🏠 CH, Dgs, CP 36, CF, 18 BGf, 4 st. £ BB £27, DB £31·50, WT (c) £84, [1], Bk £2·50, cc 1 2 3 5. ▲

BRAITHWAITE Cumbria. Map 26F
Pop 500. Keswick 2½, London 288, Carlisle 30, Cockermouth 9½.
Golf Cockermouth 18h. **See** National Park.

▣★★**Ivy House** (R), *CA12 5SY.* ☎ (059 682) 338. Open Mar–Oct. 🛏 8 bedrs, 7 bp, 1 bps, TV. ✕ LD 7.30. 🏠 CH. £ BB £14–£15·50, DB £28–£31, DBB £23–£26·50, Bk £5, D £9·75, cc 3 5. ▲
★★**Middle Ruddings,** *CA12 5RY.* ☎ (059 682) 436. Open Mar–Oct. C. 🛏 15 bedrs, 7 bp, 1 bps, 3 ba, TV. ✕ a l c, mc, at, LD 8.30. 🏠 CH, TV, CP 20, CF. £ BB £13·50–£20, DB £27–£40, WT £125–£155, WB, [2], 5%, Bk £3·50, L £3·95, D £7·50, Dep.

BRAMHALL Greater Manchester (Cheshire). Map 19B
Pop 31,595. Macclesfield 9½, London 177, Altrincham 10, Congleton 17, Knutsford 12, Middlewich 20, Sandbach 21, Stockport 4.
EC Wed. **Golf** Bramhall Ltd 18h. **See** Bramall Hall.
[i] 13 Bramhall Lane South. ☎ 061-440 8400.

★★★**Bramhall Moat House,** *Bramhall Lane South, SK7 2EB.* ☎ 061-439 8116. RS 25 Dec–2 Jan. C. 🛏 40 bedrs, 40 bp, TV, Dgs. ✕ a l c, mc, at, LD 10. 🏠 Lt, N, CH, TV, Dgs, CP 132, con 55, CF, 20 BGf, 0 st, Dis. £ BB £33–£34, DB £43–£45, WB, [2], Bk £4·15, L £5·50, D £8·40, cc 1 2 3 5 6, Dep b.

BRAMHOPE West Yorkshire. Map 25E
Pop 13,826. Leeds 8, London 199, Bradford 10, Harrogate 11, Skipton 19, York 28.
EC Wed. **MD** Mon, Fri, Sat. **Golf** Otley 18h. **See** Parish Church, Botanic Gardens.

★★★**M Post House** (TH), *Otley Rd, LS16 9JJ.* ☎ Leeds (0532) 842911. C. 🛏 120 bedrs, 120 bp, TV, Dgs. ✕ a l c, mc, at, LD 10·15. 🏠 Lt, N, CH, Dgs, CP 220, Ac, con 180, CF, 24 BGf, 0 st, Dis. £ BB £45, DB £57·50, WB, [1], cc 1 2 3 4 5 6, Dep (Xmas).

BRAMPTON Cambridgeshire. Map 15B
Pop 4,450. Biggleswade 19, London 64, Huntington 1½, Kettering 24, Peterborough 20.
Golf St Neots 18h. **See** Church, Old Cottages, Watermill.

★★★**M Brampton,** *A1 Roundabout, PE18 8NH.* ☎ Huntingdon (0480) 810434. C. 🛏 17 bedrs, 17 bp, TV, Dgs. ✕ a l c, mc, at, LD 10 (10.30 Sat). 🏠 N, CH, TV, Dgs, CP 200, G 18, Ac, con 70, CF, 0 st. £ BB £33, DB £46, WB, [1], Bk £4, L £6·85, D £6·85, cc 1 2 3 5, Dep b.
★★**Grange,** *115 High St, Brampton, Huntingdon, PE18 8TG.* ☎ Huntingdon (0480) 59516. C. 🛏 8 bedrs, 1 bp, 7 bps, 1 ba, TV. ✕ a l c, mc, at, LD 7. 🏠 CH, TV, CP 50, con 20, CF, 1 st. £ BB £20–£24, DB £30–£34, [1], Bk £3, cc 1 2 3 5 6.

BRAMPTON Cumbria. Map 30F
Pop 3,400. Alston 19, London 299, Beattock 44, Bellingham 33, Brough 42, Carlisle 9, Dumfries 39, Hawick 37,

Hexham 28, Jedburgh 47, Langholm 20, Penrith 23.
EC Thur. **MD** Wed. **Golf** Brampton 18h.
See Church (Burne-Jones windows), Moot Hall, Stocks, Prince Charlie's House, Lanecost Priory 3 m NE, Roman Wall.
🛈 Moot Hall. ☎ Brampton (069 77) 3433.

■♨★★**Farlam Hall** (R), *CA8 2NG.*
☎ Hallbankgate (069 76) 234. Closed Feb, RS Nov–Jan. C 4. ⊯ 11 bedrs, 7 bp, 2 bps, 4 ba, Dgs. ✗ mc, LD 8. ☎ CH, TV, Dgs, CP 35, CF. £ BB £32, DB £64, DBB £37·50, WB, ②, Bk £5·50, L £8·50, D £12, cc 1 2 3 6.
■★**White Lion,** *Highcross St. CA8 1RP.*
☎ (069 77) 2338.

Rescue Service: E W Cates, Carlisle Rd.
☎ (069 77) 2508.

BRAMSHAW Hampshire. Map 6C
Pop 580. Romsey 7, London 82, Lyndhurst 6, Ringwood 12, Salisbury 13, Southampton 10.
Golf Bramshaw 18h.

■♨★★**Bramble Hill,** *SO4 7JG.*
☎ Southampton (0703) 813165. RS Nov–Easter. C. ⊯ 16 bedrs, 4 bp, 3 ba, Dgs.
✗ mc, at, LD 8.15. ☎ CH, TV, Dgs, CP 50, Ac, rf, con 30, CF 2 BGf, 4 st. £ BB £15·30–£18·70, DB £30·60–£37·40, DBB £22–£27·40, WB, ②, Bk £4·20, L £6·70, D £6·70, cc 1 6.▲

Rescue Service: Bramshaw Garage (Hampshire) Ltd. ☎ Cadnam (042 127) 3206.
Rosary Garage. ☎ Cadnam (042 127) 3342.

BRANDON Suffolk. Map 16F
Pop 6,930. Newmarket 18, London 81, Bury St Edmunds 15, East Dereham 24, Ely 22, King's Lynn 25, Swaffham 15, Thetford 6½, Wisbech 29.
EC Wed. **MD** Thur, Sat. **Golf** Thetford 18h. **See** St Peter's Church, 15th cent bridge (rebuilt 1950), old craft of flintknapping.

★★**Brandon House,** *High St, IP27 0AX.*
☎ Thetford (0842) 810171. Closed Xmas Day. C. ⊯ 15 bedrs, 7 bp, 1 sh, 2 ba, TV, Dgs. ✗ a l c, mc, at, LD 8.45. ☎ CH, TV, Dgs, CP 60, Ac, con 40, CF, 4 st. £ BB £22–£30, DB £32–£40, DBB £29–£37, WB, ②, Bk £3, L £3·70, D £6·95, cc 1 2 3 5.
★**Great Eastern,** *High St. IP27 0AX.*
☎ Thetford (0842) 810229.

BRANSCOMBE Devon. Map 4F
Axminster 10, London 157, Exeter 18, Honiton 10, Lyme Regis 12, Tiverton 25.
See Church (Norman tower), cliffs.

Higher Bulstone Farm, G, xy (R).
☎ (029 780) 446. C. ⊯ 6 bedrs, 3 ba, Dgs. ☎ CH, TV, CP 20, CF. £ BB £8–£9·50, DB £16–£19, WT (b) £89–£99, DT (b) £14·50–£16, ①, Bk £2·50, D £6·50.

BRANSGORE Hampshire. Map 6E
Pop 4,700. Ringwood 6, London 99, Christchurch 4, Lyndhurst 11.
Golf Highcliffe 18h. **See** Church, 16th cent font.

Rescue Service: Bransgore Garage, Ringwood Rd. ☎ (0425) 72416.

BRAUNTON Devon. Map 4C
Pop 8,000. Barnstable 5½, London 198, Ilfracombe 8, Lynmouth 23.

EC Wed. **Golf** Saunton 18h (2). **See** 3 m of excellent sands at Saunton, 3 m, Museum.

Brookfield G, x (Rl), *45 South St, EX33 2AN.* ☎ (0271) 812382. C. ⊯ 8 bedrs, 1 ba, ns, Dgs. ☎ ch, TV, Dgs, ns, CP 12, CF, 2 BGf, 0 st, Dis.
Denham, F, x (Rl), *North Buckland, EX33 1HY.* ☎ Croyde (0271) 890297. C. ⊯ 8 bedrs, 2 ba. ☎ ch, TV, G 7, CF. £ BB £7–£8, DB £14–£16, WT (b) £80–£85, DT (b) £12–£14, ① ▲

Repairers: Braunton Garage, Exeter Rd.
☎ (0271) 812064.

BREDBURY Gtr Manchester (Cheshire).
Map 22B
Pop 14,150. Buxton 19, London 178, Barnsley 30, Chapel-en-le-Frith 15, Glossop 8¼, Huddersfield 25, Macclesfield 12, Oldham 9½, Stockport 2, Wakefield 36.
EC Wed. **Golf** Romiley 18h. **See** Arden Hall ruins, Chadkirk Chapel (early 14th cent—restored), Etherow County Park at Compstall, Chadkirk County Park at Romiley.

Specialist Body Repairer: A K Motors, Old Moor Rd, off Ashton Rd. ☎ 061-494 9997.▲
Rescue Service: A K Motors, Old Moor Rd, off Ashton Rd. ☎ 061-494 9997.▲
Stockport Road Service Station, Stockport West. ☎ 061-430 4938.
Trevan Garage Ltd, Lingard La.
☎ 061-430 4317.

BREEDON-ON-THE-HILL
Leicestershire. Map 22F
Pop 650. Hinckley 19, London 116, Ashby-de-la-Zouch 5½, Derby 10, Leicester 18, Loughborough 10, Mansfield 28, Melton Mowbray 25, Nottingham 16.
EC Wed. **Golf** Loughborough 18h. **See** 12th cent Parish Church.

Rescue Service: Breedon General Services Ltd, Main St. ☎ Melbourne (033 16) 391.

BRENDON Devon. Map 4C
Pop 80. Minehead 15, London 182, Lynmouth 3½, Tiverton 35.
EC Thur. **Golf** Ilfracombe 18h. **See** Doone Valley.

■★★**Stag Hunters Inn,** *EX35 6PS.*
☎ (059 87) 222. Open Mar–Dec. C. ⊯ 22 bedrs, 6 bp, 2 ba, Dgs. ✗ a l c, mc, at, LD 8.30. ☎ Lt, N, ch, TV, Dgs, CP, Ac, con 18, CF, 1 st. £ BB £15, DB £26·25–£32, WT £129·50, DBB £21·50–£22·50, WB, ②, Bk £3, D £6·95, cc 1 2 5, Dep a.

BRENT KNOLL Somerset. Map 5C
Pop 1,148. Wells 15, London 137, Bath 36, Bridgwater 10, Bristol 24, Glastonbury 14, Radstock 29, Weston-super-Mare 9.
Golf Burnham and Berrow 18h. **See** Brent Knoll, St Michael's Church, Iron Age Fort.
🛈 Picnic Area, M5 Southbound.
☎ Edingworth (093 472) 466

★★**Battleborough Grange** (R), *Bristol Rd.* ☎ (0278) 760208. C. 5. ⊯ 11 bedrs, 3 bp, 3 bps, 3 ba, TV, Dgs. ✗ a l c, mc, at, LD 9.30. ☎ CH, TV, CP 50, Ac, con 40, 1 st. £ BB £13–£20, DB £26–£38, WB, ①, Bk £4, D £8, cc 1 2 3 5, Dep a.▲

Rescue Service: Ivor Steer (Brent Knoll) Ltd. ☎ (0278) 760563.

BRENTWOOD Essex. Map 17F
Pop 71,935. Romford 6, London 22, Bishop's Stortford 23, Chelmsford 11, Dartford-Purfleet Tunnel 13, Dunmow 21, Epping 14, Southend 21.
EC Thur. **Golf** Hartswood, Brentford 18h.
See "White Hart" Inn (old Coaching House), 16th cent Moat House (once Hunting Lodge, now motel), RC Cathedral, Ingatestone Hall 4½ m NE.

★★★★**Brentwood Moat House** (R), *London Rd, CM14 4NR.*
☎ (0277) 225252. C. ⊯ 33 bedrs, 33 bp, 2 ba, annexe 4 bedrs, 4 bp, ns, TV, Dgs. ☎ N, CH, ns, CP 100, Ac, sb, con 60, CF, 33 BGf, 1 st, Dis. £ BB £43, DB £56, WB, ①, Bk £3·50, L £7·25, cc 1 2 3 5 6. Dep b.
★★★**M Post House** (TH), *Brook St, CM14 5NF.* ☎ (0277) 210888. C. ⊯ 120 bedrs, 120 bp, TV, Dgs. ✗ a l c, mc, at, LD 10. ☎ Lt, N, CH, Dgs, CP 148, Ac, sp, con 120, CF, 39 BGf, 0 st, Dis. £ BB £45, DB £57, WB, ①, cc 1 2 3 4 5 6.

Rescue Service: Bentley Garage, Ongar Rd. ☎ Coxtie Green (0277) 73015.

BRERETON Staffordshire. Map 22E
Lichfield 7, London 122, Burton-on-Trent 15, Stafford 9, Stone 15, Uttoxeter 12, Walsall 16, Wolverhampton 16.

★★**Cedar Tree,** *Main Rd, WS15 1DY.*
☎ Rugeley (088 94) 4241. RS Sun evening. C. ⊯ 16 bedrs, 7 bp, 3 ba, TV. ✗ a l c, mc, at, LD 10 ☎ CH, TV, CP 200, Ac, sc, con, CF. £ BB fr £16, DB £30, ①, Bk £3, L £4.50, D £4.50, cc 1 2 3 5 , Dep b.

BRIDESTOWE Devon. Map 3A
Pop 400. Okehampton 6, London 198, Launceston 12, Tavistock 11.
See Parish Church.

Linden Glade, G, xy (Unl), *EX20 4NS.*
☎ (083 786) 236. C. ⊯ 5 bedrs, 1 ba, Dgs. ☎ ch, TV, Dgs, ns, CP12, CF. £ BB £7.25, DB £14, ☎ (b) £12, ①.

BRIDGERULE Devon. M. Area 3A
Pop 400. 5 m W of Holsworthy. London 215, Bude 5, Launceston 13.
Golf Holsworthy 9h, Bude 18h.

Rescue Service: Jewells Cross Service Station. ☎ (028 881) 340.

BRIDGNORTH Shropshire. Map 13B
Pop 10,697. Kidderminster 13, London 137. Birmingham 25, Ludlow 19, Newton 47, Shrewsbury 21, Wellington 14, Wolverhampton 14.
EC Thur. **MD** Mon, Sat. **Golf** Bridgnorth 18h. **See** St Leonard's Church, St Mary's Church, 16th cent Bishop Percy's House, cliff railway, Town Hall 1652, Northgate Museum, remains of 12th cent Castle, Severn Valley Rly (steam engines) to Bewdley, Midland Motor Museum and Bird Garden.
🛈 Library, Listley St. ☎ Bridgnorth (074 62) 3358.

★★**Falcon,** *St. John St, WV15 6AG.*
☎ (074 62) 3134. C. ⊯ 16 bedrs, 3 bp, 3 ba, TV, Dgs. ✗ a l c, mc, at, LD 9.30. ☎ N, ch, TV, CP 300, U 6, Ac, con 50, CF, 1 st. £ BB £17·50–£21, DB £25–£30, ①, Bk £4, L £6, D £7, cc 1 2 3 5.
♨★★**Old Vicarage,** (R), *Worfield, WV15 5JZ.* ☎ (074 62) 498.

BRIDGWATER Somerset. Map 5C
Pop 27,000. Glastonbury 15, London 141,
M5 Motorway 2½, Bristol 32, Dunster 24,
Ilminster 19, Minehead 26, Sherborne 29,
Taunton 10, Weston-super-Mare 18,
Wincanton 32.
EC Thur. **MD** Wed. **Golf** Enmore Park 18h.
See 15th cent St Mary's Church, Town
Hall (tapestry, Blake portraits), Admiral
Blake House and Museum, Sedgemoor,
Battlefield (1685) 4 m E, Coleridge
Cottage at Nether Stowey 7 m W.

★★**Walnut Tree Inn,** Fore St, North
Petherton. ✆ (0278) 662255. C. ⊯ 11
bedrs, 11 bp, TV. ✗ a l c, mc, LD 10. 🅿 CH,
Dgs, CP 70, Ac, con, CF, 3 BGf, 0 st, Dis.
£ BB £24, DB £34, WB, Ⓣ, Bk £2·50, L
£2·50, D £8·50, cc 1 3 4 5, Dep a.
Peartree, G, x (Unl) 16 Manor Rd,
Catcott, TA7 9HF. ✆ Chilton Polden
(0278) 722390. C. ⊯ 8 bedrs, 2 ba. 🅿 ch,
TV, Dgs, CP 8, CF. £ BB fr £7·50, DB fr £15,
WT (b) fr £65, DT (b) fr £10·50, Ⓣ.

Specialist Body Repairer: Sheppards
Coachworks Ltd, Axe Rd, Colley Lane
Industrial Estate. ✆ (0278) 2238.
Rescue Service: Auto Repair & Rescue
Services, New Westway Service Centre
Ltd, Taunton Rd. ✆ (0278) 58300.
Bridgwater Motor Co Ltd, 52 Eastover.
✆ (0278) 422218.
Harry Ball (Bridgwater) Ltd, Sydenham
Garage, Market St. ✆ (0278) 422125.
K C Motor Services, Axe Rd, Colley La.
✆ (0278) 426103.
Moorlinch Garage, Moorlinch. T Ashcott
(0458) 455.
Rawlinson Garages Ltd, Heathfield
Garage, North Petherton. ✆ North
Petherton (0278) 662230 & North
Petherton (0278) 663190.
Westway Service Station, Taunton Rd.
✆ (0278) 422665.

BRIDLINGTON Humberside (North
Humberside).
Pop 28,600. Beverley 22, London 201, Hull
30, Malton 28, Pickering 31, Scarborough
17, York 41.
EC Thur. **MD** Wed, Sat. **Golf** Bridlington
18h. **See** Bayle Gate (museum), Perp
Priory Church, Zoo, Sewerby Hall and
Park, Flamborough Head and Lighthouse,
Bempton Sea Bird Colony, Burton Agnes
Hall 5½ m SW.
🛈 Garrison St. ✆ Bridlington (0262)
73474.

★★★**Expanse,** North Marine Drive, YO15
2LS. ✆ (0262) 675347. C. ⊯ 50 bedrs, 32
bp, 2 bps, 4 ba, TV. ✗ mc, at, LD 8.30.
🅿 Lt, N, CH, CP 12, G 15, con 50, CF, 5
BGf, 2 st. £ BB fr £18, DB fr £34, WT fr
£160, DT £22·75, WB, Ⓣ, Bk £2·50, cc 1 2 3 5 6, Dep.
★★**Monarch** (R), South Marine Drive,
YO15 3JJ. ✆ (0262) 674447 Open Apr-
Nov. C. ⊯ 43 bedrs, 23 bp, 1 bps, 6 ba, TV.
✗ a l c, mc, at, LD 9. 🅿 Lt, N, CH, TV, CP
10, Ac, con 40, CF. £ BB £16·50-£22, DB
£30-£37, DBB £18-£23·50, WB, Ⓣ, Bk £3,
L £4, D £7·50, cc 1 2 3 5 6.
★**Langdon,** (RI) Pembroke Terr. YO15
3BX. ✆ (0262) 73065. RS Nov-Xmas, full
service Xmas. C. ⊯ 21 bedrs, 9 bps, 4 ba,
TV. ✗ a l c, mc, at, LD 7.30. 🅿 CH, TV, Ac,
CF. £ BB £10·50-£18·50, DB £20-£27, WT
£80-£98, DBB £13·50-£21, WB, Ⓣ, Bk
£2·50, L £3·50, D £5·50, Dep.
Ap. Southcliffe, South Marine Drive,
YO15 3DA. ✆ (0262) 73589.

Repairer: Ripley's (Bridlington) Ltd, 1
Hamilton Rd. ✆ (0262) 75336.
Rescue Service: Arundale of Bridlington
Ltd, 74 Bessingby Rd. ✆ (0262) 78141.
Hall Bros, Spa Service Station, Horsforth
Av. ✆ (0262) 73346.

BRIDPORT Dorset. Map 5E
Pop 6,876. Dorchester 15, London 137,
Axminster 12, Crewkerne 13, Lyme Regis
10, Sherborne 26, Weymouth 19.
EC Thur. **MD** Wed, Sat. **Golf** West Bay
18h. **See** Museum and Art Gallery, Daniel
Taylor Almshouses, Ancient Buildings,
Golden Cap (cliffs) to SW.
🛈 32 South St. ✆ Bridport (0308) 24901.

★★★**Haddon House,** West Bay, DT6
4EL. ✆ (0308) 23626. C. ⊯ 13 bedrs, 13
bp, TV, Dgs. ✗ a l c, mc, LD 8.30, 🅿 CH,
Dgs, CP 50, G 4, con 25, 1 BGf, 0 st, Dis.
£ BB fr £21·50, DB fr £30, WB, Ⓣ, Bk
£3·50, L £4·50, D £7·50, cc 1 2 3 5 6,
Dep a.
★★**Eype's Mouth,** Eype, DT6 6AL. (2m
SW). ✆ (0308) 23300.
★**Bridport Arms,** West Bay, DT6 4EN.
✆ (0308) 22994. C. ⊯ 8 bedrs, 1 bp, 7
bps, 2 ba, annexe 5 bedrs, Dgs. ✗ mc, LD
9. 🅿 CH, TV, Dgs, CP 10, G 4, Ac, con 60,
CF, 4 st. £ BB £9-£12, DB £18-£24, WB,
Ⓣ, Bk £2·50, D £6·50, cc1 2 3 4 5 6.
Britmead House, G, y (RI) 154 West
Bay Road, DT6 4EG. ✆ (0308) 22941. C 5.
⊯ 8 bedrs, 3 bp, 1 ba, TV, Dgs. ✗ CH, TV,
CP 8, CF. £ BB £10·50, DB £21-£24, WT
£63-£101·50, Ⓣ, D £5·50, cc 1 3 4.
Roundham House, PH, y (R), West Bay
Rd. DT6 4BD. ✆ (0308) 22753.

Repairer: Star Garage, 70 East St.
✆ (0308) 22288.
Rescue Service: Green Motors (Bridport)
Ltd, East Rd. ✆ (0308) 22922 and (0308)
24559.
Harbour Garages (Bridport) Ltd, 1 West
Bay. ✆ (0308) 22207.
Stevenson's Garage, 61 East St. ✆ (0308)
22365.

BRIGG Humberside (South Humberside).
Map 23A
Pop 5,299. Lincoln 24, London 158,
Gainsborough 20, Grimsby 21, Hull 20,
Market Rasen 15, Scunthorpe 8½.
EC Wed. **MD** Tue, Thur, Sat. **Golf** Holme
Hall 18h. **See** Modernised Coaching Inns.
🛈 7 Market Pl. ✆ Brigg (0652) 52441.

Repairer: E H Smith Parkinson (Motors)
Ltd, 6 Market Pl. ✆ (0652) 52396.
Rescue Service: Whelpton, S, Foresters
Hall Garage. ✆ (0652) 52295.

BRIGHAM Cumbria. Map 26E
Pop 900. Cockermouth 2½, London 299,
Egremont 16, Workington 8
Gulf Cockermouth 10h. **See** Church, Old
Quarries.

Rescue Service: Kirkpatrick's Garage,
Low Rd. ✆ Cockermouth (0900) 825366.

BRIGHOUSE West Yorkshire. Map 25F
and 33A
Pop 35,251. Huddersfield 4, London 194,
Barnsley 19, Bradford 6½, Halifax 5, Leeds
12, Oldham 20, Rochdale 19, Skipton 19,
Wakefield 13.
EC Tue. **MD** Wed, Sat. **Golf** Lightcliffe
18h. **See** Museum and Art Gallery, Smith
Art Gallery.

Rescue Service: Donald Miller & Sons,
Spring Street Garage. ✆ (0484) 712222.

BRIGHTLINGSEA Essex. Map 17D
Pop 7,245. Colchester 10, London 66,
Clacton 10, Harwich 18, Ipswich 21,
Stowmarket 33.
EC Thur. **Golf** Clacton 18h. **See** All Saints'
Church, 13th cent Jacobes Hall.

Rescue Service: Teece Motors Ltd, Hurst
Green Garage. ✆ (020 630) 2264.

BRIGHTON East Sussex. Map 7E
See also HOVE and ROTTINGDEAN.
RAC Office, Churchill Square, Brighton,
BN1 2DW. ✆ Brighton (0273) 509253.
Pop 152,700. Crawley 22, London 53,
Arundel 20, Haywards Heath 14, Horsham
23, Lewes 8½, Newhaven 9, Pulborough
23, Worthing 11.
See Plan, p. 158.
EC Wed. **MD** Tue, Sat. **Golf** Dyke 18h,
East Brighton 18h, Waterhall 18h,
Hollingbury Park Municipal 18h. **See**
Royal Pavilion, Aquarium and
Dolphinarium, St Nicolas' Church (14th
cent Norman Fort), Museum and Art
Gallery, Booth Museum of British Birds,
Preston Manor, Marina, St Peter's Church,
The Lanes (narrow streets of shops
formerly fishermen's cottages), Regency
terraces, Newtimber Place 6½ m NW.
🛈 Marlborough House, 54 Old Steine.
✆ Brighton (0273) 23755.

★★★★**Brighton Metropole,** King's Rd,
BN1 2FU. ✆ (0273) 775432. C. ⊯ 333
bedrs, 333 bp, TV, Dgs. 🅿 Lt, N, CH, Dgs, G
200, Ac, sb, sol, gym, con 2,000, CF, 5 st.
£ WB, cc 1 2 3 4 5 6, Dep.
★★★★**Grand,** King's Rd, BN1 2FW.
✆ (0273) 26301.
Hotel under reconstruction.
★★★**Norfolk Resort,** 149 King's Rd,
BN1 2PP. ✆ (0273) 738201. C. ⊯ 65
bedrs, 56 bp, 9 bps, TV, Dgs. ✗ mc, at, LD
10. 🅿 Lt, N, CH, Dgs, CP 14, G 3, Ac, con
150, CF. £ BB fr £36, DB fr £52, WT fr
£175, WB, Ⓣ, Bk £5, L £6, D £9·50,
cc 1 2 3 4 5 6, Dep b.
★★★**Old Ship,** King's Rd, BN1 1NR.
✆ (0273) 29001. C. ⊯ 153 bedrs, 153 bp,
TV, Dgs. ✗ a l c, mc, at, LD 10 (9.30 Sun).
🅿 Lt, N, CH, TV, G 80, Ac, con 350, CF, 3
st. £ BB £39·50, DB £49·50, WB, Ⓣ, L
£3·70, D £9·50, cc 1 2 3 5 6, Dep b.
★★★**Royal Crescent,** 100 Marine Par,
BN2 1AX. ✆ (0273) 606311. C. ⊯ 50
bedrs, 50 bp, TV. ✗ a l c, mc, at, LD 9.
🅿 Lt, N, CH, TV, Dgs, G 8, Ac, con 30, CF, 3
st. £ BB £42·50-£52·50, DB £55-£65, DT
£60-£70, ②, Bk £4, L £6·95, D £8·95,
cc 1 2 3 4 5, Dep a.▲
★★**Curzon** (TH), Cavendish Pl, BN1 2HS.
✆ (0273) 25788. C. ⊯ 47 bedrs, 10 bp, 15
bps, 11 ba, TV, Dgs. ✗ a l c, mc, at, LD
9.30. 🅿 Lt, N, CH, CP 26, Ac, con 100, CF,
6 st. £ BB £39·50-£37, DB £46·25-£55,
DBB £26·50-£33·50, WB, Ⓣ, Bk £5·25, L
£3·25, D £7·95, cc 1 2 3 5, Dep.
★★**Granville** (R), 125 Kings Rd, BN1
2FA. ✆ (0273) 33516. Closed Xmas. C.
⊯ 11 bedrs, 6 bp, 5 bps, TV, Dgs. ✗ a l c,
mc, LD 10.30. 🅿 N, CH, Ac, sol, CF, 1 BGf,
5 st. £ BB £30·80, DB £43·50-£71·50, WB,
②, Bk £3·70, L £5·95, D £10·95,
cc 1 2 3 5 6, Dep b.
Abbacourt, PH, z (Unl) 33 Oriental Pl,
BN1 2LL. ✆ (0273) 25651. C7. ⊯ 12

BRIGHTON

0 miles ¼ ½

P	Car Park
C	Public Conveniences
....	Parking Meter Zone

To Bolney 13 m. **A23**

To Arundel 20 m.

To Shoreham-by-Sea 6 m.

To Lewes 9 m.

To Newhaven 9 m.

A27 **A259**

N

RAC Office
Churchill Square

West Pier (Closed)
Multi-Storey(UGC) Car Park
The Brighton Centre
Information Bureau
RAC Office
Brighton Town Hall
Dome, Public Library & Museum
Royal Pavilion
Grand Junction Rd.
Bus Station
Old Steine
Aquarium
Palace Pier
Electric Railway

Clock Tower
West St.
G.P.O.
The Lanes

Carden Avenue
Wilmington Way
Carden Hill
Withdean Park
Carden Avenue
Warnden Rd.
Brayton Avenue
Lyminster Av.
Ditchling Road
Golf Course
Hollingbury Park
Hollingbury Castle (Camp)
Moulescoomb Wild Park
Eldred Avenue
London Road
Colebrook Rd.
Longdean Lane
Hillcrest
Peacock Lane
Surrender Cres.
Surrenden Road
6th Form College
College of Technology
Moulsecoomb Station
Brighton Sports Arena
Preston Park Station
Station Road
London Road
Dyke Road
Varndean Rd.
Loder Rd.
Balfour Rd.
Ditchling Road
The Crestway
Woodruff Av.
Harrington Rd.
Preston Drove
Upper Hollingdean Rd.
Davey Dr.
The Cres.
The Avenue
Sacred Heart Convent
The Droveway
South The Drive
St. Peter's Church
Preston Park Avenue
Beaconsfield Villas
Stanford Avenue
Florence Rd.
Hollingbury Rd.
Dewe Rd.
Coombe Rd.
Lewes Road
Upper Dyke Drive
Bird Dyke Museum
Playing Fields
Dyke Road Park
Old Shoreham Road
London Road Stn.
Ditchling Rise
Ditchling Road
Upper Lewes Road
Brighton Cemetery
Crematorium
Cromwell Road
County Cricket Ground
Davigdor Rd.
Montefiore Rd.
Viaduct Rd.
Union Rd.
KEMP TOWN
Bear Road
To A259
Palmeira Avenue
Holland Road
HOVE
St. Ann's Wells Gardens
York Ave.
Dyke Road
Seven Dials
Central Station
St. Peter's Church
Richmond
The Level
Queen's Park Rd.
Southover
Islingword Rd.
Bonchurch Rd.
Kingsway
Western Road
Montpelier Rd.
Nicholas Church
Buckingham Rd.
Church St.
Victoria Gardens
John St.
Police Sta.
Queen's Park
Royal Sussex County Hospital
Whitehawk Camp
Freshfield
North St.
West St.
Edward St.
Richmond
Freshfield Rd.
Brighton College
Whitehawk Hill Road
Racecourse
Madeira Drive
Marine Parade
St. George's Rd.
Eastern Road
Dyke Road

For abbreviations see inside back cover—**RAC**

RAC

bedrs, 2 ba. 🅱 CH, TV. £ BB fr £8·50, DB fr £17, 🗓.

Adelaide, PH, z (Rl), *5 Regency Sq, BN1 2FF.* ✆ (0273) 205286. Closed mid Dec–mid Jan. C. ⊨ 12 bedrs, 9 bp, 9 bps, 2 sh, 2 ba, TV. 🅱 CH, CF, 2 st. £ BB £17·50–£19·50, DB £33–£39, WT (c) £117, 🗓, Bk £3·50, D £6·50, cc 1 2 3 5.

Ascott, G, z (Unl), *21 New Steine, Marine Parade, BN2 1PD.* ✆ (0273) 688085. C10. ⊨ 10 bedrs, 2 ba. 🅱 CH, TV, 7 st. £ BB £9–£10·50, DB £17–£20, WT (c) £56–£63, 🗓.

Byron Court, G, z (Unl), *12 Grafton St, BN2 1AQ.* ✆ (0273) 605035. Closed Dec. C7. ⊨ 11 bedrs, 11 sh, 2 ba. 🅱 ch, TV. £ BB fr £8, DB £16–£18, WT (c) £56–£60.

Cavalaire House, PH, z, *34 Upper Rock Gardens, BN2 1QF.* ✆ (0273) 696899. C. ⊨ 9 bedrs, 2 bps, 2 sh, 1 ba, TV. 🅱 CH, TV. £ BB £8–£9, DB £16–£22, WT (c) £50–£63, 🗓.

Crest, H, z (Rl), *70 Marine Par, BN2 1AE.* ✆ (0273) 689606. C. ⊨ 17 bedrs, 7 bp, 5 bps, 1 ba, TV, Dgs. 🅱 CH, TV. £ BB £14–£22, DB £22–£28, 🗓, cc 1 2 3 5.

Downlands, PH, z (Unl), *19 Charlotte St, BN2 1AG.* ✆ (0273) 601203. Closed Xmas. C. ⊨ 10 bedrs, 2 ba, TV, Dgs. 🅱 CH, TV, CF. £ BB £8·50–£10, DB £17–£20, WT (c) £56–£65.

Langham, G, z (Unl), *16 Charlotte St, BN2 1AG.* ✆ (0273) 682843. Closed Dec. C7. ⊨ 9 bedrs, 2 ba. 🅱 ch, TV. £ BB £9, DB £17–£18, 🗓.

Le Fleming's, H, z (R), *Regency Sq, BN1 2FG.* ✆ (0273) 27539.

Marina, PH, z (Rt), *8 Charlotte St, BN1 1AG.* ✆ (0273) 605349. Open Feb–Nov, C6. ⊨ 10 bedrs, 4 bps, 3 sh, 1 ba, TV, Dgs. 🅱 CH, TV, CF. £ BB £10·50–£19, DB £23–£28·50, WT (c) £69–£80·50, 🗓, Bk £2.

Melford Hall, H, z (Rl), *41 Marine Par, BN2 1PE.* ✆ (0273) 681435. Closed Xmas & New Year. C. ⊨ 12 bedrs, 6 sh, 2 ba, TV, Dgs. ✗ a l c, TV, CP 12, 7 st. £ BB £13–£20, DB £22–£26, 🗓.

Regency, H, z (R), *28 Regency Sq, BN1 2FH.* ✆ (0273) 202690. C. ⊨ 14 bedrs, 1 bp, 8 bps, 1 sh, 1 ba, TV. 🅱 CH, TV, 1 BGf, 4 st. £ BB £18–£22, DB £33–£48, 🗓, Bk £4, cc 1 2 3 5.

Rowland House, G, z (Rl), *21 St George's Ter, BN2 1JJ.* ✆ (0273) 603639. Closed Jan. C9. ⊨ 10 bedrs, 10 sh, 2 ba, TV, Dgs. 🅱 CH, TV, CP 1, 8 st. £ BB £10–£11, DB £20–£22, WT (c) £70, DT (b) £15·75–£16·75, 🗓, Bk £2, D £5·25.

The Twentyone, PH, z (Rl), *21 Charlotte St, Marine Par, BN2 1AG.*
✆ (0273) 686450. Closed Jan, C12. ⊨ 6 bedrs, 4 bps, 2 ba, TV, Dgs. 🅱 CH. £ BB £18–£23, DB £22–£30, WT (b) £182–£192, DT (b) £26–£27·50, 🗓, Bk £3·50, D £13, cc 1 2 3 5.

Trouville, PH, z (Rl), *11 New Steine, Marine Par, BN2 1PB.* ✆ (0273) 697384. C. ⊨ 9 bedrs, 4 sh, 2 ba, TV. 🅱 CH, TV. £ BB £10·50, DB £18–£21, WT (b) £89, DT (b) £14, 🗓, cc 1 3.

Repairers: Brighton Recovery, 70A St James St. ✆ (0273) 685997.
Endeavour Motor Co Ltd, 90 Preston Rd. ✆ (0273) 506331.
Wadham Stringer (Brighton) Ltd, 154 Old Shoreham Rd. ✆ (0273) 26264.
Rescue Service: Glyde Motors Ltd, Montpelier Rd. ✆ (0273) 29490.

Lee Motors Ltd, 7 Church Pl.
✆ (0273) 684022.
Lee Motors (Woodingdean) Ltd, 583 Falmer Rd, Woodingdean.
✆ (0273) 37777.
S & S Garages, 19a Hollingdean Ter.
✆ (0273) 500024.
S & S Garages, 70a St James St.
✆ (0273) 685997.
Triad Engineering Co (Three-wheelers only), 3 Queen's Place. ✆ (0273) 65896.
Well Serviced Ltd, T/As Saltdean Garage, 34 Longridge Av, Saltdean.
✆ (0273) 31061.

BRILL Buckinghamshire. M. Area 14F 6½ m NW of Thame, London 52, Aylesbury 14, Bicester 8, Oxford 11.

Rescue Service: Cooks of Brill Ltd, 12 Church St. ✆ (0844) 238217.

BRISTOL Avon. Map 5A
RAC Office, *4–6 Whiteladies Rd, Bristol, BS8 1PE.* (General) ✆ Bristol (0272) 732201. (Rescue Service only) Bristol (0272) 739311.
Pop 401,100. Chippenham 22, London 113, M32 Motorway 1, Bath 12, Bridgwater 32, Chepstow 16, Gloucester 35, Radstock 16, Shepton Mallett 20, Tetbury 26, Wells 21, Weston-super-Mare 20.
See plan, p. 160.
EC Wed, Sat. **MD** Daily. **P** See Plan. **Golf** Bristol and Clifton 18h, Filton 18h, Knowle 18h, Long Ashton 18h, Shirehampton Park 18h. **See** Cathedral, Temple Church, Merchant Seamen's Almshouses, 17th cent Llandoger Trow Inn, Theatre Royal, Cabot Tower, Lord Mayor's Chapel, Zoo, Observatory, Clifton Suspension Bridge and Avon Gorge, The Georgian House, Red Lodge, Church of St Mary Redcliffe, John Wesley's Chapel, SS "Great Britain" (at Great Western Dock), Chatterton House, Blaise Castle House Folk Museum (Henbury), RC Cathedral (Clifton).
🅿 Colston House, Colston St. ✆ Bristol (0272) 293891.

★★★★**Grand,** *Broad St, BS1 2EL.* ✆ (0272) 291645. C. ⊨ 179 bedrs, 162 bp, 17 bps, 5 ba, TV, Dgs. ✗ a l c, mc, at, LD 10.30. 🅱 Lt, N, CH, CP 20, Ac, con 600, CF, 3 st. £ BB £45–£65, DB £57–£75, WB, 🗓, cc 1 2 3 5.

★★★★**M Holiday Inn,** *Lower Castle St, BS1 3AD.* ✆ (0272) 294281. C. ⊨ 284 bedrs, 284 bp, ns, TV, Dgs. ✗ a l c, mc, at, LD 11. 🅱 Lt, N, CH, ap, sol, gym, con 500, CF, 1 st. £ BB £55·65, DB £73·50, WB, 🗓, Bk £5·65, L £10·50, D £10·50, cc 1 2 3 4 5 6, Dep b.

★★★★**Ladbroke Dragonara,** *Redcliffe Way, BS1 6NJ.* ✆ (0272) 20044. C. ⊨ 204 bedrs, 204 bp, TV, Dgs. ✗ a l c, mc, at, LD 10.30 (11 Sat, 9.30 Sun). 🅱 Lt, N, CH, Dgs, CP 160, G 10, Ac, con 300, CF, 1 st. £ BB £37·65–£46·25, DB £48·10–£58·50, WB, 🗓, Bk £5·25, L £6·95, D £9·25, cc 1 2 3 5 6, Dep b.

★★★**Avon Gorge,** *Clifton, BS8 4LD.* ✆ (0272) 738955. C. ⊨ 76 bedrs, 64 bp, 9 bps, 5 ba, TV, Dgs. ✗ a l c, mc, at, LD 10. 🅱 Lt, N, CH, Ac, con 90, CF, 0 st. £ BB £35·75, DB £46·75, WB, 🗓, cc 1 2 3 4 5.

★★★**M Crest,** *Filton Rd, Hambrook, BS16 1QX.* ✆ (0272) 564242. C. ⊨ 151 bedrs, 151 bp, ns, TV, Dgs. ✗ a l c, mc, at, LD 9.45 (9 Sun). 🅱 Lt, N, CH, Dgs, CP 200,

Ac, con 450, CF, 0 st. £ B fr £47·50, BD fr £56, WB, 🗓, Bk £5·50, D £9·95, cc 1 2 3 4 5 6, Dep b.

★★★**St Vincent's Rocks,** *Sion Hill, BS8 4BB* (Clifton) ✆ (0272) 739251. C. ⊨ 46 bedrs, 39 bp, 7 bps, TV, Dgs. ✗ a l c, mc, at, LD 9.30 (10 Fri & Sat). 🅱 N, CH, TV, Dgs, CP 18, G 10, Ac, con 50, CF, 5 BGf, 8 st. £ BB fr £40, DB fr £49, DBB fr £50, WB, 🗓, Bk £4, L £8, D £10, cc 1 2 3 4 5 6, Dep b.

■★★**Hawthorns,** *Woodland Rd, BS8 1UB* (Clifton) ✆ (0272) 738432. Closed Xmas. C. ⊨ 165 bedrs, 45 bp, 22 bps, 31 ba, TV. ✗ a l c, mc, LD 10.30. 🅱 Lt, N, CH, ns, CP 80, Ac, con 200, CF, 5 BGf, 16 st. £ BB fr £21, DB fr £36·75, WB, 🗓, Bk £2·42, L £5, D £5, cc 1 2 3 5.

★★**Seeley's** (R), *19–27 St Paul's Rd, BS8 1LX.* ✆ (0272) 738544. Closed Xmas. C. ⊨ 40 bedrs, 9 bp, 17 bps, 3 sh, 8 ba, TV, Dgs. ✗ a l c, mc, LD 11. 🅱 N, CH, Dgs, CP 10, G 18, Ac, con 42, CF, 12 BGf, 2 st. £ BB £13·50–£16·50, DB £21–£26, DT £23·25, WB, 🗓, Bk £3·50, L £3·50, D £5·25, cc 1 2 3 6, Dep b.

Birkdale, PH, z (R), *10 Ashgrove Rd, Redland, BS6 6LY.* ✆ (0272) 733635. C. ⊨ 42 bedrs, 5 bp, 7 bps, 22 sh, 8 ba. 🅱 CH, Dgs, CP 15. £ BB £17·20–£20·90, DB £34·40–£41·80, 🗓, Bk £4·05, L £4·25, D £4·75, cc 3.

Cavendish House, G, z (Unl), *18 Cavendish Rd, Henleaze, BS9 4DZ.* ✆ (0272) 621017. C. ⊨ 8 bedrs, 2 ba, Dgs. 🅱 CH, TV, Dgs, CP 5, CF, 2 st. £ BB fr £10, DB fr £18, 🗓.

Chesterfield, PH, z (Unl), *3 Westbourne Pl, BS8 1RZ.* ✆ (0272) 734606.

Clifton, PH, z, *St Paul's Rd, BS8 1LX.* ✆ (0272) 736882. C. ⊨ 63 bedrs, 4 bp, 38 bps, 6 sh, 8 ba, TV, Dgs. ✗ a l c. £ BB £13–£16·50, DB £22–£24·50, 🗓, D £6, cc 1 3.

Downlands, G, z (Unl), *33 Henleaze Gdns, Henleaze, BS9 4HH.* ✆ (0272) 621639. C. ⊨ 9 bedrs, 2 ba, TV, Dgs. 🅱 CH, TV, Dgs. £ BB £10, DB £10, WT (c) £72, DT (b) £14, 🗓, D £4.

Oakdene, PH, z (Unl), *45 Oakfield Rd, Clifton, BS8 2BA.* ✆ (0272) 735900.

Oakfield, PH, z (Unl), *52 Oakfield Rd, BS8 2BG.* ✆ (0272) 735556. C. ⊨ 27 bedrs, 7 ba, Dgs. 🅱 CH, TV, CP 20, G 2, CF, 2 BGf, 3 st. £ BB £12–£12·50, DB £18·50–£19, WT £90, DT £15·50, 🗓, Bk £2·50, D £3·50.

Pembroke, PH, z (Unl), *13 Arlington Villas, St Paul's Rd, BS8 2EG.* ✆ (0272) 735550. Closed Xmas. C. ⊨ 13 bedrs, 2 ba. 🅱 CH, TV, Dgs. £ BB £9·50, DB £18, 🗓, cc 1 3.

Washington, PH, z (Unl), *11 St Paul's Rd, BS8 1LX.* ✆ (0272) 733980. C. ⊨ 32 bedrs, 4 bps, 7 ba, Dgs. 🅱 CH, TV, Dgs, CP 13, CF, 4 BGf. £ cc 1 3.

Willsbridge House, PH, xy (Rl) *Willsbridge Hill, Willsbridge.* ✆ Bitton (027 588) 2269. C. ⊨ 15 bedrs, 5 bps, 10 sh, 2 ba, TV, Dgs. 🅱 CH, TV, CP 50, CF, 2 st. £ BB £13·22–£21·85, DB £21·85–£29·32, WT £120·04–£174·40, DT (b) £18·47–£27·10, 🗓, cc 1 3.

York House, H, z (Unl), *16 West Park, Clifton, BS8 2LT.* ✆ (0272) 733907.

Repairers: Bawns Bristol Ltd, 168 Coronation Rd. ✆ (0272) 631101.
Cathedral Garage Ltd, College Green. ✆ (0272) 20031.

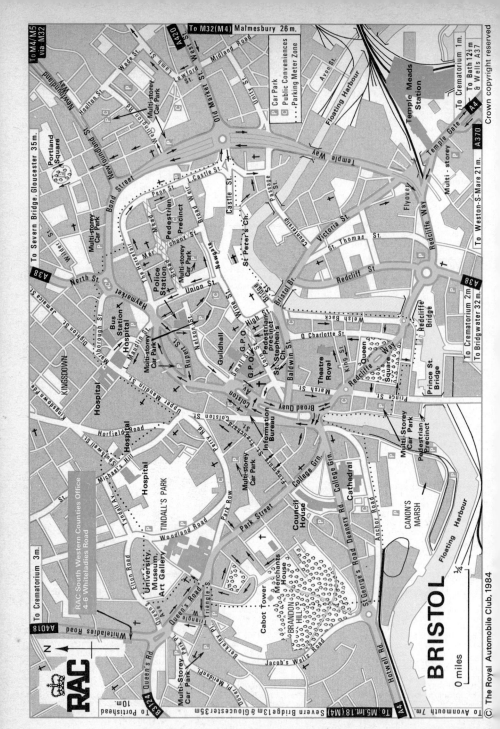

BRISTOL

0 miles ¼

Crown copyright reserved

P Car Park
G Public Conveniences
···· Parking Meter Zone

160

For abbreviations see inside back cover—**RAC**

Clist & Rattle Ltd, Cambridge Batch
Garage, Flax Bourton. ✆ Flax Bourton
(027 583) 3666.
Henlys (West) Ltd, 156 Cheltenham Rd.
✆ (0272) 48051.
Specialist Body Repairer: R H Glynn & Co
Ltd, 79 Princess Victoria St.
✆ (0272) 739078.
Specialist Radiator Repairer: Serck
Radiator Services Ltd, Clothier Rd,
Brislington Trading Estate,
✆ (0272) 779247.
MC Repairers: T T Motor Cycles, 2a
Downend Rd, Fishponds.
✆ (0272) 659690.
Rescue Service: A F S Garages, Andrews
Rd, Avonmouth. ✆ Avonmouth
(0272) 822983.
B & R Collins, Long Cross Garage,
Lawrence Weston. ✆ (0272) 822825.
Baron Motors, Gas Ferry Rd, Hotwells.
✆ (0272) 298287.
Bridgwater Road Service Station, Dundry.
✆ Long Ashton (027 580) 2212.
Clarke Bros (Bristol) Ltd, 175 Muller Rd,
✆ (0272) 513333.
Concorde Motors, 180 Newfoundland Rd.
✆ (0272) 510248.
Double "H" Service Station, Fishponds Rd.
✆ (0272) 651423.
Eastman of Eastville, 338 Stapleton Rd.
✆ (0272) 510851.
Fancoil, T/As Clifton Park Garage, 54
Clifton Park Rd. ✆ (0272) 730157.
Feeder Road Garages Ltd, Feeder Rd.
✆ (0272) 775306.
Filton Avenue Service Station, 472 Filton
Av. ✆ (0272) 696109.
Hartcliffe Motors, Whitchurch La.
✆ (0272) 645777.
Landdon Motors, School Rd, Totterdown.
✆ (0272) 776740.
Lodway Service Station, Lodway, Pill.
✆ Pill (027 581) 2561.
Longwell Green Service Station, 106 Bath
Rd, Longwell Green. ✆ Bitten
(027 588) 2317.
Midland Road Service Station, Midland
Rd. ✆ (0272) 291772.
New Station Recovery Service, New
Station Rd, Fishponds. ✆ (0272) 659423.
Park Motor Eng Co (Bristol) Ltd, 1 Hill Av.
✆ (0272) 777726.
Patchway Car Centre, Gloucester Rd,
Patchway. ✆ (0272) 694331.
Pembroke Service Station, High St,
Shirehampton. ✆ Avonmouth
(0272) 827396.
Streamside Garage, The Stream,
Hambrook. ✆ (0272) 571197 (weekends
Winterbourne (0454) 772501).
Surecar, College Rd, Fishponds.
✆ (0272) 659472.
Westward Service Station, 237 West St,
Bedminster. ✆ (0272) 665018.

BRIXHAM Torbay, Devon. Map 3D
Pop 11,900. Torquay 7½, London 107,
Dartmouth (Fy) 4½, Totnes 9½.
EC Wed. **Golf** Churston 18h. **See** Wm of
Orange statue, Museum, Aquarium,
Cavern, replica of Drake's "Golden Hind",
Parish Church of St Mary, All Saints
Church, Berry Head (Napoleonic forts,
coast guard station), Lighthouse.
🅸 Old Market House, The Quay.
✆ Brixham (08 45) 2861.

■ ★★★**Quayside,** *King St, TQ5 9TJ.*
✆ (08045) 55751. C. ◪ 32 bedrs, 22 bp, 3
bps, TV, Dgs. ✕ a l c, mc, at, LD 9.30. 🅳 N,

CH, CP 37, Ac, con 20, CF, 3 BGf, 6 st.
£ BB £22·50–£29, DB £35–£52, DBB fr
£26, WB, ⬛, Bk £3·50, L £4·85, D £8·50,
cc 1 2 3 5 6, Dep.
Au Levant, G, z *(Unl), 5 Mount Rd, TQ5
9SA.* ✆ (080 45) 2836. Closed Xmas. C.
◪ 6 bedrs, 1 ba, Dgs. 🅳 CH, TV, Dgs, CP 6,
CF. **£** BB £8–£9·50, DB £15–£18, WT (b)
£80–£90, ⬜.
Beverley Court, PH, y (Rl), *Upton
Manor Rd, TQ5 9RG.* ✆ (080 45) 3149.
Fair Winds, G, x (Unl), *New Rd, TQ5
8DA.* ✆ (080 45) 3564.
Harbour View, PH, z (Unl), *65 King St,
TQ5 9TH.* ✆ (080 45) 3052.
Kalevala, G, *13 Trafalgar Terr, Higher
Furzeham Rd, TQ5 8QT.* ✆ (080 45) 4164.
Raddicombe Lodge, G, x (Rt),
Kingswear Rd, TQ5 0EX.
✆ (080 45) 2125. C. ◪ 9 bedrs, 2 ba, Dgs.
🅳 ch, TV, CP 12, CF, 4 BGf, 7 st. **£** BB
£8·55–£13·10, DB £17·10–£21, WT
£89·60–£95, DT £12·80–£15·85, ⬜, Bk
£2, D £5·35, cc 1 3.
Ranscombe House PH, *Ranscombe Rd,
TQ5 9UP.* ✆ (080 45) 2337.
Sampford House, G, x, *57 King St, TQ5
9TH.* ✆ (080 45) 7761. Open Mar–Oct. C.
◪ 6 bedrs, 2 ba. 🅳 TV, CF. **£** BB £7–£8,
DB £14–£16, WT (c) £49–£56.

Rescue Service: Berry Head Garage, Berry
Head Rd. ✆ (080 45) 2506.
Dart Automarine Services, Hill Head
Garage. ✆ (080 45) 3887.
Kenneth Jay Ltd, T/as Brixham Garage,
New Rd. ✆ (080 45) 2952.
Prouts Garages (Churston 1970),
Churston Ferrers. ✆ Torquay
(0803) 842569 & (0803) 842245.

BRIXTON Devon. Map 3C
Pop 1,183. Ashburton 20, London 208,
Kingsbridge 14, Plymouth 5½, Totnes 17.
Golf Staddon Heights 18h.

Rescue Service: Rodgers of Brixton Ltd,
Brixton Rd Garage. ✆ Plymouth
(0752) 42623.

BROADMAYNE Dorset. Map 5F.
Pop 857. 4 m SE of Dorchester. Ringwood
33, London 126, Blandford Forum 19,
Dorchester 4, Wareham 13, Weymouth 6½.
Golf Dorchester 18h.

Rescue Service: Durant Sales & Service.
✆ Warmwell (0305) 457.

BROADSTAIRS Kent. Map 10D
See also KINGSGATE.
Pop 20,048. Canterbury 18, London 76,
Dover 20, Folkestone 26, Margate 3½.
EC Wed. **Golf** North Foreland 18h & 9h.
See St Peter's Church (12th cent), Bleak
House where Dickens lived, 16th cent
York Gate, Dickens Museum, North
Foreland Lighthouse.
🅸 Pierremont Hall, High St. ✆ Thanet
(0843) 68399.

★★★**Castle Keep,** *Kingsgate Castle,
CT10 3PQ.* ✆ Thanet (0843) 65222. C.
◪ 29 bedrs, TV, Dgs. ✕ a l c, mc, at, LD
10. 🅳 N, CH, CP 60, sp, con 30, CF, 5 BGf,
0 st, Dis. **£** BB £30–£33, DB £36–£41, WT
fr £191–£266, ⬛, 10%, Bk £3·50, L £6, D
£7, cc 1 2 3 5 6, Dep.
★★**Castlemere,** *Western Esplanade,
CT10 1TD.* ✆ Thanet (0843) 61566. RS
Nov–May. C. ◪ 37 bedrs, 30 bp, 2 ba, TV,
Dgs. ✕ mc, at, LD 7.45. 🅳 CH, TV, CP 30,
G 2, con 40, CF, 3 BGf, 1 st, Dis. **£** BB

£16·05–£22·40, DB £29·10–£41·80, DBB
£24·85–£29·70, WB, ⬜, Bk £4·50, D £8·80,
cc 1 3, Dep a.
★★**Royal Albion,** *Albion St, CT10 1LU.*
✆ Thanet (0843) 68071. RS Oct–May. C.
◪ 18 bedrs, 15 bp, 3 bps, TV, Dgs. ✕ a l c,
mc, at, LD 9.45. 🅳 N, CH, TV, CP 15, U 6,G
6, Ac, con 20, CF, 2 st. **£** BB fr £24, DB fr
£32, DBB fr £29, WB, ⬜, Bk £2·50, L £5, D
£6·50, cc 1 2 3 5 6.
Bay Tree, PH, y (Rl), *12 Eastern
Esplanade, CT10 1DR.* ✆ Thanet
(0843) 62502. Open Feb–Nov, C3. ◪ 9
bedrs, 1 bps, 2 ba, Dgs. 🅳 CH, TV, Dgs, CP
9, 2 st. **£** BB £8·50–£10·50, DB £17–£21,
WT £75–£90, DT £12·50–£14, ⬜.
Dutch House, H, y (R), *North Foreland
Rd, CT10 3NN.* ✆ Thanet (0843) 62824.
C. ◪ 10 bedrs, 2 sh. 🅳 CH, TV, CP 6, CF, 3
st. **£** BB £8·50–£9·50, DB £17–£19, WT (b)
£70–£80, DT (b) £14·50–£15·50, ⬜, Bk
£2·50, D £6.
Keston Court, H, z (Rl), *14 Ramsgate
Rd, CT10 1PS.* ✆ Thanet (0843) 62401.
C2. ◪ 10 bedrs, 2 ba, Dgs. ✕ a l c. 🅳 CH,
TV, CP 6, CF. **£** BB £10–£12, DB £17–£19,
WT (b) £85–£95, DT (b) £13·50–£15·50,
⬛, Bk £2, D £4·50.
Merriland, G, z (Unl), *The Vale, CT10
1RB.* ✆ Thanet (0843) 61064.
Rothsay, PH, z (R), ✆ (0843) 62646. C.
◪ 14 bedrs, 5 bps, 3 ba, Dgs. 🅳 CH, TV,
Dgs, CF, 0 st. **£** BB £10–£14, DB £20–£26,
WT (b) £88·50–£100·50, DT (b) £14·75–
£16·75, ⬛, Bk £2, L £4·75, D £4·75.
St Augustine's, H, z (R), *19 Granville
Rd, CT10 1QB.* ✆ Thanet (0843) 65017. C.
◪ 15 bedrs, 4 bps, 4 ba, TV, Dgs. 🅳 CH,
Dgs, CP 1, CF, 2 BGf, 0 st, Dis. **£** BB £10–
£13, DB £20–£24, WT (a) £80–£90, DT
£16–£18, ⬜, Bk £2, L £4, D £6, cc 3 6.
The White House, PH, z (Rl), *59
Kingsgate Ave, CT10 3LW.* ✆ Thanet
(0843) 63315. C. ◪ 10 bedrs, 2 bp, 1 bps,
1 sh, 2 ba, TV, Dgs. 🅳 CH, TV, CP 10, CF.
£ BB £9·50–£14·50, DB £19–£31, WT (b)
£69·50–£95, DT (b) £12·50–£18·50, ⬜, Bk
£3, D £5, cc 1 3.

BROADSTONE Dorset. Maps 5F & 6E.
Ringwood 12, London 105, Blandford
Forum 11, Bournemouth 7½, Dorchester
24, Poole 4, Wimborne Minster 3½.

Fairlight, PH, y (R), *1 Golf Links Rd,
BH18 8BE.* ✆ (0202) 694316. C. ◪ 10
bedrs, 7 bp, 2 ba, Dgs. 🅳 CH, TV, CP 10, 1
BGf. **£** BB fr £13, DB fr £22, WT fr £112, DT
fr £20, ⬜, Bk £3·50, D £8.

BROADWAY Hereford & Worcester
(Worcestershire). Map 14C
Pop 2,389. Moreton-in-Marsh 8½, London
92, Banbury 27, Cheltenham 15, Evesham
5½, Stow-on-the-Wold 10, Stratford-upon-
Avon 15, Tewkesbury 15.
EC Thur. **Golf** Broadway 18h. **See** 17th
cent Lygon Arms, Elizabethan houses, St
Eadburg's Church, 14th cent Abbots
Grange, 14th cent Priors Manse, Fish Inn,
Cross Hands signpost, Buckland Rectory
1 m SW, Snowshill Manor 2½ m S (Nat
Trust).

★★★★**Lygon Arms,** *North St, WR12
7DU.* ✆ (0386) 852255. C. ◪ 66 bedrs, 66
bp, TV, Dgs. ✕ a l c, mc, at, LD 9.15. 🅳 N,
CH, TV, Dgs, CP 150, U 4, Ac, tc, con 80,
CF, 9 BGf, 0 st, Dis. **£** BBc £45–£50, DBc
£72–£95, WB, ⬛, Bk £4, L £8·50, D £15,
cc 1 2 3 4 5 6.

★★★**Broadway,** *The Green, WR12 7AA.*
✆ (0386) 852401. C. 🚗 13 bedrs, 11 bp, 1
bps, 3 ba, annexe 11 bedrs, 9 bp, 1 bps, TV.
✗ a l c, mc, at, LD 9. 🅿 CH, CP 30, con 24,
CF, 2 BGf, 5 st. £ BB £18–£24, DBB £23–
£30, WB, 2, 5%, Bk £4, L £5·95, D £8·95,
cc 1 2 3 5 6, Dep a.

🏨★★★**Dormy House,** *Willersey Hill,*
WR12 7LF. ✆ (0386) 852711. C. 🚗 26
bedrs, 24 bp, 2 bps, annexe 23 bedrs, 23
bp, TV, Dgs. ✗ a l c, mc, at, LD 9.30. 🅿 N,
CH, CP 70, Ac, con 175, CF, 5 st. £ BB
£36–£45, DB £62–£73, WT £299·50–
£329·50, DBB £35–£38·50, WB, 2, Bk £6,
L £10·50, D £14, cc 1 2 3 5 6, Dep b.

🏨★★**Collin House** (R), *Collin La, WR12*
7PB. ✆ (0386) 858354. Closed Xmas, C8.
🚗 7 bedrs, 5 bp, 1 bps, 1 sh. ✗ a l c, LD 9.
🅿 CH, TV, Dgs, CP 32, sp. £ BB £27, DB
£47, WB, 1, Bk £3·50, L £4·50, D £10,
cc 1 3.

Old Rectory, G (Unl), *Church Street,*
Willersey, WR12 7PN. ✆ (0386) 853793.
C10. 🚗 5 bedrs, 2 bp, 3 bps, TV. 🅿 CH, TV,
CP 8, G 2. £ DB £33–£43, 1, cc 1 3.▲

Olive Branch, G, x (Unl), *78 High St,*
WR12 7AJ. ✆ (0386) 853440. Closed
Xmas. C. 🚗 8 bedrs, 2 bps, 2 ba. 🅿 ch, TV,
CP 8, CF, 1 st. £ BB £10–£11, DB £19–£25,
1.

BROCKENHURST Hampshire. Map 6E
Pop 3,305. Lyndhurst 4, London 88,
Bournemouth 17, Lymington 5, Ringwood
11.
EC Wed. **Golf** Brockenhurst Manor 18h.
See Parish Church (Norman features),
yew tree reputed to be 1,000 years old,
New Forest, Rhinefield House (3 m SW of
Lyndhurst), open to public.

★★★**Balmer Lawn,** *Lyndhurst Rd, SO4*
7ZB. ✆ Lymington (0590) 23116. C. 🚗 60
bedrs, 54 bp, 2 ba. ✗ a l c, mc, at, LD 9.45.
🅿 Lt, N, CH, CP 90, U 8, Ac, sp, tc, sol,
gym, con 120, CF, 1 st. £ BB fr £35, DB
£50, WT £200, DBB fr £48, CF, 5 st. £ Bk
£5·50, L £6, D £9, cc 1 2 3 5, Dep b.

★★★**M Carey's Manor,** *Lyndhurst Rd,*
SO4 7RH. ✆ Lymington (0590) 23551. C.
🚗 57 bedrs, 57 bp, ns, TV, Dgs. ✗ a l c, LD
10. 🅿 N, CH, CP 200, sp, sb, sol, gym, con
30, CF, 17 BGf, 4 st. £ BB £33·95–£37·95,
DB £49·90–£59·90, DBB £29·85–£37·85,
WB, 1, Bk £4·50, L £6·75, D £9·75,
cc 1 2 3 5 6, Dep a.

★★★**Forest Park,** *Rhinefield Rd, SO4*
7ZG. ✆ Lymington (0590) 22095. C.
🚗 38 bedrs, 36 bp, 2 ba, TV, Dgs. ✗ a l c,
mc, LD 10. 🅿 CH, Dgs, CP 80, Ac, sp, tc, rf,
sb, con 20, CF, 7 BGf, 3 st. £ BB £28–
£32·50, DB £38–£42, WB, 1, Bk £5·25, L
£4·75, D £8·95, cc 1 2 3 5.

◙★★**Cloud** (R), *Meerut Rd, SO4 7TD.*
✆ Lymington (0590) 22165. Closed Jan.
C. 🚗 19 bedrs, 5 ba, Dgs. ✗ mc, at, LD 8.
🅿 CH, CP 20, CF. £ BB £15·50–£20·50,
DB £31–£41, DBB £23·50–£28, WB, 2, Bk
£3·50, L £3·50, D £8·50, Dep.

🏨★★**New Park Manor,** *Lyndhurst Rd,*
SO4 7QH. ✆ Lymington (0590) 23467.

★★**Watersplash** (R), *The Rise, SO4 7ZP.*
✆ Lymington (0590) 22344. C. 🚗 26
bedrs, 13 bp, 2 bps, 11 sh, 4 ba, Dgs. ✗ mc,
at, LD 8. 🅿 CH, TV, CP 30, U 4, Ac, con
20, CF, 3 BGf, 1 st. £ BB £16–£20, DB £30–
£38, WT £139–£149, DT £24–£26, WB, 2,
Bk £3, L £4·50, D £8·50.

Wide Lane Cottage, H, x (Unl), *Sway*
Rd, SO4 7SH. ✆ Lymington
(0590) 22296. C12. 🚗 5 bedrs, 2 ba.

🅿 CH, TV, CP 5. £ BB £14–£15, DB £23–
£26, WT (b) £117–£120, DT (b) £19–
£20·50, 1, D £7·50.

Repairer: Gates Engineering Co Ltd,
Sway Rd Garage. ✆ Lymington
(0590) 23344.

BROCKFORD Suffolk. Map 16D
Pop 544. Colchester 32, London 86,
Ipswich 15, Scole 8, Stowmarket 10.
Golf Stowmarket 18h.

Repairer: Brockford Motor & Engineering
Co, Norwich Rd. ✆ Mendelsham
(044 94) 254.

BROMBOROUGH Merseyside. Map
20F
Pop 14,580. Chester 10, London 193, M53
Motorway 2, Birkenhead 4½, Ellesmere
Port 5.
EC Thur. **Golf** Bromborough 18h. **See**
Market Cross, Industrial Village.

★★★**The Dibbinsdale** (R), *Dibbinsdale*
Rd, L63 0HJ. ✆ 051-334 5171. C. 🚗 25
bedrs, 20 bp, 3 bps, 2 sh, TV. ✗ a l c, mc,
LD 10. 🅿 N, CH, CP 40, CF, 10 BGf, 1 st.
Dis. £ BB £17·71–£26·57, DB £26·57–
£36·05, WB, 1, L £8·65, D £8·65, cc
1 2 3 4 5 6.

BROME Suffolk. Map 16D.
Pop 254. Bury St Edmunds 23, London 97,
Diss 3½, Eye 2.
Golf Diss 9h. **See** Church, Castle at Eye
(2 m S).

★★**M Grange,** *IP23 8AP.* ✆ Eye
(0379) 870456. C. 🚗 22 bedrs, 20 bp, 2
bps, TV, Dgs. ✗ a l c, mc, at, LD 9.45.
🅿 CH, TV, Dgs, CP 200, Ac, con 100, CF,
22 BGf, 1 st, Dis. £ BB £24–£26, DB £35–
£37·50, WT £147–£170, WB, 1, Bk £4·50,
L £2·75, D £7·50, cc 1 2 3 5 6, Dep b.

BROMLEY Greater London (Kent).
Map 7B
Pop 65,703. London 11, Croydon 6,
Sevenoaks 14, Sidcup 4½, Westerham 11.
EC Wed. **MD** Thur. **Golf** Sundridge Park
18h. **See** Church of SS Peter and Paul
(memorial Dr Johnson's wife, Norman
Font), Bromley College, Down House,
Downe (home of Darwin) 5½ m SE.

★★★**Bromley Court,** *Bromley Hill, BR1*
4JD. ✆ 01-464 5011. C. 🚗 130 bedrs, 130
bp, TV, Dgs. ✗ a l c, mc, at, LD 9.45. 🅿 Lt,
N, CH, TV, CP 100, Ac, con, CF, 5 st. £ BB fr
£34, DB fr £45, WT fr £337·40, DT fr
£48·20, WB, 1, Bk £4, L £6·45, D £7·75,
cc 1 2 3 4 5 6, Dep a.

Bromley Continental, H, z (R), *56*
Plaistow Lane, BR1 3JE. ✆ 01-464 2415.
C. 🚗 20 bedrs, 1 bp, 2 sh, 4 ba, TV. 🅿 CH,
CP 14, U 1, CF, 3 st. £ BB £12·20–£16·50,
DB £19·50–£22·50, 1, Bk £2·85, D £5·85,
cc 1 3.

Grianan, H, y, *23 Orchard Rd, BR1 2PR.*
✆ 01-460 1795.

Villa St. Philomena, H, x (RI), *1*
Lansdowne Rd. ✆ 01-460-6311.

Rescue Service: Woods Garage (Bromley)
Ltd, 86 High St. ✆ 01-460 3000 and 2562.

BROMSGROVE Hereford & Worcester
(Worcestershire). Map 13B
Pop 87,800. Stratford-upon-Avon 20,
London 113, M5 Motorway 3,
Birmingham 13, Coventry 29, Droitwich 6,
Evesham 21, Kidderminster 9½, Warwick
23, Wolverhampton 19.

MD Tue, Fri, Sat. **Golf** Blackwell 18h. **See**
Church of St John the Baptist, Public
School 16th cent, Valley House, Fockbury
(birthplace of A E Housman), United
Reform Church; stained glass window
commemorating Bromsgrove Guild of
Applied Arts.
🛈 47 Worcester Rd. ✆ Bromsgrove
(0527) 31809.

★★★**Perry Hall,** *Kidderminster Rd, B61*
7JN. ✆ (0527) 31976. C. 🚗 53 bedrs, 53
bp, TV, Dgs. ✗ a l c, mc, at, LD 9.45. 🅿 N,
CH, Dgs, CP 180, Ac, con 180, CF, 22 BGf,
2 st. £ BB fr £35·25, DB fr £45·50, WB, 1,
Bk £4·25, L £6·20, D £7·65, cc 1 2 3 4 5 6,
Dep b.

Rescue Service: Aston Fields Recovery
Service, Aston Fields Service Station,
New Rd. ✆ Redditch (0527) 68282.
Barnt Green Garage Ltd, Hewell Rd, Barnt
Green. ✆ 021-445 1745.

BROMYARD Hereford & Worcester
(Herefordshire). Map 13C.
Worcester 14, London 128, Hereford 14,
Kidderminster 22, Ledbury 13,
Leominster 11, Ludlow 21, Tewkesbury
26.
Golf Leominster 9h. **See** Norman Church,
Lower Brockhampton House 2 m NE.

★**Hop Pole,** *The Square, HR7 4BP.*
✆ (0885) 82449.

BROOK Hampshire. Map 6C
Pop 100. Romsey 7, London 82, M27
Motorway 1, Lyndhurst 5, Salisbury 13,
Shaftesbury 30, Southampton 9.
Golf Bramshaw 18h.

★★**Bell Inn,** *SO4 7HE.* ✆ Southampton
(0703) 812214.

BROOKMANS PARK Hertfordshire.
Map 15F
Pop 3,032. Barnet 5½, London 17, Enfield
8, Hatfield 3½, Hoddesdon 11, St Albans 7,
Watford 13.
EC Thur. **Golf** Brookmans Park 18h. **See**
BBC Broadcasting Station—landmark.

Rescue Service: Brookmans Park Motors,
Gt North Rd. ✆ Potters Bar (0707) 52208.

BROUGH Cumbria. Map 26B
Pop 671. Boroughbridge 57, London 264,
Brampton 42, Darlington 34, Harrogate
66, Hawes 20, Kendal 28, Kirkby Lonsdale
29, Middleton-in-Teesdale 14,
Northallerton 44, Penrith 21, West
Auckland 29.
EC Thur. **See** Norman Castle ruins, 12th–
16th cent Church.
🛈 The "One-Stop" Shop, Main St.
✆ Brough (093 04) 260.

Rescue Service: Frank Allison Ltd, The
George Garage. ✆ (093 04) 329.

BROUGHTON-IN-FURNESS Cumbria.
Map 26F
Pop 1,037. Lancaster 41, London 277,
Ambleside 16, Barrow-in-Furness 14,
Egremont 31, Kendal 30, Kirkby Lonsdale
37, Ulverston 9½.
EC Thur. **MD** Tue. **Golf** Ulverston 18h,
Silecroft 9h. **See** St Mary Magdalene
Church, John Gilpin Obelisk.

◙★★**Eccle Riggs,** *Foxfield Rd, LA20*
6BN. ✆ (065 76) 398. C. 🚗 8 bedrs, 9 bp,
4 sh, 2 ba, TV. ✗ a l c, mc, LD 8.30. 🅿 CH,
TV, CP 100, Ac, sp, sb, sol, con 100, CF.

£ BB fr £18, DB fr £28, WB, ①, Bk £4, D £8·50, cc 1 2 3 5.

◨★**Old King's Head,** *Church St, LA20 6HJ.* ✆ (065 76) 293.

Rescue Service: Station Rd Garage, Station Rd. ✆ (065 76) 201.

BROWNHILLS West Midlands. Map 21C
Coventry 25, London 119, Birmingham 12, Lichfield 5, Newport 22, Stafford 14, Sutton Coldfield 9, Tamworth 11, Walsall 6, Wellington 25.

Rescue Service: Motormobile Services, 168 Lichfield Rd. ✆ (054 33) 3216.

BROXBOURNE Hertfordshire. Map 15F
Enfield 8, London 19, Epping 11, Hoddesdon 1, Woodford 12.
EC Wed. **Golf** East Herts 18h.

Rescue Service: Broxbourne Motors Ltd, 72 High Rd. ✆ Hoddesdon (0992) 64122.

BRUTON Somerset. Map 5D
Pop 1,731. Amesbury 33, London 112, Crewkerne 24, Frome 10, Glastonbury 13, Ilminster 26, Salisbury 33, Shaftesbury 14, Shepton Mallet 7½, Sherborne 12, Taunton 32, Warminster 15, Wincanton 5.
EC Thu. **Golf** Tower Hill 9h, Mendip, Shepton Mallet 18h. **See** Perp Church, Packhorse Bridge, 16th cent roofless dovecote (Nat Trust), 17th cent Sexey's Hospital (Almshouses).

Fryerning, H, x (R), *Burrowfield Frome Rd, BA10 0HH.* ✆ (074 981) 2343. Closed Jan–Feb, C8. ⊷ 4 bedrs, 3 bp, 1 bps, TV. ⓓ CH, ns, CP 8, 1 st. **£** BB £17–£21, DB £26–£28, WT (b) £119–£132, ①, Bk £4, D £8·50.

Repairer: West End Garage (Bruton) Ltd, West End. ✆ (074 981) 3261.

BUCKDEN Cambridgeshire. Map 15B
Pop 2,610. Biggleswade 16, London 62, Alconbury 5½, Bedford 16, Huntingdon 4½, Kettering 25, Northampton 23.
Golf St Neots 18h. **See** Perp Church (Laurence Sterne married here), remains of Palace of Bishops of Lincoln (now being restored), "Lion" and "George" (old posting inns), Grafham Water 1 m.

★**Lion** (TH), *High St, Buckden, Huntingdon, PE18 9XA.* ✆ Huntingdon (0480) 810313. C. ⊷ 14 bedrs, 4 bp, 4 bps, 2 ba, TV. Dgs. ✗ a l c, mc, at, LD 9.30. ⓓ CH, Dgs, CP 40, con 25, CF, 1 st. **£** BB fr £23·50, DB fr £29·50, WT fr £154, DBB fr £19, WB, ①, Bk £3·50, L £4·75, cc 1 2 3 5 6.

BUCKDEN North Yorkshire. Map 27A
Skipton 18, London 222, Hawes 12, Leyburn 16.
EC Wed. **Golf** Skipton 18h.

★**Buck Inn,** *BD23 5JA.* ✆ Kettlewell (076 676) 227. C. ⊷ 10 bedrs wih 1 ba, TV, Dgs. ✗ a l c, mc, LD 9.30. ⓓ CH, TV, Dgs, CP 40, CF, 3 st. **£** BB £10–£14, DB £20–£28, WB, ②, Bk £3·25, L £2·50, D £5·10, cc 1 2 3 5, Dep a.

BUCKFAST Devon. Map 3D
Ashburton 6½, London 189, Buckfastleigh ¾, Newton Abbot 10, Plymouth 23, Totnes 7, Two Bridges 11.

Black Rock, G, xy (R), *Buckfast Rd, TQ11 0EA.* ✆ Buckfastleigh (0364) 42343. C. ⊷ 11 bedrs, 2 bp, 2 ba, Dgs. ✗ a l c. ⓓ CH, TV, CP 45, CF, 1 st.

£ BB £9, DB £18–£20, WT (b) £80, DT (b) £13, ①, Bk £2·40, L £1·20, D £4·50.

BUCKFASTLEIGH Devon. Map 3D
Pop 3,000. Ashburton 3, London 190, Kingsbridge 16, Plymouth 21, Saltash 24, Tavistock 22, Totnes 6.
EC Wed. **Golf** Newton Abbot (Stover) 18h. **See** Buckfast Abbey, Caves, EE and Perp Church, Farm Museum, Dart Valley Rly (standard gauge, steam engine) to Totnes.

◨⊞♨★**Bossell House** (RI), *Plymouth Rd, TQ11 0DG.* ✆ (0364) 43294. Closed Xmas. C. ⊷ 11 bedrs, 1 bp, 1 bps, 3 ba, Dgs. ✗ a l c, mc, at, LD 9. ⓓ ch, TV, Dgs, CP 30, Ac, tc, con 60, CF, 1 BGf, 0 st. **£** WB, ①, Bk £2·75, D £5·75, Dep b.
Woodholme, G, z, (R), *113 Plymouth Rd.* ✆ (0364) 3350.

Rescue Service: Mount Pleasant Garage & Engineering Co, 116 Plymouth Rd. ✆ (0364) 3310.
West End Garage. Plymouth Rd. ✆ (0364) 2367.

BUCKHURST HILL Essex. Map 15F
Pop 11,921. London 12, Enfield 6½, Epping 6½, Hoddesdon 14, Woodford 3.
EC Wed. **Golf** Chigwell 18h. **See** Roebuck Hotel, Epping Forest.

★★**Roebuck** (TH), *North End, IG9 5QY.* ✆ 01-505 4636. C. ⊷ 23 bedrs, 23 bp, TV, Dgs. ✗ a l c, mc, LD 9.30. ⓓ CH, Dgs, CP 45, Ac, con 250, CF, 5 BGf, 1 st, Dis. **£** BB £40·50, DB £54·50, WB, ①, cc 1 2 3 4 5 6, Dep (Xmas).

Repairer: Buckhurst Hill Garages Ltd, High Rd. ✆ 01-504 7272.
Rescue Service: Montroe Motors Ltd, Epping New Rd. ✆ 01-504 1171.

BUCKINGHAM Buckinghamshire. Map 15C
Pop 5,422. Aylesbury 16, London 56, Banbury 17, Bedford 27, Bicester 11, Bletchley 11, Chipping Norton 25, Towcester 11.
EC Thur. **MD** Tue, Sat. **Golf** Buckingham 18h. **See** Manor House, Georgian Town Hall, Old Gaol (1758), 15th cent Chantry Chapel.

★★**White Hart** (TH), *Market Sq, MK18 1NL.* ✆ (0280) 815151. C. ⊷ 19 bedrs, 16 bp, 3 bps, TV, Dgs. ✗ a l c, mc, LD 9.30. ⓓ CH, Dgs, CP 30, Ac, con 90, CF, 1 st. **£** BB £37, DB £51, WB, ①, cc 1 2 3 4 5 6, Dep (Xmas).

MC Repairer: Marriott, G, 18 High St. ✆ (0280) 3153.
Rescue Service: Marriott, G, 18 High St. ✆ (0280) 3153.
Phillips & Sons (Buckingham) Ltd. ✆ (0280) 2121.

BUCKLAND-IN-THE-MOOR Devon. Map 3D
Pop 150, Ashburton 3½, London 190, Newton Abbot 10, Tavistock 18, Totnes 11.

Golf Manor House 18h. **See** 12th cent Church, 1,283 ft Beacon.
◨⊞★**Buckland Hall** (RI), *TQ13 7HL.* ✆ Ashburton (0364) 52679. Open Apr–Oct. C 8. ⊷ 6 bedrs, 5 bp, 1 bps, Dgs. ✗ mc, LD 8. ⓓ CH, TV, CP 20. **£** BB £15–£20, DB £30–£38, WT £138–£168, DT £23–£27, WB, ②, Bk £2·75, D £7·50, Dep a.

BUCKLOW HILL Cheshire. Map 20B
Pop 1,018. Knutsford 3½, London 177, M56 Motorway 2, Altrincham 4, Northwich 8½, Warrington 9.
Golf Mere G and CC 18h. **See** Tatton Park (Georgian house, gardens) (NT).

★★★**M Swan,** *Chester Rd, WA16 6RD.* ✆ (0565) 830295. RS Xmas. C. ⊷ 74 bedrs, 74 bp, TV, Dgs. ✗ a l c, mc, at, LD 9.45. ⓓ N, CH, CP 200, Ac, con 40, CF, 28 BGf, 2 st. **£** BB fr £38·50, DB fr £49·50, WB, ①, cc 1 2 3 5 6, Dep.

Rescue Service: Bucklow Garages Ltd. ✆ (0565) 830327.

BUDE Cornwall. Map 3A
Pop 6,783. Holsworthy 9½, London 220, Bideford 25, Camelford 17, Launceston 18.
EC Thur. **Golf** Bude and North Cornwall 18h. **See** Compass Hill (Tower), Poughill Church.
ⓘ The Castle. ✆ Bude (0288) 4240.

★★★**Grenville,** *Belle Vue, EX23 8JP.* ✆ (0288) 2121. Open May–Oct & Xmas. C. ⊷ 71 bedrs, 49 bp, 2 bps, 6 ba, Dgs. ✗ mc, at, LD 9. ⓓ Lt, N, TV, CP 70, G 10, sp, con 20, CF, 3 BGf. **£** BB £24·20, DB £48·40, ①, cc 1 2 3 5.
★★★**Hartland,** *Hartland Ter, EX23 8JY.* ✆ (0288) 2509. Open Apr–Oct. C. ⊷ 30 bedrs, 21 bp, 2 bps, 2 ba, TV, Dgs. ✗ a l c, mc, at, LD 8.30. ⓓ Lt, CH, CP 30, Ac, sp, con 150, CF. **£** BB £17·25–£21·80, DB £34·50–£43·60, WT £159–£199, DT £29·75–£33, Bk £3·75, L £5·50, D £7, Dep a.
★★★**Strand** (TH), *The Strand, EX23 8RA.* ✆ (0288) 3222. C. ⊷ 40 bedrs, 37 bp, 3 bps, TV, Dgs. ✗ a l c, mc, at, LD 9. ⓓ Lt, N, CH, Dgs, CP 60, Ac, con 100, CF, 2 st. **£** BB £33·50, DB £52·50, WB, ①, cc 1 2 3 4 5 6, Dep (Xmas).
★★**Burn Court** (R), *Burn View, EX23 8DB.* ✆ (0288) 2872. Closed Jan, RS winter months, C5. ⊷ 34 bedrs, 6 bp, 16 bps, 4 ba. ✗ a l c, LD 8. ⓓ CH, TV, CP 12, Ac, con 100, 1 st. **£** BB £10·50–£15·90, DB £21–£36, DBB £16–£23·90, WB, ②, Bk £4·30, L £5, D £6·50, cc 1 2 3 6, Dep.
★**Camelot,** *Downs View, EX23 8RS.* ✆ (0288) 2361. C. ⊷ 13 bedrs, 9 bps, Dgs. ⓓ CH, TV, Dgs, CP 12, CF, 2 BGf, 1 st, Dis. **£** BB £9·50–£12·25, DB £19–£37, WT (b) £96·50–£126, DT (b) £14·50–£18·50, ①, Bk £3·95, L £5·95, D £6·95, cc 1 3.
◨★**Edgcumbe** (R), *Summerleaze Cres, EX23 8HJ.* ✆ (0288) 3846. Open Mar–Oct. C. ⊷ 15 bedrs, 4 bps, 5 sh, 2 ba, Dgs. ✗ mc, at, LD 7.30. ⓓ ch, TV, Dgs, CP 11, Ac, CF. **£** BB £9·75–£11·75, DB £19·50–£21·50, DBB £14·50–£16·50, WB, ①, Bk £2·50, L £1·95, D £4·75.
◨★**Maer Lodge** (R), *Maer Down, EX23 8NG.* ✆ (0288) 3306. Open Apr–Oct & Xmas. C. ⊷ 20 bedrs, 5 bps, 2 sh, 4 ba, TV, Dgs. ✗ mc, at, LD 7.30. ⓓ TV, ns, CP 30, Ac, CF, 5 BGf, 0 st, Dis. **£** BB £9·50–£23·50, DB £12–£27, DBB £10–£16·50, ②, Bk £3, D £6, cc 1 3, Dep a.
★**Meva-Gwin** (R), *Upton, Bede Haven, EX23 0LY.* ✆ (0288) 2347. Open Mar–Oct. C. ⊷ 17 bedrs, 4 bp, 1 bps, 4 ba. ✗ mc, at, LD 6.30. ⓓ CH, TV, CP 44, Ac, CF, 1 st. **£** BB £9·20–£10·35, DB £18·40–£24·15, WT (b) £80·50–£92, WB, ①, D £4·31, Dep.
★**St. Margaret's** (R), *Killerton Rd, EX23 8EN.* ✆ (0288) 2252. C. ⊷ 10 bedrs, 3 bp,

1 sh, 3 ba, TV, Dgs. ✘ a l c, mc, LD 8.30.
🏰 CH, TV, CP 6, CF. £ BB £10–£14, DB
£20–£24, WT £80–£100, DT £17–£20, WB,
Ⓣ, Bk £2·50, L £3·50, D £5·95, cc 1 3.
Flexbury Hall, G, xy (Unl), *Poughill Rd,
EX23 8NX.* ☎ (0288) 2107. Open Mar–
Oct. C. ✆ 7 bedrs, 2 ba, Dgs. 🏰 TV, Dgs,
CF. £ BB £7–£7·75, DB £14–£15·50, WT
(b) £62·50–£72, DT (b) £10·50–£11·50, Ⓣ.
Pencarrol, G, z (Unl), *21 Downs View,
EX23 8RF.* ☎ (0288) 2478. Closed Xmas.
C. ✆ 9 bedrs, 2 ba, Dgs. 🏰 TV, Dgs, U 1,
CF, 3 st. £ BB £6–£7·50, DB £12–£15, WT
(b) £63–£73, DT (b) £9·50–£11, Ⓣ.
Sandiways, PH, x (Rl), *35 Downs View,
EX23 8RG.* ☎ (0288) 2073. C3, ✆ 11
bedrs, 1 sh, 2 ba. ✘ a l c. 🏰 ch, TV, CP 10,
CF, 2 st. £ BB £7–£8, DB £14–£18, WT (b)
£58–£75, DT (b) £10·50–£11·50, Ⓣ.
Surf Motel (Rl), *Maer Down, EX23 8NG.*
☎ (0288) 3584.
Treriven, PH, z (Rl), *24 Ocean View Rd,
EX23 8NN.* ☎ (0288) 3177. Open Mar–
Oct, C4. ✆ 5 bedrs, 1 ba. 🏰 CH, TV, CP 3,
1 st. £ BB £7·50–£9·50, DB £15–£19, WT
(b) £75–£95, DT (b) £11·50–£14·50, Ⓣ, D
£5.

Repairers: Cann Medland & Co Ltd, The
Garage, Bencoolen Rd. ☎ (0288) 2146.
Station Garage. ☎ (0288) 2255.
Specialist Battery Repairer: Cann
Medland & Co Ltd, Bencoolen Rd.
☎ (0288) 2146.
Rescue Service: Edwards of Bude, Bude
Ford, Bencoolen Rd. ☎ (0288) 2914.
Malibu Motors Ltd, Vicarage Rd.
☎ (0288) 2924.
Sam Edward & Co Ltd, Flexbury Garage.
☎ (0288) 2008.
Widemouth Service Station, Widemouth
Bay. ☎ Widemouth Bay (028 885) 279.

BUDLEIGH SALTERTON Devon.
Map 4F
Pop 4,500, Honiton 16, London 169,
Exeter 13, Lyme Regis 23, Tiverton 26.
EC Thur. **Golf** East Budleigh 18h. **See**
"Octagon", location of Millais's picture of
"Boyhood of Raleigh", Art Centre and
Museum, Hayes Barton (birthplace of Sir
Walter Raleigh) 2 m NW, Bicton Gardens
(East Budleigh).
🄿 Rolle Mews Car Park, Fore St.
☎ Budleigh Salterton (039 54) 5275.

★★★**Rosemullion,** *Cliff Rd, EX9 6JX.*
☎ (039 54) 2288.
★★**Long Range** (Unl) *Vales Rd, EX9
6HS.* ☎ (039 54) 3321. Open Apr–Oct, C4.
✆ 10 bedrs, 1 bp, 2 ba. ✘ mc, at, LD 8.
🏰 CH, TV, CP 8, U 2, 1 st. £ BB £10–£12,
DB £20–£24, WT £87–£95, DBB £15–£17,
Ⓩ, Bk £3, L £4·50, D £5·50.
★★**Southlands** (R), *9 Marine Parade,
EX9 6NS.* ☎ (039 54) 3497. C. ✆ 20
bedrs, 3 bp, 5 ba, Dgs. ✘ mc, at. 🏰 ch, TV,
CP 18, CF, 1 BGf, 2 st. £ BB £13·50–
£16·25, DB £27–£32·50, WT fr £132·50,
DT fr £23·40, WB, Ⓣ, Bk £2·75, L £3·95, D
£5·95, cc 3, Dep a.
Tidwell House, H, xy, (R), *Knowle, EX9
7AG.* ☎ (039 54) 2444. C. ✆ 9 bedrs, 1 bp,
2 sh, 4 ba, Dgs. 🏰 CH, TV, Dgs, CP 16, G 4,
CF, 12 st. £ BB £13·50–£15, DB £27–£32,
WT (b) £105–£110·25, DT (b) £17–
£18·85, Ⓣ, D £5·50.

Rescue Service: C T Staddon Ltd, High St.
☎ (039 54) 2277.
Knowle Garage, Knowle.
☎ (039 54) 5650.

BUDOCK VEAN Cornwall. Map 2F
Pop 960. Truro 13, London 267, Falmouth
5½, Helston 8, Redruth 13.
Golf Budock Vean Hotel 9h, Falmouth
18h.

■⬛★★★**Budock Vean,** *TR11 5LG.*
☎ Falmouth (0326) 250288. RS Jan–Feb,
C5. ✆ 51 bedrs, 51 bp. ✘ a l c, mc, at, LD
8.45. 🏰 Lt, N, CH, TV, ns, CP 100, Ac, sp,
gc, tc, con 50, CF, 6 BGf, 8 st. £ DBB £29–
£39·95, WB, Ⓩ, 10%, L £6, D £12,
cc 1 2 3 4 5, Dep a.

BUGBROOKE Northamptonshire.
M. Area 15C
6 m WSW of Northampton, Towcester 7,
London 69, M1 Motorway 3, Banbury 19,
Daventry 8.
See Grand Union Canal.

Rescue Service: J R Clayton Motors,
Butts Hill Garage. ☎ Northampton
(0604) 830704.

BULPHAN Essex. Maps 10A & 17F
Pop 700. London 25, Brentwood 7,
Dartford/Purfleet Tunnel 19½, Rainham 9,
Romford 11, Southend 16.
EC Wed. **Golf** Orsett 18h. **See** 14th cent
Church, 15th cent Old Plough House, 16th
cent Garlesters.

★★ **M Ye Olde Plough House** (R),
Brentwood Rd (off M25), RM14 3SR.
☎ Grays Thurrock (0375) 891592. C.
✆ 65 bedrs, 55 bp, 10 bps, TV, Dgs.
✘ a l c, mc, LD 10. 🏰 N, CH, CP 200, G 12,
Ac, sp, tc, sol, con 180, CF, 55 BGf, 2 st. £
BB fr £26, DB fr £32, WB, Ⓣ, Bk £4, L
£6·50, D £8·50, cc 1 2 3 5.

BUNGAY Suffolk. Map 16B
Pop 4,106. Scole 15, London 110, East
Dereham 31, Great Yarmouth 19,
Lowestoft 14, Norwich 15, Saxmundham
19.
EC Wed. **MD** Thur. **Golf** Bungay Common
18h. **See** Castle ruins, 17th cent Butter
Cross, St Mary's Church, Holy Trinity
Church, "Black Dog" sign.

Rescue Service: Belcher's Garage
(Bungay) Ltd, Scales St. ☎ (0986) 2467.

BUNWELL Norfolk. Map 16D.
Pop 758. Thetford 18, London 99, Bury St
Edmunds 26, East Dereham 18, Lowestoft
31, Norwich 12, Scole 12, Stowmarket 27,
Swaffham 25.
EC Wed. **Golf** Diss 9h. **See** 15th cent
Church.

■⬛★★★**Bunwell Manor,** *NOR 0IX.*
☎ (095 389) 317. Closed Xmas. C. ✆ 12
bedrs, 6 bp, 5 bps, 1 ba, TV, Dgs. ✘ a l c,
mc, at. 🏰 CH, TV, Dgs, CP 30, CF, 2 BGf, 3
st. £ BB £16–£18, DB £27–£28, DBB £20–
£21, WB, Ⓩ, 5%, Bk £4·50, L £5·50, D
£7·50, cc 1 2 3, Dep a.

Rescue Service: Days of Bunwell, The
Street. ☎ (095 389) 320.

BURFORD Oxfordshire. Map 14F
Pop 1,174. Oxford 20, London 75,
Bicester 26, Cheltenham 22, Chipping
Norton 11, Cirencester 17, Faringdon 12,
Gloucester 29, Stow-on-the-Wold 10,
Swindon 19.
EC Wed. **Golf** Burford 18h. **See** Church of
St John, old Almshouses, small museum in
15th cent Tolsey House, Old Houses, Cotswold
Wild Life Park 2 m S.

■★★**Bull,** *High St, OX8 4RH.*
☎ (099 382) 2220. C. ✆ 15 bedrs, 8 bp, 1
bps, 1 ba. ✘ a l c, mc, at, LD 9.30. 🏰 CH,
TV, Dgs, CP 8, U 3, Ac, con 12, 0 st. £ BBc
£15–£24, DBc £29·50–£35, WB, Ⓣ, Bk
£3·50, cc 3.
★★**Golden Pheasant,** *High St, OX8 4RJ.*
☎ (099 382) 3223. C. ✆ 12 bedrs, 4 bp, 8
bps, TV, Dgs. ✘ mc, at, LD 9.30. 🏰 CH,
Dgs, CP 12, con 2, CF, 2 BGf, 0 st, Dis.
£ BB £20–£28, DB £30–£45, DBB £27–
£30, WB, Ⓣ, Bk £4, L £4, D £9·50, cc 1 3.
★★**Inn For All Seasons,** The
Barringtons, OX8 4TN. ☎ Windrush
(045 14) 324.

Rescue Service: Vick's Byway Garage,
Guildenford St. ☎ (099 382) 3142.

BURGESS HILL West Sussex. Map 7D
Pop 23,635. Redhill 22, London 42,
Brighton 10, Crawley 13, Haslemere 32,
Haywards Heath 3½, Horsham 14, Lewes
10, Reigate 22, Petworth 25, Pulborough
21, Uckfield 12, Worthing 18.
MD Wed, Sat. **Golf** Pyecombe 18h. **See**
Parish Church of St John, Sussex Weald,
Ditchling Common (1 m E).

Repairer: Caffyns Ltd, Station Parade and
Mill Rd. ☎ (044 46) 2183.
Rescue Service: Cants Lane Garage,
Cants La. ☎ (044 46) 2037 and
(044 46) 41844.

BURGH HEATH Surrey. Map 7A
1½ S of Banstead, Sutton 4, London 15,
M25 Motorway 4½, Epsom 3, Dorking 8,
Reigate 5½, Croydon 8.

■★★ **M Pickard,** *Brighton Rd, KT20
6BW.* ☎ (073 73) 53355. C. ✆ 44 bedrs,
44 bp, TV, Dgs. ✘ a l c, mc, at, LD 10. 🏰 N,
CH, ns, CP 150, Ac, con 150, CF, 1 BGf, 3
st. £ BB £34–£39, DB £44–£50, WB, Ⓩ
15%, Bk £2·85, L £5·50, D £7·50,
cc 1 2 3 5 6, Dep b.

BURLESCOMBE Devon. Map 4D
Pop 738. Taunton 11, London 155, Exeter
21, Honiton 13, Ilminster 22, Tiverton 10.
Golf Tiverton 18h. **See** Ayshford Court
and Chapel, 14th cent Church,
Canonsleigh.

Rescue Service: Lamb Hill Garage.
☎ Craddock (0884) 40664.

BURLEY Hampshire. Map 6E
Pop 1,400. Lyndhurst 7, London 91,
Bournemouth 13, Lymington 9½,
Ringwood 5.
Golf Burley 9h. **See** Cricket Green.

■⬛★★★**Burley Manor,** *BH24 4BS.*
☎ (042 53) 3314. C. ✆ 22 bedrs, 21 bp, 1
bps, 1 ba, TV, Dgs. ✘ a l c, mc, at, LD 9.30.
🏰 CH, Dgs, CP 40, Ac, sp, rf, con 60, CF, 2
st. £ BB fr £28, DB fr £38, WB, Ⓩ, Bk £3·50,
D £8·95, cc 1 2 3 5 6, Dep b.
■★★**Moorhill House** (R), *BH24 4AG.*
☎ (042 53) 3285. C. ✆ 24 bedrs, 15 bp, 6
bps, 2 sh, 1 ba, ns, TV, Dgs. ✘ a l c, mc, at,
LD 8.45. 🏰 CH, TV, CP 25, U 2, G 2, sp, sb,
sol, con 20, CF, 3 BGf, 0 st, Dis. £ BB £16–
£24, DB £28–£40, WT £140–£175, WB, Ⓣ,
Bk £3, L £3, D £7, cc 1 2 3 5 6, Dep a.
★**Tree House,** (R). *The Cross, BH24 4BA.*
☎ (042 53) 3448. Open Mar–Nov. C3. ✆ 8
bedrs, 4 bps, 2 ba, TV. ✘ mc, at, LD 7.
🏰 CH, CP 12, 0 st. £ BB £15·25–£17·95,
DB £24·50–£29·90, DT £25–£30·95, WB,
Ⓣ, Bk £3·25, L £3·65, D £6·50, cc 1 2 3 5,
Dep a.

Rescue Service: Dawson Engineering
(Burley) Ltd, Pound La. ☎ (042 53) 2188.

BURNHAM MARKET Norfolk. Map
16C
Pop 943. King's Lynn 22, London 121,
Cromer 26, Fakenham 10.
EC Wed. **Golf** Royal West Norfolk,
Brancaster 18h. **See** Dec and Perp
Church, old houses, Burnham Thorpe
Church (Nelson relics), Scolt Head Bird
Sanctuary and Nature Reserve, Holkham
Hall 4 m E.

Rescue Service: Hill & Osborne (Norfolk)
Ltd. ☎ (032 873) 621.

BURNHAM-ON-CROUCH Essex.
Maps 10A and 17D
Pop 6,500. Romford 20, London 45,
Braintree 25, Brentwood 24, Chelmsford
20, Colchester 28, Dartford Tunnel 31,
Southend 24.
EC Wed. **Golf** Burnham-on-Crouch 9h.
See St Mary's Church (Norman Font).

★**Ye Olde White Harte,** *CM0 8AS.*
☎ Maldon (0621) 782106. Closed Xmas.
C. ⌘ 15 bedrs, 3 bp, 3 ba, Dgs. ✗ a l c, mc,
LD 9. ❐ CH, TV, CP 13, con 20, CF. £ BB fr
£13·75, DB fr £23·50, WT fr £125, ❑, Bk
£3·50, L £5, D £5·50, Dep a.

BURNHAM-ON-SEA Somerset. Map
5C
Pop 15,000 (inc Highbridge). Wells 17,
London 140, Bath 39, Bridgwater 9,
Bristol 27, Glastonbury 18, Radstock 32,
Weston-super-Mare 11.
EC Wed. **MD** Mon. **Golf** Burnham and
Berrow 18h. **See** St Andrew's Church
with marble altarpiece by Inigo Jones,
Gore Sands, Brean Down.
▣ Berrow Rd. ☎ Burnham-on-Sea
(0278) 787852.

★★**Dunstan House,** *Love La, TA8 1EU.*
☎ (0278) 784343. C. ⌘ 10 bedrs, 2 bp, 2
bps, 2 ba, TV, Dgs. ✗ a l c, mc, LD 10.
❐ CH, TV, Dgs, CP 40, Ac, con 40, CF, 1 st.
£ BB fr £13, DB fr £24, WB, ❷, 5%, Bk
£1·85, D £3·30, cc 1 2 3 5.▲

★★**Royal Clarence,** *The Esplanade, TA8
1BQ.* ☎ (0278) 783138. C. ⌘ 14 bedrs, 3
bp, 1 bps, 5 ba, TV, Dgs. ✗ a l c, mc, LD
8.30. ❐ CH, TV, CP 10, Ac, con, CF, 5 st.
£ BB £12·50–£13·50, DB £24–£25, WT
£120, DT £19·50, ❑, Bk £2·25, L £3·50, D
£4·25, cc 1 2 3 5, Dep.

★**Pine Grange** (R), *27 Berrow Rd, TA8
2EY.* ☎ (0278) 784214. Closed Xmas &
Jan. C. ⌘ 6 bedrs, 2 ba, Dgs. ✗ mc, at, LD
7.30. ❐ CH, TV, CP 10, U 1, CF, 0 st. £ BB
£11, DB £22, DBB £17, ❑, Bk £3·50, L
£4·50, D £6·50, Dep a.

★**Richmond** (R) *32 Berrow Rd, TA8 2EX.*
☎ (0278) 782984. C. ⌘ 12 bedrs, 4 bp, 2
bps, 1 ba, TV, Dgs. ✗ mc, at, LD 7.45.
❐ ch, TV, Dgs, CP 6, CF, 1 BGf, 3 st. £ BB fr
f9. DB fr £17, DBB fr £85, ❑, Bk £3, L
£3·50, D £5·50, cc 1 3, Dep a.
Harwood House, G, z, *123 Berrow Rd,
TA8 2PH.* ☎ (0278) 787824.

Rescue Service: Tucker's Garage Ltd,
Victoria St. ☎ (0278) 783106.

BURNLEY Lancashire. Map 27B
Pop 93,620. Rochdale 14, London 206,
Blackburn 11, Bolton 19, Bradford 25,
Bury 15, Settle 23, Skipton 18, Todmorden
8½, Whalley 8.
EC Tue. **MD** Mon, Thur, Sat. **Golf**
Towneley 18h. **See** St Peter's Church,

16th–17th cent Towneley Hall (now Art
Gallery and Museum).

★★★**M Keirby,** *Kierby Walk, BB1 2DH.*
☎ (0282) 27611. C. ⌘ 49 bedrs, 49 bp,
TV, Dgs. ✗ a l c, mc, at, LD 10. ❐ Lt, N, CH,
TV, CP 40, G 15, con 300, CF, 0 st. £ BB
£31·50, DB £54·50, DBB £38·45, WB, ❑,
Bk £5·80, L £4·10, D £6·95, cc 1 2 3 5,
Dep b.

★★**Rosehill** (R), *Rosehill Av, BB11 2PW.*
☎ (0282) 53931. C. ⌘ 20 bedrs, 10 bp, 10
bps, TV. ✗ a l c, mc, at, LD 9.30. ❐ N, CH,
CP 60, con 20, CF, 6 BGf, 1 st, Dis. £ BB
£24–£26, DB £35, DT £37–£39, WB, ❑, Bk
£3, L £4·50, D £7·50, cc 1 2 3, Dep b.▲
Oaks *under construction.*

Repairer: Holden & Hartley (Burnley) Ltd,
Accrington Rd. ☎ (0282) 27321.

BURNOPFIELD Durham. Map 32C
Pop 3,950. West Auckland 23, London
271, Corbridge 14, Durham 13, Hexham
17, Middleton-in-Teesdale 27, Newcastle
upon Tyne 8, West Auckland 23.
EC Wed. **Golf** Hobson Municipal 18h. **See**
Gibside Chapel.

Rescue Service: Pickering Nook Garage.
☎ (0207) 70248.

BURNSALL North Yorkshire. Map 27A
Pop 110. Ilkley 12, London 219,
Grassington 3, Pateley Bridge 10, Skipton
9.
EC Thur. **Golf** Skipton 12h. **See** 17th cent
Grammar School, May pole, stocks in
churchyard.

▣★★**Fell,** *BD23 6BT.* ☎ (075 672) 209.
Closed mid Dec–end Feb. C. ⌘ 16 bedrs,
12 bp, 1 bps, 1 ba. ✗ a l c, mc, LD 9. ❐ CH,
TV, CP 60, Ac, con 20, CF, 1 st. £ BB £16–
£23, DB £23–£36, WT £146–£170, DT
£23–£29, WB, ❑, Bk £3·50, L £5, D £8,
cc 1 3.

★★**Red Lion,** *BD23 6BU.*
☎ (075 672) 204. Closed Dec. C. ⌘ 8
bedrs, 3 ba, annexe 4 bedrs, 2 bp, 2 bps,
TV. ✗ mc, LD 9. ❐ CH, TV, CP 40, Ac, CF.
£ BB £15, DB £22–£34, WB, ❷, 10%, Bk
£3·50, L £4·10, D £6·20, Dep a.

BURNT YATES North Yorkshire. Map
25E
Pop 400. Harrogate 7, London 211,
Pateley Bridge 7½, Scotch Corner 35,
Thirsk 21, York 25.
Golf Harrogate 18h.

★★**M Bay Horse Inn,** *HG3 3EJ.*
☎ Harrogate (0423) 770230. RS Oct–Apr.
C. ⌘ 6 bedrs, 6 bps, annexe 10 bedrs, 10
bps, TV, Dgs. ✗ a l c, mc, LD 9.30. ❐ CH,
Dgs, CP 70, Ac, con 20, CF, 5 BGf, 1 st, Dis.
£ BB £15, DB £30, WB, ❑, Bk £3·50, L £5,
D £5·95.

BURRINGTON Devon. Map 4A
Pop 384. Tiverton 23, London 186,
Barnstaple 13, Chulmleigh 4, Okehampton
19, South Molton 10.
EC Sat. **Golf** Chulmleigh 9h.

▣★★★**Northcote Manor** *EX37 9LZ.*
☎ High Bickington (0769) 60501. Closed
Nov–Feb, Open Xmas. C. ⌘ 11 bedrs, 11
bp, TV. ✗ a l c, mc, at, LD 8.15. ❐ CH, CP
20, con 40, CF, 4 st. £ BB £22–£24, DB
£44–£48, WT £210–£224, DT £43–£39,
WB, ❑, Bk £4, L £6, D £10, cc 1 2 3 5 6.

Rescue Service: Riverside Garage.
☎ (0769) 80765.

BURSCOUGH Lancashire. Map 20E
Pop 4,997. Ormskirk 2, London 201,
Formby 4½, Skelmersdale 5, Southport 11.
EC Wed. **See** Church.

Repairer: Rob Hughes Recovery, Meadow
La, Lathom. ☎ (0704) 893395.

BURSLEM Staffordshire. Map 19D
Stoke-on-Trent 3½, London 156,
Congleton 9½, Leek 9, Nantwich 15,
Newcastle-under-Lyme 3½, Sandbach 10.
Golf Burslem 9h. **See** Old Town Hall,
Wedgwood Institute, Royal Doulton
Works (by appmt).

▣★★**George,** *Swan Sq, ST6 2AE.*
☎ Stoke-on-Trent (0782) 84021. C. ⌘ 36
bedrs, 5 bp, 8 ba, TV, Dgs. ✗ mc, at, LD 9.
❐ Lt, N, CH, Dgs, CP 6, G 8, Ac, con 300,
CF, 6 st. £ BB £16–£20, DB £26–£35, WB,
❑, Bk £4·25, L £1, D £6, cc 1 2 3 4 5 6,
Dep b.

BURTON BRADSTOCK Dorset. Map
5E
Pop 759. Dorchester 14, London 136,
Axminster 15, Crewkerne 16, Lyme Regis
12, Sherborne 29, Weymouth 16.
Golf Bridport and West Dorset 18h. **See**
15th cent Church, Cliffs-view of Chesil
Bank.

Rescue Service: Cheneys Garage, The
Garage. ☎ (0308) 897579.

BURTON-ON-TRENT Staffordshire.
Map 22E
Pop 47,616. Ashby-de-la-Zouch 9, London
122, Ashbourne 19, Atherstone 19, Derby
11, Lichfield 13, Stafford 26, Tamworth
15, Uttoxeter 13.
MD Thur, Sat. **Golf** Bretby, Branston 18h.
See Parish Church (site of Abbey
Church), Abbey ruins, Museum and Art
Gallery, Hoar Cross Hall with adj Church
of The Holy Angels at Hoar Cross.
▣ Town Hall. ☎ Burton-on-Trent
(0283) 45454.

▣★★★★**Newton Park,** *Newton Solney,
Derbys, DE15 0SS.* ☎ (0283) 703568.
Closed Xmas. C. ⌘ 27 bedrs, 26 bp, 1 bps,
3 ba, TV, Dgs. ✗ a l c, mc, at, LD 9.30. ❐ N,
CH, TV, CP 200, Ac, con 100, CF, 1 st. £ BB
£33·75, BD £44·50, DBB £42·35, WB, ❑,
Bk £4·25, L £5·60, D £8·60, cc 1 2 3 4 5,
Dep b.

★★**Midland,** *Station St, DE14 1BN.*
☎ (0283) 68723.

BURWASH East Sussex. Maps 7F and
10E
Pop 2,300. Tunbridge Wells 12, London
49, Eastbourne 20, Hastings 15, Hurst
Green 4½, Lewes 20, Maidstone 23,
Uckfield 14.
EC Wed. **Golf** Dale Hill, Ticehurst 18h.
See Bateman's (17th cent house once
home of Rudyard Kipling, Nat Trust), 11th
cent Church.

★★**M Burwash,** *High St, TN19 7HT.*
☎ (0435) 882603. RS Xmas Day. C. ⌘ 8
bedrs, 8 bp, TV, Dgs. ✗ a l c, mc, LD 9.30.
❐ N, CH, Dgs, CP 50, G 8, CF, 8 BGf, 1 st,
Dis. £ BBc £17, DBc £24, ❑, Bk £2·50, L
£5·50, D £7, cc 1 3 6, Dep b.
Admiral Vernon l, x, *Etchingham Rd,
TN19 78J.* ☎ (0435) 882230. C10. ⌘ 5
bedrs, 1 bp, TV. ✗ a l c. ❐ CH, TV, Dgs, CP
30, U 1, G 1, 3 st. £ BB £12–£14, DB £24–
£27, WT (b) fr £110, DT (b) fr £18, ❑, Bk
£3·50, L £4·50, D £6·50.

Bell Inn, l, x, *High St TN19 7EH.*
☎ (0435) 882304. Closed Xmas. C. ⊷ 5
bedrs, 1 ba, Dgs. ✗ a l c. ⓓ ch, Dgs, CP 15,
CF, 1 st. £ DB £21, WT (c) £66, ②, L £4·20,
D £5·10, cc 1 3.

BURWELL Cambridgeshire. Map 16F
Pop 4,290. Cambridge 11, London 66, Ely
12, Newmarket 4½.
EC Wed. **Golf** Newmarket 18h. **See** St
Mary's Church, Devil's Dyke.

Rescue Service: Browns of Burwell,
Central Service Station, 7 North St.
☎ Newmarket (0638) 741306.

BURY Gtr Manchester (Lancashire). Map
20A
See also RAMSBOTTOM
Pop 69,000. Manchester 8, London 192,
M66 Motorway 1½, Blackburn 15, Bolton
6, Burnley 15, Oldham 10, Rochdale 6,
Walkden 8, Whalley 18.
EC Tue. **MD** Wed, Fri, Sat. **Golf** Bury 18h.
See Art Gallery and Museum, Regimental
Museum, Statue of Sir Robert Peel, Kay
Memorial and Gardens, Parish Church,
Transport Museum, Wall Paintings.

★★Bolholt, *Walshaw Rd, BL8 1PS.*
☎ 061-764 5239. C. ⊷ 20 bedrs, 10 bp, 8
bps, 1 ba, ns, TV, Dgs. ✗ a l c. ⓓ CH, TV,
Dgs, CP 150, tc, pf, con 100, CF, 6 BGf, 1
st, Dis. £ BB £19–£25, DB £26–£30, DBB
£25–£31, WB, ①, Bk £2·75, L £3·50, D
£6·85.

■★Woolfield House (R), *Wash La, BL9
6BJ.* ☎ 061-764 7048. C. ⊷ 13 bedrs, 2
bps, 4 ba, TV. ✗ a l c, mc, at, LD 8.30.
ⓓ CH, TV, CP 30, con 50. £ BB £14–£19,
DB £24–£31, DBB £20·55–£25·55, WB, ①,
Bk £3·50, D £6·55, Dep b.

Repairer: H & J Quick Ltd, George St.
☎ 061-764 5454.
Rescue Service: Auty & Lees Ltd, 284 The
Rock. ☎ 061-764 2434.
James Street Motors, 25 James St.
☎ 061-764 5421.
Schofield, T Son & Co (Bury) Ltd,
Blackford Bridge, Manchester Rd.
☎ 061-766 2404.
White House Service Station, Manchester
Rd. ☎ 061-766 2489.

BURY West Sussex
See PULBOROUGH

BURY ST EDMUNDS Suffolk. Map 17C
Pop 31,000. Sudbury 16, London 74, Ely
24, Harwich 41, Haverhill 19, King's Lynn
41, Newmarket 14, Norwich 39, Scole 22,
Stowmarket 14, Thetford 12, Wisbech 44.
EC Thur. **MD** Wed, Sat. **Golf** Bury St
Edmunds 18h. **See** Cathedral Church of
St James, St Edmund's Abbey (remains of
the most important of the Benedictine
abbeys), St Mary's Church contains tomb
of Mary Tudor, Angel Corner (museum of
clocks and watches), Angel Hotel (assoc
Pickwick), Guildhall, restored Theatre
Royal, Unitarian Chapel, Cupola House,
Moyse's Hall Museum, Ickworth House
3 m SW, West Stow Anglo Saxon Village.
Ⓘ Abbey Gdns, Angel Hill. ☎ Bury St
Edmunds (0284) 64667.

★★★Angel, *Angel Hill, IP33 1LT.*
☎ (0284) 3926. C. ⊷ 41 bedrs, 34 bp, 1
bps, 3 ba, TV, Dgs. ✗ a l c, mc, at, LD 9.45
(10.15 Sat). ⓓ N, CH, Dgs, G 20, CP, con
120, CF, 1 st. £ BB £20–£40, DB £40–£54,
①, Bk £5, L £8, D £16, cc 1 2 3 4 5 6.

★★Everards, *Cornhill, IP33 1BD.*
☎ (0284) 5384. C. ⊷ 16 bedrs, 3 bp, 2
bps, 4 ba, TV. ✗ a l c, mc, LD 9.30. ⓓ N,
CH, CP 14, G 2, Ac, con 150, CF, 2 st. £ BB
£20–£27, DB £30–£38, ①, Bk £4·75, L
£6·25, D £6·25, cc 1 3 5 6, Dep b.

★★Suffolk (TH), *Buttermarket, IP33 1DC.*
☎ (0284) 3995. C. ⊷ 41 bedrs, 13 bp, 8
ba, TV, Dgs. ✗ mc, LD 9.30. ⓓ N, CH, Dgs,
CP 16, Ac, CF, 1 st. £ BB £31–£34, DB
£41–£50·50, WB, ①, cc 1 2 3 4 5 6, Dep
(Xmas).

Ripley House, H, z (R), *2 Northgate Av.*
☎ (0284) 4257.▲
Swan, G, z (Unl), *11 Northgate St, IP33
1HQ.* ☎ (0284) 2678. C. ⊷ 9 bedrs, 2 ba,
Dgs. ⓓ CH, TV, Dgs, CF, 2 st. £ BB £10–
£10·50, DB £19–£20, ①.

MC Repairer: Bowers, C. J & Son Ltd, 98
Risbygate St. ☎ (0284) 4635.
Rescue Service: Cowies (GM), Cotton La.
☎ (0284) 5621.

BUSHEY Hertfordshire. Map 15F
Pop 23,017. London 14, M1 Motorway 3,
Barnet 7½, Dunstable 20, Harrow 5,
Hatfield 12, Luton 17, St Albans 9,
Watford 2½.
EC Wed. **Golf** Bushey Hall 18h.

★★★★M Ladbroke, *Watford By-Pass,
WD2 8HR.* ☎ Watford (0923) 35881. RS
Xmas. C. ⊷ 155 bedrs, 155 bp, TV. ✗ mc,
at, LD 9.45 (9.30 Sun). ⓓ L t, N, CH, CP
400, Ac, con, CF, 0 st. £ BB £35–£48, DB
£45–£48, WB, ②, Bk £5·75, L £9·50, D
£10·50, cc 1 2 3 4 5 6, Dep b.

■★★M Spider's Web, *Watford By-Pass,
WD2 8HQ.* ☎ 01-950 6211. C. ⊷ 104
bedrs, 104 bp, TV, Dgs. ✗ a l c, LD 9.30.
ⓓ N, CH, TV, Dgs, CP 300, Ac, sp, sb, sol,
gym, con 250, CF, 50 BGf, 2 st. £ BB £20–
£35, DB £30–£45, WB, ①, Bk £4, L £6, D £7,
cc 1 2 3 4 5 6, Dep.

BUTTERMERE Cumbria. Map 26F
Pop 120. Keswick 8½, London 294,
Cockermouth 10, Egremont 18,
Workington 16.
Golf Cockermouth 18h. **See** Crummock
Water, Scale Force (120 ft fall).

★★Bridge, *CA13 9UZ.* ☎ (059 685) 252.
Closed Jan. C. ⊷ 22 bedrs, 17 bp, 3 bps,
Dgs. ✗ a l c, mc, at, LD 9.30. ⓓ N, CH, CP
30, U 2, con 20, CF. £ DBB £24–£27, WB,
②, L £5, D £9·50, Dep a.

BUXTON Derbyshire. Map 22C
Pop 20,797. Ashbourne 20, London 159,
Chapel-en-le-Frith 5½, Chesterfield 23,
Congleton 17, Leek 13, Macclesfield 12,
Matlock 20, Oldham 27, Sheffield 25,
Stockport 18.
EC Wed. **MD** Tue, Sat. **Golf** Buxton and
High Peak 18h. Cavendish 18h. **See** The
Crescent (18th cent houses and Pump
Room), Pavilion Gdns, Corbar Woods and
Cross, Grinlow Woods (Solomon's
Temple), Museum, Cat & Fiddle Inn
4 m SW, Speedwell Cavern 7½ m NE.
Ⓘ Natural Baths, The Crescent. ☎ Buxton
(0298) 5106.

★★★Lee Wood, *Manchester Rd, SK17
6TQ* (A 5002 Road). ☎ (0298) 3002. C.
⊷ 41 bedrs, 29 bp, 12 bps, TV, Dgs.
✗ a l c, mc, at, LD 9. ⓓ L t, N, CH, TV, CP
60, Ac, con 70, CF, 3 st. £ BB £25·50–£27,
DB £36–£39, WT £190–£210, DT £29–£32,
WB, ①, Bk £3·50, L £4, D £8, cc 1 2 3 5 6.

★★★Palace, *Palace Rd, SK17 6AG.*
☎ (0298) 2001. C. ⊷ 120 bedrs, 120 bp,
TV, Dgs. ✗ a l c, mc, at, LD 10. ⓓ L t, N, CH,
TV, CP 200, Ac, sp, sb, sol, gym, con 700,
CF, 0 st. £ WB, ②, cc 1 2 3 5 6.

★★Buckingham, *Burlington Rd, SK17
9AS.* ☎ (0298) 79414. C. ⊷ 30 bedrs, 4
bp, 13 bps, 5 ba, TV, Dgs. ✗ a l c, mc, at, LD
1. CH, TV, CP 30, con 50, CF, 1 st. £ BB £16–
£24, DB £26–£34, WT £135–£195, DT
£21–£23, WB, ②, Bk £2·75, L £4, D £7·95,
cc 1 2 3 5 6.▲

★★St Ann's, *The Crescent, SK17 6BH.*
☎ (0298) 2788.

★★Sandringham, *Broad Walk, SK17
6JT.* ☎ (0298) 3430. Closed Dec 24–Jan
10. C. ⊷ 37 bedrs, 7 bp, 6 bps, 7 ba, TV,
Dgs. ✗ LD 8.15. ⓓ ch, TV, CP 8, Ac, con
60, CF, 4 st. £ BB fr £21, DB £26, DBB
fr £18·50, ①, L £5·50, D £6·50, cc 1 3 6,
Dep b.

ⓓ★Hartington (Rl), *Broad Walk, SK17
6JR.* ☎ (0298) 2638. RS Nov–Apr. C.
⊷ 17 bedrs, 3 bp, 2 bps, 3 ba, TV. ✗ LD 8.
ⓓ ch, TV, CP 15, Ac, CF, 2 BGf, 0 st. £ BB
fr £13, DB fr £22, DBB fr £17, WB, ①, Bk
£3·90, D £6·50, Dep.

Fairhaven, G, z (Unl), *1 Dale Ter,
SK17 6LU.* ☎ (0298) 4481. C. ⊷ 7 bedrs,
1 ba, TV, Dgs. ⓓ CH, TV, Dgs, CF, 2 st.
£ BB £7–£8, DB £14–£16, WT (b) £65–
£74, DT (b) £10–£11, ①.

Guildford, G, z (Unl), *12 Compton Rd,
SK17 9DN.* ☎ (0298) 3985. C. ⊷ 6 bedrs,
2 ba. ⓓ CH, TV, CP 6, CF. £ BB £7, DB £14,
WT (b) £67, DT (b) £10, ①.

Thorn Heyes, PH, y (R), *137 London Rd.*
☎ (0298) 3539. C. ⊷ 7 bedrs, 4 bps, 1 ba,
TV, Dgs. ⓓ CH, TV, Dgs, CP 11, CF. £ BB
£12·50–£14·50, DB £19–£23, WT fr £80,
DT fr £14, ①.

Westminster, PH, z (Rl), *21 Broad Walk,
SK17 6JR.* ☎ (0298) 3929. C. ⊷ 13 bedrs,
1 bp, 2 bps, 3 ba, Dgs. ⓓ ch, TV, CP 12, CF,
2 st. £ BB fr £14, DB fr £18, WT (b) fr £90,
DT (b) fr £14, ①, D £5·50, cc 1.

CAISTER-ON-SEA Norfolk. Map 16A
Pop 6,498. Great Yarmouth 3, London
130, Cromer 31, Norwich 20.
EC Wed. **Golf** Great Yarmouth and
Caister 18h. **See** EE and Perp Church
(monuments to Caister lifeboat men in
churchyard); Caister Castle ruins and
Motor Museum.

Rescue Service: Allen's Garage, 2
Yarmouth Rd. ☎ Gt Yarmouth
(0493) 720212.

CALNE Wiltshire. Map 5B
Pop 10,421. Marlborough 13, London 85,
Chippenham 6, Cirencester 21, Devizes 8½,
Frome 22, Radstock 25, Swindon 16,
Warminster 21, Wells 36.
EC Wed. **MD** Fri. **Golf** North Wilts 18h.
See Trans and EE Church, Old
Almshouses, Town Hall, 18th cent
Coaching Hotel.

★★Lansdowne Strand, *The Strand,
SN11 0JR.* ☎ (0249) 812488. C. ⊷ 19
bedrs, 12 bp, 1 bps, 3 ba, TV. ✗ a l c,
mc, at, LD 9.30. ⓓ ch, CP 15, Ac, con 60,
CF. £ BB fr £21, DB fr £31, WT fr £205, DT
fr £32, WB, ①, Bk £3·50, L £5·50, D £7·50,
cc 1 3 4·5.

Rescue Service: Hilmarton Garage,
Hilmarton. ☎ Hilmarton (024 976) 259.

CAM Gloucestershire. M.Area 13F
Pop 7,574. Tetbury 10, London 108, Bath
27, Bristol 23, Chepstow 22, Chippenham
23, Gloucester 14, Stow-on-the-Wold 37.
EC Wed. **Golf** Stinchcombe Hill 18h. **See**
Parish Church.

Rescue Service: Cam Motors Ltd, Mill &
Draycott Garages. ✆ Dursley
(048 96) 3681.

CAMBERLEY Surrey. Map 7A
Pop 48,000 (inc Frimley). Bagshot 3,
London 30, Basingstoke 17, Farnham 10,
Guildford 12, Henley-on-Thames 18,
Reading 15.
EC Wed. **MD** Thur, Fri, Sat. **Golf**
Camberley Heath 18h. **See** St Michael's
Church, Staff College, Royal Military
Academy (Sandhurst), National Army
Museum, Frimley Parish Church (grave of
Bret Harte).

★★★**Frimley Hall** (TH), *Portsmouth Rd,
GU15 2BG.* ✆ (0276) 28321. C. ⊨ 66
bedrs, 63 bp, 3 bps, 3 ba, TV, Dgs. ✗ a l c,
mc, LD 9.45. 🄐 N, CH, Dgs, CP 200, Ac,
con 70, CF. £ BB £41·50, DB £57·50, WB,
🄣, cc 1 2 3 4 5 6.
Camberley, G, z (Unl), *116 London Rd,
GU15 3 TJ.* ✆ (0276) 24410. C. ⊨ 6
bedrs, 4 sh, 2 ba. 🄐 CH, TV, CP 6, CF. £ BB
fr £14, DB £20, 🄣.

CAMBORNE Cornwall. Map 2E
Pop 13,000. Redruth 3½, London 267,
Helston 9½, Penzance 14, St Ives 11.
EC Thur. **MD** Fri. **Golf** Tehidy Park 18h.
See School of Mines, 15th cent Church.

Pendarves Lodge, G, x (Rt), *Pendarves,
TR14 0RT.* ✆ (0209) 712691. Open May–
Sept. C. ⊨ 8 bedrs, 2 ba, Dgs. 🄐 ch, TV,
CP 8, CF. £ BB £8·50, DB £17, DT (b)
£12·50, 🄣.

MC Repairer: B M Motor Cycles, 14
Pendarves St, Tuckingmill.
✆ (0209) 719767
Carlines Motorcycles, 52 Trelowarren St.
✆ (0209) 713744.
Rescue Service: Camborne Auto's Ltd,
136 Trevenson Rd. ✆ (0209) 716491.
Glasson's Garage, Treswithian Rd.
✆ (0209) 712133.
J K Motors, Gurney's La.
✆ (0209) 715021.
Moor Street Garage, Moor St.
✆ (0209) 713862.
Pengegon Motors, Foundry Rd.
✆ (0209) 713279.
Polstrong Filling Station, Treswithian.
✆ (0209) 712358.
Williamson's Motors, Church St.
✆ (0209) 712066.

CAMBRIDGE Cambridgeshire. Map 15D
Pop 102,300. Royston 13, London 55,
M11 Motorway 1½, Bedford 30
Biggleswade 22, Bishop's Stortford 27,
Braintree 32, Dunmow 28, Ely 16,
Haverhill 18, Huntingdon 16, Newmarket
13, Northampton 50.
See Plan, p. 168.
MD Daily. **P** See Plan. **Golf** Gog Magog
18h and 9h, Girton 18h. **See** Colleges and
Gardens, 'The Backs', Churches,
Mathematical Bridge, Bridge of Sighs (St
John's), Fitzwilliam Museum, King's
College Chapel, Botanic Garden,
Cambridge and County Folk Museum,
Anglesey Abbey and Gardens 6 m NE.

🄶 Wheeler St. ✆ Cambridge (0223)
358977.

★★★★**Garden House,** *Granta Pl, Mill La,
CB2 1RT.* ✆ (0223) 63421. C. ⊨ 117
bedrs, 117 bp, TV. ✗ a l c, mc, at, LD 9.30.
🄐 Lt, N, CH, Dgs, Ac, pf, con 150, CF.
£ BBc £39·50–£42, DBc £56–£60, WB, 🄶,
Bk £7, L £9·50, D £9·50, cc 1 3 4 5 6,
Dep b.
★★★★**M Post House,** (TH), *Bridge Rd,
CB4 4PH.* ✆ Histon (022 023) 7000. C.
⊨ 121 bedrs, 121 bp, Dgs. ✗ a l c, mc, at,
LD 10.30. 🄐 Lt, N, CH, TV, Dgs, CP 250,
Ac, sp, sb, con 100, CF, 59 BGf. £ BB £47,
DB £62·50, 🄣, cc 1 2 3 4 5 6, Dep (Xmas).
★★★★**University Arms,** *Regent St, CB2
1AD.* ✆ (0223) 351241. RS Xmas. C.
⊨ 115 bedrs, 115 bp, TV, Dgs. ✗ a l c, mc,
at, LD 9.45. 🄐 Lt, N, CH, CP 75, Ac, con
250, CF, Dis. £ BB fr £30·50, DB fr £45·50,
DT fr £43·10, WB, 🄣, Bk £3·70, L £6·20, D
£7·90, cc 1 3 4 5.
★★★**Gonville,** *Gonville Pl, CB1 1LY.*
✆ (0223) 66611. Closed Xmas except for
Xmas lunch. C. ⊨ 62 bedrs, 62 bp, TV, Dgs.
✗ a l c, mc, LD 9 (9.45 Sun). 🄐 Lt, N, CH,
TV, CP 100, Ac, con 60, CF, 10 BGf, 2 st.
£ BB fr £30·50, DB fr £44·50, DT fr £45·95,
WB, 🄶, 10%, Bk £3·95, L £6·50, D £8·95,
cc 1 2 3, Dep.
■★★**Arundel House,** *53 Chesterton Rd,
CB4 3AN.* ✆ (0223) 67701. Closed Xmas.
C. ⊨ 66 bedrs, 17 bp, 25 bps, 9 ba, annexe
6 bedrs, 5 bp, 1 bps, TV, Dgs. ✗ a l c, mc,
at, LD 10. 🄐 N, CH, CP 44, Ac, con 70, CF.
£ BBc £15·25–£26·50, DBc £24·50–
£39·75, WT £196·70–£230·95, DT
£28·10–£32·95, WB, 🄣, Bk £1·85, L £5·50,
D £7·35, cc 1 3 5 6, Dep b.
★★**Blue Boar** (TH), *Trinity St, CB2 1TB.*
✆ (0223) 63121. C. ⊨ 48 bedrs, 11 bp, 8
ba, TV, Dgs. ✗ a l c, mc, at, LD 9.30. 🄐 N,
CH, Dgs, Ac, con 100, CF. £ BB fr £29·50,
DB fr £45, WB, 🄣, cc 1 2 3 4 5 6.
Ayeone Cleave, G, z (Unl), *95 Gilbert Rd,
CB4 3NZ.* ✆ (0223) 63387. C. ⊨ 6 bedrs,
2 bps, 1 ba, TV. ✗ a l c. 🄐 CH, TV, ns, CP 6
£ BB £10–£10·50, DB £18–£25, 🄣.
Cambridge Lodge, H, z (R), *139
Huntingdon Rd, CB3 0DQ.*
✆ (0223) 352833. C. ⊨ 11 bedrs, 8 bp, 8
bps, 11 sh, TV, Dgs. ✗ a l c, mc, at. 🄐 Lt,
CH, Dgs, ns, CP 24, CF, 2 st. £ BB £28·25–
£35, DB £37·65–£42·25, WT (a) £332·15,
(b) £283·50, (c) £201·25, DT (a) £47·50,
(b) £40·50, 🄶, Bk £3·75, L £6·95, D £11·75,
cc 1 3 4 5.
Hamilton, GH, z (Unl), *58 Chesterton Rd,
CB4 1ER.* ✆ (0223) 314866. C4. ⊨ 10
bedrs, 5 sh, 2 ba, TV. 🄐 CH, CP 7, CF, 1
BGf. £ BB £9·50–£11·50, DB £18–£20, WT
(c) £66·50–£80·50, 🄣, cc 1 5 ▲
Lensfield H, z (R), *53 Lensfield Rd,
CR2 1GH.* ✆ (0223) 355017. Closed Dec.
C. ⊨ 32 bedrs, 7 bp, 20 bps, 5 sh, 4 ba, ns,
TV. ✗ mc, at. 🄐 CH, TV, CP 12, CF, 4 BGf,
4 st. £ BB £16–£20, DB £22–£30, 🄣, Bk £2,
cc 1 3 4 5 ▲
Suffolk House, PH, z (Unl), *69 Milton
Rd, CB4 1XA.* ✆ (0223) 352016. C. ⊨ 8
bedrs, 1 bp, 2 sh, 2 ba, TV. 🄐 CH, TV, CP 7,
1 st. £ BB £10·50–£11·50, DB £18·50–£25,
🄢.

Repairers: Gilbert Rice (Cambridge) Ltd,
(Office & Sales, Hills Rd), Service Dept,
Cherryhinton Rd. ✆ (0223) 48151.
Marshall (Cambridge) Ltd, Austin House,
Jesus La. ✆ (0223) 62211 and Airport
Garage, Newmarket Rd. ✆ (0223) 58741.

CAMELFORD Cornwall. Map 2D
Pop 1,800. Launceston 16, London 227,
Bodmin 13, Bude 17, Liskeard 24, Saltash
31, Wadebridge 11.
EC Wed. **Golf** Launceston 18h. **See**
Church of St Thomas, Lanteglos Church,
Slaughter Bridge (scene of King Arthur's
last battle), 43rd Wessex Division
Memorial at Roughtor, Cornwall's highest
hill Brown Willy, Tintagel Castle (King
Arthur's Castle) 4½ m NW.

Sunnyside, PH, x (RI), *7 Victoria Rd,
PL32 9XB.* ✆ (0840) 212250. Closed Nov.
C. ⊨ 10 bedrs, 4 bps, 2 ba, Dgs. 🄐 CH, TV,
Dgs, CP 16, CF, 12 st. £ BB £10–£12, DB
£16–£20, WT £76–£90, DT £15–£18, 🄣, Bk
£2·80, L £4·50, D £5·50.
Warmington House, PH, x (R), *32
Market Pl, PL32 9PD.* ✆ (0840) 213380.
C. ⊨ 7 bedrs, 2 sh, 1 ba, Dgs. ✗ a l c.
🄐 CH, TV, Dgs, CP 8, CF, DB £14–
£16, WT (b) £70–£75, DT (b) £11–£12, 🄣,
Bk £2, L £2, D £4, cc 3.

Rescue Service: Camelot Garage Ltd,
Valley Truckle. ✆ (0840) 213217.
Couch, E & D, High St. ✆ (0840) 2396.
Steelspeed (Camelford) Ltd, Tintagel Rd,
Valley Truckle. ✆ (0840) 213374.

CANFORD CLIFFS Dorset
See POOLE

CANNOCK Staffordshire. Map 22E
Pop 46,200. Atherstone 23, London 127,
M6 Motorway 3½, Lichfield 9, Newport 18,
Stafford 9½, Sutton Coldfield 13, Walsall
8½, Wellington 21, Wolverhampton 9.
EC Thur. **MD** Tue, Fri, Sat. **Golf**
Beaudesert 18h. **See** Old Church (12 cent
origins), Castle Ring (Br Camp), Cannock
Chase (view of nine counties).

★★**Hollies** (R & Cl), *Hollies Av, WS11
1DW.* ✆ (05435) 3151. Closed Xmas, C6.
⊨ 6 bedrs, 1 ba, TV. ✗ a l c, mc, LD 9.30.
🄐 CH, CP 100, U 6, Ac, con 25, CF, 1 st,
Dis. £ BB fr £18, DB fr £26, 🄣, Bk £3·50, L
£6·50, D £9, cc 1 3 4 5, Dep b.

Repairer: Churchbridge Motor Garage
Ltd, Watling St. ✆ Cheslyn Hay
(0922) 417014.
Specialist Body Repairer: Shorade Motor
Bodies, New St & Church St, Bridgtown.
✆ (054 35) 71755. ▲

CANTERBURY Kent. Map 10D
Pop 36,294. Rochester 27, London 58,
Ashford 14, Dover 15, Folkestone 16,
Maidstone 27, Margate 15.
See Plan, p. 169.
EC Thur. **MD** Mon, Wed, Sat. **P** See Plan.
Golf Canterbury 18h. **See** Cathedral (site
of Becket's murder), St Martin's and other
old Churches, Christchurch Gate, King's
School, Eastbridge Hospital
(Almshouses), Beaney Institute Museum,
The Weavers, City Walls, Dane John
Gardens (Invicta Engine), Castle Keep, St
Thomas's Hospital (almshouse), Chillham
Castle Gdns 6 m SW.
🄶 22 St Peter's St. ✆ Canterbury
(0227) 66567.

★★★★**County,** *High St, CT1 2RX.*
✆ (0227) 66266. C. ⊨ 74 bedrs, 74 bp,
TV. ✗ a l c, mc, at, LD 10. 🄐 Lt, N, CH, CP
80, G 20, Ac, sol, gym, con, CF, 1 st. £ BB
£37–£40, DB £51·50–£54·50, WB, 🄣, Bk
£4·50, L £7·80, cc 1 2 3 4 5 6, Dep b. ▲
★★★**Chaucer** (TH), *Ivy La, CT1 1TT.*
✆ (0227) 64427. C. ⊨ 51 bedrs, 30 bp, 2

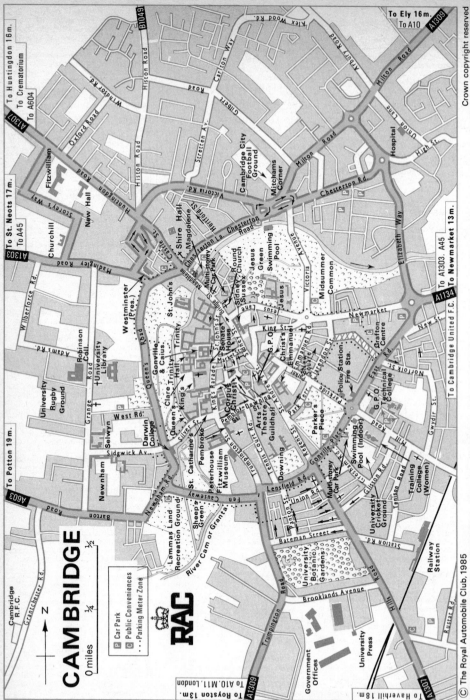

CAMBRIDGE

RAC

P Car Park
C Public Conveniences
···· Parking Meter Zone

0 miles   ¼   ½

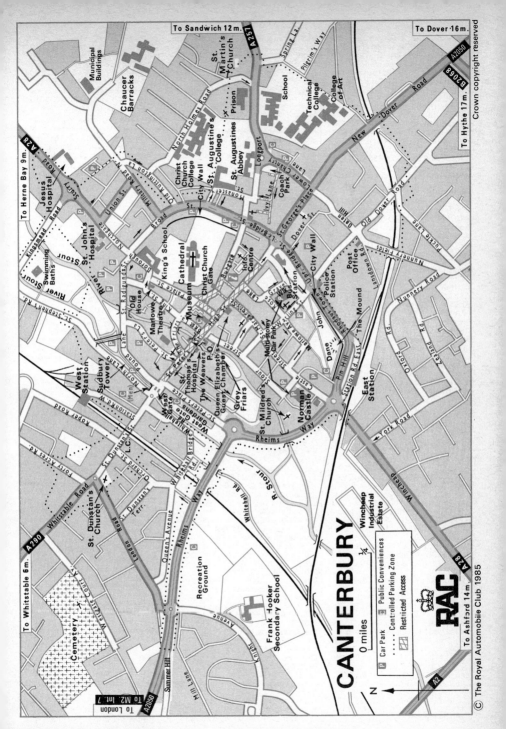

To Sandwich 12 m.
To Dover 16 m.
To Herne Bay 9 m.
To Hythe 17 m.
To Whitstable 6 m.
To London To M2. Int. 7
To Ashford 14 m.

A251
A2050
B2068
A28
A290
A28
A2

CANTERBURY

0 miles   ¼

P Car Park   Ⓒ Public Conveniences
Controlled Parking Zone
Restricted Access

N

RAC

Municipal Buildings
Chaucer Barracks
St. Martin's Church
School
Technical College
College of Art
Prison
St. Augustine's College
St. Augustine's Abbey
Christ Church College
City Wall
Coach Park
Jesus Hospital
St. John's Hospital
Swimming Baths
King's School
Cathedral
Christ Church Gate
Info Centre
City Wall
Post Office
Police Station
The Mound
East Station
Old House
Marlowe Theatre
Museum
Multi storey Car Park
Norman Castle
Grey Friars
St. Mildred's Church
West Gate
West Station
Sudbury Tower
St. Dunstan's Church
Cemetery
Recreation Ground
Frank Hooker Secondary School
Wincheap Industrial Estate

bps, 4 ba, TV, Dgs. ✗ a l c, mc, LD 9.30.
🄰 N, CH, Dgs, CP 45, Ac, con 90, CF. £ BB
fr £30·50, DB fr £43, WB, 🆃, cc 1 2 3 4 5 6.
★★★**Slatters,** *St Margaret's St, CT1 1AA.*
✆ (0227) 63271. C. ➡ 33 bedrs, 23 bp, 4
ba, TV, Dgs. ✗ a l c, LD 9. 🄰 Lt, N, CH,
Dgs, CP 25, con 35, CF, 0 st. £ BB £23–
£32, DB £35–£43, DBB £22–£25, WB, 🆃,
Bk £3·75, L £4·25, D £6·50, cc 1 2 3 5 6,
Dep b.
★★**Canterbury,** *71 New Dover Rd.*
✆ (0227) 50551. C. ➡ 30 bedrs, 12 bp, 15
bps, 1 sh, 1 ba, TV, Dgs. ✗ a l c, mc, at, LD
10. 🄰 Lt, CH, CP 50, Ac, con 25, CF, 1 BGf,
1 st, Dis. £ BB £27·50, DB £35, WB, 🆃, Bk
£3, L £4·50, D £6·50, cc 1 3 4 5 6.
★★**Victoria** (R), *59 London Rd,*
CT2 7NG. ✆ (0227) 59333. C. ➡ 24
bedrs, 15 bp, 4 bps, 2 ba, TV, Dgs. ✗ a l c,
mc, at, LD 9. 🄰 CH, CP 30, U 1, con, CF, 4
BGf, 0 st, Dis. £ BB £15–£24, DB £31–£35,
WB, 🆃, Bk £3·75, L £4, D £8, cc 1 3 4 5 6.
Abba, N, z (R), *Station Rd West, CT2
8AN.* ✆ (0227) 64771. C. ➡ 19 bedrs, 2
bp, 1 sh, 4 ba. ✗ a l c. 🄰 CH, TV, CP 7, CF,
3 st. £ BB £8·50–£12, DB £17–£24, WT (c)
£59·50–£84, 🆃, Bk £2.
Alexandra House, PH, z, *1 Roper Av,
CT2 7EH.* ✆ (0227) 67011.
Carlton, G, z (Rt), *40 Nunnery Fields,
CT1 3JT.* ✆ (0227) 65900. C. ➡ 10 bedrs,
3 ba, TV, Dgs. 🄰 CH, CP 3, CF, 15 st. £ BB
£7·50–£9·50, DB £15–£19, WT (b) fr £94,
(c) fr £66, DT (b) fr £14, 🆃.
Castle Court, G, z (Unl), *8 Castle St.*
✆ (0227) 463441. C2. ➡ 12 bedrs, 2 ba,
Dgs. 🄰 ch, TV, Dgs. £ BB £9–£10, DB £16–
£18, 🆃, L £2, D £3·65, cc 1 3.
Ebury, H, y (R), *65 New Dover Rd, CT1
3DX.* ✆ (0227) 68433. C. ➡ 15 bedrs, 13
bp, 2 bps, TV, Dgs. 🄰 CH, TV, CP 20, U 1,
CF, 6 st. £ BB £21–£25, DB £28–£34, WT
£110–£130, DT (b) £17·75–£19·25, 🆃, Bk
£3, D £7·25, cc 1 3 5.
Ersham Lodge, H, z (RI), *12 New Dover
Rd, CT1 3AP.* ✆ (0227) 63174. C. ➡ 25
bedrs, 3 bp, 7 bps, 11 sh, 3 ba, TV. 🄰 CH,
TV, CP 17, U 2, 6 BGf. £ BB £17–£20, DB
£27–£30, 🆃.
Highfield, H, y (R), *Summer Hill,
Harbledown, CT2 8NH.* ✆ (0227) 462772.
Closed Xmas & New Year, C3. ➡ 10 bedrs,
2 bps, 2 ba. 🄰 CH, TV, CP 12, 3 st. £ BB
£10–£11, DB £17–£21, cc 1 3.
Kingsbridge, G, z (R), *15 Best La, CT1
2JB.* ✆ (0227) 66415. C. ➡ 12 bedrs, 1
bp, 11 sh, 2 ba, TV, Dgs. ✗ a l c. 🄰 CH, TV,
CP 8, 3 st. £ BB £8–£10, DB £16–£19, 🆃,
Bk £2, L £5, D £6.
London, G, z (Unl), *14 London Rd, CT2
8LR.* ✆ (0227) 65860. C. ➡ 6 bedrs, 2 ba.
🄰 CH, TV, Dgs, CF. £ BB £8–£10, DB £16–
£18, 🆃.
Pilgrims, G, z (Unl), *18 The Friars, CT1
2AS.* ✆ (0227) 64531. Closed Xmas. C.
➡ 14 bedrs, 2 bps, 3 ba. 🄰 CH, TV, CP 4, G
4, CF, 2 st. £ BB £9–£10·50, DB £16–£21,
🆃.
Pointers, H z (R), *1 London Rd, CT2 8LR.*
✆ (0227) 456846. Closed Xmas & New
Year. C. ➡ 14 bedrs, 2 bp, 1 bps, 8 sh, 2 ba,
TV, Dgs. 🄰 CH, Dgs, CP 10, CF, 2 st. £ BB
£15–£17, DB £26–£28, WT (b) fr £124·50,
DT (b) fr £22, ➋, Bk £3, D £7·50, cc 1 3 4 5.
Red House, H, y (R), *London Rd, CT2
8NB.* ✆ (0227) 63578. C. ➡ 15 bedrs, 5
bp, 2 bps, 2 ba, TV. 🄰 CH, TV, CP 16, CF, 2
st. £ BB £12·65–£16·10, DB fr £23, WT (b)
fr £110, DT (b) fr £20, 🆃, Bk £2·75, D
£7·50, cc 1 5.

St Stephen's, G, z (RI), *100 St Stephen's
Rd, CT2 7JL.* ✆ (0227) 462167. C. ➡ 9
bedrs, 1 sh, 2 ba, Dgs. 🄰 CH, TV, CP 8, U 2,
3 BGf, 1 st, Dis. £ BB £8·62–£9·77, DB
£16·10–£19·55, 🆃.

Repairer: Martin Walter, 41 St Georges Pl.
✆ (0227) 66131.
MC Repairer: Hallet's of Canterbury Ltd,
St Dunstan's St. ✆ (0227) 62275.
Rescue Service: Jelley's of Canterbury,
Evenhill Garage, Littlebourne.
✆ Littlebourne (022 778) 351.

CANVEY ISLAND Essex. Map 10A.
Pop 33,847. Rainham 24, London 40,
Brentwood 19, Chelmsford 20, Colchester
39, Dartford–Purfleet Tunnel 21, Romford
24, Southend 10.
EC Thur. **MD** Sat. **Golf** Waterside Farm
9h. **See** Dutch Cottage Museum,
Coastguard cottages, "Lobster Smack"
Inn, Nature Reserve.

Rescue Service: Hickson Motor Co Ltd,
Canvey Rd. ✆ (0268) 683263.

CARBIS BAY Cornwall. Map 2E
Pop 2,500. Redruth 14, London 277,
Helston 13, Penzance 8½, St Ives 2.
EC Thur. **Golf** West Cornwall, Lelant 18h.
See North Cornwall Coast Path (view),
sandy beach, St Ives Art Galleries and Old
Mariners Church at St Ives (2 m NW).

★★**Boskerris** (RI), *Boskerris Rd, TR26
2NQ.* ✆ Penzance (0736) 795295. Open
April–Oct. C. ➡ 20 bedrs, 15 bp, 2 ba, TV,
Dgs. ✗ mc, at, LD 8. 🄰 CH, TV, CP 20, sp,
CF, 4 BGf, 8 st. £ BB £11·50–£13, DB £27–
£29, WB, 🆃, Bk £3, L £4, D £8·50, Dep a.
★★**Hendra's,** *Porthrepta Rd, TR26 2NZ.*
✆ Penzance (0736) 795030. Open May–
Sept. C. ➡ 38 bedrs, 11 bp, 2 bps, 2 sh, 8
ba, Dgs. ✗ at, LD 8. 🄰 CH, TV, CP 16, U 14,
G 3, Ac, sp, CF, 6 BGf, 2 st. £ BB £10–£12,
DB £20–£26, WT £128·80–£154·40, DT
£18·40–£22·06, WB, 🆃, Bk £3, L £3·50, D
£5·50, Dep a.
★★**Karenza** (R), *Headland Rd, TR26 2NR.*
✆ Penzance (0736) 795294. Open Mar–
Oct. ➡ 12 bedrs, 5 bp, 3 bps, 1 ba, annexe
20 bedrs, 14 bp, 4 bps, 1 ba, TV, Dgs.
✗ mc, at, LD 8. 🄰 CH, TV, CP 30, Ac, sp,
sb, sol, gym, CF, 13 st. £ BB £12·50–
£16·75, DB £25–£33·50, DBB £16·25–
£23·50, 🆃, Bk £4, L £4·25, D £6·50.
★★**St Uny** (R), *Boskerris Rd, TR26
2NQ.* ✆ Penzance (0736) 795011.
Atlantic, H, x, *St. Ives Rd, TR26 2SB.*
✆ Penzance (0736) 796177. C. ➡ 28
bedrs, 6 ba. 🄰 ch, TV, CP 24, CF, 3 BGf, 6
st. £ BB £7, DB £14, WT fr £73·50, DT
£10·50, ➋, Bk £2·50, D £3·50.
Bay View, PH, x (RI), *Headlands Rd,
TR26 2NX.* ✆ Penzance (0736) 796469.
C. ➡ 9 bedrs, 2 bps, 1 sh, 3 ba, ns, Dgs.
🄰 CH, TV, CP 9, CF, 2 BGf, 2 st. £ BB
£6·50–£10·50, DB £13–£21, WT £69·50–
£102, DT £10–£15, 🆃.
Carbis Water, G, x (RI), *St Ives Rd, TR26
2RT.* ✆ Penzance (0736) 797213. Open
Mar–Sept. C. ➡ 13 bedrs, 3 bps, 2 ba, Dgs.
🄰 TV, Dgs, CP 11, CF, 3 st. £ BB £6·90–
£9·20, DB £13·80–£19·40, WT (b) £72·45–
£88·55, DT (b) £10·35–£12·65, 🆃.
Cottage, G, x (RI), *The Valley, TR26 2JU.*
✆ Penzance (0736) 797405. C. ➡ 7
bedrs, 4 bp, 1 bps, sh, 1 ba, TV, Dgs.
✗ a l c. 🄰 CH, TV, CP 12, CF. £ DB £8–
£20, WT (b) £84–£98, DT (b) £12–£28, 🆃.

Grey Tyles, H, z (RI), *St Ives Rd, TR26
2SB.* ✆ Penzance (0736) 796408.
Tregorran, H, y (RI), *Headland Rd, TR26
2NU.* ✆ Penzance (0736) 795889. Open
April–Oct. C. ➡ 15 bedrs, 6 bps, 2 sh, 4 ba,
Dgs. ✗ a l c. 🄰 CH, TV, CP 20, CF, 1 BGf, 1
st. £ BB £9·50–£13·50, DB £19–£27, WT
(b) £84–£108·50, (c) £59·50–£80·50, ➋, D
£3·50.

CARCROFT South Yorkshire. M.Area
25D
Pop 4,446. 1 m N of Adwick-le-Street,
Doncaster 5½, London 170, Barnsley 15,
Boroughbridge 39, Goole 20, Harrogate
36, Pontefract 10, Selby 17, Thorne 13,
Wakefield 15.
EC Thur. **Golf** Doncaster 18h.

Rescue Service: Bullcroft Service Station,
Skellow Rd. ✆ Doncaster (0302) 722352.

CAREY Hereford & Worcester
(Hereford). Map 13C
M50 Motorway 7, Ross-on-Wye 6,
London 127, Hereford 8, Monmouth 13.
Golf Hereford on Ross 18h. **See** "Cottage
of Content" Inn.

Cottage of Content, I, x, *HR2 6NG.*
✆ (043 270) 242. C. ➡ 3 bedrs, 1 ba, Dgs.
✗ a l c. 🄰 CH, TV, Dgs, CP 30, CF, 3 st.
£ BB £10–£16, DB £20–£25, WT £98–
£133, DT £15–£25, D £12, 🆃, cc 1.

CARHAMPTON Somerset. Map 4D
Pop 901. Taunton 20, London 163,
Bridgwater 22, Dunster 2, Minehead 3½.
EC Wed. **Golf** Minehead and West
Somerset 18h. **See** Church (screen, ship's
bell), Dunster Castle 2 m NW.

Rescue Service: Sherrin's, Townsend
Garage. ✆ Dunster (064 382) 326.

CARLISLE Cumbria. Map 26C and 30F
See also DALSTON and WETHERAL
Pop 70,000. Penrith 18, London 294, M6
Motorway 2, Beattock 39, Brampton 9,
Cockermouth 25, Dumfries 33, Keswick
31, Langholm 20, Maryport 28.
EC Thur. **MD** All expt Thur & Sun. **P** Disc
Parking is in operation from 8.30 am to
6 pm Mondays to Saturdays, and vehicles
using the authorised parking places
within the zone must display a disc set to
indicate the time of arrival. Discs are
obtainable from Civic Centre, Town Hall,
Police Station and Traffic Wardens.
PARKING MUST NOT TAKE PLACE
WHERE THERE ARE YELLOW LINES
ALONG THE ROAD. **Golf** Stoneyholme
18h. **See** Cathedral and Monastic
buildings, Castle (Border Regt Museum),
Tullie House Museum and Art Gallery,
17th cent Market Cross, The Citadel, Tithe
Barn, St Cuthbert's Parish Church, Town
Hall, Civic Centre, Guildhall Museum
(open daily).
ℹ️ Old Town Hall, Greenmarket. ✆ Carlisle
(0228) 25517.

★★★**M Crest,** *Kingstown, CA4 0HR.*
✆ (0228) 31201. C. ➡ 100 bedrs, 100 bp,
ns, TV, Dgs. ✗ a l c, mc, at, LD 10. 🄰 Lt, N,
CH, Dgs, CP 200, Ac, con 60, CF. £ BB fr
£46·25, DB fr £62·25, WB, 🆃, Bk £5·25, D
£9·25, cc 1 2 3 4 5 6, Dep b.
★★★**Crown and Mitre,** *4 English St,
CA3 8HX.* ✆ (0228) 25491. Closed Xmas.
C. ➡ 98 bedrs, 93 bp, 5 bps, 1 ba, TV, Dgs.
✗ a l c, LD 9.45. 🄰 Lt, N, CH, TV, Dgs, CP
10, G 40, sp, gym, con 400, CF, 1 st. £ BB fr

£30·50, DB fr £49·50, WB, ⒈, Bk £3·50, L
£1·90, D £6·50, cc 1 2 3 4 5 6, Dep b.

★★★**Cumbrian Thistle,** *Court Sq., CA1
1QY.* ✆ (0228) 31951. C. ⊭ 70 bedrs, 70
bp, ns, TV, Dgs. ✗ a l c, mc, at, LD 9.30.
⒵ Lt, N, CH, TV, Dgs, CP 60, G 30, Ac, con
60, CF, 6 st. £ BB £33·75–£47·75, DB £52–
£54·50, WB, ⒉, Bk £4·75, L £6·50, D £8·50,
cc 1 2 3 4 5 6, Dep b.

★★★**Hilltop,** *London Rd, CA1 2PQ.*
✆ (0228) 29255. C. ⊭ 110 bedrs, 92 bp, 5
bps, 13 sh, 2 ba, TV, Dgs. ✗ a l c, mc, LD
9.45. ⒵ Lt, N, CH, CH, CP 300, Ac, sp, sb, sol,
gym, con 400, CF, 13 BGf, Dis. £ BB
£21·50–£34, DB £32–£45, WB, ⒈, Bk
£3·56, L £5·25, D £7·25, cc 1 3 4 5 6,
Dep b.

★★★**String of Horses,** *Heads Nook,
Faugh, CA4 9EG,* ✆ Hayton
(0228) 70297. RS Xmas. C. ⊭ 13 bedrs, 8
bp, 5 bps, TV, Dgs. ✗ a l c, mc, LD
10.30. ⒵ CH, CP 50, Ac, sp, sb, sol, con 25,
CF, 6 st. £ BB £34–£42, DB £42–£58, WB,
⒉, Bk £4·50, L £6·50, D £5·30, cc 1 3 4 5 6.

★★**Carrow House,** *Carleton, CA4 0AD.*
✆ (0228) 32073. C. ⊭ 17 bedrs, 1 bp, 4
bps, 12 sh, 3 ba, TV, Dgs. ✗ a l c. ⒵ CH, CP
150, Ac, CF, 5 BGf, 1 st, Dis. £ BB £17–
£22, DB £25·50–£30, WB (50% Nov–
March only), L a l c, D a l c, ⒈, Bk £2·55,
cc 1.

★★**Central,** *Victoria Viaduct, CA3 8AL.*
✆ (0228) 20256. RS Xmas. C. ⊭ 82 bedrs,
18 bp, 2 bps, 14 ba, TV, Dgs. ✗ a l c, mc, at,
LD 9. ⒵ Lt, N, ch, G 15, Ac, con 100, CF, 7
st. £ ⒉, Bk £3·50, L £2·25, D £5·15,
cc 1 3 4 5 6, Dep b.

▣★★**Cumbria Park** (R), *32 Scotland Rd,
CA3 9DG.* ✆ (0228) 22887. Closed Xmas.
C. ⊭ 44 bedrs, 40 bp, 2 ba, TV. ✗ a l c, LD
8. ⒵ CH, ns, CP 40, Ac, con 100, CF, 5 BGf,
1 st, Dis. £ BB £20, DB £28, ⒉, Bk £2·50, D
£6·30, cc 1 5, Dep a.

▣★★**Pinegrove,** *262 London Rd, CA1
2QS.* ✆ (0228) 24828. Closed Xmas Day.
C. ⊭ 20 bedrs, 8 bp, 4 sh, 2 ba, TV, Dgs.
✗ a l c, mc, LD 8.30. ⒵ CH, CP 30, Ac, con
130, CF, 8 BGf, 1 st, Dis. £ BB £15·53–
£20·70, DB £24·15–£32·20, ⒉, Bk £4, L
£2·70, D £5·50, cc 1 5.

★**Vallum House,** *Burgh Rd, CA2
7NB.* ✆ (0228) 21860. Closed Xmas &
New Year. C. ⊭ 11 bedrs, 2 ba, TV, Dgs.
✗ a l c, mc, LD 9. ⒵ CH, CP 50, Ac, con
30, CF. £ BB £16·50, DB £27·50, ⒉, Bk
£2·50, L £2·25, D £7·75, cc 1 4 ▲

Angus, PH, z (R), *14 Scotland Rd,
Stanwix, CA3 9DG.* ✆ (0228) 23546.
Closed Xmas–New Year. C. ⊭ 9 bedrs, 2
ba, Dgs. ⒵ CH, TV, CF, 8 st. £ BB £9·50–
£10, DB £16–£17, DT (b) £14–£15, ⒈, Bk
£3, D £4·50.

Royal, PH, z (Temp), *9 Lowther St.
CA3 8ES.* ✆ (0228) 22103. C. ⊭ 25
bedrs, 1 sh, 5 ba, TV, Dgs. ✗ a l c. ⒵ CH,
TV, CF, 4 st ✆ BB £9·50–£10 DB £18–£19,
WT (b) £98–£101·50, DT (b) £14–£14·50,
⒈, Bk £2·50, L £2, D £3, cc 1 5.

Repairers: County Motors (Carlisle) Ltd,
14 Botchergate ✆ (0228) 24387.
Specialist Radiator Repairer: Serck
Radiator Services Ltd, Newtown
Industrial Estate. ✆ (0228) 22119.
Specialist Spring Repairer: Jonas
Woodhead Ltd, Durranhill Trading Estate,
Harraby. ✆ (0228) 25528.
MC Repairer: Clarkson, J E, 1 Chapel St.
✆ (0228) 21840.

Sctr Repairer: Clarkson, J E, 1 Chapel St.
✆ (0228) 21840.
Rescue Service: Appletons Garage,
Harraby Grove. ✆ (0228) 38220.
Auto Services (Carlisle) Ltd, Hillcrest Av.
✆ (0228) 26617
Blackwood Service Station, Mealsgate.
✆ Low Ireby (096 57) 312.
Carlton Service Station, A6, Carlton.
✆ (0228) 27287.
Corby Hill Motors, Corby Hill. ✆ Wetheral
(0228) 61308.
County Garage Co Ltd, Hardwicke Circus.
✆ (0228) 24234.
Lightfoot's Garage Ltd, Lowther St.
✆ (0228) 26104.
Motor & Body Repairs Ltd, New Rd,
Viaduct Estate. ✆ (0228) 34097 and
(0228) 37033.
Waugh, R, Greenhead Garage, Greenhead.
✆ Gilsland (069 72) 251.

CARLTON Nottinghamshire. M. Area
22D
Pop 44,890. Nottingham 2½, London 125,
Grantham 26, Lowdham 4½, West
Bridgeford 4.
EC Wed. **Golf** Mapperley 18h. **See**
churches.

Rescue Service: Avondale Garages, 245
Oakdale Rd. ✆ Nottingham
(0602) 874843.

CARLYON BAY Cornwall
See ST AUSTELL

CARNFORTH Lancashire. Map 27C
Pop 4,844. London 243, M6 Motorway 2,
Ambleside 26, Broughton-in-Furness 35,
Kendal 15, Kirkby Lonsdale 10, Settle 24,
Ulveston 30.
EC Thur. **MD** Wed. **Golf** Silverdale 18h,
Morecambe 18h. **See** Borwick Hall,
Steamtown (Rly Museum), Warton Crag,
Leighton Hall 2½m N.

Rescue Service: Town End Garage, Sand
La, Warton. ✆ (0524) 3837.

CARTERTON Oxfordshire. M.Area 14F
Pop 12,000. Oxford 17, London 73,
Burford 4, Cirencester 17, Faringdon 8,
Swindon 17.
EC Wed. **MD** Thur. **Golf** Burford 18h. **See**
St Mary Church.

Rescue Service: Dowleys Garage, 12
Alvescot Rd. ✆ (0993) 842345.
Maryville Garage, Black Bourton Rd.
✆ (0993) 842399.
Philserve Motor Engineering Services,
Unit 2, Belle Terrace, Carterton Industrial
Estate. ✆ (0993) 842638.

CASTLE BROMWICH West Midlands.
Map 21D
Pop 15,952. Coventry 18, London 109,
Atherstone 14, Birmingham 6, Newport
35, Nuneaton 16, Stafford 28, Stratford-
upon-Avon 25, Sutton Coldfield 5,
Tamworth 11, Walsall 11, Warwick 21,
Wellington 38.
EC Wed, Thur. **Golf** Maxstoke Park 18h.
See Castle Bromwich Hall, Church of SS
Mary and Margaret.

▣★★**M Bradford Arms,** *Chester Rd,
B36 0AG.* ✆ 021-748 7675. Closed Xmas.
C. ⊭ 30 bedrs, 30 bp, TV, Dgs. ✗ LD 10.
⒵ N, CH, CP 30, CF, 14 BGf, 1 st, Dis.
£ WB, Bk £4, L £3, D £6, cc 1 2 3. Dep b.

CASTLE CARY Somerset. Map 5C
Pop 1,875. Wincanton 6, London 116,
Blandford Forum 26, Crewkerne 21,
Frome 10, Glastonbury 12, Ilminster 22,
Shepton Mallet 8, Sherborne 12, Taunton
33, Warminster 15.
EC Thur. **Golf** Sherborne 18h. **See** War
Memorial on its horse pond, Old
lock-up and "Round House", Church,
Norman castle remains.

Greenhills, GH, x, (R), *Ansford Hill, BA7
7JP.* ✆ (0963) 50464. C10. ⊭ 6 bedrs, 3
bp, 1 sh, 1 ba. ⒵ CH, TV, CP 12, 2 st. £ BB
fr £9·50, DB fr £19, WT (b) fr £95, DT (b) fr
£20, ⒈, D £7·50.

Repairer: Fletcher, W & G, Station Garage.
✆ (0963) 50250.
Rescue Service: Moff Motors Ltd.
✆ (0963) 50310.

CASTLE COMBE Wiltshire. Map 5B
Pop 460. Chippenham 6, London 97, M4
Motorway 6½, Bath 11, Bristol 18,
Cheltenham 34, Chepstow 26,
Cirencester 22, Frome 22, Gloucester 29,
Tetbury 12, Warminster 23.
See Very picturesque village, Market
Cross, Church, ancient three-arched
bridge.

⚑⚑★★★**Manor House,** *SN14 7HR.*
✆ (0249) 782206. C. ⊭ 34 bedrs, 11 bp, 2
bps, annexe 20 bedrs, 20 bp, TV, Dgs.
✗ a l c, mc, at, LD 9. ⒵ N, CH, CP 100, Ac,
sp, tc, gym, con 60, CF, 4 BGf, 0 st, Dis.
£ BB £35, DB £64–£74, DBB fr £36 (min 2
nights), ⒈, Bk £5, L £7·50, D £13·50,
cc 1 3 4 5, Dep a.

Rescue Service: Circuit Motors.
✆ (0249) 782596.

CASTLE DONINGTON Leicestershire.
Map 22F
Pop 5,359. M1 Motorway 2½, London 118,
Ashby-de-la-Zouch 9½, Burton-upon-Trent
16, Derby 9½, Loughborough 9,
Nottingham 12.
Golf Longcliffe 18h. **See** Donington Hall,
King's Mill (beauty spot), Church, old Key
House.

★★**Donington Manor,** *DE7 2PP.*
✆ Derby (0332) 810253. C. ⊭ 35 bedrs,
34 bp, TV. ✗ a l c, mc, LD 9.15. ⒵ N, CH,
CP 50, Ac, con 60, CF, 2 BGf, 2 st. £ BB fr
£23, DB fr £31, DT fr £38, ⒈, Bk £3·50, L
£5, D £6, cc 1 3 4 5.

Delven, G, z (RI), *12 Delven Lane, DE7
2LJ.* ✆ Derby (0332) 810153. C. ⊭ 7
bedrs, 3 ba. ✗ a l c. ⒵ CH, TV, CP 6, 1 BGf,
2 st. £ BB fr £14·38, DB fr £21·28, ⒈, D £4,
cc 1 5.

Four Poster, GH, x, (Unl), *73 Clapgun
St.* ✆ Derby (0332) 810335. C. ⊭ 7 bedrs,
2 ba, ns. ⒵ CH, TV, CP 8, CF. £ BB fr
£11·50, DB fr £19·50.

Repairer: W Boyden & Sons Ltd, Station
Rd. ✆ Derby (0332) 810221.

CASTLEFORD West Yorkshire. Map 25F
and 33B
Pop 39,814. Pontefract 3, London 181,
Boroughbridge 27, Harrogate 23, Leeds
10, Selby 14, Wakefield 9, York 23.
EC Wed. **MD** Mon, Fri, Sat. **Golf**
Pontefract 18h. **See** 12th cent Church.

Repairer: Martins (Pontefract) Ltd,
Oxford St. ✆ (0977) 558301.

Rescue Service: Burdin Motors (Castleford) Ltd, Park Rd.
℃ (0977) 552665.

CASTLETON Derbyshire. Map 22A
Pop 511. Matlock 20, London 164, Buxton 10, Chapel-en-le-Frith 7, Chesterfield 19, Sheffield 16.
EC Wed. **Golf** Bamford 18h. **See** Peveril Castle, Blue John, Speedwell, Treak Cliff and Peak Caverns, Norman Church.

Rescue Service: Castleton Garage, Buxton Rd. ℃ Hope Valley (0433) 20313.

CASTLETON North Yorkshire. Map 24D
Pop 375. Thirsk 31, London 250, Helmsley 21, Middlesbrough 18, Northallerton 27, Pickering 18, Whitby 14.
Golf Whitby 18h. **See** Church.

★★**Moorlands,** *High St, YO21 2 DB.*
℃ (0287) 60206. Open Easter–end Oct. C1. ⊞ 10 bedrs, 1 bp, 5 bps, 4 sh, 2 ba, Dgs. ✗ mc, LD 8.30. ₤ CH, TV, CP 15, Ac, 8 st. ₤ BB £12·75, D £25·50–£27·50, DBB £20·50–£21·50, WB, ①, Bk £3, Dep a.

CASTLETOWN Isle of Man. Map 27F
Pop 3,000, Douglas (Steamer service to Liverpool) 10, London 208, Peel 12.
EC Thur. **Golf** Castletown 18h. **See** Castle Rushen, Nautical Museum, Grammar School, Hango Hill.
🛈 Commissioners' Office, Parliament Sq. ℃ Castletown (0624) 823518.

★★★**Castletown Golf Links,** *Fort Island.* ℃ (0624) 822201. Open Apr–Sept. C. ⊞ 75 bedrs, 50 bp, 25 bps, 4 ba, TV, Dgs. ✗ a l c, mc, at LD 9.15. ₤ CH, TV, Dgs, CP 80, sp, tc, con 150, CF, 12 BGf, 0 st, Dis. ₤ BB £23–£24, DB £44–£45, DBB £28–£29, ②, 10%, Bk £3·50, L £6·50, D £7·50, cc 1 2 3.

Rescue Service: S & S Motors Ltd, Hope St. ℃ (0624) 823698.

CATERHAM Surrey. Map 7B
Pop 37,770 (inc Warlingham), Purley 5, London 17, Godstone 2½, Redhill 6, Reigate 7½.
EC Wed. **Golf** North Downs 18h. **See** Chaldon Church, Pilgrim's Way.

Rescue Service: Cranmer Recovery Service, 83 Eldon Rd. ℃ (0883) 43176. Station Garage, 32 Station Av. ℃ (0883) 43070.

CATLOWDY Cumbria. Map 30F
M6 Motorway 14, London 310, Canonbie 5, Carlisle 16, Greenhead 19, Longtown 8, Newcastleton 8.

Bessiestown Farm, F, xy, (Unl), *Penton CA6 5QP* ℃ Nicholforest (022 877) 219.

CATTERICK North Yorkshire. Map 24F
Pop 2,824. Boroughbridge 22, London 230, Brough 34, Darlington 13, Harrogate 31, Leyburn 11, Middlesbrough 27, Middleton-in-Teesdale 28, Northallerton 13, Stockton-on-Tees 23, West Auckland 19.
EC Wed. **Golf** Catterick Garrison 18h. **See** Catterick Racecourse, River Swale, 14th cent Church.

★★**Bridge House,** *Catterick Bridge, DL10 7PE.* ℃ Richmond (0748) 818331. Closed Xmas. C. ⊞ 16 bedrs, 4 bp, 2 bps, 3 ba, TV, Dgs. ✗ a l c, mc, LD 9.30. ₤ CH, CP 70, Ac, pf, con 120, CF. ₤ BB £15–£22·50,

DB £25–£32·50, WB, ①, Bk £3·25, L £3·95, D £7·50, cc 1 3 4 5.

CHADDERTON Gtr Manchester (Lancashire). M.Areas 19B and 27B
Pop 33,690. Oldham 2, London 187, Bury 9, Manchester 7, Rochdale 6, Walkden 13.
EC Tue. **Golf** Royton 18h. **See** Foxdenton Hall, Manor House.

Rescue Service: Eric Howarth Ltd, Nimble Nook Garage, Broadway.
℃ 061-624 3088.

CHADDESDEN Derbyshire. Map 22D
M1 Motorway 11, London 127, Ashby-de-la-Zouch 14, Derby 2, Nottingham 14.

Rescue Service: Roe Farm Service Station, Wiltshire Rd. ℃ Derby (0332) 674354.

CHAGFORD Devon. Maps 3D and 4E
Pop 1,250. Exeter 16, London 186, Ashburton 13, Barnstaple 34, Crediton 14, Newton Abbot 16, Okehampton 11, Plymouth 28, Saltash 29, South Molton 30, Tavistock 20.
EC Wed. **Golf** Okehampton 18h. **See** Dartmoor, St Michael's 13th cent Church, Old Inns, Fingle Bridge 4m, 14 cent Stannary Town.

🏩★★★**Great Tree,** *nr Sandy Park, TQ13 8JS.* ℃ (064 73) 2491. C. ⊞ 14 bedrs, 13 bp, 1 bps, TV, Dgs. ✗ a l c, mc, at, LD 9. ₤ CH, CP 20, U 3, G 4, con 15, CF, 11 BGf, 2 st. ₤ BB £24·15–£26·45, DB £46–£52·90, WB, ②, Bk £3·50, L £6·50, D £9·50, cc 1 2 3 5 6, Dep a.

🏩★★★**Mill End** (R), *Sandy Park, TQ13 8JN.* ℃ (064 73) 2282. Closed 18th Dec–28th Dec, RS Winter. C. ⊞ 17 bedrs, 17 bp, TV, Dgs. ✗ mc, at, LD 9. ₤ CH, TV, CP 17, U 4, pf, CF, 3 BGf, Dis. ₤ BB £16·50–£32·50, DB £33–£50, ①, Bk £4·50, L £8, D £11·50, cc 1 3 4 5 6.

🏩★★★**Teignworthy,** (R), *Frenchbeer, TQ13 8EX.* ℃ (064 73) 3355. C14. ⊞ 9 bedrs, 9 bp, TV. ✗ a l c, mc, at, LD 9. ₤ CH, CP 15, G 2, tc, pf, sb, sol, CF, 2 st. ₤ BB £39·50, DB £61·50, WB (win), ①, Bk £6, L £15, D £17·50.

🏩★★**Easton Court** (R), *Easton Cross, TQ13 8JL.* (1½m NE A382).
℃ (064 73) 3469.

★★**Moor Park,** *Lower St, TQ13 8BY.* ℃ (064 73) 2202.

★★**Three Crowns** (R), *High St, TQ13 8AJ.* ℃ (064 73) 3444.▲
Claremont, G, x (Rl), *Mill St, TQ13 8AW.* ℃ (064 73) 3304. C. ⊞ 5 bedrs, 2 ba, Dgs. ₤ CH, TV, CP 1, U 4, CF. ₤ BB £8, DB £16, WT (b) £81, (c) £54, DT (b) £12, ①, D £4.
Glendarah, G, x (R), *TQ13 8BZ.* ℃ (064 73) 3270. C. ⊞ 8 bedrs, 1 bp, 2 ba, Dgs. ₤ CH, TV, CP 9, CF, 1 BGf, 2 st. ₤ BB £8·50–£9·50, DB £17–£19, WT £44·50–£105, DT £14–£16, ①, Bk £3, D £5·50.

CHALE Isle of Wight. Map 6F
Pop 650. Portsmouth (Fy) 16, London 90, Cowes 14, Ryde 16, Shanklin 8½, Ventnor 6½.
EC Wed. **Golf** Ventnor 9h. **See** Blackgang Chine, Church, Monuments, St Catherine's Hill, St Catherine's Chapel, St Catherine's Point and Lighthouse.

Clarendon, H, and Wight Mouse, l, xy, *PO38 2HA.* ℃ Niton (0983) 730431. C. ⊞ 13 bedrs, 3 bp, 4 bps, 2 ba, TV, Dgs. ✗ a l c. ₤ CH, TV, Dgs, ns, CP 100, CF.

₤ BB £11·50–£13·80, DB £23–£27·60, WT (b) £126·50, DT (b) £20·70, ②, Bk £2, L £3, D £6.

CHALFONT ST PETER Buckingham. Map 7A
Pop 14,419. Gerrards Cross 1, London 21, Aylesbury 21, High Wycombe 10, Slough 7.
EC Thurs. **Golf** Gerrards Cross 18h. **See** 18 cent Church, Inn.

Greyhound, l, x, *High St, SL9 9RA.* ℃ Gerrards Cross (0753) 883404.

CHALGROVE Oxfordshire. M.Area 14F
Pop 2,519. M40 Motorway 6½, High Wycombe 17, London 47, Abingdon 12, Oxford 10, Thame 12, Wallingford 3½.
Golf Southfields 18h, Huntercombe 18h.

Rescue Service: Chalgrove Garage, (D. J. Matthews), High St. ℃ (0865) 890213.

CHANDLER'S FORD Hants. Map 6D
Winchester 6½, London 71, Cosham 20, Fareham 16, Lyndhurst 13, Petersfield 24, Romsey 6, Southampton 6.
EC Wed.

Specialist Spring Repairer: Jonas Woodhead Ltd, 4 Brickfield La.
℃ (042 15) 4474.

CHAPMANSLADE Wiltshire. Map 5D
Pop 500. Westbury 4, London 102, Bath 15, Frome 3½, Warminster 4.
EC Sat. **See** Chalcot House.

Rescue Service: Chapmanslade Garage, High St, nr Westbury. ℃ (037 388) 265.

CHARD Somerset. Map 5E
Pop 9,384. Ilminster 5, London 141, Axminster 7, Crewkerne 8, Honiton 14, Taunton 13, Tiverton 26.
EC Wed. **MD** Sat. **Golf** Windwhistle 12h. **See** 15th cent Church, old Grammar School, Manor House (Judge Jeffreys assoc), Guildhall, Waterloo House, Choughs Inn, Cricket St Thomas Wild Life Park 3m E, Museum, Forde Abbey, Chard Reservoir.

Watermead, G, x (R), *83 High St, TA20 1QT.* ℃ (04606) 2834. C. ⊞ 9 bedrs, 2 ba, ns, Dgs. ₤ CH, TV, Dgs, ns, CP 9, G 2, CF, 1 st. ₤ BB £8–£8·50, DB £16–£17, WT (c) £50–£55, DT £76·25–£81·25, ①, Bk £2, D £3·75.

Rescue Service: Hillside Filling Station, Ham Hill, Combe-St-Nicholas. ℃ Buckland St Mary (046 034) 272. Premier Motors, Crewkerne Rd. ℃ (046 06) 3146.

CHARING Kent Map 10C
Maidstone 13, London 50, Ashford 6, Canterbury 14, Hawkhurst 20, Rochester 21, Tenterden 14, Tunbridge Wells 28.

★**Swan,** *Ashford Rd, TN27 0JS.* ℃ (023 371) 2357.

CHARLBURY Oxfordshire. Map 14F
Pop 2,637. Oxford 15, London 71, Banbury 15, Bicester 16, Burford 9, Chipping Norton 6½, Faringdon 19, Wantage 24.
Golf Chipping Norton 9h, Burford 18h. **See** Museum, Combe Mill, Church of St. Mary.

★★**Bell,** *Church St, OX7 3AP.* ℃ (0608) 278.

CHARLECOTE Warwickshire. Map 14D
Banbury 17, London 89, Chipping Norton 23, Moreton-in-Marsh 18, Stratford-upon-Avon 5, Warwick 6.

★★★**Charlecote Pheasant,** *CV35 9EW.* ☎ Stratford-on-Avon (0789) 840200. C. 🛏 16 bedrs, 5 bp, 11 bps, TV, Dgs. ✕ a l c, mc, at, LD 10. 🏠 CH, CP 130, Ac, tc, sb, sol, con 60, CF, 1 BGf, 1 st, Dis. £ BB £26, DB £34, WB, [1], Bk £3·50, L £6·20, D £7·40, cc 1 3.

CHARLTON KINGS Glos. Maps 13F and 14E
Pop 10,190. Burford 21, London 96, Cheltenham 1½, Cirencester 13, Stow-on-the-Wold 16.
EC Wed. **Golf** Lilleybrook 18h. **See** Parish Church of St Mary, Old Stocks.

Rescue Service: Lyefield Garage, 21 Lyefield Rd West. ☎ Cheltenham (0242) 21131.▲
Station Garage (Charlton Kings) Ltd, Cirencester Rd. ☎ Cheltenham (0242) 23747.

CHARLWOOD Surrey. Map 7C
Pop 2,795. Redhill 8, London 29, Crawley 4, Dorking 9, Lingfield 12
EC Wed. **Golf** Ifield 18h. **See** 'The Half Moon' Inn, stone causeways, church.

★★★**Russ Hill** (R), *Russ Hill, RH6 0EL.* ☎ Norwood Hill (0293) 862171. C. 🛏 80 bedrs, 80 bp, TV, Dgs. ✕ a l c, mc, at, LD 9.45. 🏠 N, CH, CP 250, Ac, sp, tc, sb, sol, con 300, CF, 2 BGf, 1 st, Dis. £ BB fr £30, DB fr £46, WB, [2], Bk £4, L £6·75, D £7·75, cc 1 3 4 5 6, Dep b.
Trumble's H, xy (R), *Stanhill, RH6 0EP.* ☎ Crawley (0293) 862212. Closed Xmas & New Year. 🛏 5 bedrs, 2 bp, 3 bps, TV. ✕ a l c. 🏠 CH, CP 30. £ BB £28, DB £35, [1], Bk £3, D £12, cc 1 3 4 5.

CHARMOUTH Dorset. Map 5E.
Pop 1,122. Dorchester 22, London 144, Axminster 6, Crewkerne 13, Lyme Regis 3, Taunton 27, Weymouth 26.
Golf Lyme Regis 18h. **See** Old Toll House, 16th cent Queen's Armes, Devil's Bellows, Fossil Exhibition.

▣★★**Charmouth House,** *The Street, DT6 6PH.* ☎ (0297) 60319. C. 🛏 9 bedrs, 2 bp, 4 ba, Dgs. ✕ a l c, LD 9.30. 🏠 ch, TV, CP 24, sp, sb, CF, 1 st. £ BB £14, DB £28–£31, [2], Bk £2·50, D £4, cc 1 3, Dep.
▣★★**Fernhill,** *DT6 6BX.* ☎ (0297) 60492. C. 🛏 15 bedrs, 5 bp, 3 bps, 4 sh, 3 ba, Dgs. ✕ mc, LD 8.45. 🏠 CH, TV, Dgs, CP 60, sp, sc, con 20, CF, 2 st. £ BB £17–£22, DB £34–£41·20, DBB £24–£28·10, WB, [2], Bk £2·95, L £2·95, D £8·95, cc 1 3.
▣★★**Queen's Armes** (R), *The Street, DT6 6QF.* ☎ (0297) 60339. Closed Xmas. C4 🛏 11 bedrs, 5 bp, 4 bps, 1 ba, Dgs. ✕ a l c, mc, LD 8.30. 🏠 CH, ns, CP 20. £ BB £14·50–£17, DB £29–£34, WT £128–£145, WB, [2], Bk £3·50, D £7·95, Dep a.
★**Sea Horse** (R), *Higher Sea La, DT6 6BB.* ☎ (0297) 60414. Open Mar–Oct. C. 🛏 8 bedrs, 3 bp, 2 ba, annexe 2 bedrs, 1 bp, 1 ba, Dgs. ✕ mc, at, LD 8. 🏠 CH, TV, CP 14, U 2, CF, 2 BGf, 4 st. £ BB £10–£15·50, DB £20–£31, WT £116–£136, DT £17–£19·50, WB, [2], Bk £2·50, L £3, D £4, Dep b.
Newlands House, G, x (RI), *Stonebarrow Lane, DT6 6RA.* ☎ (0297) 60212.
The Cottage, PH, *The Street, DT6 6PQ.* ☎ (0297) 60407.

CHARNOCK RICHARD Lancs. Map 27D
Pop 2,000. Wigan 7, London 202, Chorley 3, Liverpool 24, Ormskirk 12, Preston 10, St Helens 14, Southport 18.
EC Wed. **Golf** Leyland 18h. **See** Church, Almshouses.

▣★★★**M TraveLodge** (TH), (RI), *Mill La, PR7 5LR* (M6 Motorway). ☎ Coppull (0257) 791746. C. 🛏 108 bedrs, 108 bp, TV, Dgs. ✕ a l c. 🏠 CH, Dgs, CP 120, con 40, CF, 50 BGf, 1 st. £ BBc £26, DBc £34·50, WB, [1], cc 1 2 3 4 5 6. (Meals served in adjacent Motorway Service Area Restaurant).
★★**M Hunters Lodge** (Rt), *Preston Rd, PR7 5LH.* ☎ Coppull (0257) 791324. C. 🛏 21 bedrs, 2 bp, 19 bps, TV, Dgs. ✕ a l c, mc, LD 10. 🏠 CH, CP 100, Ac, sol, con 70, CF, 12 BGf, Dis. £ BB £24, DB £33, DT £30–£35, WB, [2], Bk £3·95, L £2·95, D £4·95, cc 1 3 4 5 6, Dep b.

Rescue Service: J. Boardman (Garages) Ltd, M6 Motorway. ☎ Forton (0524) 791666.

CHATHAM Kent. Map 10C
Rochester 1, London 31, M2 Motorway 8, Maidstone 3½, Sittingbourne 10.
EC Wed. **See** Almshouses, Heritage Centre, Napoleonic Fort, Rochester Castle, Cathedral and Museum (1 m W), RE Museum (Gillingham).

★★★**M Crest,** *Maidstone Rd, ME5 9SF.* ☎ Medway (0634) 687111. C. 🛏 106 bedrs, 106 bp, ns, TV, Dgs. ✕ a l c, mc, at, LD 9.30. 🏠 Lt, N, CH, CP 180, Ac, con 110, CF, 2 BGf, Dis. £ BB fr £47·75, DB fr £63, WB, [1], Bk £2·55, D £9·60, cc 1 2 3 4 5 6, Dep b.

Rescue Service: Autotrend Motor Services, 101 Beacon Rd. ☎ Medway (0634) 46967 & (0634) 811666.

CHEADLE Gtr Manchester (Cheshire). Map 19B
Pop 26,350. Congleton 17, London 178, Altrincham 7, Knutsford 12, Macclesfield 11, Manchester 7, Sandbach 21, Stockport 3½, Walkden 13.
EC Wed. **Golf** Cheadle 9h. **See** Church (16th cent), Moseley Old Hall (grounds), Abney Hall.

Repairer: Quick, H & J Ltd, Wimslow Rd. ☎ 061-437 2345.

CHEADLE Staffordshire. Map 22C
Pop 10,876. Uttoxeter 9½, London 145, Ashbourne 13, Buxton 23, Macclesfield 23, Newcastle-under-Lyme 12, Stafford 18.
EC Wed. **MD** Fri, Sat. **Golf** Whiston 18h. **See** Gothic Church (R.C.), 17 cent Market Cross.

Royal Oak, H, z, *69 High St, ST10 1AN.* ☎ (0538) 753116. C. 🛏 6 bedrs, 2 ba, TV, Dgs. ✕ a l c. 🏠 CH, TV, Dgs, CP 30, CF. £ BB £10·50, DB £16·50, [1], Bk £2·75, L £3, D £5, cc 5.

CHEADLE HULME Gtr Manchester (Cheshire). Map 19B
Pop 29,145. Congleton 17, London 178, Altrincham 8, Knutsford 12, Macclesfield 11, Manchester 9, Sandbach 21, Stockport 3½, Walkden 15.
EC Wed. **Golf** Cheadle 9h.
[i] 6 Station Rd. ☎ 061-486 0283.

▣★★**M Ravenoak,** (Cl), *Ravenoak Rd, SK8 7EQ.* ☎ 061-485 3376. C. 🛏 19 bedrs, 1 bp, 1 bps, 3 sh, 3 ba, annexe 18 bedrs, 4 bp, 14 bps, TV, Dgs. ✕ a l c, mc, at, LD 8.45. 🏠 CH, CP 60–80, Ac, con 100, CF, 18 BGf, 2 st, Dis. £ BB fr £18·98, DB fr £27·60, DBB fr £28·18, [1], Bk £2·50, D £5·50, cc 1 3 4 5, Dep b.

Rescue Service: Kendor Recovery, Church Road Garage, Church Rd. ☎ 061-437 8400.
Mellor Road Garage, Mellor Rd. ☎ 061-485 3341 & 7447.

CHEAM Greater London (Surrey). Map 7A
Pop 79,008 (inc Sutton), Mitcham 4, London 12, Croydon 5½, Epsom 3½, Kingston upon Thames 6, Purley 6, Reigate 9½, Thornton Heath 6½.
EC Wed. **See** St Dunstan's Church, Nonsuch Park.

Repairer: Godfreys (Sutton & Cheam) Ltd, 50 Malden Rd. ☎ 01-644 8878.

CHEDDAR Somerset. Map 5C
Pop 3,500. Wells 8, London 130, Bath 23, Bridgwater 18, Bristol 17, Glastonbury 13, Radstock 17, Weston-super-Mare 12.
EC Wed, Sat. **MD** Wed. **Golf** Burnham and Berrow 18h. **See** Market Cross, Gorge, Caves, Jacob's Ladder, Motor and Transport Museum, Museum with prehistoric remains, Ambleside Water Gardens and Aviaries 2 m NW.
[i] The Library, Union St. ☎ Cheddar (0934) 742769.

★**Gordons** (R), *Cliff St, BS27 3PT.* ☎ (0934) 742497. Closed Jan. C. 🛏 13 bedrs, 2 sh, 2 ba, TV, Dgs. ✕ a l c, mc, at, LD 9. 🏠 CH, TV, Dgs, CP 10, Ac, con 40, CF, 2 st. £ BB fr £8·50, DB fr £16, DBB fr £12, WB, [1], Bk £2·75, L £4, D £4, cc 1 5, Dep a.
Fairlands House, G, x (Unl), Froglands Lane. ☎ 742629.
The Market Cross, PH, x (RI), *Church St, BS27 3RA.* ☎ (0934) 742264. C. 🛏 6 bedrs, 2 ba, Dgs. 🏠 CH, TV, CP 6, CF. £ BB £8·50–£10, DB £15–£16, [1], Bk £5·50.
Poacher's Table, G, x, *Cliff St.* ☎ (0934) 742271. C. 🛏 6 bedrs, 3 ba, TV, Dgs. ✕ a l c. 🏠 CH, Dgs, CP 9, CF. £ DB £13–£14, WT (b) £84–£87·50, DT (b) £12–£12·50, [2], cc 1 3 4 5.

Rescue Service: Cheddar Motors Ltd, Tweentown. ☎ (0934) 742955.

CHELFORD Cheshire. Map 19B
Pop 690. Congleton 8½, London 169, Glossop 21, Knutsford 5½, Macclesfield 7, Middlewich 10, Sandbach 11, Stockport 12
EC Sat. **MD** Mon to Fri. **Golf** Wilmslow 18h. **See** Church, Traction Engine Rally 2nd wknd Aug.

Repairer: Blackhurst Bros, Station Garage, Knutsford Rd. ☎ (0625) 861239.

CHELLASTON Derbyshire. M.Area 22F
Pop 3,990. Ashby-de-la-Zouch 10, London 123, Burton upon Trent 11, Derby 4, Loughborough 14, Nottingham 15.
EC Wed. **See** St Peter's Church (alabaster pulpit).

Lawn, H, z, *23 High St.* ✆ Derby (0332) 701553.

Rescue Service: Chellaston Garages Ltd, 3 Derby Rd. ✆ Derby (0332) 700178.

CHELMSFORD Essex. Map 17F
Pop 58,974. Brentwood 11, London 33, Bishop's Stortford 18, Braintree 11, Colchester 22, Dunmow 12, Epping 17, Hatfield 36, Southend 19.
EC Wed. **MD** Mon, Tue, Fri, Sat. **Golf** Chelmsford 18h (2). **See** Cathedral, Shire Hall, Chelmsford and Essex Museum, Grammar School, Springfield Church, Hylands Park (Writtle).

★★★**M Miami,** *Princes Rd, CM2 9AJ.* ✆ (0245) 269603. RS Xmas. C. ⇔ 46 bedrs, 4 bp, 42 bps, 5 ba, TV, Dgs. ✗ a l c, mc, at, LD 9.30. 🅐 N, CH, Dgs, CP 80, Ac, sb, con 45, CF, 4 BGf, 1 st. £ BB fr £14, DB fr £25, WB, ①, Bk £3·75, L £4·50, D £5·25, cc 1 2 3 5 6.

⇕★★★**Pontlands Park,** *West Hanningfield Rd, CM2 8HR.* ✆ (0245) 76444. Closed 1st week Jan. C. ⇔ 8 bedrs, 8 bp, TV, Dgs. ✗ a l c, mc, at, LD 9. 🅐 CH, Dgs, sp, sb, sol, gym, con, CF, 1 st. £ BBc £37·75, DBc £54·50, WB, ② 10%, Bk £4·75, L £7, D £7, cc 1 3 4 5.

★★★**South Lodge,** *196 New London Rd, CM2 0AR.* ✆ (0245) 264564. C. ⇔ 41 bedrs, 41 bp, TV, Dgs. ✗ a l c, mc, at, LD 10. 🅐 N, CH, CP 45, con 70, CF, 1 st. £ cc 1 3 4 5 6, Dep b.

★★**County,** *29 Rainsford Rd, CM1 2QA.* ✆ (0245) 266911. Closed week after Xmas, C. ⇔ 31 bedrs, 18 bp, 6 bps, 3 ba, annexe 23 bedrs, 7 bps, 6 ba, Dgs. ✗ a l c, mc, at, LD 9.15. 🅐 N, CH, TV, Dgs, CP 70, Ac, con, CF, 3 BGf. £ BB fr £22, DB fr £40, WB, ②, Bk £5, L £6, D £7, cc 1 2 3 5 6, Dep b.

Beechcroft, PH, z (Unl), *211 New London Rd, CM2 0AJ.* ✆ (0245) 352462. Closed Xmas & New Year. C. ⇔ 24 bedrs, 1 bp, 6 bps, 4 ba, Dgs. 🅐 CH, TV, CP 15, CF, 7 st. £ BB £14·40–£19·50, DB £23–£30, WT £100·80, ①, Bk £2·50.

Boswell House, PH, z (R), *118 Springfield Rd, CM2 6LF.* ✆ (0245) 87587. C. ⇔ 13 bedrs, 9 bp, 4 bps, TV, Dgs. 🅐 CH, TV, ns, CP 15, CF, 3 BGf, 1 st. £ BB £17·25–£24·50, DB £30–£35, DT (b) £22·75–£26·25, ①, Bk £2·50, D £5·50.

Tanunda, H, z (RI) *217 New London Rd, CM2 0AJ.* ✆ (0245) 354295. Closed Xmas. C. ⇔ 20 bedrs, 2 bp, 7 bps, 3 ba, TV, Dgs. ✗ a l c. 🅐 CH, TV, CP 20, 1 BGf, 1 st. £ BB fr £14, DB fr £24, ①, Bk £3·25, D £6·25.

MC Repairer: Hadler's Garage Ltd, 200 Baddow Rd. ✆ (0245) 54844.
Rescue Service: Oasis Autopoint, Springfield Rd. ✆ (0245) 57047. Service on Site, Boreham Industrial Estate, Waltham Rd, Boreham. ✆ (0245) 465317 & (0245) 59666.

CHELSFIELD Greater London (Kent) Map 7B
Orpington 2, London 16, Croydon 12, Dartford 10, Sevenoaks 7½.
See North Downs.

Rescue Service: DW Recovery & Towing Services, Longlands, Jubilee Rd.
✆ Knockholt (0959) 34476.

CHELTENHAM Gloucestershire. Maps 13F and 14E.
See also SOUTHAM.
Pop 86,000. Burford 22, London 97, M5 Motorway 3½, Bath 42, Cirencester 14, Evesham 16, Gloucester 9, Ledbury 22, Stratford-upon-Avon 30, Stow-on-the-Wold 18, Tetbury 24, Tewkesbury 9.
See Plan, p. 175.
EC Wed. **MD** Thur. **Golf** Cleeve Hill 18h.
See Cheltenham College, Cheltenham Ladies College, Art Gallery and Museum, Racecourse, St Mary's Parish Church, Montpellier Rotunda, Regency houses, Hailes Abbey 7½m NE, Chedworth Roman Villa 8½ m SE, Mineral Springs, Devil's Chimney (964 ft), Sudeley Castle and Winchcombe Railway Museum (7 m NE).
🛈 The Promenade. ✆ Cheltenham (0242) 22878.

★★★★**M Golden Valley Thistle,** *Gloucester Rd, GL51 0TS.*
✆ (0242) 32691. C. ⇔ 103 bedrs, 103 bp, ns, TV, Dgs. ✗ a l c, mc, at, LD 9.30. 🅐 Lt, N, CH, CP 279, Ac, con 500, CF, 33 BGf, 0 st, Dis. £ BB £44·45–£48·95, DB £60·90–£65·40, WB, ②, Bk £4·95, cc 1 2 3 4 5 6, Dep b.

★★★★**Queen's** (TH), *Promenade, GL50 1NN.* ✆ (0242) 514724. C. ⇔ 77 bedrs, 77 bp, TV, Dgs. ✗ a l c, mc, at, LD 9.45. 🅐 Lt, N, CH, CP 32, Ac, con 280, CF, 2 st. £ BB £47·50, DB £63·50, WB, ①, cc 1 2 3 4 5 6, Dep (Xmas).

★★★**Carlton,** *Parabola Rd, GL50 3AQ.* ✆ (0242) 514453. C. ⇔ 49 bedrs, 48 bp, 1 bps, TV, Dgs. ✗ a l c, mc, at, LD 9. 🅐 Lt, N, CH, CP 20, Ac, con 150, CF, 8 BGf, 9 st. £ BB £30·50, DB £42, WT £175, WB, ①, Bk £4, L £6·75, D £8, cc 1 3 4 5 6, Dep b.

★★**George,** *41 St George's Rd, GL50 3DZ.* ✆ (0242) 35751. C. ⇔ 41 bedrs, 22 bp, 4 bps, 5 ba, TV, Dgs. ✗ a l c, mc, at. 🅐 N, CH, CP 15, U 4, Ac, con, CF, 1 BGf, 4 st. £ BB £20–£26, DB £30–£36, WT £223·65, DBB £28, WB, ①, Bk £3, L £3·95, D £7·50, cc 1 3 4 5 6, Dep b.

★★**Park Place,** *Park Pl, GL50 2RB.* ✆ (0242) 525353. C. ⇔ 50 bedrs, 31 bp, 19 sh, 3 ba, TV, Dgs. ✗ a l c, mc, at, LD 8.30. 🅐 Lt, N, CH, CP 25, Ac, con 85, CF. £ BB £18·50–£25, DB £28·50–£36. WB, Bk £3·50, L £4·75, D £8·50, ①, cc 1 2 3 4 5 6.

★★**Savoy,** *Bayshill Rd, GL50 3AS.* ✆ (0242) 527788. C. ⇔ 59 bedrs, 26 bp, 3 bps, 1 sh, 9 ba, TV, Dgs. ✗ mc, at, LD 9. 🅐 Lt, N, CH, CP 25, U 1, Ac, sb, sol, con 60, CF, 4 BGf. £ BBc fr £22, DBc fr £34, WB, Bk £3, L £4, D £6·95, ①, cc 1 2 3 4 5 6.

★**Wellesley Court,** *Clarence Sq, GL50 4JR.* ✆ (0242) 31632. RS Bank Holidays & Sun, C5. ⇔ 21 bedrs, 3 bp, 3 ba, TV, Dgs. ✗ a l c, mc, at, LD 9.30. 🅐 Lt, CH, TV, CP 18, Ac, con 40, CF, 2 BGf, 7 st. £ BB £17–£23, DB £30–£40, WT £206·50, DT £29·50, WB, ①, Bk £3, L £5·50, D £7, cc 1 2 3 5, Dep b.

Bowler Hat, PH, z (RI), *130 London Rd, GL52 6HJ.* ✆ (0242) 523614. C. ⇔ 6 bedrs, 1 bp, 1 ba, TV. 🅐 CH, CP, CF, 6 st. £ BB £9–£11, DB £16–£22, WT (b) £80–£90, DT (b) £13·50–£15, ①.

Broomhill, G, z (Unl), *218 London Rd, GL52 6HW.* ✆ (0242) 513086.

Clevelands House, G, z (Unl), *38 Evesham Rd, GL52 2AH.*
✆ (0242) 518898. C. ⇔ 14 bedrs, 3 ba, TV, Dgs. ✗ a l c. 🅐 CH, TV, Dgs, CP 10, CF,

---

2 BGf, 1 st. £ BB £8–£10, DB £16–£20, ①, Bk £3·50.

Cotswold Grange, PH, x (RI) *Pittville Circus Rd, GL52 2QH.* ✆ (0242) 515119. C. ⇔ 20 bedrs, 9 bp, 4 ba, Dgs. ✗ a l c. 🅐 CH, TV, Dgs, CP 20, CF, 6 st. £ BB £14–£17·50, DB £23–£29, ①, Bk £2·50, L £2·95, D £5.

Hollington House, PH, y (RI), *115 Hales Rd, GL52 6ST.* ✆ (0242) 570280. C. ⇔ 6 bedrs, 2 bps, 1 ba, TV, Dgs. 🅐 ch, TV, CP 8, CF, 4 st. £ BB £11·20–£12·20, DB £21–£27, WT (c) £70–£80, DT £17·20–£18·20, ②.

Ivy Dene, G, y (Unl), *145 Hewlett Rd, GL52 6TS.* ✆ (0242) 521726. C. ⇔ 9 bedrs, 3 ba, Dgs. 🅐 CH, TV, Dgs, CP 9, CF, 1 BGf. £ BB £7–£7·50, DB £14–£15, WT (c) fr £49, ①.

Leeswood, G, z (Unl), *14 Montpellier Dr, GL50 1TX.* ✆ (0242) 524813. Closed Xmas. C. ⇔ 7 bedrs, TV, Dgs. 🅐 ch, CP 4, 2 st. £ BB £8·50–£10, DB £17–£20, WT (c) £51–£60, ①, Bk £2.

Micklinton, PH, z (Unl) *12 Montpellier Dr, GL50 1TX.* ✆ (0242) 520000. C1. ⇔ 9 bedrs, 1 sh, 2 ba, TV, Dgs. 🅐 CH, TV, Dgs, CP 4, U 1, CF, 1 BGf. £ BB £8–£10, DB £9–£11, DT (b) £13·50–£14, ①.

Montpellier, PH, z (R), *33 Montpellier Terr.* ✆ (0242) 526009. C10. ⇔ 12 bedrs, 10 sh, 3 ba. ✗ a l c. 🅐 CH, TV, CP 40, CF. £ BB £12–£16, DB £20–£24, WT £84–£120, DT £14–£16, ①, Bk £2·60, L £4·60, D £5·50.

North Hall, PH, z (R), *Pittville Circus Rd, GL52 2PZ.* ✆ (0242) 520589. C. ⇔ 21 bedrs, 7 ba, TV, Dgs. 🅐 CH, TV, CP 20, CF, 6 st. £ BB fr £11·21, DB fr £18·98, WT (b) fr £91·44, DT (b) fr £15·24, ②, Bk £3·45, D £4·03.

Regency House, PH, z, (RI) *50 Clarence Sq, GL50 4JR.* ✆ (0242) 582718. C. ⇔ 8 bedrs, 2 bp, 3 ba, TV, Dgs. 🅐 CH, TV, G 2, CF, 8 st. £ BB fr £9, DB fr £18, WT fr £85, DT (b) fr £14, ①.

Wayside House, H, yz (Unl), *125 London Rd, GL52 6HN.* ✆ (0242) 20250.

Wellington, PH, z (R), *Wellington Sq, GL50 4JZ.* ✆ (0242) 521627. C. ⇔ 10 bedrs, 2 sh, 3 ba. ✗ a l c. 🅐 CH, TV, ns, CP 6, CF, 6 st. £ BB fr £10·50, DB fr £20, DT (b) £16, Bk £2·50, L £3·50, D £5·50.

Willoughby, G, z (Unl), *1 Suffolk Sq, GL50 2DR.* ✆ (0242) 522798. Closed Dec. C. ⇔ 10 bedrs, 3 sh, 3 ba, TV, Dgs. 🅐 ch, TV, CP 10, CF, 2 BGf, 4 st. £ BB £10·50, DB £21, WT (b) £95, (c) £70, DT (b) £15, ②.

Repairer: Ebdons Automobiles Ltd, 28 Bath Rd. ✆ (0242) 515391.
Lex Mead, Princess Elizabeth Way.
✆ (0242) 520441.
Rescue Service: Michael Smith Motors, Keynsham St, London Rd.
✆ (0242) 519616.
Pihlens Motors, 60, 66 & 84 Fairview Rd.
✆ (0242) 513880.
Witcombe Garage Group, Witcombe Pl.
✆ (0242) 34797.

CHELWOOD GATE East Sussex. M.Area 7D
Pop 1,451. East Grinstead 6½, London 36, Crawley 11, Hastings 32, Haywards Heath 7½, Hurst Green 23, Lewes 13, Tunbridge Wells 14, Uckfield 7½.
Golf Royal Ashdown Forest 18h.(2).

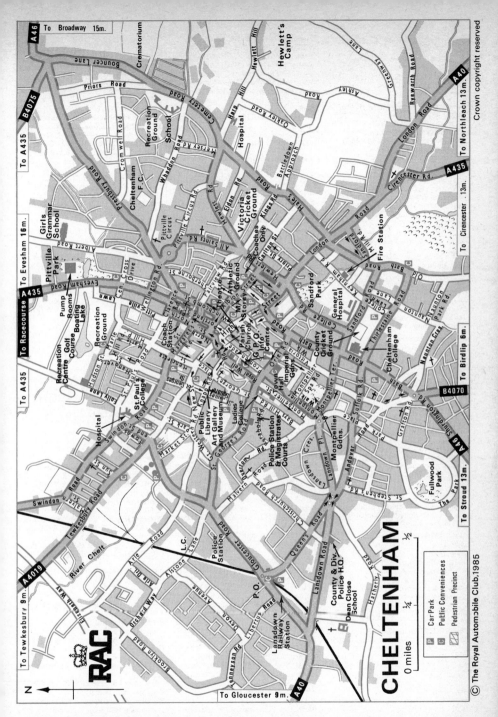

CHELTENHAM

0 miles   ¼   ½

P	Car Park	
C	Public Conveniences	
	Pedestrian Precinct	

Repairer: Mid Sussex Garage Ltd.
✆ (082 574) 355.

CHENIES Buckinghamshire. Map 15E
Pop 1,063. Rickmansworth 4, London 22,
Aylesbury 18, Bletchley 30, Dunstable 20,
High Wycombe 12, Oxford 36, Slough 14.
See Church. Mill.

★★★**Bedford Arms,** *Thistle, WD3 6EQ.*
✆ (092 78) 3301. C. ⊷ 10 bedrs, 10 bp,
TV. ✗ a l c, LD 9.30. 🅟 N, CH, CP 80, CF, 0
st. £ BB £48·45–£53·95, DB £66·40–
£71·40, WB, ②, Bk £5·95, L £17·45, D
£21·50, cc 1 2 3 4 5 6, Dep a.

CHERITON BISHOP Devon. Maps 3B
and 4E
Pop 606. Exeter 9, London 178,
Ashburton 19, Crediton 7, Newton Abbot
18, Okehampton 12.
Golf Downes Crediton 18h. **See** 13th
cent Church, 16th cent Carved Wooden
Panels, 18th cent Well.

Rescue Service: Moorlands Garage,
Cheriton Cross. ✆ (064 724) 256.

CHERTSEY Surrey. Map 7A
Pop 11,620. Richmond-upon-Thames 11,
London 19, Bagshot 9½, Kingston upon
Thames 10, Leatherhead 12, Reading 23,
Ripley 9, Staines 3½, Weybridge 3, Woking
3.
EC Wed. **MD** Sat. **Golf** Laleham 18h. **See**
St Peter's Church founded 1310, Museum,
18th cent Bridge.

★**Bridge,** *Chertsey Bridge Rd, KT16 8JZ.*
✆ (093 28) 64408. C. ⊷ 11 bedrs, 2 ba.
✗ a l c, mc, at, LD 10.15. 🅟 ch, TV, CP 60,
pf, con 20, 1 st. £ BB £18·11, DB £27·17,
WB, ①, Bk £2, L £4, D £6, cc 1 4 5, Dep b.

Repairer: Bridge Garage (Chertsey) Ltd,
102 Bridge Rd. ✆ (093 28) 62702.
Specialist Body Repairer: Medcalf & Co
(Coachbuilders) Ltd, Fordwater Trading
Estate. ✆ (093 28) 63026 and
(093 28) 63560.

CHESHUNT Hertfordshire. Map 15F
Pop 49,000 (inc Waltham Cross), London
15, Enfield 4½, Epping 8, Hatfield 11,
Hoddesdon 4½, Romford 15, Woodford 8½.
EC Thur. **Golf** Cheshunt Park 18h. **See**
Eleanor Cross (1294), 15th cent Church,
Temple Bar. Cedars Park.

Rescue Service: Kilsmore Filling Station,
238 Gt Cambridge Rd. ✆ Waltham Cross
(0992) 22899.

CHESSINGTON Greater London.
M.Area 7A
London 13, Croydon 10, Epsom 3½,
Kingston upon Thames 3½, Leatherhead 5,
Mitcham 8½, Ripley 11, Staines 12,
Weybridge 8½, Woking 14.
EC Wed. **See** 13th cent Church,
Zoological Gardens.

Specialist Body Repairer: George F Ray
(Coachworks), Green La. ✆ 01-397 4566.

CHESTER Cheshire. Map 19C
Pop 114,045. Nantwich 21, London 183,
M56 Motorway 5½, Birkenhead 15,
Colwyn Bay 42, Corwen 28, Middlewich
20, Mold 11, Northwich 18, Queensferry
6½, St Helens 23, Warrington 20,
Whitchurch 20, Wrexham 11.
See Plan p. 177.
EC Wed. **MD** Daily exc Wed. **P** See Plan.
Golf Vicars Cross 18h, Upton-by-Chester
18h, Chester Curzon Park 18h. **See**

Cathedral, The Rows, City Walls, Gates
and Towers, High Cross, Roman
amphitheatre, St John's Church and ruins,
Castle remains house Regimental
Museum of the Cheshire Regt, Town Hall,
13th cent Old Dee Bridge, old Inns, Gods
Providence House, Leche House, Bishop
Lloyds House, Grosvenor Museum, 16th
cent Stanley Palace, Zoological Gardens.
Upton-by-Chester 2 m NNE, City Record
Office.
ℹ️ Town Hall, Northgate St. ✆ Chester
(0244) 40144, ext 2111.

★★★★**Chester Grosvenor,** *56 Eastgate
St, CH1 1LT.* ✆ (0244) 24024. Closed
Xmas. C. ⊷ 98 bedrs, 98 bp, TV, Dgs.
✗ a l c, mc, at, LD 10. 🅟 Lt, N, CH, Dgs.
Ac, con 250, CF, 2 st. £ BB fr £51, DB fr
£75, WB, ①, Bk £6, L £7·50, D £12,
cc 1 2 3 4 5 6, Dep b.

★★★**M Abbots Well,** *107 Whitchurch
Rd, Christleton, CH3 5QL.*
✆ (0244) 332121. C. ⊷ 127 bedrs, 127
bp, TV, Dgs. ✗ a l c, mc, at, LD 10. 🅟 N,
CH, Dgs, CP 200, Ac, con 120, CF, 58 BGf,
1 st, Dis. £ BB fr £35, DB fr £47, WB, ①, Bk
£4·25, L £6·10, D £9, cc 1 2 3 4 5 6, Dep b.

★★★**Blossoms,** *St Johns St, CH1 1HL.*
✆ (0244) 23186. C. ⊷ 71 bedrs, 71 bp,
TV, Dgs. ✗ LD 9.30. 🅟 Lt, N, CH, Ac, sb,
sol, gym, con 70, CF, 7 st. £ WB, ①, Bk
£4·50, L £5·75, D £7·45, cc 1 3 4 5 6,
Dep b.

★★★**M Ladbroke,** *Backford Cross, CH1
6PE.* Junction of A41 & A5117. ✆ Great
Mollington (0244) 851551. C. ⊷ 118
bedrs, 118 bp, TV, Dgs. ✗ a l c, mc, at, LD
10. 🅟 N, CH, CP 150, Ac, pf, con 150, CF.
£ BB £44·75, DB £55·75, WB, ②, Bk £5·25,
L £6·50, D £9, cc 1 2 3 4 5 6, Dep.

★★★**Mollington Banastre,** *Parkgate
Rd, CH1 6NN.* (A540). ✆ Gt Mollington
(0244) 851471. C. ⊷ 48 bedrs, 48 bp, TV,
Dgs. ✗ a l c, mc, at. 🅟 Lt, N, CH, CP 250,
Ac, rf, sb, sol, gym, con 250, CF, 5 BGf, 0 st,
Dis. £ BB £41–£50, DB £52–£60, WB, ①,
Bk £6, L £5·50, D £11, cc 1 3 5, Dep b.

★★★**M Post House** (TH), *Wrexham Rd,
CH4 9DL.* ✆ (0244) 674111. C. ⊷ 62
bedrs, 62 bp, TV, Dgs. ✗ a l c, mc, LD 9.45.
🅟 N, CH, Dgs, CP 250, Ac, con 75, CF, 28
BGf, 1 st. £ BB £39, DB £51·50, WB, ①,
cc 1 2 3 4 5 6, Dep (Xmas).

★★★**Queen** (TH), *City Rd, CH1 3AH.*
✆ (0244) 28341. C. ⊷ 91 bedrs, 91 bp,
TV, Dgs. ✗ a l c, mc, LD 9.15. 🅟 Lt, N, CH,
Dgs, CP 130, Ac, con 250, CF, 11 BGf, 8 st.
£ BB £38, DB £54, WB, ①, cc 1 2 3 4 5 6,
Dep (Xmas).

★★★**Rowton Hall,** *Whitchurch Rd,
Rowton, CH3 6AF.* ✆ (0244) 335262. C.
⊷ 42 bedrs, 42 bps, TV, Dgs. ✗ a l c, mc,
at, LD 9.30. 🅟 N, CH, TV, Dgs, CP 120, U 9,
Ac, con, CF, 0 st. £ BB £28–£38, DB £42,
DT fr £40·60, DBB £34·95–£44·95, WB, ②,
Bk £3·50, L £5·65, D £6·95, cc 1 2 3 5.

★★**Chester Court** (R), *48 Hoole Rd, CH2
3NL.* ✆ (0244) 20779.

★★**Dene** (R), *75 Hoole Rd, CH2 3ND.*
✆ (0244) 21165. C. ⊷ 44 bedrs, 30 bp, 13
bps, 6 ba, TV, Dgs. ✗ a l c, mc, at, LD 8.
🅟 CH, CP 55, Ac, con 20, CF, 24 BGf, 0 st.
Dis. £ BB £15·50–£22, DB £25·50–£32,
WB, ①, Bk £3, D £5·50.

★★**Oaklands,** *93 Hoole Rd, CH2 3NB.*
✆ (0244) 22156. C. ⊷ 18 bedrs, 10 bp, 2
ba, TV, Dgs. ✗ a l c, mc, LD 9.30. 🅟 ch, TV,
Dgs, CP 50, Ac, con 60, CF, 4 BGf, 4 st.

£ BB £14·25–£19·75, DB £21·65–£25, ②,
Bk £2·50, L £5·95, D £5·95, cc 1 2 3 5 6.
★**Green Bough** (R), *60 Hoole Rd,
CH2 3NL.* ✆ (0244) 26241. Closed Xmas
2 wks. C4. ⊷ 11 bedrs, 2 bp, 6 bps, 2 ba,
TV, Dgs. ✗ mc, LD 7. 🅟 CH, TV, CP 11, Ac,
1 BGf, 3 st. £ BB £12·50–£20, DB £18–
£27, WT £142–£200, DT £21–£31, WB, ②,
Bk £3·50, L £5·50, D £6, cc 1 5 6, Dep.

★**Ye Olde King's Head,** *48 Lower Bridge
St, CH1 1RS.* ✆ (0244) 24855. RS Xmas.
C. ⊷ 11 bedrs, 3 ba, TV, Dgs. ✗ a l c, mc,
at, LD 9. 🅟 CH, G 6, Ac, CF, 0 st. £ BB
£12·50–£17·50, DB £19–£25, WB, ②, 10%,
Bk £3·50, L £4·50, D £5·50, cc 1 2 3 5 6,
Dep a.

Belgrave, H, z, *City Rd, CH1 3AE.*
✆ (0244) 31138. C. ⊷ 31 bedrs, 1 bp, 4
bps, 1 sh, 5 ba, Dgs. 🅟 ch, TV, Dgs, CF.
£ BB £14–£20, DB £24–£34, ②, Bk £3, D
£4·95, cc 1 3.

Brookside, PH (Rl) *12 Brook Lane, CH2
2AP.* ✆ (0244) 381943. Closed Xmas. C.
⊷ 23 bedrs, 10 bps, 3 ba, TV, Dgs.
🅟 CH, TV, CP 14, CF, 4 BGf, 2 st. £ BB
£12·07–£17·25, DB £23–29·32, ①, cc 5.

Cavendish, H, z (Rl), *44 Hough Green.*
✆ (0244) 675100. C. ⊷ 11 bedrs, 1 bp, 3
ba, TV, Dgs. 🅟 CH, TV, Dgs, CP 12, CF, 2 st.
£ BB £16–£17·50, DB £25–£32·50, WT (b)
fr £120, (c) fr £80, DT fr £19, ①, cc 1 2 3 5.

Devonia, G, *33–35 Hoole Rd, CH2 3NH.*
✆ (0244) 22236.

Eaton, H, z (R), *29 City Rd, CH1 3AE.*
✆ (0244) 312091. C. ⊷ 17 bedrs, 1 bp, 3
bps, 13 sh, 1 ba, TV, Dgs. ✗ a l c. 🅟 CH, TV,
CP 4, G 2, CF, 1 BG, 0 st, Dis. £ BB fr £15,
DB fr £22, ①, cc 1 3 4 5.

Gables, G, z (Unl), *5 Vicarage Rd, Hoole,
CH2 3HZ.* ✆ (0244) 23969. ⊷ 7 bedrs, 2
ba, Dgs. 🅟 CH, TV, Dgs, CP 7, CF, 1 st.
£ BB £7–£9·50, DB £14–£19, WT £98–
£126, ①.

Hamilton Court, PH, x (Rl), *5–7
Hamilton St, Hoole, CH2 3A.*
✆ (0244) 45387. C. ⊷ 12 bedrs, 2 ba,
Dgs. 🅟 CH, TV, Dgs, CF. £ BB £9·50–£11,
DB £18–£20, WT £70–£90, DT £12–£14,
①, Bk £2·50, D £4.

Riverside, H, z (R), *22 City Walls, CH1
1SB.* ✆ (0244) 26580. Closed Xmas. C.
⊷ 14 bedrs, 11 bp, 3 bps, 3 ba, TV, Dgs.
✗ a l c. 🅟 CH, TV, Dgs, CF, 24 st. £ BB
£19·55, DB £31·05, DT (b) fr £25·55, ①, Bk
£3·50, D £6.

Weston, H, y (R), *82 Hoole Rd, CH2 3NT.*
✆ (0244) 26735. Closed Xmas Week. C5.
⊷ 22 bedrs, 14 bp, 1 bps, 3 ba. ✗ a l c.
🅟 CH, TV, Dgs, CF, 1 st. £ BB £14·50–£21,
DB £23–£35, DT fr £18·50, ①, cc 1 3 4 5.

Repairers: Chester Engineering Co Ltd,
Hoole La. ✆ (0244) 24611.
James Edwards (Chester) Ltd, Victoria
Rd. ✆ (0244) 378479.
Henlys (Midland) Ltd, 14 City Rd.
✆ (0244) 313901.
Ben Whitehouse Ltd, Parkgate Rd.
✆ (0244) 372666.
Specialist Body Repairer: James Edwards
(Chester) Ltd, The Northgate.
✆ (0244) 378479.
Quicks of Chester Ltd, The Newgate.
✆ (0244) 20444.
Rescue Services: Deva Garages, 62–66
Boughton. ✆ (0244) 317127.
R A Edwards Engineering Ltd, T/As G. A.
Engineering, Unit 2, Dale St, Great
Boughton. ✆ (0244) 314786

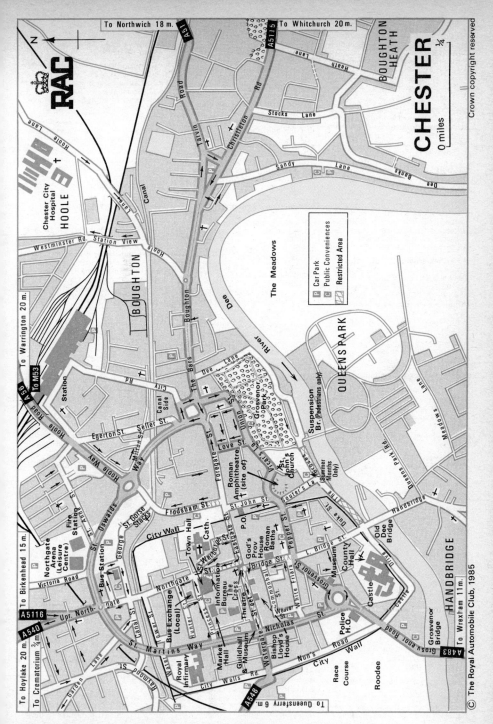

CHESTER

© The Royal Automobile Club, 1985

Recovery North West, Deva Service Station, Whitchurch Rd, Great Boughton. ✆ 051–342 7146.
Richmond Hill Garage, 136 Boughton. ✆ (0244) 25761.
Tom Houghton & Sons Ltd, Foregate Garage, 105a Foregate St. ✆ (0244) 22149.

CHESTERFIELD Derbyshire. Map 22D
Pop 97,000. Nottingham 26, London 149, M1 Motorway 5, Buxton 23, Chapel-en-le-Frith 23, Derby 23, Glossop 31, Mansfield 12, Matlock 10, Ollerton 19, Rotherham 16, Sheffield 12, Worksop 14.
EC Wed (exc Town centre). MD Mon, Fri, Sat. Golf Tapton 18h. See 14th cent Parish Church ('crooked' spire), Trinity Church (George Stephenson's grave), Stephenson Memorial Hall (Civic Theatre and Public Library), Revolution House, now Museum (Old Whittington), Bolsover Castle 6½ m E. Pomegranate Theatre. 🛈 Peacock Tourist Information and Heritage Centre, Low Pavement. ✆ Chesterfield (0246) 207777.

★★★**Chesterfield,** (late **Station**), Malkin St, S41 7UA. ✆ (0246) 71141. C. ➡ 61 bedrs, 61 bp, TV, Dgs. ✗ a l c, mc, at, LD 10. 🅿 Lt, N, CH, CP 60, G 8, Ac, con 250, CF, 6 st. £ BB £33–£36, DB £46–£48, WB, 🔟, Bk £4·50, L £7·45, D £7·45, cc 1 3 4 5, Dep b.
★★**Portland,** West Bars, S40 1AY. ✆ (0246) 34502.

Rescue Service: Hillside Garage, 41 Chesterfield Rd, Shuttlewood. ✆ (0246) 822275.

CHESTER-LE-STREET Durham. Map 32E
Pop 20,000. Durham 6, London 265, A1 (M) Motorway ½, Alston 43, Corbridge 23, Hexham 26, Middlesbrough 28, Newcastle upon Tyne 8½, Sunderland 9½.
EC Wed. MD Tue, Fri. Golf Chester-le-Street 18h. See Lumley Castle, Lambton Park.

★★★**Lumley Castle,** DH3 4NX. ✆ (0385) 885326. Closed Xmas & New Year. C. ➡ 50 bedrs, 41 bp, 9 bps, TV, Dgs. ✗ a l c, mc, at, LD 9.45. 🅿 N, CP 200, Ac, gc, sb, con 200, CF, 27 BGf, 2 st. £ WB, 🔟, Bk £4·50, L £6·95, D £8·95, cc 1 3 4 5 6, Dep b.▲
★★**Lambton Arms,** Front St, DH3 3BJ. ✆ (0385) 8832. C. ➡ 10 bedrs, 4 ba, TV. ✗ a l c, mc, at, LD 9. 🅿 CH, Dgs, CP 32, Ac, con 50, CF. £ BB £13·50, DB £23, 🔟, Bk £3, L £4·50, D £4·95, cc 1 5, Dep b.

CHEW MAGNA Avon. M.Area 5A
Pop 1,300. Bath 12, London 117, Bridgwater 29, Bristol 7, Radstock 10, Shepton Mallet 15, Wells 12, Weston-super-Mare 18.
EC Sat. MD Tue. Golf Long Ashton 18h. See 12th cent Church, 15th cent Old Schoolroom, Old Bridge ('Tunbridge'), Chew Valley Lake.

Rescue Service: Winford Road Garage, Littleton Mills, Winford. ✆ (027 589) 2857.

CHICHESTER West Sussex. Map 6F
See also GOODWOOD
Pop 24,188. Midhurst 12, London 61, Arundel 11, Bognor Regis 6½, Cosham 13, Haywards Heath 37, Littlehampton 13,

Petersfield 18, Petworth 14, Pulborough 17.
EC Thur. MD Wed. Golf Goodwood 18h. See Cathedral, Market Cross, ancient Walls, Council House (Corporation plate), remains of Greyfriars Monastery, St Mary's Hospital Almshouses, Chichester Festival Theatre, The Roman Palace and Museum at Fishbourne, Goodwood House 3 m NE.
🛈 Council House, North St. ✆ Chichester (0243) 775888.

★★★**Chichester Lodge,** Westhampnett, PO19 4UL. ✆ (0243) 786351. C. ➡ 43 bedrs, 43 bp, TV, Dgs. ✗ a l c, mc, at, LD 9.30. 🅿 N, CH, CP 100, G 7, Ac, con 120, CF, 25 BGf, 0 st, Dis. £ BB fr £31·50, DB £42·50, WB, 2️⃣, Bk £4·25, L £6·50, D £8·25, cc 1 2 3 5 6, Dep b.
★★★**Dolphin & Anchor** (TH), West St, PO19 1QE. ✆ (0243) 785121. C. ➡ 54 bedrs, 49 bp, 5 bps, TV, Dgs. ✗ a l c, mc, at, LD 10.30. 🅿 N, CH, Dgs, G 16, Ac, con 200, CF, 4 st. £ BB fr £40, DB fr £55·50, WB, 🔟, cc 1 2 3 4 5 6, Dep (Xmas).
★★**Ship,** North St, PO19 1NH. ✆ (0243) 782028. C. ➡ 36 bedrs, 22 bp, 8 ba, TV. ✗ a l c, mc, at, LD 9.15. 🅿 Lt, N, CH, Dgs, CP 30, Ac, con 60, CF, 5 st. £ BB £18·50–£23, DB £29–£36·50, DBB £26·25–£30·75, WB, 2️⃣, 10%, Bk £4, L £5·50, D £7·75, cc 2 3 4 5.

Repairer: Whyke Motors Ltd, 51 Bognor Rd. ✆ (0243) 783888.
Rescue Service: Iain Archibald Garages Ltd, Paddock Service Station, Selsey Rd, Sidlesham. ✆ Sidlesham (024 356) 277.
Pearmans Garage, Childown. ✆ Singleton (024 363) 229.

CHICKLADE Wiltshire. Map 5D
Pop 100. Amesbury 17, London 96, Salisbury 16, Shaftesbury 9, Warminster 9, Wincanton 14.
See Parish Church.

Old Rectory, G, xy (Unl), (A303), Hindon, SP3 5SU. ✆ Hindon (074 789) 226. Closed 1st two weeks Oct & Xmas. C. ➡ 8 bedrs, 3 ba, Dgs. 🅿 ch, TV, Dgs, CP 8, U1, CF, 1 st. £ BB £9–£10, DB £18–£20, WT (b) £80–£87, DT (b) £13–£14·50, 🔟, cc 1 5 6.

CHIDEOCK Dorset. Map 5E
Pop 650. Dorchester 18, London 150, Axminster 9½, Crewkerne 15, Lyme Regis 7, Sherborne 28, Weymouth 21.
See Church. Golf Lyme Regis 18h.

◼★**Clock House,** DT6 6JW. ✆ (029 789) 423.
Betchworth, G, x, (Rt), Chideock, DT6 6JW. ✆ (029 789) 478. C. ➡ 6 bedrs, 2 bps, 2 ba, Dgs. ✗ a l c. 🅿 CH, TV, CP 15, CF, 1 BGf, 1 st. £ BB £9–£9·50, DB £18–£22, WT (b) £88–£95, DT (b) £13·50–£14·50, 🔟, Bk £3, D £5·50, cc 1 3 4 5.

Rescue Service: Frodsham Motors, Morcombelake. ✆ (029 789) 312 and Bridport (0308) 3340.

CHILCOMPTON Somerset. Map 5C
Pop 1,500. Radstock 4, London 114, Bristol 16, Frome 11, Shepton Mallet 6½, Wells 8, Weston-super-Mare 25.
EC Sat. Golf Mendip 18h, Midsomer Norton 9h.

Rescue Service: Veale, H F & Sons, Broadway Garage. ✆ Stratton-on-the-Fosse (0761) 232298.

CHILD OKEFORD Dorset. Map 5F.
Pop 957, Salisbury 28, London 111, Blandford Forum 6½, Sturminster Newton 4, Shaftesbury 6½.
Golf Ashley Wood 9h. See Hambledon Hill, (Iron Age earthworks), Hod Hill (Roman Camp).

Rescue Service: Millbrook Garage, The Hollow. ✆ (0258) 860537.

CHILHAM Kent. Map 10D
Pop 1,500, M2 Motorway 5, Sittingbourne 14, London 56, Ashford 9, Canterbury 6½, Charing 8.
See 15th cent Church, Castle.

★★**Woolpack,** High St, CT4 8DL. ✆ Canterbury (0227) 730208.

CHILLINGTON Devon. Map 3F
Pop 800. Kingsbridge 4½, London 209, Dartmouth 10.
Golf Thurlestone 18h.

◼⬛★★**Oddicombe House,** (R), TQ7 2JD. ✆ Frogmore (054 853) 234. Open Apr–Oct. C 3 months. ➡ 8 bedrs, 6 bp, 1 ba, annexe 2 bedrs, 1 ba, Dgs. ✗ mc, at, LD 8.30. 🅿 CH, TV, ns, CP 15, sp, CF, 2 BGf. £ BB £14–£21, DB £30–£40, WT £140–£170, DBB £21–£27, 2️⃣, Bk £5, L £5·75, D £8·50, Dep a.
White House, H, xy (R), TQ7 2JX. ✆ Kingsbridge (0548) 580580. Open Apr–Oct. C. ➡ 9 bedrs, 1 bp, 3 sh, 2 ba. 🅿 CH, TV, CP 9, CF. £ BB fr £17·50, DB fr £23, WT (b) fr £98, DT (b) fr £16·50, 2️⃣, D £5·50, cc 3.

Rescue Service: Chillington Garage. ✆ Kingsbridge (0548) 580238.

CHILWELL Nottinghamshire. M.Area 22D
See also BEESTON.
Pop 12,000. M1 Motorway 7, London 123, Ashby-de-la-Zouch 17, Chesterfield 26, Derby 12, Hinckley 31, Loughborough 14, Matlock 24, Nottingham 5.
EC Thur. Golf Chilwell Manor 18h.

Rescue Service: Clifford, H & Sons Ltd, Bramcote Av. ✆ Nottingham (0602) 256117.

CHILWORTH Surrey. M.Area 7C
Pop 646. Guildford 3½, London 32, Dorking 10, Haslemere 14, Hindhead 13, Horsham 19.
Golf Bramley 18h. See St Martha's Hill, Powder Mills. Manor.

Rescue Service: Chilwell Garage, 97 New Rd. ✆ Guildford (0483) 62221.

CHIPPENHAM Wiltshire. Map 5B
Pop 21,000. Marlborough 19, London 91, M4 Motorway 4, Bath 13, Bristol 22, Chepstow 32, Cirencester 21, Devizes 11, Frome 21, Swindon 20, Tetbury 14, Warminster 20.
EC Wed. MD Fri, Sat. Golf Chippenham 18h. See 'Maud Heath's Causeway' (1474), Corsham Court 3½ m SW, Lacock Abbey and village 4 m, Castle Combe village 6 m NW, Museum.
🛈 The Neeld Hall, High St. ✆ Chippenham (0249) 57733.

★★**M Angel,** Market Place, SN15 3HD. ✆ (0249) 652615. C. ➡ 46 bedrs, 40 bp, 3 ba, TV, Dgs. ✗ a l c, mc, at, LD 9.45. 🅿 N,

ch, Dgs, CP 60, Ac, con 90, CF, 20 BGf, 2 st. **£** BB fr £19, DB fr £29, WT fr £220·50, DT fr £31, WB, ▯, L £7·50, D £9·50, cc 1 3 4 5 6, Dep.

★Bear, *Market Place, SN15 3HJ.* **✆** (0249) 653272. C. **↫** 8 bedrs, 1 bp, 2 bps, 2 ba, Dgs. ✘ a l c, mc, at, LD 9. ▣ ch, TV, ns, G 4, con 25, CF, 3 st. **£** BB £13·20, DB £26·40–£32, ▯, Bk £2·25, L £2·50, D £5, cc 1 5, Dep.

Oxford, PH, z (R), *32–36 Langley Rd, SN15 1BX.* **✆** (0249) 652542. C2. **↫** 16 bedrs, 7 bps, 1 ba, TV, Dgs. ▣ CH, TV, CP 8, 3 BGf, 1 st. **£** BB £11–£12·50, DB £19–£22, WT (c) £70, DT (b) £15·75, ▯, Bk £2·25, D £4·75, cc 1 3 4 5.

MC Repairer: Chequer, C N & Son Ltd, Lowden Garage, Lowden Rd. **✆** (0249) 655225.
Rescue Service: Causeway Garage (Chippenham) Ltd, London Rd. **✆** (0249) 655871.
Earle of Chippenham Ltd, Cocklesbury Rd. **✆** (0249) 653255.
Kington Langley Filling Station, A429, Kington Langley. **✆** Kington Langley (024 975) 228.
Sheppard's Garage, Fritterswell. **✆** Brinkworth (066 641) 501.

CHIPPING CAMPDEN Glos. Map 14C
Pop 1,964. Moreton-in-Marsh 6½, London 90, Banbury 22, Cheltenham 21, Evesham 9, Stow-on-the-Wold 10, Stratford-upon-Avon 12, Tewkesbury 21.
EC Thur. **Golf** Broadway 18h. **See** 15th cent Parish Church, 14th cent Grevel's House, Market Hall, Almshouses, 17th cent Town Hall, Campden House ruins, Woolstaplers Hall, old Grammar School, Hidcote Manor Gdns 2½ m NE.
ⓘ Woolstaplers Hall Museum, High St. **✆** Evesham (0386) 840289.

★★Cotswold House, *The Square, GL55 6AN.* **✆** Evesham (0386) 840330. Closed 23rd Dec–2nd Jan. C6. **↫** 25 bedrs, 11 bp, 1 bps, 6 ba, Dgs. ✘ a l c, mc, at, LD 9. ▣ CH, CP 12, G 6, con 16, 5 BGf, 2 st. **£** BBc £14–£27·80, DBc £28–£45·40, WB, ▯, Bk £3·20, L £3·85, D £9, cc 1 5 6.

★★King's Arms (Rt), *High St, GL55 6AW.* **✆** Evesham (0386) 840256. RS Jan & Feb. C. **↫** 14 bedrs, 2 bp, 4 ba, Dgs. ✘ mc, at, LD 9. ▣ ch, at, CF. **£** BB £17·71, DB £29·10–£44·28, WB, ▯, D £10·95, cc 1 3 4 5.

★★Noel Arms, *High St, GL55 6AT.* **✆** Evesham (0386) 840317.

CHIPPING NORTON Oxon. Map 14D
Pop 5,000. Oxford 20, London 75, Banbury 13, Bicester 19, Buckingham 25, Burford 11, Moreton-in-Marsh 8½, Stow-on-the-Wold 9, Stratford-upon-Avon 21, Warwick 27.
EC Thur. **MD** Wed. **Golf** Chipping Norton 9h. **See** 15th cent Parish Church, 1/th cent Almshouses, Old Guildhall, old 'White Hart' Inn, 'Rollright Stones' and 'Whispering Knights' 3 m.
ⓘ 22 New St. **✆** Chipping Norton (0608) 41320.

★★Crown & Cushion, *23 High St, OX7 5AD.* **✆** (0608) 2533. RS Xmas & New Year. C. **↫** 14 bedrs, 14 bp, TV, Dgs. ✘ a l c, mc, LD 9. ▣ CH, Dgs, CP 16, U 4, G 4, Ac, con, CF, 1 st. **£** BB £15–£23, DB £30–£43, WT £182–£238, DT £26–£34, DBB £23–£31, WT £182–£238, DT £26–

£34, WB, ▯, L £7·75, D £7·75, cc 2 3 5, Dep a.▲

★★White Hart (TH), *High St, OX7 5AD.* **✆** (0608) 2572. C. **↫** 22 bedrs, 6 bp, 6 ba, TV, Dgs. ✘ a l c, mc, at, LD 9.45. ▣ CH, Dgs, CP 10, G 6, Ac, con 25, CF, 5 BGf, 3 st. **£** BB fr £31, DB fr £41·50, WB, ▯, cc 1 2 3 4 5 6, Dep (Xmas).

Rescue Service: Brian Kimberley Garages, Station Road Garage, Hook Norton. **✆** Hook Norton (0608) 737551.
Souch Autos, 22 The Green. **✆** (0608) 2656.

CHIPPING SODBURY Avon. Map 5B
Pop 5,000. Chippenham 15, London 106, Bath 13, Bristol 11, Cheltenham 33, Chepstow 16, Gloucester 26, Swindon 31, Tetbury 13.
EC Thur. **Golf** Chipping Sodbury 18h. **See** Market Cross, Tudor House (Hatters La), Disused Quaker Meeting House, Parish Church, Roman Camp (Old Sodbury), Horton Court 3 m NE, Badminton House 5 m NE, Dodington House and Park, 2½ m SE.

Rescue Service: M & S Motors, Stanshawes Court Garage, Yate. **✆** (0454) 318798 and (0454) 314032.
Yate Motors, 452 Badminton Rd. **✆** (0454) 313496.

CHITTERNE Wiltshire. Map 5D
Pop 257. Amesbury 11, London 90, Devizes 13, Salisbury 16, Warminster 8.
EC Wed.

Chitterne Lodge, G, y (Unl), *BA12 0LQ.* **✆** (0985) 50155. Closed Xmas. C. **↫** 7 bedrs, 2 ba. ▣ CH, TV, Dgs, CF. **£** BB £9–£9·50, DB £16, DT (b) £70–£75, ▯.

CHOLDERTON Wiltshire. Map 6C
Pop 200. Andover 10, London 75, Amesbury 5, Devizes 20, Marlborough 18, Romsey 17, Salisbury 10, Winchester 19.
Golf High Post, Salisbury 18h. **See** Manor House, Church, Beacon Hill.

Rescue Service: Park House Garage (F Hall) Ltd. **✆** (098 064) 220.

CHOLLERFORD Northumberland. Map 31E
Hexham 5, London 285, Alnwick 39, Alston 24, Bellingham 11, Berwick-upon-Tweed 64, Brampton 26, Corbridge 7½, Hawick 48, Jedburgh 32, Newcastle upon Tyne 22.
See Bridge, Chesters Roman Fort and Museums. **Golf** Hexham 9h & 18h.

★★★George, *NE46 4EW* (Humshaugh). **✆** Humshaugh (043 481) 611. C. **↫** 54 bedrs, 54 bp, TV, Dgs. ✘ a l c, mc, at, LD 9. ▣ CH, CP 100, Ac, sp, pf, sb, sol, gym, con 50, CF, 6 BGf, Dis. **£** BB £30, DB £46, WT £211, DT £45·50, WB, ▯, Bk £5·50, L £6·50, D £9, cc 1 3 4 5 6, Dep b.

Rescue Service: Robson & Bestford Ltd, Service Garage. **✆** Humshaugh (043 481) 219.

CHORLEY Lancashire. Map 27D.
Pop 35,250. Walkden 14, London 203, Blackburn 10, Bolton 11, Ormskirk 15, Preston 9, Southport 19, Wigan 8.
EC Wed. **MD** Tue, Fri, Sat. **Golf** Duxbury Chorley 18h. **See** Astley Hall and Park, St Mary's RC Church, St Laurence's Church, Art Gallery and Museum, Rivington Pike and Lakes.

Repairer: Northern Motor & Engineering Co (Chorley) Ltd, Phoenix Works, Steeley La. **✆** (025 72) 62195.
Rescue Service: Chorley Service Station, Harpers La. **✆** (025 72) 63542 and (025 72) 78275.
Withnell Service Station, Withnell. **✆** Blackburn (0254) 21403.

CHRISTCHURCH Dorset. Map 6E
See also MUDEFORD
Pop 27,751, Lyndhurst 14, London 98, Blandford Forum 21, Bournemouth 5, Lymington 12, Ringwood 9.
EC Wed. **MD** Mon. **Golf** Ilford Bridge 9h.
See Priory Church, Red House Museum.

★★★King's Arms Crest, *Castle St, BH23 1DT.* **✆** (0202) 484117.

★★Fisherman's Haunt, *Winkton, BH23 7AS.* **✆** (0202) 484071. RS Xmas. C. **↫** 4 bedrs, 2 bp, 2 bps, 1 ba, annexe 9 bedrs, 5 bp, 2 bps, 1 ba, TV, Dgs. ✘ a l c, mc, at, LD 10. ▣ CH, TV, Dgs, CP 150, Ac, CF, 2 BGf, 1 st, Dis. **£** BB £15·50–£17·50, DB £29–£32, DBB fr £16, ▯, Bk £4·50, L £4·75, D £10, cc 1 2 3 5 6, Dep a.

Belvedere, PH, z, (RI), *59 Barrack Rd, BH23 1PD.* **✆** (0202) 485978. C. **↫** 10 bedrs, 1 bp, 9 bps, 2 ba, TV, Dgs. ▣ CH, Dgs, CP 12, U 1. **£** BB £8–£10, DB £16–£18, WT (b) £80–£90, (c) £50–£60, DT (b) £12–£14, ▯.

Broomway, PH, z (RI), *46 Barrack Rd, BH23 1PF.* **✆** (0202) 483405. Open Dec. C2. **↫** 9 bedrs, 2 ba, Dgs. ▣ ch, TV, CP 12. **£** BB £10–£11·50, DB £20–£23, WT £72–£85, DT £10–£11·50, ▯.

Ferndale, G, z (Unl), *41 Stour Rd, BH23 1LN.* **✆** (0202) 482616. Closed Xmas. C. **↫** 6 bedrs, 1 ba, Dgs. ▣ CH, TV, Dgs, CP 6, CF, 1 st.

Laurels Touring Hotel, PH, z (RI), *195 Barrack Rd, BH23 2AR.* **✆** (0202) 485530.
Park House, H, x (RI), *48 Barrack Rd, BH26 1PF.* **✆** (0202) 482124. Closed Xmas & New Year. C3. **↫** 9 bedrs, 1 bps, 2 ba, TV. ▣ CH, TV, CP 12. **£** BB £12–£15, DB £24–£30, WT (c) £72, ▯, Bk £2·75, D £2·50, cc 1 5.

Pines, PH, x (RI), *39 Mudeford, BH23 3HQ.* **✆** (0202) 482393. C. **↫** 13 bedrs, 6 bps, 1 ba, ns, TV, Dgs. ▣ CH, TV, Dgs, CP 14, CF, 2 BGf, 1 st, Dis. **£** BB £11–£15·50, DB £22–£27·50, WT (b) £93–£99, (c) £69–£72, DT (b) £15·25–£16·50.

St. Albans, PH, z (RI), *8 Avenue Rd, BH23 2BY.* **✆** (0202) 471096. C. **↫** 9 bedrs, 2 bps, 1 sh, 3 ba, Dgs. ▣ CH, TV, CP 12, CF, 1 BGf, 1 st. **£** BB £8–£8·50, DB £15·50–£19·50, WT (b) £55–£58, DT (b) £12–£13, ▯, D £4.

Sea Witch, PH, z (RI), *153 Barrack Rd, BH23 2AP.* **✆** (0202) 482846. C. **↫** 9 bedrs, 2 ba, Dgs. ▣ CH, TV, CP 15, CF. **£** BB £9·50–£10·50, DB £19–£21, WT (b) £93–£99, DT (b) £14·25–£15·25, ▯, Bk £2·50, D £4·75.

Two Wings, G, y (RI), *1 Avenue Rd, BH23 2BU.* **✆** (0202) 483181. C8. **↫** 7 bedrs, 1 ba. ▣ CH, TV, CP 8, 1 BGf, 1 st. **£** BB £7–£9, WB, TV £16, WT (c) £52·50–£56, ▯, Bk £2·50, D £6.

Rescue Service: Airspeed Motors, Unit 16, Airspeed Rd, Airspeed Industrial Estate. **✆** Highcliffe (042 52) 78265.

CHRISTOW Devon. Map 3D
Pop 650. M5 Motorway 9, London 178, Chudleigh 5, Exeter 9, Moretonhampstead 6½.

Golf Newton Abbot (Stover) 18h. **See** 10th cent Church, Reservoirs.

Rescue Service: Christow Garages Ltd, Meadowcroft, Wet La. ✆ (0647) 52249.

CHULMLEIGH Devon. Map 3B
Tiverton 19, London 182, Barnstaple 18, Bideford 22, Exeter 23, Okehampton 17, South Molton 10.

Rescue Service: Eggesford Garage.
✆ (0769) 80056.

CHURCH STRETTON Shropshire. Map 13A
Pop 3,350. Bridgnorth 19, London 156, Knighton 22, Ludlow 15, Newton 28, Shrewsbury 13, Welshpool 26.
EC Wed. **MD** Thur. **Golf** Church Stretton 18h. **See** Parish Church, The Longmynd 5,000 acres. (N.T.) Waterfall.
🛈 Church St. ✆ Church Stretton (0694) 722535.

★★★**Long Mynd,** *Cunnery Rd, SY6 6AG.*
✆ (0694) 722244. C. ⇄ 60 bedrs, 43 bp, 3 bps, 6 ba, TV, Dgs. ✗ a l c, mc, at, LD 9.30.
🅿 Lt, ch, CP 150, Ac, sp, gc, sb, sol, con 150, CF. £ BB fr £23·50, DB fr £34, WT £173, DT £27–£31, WB, 🄑, Bk £2·50, L £4, D £5·50, cc 1 3 4 5 6.

★★★★**Stretton Hall,** *All Stretton, SY6 6HG.* ✆ (0694) 723224. C. ⇄ 12 bedrs, 8 bp, 2 ba, TV, Dgs. ✗ a l c, mc, at, LD 9.30.
🅿 CH, CP 30, con 30, CF, 1 BGf, 3 st.
£ WB, 🄑, cc 1 3 4 5 6, Dep.

★★**Sandford,** *Watling St South, SY6 7BG.* ✆ (0694) 722131. C. ⇄ 24 bedrs, 9 bp, 3 bps, 4 ba, TV, Dgs. ✗ a l c, mc, at, LD 9. 🅿 CH, TV, Dgs, CP 30, con 170, CF, 0 st.
£ BB £14–£16·50, DB £25–£29, DBB £19·50–£22·50, WB, 🄑, Bk £3, L £4·10, D £5·50, cc 1 3, Dep b.▲

Mynd House, PH, x (R), *Little Stretton, SY6 6RB.* ✆ (0694) 722212. Closed Dec, Jan. C10. ⇄ 13 bedrs, 3 bp, 1 bps, 3 sh, 2 ba, Dgs. 🅿 CH, TV, CP 16, CF, 2 st. £ BB £10–£15, DB £20–£29·50, WT (b) £100–£121, DT (b) £15–£20, 🄑, Bk £2·50, D £5·25, cc 1 5.▲

Rescue Service: Brian R Evans, Marshbrook Garage. ✆ (069 46) 340.

CHURSTON FERRERS Devon. Map 3D
Pop 1,582. Torquay 6½, London 196, Dartmouth (Fy) 5, Totnes 7½.
See Church.

White Horse, PH, xy, (R), *Dartmouth Rd, TQ5 0LL,* ✆ Churston (0803) 842381. C. ⇄ 10 bedrs, 1 bps, 2 ba. 🅿 ch, TV, CP 10, CF, 2 st. £ BB £6·50–£9·35, DB £13–£18·70, WT (b) £64–£88, DT (b) £10·25–£13·10, 🄑, Bk £1·75, D £3·75, cc 1 5.

Rescue Service: Prouts Garage (Churston 1970) Ltd. ✆ Churston (0803) 842245.

CINDERFORD Gloucestershire. Map 13E
Pop 7,224. Gloucester 14, London 118, Chepstow 18, Hereford 22, Ledbury 17, Monmouth 12, Ross 8½.
EC Thur. **MD** Fri. **Golf** Coleford 18h. **See** Forest of Dean, Speech House, St Anthony Well 2½ m NE, Roman road at Soudley 3 m S.
🛈 Library. Belle Vue Rd. ✆ Dean (0594) 22581.

Overdean, G, x (Unl), *31 St Whites Rd, GL14 3DB.* ✆ Dean (0594) 22136. C. ⇄ 6 bedrs, 2 ba, Dgs. ✗ a l c. 🅿 CH, TV, CP 6, G

2, CF, 1 BGf, 1 st. £ BB £8–£9, DB £15–£17, WT (b) £85–£95, DT £13–£14, 🄑.
White Hart, I, x, *85 St White's Rd, Ruspidge.* ✆ Dean (0594) 23139.

MC Repairer: Haines & Co, 125 High St.
✆ Dean (0594) 22202.
Rescue Service: Tramway Road Garage, Tramway Rd, Ruspidge. ✆ Dean (0594) 22238.

CIRENCESTER Gloucestershire. Map 14E
See also EWEN
Pop 15,535. Faringdon 18, London 88, Burford 17, Cheltenham 14, Chippenham 21, Gloucester 18, Stow-on-the-Wold 19, Swindon 15, Tetbury 10.
EC Thur. **MD** Mon, Tue, Fri. **Golf** Cirencester 18h. **See** Corinium Museum, Parish Church, Royal Agricultural College, Abbey grounds park (Roman Wall).
🛈 Corn Hall, Market Pl. ✆ Cirencester (0285) 4180

★★★**King's Head,** *Market Place, GL7 2NR.* ✆ (0285) 3322. Closed 27–30 Dec. C. ⇄ 70 bedrs, 70 bp, TV, Dgs. ✗ a l c, mc, at, LD 9.30. 🅿 Lt, N, CH, CP 20, Ac, con 200, CF. £ BB £37–£40, DB £50–£53, WT £204–£210, WB, 🄑, Bk £4·90, L £7·40, D £9·50, cc 1 2 3 4 5 6.

★★★★**Stratton House,** *Gloucester Rd, GL7 2LE.* ✆ (0285) 61761. C. ⇄ 26 bedrs, 20 bp, 2 bps, 3 ba, TV, Dgs. ✗ a l c, mc, at, LD 9.45. 🅿 CH, CP 100, U 2, Ac, con 100, CF, 2 BGf, Dis. £ BB fr £23·75, DB fr £35·50, WT £248·50–£264·25, DT fr £38·60, WB, 🄑, Bk £4·50, L £6·75, D £8·10, cc 1 3 4 5 6.

★★**Corinium Court,** *Gloucester St, GL7 2DG.* ✆ (0285) 4499.

★★**Fleece,** *Market Pl, GL7 4NZ.*
✆ (0285) 68507. C. ⇄ 19 bedrs, 19 bp, TV, Dgs. ✗ a l c, mc, at, LD 9.30. 🅿 CH, Dgs, CP 34, Ac, CF, 2 st. £ BB fr £35·50, DB fr £45·50, WB, 🄑, Bk £4·25, L £6·50, D £9·50, cc 1 2 3 5, Dep b.

Arkenside, H, *44 Lewis La, GL7 1EB.*
✆ (0285) 3072. Closed Jan. C. ⇄ 19 bedrs, 4 ba, Dgs. 🅿 ch, TV, CP 14, CF. £ BB fr £10, DB fr £17, 🄑.

Raydon, PH, z (Rl), *3 The Avenue, GL7 1EH.* ✆ (0285) 3485. Closed Xmas. C. ⇄ 16 bedrs, 6 bp, 2 bps, 3 ba, TV. ✗ a l c. 🅿 CH, TV, ns, CP 12, CF, 1 BGf, 3 st. £ BB £10–£18, DB fr £25, WT fr £115, DT £16·50–£18·50, 🄑, Bk £2·95, L £2·50, D £6·50, cc 1 5.

Wimborne, G, y (Unl), *91 Victoria Rd, GL7 1ES.* ✆ (0285) 3890. C5. ⇄ 7 bedrs, 2 ba. 🅿 CH, TV, ns, CP 6, 2 st. £ BB £8–£9, DB £16–£18, WT (c) £50–£56, DT (b) £13–£14, 🄑, D £5.

MC Repairer: Peter Hammond Motor Cycles, Watermoor Rd. ✆ (0285) 2467.
Sctr Repairer: Peter Hammond Motor Cycles, Watermoor Rd. ✆ (0285) 2467.

CLACTON-ON-SEA Essex. Map 17D
See also HOLLAND-ON-SEA
Pop 32,868. Colchester 15, London 71, Harwich 16, Ipswich 24, Stowmarket 35.
EC Wed. **MD** Tue, Sat. **Golf** Clacton-on-Sea 18h. **See** Norman Church, St Osyth's Priory 3½ m W.
🛈 Town Hall, Station Rd. ✆ Clacton-on-Sea (0255) 425501.

★★**King's Cliff,** *King's Par, Holland-on-Sea, CO15 5JB.* ✆ (0255) 812343. C. ⇄ 15 bedrs, 10 bp, 3 bps, 1 ba, TV. ✗ a l c,

mc, at, LD 9.30. 🅿 N, CH, Dgs, CP 80, U, G 5, Ac, con, CF, 1 st. £ BB £16–£20, DB £28–£35, WT £178·50–£245, DT £25·50–£29·50, WB, 🄑, Bk £4, L £4, D £5·50, cc 1 5.

Stonar, PH, z (Unl), *19 Agate Rd, CO15 1RA,* ✆ (0255) 426554. Closed Xmas. C. ⇄ 9 bedrs, 2 ba, TV, Dgs. ✗ a l c. 🅿 CH, TV, Dgs, ns, CP 3, CF. £ BB £8·50, DB £17, WT £72–£75, DT £13·50, 🄑.

Rescue Service: Carlton Garage, 65 High St. ✆ (0255) 420444.
Chaswin Autos, 301 Old Rd.
✆ (0255) 423707.
Marina Services, 7 St Osyth Rd.
✆ (0255) 423462.

CLANFIELD Hampshire. Map 6D
Petersfield 6½, London 59, Alton 18, Chichester 16, Fareham 14, Portsmouth 14, Southampton 27, Winchester 18.
EC Wed. **Golf** Havant 18h.

Rescue Services: James Watts Automobiles (Clanfield) Ltd, 33 South La. ✆ Horndean (0705) 595315.

CLAPHAM North Yorkshire. Map 27A
Pop 250. Settle 6, London 235, Hawes 20, Kirkby Lonsdale 11, Lancaster 20.
EC Thur. **Golf** Bentham 9h. **See** Ingleborough Estate (wooded grounds and Cave).

Repairer: E S Hartley Ltd, Clapham Garage. ✆ (046 85) 247.

CLARE Suffolk. Map 17E
Pop 2,025. Dunmow 19, London 57, Bishop's Stortford 27, Braintree 15, Bury St Edmunds 15, Haverhill 8, Newmarket 16, Stowmarket 23, Sudbury 9.
EC Wed. **MD** Mon, Sat. **Golf** Bury 18h. **See** Norman castle ruins, 13th cent Augustine Priory remains (Clare Priory), Church, Country Park.

★★**Bell,** *Market Hill, CO10 8NN.*
✆ (0787) 277741.

CLAVERING Essex
Map Areas 15D & 17E
Bishops Stortford 8, London 39, Braintree 26, Puckeridge 10, Stevenage 17.

Rescue Service: D J Herbert, Arkesden Rd, CB11 4QU. ✆ (079 985) 639.

CLAWTON Devon. Map 3A
Pop 291. Holsworthy 3, London 213, Launceston 10.
Golf Holsworthy 18h. **See** 14th cent Church.

★★**Court Barn** (R), *nr Holsworthy, EX22 6PS.* ✆ North Tamerton (040 927) 219. RS Nov, Dec, Jan. C. ⇄ 8 bedrs, 4 bp, 2 bps, 2 ba, Dgs. ✗ a l c, mc, LD 8.30. 🅿 CH, TV, CP 12, CF, 1 st. £ BB £14–£22·50, DB £28–£40, WB, 🄑, Bk £3, L £2·50, D £8·50.

CLAYTON West Yorkshire. M.Area 25F and 33A
Huddersfield 11, London 198, Bradford 3, Halifax 5½, Skipton 20, Wakefield 17.
Golf Clayton 9h.

Rescue Service: Curtis & Robinson Ltd, Bradford Rd. ✆ Bradford (0274) 882315.

CLAYTON LE WOODS Lancs. Map 27D
Pop 6,600. M6 Motorway ½, London 207, Blackburn 9.
EC Wed. **Golf** Shaw Hill 18h. **See** RC Church of St Bedes, Convent.

★★★**Pines,** *Preston Rd, PR6 7ED.*
☎ (0772) 38551. Closed Xmas. C. ⊨ 25
bedrs, 25 bp, TV. ✗ a l c, mc, at, LD 9.30.
🅿 N, CH, CP 120, Ac, sc, sol, con 150, CF,
8 BGf, 1 st, Dis. £ WB, 🔟, Bk £4·75, L
£5·50, D £9·50, cc 1 3 4 5.

Rescue Service: Halfway Garage, Preston
Rd. ☎ Preston (0772) 85139.
Swansey Garage, 350 Preston Rd.
☎ Chorley (025 72) 2461.

CLEATOR MOOR Cumbria. M.Area 26F
Pop 7,355. Egremont 3, London 311,
Cockermouth 13, Workington 11.
EC Wed. **MD** Fri. **Golf** St Bees 9h. **See** St
Leonard's Church, The Grotto, St Mary's
Priory (Cleator).

Rescue Service: Frank Whelan, Princes
Garage. ☎ (0946) 272.

CLECKHEATON West Yorkshire. Map
25F and 33A
Pop 13,984. Wakefield 10, London 192,
Bradford 6, Halifax 7, Huddersfield 7½,
Leeds 9½.
EC Wed. **MD** Sat. **Golf** Cleckheaton and
District 18h. **See** Red House Museum.

Repairer: Cleckheaton Motor Co Ltd, 179
Bradford Rd. ☎ (0274) 874202.
Rescue Service: Highway Recovery M62
Ltd, Hartshead Moor Service Area.
☎ (0274) 873391.
Motoross Ltd, M62 Service Area,
Hartshead Moor, Clifton. ☎ (0274)
876584.

CLEETHORPES Humberside (South
Humberside). Maps 23B and 24A
Pop 35,500. Louth 16, London 164,
Gainsborough 37, Grimsby 6½, Hull 34,
Market Rasen 20, Scunthorpe 31.
EC Thur (winter). **MD** Wed. **Golf**
Cleethorpes 18h. **See** Beacon, Leisure
Park.
🛈 43 Alexandra Rd. ☎ Cleethorpes (0472)
697472.

★★★**Kingsway** (R), *Kingsway, DN35
0AE.* ☎ (0472) 601122. RS Xmas. C. ⊨ 53
bedrs, 48 bp, 3 ba, TV. ✗ a l c, mc, LD 9.
🅿 Lt, N, CH, CP 30, G 20, con 25, CF, 1 st.
£ BB £24–£31, DB £34–£45, WB, 🔟, Bk
£4·50, D £7·75, cc 1 3 4 5.

★★**M Wellow,** *Kings Rd, DN35 0AQ.*
☎ (0472) 695589. Closed Xmas. C. ⊨ 10
bedrs, 10 bp, TV, Dgs. ✗ a l c, mc, at, LD
10. 🅿 CH, TV, CP 80, Ac, con 10, CF, 1 st.
£ WB, cc 1 2 3, Dep a.

Mallow View, G, z (RI), *9 Albert Rd,
DN35 8LX.* ☎ (0472) 691297.
Seacot, H, z (R), *40 Bradford Av, DN35
0BD.* ☎ (0472) 693014. C. ⊨ 9 bedrs, 1
bp, 1 bps, 4 sh, 2 ba, TV, Dgs. 🅿 CH, TV, CP
12, CF, 0 st. £ BB £15·50–£18, DB £25–
£27·50, WT £95, DT £21, Bk £2·85, D
£5·50.

CLEEVE Avon. Map Area 5A
Bristol 10, London 123, Bath 21, Weston-
super-Mare 11.

Rescue Service: Weston Road Garage,
171 Main Rd. ☎ Flax Bourton
(027 583) 2257.

CLEEVE HILL Gloucestershire. Map 14C
Cheltenham 4, London 101, Broadway 9,
Evesham 14, Gloucester 12, Stow-on-the-
Wold. 17
Golf Municipal 18h.

★★**The Rising Sun,** *GL52 3PX.*
☎ Bishop's Cleeve (0242 67) 2002. C.
⊨ 13 bedrs, 4 bp, 9 bps, TV. ✗ a l c, mc,
LD 10. 🅿 CH, CP 55, CF, 6 st. £ BB fr
£27·50, DB fr £37·50, WB, 🔟, Bk £4, L
£5·50, D £7, cc 1 3 4 5, Dep.

CLEOBURY MORTIMER Shropshire.
Map 13B
Pop 1,750. Kidderminster 11, London 134,
Bridgnorth 13, Droitwich 20, Leominster
18, Ludlow 11, Worcester 20.
EC Thur. **Golf** Ludlow 18h. **See** St Mary's
Church.

★★**The Redfern** (late **Old Lion Inn**) (R),
DY14 8AA. ☎ (0299) 270395. C. ⊨ 11
bedrs, 5 bp, 6 bps, TV, Dgs. ✗ a l c, mc, LD
9.30. 🅿 N, CH, CP 30, con 20, CF. £ BB
£21, DB £32, WT £154, DT £25, WB, 🔟, Bk
£3, L £3, D £8, cc 1 3 4 5 6.

Rescue Service: G B Motors (Hopton),
Hopton Bank Garage, Hopton Bank.
☎ Ludlow (0584) 890225

CLEVEDON Avon. Map 5A
Pop 14,330. Bristol 12, London 126, M5
Motorway 1, Bridgwater 28, Radstock 27,
Shepton Mallet 26, Wells 24, Weston-
super-Mare 14.
EC Wed. **Golf** Clevedon 18h. **See** St
Andrew's Church (tombs of Arthur and
Henry Hallam), Clevedon Court 1 m E,
14th cent Manor House.

★★★**Walton Park,** *1 Wellington Ter,
BS21 7BL.* ☎ (0272) 874253. C. ⊨ 35
bedrs, 22 bp, 3 bps, 2 ba, TV, Dgs. ✗ mc,
at, LD 9. 🅿 Lt, CH, CP 40, G 10, Ac, con 60,
CF, 1 st. £ BB £26·50–£30, DB £35·95–
£41·95, WT £158–£168, DT £41·65–
£43·65, WB, ②, Bk £4·50, L £6·45, D £8·70,
cc 1 3 4 5.

Amberley House, G, z (RI), *146 Old
Church Rd, BS21 7XP.* ☎ (0272) 874402.
Closed Xmas. C. ⊨ 8 bedrs, 2 bp, 1 bps, 2
sh, 1 ba. ✗ a l c. 🅿 CH, TV, CP 3, CF, 3 BGf,
2 st. £ BB £9·50–£11, DB £19–£22, 🔟, D
£5, cc 3.

Repairer: Binding & Payne Ltd, Austin
House, Old Church Rd. ☎ (0272) 872201.
Rescue Service: Clevedon Garages Ltd,
Bristol Rd. ☎ (0272) 873701.
Tickenham Garage, Clevedon Rd,
Tickenham. ☎ Nailsea (0272) 852035.

CLEVELEYS Lancashire
See THORNTON CLEVELEYS.

CLIFTON Avon
See BRISTOL

CLIFTON Gtr Manchester (Lancashire).
M.Area 20F
Pop 5,000. 5½ m NW of Manchester,
London 189, Bolton 5, Walkden 3½.
EC Wed. **Golf** Swinton Park 18h.

Rescue Service: Jacks Bros (Garages)
Ltd, 53 Manchester Rd. ☎ 061-794 1928.

CLIFTONVILLE Kent. Map 10D
See also MARGATE.
Pop 6,284. Eastern side of Margate.
Margate 1, London 74.
EC Thur. **Golf** North Foreland, Broadstairs
18h, Westgate and Birchington 18h, St
Augustine's, Ramsgate 18h. **See** Winter
Gardens, King Vortigern Caves, Grotto,
Shell Temple.

Cartwheel, G, z (RI), *41 Norfolk Rd,
CT9 2HU.* ☎ Thanet (0843) 22406.

Falcon Holiday Hotel, PH, z (R), *2
Ethelbert Rd, CT9 1RY.* ☎ Thanet
(0843) 23846. C. ⊨ 32 bedrs, 15 bps, 3
ba, TV. 🅿 Lt, ch, TV, CP 11, CF, 6 st. £ BB
£8–£10, DB £25–£29, WT £65–£83, DT
£8–£9, 🔟.

Galleon Lights, PH, z (RI), *12 Fort Cres,
CT9 1HX.* ☎ Thanet (0843) 291703. C10.
⊨ 21 bedrs, 5 bp, 2 bps, 4 ba, TV. 🅿 CH,
TV, 8 st. £ BB £7·50–£10·50, DB £15–£21,
WT (b) £69·50–£85, DT (b) £11–£15, 🔟,
Bk £2·75, D £3·50, cc 1 3. ▲

Repairer: Invicta Motors (Thanet) Ltd,
Northdown Rd and at St Georges Garage.
☎ Thanet (0843) 26554.

CLIMPING W. Sussex. Map 7E
Arundel 3, London 59, Bognor Regis 5½,
Chichester 9, Littlehampton 2.
Golf Littlehampton 18h.

🏨★★★**Bailiffscourt,** *BN17 5RW.*
☎ Littlehampton (090 64) 23511.

CLITHEROE Lancashire. Map 27A
Pop 13,671. Whalley 4, London 214,
Settle 19, Skipton 18.
EC Wed. **MD** Mon, Tue, Fri, Sat. **Golf**
Clitheroe 18h. **See** Castle Keep, Pendle
Hill 1,830 ft, Sawley Abbey, Stonyhurst
College, Castle House (Museum).
🛈 Council Offices, Church Walk.
☎ Clitheroe (0200) 25566.

Fairway House, PH, z (R), *48 King St.*
☎ (0200) 22025. C. ⊨ 9 bedrs, 3 bps, 1
ba, Dgs. ✗ a l c. 🅿 CH, TV, CP 9, CF. £ BB
£9·20–£16·10, DB £18·40–£21·85, 🔟, Bk
£2, D £4, cc 1.
White Lion, H, x (RI), *Market Pl.*
☎ (0200) 26955.

Rescue Service: Greenacre Garage,
Greenacre St. ☎ (0200) 23108.
Robinson, ☎ (Clitheroe) Ltd, Low Moor
Garage, 57 Henthorn Rd. ☎ (0200) 23551.

CLOVELLY Devon. Map 3A
Pop 422. Bideford 11, London 214, Bude
16, Holsworthy 17, Launceston 30.
Golf Westward Ho! 18h. **See** Picturesque
little harbour, 'Up-along' (quaint stepped
street), Hobby Drive (toll).

Red Lion, H, *The Quay, EX39 5TF.*
☎ (023 73) 237. Open Apr–Oct. C. ⊨ 9
bedrs, 9 sh, 3 ba. 🅿 CH, TV, CP 6, CF, 6 st.
£ BB fr £9·75, DB fr £19·50, 🔟, Bk £2·50, L
£3·50, D £7·50, cc 1 3.

CLOWNE Derbyshire. M.Area 22B
Pop 6,847. Mansfield 10, London 148,
Chesterfield 8½, Doncaster 20, Ollerton 12,
Rotherham 12, Sheffield 12, Worksop 7.
EC Wed. **MD** Thur. **Golf** Renishaw Park,
Sheffield 18h. **See** Norman Church.

MC Repairer: High St Motors, High St.
☎ Chesterfield (0246) 810469.

CLYST ST MARY Devon. Maps 3B and
4F
Pop 1,304. Honiton 14, London 167,
Axminster 24, Exeter 4, Lyme Regis 25,
Taunton 36, Tiverton 15.
Golf Exeter G and CC 18h. **See** Medieval
Church, Oldest Bridge in Devon.

Rescue Service: C & P Motors, Sandpit,
Sidmouth Rd. ☎ Topsham
(039 287) 5009.

COALEY Gloucestershire. Map 13F
Pop 857. Tetbury 11, London 107,
M5 Motorway 5½, Bristol 26, Dursley 3½,
Stroud 7.

Golf Stinchcombe Hill 18h.

School Cottage, G, x (Unl), *GL11 5ED.*
✆ Cambridge (Glos) (045 389) 459. C.
🚗 5 bedrs, 2 ba, TV, Dgs. 🅿 CH, TV, Dgs,
ns, CP 4, CF. £ BB £7, DB £14, WT (b) £65,
DT (b) £10, 1.

COBHAM Surrey. Map 7A
Pop 9,518. Kingston upon Thames 8,
London 18, Epsom 7½, Leatherhead 5,
Ripley 5, Weybridge 5, Woking 8.
EC Wed. **Golf** Fairmile & Silvermere 18h.
See Church of St Andrew, 15th–18th cent
'The Cedars', 17th cent White Lion Inn,
Old Mill.

★★★**Seven Hills**, *Seven Hills Rd, KT11
1EW.* ✆ (0923) 64471. C. 🚗 115 bedrs,
115 bp, TV, Dgs. ✗ a l c, mc, at, LD 10.
🅿 Lt, N, CH, TV, CP 250, Ac, sp, tc, sb, con
300, CF, 10 BGf, 2 st. £ BB £50, DB £62,
WB, 1, Bk £5·50, L £8, D £10,
cc 1 2 3 4 5 6, Dep b.

Repairer: Rowland Weller (Garage) Ltd,
The Tilt. ✆ (0923) 4244.

COBRIDGE Staffordshire.
See STOKE-ON-TRENT.

COCKERMOUTH Cumbria. Map 26E
Pop 6,290. Keswick 11, London 297,
Carlisle 25, Egremont 15, Maryport 7,
Workington 8½.
EC Thur. **MD** Mon. **Golf** Embleton
Cockermouth 18h. **See** Wordsworth
House (Nat Trust) birthplace of the poet,
All Saints' Church, Moorland Close
(birthplace of Fletcher Christian 1764),
12th cent Castle remains.
🅿 Riverside Car Park, Market St.
✆ Cockermouth (0900) 822634.

★★★**Broughton Craggs**, *Gt Broughton,
CA13, 0XW.* ✆ (0900) 824400. C. 🚗 10
bedrs, 10 bp, TV. ✗ a l c, mc, at, LD 9.30.
🅿 CH, CP 50, con 40, CF, 1 st. £ BB £17–
£23, DB £25–£35, WT £220–£262, DT
£31·50–£37·50, WB, 2, Bk £2·50, L £2·50,
D £8·50, cc 1 3 5 6.

★★★**Trout**, *Crown St, CA13 0EJ.*
✆ (0900) 823591. Closed Xmas Day. C.
🚗 16 bedrs, 11 bp, 4 bps, 1 ba, TV, Dgs.
✗ a l c, mc, LD 9.30. 🅿 N, CH, Dgs, CP 75,
Ac, pf, con 20, CF, 1 st. £ BB £22–£23, DB
£35, WT £273, DT £39, DBB £32–£33, WB,
2, Bk £2·75, L £6, D £10, cc 3.

★★**Allerdale Court**, *Market Place, CA13
9HQ.* ✆ (0900) 823654. RS Xmas. C. 🚗 24
bedrs, 17 bp, 2 bps, 2 ba, TV, Dgs. ✗ a l c,
LD 9.30. 🅿 CH, TV, Dgs, Ac, CF, 1 st. £ BB
£15–£19, DB £22–£28, WT £170–£185, DT
£28·20, WB, 1, Bk £3, L £5·50, D £8·50,
cc 1 2 3, Dep.

★★**Globe**, *Main St, CA13 9LA.*
✆ (0900) 822126.
★★**Wordsworth**, *Main St, CA13 9JS.*
✆ (0900) 822757. Closed Xmas Day. C.
🚗 18 bedrs, 4 bp, 9 sh, 2 ba, TV. ✗ a l c,
mc, at, LD 9. 🅿 ch, TV, CP 30, Ac, con 100,
CF, 2 st. £ BB £16–£22·50, DB £24–£32,
WB, 1, Bk £3·50, D £7·50, cc 1 5 6, Dep a.

CODICOTE Hertfordshire. Map 15F
Pop 2,896. Hatfield 6½, London 27,
Baldock 12, Bedford 24, Biggleswade 18,
Bishop's Stortford 23, Hoddesdon 13,
Luton 10, St Albans 9.
Golf Knebworth 18h & 9h. **See** 14th cent
'George and Dragon' Inn, St Giles' Church.

Repairer: Codicote Motors Ltd, High St.
T Stevenage (0438) 820288.

CODSALL West Midlands. Map 19F
Pop 9,603. Wolverhampton 4½, London
129, Newport 14, Stafford 16, Wellington
15.
EC Wed. **Golf** Patshull 18h. **See** Church,
Chillington Hall—Capability Brown
grounds.

Moors Farm (R), **F, x** *Chillington Lane,
WV8 1QM.* ✆ (090 74) 2330. C4. 🚗 6
bedrs, 2 bps, 2 ba. ✗ a l c. 🅿 TV, CP 20,
CF, 1 st. £ BB £10–£12, DB £18–£22, WT
(a) £115–£120, DT (a) £19·50–£23, 2, L
£5, D £8, cc 1.

Rescue Service: Birches Bridge Garage,
Wolverhampton Rd. ✆ (090 74) 2316.

COLCHESTER Essex. Map 17C
Pop 138,700. Chelmsford 22, London 56,
Braintree 15, Clacton 15, Harwich 18,
Haverhill 28, Ipswich 18, Scole 40,
Southend 37, Stowmarket 27, Sudbury
14.
EC Thur. **MD** Thur, Sat. **Golf** Colchester
18h. **See** Colchester and Essex Museum
(incorp the Castle, Hollytrees mansion and
All Saints' Church), St. John's Abbey
Gateway, Siege House, St Martin's
Church, St Botolph's Priory remains, Layer
Marney Tower (B1022—Tiptree Rd),
famous oyster fisheries, Bourne Mill (NT),
Roman walls and Balkerne Gate, Minories
Art Gallery, 74 High St.
🅿 Town Hall, High St. ✆ Colchester
(0206) 46379.

★★★**Marks Tey**, *London Rd, Marks Tey,
CO6 1DU.* ✆ (0206) 210001. C. 🚗 106
bedrs, 106 bp, TV, Dgs. ✗ a l c, mc, at, LD
10.30. 🅿 N, CH, TV, CP 160, con 250, CF,
50 BGf, 0 st, Dis. £ BB £32·50, DB £42,
WB, 1, Bk £3·45, L £6·60, D £6·60.
★★**George**, *116 High St, CO1 1WJ.*
✆ (0206) 578494. C. 🚗 47 bedrs, 47 bp,
TV, Dgs. ✗ mc, at, LD 10. 🅿 N, CH, CP 50,
Ac, con 80, CF. £ BB fr £31, DB fr £42, WB,
1, Bk £3·75, L £7·25, D £7·25, cc 1 2 3 4 5,
Dep b.
■★**Red Lion**, *High St, CO1 1DJ.*
✆ (0206) 577986. C. 🚗 20 bedrs, 15 bp, 2
ba, TV, Dgs. ✗ mc, at, LD 10.30. 🅿 N, CH,
TV, Dgs, Ac, con 35, CF, 1 st. £ Bk £4,
cc 1 2 3 5.

Repairer: Cowies G M of Colchester,
Ipswich Rd. ✆ (0206) 61339.
Specialist Body Repairer: Lufax Motor
Works, Fairfax Rd. ✆ (0206) 74927.
Rescue Service: B & B Motors
(Colchester) Ltd, 77 Military Rd.
✆ (0206) 72514.
Evans Motors, 199 Lexden Rd.
✆ (0206) 74683.
Maldon Road Garage, 84 Maldon Rd.
✆ (0206) 73657.
Scottspray, Hawkins Rd. ✆ (0206) 68813
& (0206) 70091.
Trident Motors, 108 Military Rd.
✆ (0206) 77313 & (0206) 47462.

COLDEN COMMON Hampshire. Map
6D
Winchester 5, London 69, Cosham 17,
Romsey 10, Southampton 9

Rescue Service: The Village Garage, Main
Rd. ✆ Twyford (0962) 712185

COLEFORD Gloucestershire, Map 13E
Pop 4,305. Gloucester 20, London 124,
Chepstow 13, Monmouth 5½, Ross-on-
Wye 12.

EC Thur. **Golf** Coleford 18h. **See** Remains
of 14th cent Church, Forest of Dean,
Speech House 2½m E.

★★**M Bells**, *Lord Hill, GL16 8BD.* ✆ Dean
(0594) 32583. Closed Xmas Day. C. 🚗 25
bedrs, 25 bp. ✗ a l c, mc, at, LD 10. 🅿 CH,
TV, CP 250, sp, tc, con 150, CF, 25 BGf,
Dis. £ BB fr £12·50, DB fr £22, WT fr £140,
DT fr £24, WB, 1, Bk £3·50, L £5·50, D
£5·75, cc 1 5, Dep a.
★★**Speech House** (TH), *Forest of Dean,
GL16 7EL.* (3 m E on B4226).
✆ Cinderford (0594) 22607. C. 🚗 14
bedrs, 3 bp, 6 ba, 1 st. ✗ a l c, mc, at, LD
9.30. 🅿 CH, TV, CP 50, Ac, con 30,
CF. £ BB fr £34, DB fr £44, WB, 1,
cc 1 2 3 4 5 6, Dep (Xmas).
★**King's Head**, *Bank St, GL36 8BA.*
✆ Dean (0594) 34094.
Greenmoors, G, xy (Unl), *Crossways,
GL16 8QP.* ✆ Dean (0594) 32556.

Rescue Service: Christchurch Garage,
Christchurch. ✆ Dean (0594) 32586.
Five Acres Garage. ✆ Dean (0594) 33517.

COLESHILL Warwickshire. Map 21B
Pop 6,670. Coventry 12, London 106,
Atherstone 10, Birmingham 9½, Evesham
34, Lichfield 15, Nuneaton 12, Stratford-
upon-Avon 24, Sutton Coldfield 7½,
Tamworth 10, Warwick 18.
EC Mon, Thur. **Golf** Maxstoke Park 18h.
See Pillory, Whipping Post and Stocks on
Church Hill, 14th cent Church.

★★★**Coleshill**, *High St, B46 3BG.*
✆ (0674) 65527. C. 🚗 15 bedrs, 13 bp, 2
bps, TV. ✗ a l c, mc, at, LD 10.30. 🅿 N, CH,
CP 52, U 2, Ac, con 240, CF. £ BB £27, DB
£30, WT £286·30, DT £40·90, WB, 2, Bk
£3, L £5·95, D £7·95, cc 1 2 3 4 5 6, Dep b.

Sctr Repairer: Wood Scooters Ltd, 122
High St. ✆ (0674) 63586.

COLLIERS END Hertfordshire. M.Area
15F
Pop. 3,747. Hoddesdon 8, London 28,
Baldock 15, Bishop's Stortford 9, Hatfield
14, Royston 13.
EC Wed. **Golf** Hamels Park 18h.

Repairer: Colliers End Garage Ltd, A10
Road. ✆ Ware (0920) 821705.

COLNBROOK Buckinghamshire. Map
7A
Chiswick 12, London 17, M4 Motorway
1½, Harrow 13, Kingston upon Thames 13,
Slough 4, Staines 5, Windsor 4½.

Rescue Service: Just Transit Ltd, Unit 8,
Trident Industrial Estate, Blackthorne Rd.
✆ (028 12) 5018.

COLNE Lancashire. Map 27A
Pop 18,150. Burnley 6½, London 212,
Blackburn 16, Bradford 19, Halifax 20,
Settle 20, Skipton 11, Whalley 12.
EC Tue. **MD** Wed, Fri, Sat. **Golf** Colne 18h.
See St Bartholomew's Church (1122),
Wycoller Hall ruins.

Repairer: Kitchen, D Ltd, Atlas Garage,
Skipton Rd. ✆ (0282) 865959.
Rescue Service: John Macadam & Son,
Hyde Park Garage, North Valley Rd.
✆ (0282) 863851.

COLNEY HEATH Hertfordshire. Map
15F
Pop 4,500. Barnet 8½, London 19, Hatfied
3, St Albans 3½, Watford 10.

EC Wed. **Golf** Welwyn Garden City 18h. **See** St Mark's Church.

Rescue Service: Butterfields Car Recovery, Colney Heath Service Station, High St, St Albans. ℓ Bowmansgreen (0727) 22146.

COLSTERWORTH Lincolnshire. Map 23E
Pop 1,121. Stamford 13, London 103, Grantham 8, Melton Mowbray 13, Spalding 24.
EC Wed. **Golf** Stoke Rochford 18h. **See** EE Church (Memorial Chapel to Sir Issac Newton), Woolsthorpe Manor (Nat Trust)—birthplace of Issac Newton.

Rescue Service: Jubilee Garage (Colsterworth) Ltd, The By-pass. ℓ Grantham (0476) 860244.

COLWELL BAY Isle of Wight. M.Area 6E
Pop 2,230. Yarmouth 2, London (Fy) 88, Cowes 15, Newport 12, Totland 1.
EC Wed. **Golf** Freshwater 18h.

Sandy Lane, G, x, *Colwell Common Rd, PO39 0DD.* ℓ (0893) 753330. C. ⋈ 9 bedrs, 2 ba, Dgs. ⌂ ch, TV, Dgs, CP 5, CF, 2 BGf, 2 st. **£** BB £8·10–£8·65, DB £16·20–£17·30, WT (b) £72·45–£76·65, DT (b) £11·55–£12·60, ⬚, Bk £1·50, D £3·75.

COLYTON Devon. Map 5D
Pop 2,422. Lyme Regis 7, London 154, Honiton 8, Seaton 2½, Axminster 5.
EC Wed. **Golf** Axe Cliffe, Axmouth 18h. **See** Church, Monuments.

St Edmunds, G, x (Unl), *Colyford, EX13 6QQ.* ℓ (0297) 52431. Open Easter & May-Sept. C. ⋈ 7 bedrs, 2 ba, Dgs. ⌂ CH, TV, Dgs, CP 8, 1 BGf, 0 st, Dis. **£** BB £7·75–£8·25, DB £15·50–£16·50, WT £52·50–£56, ⬚.

COMBE MARTIN Devon. Map 4C
Pop 2,500. Dunster 31, London 196, Barnstaple 10, Ilfracombe 5, Lynmouth 12, South Molton 18.
EC Wed. **Golf** Ilfracombe 18h. **See** 'Pack of Cards' Inn, Church with fine Perp tower. ⓘ Sea Cottage, Cross St. ℓ Combe Martin (027 188) 3319.

■▥★★Coulsworthy House (R), *EX34 0PD.* ℓ (027 188) 2463. Closed mid-Dec–Jan. C. ⋈ 10 bedrs, 2 ba, 4 bps, 1 sh, 2 ba, TV, Dgs. ✘ mc, at, LD 9.15. ⌂ CH, TV, Dgs, CP 20, sp, tc, CF, 2 st. **£** BB £12–£38, DB £24–£50, WT £134–£218, DT £22–£36·50, WB, ⬚, Bk £4, L £4, D £11.

■★★M White Gates (R & Cl), *Woodlands, EX34 0AT.*
ℓ (027 188) 3511.
■★Britannia (RI), *Moorey Meadow, Seaside, EX34 0DG.* ℓ (027 188) 2294. C. ⋈ 10 bedrs, 2 ba. ✘ a l c, mc, at, LD 7.30. ⌂ CH, TV, CP 14, G 2, CF, 4 st. **£** BB £12–£13·76, DB £16·£52, WT £130·75–£143, DT £20–£21·50, ⬚, Bk £4·50, L £5, D £7·50, Dep a.
■★Rone House (R), *Kings St, EX34 0AD.* ℓ (027 188) 3428. Closed Nov. C. ⋈ 12 bedrs, 2 bp, 5 sh, 3 ba, Dgs. ✘ mc, LD 7.30. ⌂ CH, TV, CP 15, Ac, sp, con 30, CF. **£** WB, ⬚, Bk £3, L £2·50, D £6, cc 1, Dep a.

Firs, PH, x (RI), *Woodlands, Seaside, EX34 0AS.* ℓ (027 188) 3404. Open Mar–Oct. C. ⋈ 9 bedrs, 2 ba. ⌂ CH, TV, CP 10, CF, 1 st. **£** BB £7, DB £14, WT £65–£75, DT £12, ⬚.

Newbury Lodge, PH, x (RI), *Newbury Rd, EX34 0AP.* ℓ (027 188) 3316.
Saffron House, PH, x (RI), *King St, EX34 0BX.* ℓ (027 188) 3521. Closed Oct. C. ⋈ 10 bedrs, 2 ba, Dgs. ⌂ CH, TV, Dgs, CP 12, CF, 0 st. **£** BB £7·50–£8·50, DB £15–£16, WT (b) £80–£88, DT (b) £12–£13, ⬚, cc 1 3.
Woodlands, G, x (RI), *2 The Woodlands, EX34 0AT.* ℓ (027 188) 2769. Open Mar–Oct & Xmas, closed Nov–Feb (except for bookings). C3. ⋈ 8 bedrs, 4 sh, 2 ba. ⌂ ch, TV, CP 16, G 2, 5 st. **£** BB £7–£8, DB £14–£16, WT (b) £70–£80, DT (b) £11–£12, ⬚, Bk £2·50, D £4, cc 3.

Repairers: Combe Martin Motor Co, Victoria St. ℓ (027 188) 3395. Loverings of Combe Martin Ltd, Borough Rd. ℓ (027 188) 3257.
Rescue Service: S G Irwin, Glen Lyn Garage. ℓ (027 188) 2391.

COMPSTALL Gtr Manchester (Cheshire). Map 22A
Pop 16,096. Marple 2, London 176, Buxton 13, Glossop 6, Hyde 3, Manchester 10, Stockport 5.
EC Wed. **Golf** Romiley 18h, Mellor 18h, Marple 18h. **See** Country Park.

MC Repairer: Compstall Motorcycle Services, Weirside Garage, Andrew St. ℓ 061-494 8494 and 061-427 5133.

COMPTON Surrey. Map 7C
Guildford 3½, London 31, Alton 18, Basingstoke 24, Midhurst 20.

Rescue Service: Autotek, Jackson's Corner, A3 By-Pass Rd. ℓ Guildford (0483) 810103.

CONGLETON Cheshire. Map 19D
Pop 23,850. Stoke-on-Trent 13, London 161, Altrincham 20, Buxton 17, Knutsford 31, Leek 9½, Macclesfield 8½, Manchester 24, Middlewich 10, Nantwich 15, Newcastle-under-Lyme 12, Northwich 15, Sandbach 7.
EC Wed. **MD** Tue, Sat. **Golf** Astbury 18h, Congleton 9h. **See** Town Hall, old inns, Little Moreton Hall (NT) 3 m SW, Capesthorne Hall 6½ m N.
ⓘ Town Hall, High St. ℓ Congleton (026 02) 71095.

Rescue Service: Burns Garages Ltd, Canal St. ℓ (026 02) 3553. Lawrence Motors Ltd, Canal Rd. ℓ (026 02) 4965.

CONINGTON Cambridgeshire. M.Area 15B
Pop 215. Alconbury 7, London 74, Ely 30, Huntingdon 11, Kettering 25, Market Harborough 33, Northampton 36, Peterborough 9½, Stamford 17.
Golf Ramsey 18h. **See** Moated enclosures, Holme Fen Nature Reserve, Parish Church.

Rescue Service: Ratcliffe, F, Cross Roads Garage. ℓ Ramsey (0487) 830253.

CONISTON Cumbria. Map 26F
Pop 1,063. Ambleside 7, London 275, Broughton-in-Furness 9, Ulverston 13.
EC Wed. **Golf** Ulverston 18h. **See** Brantwood (Ruskin Museum), Parish Church (Ruskin's grave), Donald Campbell Memorial, Tent Lodge (where the Tennyson), Coniston Old Man, 2,633 ft, Coniston Water, Tarn Hows (Nat Trust).

ⓘ Main Car Park. ℓ Coniston (096 64) 533.

■★★Sun, *LA21 8HQ.* ℓ (0966) 41248. RS Nov–Feb. C. ⋈ 10 bedrs, 3 bps, 3 ba, Dgs. ✘ a l c, mc, at, LD 8. ⌂ ch, TV, CP 25, G 4, Ac, con 30, CF, 0 st. **£** BB £16–£20·50, DB £31–£39, DBB £24·50–£28·50, ⬚, Bk £4, L £3·15, D £7·50, cc 1 3 6.
■★Black Bull, *Yewdale Rd, LA21 8DU,* ℓ (0966) 41335. C. ⋈ 7 bedrs, 3 sh, 2 ba, TV, Dgs. ✘ a l c, mc, at, LD 9. ⌂ ch, TV, CP 8, U 2, CF. **£** Bk £3, L £2·50, D £6·50, Dep.

CONNOR DOWNS Cornwall. M. Area 2E
2½ m NE of Hayle, Camborne 3½, London 271, Falmouth 17, Helston 10, Penzance 11, St Ives 7½.

Rescue Services: Connor Downs Service Station, Connor Hill. ℓ Hayle (0736) 755044.

CONSETT Durham. Map 24E
Pop 30,750 (Inc. Leadgate). West Auckland 19, London 268, Alston 32, Corbridge 13, Durham 12, Hexham 16, Middleton-in-Teesdale 24, Newcastle upon Tyne 13, Sunderland 21.
EC Wed. **MD** Fri, Sat. **Golf** Consett 18h. **See** Moors, Derwent Reservoir, Roman Bath-house at Ebchester.

Rescue Service: Edge Garage, Leedham Motor Services, Medomsley. ℓ Ebchester (0207) 560274.
Heaton Motor Co Ltd, Ann St. ℓ (0207) 508337 and (0207) 503137.
Keith Morton Ltd, Delves Garage. ℓ (0207) 503561.

CONSTANTINE BAY Cornwall. Map 2D
Pop 100. Wadebridge 11, London 250, Newquay 12.
Golf Trevose G and CC 18h and 9h. **See** Trevose Head (Lighthouse, Cliffs).

★★★Treglos (R), *PL28 8JH.* ℓ Padstow (0841) 520727. Open Mar–Nov. C. ⋈ 44 bedrs, 44 bp, TV, Dgs. ✘ a l c, mc, at, LD 9.30. ⌂ Lt, CH, CP 50, U 8, sp, con 30, CF, 1 BGf, 1 st, Dis. **£** BB £22–£31, DB £42–£60, WT £190–£260, DT £34·50–£43·50, ⬚, Bk £5·50, L £6·50, D £9.

COODEN BEACH East Sussex. Map 10E
Hurst Green 15, London 65, Eastbourne 9, Hastings 7½, Lewes 21, Uckfield 23.
EC Wed. **Golf** Cooden Beach 18h.

★★★Cooden Beach, *Cooden Sea Rd, TN39 4TT.* ℓ Cooden (042 43) 2281. C. ⋈ 32 bedrs, 30 bp, 5 bps, 2 ba, TV, Dgs. ✘ a l c, mc, at, LD 10. ⌂ N, CH, TV, CP 100, U 8, sp, con 35, CF, 1 st. **£** BBc £23–£28, DBc £35·50–£42·50, WT £175·20–£198·25, DT £37·45–£42·45, WB, ⬚, Bk £4·50, L £6·50, D £7·95, cc 1 3 4 5.

COOKHAM Berkshire. Map 7A
Pop 8,000. Slough 7½, London 28, Denham 12, Henley-on-Thames 12, High Wycombe 7½, Reading 16, Windsor 9.
EC Wed, Sat. **Golf** Maidenhead 18h. Temple 18h. **See** Stanley Spencer Gallery, 12th cent Parish Church, 15th cent Bel and the Dragon Inn, Cliveden Reach, Nat Trust Commons.

Repairer: Barnside Motors Ltd, High St. ℓ Bourne End (062 85) 22029.

COOMBE HILL Gloucestershire. Map 13D

Pop 287. Cheltenham 5, London 102, Gloucester 7, Tewkesbury 4.
Golf Tewkesbury Park 18h. **See** Leigh Perp. church.

Rescue Service: Barters Garage.
✆ (024 268) 362.

COPTHORNE West Sussex. Map 7D
Pop 3,048. Redhill 8, London 28, M23 Motorway 5, Crawley 4½, East Grinstead 6½, Godstone 12.
Golf Copthorne 18h.

★★★★**M Copthorne,** *Copthorne Rd, RH10 3PG.* ✆ (0342) 714971. C. ⇔ 221 bedrs, 175 bp, 46 bps, 2 ba, TV, Dgs. ✗ a l c, mc, at, LD 10.30. ⓐ N, CH, TV, CP 300, Ac, sp, gc, tc, sc, sb, sol, gym, con 150, CF. £ BB £47·75, DB £63·75, WB, ⅉ, Bk £5, L £10, D £15, cc 1 3 4 5 6, Dep a.

CORBRIDGE-ON-TYNE
Northumberland. Map 26A
Pop 2,200. West Auckland 31, London 280, Alnwick 43, Bellingham 18, Durham 25, Hawick 52, Hexham 3½, Jedburgh 47, Newcastle upon Tyne 17.
EC Thur. **Golf** Hexham 18h & 9h. **See** St Andrew's Church, Market Cross, 17th cent bridge, 17th cent Angel Inn, ruins of Aydon and Dilston castles. Museum of Roman relics at Corstopitum.
ⅉ Vicars Pele Tower, Market Pl.
✆ Corbridge (043 471) 2815.

★★**Angel Inn,** *Main St, NE45 5LA.* ✆ (043 471) 2119. C. ⇔ 6 bedrs, 2 ba, TV, Dgs. ✗ a l c, mc, LD 10. ⓐ ch, CP 30, Ac, CF, 1 st. £ BB fr £15, DB fr £19·80, ⅉ, Bk £2·40, L £1·75, D £4·95, cc 1 3 4 5, Dep b.
Tynedale, H, x, *Market Pl, NE45 5AW.* ✆ (043 471) 2149. C. ⇔ 8 bedrs, 8 bps, TV. ⓐ CH, 1 st. £ BB £16, DB £25, ⅉ, Bk £2·50.

CORBY Northamptonshire. Map 15A
Pop 52,395. Kettering 7½, London 82, Huntingdon 27, Market Harborough 12, Melton Mowbray 24, Peterborough 23, Stamford 16.
EC Wed. **MD** Fri, Sat. **Golf** Corby 18h. **See** Castle 2m N.

★★★**M Grosvenor,** *George St, NN17 1QQ.* ✆ (053 63) 3441.

CORLEY Warwickshire. Map 14B
Pop 699. Coventry 5, London 99, Birmingham 16, Nuneaton 6, Tamworth 14.
Golf Maxstoke 18h. **See** Parish Church, Corley Rocks, Ruins Roman Camp (A.M.).

Rescue Service: Corley Ash Garage, Tamworth Rd. ✆ Fillongley (0676) 40335. Cowan Recovery Ltd, Corley Service Area, M6 Motorway. ✆ Fillongley (0676) 40136

CORNHILL-ON-TWEED
Northumberland. Map 31A
Pop 320. Newcastle upon Tyne 59, London 333, Alnwick 30, Berwick-upon-Tweed 13, Coldstream 1½, Kelso 10.
EC Thur. **Golf** Coldstream 9h. **See** Castles, Abbeys.

▣⌘★★★★**Tillmouth Park,** *TD12 4UU.* ✆ Coldstream (0890) 2255. C. ⇔ 16 bedrs, 7 bp, 4 ba, TV, Dgs. ✗ mc, LD 8.45. ⓐ ch, TV, Dgs, CP 50, U 2, Ac, pf, CF, 1 BGf, 6 st. £ ⅉ, Bk £5, L £6·95, D £9·25, cc 1 3 4 5.
★★**Collingwood Arms,** *Main St, TD12 4UH.* ✆ Coldstream (0890) 2424.

Rescue Service: Station Garage.
✆ Coldstream (0890) 2146.

CORSHAM Wiltshire. Map 5B
Pop 10,440. Chippenham 4, London 95, Bath 9½, Bristol 21, Chepstow 31, Devizes 12, Frome 17, Westbury 14.
EC Wed. **MD** Tue. **Golf** Chippenham 18h. **See** Corsham Court.

★★★**Rudloe Park,** *Leafy La, SN13 0PA.* ✆ Hawthorn (0225) 810555. C. ⇔ 8 bedrs, 8 bp, TV. ✗ a l c, mc, at, LD 10. ⓐ CH, ns, CP 80, U 2, G 2, Ac, con 120, CF, 2 st. £ BB £32·50–£35, DB £55–£65, WT £287–£322, DT £43·50–£48·50, WB, ② 10%, Bk £5, L £6·25, D £9·75, cc 1 2 3 4 5 6.▲
★★**M Stagecoach** (Rt) *Park La, Pickwick, SN13 9LG.* ✆ (0249) 713162. C. ⇔ 22 bedrs, 22 bp, 1 sh, TV. ✗ a l c, mc, at, LD 9.30. ⓐ N, CH, TV, Dgs, ns, CP 40, Ac, con 50, CF, 21 BGf, 1 st, Dis. £ BB £25–£27, DB £37·75–£42·25, WT £165–£185, DT £28·75–£29·75, WB, ⅉ, Bk £3·50, L £5·50, D £7·50, cc 1 3 4 5.

COSHAM Hampshire. Map 6F
Petersfield 13, London 66, Chichester 13, Fareham 5, Midhurst 21, Portsmouth 4, Winchester 22.
EC Wed. **Golf** Crookhorn Lane, Purbrook 18h.

Rescue Service: Safety Autos, Unit J, Paulsgrove Industrial Estate.
✆ (0705) 324214.

COTTERED Hertfordshire. Map 15D.
Pop 587. Buntingford 3, London 37, Baldock 8, Bishops Stortford 14, Cambridge 24, Stevenage 7.
Golf Letchworth 18h. **See** Japanese Gdns.

Rescue Service: Cottered Service Station.
✆ (076 381) 267.

COULSDON Greater London (Surrey). Map 7B
Pop 46,190 (Coulsdon and Purley in the London Borough of Croydon), Purley 2, London 14, Dorking 12, Epsom 7, Godstone 6½, Redhill 6, Reigate 7½.
EC Wed. **Golf** Coulsdon Court Municipal 18h.

Repairer: Forder Motors Ltd, Smitham House, 127 Brighton Rd. ✆ 01-668 2331.

COUND Shropshire. Map 19F
Much Wenlock 7, London 152, Shrewsbury 7, Wellington 10.
Golf Hawkestone Park (2) 18h.

Rescue Service: Cound Garage (H M & C A Webb), nr Shrewsbury. ✆ Cressage (095 289) 248.

COUNDON Durham. Map 24E
Pop 2,493. West Auckland 4½, London 255, Alston 37, Corbridge 30, Darlington 12, Durham 10, Hexham 33, Stockton-on-Tees 16.
Golf Bishop Auckland 18h.

Rescue Service: Kemble Motors, Lorne Garage, Cleveland View. ✆ Bishop Auckland (0388) 2788.

COVENTRY West Midlands. Map 21B
Pop 318,000. Daventry 19, London 94, M6 Motorway 4, Banbury 27, Birmingham 18, Bromsgrove 29, Leicester 25, Market Harborough 28, Nuneaton 8½, Rugby 12, Sutton Coldfield 19, Tamworth 19, Walsall 26, Warwick 10.

See Plan, p. 185.
MD Daily expt Thur. **P** See Plan. **Golf** Coventry 18h, Coventry Hearsall 18h, Grange 9h. **See** Cathedral remains and new Cathedral, St Mary's Hall, Holy Trinity Church, Lady Godiva Statue, Herbert Art Gallery and Museum, City Wall and Lady Herbert's Garden, new City centre, Belgrade Theatre, Ford's Hospital and Bonds Hospital (Almshouses), Christ Church, Whitefriars Monastery Museum, reconstructed Roman Fort at Baginton.
ⅉ 36 Broadgate. ✆ Coventry (0203) 20084.

★★★★**De Vere,** *Fairfax St, CV1 5RP.* ✆ (0203) 51851. C. ⇔ 215 bedrs, 215 bp, TV, Dgs. ✗ a l c, mc, at, LD 11. ⓐ Lt, N, CH, TV, Dgs, G 130, con, CF, 0 st. £ BB fr £47, DB fr £62, WB, ⅉ, Bk £5, L £5, D £5, cc 1 2 3 4 5 6, Dep b.
★★★★**Hotel Leofric,** *Broadgate, CV1 1LZ.* ✆ (0203) 21371. C. ⇔ 91 bedrs, 91 bp, TV, Dgs. ✗ a l c, mc, at, LD 10. ⓐ Lt, N, CH, Dgs, Ac, con 500, CF. £ B fr £39, BD fr £49, WB, ⅉ, Bk £4·25, L £6·95, D £7·75, cc 1 2 3 4 5 6, Dep b.
★★★**Brandon Hall** (TH), *Main St, Brandon, CV8 3FW.* ✆ (0203) 542571. C. ⇔ 68 bedrs, 44 bp, TV, Dgs. ✗ a l c, mc, at, LD 9.30. ⓐ N, CH, Dgs, CP 250, Ac, con 70, CF, 20 BGf, 1 st. £ BB fr £26·50, DB fr £41, WB, ⅉ, cc 1 2 3 4 5 6, Dep (Xmas).
★★★**M Chace Crest,** *London Rd, Willenhall, CV3 4EQ.* ✆ (0203) 303398. C. ⇔ 68 bedrs, 68 bp, ns, TV, Dgs. ✗ a l c, mc, LD 9.45. ⓐ N, CH, Dgs, CP 150, Ac, con 50, 25 BGf, Dis. £ BB fr £43·45, DB fr £58·40, WB, ⅉ, Bk £4·95, D £8·95, cc 1 2 3 4 5 6, Dep b.
★★★**M Crest,** *(M6, Junction 2), Hinckley Rd, Walsgrave, CV2 2HP* (3 m NE junc A46 and M6). ✆ (0203) 613261. C. ⇔ 160 bedrs, 160 bp, ns, TV, Dgs. ✗ a l c, mc, at, LD 9.45. ⓐ Lt, N, CH, Dgs, CP 250, Ac, con 450, CF, Bk £5·25, D £9·60, cc 1 2 3 4 5 6, Dep b.
★★★**M Novotel,** *Wilsons La, CV6 6HL.* ✆ (0203) 365000. C. ⇔ 100 bedrs, 100 bp, TV, Dgs. ✗ a l c, mc, at, LD 11.15. ⓐ Lt, N, CH, Dgs, CP 120, Ac, sp, sc, sb, sol, gym, con 200, CF, 28 BGf, Dis. £ BB £38, DB £44, WB, ⅉ, Bk £4, L £7, D £9, cc 1 2 3 4 5 6.
★★★**M Post House** (TH), *Rye Hill, Allesley, CV5 9PH.* ✆ (0203) 402151. C. ⇔ 196 bedrs, 196 bp, TV, Dgs. ✗ a l c, mc, at, LD 10.15. ⓐ Lt, N, CH, Dgs, CP 297, Ac, con 130, CF. £ BB fr £40, DB fr £52·50, WB, ⅉ, cc 1 2 3 4 5 6.
★★**Allesley,** *Allesley Village, CV5 9GP.* ✆ (0203) 403272. Closed Xmas Day. C. ⇔ 24 bedrs, 14 bp, 3 ba, annexe 13 bedrs, 13 sh, TV, Dgs. ✗ a l c, mc, at, LD 10.30. ⓐ N, CH, CP 350, Ac, con 350, CF, 1 st. £ BB £17·10–£25·95, DB £32·50–£36·25, WT fr £224, DT fr £32, WB, ⅉ, Bk £3·50, L £7·50, D £8, cc 1 2 3 4 5 6, Dep b.
★★**Beechwood** (RI), *Sandpits La, CV6 2FR.* (3 m N on A51, Tamworth Rd). ✆ Keresley (0203) 334243. C. ⇔ 27 bedrs, 1 bp, 17 bps, 2 sh, 3 ba. ✗ a l c, mc, at, LD 10. ⓐ N, CH, Dgs, CP 160, con 12, CF, 7 BGf, Dis. £ BB fr £19·50, DB fr £26, WT fr £220·50, DT fr £32·50, WB, ②, Bk £3, L £6·50, D £7·50, cc 1 3 4 5 6.
Croft, H, z (RI), *Stoke Green, CV3 1FP.* ✆ (0203) 457846. C. ⇔ 12 bedrs, 3 sh, 3 ba, TV, Dgs. ✗ a l c. ⓐ CH, TV, CP 22, CF, 4

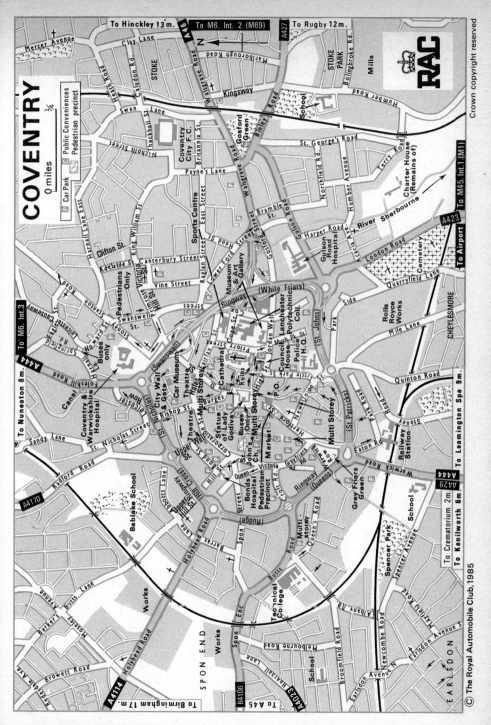

st. **£** BB £13–£13·75, DB £21–£28, ☑, Bk
£2·95, D £5.

Trinity House, H, z (R), *28 Lower
Holyhead Rd, CV1 3AU.* ✆ (0203) 555654.
C. ⊷ 8 bedrs, 2 ba, Dgs. ✗ a l c. ◪ CH, TV,
CP 2, CF, 2 st. **£** BB £11·50, DB £18·50,
WT (b) £108, (c) £72, DT (b) £17·25, ☐, D
£6.

Repairer: Henlys (Coventry) Ltd, Kenpas
Highway. ✆ (0203) 411515.
Specialist Radiator Repairer Serck
Radiator Services Ltd, Henrietta St.
✆ (0203) 89336.
Rescue Service: Allesley Garage, 244
Birmingham Rd. ✆ (0203) 403466.
Binley Woods Service Station Ltd, 60
Rugby Rd, Binley Woods. ✆ Wolston
(0203) 2202.
City Garage, Roseberry Av, Bell Green.
✆ (0203) 87904.
Heath Road Motors Ltd, 25 Heath Rd.
✆ (0203) 454229 & (0203) 442328.
Potters Green Service Station, Ringwood
Highway. ✆ (0203) 614570.
Rayfield Autos Ltd, 142 Lowerford St.
✆ (0203) 20475 & (0203) 20492.

COVERACK Cornwall. Map 2F
Pop 375. Truro 24, London 278, Falmouth
18, Helston 11.
Golf Mullion 18h.
See Cliffs, South Cornwall Coast Path,
Goonhilly Downs.

◪★★**Coverack Headland,** *TR12 6SB.*
✆ St Keverne (0326) 280243. Open April–
Sept. C. ⊷ 20 bedrs, 8 bp, 4 ba, Dgs.
✗ a l c. mc, at. ◪ ch, TV, Dgs, CP 20, Ac,
CF. **£** BB £10–£16, DB £17–£25, ☐, Bk
£3·50, L 60p, D £6·50, cc 3 4.

COWES Isle of Wight. Map 6F
Pop 16,255. Ferry service to
Southampton. London 76, Newport 4½,
Ryde (Fy) 8, Yarmouth 13.
EC Wed. **Golf** Cowes 9h. **See** Osborne
House (Royal Apartments, Swiss Cottage,
Museum, Gardens), 16th cent Cowes
Castle, East Cowes (H.Q. of Royal Yacht
Squadron), Whippingham Church 2 m SE.

★★**Holmwood** (R), *Queens Rd, PO31
8BW.* ✆ Isle of Wight (0983) 292508. C.
⊷ 16 bedrs, 5 bp, 6 bps, 2 ba, TV, Dgs.
✗ a l c. mc, at, LD 9.30. ◪ CH, TV, Dgs, CP
14, con 100, CF, 4 st, Dis. **£** BB
£19·80–£26·40, DB £39·60–£44, DBB
£24·50, WB, ☑ 10%, Bk £3·50, L £7, D £9,
cc 1 2 3 5.

★**Cowes**, (R), *260 Arctic Rd, PO31 7PJ.*
✆ Isle of Wight (0983) 291541. Closed
Xmas. C. ⊷ 13 bedrs, 12 bp, 1 bps, TV,
Dgs. ◪ N, CH, Dgs, CP 15, sp, sb, con 12,
CF, 4 BGf, 6 st. **£** BB fr £19·50, DB fr
£29·50, WB, ☐, Bk £7·99, L £7·99, D £7·99,
cc 1 3 4 5.

COWFOLD West Sussex. Map 7C
Pop 1,400. M23 Motorway 8, Crawley 10,
London 41, Haywards Heath 8, Worthing
15.
EC Wed. **Golf** Mannings Heath 18h. **See**
Old Buildings, St Peter's Church.

Rescue Service: Noahs Ark Service
Station, Henfield Rd. ✆ (040 386) 511.

COWLING North Yorkshire. Map 27A
Pop 1,800. Halifax 20, London 213,
Blackburn 22, Bradford 18, Burnley 12,
Harrogate 28, Huddersfield 26, Leeds 25,
Skipton 8, Whalley 18.

EC Wed. **Golf** Skipton 18h. **See**
Ickornshaw Moor, panoramic views.

Rescue Service: Brigg, Walter C Ltd,
North End Garage. ✆ Cross Hills
(0535) 33241.

CRACKINGTON HAVEN Cornwall.
Map 2B
Pop 1,500. Launceston 18, London 229,
Bideford 35, Bude 10, Camelford 10,
Holsworthy 18.
Golf Bude and North Cornwall 18h. **See**
Fine cliffs (Nat Trust area), good surf-
bathing beaches.

◪★★**Coombe Barton,** *EX23 0JG.* ✆ St
Gennys (08403) 345. Open Mar–Oct. C.
⊷ 10 bedrs, 3 bp, 3 ba, Dgs. ✗ a l c. mc,
LD 9. ◪ CH, TV, Dgs, CP 60, Ac, CF. **£** BB
£14·75–£15·75, DB £27·50–£32·50, WT
£129–£135, ☐, Bk £3·75, L £2·75, D £8·50,
cc 1 3 5.

CRADLEY HEATH Warley, West
Midlands. M.Area 21F
Pop 15,600. Birmingham 9½, London 121,
Bridgnorth 17, Bromsgrove 14,
Kidderminster 10, Walsall 10,
Wolverhampton 9.
EC Thur. **MD** Fri. **Golf** Dudley 18h. **See**
Haden Hill Park.

Rescue Service: S & S Services, Cox Lane
Garage, Old Hill. ✆ (0384) 62385.

CRAFTHOLE Cornwall. Map 3C
Pop 660. Saltash 12, London 224 (Fy
219), Liskeard 11, Looe 11, Plymouth (Fy)
7½.
EC Thur. **Golf** Whitsand Bay 18h. **See**
13th cent Dovecot, 12th cent Church,
Tithe Barn. Celtic Cross.

◪★**Finnygook Inn,** *PL11 3BQ.* ✆ St.
Germans (0503) 30338. C14. ⊷ 6 bedrs,
5 bp, 1 ba, TV. ✗ a l c. mc, LD 9.30. ◪ CH,
CP 50, con 50, 1 st. **£** ☐, Bk £3·50, L £1, D
£5, Dep a.
Ap. Whitsand Bay, *Portwrinkle, PL11
3BU.* ✆ St. Germans (0503) 30276. Open
Mar–Nov. C. ⊷ 30 bedrs, 25 bp, 6 ba, Dgs.
✗ a l c. mc, at, LD 8.30. ◪ CH, TV, Dgs, CP,
Ac, gc, con 100, CF, 1 st. **£** BB £10–£14,
DB £20–£28, WT £80–£125, DT £14–£18,
WB, ☐, Bk £3, L £3·50, D £7.

CRANBORNE Dorset. Maps 5F and 6C.
Pop 592. Salisbury 14, London 97,
Blandford Forum 14, Bournemouth 17,
Southampton 26, Wimborne Minster 10.
Golf Ferndown 18h.

Fleur de Ly's, H, x, *5 Wimborne St.*
✆ (07254) 282. Closed Xmas. C. ⊷ 4
bedrs, 1 sh, 1 ba, TV, Dgs. ✗ a l c. ◪ CH,
Dgs, CP 35, CF. **£** BB £10–£12, DB £19–
£21, ☐, Bk £2·50, L £6·50, D £8.

CRANBROOK Kent. Map 10C
Pop 4,247. Tonbridge 17, London 49,
Ashford 18, Canterbury 30, Hawkhurst 4,
Maidstone 14, Rye 17, Tenterden 8½,
Tunbridge Wells 14½.
EC Wed. **Golf** Cranbrook 18h. **See**
Church (15th cent), old Smock Mill open
to public on request, Cranbrook School,
George Inn, Angley House Gardens,
Sissinghurst Castle 2½ NE, Sissinghurst
Place Gardens 2 m NE.
[🛈] Vestry Hall, Stone St. ✆ Cranbrook
(0580) 712538.

◪⬤★★**Kennel Holt** (R). *Goudhurst Rd,
TN17 2PT.* ✆ (0580) 712032. Closed

Xmas. C. ⊷ 7 bedrs, 7 bp, TV, Dgs. ✗ at,
LD 8. ◪ CH, CP 30, con 15, 2 st. **£** BB
£18–£26, DB £32–£56, WT £175–£227,
WB, ☐, cc 1 3 4 5 6, (Rest only).

★★**Willesley,** *Angley Rd, TN17 2LE.*
✆ (0580) 713555. Closed 1st week Feb.
C. ⊷ 16 bedrs, 16 bp, TV, Dgs. ✗ a l c. mc,
LD 9.30. ◪ CH, TV, Dgs, CP 60, Ac, con 60,
CF, 4 BGf, Dis. **£** BB £27·50–£33, DB £40–
£44, DT £39–£43, WB, ☐, Bk £4·50, L £6, D
£9·50, cc 1 2 3 4 5 6, Dep b.▲
★**George,** *Stone St, TN17 3HE.*
✆ (0580) 713348.

Repairer: Cranbrook Engineering Works,
Stone St. ✆ (0580) 712121.

CRANFIELD Bedfordshire. M.Area 15C
Pop 4,183. M1 Motorway 4, London 49,
Aylesbury 23, Baldock 22, Bedford 9,
Biggleswade 19, Bletchley 8½, Daventry
30, Dunstable 16, Kettering 28, Luton 18,
Northampton 20, Rugby 39, Towcester
21.
Golf Millbrook 18h. **See** Parish Church,
Old Rectory.

Repairer: Allon White & Son (Cranfield)
Ltd, 119 High St. ✆ Bedford
(0234) 750205.
Rescue Service: R G R Garage, High St.
✆ Bedford (0234) 750207.

CRANFORD Greater London (Middx)
M.Area 7A
See also LONDON AIRPORT.
Brentford & Chiswick 8, London 12, M4
Motorway 1¼, Harrow 10, Richmond-
upon-Thames 6, Slough 8, Staines 6½,
Uxbridge 6½, Windsor 9.

Rescue Service: Rectory Autos, The Old
Rectory, Church Rd. ✆ 01-573 4101 and
848 9201.

CRANTOCK Cornwall. Map 2D
Pop 911. Bodmin 21, London 254,
Newquay 3½, Redruth 15, St Austell 17,
Truro 12, Wadebridge 18.
EC Wed. **Golf** Newquay 18h. **See** 12th
cent Church, St Ambrose Well.

◪★★**Crantock Bay** (R), *West Pentire,
TR8 5SE.* ✆ (0637) 830229. Open Apr–
Oct. C. ⊷ 30 bedrs, 27 bp, 1 bps, 1 ba, TV,
Dgs. ✗ mc, at, LD 8. ◪ CH, TV, CP 35, CF,
1 BGf, 1 st, Dis. **£** DBB £14·50–£23·50,
WB, ☑, Bk £1·50, L £2·65, D £6·25, cc 3.
◪★★**Fairbank** (R), *West Pentire Rd. TR8
5SA.* ✆ (0637) 830424. Open Apr–Oct. C.
⊷ 30 bedrs, 22 bp, 1 sh, 4 ba, TV. ✗ mc, at,
LD 8. ◪ CH, TV, CP 40, con 20, CF. **£** BB
£14–£17·25, DB £28–£34·50, DBB
£19·50–£25·87, WB, ☑, Bk £2, D £6·84,
cc 1 3 5 6.
Crantock Cottage, PH, x (R), *West
Pentire Rd, TR8 5SA.* ✆ (0637) 830232.
Open Apr–Oct. C 7. ⊷ 10 bedrs, 2 ba, Dgs.
◪ ch, TV, CP 6, 4 BGf, 2 st. **£** BB £8·05–
£9·28, DB £16·10–£18·50, WT (b) £71·30–
£83·95, (c) £51·75–£59·80, DT (b)
£11·50–£13·80, ☑.
Tregenna, G, xy (RI), *TR8 5RZ.*
✆ (0637) 830381. Open April–Oct. C. ⊷ 5
bedrs, 1 bps, 2 ba, Dgs. ✗ a l c. ◪ CH, TV,
CP 8, CF, 2 st.

CRAVEN ARMS Shropshire. Map 13A
Pop 1,450. Ludlow 8, London 152,
Bridgnorth 21, Knighton 14, Newtown 27,
Shrewsbury 20, Wellington 27, Welshpool
24.

EC Wed. **MD** Fri. **Golf** Church Stretton 18h. **See** Stokesay Castle, old Mileage Pillar, Iron Age Hill Fort nearby.

◨★★**Craven Arms,** *Shrewsbury Rd, SY7 9QA.* ✆ (058 82) 3331.

CRAWLEY West Sussex. Map 7C
Pop 82,000. Redhill 10, London 31, M23 Motorway 3, Brighton 22, Dorking 13, East Grinstead 9, Godstone 14, Haywards Heath 12, Horsham 8, Reigate 11.
EC Wed. **MD** Fri, Sat. **Golf** Tilgate Park 18h. **See** 'George Inn (16th cent 'Gallows' sign), 15th cent Parish Church, medieval Prior's House now cafe, Nymans Gdns 4½ m S, Tilgate Park, Gatwick Airport (public viewing area), Worth Abbey Church, Worth Forest, Gatwick Gardens and Aviaries.

★★★**M Crest Gatwick Airport,** *Langley Drive, Tushmore Roundabout, RH11 7SX.* ✆ (0293) 29991. C. ⊷ 230 bedrs, 230 bp, ns, TV, Dgs. ✗ a l c, mc, at, LD 11. ⌂ Lt, N, CH, Dgs, CP 300, Ac, con 350, CF, 4 st. £ B fr £41·50, BD fr £52, WB, ①, Bk £5·25, D £8·95, cc 1 2 3 4 5 6, Dep b.

★★★**M Gatwick Concorde** (formerly **Saxon Inn**), *Church Rd, Lowfield Heath, RH11 0PQ.* ✆ (0293) 33441. C. ⊷ 92 bedrs, 92 bp, TV. ✗ a l c, mc, at, LD 10.15. ⌂ Lt, N, CH, CP 150, Ac, con 70, CF, 0 st. £ BB £38·50, BD £49·50, WB, ①, Bk £4·75, L £5·95, D £7·95, cc 1 2 3 5 6, Dep b.

★★★**George** (TH), *High St, RH10 1BS.* ✆ (0293) 24215. C. ⊷ 76 bedrs, 76 bp, TV, Dgs. ✗ a l c, mc, at, LD 9.30. ⌂ N, CH, Dgs, CP 75, Ac, con 250, CF, 13 BGf, 1 st. £ BB fr £43, DB fr £55·50, WB, ①, cc 1 2 3 4 5 6.

★★★**M Goffs Park,** *45 Goffs Park Rd, RH11 8AX.* ✆ (0293) 35447. C. ⊷ 38 bedrs, 37 bp, 1 sh, 1 ba, TV, Dgs. ✗ a l c, mc, LD 9.30. ⌂ N, CH, Dgs, CP 200, Ac, rf, con 150, CF, 14 BGf, 1 st, Dgs. £ BB £23–£28, DB £33–£42, DT £34·70–£36·70, WB, ②, Bk £1·75, L £5·10, D £5·80, cc 1 2 3 5, Dep b.

◨★★**Ifield Court,** *Ifield Av, RH11 0JH.* ✆ (0293) 34807.

Barnwood, PH, x (R), *Balcombe Rd, Pound Hill, RH10 4RU.* ✆ (0293) 882709. C. ⊷ 27 bedrs, 1 bp, 26 bps, 1 ba, TV. ✗ a l c. ⌂ CH, CP 30, CF, 3 BGf, 2 st. £ BB fr £24, DB fr £38, ①, Bk £3·50, D £7, cc 1 2 3 4 5. 6

Repairers: Crawley Down Garage Ltd, Snow Hill, Copthorne. ✆ Copthorne (0342) 713933.
Fieldale Ltd, Overdene Dr, Ifield. ✆ (0293) 515551.
G Gadsdon Ltd, 5 Brighton Rd. ✆ (0293) 35264.
Southern Counties Garages Ltd, 27 Ifield Rd ✆ (0293) 20191.
Southern Counties Garages (Barkers) Ltd, 263 Haslett Av, Three Bridges. ✆ (0293) 27101.
Specialist Body Repairer Fieldale Ltd, Ifield Green. ✆ (0293) 37577.
Rescue Service: H R S Recoveries, Dales Coachyard, Spindle Way, ✆ (0293) 26357.
Shaw's Garage (Crawley) Ltd, Orchard St. ✆ (0293) 23323.
Tates (Portslade Garages) Ltd, Fleming Way. ✆ (0293) 29771.
Windmill Garage (Gatwick) Ltd, Old Brighton Rd, Lowfield Heath. ✆ (0293) 29955.

CREDITON Devon. Maps 3B and 4F
Pop 6,169. Exeter 7½, London 177, Barnstaple 33, Bideford 34, Holsworthy 34, Okehampton 17, Plymouth 41, Saltash 41, South Molton 20, Tavistock 32, Tiverton 12.
EC Wed. **Golf** Downes Crediton 18h. **See** Restored 13th cent Lawrence's Chapel, Statue of St Boniface, Parish Church of the Holy Cross.

Ship, H, *131 High St, EX17 3LQ.* ✆ (036 32) 2963. Closed Xmas. C. ⊷ 5 bedrs, 1 sh, 1 ba, Dgs. ✗ a l c. ⌂ ch, TV, Dgs. CP, CF, 2 st. £ BB £10·50–£12·50, DB £21–£25, WT (c) £73·50, ①, Bk £2·50, L £2·50, D £2·50, cc 5.

Rescue Service: Moore Bros, 36 High St. ✆ (036 32) 2074.

CREWE Cheshire. Map 19D
Pop 48,000. Newcastle-under-Lyme 12, London 162, Middlewich 7½, Nantwich 4½, Newport 27, Sandbach 6.
MD Mon, Fri, Sat. **Golf** Crewe 18h. **See** Weather vane on Municipal Buildings (model of Stephenson's 'Rocket').
⚏ Delamere House, Delamere St. ✆ Crewe (0270) 583191.

★★★**Crewe Arms,** *Nantwich Rd, CW1 1DW* ✆ (0270) 213204. C. ⊷ 36 bedrs, 31 bp, 3 bps, 1 ba, TV, Dgs. ✗ a l c, mc, at, LD 9.30, (10 Fri). ⌂ N, CH, Dgs, CP 120, Ac, con 160, CF. £ B fr £29·50, BD fr £35, WB, ①, Bk £4·25, L £6·95, D £6·95, cc 1 2 3 4 5 6, Dep b.

Repairer: Coppenhall Garage Ltd. Cross Green. ✆ (0270) 583437.
Rescue Service: Brian Peake Developments, Shavington Service Station, Newcastle Rd. Shavington. ✆ (0270) 60892.
Ringways Garages (Crewe) Ltd, Macon Way. ✆ (0270) 583511 and (0270) 586744.
Stewart Street Motors (Crewe) Ltd, Stewart St. ✆ (0270) 60688.

CREWKERNE Somerset. Map 5E
Pop 5,330. Sherborne 14, London 134, Axminster 13, Dorchester 21, Frome 35, Glastonbury 22, Honiton 21, Ilminster 8, Lyme Regis 16, Shepton Mallet 26.
EC Thur. **Golf** Windwhistle 9h. **See** 15th cent St Bartholomew's Church, old Grammar School, Wayford Manor Gardens, Forde Abbey, West Country Wild Life Park, Royal Nurseries at Merriott (1½ m N).

◨★★**Old Parsonage** (R), *59 Barn St, TA18 8BP.* ✆ (0460) 73516.

Rescue Service: Rivermead Garage, South St. ✆ (0460) 73565.
Swaffield, J H & Sons Ltd, East St. ✆ (0460) 72059.

CRICK Northamptonshire.
See RUGBY.

CROCKERNWELL Devon, Maps 3B & 4E
Pop 200. Exeter 12, London 181, Ashburton 19, Crediton 9, Newton Abbot 19, Okehampton 11, Plymouth 34, Saltash 35, Tavistock 26.
See Fingle Bridge.

Rescue Service: Crockernwell Motor Works Ltd. ✆ Cheriton Bishop (064 724) 333.

CROMER Norfolk. Map 16A
Pop 6,192. Fakenham 22, London 133, East Dereham 26, Great Yarmouth 34, Norwich 23.
EC Wed. **Golf** Royal Cromer 18h. **See** 14th cent Church, Lighthouse, Lifeboat Stations and Museum, Birdland, Model Village, Felbrigg Hall 3 m SW.
⚏ North Lodge Park, ✆ Cromer (0263) 512497

★★**Cliftonville,** *Runton Rd, NR27 9AS.* ✆ (0263) 512543. C. ⊷ 46 bedrs, 9 bp, 4 bps, 9 ba, TV, Dgs. ✗ mc, at, LD 9. ⌂ Lt, N, ch, TV, Dgs, CP 20, U 3, Ac, sb, con 200, CF, 3 st. £ BB fr £13, DB fr £17, WB fr £147, DT fr £26·50, WB, ②, Bk £3, L £4·50, D £7·50, cc 1 2 3 5 6, Dep a.▲

★★**Hotel de Paris,** *Jetty Cliff, NR27 9HG.* ✆ (0263) 513141. C. ⊷ 55 bedrs, 31 bp, 2 bps, 9 sh, 19 ba, TV, Dgs. ✗ mc, at, LD 9. ⌂ Lt, N, CH, TV, Dgs, CP 30, Ac, con 120, CF, 1 st. £ BB £16·50–£20, DB £31–£35, WT £140–£160, DT fr £29·50, WB, ①, Bk £3·75, L £5·50, D £7·50, cc 1 2 3 5 6, Dep a.

◨★**Virginia Court** (RI), *Cliff Av, NR27 0AN.* ✆ (0263) 512398. Open April–Sept. C. ⊷ 23 bedrs, 11 bp, Dgs b. ✗ mc, at, LD 7.45. ⌂ ch, TV, Dgs, CP 22, Ac, con 120, CF, 4 BGf, 2 st. £ BB £15–£26, DB £30–£42, ②, Bk £3, cc 1.

◨★**West Parade,** *5 Runton Rd, NR27 9AR.* ✆ (0263) 512443. Open May–Sept, Easter & Xmas. C. ⊷ 29 bedrs, 8 ba, Dgs. ✗ a l c, mc, at, LD 8. ⌂ ch, TV, Dgs, CP 26, Ac, CF. £ WB (Easter), ②, Bk £3·50, L £3·50, D £6·50.

Chellow Dene, G, x (RI), *23 Macdonald Rd, NR27 9AP.* ✆ (0263) 513251.

Overstrand Court, H, y *5 High St, Overstrand, NR27 0AB.* ✆ Overstrand (026 378) 282. C. ⊷ 18 bedrs, 1 bp, 3 bps, 1 sh, TV, Dgs. ⌂ ch, TV, Dgs, CP 50, CF. £ BB £12·50–£18·50, DB £25–£37, WT (b) £99–£119, DT (b) £16·50–£20·50, ②, L £2·50, D £6·50.

Sandcliff, H, x *Runton Rd, NR27 0HJ.* ✆ (0263) 512888. Closed Dec 15–Jan 15. C. ⊷ 22 bedrs, 10 bp, 5 ba, TV, CP 7, CF, 3 st. £ BB £11·20–£12·20, DB £22·40–£23·40, WT (b) £72–£84, DT (b) £14·50, Bk £4, D £4.▲

Westgate Lodge, PH, y (RI), *Macdonald Rd, NR 27 9AP.* ✆ (0263) 512840. C3. ⊷ 12 bedrs, 4 bps, 2 ba. ⌂ CH, TV, CP 14, CF, 1 st. £ BB fr £10·35, DB fr £18·40, WT fr £86·25, DT fr £13·80, ①, cc 1 5.

Repairers: Allen's Garage, West St. ✆ (0263) 512557.
East Coast Motor Co Ltd, Church St. ✆ (0263) 512203.

CROOK Cumbria.
See WINDERMERE.

CROOK Durham. Maps 24F & 26A,
Pop 10,500. Bishop Auckland 5½, London 257, Consett 14, Durham 10, Sedgefield 14, Stanhope 11.
EC Wed. **MD** Tue, Sat. **Golf** Crook 18h. **See** Churches, Market Place, Auckland Castle (5 m S).

Rescue Service: Crook Motor Centre Ltd, Croft St, Crook, Darlington. ✆ Bishop Auckland (0388) 764484.

CROOKLANDS Cumbria. Map 26D
London 249, M6 Motorway 1, Brough 32, Broughton-in-Furness 28, Kendal 6,

Kirkby Lonsdale 6, Lancaster 15, Ulverston 23.
Golf Kendal 18h.

★★★**Crooklands**, *LA7 7NW.*
✆ (044 87) 432. C. ✉ 15 bedrs, 15 bp, TV, Dgs. ✗ a l c, mc, at, LD 9.30. ⓕ CH, Dgs, CP 120, Ac, pf, con 80, CF, 6 BGf, 1 st, Dis. £ BB £23–£34, DB £30–£46, DT £45·50–£49·50, WB, 🔟, Bk £5, L £6, D £10, cc 1 2 3, Dep b.

Rescue Service: Atkinson, J & Son, Canal Garage. ✆ (044 87) 401.
Crooklands Mill Garage. ✆ (044 87) 216.
Crooklands Motor Co (Crooklands), nr Milnthorpe. ✆ (044 87) 414.

CROWBOROUGH East Sussex. Map 7D
Pop 17,000, Tunbridge Wells 7, London 44, Eastbourne 25, East Grinstead 12, Hastings 28, Hurst Green 16, Uckfield 7½.
EC Wed. **Golf** Crowborough Beacon 18h.
See Home of Richard Jeffries in London Rd (tablet), Crowborough Beacon 792 ft.

★★★**Crest**, *Beacon Rd, TN6 1AD.*
✆ (089 26) 2772. C. ✉ 31 bedrs, 14 bp, 8 bps, 4 ba, TV, Dgs. ✗ a l c, mc, at, LD 9.15. ⓕ Lt, N, CH, TV, Dgs, CP 70, Ac, con, CF. £ BB fr £20, DB fr £32, WT fr £204·75, DT fr £32·50, WB, 🔟, Bk £4, L £6·50, D £7, cc 1 3 4 5 6.

Rescue Service: Care's Garage, School La, St John's. ✆ (089 26) 3519 and (089 26) 4374.

CROWTHORNE Berkshire. Map 6B
Pop 8,330, Staines 15, London 32, Alton 20, Bagshot 6½, Basingstoke 17, Farnham 13, Henley-on-Thames 15, High Wycombe 32, Reading 12, Windsor 13.
MD Fri. **Golf** Downshire 18h.

★★★**M Waterloo**, *Duke's Ride, RG11 7NW.* ✆ (0344) 777711. C. ✉ 54 bedrs, 34 bp, 20 bps, TV, Dgs. ✗ a l c, mc, at, LD 10. ⓕ N, CH, Dgs, CP 100, Ac, con, CF, 16 BGf, 0 st, Dis. £ BB £46, DB £50, WB, 🔟, Bk £4·50, L £7·50, D £9, cc 1 2 3 5 6, Dep.

Rescue Service: W Pearmain & Sons Ltd, Central Garage, High St.
✆ (0344) 777777.
A C Barnes (Wokingham) Ltd, Dukes Ride ✆ (0344) 771555

CROYDE BAY Devon. Map 4C
Barnstaple 10, London 203, Blackmoor Gate 6, Ilfracombe 8½, Woolacombe 5.

Moorsands, PH, x (Rl) *Moor Lane.*
✆ Croyde (0271) 890781. Open Apr–Oct. C4. ✉ 8 bedrs, 8 sh, 1 ba. ⓕ CH, TV, CP 8, CF. £ BB £9–£10·50, DB £18–£21, WT (b) £88–£102, DT £13–£15, 🔟.
Bay View, H, x (R), *Baggy Point.*
✆ Croyde (0271) 890224.

CROYDON Greater London (Surrey).
Map 7B
RAC Office, *PO Box 8, Marco Polo House, 3–5 Lansdowne Rd, Croydon, CR9 2JH.*
✆ (General) 01-686 2314 (Rescue Service only) 01-681 3611.
Pop 320,500. Thornton Heath 2, London 10, Bromley 6, Epsom 8½, Kingston upon Thames 10, Mitcham 4, Purley 2½, Westerham 12.
See Plan, p 189.
MD Daily. **P** See Plan. **Golf** Addington Palace 18h. Addington Court Public Courses 18h and 9h, Shirley Park 18h, Selsdon Park Hotel Course 18h, Croham

Hurst 18h. **See** Parish Church, Whitgift Hospital (almshouses), Archbishop's Palace (now school—viewable on application).

🄵★★★★**Selsdon Park**, *Addington Rd, South Croydon, CR2 8YA.* ✆ 01-657 8811. C. ✉ 160 bedrs, 160 bp, TV, Dgs. ✗ a l c, mc, LD 9.15. ⓕ Lt, N, CH, Dgs, CP 200, U 20, Ac, sp, gc, tc, rf, sb, sol, con 150, CF, 4 BGf, 0 st, Dis. £ B £48–£58, DB £64–£78, WT £294–£476, DT £54–£80, WB, 🔟, Bk £4, L £10·25, D £11·75, cc 1 3 4 5 6, Dep.▲

★★★**Aerodrome**, *Purley Way, CR9 4LT.*
✆ 01-688 5185. C. ✉ 85 bedrs, 85 bp, TV, Dgs. ✗ a l c, mc, at, LD 9.30. ⓕ N, CH, CP 80, Ac, con 150, CF, 4 st. £ BB £39·50, DB £46, WB, 🔟, Bk £4·50, L £4, D £9, cc 1 2 3 5, Dep b.

★★★**Central**, *3 South Park Hill Rd, CR2 7DY.* ✆ 01-688 5644. C. ✉ 25 bedrs, 7 bp, 7 bps, 3 ba, TV. ✗ a l c. ⓕ CH, TV, ns, CP 20, CF, 2 BGf, 3 st. £ BB fr £18, DB fr £27, DT fr £25, 🔟, Bk £4, L £5·95, D £5·95.▲

★**Briarley** (R), *8 Outram Rd, CR0 6XE.*
✆ 01-654 1000. C. ✉ 19 bedrs, 5 bp, 6 bps, 3 ba. ✗ LD 10. ⓕ CH, TV, CP 9, Ac, con 40, CF, 3 st. £ BB fr £18, DB fr £30, WB, 🔟, Bk £3·50, L £7·50, D £7·50, cc 1 2 3 5 6, Dep.

★**Oakwood** (Rl) *69 Outram Rd, CR0 6XJ.* ✆ 01-654 2835. C. ✉ 15 bedrs, 9 bp, 6 bps, ns, TV, Dgs. ✗ a l c, mc, at, LD 7. ⓕ CH, TV, ns, CP 10, U 3, Ac, con 20, CF, 2 BGf, 2 st. £ BB fr £24, DB fr £30, WB, 🔟, Bk £3·50, D £5·50, cc 1 2 3 4 5 6, Dep.
Holiday Inn, *Under construction.*
Alpine, H, x (Rl), *16 Moreton Rd, South Croydon, CR2 7DL.* ✆ 01-688 6116. C. ✉ 25 bedrs, 12 bps, 13 sh, 4 ba, TV. ✗ a l c. ⓕ CH, TV, ns, CP 20, CF, 2 BGf, 1 st. £ BB £17–£22, DB £26–£29·50, WT £150, DT £25, 🔟, Bk £2, L £5·50, D £5·50, cc 1 3 4 5.▲
Beech House, PH, z (Rl). *7 Beech House Rd, CR0 1JQ.* ✆ 01-688 4385.
Beulah House, PH, (Rl), *31 Beulah Rd, Thornton Heath, CR4 8JH.*
✆ 01-653 1788. C. ✉ 15 bedrs, 1 bp, 1 bps, 13 sh, 2 ba, TV. ⓕ CH, TV, CP 6, CF, 0 st. £ BB £9·77–£15·25, DB £17·50–£21·50, 🔟, cc 3.
Friends, PH, z (Unl) *50 Friends Rd, CR0 1EB.* ✆ 01-688 6215. C. ✉ 11 bedrs, 2 ba, TV. ⓕ CH, TV, ns, CP 5, CF, 1 st. £ BB £13–£14, DB £23–£24, 🔟, Bk £2.
Hayesthorpe, H, z (Rl), *48 St Augustine's Ave, CR2 6JJ.* ✆ 01-688 8120. C. ✉ 27 bedrs, 9 bp, 3 bps, 6 ba, Dgs. ⓕ CH, TV, Dgs, ns, CP 12, CF, 1 BGf, Dis. £ BB £13–£17·50, DB £25–£27·50, WT (b) £90, DT (b) £18, 🔟, Bk £2·50, D £5·50, cc 5.
Lonsdale, H, z, (Rl), *158 Lower Addiscombe Rd.* ✆ 01-654 2276. C. ✉ 9 bedrs, 5 ba, TV. ⓕ CH, TV, CP 10, CF. £ BB fr £16, DB fr £26, DT (b) fr £21·50, Bk £2·50, D £5·50.
Markington, PH, z (Rl), *9 Hayling Park Rd, CR2 6NG.* ✆ 01-681 6494. Closed Xmas. C. ✉ 15 bedrs, 1 bp, 10 bps, 2 ba, TV. ✗ a l c. ⓕ CH, TV, ns, CP 7, 2 st. £ BB fr £17, DB fr £27, 🔟, Bk £4, D £8, cc 1 3 5.▲

Repairers: Dees of Croydon Ltd, 15 Brighton Rd. ✆ 01-686 8888.
Dove, L F Ltd, Imperial Way, Purley Way. ✆ 01-680 9888.▲
MV Trucks (Aftersales), 22 Lansdowne Rd. ✆ 01-680 5533 or 01-686 1883.

Rescue Service: Leathwood's Garages Ltd, 203 St James's Rd. ✆ 01-684 8222.
Parsons Bros, 2a Tavistock Grove.
✆ 01-684 9370.
Purley Oaks Service Station Ltd, 443a Brighton Rd, South Croydon.
✆ 01-660 0727.
Shirley Service Station, 179 Shirley Rd.
✆ 01-654 8822.

CRUDWELL Wiltshire. Map 14E
Pop 1,000. Swindon 19, London 96, Bristol 30, Chippenham 13, Cirencester 7½.
Golf Chippenham 18h. **See** Norman Church.

Mayfield, PH, y (R). ✆ (066 67) 409.
Closed 23rd Dec–14th Jan. C. ✉ 21 bedrs, 8 bp, 1 sh, 3 ba, TV, Dgs. ✗ a l c. ⓕ CH, TV, CP 30, CF, 1 st. £ BB fr £14·50, DB fr £26, 🄾, Bk £2·50, L £5, D £6·90, cc 1 5.▲

CUCKFIELD West Sussex. Map 7D
Pop 2,800. Redhill 17, London 37, Arundel 27, Bognor Regis 32, Brighton 14, Chichester 33, Crawley 9½, Godstone 20, Haywards Heath 2, Horsham 11, Littlehampton 25, Petworth 24, Pulborough 20, Reigate 18, Worthing 22.
EC Wed. **Golf** Haywards Heath 18h. **See** Ancient Church, Old Coaching Inns, 'Marshells' (Jacobean Manor House), Cuckfield Park.

🄵★★★★**Ockenden Manor**, *Ockenden La, RH17 5LD.* ✆ Haywards Heath (0444) 416111. C7. ✉ 10 bedrs, 10 bp, TV. ✗ a l c, mc, at, LD 9.45 (9 Sun). ⓕ CH, CP 40, U 2, G 2, Ac, con 40, CF. £ BBc £32, DBc £45·60, WB, 🔟, Bk £5·50, L £7·50, D £10·50, cc 1 3 4 5, Dep b.
🄵★★**Hilton Park** (R), *RH17 5EG.*
✆ Haywards Heath (0444) 454555. C. ✉ 14 bedrs, 5 bp, 2 bps, 7 sh, 3 ba, TV, Dgs. ✗ mc, at, LD 8. ⓕ CH, TV, ns, CP 50, U 2, G 2, con 25, CF, 1 st. £ BB fr £28, DB fr £38, WB, 🄾, Bk £4·50, D £8·50, cc 1 3 4 5.

CULLOMPTON Devon. Map 4F
Pop 5,031. Ilminster 24, London 159, Crediton 14, Exeter 13, Honiton 11, Taunton 19, Tiverton 6.
EC Thur. **Golf** Tiverton 18h. **See** Parish Church, old houses.

Repairer: Culm Garage Ltd, Willand Rd.
✆ (0884) 33551.
Rescue Service: Highway Garage, Station Rd. ✆ (0884) 33316.

CULMSTOCK Devon. Map 4F
Pop 804. Ilminster 17, London 152, Crediton 21, Crewkerne 23, Dunster 25, Exeter 19, Honiton 11, Taunton 12, Tiverton 6½.
EC Wed. **Golf** Tiverton 18h. **See** Perp Church, Beacon.

Rescue Service: Culmstock Garage, The Strand. ✆ Craddock (0884) 40570.

DALSTON Cumbria. Maps 26C & 30F
M6 Motorway 5½, Penrith 20, London 296, Brampton 13, Carlisle 4½, Wigton 8½.

★★★**Dalston Hall**, *CA5 7JX.*
✆ (0228) 710271. C. ✉ 18 bedrs, 13 bp, 1 bps, 2 ba, TV, Dgs. ✗ mc, at, LD 9. ⓕ CH, TV, CP 200, gc, tc, pf, con 150, CF, 0 st. £ BB £22–£29, DB £41–£45, WB, 🔟, Bk £3·50, L £2·50, D £7·55, cc 1 2 3 5 6.

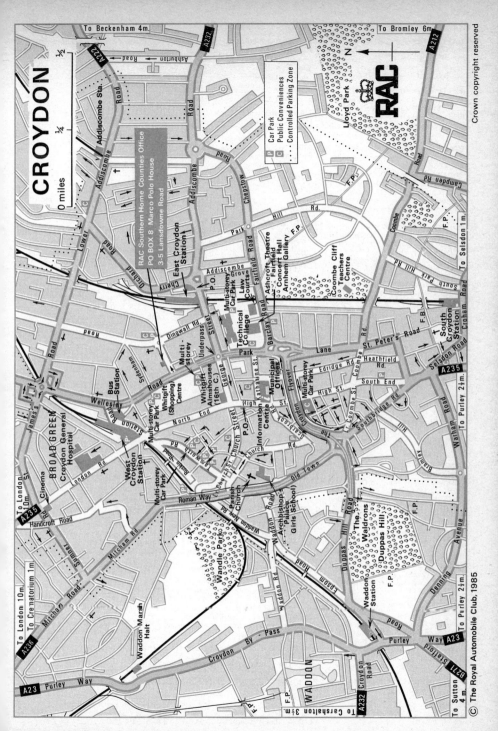

CROYDON

0 miles

RAC Southern Home Counties Office
PO BOX 8 Marco Polo House
3-5 Lansdowne Road

N

RAC

To Beckenham 4m.

To Bromley 6m.

To Selsdon 1m.

To Purley 2½m.

Lloyd Park

P	Car Park
C	Public Conveniences
	Controlled Parking Zone

Coombe Cliff
Teachers
Centre

Ashcroft Theatre
Fairfield
Concert Hall
Arnhem Gallery

East Croydon Station

Law Courts

Technical College

Multi-storey Car Park

South Croydon Station

Heathfield Rd.

St. Peter's Road

South End

Municipal Offices

Information Centre

Whitgift Almshouses 16th C.

Whitgift (Shopping) Centre

Bus Station

Croydon General Hospital

Cinema

West Croydon Station

Multi-storey Car Park

Roman Way

Parish Church

Archbishops Palace (Girls School)

Wandle Park

Waddon Marsh Halt

The Waldrons

Duppas Hill

Waddon Station

To London 10m.

To Crematorium 1m.

To London 10m.

Handcroft Road

Mitcham Road

Croydon By - Pass

Purley Way

WADDON

To Carshalton 3½m.

To Sutton 4 m.

To Purley 2½m.

Purley Way

A23

To London 10m. A236

A23 A232 B271 Stafford

DARESBURY Cheshire. Map 19B
Pop 1,399. Northwich 10, London 183,
Chester 15, Knutsford 13, Liverpool 17,
St Helens 13, Warrington 5.
EC Wed. **Golf** Runcorn 18h. **See** Church.

★★★**Lord Daresbury**, *WA4 4BB.*
📞Warrington (0925) 67331. C. 📧 141
bedrs, 141 bp, TV, Dgs. ✗ mc, at. 🄼 Lt, N,
CH, Dgs, CP 400, con 800, CF, 46 BGf, 1 st.
Dis. **£** DB £41, DB £50, WB, 🄻, Bk £4·50, L
£8, D £8, cc 1 2 3 5 6, Dep b.

DARLINGTON Durham. Map 24F
Pop 97,219. Boroughbridge 36, London
244, A66(M) Motorway 2, Brough 34,
Durham 18, Harrogate 46, Leyburn 27,
Middleton-in-Teesdale 24, Northallerton
16, Stockton-on-Tees 11, West Auckland
10.
EC Wed. **MD** Mon, Thur, Sat. **Golf**
Darlington 18h, Blackwell 18h. **See**
Stephenson's 'Locomotion No 1' on view
at North Rd Rail Museum, St Cuthbert's
Church (12th–15th cent), Museum and
Art Gallery, Town Hall.
🄸 Library, Crown St. 📞 Darlington (0325)
62034.

★★★★**M Blackwell Grange Moat
House,** *Blackwell Grange, DL3 8QH.*
📞 (0325) 460111. C. 📧 98 bedrs, 98 bp,
TV, Dgs. ✗ a l c, mc, at, LD 9.45. 🄼 Lt, N,
CH, Dgs, CP 150, U 3, Ac, tc, con 120, CF,
29 BGf, Dis. **£** BB fr £34, DB fr £44, WB, 🄻,
Bk £4·25, L £7·50, D £7·50, cc 1 2 3 4 5 6,
Dep b.
🄸★★★**Kings Head**, *Priestgate, DL1
1NW.* 📞 (0325) 467612. C. 📧 86 bedrs,
86 bp, TV, Dgs. ✗ a l c, mc, at, LD 9.30.
🄼 Lt, N, CH, TV, Dgs, CP 25, G 6, Ac, con
250, CF, 1 st. **£** BB £20–£35, DB £30–£45,
WT £140–£294, DT £31–£46, DBB £27–
£42, WB, 🄻, Bk £5·25, L £3·95, D £6·95,
cc 1 2 3 5, Dep b.
🄸★★★**St. George**, *Teesside Airport,
DL2 1RH.* 📞 (0325) 332631. C. 📧 58
bedrs, 58 bp, TV, Dgs. ✗ a l c, mc, at, LD
9.45. 🄼 N, CH, CP 100, G 6, Ac, sb, sol,
con 75, CF, 27 BGf, 2 st. **£** BB fr £32·45,
DB fr £41·25, WB, 🄻, cc 1 2 3 5.
★★★**White Horse**, *Harrowgate Hill, DL1
3AD.* 📞 (0325) 487111. C. 📧 40 bedrs, 40
bp, TV, Dgs. ✗ a l c, mc, LD 10.30. 🄼 Lt, N,
CH, CP 150, Ac, con 50, CF, 10 BGf, Dis.
£ WB, Bk £2·50, L £6·50, D £7·50,
cc 1 3 4 5 6, Dep b.

Repairers: Motor Delivery Co Ltd, Grange
Rd. 📞 (0325) 69231.
Specialist Spring Repairer Jonas
Woodhead Ltd, Coronation Works, Spring
Road, Aycliffe Industrial Estate, Aycliffe.
📞 Aycliffe (0325) 312371.
Rescue Service: Sherwoods of Darlington
Ltd, Chestnut Rd. 📞 (0235) 66155.

DARRINGTON West Yorkshire. Map
25D
Pop 1,125. Doncaster 13, London 176,
Barnsley 14, Boroughbridge 31, Goole 19,
Harrogate 29, Pontefract 2½, Rotherham
20, Selby 13, Thorne 16, York 25.
EC Thur. **Golf** Pontefract 18h. **See** Old
Windmill (Domesday Survey), Church.

★★**Darrington**, *Great North Rd, WF8
3BL.* 📞 Pontefract (0977) 71458.

Rescue Service: Waterfalls of Darrington,
Gt North Rd. 📞 Pontefract
(0977) 704061.

DARSHAM Suffolk. M.Area 16B
Pop 301. Saxmundham 6, London 101,
Aldeburgh 11, Lowestoft 18, Norwich 29,
Scole 23.
Golf Thorpeness 18h.

Repairer: A E Kerridge & Sons Ltd,
Station Rd. 📞 Yoxford (072 877) 337.

DARTFORD Kent. Map 7B
Pop 78,345. M25 Motorway 2,
Bexleyheath 4, London 17, Erith 4,
Gravesend 7, Orpington 8.
MD Thur, Sat. **Golf** Dartford Heath 18h.
See Museum, Holy Trinity Church, The
Spital Almshouses.

★★**Royal Victoria & Bull,** *1 High St,
DA1 1DU.* 📞 (0322) 23104.

Repairers: K T (Dartford) Ltd, The Brent.
📞 (0322) 22171.

DARTMOUTH Devon. Map 3D
Pop 5,250. Totnes 13 (Fy 11), London 205
(Fy 199), Kingsbridge 15, Plymouth 28,
Tavistock 35, Torquay (Fy) 10.
EC Wed. **MD** Tue, Fri. **Golf** Churston 18h.
See RN College (by permit only), St
Pryroc's Church, Butterwalk, Butterwalk
Museum, Castle, St Saviour's Church
(14th cent), Mayflower Stone, Newcomen
Engine House, Borough Museum.
🄸 Guildhall, Victoria Rd. 📞 Dartmouth
(080 43) 2281.

★★★**Dart Marina** (TH), *Sandquay Rd,
TQ6 9PH.* 📞 (080 43) 2580. C. 📧 37
bedrs, 26 bp, 5 ba, TV, Dgs. ✗ a l c, mc, LD
9. 🄼 CH, Dgs, CP 75, CF, 1 st. **£** BB
£27·50–£35·50, DB £40–£54·50, WB, 🄻,
cc 1 2 3 4 5 6, Dep (Xmas).
🄸★★**Royal Castle,** *The Quay, TQ6 9PS.*
📞 (080 43) 2397. RS Jan, Feb, Oct. 📧 20
bedrs, 12 bp, 4 bps, 3 ba, TV, Dgs. ✗ a l c,
mc, at, LD 9. 🄼 N, Dgs, G 8, Ac, con 30, CF.
£ BB fr £20·95, DB fr £36·95, WT fr £165,
DT fr £25·50, WB, 🄻, cc 1 5 6.
★**Royle House** (R), *Mount Boone, TQ6
9HZ.* 📞 (080 43) 3649. C. 📧 8 bedrs, 7 bp,
TV, Dgs. ✗ a l c, mc, at, LD 9. 🄼 ch, TV, sb,
sol, CF. **£** BB £23–£25, DB £42–£46, WT
£155–£167, DBB £27–£29, 🄻, L £3·25, D
£6·25, cc 1 2 3 5, Dep.
🄸★**Victoria**, *Victoria Rd, TQ6 9EJ.*
📞 (080 43) 2572.

Repairer: Dennings of Dartmouth Ltd,
Mayor's Av. 📞 (080 43) 2134.
Rescue Service: Dennings of Dartmouth
Ltd, Townstal Garage, Townstal Rd.
📞 (080 43) 2610.
Premier Garage, Dartmouth Rd. 📞 Stoke
Fleming (080 427) 324.
Start Bay Garage, Totnes Rd, Strete.
📞 Stoke Fleming (080 427) 302.

DARWEN Lancashire. Map 27D
Pop 29,769. Bolton 9, London 204,
Blackburn 4, Preston 14.
EC Tue. **MD** Mon, Fri, Sat. **Golf** Darwen
18h. **See** Darwen Tower, old steam cotton
mill engine (India Mills).

★★★**Whitehall**, (R & Cl), *Springbank,
BB3 2JU.* 📞 Blackburn (0254) 71595. C
📧 18 bedrs, 14 bp, 2 ba, TV, Dgs. ✗ a l c,
mc, at, LD 9.30. 🄼 CH, TV, Dgs, CP 60, Ac,
sp, sb, con, CF, 10 BGf, 5 st. **£** BB fr £17·50,
DB fr £37·50, WB, 🄻, Bk £3·50, L £5, D
£7·50, cc 1 4 5.

Rescue Service: Anchor Service Station
Ltd, Blackburn Rd. 📞 (0254) 73203.

DAVENTRY Northamptonshire. Map
14D
Pop 16,500. Towcester 12, London 74,
Banbury 16, Coventry 19, Hinckley 32,
Leicester 28, Market Harborough 21,
Northampton 12, Rugby 10, Warwick 19.
EC Thur. **MD** Tue, Fri. **Golf** Daventry and
District 9h.
See Borough Hill (British Camp, Roman
villa remains), Moot Hall.

Rescue Service: Giles Garage, London Rd.
📞 (032 72) 2576.

DAWLISH Devon Map 3D
Pop 10,000. Honiton 26, London 179,
Exeter 13, Newton Abbot 9, Okehampton
30, Torquay 11.
EC Thur. **Golf** Dawlish Warren 18h,
Teignmouth (Haldon) Ltd 18h. **See**
Powderham Castle 5 m N.
🄸 The Lawn. 📞 Dawlish (0626) 863589.

★★**Charlton House** (R), *Exeter Rd, EX7
0BP.* 📞 (0626) 863260. C. 📧 22 bedrs, 14
bp, 3 bps, 1 sh, 3 ba, TV. ✗ a l c, mc, at, LD
8.50. 🄼 CH, TV, Dgs, CP 40, sp, sb, sol,
gym, con 80, CF. **£** BB £14·50–£16·50, DB
£28–£31·50, WT £125–£140, DT £23·50–
£26·50, 🄲, Bk £2·20, L £4·75, D £7·75,
cc 1 3 4 5 6, Dep a.
Broxmore, P H, z (RI), *20 Plantation Ter,
EX7 9DR.* 📞 (0626) 863602. Closed Jan &
Feb. C5. 📧 8 bedrs, 2 ba. 🄼 CH, TV, ns, CF,
2 st. **£** BB £6·80–£8·70, DB £15·20–
£17·40, WT (b) £74·50–£86, DT (b)
£11·60–£13, 🄻.
Mimosa, G, z (Unl), *11 Barton Ter, EX7
9QH.* 📞 (0626) 863283. Open Apr–Sept.
C5. 📧 9 bedrs, 1 bps, 2 ba. 🄼 CH, TV, CP
2, 6 st. **£** BB £6–£7·50, DB £13–£15, WT
(b) £59–£68, DT (b) £9·50–£10·50, 🄻.
Rosemount, P H, z (RI), *8 Barton Ter,
EX7 9QH.* 📞 (0626) 863368. Open Mar–
Nov. C. 📧 9 bedrs, 2 ba. 🄼 CH, TV, CP 7,
CF, 8 st. **£** BB £6·50–£8, DB £13–£16, WT
(b) £65–£78, DT £10–£11·50, 🄻, D £3·50.

Rescue Service: J. Kayley Motors,
Shutterton Bridge, Exeter Rd.
📞 (0626) 864912.
Marine Garage, Exeter Rd.
📞 (0626) 863298.
Shapter's Garages Ltd, Richmond Place.
📞 (0626) 862113.

DAYBROOK Nottinghamshire. M.Area
22D
Nottingham 3, London 126, Derby 18,
Mansfield 11, Matlock 24, Newark-upon-
Trent 19, Ollerton 16.
EC Wed. **MD** Fri, Sat. **Golf** Mapperley 9h.

Repairer: Hammond, S & Co (Daybrook)
Ltd, 119 Mansfield Rd. 📞 Nottingham
(0602) 268655.

DEAL Kent. Map 10D
Pop 26,100. Canterbury 17, London 76,
Dover 8, Margate 14.
EC Thur. **MD** Sat. **Golf** Royal Cinque
Ports 18h, Prince's, Sandwich Bay 18h
and 9h, Walmer and Kingsdown 18h. **See**
St Leonard's Church, St George's Church
(18th cent), Lifeboat Station, Walmer
Castle, Deal Castle.
🄸 5 King St. 📞 Deal (0304) 361161 Ext
263.

Rescue Service: Campbells of Deal Ltd, 6
The Marina. 📞 (0304) 363166.
Hinkins, G E J, London Rd Service Station.
📞 (0304) 372377.

Park Avenue Motors, 71 Albert Rd.
✆ (0304) 366800.
Sandown Garage, Sandown Rd.
✆ (0304) 374239.

DEDHAM Essex. Map 17C
Pop 1,983. Colchester 7, London 63, Bury
St Edmunds 28, Clacton 17, Harwich 15,
Ipswich 11, Scole 32, Stowmarket 20,
Sudbury 14.
EC Wed. **Golf** Colchester 18h. **See** 15th
cent Church, Weaver's Cottages, Castle
House (home of the late Sir Alfred
Munnings RA).
🛈 Countryside Centre, Duchy Barn.
✆ Colchester (0206) 323447.
★★★**Dedham Vale** (R), *Stratford Rd,
CO7 6HW.* ✆ Colchester (0206) 322273.
C. ⊨ 6 bedrs, 6 bp, TV. ✗ a l c, mc, at, LD
10. 🄰 CH, CP 100, con 50, CF, 3 st. **£** BBc
fr £40, DBc fr £55, 🄰 10%, L £5·95, D £17,
cc 1 3 4 5 6.
★★★★**Maison Talbooth,** *Stratford Rd,
CO7 6HN.* ✆ Colchester (0206) 322367.
C. ⊨ 10 bedrs, 9 bp, 1 bps, TV. ✗ a l c, mc,
at, LD 9.30. 🄰 CH, CP 15, con 40, CF, 5
BGf, 1 st. **£** BB £44–£69, DB £73–£98, 🄰,
Bk £4, L £10·50, cc 1 2 3 4 5 6.

DEEPCUT Surrey. M.Area 7A
2 m E of Frimley. Bagshot 5, London 32,
M3 Motorway 3, Basingstoke 20,
Farnham 10, Guildford 10, Reading 20,
Woking 8.
See Flight of locks on Basingstoke Canal.

Rescue Service: Deepcut Garage Ltd, 88
Deepcut Bridge Rd. ✆ (025 16) 5631.

DELABOLE Cornwall. M.Area 2D
3 m W of Camelford. Pop 1,131.
Launceston 19, London 230, Bodmin 13,
Bude 20, Wadebridge 10.
EC Wed. **Golf** St Enodoc Rock 18h and
9h. **See** Slate Quarries.

Rescue Service: Lugg W E & Son,
Rockland Garage, Rockland St.
✆ Camelford (0840) 213284.

DENHAM Buckinghamshire. Maps 7A
and 15E
Pop 6,500. London 17, Harrow 9, High
Wycombe 12, Rickmansworth 6, Slough
6½, Uxbridge 2.
EC Wed. **Golf** Denham 18h. **See** Denham
House.

Rescue Service: Orbital Service Station
Ltd, North Orbital Rd. ✆ (0895) 2180.

DENT Cumbria. M.Area 26D
4½ m SE of Sedbergh. Kirkby Lonsdale 10,
London 255, Kendal 15, Hawes 14.

Rescue Service: Len Haygarth, Main St.
✆ (058 75) 202.

DENTON Gtr Manchester (Lancashire).
Map 19B
Pop 38,383. Stockport 5, London 182,
Glossop 0, Manchester 6½, Oldham 6½
EC Tue. **MD** Fri, Sat. **Golf** Hyde 9h. **See**
Timbered Church, Hyde Hall.

Repairer: Kirbys of Denton Ltd,
Manchester Rd. ✆ 061-336 3911.
Specialist Body Repairer: Kirbys of
Denton Ltd, Manchester Rd.
✆ 061-336 3911.

DERBY Derbyshire. Map 22D
Pop 217,000. M1 Motorway 10, London
126, Ashbourne 13, Ashby-de-la-Zouch
14, Burton-upon-Trent 11, Chesterfield 23,
Loughborough 16, Mansfield 23, Matlock

18, Melton Mowbray 29, Nottingham 15,
Uttoxeter 18.
See Plan, p. 192.
EC Wed. **MD** Tue, Thur, Fri, Sat. **P** See
Plan. **Golf** Allestree Park 18h. Kedleston
Park 18h, Mickleover 18h. **See** Cathedral,
St Werburgh's Church, RC Church of St
Mary by Pugin, St Mary's Bridge (13th
cent Bridge Chapel), St Peter's Church,
Sadler Gate, Royal Crown Derby Works
(tours by appmt), Art Gallery and Museum,
Kedleston Hall 3½ m NW, Elvaston Castle
Country Park 4 m SE, Melbourne Hall 7 m
SE. "Old Bell" coaching inn, St. Helen's
Hse.
🛈 Central Library, Wardwick. ✆ Derby
(0332) 31111.

★★★★**Breadsall Priory,** *Moor Rd,
Morley DE7 6DL.* ✆ (0332) 832235.
Closed Xmas. C. ⊨ 23 bedrs, 23 bp, TV,
Dgs. ✗ a l c, mc, at, LD 9.45. 🄰 CH, Dgs,
CP 150, Ac, gc, sc, con 80, CF, 3 BGf, 0 st.
Dis. **£** BB £29·50, DB £41·50, WB, 🄰, Bk
£4·50, L £5·50, D £9, cc 1 3 4 5 6.
★★★**M Crest,** *Pasture Hill, Littleover,
DE3 7BA.* ✆ (0332) 514933. C. ⊨ 66
bedrs, 66 bp, ns, TV, Dgs. ✗ a l c, mc, LD
10. 🄰 N, CH, Dgs, CP 200, Ac, con 45, CF,
18 BGf, Dis. **£** B fr £42, BD fr £53, WB, 🄰,
Bk £5·25, D £8·95, cc 1 2 3 4 5 6, Dep b.
★★★**Hotel International** (R), *Burton Rd,
DE3 6AD.* ✆ (0332) 369321. Closed after
Xmas to 31st Dec. C. ⊨ 44 bedrs, 42 bp, 2
bps, TV, Dgs. ✗ a l c, mc, at, LD 9. 🄰 Lt,
N, CH, CP 60, con 150, CF, 2 BGf, 1 st, Dis.
£ BB £35, DB £45, WT £329, DT £47, WB,
🄰, Bk £2·50, L £4·50, D £7·75, cc 1 3 4 5 6.
★★★**Midland,** *Midland Rd, DE1 2SQ.*
✆ (0332) 45894. C. ⊨ 63 bedrs, 34 bp, 6
ba, TV, Dgs. ✗ a l c, mc, at, LD 10. 🄰 N,
CH, TV, CP 50, G 10, Ac, con 200, CF, 2 st.
£ BB £22–£34, DB £35–£41, WB, 🄰, Bk
£3·80, L £3·70, D £7·50, cc 1 2 3 5 6,
Dep b.
★★★**Pennine,** *Macklin St, DE1 1LF.*
✆ (0332) 41741. Closed Dec 24–Jan 1. C.
⊨ 100 bedrs, 55 bp, 45 bps, TV, Dgs.
✗ mc, at, LD 9.45. 🄰 Lt, N, CH, Dgs, CP
30, Ac, con 400, CF, 1 st. **£** BB fr £34, DB
£43·50, WB, 🄰, Bk £3·50, L £3·10, D£6·75,
cc 1 2 3 5 6, Dep b.
★★**Aston Court,** *Midland Rd, DE1 2SL.*
✆ (0332) 42716.▲
★★**Clarendon,** *Midland Rd, DE1 2SL.*
✆ (0332) 365235. C. ⊨ 49 bedrs, 13 bp, 6
bps, 8 ba, TV, Dgs. ✗ a l c, mc, at, LD
10.30. 🄰 N, CH, TV, Dgs, CP 100, Ac, con
80, CF, 1 st. **£** BB £11·50–£26·50, DB
£18·50–£32·50, WB, 🄰, L £3·45, D £6,
cc 1 3 4 5 6.
★★**Gables** (R), *119 London Rd, DE1 2QR.*
✆ (0332) 40633. Closed 1 wk Xmas. C.
⊨ 54 bedrs, 14 bp, 18 bps, 7 ba, TV.
✗ a l c, mc, at, LD 9.45. 🄰 N, CH, TV, CP
70, Ac, con 20, CF, 20 BGf, Dis. **£** BB fr
£16·50, DB fr £25, WB, 🄰, Bk £3·50, L
£4·95, D £6·50, cc 1 5.
Ascot, PH, z (R), *724 Osmaston Rd, DE2
8GT.* ✆ (0332) 41916.
Rangemoor, PH, z (Unl), *67 Macklin St,
DE1 1LF.* ✆ (0332) 47252. C. ⊨ 20 bedrs,
6 ba, Dgs. 🄰 CH, TV, CP 20, CF, 2 BGf, 3 st.
£ BB fr £9, DB fr £16·50.

Specialist Radiator Repairer: Serck
Radiator Services Ltd, Cranmer Rd, West
Meadows Industrial Estate (off
Nottingham Rd). ✆ (0332) 361711.
MC Repairer: Macton Motors, 178
Normanton Rd. ✆ (0332) 45665.

Rescue Service: Ingles Motors (Derby)
Ltd, Walbrook Rd. ✆ (0332) 767920.
Miles, K F, Stoney Cross, off Old
Nottingham Rd, Spondon.
✆ (0332) 663123.
Rainbow Motor Services, Oathbrook Ltd,
Mount St. ✆ (0332) 363595.▲

DEREHAM Norfolk. Map 16C
Pop 11,845. Newmarket 43, London 105,
Cromer 27, Fakenham 12, Norwich 16,
Scole 28, Stowmarket 39, Swaffham 12,
Thetford 24.
EC Wed. **MD** Tue, Fri. **Golf** Dereham 9h.
See Fine EE and Perp Church (Cowper's
tomb), St Withburga's Well.

★★★**Phoenix** (TH), *Church St, NR19
1DL.* ✆ (0362) 2276. C. ⊨ 28 bedrs, 17
bp, 3 ba, TV, Dgs. ✗ a l c, mc, LD 9.30.
🄰 CH, Dgs, CP 40, Ac, con 75, CF, 0 st.
£ BB £30·50–£33·50, DB £43–£49·50, WB,
🄰, cc 1 2 3 4 5 6, Dep (Xmas).
★★**King's Head,** *Norwich St, NR19 1AD.*
✆ (0362) 3842. RS Xmas Night. C. ⊨ 10
bedrs, 4 bp, 2 bps, 2 ba, 5 bedrs, annexe 2
bp, 3 bps, TV, Dgs. ✗ a l c, mc, at, LD 9. 🄰 CH,
Dgs, CP 30, G 3, tc, con 45, CF, 5 BGf, 1 st.
£ BB £19·50–£23·50, DB £28–£33, 🄰, Bk
£4·25, L £4·50, D £6, cc 1 3 4 5.

Repairer: Dereham Motors Ltd, Norwich
Rd. ✆ (0362) 2293.

DERSINGHAM Norfolk. Map 16E
Pop 3,268. King's Lynn 9, London 108,
East Dereham 25, Fakenham 16,
Swaffham 17.
EC Wed. **Golf** Hunstanton 18h. **See** Dec
and Perp Church, Tithe Barn, Sandringham
Gdns 2 m SE.
Westdene House, PH, x (R), *60
Hunstanton Rd, PE31 6HQ.* ✆ (0485)
40395. Closed Nov–Dec. C. ⊨ 5 bedrs, 1
bp, 1 ba. ✗ a l c, 🄰 CH, TV, ns, CP12, CF.
£ BB £10–£15, DB £20–£25, 🄰, Bk £2·50,
L £4·50, D £4·80.

DESBOROUGH Northants. Map 15A
Pop 5,500. Kettering 5½, London 80,
Market Harborough 5, Northampton 17,
Peterborough 29, Stamford 22.
EC Wed, Sat. **Golf** Kettering 18h. **See**
13th cent Parish Church, "Toll" Cross.

Rescue Service: Desborough Motor &
General Engineers Ltd, Harborough Rd.
✆ Kettering (0536) 760457.
Recreation Garage Ltd, Union St.
✆ Kettering (0536) 760250

DEVIZES Wiltshire. Map 5B
Pop 11,000. Marlborough 14, London 86,
Amesbury 18, Andover 27, Bath 19,
Chippenham 11, Frome 18, Pewsey 12,
Radstock 23, Salisbury 25, Swindon 15,
Warminster 15.
EC Wed. **MD** Thur, Sat. **P** Disc Parking is
in operation on weekdays from 8 am to
6 pm. Sundays and Bank Holidays are
exempt. PARKING IS FREE in the town
centre on the streets and Market Place
where indicated with broken White Lines.
Vehicles can be parked either parallel with
the kerb or in individual marked-out
spaces. PARKING DISCS must be
displayed on the nearside front of the
vehicle and can be obtained at most
shops in the town or from Parking
Attendants or from the Council's Offices
at Northgate House or from the Police.
PARKING MUST NOT TAKE PLACE
WHERE THERE ARE YELLOW LINES

DERBY

0 miles ¼

Legend:
- P Car Park
- C Public Conveniences
- Pedestrian Precinct

To Nottingham 15½ m. A52
To M1. (Int. 25)

To Sheffield 39 m. A61

To Leicester 28 m. A6

Derbyshire Royal Infirmary A514

To Swarkestone 5½ m.

To Burton-on-Trent 11 m. A5250

To Matlock 18 m. A6

To Uttoxeter 18½ m. A516

To Crematorium 1 m.
To Macclesfield 4 m. A52

Railway Terrace
Derby Station

R. Derwent

RAC Service Centre
Cockpit Car Park

Bass's Rec. Grd.

Station Approach

Florence Nightingale Statue

Traffic Street

Park St.

London Rd.

Osmaston Rd.

Council House

Magistrates Court

Police Sta.

Museum

Cathedral

St. Alkmunds Way

Derwent St.

Nottingham Rd.

Clarke St.

Fox St.

Stores Rd.

Mansfield Rd.

City Road

Handyside St.

St. Mary's Church

Darley La.

Edward St.

Arthur St.

North St.

Duffield Rd.

Lodge Lane

Bridge St.

Ashbourne Rd.

Old Uttoxeter Road

Northern Rd.

Friar Gate

Ford St.

Stafford St.

Curzon St.

Friary St.

Abbey Street

Monk St.

Wilson St.

Macklin St.

Becket St.

Green Lane

Sitwell St.

Babington La.

Sacheverel St.

Normanton Rd.

Burton Rd.

Gerald St.

Markeaton Rec. Grd.

Greyhound Stadium

Hosp. (Womens)

Hosp. (Childrens)

Art Gallery and Museum

St Werburgh's Church

King's Hall

Assembly Rooms

Irongate

Full St.

Queen St.

King St.

St. Mary's Gate

Walker La.

Cathedral Rd.

Jury St.

Bold Lane

Information Centre

Guildhall

Market Hall

Corpn. St.

Market Pl.

St. James

Albert St.

Victoria St.

Strand

Wardwick

St. Peters St.

St. James St.

P.O.

County Court

Eagle Centre Shopping Area

Playhouse

Central Bus Station

(Sat. only)

New Road

Graal

Uttoxeter New Road

Old Cemy.

F.P.

N

RAC

192   For abbreviations see inside back cover—RAC

ALONG THE ROAD. **Golf** Bishops Cannings 18h. **See** Market Cross, St John's Church, Wiltshire Archaeological Society Museum, Bear Hotel (old coaching hostelry), Town Hall, St Mary's Church, St James Church, Corn Exchange, St John's Alley.
🛈 Canal Centre, Couch La. ✆ Devizes (0380) 71279.

★★**Bear**, *Market Pl, SN10 1HS*. ✆ (0380) 2444. C. 🚗 26 bedrs, 14 bp, 12 bps, 6 ba, TV, Dgs. ✖ a l c, mc, at, LD10. 🅱 CH, TV, Dgs, CP 50, G 50, Ac, con 200, CF. £ BB fr £22, DB fr £30, DT fr £38, WB, 🔟, Bk £5, L £5·50, D £7·50, cc 1 3 5, Dep b.

Rescue Service: Cannings Hill Garage, London Rd. ✆ (0380) 2569.
Devizes Motor Co Ltd, 91 New Park St. ✆ (0380) 3456.

DEWSBURY West Yorkshire. Map 25F
See also BATLEY.
Pop 49,386. Wakefield 6, London 187, Barnsley 14, Bradford 19, Halifax 11, Huddersfield 8½, Leeds 9, Selby 27, York 32.
EC Tue. **MD** Wed, Sat. **Golf** Hanging Heaton 9h. **See** All Saints' Church (13th cent), Museum in Crow Nest Park, 16th cent Lees House. Open Market (360 Stalls).

Repairer: Rocar (Dewsbury) Ltd, Aldams Rd. ✆ (0924) 465652.
Rescue Service: Woodkirk Garage & Service Station Ltd, Leeds Rd, Woodkirk. ✆ Batley (0924) 474212.

DIDCOT Oxfordshire. Map 6B
Pop 16,000. Wallingford 6½, London 52, Burford 29, Newbury 17, Oxford 13, Reading 18, Wantage 7½.
EC Wed. **MD** Fri, Sat. **Golf** Frilford Heath 18h (2). **See** Dec and Perp Church.
🛈 128 Broadway. ✆ Didcot (0235) 815334.

Rescue Service: Didcot Motors Ltd, The Broadway. ✆ (0235) 812914.

DINNINGTON South Yorkshire. M.Area 22B
Pop 7,330. Worksop 6½, London 149, Chesterfield 15, Doncaster 13, Gainsborough 22, Mansfield 18, Rotherham 8, Sheffield 12.
EC Wed. **MD** Fri. **Golf** Lindrick 18h.
Sctr Repairer Speed-On Garage, Clarence St. ✆ (0909) 2543.

DIPTON Durham. Map 32C
Pop 1,500. West Auckland 23, London 271, Corbridge 15, Durham 12, Hexham 18, Newcastle upon Tyne 8, Sunderland 17.
EC Wed. **Golf** Hobson Municipal 18h.

Rescue Service: Mountsett Garage (Dipton) Ltd, Mountsett, Burnopfield. ✆ (0207) 570333.

DISEWORTH Leicestershire. M.Area 22F
2 m S of Castle Donington. Pop 1,597. Loughborough 6½, London 115, Ashby-de-la-Zouch 9, Burton-upon-Trent 16, Derby 12, Hinckley 21, Melton Mowbray 21, Nottingham 14, Uttoxeter 26.
EC Wed. **See** Church, Whatton Hall, Long Whatton Church, Donington Park Motor Racing Circuit & Museum.

Rescue Service: Smith's Garage (Diseworth) Ltd, 1 The Green. ✆ Derby (0332) 810467.

DISLEY Cheshire. Map 22A
Pop 5,000. Buxton 11, London 170, Chapel-en-le-Frith 7½, Glossop 9½, Knutsford 17, Macclesfield 10, Oldham 15, Stockport 7.
EC Wed. **Golf** Disley 18h. **See** Lyme Park (Elizabethan) (Nat Trust).

★★★**Moorside**, *Higher Disley, SK12 2AP*. ✆ (066 32) 4151. C. 🚗 33 bedrs, 33 bp, TV, Dgs. ✖ a l c, mc, at, LD 10. 🅱 N. CH, CP 200, Ac, gc, con 250, CF. £ BB fr £33, DB fr £44, WT £365, DT fr £52·50, DBB fr £44·50, WB, 🔟, cc 1 2 3 5, Dep b.

Rescue Service: Holmes, R C & Sons, Seven Springs Garage, Buxton Rd. ✆ (066 32) 2105.

DISS Norfolk Map 16D
Pop 5,276. Colchester 41, London 97, Bury St Edmunds 19, Ipswich 24, Saxmundham 23, Scole 2½, Stowmarket 19, Thetford 19.
EC Tue. **MD** Fri. **Golf** Diss 9h. **See** Diss Mere, St Mary's Church.

Hamblyn House Inn, I, x, *The Street, Bickinghall, IP22 1BN*. ✆ (0379) 898292.

Rescue Service: Watson & Smith Ltd, Victoria Rd. ✆ (0379) 2241.

DONCASTER South Yorkshire. Map 25D
Pop 81,611. Newark 37, London 164, A1(M) Motorway 2½, Barnsley 15, Boroughbridge 44, Gainsborough 20, Harrogate 40, Ollerton 25, Pontefract 14, Rotherham 11, Scunthorpe 22, Selby 20, Thorne 9½, Wakefield 19, Worksop 16.
EC Thur. **MD** Tue, Fri, Sat. **Golf** Doncaster 18h. Wheatley 18h, Doncaster Town Moor 18h. **See** St George's Church, Christ Church, Museum and Art Gallery, Mansion House, Racecourse and exhibition.
🛈 Central Library, Waterdale. ✆ Doncaster (0302) 69123.

★★★**Danum**, *High St, DN1 1DN*. ✆ (0302) 62261. C. 🚗 66 bedrs, 58 bp, 8 bps, TV, Dgs. ✖ a l c, mc, at, LD 9·30. 🅱 Lt N, CH, Dgs, CP 60, G 15, Ac, con 100, CF. £ BB £25–£37·50, DB £34–£47, WB, 🔟, Bk £5·50, L £6·95, D £8·95, cc 1 2 3 5 6, Dep b.

★★★**Earl of Doncaster**, *Bennetthorpe, DN2 6AD*. ✆ (0302) 61371. C. 🚗 53 bedrs, 49 bp, 4 bps, TV, Dgs. ✖ mc, at, LD 9·45. 🅱 Lt, N, CH, Dgs, Ac, con, CF, 4 st. £ BB fr £35, DB fr £42, WB, 🔟, Bk £3, L £7·20, D £7·20, cc 1 2 3 4 5 6, Dep b.

★★★**Punch's**, *Bessacarr, DN4 7BS*. ✆ (0302) 535235. C. 🚗 25 bedrs, 15 bp, 3 ba, TV, Dgs. ✖ a l c, mc, at, LD 9.15. 🅱 N, CH, Dgs, CP 100, G 5, Ac, con 60, CF, 6 BGf, 2 st. £ B £17–£36, DB £28–£47, WB, 🔟, Bk £4·25, L £7, D £7, cc 1 2 3 4 5 6, Dep b.

★★**Mount Pleasant** (R), *Gt North Rd, Rossington, DN11 0HW*. ✆ (0302) 868219.

★★**Regent**, *Regent Sq, DN1 2DS*. ✆ (0302) 64180. RS Xmas & New Years Day. C. 🚗 34 bedrs, 11 bp, 23 bps, TV, Dgs. ✖ a l c, mc, at, LD 10. 🅱 Lt, N, CH, CP 20, Ac, sb, con, CF, 2 BGf, Dis. £ BB fr £30, DB fr £37, DT fr £41, WB, 🔟, Bk £3, L £2·50, cc 1 3 4 5 6.

Maulea, H, z (Unl), *2/4 Morley Rd, Wheatley, DN1 2TN*. ✆ (0302) 68365. C.

🚗 14 bedrs, 3 ba, Dgs. 🅱 CH, TV, Dgs, CP 4, CF. £ BB £7·50, DB £14, WT (b) £69·30, DT (b) £9·90, 🔟, D £2·90.

Specialist Body Repairer: Ringways Garages (Doncaster) Ltd, York Rd. ✆ (0302) 785221.
MC Repairer: Binks, Alan (Motor Cycles) Ltd, 71 Balby Rd. ✆ (0302) 65836.
Sctr Repairer: Cusworths Distributors Ltd, Princegate. ✆ (0302) 4594.
Rescue Service: Frederick Camm & Partners, Barnsley Rd. ✆ (0302) 782332.
Ringways Garages (Doncaster) Ltd, York Rd. ✆ (0302) 785221.
T.T. Garages (Doncaster), 33 Sandford Rd, Balby. ✆ (0302) 853524.

DONINGTON Lincolnshire. Map 23D
Pop 1,773. Spalding 8½, London 110, Boston 10, Grantham 20, Horncastle 24, King's Lynn 33, Sleaford 14, Stamford 27, Wisbech 28.
Golf Surfleet, Spalding 18h. **See** Parish Church, Cowley's School (1711).

Rescue Service: Burdall, W A Ltd, Station St. ✆ Spalding (0775) 820219.

DONNINGTON Shropshire. Map 19F
Pop 4,600. Wolverhampton 18, London 142, M54 Motorway 3, Newport 4, Wellington 4.
Golf Lilleshall 18h.

★**White House**, *Wellington Rd, TF2 8NG*. ✆ Telford (0952) 604276. RS Xmas. C. 🚗 9 bedrs, 3 ba, TV, Dgs. ✖ a l c, mc, LD 9. 🅱 CH, TV, Dgs, CP 100, CF, 1 st. £ BB fr £16·50, DB fr £20·50, WB, 🔟, Bk £2·50, L £4·95, D £7·50, cc 1 5.

DORCHESTER Dorset. Map 5F
Pop 14,049. Blandford Forum 16, London 122, Axminster 27, Bournemouth 27, Crewkerne 21, Glastonbury 36, Lyme Regis 24, Ringwood 32, Sandbanks 27, Sherbourne 18, Wareham 16, Weymouth 8.
EC Thur. **MD** Wed. **Golf** Dorchester (2 m) 18h. **See** Mambury Rings, Poundbury Camp, Hangman's Cottage, Dorset County Museum, Thomas Hardy Monument, Barnes' Monument, Dorset Military Museum, Judge Jeffrey's Lodgings (now Restaurant), Old Crown Court (assoc with Tolpuddle Martyrs), St Peter's Church, Nappers Mite Almshouses, Hardy's House, "Max Gate", Maiden Castle earthworks 1½ m SW, 15th cent Athelhampton 5½ m NE.
🛈 Antelope Yard, South St. ✆ Dorchester (0305) 67992.

★★★**King's Arms**, *High East St, DT1 1HF*. ✆ (0305) 65353. C. 🚗 27 bedrs, 18 bp, 2 bps, 3 ba, TV, Dgs. ✖ mc, at, LD 9.15, CH, TV, Dgs, CP 36, G 4, Ac, sol, con, CF. £ BB £19–£28, DB £34·50–£42·50, DBB £23·50–£28, WB, 🔟, Bk £4·50, L £5·50, D £9·50, cc 1 2 3.

★★**Antelope**, *South St, DT1 1BH*. T (0305) 63001. C. 🚗 19 bedrs, 4 bp, 1 bps, 2 sh, 3 ba, Dgs. ✖ a l c, mc, LD 8·30. 🅱 TV, Dgs, CP 10, G 4, Ac, con 70, CF, 1st. £ BB £13·50–£22·50, DB £20–£30, WB, 🔟, Bk £2·50, L £3·50, D £7, cc 1 2 3 4 5 6, Dep b.

Specialist Body Repairer: Leeline Bodyworks Ltd, Poundbury West Trading Estate. ✆ (0305) 4363.

Rescue Service: Leeline Bodyworks Ltd,
Poundbury West Trading Estate. ✆ (0305)
4363.
Wadham Stringer (Dorchester) Ltd, 21–
26 Trinity St. ✆ (0305) 63031.
Weatherbury Garage, Athelhampton Rd,
Puddletown. ✆ Puddletown (030 584)
211.

DORCHESTER-ON-THAMES
Oxfordshire. Map 14F
Pop 1008. Wallingford 4, London 50,
Aylesbury 20, Burford 28, Faringdon 20,
Oxford 9.
Golf Frilford Heath 18h. **See** Dec. Abbey
Church, Museum, George Inn, 17th cent
White Hart, Roman–British Earthworks.

★★★White Hart, *26 High St, OX9 8HN.*
✆ Oxford (0865) 340074. C. ⊷ 16 bedrs,
16 bp, 3 ba, TV. ✗ a l c, mc, at, LD 9.30.
⊡ CH, TV, CP24, con 20, CF, 4 BGf. £ BB
£40–£45, DB £55–£60, WB, ⏹, Bk £5, L £3,
D £12, cc 1 3 4 5 6, Dep b.

DORKING Surrey. Map 7C
Pop 23,010. Leatherhead 5, London 23,
Crawley 13, Guildford 12, Haslemere 23,
Hindhead 23, Horsham 13, Petworth 26,
Pulborough 23, Purley 14, Reigate 6.
EC Wed. **MD** Fri. **Golf** Betchworth Park
18h, Dorking 9h. **See** Old Inns, Parish
Church of St Martin, Box Hill, Polesden
Lacey 2½ m NW, 18th cent Clandon Park
5 m W.

★★★★Burford Bridge (TH), *Burford
Bridge, Box Hill, RH5 6BX* (2 m N on A24).
✆ (0306) 884561. C. ⊷ 52 bedrs, 52 bp,
TV, Dgs. ✗ a l c, mc, at, LD 9.30. ⊡ N, CH,
Dgs, CP 80, Ac, sp, con 350, CF, 3 st. £ BB
£49·50, DB £70, WB, ⏹, cc 1 2 3 4 5 6,
Dep (Xmas).

★★★M Punch Bowl, *Reigate Rd, RH4
1QB.* ✆ (0306) 889335. C. ⊷ 29 bedrs, 29
bp, 2 ba, TV, Dgs. ✗ a l c, mc, LD 10 (9.15
Sun). ⊡ N, CH, Ac, con 20, CF, 1 st. £ BB
£25–£40, DB £35–£48, WB, ⏹, Bk £4·50, L
£6.95, D £6.95, cc 1 2 3 5 6, Dep b.

★★★White Horse (TH), *High St, RH4
1BE.* ✆ (0306) 881138. C. ⊷ 70 bedrs, 67
bp, 3 bps, TV, Dgs. ✗ a l c, mc, at, LD 9.15.
⊡ Lt, CH, Dgs, CP 73, Ac, sp, con 35, CF, 5
st. £ BB £39, DB £54·50, WB, ⏹,
cc 1 2 3 4 5 6, Dep (Xmas).

Repairer: Mays, F W & Co Ltd, 105 South
St. ✆ (0306) 882244.
Rescue Service: Dorking Autos, Curtis Rd.
✆ (0306) 883022.

DORNEY Buckinghamshire. M. Area 7A
Pop 800. Windsor 3, London 24, M4
Motorway 2, Bagshot 13, Henley-on-
Thames 13, High Wycombe 12, Reading
17, Slough 4½.

Rescue Service: White Heather Garage
(Dorney) Ltd, Village Rd. ✆ Burnham (062
86) 3188.

DORRINGTON Shropshire. Map 19E
Pop 470. Shrewsbury 6½, London 159,
Knighton 28, Ludlow 21.
Golf Condover 18h. **See** EE St Edward's
Church, The Olde Hall (now Restaurant).

Rescue Service: Dorrington Garage, Main
Rd. ✆ (074 373) 228.

DOUGLAS Isle of Man. Map 27F
Pop 19,897. Steamer Service to Liverpool.
London 198, Castletown 10, Peel 11,
Ramsey 15.

EC Thur. **Golf** Pulrose 18h. **See** Villa
Marina Gdns, Lighthouse, Manx Museum
and Art Gallery, House of Keys and
Tynwald, Tower of Refuge, St George's
Church, Derby Castle Aquadrome and
Solarium. TT Races June, Manx Grand Prix
Sept, Manx Motor Museum (Crosby) 4 m
NW.
🛈 13 Victoria St. ✆ Douglas (0624) 4323.

★★★Palace, *Central Promenade.*
✆ (0624) 4521. C. ⊷ 137 bedrs, 137 bp,
TV, Dgs. ✗ a l c, LD 11.30. ⊡ Lt, N, CH, CP
80, Ac, sp, con 200, CF, 1 st. £ BB £31·45,
DB £46·40, WT £303.80, DT £43·40, WB,
⏹, Bk £3·95, L £5, D £6.95, cc 1 2 3 4 5 6,
Dep b.

▣★Woodbourne, *Alexander Dr.*
✆ (0624) 21766.
Hydro, PH, z (RI), *Queen's Promenade.*
✆ (0624) 6870. C. ⊷ 71 bedrs, 7 bp, 13
ba. ⊡ Lt, CH, TV, CF, 7 st. £ BB £9·77–
£14·37, DB £16·10–£25·30, WT (a)
£88·55–£104·65, (b) £68·42–£84·52, (c)
£9·77–£12·07, ⏹, Bk £2·50, L £2·50, D £3.
Rothesay, *15–16 Lock Promenade.*
✆ (0624) 5274.

Repairers: Athol Garage (1945) Ltd, Hill
St. ✆ (0624) 4428.
Christian, E B & Co Ltd, Bridge Garage.
✆ (0624) 3211.
Rescue Service: Mylchreests Motors Ltd,
Westmoreland Rd. ✆ (0624) 24519.

DOUSLAND Devon.
See Yelverton.

DOVEDALE Derbyshire. Map 22C
Pop 225. Ashbourne 4½, London 143,
Buxton 17, Leek 13, Macclesfield 24,
Matlock 15, Newcastle-under-Lyme 22,
Sheffield 31, Stoke-on-Trent 21, Stone 22,
Uttoxeter 15.
Golf Clifton 9h. **See** Lovely Dale
(explorable on foot), Pike Pool (Beresford
Dale), Thorpe Cloud, Lion's Head Rock,
Ilam Hall.

★★★Izaak Walton, *DE6 2AY.* ✆ Thorpe
Cloud (033 529) 261.
★★★Peveril of the Peak (TH), *Thorpe,
DE6 2AW.* ✆ Thorpe Cloud (033 529) 333.
C. ⊷ 41 bedrs, 41 bp, TV, Dgs. ✗ a l c, mc,
at, LD 9.30. ⊡ CH, Dgs, CP 100, Ac, tc, con
250, CF, 3 st. £ BB £37·50, DB £52·50, WB,
⏹, cc 1 2 3 4 5 6, Dep (Xmas).
Hillcrest House, G, *Thorpe, DE6 2AW*
✆ Thorpe Cloud (033 529) 436.

DOVER Kent. Map 10D
RAC Port Office, *Terminal Building,
Eastern Docks, Dover Harbour, CT16 1JA.*
✆ Dover (0304) 204256 and 204153.
Pop 33,000. Canterbury 15, London 74,
Folkestone 7, Margate 20.
See Plan, p. 195.
EC Wed. **MD** Tue, Thur, Fri, Sat. **P** See
Plan. **Golf** Walmer and Kingsdown 18h.
See Castle and Roman Pharos
(lighthouse), Keep and underground
passages, Church, Town Hall incorp 13th
cent Maison Dieu, Museum, Bleriot
Memorial, Roman Painted House.
🛈 Townwall St. ✆ Dover (0304) 205108.

★★★★M Holiday Inn, *Townwall St,
CT16 1JP.* ✆ (0304) 203270. C. ⊷ 80
bedrs, 80 bp, TV, Dgs. ✗ a l c, mc, LD 10.
⊡ Lt, N, CH, Dgs, Ac, sp, con 60, CF, 1 st.
£ BB fr £38, DB fr £47·25, WB, ⏹, Bk

£4·25, L £6·85, D £12, cc 1 2 3 4 5 6,
Dep b.
★★★M Dover (RI), *Whitfield, CT16 3LF.*
✆ (0304) 821222. C. ⊷ 67 bedrs, 67 bp,
TV, Dgs. ✗ a l c, mc, at, LD 10.45. ⊡ N, CH,
Dgs, ns, CP 75, Ac, tc, con 80, CF, 30 BGf,
Dis. £ BB fr £36·45, DB fr £48·90, WB, ⏹,
Bk £3·45, L £4·95, D £4·95, cc 1 2 3 4 5 6.
★★★White Cliffs, *Esplanade, CT17
9BW.* ✆ (0304) 203633. Closed Xmas. C.
⊷ 62 bedrs, 36 bp, 5 bps, 8 ba, TV, Dgs.
✗ a l c, mc, at, LD 9.30. ⊡ Lt, N, CH, TV, G
25, Ac, con 25, CF, 4 st. £ BB £19–£24, DB
£33·50–£38, WB, ▣, Bk £3·50, L £4·85, D
£5·50, cc 1 2 3 4 5 6, Dep b.
★★Cliffe Court (R), *25 East Cliffe, CT16
1LU.* ✆ (0304) 211001.▲
★★Dover Stage, *Marine Par, CT16 1LE.*
✆ (0304) 201001. C. ⊷ 42 bedrs, 5 bps,
10 ba, TV, Dgs. ✗ a l c, mc, at, LD 8.45.
⊡ Lt, N, TV, Dgs, CP 18, Ac, con 100, CF.
£ BB £21, DB £37–£40, DT £29–£31, WB,
⏹, Bk £3·50, L £4, D £6, cc 1 3 4 5 6, Dep.
★★Granham Webb, *165 Folkestone Rd,
CT17 9SJ.* ✆ (0304) 201897. C. ⊷ 29
bedrs, 13 bp, 4 bps, 6 ba, TV, Dgs. ✗ a l c
mc, at, LD 10. ⊡ N, CH, TV, Dgs, CP 80, U
3, Ac, con 80, CF, 2 BGf. £ BB £15·50–
£24, DB £30–£38, WB, ⏹, Bk £3, L £5·80, D
£5·80, cc 1 3 4 5 6.
Amsterdam, G, z (Unl), *147 Folkestone
Rd, CT17 9SG.* ✆ (0304) 201792. Closed
Jan, Feb. C. ⊷ 11 bedrs, 3 ba, Dgs. ⊡ CH,
TV, Dgs, CP 11, 2 BGf, 1 st. £ BB £8, DB
£16, ⏹.
Ashmor, G, z (Unl), *331 Folkestone Rd,
CT17 9SG.* ✆ (0304) 205305. Open Apr–
Sept. C4. ⊷ 5 bedrs, 2 ba. ⊡ CH, TV, ns,
CP 7, G 2, £ BB £9, DB £18, ⏹.
Beulah House, G, yz (Unl), *94 Crabble
Hill, CT17 0SA.* ✆ (0304) 824615. C. ⊷ 7
bedrs, 1 sh, 3 ba. ⊡ CH, ns, CP 10, U 2, CF,
3 st. £ BB £12, DB £20, WT (c) £63, ⏹, Bk
£3.
Byways, H, z (RI), *247 Folkestone Rd,
CT17 9LL.* ✆ (0304) 204173. C. ⊷ 16
bedrs, 4 bps, 4 sh, 4 ba, TV. ✗ a l c. ⊡ CH,
TV, ns, CP 18. £ BB £11–£18, DB £18–£26,
WT (b) £96–£110, DT (b) £16·50–£18·50,
⏹, Bk £3·20, D £5·50.
Castle, G, z (Unl), *10 Castle Hill Rd, CT16
1QW.* ✆ (0304) 201656.
Clare House, PH, z (RI), *167 Folkestone
Rd, CT17 9SJ.* ✆ (0304) 204553. C. ⊷ 8
bedrs, 2 ba. ⊡ TV, CP 6, CF. £ BB £9–
£10, DB £18–£20, ⏹.
Cleveland, G, z (Unl), *2 Laureston Pl,
CT16 1QX.* ✆ (0304) 204622. ⊷ 8 bedrs,
1 ba. ⊡ CH. £ BB £8·50–£9, DB £16–
£17·50, ⏹.
Dell, G, z (Unl), *233 Folkestone Rd, CT17
9SL.* ✆ (0304) 202422. C. ⊷ 4 bedrs, 1 ba.
⊡ CH, TV, CP 4, 3 st. £ BB £7·50–£9, DB
£15–£17, WT (c) fr £52·50, ⏹.
Dover Stop, H, x (RI), *43 London Rd,
River, CT17 0SG.* ✆ (0304) 822751. C.
⊷ 11 bedrs, 1 sh, 3 ba, TV, Dgs. ⊡ CH, TV,
CP 14, G 1, CF, 1 BGf, 1st. £ BB £16·50,
DB fr £26, WT (b) fr £133, (c) fr £90, DT
(b) fr £19, ⏹, Bk £3.
Eightynine, G, z (Unl), *89 Maison Dieu
Rd, CT16 1RU.* ✆ (0304) 204033. C. ⊷ 7
bedrs, 2 ba. ⊡ CH, TV, CP5, CF. £ BB
£7·50–£8, DB £15–£16, WT £49, DT
£7·50–£8, ⏹.
Gordon, G, z (Unl), *23 Castle St, CT16
1PT.* ✆ (0304) 201894. C. ⊷ 6 bedrs, 2 ba,
TV. ⊡ CH, TV, ns. £ BB £12–£15, DB £17–
£19, WT (c) £59·50–£66·50, DT £13–£14,
⏹, Bk £2·50, D £5.

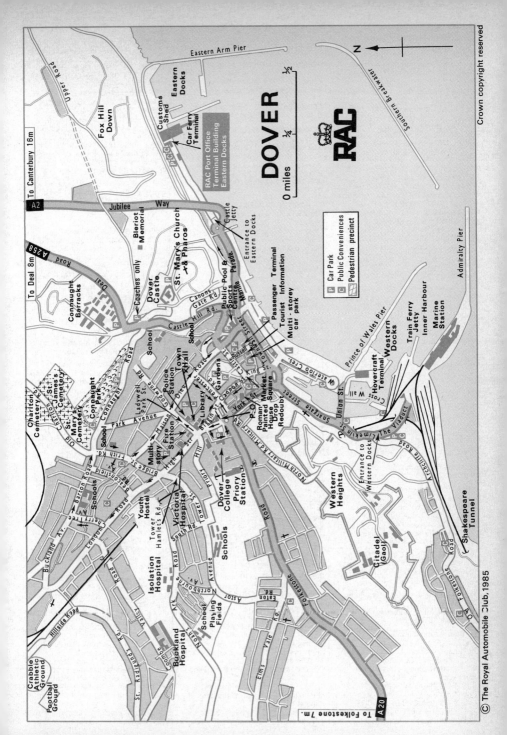

DOVER

RAC

Number One, G, z (Unl), *1 Castle St, CT16 1QH.* ✆ (0304) 202007. C. ➡ 5 bedrs, 3 bps, 2 sh, TV. ⓟ CH, Dgs, CP 2, G 4, CF. £ BB £11–£15, DB £17–£21, Ⓣ

Palma Nova, G, z (Unl), *126 Folkestone Rd, CT17 9SP.* ✆ (0304) 208109.

Penny farthing, G, z, (Unl) *109 Maison Dieu Rd, CT16 1RT.* ✆ (0304) 205563. C. ➡ 6 bedrs, 1 bps, 3 sh, 1 ba. ⓟ CH, TV, CP 6, CF. £ BB £9–£10, DB £16–£19, Ⓣ.

Peverell House, PH, z (Rl), *28 Park Av, CT16 1HD.* ✆ (0304) 202573. Open Apr–Sept. C (Babies). ➡ 7 bedrs, 2 sh, 2 ba ⓟ CH, TV, CP 6, CF. £ BB £9·50–£10·50, DB £16·50–£18·50, WT (b) £105–£112, DT (b) £15·50–£16·50, Ⓣ.

St Brelade's, G, z (R), *82 Buckland Av, CT16 2NW.* ✆ (0304) 206126. C. ➡ 8 bedrs, 2 ba. ⓟ CH, TV, ns, CP 7, CF. £ BB £10–£12, DB £17–£18, Ⓣ, Bk £3·50.

St Martins, G, z (Rl), *17 Castle Hill Rd, CT16 1QW.* ✆ (0304) 205938. Closed Xmas. C. ➡ 6 bedrs, 5 sh, 1 ba, TV. ⓟ CH. £ DB £15–£18, WT (c) £105–£126, Ⓣ.

Tower, G, z (Unl), *98 Priory Hill, CT17 0AD.* ✆ (0304) 208212. Closed Xmas–New Year. C. ➡ 5 bedrs, 2 bps, 2 ba, TV, Dgs. ⓟ CH, Dgs, U 1, CF. £ DB £17–£22, Ⓣ.

Westbank, G, z (Unl), *239 Folkestone Rd, CT17 9LL.* ✆ (0304) 201061. C. ➡ 6 bedrs, 2 ba, TV, Dgs. ✖ a l c. ⓟ CH, Dgs, CP 6, CF, 1 st. £ BB £7·50–£9·50, DB £13–£17, WT (b) £66–£75, DT (b) £11–£13, Ⓣ, Bk £2·50, D £4·50.

Windmill, G, z (Unl), *209 Folkestone Rd, CT17 9SL.* ✆ (0304) 202054. C. ➡ 5 bedrs, 1 ba. ⓟ CH, TV, CP 6, 2 st. £ BB £6·50–£7·50, DB £13–£15, WT £66·50–£77, DT £10–£11, Ⓣ.

Repairers: BCB (Enterprises) Dover Ltd, Centre Road Garage, Western Heights. ✆ (0304) 202974.
Henlys (South East) Ltd, Woolcomber St. ✆ (0304) 201904.
R P Greaves, Mechanical, Poulton Close. ✆ (0304) 205427.
Rescue Service: R W Couzens Ltd. Maison Dieu Rd. ✆ (0304) 207751.
Thompson's of Dover, Woolcomber St. ✆ (0304) 206518.

DOVERCOURT Essex. Map 17A
See also HARWICH
Colchester 17, London 78, Bury St Edmunds 40, Clacton 16, Harwich 1, Ipswich 23, Stowmarket 32.
EC Wed. **Golf** Harwich and Dovercourt 9h. **See** All Saints' Church.

Ivy Lea, G, z (Rl), *42 Cliff Rd, CO12 3PP.* ✆ Harwich (0255) 507816. Closed Xmas. C. ➡ 5 bedrs, 2 ba. ⓟ CH, TV, ns, CP 4, CF, 0 st. £ BB £7, DB £14, ②.

Rescue Service: Smith's Motors, Fronks Rd. ✆ Harwich (02555) 2301.
Starling, G E & Sons Ltd, High St. ✆ Harwich (02555) 2537.

DOWNDERRY Cornwall. Map 3C
Pop 2275. Saltash 11, London 233 (Fy 221), Launceston 22, Liskeard 9, Looe 6, Plymouth (Fy) 12, Tavistock 21.
EC Thur. **Golf** Looe Bin Down 18h.
■✖▲**Wide Sea** (R), *PL11 3LB.* ✆ (050 35) 240. C. ➡ 32 bedrs, 6 bp, 9 ba, Dgs. ✖ mc, at, LD 7.30. ⓟ ch, TV, CP 30, U 6, CF, 2 BGf, 2 st. £ BB £6–£11, DB £12–£22, DBB £11·50–£17·50, WB, Ⓣ, Bk £2, L £3·50, D £6.75, cc 3 6, Dep a.

Rescue Service: Palmers Garage, ✆ (050 35) 214.

DOWNHAM MARKET Norfolk. Map 16F
Pop 4,700. Ely 17, London 88, King's Lynn 11, Swaffham 15, Thetford 22, Wisbech 13.
EC Wed. **MD** Fri, Sat. **Golf** Denver 9h. **See** St Edmund's Parish Church.

★**Castle,** *High St, PE38 9HF,* ✆ (0366) 382157.
★**Crown,** *Bridge St, PE38 9DH.* ✆ (0366) 382322. C 14. ➡ 10 bedrs, 7 bp, 2 ba, TV. ✖ a l c, mc, at, LD10. ⓟ CH, TV, CP 50, G 2, con 60, CF. £ BB £13–£17, DB £22–£27, WT £120–£126, WB, Ⓣ, Bk £3, L £5·60, D £7, cc 3 4 5.

DOWNTON Wiltshire. Map 6C
Pop 2,900. Romsey 13, London 88, Andover 23, Blandford Forum 26, Lyndhurst 12, Ringwood 12, Salisbury 6½, Shaftesbury 25.
EC Wed. **See** St Lawrence Church, Borough Cross, The Moat.

The Warren, G, y, (Unl), *High St, SP5 3PG.* ✆ (0725) 20263. Closed 2 weeks Dec, 2 weeks Jan. C 5. ➡ 7 bedrs, 1 bp, 2 ba, Dgs. ⓟ CH, TV, Dgs, CP 8. £ BB £9·50–£10, DB £19–£22, Ⓣ, Bk £1·50.

DRAYCOTT Derbyshire. Map 22F
M1 Motorway 3, Long Eaton 3, London 124, Castle Donington 5, Derby 6, Loughborough 11, Nottingham 10.

Rescue Service: Draycott Garage (Sawley Garage Ltd), Victoria Rd. ✆ (033 17) 2359.

DRIFFIELD, GREAT Humberside (North Humberside). Map 25A
Pop 8,400. Beverley 13, London 192, Bridlington 11, Malton 19, Scarborough 21, York 29.
EC Wed. **MD** Thur, Sat. **Golf** Driffield 9h. **See** All Saints Church, St Mary's Church (Little Driffield), Sledmere House 7 m NW.

★★★**Bell,** *Market Pl, YO25 7AP.* ✆ (0377) 46661. C 12. ➡ 14 bedrs, 14 bp, ns, TV. ✖ a l c, mc, at, LD 9.30. ⓟ CH, ns, CP 50, AC, con 150, 2 BGf. £ BB fr £25, DB fr £35, WB, Ⓣ, Bk £3·25, L £4·95, D £7·95, cc 1 3 4 5.
■✖▲**Wold House** (R), *YO25 0LD.* ✆ (0377) 44242. C. ➡ 13 bedrs, 6 bp, 2 ba, TV, Dgs. ✖ mc, at, LD 8.30. ⓟ ch, TV, CP 40, G 3, AC, sp, gc, con 20, CF, 1 BGf, 2 st. £ BB £17·50–£19, DB £27–£30, WB, Ⓣ, Bk £1·75, L £5·75, D £7·50.

Rescue Service: David Thorley, T/As Cranswick Autopoint, Beverley Rd, Cranswick. ✆ (0377) 70177.

DROITWICH Hereford & Worcester (Worcestershire). Map 14C
Pop 13,270. Stratford-upon-Avon 21, London 114, M5 Motorway 2, Bromsgrove 6, Evesham 19, Kidderminster 10, Ludlow 29, Warwick 28, Worcester 6½.
EC Thur. **MD** Sat. **Golf** Droitwich G and CC 18h. **See** Brine Baths, Churches of St Andrew, St Peter, Sacred Heart (mosaics), Elizabethan Raven Hotel, old houses, Hanbury Hall 2½ m E.
ⓘ Heritage Way. ✆ Droitwich (0905) 775155.

★★★★**Chateau Impney,** *WR9 0BN.* ✆ (0905) 774411. Closed Xmas. C. ➡ 67 bedrs, 63 bp, 4 bps, TV, Dgs. ✖ a l c, mc, at, LD 10. ⓟ Lt, N, CH, TV, CP 600, Ac, tc, con, CF, 5 st. £ BB fr £60·90, DB fr £71·85, WB, Ⓣ, Bk £5·95, L £7·99, D £8·99, cc 1 3 4 5 6, Dep b.
★★★**Raven,** *St Andrews St, WR9 8DU.* ✆ (0905) 772244. RS Xmas. C. ➡ 55 bedrs, 55 bp, TV, Dgs. ✖ a l c, mc, at, LD 10. ⓟ Lt, N, CH, TV, CP 250, Ac, con 150, CF, £ BB fr £45·90, DB fr £61·85, WB, Ⓣ, Bk £5·95, L £7·99, D £8·99, cc 1 3 4 5, Dep b.
▲Ap. **St Andrew's House,** *Worcester Rd, WR9 8 AL.* ✆ (0905) 773202.
Worcester Brine Baths. Under construction.

Repairers: Droitwich Garages Ltd, St George's Sq. ✆ (0905) 773337.
Paul Newbury Ltd, Worcester Rd. ✆ (0905) 773119.

DRONFIELD Derbyshire. Map 22B
Pop 25,000. Chesterfield 5½, London 154, Buxton 23, Chapel-en-le-Frith 21, Glossop 27, Ollerton 22, Sheffield 6½, Worksop 16.
EC Wed. **Golf** Hallowes 18h. **See** Corn Memorial, Parish Church, Old buildings.

★★**Manor,** *High St, S18 6PY.* ✆ (0246) 413971. RS Sun. C. ➡ 10 bedrs, 1 bp, 9 bps, TV, Dgs. ✖ a l c, mc, at, LD 9.30, 10 (Sat). ⓟ CH, TV, Dgs, CP 30, Ac, con, CF, 14 st. £ BB £25, DB £32, WB, ②, L £4·50, D £7·95, cc 1 3 5.

Rescue Service: Dronfield Service Station, Sheffield Rd. ✆ (0246) 412315.

DROXFORD Hampshire. M.Area 6D.
Pop 600. Alton 16, London 62, Chichester 21, Cosham 10, Fareham 8½, Petersfield 11, Romsey 18, Southampton 14, Winchester 11.
EC Wed. **Golf** Corhampton 18h. **See** Church mentioned in Doomsday Book.

Little Uplands (late Meon Valley), G, xy (Rl), *Little Uplands, SO3 1QL.* ✆ (0489) 878507. Closed Xmas, 23rd Dec–3rd Jan. C. ➡ 14 bedrs, 8 bps, 2 ba, TV. ⓟ CH, TV, CP 20, CF, 10 BGf, 1 st. £ Ⓣ, cc 1 3 5.

Rescue Service: Merington's Garage Ltd, Garrison Hill Motor Works. ✆ (0489) 877431.

DRYBROOK Gloucestershire. M.Area 13E
Pop 2,719. Gloucester 12, London 116, Chepstow 19, Monmouth 11, Ledbury 16, Ross-on-Wye 6½.
EC Thur. **Golf** Coleford 18h. **See** Wigpool Common Hill, Forest of Dean National Forest Park.

Rescue Service: Brierley Service Station, Brierley. ✆ Dean (0594) 60227.
Overbrook Garage, Drybrook Rd. ✆ Dean (0594) 542279.

DUDLEY West Midlands. Map 21F
Pop 180,000. Birmingham 8½, London 120, Bridgnorth 17, Bromsgrove 13, Kidderminster 12, Sutton Coldfield 13, Walsall 7½, Wolverhampton 6.
EC Wed. **MD** Daily (Ex. Wed.). **Golf** Dudley 18h. **See** Castle ruins, remains of 12th cent Cluniac Priory, Art Gallery, Geological Museum, Zoo, Wrens Nest, Geological Nature Reserve, Black Country Museum.
ⓘ 39 Churchill Precinct. ✆ Dudley (0384) 50333.

*For abbreviations see inside back cover—***RAC**

★★Station, *Castle Hill, Birmingham Rd, DY1 4RA.* ✆ (0384) 53418. C. ⊞ 29 bedrs, 9 bp, 2 sh, 5 ba, TV, Dgs. ✘ a l c, mc, at, LD 9.45. ⬚ Lt, N, CH, TV, Dgs, CP 100, Ac, con 250, CF. £ BB fr £20, DB fr £26, WB, ⬚, Bk £3, L £4·25, D £5·95, cc 1.

★Ward Arms, *Birmingham Rd, DY1 4RN,* ✆ (0384) 52723. C. ⊞ 12 bedrs, 6 sh, 4 ba, TV, Dgs. ✘ a l c, mc, at. ⬚ CH, TV, Dgs, CP 100, Ac, con 25, CF, 1 st. £ BB fr £15, DB fr £23, WB, ⬚, Bk £3, L £4·25, D £5·25, cc 1 5.

Repairer: Westley's Dudley Garage Ltd, Castle Hill. ✆ (0384) 52474.
Specialist Body Repairer: Edward Evans (Coachbuilders) Ltd, Bath St. ✆ (0384) 52010 and (0384) 53189.

DULVERTON Somerset. Map 4D
Pop 1,293. Taunton 25, London 168, Dunster 14, Ilfracombe 32, Lynmouth 22, South Molton 12, Tiverton 18.
EC Thur. **Golf** Tiverton 18h. **See** 12th cent Church Tower, Tarr Steps 5 m NW, Earthworks.

⚹★★Ashwick (R) TA22 9QD. ✆ (0398) 23868. C 10. ⊞ 6 bedrs, 6 bp, TV, Dgs. ✘ mc, at, LD 8.45. ⬚ CH, CP 30, con 20. £ BB £16·50–£19, DB £27–£32, WT £153–£166, WB, ⬚, Bk £3, L £4, D £7.

◩★★Lamb, *High St. TA22 9HB.* ✆ (0398) 23369. C. ⊞ 16 bedrs, 7 bp, 3 ba, Dgs. ✘ a l c, mc, LD 9. ⬚ CH, TV, DGs, CP 100, Ac, con 60, CF, 1 BGf. £ BB £9–£11·50, DB £18–£20·50, ⬚ 10%, Bk £2·50, L £3, D £4·50, cc 1 3 4 5 6.

⚹★★Three Acres Captain's Country (RI), *Brushford, TA22 9AR* (2 m S B3222). ✆ (0398) 23426. Closed Jan, Feb. C 9. ⊞ 7 bedrs, 2 bp, 1 bps, 3 ba, TV, Dgs. ✘ a l c, mc, at, LD 8 ⬚ CH, TV, Dgs, CP 16, U 2, con 20. £ BB £12·50–£14·50, DB £25–£27, WT £154, DT £25, WB, ⬚ 10%, Bk £3·50, L £3·95, D £7·50, Dep a.

◩★Lion, *Bank Sq, TA22 9BU.* ✆ (0398) 23444. C 14. ⊞ 16 bedrs, 12 bps, 3 ba, Dgs. ✘ a l c, mc, LD 9. ⬚ CH, TV, Dgs, CP 6, Ac, con 40, CF. £ BB £9–£11·50, DB £18–£20·50, ⬚ 10%, Bk £2·50, L £4, D £5·50, cc 1 3 4 5 6, Dep a.

Rescue Service: G C Stanbury & Sons, Fore St and High St. ✆ (0398) 23545.

DUNHOLME Lincolnshire. Map 23A
Lincoln 5½, London 138, Gainsborough 17, Horncastle 17, Market Rasen 9½.

★★M. Four Seasons, *Scothern Lane, LN2 3SL.* ✆ Welton (0673) 60108. C. ⊞ 12 bedrs, 8 bp, 4 bps, TV. ✘ a l c, mc, LD 10. ⊞ TV, Ac, gc, con 200, CF, 3 st. £ BB £22·50, DB £35, WB, ⬚, Bk £2·50, L £6·50 D £8·50, cc 1 3 5 6, Dep b.

Rescue Service: Centurion Garage, Lincoln Rd. ✆ Welton (0673) 60303.

DUNMOW Essex. Map 17E
Pop 4,529. Woodford 27, London 38, Bishop's Stortford 9, Braintree 8½, Brentwood 21, Cambridge 28, Chelmsford 12, Epping 19, Haverhill 17, Hoddesdon 22.
EC Wed. **Golf** Bishop's Stortford 18h, Braintree 18h. **See** Parish Church, old Town Hall.

★★Saracen's Head (TH), *High St, CM6 1AG.* ✆ Gt Dunmow (0371) 3901. C. ⊞ 24 bedrs, 24 bp, TV, Dgs. ✘ a l c, mc, at, LD 9.30. ⬚ CH, Dgs, CP 60, Ac, con 70,

CF, 1 st. £ BB £41, DB £57, WB, ⬚, cc 1 2 3 4 5 6, Dep (Xmas).

Repairer: J L Smith (Cars) Ltd, Stortford Rd. ✆ Gt Dunmow (0371) 2101.

DUNNINGTON North Yorkshire. M.Area 25C
Pop 3,048. Selby 17, London 201, Bridlington 37, Goole 23, Helmsley 24, Market Weighton 15, York 4½.
Golf Fulford York 18h. **See** St Nicholas Church.

Repairers: Myers & Burnell Ltd, Stamford Bridge Rd. ✆ York (0904) 489231.
Till & Elliot Ltd, Station Garage. ✆ York (0904) 489328.

DUNSFORD Devon. Maps 3B and 4F
Pop 700. Exeter 7½, London 177, Ashburton 16, Crediton 8½, Newton Abbot 13, Okehampton 16, Plymouth 35, Saltash 36, Tavistock 26.
EC Sat. **Golf** Exeter G and CC 18h. **See** 15th cent Church.

Rescue Service: Dicker, G, Moor Park Garage. ✆ Christow (0647) 52458.

DUNSOP BRIDGE Lancashire. M.Area 27C
Pop 167. Whalley 11, London 222, Blackburn 18, Blackpool 30, Hawes 36, Kirkby Lonsdale 24, Lancaster 15, Preston 18, Settle 16, Skipton 24.
Golf Clitheroe 18h. **See** Trough of Bowland.

Rescue Service: Leedham's Garage, Smith Garage. ✆ (020 08) 237.

DUNSTABLE Bedfordshire. Map 15E
Pop 31,371. London 34, M1 Motorway 2½, Aylesbury 15, Bedford 19, Bletchley 12, High Wycombe 25, Luton 5, Northampton 31, St Albans 13, Slough 32, Watford 18.
EC Thur. **MD** Wed, Sat. **Golf** Dunstable Downs 18h. **See** Priory Church of St Peter, incorp remains of 12th cent Augustinian priory, St Mary's RC Church, old inns, Chew's Almshouses, Dunstable Downs (Nat Trust) (gliding centre), Whipsnade Zoo.
⬚ Queensway Hall, Vernon Pl. ✆ Dunstable (0582) 603326.

★★Highwayman, *London Rd, LU6 3DX.* ✆ (0582) 61999. Closed Xmas. C. ⊞ 26 bedrs, 12 bp, 14 bps, TV, Dgs. ✘ a l c, mc, at, LD 9. ⬚ N, CH, CP 40, Ac, con 35, CF, 10 BGf, 10 st. £ BB fr £24, DB fr £34, WB Bk £3, D £7, ⬚, cc 1 3 4 5 6.

Repairer: Booth, G P, 102 Gt Northern Rd. ✆ (0582) 61651.
Rescue Service: Goodley Garages Ltd, Unit 6, King St, Houghton Regis. ✆ (0582) 67256.

DUNSTER Somerset. Map 4D
Pop 786. Taunton 22, London 165, Barnstaple 34, Bridgwater 24, Ilfracombe 36, Minehead 2, South Molton 24, Tiverton 26.
EC Wed. **Golf** Minehead and West Somerset 18h. **See** Historic Castle, Yarn Market, Church with 15th cent font and rood screen, Dovecote (unique revolving ladder), Nunnery (pantiled cottages), old Grist Mill with double wheel, old Buttercross, ancient packhorse bridge, Cleeve Abbey 4 m SE, West Somerset Rly (Steam Engines).

★★★Luttrell Arms (TH), *High St, TA24 6SG.* ✆ (064 382) 555. C. ⊞ 21 bedrs, 21 bp, TV, Dgs. ✘ mc, at, LD 9.30. ⬚ ch, Dgs, G 2, CF, 2 st. £ BB £38·50. DB £54, WB, ⬚, cc 1 2 3 4 5 6, Dep (Xmas).

Rescue Service: Luttrell Arms Garage Ltd. ✆ (064 382) 284.

DUNTISBOURNE ABBOTS Gloucestershire. M. Area 14E
Pop 230. Cirencester 6, London 94, Gloucester 14, Stroud 12.

Rescue Service: Centurion Garage, Gloucester Rd. ✆ Miserden (028 582) 256.

DUNTON Essex. M. Area 8A
Romford 10, London 26, Brentwood 6, Chelmsford 12, Dartford–Purfleet Tunnel 13, Rainham 12, Southend 15.
EC Wed.

Rescue Service: Arterial Filling Station, Southend Arterial Rd. ✆ Brentwood (0277) 811748.

DUNTON GREEN Kent. Map 7B
Pop 1,850. Bromley 12, London 23, M25 Motorway 2, Maidstone 17, Sevenoaks 2, Westerham 6.
EC Wed. **Golf** Sevenoaks, Seal 18h. **See** Old Stone Bridge 200 yrs old, Parish Church, Broughton House.

★★Emma, *TN13 2TD.* ✆ (0732 73) 681. C. ⊞ 45 bedrs, 45 bp, TV, Dgs. ✘ a l c, mc, at, LD 10. ⬚ N, CH, Dgs, ns, CP 150, Ac, con 150, CF, 22 BGf, Dis. £ BB £24–£26, DB £34–£36, WB, ⬚, Bk £3, L £5·50, D £6·50, cc 1 3 4 5 6, Dep. ▲

Repairer: Morants Motors Ltd, London Rd. ✆ (073 273) 382.

DURHAM Durham. Map 24E
Pop 24,777. Darlington 19, London 260, A1(M) Motorway 3, Alston 41, Corbridge 24, Hexham 27, Middleton-in-Teesdale 28, Newcastle upon Tyne 14, Stockton-on-Tees 19, Sunderland 13, West Auckland 13.
EC Wed. **MD** Sat. **Golf** Durham City 18h. **See** Cathedral, Norman Castle, St Giles and St Margaret's Churches (both 12th cent), St Oswald's Church, remains of 14th cent Almshouses, Art Gallery, Gulbenkian Museum of Oriental Art and Archaeology, Finchale Priory 5½ m NE.
⬚ 13 Claypath. ✆ Durham (0385) 43720.

★★★★Royal County, *Old Elvet, DH1 3JN.* ✆ (0385) 66821. C. ⊞ 120 bedrs, 120 bp, TV, Dgs. ✘ a l c, mc, at. ⬚ Lt, N, CH, CP 120, Ac, sb, con 120, CF, 21 BGf. £ BB £38, DB £48·75, WB, ⬚, Bk £5·50, L £6·50, D £8·50, cc 1 2 3 5 6, Dep b.

◩★★★M Bridge, *Croxdale, DH1 3SP* (3¾ m S on A167). ✆ (0385) 780524. C. ⊞ 50 bedrs, 46 bp, 2 ba, TV, Dgs. ✘ a l c, mc, at, LD 9.45. ⬚ N, CH, Dgs, CP 200, Ac, con 20, CF, 2 BGf. £ BB £16–£26, DB £25–£32, WB, ⬚, Bk £4, L £5·50, D £7, cc 1 3 4 5 6.

◩★★★Ramside Hall, *DH1 1TD* (3 m NE A690). ✆ (0385) 65282. C. ⊞ 11 bedrs, 6 bp, 5 sh, 2 ba, TV, Dgs. ✘ a l c, mc, LD 9.30. ⬚ CH, CP 500, Ac, con 300, CF. £ BB fr £25, DB fr £33, WB, ⬚, Bk £5·50, L £5·50, D £7·50, cc 1 3 4 5 6, Dep b.

★★★Three Tuns, *New Elvet, DH1 3AQ,* ✆ (0385) 64326. RS Bank Holidays. C. ⊞ 51 bedrs, 51 bp, TV, Dgs. ✘ a l c, mc, at, LD 9.30. ⬚ N, CH, CP 60, con 308, CF, 1 st.

£ BB £30–£35, DB £35–£42, WB, □, Bk £5·50, L £6, D £8·50, cc 1 2 3 4 5 6, Dep.

Specialist Body Repairer: Moor Coachworks Ltd, Finchdale Rd, Framewellgate Moor. ☎ (0385) 47656.
Rescue Service: Ansa Motors Ltd, Newbridge Service Station, Neville's Cross. ☎ (0385) 67561.
Crescent Garage (Sherburn Hill) Ltd, Former Colliery Yard, Sherburn Hill. ☎ (0385) 720009.
Fowler & Armstrong Ltd, 74 New Elvet. ☎ (0385) 47278.
Fred Henderson, Auto Engineers, Ainsley St. ☎ (0385) 67658.
Gladstone Motors, East View, Ludworth. ☎ Wellfield (0429) 820507.

DUXFORD Cambridgeshire. M.Areas 15D and 17E
Pop 1,730. Hoddesdon 28, London 48, Bishop's Stortford 18, Braintree 17, Cambridge 9, Dunmow 21, Hatfield 34, Haverhill 15, Newmarket 16, Royston 9½.
Golf Gog Magog 9h and 18h. **See** 15th cent St Peter's Church, Duxford Chapel, Imperial War Museum (RAF).

Rescue Service: Duxford Service Station, Newmarket Rd. ☎ Cambridge (0223) 832136.

DYMCHURCH Kent. Map 10F
Pop 5,600. Ashford 12, London 68, Canterbury 21, Folkestone 9½, Rye 16, Tenterden 17.
EC Wed. **Golf** Littlestone 9h & 18h. **See** Romney, Hythe & Dymchurch Railway, 12th cent Church, Smugglers Inn, Martello Towers.

Chantry, PH, x (R), *Sycamore Gdns, TN29 0LA.* ☎ (0303) 873137. Open Feb–Oct. C. ☞ 8 bedrs, 2 bp, 1 bps, 1 ba, TV. ⊞ CH, TV, CP 8, CF, 1 BGf, 1 st, Dis. £ BB £10–£15·50, DB £20–£26, WT (b) £86–£96, DT (b) £155·50–£18·50, □, D £5·50.

EAGLESCLIFFE Cleveland. Map 24F
Thirsk 20, London 239, Darlington 9, Helmsley 28, Northallerton 16, Stockton-on-Tees 4, Whitby 35.
Golf Eaglescliffe 18h. **See** Preston Park, Museum.
★★★**Parkmore** (R), *636 Yarm Rd, TS16 0DH.* ☎ (0642) 786815.

EARBY Lancashire. Map 27A
Pop 4,955. Burnley 10, London 216, Bradford 28, Skipton 7½.
EC Tue. **See** Museum of Mines, old Grammar School.

Repairer: C S Whitaker, Ltd, Skipton Rd. ☎ (028 284) 3453.

EASINGWOLD North Yorkshire. Map 25C
Pop 3,640. York 13, London 211, Boroughbridge 11, Helmsley 13, Leeds 31, Malton 19, Pontefract 36, Thirsk 10.
EC Wed. **MD** Fri. **Golf** Easingwold 18h. **See** Church of St John the Baptist, Market Cross, Bull Ring, Byland Abbey.

★★**George**, *Market Pl, YO6 3AD.* ☎ (0347) 21698. Closed Xmas. C. ☞ 18 bedrs, 16 bp, 2 bps, TV, Dgs. ✗ a l c, mc, LD 9. ⊞ CH, TV, con 40, CF, 6 BGf, 1 st, Dis. £ BB £15–£20, DB £25–£27, WT £137–£158, WB, ②, cc 5.

EAST ANSTEY Devon. Map Area 4D
Bampton 9, London 172, Barnstaple 24, Dulverton 5, Minehead 21, Tiverton 17. **See** Church.

Rescue Service: Mid Western Cars Ltd, Blackerton Cross Garage. ☎ Anstey Mills (039 84) 405.

EASTBOURNE East Sussex. Map 7F
Pop 77,000. Uckfield 19, London 63, Hastings 20, Hurst Green 23, Lewes 16, Newhaven 12, Tunbridge Wells 29.
See Plan, p. 199.
EC Wed. **MD** Daily. **P** See Plan. **Golf** Royal Eastbourne 18h and 9h. Eastbourne Downs, 18h, Willingdon 18h. **See** Beachy Head and Lighthouse, Towner Art Gallery, Wish Tower, Winter Gardens, Congress Theatre, Devonshire Park Theatre, Redoubt Tower (Blue Temple, Grotto, Aquarium and Model Village), St Mary's Church, 13th cent Lambe Inn, Pevensey Castle 4 m NE, Michelham Priory 7 m NW, Herstmonceux Castle Gdns (and Isaac Newton Telescope), 7 m N.
ℹ 3 Cornfield Ter. ☎ Eastbourne (0323) 27474.

★★★★★**Grand**, *King Edward's Par, BN21 4EQ.* ☎ (0323) 22611. C. ☞ 178 bedrs, 178 bp, TV, Dgs. ✗ a l c, mc, at, LD 9.30. ⊞ Lt, N, CH, CP 100, sp, con 350, CF. £ BB fr £45, DB fr £70, WB, □, Bk £5·50, L £10, D £13·50, cc 1 2 3 4 5 6, Dep b.
★★★★**Cavendish**, *Grand Par, BN21 4DH.* ☎ (0323) 27401. C. ☞ 115 bedrs, 115 bp, TV, Dgs. ✗ a l c, mc, at, LD 9. ⊞ Lt, N, CH, Dgs, CP 50, Ac, con 255, CF, 10 st. £ BB fr £39, DB fr £64, □, L £10·50, D £12, cc 1 2 3 4 5, Dep b.
★★★★**Queen's**, *Marine Par, BN21 3DY.* ☎ (0323) 22822. C. ☞ 112 bedrs, 112 bp, TV, Dgs. ✗ a l c, mc, at, LD 9. ⊞ Lt, N, CH, Dgs (guide dogs only), CP 80, Ac, con 200, CF, 0 st. £ BB £34–£38, DB £60–£68, WT £265, DBB fr £32, WB, □, L £8·50, D £10, cc 1 2 3 4 5 6, Dep b.
★★★**Burlington**, *Grand Par, BN21 3YN.* ☎ (0323) 22724. C. ☞ 160 bedrs, 130 bp, 11 bps, 14 ba, TV, Dgs. ✗ a l c, mc, at, LD 8.15. ⊞ Lt, N, CH, Dgs, Ac, con 150, CF, 6 st. £ BB £22–£25, DB £44–£50, WT £169–£190, DT £33–£36, WB, □, Bk £3·25, L £4·95, D £5·95, cc 1 3 4 5, Dep a.
★★★**Chatsworth** (RI), *Grand Par, BN21 3YR.* ☎ (0323) 30327. Open March–Dec. C. ☞ 45 bedrs, 14 bp, 31 bps, 2 ba, TV, Dgs. ✗ a l c, mc, at. ⊞ Lt, N, CH, TV, Dgs, Ac, con 25, CF, 6 st. £ BB £21·85–£23, DB £43·70–£46, DBB £23–£29·90, WB, ②, Bk £5·20, D £7·70, cc 1 3.▲
★★★**Cumberland**, *Grand Par, BN21 3YT.* ☎ (0323) 30342. C. ☞ 70 bedrs, 65 bp, 5 bps, TV, Dgs. ✗ a l c, mc, at, LD 7.45. ⊞ Lt, N, CH, TV, ns, con 200, CF. £ BB £19–£27, DB £36–£52, WT £155–£175, DT £26–£31, WB, □, Bk £3·45, L £4·03, D £6·33, Dep b.▲
■★★★**M Eastbourne**, *Pevensey Bay Rd, BN23 6JG.* ☎ (0323) 764188.
★★★**Lansdowne**, *King Edward's Par, BN21 4EE.* ☎ (0323) 25174. C. ☞ 137 bedrs, 77 bp, 16 bps, 15 ba, TV, Dgs. ✗ a l c, mc, at, LD 8.30. ⊞ Lt, N, CH, TV, ns, U 21, Ac, con 110, CF, 2 BGf. £ BB £20–£27·50, DB £34–£55, DBB £19·50–£33·50, WB, □, Bk £4·25, L £4·25, D £7·50, cc 1 2 3 6, Dep (Xmas).▲
★★**Mansion**, *Grand Par, BN21 3YS.* ☎ (0323) 27411. C. ☞ 103 bedrs, 73 bp, 4 bps, 15 ba, TV. ✗ mc, at, LD 8.30. ⊞ Lt, N, ch, TV, Ac, con 200, CF, 3 BGf, 9 st. £ BB £15·50–£25·50, DB £30–£50, WT £146–£206, DT £23–£33, WB, ②, Bk £2·75, L £4·75, D £5·95, cc 1 2 3 5 6, Dep.▲
★★★**Princes**, *Lascelles Ter, BN21 4BL.* ☎ (0323) 22056. Closed Jan, Feb. C. ☞ 50 bedrs, 35 bp, 15 sh, 4 ba, TV, Dgs. ✗ mc, at, LD 8.30. ⊞ Lt, N, CH, TV, Dgs, Ac, con 50, CF, 6 st. £ BB £15·50–£19·25, DB £29–£36·50, WB, □, Bk £3·50, L £5·75, D £7·25, cc 1 3 4 5 6.
★★★**Sandhurst**, *Grand Par, BN21 4DJ.* ☎ (0323) 27868. C. ☞ 64 bedrs, 32 bp, 13 bps, 10 ba, TV, Dgs. ✗ mc, at, LD 8.30. ⊞ Lt, N, Dgs, con 100, CF, 5 st. £ BB £17·50–£24, DB £35–£48, DBB £23·50–£30, WB, ②, Bk £4, L £5, D £6, cc 2 5, Dep b.
★★★**Wish Tower** (TH), *King Edward's Par, BN21 4AB.* ☎ (0323) 22676. C. ☞ 74 bedrs, 40 bp, 10 ba, TV, Dgs. ✗ mc, at, LD 8.30. ⊞ Lt, N, CH, Dgs, G 3, con 90, CF, 9 st. £ BB £26–£33·50, DB £43–£50, WB, □, cc 1 2 3 4 5 6, Dep (Xmas).
★★**Congress**, *31 Carlisle Rd, BN21 4JS.* ☎ (0323) 32118.
★★**Croft** (R), *18 Prideaux Rd, BN21 2NB.* ☎ (0323) 642291.
★★**Farrar's** (R), *3 Wilmington Gdns, BN21 4JN.* ☎ (0323) 23737. C. ☞ 42 bedrs, 24 bp, 6 bps, 10 ba, TV Dgs. ✗ a l c, mc, at, LD 8. ⊞ Lt, N, CH, TV, Dgs, CP 26, U 1, Ac, CF, 0 st. £ BB £16·50–£22, DB £33–£44, WT £110–£185, DT £24–£32·50, WB, ②, Bk £3·50, D £6, cc 1 3 5.▲
★★**Langham**, *Royal Par, BN22 7AH.* ☎ (0323) 31451. Open Mar–Oct. C. ☞ 83 bedrs, 40 bp, Dgs. ✗ a l c, mc, at, LD 7.30. ⊞ Lt, N, ch, TV, U 3, Ac, con 85, CF, 3 BGf. £ BB fr £14, DB fr £28, WT fr £90, DT fr £18, WB, ②, Bk £2·75, L £4·75, D £6·25, Dep b.
★★**Lathom House** (R), *Howard Sq, BN21 4BG.* ☎ (0323) 641986. Open Mar–Oct & Xmas. C. ☞ 38 bedrs, 2 bp, 10 bps, 8 ba, TV. ✗ mc, at, LD 8. ⊞ Lt, N, ch, CP 11, U 2, Ac, con 25, CF, 2 BGf, 7 st. £ BB £13·50–£16, DB £23–£29, WT £99·50–£105, DT £19–£22, WB, □, Bk £2·75, L £4·50, D £5·50, cc 1 5 6, Dep a.
★★**Sussex**, *Cornfield Ter, BN21 4NS.* ☎ (0323) 27681.
★★**York House** (RI), *14 Royal Par, BN22 7AR.* ☎ (0323) 20918. Open April–Oct. C. ☞ 103 bedrs, 35 bps, 18 ba, Dgs. ✗ mc, at, LD 7.30. ⊞ Lt, N, ch, TV, Ac, sp, con 4, CF, 7 st. £ BB £17·40–£21·10, DB £30·40–£42·20, WT £133–£159·50, DT £22·20–£26·60, WB, □, Bk £2·75, L £5, D £6·50, Dep.
★**Downland** (R), *37 Lewes Rd, BH21 2BU.* ☎ (0323) 32689. Open Mar–Nov. C. ☞ 16 bedrs, 8 bp, 8 bps, 1 ba, TV. ✗ mc, at, LD 7.30. ⊞ CH, TV, Dgs, CP 16, Ac, con 16, CF, 1 st. £ BB £15–£19·50, DB £28–£37, WT £107·50–£149·50, DT £23–£30, ②, Bk £2·50, L £3·25, D £5·50, cc 1 3 5 6, Dep.▲
★**Lynwood** (R), *31 Jevington Gdns, BN21 4HP.* ☎ (0323) 23982. C. ☞ 76 bedrs, 22 bp, 10 ba, TV, Dgs. ✗ mc, at, LD 7·45. ⊞ Lt, N, ch, TV, CP 5, G 4, Ac, con 30, CF, 2 BGf, 2 st. £ BB £13·75–£22·50, DB £27·50–£45, WT £120–£200, DT £22–£35, DBB £18·50–£31·50, WB, □, Bk £3, L £4·50, D £6·50, cc 6, Dep.
★**New Wilmington** (Rt), *25 Compton St, BN21 4DU.* ☎ (0323) 21219. Open Mar–Oct & Xmas. C. ☞ 30 bedrs, 13 bp, 5 bps, 2

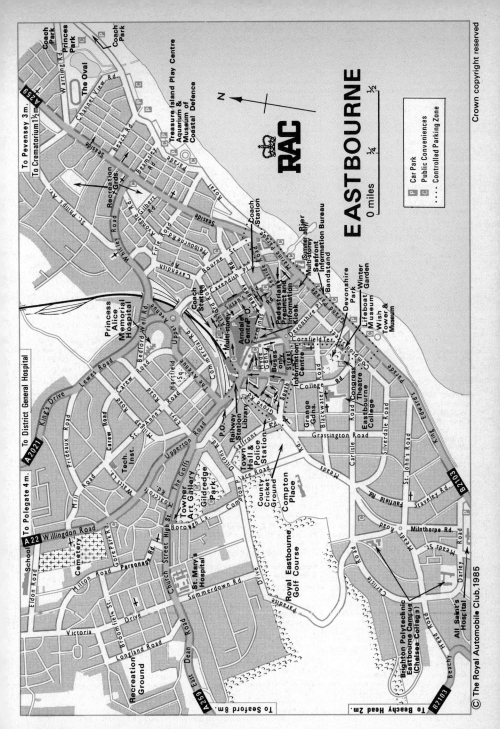

EASTBOURNE

ba, TV, Dgs. ✗ mc, at, LD 6. 🅿 Lt, N, ch, TV, Ac, CF, 3 BGf, 4 st. £ BB £13·50–£17·50, DB £24–£37, WB, ②, Bk £2·50, L £2·50, D £5, Dep.

★**Oban,** *King Edward's Par, BN21 4DS.* ✆ (0323) 31581.

★**San Remo,** *Royal Par, BN22 7AJ.* ✆ (0323) 21831. Open April–Oct & Xmas. C. ⬤ 64 bedrs, 12 bp, 12 ba, Dgs. ✗ mc, at, LD 7. 🅿 Lt, N, ch, TV, Ac, CF, 6 st. £ BB £14–£18, DB £28–£40, WT £80–£109, DT £20–£23, WB, ①, Bk £2·50, L £3·50, D £4·50, cc 1 3, Dep a.▲

Alfriston, PH, z (RI), *16 Lushington Rd, BN21 4LL.* ✆ (0323) 23454.

Avondale, H, z (RI), *77 Royal Par, BN22 7AE.* ✆ (0323) 23510. Open April–Oct. C 5. ⬤ 8 bedrs, 5 ba. 🅿 TV. £ BB £9–£11, DB £18–£22, WT (b) £85–£98, DT (b) £13–£15, ②, Bk £2·50, D £6·50.

Beachy Rise, G, z (Unl), *93 Royal Par, Rd, BN20 7QN.* ✆ (0323) 639171. Closed Dec. C 5. ⬤ 6 bedrs, 1 ba, Dgs. 🅿 CH, TV. 0 st. £ DB £16–£21, WT (b) £60–£73, DT (b) £10–£12, ①▲

Courtlands, PH, z (R), *68 Royal Par, BN22 7AQ.* ✆ (0323) 26915. Open Mar–Nov & Xmas. C. ⬤ 12 bedrs, 1 bp, 3 sh, 5 ba. ✗ a l c. 🅿 ch, TV, CP 1, G 1, CF, 6 st. £ BB fr £11·50, DB fr £23, WT fr £113·85, DT fr £18·40, ①, Bk £2, D £4.

Delladale Lodge, PH, x (RI), *35 Lewes Rd, BN21 2BU.* ✆ (0323) 25207. Open April–Oct. C 5. ⬤ 10 bedrs, 6 bps, 1 ba. 🅿 CH, TV, CP 10, 2 st. £ DB £18·50–£27, ①.

Edmar, G, z (Unl), *30 Hyde Gardens, BN21 4PX.* ✆ (0323) 33024. Open Mar–Oct. ⬤ 9 bedrs, 3 bp, 1 ba. 🅿 ch, TV, 1 BGf, 8 st. £ BB £7·50–£12·50, DB £14–£19, WT (b) £59·95–£102·95, DT (b) £8·56–£14·70, ①, D £4.

Ellesmere, H, *31 Wilmington Square, BN21 4EA.* ✆ (0323) 31463.

Gilday, PH, z (R), *1 Marine Par, BN21 3DX.* ✆ (0323) 21818.

Hanburies, H, z, *4 Hardwick Rd, BN21 4NY.* ✆ (0323) 30698. C 12. ⬤ 14 bedrs, 9 bp, 1 bps, 1 ba, TV. 🅿 CH, TV, CP 4. £ BB £11·50–£12·50, DB £23–£28, WT (b) £92–£110, DT (b) £13·50–£15·50, ①.

Little Crookham, PH, z (Unl), *16 South Cliff Av, BN20 7AH.* ✆ (0323) 34160. Open Mar–Oct. C. ⬤ 7 bedrs, 1 ba, Dgs. 🅿 CH, TV, Dgs, 3 st. £ BB £9, DB £18, WT £84, DT £13.

Mandalay, H, y (R), *16 Trinity Trees, BN21 3LE.* ✆ (0323) 29222. Closed Xmas. C 5. ⬤ 12 bedrs, 1 bp, 7 bps, 2 ba, TV. 🅿 CH, CP 20, 1 BGf. £ BB £14·65–£15·80, DB £25·20–£32·20, WT £94·30–£121·90, DT £14·95–£19·55, ②, D £8, cc 1 3.

Marina, PH, z (R), *86 Royal Par, BN22 7AE.* ✆ (0323) 20297. Open Mar–Oct & Xmas. C. ⬤ 19 bedrs, 6 bps, 5 ba, TV, Dgs. 🅿 CH, TV, Dgs, CF, 8 st. £ BB £8·50–£10·50, DB £17–£23, WT (b) £68–£95, DT (b) £11·50–£14·50, ①, Bk £2, D £4.

Meridale, G, z (Unl) *91 Royal Par, BN22 7AE.* ✆ (0323) 29686. Open April–Sept. C 2. ⬤ 8 bedrs, 2 ba. 🅿 ch, TV, CP 1. £ BB £8–£9, DB £16–£18, WT (b) £65–£72, DT (b) £10·25–£11·75, ①.

Mowbray, PH, z (Unl), *Lascelles Ter, BN21 4BJ.* ✆ (0323) 20012. Closed Jan.–Mar. C 6. ⬤ 16 bedrs, 4 bps, 2 ba, TV, Dgs. 🅿 Lt, TV, Dgs, 8 st. £ BB £11, DB fr £22, WT (c) fr £70·50, DT (b) fr £16·75, L £2·50, D £5·75, ②, cc 1 5.

New Alwyn, PH, z (RI), *Jevington Gdns.* ✆ (0323) 24169. Closed Jan, Feb. C. ⬤ 28 bedrs, 2 bp, 10 bps, 3 ba, Dgs. 🅿 CH, TV, Dgs, CF. £ BB £12–£15, DB £24–£30, WT (b) £100–£108, DT (b) £16–£17, ①.

Oakwood, PH, z (RI), *28 Jevington Gdns, BN21 4HN.* ✆ (0323) 21900. C. ⬤ 15 bedrs, 2 ba, Dgs. 🅿 ch, TV, CF, 6 st. £ BB £9·50, DB £19, WT (b) £73–£78, DT (b) £12–£12·50, ①.

Orchard House, PH, z (Unl), *10 Old Orchard Rd, BN21 1DB.* ✆ (0323) 23682. C 5. ⬤ 8 bedrs, 5 bp, 3 bps, TV. 🅿 ch, TV, CP 3. £ BB £11–£12, DB £22–£24, WT £89–£93, DT £15–£16·50, ①.

Rosforde, PH, z (RI), *51 Jevington Gdns, BN21 4EH.* ✆ (0323) 32503. C. ⬤ 12 bedrs, 4 bps, 2 ba. 🅿 ch, TV, CF, 10 st. £ BB £10–£12, DB £20–£27, WT (b) £75–£90, DT (b) £12·50–£15, ①.

Sovereign View, G, z (RI), *93 Royal Par, BN22 7AE.* ✆ (0323) 21657. Open Mar–Oct. C 9. ⬤ 8 bedrs, 2 ba. 🅿 ch, TV, ns. £ BB £9–£9·50, DB £18–£19, WT (b) £67–£74, DT (b) £13·50–£14·50, ①.

Traquair, PH, z (RI), *25 Hyde Gdns, BN21 4PX.* ✆ (0323) 25198. C. ⬤ 11 bedrs, 5 bps, 2 ba, TV, Dgs. 🅿 CH, TV, CF. £ BB £10–£13·50, DB £17–£24, WT (b) £85–£130, DT (b) £14·50–£18, ②, Bk £3·50, L £5, D £6.

Wynstay, PH, z (Unl), *13 Lewes Rd, BN21 2BY.* ✆ (0323) 21550. Closed Xmas & New Year. C. ⬤ 7 bedrs, 5 bps, 1 ba, TV. 🅿 CH, CP 7, CF, 1 st. £ BB £11–£15·50, DB £18–£25, WT (b) £65–£78, (c) £55–£68, DT (b) £13–£14·50, ①.

MC Repairers: Motcombe Motorcycles, 10 Motcombe La. ✆ (0323) 29727. Park Motorcycles, Mountfield Rd. ✆ (0323) 52187.
Rescue Service: Colin Cars Ltd, 89 Pevensey Bay Rd. ✆ (0323) 761150. Robin Kay Motors, Marine Rd. ✆ (0323) 26462 & (0323) 25563.

EAST BUDLEIGH Devon. M. Area 4F
2 m N of Budleigh Salterton. Honiton 14, London 167, Exeter 11, Exmouth 5½, Sidmouth 4½.

Rescue Service: East Budleigh Garage, Lower Budleigh. ✆ Budleigh Salterton (039 54) 5595.

EAST CHINNOCK Somerset. M.Area 5E
Pop 463. Sherborne 9½, London 129, Bridgwater 25, Crewkerne 4, Dorchester 21, Ilminster 10, Shepton Mallet 27, Wells 26, Wincanton 19.
Golf Yeovil 18h. **See** Parish Church.

Rescue Service: Barrow Hill Garage. ✆ West Coker (093 586) 3279.

EASTCHURCH Kent. Map 10C
Pop 3,200. Rochester 19, London 51, Sheerness 5½.
EC Wed. **Golf** Sheerness 18h. **See** Warden Manor, Shurland Hall, Church.

Rescue Service: Eastchurch Motors Ltd, High St. ✆ (079 588) 262.

EAST DEREHAM Norfolk
See DEREHAM.

EASTERGATE West Sussex. Map 7E
Pop 2,105. Pulborough 11, London 58, Arundel 5½, Bognor Regis 4½, Chichester 6½, Haywards Heath 32, Littlehampton 6, Midhurst 21, Petersfield 20, Petworth 11.

Golf Bognor Regis 18h. **See** Old Whipping Post, War Memorial Hall, Church, Lion War Memorial.

Repairer: Aldingbourne Motors (Sussex) Ltd, Irene Garage, Nyton Rd, Aldingbourne. ✆ (024 368) 3128.

EAST GRINSTEAD West Sussex. Map 7D
Pop 22,395. Godstone 10, London 30, Crawley 9, Haywards Heath 11, Hurst Green 27, Lewes 21, Redhill 13, Reigate 14, Sevenoaks 17, Tonbridge 16, Tunbridge Wells 13, Uckfield 15, Westerham 13.
EC Wed. **MD** Sat. **Golf** Copthorne 18h. **See** Sackville College (17th cent almshouses), Museum, old buildings in High St, St Swithin's Church, Mormon Temple Gardens at Newchapel 3 m NW, Tanyard medieval tannery at Sharpthorne 5 m S.

★★★**M Felbridge,** *RH19 2BH.* ✆ (0342) 26992. C. ⬤ 48 bedrs, 48 bp, TV, Dgs. ✗ a l c, mc, LD 9.30. 🅿 N, CH, CP 600, Ac, sp, sb, sol, gym, con 60, CF, 24 BGf, 4 st. £ BB fr £36, DB fr £46, WB, ①, Bk £5·50, L £7·50, D £9, cc 1 2 3 4 5 6, Dep.

≋★★★**Gravetye Manor** (R), *nr East Grinstead, RH19 4LJ.* ✆ Sharpthorne (0342) 957239. C 7. ⬤ 14 bedrs, 12 bp, 2 bps, TV. ✗ a l c, LD 9.30. 🅿 CH, CP 30, pf, con 14, CF, 0 st. £ BB fr £53, DB fr £75, ①, Bk £5.

Cranfield, PH, x (RI) *Maypole Rd, RH19 1HW.* ✆ (0342) 21251. C. ⬤ 19 bedrs, 1 bp, 6 bps, 2 sh, 2 ba, TV, Dgs. 🅿 CH, TV, Dgs, CP 12, CF. £ BB fr £13·80, DB fr' £21·85, ① Bk £3·15, D £6·50.

EAST HARLING Norfolk. Map 16D
Pop 1,874. Thetford 9, London 91, Bury St Edmunds 19, East Dereham 21, Norwich 23, Scole 12, Stowmarket 21, Swaffham 20.
EC Wed. **Golf** Thetford 18h. **See** Church.

Rescue Service: White Hart Garage (East Harling) Ltd, White Hart St. ✆ (0953) 717321.

EAST HECKINGTON Lincolnshire. Map 23C
Pop 180. Donington 8, London 118, Boston 9, Horncastle 22, Sleaford 8½.

Rescue Service: Four Winds Service Station, nr. Boston. ✆ Boston (0205) 820600.

EAST HORSLEY Surrey. Map 7C
Pop 4,080. Leatherhead 6, London 24, Cobham 4½, Dorking 9, Guildford 8.
EC Thur. **Golf** East Horsley 18h. **See** St. Martins Church, Horsley Tower.

★★★**M Thatchers,** *Epsom Rd, KT24 6TB.* ✆ (04865) 4291. C. ⬤ 28 bedrs, 28 bp, TV, Dgs. ✗ a l c, mc, at, LD 9.30. 🅿 N, CH, Dgs, CP 100, Ac, sp, con 120, CF, 3 BGf, 1 st, Dis. £ BB £37·25, DB £53–£59·50, WB, ①, Bk £4·75, L £6·50, D £9·25, cc 1 3 4 5 6.

EAST LEAKE Leicestershire. M.Area 22F
M1 Motorway 8½, Loughborough 5, London 114, Kegworth 5, Melton Mowbray 14, Nottingham 10.

Rescue Service: East Leake Garage Ltd, Main St. ✆ (050 982) 2377.

EASTLEIGH Hampshire. Map 6D.
Pop 94,000. Winchester 7½, London 72,
Cosham 18, Fareham 12, Lyndhurst 17,
Petersfield 23, Ringwood 24, Romsey 7,
Southampton 5. **EC** Wed. **MD** Thur. **Golf**
Fleming Park 18h.

★★★**M Crest,** *Leigh Rd, SO5 5PG.*
✆ (0703) 619700. C. ⊨ 120 bedrs, 120
bp, ns, TV, Dgs. ✗ a l c, mc, at. ⊡ Lt, N, CH,
CP 178, Ac, con 250, 4 BGf, 0 st. £ B fr
£45·50, BD fr £56, WB, ①, Bk £5·25, D
£9·60, cc 1 2 3 4 5 6.

EASTON Hampshire. M.Area 6D
Pop 439. Alton 15, London 63, Andover
15, Basingstoke 18, Lyndhurst 24,
Petersfield 19, Salisbury 26, Southampton
14, Winchester 2½.
Golf Hockley 18h. **See** 12th cent Church.

Rescue Service: Mould & Thompson, The
Garage. ✆ Itchen Abbas (096 278) 319.

EAST PORTLEMOUTH Devon. Map 3F.
Kingsbridge 8, London 211, Dartmouth
15.

West Waterhead, PH, xy (Rt), *nr
Salcombe, TQ8 8PA.* ✆ (054 851) 240.
Open Mar–Oct & New Year. C 6. ⊨ 8
bedrs, 5 bpa, 2a, Dgs. ⊡ CH, TV, Dgs, CP
8, 3 BGf, 16 st. £ BB £9–£14·50, DB £18–
£29, WT (b) £108·50–£136·50, DT (b)
£15·50–£21, ②, Bk £2·75, D £6·50.

EAST RAINTON Tyne & Wear. Map 32F.
Durham 6, London 266, A1 (M) Motorway
2½, Consett 19, Hartlepool 16, Newcastle
upon Tyne 14, Sunderland 7½.
Golf Houghton 18h.

Rescue Service: Pit Stop Garage Services,
Old Durham Rd. ✆ Houghton-le-Spring
(0783) 842506.

EAST RETFORD Nottinghamshire
See RETFORD.

EAST RUDHAM Norfolk. Map 16C
Pop 579. Swaffham 13, London 110, East
Dereham 16, Fakenham 6½, King's Lynn
15.
EC Thur. **Golf** Fakenham 18h. **See**
Ancient Parish Church, Coxford Priory
remains.

Rescue Service: Freeman, W T, The
Garage. ✆ (048 522) 273.

EAST WITTERING West Sussex. M.Area
6F
Pop 2,593. Chichester 7, London 68,
Bognor Regis 12.
EC Wed. **Golf** Selsey 9h. **See** 12th cent
Church, Fossil Beds at Bracklesham Bay.

Repairer: Shore Road Garage Ltd, Shore
Rd. ✆ West Wittering (024 366) 2711.

EASTWOOD Nottinghamshire. Map 22D
Pop 11,805. M1 Motorway 3½, London
131, Ashbourne 21, Chesterfield 18, Derby
11, Loughborough 21, Mansfield 12,
Matlock 17, Nottingham 8½.
MD Wed, Sat. **Golf** Alfreton 9h. **See**
Birthplace of D H Lawrence, now
Museum. (Victoria St), Sun Inn.

★**Sun Inn,** *Market Pl, NG16 3NR.*
✆ Langley Mill (0773) 712940. ⊨ 17
bedrs, 3 ba, Dgs. ✗ a l c, mc, at. LD 7.30.
⊡ CH, TV, Dgs, CP 50, Ac, 1 BGf, 3 st. £ BB
£11·50, DB £23, WT £126, DT £18, ①, Bk
£3, L £4, D £4·20.

Repairer: Smaller Bros, 151 Nottingham
Rd. ✆ Langley Mill (077 37) 3586.

EATHORPE Warwickshire. Map 14B
Princethorpe 1, London 87, Coventry 8,
M45 Motorway 5½, Royal Leamington Spa
7, Southam 6.

⬕★★**Eathorpe Park,** *Fosse Way.*
✆ Marton (0926) 632245. Closed Xmas
Night. C. ⊨ 10 bedrs, 4 bp, 4 bps, 2 ba, TV,
Dgs. ✗ a l c, mc, LD 9.45. ⊡ CH, TV, CP
200, Ac, con 100, CF, 1 st. £ BB fr £20·25,
DB fr £30·50, WB, ②, Bk £3, L £3·65, D
£8·75, cc 1 3 4 5.

ECCLES Gtr Manchester (Lancashire).
Map 20A
Pop 40,000. Altrincham 8, London 188,
Bury 10, Manchester 4, Rochdale 14, St
Helens 18, Walkden 4, Warrington 14,
Wigan 14.
EC Wed. **MD** Thur, Sat. **Golf** Worsley 18h.
See 15th cent Church, Monks Hall
Museum and Art Gallery, Barton Swing
Bridge and Aqueduct.

Repairer: Ashmall & Parkinson Ltd, 1a
Cambridge Grove. ✆ 061-789 5141.

EDENHALL Cumbria. Map 26C
Pop 685. Kendal 29, London 286, Alston
16, Ambleside 25, Brampton 21, Brough
22, Carlisle 19, Hawes 40, Penrith 4,
Ulverston 46.
Golf Penrith 18h. **See** St. Cuthbert
Church.

★★**Edenhall,** *CA11 8SX.* ✆ Langwathby
(0768 81) 454. C. ⊨ 27 bedrs, 27 bp, TV.
✗ a l c, mc, at. LD 8.45. ⊡ CH, TV, CP 60,
U 1, con, CF, 1 BGf. £ BB £14·50, DB
£27·50, WT £158·70–£164·95, WB, ①, Bk
£2·75, L £3·95, D £7·15, cc 1 3 4 5.

EDGBASTON Part of Birmingham
See BIRMINGHAM.

EDGWARE Greater London (Middx).
Map 8.
London 9, Barnet 5½, Brentford &
Chiswick 10, Harrow 3, Hatfield 12, St
Albans 11, Woodford 16.
EC Thur. **MD** Fri, Sat. **See** Church, grave
of harmonious blacksmith, Handel's organ.

Repairer: W Harold Perry Ltd (Ford
Products), 51 High St. ✆ 01-952 2353.

EDINGWORTH Somerset. Map 5C
Pop 125. M5 Motorway 4, Axbridge 6,
London 138, Bath 30, Bridgwater 12,
Bristol 21, Wells 16, Weston-super-Mare
6. **Golf** Berrow 18h.

Rookery, F, x (Unl), *BS24 0JB.*
✆ (093 472) 200.

EFFINGHAM Surrey. M.Area 7A
Pop 2,700. Leatherhead 3½, London 21,
Dorking 5, Guildford 8, Ripley 6, Woking
11.
EC Wed. **Golf** Effingham 18h. **See** Church.

Rescue Service: F W Mays & Co Ltd,
Effingham Garage. ✆ Bookham (0372)
2066.

EGGLESTON Durham. Map 26B
Pop 360. Barnard Castle 6, London 254,
Alston 25, Bishop Auckland 16, Brough
16, Darlington 22.
Golf Barnard Castle 18h.

Moorcock, I, x, *Hill Top, Eggleston, nr
Barnard Castle, DL12 0AU.* ✆ Teesdale
(0833) 50395.

EGHAM Surrey. Map 7A
Pop 15,733. Staines 1½, London 18, M25
Motorway ½, Bagshot 8½, Reading 21,
Weybridge 7, Windsor 6, Woking 10.
EC Thur. **Golf** Wentworth 18h (2) and 9h.
See Virginia Water, Runnymede
Memorials: President Kennedy,
Commonwealth Air Forces, Magna Carta,
Savill Gdns.

★★★★**Great Fosters,** *Stroude Rd, TW20
9UR.* ✆ (0784) 33822. C. ⊨ 23 bedrs, 18
ba, 5 bps, annexe 21 bedrs, 11 bp, 10 bps,
TV. ✗ a l c, mc, at, LD 9.30. ⊡ N, CH, TV,
CP 200, Ac, sp, tc, sb, con 60, CF, 2 BGf, 2
st. £ BB fr £35, DB fr £54, WB, ①, Bk £4·75,
L £9·50, D £12·75, cc 1 2 3 5 6, Dep b.

EGREMONT Cumbria. Map 26F
Pop 8,035. Broughton-in-Furness 31,
London 308, Cockermouth 15, Keswick
25, Workington 13.
EC Wed. **MD** Fri. **Golf** St. Bees 9h. **See**
Castle ruins.

🄸 12 Main St. ✆ Egremont (0946)
820693.

Rescue Service: Jubilee Garage
(Egremont) Ltd, North Rd. ✆ (0946)
820245.

ELBERTON Avon. M. Area 5A
Pop 50. 2½ m W of Alveston. M4
Motorway 2, London 117, Bristol 11,
Chepstow 7, Gloucester 26.

Rescue Service: Forge Cars (Elberton)
Ltd. ✆ Thornbury (0454) 419051.

ELLESMERE Shropshire. Map 19C
Pop 2,474. Wellington 25, London 169,
Chester 23, Llangollen 15, Newport 30,
Shrewsbury 16, Welshpool 24,
Whitchurch 11, Wrexham 12.
EC Thur. **MD** Fri. **Golf** Oswestry 18h. **See**
Rebuilt St Mary's Church, Kynaston
Monument, The Mere, half-timbered
houses.

⬕★★**Grange** (R), *Grange Rd, SY12 9DE.*
✆ (069 171) 2735. Closed 27 Dec–3 Jan.
C. ⊨ 15 bedrs, 13 bp, 1 bps, 2 ba, TV, Dgs.
✗ mc, at, LD 8.30. ⊡ ch, Dgs, CP 20, tc,
CF, 1 BGf. £ BB £12–£17·50, DB £28, WT
£145, DT £27, WB, ②, Bk £3·50, L £3, D
£7·50, cc 1 4 5.

Rescue Service: Mere Motors Ltd, Church
St. ✆ (069 171) 2343.
Shropshire Breakdown & Recovery
Services, Trotting Mare Garage, Trench.
✆ Overton-on-Dee (097 873) 300.

ELLESMERE PORT Cheshire. Map 19A
Pop 63,300. Chester 7½, London 149,
Birkenhead 10, Northwich 22,
Queensferry 9, Warrington 23.
MD Tue, Fri, Sat. **Golf** Municipal 18h. **See**
Museum.

Repairer: Offley Bros Ltd, Chester Rd.
✆ 051-355 1821.
Specialist Body Repairer: Offley Bros Ltd,
Chester Rd. ✆ 051-355 1821.
Rescue Service: Graham Thomas Motors,
1 Ross Rd, Trading Estate. ✆ 051-355
1928.

ELSTREE Hertfordshire. Map 15F
Pop 3,028, London 12, M1 Motorway 4,
Barnet 4½, Harrow 5, Hatfield 12, St Albans
8, Watford 5½.
EC Thur. **Golf** Aldenham 18h. **See** St
Nicholas Church, Aldenham Reservoir.

Rescue Service: Autoport (LAP) Ltd,
Allum La. ☎ 01-953 3618.

ELTERWATER Cumbria. M. Area 26D
3 m W of Ambleside. M6 Motorway 28,
London 272, Broughton-in-Furness 15,
Kendal 16, Keswick 15, Penrith 25,
Ulverston 19.

■♨★★**Eltermere** (R), *LA22 9HY.*
☎ Langdale (096 67) 207.

ELVINGTON North Yorkshire. Map 25C
Pop 550. Selby 15, London 198,
Bridlington 35, Goole 19, Malton 18,
Market Weighton 13, York 7½.
Golf Fulford York 18h. **See** Cottages,
Church.

Rescue Service: John I Jacques, Rydal
Garage. ☎ (090 485) 268.

ELY Cambridgeshire. Map 16F
Pop 9,640. Cambridge 16, London 71,
Bury St Edmunds 24, Huntingdon 21,
King's Lynn 28, Newmarket 13,
Peterborough 32, Swaffham 26, Wisbech
23.
EC Tue. **MD** Thur. **Golf** Cambridge Rd.
18h. **See** Cathedral, Bishop's Palace, Prior
Crauden's Chapel and Ely Porta (King's
School), 15th cent Monk's Granary, 13th
cent St Mary's Church, Goldsmith Tower,
Museums, Brass Rubbing Centre.
🛈 24 St Mary's St. ☎ Ely (0353) 3311.

★★**Lamb,** *Lynn Rd, CB7 4EJ.* ☎ (0353)
3579. RS 24–31 Dec incl. C. ⇔ 32 bedrs,
31 bp, 1 bps, TV, Dgs. ✗ a l c, mc, at, LD
9.15. 🄰 N, CH, TV, Dgs, CP 20, Ac, con 35,
CF, 1 st. £ BB £26–£28·50, DB £34–
£36·50, WB, 2, Bk £5, L £7, D £7,
cc 1 3 4 5 6, Dep b.

Nyton, G, x y (RI), *7 Barton Rd, CB7 4HZ.*
☎ (0353) 2459. C. ⇔ 13 bedrs, 4 bps, 4 ba.
🄰 ch, TV, CP 12, CF, 2 BGf, 2 st. £ BB £12–
£14, DB £20–£22, WT (c) £63–£91, 1.

Rescue Service: Ely Service Motor Co Ltd,
Lynn Rd. ☎ (0353) 2981.

EMBLETON Northumberland. Map 31B
Pop 435. Alnwick 7½, London 315,
Berwick-upon-Tweed 30, Coldstream 36.
EC Wed. **Golf** Embleton Village 18h. **See**
Dunstanburgh Castle ruins, old Church,
Vicarage with Pele Tower.

★★**Dunstanburgh Castle,** *Nr Alnwick,
NE66 3UN.* ☎ (066 576) 203. C. ⇔ 17
bedrs, 9 bp, 4 ba, Dgs. ✗ mc, at, LD 7.45.
🄰 ch, TV, CP 20, G 1, CF. £ BB fr £11·75,
DB fr £23·50, DBB £19·50, 1, Bk £3·50,
L £4·50, D £8.

EMBOROUGH Somerset. Map 5C
Pop 163. Radstock 6, London 116, Wells
5½, Bath 14, Bristol 16.
Golf Wells 9h, Mendip 18h.

★★**Court** (R), *Lynch Hill, BA3 4SA.*
☎ Stratton-on-the-Fosse (0761) 232237.
Closed Dec 26–Jan 11. C. ⇔ 10 bedrs, 2
bp, 7 bps, 1 ba, TV, Dgs. ✗ mc, at, LD 9.
🄰 CH, ns, CP 30, G 2, tc, con 50, CF, 4 BGf,
1 st, Dis. £ BB £15–£22, DB £32–£35, WT
£153·22, DT £25·75, WB, 2, Bk £3, L
£2·75, D £7, cc 1 3, Dep a.

EMSWORTH Hampshire. Map 6F
Petersfield 13, London 66, A3 (M)
Motorway 3, Chichester 7, Cosham 6.
EC Wed. **Golf** Rowlands Castle 18h. **See**
St James's Church. Oyster beds.

■★★**Brookfield** (R), *Havant Rd. PO10
7LF.* ☎ (024 34) 3363. C. ⇔ 17 bedrs, 11

bp, 6 bps, TV. ✗ a l c, mc, LD 9.30. 🄰 CH,
TV, CP 100, con 50, CF, 3 BGf, 1 st. £ BB
£27, DB £34, 2, 10%, Bk £3·75, L £7·50, D
£8·50, cc 1 2 3 5 6.

Chestnuts, G, x (Unl), *55 Horndean Rd,
PO10 7PU.* ☎ (024 34) 2233. C. ⇔ 6
bedrs, 3 ba, Dgs. 🄰 CH, TV, CP 10, CF, 1
BGf, 3 st. £ BB £10–£12, DB £18–£20, DT
(b) £13·50–£15·50, 2, Bk £2·50, D £3·50.

Jingles, G, x (Unl) *77 Horndean Rd,
PO10 7PU.* ☎ (024 34) 3755. C. ⇔ 9
bedrs, 3 ba, Dgs. 🄰 CH, TV, Dgs, ns, CF, 2
BGf, 3 st. £ BB £10·35–£11, DB £20·70–
£22, WT (b) £95, DT £13·80–£14·50, 1,
cc 1 5.

Merry Hall, H, x (R), *73 Horndean Rd,
PO10 7PU.* ☎ (024 34) 2424. C. ⇔ 10
bedrs, 7 bp, 3 sh, TV. ✗ a l c. 🄰 CH, CP 12,
CF, 2 BGf, 1 st. Dis. £ BB fr £21·50, DB fr
£32·50, 1, Bk £3·75, L £5, D £7·50,
cc 1 3.▲

Queensgate, H, z (RI), *80 Havant Rd,
PO10 7LH.* ☎ (024 34) 7190. Closed 18
Dec–7 Jan. C. ⇔ 11 bedrs, 9 sh, 2 ba, TV,
Dgs. ✗ a l c. 🄰 CH, TV, CP 11, CF, 2 st.
£ BB £13·80–£17·25, DB £27·60–£31·05,
1.

Rescue Service: Chequers Garage, 39
Queen St. ☎ (024 34) 3122 and (024 34)
2781.
Dave Lashly, Commonside (Westbourne).
☎ (024 34) 2946.
R & K Autos, 28a Queen St. ☎ (024 34)
6243.

ENDERBY Leicestershire. M.Areas 14B
and 22F
Pop 4,047. M1 Motorway 11, London 97,
Ashby-de-la-Zouch 18, Atherstone 17,
Coventry 20, Daventry 26, Hinckley 9½,
Leicester 5, Market Harborough 17,
Northampton 31, Rugby 17, Towcester
37.
EC Wed. **Golf** Cosby, Leicester 18h.

Rescue Service: H & C West Ltd, The
Quarry. ☎ Narborough (0760) 2231.

ENFIELD Greater London (Middx). Map
15F
Pop 109,543. London 12, Barnet 6,
Brentford & Chiswick 17, Epping 11,
Hatfield 12, Hoddesdon 9, Woodford 6½,
St Albans 15.
EC Wed. **MD** Sat. **Golf** Enfield 18h, Bush
Hill Park 18h.

★★★**Royal Chace,** *The Ridgeway, EN2
8AR.* ☎ 01-366 6500. C. ⇔ 90 bedrs, 62
bp, 28 bps, TV. ✗ a l c, mc, LD 9.45. 🄰 N,
CH, CP 300, sp, con 200, CF, 1 BGf, 2 st.
£ BB fr £33, DB fr £44·50, 1, Bk £4·25, L
£6·60, D £7, cc 1 2 3 4 5 6, Dep b.

★★**Enfield,** *Rowantree Rd, EN2 8PW.*
☎ 01-366 3511.

★★**Holtwhites** (RI), *92 Chase Side, EN2
0QN.* ☎ 01-363 0124. C 3. ⇔ 28 bedrs, 17
bp, 3 bps, 2 sh, 2 ba, TV, Dgs. ✗ a l c, mc,
at, LD 8. 🄰 N, CH, TV, Dgs, CP 25, G 7, Ac,
3 st. £ BB £24·50–£31·50, DB £34·50–
£42·50, WB, 2, 10%, Bk £3·95, D £9,
cc 1 3 4 5 6, Dep b.

Rescue Services: Elmsleigh of Enfield,
Redburn Industrial Estate, Woodall Rd.
☎ 01-805 2202.
Grindrod & Higgs (Enfield) Ltd, Alexandra
Rd. ☎ 01-804 4817.
Lavender Hill Garage, The Ridgeway.
☎ 01-363 3456.

ENGLEFIELD GREEN Surrey. Map 7A
Staines 2½, London 19, Bagshot 7½,
Reading 20, Weybridge 8, Windsor 4,
Woking 10.
EC Thur. **Golf** Sunningdale 18h (2). **See**
Commonwealth Air Forces Memorial.

Repairer: Fletcher's Garage, 63 St Jude
Rd. ☎ Egham (0784) 2166.

ENNERDALE BRIDGE Cumbria. Map
26F
Pop 296. Cockermouth 10, London 307,
Egremont 5½, Whitehaven 7½, Keswick 20.
Golf St Bees 9h. **See** Ennerdale Lake.

■★**Shepherds Arms** (RI), *CA23 3AR.*
☎ Lamplugh (0946) 861249. Closed Jan &
1 week mid Nov. C. ⇔ 6 bedrs, 2 bps, 2 ba,
Dgs. ✗ mc, LD 8.30. 🄰 CH, TV, Dgs, CP
12, CF, 0 st. £ BB £11–£12, DB £22–£26,
DBB £18–£20, WB, 2, Bk £3, L £3·50, D £7.

EPPING Essex. Maps 15F and 17F
Pop 12,336. Woodford 8½, London 18,
M11 Motorway 3½, Bishop's Stortford 13,
Brentwood 14, Chelmsford 17, Dunmow
19, Enfield 11, Hoddesdon 9, Romford 12.
EC Wed. **MD** Mon. **Golf** Theydon Bois
18h. **See** Epping Forest—5,000 acres.

★★★**M Post House** (TH), *High Rd, CM16
4DG.* ☎ (0378) 73137. C. ⇔ 82 bedrs, 82
bp, TV, Dgs. ✗ a l c, mc, at, LD 10.15. 🄰 N,
CH, Dgs, CP 95, Ac, CF, 2 st. £ BB £43·50,
DB £56, WB, 1, cc 1 2 3 4 5 6,
Dep (Xmas).

Specialist Body Repairers: Brian Shilton &
Co Ltd, 73 Lindsey St. ☎ (0378) 74341.
Popplewells Coachworks Ltd, High St,
Thornwood. ☎ (0378) 74040.
Rescue Service: B & G Automotives, Half
Moon La, High St. ☎ (0378) 74753.
Brian Shilton & Co Ltd, 73 Lindsey St.
☎ (0378) 74341.

EPSOM Surrey. Map 7A
RAC Country Club, *Woodcote Park,
Epsom, KT18 7EW.* ☎ Ashtead
(037 22) 76311.
Pop 68,538 (inc Ewell). Mitcham 7½,
London 14, Croydon 8½, Kingston upon
Thames 7, Leatherhead 4, Purley 7½,
Reigate 9, Thornton Heath 10, Weybridge
12.
EC Wed. **MD** Sat. **Golf** Epsom 18h,
Cuddington, Banstead 18h, the RAC
Country Club (members to accompany all
visitors) 18h (2). **See** Racecourse, St
Martin's Church.

★★**Chalk Lane** (Rt), *Chalk La, KT18 7BB.*
☎ (037 27) 21179.

■★★**Drift Bridge,** *Reigate Rd, KT17
3JZ.* ☎ Burgh Heath (073 73) 52163.

Repairers: Edwards, H F & Co Ltd, 28
Upper High St. ☎ (037 27) 25611.
Page Motors Ltd, Nonsuch Industrial
Estate, East St. ☎ (037 27) 26246.
University Motors (Woodcote) Ltd, 4
Church St. ☎ (037 27) 26611.
Specialist Body Repairer: University
Coachworks Ltd, Blenheim Rd, Longmead
Industrial Estate. ☎ (037 27) 27133.
Rescue Service: Allam Motor Services
Ltd, 48 Upper St. ☎ (037 27) 25920.

ERITH Greater London (Kent). Map 7B
Pop 45,026. London 16, Dartford 3½,
Sidcup 6½, M25 Motorway 7½.
EC Thur. **See** Lessnes Abbey remains.

Specialist Body Repairer: Hodges Motor Services Ltd, Anchor Bay Industrial Estate, Manor Rd. ✆ (032 24) 49433.

Repairers: Hodges Motor Services Ltd, Anchor Bay Industrial Estate, Manor Rd. ✆ (032 24) 49433.
K T (Dartford) Ltd, 391 Erith Rd, North Heath. ✆ (032 24) 38191.▲
Rescue Service: Hodges Roadside Rescue Ltd, Anchor Bay Industrial Estate, Manor Rd. ✆ (032 24) 49433.
Royal Oak Garage (Bexley) Ltd, Bexley Rd. ✆ (032 24) 36666.

ERMINGTON Devon. Map 3D
Pop 869. Ashburton 15, London 203, Plymouth 11, Totnes 12.
Golf Wrangaton 9h. **See** Parish Church.

▣★★**Ermewood House,** *PL21 9NS.*
✆ Modbury (0548) 830741. Closed Dec 23–31. C. 🛏 9 beds, 5 bp, 4 bps, TV, Dgs. ✗ a l c, mc, at, LD 9.30. 🅿 CH, CP 20, CF, 1 st. £ BB £25–£27, DB £46–£50, DBB £30–£34, WB, ⬜, Bk £3·50, L £4, D £8, cc 1 2 3 5 6.

ESHER Surrey. Map 7A
Pop 5,555. Kingston 3½, London 13, Croydon 14, Guildford 15, Leatherhead 6½, Staines 10, Chertsey 6½, M3 Motorway 6.
EC Wed. **Golf** Moore Place 9h. **See** Racecourse, Claremount House, Church.

★★**Haven** (R), *Portsmouth Rd, KT10 9AR.*
✆ 01-398 0023. RS Sats pm and Bank Hols. C. 🛏 16 beds, 2 bp, 4 bps, 5 ba, annexe 4 bedrs, 2 bp, 2 bps, TV, Dgs. ✗ mc, at, LD 8.30. 🅿 CH, TV, CP 20, U 1, con 48, CF, 2 BGf, 2 st. £ BB £18·50–£25, DB £28·50–£33·50, ⬜, Bk £2·50, D £5·50, cc 1 2 3 5 6, Dep b.

ESKDALE Cumbria. Map 26F
Pop 305 (inc Boot). Ambleside 17, London 285, Broughton-in-Furness 25, Egremont 12.
EC Wed. **Golf** Seascale 18h. **See** Ravenglass and Eskdale Rly, Dalegarth Force 2 m E, Hardknott Pass.

Rescue Service: Postlethwaite, R & A, Fell View Garage, Main Rd. ✆ (094 03) 239.

ESSINGTON Staffordshire. Map 21E
Pop 3,970. Walsall 4½, London 125, Birmingham 13, Lichfield 12, Stafford 13, Tamworth 17, Uttoxeter 23, Wolverhampton 4.
Golf Bloxwich 18h. **See** Moseley Old Hall (NT). Hilton Park and Tower.

Rescue Service: J. Boardman (Garages) Ltd, Hilton Park Motorway Services.
✆ Cheslyn Hay (0922) 416803.
Top Rank Motorport, Hilton Park (M6).
✆ Cheslyn Hay (0922) 415537.

ETWALL Derbyshire. Map 22E
Pop 2,740. Ashby-de-la-Zouch 12, London 125, Ashbourne 13, Burton-on-Trent 6½, Derby 6, Uttoxeter 13, M25 Motorway 9.
EC Thur. **Golf** Mickleover 18h. **See** St Helen's Church, Almshouses built by Sir John Port (founder of Repton School).

Rescue Service: Ian Jones Motors, Etwall Garage, Uttoxeter Rd. ✆ (028 373) 2333.

EVERCREECH Somerset. Map 5C
Pop 1,906. Frome 11, London 116, Ilminster 26, Radstock 11, Shepton Mallet 4, Sherbourne 15, Wincanton 8, Shaftesbury 17.

EC Wed. **Golf** Mendip 18h. **See** St Peter's Church.

♨★★★**Glen,** *Queens Rd, BA4 6JS.*
✆ (0749) 830369. Closed Xmas. C. 🛏 12 beds, 7 bp, 2 bps, 2 ba, 4 bedrs annexe, 1 ba, TV. ✗ a l c, mc, at, LD 9.45. 🅿 CH, TV, CP 40, Ac, con 20, CF. £ BB £14–£20, DB £24–£30, ⬜, Bk £3, L £1, D £3·50, cc 1 3 4 5 6, Dep b.

EVESHAM Hereford & Worcester (Worcestershire). Map 14C
Pop 15,271. Moreton-in-Marsh 14, London 98, Banbury 30, Birmingham 30, Bromsgrove 21, Cheltenham 16, Droitwich 19, Ledbury 26, Stratford-upon-Avon 14, Stow-on-the-Wold 16, Tewkesbury 13, Worcester 16.
EC Wed. **MD** Tue, Thur, Fri, Sat. **Golf** Broadway 18h, Hadbury 18h. **See** Abbey ruins, All Saints' Church, St Lawrence Church, Walker Hall, Tudor Vicarage (now a church house), Abbey Almonry (now local history museum), Old Town Hall, Abbey Park and Gardens.
🛈 Almonry Museum, Merstow Green.
✆ Evesham (0386) 6944.

★★★**Evesham,** *Coopers La, off Waterside (A44), WR11 6DA.* ✆ (0386) 49111.
Closed Xmas. C. 🛏 34 beds, 28 bp, 5 bps, 1 ba, TV, Dgs. ✗ a l c, mc, at, LD 9.30. 🅿 CH, CP 45, con 20, CF. £ BB £30–£35, DB £40–£48, WT £197–£266, WB, ⬜, Bk £3·30, L £4·85, D £9·50, cc 1 3 4 5 6.

★★★**Northwick Arms,** *Waterside WR11 6BT.* ✆ (0386) 6109. Closed Xmas. C.
🛏 22 bedrs, 4 bp, 5 ba, Dgs. ✗ a l c, mc, at, LD 9.30. 🅿 ch, TV, Dgs, CP 100, Ac, con 20, CF. £ BB £14–£25, DB £20–£38, WB, ⬜, Bk £3, D £4·50, cc 1 5.

♨★★**Salford Hall,** *Abbots Salford, WR11 5UT.* ✆ (0386) 870561.
Ap. Park View (R), *Waterside, WR11 6BS.* ✆ (0386) 2639. Closed Dec 23rd–Jan 2nd. C. 🛏 29 bedrs, 6 ba, Dgs. ✗ mc, at, LD 7. 🅿 ch, TV, CP 50, Ac, CF. £ BB £11·35–£12·25, DB £22·70–£24·50, ⬜, Bk £2·70, L £1, D £5·50, cc 1 5 6.

Dayleen, G, z (Unl), *16 Broadway Rd, WR11 6BQ.* ✆ (0386) 6676. C. 🛏 6 bedrs, 1 ba, Dgs. 🅿 CH, TV, CP 6, CF. £ BB £8·50–£9, DB £17–£18, ⬜.

Repairer: Howard, A & Son, Worcester Rd. ✆ (0386) 6140.
Rescue Service: Bright, S & Sons Ltd, Bright's Garage, Cheltenham Rd. ✆ (0386) 2301.
Morrall, V A Ltd, The Motor House, Broadway Rd. ✆ (0386) 6441.

EYNSHAM Oxfordshire. Map 14F
Oxford 6½, London 63, Banbury 23, Cheltenham 34, Swindon 28.

Rescue Service: Wastie's Motors A40.
✆ Oxford (0865) 881367.

EWEN Gloucestershire. Map 14E
Pop 150. Cirencester 3½, London 91, Chippenham 18, Marlborough 25, Newbury 38, Swindon 16, Tetbury 9.
Golf Cirencester 18h.

★★★**Wild Duck Inn,** *GL7 6BY.* ✆ Kemble (028 577) 364.▲

EWYAS HAROLD Hereford & Worcester (Herefordshire). Map 13C
Pop 449. Ross-on-Wye 15, London 137, Abergavenny 13, Brecon 34, Builth Wells 38, Hereford 13, Monmouth 15.

Golf Monmouthshire (Abergavenny) 18h.
Rescue Service: Smith, D C, Forge Garage, ✆ Golden Valley (0981) 240261.

EXBOURNE Devon. Map 3A.
Pop 198. Crediton 16, London 193, Barnstaple 24, Exeter 25, Holsworthy 18, Okehampton 6.

Rescue Service: Guys Garage.
✆ (083 785) 213.

EXEBRIDGE Somerset. Map 4D
Taunton 22, London 166, Dunster 17, Ilfracombe 35, Lynmouth 25, South Molton 14, Tiverton 10.

★**Anchor Inn,** ✆ Dulverton (0398) 23433.

EXETER Devon. Maps 3B and 4F
RAC Office, *188 Sidwell St, Exeter, EX4 6RD.* ✆ Exeter (0392) 58333.
Pop 98,800. Honiton 17, London 169, M5 Motorway 3, Ashburton 19, Crediton 7½, Lyme Regis 29, Newton Abbot 15, Okehampton 22, Saltash 42, Taunton 33, Tavistock 33, Tiverton 15.
See Plan, p. 204.
MD Daily. **P** See Plan. **Golf** Exeter G and CC 18h. **See** Cathedral, Museum and Art Gallery, Northernhay Gardens, Southernhay (old houses and fine gardens), Customs House, Mol's Coffee House, Tucker's Hall, Rougemont, Castle ruins, Maritime Museum, Guildhall, St Nicholas' Priory (16th cent), remains of City Walls, ancient underground passage, Museum (Rougemont House), Wynard's Almshouses, Killerton Gdns 6 m NE, Powderham Castle 6 m SE.
🛈 Civic Centre. ✆ Exeter (0392) 72434.

★★★**Buckerell Lodge Crest,** *Topsham Rd, EX2 4SQ.* ✆ (0392) 52451. C. 🛏 54 bedrs, 54 bp, ns, TV, Dgs. ✗ a l c, mc, LD 9.45. 🅿 N, CH, Dgs, CP 36, con 50, CF, 2 BGf, 2 st. £ B fr £41, BD fr £52, WB, ⬜, Bk £5·25, D £9·95, cc 1 2 3 4 5 6, Dep b.

★★★**M Devon,** *Exeter By-pass, Matford, EX2 8XU.* ✆ (0392) 59268. C. 🛏 40 bedrs, 38 bp, 2 bps, 1 ba, TV, Dgs. ✗ a l c, mc, LD 10. 🅿 N, CH, Ac, con, CF, 12 BGf. £ BB fr £23, DB fr £29·90, Bk £1·25, D £6·75, cc 1 2 3 4 5 6.

▣★★★**M Exeter Arms,** *Rydon La, Middlemoor, EX2 7HL.* ✆ (0392) 35353.

★★★**Gipsy Hill Hotel & Restaurant,** *Pinhoe, EX1 3RN.* ✆ (0392) 65252. C.
🛏 19 bedrs, 18 bp, 1 bps, TV. ✗ a l c, mc, at, LD 9. 🅿 N, CH, Dgs, CP 50, Ac, con 150, 0 st. £ BB £26·50, DB £37, WB, ⬜, Bk £3·75, L £5·50, D £7, cc 1 2 3 6, Dep b.

★★★**Imperial,** *New North Rd, EX4 4JX.* ✆ (0392) 211811. C. 🛏 25 bedrs, 18 bp, 2 bps, 4 ba, TV, Dgs. ✗ mc, at, LD 9. 🅿 N, CH, TV, Dgs, CP 80, U 3, G 10, gc, con 200, CF. £ BB fr £17–£29·50, DB £28–£39, WT £199, DT £28·70, WB, ⬜, Bk £3·50, L £4·95, D £6·95, cc 1 3 4 5 6.

▣★★★**M Ladbroke,** *Kennford, EX6 7UX.* ✆ Kennford (0392) 832121. C. 🛏 61 bedrs, 61 bp, 2 ba, TV, Dgs. ✗ a l c, mc, at, LD 9.45. 🅿 N, CH, TV, Dgs, CP 200, Ac, con 150, CF, 1 st. £ BB £31–£33, DB £41–£44, DT £49, WB, ⬜, Bk £3·25, L £2·50, D £5·25, cc 1 2 3 5, Dep b.

★★★**Rougemont,** *Queen St, EX4 3SP.* ✆ (0392) 54982. C. 🛏 63 bedrs, 59 bp, 4 bps, TV, Dgs. ✗ a l c, mc, at, LD 9.30. 🅿 Lt, N, CH, Dgs, CP 35, Ac, con 300, CF, 5 st.

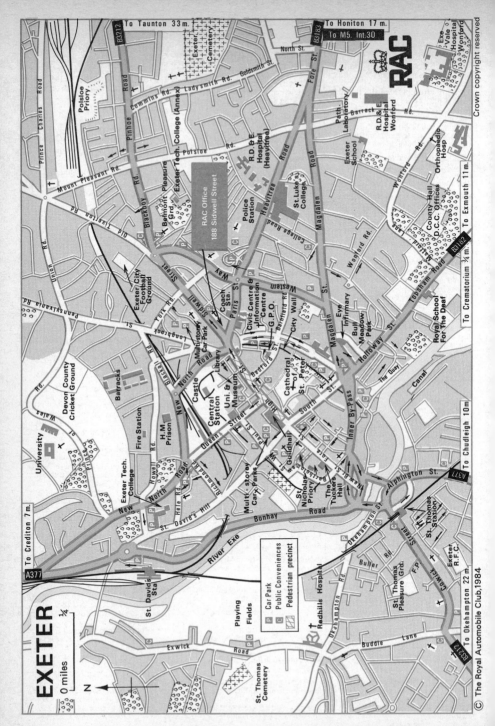

EXETER

0 miles ¼

To Taunton 33m.
To Honiton 17m.
To M5. Int.30
To Exmouth 11m.
To Chudleigh 10m.
To Crematorium ¾m.
To Okehampton 22 m.
To Credion 7m.

RAC Office 188 Sidwell Street

Legend:
P Car Park
C Public Conveniences
Pedestrian precinct

£ BB fr £32·45, DB fr £43·45, WB, ▣, cc 1 2 3 5.

★★★**Royal Clarence,** *Cathedral Yard, EX1 1HD.* ✆ (0392) 58464. C. ⇔ 62 bedrs, 53 bp, 9 bps, TV, Dgs. ✗ a l c, mc, at, LD 9.30. ▣ Lt, N, CH, Dgs, CP 19, Ac, con 120, CF, 2 st. **£** BB fr £32·50, DB fr £49, WT fr £269·50, DT fr £38·50, WB, ▣, L £6, D £8, cc 1 3 4 5 6, Dep.

★★★**White Hart,** *South St, EX1 1EF.* ✆ (0392) 79897.

▣★★**Bystock,** *Bystock Ter, EX4 4HY.* ✆ (0392) 72709. Closed Xmas. C. ⇔ 24 bedrs, 4 bp, 3 bps, 3 sh, 7 ba, TV, Dgs. ✗ a l c, mc, at, LD 9.45. ▣ CH, TV, Dgs, Ac, con 30, CF, 1 BGf, 5 st. **£** BB £14–£18, DB £26–£30, ▣, Bk £2, L £5·10, D £5·50, cc 1 3.

★★**Edgerton Park,** *Pennsylvania Rd, EX4 6DH.* ✆ (0392) 74029. C 5. ⇔ 17 bedrs, 5 bp, 12 bps, 5 ba. ✗ a l c, mc, LD 9. ▣ CH, TV, CP 60, con 70. **£** BB £18–£18·50, DB £30–£31, WB, ▣, Bk £3, L £4·50, D £4·50, cc 1 3 4 5.

★★**M Exeter Moat House,** *Topsham Rd, Exeter By-Pass, EX2 6HE.* ✆ Topsham (039 287) 5441. C. ⇔ 44 bedrs, 44 bp, TV, Dgs. ✗ a l c, mc, at, LD 10. ▣ N, CH, Dgs, CP 44, Ac, tc, con 130, CF, 33 BGf, 1 st, Dis. **£** BB £20–£29·45, DB £25–£37, WT fr £175, DT fr £27, WB, ▣, Bk £4, L £5·95, D £6·50, cc 1 3 4 5 6, Dep.

★★**Gt Western,** *St David's, Station Approach, EX4 4NU.* ✆ (0392) 74039. C. ⇔ 45 bedrs, 8 bp, 9 ba, TV, Dgs. ✗ a l c, mc, at, LD 9.30. ▣ CH, TV, Dgs, CP 40, Ac, con 50, CF. **£** BB £15–£17·50, DB £24–£28, WT £129·15, DT £20·95, WB, ▣, Bk £3, L £4·25, D £5·95, cc 1 3 4 5 6, Dep b.

★★**Red House,** *2 Whipton Village Rd, EX4 8AR.* ✆ (0392) 56104. C 5. ⇔ 13 bedrs, 3 bp, 4 bps, 3 ba, TV, Dgs. ✗ a l c, mc, LD 9.30. ▣ CH, CP 40. **£** BB £12–£19·25, DB £24·20–£30·25, WT £148–£168, DT £21–£24, WB, ▣, Bk £3·75, L £4·60, D £6·65, cc 1 2 3 5, Dep a.

★★**St Andrews,** *28 Alphington Rd, EX2 8HH.* ✆ (0392) 76784. Closed Xmas. C. ⇔ 16 bedrs, 6 bp, 6 ba, TV, Dgs. ✗ a l c, mc, at, LD 8. ▣ CH, TV, Dgs, CP 20, CF, 3 st. **£** BB £14–£20, DB £24–£33, WB, ▣, Bk £3·50, L £3, D £5·50, cc 1 3 5.

Braeside, G, z (Unl), *21 New North Rd, EX4 4HF.* ✆ (0392) 56875.

Cre-Ber, G, z (Unl), *32 Heavitree Rd, EX1 2LQ.* ✆ (0392) 76102. Closed Xmas. C 3. ⇔ 12 bedrs, 2 bps, 1 sh, 3 ba, ns, TV. ▣ CH, TV, CP 2, CF. **£** BB £9–£11, DB £16–£20, WT (b) £82, (c) £54, DT (b) £13, ▣.

Park View, H, z (Unl) *8 Howell Rd, EX4 4LG.* ✆ (0392) 71772. Closed Mid Dec–Mid Jan. C. ⇔ 15 bedrs, 2 bp, 3 bps, 4 sh, 2 ba, TV, Dgs. ✗ a l c. ▣ CH, TV, Dgs, CP 6, CF, 2 st. **£** BB £9·78–£12, DB £18·40–£23, DT (b) £15–£17, ▣, Bk £3·50, L £4·50, D £5, cc 1 5.

Radnor, H, z (Unl), *79 St David's Hill, EX4 4DW.* ✆ (0392) 72004. Closed Dec. C. ⇔ 7 bedrs, 2 bps, 2 ba, Dgs. ▣ CH, TV, Dgs, CP 7, CF. **£** BB £8·05–£8·62, DB £14·95–£18·40, DT (b) £12·07–£12·65, ▣, D £4·60. ▲

Regents Park, H, z (Unl) *Polsloe Rd, EX1 2NU.* ✆ (0392) 59749. Closed 2 weeks Xmas. C. ⇔ 11 bedrs, 3 ba, Dgs. ▣ TV, Dgs, CP 16, 1 BGf, 4 st. **£** BB £9·50, DB £18, WT (c) £66·50, DT (b) £15, ▣.

Rowhorne House Farm, F xy, *Rowhorne, Whitestone, EX4 2LQ.*

✆ (0392) 74675. Open Feb–Oct. C. ⇔ 3 bedrs, 2 ba. ▣ TV. **£** BB £7, DB £14, WT £70, DT £10.

Shene, G, z (Unl), *328 Pinhoe Rd, EX2 8AS.* ✆ (0392) 55786. C. ⇔ 7 bedrs, 1 bp, 1 ba, Dgs. ▣ CH, TV, CP 10, CF, 1 BGf, 2 st. **£** BB £8–£9·50, DB £15–£18, WT (b) £80–£83·50, DT (b) £12–£12·50, ▣.

Sylvania House, PH, z (Unl) *64 Pennsylvania Rd, EX4 6DF.* ✆ (0392) 75583. Closed Dec 14–31. C. ⇔ 8 bedrs, 1 bp, 4 bps, 1 ba. ▣ CH, TV, CP 4, CF, 1 st. **£** BB £10–£11·50, DB £19–£22, ▣, Bk £2, cc 1 3.

Sunnymead, G, z (Unl), *24 New North Rd, EX4 4HF.* ✆ (0392) 73844. Closed Xmas. ⇔ 6 bedrs, 1 ba, TV. ▣ CH, TV. **£** BB £8·50, DB £16, WT £74·50, DT £12, ▣, D £3·50, cc 5.

Telstar, PH, z (Unl), *77 St David's Hill, EX4 4DW.* ✆ (0392) 72466. Closed Xmas. C. ⇔ 8 bedrs, 2 sh, 1 ba. ▣ CH, TV, CP 5. **£** BB £8–£8·50, DB £15·50, DT (b) fr £11·50, ▣.

Trees (Mini), PH, z (Unl), *2 Queen's Cres, York Rd, EX4 6AY.* ✆ (0392) 59531. C 1. ⇔ 12 bedrs, 1 ba. ▣ CH, TV, U 1. **£** BB £9, DB £16, WT (c) £59·50, ▣.

Westholme, PH, z (Unl), *85 Heavitree Rd, EX1 2ND.* ✆ (0392) 71878. Closed Mid Dec–Mid Jan. C. ⇔ 7 bedrs, 2 ba, Dgs. ▣ ch, TV, CP 9, CF, 2 BGf, Dis. **£** BB £8·50–£9, DB £17–£18, WT (c) £56–£59, ▣.

Willowdene, H, z (Unl), *161 Magdalen Rd, EX2 4TT.* ✆ (0392) 71925. C. ⇔ 8 bedrs, 2 ba. ✗ a l c. ▣ TV, CF. **£** BB £9, DB £18, ▣.

Repairers: Dunns Motors (Exeter) Ltd, Trusham Rd, Marsh Barton. ✆ (0392) 77311.

W. Mumfords Ltd, Marsh Barton Rd. ✆ (0392) 37752.

U B M Ford, 9 Marsh Barton Rd. ✆ (0392) 50141.

MC Repairers: Fred Hutchings Ltd, Swan Yard, Okehampton St. ✆ (0392) 72524. Len Born Ltd, 16 Bartholomew St East. ✆ (0392) 73141.

Rescue Service: Countess Wear Service Station, 399 Topsham Rd. ✆ Topsham (039 287) 3110.

Cowley Road Garage, Cowley Rd. ✆ (0392) 54414 and (0392) 70229.

D & T Motors, Longbrook Terrace. ✆ (0392) 37846.

George Tancock's Motor Engineers, Landscore Rd, St Thomas. ✆ (0392) 55686.

Oaklands Garage, Sidmouth Rd, Aylesbeare. ✆ Woodbury (0395) 32241.

Seabrook Service Station, Topsham Rd. ✆ Topsham (039 287) 7272.

Sports Classic & Performance Cars, No. 6, Bittern Units, Sowton Industrial Estate. ✆ (0392) 59786.

U B M Ford, 9 Marsh Barton Rd. ✆ (0392) 50141.

Woods Western Garages Ltd, 52 Alphington Rd. ✆ (0392) 74458.

EXMINSTER Devon. Maps 3D and 4F. Pop 3500. Exeter 4½, London 170, Ashburton 18, Newton Abbot 13.

EC Thur. **Golf** Dawlish Warren 18h. **See** 14 cent Church (restored).

Rescue Service: Swan Nest Garage, Dawlish Rd. ✆ Exeter (0392) 832577.

EXMOUTH Devon. Maps 3D and 4F Pop 31,000. Honiton 17, London 170, Axminster 26, Exeter 11, Lyme Regis 27.

EC Wed. **Golf** East Devon, Budleigh Salterton 18h. **See** A La Ronde–18th cent house with Shell Gallery.

🛈 Alexandra Ter. ✆ Exmouth (039 52) 63744.

★★★**Devoncourt,** *Douglas Av, EX8 2EX.* ✆ (0395) 272277. C. ⇔ 68 bedrs, 68 bp, 1 ba, TV, Dgs. ✗ a l c, mc, at, LD 8.30. ▣ Lt, N, CH, CP 45, G 10, sp, tc, sb, sol, gym, con 100, CF, 5 BGf, 2 st. **£** BB £20·25–£22·15, DB £40·50–£44·30, WT £181·50–£208·95, DT £27·20–£31, WB, ▣, Bk £2·50, L £5, D £6·30, cc 1 3 5, Dep b. ▲

★★★**Imperial** (TH), *Esplanade, EX8 2SW.* ✆ (03952) 74761. C. ⇔ 61 bedrs, 61 bp, TV, Dgs. ✗ a l c, mc, at, LD 9. ▣ Lt, N, CH, Dgs, CP 55, sp, tc, sb, con 120, CF, 0 st. **£** BB £34·50, DB £57·50, WB, ▣. cc 1 2 3 4 5 6, Dep (Xmas).

★★★**Royal Beacon,** *The Beacon, EX8 2AF.* ✆ (0395) 264886. C. ⇔ 35 bedrs, 32 bp, 6 ba, TV, Dgs. ✗ a l c, mc, at, LD 9. ▣ Lt, CH, TV, Dgs, CP 20, U 10, Ac, sb, sol, gym, con, CF, 7 st. **£** BB fr £17, DB fr £34, WB Bk £4, L £5, ▣, cc 1 2 3 4 5 6, Dep.

★★**Balcombe House,** (RI), *7 Stevenstone Rd, EX8 2EP.* ✆ (0395) 266349. Open April–Oct. C 10. ⇔ 12 bedrs, 12 bps, TV. ✗ mc, LD 5·30. ▣ CH, TV, ns, CP 14, CF, 3 BGf, Dis. **£** BB £13–£14, DB £26–£28, WT £149–£159, DT £23·50–£26, Bk £3·50, L £4, D £5·75, ▣, Dep a.

★★**Barn,** (RI), *Foxholes, off Marine Dr, EX8 2DF.* ✆ (0395) 274411. C. ⇔ 12 bedrs, 10 bp, 1 bps, 1 ba, TV, Dgs. ✗ a l c, mc, at, LD 8.30. ▣ CH, TV, CP 30, G 3, sp, tc, con 100, CF, 1 BGf, 4 st. **£** BB £16·50–£19, DB £33–£38, WB, ▣, Bk £4, L £6·50, D £7·50, Dep a.

★★**Grand,** *Sea Front, EX8 1BE.* ✆ (0395) 263278. C. ⇔ 85 bedrs, 41 bp, 17 bps, 12 ba, TV, Dgs. ✗ a l c, mc. ▣ Lt, CH, CP 30, Ac, con 130, CF, 4 BGf, 0 st. **£** BB £13·50–£20, DB £27–£38, WT £115·50–£130, DT £22–£25, ▣, Bk £2·50, L £4, D £5·50, Dep.

★★**Manor,** *The Beacon, EX8 2AG.* ✆ (0395) 272549. C. ⇔ 40 bedrs, 38 bp, 2 bps, TV, Dgs. ✗ a l c, mc, LD 8. ▣ Lt, CH, Dgs, CP 12, U 3, Ac, CF, 6 st. **£** BB £15·50–£17·80, DB £31–£35·80, WT £110–£128, DT £24·50–£29·32, WB, ▣, Bk £3·50, L £4·50, D £5·50, cc 1 3.

Aliston House, PH, y (R), *58 Salterton Rd, EX8 2EW.* ✆ (0395) 274119. Open Mar–Oct. C. ⇔ 12 bedrs, 6 bps, 2 ba, TV Dgs. ▣ ch, TV, Dgs, CP, CF, 0 st. **£** BB £12·50–£15, DB £25–£30, WT (c) £125–£132, DT (b) £18·50–£19·50, ▣, Bk £2·75, D £6.

Blenheim, G, z (RI), *39 Morton Rd, EX8 1BA.* ✆ (0395) 4230.

Carlton Lodge, H, x *Carlton Hill, EX8 2AJ.* ✆ (0395) 263314. C. ⇔ 6 bedrs, 4 bps, 1 ba, Dgs. ▣ CH, Dgs, CP, CF, 1 st. **£** BB £11–£12·50, DB £22–£25, WT (b) £96, (c) £70, ▣, Bk £2, D £18.

Clinton House, G, z (Unl), *41 Morton Rd, EX8 1BA.* ✆ (0395) 271969. C 5. ⇔ 8 bedrs, 2 ba. ▣ ch, TV, 0 st. **£** BB £8, DB £16, WT (c) £51, DT (b) £11, ▣.

Dawsons, G, z (Temp), *8 Morton Rd, EX8 1AZ.* ✆ (0395) 72321.

Dolphin, PH, x (RI), *4 Morton Rd, EX8 1AZ.* ✆ (0395) 263832. C. ⊷ 27 bedrs, 16 bp, 11 bps, 4 sh, 3 ba, TV, Dgs. ✗ a l c. ⚑ CH, TV, CP 6, CF, 4 BGf. £ BB £7–£11, DB £14–£22, WT £56–£76, DT £9–£11, ②.
Redcliff Court, PH, z (RI), *4 Cyprus Rd, EX8 2DZ.* ✆ (0395) 3363.

Rescue Service: Brixington Service Station, Churchill Rd. ✆ (0395) 72976. Carlton Garage, 27 Rolle Rd. ✆ (0395) 263524.
Highfield Coachworks, Dinan Way Industrial Estate, off Salterton Rd. ✆ (0395) 263381.
Leese's Garage, 46 Park Rd. ✆ (0395) 263791.
Miller & Son (Exmouth) Ltd, Strand Garage. ✆ (0395) 72893.
Palmers Garage (Exmouth) Ltd, Withycombe Village Rd. ✆ (0395) 77633.
Richards and Sons, Victoria Way. ✆ (0395) 266375.

EYE Cambridgeshire. Map 23F
Pop 3,000. Peterborough 4, London 87, Spalding 14, Wisbech 17.
EC Wed, Sat. **Golf** Milton Peterborough 18h. **See** Church.

Rescue Service: Barron, C C, 17 High St. ✆ Peterborough (0733) 222293.

EYE Suffolk. Map 16D
Pop 1,650. Colchester 38, London 94, Bury St Edmunds 23, East Dereham 31, Great Yarmouth 36, Ipswich 21, Lowestoft 32, Saxmundham 19, Scole 4, Stowmarket 10, Swaffham 30, Thetford 21.
EC Tue. **Golf** Diss 9h. **See** Church with notable flintwork.

Rescue Service: Roy Humphrey, Yaxley Garage, Yaxley. ✆ Mellis (037 983) 224.

EYNSFORD Kent. Map 7B
Pop 3,200. Sidcup 7½, London 20, M20/ M25 Motorway 2½, Bromley 11, Croydon 16, Dartford 6½, Dartford–Purfleet Tunnel 9½, Maidstone 18, Purley 17, Rochester 16, Sevenoaks 7½, Westerham 11.
EC Wed. **Golf** Lullingstone Park 18h. **See** Norm and EE Church, Castle ruins, Tudor Cottages. At Lullingstone—Roman Villa.

★**Castle**, *High St, DA4 0AB.*
✆ Farningham (0322) 863162.

FAILAND Avon. Map 5A
Bristol 5, London 118, Avonmouth 2, Clevedon 8, M5 Motorway 6½, Weston-super-Mare 16. **Golf** Long Ashton 18h.

★★★**M Redwood Lodge & Country Club.** *Beggar Bush La, Failand, nr Bristol, BS8 3TG.* ✆ Long Ashton (0272) 393901. RS Xmas & New Year. C. ⊷ 72 bedrs, 72 bp, ns, TV. ✗ mc, at, LD 9.45. ⚑ N, CH, Dgs, CP 1000, Ac, sp, tc, sc, sb, sol, gym, con 200, CF, 30 BG f, 4 st. £ BB £35, DB £42, DT fr £50·75, WB, ①, Bk £4·50, L £6·50, D £9·25, cc 1 2 3 5 6, Dep b.

FAIRFORD Gloucestershire. Map 14E
Pop 2,308. Faringdon 10, London 80, Burford 13, Cirencester 9, Swindon 15.
EC Thur. **Golf** Cirencester 18h. **See** Perp St Mary's Church.

★**Hyperion House** (R), *London St, GL7 4AH.* ✆ Cirencester (0285) 712349. C. ⊷ 24 bedrs, 21 bp, 2 ba, TV, Dgs. ✗ mc, at, LD 8. ⚑ CH, TV, CP 50, CF, 2 BGf. £ BB fr

---

£17·50, DB fr £29, WT, £147, DBB fr £22, WB, ①, Bk £3·75, D £7·95, cc 1 2 3 5 6.

Rescue Service: H M Auto Bodies (Cricklade) Ltd, London Rd Garage, London Rd. ✆ Cirencester (0285) 713365.

FAIRLIGHT East Sussex. Map 10E
Pop 1,420. Hastings 3, London 66, Battle 9, Rye 7, Tunbridge Wells 30.
See Church tower. Firehills country park. Cliff End.

Fairlight Hall, G, xy (Unl), *North Wing, Martineau Lane, TN35 5DR.* ✆ Pett (042 486) 3145.

FAKENHAM Norfolk. Map 16C
Pop 5,550. Swaffham 16, London 113, Cromer 22, East Dereham 12, King's Lynn 22, Norwich 26.
EC Wed. **MD** Thur. **Golf** Fakenham 9h.
See Parish Church (fine masonry, windows, etc), Walsingham RC Slipper Chapel at Houghton St Giles 3½ m N. Walsingham Abbey ruins 4½ m N.

Rescue Service: Carley Motors Ltd, Norwich Rd. ✆ (0328) 2251.

FALFIELD Avon. Map 13F
Pop 657. Tetbury 15, London 114, Bath 23, Bristol 16, Chepstow 14, Chippenham 23, Gloucester 19.
Golf Cotswold Edge 18h.

■◆★★**Park**, *GL12 8DR.* ✆ (0454) 260550. C. ⊷ 10 bedrs, 4 bp, 2 bps, 2 ba, TV, Dgs. ⚑ ch, Dgs, CP 100, Ac, con 30, CF, 0 st. £ BB fr £26·50, DB fr £34, WB, ①, Bk £3·25, L £9·50, D £10·50, cc 1 2 3 5 6

FALMOUTH Cornwall. Map 2F
Pop 18,000. Truro 11, London 266, Helston 13, Redruth 10.
EC Wed. (Win) **Golf** Falmouth 18h. **See** Church (17th cent), Pendennis Castle, Arwenack Manor ruins, Jacob's Ladder (111 steps), St Mawes Castle 1½ m E, Penjerrick Garden at Budock Water 2 m SW, Glendurgan grounds and gardens 4 m SW.
ℹ Town Hall, The Moor. ✆ Falmouth (0326) 312300.

■★★★**Bay**, *Cliff Rd, TR11 4NU.* ✆ (0326) 312094. Open Apr–Oct. ⊷ 36 bedrs, 36 bp, TV, Dgs. ✗ mc, at, LD 9. ⚑ Lt, N, CH, Dgs, CP 60, Ac, sb, con 70, CF. £ BB £18·50–£23, DB £37·50–£46, WT £162–£195, DBB £26–£31, WB, ①, L £4·85, D £10·85, cc 1 2 3 5 6.
■★★★**Falmouth**, *Cliff Rd, TR11 4NZ.* ✆ (0326) 312671. Closed Xmas–New Year. C. ⊷ 73 bedrs, 73 bp, TV. ✗ mc, at, LD 9. ⚑ Lt, N, CH, Dgs, CP 100, Ac, sp, con 200, CF, 4 st. £ BB £20–£30·25, DB £40–£60·50, DBB £28–£38·50, L £4·85, D £10·50, cc 1 2 3 5 6, Dep.
■★★★**Falmouth Beach**, *Seafront, TR11 4NA.* ✆ (0326) 318084. Open Mar–Oct & Xmas–New Year. C. ⊷ 67 bedrs, 48 bp, 19 bps, TV, Dgs. ✗ mc, at, LD 9.30. ⚑ Lt, N, CH, Dgs, CP 40, Ac, sp, ns, sb, sol, gym, con 120, CF, 5 BGf, 0 st. £ WB, Bk £4, L £1·50, D £9, cc 1 2 3 5, Dep.
★★★**Green Bank**, *TR11 2SR.* ✆ (0326) 312440. Closed Jan. C. ⊷ 40 bedrs, 35 bp, 5 bps, 1 ba, TV, Dgs. ✗ mc, at, LD 10. ⚑ Lt, N, CH, Dgs, CP 45, G 30, Ac, CF, 5 st. £ BB £25–£30·50, DB £42·50–£51·50, DBB £26–£36·50, WB, ①, Bk £5, D £10, cc 1 2 3 5, Dep b.▲

★★★**Green Lawns** (R), *Western Ter, TR11 4EW.* ✆ (0326) 312734. C. ⊷ 43 bedrs, 36 bp, 3 bps, 1 sh, 1 ba, TV, Dgs. ✗ a l c, mc, at, LD 10. ⚑ N, CH, CP 60, sp, gc, tc, sc, sb, sol, gym, con 100, CF, 11 BGf, 1 st, Dis. £ BB £12–£27, DB £20–£40, DBB £19–£36, WB, ②, Bk £3, D £8·50, cc 1 2 3 4 5 6.▲
★★★**Gyllyngdune**, *Melvill Rd, TR11 4AR.* ✆ (0326) 312978. C. ⊷ 35 bedrs, 30 bp, 1 ba, TV, Dgs. ✗ a l c, mc, at, LD 9. ⚑ N, CH, CP 15, G 4, Ac, sp, sb, sol, gym, con 50, CF, 5 BGf, 1 st, Dis. £ BB £14·50–£19·50, DB £29–£39, DBB £19·50–£25·50, WB, ②, Bk £2·50, L £4, D £7, cc 1 2 3 5 6, Dep a.
■◆★★**Meudon** (R), *Maenporth Road, TR11 5HT.* ✆ (0326) 250541. C. ⊷ 30 bedrs, 30 bp, 2 ba, TV, Dgs. ✗ a l c, mc, at, LD 9. ⚑ N, CH, Dgs, CP 90, sp, con 80, CF, 17 BGf, 1 st. £ BB £22–£36, DB £44–£68, DBB £30–£42, WB, ②, Bk £5, L £7, D £10, cc 1 2 3 5.▲
■◆★★★**Penmere Manor** (R), *Mongleath Rd, TR11 4PN.* ✆ (0326) 314545. C. ⊷ 27 bedrs, 24 bp, 3 bps, annexe 2 bedrs, 2 bp, TV, Dgs. ✗ mc, at, LD 8.30. ⚑ CH, ns, CP 40, sp, con, CF, 12 BGf, 1 st, Dis. £ BB £22·50–£26·50, DB £38–£45, WT £160–£196, DBB £30·50–£34·50, WB, Bk £3·50, D £8, cc 1 2 3 5 6.
★★★**Royal Duchy**, *Cliff Rd, TR11 4NX.* ✆ (0326) 313042. C. ⊷ 44 bedrs, 39 bp, 1 bps, 2 ba, TV, Dgs. ✗ a l c, mc, at, LD 8·45. ⚑ Lt, N, CH, TV, CP 50, Ac, con 75, CF, 1 st. £ cc 1 2 3 5, Dep a.
★★★**St Michaels**, *Gyllyngvase Beach, Sea Front, TR11 4ND.* ✆ (0326) 312707. C. ⊷ 62 bedrs, 47 bp, 15 bps, TV, Dgs. ✗ a l c, mc, at, LD 10.30. ⚑ N, CH, TV, sp, sb, sol, gym, con 100, CF, 17 BGf, 7st. £ BB £21·50–£28·50, DB £38–£51, DBB £29–£36, ②, Bk £5·75, D £10·25, cc 1 2 3 5 6, Dep.
■★★**Carthion** (R), *Cliff Rd, TR11 4BG.* ✆ (0326) 313669. Open Mar–Oct. C 10. ⊷ 14 bedrs, 10 bp, 4 bps, 2 ba, TV, Dgs. ✗ a l c, mc, at LD 8. ⚑ CH, ns, CP 18. £ BB £11·55–£17·35, DB £23·10–£34·70, DBB £17·85–£23·65, WB, ②, Bk £3·75, D £7·75, cc 1 2 3 5, Dep a.
■★★**Crill House** (R), *Golden Bank, TR11 5BL.* ✆ (0326) 312994. Open Mar–Oct. C. ⊷ 11 bedrs, 10 bp, 1 bps, 1 ba, TV, Dgs. ✗ a l c, mc, at, LD 8. ⚑ CH, Dgs, CP 22, U 1, sp, CF, 4 st. £ BB £14–£22, DB £28–£44, ②, Bk £3·50, L £1, D £6, cc 1 3.
■★★**Madeira**, *Cliff Rd, TR11 4NY.* ✆ (0326) 313531. C. ⊷ 49 bedrs, 16 bp, 33 bps, 2 ba, TV, Dgs. ✗ mc, at, LD 8·15. ⚑ Lt, N, CH, Dgs, ns, CP 10, Ac, CF, 7 BGf, 4 st. £ Bk £3·50, D £7, cc 1 2 3, Dep a.
■★★**Melville** (R), *Sea View Rd, TR11 4NL.* ✆ (0326) 312134. ⊷ 20 bedrs, 3 bp, 12 bps, 2 ba, TV, Dgs. ✗ mc, at, LD 8. ⚑ ch, TV, CP 20, U 10, Ac, con 30, CF, 1 BGf, 0 st, Dis. £ BB £13–£16, DB £24–£28, DBB £21–£27, WB, ①, Bk £3·95, L £4·25, D £7·45, Dep a.
★★**Pendower** (R), *Sea View Rd, TR11 4EF.* ✆ (0326) 312108. C. ⊷ 29 bedrs, 12 bp, 6 bps, 11 sh, 3 ba, TV, Dgs. ✗ mc, at, LD 7.30. ⚑ CH, TV, CP 25, Ac, sp, sb, sol, con 50, CF, 9 BGf, 4 st. £ BB £12·75–£15·50, DB £24–£26, DBB fr £14, WB, Bk £4·50, L £4·75, D £6·50, cc 1 3.▲
■★★**Somerdale** (R), *Sea View Rd, TR11 4EF.* ✆ (0326) 312566. Closed Jan–Feb. ⊷ 18 bedrs, 10 bp, 2 bps, 2 ba, TV. ✗ mc, at, LD 9.30. ⚑ CH, CP 13, Ac, con 20, CF, 0 st. £ BB £12–£16, DB £24–£32, WT £131–

£163, DT £21·75–£24·75, DBB £18·75–
£23·75, WB, ☑, Bk £4·50, L £3, D £7·75,
cc 1 2 3 5 6, Dep.

◼★**Suncourt** (Rl), *Boscawen Rd, TR11
4EL.* ✆ (0326) 312886.

◼★**Tresillian House** (R), *Stracey Rd,
TR11 4DW.* ✆ (0326) 312425. C. ⊶ 12
bedrs, 5 bp, 7 bps, TV. ✘ mc, at, LD 7.30.
🅐 ch, TV, ns, CP 8, CF, £ BB £12·15–
£14·15, DB £24·30–£28·30, DBB £14·15–
£16·20, ☑, Bk £2·50, L £2, D £6·50, Dep.

Bedruthan, G, z (Rl), *Sea Front, Castle
Dr, TR11 4NF.* ✆ (0326) 311028. C. ⊶ 7
bedrs, 1 bps, 6 sh, 2 ba. 🅐 CH, TV, CP 4,
CF, 1 BGf, 12 st. £ BB £7·50–£8, DB £15–
£16, WT (b) £75–£78, (c) £50–£52, DT (b)
£11·50–£12, ☑, Bk £2, D £4.

Chellowdene, G, x, *Gyllyngvase Hill,
TR11 4DN.* ✆ (0326) 314950. Open May–
Oct. C 12. ⊶ 6 bedrs, 2 sh, 1 ba. 🅐 ch, TV,
ns, CP 6. £ BB £8–£9, DB £15–£18, WT (b)
£74–£84, DT (b) £11–£12·50, ☑.

Cotswold House, PH, z (Rl), *49 Melvill
Rd, TR11 4DF.* ✆ (0326) 312077. C 10.
⊶ 11 bedrs, 2 bp, 3 sh, 2 ba. 🅐 ch, TV, CP
12. £ BB £7·95–£10·50, DB £15·90–£21,
WT (b) £79–£85, DT (b) £12·95–£14, ☑, D
£5.

Dolvean, PH, z (Unl), *50 Melvill Rd,
TR11 4DQ.* ✆ (0326) 313658. C 3. ⊶ 14
bedrs, 2 bp, 4 ba, TV, Dgs. 🅐 TV, ns, CP 18,
U 1, G 3, CF, 4 BGf, 4 st. £ BB £10·81–
£14·45, DB £20·12–£30·50, WT (b)
£72·45–£96·60, DT (b) £12·08–£16·10, ☑,
cc 1.

Dunmede, G, z (Rl), *11 Melvill Rd, TR11
4AS.* ✆ (0326) 313429. C 5. ⊶ 5 bedrs, 1
ba, Dgs. 🅐 CH, TV, CP 3. £ BB £6–£7, DB
£12–£14, DT (b) £9·50–£10·50, ☑, D
£3·50.

Gyllyngvase House, PH, z (Rl),
Gyllyngvase Rd, TR11 4DJ. ✆ (0326)
312956.▲

Hawthorne Dene, PH, z (Rl), *12
Pennance Rd, TR11 4EA.* ✆ (0326)
311427. Closed Dec. C. ⊶ 10 bedrs, 10
bps. 🅐 CH, TV, CP 10, 6 st. £ BB £9–£12,
DB £18–£24, WT (b) £87–£100, DT (b)
£12·50–£14·50, ☑.

Headlands, PH, z (Unl), *4 Avenue Rd,
TR11 4AZ.* ✆ (0326) 311141.

Maenheere, H, z, *3 Grove Place, TR11
4AU.* ✆ (0326) 312009. C. ⊶ 18 bedrs, 6
bps, 3 sh, 3 ba, TV, Dgs.🅐 ch, TV, CF, 4
BGf. £ BB £10·89–£14·75, DB £21·78–
£28·30, WT (c) £69·52–£84·21, DT (b)
£14·47–£17·71, ☑, Bk £1·50, D £4·50,
cc 1 3.

Maskee House, G, z (Unl), *4 Spernen
Wyn Rd, TR11 4EH.* ✆ (0326) 311783.

Milton House, G, z (Unl), *33 Melvill Rd,
TR11 4AR.* ✆ (0326) 314390. C. ⊶ 6
bedrs, 1 ba, Dgs. 🅐 ch, TV, Dgs, CP 6, CF, 6
st. £ BB £7–£8, DB £14–£16, WT (b) £60–
£73, DT (b) £9–£10·50, ☑.

Penty Bryn, PH, z (Rl), *10 Melvill Rd,
TR11 4AS.* ✆ (0326) 314988. Open Feb–
Oct. C 5. ⊶ 7 bedrs, 3 bps, 1 sh, 1 ba, Dgs.
🅐 CH, TV, CP 2. £ BB £7·50–£8·50, DB
£15–£20, WT (b) £70–£87, DT (b) £11–
£13, ☑, D £4.

Rathgowry, H, x (Rl), *Gyllyngvase Hill,
TR11 4DN.* ✆ (0326) 313482. C.
⊶ 9 bedrs, 2 bp, 6 bps, 1 ba, Dgs. 🅐 CH,
TV, CP 9, CF, 2 st. £ BB £9·90–£12·65, DB
£19·80–£25·30, WT (b) £73·60–£97·75,
DT (b) £12·19–£14·95, ☑.

Tregenna, G, z (Rl), *28 Melvill Rd, TR11
4AR.* ✆ (0326) 313881. C. ⊶ 6 bedrs, 1
ba, Dgs. 🅐 CH, TV, Dgs, CP 6, CF, £ BB £7–

£8, DB £14–£16, WT (b) fr £70, DT (b)
£10·50–£11·50, ☑.

Trevaylor, G, y (Rl), *8 Pennance Rd,
TR11 4EA.* ✆ (0326) 313041. Open Apr–
Sep. C 2. ⊶ 6 bedrs, 3 bps, 1 sh, 2 ba.
🅐 CH, TV, CP 6. £ DB £14–£18, WT (b)
£68·25–£80·50, DT (b) £9·75–£11·50, ☑.

Wentworth, G, z (Unl), *10 Gyllyngvase
Ter, TR11 4DL.* ✆ (0326) 314337. Open
Mar–Oct. C 3. ⊶ 6 bedrs, 1 ba, Dgs. 🅐 TV,
Dgs, CF, 5 st. £ BB £6–£7, DB £12–£14,
WT (b) £63–£72, DT (b) £9–£10·25, ☑.

Wickham, G, z (Unl), *21 Gyllyngvase Ter,
TR11 4DL.* ✆ (0326) 311140. Open Apr–
Oct. C 3. ⊶ 10 bedrs, 2 ba. 🅐 ch, TV, CP 3,
CF. £ BB £7·50–£8·50, DB £15–£17, WT
£70–£80, DT £10·50–£12·50, ☑.

Winnick, G, z, *17 Castle Dr, TR11 4NF.*
✆ (0326) 313913. Open Mar–Oct. C 12.
⊶ 4 bedrs, 1 ba. 🅐 CH, TV, ns, CP 4. £ BB
£8, DB £16, WT (c) £52·50, ☑.

Repairers: Dales of Falmouth,
Ponsharden. ✆ (0326) 72011.
J D F Motors Ltd, Dracaena Av. ✆ (0326)
311616.
Riders Garages Ltd, 4 Berkeley Vale.
✆ (0326) 316333.
Rescue Service: Boslowick Garage,
Boslowick Rd, Swanvale. ✆ (0326)
312765.
Dell Garage, Avenue Rd. ✆ (0326)
312280.
Falmouth Coachworks Ltd, Penwerris
Lane. ✆ (0326) 314963.
Parkside Garage Ltd, Kimberley Park Rd.
✆ (0326) 312449.
Riders Garages Ltd, The Moor. ✆ (0326)
312316.

FAREHAM Hampshire. Map 6F
Pop 84,200. Cosham 5, London 72, M27
Motorway 1, Alton 24, Portsmouth 9,
Romsey 20, Southampton 12, Winchester
19.
EC Wed. **MD** Mon. **Golf** Lee-on-the-
Solent 18h. **See** St Peter's Church.
Titchfield Abbey 2 m W, Portchester
Castle, Church and Roman Fort 3 m E,
Titchfield Abbey 2 m W, Bishop's Waltham
Palace (ruins) 7 m N.
🛈 6 West Quay House, West St.
✆ Fareham (0329) 285432.

★★**Red Lion,** *East St, PO16 0BP.*
✆ (0329) 239611. C. ⊶ 33 bedrs, 33 bp,
TV. ✘ a l c, mc. 🅐 CH, TV, CP 100, Ac, con
30, CF, 1 st. £ BB fr £35, DB fr £45, WB, ☑,
Bk £4, L £6, D £8, cc 1 2 3 5.

★**Maylings Manor** (R), *11a Highlands
Rd, PO16 7XJ.* ✆ (0329) 286451. C. ⊶ 30
bedrs, 30 bp, 10 bps, 2 ba, TV, Dgs. ✘ a l c,
mc, at, LD 9.45. 🅐 CH, TV, CP 85, Ac, con
150, CF, 1 st. £ BB fr £16·95, DB fr £26,
DBB fr £24·95, WB, ☑, Bk £2, L £3·20, D
£5, cc 1 2 3 5, Dep a.

Seven Sevens, PH, x (Unl), *Hillhead Rd,
Hillhead, PO14 3JH* ✆ Stubbington
(0329) 662408.

White Cockade, H, z (R), *207 West St,
PO16 0EN.* ✆ (0329) 232697. Closed 24
Dec–2 Jan. C. ⊶ 5 bedrs, 3 ba, TV.
✘ a l c. 🅐 ch, TV, CP 10, CF, 3 st. £ BB fr
£16, DB fr £23, WT fr £96, ☑, Bk £4·50, L
£4, D £4·50, cc 1 2 3 5.

Rescue Service: A & D Auto Repair Ltd,
Unit 6, Bridge Industries, Broadcut,
Wallington. ✆ (0329) 289643.
Paul Huxford (AE) Ltd, Newgate La.
✆ (0329) 282811.

FARINGDON Oxfordshire. Map 14F
Pop 5,107. Wantage 9, London 70,
Burford 12, Cirencester 18, Marlborough
20, Oxford 17, Swindon 12.
EC Thur. **MD** Tue. **Golf** Bremhill Park,
Shrivenham 18h. **See** Gothic Church, old
arcaded Town Hall (now Library), Folly
Tower, Pusey House Gardens, Buscot
Park 3 m NW, Radcot Bridge (13th cent),
Uffington Castle (Iron Age Camp) 6 m S.
🚗 Car Park, Southampton St.

★★**Bell,** *Market Pl, SN7 7HP.* ✆ (0367)
20534. C. ⊶ 11 bedrs, 6 bp, 4 bps, 1 sh, 1
ba, TV, Dgs. ✘ a l c, mc, at, LD 9.30. 🅐 CH,
TV, CP 12, G 3, Ac, con 10, CF, 0 st. £ Bk
£3·60, L £6·55, D £8·75, cc 1 2 3 5.

★**Salutation,** *Market Pl, SN7 7HL.*
✆ (0367) 20536. C. ⊶ 7 bedrs, 1 bps, 1 ba,
TV, Dgs. ✘ mc, LD 9.30. 🅐 CH, TV, Dgs,
CP 4, U 1, G 2, Ac, con 60, CF, 1 Bgf, 0 st.
£ BB £17·25–£19·55, DB £23–£31, WT
£150, DT £27, DBB £22–£25, WB, ☑, Bk
£3, L £5, D £6, cc 2 3.

Rescue Service: All Saints Service
Station, Church St. ✆ (0367) 22070.

FARLINGTON Hampshire. M. Area 6F.
2 m W of Havant, M27 Motorway 2½,
Petersfield 14, London 67, Chichester 12,
Southampton 20, Portsmouth 6.
See Fort Widley.

Rescue Service: Abcar Auto Engineers,
Jet Service Station, Fitzherbert Rd.
✆ Cosham (0249) 324035.

FARNBOROUGH Hampshire. Map 7A
Pop 80,300. Bagshot 7, London 34, M3
Motorway 3, Basingstoke 18, Farnham 5½,
Guildford 11, Henley-on-Thames 22,
Reading 19, Woking 10.
EC Wed. **MD** Tue. **Golf** Southwood 9h.
See St Michael's Abbey and Benedictine
Monastery, 12th cent Parish Church, 19th
cent RC Church, Imperial Mausoleum.
🛈 Public Library, Pinehurst Av.
✆ Farnborough (0252) 513838.

★★★**M Queen's,** *Farnborough Rd, GU14
6AZ.* ✆ (0252) 545051. C. ⊶ 85 bedrs, 80
bp, 2 ba, TV, Dgs. ✘ a l c, mc, at, LD 10.
🅐 N, CH, Dgs, CP 200, Ac, con 140, CF, 2
st. £ BB £22–£39·50, DB £27–£46, WB, ☑,
Bk £4·50, L £6·25, D £6·25, cc 1 2 3 4 5 6,
Dep b.

MC Repairer: Motor Cycle City Sales, 209
Lynchford Rd. ✆ (0252) 513231.

FARNHAM Surrey. Map 6D
Pop 35,160. Guildford 10, London 38,
Alton 9½, Bagshot 12, Basingstoke 15,
Henley-on-Thames 28, Hindhead 8½,
Horsham 27, Petersfield 17, Reading 25,
Woking 14.
EC Wed. **Golf** Farnham 9h. **See** 12th cent
Castle Keep, 14th cent Church, "The
William Cobbett" (birthplace of William
Cobbett 1762–1835) and formerly
known as the Jolly Farmer Inn, Wilmer
House Museum—Queen Anne House of
great merit, Waverley Abbey (Cistercian
monastery ruins), Ridgway House Farm,
Runwick (rare sheep).
🛈 Locality Office, South St, Godalming.
✆ Godalming (048 68) 4104.

★★★**Bush,** *The Borough, GU9 7NN.*
✆ (0252) 715237. C. ⊶ 66 bedrs, 58 bp, 3
bps, 3 ba, TV, Dgs. ✘ a l c, mc, at, LD 9.45.
🅐 N, Dgs, CP 70, Ac, con 50, CF. £ BB
£39·50, DB £47·50, DBB £44·50–£55, WB,

---

① , Bk £4·50, L £7·50, D £7·50, cc 1 2 3 5 6,
Dep b.
★★★**Frensham Pond,** *Bacon Road,*
Churt, GU10 2QD. ✆ Frensham (025 125)
3175. C. ◄ 7 bedrs, 7 bp, annexe 12 bedrs,
12 bp, TV. ✗ a l c, mc, LD 9.30. ⓐ N, CH,
CP 100, con, CF, 12 BGf. £ BB £36–£40,
DB £46–£70, WB, ①, Bk £4·50, L £11·50, D
£15, cc 1 2 3 5 6, Dep b.
★★**Bishop's Table,** *27 West St, GU9*
7DR. ✆ (0252) 715545. C. ◄ 7 bedrs, 7
bp, annexe 9 bedrs, 3 bp, 4 bps, 1 ba, TV,
Dgs. ✗ a l c, mc, at, LD 9.30. ⓐ CH, Dgs,
Ac, con 10, CF, 6 BGf, 2 st. £ BB £28·50–
£30, DB £40, WB, ①, Bk £3·50, L £8, D £8,
cc 1 2 3 5.
◨★★**Pride of the Valley,** *Jumps Rd,*
GU10 2LE. ✆ Hindhead (042 873) 5799.
◨◗★★**Trevena House,** (R), *Alton Rd,*
GU10 5ER. ✆ (0252) 716908. Closed
Xmas & 1st 2 weeks Jan. C. ◄ 10 bedrs,
17 bp, 2 bps, TV. ✗ at, LD 9.15. ⓐ CH, CP
30, sp, tc, sb, con 30, CF. £ BB £28, Dgs,
£35, WB, ①, Bk £2·95, D £10, cc 1 2 3 5 6,
Dep.

FARNWORTH Gtr Manchester
(Lancashire). Map 20A
Pop 24,000. Walkden 2, London 193,
Bolton 2½, Bury 6½, Chorley 14,
Manchester 8½, Oldham 14, Wigan 10.
EC Wed. **MD** Mon, Fri, Sat. **Golf** Bolton
Municipal 18h.

Repairer: Marland, A G & Sons Ltd,
Parkside Motor Co, Bolton Rd. ✆ (0204)
72871.

FAR SAWREY Cumbria. Map 26D
M6 Motorway 29, London 269, Coniston
6, Windermere 11 (Fy 3).
Golf Windermere 18h. **See** Hill Top (NT),
Courthouse (Museum).

◨★★**Sawrey,** *LA22 OLQ.* ✆ Windermere
(096 62) 3425. RS Xmas. C. ◄ 18 bedrs, 3
bp, 4 ba, TV, Dgs. ✗ mc, LD 8·45. ⓐ ch, TV,
Dgs, CP 30, con 35, CF, 5 BGf, 0 st, Dis.
£ BB £11·95–£14·50, DB £23·90–£27,
DBB £15–£18·50, WB, ②, Bk £2·75, L
£4·90, D £7·50, Dep.
Sawrey House, PH, xy (R), *Far Sawrey,*
LA22 OLF. ✆ Hawkshead (058 05) 387.
West Vale, G, *LA22 OLQ.* ✆ Windermere
(096 62) 2817.

FAUGH Cumbria
See CARLISLE.

FAVERSHAM Kent. Map 10C
Pop 23,500. Rochester 18, London 49,
Ashford 13, Canterbury 11, Maidstone 20,
Margate 24, Hawkhurst 30.
EC Thur. **MD** Wed, Fri, Sat. **Golf** Belmont
18h. **See** Town Hall on pillars, restored
period houses in Abbey St, Parish Church,
Davington Priory, Globe House (formerly
Globe Inn), 16th cent Queen Elizabeth
Grammar School, 15th cent Maison Dieu
1 m SW.
🛈 Fleur de Lis Heritage Centre, Preston
St. ✆ Faversham (0795) 534542.

Rescue Service: G & E Newbery & Son
(Faversham) Ltd, Ospringe Road Garage,
Ospringe Rd. ✆ (0795) 534566.

FAYGATE West Sussex. Map 7C
Crawley 3½, London 35, Brighton 23,
Dorking 13, Guildford 19, Haywards
Heath 17, Horsham 3½, Lewes 25, Redhill
13, Reigate 13.
EC Wed. **Golf** Mannings Heath 18h.

Rescue Service: Thornley Engineering Co,
Crawley Rd. ✆ (029 383) 249.

FEATHERSTONE Staffordshire. M. Area
21E
Walsall 7, London 127, Wolverhampton 5,
Cannock 4.

Rescue Service: Hilton Service Station,
Cannock Rd. ✆ Wolverhampton (0902)
732566.

FELIXSTOWE Suffolk. Map 17A
Pop 20,858. Ipswich 12, London 86,
Aldeburgh 29, Saxmundham 25, Scole 36.
EC Wed. **MD** Thur, Sun. **Golf** Felixstowe
Ferry 18h. **See** St Peter's Church, St
Andrew's Church is modern.
🛈 91 Undercliff Road West. ✆ Felixstowe
(039 42) 2122.

★★★★**Orwell Moat House,** *Hamilton*
Rd, IP11 7DX. ✆ (0394) 285511. C. ◄ 58
bedrs, 58 bp, 1 ba, TV, Dgs. ✗ a l c, mc, at,
LD 9·45. ⓐ Lt, N, CH, Dgs, CP 200, G 15,
Ac, con 200, CF, 0 st. £ BB £38–£42, DB
£55–£60, WT £165, WB, ①, Bk £4·50, L
£7·50, D £9, cc 1 2 3 5 6.
★★**De Novo,** *Orwell Rd, IP11 7PC.*
✆ (0394) 278441. C. ◄ 26 bedrs, 9 bp, 5
ba, TV, Dgs. ✗ a l c, LD 9.15. ⓐ CH, TV,
Dgs, CP 35, Ac, con 50, CF, 3 BGf, 1 st.
£ BB £19–£21, DB £27–£29, WT £224,
DBB £34·75–£36·75, Bk £3·75, L £5, D
£6·50, cc 1 2 3 5.
★★**Marlborough,** *Sea Rd, IP11 8BJ.*
✆ (0394) 285621. C. ◄ 50 bedrs, 37 bp, 3
ba, TV, Dgs. ✗ a l c, mc, at, LD 10. ⓐ Lt, N,
ch, TV, CP 25, Ac, con 100, CF, 0 st. £ BB
£19–£25, DB £28–£34, DBB £24·95–
£30·95, WB, ①, Bk £3·25, L £4·75, D £5·75,
cc 1 2 3 5, Dep b.
★★**North Sea,** *Sea Rd, IP11 8AU.*
✆ (0394) 282103. C. ◄ 25 bedrs, 10 bp, 2
bps, 6 ba, TV, Dgs. ✗ a l c, LD 9.30. ⓐ N,
CH, TV, Dgs, CP 16, Ac, con 50, CF, 1 st.
£ BB £20–£24, DB £27–£30, WT £158·55,
DT £24, DBB £19–25–£20·75, ①, Bk £3·50,
L £5·25, D £6·25, cc 1, Dep.
★★**Waverley,** *Wolsey Gdns, IP11 7DF.*
✆ (0394) 282811▲.
◨★**Cavendish,** *Sea Rd, IP11 8DP.*
✆ (0394) 282696. C. ◄ 14 bedrs, 3 ba,
Dgs. ✗ mc, LD 8. ⓐ Lt, CH, TV, CP 150,
Ac, con 200, CF, 2 st. £ BB £10–£14, DB
£20–£24, DBB £16–£18, ①, Bk £2, D £7,
Dep a.

Rescue Service: French's Garage, 31
Undercliff Rd West. ✆ (0394) 286339.

FELSTED Essex. Map 17F
Pop 2,507. Chelmsford 10, London 43,
Braintree 4½, Dunmow 4½.
Golf Braintree 18h. **See** Public School,
founded 16th cent, interesting old Parish
church, 16th cent Almshouses and
Chapel, 17th cent Vicarage.

Rescue Service: Woodley, L H, The
Garage. ✆ Gt Dunmow (0371) 820347.

FELTHAM Greater London (Middx).
M. Area 7A
3 m SW of Hounslow. Pop 55,000.
Brentford and Chiswick 7, London 13,
Ealing 13, Harrow 10, Kingston upon
Thames 6, Leatherhead 13, Richmond-
upon-Thames 5½, Ripley 13, Slough 10,
Staines 5, Uxbridge 9, Weybridge 7,
Windsor 10.
EC Wed.

Repairer: Fern Automobiles Ltd, Adj
Heron Service Station, Hounslow Rd.
✆ 01-890 0395.

FENNY BRIDGES Devon. Map 4F
Pop 300. Honiton 3, London 156, Exeter
13, Tiverton 20.
Golf Honiton 9h.

★**Fenny Bridges,** *EX14 0BQ.* ✆ Honiton
(0404) 850218. C. ◄ 6 bedrs, 2 ba, Dgs.
✗ a l c, mc, at, LD 9.30. ⓐ CH, TV, Dgs, CP
120, Ac, pf, CF, 0 st. £ BB £10, DB £18·50,
WB, ①, Bk £2·50, L £3·50, D £4·50,
cc 1 2 3 5 6, Dep a.

Rescue Service: Lanson Garage, Beacon.
✆ Honiton (0404) 850002.

FENTON Staffordshire.
See STOKE-ON-TRENT.

FERNDOWN Dorset. Maps 5F and 6E
Pop 15,474. Ringwood 6, London 99,
Blandford Forum 14, Bournemouth 7,
Dorchester 28, Lymington 20, Sandbanks
10, Shaftesbury 23, Wareham 15.
EC Wed. **Golf** Ferndown 18h. **See**
Church.

★★★★**Dormy,** *New Rd, BH22 8ES.*
✆ (0202) 872121.
Broadlands, H, y (R), *West Moors Rd,*
BH22 9SA. ✆ (0202) 877884. C. ◄ 17
bedrs, 4 bp, 3 bps, 2 ba, Dgs. ⓐ CH, TV,
Dgs, CP 15, CF. £ BB £12·50–£15, DB
£25–£30, WT (c) £80, DT (b) £17·75, ①, Bk
£3, D £5·25.

Repairer: Victoria Garage (Ferndown)
Ltd, Ringwood Rd. ✆ (0202) 872212.
Rescue Service: D C Mant, Colonial
Garage, 443 Wimborne Rd. ✆ (0202)
875802 & (0202) 871823.

FILEY North Yorkshire. Map 25A
Pop 5,480. Gt Driffield 21, London 213,
Bridlington 10, Malton 23, Pickering 22,
Scarborough 7½.
EC Wed. **Golf** Filey 18h. **See** St Oswald's
Church, old houses, extensive sands.
🛈 John St. ✆ Scarborough
(0723) 512204.

★★★**White Lodge,** *The Crescent, YO14*
9JX. ✆ Scarborough (0723) 514771. C.
◄ 21 bedrs, 16 bp, 3 bps, 2 sh, 3 ba, TV,
Dgs. ✗ a l c, mc, at, LD 8. ⓐ Lt, ch, CP 10,
Ac, con 60, CF, 3 st. £ BB £15–£19·40, DB
£32·20–£38·80, WB, ①, Bk £4, L £6, D
£8·50, cc 1 2 3 5 6, Dep a.
★★**Hylands,** *The Crescent, YO14 9JR.*
✆ Scarborough (0723) 512091. C. ◄ 47
bedrs, 9 bp, 9 bps, 7 ba. ✗ mc, at, LD 8.
ⓐ Lt, N, ch, Ac, con 40, CF, 4 st. £ BB £10–
£13, DB £20–£28, WT £130–£144, DT
£20–£24, DBB £16–£20, WB, ②, Bk £3, L
£4, D £6·50, cc 1 3 5 6.
Beach, PH, z (Rl), *The Beach, YO14 9LA.*
✆ Scarborough (0723) 513392. Closed
Nov. C 6. ◄ 23 bedrs, 1 bp, 5 bps, 3 ba,
Dgs. ⓐ CH, TV, CF. £ BB £11·50–£16·50,
DB £23–£31, WT (b) £193–£206·50, DT
(b) £13·50–£17·50, ①, Bk £2·95, L £2·50,
D £5·95, cc 1 3 5.
Southdown, H, x (Rl), *The Beach, YO14*
9LA. ✆ Scarborough (0723) 513392.

Rescue Service: Newtons Garage, South
Crescent Rd. ✆ Scarborough (0723)
512233.
Rosedale Garage, Hunmanby.
✆ Scarborough (0723) 890552.

FILLEIGH Devon. Map 4C
South Molton 4, London 184, Barnstaple
8, Holsworthy 28, Lynmouth 18,
Okehampton 26.

North Lodge, G, y (Unl), *EX32 0RE.*
☎ (059 86) 332. Open Mar–Oct. C. ⇄ 4
bedrs, 1 ba. ⌂ CH, Dgs, CP 4, CF. £ BB £7,
DB £14, WT (b) £53·20–£66·50, DT (b)
£9·50, ①.

FINCHINGFIELD Essex. Map 17E
Pop 1,900. Dunmow 9, London 46,
Bishop's Stortford 18, Braintree 9½,
Cambridge 25, Haverhill 9, Royston 25,
Sudbury 16.
EC Wed. **See** Church (Norman tower),
Guildhall, Museum, Windmill.

Repairer: Eastern Garage. ☎ Gt Dunmow
(0371) 810238.

FINDERN Derbyshire. Map 22F
Pop 1,755. Ashby-de-la-Zouch 11, London
124, Ashbourne 15, Burton-on-Trent 7,
Derby 5½, Loughborough 19, Melton
Mowbray 33, Uttoxeter 16.
EC Thur. **Golf** Mickleover 18h. **See**
Remains of Norman Chapel, Parish
Church, Village Green and old smithy.

Rescue Service: Archway Motors of
Findern Ltd, 14 Doles La. ☎ Burton (0283)
702378.

FITTLEWORTH West Sussex. Map 7C
Pop 888. Petworth 3, London 51,
Horsham 15, Pulborough 2½.
Golf West Sussex 18h. **See** Church 13th
cent.

★★Swan, *Lower St, RH20 1EN.* ☎ (079
882) 429.

FLAMBOROUGH Humberside. Map
25A
Bridlington 4½, London 206, Great Driffield
16, Scarborough 17.

⚑★★Timoneer Country Manor, *South
Landing, YO15 1AG.* ☎ (0262) 850219. C.
⇄ 10 bedrs, 5 bp, 5 bps, TV, Dgs. ✗ a l c,
mc, LD 9.45. ⌂ CH, Dgs, CP 150, G 10,
con, CF. £ BB £19·50–£21·50, DB £32–
£35, DBB £23·50–£28·50, WB,②, Bk £2·50,
D £6·50, cc 1 2 3 5 6, Dep b.

FLEET Hampshire. Map 6D
Pop 25,993. Bagshot 10, London 37, M3
Motorway 6½, Alton 12, Basingstoke 12,
Farnham 6, Guildford 14, Henley-on-
Thames 20, High Wycombe 28, Reading
15, Woking 14.
EC Wed. **MD** Sat. **Golf** North Hants 18h.
🛈 Fleet Service Area, M3 Motorway.
☎ (025 14) 21154.

★★★Lismoyne, *Church Rd, GU13
8NA.* ☎ (025 14) 28555. C. ⇄ 39 bedrs,
28 bp, 3 bps, 2 ba, TV, Dgs. ✗ a l c, mc, at,
LD 9·30. ⌂ N, CH, Dgs, CP 80, Ac, con
167, CF, 6 Bgf, 1 st, Dis. £ BB £22–£34. DB
£32–£40, WB, ①, Bk £3, L £5·50, D £6·35,
cc 1 2 3 5 6, Dep b.

Rescue Service: Ravenscroft Motors,
Fleet Service Area. ☎ (025 14) 7353.

FLEETWOOD Lancashire. Map 27C
Pop 30,000. Preston 22, London 223,
Blackpool 8½, Lancaster 25.
EC Wed. **MD** Tue, Fri. **Golf** Fleetwood
18h. **See** Fish dock and fish market
(permits to view from Docks Manager).
🛈 Marine Hall, Esplanade. ☎ Fleetwood
(039 17) 71141.

★★★North Euston, *Esplanade, FY7
6BN.* ☎ (039 17) 6525. C. ⇄ 57 bedrs, 33
bp, 5 bps, 11 ba, TV, Dgs. ✗ a l c, mc, at,
LD 9.30. ⌂ Lt, N, CH, CP 65, Ac, con 200,
CF, 1 st. £ BB £18–£20, DB £31–£35, DBB
£25·50–£27·50, WB, ②, Bk £3·75, L £4·50,
D £7·50, cc 1 2 3 5, Dep b.

Repairer: Lawton's Garage Ltd, Copse Rd.
☎ (039 17) 6511.
Rescue Service: Central Garage, Albany
Rd. ☎ (039 17) 3710.
P R Hutton, Victoria Street Garage,
Victoria St. ☎ (039 17) 6132.

FLIXTON Gtr Manchester (Lancs). Map
20B
Altrincham 6, London 186, Bolton 12,
Manchester 7, Warrington 11.

Rescue Service: Dyson Motors, 58
Woodsend Rd. ☎ 061-748 6946.

FLORE Northamptonshire. Map 14D
Pop 1,170. Towcester 8½, London 70,
Atherstone 34, Banbury 20, Daventry 5½,
Hinckley 27, Leicester 32, Luton 39,
Market Harborough 20, Northampton 7,
Rugby 14.
Golf Farthingstone 18h. **See** Watermill,
old houses.

Rescue Service: Green, P J & Co, 81 High
St. ☎ Weedon (0327) 40287.

FLUSHING Cornwall. Map 2F
Pop 800. Truro 9, London 255, Falmouth 5,
Redruth 9.
EC Wed. **Golf** Falmouth 18h.

Nankersey, PH, x (Rl), *St Peter's Rd,
TR11 5TP.* ☎ Falmouth (0326) 74471. C.
⇄ 7 bedrs, 2 ba. ⌂ ch, TV, 3 st. £ BB
£10·50–£11·50, DB £21–£23, WT (b)
£100–£108, (c) £66·50–£73·50, DT (b)
£17·50–£18·50, ①, Bk £3·50, D £7, cc 1 3.

FOLKESTONE Kent. Map 10D
RAC Port Office, *West Side Terminal,
Folkestone Harbour, CT20 1QG.*
☎ Folkestone (0303) 58560.
Pop 46,500. Ashford 16, London 71, M20
Motorway 2, Canterbury 16, Dover 7,
Margate 26, Rye 25, Tenterden 23.
See Plan, p. 210.
EC Wed. **MD** Thur, Sun. **P** See Plan. **Golf**
Sene Valley 18h. **See** Church of St Mary
and St Eanswythe, Kingsnorth Gdns, The
Leas, The Arts Centre (New Metropole),
Sports Centre (Radnor Park Av) with
extensive facilities, including artificial ski-
slope, Racecourse, Giant Sunday Market
(Rotunda Park).
🛈 Harbour St. ☎ Folkestone (0303)
58594.

★★★Burlington, *Earls Av, The Leas,
CT20 2HR.* ☎ (0303) 55301. C. ⇄ 57
bedrs, 57 bp, TV. ✗ a l c, mc, at, LD 9.15.
⌂ Lt, N, CH, CP 15, Ac, con 150, CF, 5 Bgf,
10 st. £ WB, Bk £3·50, L £7·75, D £9,
cc 1 2 3 5 6, Dep b.

★★★Clifton (TH), *The Leas, CT20 2EB.*
☎ (0303) 41231. C. ⇄ 62 bedrs, 35 bp, 1
bps, 11 ba, TV, Dgs. ✗ mc, at, LD 9. ⌂ Lt,
N, CH, Dgs, Ac, con 60, CF, 8 st. £ BB £24–
£31·50, DB £38·50–£49, WB, ①,
cc 1 2 3 4 5 6, Dep (Xmas).

★★Chilworth Court, *39 Earls Av, CT20
2HB.* ☎ (0303) 41583.
Argos, PH, z (Rl), *6 Marine Ter, CT20
1PZ.* ☎ (0303) 54309. C 3. ⇄ 9 bedrs, 3
ba. ⌂ CH, TV, CF. £ BB £9–£10, DB £17–

£20, WT £57·50–£65, DT £12·50–£13·50,
①, Bk £2·50, L £3, D £3·50.
Arundel, PH, z (Rl), *3 Clifton Rd,
CT20 2EH.* ☎ (0303) 52442. Open Mar–
Oct. C. ⇄ 13 bedrs, 3 ba. ⌂ ch, TV, CF, 1
BGf, 12 st. £ BB £9·20–£11·50, DB
£18·40–£23, WT (b) £62·10–£66·70, DT
(b) £12·65–£16·10, ①.
Beaumont, PH, z (Rl), *5 Marine Ter,
CT20 1PZ.* ☎ (0303) 52740.
Belmonte, PH, z (Unl), *30 Castle Hill Av,
CT20 2RE.* ☎ (0303) 54470. Open Mar–
Oct. C. ⇄ 11 bedrs, 3 ba, Dgs. ⌂ ch, TV,
CP 8. £ BB £9–£9·50, DB £17·50–£18, WT
£74–£78, DT (b) £11·95–£12·50, ①.
Gresham, PH, z (R), *18 Clifton Cres,
CT20 2EP.* ☎ (0303) 53906. C 5. ⇄ 14
bedrs, 3 ba, TV, Dgs. ⌂ ch, TV, Dgs. £ BB
£11·95–£13·25, DB £23·90–£26·50, WT
(b) £90·15–£104, DT (b) £17·20–£18·95,
②, Bk £2·50, D £4·55, cc 1.
Kasfaret, G, z (Unl), *91 Bouverie Rd
West, CT20 2PP.* ☎ (0303) 53705.
Shannon, PH, z (Rl), *59 Cheriton Rd,
CT20 1DF.* ☎ (0303) 54905.
Wearbay, PH, z (R), *23 Wear Bay Cres,
CT19 6AX.* ☎ (0303) 52586. C. ⇄ 12
bedrs, 1 bp, 3 sh, 3 ba, TV, Dgs. ✗ a l c.
⌂ CH, TV, U 1, CF. £ BB £7·70–£20, DB
£15·40–£26·62, WT (b) £87·30–£115·86,
DT (b) £13·20–£19·31, ①, Bk £2·50, L £5,
D £5, cc 1.
Westward Ho, PH, x (R), *13 Clifton
Cres, CT20 2EL.* ☎ (0303) 52663. Closed
Xmas. C. ⇄ 11 bedrs, 1 bps, 3 ba, Dgs.
⌂ Lt, CH, TV, CF. £ BB £10–£13, DB £20–
£26, WT (b) £83–£90, (c) £63–£70, DT (b)
£14–£15, ①, Bk £2·50, D £5.

Repairers Henlys (South East) Ltd, Clifton
Garage, Bouverie Rd West. ☎ (0303)
55101.
Peacocks of South Kent Ltd, Foord Rd
North. ☎ (0303) 41234.

FONTMELL MAGNA Dorset. Map 5D
Pop 590. Shaftesbury 4½, London 107,
Blandford Forum 7.
Golf Ashley Wood, Blandford 9h.

Rescue Service: Crown Garage,
Shaftesbury Rd. ☎ (0747) 811256.

FORD Wiltshire. Map 5B
Pop 80. M4 Motorway 7, Chippenham 5,
London 96, Bath 10, Bristol 16, Chipping
Sodbury 11, Melksham 9.
Golf Kingsdown 18h.

★★White Hart Inn, *SN14 8RP.* ☎ Castle
Combe (0249) 782213. Closed Dec 24–
30. C 3. ⇄ 3 bedrs, annexe 8 bedrs, 8 bp,
TV. ✗ a l c, mc, LD 9.30. ⌂ ch, TV, Dgs, CP
100, Ac, sp, con 40, 4 Bgf, 2 st. £ BB £20–
£26, DB £26–£34, WB, ①, Bk £3, D £8, cc 1,
Dep a.

FORDHAM Cambridgeshire. Map 16F
Newmarket 5, London 68, Cambridge 16,
Ely 9, Thetford 10.

Rescue Service: New Path Motors, 16
New Path. ☎ Newmarket (0638) 720912.

FORDINGBRIDGE Hampshire. Map 6C
Pop 5,075. Romsey 15, London 91,
Blandford Forum 21, Lyndhurst 13,
Ringwood 6, Salisbury 10, Shaftesbury 23,
Southampton 19.
EC Thur. **Golf** Bramshaw 18h. **See**
Modernised 14th cent 7-arch bridge, EE
and Dec Church, Augustus John statue.
Breamore House 3 m N, Hale Park.

FOLKESTONE

0 miles ¼ ½

To Dover 7 m.
The Warren
Camping Site
Martello Tower
A20
Dover Road
Wear Bay Road
Tennis Grounds
Martello Tower
West Bay Road
Martello Tower
Wear Bay Cres.
Foreland Av.
Martello Tower
East Cliff Golf Links
East Cliff Pavilion

To Crematorium 2 m.
To Canterbury 17 m.
A260
Canterbury Road
School
Dover Road
Sidney St.
Joyes Road
Canterbury Rd.
Rec. Ground
Black Bull Road
Museum & Library
Foord Rd.
Dover Rd.
Radnor Bridge Rd.
Tram Road
Harbour
Info. Centre
The Stade
Info. Centre
High St.
Town Hall
Information Centre
East Pier
Harbour
Harbour Station
Car Ferry Terminal
Pier
Pavilion
Parish Church
Amusement Park
Marine Parade
Boating Pool

Churchill Avenue
Victoria Hospital
Pavilion Rd.
Bournemouth Rd.
Park Rd.
Radnor Park
Foord Rd.
Cheriton Rd.
Cheriton Gdns.
P.O.
War Meml.
Cliff Lifts
Theatre
Tontine Road
Leas
The Leas
Cliff Hall
Park Farm Industrial Estate
Sch.
Sch.
Sch.
Sports Centre
Police Station
Central Station
Manor Rd.
Bouverie Road West
Castle Hill Avenue
Civic & Information Centres
Law Courts
Augusta Gdns.
Sandgate
Clifton Gdns.
Bus Sta.
Guildhall St.

Cherry Garden Avenue
Cherry Garden Lane
Recreation Ground
Municipal Sports Ground
Cemetery
Technical College
Cornwallis Av.
Wilton Rd.
Cheriton Road
Earl's Avenue
Grimston Avenue
Shorncliffe Road
Station Rd.
West Station
Turketel Rd.
Audley Rd.
Coolinge Lane
Bathurst Rd.
Bouverie Road
Sandgate Road
The Leas
Lower Sandgate Road
Picnic
Toll
New Metropole
Toll Road
Martello Tower
School
School
School
School
Martello Tower
Castle
A259
To Hythe 5 m.

M20
Surrenden Road
A20
To Ashford 17 m.

N

RAC

P Car Park
C Public Conveniences
▨ Pedestrian precinct

RAC Port Office
West Side Terminal

© Crown copyright reserved

© The Royal Automobile Club, 1985

For abbreviations see inside back cover—RAC

Oakfield Lodge, G, x (Unl), *1 Park Rd, SP6 1EQ.* ✆ (0425) 52789. Closed Nov & Dec. C. ⊯ 10 bedrs, 1 bps, 2 sh, 2 ba. ⌂ CH, TV, CP 10, CF. 1 BGf, 0 st, Dis. £ BB £9, DB £18–£19, WT (b) £57, ②.

Waverley, G, z (Unl), *Salisbury Rd, SP6 1EX.* ✆ (0425) 52751. Open Mar–Nov. C 3. ⊯ 10 bedrs, 3 ba. ⌂ ch, TV, CP 9, 1 st. £ BB £7·50–£8, DB £15–£16, WT (b) £58–£63, DT (b) £10·25–£11, ①.

Rescue Service: Damerham Garage, Damerham. ✆ Rockbourne (072 53) 224. Lewtas Motors, Salisbury St. ✆ (0425) 52385.
RMJ Waters (Albion Road Garage) ✆ (0425) 52145.

FORDWICH Kent. Map 10D
Pop 175. Canterbury 2½, London 61, Dover 16, Folkestone 17, Margate 13.
Golf Canterbury 18h. **See** Old Town Hall, Ducking Stool, Stocks, Saxon and Norman Church.

◼★★**George & Dragon,** *CT2 0BX.* ✆ Canterbury (0227) 710661.

FOREST OF DEAN Gloucestershire *See* COLEFORD.

FOREST ROW East Sussex. Map 7D
Pop 4,246. East Grinstead 3, London 33, Hawkhurst 25, Haywards Heath 10, Hurst Green 24, Lewes 17, Tonbridge 15, Tunbridge Wells 12, Uckfield 10.
EC Wed. **Golf** Royal Ashdown Forest 18h (2). **See** Ruins of Brambletye Castle (17th cent), 15th cent "Chequers", once Posting Inn.

★★★**Roebuck,** *Wych Cross, RH18 5JL* (2 m S A22). ✆ (034 282) 3811. C. ⊯ 31 bedrs, 31 bp, TV, Dgs. ✗ a l c, mc, at, LD 9.30. ⌂ N, CH, Dgs, CP 100, Ac, con 100, CF, 8 BGf, 0 st, Dis. £ B£23, BD £33, WB, ①, Bk £4·25, L £7·50, D £7·50, cc 1 2 3 4 5 6, Dep b.

★★**M Brambletye,** *The Square, RH18 5EZ.* ✆ (034 282) 4144. Closed Xmas. C. ⊯ 13 bedrs, 13 bp, TV, Dgs. ✗ mc, at, LD 10. ⌂ CH, Dgs, CP 50, CF, 6 BGf. 1 st. £ BB £20·50, DB £31·50, WB, cc 1 2 3 5 6.

Rescue Service: Martin's Garage, Lower Sq. ✆ (034 282) 2412.

FORMBY Merseyside. Map 20E
Pop 25,581. Northwich 34, London 207, Liverpool 11, Ormskirk 8½, St Helens 17, Southport 7½, Warrington 25.
EC Wed. **Golf** Formby 18h. **See** St Luke's Church, Beach Walk.

Repairer: Woodward, H & Son Ltd, Altcar Works, By-Pass Rd. ✆ (070 48) 78121.

FOUR MARKS Hampshire. Map 6D
Pop 2,500. Alton 4, London 52, Basingstoke 13, Cosham 23, Fareham 22, Midhurst 19, Petersfield 11, Winchester 13.
EC Wed. **Golf** Alton 9h. **See** Swelling Hill Pond. "Pilgrim's Way".

Rescue Service: Chawton End Garage Ltd. ✆ Alton (0420) 62354.

FOWEY Cornwall. Map 2D
Pop 2,447. Liskeard 18, London 239 (Fy 236), Bodmin 8, Looe 19 (Fy 10), St Austell 7½.
EC Wed. **Golf** St Austell 18h, Carlyon Bay 18h. **See** Parish Church, Museum, Aquarium, St Catherine's Castle ruins, St Catherine's and St Saviour's Point (Nat Trust).
⑦ Albert Quay. ✆ Fowey (072 683) 3320.

◼★★★**Fowey,** *PL23 1HX.* ✆ (072 683) 2551.

◼★★**Cormorant** (R), *Golant, PL23 1LL.* ✆ (072 683) 3426. C. ⊯ 10 bedrs, 10 bp, TV, Dgs. ✗ mc, at, LD 8.30. ⌂ CH, CP 20, sp, con 15, 4 BGf. £ BB £17·50–£23, DB £35–£40, DBB £22–£28, WB, ②, Bk £4·50, D £8·80, cc 3, Dep a.

◼★★**Marina** (R), *Esplanade, PL23 1HY.* ✆ (072 683) 3315. RS Nov–Feb. C. ⊯ 14 bedrs, 8 bp, 1 bps, 2 ba, TV, Dgs. ✗ a l c, mc, at, LD 8.30. ⌂ CH, TV, CP 1, pf, CF, 3 Bgf, 0 st. £ BB £11–£19, DB £22–£39, DBB £19–£27·50, ②, 10%, Bk £3, D £8, cc 1 2 3 5 6, Dep a.

◼★★**Penlee** (R), *Esplanade, PL23 1JB.* ✆ (072 683) 3220. C. ⊯ 12 bedrs, 9 bp, 4 bps, 2 ba, ns, TV, Dgs. ✗ mc, at, LD 8.30. ⌂ CH, TV, Dgs, ns, CP 10, Ac, con 50, CF, 12 st. £ BB £12–£20·50, DB £24–£41, WT £140–£182, DT £20–£28·50, WB, ①, Bk £2·50, L £1·85, D £8, cc 1 2 3 4 5 6.

◼★★**Riverside,** *32 Passage St, PL23 1DE.* ✆ (072 683) 2275. Open Mar–Sep. C. ⊯ 14 bedrs, 5 bp, 2 bps, 2 ba, TV, Dgs. ✗ mc, at, LD 9. ⌂ ch, TV, Dgs, ns, CP 5, G, pf, con 50, CF, 2 st. £ BB £10–£20, DB £20–£40, WB, ②, 10%, Bk £2·50, D £9·50, cc 1.

◼★**Old Quay House** (R), *Fore St, PL23 1AQ.* ✆ (072 683) 3302. Closed Xmas & New Year. C. ⊯ 13 bedrs, 7 bp, 1 bps, 2 sh, 1 ba, TV, Dgs. ✗ mc, at, LD 8. ⌂ ch, TV, Dgs, Ac, pf, CF, 1 BGf, 3 st. £ BB £10·50–£13·50, DB £21–£27, DBB £17–£21, WB, ①, Bk £2·50, D £6·50, cc 1 3.

Carnethic House, PH, xy, (RI), *Lambs Barn, PL23 1HQ.* ✆ (072 683) 3336. Open Mar–Sep. C 12. ⊯ 8 bedrs, 4 bps, 1 sh, 2 ba, TV. ⌂ CH, CP 20, 0 st. £ BB £12–£18, DB £22–£30, ①, Bk £3·50, L £2·50, D £7·50, cc 1 2 3 5.

Wheelhouse, G, z (RI), *60 Esplanade, PL23 1JA.* ✆ (072 683) 2452. Closed Jan & Feb. C 12. ⊯ 7 bedrs, 3 ba. ⌂ CH, TV. £ BB £9·50, DB £19, WT (b) £108, DT (b) £16, ①.

Rescue Service: Cotswold Garage, Lambs Barn, Polvillion Rd. ✆ (072 683) 3393. Fowey Garage & Marine, Lostwithiel St. ✆ (072 683) 2202 & (072 683) 2224.

FRADDON Cornwall. Map 2D
Pop 871. Bodmin 12, London 245, Newquay 7½, Redruth 17, St Austell 9½, Truro 11, Wadebridge 12.
EC Wed. **Golf** Newquay 18h.

Rescue Service: R & H Motors, Fraddon Garage. ✆ St Austell (0726) 860675.

FRAMLINGHAM Suffolk. Map 17A
Pop 2,190. Ipswich 15, London 89, Aldeburgh 13, Lowestoft 29, Norwich 33, Saxmundham 7, Scole 15, Stowmarket 17, Sudbury 24.
EC Wed. **MD** Sat. **Golf** Woodbridge 18h. **See** Norman Castle ruins, Parish Church.

★★**Crown** (TH), *Market Hill, IP13 9AN.* ✆ (0728) 723521. C. ⊯ 17 bedrs, 4 bp, 3 ba, TV, Dgs. ✗ a l c, mc, at, LD 9.15. ⌂ CH, Dgs, CP 15, Ac, con 40, CF, 1 st. £ BB £31–£34, DB £43–£49·50, WB, ①, cc 1 2 3 4 5 6, Dep (Xmas).

FRAMPTON Dorset. Map 5E
Pop 390. Dorchester 5½, London 128, Axminster 25, Crewkerne 15, Glastonbury 32, Lyme Regis 22, Shaftesbury 27, Sherborne 17, Weymouth 12.
Golf Dorchester 18h. **See** Parish Church.

Wessex Barn, G, x (Rt), *DT2 9NB.* ✆ Maiden Newton (0300) 20282.

Rescue Service: Frampton Garage, 8 Dorchester Rd. ✆ Maiden Newton (0300) 20347.

FRECKENHAM Suffolk. Map Area 16F.
Newmarket 7, London 70, Downham Market 25, Ely 11, Thetford 16

Rescue Service: New Lodge Garage, Turnpike Rd, Freckenham Red Lodge. ✆ Newmarket (0638) 750534

FRESHWATER Isle of Wight. Map 6E
Pop 4,949. Portsmouth (Fy) 16, London 77, Newport 11, Ventnor 18, Yarmouth 2½.
EC Thur. **Golf** Freshwater 18h. **See** Tennyson's Home and Memorial, All Saints Church, St Agnes thatched Church.

★★★**Albion,** *Freshwater Bay, PO40 9RA.* ✆ Isle of Wight (0983) 753631. Open Apr–Oct. C. ⊯ 43 bedrs, 37 bp, 3 ba, TV, Dgs. ✗ mc, at, LD 8.15. ⌂ CH, TV, CP 75, CF, 8 BGf, 2 st. £ BB £13·50–£16·75, DB £24·75–£33·75, DT £23–£27·50, DBB £19·50–£24·50, ①, Bk £4, L £5, D £8·25, cc 1 3, Dep.

◼♨★★★**Farringford,** *Bedbury La, Freshwater Bay, PO40 9PE.* ✆ Isle of Wight (0983) 752500. Open Apr–Sep. C. ⊯ 16 bedrs, 16 bp, annexe 36 bedrs, 34 bp, TV, Dgs. ✗ a l c, mc, at, LD 9.30. ⌂ N, CH, TV, CP 100, G 2, Ac, sp, gc, tc, con 25, CF, 4 BGf, 1 st, Dis. £ BB £20–£25, DB £40–£50, Bk £4, L Sun £5·25, D £7·75, cc 1 2 3 5 6, Dep a.

Blenheim House, PH, x (R), *PO40 9QD.* ✆ Isle of Wight (0983) 75285. Open May–Oct. C. ⊯ 18 bedrs, 8 bps, 2 ba, TV. ⌂ CH, CP 6, U 1, CP, 2 st. £ BB £10–£13·68, DB £20–£26·36, WT (b) £92–£110, DT £14·50–£16·50, ①, Bk £2·50, L £3, D £5.

FRINTON-ON-SEA Essex. Map 17B
Pop 4,577. Colchester 17, London 73, Bury St Edmunds 43, Clacton 7, Harwich 14, Ipswich 23, Stowmarket 35.
EC Wed. **Golf** Frinton 18h and 9h. **See** Old Parish Church.

★★★**Frinton Lodge,** *Esplanade, CO13 9HL.* ✆ (025 56) 4391. C. ⊯ 24 bedrs, 16 bp, 1 bps, 3 ba, TV, Dgs. ✗ a l c, mc, at, LD 9.30. ⌂ Lt, N, CH, TV, Dgs, CP 14, U 3, Ac, con 140, CF, 1 st. £ BB £21–£32, DB £43–£53, WT £149–£231, DT £34·95–£39·95, DBB £28–£34, WB, ②, Bk £4·25, D £6·95, cc 1 2 3 5, Dep b.

★★**Maplin** (R), *Esplanade, CO13 9EL.* ✆ (025 56) 3832. Closed Jan. C 10. ⊯ 12 bedrs, 9 bp, 1 bps, 1 ba, TV, Dgs. ✗ a l c, mc, LD 9.30. ⌂ CH, TV, Dgs, CP 15, G 2, sp, CF. £ BB £20–£21·50. DB £43, DBB £32·75, WB, ①, Bk £5, L £8·25, D £11·25, cc 1 2 3 5.

★**Rock (R),** *1 Third Avenue, Esplanade, CO13 9EG.* ✆ (025 56) 5173. C. ⊯ 9 bedrs, 1 bp, 1 bps, 2 ba, TV, Dgs. ✗ a l c, mc, at, LD 10. ⌂ CH, TV, Dgs, CP 12, con 26, CF, 2 st. £ BB £16·50–£17·50, DB £29·50–£33·50, DBB £21·25–£23·25, WB, ①, cc 1 2 3 5 6.

Forde, G, x (Unl), *18 Queens Rd, CO13 9BL.* ✆ (025 56) 4758.

Linnets (R), *Thorpe Rd, Kirby Cross, CO13 0LT.* ✆ (025 56) 4910.

Montpellier, PH, z (Rl), *2 Harold Grove, CO13 9BD.* ✆ (025 56) 4462. C. ➄ 6 bedrs, 5 bp, 1 bps, TV. 🅗 CH, TV, ns, CP 6, U 1, CF, 2 st. £ BB £13·75–£16·50, DB £21·50–£27, WT (b) £98–£114, DT (b) £16·25–£19, ②, cc 1 3.

Repairer: Branwhite Motor Co Ltd, Kirby Cross Garage. ✆ (025 56) 4383.

FRODSHAM Cheshire. Map 19A
Pop 8,965. Northwich 10, London 184, M56 Motorway 4½, Chester 11, Ellesmere Port 10, Runcorn 5, Warrington 9.
EC Wed. **MD** Thur. **Golf** Helsby 18h. **See** Ornamental gardens, 17th cent "Bear's Paw" Inn.

★★**Old Hall** (R), *Main St, WA6 7AB.* ✆ (0928) 32052. C. ➄ 12 bedrs, 12 bp, ns, TV, Dgs. ✗ a l c, mc, at, LD 10. 🅗 CH, Dgs, CP 20, Ac, con, CF, 2 BGf, 0 st. Dis. £ BB £25, DB £35, ①, Bk £3·75, L £5·50, D £9, cc 1 2 3 5 6.

FROGMORE Hertfordshire. Map 15F
Pop 1,481. London 18, Aylesbury 23, Barnet 9½, Enfield 14, Harrow 11, Hatfield 7½, St Albans 2½, Watford 6½.
Golf St Albans 18h.

Repairer: Frogmore Garage & Coachworks, Park St. ✆ Park Street (0727) 72626.
Specialist Body Repairer Rand & Robson Coachworks Ltd, 51 Radlett Rd. ✆ Park Street (0727) 72844.

FROME Somerset. Map 5D
Pop 17,000. Warminster 7, London 105, Bath 13, Chippenham 21, Crewkerne 35, Devizes 18, Ilminster 36, Pewsey 29, Radstock 8, Shaftesbury 19, Shepton Mallet 11, Sherborne 22, Wincanton 15.
EC Thur. **MD** Wed. **Golf** W Wilts. Warminster 18h. **See** Church (14th cent), Jacobean houses, Blue House.
🅿 Cattle Market Car Park. ✆ Frome (0373) 67271.

★★★**M Mendip Lodge,** *Bath Rd, BA11 2HP.* ✆ (0373) 63223. C. ➄ 40 bedrs, 40 bp, TV, Dgs. ✗ mc, at, LD 9.45. 🅗 N, CH, CP 60, G 12, Ac, con 80, CF 12, 2 BGf, 1 st, Dis. £ BB £31, DB £43, WB, ①, Bk £6, D £8·95, cc 1 2 3 5, Dep b.

★★**George,** *4 Market Pl, BA11 1AE.* ✆ (0373) 62584. C. ➄ 12 bedrs, 4 bp, 3 ba,TV, Dgs. ✗ a l c, mc, at, LD 9. 🅗 CH, Dgs, CP 20, Ac, sol, con 40, CF, 1 st. £ BB £18, DB £22–£31, WT £171·50, DT £30, DBB £24–£37·50, ②, Bk £3, L £3·75, D £6·50, cc 1 2 3 5 6.
Cork Villas, G, z (Rt), *3 The Butts, BA11 4AB.* ✆ (0373) 62101.
Keyford Elms, G, x (Rl), *92 Locks Hill, BA11 1NG.* ✆ (0373) 62681.

Rescue Service: Car Renovations (Frome) Ltd, Butts Hill. ✆ (0373) 62882.
Linwood Motors, Keyford Garage, Keyford. ✆ (0373) 63433.

GAILEY Staffordshire. Map 22E
Pop 150. Wolverhampton 8, London 132, Atherstone 27, Burton-on-Trent 27, Newport 14, Stafford 8, Sutton Coldfield 17, Tamworth 20, Walsall 10, Wellington 16.
Golf Oxley 18h. **See** Gailey Toll House.

Rescue Service: Gailey Service Station, A5 Watling St. ✆ Standeford (0902) 790490.
Midland Motorway Services (Gailey), Croft La. ✆ Standeford (0902) 790348.

GAINSBOROUGH Lincolnshire. Map 23A.
Pop 18,715. Newark 24, London 150, Doncaster 20, Grimsby 35, Hull 38, Lincoln 18, Market Rasen 20, Scunthorpe 16.
EC Wed. **MD** Mon, Tue, Sat. **Golf** Thonock 18h, Torksey 18h. **See** Model Railway, Elswitha Hall, Trinity Arts Centre.

★★**Hickman-Hill,** *Cox's Hill, DN21 1HH.* ✆ (0427) 3639. C. ➄ 8 bedrs, 3 bp, 1 bps, 3 sh, 1 ba, TV, Dgs. ✗ a l c, mc, at, LD 9. 🅗 CH, TV, Dgs, CP 25, con 35, CF, 0 st. £ BB fr £20·50, DB fr £27·50, WB, ②, Bk £2·95, L £4·95, D £6·95.

GALLOWSTREE COMMON Oxfordshire. M. Area 6B
Pop 100. 4½ m NNW of Reading. Maidenhead 17, London 43, Oxford 22.
Golf Huntercombe 18h.

Rescue Service: Gallowstree Common Garage. ✆ Kidmore End (0734) 2266.

GARFORTH West Yorkshire. Map 25F
See also LEEDS.
Pop 15,370. Pontefract 9½, London 187, Boroughbridge 23, Goole 28, Harrogate 19, Leeds 7½, Selby 14, Thorne 28, Wakefield 10, York 19.
EC Wed. **Golf** Garforth 18h (2). **See** Modern RC Church.

Rescue Service: Littler Bros, 63 Wakefield Rd. ✆ Leeds (0532) 862607.

GARGRAVE North Yorkshire. Map 27A
Pop 1,400. Skipton 4½, London 218, Burnley 18, Settle 12, Whalley 21.
EC Tue. **Golf** Skipton 12h. **See** Roman Villa, Church.

Rescue Service: Gargrave Service Station, Skipton Rd. ✆ (075 678) 445.

GARSTANG Lancashire. Map 27C
Preston 10, London 221, M55 Motorway 7½, Blackpool 15, Lancaster 10.
EC Wed. **MD** Thur. **Golf** Lancaster 18h. **See** Castle ruins, Wyre bridge, Parish Church.

★★**M Crofters,** *A6 Cabus, PR3 1PH.* ✆ (099 52) 4128. C. ➄ 23 bedrs, 3 bp, 20 bps, TV, Dgs. ✗ mc, LD 10. 🅗 N, CH, CP 200, Ac, con 300, CF, 1 st. £ BB £27·50, DB £33·50, WT £120, WB, ②, Bk £3·50, L £5·25, D £8·75, cc 1 2 3 5, Dep b.

GATESHEAD Tyne & Wear. Map 32C
See also NEWCASTLE UPON TYNE.
Pop 76,969. Durham 14, London 272, Newcastle upon Tyne 1, Sunderland 11.
EC Wed. **Golf** Ravensworth 18h. **See** Shipley Art Gallery, St Mary's Church, Holy Trinity Church, Bridges, Saltwell Towers and Park.
🅿 Central Library, Prince Consort Rd. ✆ Gateshead (0632) 773478.

★★★**Five Bridges,** *High West St NE8 1PE.* ✆ (0632) 771105. RS Sat. C. ➄ 106 bedrs, 106 bp, TV, Dgs. ✗ a l c, mc, at, LD 10. 🅗 Lt, N, CH, Dgs, CP 80, G 80, Ac, con 350, CF, 1 st. £ BB £21·50–£34·50, DB £26·50–£38·50, WB, ①, Bk £5·50, L £5, D £7, cc 1 2 3 5 6, Dep b.

★★★**Springfield,** *Durham Rd, NE9 5BT.* ✆ (0632) 774121. C. ➄ 40 bedrs, 40 bp, TV, Dgs. ✗ a l c, mc, at, LD 9.30. 🅗 N, CH, Dgs, CP 100, Ac, con 100, CF, 3 st. £ B £31·50, BD £39·50, WB, ①, Bk £4·75, L £4, D £6·75, cc 1 2 3 5 6, Dep b.

Rescue Service: Harry Nichols (Auto Repairs), 610 Durham Rd, Low Fell. ✆ Low Fell (0632) 877014.
Wardley Service Station, Sunderland Rd. ✆ Felling (0632) 692433.

GATWICK AIRPORT West Sussex. Map 7C
See CHARLWOOD, COPTHORNE, CRAWLEY, and HORLEY.

GAYDON Warwickshire. Map 14D
Pop 384. Banbury 11, London 83, Warwick 9, Leamington Spa 9, Southam 6½, Shipston-on-Stour 12.
EC Sat. **Golf** Leamington Spa 18h.

Rescue Service: Charles Blackwell Motor Co Ltd, Banbury Rd. ✆ Kineton (0926) 640303.

GERRARDS CROSS Bucks. Maps 7A and 15E
Pop 6,500. Denham 3, London 20, M40 Motorway 3, Aylesbury 22, High Wycombe 10, Slough 6.
EC Wed. **Golf** Gerrards Cross 18h. **See** Interesting modern Church.

★★★**Bull,** *Oxford Rd. SL9 7PA.* ✆ (0753) 885995. C. ➄ 40 bedrs, 40 bp, TV, Dgs. ✗ mc, at, LD 9.30. 🅗 N, CH, CP 166, con 130, CF, 1 st. £ BB fr £49, DB fr £64, DT fr £69·25, WB, ①, Bk £5, L £9·75, D £10·50, cc 1 2 3 5 6, Dep b.

■★★**Elthorpe,** *Packhorse Rd, SL9 8MX.* ✆ (0753) 882039. C. ➄ 28 bedrs, 28 bp, TV. 🅗 N, CH, CP 40, con 25, CF, 9 BGf, 1 st, Dis. £ BB fr £30, DB fr £42·50, WB, ①, Bk £2·50, L £3, D £3·79, cc 1 2 3 5 6, Dep b.

GIGGLESWICK North Yorkshire. Map Area 27a.
Burnley 24, London 230, Hawes 23, Kirkby Lonsdale 17, Skipton 17, Whalley 24.

Rescue Service: Scar Top garage, Buckhaw Brow, ✆ Settle (072 92) 3267.

GILLAN Cornwall. Map 2F
Pop 180. Truro 24, London 279, Falmouth 17, Helston 11.
Golf Mullion 18h.

■★**Tregildry,** *Manaccan, TR12 6HG.* ✆ Manaccan (0236 23) 378. Open Mar–Oct. C. ➄ 13 bedrs, 1 bp, 3 ba, TV, Dgs. ✗ mc, at, LD 8. 🅗 N, CH, TV, CP 50, tc, con 25, CF. £ BB £11–£12, DB £22–£24, DBB £18–£21, ①, Bk £4, L £3, D £8.

GILLINGHAM Dorset. Map 5D
Pop 5,514. Shaftesbury 4½, London 108, Amesbury 28, Frome 15, Sherborne 14, Warminster 14, Wincanton 7.
EC Thur. **Golf** Ashley Wood 9h. **See** St Mary's Church, Museum.

Rescue Service: Elfords Garage, Peacemarsh. ✆ (074 76) 2307.

GILLINGHAM Kent. Map 10C
Pop 95,200. Rochester 3, London 33,
Canterbury 26, Maidstone 10, Margate 41.
EC Wed. **MD** Mon. **Golf** Gillingham 18h.
See St Mary's Church Clock Tower
(memorial to William Adams, 17th cent
navigator), Rainham Church.

★**Park,** *Nelson Rd, ME7 4NA.* ✆ Medway
(0634) 51546.

Repairer: Autoyachts Ltd, 171 Pier Rd.
✆ Medway (0634) 52333.
Rescue Service: Burtons, 31 Duncan Rd.
✆ Medway (0634) 51294.

GISLAND Cumbria (Northumberland).
Map 30F.
Brampton 8½, London 304, Alston 23,
Hexham 22, Langholm 28.
See Hadrian's Wall.

■★**Station,** *CA6 7OS.* ✆ (06972) 206. C.
⚑ 6 bedrs, 2 sh, 1 ba, TV, Dgs. ✖ mc, LD
9.30. ⓗ ch, TV, CP 80, Ac, con 50, CF, 0 st.
£ BB £8–£12, DB £18–£20, ①, Bk £2·50, L
£2·50, D £9·50.

GISBURN Lancashire. Map 27A
Pop 356. Nelson 8, London 218, Clitheroe
7, Preston 23, Settle 12, Skipton 11.
EC Wed. **MD** Sat. **Golf** Clitheroe 18h.

★★★**Stirk House,** *Gisburn Rd, BB7 4LJ.*
✆ (020 05) 581. C. ⚑ 40 bedrs, 37 bp, 3
bps, TV, Dgs. ✖ a l c, mc, LD 9·45. ⓗ N,
CH, CP 100, Ac, sp, sc, sb, sol, con, CF, 24
BGf, 2 st. £ BB £29, DB £43, WT £273, DT
£40. DBB £37, WB, ①, Bk £4·25, L £6·95, D
£8·25, cc 1 2 3 5.
Park House, PH, x (Rt), *Church View,
BB7 4HG.* ✆ (020 05) 269. Closed Xmas.
C. ⚑ 11 bedrs, 3 ba. ✖ a l c. ⓗ CH, TV, CP
5, CF, 12 st. £ BB £8·50, DB £17, L £3·25,
D £6.

GLAPWELL Derbyshire. Map 22D
Pop 1,663. Mansfield 5, London 143,
Chesterfield 7½, Matlock 14, Ollerton 13,
Rotherham 21, Sheffield 17, Worksop 15.
Golf Chesterfield 18h. **See** Hardwick Hall
4 m SE, NT.

Rescue Service: Staley, R & Son, Regent
Garage, Mansfield Rd. ✆ Mansfield (0623)
810634.

GLASTONBURY Somerset. Map 5C
Pop 6,773. Shepton Mallet 9, London 126,
Bridgwater 15, Crewkerne 22, Dorchester
36, Ilminster 23, Sherborne 20, Taunton
22, Wells 5½, Weston-super-Mare 24,
Wincanton 23.
EC Wed. **MD** Tue. **Golf** Wells (Somerset)
9h. **See** Ruins of Benedictine Abbey,
oldest religious foundation in Britain with
Abbot's kitchen (intact) and St Mary's
Chapel, Weary-all Hill (site of
"Glastonbury Thorn"), Ye Olde Pilgrim's
Inn (15th cent), Abbot Bere's Almshouses,
St Michael's Tower on the Tor, Tribunal
House (with relics from a prehistoric lake
village).
ⓘ 1 Marchant's Buildings, Northload St.
✆ Glastonbury (0458) 32954.

★★**George and Pilgrims,** *High St, BA6
9DP.* ✆ (0458) 31146. C. ⚑ 12 bedrs, 4
bp, 1 bps, 4 ba. ✖ a l c, mc, at, LD 9.30.
ⓗ CH, TV, Dgs, CP 4, U 6, Ac, CF, 0 st.
£ BB £22, DB £31–£42, WB, ②, Bk £4·50, D
£9·50, cc 1 2 3 4 5 6, Dep.
Cradlebridge Farm, F, y (Unl), *BA6 9SD.*
✆ (0458) 31827. Closed Xmas. C. ⚑ 4
bedrs, 1 ba, Dgs. ⓗ CH, TV, CP, 1 Bgf.

£ BB £9–£9·50, DB £18–£19, WT (c) £54–
£57, DT (b) £16–£16·50.
Dower House, F, x (Unl), *Butleigh,
BA6 8TG.* ✆ Baltonsborough (0458)
50354.
Hawthorns PH, z, *Northload St, BA6
9JJ.* ✆ (0458) 31255. C. ⚑ 12 bedrs, 3
bps, 2 sh, 2 ba. ✖ a l c. ⓗ CH, TV, ns, CF, 3
BGf, 1 st, Dis. £ BB £12–£15, DB £22–£33,
WT £90–£100, DT £18–£21, Bk £1·75, D
£5·75, cc 1 3 5.
Tor Down, G, z (Unl), *Ashwell La, BA6
4BG.* ✆ (0458) 32287.

Repairer: Rapson, C R & Co, Station Rd
Garage, Benedict St. ✆ (0458) 31130.
Rescue Service: S G Bartlett Ltd, Street
Rd. ✆ (0458) 32137.
Tor View Garage, Edgarley. ✆ (0458)
31124.

GLENRIDDING Cumbria. Map 26D
Pop 599. Ambleside 9, London 277,
Kendal 21, Keswick 16, Penrith 13.
EC Tue. **Golf** Penrith 18h. **See** Ullswater,
Helvellyn (3,118 ft), Aira Force.
ⓘ Beckside Car Park. ✆ Glenridding
(085 32) 414.

■★★**Glenridding,** *CA11 0PB.*
✆ (085 32) 228. C. ⚑ 42 bedrs, 37 bp, 2
ba, Dgs. ✖ mc, at, LD 8.15. ⓗ CH, TV, Dgs,
CP 43, Ac, CF, 6 BGf, 6 st. £ BB £17–£20,
DB £25–£41, WT £140–£168, DT £25–£35,
DBB £20–£29·50, WB, ①, Bk £3·50, L £5, D
£9, cc 1 2 3 5 6.

Rescue Service: Ullswater Garage, Brown
Howe. ✆ (085 32) 213.

GLENTHAM Lincolnshire. Map 23A.
Lincoln 15, London 148, Gainsborough
13, Humber Bridge 25, Grimsby 25,
Market Rasen 7½.

Rescue Service: R & M Service Centres,
High St. ✆ (067 37) 591.

GLOSSOP Derbyshire. Map 22A
Pop 25,395. Chapel-en-le-Frith 9, London
174, Barnsley 24, Huddersfield 19,
Macclesfield 19, Manchester 14, Oldham
12, Sheffield 24, Stockport 11.
EC Tue. **MD** Thur, Fri, Sat. **Golf** Glossop
9h. **See** Dinting Rly Centre (rides on
restored steam trains), Saxon Cross (Old
Glossop), Snake Pass, Site of Melandra
Roman Fort, Peak National Park.
ⓘ Station Forecourt, Norfolk St.
✆ Glossop (045 74) 5920.

Hurst Lee, PH, x (Rt), *Derbyshire Lane,
off Sheffield Rd. SK13 9PT.* ✆ (045 74)
3354. C 7. ⚑ 8 bedrs, 8 bps, Dgs. ⓗ CH,
TV, CP 12, 2 st. £ BB £25, DB £32, WT (b)
£157·50–£220·50, DT (b) £22·50–£31·50,
cc 3.

Repairer: Newton & Heap Ltd, Arundel St.
✆ (045 74) 2180.
Rescue Service: Charlesworth (Derbys)
Garage Ltd, 7 Marple Rd, Charlesworth.
✆ (045 74) 3443.
Glossop Motor Repairs, Excelsior Garage,
Derby St, off Victoria St. ✆ (045 74)
64129.

GLOUCESTER Gloucestershire.
Map 13F
RAC Office, *Kings Square, Gloucester,
GL1 1RP.* ✆ Gloucester (0452) 20460;
Rescue service only ✆ Gloucester (0452)
502011.
Pop 93,000. Cheltenham 9, London 104,
M5 Motorway 4½, Bath 38, Bristol 35,

Chepstow 28, Cirencester 18, Hereford
28, Ledbury 16, Monmouth 24, Ross-on-
Wye 16, Tetbury 19, Tewkesbury 10.
See Plan, p. 214.
MD Daily. **P** See Plan. **Golf** Gloucester
G.C. 18h & 9h. **See** Cathedral, St Mary de
Crypt Church, Bishop Hooper's Lodging
(Gloucester Folk Museum), Hooper
Monument, City Museum and Art Gallery,
Robt Raikes' House, St Oswald's Priory
ruins, The New Inn (medieval hostelry),
16th cent Maverdine House, Greyfriars,
Blackfriars Priory, St Mary de Lode
Church, Llanthony Priory, Prinknash
Abbey (Grounds, Church/Pottery) 4½ m
SE, Regimental Museum.
ⓘ 6 College St. ✆ Gloucester (0452)
421188.

★★★**Bowden Hall,** *Upton St Leonards,
GL4 8ED.* ✆ (0452) 64121. C. ⚑ 24 bedrs,
24 bp, 1 ba, TV, Dgs. ✖ a l c, mc, at, LD 10.
ⓗ N, CH, Dgs, CP 100, Ac, pf, con 200, CF,
1 st. £ BB £25, DB £38, DT £40, DBB £32,
WB, ②, Bk £3·50, L £6·90, D £6·90,
cc 1 2 3 5 6, Dep b.
★★★**M Crest,** *Crest Way, Barnwood,
GL4 7RX.* ✆ (0452) 63311. C. ⚑ 100
bedrs, 100 bp, ns, TV, Dgs. ✖ a l c, mc, at,
LD 9·45. ⓗ N, CH, Dgs, CP 178, Ac, con
100, CF, 50 BGf, 0 st, Dis. £ B fr £43·50,
BD fr £55, WB, ①, Bk £5·25, D £9·60,
cc 1 2 3 4 5 6, Dep b.
★★★**Tara,** *Upton Hill, GL4 8DE.* (3¾m SE
on B4073). ✆ (0452) 67412. RS Dec 26–
Jan 2 & Bank Holidays except Xmas. C.
⚑ 22 bedrs, 9 bp, 8 bps, 3 ba. ✖ a l c, mc,
at, LD 9·45. ⓗ CH, CP 100, sp, con 100,
CF, 1 st. £ BB £25–£36, DB £43–£52, WB,
②, Bk £4, L £15, D £15, cc 1 2 3 5, Dep b.
★★**Fleece,** *19 Westgate St. GL1 2NR.*
✆ (0452) 22762. C. ⚑ 40 bedrs, 6 bp, 3
bps, 8 ba. ✖ mc, at, LD 9·30. ⓗ N, ch, TV,
Dgs, CP 15, £20, Ac, con 90, CF, 1 BGf, 0
st. £ BB £12–£16, DB £20–£27, ①, Bk
£2·50, L £2·50, D £3·75, Dep b.
★★**New County,** *44 Southgate St, GL1
2DU.* ✆ (0452) 24977. C. ⚑ 36 bedrs, 4
bp, 9 ba, TV, Dgs. ✖ mc, at, LD 9.15. ⓗ N,
ch, Dgs, Ac, con 175, CF. £ BB £18·50, DB
fr £27·50, WB, ①, Bk £4·50, L £4·50, D
£6·50, cc 1 2 3 4 5 6.
Montieth, G, z, (Rl), *127 Stroud Rd,
GL1 5AJ.* ✆ (0452) 25369. Closed Xmas.
C. ⚑ 8 bedrs, 2 bp, 2 ba, TV, Dgs. ⓗ CH,
TV, CP 8, CF. £ BB £10, DB £17–£23.
Rotherfield House, PH, z (R), *5 Horton
Rd, GL1 3PX.* ✆ (0452) 410500. C. ⚑ 11
bedrs, 2 ba. ⓗ CH, TV, CP 9, 2 st. £ BB £13,
DB £22, WT (b) £133, DT (b) £19, Bk £3, D
£6.
Stanley House, PH, z, (R), *87 London
Rd, GL1 3HH.* ✆ (0452) 20140. C. ⚑ 22
bedrs, 3 bp, 5 bps, 14 sh, 6 ba, TV, Dgs.
ⓗ CH, TV, CP 40, CF, 4 BGf, 1 st, Dis. £ BB
£10–£11, DB £22–£40, WT £105, DT (b)
£15–£16, Bk £3, D £5.

Repairer: Moons of Gloucester Ltd,
London Rd. ✆ (0452) 24081.
Specialist Radiator Repairer Serck
Radiator Services Ltd, Ashville Rd.
✆ (0452) 26424.
MC Repairer: The Motor Cyclist
(Gloucester), 99 Barton St. ✆ (0452)
25128.
Rescue Service: Barters Garage Ltd,
Coombe Hill. ✆ Coombe Hill (024 268)
362.
Glevum Garage, Unit 2, Glevum Works,
Upton St. ✆ (0452) 500015.

GLOUCESTER

To Tewkesbury 11 m. A38
To Ross-on-Wye 16 m.
To Cheltenham 9 m.
To M5 Int.11
A40
To Cirencester 18 m.
A417
To Cheltenham 9 m.
A38
To Painswick 6 m.
B4073
To Stroud 9 m.
A4173
To Bristol 35 m. To M5. Int.12
A38
To A38
A430

RAC

N

RAC Office
Kings Square

College
Cheltenham Road
A40
Merevale Rd.
Barnwood Road
School
Stadium
Horton Road Hospital
Horton Road
Gt. Western Road
L.C.
Eastern Avenue
Crematorium
Cemetery
Cotswold Rd.
Painswick Rd.
Robinswood Hill Country Park
Rec. Ground
Reservoir Rd.
Finlay Road
Southern Av.
Cole Avenue
Crypt School
Recreation Ground
Tuffley Rd.
Witton Rd.
Podsmead
Seymour Rd.
Linden Road
Calton Rd.
King Edward's Av.
Churchill Road
Rec. Ground
Bristol Road
Alma Rd.
Stroud Road
Whetstone Rd.
Tredworth Rd.
Hatherley Rd.
High St.
Conduit St.
Adelaide St.
Upton St.
Victoria St.
Ryecroft St.
Hopewell St.
Barton St.
Millbrook St.
Derby Rd.
Station Rd.
Weston Rd.
Park Road
The Park
Parliament St.
Brunswick Rd.
Southgate Street
Commercial Rd.
Police Station
Robert Raike's House
The Docks
Severn Rd.
Gloucester & Sharpness Canal
River Severn (East Channel)
Castle Meads
Bishop Hooper's House
Rec. Grounds
Information Centre
St. Oswald's Priory (ruins)
Cattle Market
Lorry Park
St. Oswald's Road
Deans Way
Kingsholm Rd.
Sports Ground
R.F.C. Ground
Worcester St.
Rec. Grd.
Oxford Rd.
Denmark Road
Kingsholm Rd.
Escourt
Ostalls Lane
London Road
Gloucestershire Royal Hospital
RAC Office
Alvin St.
Folk Museum
Cathedral
Archdeacon St.
Westgate St.
The Quay
Quay St.
Shire Hall
Multi-storey Car Park
New Inn
King St.
Northgate Street
Westgate Street
P.O.
Eastgate
Multi-storey
Guildhall
Wellington St.
Leisure Centre
Bus Station
Central Station
Saturday Only
Greyfriars

Car Park
Public Conveniences
Roof Car Park & Access

0 mile   ¼   ½

H & A Motors (Gloucester) Ltd, Lawn Garage, Barnwood Rd. ✆ (0452) 66514.
Wil-el-Mil Engineering, Lower Tuffley La. ✆ (0452) 25259.

GOATHLAND North Yorkshire. Map 24D
Pop 394. Pickering 14, London 227, Whitby 9.
EC Thur. **Golf** Whitby 18h. **See** Church, Moors, Waterfalls, Roman Road.

♨★★**Goathland Hydro** (R), *YO22 5LZ.*
✆ Whitby (0947) 86296. Open Apr–Sep.
C. ✉ 32 bedrs, 13 bp, 4 ba. ✗ mc, at, LD 7.45. ☎ ch, TV, CP 25, con 30, CF, 2 BGf, 2 st. £ BB £16·50–£19·15, DB £33–£38·30, WT fr £141·75, DT fr £20·25, DBB fr £20, WB, ①, Bk £3·85, L £5, D £6·75, cc 5.

GOBOWEN Shropshire. Map 19E
Pop 2,100. Shrewsbury 19, London 173, Llangollen 10, Wrexham 13.
EC Wed. **Golf** Oswestry (Aston) 18h.
See Whittington Castle 2 m SE, Chirk Castle 3 m NW.

Rescue Service: Perry Garage, St Martins Rd. ✆ Oswestry (0691) 661295.

GODALMING Surrey. Map 7C
Pop 18,209. Guildford 4, London 32, Dorking 15, Farnham 9, Haslemere 8½, Hindhead 8, Horsham 18, Petworth 16.
EC Wed. **MD** Fri. **Golf** West Surrey 18h, Bramley 18h. **See** Charterhouse School, Norm and EE Church, Church House, Local Interest Museum, Winkworth Arboretum 2 m SE.

Meads, H, x (RI), *65 Meadrow, GU7 3HS.*
✆ (048 68) 21800. C. ✉ 15 bedrs, 3 bps, 5 sh, 3 ba, TV, Dgs. ☎ CH, TV, CP 14, CF, 5 st. £ BB £11–£19, DB £18·50–£24, WT (c) £80–£90, Bk £3·50, D £5·30, cc 2 3.

Repairers: H A Jackson Ltd, Hurtmore Rd. ✆ (048 68) 4311.
Jordans Garage Ltd, The Wharf. ✆ (048 68) 5201.
MacDonald Garages (Surrey) Ltd, Guildford Rd. ✆ (048 68) 23555.

GODSHILL Isle of Wight. Map 6F
Pop 2,014. Portsmouth (Fy) 8½, London 80, Newport 5½, Ryde 9½, Sandown 5½, Shanklin 4, Ventnor 5.
EC Sat. **Golf** Sandown & Shanklin 18h.
See 14th cent Church, Thatched Cottages, Model Village, Old Smithy, Shell Museum.

Rescue Service: Sandford Garage, Sandford. ✆ Isle of Wight (0983) 840211.

GODSTONE Surrey. Map 7D
Pop 5,800. Purley 7, London 20, M25 motorway ¾, M23 motorway 3¼, Crawley 14, East Grinstead 10, Haywards Heath 20, Redhill 5, Westerham 6½.
Golf Tandridge, Oxted 18h. **See** 12th cent Church, St Mary's Almshouses, 14th cent "White Hart" (formerly "Clayton Arms" and assoc with William Cobbett).

♨★**Wonham House,** *Eastbourne Rd, South Godstone, RH9 8EJ.* ✆ South Godstone (034 285) 3188.

GOODRINGTON Devon
See PAIGNTON.

GOODWOOD West Sussex. Map 7E.
Midhurst 9, London 58, Chichester 4½.
See Goodwood House, race-course, Trundle Hill (View), Boxgrove Priory 1 m SE, Weald and Downland Open Air Museum at Singleton (2 m N), West Dean Gardens.

★★★**Richmond Arms,** *PO18 0QE.*
✆ Chichester (0243) 775537. C. ✉ 18 bedrs, 16 bp, 2 ba, TV, Dgs. ✗ a l c, mc, at, LD 9·30. ☎ CH, Dgs, CP 60, con 12, CF, 0 st. £ BB fr £28·25, DB fr £38, WB, ②, Bk £3·75, L £5·50, D £8·95, cc 1 2 3 5, Dep.

GOOLE Humberside (South Humberside). Map 25D
Pop 17,100. Thorne 11, London 179, Beverley 23, Gainsborough 32, Hull 33, Market Weighton 16, Pontefract 20, Scunthorpe 21, Selby 12, York 24.
EC Thur. **MD** Mon, Wed, Fri, Sat. **Golf** Selby 18h. **See** Port.
ℹ Central Library. ✆ Goole (0405) 2187.

MC Repairer: Reg Kay & Son, Second Avenue Garage, Pasture Rd. ✆ (0405) 3719.
Rescue Service: Clews Garage, Rawcliffe Rd. ✆ (0405) 357.0.

GORING BY SEA West Sussex. Map 7E
Horsham 19, London 56, Arundel 8, Crawley 28, East Grinstead 34, Guildford 34, Littlehampton 7, Pulborough 14, Worthing 2.
EC Wed. **Golf** Worthing 18h. **See** Highdown Gardens, Highdown Hill (Nat Trust).

Repairer: Brook Lane Garage Ltd, Palatine Rd. ✆ Worthing 43271.
Specialist Body Repairer J S Arnold (Coachbuilders) Ltd, Woods Way. ✆ Worthing (0903) 40304.

GORLESTON-ON-SEA Norfolk. Map 16B
Lowestoft 8, London 125, Gt Yarmouth 2, Scole 32.
EC Wed. **Golf** Gorleston 18h. **See** St Andrew's Parish Church, Lifeboat Station, Caister Castle ruins (with Motor Museum adj 5 m N).

★★★**Cliff,** *Cliff Hill, NR31 6DH.* ✆ (0493) 662179. C. ✉ 28 bedrs, 22 bp, 6 bps, 1 ba, TV, Dgs. ✗ a l c, mc, at, LD 9.30. ☎ N, CH, CP 70, Ac, con 50, CF, 0 st. £ BB £26, DBB £45, DBB £32·90, WB, ②, Bk £3·75, L £5·75, D £6·90, cc 1 2 3 5 6.

★**Pier,** *Harbour Mouth, NR31 6PL.* ✆ (0493) 662631. C. ✉ 20 bedrs, 10 bp, 3 ba, TV, Dgs. ✗ mc, at, LD 8·30. ☎ CH, TV, Dgs, CP 40, Ac, pf, con, CF, 2 st. £ BB fr £19·55, DB fr £34·50, WB, ①, Bk £3·50, D £6, cc 1 3.

Frandor, G, z (RI), *120 Lowestoft Rd, NR31 6ND.* ✆ Gt Yarmouth (0493) 662112.
Seacliffe, PH, z (RI). *60 Clarence Rd, NR31 6DR.* ✆ Gt Yarmouth (0493) 662734. C. ✉ 10 bedrs, 2 ba, Dgs. ☎ ch, TV, Dgs, CF, 1 st. £ BB fr £8–£10, DB £16–£20, WT (h) £65–£72, DT (h) £12–£14, ①, Bk £3, D £4.
Squirrels Nest, H, z (R), *71 Avondale Rd.* ✆ Gt Yarmouth (0493) 662746. C. ✉ 10 bedrs, 7 sh, 2 ba, TV, Dgs. ✗ a l c. ☎ CH, TV, Dgs, CP 5, CF, 2 st. £ BB £12–£19, DB £24–£28, WT £70–£90, DT (b) £16–£19, ①, Bk £3·50, L £4·25, D £4·50, cc 1 3.

GOSBERTON Lincolnshire. Map 23F
Pop 1,235. Spalding 6, London 107, Boston 10, Grantham 23, Horncastle 29, King's Lynn 31, Sleaford 19.

Golf Surfleet 18h. **See** 15th cent Parish Church.

Rescue Service: A & W Elsey Ltd, High St. ✆ (077 584) 218.

GOSFIELD Essex. Map 17E.
Braintree 5, London 65, Cambridge 32, Colchester 17, Sudbury 10.
See Gosfield Hall.

Rescue Service: Gosfield Cars, The Street. ✆ Halstead (0787) 472131

GOSFORTH Tyne & Wear. Map 32A
Pop 24,421. Newcastle upon Tyne 3, London 276, Alnwick 31, Coldstream 57, Corbridge 17, Hawick 61, Jedburgh 56.
EC Wed. **Golf** Gosforth 18h.

★★★★**Gosforth Park Thistle,** *High Gosforth Park, NE3 5HN.* ✆ (0632) 364111. C. ✉ 178 bedrs, 178 bp, ns, TV, Dgs. ✗ a l c, mc, at, LD N, CH, TV, Dgs, CP 300, Ac, sp, sc, sb, sol, gym, con 650, CF, 0 st. £ BB £51·25–£54·75, DB £66·50–£74, WB, ②, Bk £5·25, L £7·50, D £10·50, cc 1 2 3 4 5 6, Dep b. ▲

GOSPORT Hampshire. Map 6F
Pop 80,000. Fareham 5, London 81, Romsey 23, Southampton 16.
EC Wed. **MD** Tue. **Golf** Gosport and Stokes Bay 18h, Lee-on-the-Solent 18h.
See Holy Trinity Church (1696) (organ once played by Handel), Submarine Museum.
ℹ Ferry Gdns. ✆ Gosport (070 17) 22944.

★★**Anglesey,** *Crescent Rd, Alverstoke, PO12 2DH.* ✆ (0705) 582157. C. ✉ 19 bedrs, 5 bp, 14 bps, TV, Dgs. ✗ a l c, mc, LD 9.45. ☎ CH, Dgs, U 3, Ac, con 20, CF. £ BB £22·50–£24·50, DB £28·50–£32·50, WB, ①, Bk £2·75, L £3·50, D £6, cc 1 2 3, Dep b.
Bridgemary Manor, PH, z (R), *Brewers Lane, PO13 0JY.* ✆ Fareham (0329) 232946. C. ✉ 16 bedrs, 3 ba, Dgs. ☎ TV, Dgs, CP 16, CF, 2 st.

Rescue Service: Southern Auto Repairs, Unit 7, Quay La. ✆ (0705) 526223.
Repairer: Auto-Mech (Commercials) Ltd, Dock Rd, Cranbourne Industrial Estate. ✆ (0705) 528525.

GOUDHURST Kent. Map 10C
Pop 2,663. Tonbridge 12, London 44, Ashford 21, Canterbury 33, Hawkhurst 6, Hurst Green 7, Tunbridge Wells 10.
EC Wed. **Golf** Lamberhurst 18h. **See** Parish Church of St Mary (Culpeper tombs), Weavers' Cottages, old "Star and Eagle" Inn, Bedgebury National Pinetum 2½ m S, Pattyndenne Manor.

★★**Star & Eagle,** *High St, TN17 1AL.* ✆ (0580) 211512. RS Mon L. C. ✉ 11 bedrs, 9 bp, 2 bps, TV. ✗ a l c, mc, LD 9.30. ☎ CH, Dgs, CP 25, Ac, 3 st. £ BB £22–£25, DB £25–£35, WB, ②, Bk £3, L £4·95, D £7·25, cc 1 2 3 6.
★**Green Cross** (late **Goudhurst**), *Station Rd, TN17 1HA.* (1 m W of village on A262). ✆ (0580) 211200.

GRANGE IN BORROWDALE Cumbria. Map 26F
Pop 50. Keswick 4, London 289.
EC Sat. **Golf** Keswick 9h. **See** Bowder Stone, old Bridge, Castle Crag, Grange Fell.

■★★★**Borrowdale Gates** (R), *CA12 5UQ.* ✆ Borrowdale (059 684) 204. C.

⊷ 20 bedrs, 15 bp, 3 ba, TV, Dgs. **✗** a l c, mc, at, LD 8.45. 🅟 CH, TV, CP 40, Ac, CF, 5 BGf, 0 st, Dis. **£** BB fr £12, DB fr £25, WT £145–£155, DBB £20·70–£24, WB, ①, Bk £2·50, D £9, cc 1 2 3 5, Dep a.

GRANGE-OVER-SANDS Cumbria. Map 27C
Pop 3,474. Lancaster 24, London 259, Ambleside 19, Kendal 13, Kirkby Lonsdale 20, Ulverston 15.
EC Thur. **Golf** Grange-over-Sands 18h. **See** 12th cent Cartmel Priory Gatehouse 1½ m W, Holker Hall 3 m SW.
🆔 Council Offices, Main St. ✆ Grange-over-Sands (044 84) 4331.

★★★**Cumbria Grand,** Lindale Rd, LA11 6EN. ✆ (044 84) 2331.
★★**Grange,** Lindale Rd, LA11 6EJ. ✆ (044 84) 3666. C. ⊷ 40 bedrs, 32 bp, 3 ba, TV, Dgs. ✗ mc, at, LD 9. 🅟 ch, TV, Dgs, CP 100, Ac, con 150, CF, 1 BGf, 2 st. £ BB £14–£22, DB £24–£40, cc 1 2 3 6.
↡★★**Graythwaite Manor** (R), Fernhill Rd, LA11 7JE. ✆ (044 84) 2001. RS Xmas. C. ⊷ 24 bedrs, 12 bp, 2 bps, 6 ba, TV. ✗ mc, at, LD 8. 🅟 CH, TV, CP 18, U 4, G 10, tc, CF, 1 BGf, 1 st, Dis. £ WT £129·50–£199·50, DT £19·50–£32·50, ①, Bk £3, L £4, D £8·50.
★★**Kents Bank,** Kensford Rd, LA11 7BB. ✆ (044 84) 2054. RS Xmas & New Year's Eve. C. ⊷ 8 bedrs, 3 bp, 2 ba, Dgs. ✗ a l c, mc, at, LD 9. 🅟 CH, TV, Dgs, CP 30, Ac, CF, 4 st. £ BB £11·75–£13·50, DB £22–£23, WT £146–£156, DT £22–£23, DBB £19–£20, WB, ②, Bk £4, L £3, D £7·50, cc 1 3
★★**Netherwood,** Lindale Rd, LA11 6ET. ✆ (044 84) 2552. C. ⊷ 23 bedrs, 15 bp, 2 bps, 3 ba, Dgs. ✗ mc, at, LD 8.15. 🅟 N, CH, TV, Dgs, CP 60, Ac, con 200, CF, 1 st. £ BB £15·50–£18, DB £31–£36, WT £171·50–£185, DT £24·50–£26·50, DBB £21–£23, WB, ①, Bk £3, L £4·25, D £6·50.
★**Commodore,** Main St, LA11 6DY. ✆ (044 84) 2381.
▣★**Methven** (R), Methven Rd, LA11 7DU. ✆ (044 84) 2031. Open Apr–Oct. C 3. ⊷ 14 bedrs, 1 bp, 2 bps, 4 ba, Dgs. ✗ mc, at, LD 7. 🅟 ch, TV, CP 14, 1 BGf, 5 st. £ BB £10–£12, DB £20–£30, DBB £15–£17, ②, Bk £2·75, D £4, Dep.
🅿**Ap. Grayrigge,** (R), Kents Bank Rd, LA11 7HD. ✆ (044 84) 2345.
Elton, PH, x (Unl), Windermere Rd, LA11 6EQ. ✆ (044 84) 2838. C. ⊷ 10 bedrs, 1 sh, 2 ba, ns, TV. 🅟 ch, TV, Dgs, ns, CP 8, CF, 1 st. £ BB £9–£9·50, WT (b) £70–£75, DT (b) fr £11–£11·50, ①.
Thornfield House, G, x (Unl), Kents Bank Rd, LA11 7DT. ✆ (044 84) 2512. Open Apr–Oct. C 5. ⊷ 6 bedrs, 1 ba, TV. 🅟 CH, CP 6, 1 st. £ DB fr £15, WT (b) fr £75, DT (b) fr £11·50, ①.
Uplands, G, y (Rl), Haggs La, Cartmel, CA11 6HD. ✆ Cartmel (044 854) 249. C 9. ⊷ 3 bedrs, 3 bps, 1 ba. 🅟 CH, CP 4, 4 st. £ BB £10–£13·50, DB £20–£27, ①, D £8.

GRANTHAM Lincolnshire. Map 23C
Pop 30,502. Stamford 21, London 111, Boston 30, Lincoln 25, Melton Mowbray 16, Newark 15, Nottingham 24, Sleaford 14, Spalding 30.
EC Wed. **MD** Thur, Sat. **Golf** Belton Park 18h. **See** Market Cross, Isaac Newton statue, Grammar School (Isaac Newton educ), St Wulfram's Church 14th cent, Grantham House, Old Inns, Belton House

2½ m NE, Woolsthorpe Manor 7 m S, Belvoir Castle 6 m SW.
🆔 Guildhall. ✆ Grantham (0476) 66444.

★★★**Angel & Royal** (TH), High St, NG31 6PN. ✆ (0476) 65816. C. ⊷ 32 bedrs, 14 bp, 7 ba, TV, Dgs. ✗ a l c, mc, at, LD 10. 🅟 N, CH, Dgs, CP 60, Ac, con 75, CF, 1 st. £ BB £31–£34, DB £43·50–£50·50, WB, ①, cc 1 2 3 4 5 6, Dep (Xmas).
★★★**George,** High St, NG31 6NN. ✆ (0476) 63286. ⊷ 47 bedrs, 41 bp, 6 bps, TV, Dgs. ✗ a l c, mc, at, LD 10. 🅟 N, CH, Dgs, CP 70, U 2, Ac, con 120, CF, 2 st. £ BB £28–£35, DB £38–£45, DBB £36–£45, WB, ①, Bk £3·50, L £6·95, D £8·25, cc 1 2 3 5, Dep.
★★**Kings,** North Par, NG31 8AU. ✆ (0476) 65881. C. ⊷ 17 bedrs, 5 bp, 5 bps, 2 ba, TV, Dgs. ✗ a l c, mc, LD 9.30. 🅟 N, CH, Dgs, CP 70, Ac, con 100, CF, 3 BGf, 6 st. £ BB £17–£23, DB £25–£31, DBB fr £23, WB, ①, Bk £3·50, L £5·55, D £6·85, cc 1 2 3 5.
Garden, H, (R), 86 Barrowby Rd, NG31 9AF. ✆ (0476) 62040. C. ⊷ 10 bedrs, 3 ba. 🅟 CH, TV, CP 20, CF, 2 st. £ BB fr £13·75, DB fr £21·50, ①.

Rescue Service: B & B Garages, Spittlegate Level. ✆ (0476) 64688. Levick's Garage, North Par. ✆ (0476) 3177. Ponton Main Service Station, Gt North Rd, A1. ✆ Great Ponton (047 683) 261.

GRAPPENHALL Cheshire. Map 20D
Pop 6,613. Knutsford 9½, London 181, Altrincham 10, Chester 21, Northwich 11, Warrington 3.
Golf Lymm 18h. **See** 17th cent St Wilfrid's Church, Village Stocks adjoining.

▣★**Rockfield** (R), Alexandra Rd, WA4 2EL. ✆ Warrington (0925) 62898. Closed Xmas–New Year. RS Sun. C. ⊷ 7 bedrs, 3 bp, 1 ba, annexe 8 bedrs, 2 bp, 2 ba, TV, Dgs. ✗ mc, LD 9. 🅟 CH, TV, CP 30, Ac, con 25, CF, 3 BGf, 3 st. £ BB £17–£25, DB £26–£36, DBB £24–£32, ①, Bk £3·50, D £7, cc 1 3 6.

GRASMERE Cumbria. Map 26D
Pop 1,029. Ambleside 4, London 273, Keswick 12, Penrith 25.
EC Thur. **Golf** Windermere 18h. **See** Dove Cottage and Wordsworth Museum, St Oswald's Church, graves of Wordsworth and Coleridge in churchyard, Rush-bearing ceremony Aug, Grasmere Sports Aug.
🆔 Broadgate News Agency. ✆ Grasmere (096 65) 245.

★★★★**Wordsworth,** LA22 9TA. ✆ (096 65) 592. C. ⊷ 35 bedrs, 34 bp, 1 bps, TV. ✗ a l c, mc, at, LD 9. 🅟 Lt, N, CH, CP 54, Ac, sp, sb, sol, con 150, CF, 2 BGf, 1 st, Dis. £ WB, cc 1 2 3 5, Dep b.
▣★★★**Gold Rill,** LA22 9PU. ✆ (096 65) 486. C 5. ⊷ 22 bedrs, 17 bp, 5 sh, 1 ba, TV. ✗ mc, at, LD 8·30. 🅟 CH, TV, CP 30, sp, 2 BGf, 1 st, Dis. £ BB £18–£29, DB £36–£58, DBB £21–£36, ①, Bk £4·50, D £10·50, cc 1 2 3 5, Dep a.▲
▣★★★**Grasmere Red Lion,** Red Lion Sq, LA22 9SS. ✆ (096 65) 456. Open Mar–Nov. C. ⊷ 36 bedrs, 34 bp, 2 bps, 2 ba, TV, Dgs. ✗ mc, at. 🅟 Lt, CH, Dgs, CP 40, Ac, con, CF, 2 st. £ BB £23·50–£23·50, DB £37–£45, DBB £27–35, WB, ①, Bk £4·60, L £5·75, D £9·50, cc 1 2 3 5.

★★★**Prince of Wales,** LA22 9PR. ✆ (096 65) 666. C. ⊷ 81 bedrs, 72 bp, 9 bps, TV, Dgs. ✗ mc, at, LD 9. 🅟 N, CH, CP 90, Ac, con 150, CF, 6 st. £ BB fr £33, DB fr £50·60, WB, ①, cc 1 2 3 5.
★★★**Swan** (TH), LA22 9RF. ✆ (096 65) 551. C. ⊷ 41 bedrs, 25 bp, 5 ba, TV, Dgs. ✗ mc, at, LD 8.45. 🅟 N, CH, Dgs, CP 40, CF, 0 st. £ BB £34·50–£41, DB £46·50–£58, WB, ①, cc 1 2 3 4 5 6, Dep (Xmas).
▣★★**Grasmere** (R), LA22 9TA. ✆ (096 65) 277. Closed Dec–Feb. C. ⊷ 10 bedrs, 2 bp, 6 bps, 2 ba, Dgs. ✗ mc, at, LD 8. 🅟 TV, ns, CP 16, con 20, CF, 2 st. £ DB £26–£36, ②, Bk £4, D £10, Dep b.▲
▣★★**Oak Bank** (R), Broadgate, LA22 9TA. ✆ (096 65) 217. Closed Dec–Jan. RS. Feb & Nov. C. ⊷ 14 bedrs, 6 bp, 8 bps, Dgs. ✗ mc, at, LD 7.30. 🅟 ch, TV, CP 12, con 10, CF. £ BB £14–£18, DB £28–£36, WB, ①, Bk £5, D £9, cc 1 3, Dep b.
▣★★**Rothay Bank,** LA22 9RH. ✆ (096 65) 334. Open Feb–Nov, RS Feb. C. ⊷ 17 bedrs, 2 bp, 5 bps, 5 ba, Dgs. ✗ mc, LD 7.30. 🅟 CH, TV, Dgs, pf, CF, 1 st. £ BB £12·75–£20, DB £25–£34, DBB £21–24·95, WB, ②, Bk £3·75, D £8·50, cc 1 2 3 5 6, Dep a.
▣★**Moss Grove** (R), LA22 9SW. ✆ (096 65) 251.
Dunmail, G, x (Unl), Keswick Rd, LA22 9RE. ✆ (096 65) 256.

GRASSINGTON North Yorkshire. Map 27A
Pop 1,310. Leeds 31, London 222, Boroughbridge 29, Harrogate 25, Hawes 26, Leyburn 26, Settle 18, Skipton 9, Thirsk 34, York 44.
EC Thur. **Golf** Skipton 18h, Ilkley 18h. **See** Cobbled square, Linton Church, Old lead mines on Moor, Linton Church, Stump Cross caverns 5 m E, Museum.

★★★**Wilson Arms,** Station Rd, Threshfield, BD23 5EL. ✆ (0756) 752666. C. ⊷ 28 bedrs, 28 bp, TV, Dgs. ✗ a l c, mc, at, LD 9.45. 🅟 Lt, CH, TV, CP 55, U 1, Ac, con 50, CF, 0 st. £ BB £25–£27·50, DB £41·50–£46·50, WT £202–£236, WB, ①, Bk £4·25, L £5·75, D £9, cc 1 2 3 5 6, Dep b.

GRAVESEND Kent. Map 10A
Pop 52,532. Dartford 8, London 24, Dartford Tunnel 8½, Rochester 7, Sevenoaks 18, Tonbridge 19.
EC Wed. **MD** Daily. **Golf** Mid Kent 18h. **See** Chapel of Milton Chantry, Town Hall, Princess Pocahontas Memorial Church and Statue.

★★**Clarendon Royal,** Royal Pier Rd, DA12 2BE. ✆ (0474) 63151. Closed Xmas. C. ⊷ 22 bedrs, 3 bp, 5 ba, TV. ✗ a l c, mc, LD 10.30. 🅟 N, CH, CP 50, Ac, CF, 6 st. £ BB £17·80–£22·60, DB £31–£40·20, WB, ①, Bk £2·42, L £5, D £5, cc 1 2 3 5.
★★**M Tollgate Moat House,** Watling St, DA13 9RA. ✆ (0474) 57655. C. ⊷ 122 bedrs, 122 bp, TV, Dgs. ✗ a l c, mc, LD 9.45. 🅟 N, CH, Dgs, CP 200, Ac, con 120, CF. £ BB £27·50–£32·50, DB £34–£40, WB, ①, Bk £3·75, D £6·50, cc 1 2 3 4 5 6, Dep.
Sunnyside, M, G, yz (Unl), 3 Sunnyside, Windmill St, DA12 1LG. ✆ (0474) 65445.

Specialist Body Repairer: Motor Body Repair Centre, Norfolk Rd. ✆ (0474) 65840 and (0474) 63041.

Rescue Service: G & M Motors, Dover Rd, Northfleet. ☎ (0474) 22909.
Motor Body Repair Centre, Norfolk Rd. ☎ (0474) 63041.

GREAT AYTON North Yorkshire. Map 24D
Pop 5,160. Thirsk 22, London 241, Darlington 19, Helmsley 21, Middlesbrough 8½, Northallerton 18, Pickering 30, Stockton-on-Tees 11, Whitby 26.
EC Wed. **Golf** Nunthorpe 18h. **See** Captain Cook's Obelisk, School Room and Museum, Pre-Reformation All Saints' Church (graves of Capt Cook's family), Roseberry Topping.

★★★Ayton Hall (R), Low Green, TS9 6PS. ☎ (0642) 723595. C 10. ⌘ 7 bedrs, 7 bp, ns, TV. ✗ mc, at, LD 9.30. ⓑ CH, ns, CP, U 3, tc, con 30, 1st. £ BB £33–£43·95, DB £43–£58·90, DT £43·35–£56·35, DBB £47·80–£50·80, WB, ①, Bk £2·95, L £6·95, D £9·95, cc 1 2 3, Dep b.

GREAT BOUGHTON Cheshire.
See CHESTER.

GREAT DRIFFIELD Humberside (North Humberside)
See DRIFFIELD, GREAT.

GREAT DUNMOW Essex.
See DUNMOW.

GREAT GRIMSBY Humberside (South Humberside)
See GRIMSBY.

GREAT MALVERN Hereford & Worcester (Worcestershire)
See MALVERN.

GREAT MISSENDEN Bucks. Map 15E
Pop 9,844. Denham 14, London 31, Aylesbury 9½, Dunstable 18, High Wycombe 7, Oxford 27, Rickmansworth 12, St Albans 19, Slough 17.
EC Thur. **Golf** Ellesborough, Wendover 18h. **See** Church (12th cent), Missenden Abbey (College), Little Missenden Church, (10th cent Saxon), 2 m E.

Rescue Service: Prestwood Motor Co. Ltd, High St, Prestwood. ☎ (024 06) 3161.

GREAT SHELFORD Cambridgeshire. Map 15D
Pop 3,995. Royston 11, London 52, Bishop's Stortford 22, Cambridge 4, Haverhill 16, Newmarket 16.
EC Wed. **Golf** Gog Magog 18h. **See** Parish Church.

Rescue Service: A J Rayment, 28 Woollards La. ☎ Cambridge (0223) 843048.

GREAT SMEATON North Yorkshire. Map 24F
Pop 180. Northallerton 7, London 234, Darlington 0½, Richmond 13, Stockton on Tees 13.
Golf Darlington 18h. **See** Church.

Rescue Service: Toll Bar Garage, Entercommon. ☎ (060 981) 225.

GREAT SOMERFORD Wiltshire. Map 5B.
Swindon 14, London 91, Bath 20, Bristol 29, Cirencester 16, Marlborough 21, Warminster 27.

Rescue Service: Forge Garage. ☎ Seagry (0249) 720410.

GREATSTONE-ON-SEA Kent. Map 10F
Littlestone-on-Sea 1, London 70, Folkestone 15, Lydd 6, New Romney 2, Rye 13.
EC Wed. **Golf** Littlestone 18h. **See** Romney, Hythe & Dymchurch Railway.

Rescue Service: Philbor Motors Ltd, Greatstone Garage, 113 Coast Dr, nr New Romney. ☎ New Romney (067 93) 3136.

GREAT TORRINGTON Devon
See TORRINGTON.

GREAT WAKERING Essex. Maps 10A and 17D
Pop 4,770. Southend-on-Sea 5, London 47.
EC Wed. **Golf** Rochford Hundred 18h. **See** Church of St Nicholas, Early Roman settlement.

Rescue Service: Service Garage, High St, Little Wakering corner. ☎ Southend-on-Sea (0702) 219252.

GREAT WITCHINGHAM Norfolk. Map 16C
Pop 400. Norwich 11, London 122, Cromer 19, East Dereham 9½, Fakenham 14, King's Lynn 32.
EC Sat. **Golf** Royal Norwich 18h. **See** Lenwade Mill, Norfolk Wildlife Park and Pheasant Trust, Great Witchingham Hall, St Mary's Church.

★★Lenwade House (R & Cl), NR9 5QP. ☎ (060 544) 288. C 5. ⌘ 14 bedrs, 9 bp, 5 bps, TV. Dgs. ✗ a l c, mc, LD 9.15. ⓑ CH, TV, Dgs, CP 40, sp, tc, pf, sc, sol, con 30, CF, 1 st. £ BB £24·80, DB £36·75, DT £37·50, DBB £32·80, WB, ②, Bk £3·50, L £6·50, D £7·95, cc 1 2 3 5.

GREAT YARMOUTH Norfolk
See YARMOUTH, GREAT.

GREAT YELDHAM Essex. M.Area 17E
6 m NW of Halstead. Pop 1,450. Braintree 10, London 54, Bury St Edmunds 21, Colchester 20, Haverhill 9, Sudbury 9.
See 900-year-old Great Oak, 17th cent White Hart Hotel.

Rescue Service: G S Last Ltd, Oak Garage, The Street. ☎ (0787) 237218.

GREENODD Cumbria. Map 26F
Pop 250. M6 Motorway 25, London 268, Ambleside 17, Broughton-in-Furness 9, Kendal 21, Kirkby Lonsdale 28, Lancaster 37, Ulverston 3½.
Golf Ulverston 18h.

Rescue Service: Hurley & Peake, Service Garage. ☎ (022 986) 208.

GRETA BRIDGE Durham. Map 24F
Pop 90. Boroughbridge 37, London 244, Brough 19, Darlington 16, Harrogate 46, Leyburn 23, Middleton-in-Teesdale 13, Northallerton 25, West Auckland 13.
Golf Barnard Castle 18h. **See** 'Meeting of the Waters', Mortham Towers.

★★Morritt Arms, Rokeby, DL12 9SE. ☎ (0833) 27232. C. ⌘ 23 bedrs, 14 bp, 5 ba, TV, Dgs. ✗ a l c, mc, at, LD 9. ⓑ ch, TV, Dgs, CP 100, G 10, pf, con 200, CF, 0 st. £ BB £20–£25, DB £30–£37, WT £160, DB £30–£37, WT £160, DBB £26–£28, WB, ①, Bk £4, L £6, D £10, cc 1 3 5.

GRIMOLDBY Lincolnshire. Map 23B.
Louth 5½, London 153, Cleethorpes 17, Mablethorpe 10, Skegness 24.

Rescue Service: M. J. Watts, Central Garage, Tinkle St. ☎ South Cockerington (050 782) 231.

GRIMSBY Humberside (South Humberside). Maps 23B and 24A
See also CLEETHORPES.
Pop 92,000. Louth 16, London 164, Hull 31, Gainsborough 36, Market Rasen 20, Scunthorpe 30.
MD Tue, Fri, Sat. **Golf** Grimsby 18h, Cleethorpes 18h. **See** Fish Docks, new Law Courts, Historic Churches (St James'), Old Clee Church.

★★★★M Humber Royal Crest, Littlecoates Rd, DN34 4LX. ☎ (0472) 50295. C. ⌘ 52 bedrs, 52 bp, ns, TV, Dgs. ✗ a l c, mc, LD 9.45. ⓑ Lt, N, CH, Dgs, CP 90, Ac, con 285, CF, 2 st. £ B fr £46·50, BD fr £55, WB, ①, Bk £5·50, D £9·95, cc 1 2 3 4 5 6.

★★★M Crest, St James Sq, DN31 1EP. ☎ (0472) 59771. C. ⌘ 132 bedrs, 132 bp, ns, TV, Dgs. ✗ a l c, mc, LD 9.45. ⓑ Lt, N, CH, Dgs, CP 90, Ac, sb, con 40, CF, 2 st. £ B fr £41, BD fr £51, WB, ①, Bk £5·25, D £8·95, cc 1 2 3 4 5 6.

★★Oaklands, Barton St, Laceby, DN37 7LF. ☎ (0472) 72248. C. ⌘ 50 bedrs, 50 bp, 2 ba, TV. ✗ a l c, mc, at, LD 9. ⓑ N, CH, CP 250, sb, con 150, CF, 10 BGf. £ BB £30–£40, DB £40–£50, WT £270, DT £42, DBB £37, WB, ①, Bk £4·50, L £5, D £7, cc 1 2 3 4 5.

Repairer: Hartford Motors (Grimsby) Ltd, Corporation St. ☎ (0472) 58941.
Specialist Body Repairer: Grimsby Motors Ltd, Victoria St. ☎ (0472) 56161.
MC Repairer: Freddie Frith Ltd, 119 Victoria St. ☎ (0472) 54031.
Rescue Service: Burchell & Blackburn Ltd, Estate Road No 5, Pyewipe Industrial Estate. ☎ (0472) 41281.
Grimsby Motors Ltd, 415 Victoria St. ☎ (0472) 56161.

GRIMSTON Norfolk. Map 16E
Pop 1,706. King's Lynn 7, London 106, East Dereham 21, Fakenham 16, Norwich 39, Swaffham 12.
EC Tue. **Golf** King's Lynn 18h. **See** Site of Roman villa, 13th cent church.

★★★★Congham Hall (R), King's Lynn, PE32 1AH. ☎ Hillington (0485) 600250. Closed Dec 23–Jan 8. C 12. ⌘ 10 bedrs, 8 bp, 1 bps, 1 ba, TV. ✗ a l c, LD 9.30. ⓑ CH, CP 50, U 2, sp, tc, con 12, 2 st. £ BB £42, DB £52, WB, ②, Bk £3·95, L £8·50, D fr £16, cc 1 2 3 5.

Rescue Service: S R V Motors, Lynn Rd. ☎ Hillington (0485) 600248.

GRINDLEFORD Derbyshire. Map 22A
Pop 411. Matlock 13, London 158, Ashbourne 24, Buxton 15, Chapel-en-le-Frith 14, Chesterfield 13, Glossop 20, Leek 25, Sheffield 10.
Golf Bakewell 9h. **See** Padley Chapel, Priory ruins, Pilgrimage in July.

★★★Maynard Arms, Main Rd, Grindleford Bridge, S30 1HP. ☎ (0433) 30321. C. ⌘ 13 bedrs, 9 bp, 2 bps, 2 ba, TV, Dgs. ✗ mc, LD 9.30. ⓑ CH, CP 70, G 4, con 120, CF, 1 st. £ BB £29, DB £40, DBB £23, WB, ②, Bk £4, L £6·25, D £9·75, cc 1 2 5, Dep b.

GROBY Leicestershire. Map 22F.
Pop 4,890. Leicester 5, London 102,
Burton-on-Trent 21, Coventry 27, Melton
Mowbray 19.
Golf Charnwood Forest 9h.

★★**Brant Inn,** *Leicester Rd, LE6 ODU.*
☎ Leicester (0533) 872703. RS Xmas. C.
⇔ 10 bedrs, 8 sh, 1 ba, TV. ✘ a l c, mc, LD
10. ⓕ CH, Dgs, CP 200, G 2, Ac, con 200,
CF, 2 st. £ BB £12·50–£18·50, DB £28·50,
②, L £4·95, D £7, cc 1 3 5.

GROOMBRIDGE Kent. Map 7D
Pop 1,056. Tunbridge Wells 4, London 40,
East Grinstead 11, Edenbridge 10,
Crowborough 4.

Rescue Service: D B G Motor Engineers,
Station Rd. ☎ (089 276) 204

GUILDFORD Surrey. Map 7C
Pop 60,000. Ripley 6, London 28, Bagshot
11, Dorking 13, Farnham 10, Haslemere
12, Hindhead 12, Horsham 19,
Leatherhead 12, Petworth 20, Pulborough
22, Woking 6½, Worthing 34.
See Plan, p. 219.
MD Tue, Fri, Sat. **P** See Plan. **Golf**
Guildford 18h. **See** Cathedral, Castle
ruins, Abbot's Hospital (1619), Guildhall,
St Mary's Church Tower (late Norman),
Museum, Yvonne Arnaud Theatre, Royal
Grammar School (by arr), Albury Park,
Watts Gallery, Compton (Watts Mortuary
Chapel nearby), Loseley House 2 m SW,
Hatchlands 5 m NE, 18th cent Clandon
Park 3½ m NE.
ⓘ Civic Hall, London Rd. ☎ Guildford
(0483) 67314.

★★★**Angel** (TH), *High St, GU1 3DR.*
☎ (0483) 64555. C. ⇔ 25 bedrs, 24 bp, 1
bps, TV, Dgs. ✘ mc, at, LD 9.30. ⓕ N, CH,
Dgs, Ac, CF, 2 st. £ BB £40·50, DB £55·50,
WB, ①, cc 1 2 3 4 5 6, Dep (Xmas).
★★★**White Horse,** *Upper High St, GU1
3JG.* ☎ (0483) 64511. RS Dec 24–27. C.
⇔ 38 bedrs, 31 bp, 2 ba, TV, Dgs. ✘ a l c,
LD 9.15. ⓕ N, CH, Dgs, G 14, Ac, con 35,
CF, 0 st. £ B £33, BD £40, WB, ①, Bk £4·25,
D £6·50, cc 1 2 3 4 5 6, Dep.
Blanes Court (R), *Albury Rd, GU1 2BT.*
☎ (0483) 573171.
Carlton, H, (R), *36 London Rd, GU1 2AF.*
☎ (0483) 576539. C. ⇔ 36 bedrs. 12 bp, 6
bps, 7 ba, TV. ⓕ CH, TV, CP 40, CF, 2 BGf,
4 st. £ BB £15–£19, DB £22–£25, DT (b)
£16·75, ①, Bk £2·75, D £3·75, cc 1 2 3.

Repairers: Grays of Guildford, By-pass,
Woodbridge Meadows. ☎ (0483) 60601.
Puttocks Ltd, Aldershot Rd. ☎ (0483)
60751.
Wadham Stringer (Guildford) Ltd, By-
pass and Woodbridge Rd. ☎ (0483)
69231.

GUISBOROUGH Cleveland. Map 24D
Pop 19,100. Thirsk 27, London 246,
Helmsley 27, Stockton-on-Tees 13,
Whitby 20.
EC Wed. **MD** Thur, Sat. **Golf** Saltburn
18h. **See** Upleathem Church (Smallest in
England).

★**M Moor Cock,** *West End Rd.
TS14 6RL.* ☎ (0287) 32342.

GUISELEY West Yorkshire. Map 25E
Pop 12,000. Leeds 9, London 200,
Bradford 7, Burnley 29, Harrogate 14,
Hawes 50, Skipton 12, Todmorden 23,
York 31.

EC Tue. **Golf** Hawksworth 18h. **See** St
Oswald's Church, 17th cent Rectory,
Harry Ramsden's 'Biggest Chip Shop in
the World' on the Guiseley to Menston
road.

Rescue Service: Oxford Road Garage,
Oxford Rd. ☎ (0943) 73808.

GUNNISLAKE Cornwall. Map 3C
Pop 4,955. Tavistock 4½, London 207,
Camelford 26, Launceston 14, Liskeard
13, Saltash 13.
EC Wed. **Golf** St. Mellion 18h. **See**
Morwell Rocks, Weir Head.

◨★**Cornish Inn,** *PL18 9BW.* ☎ Tavistock
(0822) 832475.
★**Tavistock Arms,** *Fore St, PL18 9BN.*
☎ Tavistock (0822) 832217. C. ⇔ 6
bedrs, 1 sh, 2 ba, Dgs. ✘ mc, LD 9.30.
ⓕ ch, TV, Dgs, CP 12, Ac, CF. £ BB £8, DB
£16–£17, WB, ①, Bk £1·80, D £3·50,
cc 1 3 5.

Rescue Service: Central Motors.
☎ Tavistock (0822) 832432.

GUNTHORPE Nottinghamshire. M.Area
22D
9 m NE of Nottingham. Pop 726.
Grantham 17, London 128, Newark 12.
Golf Oxton 18h. **See** Gunthorpe Hall.

Rescue Service: Newbridge Garage
(Gunthorpe) Ltd, Lowdham Rd.
☎ Nottingham (0602) 663808.

GURNEY SLADE Somerset. Map 5C
Pop 300. Radstock 6, London 116,
Shepton Mallet 7, Wells 5½, Bristol 16.

Rescue Service: Motor Services (Mendip)
Ltd. ☎ Oakhill (0749) 840252.

GWITHIAN Cornwall. Map 2E
Pop 300. Redruth 10, London 273,
Falmouth 18, Helston 11, Penzance 10, St
Ives 7.
Golf Lelant 18h. **See** Godrevy Point,
North Cornwall Coastal Path.

◨★★**Glencoe House** (R), *23
Churchtown Rd, TR27 5BX.* ☎ (0736)
752216. Closed Dec–Jan. C. ⇔ 11 bedrs,
9 bp, 2 bps, TV, Dgs. ✘ a l c, mc, LD 9.
ⓕ CH, TV, CP 14, sp, 3 st. £ BB
£18·50–£21, DB £28·50–£33, DT £28–£30,
DBB £25–£28, WB, ①, BR £2·75, D £7·50,
cc 1 3 6.▲

HADDENHAM Buckinghamshire. Map
15E.
Pop 5,000. High Wycombe 14, London 43,
Aylesbury 6, Bicester 16, Henley-on-
Thames 22, Oxford 16, Reading 27,
Rickmansworth 24, Wallingford 19,
Wantage 28.

Rescue Service: Haddenham Motors Ltd,
15 High St. ☎ (0844) 291262.

HADLEIGH Suffolk. Map 17C
Pop 5,985. Colchester 14, London 70,
Bury St Edmunds 20, Clacton-on-Sea 24,
Harwich 21, Ipswich 10, Stowmarket 14,
Sudbury 11.
MD Fri. **Golf** Nayland 18h. **See** Deanery
Tower, 15th cent Almshouses, EE and
Perp Church, Guildhall.

Rescue Service: F Holbrow Ltd, High St.
☎ (047 32) 823286.

HADLEY WOOD Greater London
(Middx.). M. Area 15F
Barnet 1½, London 13, Enfield 5, Hatfield 9,
St Albans 11.

EC Thur. **Golf** Hadley Wood 18h.

♨★★★★**West Lodge Park** (R), *EN4 0PY.*
☎ 01-440 8311. C. ⇔ 50 bedrs, 50 bp, TV.
✘ a l c, mc, LD 9.30. ⓕ Lt, N, CH, CP 200,
con 40, CF, 2 st. £ BB £40, DB £54, WB, ①,
cc 1 2 3 5 6.

HAGLEY Hereford & Worcester
(Worcestershire). Maps 13B & 14A
Pop 4,500. Birmingham 11, London 120,
M5 Motorway 5, Bromsgrove 7,
Kidderminster 6, Stourbridge 2½.
Golf Stourbridge 18h.

Rescue Service: Clark's Motor Services
(Rednal) Ltd, Forge Garage,
Kidderminster Rd. ☎ Kidderminster
884873 & 021-453 7127.

HAILSHAM East Sussex. Map 7F
Pop 17,000. Uckfield 12, London 56,
Eastbourne 8, Hastings 17, Hurst Green
18, Lewes 13, Newhaven 15, Rye 26,
Tunbridge Wells 22.
EC Thur. **MD** Wed. **Golf** Willingdon,
Eastbourne 18h. **See** Restored Perp.
Church, Mickelham Priory 2 m.
ⓘ Area Library, Western Rd. ☎ Hailsham
(0323) 840604.

Old Forge, G, x (R), *Magham Down,
BN27 1PN.* ☎ (0323) 842893. C. ⇔ 4
bedrs, 1 ba. ✘ a l c. ⓕ CH, TV, CP 20. £ BB
£12–£18, DB £18, ①, Bk £3, L £2·95, D fr
£4·50.

HALE Gtr Manchester (Cheshire). Maps
19B and 20B
Pop 16,247. Knutsford 7½, London 180,
Altrincham 1, Macclesfield 14, Northwich
12, Warrington 14.
EC Wed. **Golf** Altrincham 18h. **See** War
Memorial Gdns, Halecroft (Hale Rd),
Bolling Valley, 18th cent Chapel.

★★★**M Ashley,** *Ashley Rd, WA15 9SF.*
☎ 061-928 3794. C. ⇔ 49 bedrs, 48 bp, 1
bps, TV, Dgs. ✘ a l c, mc, at, LD 9.45. ⓕ Lt,
N, CH, Dgs, Ac, con 180, CF, 6 st. £ BB
£32, DB £42, WB, ② WB, Bk £3·30, L
£5·80, D £6·80, cc 1 2 3 5 6, Dep b.

Repairer: Hale Barns Garage, Hale Rd.
☎ 061-980 4116.
Rescue Service: Tom Davies (Motors)
Ltd, Grove La. ☎ 061-980 7010.

HALES Norfolk. Map 16B
1 m SE of Loddon. Pop 448. Scole 20,
London 116, Aldeburgh 28, Great
Yarmouth 14, Lowestoft 14, Norwich 12,
Saxmundham 25.
Golf Beccles 9h. **See** 10th cent Church.

MC Repairer: Ball, C J & Son, Yarmouth
Rd. ☎ Raveningham (050 846) 302
Sctr Repairer: Ball, C J & Son, Yarmouth
Rd. ☎ Raveningham (050 846) 302

HALESOWEN West Midlands. Map 21F
Pop 60,000. Birmingham 7, London 118,
Bridgnorth 18, Bromsgrove 8½, Droitwich
14, Kidderminster 10, Walsall 11,
Wolverhampton 11.
EC Thur. **Golf** Halesowen 18h. **See** Abbey
ruins, 11th cent St John the Baptist
Church, Leasowes Park.

Rescue Service: Hunnington Motor Co
Ltd, Red Hill Garage, 183 Bromsgrove Rd,
Hunnington. ☎ Romsley (0562) 710243.

HALESWORTH Suffolk. Map 16B
Pop 3,927. Ipswich 31, London 105,
Lowestoft 16; Beccles 9, Bury St
Edmunds 42.

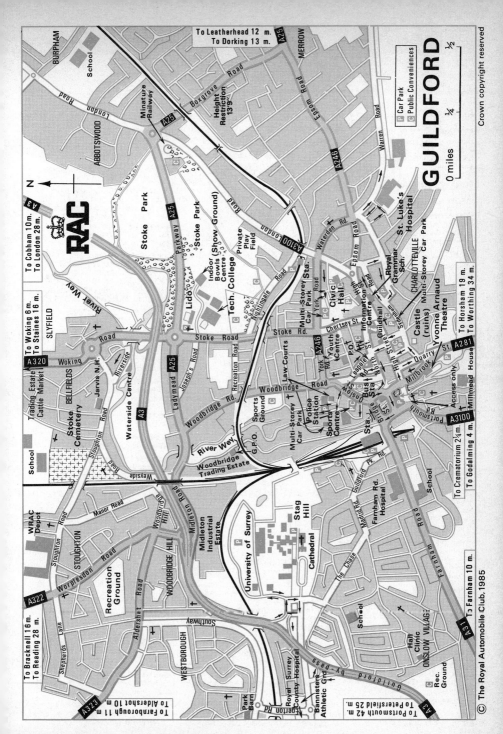

GUILDFORD

EC Thur. **MD** Wed. **Golf** Southwold 9h.
See Parish Church, Heveningham Hall,
Holton Mill 1 m.

Rescue Service: Kerridge (Halesworth)
Ltd, London Rd. ✆ (098 67) 2138.
M R King & Sons Ltd, 46 Quay St.
✆ (098 67) 3580.

HALIFAX West Yorkshire. Map 25F/33A
Pop 87,488. Huddersfield 7, London 187,
M62 Motorway 4½, Bradford 8, Leeds 15,
Oldham 19, Rochdale 17, Skipton 17,
Todmorden 12, Wakefield 17.
MD Daily. **Golf** Halifax 18h, West End
18h. **See** St John's Parish Church, Piece
Hall, Shibden Hall Folk Museum and Park,
Bankfield Museum, Town Hall, Wainhouse
Tower.
ℹ Piece Hall. ✆ Halifax (0422) 68725.

▣**⌂★★★Holdsworth House,**
Holdsworth Rd, Holmfield, HX2 9TG.
✆ (0422) 244270. Closed 1 week Xmas. C.
🚗 30 bedrs, 18 bp, 12 bps, TV, Dgs.
✗ a l c, mc, at, LD 9.30. ⓟ N, CH, Dgs, CP
40, Ac, con 100, CF, 2 st. £ BB £24–£38,
DB £42–£52, WT £240–£320, DT £35–£62,
DBB £28–£52, WB, ⚼, Bk £3, L £8, D £10,
cc 1 2 3 4 5 6.

★★★Princess, *Princess St, HX1 1TR.*
✆ (0422) 54227. C. 🚗 50 bedrs, 29 bp, 3
bps, 3 ba, TV, Dgs. ✗ mc, LD 9.45. ⓟ Lt, N,
CH, Dgs, G 8, Ac, con 120, CF, 3 st. £ BB
£12·75–£29·75, DB £25–£40·50, DT £25–
£40, DBB £21–£37·25, WB, ⚹ 10%, Bk
£1·95, L £3·50, D £7·50, cc 1 2 3 5 6, Dep.

Repairers: Hoffmans of Halifax Ltd,
Huddersfield Rd. ✆ (0422) 65944.
Mayfield Garage (Halifax) Ltd, Queens Rd.
✆ (0422) 67711.▲
Rescue Service: Bradshaw Garage Ltd,
Bradshaw La, Bradshaw. ✆ (0422) 44958.
Prospect Service Station, Keighley Rd,
Ovenden. ✆ (0422) 67377.
Salterhebble Garage Ltd, Huddersfield
Rd. ✆ (0422) 54077 and (0422) 67800.

HALLAND East Sussex. Map 7D
Pop 780. Uckfield 3½, London 47,
Eastbourne 15, Hastings 25, Hurst Green
17, Lewes 7½, Rye 33, Tunbridge Wells 19.
Golf Piltdown, Uckfield 18h.

★★★M Halland Forge, *BN8 6PW.*
✆ (082 584) 456. C 5. 🚗 20 bedrs, 17 bp,
3 bps, TV, Dgs. ✗ a l c, mc, at, LD 9.30.
ⓟ CP 70, Ac, con 70, 8 BGf, 1st, Dis. £ BB
£29·50, DB £45, WT £216, DT £38, DBB
£31·50, WB, ⚹ L £7, D £9, cc 1 2 3 5 6.

HALLWORTHY Cornwall. Map 3C.
Launceston 11, London 222, Bodmin 19,
Bude 15, Tavistock 23, Wadebridge 16.

Wilsey Down, H, x, *Nr Camelford,*
PL32 9SH. ✆ Otterham Station (084 06)
205. C. 🚗 7 bedrs, 1 sh, 2 ba, Dgs. ✗ a l c.
ⓟ Lt, CH, TV, Dgs, CP 75, CF, 2 st. £ BB
£8·50, DB £17, DT £11, ⚼, Bk £2, L £2, D
£2, cc 1 2 3.

HALSTEAD Essex. Map 17C
Pop 9,385. Braintree 6½, London 50,
Colchester 13, Haverhill 15, Sudbury 8.
EC Wed. **MD** Tue, Fri. **Golf** Braintree 18h.
See St Andrew's Church, Gosfield Hall 2½
m SW, Hedingham Castle Keep 4 m NNW,
round church.

Rescue Service: Kendall & Morrall, Mount
Hill Auto Point. ✆ (0787) 473803

HALSTEAD Kent. M.Area 7B
Pop 1,800. Bromley 9, London 21,
Croydon 13, Maidstone 21, Sevenoaks 5,
Sidcup 8½, Westerham 7½.
EC Wed. **Golf** Knole Park, Sevenoaks 18h.

Repairer: Wood, C R & Sons, Retreat
Garage, Polhill. ✆ Badgers Mount 247.
Specialist Body Repairer: Wood, C R &
Son, Retreat Garage, Polhill. ✆ Badgers
Mount (095 97) 247.

HALTWHISTLE Northumberland. Maps
26A and 31E
Pop 2,500. Alston 17, London 298,
Bellingham 26, Brampton 13, Hexham 16.
EC Wed. **MD** Thur. **Golf** Greenhead 12h.
See EE Church, 12th cent Bellister Castle,
Roman Wall, Featherstone Castle.
ℹ Market Pl. ✆ Haltwhistle (0498) 20920.

Vallum Lodge, H, x (R), *Military Rd,*
Twice Brewed, Bardon Mill, Hexham,
NE47 7AN. ✆ Bardon Mill (049 84) 248.
C. 🚗 7 bedrs, 2 ba, Dgs. ✗ a l c. ⓟ CH, TV,
CP 25, CF, 1 BGf, 4 st. £ BB £10–£10·50,
DB £20–£21, DBB £15·75–£16·25, ⚹ Bk
£3·10, L £3·75, D £5·75.

Rescue Service: John Elliot (Garage) Ltd,
West End Garage. ✆ (049 84) 20074.

HAMBLETON Lancashire. Map 27C
Pop 2,550. Preston 17, London 228,
Blackpool 7, Lancaster 17, Whalley 29.
EC Wed. **Golf** Knott End 18h, Poulton 9h.
See Shard Bridge Inn.

Repairers: Gornalls Garage. ✆ (0253)
700214.
Storeys of Hambleton, Shard La. ✆ (0253)
700217.
Rescue Service: Jenkinson, J & Son Ltd,
Rycroft Garage. ✆ (0253) 700233.

HAMPSON GREEN Lancashire. Map
27C
M6 Motorway 1, Preston 17, London 230,
Blackpool 20, Lancaster 5.
Golf Lancaster 18h.

▣**★★Hampson House,** *Galgate,*
LA2 0JB. ✆ (0524) 751188. C. 🚗 13
bedrs, 4 bp, 1 bps, 1 sh, 2 ba, TV. ✗ mc, LD
9.15. ⓟ CH, TV, CP 50, Ac, con 40, CF, 1 st.
£ BB £15·50–£19, DB £26–£28, ⚹ 10%, Bk
£3, L £5·50 (Sun), D fr £7, Dep b.

HAMPTON Greater London. (Middx).
Maps 7A & 8
1 m S of Twickenham, London 8, Feltham
3, Sunbury 4, Teddington 1.
EC Wed.

Rescue Service: Broad Lane Garage, 163
Broad La. ✆ 01-979 2233.
Speedwell Motor Works, 70 Wellington
Rd, Fulwell. ✆ 01-943 2937.

HAMPTON COURT Greater London.
(Middx). Map 7A
Kingston upon Thames 2, London 11,
Ealing 9½, Epsom 7, Leatherhead 8½, Purley
13, Richmond-upon-Thames 5½, Ripley 10,
Staines 8, Uxbridge 13, Weybridge 6½.
EC Wed. **Golf** Home Park 18h, Fulwell
18h, Strawberry Hill 9h, Thames Ditton
and Esher 9h, Surbiton 18h. **See** Palace,
Maze and Gardens, Bushy Park.

▣**★★Greyhound** (TH), *Hampton Court*
Rd, KT8 9BZ. ✆ 01-977 8121.

HAMPTON HEATH Cheshire. Map 19C
Pop 354. Whitchurch 6½, London 170,
Chester 14, Llangollen 24, Middlewich 22,

Nantwich 13, Northwich 20, St Helens 34,
Warrington 28, Wrexham 13.
EC Wed. **MD** Sat.

Rescue Service: Hampton Heath Service
Station Ltd, (A41). ✆ 564.

HAMPTON-IN-ARDEN West Midlands.
Map 21B
Pop 1,552. M6 Motorway 4½, Coventry 8½,
London 102, Birmingham 10, Nuneaton
11, Stratford-upon-Avon 20, Tamworth
16, Warwick 13.
Golf N Warks 9h. **See** Packhorse Bridge,
Church.

Rescue Service: Ring of Bells Garage,
Solihull Rd. ✆ (067 55) 2288.

HANDFORTH Cheshire. Map 19B
Pop 6,843. Congleton 14, London 175,
Altrincham 9, Knutsford 9, Macclesfield 9,
Manchester 10, Middlewich 17,
Sandbach 18, Stockport 6.
EC Wed. **Golf** Wilmslow 18h. **See**
Handforth Hall.

★★★★Belfry (R), *Stanley Rd, SK9 3LD.*
✆ 061-437 0511. C. 🚗 92 bedrs, 92 bp,
TV. ✗ a l c, mc, LD 10. ⓟ Lt, N, CH, CP
150, Ac, con 80, CF, 19 BGf, 1 st. £ BB
£39·50, DB £54, DBB £48, WB, ⚼, Bk
£4·50, L £7·25, D £8·50, cc 1 2 3 5 6, Dep.

HANDSWORTH West Midlands. Map
21D
M6 Motorway 3, Birmingham 4, London
115, Sutton Coldfield 7, Walsall 7,
Wolverhampton 11.

Repairer: Murco Service Station,
Holyhead Rd. ✆ 021-554 8679.

HANKERTON Wiltshire. Map 14E
4 m NE of Malmesbury. Pop 230. Swindon
15, London 92, Chippenham 14,
Cirencester 10, Faringdon 22, Tetbury 6½.
Golf Chippenham 18h. **See** 13th cent
Church.

Rescue Service: L J Cooper & Son.
✆ Crudwell (066 67) 273.

HANLEY Staffordshire. Map 19D
RAC Office, *2 Broad St, Hanley, ST1 4HL.*
✆ Stoke-on-Trent (0782) 266783.
See also STOKE-ON-TRENT.
Stoke-on-Trent 2, London 154, M6
Motorway 4½, Congleton 11, Leek 10,
Nantwich 16, Newcastle-under-Lyme 2,
Sandbach 12.
See Plan p. 221.
P See Plan. **See** Museum and Art Gallery,
Site of birthplace of Arnold Bennett at 92
Hope St.

★★★Stakis Grand, *66 Trinity St,*
ST1 5NB. ✆ (0782) 22361. C. 🚗 93 bedrs,
93 bp, TV, Dgs. ✗ a l c, mc, at, LD 10.30.
ⓟ Lt, N, CH, TV, Dgs, CP 42, Ac, con 290,
CF, 0 st. £ WB, Bk £3·50, L £4·75, D £4·40,
cc 1 2 3 5, Dep b.
For Appointed Garages see STOKE-ON-
TRENT.

HARBURY Warwickshire. Map 14B
Pop 2,496. M1 Motorway 20, Southam 3½,
London 83, Banbury 4½, Coventry 15,
Leamington Spa 6½, Stratford-on-Avon 12.
Golf Whitnash 18h. **See** 13th cent Parish
Church, 17th cent Windmill (1 m W),
Manor House.

Rescue Service: Martin D Shepherd,
Fosse Garage, Fosse Way. ✆ Leamington
Spa (0926) 613260.

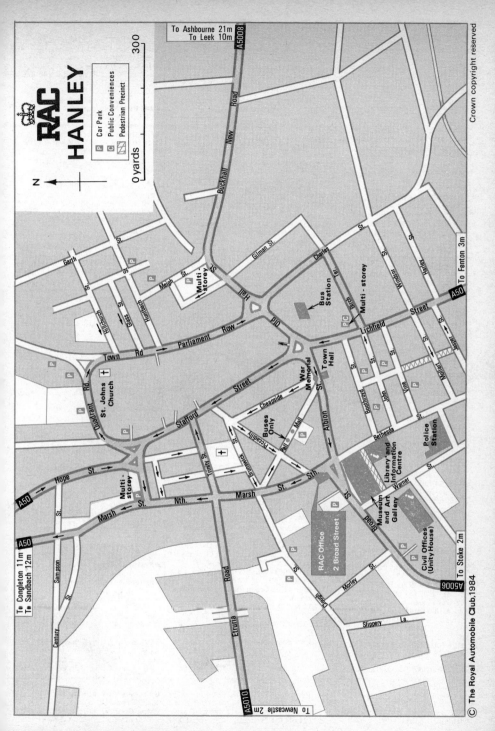

RAC HANLEY

Car Park
Public Conveniences
Pedestrian Precinct

0 yards — 300

To Ashbourne 21m
To Leek 10m

A5008

New Road
Bucknall

Garth
St.
Meigh
Hillchurch
Humback
Glass
St.
St.
Garth St.
Multi-storey
P

Gilman St.
Hall St.

Parliament Row
Town Rd
St. Johns Church
Quadrant Rd.
P
P
P
P

Stafford Street

Cheapside
Piccadilly
Mall
Buses Only

War Memorial
Old Hall St.

Bus Station
Charles St.
Birch
Multi-storey
P G
Lichfield Street

A50 To Fenton 3m

Town Hall
Albion St.
Boothband
John
Vine
Bethesda
Mollart St.
Piccadilly

Library and Information Centre
Police Station
Warner St.

Museum and Art Gallery

Civil Offices (Unity House)

A5006 To Stoke 2m

Hope St.
Marsh St.
Multi-storey
Nth.
Marsh St.
Trinity St.
Brunswick St.
Sth. St.
Broad Road

RAC Office
2 Broad Street
P
P
P

A50
A50

Samson St.
Century
Etruria Road

Morley
Slippery La.
Clough St.

A5010 To Newcastle 2m

To Congleton 11m
To Sandbach 12m

N

HARLESTON Norfolk. Map 16B
Pop 3,028 (inc Redenhall). Scole 7½,
London 103, East Dereham 30, Great
Yarmouth 27, Lowestoft 22, Norwich 19,
Saxmundham 22, Swaffham 37.
EC Thur. **MD** Wed. **Golf** Bungay 18h, Diss
9h. **See** 15th cent Church.

★★**Swan,** *The Thoroughfare, IP20 9AS.*
✆ (0379) 852221.

HARLOW Essex. Map 17F
Pop 79,000. Epping 6, London 25, M11
Motorway 3, Bishop's Stortford 6½,
Brentwood 16, Chelmsford 18, Dunmow
14, Hoddesdon 8.
EC Wed. **MD** Tue, Thur, Fri, Sat. **Golf**
Canons Brook 18h.

★★★**M Green Man,** *Mulberry Rd, CM17
0ET.* ✆ (0279) 29412. C. ⇥ 55 bedrs, 55
bp, ns, TV, Dgs. ✖ a l c, mc, at, LD 10
(10,30 Fri-Sat, 9.30 Sun). 🅐 N, CH, CP 75,
Ac, con 60, CF, 15 BGf, 0 st, Dis. £ BB
£36·50, DB £45, ①, WB, Bk £4·50, L £8·50,
D £8·50, cc 1 2 3 4 5 6, Dep b.
★★★**M Harlow Moat House** (late
Saxon Inn), *Southern Way, CM18 7BA.*
✆ (0279) 22441. C. ⇥ 120 bedrs, 120 bp,
TV, Dgs. ✖ a l c, mc, at, LD 10·30. 🅐 N,
CH, Dgs, CP 200, Ac, con 200, CF, 60 BGf,
1 st, Dis. £ BB £38·50, DB £48, DBB £45,
WB, ①, Bk £3·95, L £5·75, D £6·95,
cc 1 2 3 5, Dep b.▲

Repairers: Arlington Motor Co (Harlow)
Ltd, Potter St. ✆ (0279) 22391.
Fullers Motors, 107 Fullers Mead.
✆ (0279) 27258.

HARMONDSWORTH Greater London
(Middx). M.Area 7A
Brentford and Chiswick 9, London 15,
Ealing 9, Harrow 10, Kingston-upon-
Thames 11, Richmond-upon-Thames 9,
Slough 6, Staines 5, Uxbridge 4½, Watford
16, Windsor 6½.

Rescue Service: Radley Autos
(Heathrow) Ltd, 1 The Village.
✆ 01-897 8841.

HARPENDEN Hertfordshire. Map 15F
Pop 24,188. St Albans 5, London 25, M1
Motorway 4½, Aylesbury 25, Baldock 17,
Hatfield 8, High Wycombe 26, Luton 5½.
EC Wed. **Golf** Harpenden 18h, Harpenden
Common 18h. **See** Church with 15th cent
tower, Rothamsted Agricultural
Experimental Station, Luton Hoo 3 m N.

★★★★**Harpenden Moat House,** *18
Southdown Rd, AL5 1PE.* ✆ (058 27)
64111. C. ⇥ 19 bedrs, 16 bp, 3 bps,
annexe 16 bedrs, 16 bp, TV, Dgs. ✖ a l c,
mc, at, LD 10. 🅐 N, CH, CP 50, con 20, CF.
£ BB £38, DB £52·50, WB, ①, Bk £4·50, L
£8, D £11·75, cc 1 2 3 5 6, Dep b.
★★★**Glen Eagle,** *Luton Rd, AL5 2PX.*
✆ (058 27) 60271. C. ⇥ 51 bedrs. 48 bp,
3 bps, TV, Dgs. ✖ a l c, mc, at, LD 10. 🅐 Lt,
N, CH, CP 100, Ac, con 70, CF, 11 BGf.
£ BB £40–£42·50, DB £47–£51, WB, ①, Bk
£5, L £15, D £15, cc 1 2 3 5 6, Dep b.

Specialist Body Repairer Oggelsbys,
Southdown Industrial Estate, Southdown
Rd. ✆ (058 27) 67776.
Repairers: Oggelsbys, Luton Rd.
✆ (058 27) 67776.
Pinneys of Harpenden Ltd, Station Rd.
✆ (058 27) 64311.

HARROGATE North Yorkshire. Map 25E
Pop 65,000. Doncaster 40, London 204,
Boroughbridge 10, Bradford 18, Brough
66, Darlington 46, Leeds 15, Leyburn 31,
Middleton-in-Teeside 61, Northallerton
29, Pontefract 27, Selby 29, Skipton 22,
West Auckland 52, York 22.
See Plan p. 223.
EC Wed. **MD** Daily. **P** Disc parking is in
operation on weekdays, from 8 am to 6
pm, Sundays and Bank Holidays are
exempt. PARKING IS FREE in spaces
marked out in the principal shopping and
commercial streets. PARKING DISCS
must be displayed on the nearside front of
the vehicle and can be obtained from
shops, banks, offices, etc, within the disc
area and from the Municipal Offices.
PARKING MUST NOT TAKE PLACE
WHERE THERE ARE YELLOW LINES
ALONG THE ROAD. **Golf** Harrogate 18h,
Pannal 18h, Oakdale 18h. **See** Valley
Gardens, The Stray, Harlow Car Gardens,
Pump Room Museum, Moors and Dales,
Rudding Park Gardens 2½ m SE,
Knaresborough Castle ruins 3½ m NE,
Ripley Castle 4 m N, Harewood House 7 m
S, Fountains Abbey, Newby Hall.
🅘 Royal Bath Assembly Rooms, Crescent
Rd. ✆ Harrogate (0423) 65912.

★★★★**Crown** (TH), *Crown Pl, HG1 2RZ.*
✆ (0423) 67755. C. ⇥ 120 bedrs, 98 bp,
22 bps, TV, Dgs. ✖ a l c, mc, at, LD 9.30.
🅐 Lt, N, CH, Dgs, CP 50, Ac, con 300, CF,
0 st. £ BB £44, DB £56·50, WB, ①,
cc 1 2 3 4 5 6, Dep (Xmas).
★★★★**Majestic** (TH), *Ripon Rd, HG1
2HU.* ✆ (0423) 68972. C. ⇥ 151 bedrs,
150 bp, 1 bps, TV, Dgs. ✖ a l c, mc, at, LD
9.15. 🅐 Lt, N, CH, Dgs, CP 180, Ac, sp, tc,
sc, con 500, CF, 0 st. £ BB £45·50, DB
£59·50, WB, ①, cc 1 2 3 4 5 6, Dep (Xmas).
★★★★**Old Swan,** *Swan Rd, HG1 2SR.*
✆ (0423) 504051. C. ⇥ 137 bedrs, 130
bp, 7 bps, TV, Dgs. ✖ mc, at, LD 10. 🅐 Lt,
N, CH, Dgs, CP 150, Ac, tc, sb, sol, con, CF,
0 st. £ BB £27–£46, DB £54–£65, DT £45–
£62, DBB £37·50–£46, WB, ①, Bk £5, L
£7·50, D £8·50, cc 1 2 3 4 5 6, Dep b.
★★★**Cairn,** *Ripon Rd, HG1 2JD.*
✆ (0423) 504005. C. ⇥ 140 bedrs, 119
bp, 3 bps, 6 ba. ✖ a l c, mc, at, LD 9.15.
🅐 Lt, N, ch, Dgs, CP 250, Ac, tc, con 450,
CF, 1 st. £ BB £36–£40, DB £47–£54, WB,
②, Bk £3, L £5·75, D £6·70, cc 1 2 3 4 5 6.
★★★**Grants,** *3 Swan Rd, HG1 2SS.*
✆ (0423) 60666. C. ⇥ 17 bedrs, 7 bp, 10
bps, 1 ba, TV. ✖ a l c, mc, at, LD 10. 🅐 Lt,
N, CH, CP 15, Ac, sol, con 60, CF, 1 BGf, 0
st, Dis. £ BB £32·50, DB £48·50, WT
£246·75, DT £35·25, WB, ②, Bk £4, L
£5·50, D £5·50, cc 1 2 3 5 6.
★★★★**Hob Green** (R), *Markington, HG3
3PJ.* ✆ (0423) 770031. C 4. ⇥ 11 bedrs,
10 bp, 1 bps, TV. ✖ mc, at, LD 10. 🅐 CH,
CP 50, con 10, CF, 0 st. £ BB £32·50–
£37·50, DB £45–£52·50, WB, ②, L £5, D
£10·75, cc 1 2 3 5 6, Dep b.
★★★**Hospitality Inn,** *West Park, HG1
1LB.* ✆ (0423) 64601. C. ⇥ 71 bedrs, 71
bp, TV, Dgs. ✖ mc, at, LD 10. 🅐 Lt, N, CH,
TV, CP 35, Ac, con 100, CF, 12 BGf, 0 st,
Dis. £ BB £38·50, DB £49·50, WB, ①,
cc 1 2 3 5.
★★★**Hotel St George,** *Ripon Rd, HG1
2SY.* ✆ (0423) 61431. C. ⇥ 82 bedrs, 79
bp, 4 bps, TV, Dgs. ✖ a l c, mc, at, LD 9.30.
🅐 Lt, N, CH, Dgs, CP 40, Ac, con 300,

CF, 3 st. £ BB £26–£42, DB £40–£58, WB,
①, Bk £5·50, L £6·25, D £9·50, cc 1 2 3 5 6.
■★★★**Prospect,** *Prospect Pl, HG1 1LA.*
✆ (0423) 65071. C. ⇥ 97 bedrs, 48 bp, 7
bps, 9 ba, TV, Dgs. ✖ mc, at, LD 8.45. 🅐 Lt,
N, CH, TV, Dgs, CP 50, Ac, con 140, CF, 0
st. £ BB £21–£25, DB £30–£42, WB, ①, Bk
£1·75, D £6·50, cc 1 2 3 5, Dep b.
★★★**M Bay Horse Inn,** *Burnt Yates, HG1
3LA.* ✆ (0423) 770230.
★★**Caesars** (RI), *Valley Dr, HG2 0JH.*
✆ (0423) 65818. Closed Xmas–New Year.
C. ⇥ 10 bedrs, 10 bp, TV. ✖ mc, at, LD 9.
🅐 CH, Ac, CF, 15 st. £ BB £21, DB £37,
DBB £25, WB, ②, Bk £2·75, D £8, cc 1 6,
Dep a.
★★**Fern** (late **Fernlea**) (R), *Swan Rd,
HG1 2SS.* ✆ (0423) 523866. C. ⇥ 28
bedrs, 26 bp, 2 sh, 2 ba, TV. ✖ mc, at, LD
10. 🅐 N, CH, Ac, con 40, CF, 3 st. £ BB
£27·95–£29·95, DB £42·95–£46·95, DBB
£33·95–£36·95, WB, ①, Bk £3·50, L £5·50,
D £7, cc 1 2 3 5 6.
★★**Gibsons,** *105 Valley Dr, HG2 0JP.*
✆ (0423) 522246. C. ⇥ 21 bedrs, 18 bp, 3
bps, TV, Dgs. ✖ a l c, mc, LD 9.30. 🅐 CH,
Ac, con 36, CF. £ BB £23–£30, DB £35–
£46, WB, ①, Bk £3·45, D £7·50, cc 1 2 3 5.
★★**Green Park,** *Valley Dr, HG2 0JT.*
✆ (0423) 504681. C. ⇥ 44 bedrs, 27 bp,
17 bps, TV, Dgs. ✖ mc, at, LD 9. 🅐 Lt, N,
ch, TV, CP 12, Ac, con 50, CF, 3 BGf, 9 st.
£ BB £23·50–£25, DB £38·50–£40, DBB
£26·50–£27·25, WB, ②, Bk £3·50, L £7·25,
cc 1 2 3 5 6, Dep b.
★★**Italia,** *53 Kings Rd, HG1 5HJ.*
✆ (0423) 67404.
★★**Langham** (RI), *Valley Dr, HG2 0JL,*
✆ (0423) 502347. C. ⇥ 51 bedrs, 48 bp, 3
bps, Dgs. ✖ mc, LD 6. 🅐 Lt, CH, TV, Dgs,
Ac, con 20, CF, 14 st. £ BB £18·50–£23,
DB £36·80–£46, DBB £25·30–£30, WB, ②,
Bk £4, D £6·90.
■★★**Russell,** *Valley Dr, HG2 0JP.*
✆ (0423) 509866. C. ⇥ 34 bedrs, 29 bp, 5
bps, 3 ba, TV, Dgs. ✖ a l c, mc, LD 10.30.
🅐 Lt, N, CH, Ac, con 40, CF, 2 st. £ BB
£25·95–£29·95, DB £38·95–£42·95, DBB
£29·22–£31·22, WB, ①, Bk £4·25, D £9·75,
cc 1 2 3 4 5 6, Dep b.
★★**Wessex** (RI), *22 Harlow Moor Dr, HG2
0JY.* ✆ (0423) 65890. C. ⇥ 15 bedrs, 15
bps, 1 ba, Dgs. ✖ mc, at, LD 8. 🅐 CH, TV,
Ac, CF, 2 st. £ BB £16, DB £31·50, WT
£145, DBB £23, WB, ② 10%, D £7.
■★**Alvera Court** (R), *76 Kings Rd, HG1
5JX.* ✆ (0423) 55735. C. ⇥ 10 bedrs, 3
bp, 5 bps, 2 sh, 1 ba, TV. ✖ LD 7.30. 🅐 CH,
TV, CP 4, G 1, CF. £ BB £15–£18·50, DB
£29–£34, WT £105–£125, DT £24–£27·50,
WB, ①, Bk £2, D £6·50.
★**Bastille,** *2 Strawberry Dale, HG1 5EF.*
✆ (0423) 501601.
★**Britannia Lodge.** (RI) *16 Swan Rd,
HG1 2SA.* ✆ (0423) 502029. C. ⇥ 11
bedrs, 6 bp, 5 bps, 1 ba, TV. ✖ a l c, mc, at,
LD 7. 🅐 CH, TV, CP 6, U 1, CF, 5 st. £ BB
£15–£18, DB £30–£36, WT £110–£130, DT
£25–£28, DBB £22–£25, WB, ①, Bk £3, L
£3·50, D £7, cc 1 3 6.
★**Gables,** *2 West Grove Rd, HG1 2AD.*
✆ (0423) 55625. C. ⇥ 9 bedrs, 4 bp, 3
bps, 2 sh, TV. ✖ a l c, mc, at, LD 8. 🅐 CH,
CP 6, CF, 6 st. £ BB £18·50, DB £35, DBB
£24·75–£25·75, WB, ①, Bk £3·50, L £4, D
£7·25.
Harrogate International. *Under
construction.*
Abbey Court, G, z (Unl), *61 Franklin Rd,
HG1 5EH.* ✆ (0423) 68302. C. ⇥ 5 bedrs,

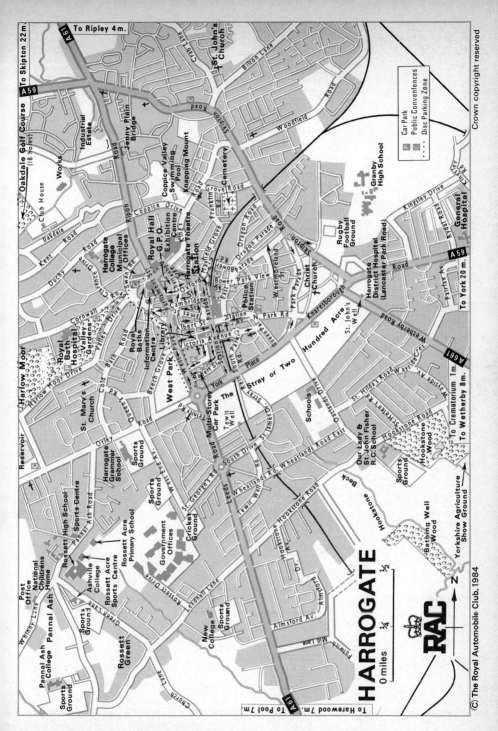

HARROGATE

1 ba. ⓓ CH, TV, CP 2, CF, 3 st. £ BB £8–£9, DB £16–£18, WT (b) £84–£91 (c) £56–£63, DBB £12–£13.

Abbey Lodge, G, z (RI), *31 Ripon Rd, HG1 2JL.* ☎ (0423) 69712. C. 🖛 8 bedrs, 1 bp, 3 bps, 2 ba, TV, Dgs. ⓓ CH, TV, CP 14, G 2, CF, 6 st. £ BB £8, DB £19–£22, ⚀, D £5·50.

Alphen Lodge, *2 Esplanade, HG1 0LN.* ☎ (0423) 502882. Closed Xmas, RS Sun. C. 🖛 11 bedrs, 6 bp, 1 bps, 1 ba, TV, Dgs. ⓓ CH, CP 10, CF, 14 st. £ BB £18–£21, DB £30·50–£36, DT fr £27, ⚁, Bk £4·50, L £4, D £7·50, cc 1 2 3.

Arden House, PH, z (RI), *69 Franklin Rd, HG1 5EH.* ☎ (0423) 509224. Closed Xmas. C. 🖛 14 bedrs, 12 bps, 1 ba, TV, Dgs. ⓓ CH, CP 12, CF, 3 st. £ BB £11·75–£15·75, DB £19·50–£27·50, WT (c) £61·25–£75·25, DT (b) £16–£18, ⚀, Bk £2·50, L £3, D £6·25.

Aston (late Hartington), G, z (Unl), 7 *Franklin Mount, HG1 5EJ.* ☎ (0423) 69534.

Aston Lodge, PH, z (RI), *5–7 Franklin Mount, HG1 5EJ.* ☎ (0423) 69534. Closed Xmas. C. 🖛 25 bedrs, 15 bps, 2 ba, TV, Dgs. ⓓ CH, TV, Dgs, ns, CP6, CF, 2 st. £ BB £9·50–£15·50, DB £18–£25, WT (b) £92·75–£106·75, DT (b) £14·25–£15·75, ⚀, Bk £1·25, D £4·95.

Carlton, PH, z (RI), *98 Franklin Rd, HG1 5EN.* ☎ (0423) 64493. C. 🖛 11 bedrs, 2 ba, ⓓ CH, TV, CP 8, 6 st. £ BB £11, DB £20, WT (c) £70, DT (b) £16·50.

Cavendish, PH, z (RI), *3 Valley Dr, HG2 0JJ.* ☎ (0423) 509637. C. 🖛 11 bedrs, 1 bp, 5 bps, 1 sh, 2 ba, TV, Dgs. ✗ a l c. ⓓ CH, TV, CF, 10 st. 🖛 BB £12·50–£16·50, DB £25–£32, WT (b) £126–£147, DT (b) £18–£21, ⚀, Bk £2·50, L £3·50, D £4·50, cc 1 2 3 5.

Cheltenham Lodge, H, z (R), *Cheltenham Parade, HG1 1DB.* ☎ (0423) 55041. C. 🖛 14 bedrs, 1 bp, 3 bps, 10 sh, 2 ba, TV. ✗ a l c. ⓓ CH, CP 10, CF, BB £14–£17, DB £28–£34, WT (c) £77–£84, ⚀, Bk £2·50, L £3, D £5, cc 1 2 3 5.▲

Croft, H, z (R), *42 Franklin Rd.* ☎ (0423) 63326.

Gillmore, PH, z (R), *98 Kings Rd, HG1 5HH.* ☎ (0423) 503699. 🖛 20 bedrs, 2 bps, 5 ba, TV, Dgs. ⓓ CH, Dgs, CP 20, CF, 2 BGf, 1 st. £ BB £12, DB £24, WT (b) fr £95, DT (b) £16, ⚀, Bk £2, D £4·50.▲

Grafton, PH, z (R), *1 Franklin Mount, HG1 5EJ.* ☎ (0423) 58491. Closed Dec. C. 🖛 16 bedrs, 5 bps, 4 ba, TV. ⓓ CH, TV, CF, 2 st. £ BB £9·50–£14, DB £19–£27, WT (b) fr £91, DT (b) fr £14, ⚀, Bk £2·50, D £4·50.

Ingleside, H, z (RI), *37 Valley Dr. HG2 0JH.* ☎ (0423) 502088. C. 🖛 6 bedrs, 1 sh, 3 ba, TV, Dgs. ⓓ CH, TV, ns. £ BB fr £16, DB £30, DT (b) fr £22·90, ⚁, Bk £2·50, D £6·90.

Kingsway, G, z (RI), *36 Kings Rd, HG1 5JW.* ☎ (0423) 62179. C. 🖛 7 bedrs, 1 bp, 6 bps, Dgs. ⓓ CH, TV, Dgs, CP 2, U 1, CF, 1 BGf, 7 st. £ BB £12, DB £24, WT (c) £80, DBB £16·50.

Manor, PH, z (Rt), *3 Clarence Dr. HG1 2QE.* ☎ (0423) 503916. C. 🖛 14 bedrs, 3 bp, 6 bps, 2 ba, TV, Dgs. ⓓ CH, TV, CP 6, CF, 10 st. £ BB £15–£20, DB fr £30, WT (a) £147–£175, DT (a) £22–£26, ⚀, Bk £2·50, D £6.

Princes, G, z (Rt), *7 Granby Rd, HG1 4ST.* ☎ (0423) 883469. C. 🖛 8 bedrs, 1 bp, 2 bps, 3 sh, 4 ba, TV. ⓓ CH, TV, G 4, 2 st. £ BB £9·75–£11·50, DB £21·50–£28,

WT (b) £98–£111, DT (b) £14·55–£16·50, ⚀, Bk £4, D £5·75.

Roan, G, z (Unl), *90 Kings Rd, HG1 5JX.* ☎ (0423) 503087. Closed Dec 25 & 26. C. 🖛 7 bedrs, 2 bps, 1 ba. ⓓ CH, TV. £ BB £9, DB £18, DT (b) £13·25, ⚀.

Ross, H, z (R), *56 Cheltenham Mount, HG1 1DL.* ☎ (0423) 503795. C. 🖛 6 bedrs, 2 ba, TV, Dgs. ⓓ CH, TV, Dgs, CP 3, CF, 5 st. £ BB £10–£15, DB £20, WT £80–£110, DT £16·50–£20·50, ⚀, Bk £2, L £3, D £6·50, cc 2 3 5.

Scotia House, PH, z (RI), *66 Kings Rd, HG1 5JR.* ☎ (0423) 504361. C. 🖛 6 bedrs, 1 bps, 3 sh, 1 ba, TV, Dgs. ⓓ CH, TV, Dgs, ns, CP 2, CF, 8 st. £ BB £10–£12·50, DB £20–£22, WT (a) £126, (b) £98, (c) £63, DT (a) £18·50, (b) £14·50, ⚀, Bk £2, L £4, D £5·50.▲

Shelbourne, G, z (RI), *78 Kings Rd, HG1 5JX.* ☎ (0423) 504390. C. 🖛 7 bedrs, 2 ba. ⓓ CH, TV, CP 1, CF. £ BB £9–£11·50, DB £17·50–£20, WT (b) £84–£95, DT (b) £14–£16, ⚀, D £5, cc 3.

Springfield, G, z (Unl). *80 Kings Rd, HG1 5JX.* ☎ (0423) 67166.

Young's, PH, z (RI), *15 York Rd, HG1 2QL.* ☎ (0423) 67336.

Repairers: Appleyard of Harrogate Ltd, 91 Leeds Rd. ☎ (0423) 81263 and (0423) 84561.
Croft & Blackburn Ltd, Leeds Rd, Pannal. ☎ (0423) 879236.
Emsley, V J, North Park Road Garage, North Park Rd. ☎ (0423) 61929.
Massingberd Ltd, Ripon Rd. ☎ (0423) 55141.
Nash, E & Co Ltd, 95 Leeds Rd. ☎ (0423) 81269.
MC Repairer: P Reed, 43 High St, Spa La, Starbeck. ☎ (0423) 83184.
Rescue Service: J W Harrison & Sons Ltd, Links Side Garage, Forest Lane Head, Knaresborough. ☎ (0423) 862364.

HARROW-ON-THE-HILL Greater London (Middx). Maps 7A and 15F.
Pop 208, 963. London 10, Barnet 9½, Denham 8½, Ealing 5½, Hatfield 16, Rickmansworth 7½, St Albans 13, Staines 15, Uxbridge 8, Watford 7.
EC Wed. **MD** Thur. **See** Harrow School, St Mary's Church, 16th cent King's Head.

★★**Cumberland,** *St Johns Rd, HA1 2EF.* ☎ 01-863 4111. C. 🖛 28 bedrs, 8 bp, 20 bps, annexe 49 bedrs, 18 bp, 14 bps, 17 sh, 6 ba, TV. ✗ a l c, mc, at, LD 9.30. ⓓ N, CH, TV, CP 65, Ac, CF, 17 BGf, 3 st. £ BB £27–£34, DB £42, WT £254·14, DT £40·49, DBB £35·50–£42·50, WB, ⚁, Bk £3·75, L £4·99, D £8·50, cc 1 2 3 5, Dep.

★★**Harrow,** *12 Pinner Rd, HA1 4HZ.* ☎ 01-427 3435. RS Xmas–New Year. C. 🖛 65 bedrs, 29 bp, 33 bps, 3 sh, 4 ba, annexe 28 bedrs, 15 bp, 13 bps, TV. ✗ a l c, mc, at, LD 9.30. ⓓ N, CH, CP 55, Ac, con 120, CF, 4 BGf, 1st, Dis. £ BB £35–£42, DB £47–£54, DT £50–£54, DBB £44–£51, WB, ⚀, Bk £4·50, L £9, D £9, cc 1 2 3 5, Dep.

Hindes, H, z, *8 Hindes Rd, HA1 1SJ.* ☎ 01-427 7468.

Rescue Service: Harold W Perry Ltd, 372 High Rd. ☎ 01-427 4282.
Sixsmiths Garage, 140 Greenford Rd. ☎ 01-422 1081.

HARROW WEALD Greater London (Middx). Maps 7A, 8 and 15F.

Wealdstone 1, London 12, M1 Motorway (Northbound) 3, Potters Bar 6, Richmond 12, Rickmansworth 7½, Watford 5.

★★★**Grimsdyke,** *Old Redding, HA3 6SH.* ☎ 01-954 4227. C. 🖛 8 bedrs, 8 bp, annexe 40 bedrs, 40 bp, TV, Dgs. ✗ a l c, mc, at, LD 9.45. ⓓ N, CH, Dgs, CP, con, CF. £ BB £42, DBB £60, WB, ⚁, L £9·50, D £9·50, cc 1 2 3 5, Dep b.

HARTHILL South Yorkshire. M. Area 22B. 6½ m W of Worksop. Mansfield 14, London 153, M1 Motorway 4, Chesterfield 10, Doncaster 19, Sheffield 11.
See Barlborough Hall (1 m S), Creswell Crags (6 m SE).

Rescue Service: Dinnington Auto Electrical Services Ltd, Woodall Service Area, M1 Southbound. ☎ Sheffield (0742) 486448.

HARTINGTON Derbyshire. Map 22C Pop 343. Ashbourne 12, London 151, Buxton 12, Chesterfield 20, Leek 12, Matlock 13, Sheffield 26.
Golf Buxton 18h. **See** Dovedale and Beresford Dale (explorable on foot).

★**Charles Cotton,** *Market Pl, SK17 0AL.* ☎ (029 884) 229. C. 🖛 11 bedrs, 3 ba, Dgs. ✗ a l c, mc, at, LD 9. ⓓ CH, TV, CP 50, Ac, pf, con, CF. £ BB fr £9·50, DB fr £17·50, WT fr £92, DT £17, WB, ⚁ 10%, Bk £4, L £4·25, D £6·50.

Minton House, G, x (R), *Market Pl, SK17 0AL.* ☎ (029 884) 368.

HARTLAND Devon. Map 3A Pop 1,420. Bideford 14, London 216, Bude 15, Holsworthy 16, Launceston 29.
EC Tue. **Golf** Westward Ho! 18h. **See** Hartland Point, Town Clock, Abbey, St Nectans Church, Bronze Age hill fort, Burial Mounds.

★★**Hartland Quay,** *EX29 6DU.* ☎ (023 74) 218. Open Easter–mid Nov. RS mid Oct–mid Nov.C. 🖛 16 bedrs, 5 bp, 1 bps, 3 ba, Dgs. ✗ mc, at, LD 8.30. ⓓ ch, TV, CP 100, G 10, sp, CF, 2 st. £ BB £11–£12·50, DB £22–£25, DBB £16–£18, ⚀, Bk £2, D £5·50, Dep a.

Rescue Service: W L Heard, Heard's Garage. ☎ (023 74) 233.

HARTLEPOOL Cleveland. Map 24C Pop 94,300. Stockton-on-Tees 9½, London 253, Durham 17, Middlesbrough 8, Newcastle-upon-Tyne 29, Sunderland 18.
EC Wed. **MD** Thur. **Golf** Hartlepool 18h, Seaton Carew 18h. **See** St Hilda's Church, Stranton Church (11th cent), Fish Quay and Market, good beaches, Art Gallery & Museums.
[i] Leisure & Amenities Dept, Civic Centre. ☎ Hartlepool (0429) 66522.

■★★★**Grand,** *Swainson St, TS24 8AA.* T (0429) 66345. Closed Xmas. C. 🖛 44 bedrs, 22 bp, 6 ba, TV, Dgs. ✗ a l c, mc, at, LD 9. ⓓ Lt, N, CH, Ac, con 200, CF 2 st. £ BB fr £26·50, DB fr £36, WB, ⚀, Bk £4, L £4·60, D £7·25, cc 1 2 3 4 5 6, Dep b.

Repairer: Gales Motors Ltd, 128 York Rd. ☎ (0429) 66393.
Rescue Service: Bradley, C R & Sons (Peterlee) Ltd, Coast Rd, Blackhall Colliery. ☎ Peterlee (0783) 866211.
Ron Perry & Son, A19 Service Station, Elwick. ☎ Wolviston (074 04) 223.
Seaton Service Station, Station La, Seaton Carew. ☎ (0429) 66274.

HARVINGTON Hereford & Worcester (Worcestershire). Map 4c
Pop 1,391. Evesham 4, London 102, Birmingham 26, Bromsgrove 18, Droitwich 18, Ledbury 27, Stratford-upon-Avon 10, Worcester 17.
EC Thur. **Golf** Evesham 18h. **See** Church, Old cottages.

Repairer: Black & White Garages (Harvington) Ltd, Evesham Rd.
☎ Evesham (0386) 870612.

HARWICH Essex. Map 17A
See also DOVERCOURT.
RAC Port Office, *Parkeston Quay, CO12 4SH.* ☎ Harwich (0255) 503567.
Pop 14,964. Colchester 18, London 74, Bury St Edmunds 41, Clacton 16, Ipswich 22, Stowmarket 33, Sudbury 30.
EC Wed. **MD** Fri. **Golf** Harwich and Dovercourt 18h. **See** 17th cent Guildhall, old houses, Treadmill Crane on Green, Redoubt (Napoleonic Fort).
ℹ Parkeston Quay ☎ Harwich (025 55) 6139.

★★**Cliff,** *Marine Par, Dovercourt, CO12 3RE.* ☎ (025 55) 3345. C. ⇔ 34 bedrs, 18 bp, 3 bps, 4 sh, 4 ba, TV, Dgs. ✗ a l c, mc, at, LD 9.15. ⓟ N, CH, TV, Dgs, CP 70, U 4, Ac, con 200, CF, 1 BGf, 8 st. £ BB £21–£23, DB £37–£39, ⑪ Bk £3·50, L £5·10, D £5·95, cc 1 2 3 4 5 6.

Rescue Service: Harwich Body Works Ltd, Tollgate Main Rd, Dovercourt.
☎ (025 55) 2166.
King's Head Motors, 43 King's Head St.
☎ (025 55) 4645.

HASLEMERE Surrey. Map 7C
Pop 14,022 (inc Hindhead). Guildford 12, London 41, Dorking 23, Hindhead 3½, Horsham 20, Midhurst 8, Petersfield 12, Petworth 10.
EC Wed. **Golf** Hindhead 18h. **See** Educational Museum, Dolmetsch Workshops (early musical instruments).

★★★**Georgian,** *High St, GU12 2JY.* ☎ (0428) 51555. C. ⇔ 18 bedrs, 10 bp, 1 bps, 2 ba, TV, Dgs. ⇔ mc, at, LD 9.30. ⓟ CH, TV, CP 30, Ac, sc, sb, con 60, CF, 0 st. £ BB £23–£28, DB £33–£38, DBB £30, WB, ⑪ Bk £3, L £5, D £9·50, cc 1 2 3 5.
★★★**Lythe Hill,** *Petworth Rd, GU 27 3QB.* ☎ (0428) 51251. C. ⇔ 37 bedrs, 33 bp, 2 bps, 1 ba, TV, Dgs. ✗ a l c, mc, at, LD 10.30. ⓟ N, CH, TV, Dgs, CP 200, tc, pf, sb, con 120, CF, 4 BGf, 7 st. £ BBc £36–£45, DBc £50–£70, DBBc £46–£57, WB, ⑪ Bk £5, L £7·50, D £10, cc 1 2 3 5 6, Dep a.
White Horse, I, x, *22 High St, GU27 2HJ.* ☎ (0428) 2103.

Repairer: Cowie's of Haslemere, Farnham La. ☎ (0428) 3222.
Rescue Service: Carcare, Hindhead Rd. ☎ (0428) 3060.

HASSOP Derbyshire. Map 22C
Pop 104. Chesterfield 10, London 159, Ashbourne 20, Buxton 12, Chapel-en-le-Frith 15, Matlock 11, Sheffield 14.
Golf Bakewell 18h. **See** Church.

⇔★★★**Hassop Hall,** *DE4 1NS.* ☎ Gt Longstone (062 987) 488. C. ⇔ 12 bedrs, 12 bp, TV, Dgs. ⓟ Lt, N, CH, CP 80, con, CF, 3 st. £ BB £40, DB £54, WT £410, DBB £57, ⑪ L £8, D £13, cc 1 2 3 5.

HASTINGS AND ST LEONARDS East Sussex. Map 10E

Pop 73,622. Hurst Green 13, London 63, Eastbourne 20, Hawkhurst 15, Lewes 29, Rye 11, Tenterden 20, Uckfield 26.
See Plan p. 226.
EC Wed. **MD** Wed, Sat. **P** See Plan. **Golf** Hastings Municipal 18h. **See** Ruins of Castle, Museum and Art Gallery, St Clement's Caves, St Clement's Church, All Saints' Church, Fisherman's Church, boat pulpit, fossils in stonework, Hastings Historical Embroidery (81 episodes in British history from 1066–the present-day) being 243 ft long and 3 ft deep on view in 'The Embroidery Room', Fishermen's Museum, Country Park.
ℹ 4 Robertson Ter. ☎ (0424) 424242.

⇔★★★**Beauport Park,** *Beauport Park (On A2100 3 m S. Battle), TN38 8EA.* ☎ (0424) 51222. C. ⇔ 23 bedrs, 23 bp, TV, Dgs. ✗ a l c, mc, at, LD 10. ⓟ CH, Dgs, CP 70, U 4, G 4, sp, gc, tc, sc, rf, con 70, CF, 3 st. £ BB £29·50–£32, DB £42–£46, WT £248·50, DT £35·50–£42·50, DBB £28·50–£40·50, WB, ⑪ Bk £4, L £7, D £8·50, cc 1 2 3 5 6, Dep b.
★**Burlington,** (R), *2 Robertson Ter, TN34 1JE.* ☎ (0424) 424303. Closed Dec 24–25. C. ⇔ 17 bedrs, 6 bp, 1 sh, 2 ba, TV, Dgs. ✗ mc, at, LD 8. ⓟ N, CH, ns, Ac, CF, 1 BGf, 3 st. £ BB £12·45–£18·95, DB £17–£29·90, WT £149–£178, DT £25–£32, DBB £14·20–£31·25, WB, ⑪ Bk £3, L £4·75, D £4·25, cc 1 2 3 4 5 6, Dep.
Argyle, G z (Unl), *32 Cambridge Gdns, TN34 1EN.* ☎ (0424) 421294. Closed Xmas, C 4. ⇔ 8 bedrs, 2 bps, 1 ba. ⓟ CH, TV, ns, 5 st. £ BB £8, DB fr £15, WT (b) £59·50, DT (b) £10·50, ⑪.
Beechwood, PH, z, *59 Baldslow Rd, TN34 2EY.* ☎ (0424) 420078. C. ⇔ 5 bedrs, 1 ba, TV, Dgs. ✗ a l c. ⓟ CH, TV, Dgs, ns, CP 6, CF, 3 st. £ BB £8–£10, DB £15–£20, WT (a) £80, (b) £75, (c) £50, DT (a) £15, (b) £12, ⑪, Bk £2, L £5, D £5.
Bryn-y-Mor, H, yz (R). *12 Godwin Rd, TN35 5JR.* ☎ (0424) 441755. Closed Dec 25. C. ⇔ 6 bedrs. 1 bp, 5 bps, 1 ba, TV. ✗ a l c. ⓟ CH, TV, ns, CF, 3 BGf, 0 st, Dis. £ BB £18–£21, DB £30–£36, WT (b) £135–£153, DT (b) £22·50–£25·50, ②, Bk £2·50, L £6·50, D £7·50, cc 1 2 3 5.
Chimes, H, z (RI), *1 St Matthews Gdns, St Leonards, TN38 OTS.* ☎ (0424) 434041. C. ⇔ 10 bedrs, 3 bp, 2 ba, TV, Dgs. ⓟ CH, TV, Dgs, CF, 20 st. £ BB £10·50–£12·50, DB £19–£33, WT (b) £95, (c) £60, DT (b) £15·50, ⑪, D £6.
Eagle House, H, y (R), *12 Pevensey Rd, TN38 0JZ.* ☎ (0424) 430535. C 5. ⇔ 14 bedrs, 1 bp, 10 bps, 2 ba, TV, Dgs. ✗ a l c. ⓟ CH. £ BB £12·75–£15, DB £20–£24, WT £281, DT £23·50, ②, Bk £2·50, L £8·50, D £8·50.▲
French's, I, z, (R), *24 Robertson St.* ☎ (0424) 421195. C. ⇔ 4 bedrs, 2 ba, TV, Dgs. ✗ a l c. ⓟ CH, TV, Dgo, 2 st. £ DD £14–£15, DB £23–£24·50, DT (b) £21–£22, ② 10%, Bk £3·50, L £5, D £7, cc 2 3 5.
Gainsborough, PH, z (R) *5 Carlisle Par, TN34 1JG.* ☎ (0424) 434010. C. ⇔ 12 bedrs, 2 bp, 2 sh, 2 ba, TV, Dgs. ⓟ CH, CF, 6 st. ⓟ BB £8·75–£11·50, DB £17·25–£23, WT £95, (c) £52–£56, DT (b) £13·35–£16, ⑪, Bk £2·30, D £4·60.
Gresford, G, z (Unl), *12 Devonshire Rd, TN34 1NE.* ☎ (0424) 424745. C. ⇔ 9 bedrs, 1 sh, 2 ba ⓟ ch, TV, CF. £ BB £6·75–£7·50, DB £13·50–£15, ⑪.

Sandhurst, G, z (Unl). *21 Cambridge Gdns, TN34 1EH.* ☎ (0424) 422307. C. ⇔ 8 bedrs. 5 sh, 2 ba, TV, Dgs. ⓟ CH, TV, CF, 2 BGf, 2 st.
Tamar, G, z (Unl), *7 Devonshire Rd, TN34 1NE.* ☎ (0424) 434076. C. ⇔ 5 bedrs, 2 ba. ⓟ CH, TV, ns, CF. £ BB £7–£8, DB £14–£16, WT (c) £45–£52, ⑪.
Waldorf, H, z (RI), *4 Carlisle Par. TN34 1JG.* ☎ (0424) 422185. C. ⇔ 12 bedrs, 3 ba, TV. ⓟ CH, TV, CF, 7 st. £ BB £8·50–£10, DB £17–£20, WT (b) £79·50–£91, DT (b) £11·50–£13, ⑪.

Specialist Body Repairer: J Hollingsworth Ltd, York Rd, St Leonards. ☎ (0424) 432025.
Rescue Service: Alexander Garage Ltd, 20 St Margaret's Rd. ☎ (0424) 436295.
Boardman's Garage, 8a The Ridge.
☎ (0424) 421566.
Elva Service Station, Sedlescombe Road North. ☎ (0424) 751389.
J Hollingsworth Ltd, Braybrooke Rd.
☎ (0424) 422727.
Skinners (Hastings) Ltd, 5 Western Rd.
☎ (0424) 437628.

HATCH BEAUCHAMP Somerset. Map 5C
Pop 400. Wincanton 27, London 137, Bridgwater 12, Glastonbury 21, Honiton 17, Ilminster 6, Taunton 6.
Golf Taunton & Pickeridge 18h. **See** 16th cent Church.

Rescue Service: W F Stanford, Hatchgreen Garage. ☎ (0823) 480338.

HATFIELD Hertfordshire, Map 15F
Pop 27,000. Barnet 9, London 20, A1 (M) Motorway 2, Baldock 17, Bedford 31, Bishop's Stortford 22, Enfield 12, Harrow 16, Hoddesdon 11, Luton 13, St Albans 6, Watford 13.
EC Thur. **MD** Wed, Sat. **Golf** Panshanger 18h. **See** Church, Hatfield House, Swimming Pool with largest hyperbolic paraboloid roof in Europe, Mill House & Museum.

★★★**Comet,** *301 St Albans Rd West, AL10 9RH* (junc A1/A414). ☎ (070 72) 65411. RS Xmas. C. ⇔ 57 bedrs, 54 bp, 2 ba, TV, Dgs. ✗ mc, at, LD 9.45. ⓟ N, CH, Dgs, CP 150, Ac, con 40, CF, 26 BGf, 1 st. £ B fr £21, BD £38, WB, ⑪, Bk £4·25, L £7, D £7, cc 1 2 3 4 5 6, Dep.

HATFIELD South Yorkshire. Map 25D
Pop 4,910. Newark 40, London 166, Doncaster 7½, Gainsborough 23, Ollerton 29, Scunthorpe 16, Thorne 3, Worksop 22.
EC Thur. **Golf** Wheatley 18h.

Repairer: F Cross & Sons, Carr Garage, Old Thorne Rd. ☎ Doncaster (0302) 840348.

HATHERLEIGH Devon. Maps 3A and 4E
Pop 974. Crediton 20, London 197, Barnstaple 23, Bideford 19, Holsworthy 13, Launceston 24, Okehampton 7, South Molton 24, Tavistock 21.
EC Wed. **MD** Mon, Tue. **Golf** Okehampton 18h. **See** Church (1184).

★★**George,** *Market St, EX20 3JN.* ☎ Okehampton (0837) 810454. Closed 3 days Xmas. RS Sun. C. ⇔ 12 bedrs, 6 bp, 4 bps, 1 ba, Dgs. ✗ a l c, mc, LD 9.30. ⓟ CH, TV, CP 40, Ac, con 20, CF, 1 st. £ BB £13·75–£18·25, DB £17·50–£22, ②, Bk £3·75, L £6, D £10, cc 3.

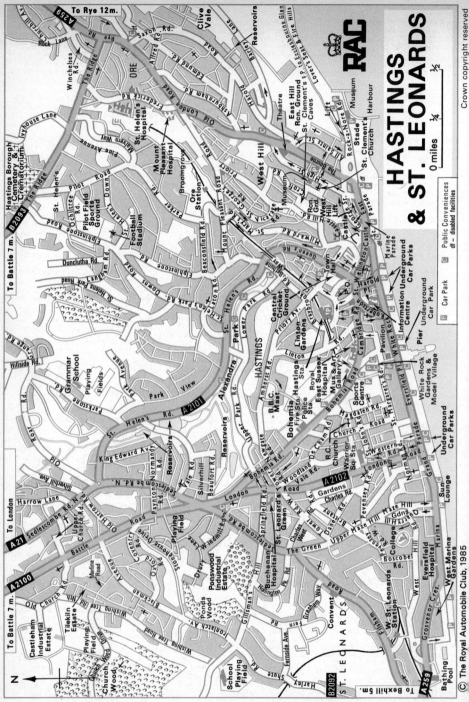

HASTINGS & ST. LEONARDS

© The Royal Automobile Club, 1985

*For abbreviations see inside back cover—***RAC**

Bridge, l *Bridge St, EX20 3JA.*
✆ Okehampton (0837) 810357. C. ⊷ 4
bedrs, 1 ba, Dgs. ✗ a l c. ⌂ CH, TV, Dgs,
CP 20, CF, 0 st. £ BB £9·50–£12·50, DB
£16–£17·50, WT (b) £85–£105, (c) £64–
£85, DT (b) £12·50–£16, ②, Bk £2·50, L
£3·70, D £6·95.

Rescue Service: Jones Bros, Bridge
Garage. ✆ (083 781) 244.

HATHERSAGE Derbyshire. Map 22A
Pop 1,426. Matlock 19, London 163,
Chesterfield 15, Glossop 18, Sheffield 11.
Golf Chapel-en-le-Frith 18h. **See** Iron Age
Fort, Norman Castle (earthworks), 14th
cent Church, assns with Robin Hood.

★★★**George,** *Main St, S30 1BB.* ✆ Hope
Valley (0433) 50436. C. ⊷ 18 bedrs, 16
bp, 2 bps, TV, Dgs. ✗ a l c, mc, LD 10.
⌂ CH, CP, con 16, CF, 0 st. £ BB £30–
£35, DB £40–45, WB, ①, Bk £4·50, L £5·50,
D £8·50, cc 1 2 3 5 6.

★★**Hathersage Inn,** *Main St, S30 1BB.*
✆ Hope Valley (0433) 50259. C. ⊷ 11
bedrs, 9 bp, 2 bps, 1 ba, TV, Dgs. ✗ mc, at,
LD 9.30. ⌂ CH, Dgs, CP 20, con 10, CF, 1
BGf, 3 st. £ BB £22–£35, DB £30–£50, WT
£140–£195, WB, ①, Bk £5, L £4·50, D
£6·95, cc 1 2 3 5, Dep a.

Highlow Hall, PH, xy (R), *via Sheffield,
S30 1AX.* ✆ Hope Valley (0433) 50393.

HATT Cornwall. Map 3C
Saltash 3, London 215, Callington 6,
Liskeard 11, Looe 13.

Holland Inn, *nr Saltash, PL12 6PJ.*
✆ Saltash (075 55) 3635.

HAVANT Hampshire. Map 6F
See also EMSWORTH.
Pop 115,900. Petersfield 12, London 65,
Chichester 9, Cosham 4.
EC Wed. **MD** Tue, Sat. **Golf** Crookhorn
18h. **See** Parish Church, Ancient Houses.

Rescue Service: Alandown (Motors) Ltd,
98 West St. ✆ (0705) 482369.

HAVEN STREET Isle of Wight. Map 6F
Pop 658. Portsmouth (Fy) 2½, London (Fy)
74, Cowes (Fy) 6½, Newport 4½, Ryde 3½,
Sandown 7, Ventnor 10.
Golf Ryde 9h.

Rescue Service: Winter, F H & Sons. ✆ Isle
of Wight (0983) 882455.

HAWES North Yorkshire. Map 26B
Pop 1,100. Leyburn 16, London 250,
Brough 21, Kendal 26, Kirkby Lonsdale
23, Lancaster 34, Leeds 58, Penrith 40,
Settle 36, Skipton 36.
EC Wed. **MD** Tue. **Golf** Catterick 18h.
See Waterfalls.

◼★★**Fountain,** *Main St, DL8 3RD.*
✆ (096 97) 206. C. ⊷ 12 bedrs, 5 bp, 7
bps, Dgs. ✗ mc, LD 8.45. ⌂ ch, CP 12, Ac,
3 st. £ BB £18–£20, DB £28–£30, DBB
£38–£40, ①, Bk £3·50, L £4·50, D £6·95,
Dep.

◼★★**Simonstone Hall,** (R) *DL8 3LY.*
✆ (096 97) 255. C. ⊷ 10 bedrs, 7 bp, 1
bps, 1 ba, TV, Dgs. ✗ mc, at, LD 8. ⌂ CH,
TV, Dgs, CP, con 20, CF, 1 st. £ BB £22, DB
£36, DBB £27·75, WB, ②, Bk £3·75, L
£4·95, D £9, cc 1 5 6, Dep a.

Rescue Service: Central Garage (Hawes)
Ltd. ✆ (096 97) 202.
Town Head Garage. ✆ (096 97) 216.

HAWESWATER Cumbria. Map 26D
Pop 50. Kendal 22, London 279,
Ambleside 27, Brough 26, Keswick 20,
Penrith 12.
Golf Penrith 18h. **See** Haweswater
(Manchester Corp. Reservoir), Fells.

◼★★**Haweswater,** *Lakeside Rd, CA10
2RP.* ✆ Bampton (Penrith) (093 13) 235.
C. ⊷ 16 bedrs, 3 sh, 4 ba. ✗ mc, at, LD 8.
⌂ CH, TV, CP 12, U 4, pf, con 16, CF, 1 st.
£ BB £14, DB £28, WT £114–£126, DT
£19–£21, DBB £18, WB, ①, D £6·50,
cc 1 3 5, Dep a.

HAWKCHURCH Devon. Map 5E
Pop 561. Crewkerne 9, London 143,
Axminster 6, Ilminster 11, Lyme Regis 7,
Taunton 18.
EC Wed, Sat. **Golf** Axe Cliff 18h.
See Church, Lamberts Castle–2 m.

◼★★★**Fairwater Head,** *EX13 5TX.*
✆ (029 77) 349. Closed Jan. C. ⊷ 14
bedrs, 14 bp, TV. ✗ a l c, at, LD 9. ⌂ CH,
TV, Dgs, CP 35, con 20, CF, 4 BGf, 1 st, Dis.
£ BB £24–£26, DB £44–£48, WB, ①, Bk
£3·50, L £4·50, D £8, cc 1 3, Dep a.

HAWKHURST Kent. Map 10E
Pop 3,908. Tonbridge 16, London 50,
Hastings 15, Hurst Green 3, Maidstone 17,
Rye 13, Tenterden 10, Tunbridge Wells 15.
EC Wed. **Golf** Hawkhurst 9h. **See** Church,
Bodiam Castle 3 m S.

★★**Tudor Arms,** *Rye Rd, TN18 5DA.*
✆ (058 05) 2312. C. ⊷ 14 bedrs, 6 bp, 3
bps, 2 ba, Dgs. ✗ a l c, mc, at, LD 9.15.
⌂ CH, TV, Dgs, CP 40, U 3, Ac, tc, con 20,
CF, 0 st. £ BB fr £17, DB fr £34, WT £168–
£196, DT £29·50–£33·50, DBB £24–£28,
WB, ①, Bk £3·50, L £5·50, D £7·50,
cc 1 2 3 5 6, Dep a.

Repairers: Sandhurst Service Station,
Sandhurst. ✆ Sandhurst (058 085) 295.
T G Waters, Four Throws Garage.
✆ (058 05) 2399.

HAWKSHEAD Cumbria. Map 26D
Pop 684. M6 Motorway 24, London 271,
Ambleside 5, Broughton-in-Furness 13,
Kendal 17, Lancaster 36, Ulverston 14.
EC Thur. **Golf** Windermere 18h. **See** 12th-
14th cent Church, 12th cent Court House
and Folk Museum, Tarn Hows, Grammar
School, Quaker Meeting House, Grisedale
Forest Nature Reserve.
🛈 Brown Cow Laithe. ✆ Hawkshead
(096 66) 525.

◼★★★**Tarn Hows,** *Hawkshead Hill,
LA22 0PR.* ✆ (096 66) 330.

◼★◾★**Ees Wyke,** (RI) *Near Sawrey,
LA22 0JZ.* ✆ (096 66) 393. C 14. ⊷ 6
bedrs, 2 bp, 4 bps, TV. ✗ LD 5.30. ⌂ CH,
CP 10, Ac, pf. £ BB £20, DB £30, DBB £22,
①, Dep a.

★★**Ormandy,** (R), *Grizedale.* ✆ (096 66)
532. Closed Jan–Feb. C. ⊷ 6 bedrs, 6 bps,
Dgs. ✗ LD 8.30. ⌂ CH, TV, Dgs, CP 25, pf,
2 st. £ BB £15·62, DB £25, ① 10%, L £4·50,
D £10, Dep a.

Highfield House, P, y, (R), *Hawkshead
Hill, LA22 0PN.* ✆ (096 66) 344. C. ⊷ 12
bedrs, 3 bp, 3 ba, TV, Dgs. ✗ mc, LD 7.15,
CF, 2 st. £ BB £10·50–£17, DB £20–£34,
WT (b) £100–£168, DT (b) £15–£24, ①, Bk
£2·50, L £3, D £7·50.

Repairer: C W Battersby, The Garage,
Main St. ✆ (096 66) 322.

HAWORTH West Yorkshire. Map 27A
Halifax 9½, London 203, Bradford 9,
Keighley 3½, Todmorden 8. **See** Old
Vicarage—Home of Bronte Sisters.
🛈 2 West Lane. ✆ Haworth (0535) 42329.

★★**Old White Lion,** *6 West Lane, BD22
8DU.* ✆ (0535) 42313. C. ⊷ 12 bedrs, 4
bp, 4 bps, 2 ba. ✗ a l c, mc, at, LD 10.
⌂ CH, TV, Dgs, CP 9, G 1, Ac, con 60, CF, 1
st. £ BB £18–£20·50, DB £26–£30·50,
DBB £25–£27·50, WB, ①, Bk £3·50, L
£4·80, D £7·50, cc 1 2 3 5 6, Dep.

Fernchiffe, PH, x (R), *Hebden Rd, BD22
8RS.* ✆ (0535) 43405. Closed Feb. C. ⊷ 6
bedrs, 6 bps, TV, Dgs. ✗ a l c. ⌂ CH, TV,
CP 15, CF. £ BB £12·50–£15, DB £25–£30,
WT (a) £147, (b) £120, (c) £87·50, DT (a)
£21, (b) £17, ②, Bk £2·75, L £3·75, D £4·75,
cc 3 5.

HAXBY North Yorkshire. Map 25C
Pop 9,150. York 4½, London 197,
Harrogate 24, Malton 17, Market
Weighton 24, Selby 18.
EC Wed. **Golf** Strensall 18h.

★★**Hilbra Court,** *York Rd, YO3 8HB.*
✆ York (0904) 768335. C. ⊷ 12 bedrs, 4
bps, 8 sh, 1 ba, TV, Dgs. ✗ a l c, LD 10.
⌂ ch, TV, CP 40, Ac, con, CF, 0 st. £ BB
£21–£25, DB £36–£38, WT £203, DT £32,
DBB £28·50, WB, ①, Bk £4·50, L £6·50, D
£8·50, cc 1 2 3 5 6.

HAYDOCK Merseyside. Map 20c
M6 Motorway 1½, London 194, Newton-
le-Willows 2½, St Helens 4½, Wigan 6.

★★★★**M Post House** (TH), *Lodge Lane,
WA12 0JG.* ✆ Wigan (0942) 717878, C.
⊷ 98 bedrs, 98 bp, TV, Dgs. ✗ a l c, mc, at,
LD 10·15. ⌂ N, CH, Dgs, CP 130, Ac, con
60, CF, 25BGf, 1 st, Dis. £ BB £44·50, DB
£57, WB, ①, cc 1 2 3 4 5 6, Dep (Xmas).

HAYDON BRIDGE Northumberland.
Map 31E
Pop 1,800. Hexham 6, London 288, Alston
17, Corbridge 10, Haltwhistle 9, Jedburgh
51.
EC Wed. **Golf** Hexham 9h & 18h. **See**
Church.

★★**Anchor,** *John Martin St, NE47 6AB.*
✆ (043 484) 227. C. ⊷ 10 bedrs, 5 bps, 2
ba, TV, Dgs. ✗ mc, LD 9. ⌂ CH, TV, Dgs,
CP 20, Ac, pf, con 40, CF, 2 st. £ BB £15–
£20, DB £23–£29, DBB £15–£22, ①, Bk £3,
D £6, cc 1 2 3 5.

HAYES Greater London (Middx). Map 7A
2½ m W of Southall. Pop 67,915 (inc
Harlington), London 13, London 13,
Brentford & Chiswick 6½, Harrow 6½,
Kingston upon Thames 9½, Richmond-
upon-Thames 8, Rickmansworth 10,
Staines 8, Slough 9, Uxbridge 4, Watford
13, Windsor 10.
EC Wed. **Golf** Ealing 18h. West Middlesex
18h.

Rescue Service: Airways Garage Ltd,
Bath Rd. ✆ 01-759 9661.
North Hyde Service Station, North Hyde
Rd. ✆ 01-573 6912.

HAYFIELD Derbyshire (Cheshire) Map
22A
Pop 2,344. Chapel-en-le-Frith 5, London
170, Glossop 5, Manchester 17, Sheffield
26, Stockport 10.
Golf New Mills 9h

Hazel Villas, G, x (Unl). *1 & 2 Valley Rd.*
✆ New Mills (0663) 43671. ⊨ 8 bedrs, 2
bps, 2 ba, TV, Dgs. ⌂ TV, Dgs, CP 8, G 1,
CF, 2 BGf, 1 st. £ BB £9·50–£11·50, DB
£15·50–£17·50, ⊡, cc 1.

HAYLE Cornwall. Map 2E
Pop 6,200. Redruth 10, London 275,
Helston 10, Penzance 7½, St Ives 5.
EC Thur. **Golf** West Cornwall, Lelant 18h.
See Ancient Church of St Felicitas,
inscribed 5th cent stone.

◨★**Hillside** (Rl), *Angarrack, TR27 5HZ.*
✆ (0736) 752180. RS Dec 22–Jan 4. C.
⊨ 7 bedrs, 1 bp, 2 bps, 1 sh, 2 ba. ✘ mc,
at, LD 6. ⌂ CH, TV, CP 8, CF, 2 st. £ BB
£10·25–£12·75, DB £19·50–£24, DBB
£13·95–£16·95, ⊡, Bk £3·25, D £5·75.

Specialist Radiator Repairer: Serck
Radiator Services, The Causeway.
✆ (0736) 752677.
Rescue Service: Fraddam Garage,
Fraddam. ✆ Leedstown (073 685) 213.
Hawkins Motors Ltd, Hayle Ter. ✆ (0736)
753143.

HAYLING ISLAND Hampshire. Map 6F
Pop 12,225. Petersfield 18, London 71,
Chichester 14, Cosham 9.
EC Wed. **Golf** Hayling 18h. **See** St Mary's
Church, St Peter's Church.
⏹ 32 Seafront. ✆ Hayling Island (070 16)
67111.

★★★★**M Post House** (TH), *Northney Rd,
PO11 0NQ.* ✆ (070 16) 5011. C. ⊨ 96
bedrs, 96 bp, TV, Dgs. ✘ a l c, mc, LD
10.30. ⌂ N, CH, Dgs, CP 150, Ac, sp, con
140, CF, 40 BGf, 0 st, Dis. £ BB £42·50, DB
£54·50, WB, ⊡, cc 1 2 3 4 5 6, Dep (Xmas).
◨★★**Newtown House** (R), *Manor Rd,
PO11 0QR.* ✆ (070 16) 66131. Closed Dec
24–Jan 2. C. ⊨ 21 bedrs, 10 bp, 9 bps, 2
ba, ns, TV, Dgs. ✘ a l c, mc, at, LD 9.30.
⌂ N, CH, CP 45, sp, tc, sb, con 30, CF, 8
BGf, 2 st. £ WB, cc 1 2 3 5 6, Dep b.

Rescue Service: Hayden Garages, 62
Station Rd. ✆ (070 16) 2660.
Vick Autos (Hayling) Ltd, Hayling Service
Station, 181 Havant Rd. ✆ (070 16) 3570.

HAYTOR Devon. Map 3D
Exeter 17, London 185, Ashburton 5½,
Newton Abbot 7½, Okehampton 21.
EC Wed. **Golf** Newton Abbot (Stover)
18h. **See** Haytor Rocks 1,491 ft above sea
level.

◨⬛★★**Bel Alp** (R), *TQ13 9XX.*
✆ (036 46) 217. C. ⊨ 9 bedrs, 8 bp, 1 bps,
TV, Dgs. ✘ mc, at, LD 8.30. ⌂ Lt, CH, Dgs,
CP 20, tc, con 20, CF, 1 BGf, 3 st. £ BB
£24, DB £42, DBB £24–£33, ⊡, Bk £4, D
£11, cc 1 3 5, Dep a.
◨⬛★★**Haytor,** *Ilsington, TQ13 9RR*
✆ (036 46) 200. C. ⊨ 16 bedrs, 3 bp, 2
bps, 4 ba, Dgs. ✘ mc, LD 8. ⌂ ch, TV, Dgs,
CP 30, Ac, gc, con 100, CF, 2 st. £ BB
£11·50, DB £23–£26, DBB £18·50–£21·50,
WB, ⊡, Bk £3·50, D £6·90.

HAYWARDS HEATH West Sussex.
Map 7D
Pop 25,310. Redhill 17, London 38,
Arundel 29, Bognor Regis 35, Brighton 14,
Chichester 37, Crawley 12, East Grinstead
11, Godstone 20, Horsham 13, Lewes 13,
Petworth 27, Pulborough 23, Reigate 18,
Tunbridge Wells 21, Uckfield 12.
EC Wed. **MD** Tue, Sun. **Golf** Haywards
Heath 18h. **See** Church.

Repairers: Dinnages, Wivelsfield Rd.
✆ (0444) 50222.
Wadham Stringer (Haywards Heath) Ltd,
Milgreen Rd. ✆ (0444) 50404.

HAZEL GROVE Gtr Manchester
(Cheshire). M. Area 22A
Pop 15,560, Buxton 14, London 174,
Chapel-en-le-Frith 11, Glossop 10,
Knutsford 13, Macclesfield 8½, Oldham 13,
Stockport 3.
EC Wed. **Golf** Hazel Grove 18h. **See**
Bramall Hall, 14th cent half-timbered.
⏹ Civic Hall, London Rd. ✆ 061-456 4195.

MC Repairer: Derek Warburton Ltd, 260
London Rd. ✆ 061-483 4500.

HAZLEHEAD South Yorkshire. Map
Areas 22A and 33C
Sheffield 16, London 170, Barnsley 10,
Huddersfield 11, Manchester 26.

Flouch, I, x, *Crowedge, S30 5HH.*
✆ (0226) 762037. ⊨ 5 bedrs, 4 bp, 1 ba,
TV, Dgs. ✘ a l c ⌂ CH, Dgs, CP 50, CF, 1
st. £ BB £15, DB £25, ⊡, Bk £3·75, L £3·75,
D £6·50, cc 1.

HEACHAM Norfolk. Map 16E.
Kings Lynn 14, London 113, Cromer 38,
Fakenham 18, Norwich 44, Swaffham 24.

St Anne's, G, x (Rl), *53 Neville Rd.
PE31 7HB.* ✆ (0485) 70021. Open Feb–
Nov. C. ⊨ 6 bedrs, 2 bps, 2 ba, TV, Dgs.
⌂ ch, TV, Dgs, CP 6, 2 BGf, 1 st, Dis. £ BB
£8·25–£11·75, DB £16·50–£23·50, WT (b)
£92·75–£117·25, (c) £57·75–£82·25, DT
(b) £13·25–£15·75, ⊡.

HEADINGTON Oxfordshire. Map 14F
High Wycombe 23, London 53, M40
Motorway 6, Oxford 3, Witney 13.

Conifer, G, z (Unl). *116 The Slade, OX3
7DX.* ✆ Oxford (0865) 63055. C. ⊨ 8
bedrs, 1 bp, 2 bps, 1 ba, TV, Dgs. ✘ CP
8, CF. £ BB £10–£12, DB £18–£24, ⊡.

HEADLEY DOWN Hampshire. M. Area
6D
Pop 5,000. 3 m W of Hindhead, London 44,
Alton 9½, Farnham 8, Petersfield 11.
EC Wed. **Golf** Blackmoor 18h. **See**
Headley Mill.

Rescue Service: Healey & Jacobs Ltd,
Crabtree Garage. Crabtree La. ✆ (0428)
2381.

HEATH Derbyshire. Map 22D
Pop 186. M1 Motorway ½, London 144,
Chesterfield 6, Derby 23, Mansfield 6½,
Matlock 12, Ollerton 15, Rotherham 18,
Sheffield 16, Worksop 14.
EC Wed. **Golf** Chesterfield 18h (2). **See**
All Saint's Church.

Rescue Service: Red House Service
Station. ✆ Chesterfield (0246) 850329.

HEDNESFORD Staffordshire. M. Area
22E
Pop 13,300. Atherstone 23, London 127,
M6 Motorway 5½, Burton-on-Trent 22,
Shrewsbury 36, Stafford 9, Rugeley 4½.
EC Thur. **MD** Fri, Sat. **Golf** Cannock
Chase 18h.

Rescue Service: Chase Service Centre,
172A Belt Rd. ✆ (054 38) 76908 &
(054 38) 77888.

HEDON Humberside (North
Humberside). Map 25B
Pop 4,700. Hull 6, London 181, Bridlington
28.

EC Wed. **Golf** Ganstead 9h, Sutton 18h.
See St Augustine's Church.

Rescue Service: Johnson's Garage
(Hedon) Ltd, Thorn Rd. ✆ Hull (0482)
895121.

HELMSLEY North Yorkshire. Map 24D
Pop 1,450. York 24, London 222,
Boroughbridge 21, Malton 16,
Middlesbrough 28, Pickering 13,
Stockton-on-Tees 29, Thirsk 14.
EC Wed. **MD** Fri. **Golf** Kirbymoorside 9h.
See Castle ruins, Rievaulx Terrace
frescoes 2 m NW, Rievaulx Abbey 3 m NW,
Nunnington Hall 4½ m SE, remains of
12th-13th cent Byland Abbey 4½ m SW.
⏹ 23a Market Pl. ✆ Helmsley (0439)
70775.

★★★**Black Swan** (TH), *Market Pl, YO6
5BJ.* ✆ (0439) 70466. C. ⊨ 38 bedrs, 38
bp, TV, Dgs. ✘ a l c, mc, at. ⌂ N, CH, Dgs,
CP 36, G 2, Ac, con 60, CF, 0 st. £ BB £41,
DB £59·50, WB, ⊡, cc 1 2 3 4 5 6, Dep
(Xmas).
★★★**Feversham Arms,** *YO6 5AG.*
✆ (0439) 70766. C. ⊨ 15 bedrs, 15 bp, TV,
Dgs. ✘ a l c, mc, LD 9. ⌂ CH, CP 30, Ac,
tc, con 30, CF, 4 BGf, 3 st. £ BB £28–£30,
DB £36–£40, WB, ⊡, Bk £6, L £6, D £10,
cc 1 2 3 6, Dep a.
★★**Crown,** *Market Pl, YO6 5BJ.* ✆ (0439)
70297. C. ⊨ 15 bedrs, 1 bp, 9 bps, 2 ba,
TV, Dgs. ✘ a l c, mc, LD 8. ⌂ CH, TV, CP 15,
G 3, 3 BGf, 0 st, Dis. £ BB £16–£18, DBB
£32–£36, WT £169–£182, DT £26–£28,
DBB £22–£24, WB, ⊡, Bk £2·50, L £4, D
£7·50.▲
★★**Feathers,** *Market Pl, YO6 5BH.*
✆ (0439) 70275. RS Xmas–New Year. C.
⊨ 18 bedrs, 6 bp, 7 bps, 3 ba, TV, Dgs.
✘ mc, at, LD 8.30. ⌂ CH, TV, Dgs, CP 10,
Ac, CP 100, CF, 2 st. £ BB £15–£18, DB
£30–£36, WT £205, DT £30, DBB £22·50–
£25, WB, ⊡, Bk £3·50, L £5, D £8·50,
cc 1 2 3 5.

HELSBY Cheshire. Maps 20D & 19A
Pop 4,326. Tarporley 12, London 184,
M56 Motorway 1½, Chester 7½, Runcorn
7½, Warrington 12.
Golf Helsby 18h. **See** The Hill (N.T.).

Poplars, G, (Unl). *130, Chester Rd, WA6
9NN.* ✆ (092 82) 3433. Closed Dec. 24–
31. C. ⊨ 6 bedrs, 2 ba. ⌂ CH, TV, CP 10, 2
st. £ BB £11·50, DB £18, WT (c) £80, DT
(b) £15·50, ⊡, D £4.

HELSTON Cornwall. Map 2E
Pop 7,975. Truro 16, London 271,
Falmouth 13, Penzance 13, Redruth 10, St
Ives 15.
EC Wed. **MD** Mon, Sat. **Golf** Mullion 18h,
Praa Sands 9h. **See** 'Furry Day'
celebrations (May), Museum, St Michael's
Church, Godolphin House 4½ m NW.
⏹ Greenacres, Clodgey La. ✆ Helston
(032 65) 62505

◨★★**Gwealdues,** *TR13 8JX.* ✆ (032 65)
2808.
◨★**Angel,** *Coinagehall St, TR13 8EB.*
✆ (032 65) 2701. C. ⊨ 21 bedrs, 1 bps, 6
ba. ✘ a l c, mc, at, LD 9 (10 in summer).
⌂ ch, TV, Dgs, CP 14, G 1, Ac, CF, 2 st.
£ BB £15–£17, DB £20–£25, WT £133–
£164, DT £22–£27, DBB £20–£25, WT, ⊡,
Bk £3, L £3, D £7, cc 1 2 3 5 6, Dep a.
Boscadjack, F, x (Unl), *Coverack
Bridges, TR13 0LZ.* ✆ (032 65) 2086.
Open Mar–Sep. C. ⊨ 4 bedrs, 1 ba. ⌂ CH,

TV, CP, CF, 2 st. **£** BB fr £7, DB £14, WT (b)
fr £67, (c) fr £49, DT (b) fr £10, ⊡.
Hillside, G, z (Rl), *Godolphin Rd, TR13
8PX.* **✆** (032 65) 4788.
Tenderah, H, yz, *Church Hill, TR13 8NT.*
✆ (032 65) 2703.
Wheal Tor, PH, z (R), *26 Godolphin Rd,
TR13 8PY.* **✆** (032 65) 61211. Closed
Xmas. C. **➡** 8 bedrs, 1 bps, 2 ba. ⓓ CH, TV,
CF, 2 st. **£** BB £7–£7·75, DB £14–£18·50,
WT (c) £49–£54·25, ⊡.

MC Repairer: Helston Motorcycle Centre
Ltd, Turnpike. **✆** (032 65) 62929.
Rescue Service: Flora Motors Ltd,
Lakeside Garage. **✆** (032 65) 2337.▲
Helston Auto Centre, Clodgey La.
✆ (032 65) 63671.
Helston Garages Ltd, Meneage St.
✆ (032 65) 3415.
J H Pollard & Son (Garage) Ltd, Kennack
Sands, Ruan Minor. **✆** The Lizard (0326)
290503.

HEMEL HEMPSTEAD Herts. Map 15E
Pop 79,588. Watford 7½, London 24, M1
Motorway 2½, Aylesbury 17, Barnet 16,
Bletchley 22, Dunstable 12, Enfield 21,
High Wycombe 18, Luton 12, St Albans 7.
EC Wed. **MD** Thur, Fri, Sat. **Golf** Little
Hay 18h. **See** Civic Centre, Church of St
Mary (Norman), Water Gardens, Piccotts
End (Medieval Murals) 1 m N.
ⓘ The Pavilion, The Marlowes. **✆** Hemel
Hempstead (0442) 64451.

★★★M Post House (TH), *Breakspear
Way, HP2 4UA.* **✆** (0442) 51122. C.
➡ 107 bedrs, 107 bp, TV, Dgs. **✗** a l c, mc,
at, LD 9.45. ⓓ Lt, N, CH, Dgs, CP 140, Ac,
con 100, CF, 38 BGf, 0 st, Dis. **£** BB £43,
DB £55·50, WB, ⊡, cc 1 2 3 4 5 6, Dep
(Xmas).
Southville, PH, z (Unl), *9 Charles St,
HP1 1JH.* **✆** (0442) 51387. C. **➡** 12 bedrs,
3 ba, Dgs. ⓓ CH, TV, CP 8, 1 st. **£** BB
£13·50, WT (c) £94·50, ⊡.

Repairer: Hemel Hempstead Motors Ltd,
London Rd. **✆** (0442) 42841.
Specialist Body Repairers: D R Bradshaw
& Co Ltd, London Rd. **✆** (0442) 57491.
Shaw & Kilburn Ltd, Two Waters Rd.
✆ (0442) 51212.
Rescue Service: Adeyfield Recovery &
Breakdown Service, 1 St Albans Hill.
✆ (0442) 52515.
R V James Ltd, Marlowes Garage, Hillfield
Rd. **✆** (0442) 49494.
Hemel Car Recovery, 194 Belswains La.
✆ (0442) 45678.

HEMINGFORD ABBOTS
Cambridgeshire. M. Area 15B
1 m W of Hemingford Grey. Pop 580.
Royston 21, London 62, Biggleswade 20,
Cambridge 13, Ely 17, Huntingdon 4,
Wisbech 33.
Golf St Ives 9h. **See** Church, old houses.

Rescue Service: Abbots Service Area,
A604 Cambridge Rd. **✆** St Ives (0480)
67352.
Lion Garage (Huntingdon) Ltd,
Cambridge–Huntingdon Rd. **✆** St Ives
(0480) 63240.

HEMSWORTH West Yorkshire. Map
25F and 33D
Pop 21,089. Rotherham 14, London 175,
Barnsley 7½, Doncaster 12, Pontefract 6½,
Wakefield 8½.

EC Wed. **MD** Tues, Fri, Sat. **Golf**
Pontefract 18h. **See** Nostell Priory 3 m
NW.

Rescue Service: Taits of Hemsworth,
Barnsley Rd. **✆** (0977) 610231.

HEMYOCK Devon. Map 4E
Pop 1,232. Ilminster 15, London 150,
Crewkerne 21, Dunster 26, Exeter 22,
Honiton 10, Minehead 20, Taunton 11,
Tiverton 12.
EC Thur. **Golf** Tiverton 18h. **See**
'Wellington' Monument, 13th cent Church.

Rescue Service: Hemyock Motors,
Culmstock Rd. **✆** (0823) 680591.

HENLEY-IN-ARDEN Warwicks. Map
14A
Pop 1,640. Stratford-upon-Avon 8,
London 101, Birmingham 15, Bromsgrove
14, Coventry 19, Evesham 18, Sutton
Coldfield 23, Warwick 9, Worcester 25.
EC Thur. **MD** Mon. **Golf** Redditch 18h.
See Perp Church, Market Cross, Guildhall,
Old inns and houses.

Ashleigh House, G, x, y (Unl), *Whitley
Hill, B95 5DL.* **✆** (056 42) 2315. C 5. **➡** 8
bedrs, 4 ba, TV. ⓓ CH, TV, CP 8, G 1, 1 BGf,
3 st. **£** BB £10–£15, DB £20–£30, ⊡.

Repairer: Henley Garages Ltd, 57 High St.
✆ (056 42) 2543.
Rescue Service: Market Garage, Warwick
Rd. **✆** (056 42) 3050.

HENLEY-ON-THAMES Oxfordshire.
Map 6B
Pop 12,000. Slough 14, London 35, A423
(M) Motorway 6½, Aylesbury 27, Bagshot
19, Bicester 34, Denham 21, Farnham 28,
High Wycombe 12, Reading 8, Wallingford
11, Windsor 14.
MD Thur. **Golf** Henley 18h. **See** Bridge,
Chantry House (14th cent), St Mary's
Church, Kenton Theatre 1798, Royal
Regatta in June/July, 16th cent Greys
Court 2½ m NW (NT).
ⓘ West Hill House, 4 West St. **✆** Henley-
on-Thames (049 12) 2626.

★★★Red Lion, *Hart St, RG9 2AR.*
✆ (0491) 572161. C. **➡** 28 bedrs, 19 bp, 2
ba, TV. ⓓ N, CH, Dgs, CP 30, U 1, G 4, con
20, CF, 0 st. **£** BB fr £25, DB fr £40, WT
£185, DT £30, DBB £25, WB, ⊡, Bk £5, L
£6·50, D £7·50, cc 2 3.
★Sydney House, (R), *Northfield End,
RG9 2JG.* **✆** (0491) 573412. C. **➡** 8
bedrs, 2 bp, 1 sh, 2 ba, TV, Dgs. **✗** a l c, LD
10.30. ⓓ CH, TV, Dgs, CP 5, CF, 3 st. **£** BB
£11·50–£15, DB £20–£30, WB, Bk £3, L £8,
D £12, cc 1 2 3 5 6, Dep b.

Repairers: Bell Street Motors Ltd, Bell St.
✆ (0491) 3077.
Ray Sargeant Ltd, 58 Reading Rd.
✆ (0491) 3902.
Rescue Service: Julians of Henley Ltd, 49
Station Rd. **✆** (0491) 4136.

HENSTRIDGE Somerset. Map 5D
Pop 1,331. Shaftesbury 10, London 113,
Blandford Forum 16, Dorchester 20,
Sherborne 6, Wincanton 7.
EC Wed. **Golf** Sherborne 18h. **See**
Church.

Rescue Service: Vale Motors, Bazeland
Hill. **✆** Stalbridge (0963) 62268.

HEREFORD Hereford & Worcester
(Herefordshire). Map 13C

Pop 48,300. Gloucester 28, London 132,
Abergavenny 23, Brecon 36, Bromyard 14,
Builth Wells 40, Kington 18, Ledbury 14,
Leominster 12, Monmouth 17, Ross-on-
Wye 14, Worcester 25.
EC Thur. **MD** Mon, Wed, Thur, Fri. **Golf**
Wormsley 18h. **See** Cathedral (Medieval
Maps, Chained Library), The Old House
(museum), 15th cent Booth Hall (now
dining hall of Booth Hall Hotel), Museum
and Art Gallery, 'Raven' Inn (Garrick's
birthplace), All Saints' Church, St Peter's
Church, birthplace of Nell Gwynne in
Gwynne St (tablet), Coningsby Hospital
(Almshouse), 15th cent Wye Bridge, Three
Choirs Festival held trienially, Dinmore
Manor 6½ m N.
ⓘ Shirehall Forecourt, 1a St Owen St.
✆ Hereford (0432) 268430.

★★★Green Dragon (TH), *Broad St, HR4
9BG.* **✆** (0432) 272506. C. **➡** 88 bedrs, 88
bp, TV, Dgs. **✗** a l c, mc, at, LD 9.15. ⓓ Lt,
N, CH, Dgs, G 90, Ac, con 200, CF, 0 st.
£ BB £40, DB £51·50, WB, ⊡,
cc 1 2 3 4 5 6, Dep (Xmas).
★★★M Hereford Moat House, *Belmont
Rd, HR2 7BP.* **✆** (0432) 54301. C. **➡** 32
bedrs, 32 bp, TV, Dgs. **✗** a l c, mc, at, LD
9.45. ⓓ N, CH, CP 200, Ac, con 300, CF, 32
BGf, 2 st. **£** BB £33, DB £40, DT £46·75,
DBB £40·50, WB, ⊡, Bk £3·50, L £6·25, D
£7·50, cc 1 2 3 5, Dep b.
★★Graftonbury, *Grafton La, HR2 8BN.*
✆ (0432) 56411. C. **➡** 21 bedrs, 10 bp, 4
bps, 3 ba, annexe 15 bedrs, 2 bps, 3 ba, TV,
Dgs. **✗** a l c, mc, LD 9.15. ⓓ Lt, N, ch, TV,
Dgs, CP 100, Ac, sp, sb, sol, gym, CF, 10
BGf, 1 st, Dis. **£** BB £16·50–£22, DB £25–
£35, WB, ⊡, Bk £3·50, L £5·05, D £5·50,
cc 1 2 3 5.▲
★★Litchfield Lodge (R), *Bodenham Rd,
HR1 2TS.* **✆** (0432) 273258. Closed Xmas.
C 5. **➡** 14 bedrs, 4 bp, 5 bps, 1 ba, TV.
✗ a l c, mc, at, LD 8. ⓓ CH, TV, CP 15, CP
20, **£** BB £17·05–£20·35, DB £28·60–
£31·90, DBB £22·05–£28, ⊡, cc 1 2 3.
★★Merton, *Commercial Rd, HR1 2BD.*
✆ (0432) 265925.
Munstone House, G, y (Unl), *Munstone.*
✆ (0432) 267122. Open Apr–Oct. C. **➡** 6
bedrs, 2 ba, ns, ⓓ ch, TV, CP 10, CF, 0 st.

Repairers: Henlys (West) Ltd, Widemarsh
St. **✆** (0432) 67611.
Victory Garage, St Owen St. **✆** (0432)
266443.
Vincent Greenhous (Hereford) Ltd,
Blackfriars St. **✆** (0432) 267441.
Rescue Service: Hereford Auto Repairs,
Field Yard, Plough La. **✆** 57241.

HERMITAGE Berkshire. Map 6B
Pop 850. Reading 14, London 53,
Basingstoke 18, Newbury 4½, Oxford 24,
Wallingford 14, Wantage 14.
EC Wed. **Golf** Newbury and Aldworth
18h. **See** Grimsbury Castle, Wessex
Downs Park, Well.

Rescue Service: A & B Motors
(Hermitage) Ltd, Hermitage Garage.
✆ (0635) 200257.

HERNE BAY Kent. Map 10D
Pop 26,000. Rochester 30, London 62,
Canterbury 8½, Maidstone 31, Margate 12.
EC Thur. **MD** Sat. **Golf** Herne Bay 18h.
See Reculver (remains of Roman fort),
Clock Tower, King's Hall (The Downs),
Windmill.

🛈 Council Offices, William St. ✆ Herne Bay (022 73) 66031.

Beauville, G, z (Unl), *92 Central Parade, CT6 5JJ.* ✆ (022 73) 5330. C. ⚫ 5 bedrs, 1 ba, Dgs. 🅿 CH, TV, Dgs, CF, 1 st. £ BB £10–£11, DB £18, 🛈.

Four Fathoms, H, z, *2 High St, CT6 5LH.* ✆ (022 73) 4987. C. ⚫ 6 bedrs, 2 ba, Dgs. 🅿 TV, Dgs, 1 st. £ BB £9·50–£10·50, DB £19–£21, WT (c) £60–£70, 🛈.

Victoria, PH, z (Unl), *85 Central Parade, CT6 5JQ.* ✆ (0227) 69660. C. ⚫ 4 bedrs, 1 bp, 1 ba, TV, Dgs. 🅿 CH, sp, sb, CF. £ BB £10, DB £17–£30, WT (c) fr £70.

Repairers: County Garage (Herne Bay) Ltd, 15 Sea St. ✆ (022 73) 4939.
L H Jackson Motors Ltd, Kings Rd. ✆ (022 73) 3871.

HERSTMONCEUX East Sussex. Map 7F
Pop 1,400. Lower Dicker 5½, London 58, Battle 8, Bexhill 9, Eastbourne 11.
EC Wed. **Golf** Willingdon 18h. **See** Castle, now Royal Greenwich Observatory, Ornamental gardens open, 14th cent Tithe Barn, Isaac Newton telescope.

Cleavers Lyng, H, xy (R), *Church Rd, BN27 1QJ.* ✆ (0323) 833131, Closed Xmas & Jan. C. ⚫ 8 bedrs, 4 ba, Dgs. 🅿 CH, TV, Dgs, CP 15, CF, 0 st. £ BB £10·25–£10·75, DB £20·50–£21·50, WT (b) £91–£95, DT (b) £14·25–£14·95, 🄌, Bk £2·50, L £3·50, D £4·75.

Rescue Service: Geo Collins (Engineers) Ltd, Hailsham Rd. ✆ (0323) 833488.

HERTFORD Hertfordshire. Map 15F
Pop 25,000. Hoddesdon 4½, London 24, Baldock 17, Barnet 13, Bedford 32, Bishop's Stortford 13, Chelmsford 27, Epping 13, Hatfield 7, Luton 18, Royston 19.
EC Thur. **MD** Mon, Thur, Sat. **Golf** Chadwell Springs 9h. **See** Municipal buildings (once castle), St Leonard's Church, All Saints' Church, Old houses, Haileybury College.
🛈 Vale House, 43 Cowbridge. ✆ Hertford (0992) 54977 ext 287.

★★★M White Horse Inn (TH), *Hertingfordbury, SG14 2LB.* (1½ m W A414). ✆ (0992) 56791. C. ⚫ 30 bedrs, 30 bp, TV, Dgs. ✗ mc, LD 9.45. 🅿 CH, Dgs, CP 60, Ac, con 30, CF, 0 st. £ BB £40·50, DB £54·50, WB, 🛈, cc 1 2 3 4 5 6, Dep (Xmas)

★★Salisbury Arms, *Fore St, SG14 1BZ.* ✆ (0992) 53091. RS Dec 25–27. C. ⚫ 32 bedrs, 11 bp, 1 sh, 7 ba, Dgs. ✗ a l c, mc, LD 9. 🅿 N, CH, CP 40, Ac, con 35, CF, 0 st. £ BB fr £18, DB fr £26·25, 🛈, Bk £4, L £6, D £6, cc 1 3, Dep b.

Rescue Service: Abbey Garage (Hertford) Ltd, 26 Church Rd, Little Berkhamsted. ✆ Cuffley (070 787) 5151.
Neal of Hertford, Old London Rd. ✆ (0992) 2561.

HERTFORD HEATH Hertfordshire. M. Area 15F
Pop 1,391. Hoddesdon 2, London 22, Baldock 19, Barnet 15, Bedford 34, Hatfield 9, Luton 20, Royston 21.
Golf Chadwell Springs 9h. **See** Haileybury College, Hertford Heath (rare plants).

Rescue Service: Haileybury Motor Works, College Rd. ✆ Hoddesdon (099 24) 62348.

HESSLE Humberside (North Humberside). Map 25B
Pop 14,040. Goole 23, London 202, Beverley 9, Hull 4½, Market Weighton 16, Selby 30.
Golf Hessle 18h. **See** All Saints' Church, part 12th cent.

Rescue Service: Hessle Auto Engineers Ltd, Westbourne Garage. ✆ Hull (0482) 642266.

HESWALL Merseyside. Map 19A
Pop 26,395. Chester 13, London 197, Birkenhead 7, Queensferry 11.
EC Wed. **Golf** Gayton 18h. **See** Wirral County Park.

Repairers: Hall's Garage, Lower Village. ✆ 051-342 6059.
Heswall Autos Ltd, May Rd. ✆ 051-342 6316.
Specialist Body Repairer: Heswall Autos Ltd, May Rd. ✆ 051-342 6316.
Rescue Service: James Edwards (Chester) Ltd, Heswall Garage, 77 Telegraph Rd. ✆ 051-342 6171.

HETHERSETT Norfolk. Map 16D
Thetford 22, London 104, East Dereham 14, Lowestoft 34, Norwich 6, Scole 21.

★★★Park Farm (R), *NR9 3DL.* ✆ Norwich (0603) 810264. C. ⚫ 21 bedrs, 11 bp, 10 sh, 1 ba, TV. ✗ a l c, mc, at, LD 9. 🅿 CH, TV, CP 50, sp, tc, sb, sol, con, CF, 6 BGf, 2 st. £ BB £25–£28, DB £35–£38, WT £245, DT £38–£40, DBB £33–£38, WB, 🛈, Bk £4, L £4·95, D £7·50, cc 1 3.

HEVERSHAM Cumbria. Map 26D
Pop 703. M6 Motorway 3½, London 253, Ambleside 18, Broughton-in-Furness 27, Kendal 6½, Kirkby Lonsdale 9, Lancaster 15, Ulverston 22.
Golf Kendal 18h. **See** Church, Old Hall.

★★★Blue Bell at Heversham, *Prince's Way, LA7 7EE.* ✆ Milnthorpe (044 82) 3159. Closed Dec 25 & 26. C. ⚫ 28 bedrs, 12 bp, 5 bps, 4 ba, ns, Dgs. ✗ a l c, mc, at, LD 9.15. 🅿 CH, TV, Dgs, CP 104, con 45, CF, 1 st. £ BB fr £19, DB fr £32, WT £165, DBB fr £27, WB, 🛈, Bk £5·50, L £5·50, D £10, cc 1 3.

HEWISH Avon. Map 5A
Pop 250. 2½ m W of Congresbury. Bristol 14, London 128, M5 Motorway 3, Bath 25, Glastonbury 22, Radstock 24, Shepton Mallet 23, Wells 18, Weston-super-Mare 6.
Golf Worlebury, Weston-super-Mare 18h.

Kara, G, x (Rl). *BS24 6RQ.* ✆ Yatton (0934) 834442. C. ⚫ 6 bedrs, 2 ba. 🅿 CH, TV, CP 5, CF, 0 st. £ BB £6·50–£7·50, DB £13–£15, WT (b) £59·75–£66, DT (b) £9·50–£10·50, 🛈.

Rescue Service: Hewish Service Station, Bristol Rd. ✆ Yatton (0934) 832853.

HEXHAM Northumberland. Maps 26A and 31E
Pop 10,000. West Auckland 33, London 282, Alnwick 44, Alston 21, Bellingham 17, Brampton 28, Corbridge 3½, Durham 27, Hawick 53, Jedburgh 48, Middleton-in-Teesdale 31.
EC Thur. **MD** Tue, Fri. **Golf** Hexham 18h. **See** Priory Church, 15th cent Moot Hall, Roman Wall, Housesteads Roman Camp,

Chesters Roman Camp, Brunton Turret (Roman Milecastle), Vindolanda excavations, Kielder Water (largest reservoir in England).
🛈 Manor Office, Hallgates. ✆ Hexham (0434) 605225.

■★★Beaumont, *Beaumont St, NE46 3LT.* ✆ (0434) 602331. Closed Xmas. C. ⚫ 22 bedrs, 4 bp, 14 bps, 2 ba, TV, Dgs. ✗ mc, LD 9.45. 🅿 CH, Dgs, Ac, con 25, CF, 2 st. £ BB £17·50–£18·50, DB £29·50, WB, 🛈, Bk £3·50, L £5, cc 1 2 3 5 6, Dep b.

★★County, *Priestpopple, NE46 1PS.* ✆ (0434) 602030. C. ⚫ 10 bedrs, 4 bps, 5 sh, 2 ba, TV, Dgs. ✗ mc, at, LD 9.30. 🅿 N, CH, Dgs, Ac, con 65, CF, 3 st. £ BB fr £16, DB fr £24, WB, 🄌, Bk £3, L £6, D £6, cc 1 2 3.

■★★Royal, *Priestpopple, NE46 1PQ.* ✆ (0434) 602270. C. ⚫ 25 bedrs, 14 bp, 5 ba, TV, Dgs. ✗ a l c, mc, LD 9.30. 🅿 CH, CP 25, Ac, con 100, CF. £ BB £15·50–£23·50, DBB £20·25–£24·50, WB, 🛈, Bk £3·50, L £4·75, D £6·75, cc 1 3.

Rescue Service: Broadway Garage, West Rd. ✆ (0434) 603861.
Carr, A & Son (Hexham) Ltd, Station Garage. ✆ (0434) 602179.
Tynedale Motor Co, Corbridge Rd. ✆ (0434) 604444.

HEXWORTHY Devon. Map 3D
Pop 50. Ashburton 9, London 196, Crediton 28, Plymouth 21, Saltash 22, Tavistock 13.
Golf Tavistock 18h. **See** Dartmeet and Huccaby (beauty spots).

★★Forest Inn, *PL20 6SD.* ✆ Poundsgate (036 43) 211. C. ⚫ 10 bedrs, 5 ba, Dgs. ✗ a l c, mc, at, LD 9. 🅿 CH, TV, Dgs, CP 50, pf, rf, con 30, CF, 1 st. £ BB £11·50–£13·50, DB £23–£30, DBB £18·25–£20, WB, 🛈, Bk £3·50, L £5·50, D £6·75, cc 2 3.

HEYSHAM Lancashire. Map 27C
See also MORECAMBE.
Pop 41,863 (with Morecambe). Lancaster 6½, London 244, Ambleside 37, Broughton-in-Furness 46, Kendal 25, Kirkby Lonsdale 20, Ulverston 40.
EC Wed. **MD** Tue, Thur (Mon–June to Sept). **Golf** Heysham 18h. **See** Heysham Head Entertainment Centre (inc Kart Racing Circuit).

Rescue Service: Heysham Motor Co Ltd, 362 Heysham Rd. ✆ (0524) 51093.
Tibicar Motor Eng Co Ltd, Oxcliffe Rd. ✆ (0524) 52461.

HEYWOOD Gtr Manchester (Lancashire). Map 27B
Pop 30,650. Manchester 8½, London 192, Bury 3½, Oldham 7, Rochdale 3½.
EC Tue. **MD** Fri, Sat. **Golf** Springfield Park 18h. **See** St Luke's Church, Ashworth Valley.

Rescue Service: Aspinall, E J W, Park Garage, Langton St. ✆ (0706) 60097.
Derbyshire Motors, River St. ✆ (0706) 623068.
Kempster, F & Sons Ltd, Hardfield Garage. ✆ (0706) 69817.

HICKLING Norfolk. Map 16A
Pop 934. Stalham 3, London 129, Cromer 17, Great Yarmouth 16, Norwich 18, Potter Heigham 4.
EC Wed. **Golf** Mundesley 9h.

Jenter House, G, x (Unl), *Town St, NR12 0AY.* ☎ (069 261) 372. C. 🛏 10 bedrs, 3 ba, Dgs. 🅿 CH, TV, Dgs, CP 10, CF, 1 BGf, 0 st, Dis. **£** BB £9, DB £18, WT (b) £84, DT (b) £13, Bk £3, D £4.

HIGHBRIDGE Somerset. Map 5C
Pop 12,400 (inc Burnham), Wells 16, London 138, M5 Motorway 2, Bath 35, Bridgwater 7½, Bristol 25, Glastonbury 17, Radstock 28, Weston-super-Mare 10.
EC Wed. **MD** Mon. **Golf** Burnham and Berrow 18h.
See Bridgwater Bay.

★★Sundowner, (R), *Main Street, West Huntsplil, TA9 3QU.* ☎ Burnham-on-Sea (0278) 784766. C. 🛏 8 bedrs, 2 bp, 1 bps, 2 sh, 3 ba, TV, Dgs. ✗ a l c, mc, LD 10. 🅿 CH, TV, CP 25, con 20, CF, 1 st. **£** BB fr £14, DB fr £21, WT £137–£144, WB, ②, Bk £4, L £5·50, D £6, cc 1 2 3 5 6.

Rescue Service: Stedda Motor Services, Viscount Service Station, Burnham Rd. ☎ Burnham-on-Sea (0278) 788688.

HIGHCLIFFE-ON-SEA Dorset. Map 6E
Pop 9,536. Lyndhurst 12, London 96, Blandford Forum 25, Bournemouth 9, Lymington 8, Ringwood 10.
EC Wed. **MD** Fri. **Golf** Highcliffe Castle 18h. **See** St Mark's Parish Church, Highcliffe Castle open to public.

Repairer: Sea Corner Garage Ltd, Lymington Rd. ☎ (042 52) 72333.

HIGHER INCE Greater Manchester (Lancashire). Map Area 20C.
See also WIGAN.
London 195, M6 Motorway 3½, Bolton 9, Chorley 8½, Manchester 18, Warrington 11.
See Powell Museum.

Rescue Service: J Boardman (Garages) Ltd, Wilsons Garage, Manchester Rd. ☎ Forton 791666.

HIGH WYCOMBE Bucks. Map 15E
Pop 60,000. Denham 12, London 30, M40 Motorway 1½, Aylesbury 16, Bagshot 23, Bicester 31, Dunstable 25, Henley-on-Thames 12, Oxford 26, Reading 18, Rickmansworth 15, St Albans 24, Wallingford 21, Windsor 15.
EC Wed. **MD** Tue, Fri, Sat. **Golf** Flackwell Heath 18h. **See** All Saints Church, Guildhall, Art Gallery and Museum, The Priory (now shops), Little Market House, Hughenden Manor, home and burial place of Disraeli (Nat Trust), West Wycombe Park.
🏛 Council Offices, Queen Victoria Rd. ☎ High Wycombe (0494) 26100.

★★★M Crest, *Crest Rd, HP11 1TL.* ☎ (0494) 442100. C. 🛏 108 bedrs, 108 bp, ns, TV, Dgs. ✗ a l c, mc, at, LD 10·30. 🅿 Lt, N, CH, Dgs, CP 178, Ac, con 100, CF £ B fr £47·50, BD fr £57, WB, ①, Bk £5·25, D £9·60, cc 1 2 3 4 5 6.

★★Falcon, *Cornmarket, HP11 2AX.* ☎ (0494) 22173. C. 🛏 12 bedrs, 7 sh, 4 ba, TV. ✗ a l c, mc, at, LD 10. 🅿 CH, G 10, Ac, con 20, CF, 1 st. **£** BB £23–£26, DB £35–£38, WT £220, DT £39, DBB £29–£32, WB, ①, Bk £1·90, L £3·75, D £5·50, cc 1 2 3 5 6, Dep b.

Clifton Lodge, H, y, z (RI), *210 West Wycombe Rd, A40, HP12 3AR.* ☎ (0494) 40095. Closed 10 days Xmas. C. 🛏 17 bedrs, 1 bp, 3 ba, TV. ✗ a l c. 🅿 CH, TV, CP

16, CF, 3 BGf, 4 st. **£** BBc £13·80, DBc £20·70–£24·15, ②, Bkc £2·25, L £3·50, D £5·50, cc 1 2 5.▲

Drake Court, PH, z (R), *London Rd, HP11 1BT.* ☎ (0494) 23639. C. 🛏 20 bedrs, 2 ph, 2 sh, 4 ba, TV. ✗ a l c. 🅿 CH, TV, CP 30, CF, 4 st. **£** BB £18–£30, DB £25–£32, ①, L £5, D £6, cc 1 2 3 5.▲

Repairer: Davenport Vernon Co Ltd, London Rd. ☎ (0494) 30021.
Specialist Body Repairer: Markhams Motor Body Repair Centre Ltd, 6 West Wycombe Rd. ☎ (0494) 30614.
Rescue Service: G I Thomas, Unit 3, Abercrombie Industrial Estate. ☎ (0494) 37414.

HILDENBOROUGH Kent. M. Area 7D
Sevenoaks 1, London 26, M25/26 Motorway 7½, M20 Motorway 10, Maidstone 15, Tonbridge 3.

Rescue Service: Stormont Engineering Co Ltd, Commercial Vehicle Division. ☎ (0732) 833005.

HILGAY Norfolk. Map 16F
Pop 1,125. Ely 14, London 85, Downham Market 3, King's Lynn 15, Thetford 22, Wisbech 16.
EC Wed. **Golf** Denver 9h.

Crosskeys Riverside, H, xy (R), *nr Downham Market.* ☎ Downham Market (0366) 387777. Closed Jan. C. 🛏 5 bedrs, 5 bp, TV. 🅿 CH, CP 10, 2 BGf, 0 st. **£** BB £17–£18·70, DB £24–£26·40, WT (b) £109·50–£120·45, DT £18·25–£19·95, ①, Bk £3·50, D £6·25.

HILLINGDON Greater London (Middx). Map 7A
2 m E of Uxbridge. Ealing 7, London 15, Brentford and Chiswick 9, Harrow 8, Kingston upon Thames 12, Richmond-upon-Thames 10, Rickmansworth 9, Staines 9.
EC Wed. **Golf** Hillingdon, Uxbridge 9h. **See** 13th cent Church.

★★★M Master Brewer, *Western Av, Hillingdon Circus, UB10 9NX.* ☎ Uxbridge (0895) 51199. RS Dec 26. C. 🛏 64 bedrs, 64 bp, TV, Dgs. ✗ a l c, mc, at, LD 11. 🅿 N, CH, CP 64, Ac, con 200, CF, 32 BGf, 1 st, Dis. **£** BB £33·75, DB £46·50, WB, ②, 12½%, Bk £3·10, L fr £4·95, D fr £5·50, cc 1 2 3 5 6, Dep b.

Rescue Service: Colham Green Garage Ltd, 148 West Drayton Rd. ☎ 01-933 4122.

HILTON Cambridgeshire. Map 15B
Pop 560. Royston 18, London 59, Cambridge 14, Huntingdon 5½, M11 Motorway 10, St Neots 10.
See Circular Maze on Village Green. 13th cent Church.

Rescue Service: Hilton Service Station, Potton Rd. ☎ Huntingdon (0480) 830316.

HIMLEY Staffordshire. Maps 13B & 14A.
Pop: 841. Birmingham 13, London 124, Bridgnorth 13, Bromsgrove 14, Kidderminster 10, Sutton Coldfield 17, Walsall 11, Wellington 21, Wolverhampton 21.
Golf Himley 18h. **See** Himley Hall.

◼**★★Himley House,** *nr, Dudley, DY3 4ED.* ☎ Wombourne (0902) 892468.

HINCKLEY Leicestershire. Map 14B
Pop 38,231. London 97, M69 Motorway 2, Ashby-de-la-Zouch 16, Atherstone 8½, Daventry 23, Leicester 13, Loughborough 22, Market Harborough 24, Northampton 32, Nottingham 35, Nuneaton 4½, Rugby 15, Towcester 34.
EC Thur. **MD** Mon, Sat. **Golf** Burbage Common 18h. **See** Church (13th-14th cent), Bosworth Field 4 m NNW.
🏛 Hinckley Library, Lancaster Rd. ☎ Hinckley (0455) 635106.

Fernleigh, PH, x (R), *32 Wood St, Earl Shilton, LE9 7ND.* ☎ (0455) 47011. Closed Dec 25–Jan 2. C. 🛏 12 Bedrs, 1 bp, 11 bps, TV. ✗ a l c. 🅿 CH, CP 12, CF, 2 st. **£** BB £23, DB £30, ①, Bk £3, L £4·75, D £4·75, cc 1 3.

Kings, H, y (R), *13 Mount Rd, LE10 1AD.* ☎ (0455) 637193. Closed Xmas. C. 🛏 7 bedrs, 2 bp, 5 bps, 1 ba, TV. ✗ a l c. 🅿 CH, CP 20, U 3, CF, 2 st. **£** BB £13·50–£25, DB £25–£45, WT (b) £105–£150, DT (b) £20–£30, ①, Bk £5, L £6, D £9·50, cc 1 2 3 5.

Rescue Service: Dudley Bedford Ltd, County Garage, Leicester Rd. ☎ (0455) 637310 & (0455) 613051.
Hinckley Mota-Care Ltd, Ashby Rd. ☎ (0455) 637339.

HINDHEAD Surrey. Map 7C
Pop 3,000. Guildford 12, London 41, Alton 13, Dorking 23, Farnham 8½, Haslemere 3½, Midhurst 10, Petersfield 12.
Golf Hindhead 18h. **See** Devil's Punch Bowl, Waggoners Wells (Nat Trust). Greensand Way footpath, Frencham Common (3 m N).

Repairer: Hindhead Automobile Centre, London Rd. ☎ (042 873) 5000.

HINDLEY Gtr Manchester (Lancashire). Map 20C
Pop 26,183. M6 Motorway 5, London 192, Bolton 8, Manchester 17, St Helens 9½, Warrington 11, Wigan 2½.
EC Wed. **MD** Fri. **Golf** Hindley Hall 18h.

Rescue Service: Alan's Motors (Hindley), Low Mill La. ☎ Wigan (0942) 55015.

HINDON Wiltshire. Map 5D
Pop 600. Amesbury 17, London 97, Frome 14, Glastonbury 31, Salisbury 16, Shaftesbury 7½, Shepton Mallet 25, Warminster 9½, Wincanton 14.
Golf W Wilts. Warminster 18h. **See** Parish Church.

★★Lamb, *High St, SP3 6DP.* ☎ (074 789) 225. Closed Dec 25 & 26. C. 🛏 16 bedrs, 6 bp, 4 ba, ✗ mc, LD 9. 🅿 CH, TV, Dgs, CP 12, CF, 3 st. **£** BB £16–£30, DB £30–£36, WT £175–£182, DT £26–£28, DBB £20–£24, WB, ①, Bk £3, L £6, D £8, cc 1.

HITCHIN Hertfordshire. Map 15D
See also LITTLE WYMONDLEY.
Pop 30,317. Hatfield 14, London 35, A1 (M) Motorway 3, Baldock 5, Bedford 16, Biggleswade 10, Epping 27, Hoddesdon 19, Luton 8, St Albans 16.
EC Wed. **MD** Tue, Sat. **Golf** Letchworth 18h. **See** Priory, St Mary's Church, The Biggin (17th cent Almshouses), Skynner's Almshouses (1670).
🏛 The Library, Paynes Park. ☎ Hitchin (0462) 4738.

★★Sun, *Sun St, SG5 1AF.* ☎ (0462) 32092. C. 🛏 32 bedrs, 32 bp, TV. ✗ mc, at, LD 10. 🅿 N, CH, CP 36, Ac, con 200, CF, 6

BGf, 2 st. £ BB £29, DB £36, DBB £35, WB,
①, Bk £2·75, L £4·95, D £4·95, cc 1 3 5 6.
Firs, PH, z (R), *83 Bedford Rd, SG5 2TY.*
✆ (0462) 59288. C. ⌘ 22 bedrs, 8 bps, 9
sh, 1 ba, TV, Dgs. ⑩ CH, CP 23, 8 BGf, 1 st.
£ BB £16·50–£21, DB £28·50, WT (a)
£207·50, DT (a) £41·50, ①, Bk £2·50, L
£4·50, D £8, cc1 2 3.

HODDESDON Hertfordshire. Map 15F
Pop 32,000. London 20, Baldock 21,
Barnet 14, Bedford 36, Bishop's Stortford
14, Enfield 8, Epping 9, Hatfield 11, Luton
23, Newmarket 43, Royston 21.
EC Thur. **MD** Wed. **Golf** Cheshunt. 18h.
See Rye House remains, Old Coaching
Inns.

Rescue Service: Dave's Car Recovery
Service, Brewery Yard, Brewery Rd.
✆ (0992) 45169.

HOGHTON Lancashire. Map 27D
Pop 800. Bolton 13, London 206,
Blackburn 5, Chorley 7, Ormskirk 21,
Preston 8, Southport 22.
EC Wed. **Golf** Shaw Hill 18h. **See** Tower.

Rescue Service: Old Oak Garage,
Hoghton La. ✆ (025 485) 2412.

HOG'S BACK Surrey. Map 7C
Guildford 6½, London 35, Bagshot 11,
Basingstoke 18, Farnham 3½, Haslemere
13, Henley-on-Thames 27, Hindhead 10,
Petworth 20, Reading 23, Woking 11.

★★★**Hog's Back,** *Nr Seale, Farnham,*
GU10 1EX. ✆ Runfold (025 18) 2345. C.
⌘ 50 bedrs, 50 bp, TV, Dgs. ✖ a l c, mc, at,
LD 9.30. ⑩ N, CH, Dgs, CP 120, Ac, con
100, CF, 17 BGf, 0 st, Dis. £ BB £36, DB
£44, WB, ①, Bk £4·25, L £6·50, D £6·50,
cc 1 2 3 4 5 6, Dep b.

HOGSTHORPE Lincolnshire. M. Area
23D
Pop 687, Skegness 6½, London 146, Alford
6½, Lincoln 42, Louth 19, Mablethorpe 10.
Golf Skegness 18h.

Rescue Service: South End Garage, South
End. ✆ Skegness (0754) 72206.

HOLBEACH Lincolnshire. Map 23F
Pop 2,000. Peterborough 23, London 106,
Boston 15, Grantham 34, King's Lynn 19,
Sleaford 26, Spalding 8, Wisbech 14.
EC Wed. **MD** Thur, Sat. **Golf** Sutton
Bridge 9h.

Rose & Crown, H, x, *5 West End, PE12*
1LW. ✆ (0406) 23941. C. ⌘ 11 bedrs, 3
bp, 1 bps, 1 ba, TV, Dgs. ✖ a l c. ⑩ CH,
Dgs, CP 50, CF, 1 st. £ BB £8·50–£10, DB
£17–£20, WT (b) £77, DT (b) £12, ①, Bk
£2·75, L £4·50, D £4·95, cc 1 3.

HOLBETON Devon. Map 3C
Ashburton 19, London 206, Plymouth 10,
Tavistock 22, Torquay 25.

♨★★★**Alston Hall,** *Battisborough Cross,*
PL8 1HN. ✆ (075 530) 259. C. ⌘ 9 bedrs,
8 bp, 1 bps, TV. ✖ a l c, mc, at, LD 9.30.
⑩ CH, CP 60, Ac, sp, tc, con 70, CF, 4 st.
£ BB £27·50–£38·50, DB £36·50–£49·50,
DBB £28·50–£35, WB, ①, Bk £3·75, L
£5·95, D £9, cc 1 2 3 5, Dep.

HOLCOMBE Devon. Map 3D
Exeter 13, London 182, Honiton 26,
Newton Abbot 7, Torquay 9.
EC Thur. **Golf** Haldon, Teignmouth 18h.

■★**Holcombe Head** (R), *Windward La,*
EX7 0JQ. ✆ Dawlish (0626) 862130.

HOLFORD Somerset. Map 4D
Pop 265. Bridgwater 11, London 152,
Dunster 13, Minehead 15, Taunton 15,
Tiverton 31.
Golf Enmore Park 18h. **See** Holford Glen,
Holford Combe, Hodder's Combe,
Alfoxton House (home of Wordsworth).

■♨★★★**Alfoxton Park** (R), *TA5 1SG.*
✆ (027 874) 211. Open Apr–Oct. C. ⌘ 18
bedrs, 17 bp, 1 ba, TV. ✖ mc, LD 8.45.
⑩ CH, CP, sp, tc, CF, 1 BGf, 2 st. £ BB £27,
DB £44–£46, DBB £27–£28, WB, ①, D £9,
cc 1 2 3 5.

■♨★★**Combe House** (RI), *TA5 1RZ.*
✆ (027 874) 382. Closed Dec & Jan. C.
⌘ 16 bedrs, 10 bp, 3 ba, TV, Dgs. ✖ mc, at,
LD 8.15. ⑩ CH, TV, CP 40, Ac, sp, tc, sb,
sol, con 40, CF, 1 BGf, 2 st. £ BB £14·75–
£19, DB £27–£31·50, WT £148–£155, DT
£22·50–£23·25, DBB £21–£25·25, WB, ②,
Bk £2·95, D £7·50.

HOLKHAM Norfolk. Map 16C
Pop 295. Fakenham 11, London 124,
Cromer 23, King's Lynn 25, Norwich 35.
EC Wed. **Golf** Hunstanton 18h. **See**
Holkham Hall Gardens and Pottery.

★**Victoria,** *NR23 1RG.* ✆ Fakenham
(0328) 710469. C. ⌘ 8 bedrs, 2 ba, Dgs,
✖ mc, LD 8.30. ⑩ TV, Dgs, CP 50, Ac, CF,
0 st. £ BB £12·50–£15, DB £23–£29, WB,
①, D £6·50.

HOLLAND-ON-SEA Essex. Map 17B
Pop 10,701. Colchester 16, London 72,
Clacton-on-Sea 2, Harwich 17, Ipswich
25, Stowmarket 36.
EC Wed. **Golf** Clacton 18h. Frinton 18h
and 9h.

York House, G, y (RI), *19 York Rd, CO15*
5NS. ✆ Clacton-on-Sea (0255) 814333.
C. ⌘ 6 bedrs, 1 ba, TV, Dgs. ⑩ CH, CP 4, U
2, CF, 1 BGf, 3 st. £ BB £12·50, DB £25,
WT (b) £105, (c) £75, DT (b) £17·50, ①, Bk
£1·75, D £6·50.

HOLLINGBOURNE Kent. Map 10C
Pop 1200. Maidstone 6, London 42, M20
Motorway 1½, Ashford 16, Canterbury 23,
Dartford 26, Dartford Tunnel 27,
Hawkhurst 19, Margate 38, Rochester 14,
Tenterden 18.
EC Wed. **Golf** Leeds Castle 18h. **See**
Eyhorne Manor.

★★★**Great Danes,** *Ashford Rd, ME17*
1RE. ✆ Maidstone (0622) 30022. C.
⌘ 128 bedrs, 128 bp, TV, Dgs. ✖ a l c, mc,
at, LD 10·45. ⑩ Lt, N, CH, Dgs, CP 500, Ac,
sp, con 500, CF, 0 st. £ BB £35, BD £42·50,
WB, ①, Bk £4·25, L £6·50, D £7·50,
cc 1 2 3 4 5 6, Dep b.

HOLLINGWORTH Gtr Manchester
(Cheshire). Map 22A
Pop 11,115. Chapel-en-le-Frith 11,
London 177, Barnsley 24, Glossop 2½,
Huddersfield 19, Knutsford 24,
Macclesfield 18, Manchester 11, Oldham
9, Stockport 8½, Wakefield 30.
Golf Hyde 9h.

Rescue Service: W Frost & Sons,
Longendale Garage. ✆ Mottram (0457)
3269.

HOLME Cumbria. Map 27C
Pop 861. M6 Motorway 6, London 254,
Barrow-in-Furness 33, Kendal 10,
Lancaster 12.
Golf Kendal 18h.

Rescue Service: E & D E Towers, Service
Garage, Station Rd. ✆ Burton (0524) 321.

HOLMFIRTH West Yorkshire. Maps 22A
and 25F and 33C
Pop 29,294. Sheffield 21, London 181,
Barnsley 14, Glossop 13, Huddersfield 6½,
Oldham 15, Rotherham 23, Stockport 22,
Wakefield 17.
EC Tue. **MD** Tue, Thur. **Golf** Meltham 9h.
See Picturesque streets ('Summer Wine'
country).
⑰ 50 Huddersfield Rd. ✆ Holmfirth (0484)
684992.

White Horse, I, x, *Jackson Bridge,*
HD7 7HF. ✆ (0484) 683940. C. ⌘ 5
bedrs, 2 ba, TV, Dgs. ✖ a l c. ⑩ CH, Dgs,
CP 12, U 1, CF, 0 st. £ BB £10, DB £16, ①,
Bk £1·50, L £1, D £2·35.

Repairer: Castle, G W Ltd, Huddersfield
Rd. ✆ (048 489) 3676.
Rescue Service: Holme Valley Garage Ltd,
Huddersfield Rd. ✆ (048 489) 3172.

HOLMROOK Cumbria. Map 26F
Pop 296. Broughton-in-Furness 21,
London 299, Ambleside 21, Egremont 9.
EC Wed. **Golf** Seascale 18h.

■★★**Lutwidge Arms,** *CA19 1UH.*
✆ (094 04) 230. C. ⌘ 20 bedrs, 9 bp, 11
bps, TV. ✖ a l c, mc, at, LD 8.30. ⑩ CH, CP
40, Ac, pf, con 50, 3 st. £ BB fr £16·50, DB
fr £31, ②, cc 1.

Rescue Service: Mitchell, H & Son.
✆ (094 04) 228.

HOLNE Devon. Map 3D
Pop 100. Ashburton 3, London 194,
Plymouth 26, Tavistock 18.
Golf Stover 18h. **See** Church, 14th cent
inn.

Church House, I, x, *TQ13 7SJ.*
✆ Poundsgate (036 43) 208. C 12. ⌘ 7
bedrs, 2 bps, 1 ba, TV. ✖ a l c. ⑩ CH,
TV, Dgs, CP 7, 2 st. £ BB £8·50–£11, DB
£17–£28, WT (b) £88–£98, ①, Bk £3·50, L
£4, D £6, cc 1 3.

HOLSWORTHY Devon. Map 3A
Pop 1,645. Crediton 36, London 210,
Bideford 18, Bude 9½, Launceston 13,
Okehampton 20, South Molton 31.
EC Tue. **MD** Wed, Thur. **Golf** Holsworthy
18h. **See** Perp Church, Museum, St Peter's
Fair (July), Agricultural Show (May).

★**White Hart,** *Fore St, EX22 6EB.*
✆ (0409) 253475.
Coles Mill, PH, xy (RI), *EX22 6LX.*
✆ (0409) 253313. Open Apr–Oct. C 6.
⌘ 5 bedrs, 5 bps, TV. ⑩ ch, TV, ns, CP 12,
1 BGf, 0 st, Dis. £ BB £9·50–£11, DB £17–
£20, WT (b) £78–£91·50, DT (b) £14·50–
£16, ①.
Leworthy, GF, xy (R), *EX22 6SJ.*
✆ (0409) 253488. C. ⌘ 16 bedrs, 3 bps, 4
ba. ⑩ ch, TV, ns, CP 20, G 2, CF, 4 BGf, 3 st.
£ BB £8·50–£10·50, DB £16–£22, WT (b)
£85–£105, DT (b) £13–£15, ①, Bk £3, D
£4·50.

Rescue Service: Bude Road Garage Ltd,
Bude Rd. ✆ (0409) 253477.
West Devon and North Cornwall Farmers
Ltd, Bodmin St. ✆ (0409) 253382.

HOLT Norfolk. Map 16C
Pop 2,529. Fakenham 21, London 123,
Cromer 10, East Dereham 18, Great
Yarmouth 40, Norwich 22.

EC Thur. **Golf** Sheringham 18h. **See** Parish Church, Kelling Park Aviaries and Zoo. Shell Museum at Glandford 3 m NW.

Lawn's, H, z (Rt), *26 Station Rd, NR25 6BS.* ✆ (026 371) 3390.

HONEYBOURNE Hereford & Worcester (Worcestershire). Map 14C
Pop 1,466. Moreton-in-Marsh 12, London 95, Birmingham 34, Bromsgrove 22, Cheltenham 20, Evesham 6, Stow-on-the-Wold 14, Stratford-upon-Avon 11.
EC Tue. **Golf** Evesham 18h. **See** 13th/14th cent Church.

Rescue Service: D & M Francatt Ltd, 35 High St. ✆ Evesham (0386) 830382.

HONITON Devon. Map 4F
Pop 7,000. Ilminster 17, London 153, Axminster 10, Crewkerne 13, Exeter 17, Taunton 18, Tiverton 19.
EC Thur. **MD** Tue, Sat. **Golf** Honiton 18h. **See** Museum, Honiton Pottery, Priory.
[i] Angel Hotel Car Park, High St. ✆ Honiton (0404) 3716.

★★★**Deer Park** (R), *Weston, EX14 0PG.* (2½ m W off A30). ✆ (0404) 2064. C. ✉ 17 bedrs, 15 bp, annexe 14 bedrs, 14 bp, TV, Dgs. ✗ a l c, mc, at, LD 10.30.
① CH, TV, ns, CP 60, U 4, Ac, sp, tc, pf, sc, sb, sol, con 60, CF, 8 BGf, 1 st, Dis. **£** BB £23–£28, DB £45–£60, DBB £30–£40, WB, **①**, Bk £5, L £5·50, D £11, cc 1 2 3 5, Dep a.
★**Angel**, *High St, EX14 8PE.* ✆ (0404) 2829. ✉ 6 bedrs, 1 bp, 1 bps, 1 ba. ✗ mc, LD 9. **①** CH, TV, CP 25, con 30, 0 st. **£** BB £14·53–£16·26, DB £23·58–£27·25, WB, **②**, Bk £3·50, L £4·75, D £7·50, cc 6, Dep a.
Colestocks House, PH, y (R), *Colestocks, nr Feniton, EX14 0JR.* ✆ (0404) 850633. Open Feb–Oct & Xmas. C 12. ✉ 8 bedrs, 3 bp, 1 bps, 2 ba. **①** CH, TV, CP 8, 1 BGf, 0 st, Dis. **£** BB £9·50–£11, DB £18–£20, WT (b) £87·50–£115, DT (b) £13·50–£17·50, **①**, D £5·50.
Hill House, H, y (R), *Combe Raleigh, EX14 0UQ.* ✆ (0404) 3371. Open Apr–Oct. C. ✉ 10 bedrs, 2 bp, 3 bps, 2 ba, Dgs. **①** CH, TV, CP 14, CF, 2 BGf, 1 st, Dis. **£** BB £11·38, DB £22·76–£29·08, WT (b) £98·67, DT (b) £15·81, **①**, D £6·65.

Repairer: Read's Garage (Honiton) Ltd. ✆ (0404) 2737.

HOOK Hampshire. Map 6B
Pop 2,869. Bagshot 14, London 41, Alton 10, Basingstoke 6, Farnham 10, Guildford 19, Reading 13.
Golf Tylney Park 18h. **See** Old Coaching Inns.

Rescue Service: Munro Motors, London Rd. ✆ (025 672) 2284 and (025 672) 2693.

HOOK NORTON Oxfordshire. M. Area 14D
Pop 1,758. Woodstock 13, London 76, Banbury 8, Moreton-in-Marsh 11, Stratford-upon-Avon 19.
EC Thur, Sat. **Golf** Tadmartin Heath 18h, Chipping Norton 9h. **See** Church.

Rescue Service: Brian Kimberley Garages, Station Road Garage. ✆ (0608) 737551.

HOPE COVE Devon. Map 3F
Pop 350. Kingsbridge 5, London 209, Plymouth 23, Tavistock 33.
Golf Thurlestone 18h.

★★**Cottage,** *TQ7 3HJ.* ✆ Kingsbridge (0548) 561555. Closed Jan. C. ✉ 36 bedrs, 10 bps, 4 bps, 7 ba, Dgs. ✗ a l c, mc, at, LD 8.45. **①** ch, TV, Dgs, CP 50, con 30, CF, 3 BGf, 2 st. **£** BB £9·64–£16·88, DB £19·28–£53·51, WT £160·20–£217·13, DT £23·47–£32·34, DBB £17·75–£30·54, WB, **①**, Bk £3·75, L £5·64, D £9·85, Dep a.
■★★**Sun Bay** (R), *TQ7 3HH.*
✆ Kingsbridge (0548) 561371. Open Apr–Oct. C. ✉ 14 bedrs, 12 bp, 1 bps, 1 ba, Dgs. ✗ a l c, mc, at, LD 8.15. **①** ch, TV, Dgs, CP 14, CF, 1 st. **£** BB £9·50, DB £19, WT £116·90–£131·95, DBB £17·70–£19·85, WB, **②**, Bk £4·50, D £5·75, Dep.
■★**Greystone** (RI), *TQ7 3HH.*
✆ Kingsbridge (0548) 561233. C. ✉ 11 bedrs, 3 ba, Dgs. ✗ a l c, mc, at, LD 10.
① CH, TV, CP 15, G 4, CF, 3 BGf, 1 st, Dis. **£** BB£10·50, DB £21, WT £91·25–£105, DT £20, DBB £15·50, WB, **①**, Bk £3, L £4·50, D £6·50, cc 1 2 3, Dep a.
Lantern Lodge, H, x (R), *TQ7 3HE.*
✆ Kingsbridge (0548) 561280.

HORLEY Surrey. Map 7C
Pop 20,353. Redhill 5, London 25, M23 Motorway 3, Crawley 5½, East Grinstead 8½, Haywards Heath 12, Reigate 5½.
EC Wed. **Golf** Earlswood 18h. **See** EE Church, 15th cent 'Six Bells' Inn.

★★★★**M Gatwick Penta,** *Povey Cross Rd, RH16 0BE.* ✆ (029 34) 5533. C. ✉ 260 bedrs, 260 bp, TV, Dgs. ✗ a l c, mc, con 180, CF, 0 st. **£** BB £53·20, DB £69·40, **①**, Bk £5·20, L £8·50, D £10·95, cc 1 2 3 4 5, Dep.
★★★**Gatwick Moat House,** *Longbridge Roundabout, RH6 0AB.* ✆ (029 34) 5599. C. ✉ 122 bedrs, 122 bp, TV. ✗ a l c, mc, at, LD 10·30. **①** Lt, N, CH, G 136, Ac, con 180, CF, 0 st. **£** BB £38·50, BD £49·50, WB, **①**, Bk £4·75, D £7·95, cc 1 2 3 5 6, Dep b.
★★★**M Chequers Thistle,** *Brighton Rd, RH6 8PH.* ✆ (0293) 346992. C. ✉ 78 bedrs, 78 bp, ns, TV, Dgs. ✗ a l c, mc, LD 9.30. **①** N, CH, TV, Dgs, CP 160, Ac, sp, con 60, CF, 39 BGf, 0 st, Dis. **£** BB £40·50–£46·50, DB £46·50–£52·50, WB, **②**, Bk £4·50, L £7·25, D £10, cc 1 2 3 4 5 6, Dep b.
★★★**M Post House** (TH), *Povey Cross Rd, RH6 0BA.* ✆ (029 34) 71621. C. ✉ 149 bedrs, 149 bp, TV, Dgs. ✗ a l c, mc, at, LD 10.15. **①** Lt, N, CH, Dgs, CP 350, Ac, sp, con 250, CF, 25 BGf, 0 st, Dis. **£** BB £46·50, DB £63·50, **①**, cc 1 2 3 4 5 6, Dep (Xmas).
Gainsborough Lodge, PH, z (Unl), *39 Massetts Rd, RH6 7DT.* ✆ (029 34) 3982. C. ✉ 8 bedrs, 3 bp, 5 bps. **①** CH, TV, ns, CP 16. **£** BB £11–£17, DB £20–£27, **①**, Bk £2·50.
Woodlands, G, z (Unl), *42 Massetts Rd, RH6 7DS.* ✆ (029 34) 2994. C. ✉ 6 bedrs, 2 sh, 2 ba, TV. **①** CH, TV, CP 8, G 2, CF, 1 BGf.
Repairers: Horley Motor Co Ltd, Brighton Rd. ✆ (029 34) 2301.

HORNCASTLE Lincolnshire. Map 23D
Pop 4,207. Spalding 35, London 144, Boston 18, Lincoln 21, Louth 13, Market Rasen 19, Skegness 21, Sleaford 23.
EC Wed. **MD** Thur, Sat. **Golf** Woodhall Spa 18h. **See** 16th cent Bull Hotel, St Mary's Church, remains of Roman Wall,

Somersby (Tennyson's birthplace) 7 m E, Tattershall Castle 8 m SW.

★**Bull**, *Bull Ring, LN9 5HU.* ✆ (065 82) 3331. C. ✉ 8 bedrs, 1 bp, 2 ba, TV, Dgs.
① CH, TV, Dgs, CP 30, Ac, con, CF, 0 st. **£** BB fr £14, DB fr £21, DBB fr £20·55, WB, **①**, Bk £3, D £6·55, cc 1 3 5.

Rescue Service: Bullwinkle's of Baumber, Red Lion Garage, Baumber. ✆ Baumber (065 887) 252.
G L Clarke & Sons, The Garage, Spilsby Rd. ✆ (065 82) 2391.

HORNCHURCH Greater London. M. Area 7B
Pop 84,000. London 18, Brentwood 6½, Dartford Tunnel 8, Rainham 4, Romford 2½, Southend-on-Sea 24.
EC Thur. **See** Parish Church.

★★★**M Ladbroke,** *Southend Arterial Rd, RM11 5UT.* ✆ Ingrebourne (040 23) 46789. RS Bank Holidays. C. ✉ 140 bedrs, 140 bp, TV, Dgs. ✗ mc, LD 9.45. **①** N, CH, Dgs, CP 170, Ac, con 250, CF, 60 BGf, 0 st, Dis. **£** BB £47·30, DB £60·50, DBB £56·80, WB, **②**, Bk £5·50, L £7·50, D £9·50, cc 1 2 3 5 6, Dep b.

Repairer: Frost Bros Motors Ltd, 117 North St. ✆ (040 24) 46772.

HORNING Norfolk. Map 16A
Pop 1,028. Norwich 10, London 122, Cromer 19, Fakenham 32, Great Yarmouth 17.
EC Wed. **Golf** Royal Norwich 18h, Mundesley 9h. **See** St Benet's Abbey ruins, windmills.

★★★**Petersfield House,** *Lower St, NR12 8PF.* ✆ (0692) 630741.

HORNS CROSS Devon. Map 3A
Pop 147. Bideford 5½, London 207, Bude 20, Holsworthy 14.
Golf Westward Ho! 18h.

■★★**Foxdown Manor,** *nr Bideford, EX39 5PJ.* ✆ (023 75) 325. C. ✉ 7 bedrs, 5 bp, 1 bps, 1 sh, 1 ba, TV, Dgs. ✗ mc, at, LD 8.45. **①** CH, CP 40, sp, tc, sb, sol, CF, 0 st. **£** BB £17–£24, DB £34–£48, DBB £27–£34, WB, **②**, Bk £4·50, L £5·50, D £10, cc 1 2 3 5, Dep a.

Rescue Service: Robinson's Garage. ✆ (023 75) 248.

HORNSEA Humberside (North Humberside). Map 25A
Pop 7,260. Beverley 13, London 192, Bridlington 15, Hull 17, Malton 36.
EC Wed. **MD** Sun. **Golf** Hallgate Park 18h. **See** Church Market Cross, Hornsea Potteries, Hornsea Mere (largest freshwater lake in Yorkshire and noted bird reserve).
[i] Floral Hall. ✆ Hornsea (040 12) 2919.

★★**Seaforth, PH, z** (Unl), *Esplanade, HU18 1NQ.* ✆ (040 12) 2616. C. ✉ 7 bedrs, 2 ba, Dgs. **①** CH, TV, Dgs, CP 4, CF, 1 st. **£** BB £6·75, DB £13·50, WT (b) £62·50, DT (b) £10·25, **①**.

HORRABRIDGE Devon. Map 3C
Pop 2,155. Exeter 34, London 203, Ashburton 20, Crediton 32, Dartmouth 32, Kingsbridge 25, Plymouth 11, Saltash 12, Tavistock 4½, Totnes 24.
EC Wed. **Golf** Tavistock 18h. **See** Dartmoor.

Overcombe, PH, x (R), *PL20 7RN.*
☎ Yelverton (0822) 853501. C. ⊨ 7
bedrs, 1 bp, 2 bps, 2 ba, TV, Dgs. ⓓ CH, TV,
Dgs, CP 10, CF. £ BB £12·25–£14·25, DB
£24·50–£26·50, WT (b) £115–£119, DT
(b) £18·75, ⊞, Bk £3, L £3, D £6·50,
cc 1 2 3 5.

HORSFORTH West Yorkshire. Map 25F
Pop 19,870. Leeds 5, London 196,
Bradford 6, Halifax 14, Harrogate 14,
Hawes 54, Huddersfield 16, Skipton 20,
York 28.
Golf Gotts Park 18h. **See** Trees of
Remembrance forming War Memorial
(Stanhope Drive and Broadway).

Rescue Service: Horsforth Garage Ltd,
New Road Site. ☎ (0532) 582271.

HORSHAM West Sussex. Map 7C
Pop 26,000. Dorking 13, London 36,
Brighton 23, Crawley 8, Farnham 27,
Guildford 19, Haslemere 20, Haywards
Heath 13, Petworth 16, Pulborough 12,
Worthing 20.
EC Thur. **Golf** Mannings Heath 18h. **See**
St Mary's Church, 16th cent North Chapel,
Museum, Christs Hospital (School) 2 m
SW, Leonardslee Gardens 4½ m SE, Blue
Idol Guest House and Meeting House
(assoc with William Penn) 6 m SW.

★★**Ye Olde King's Head,** *Carfax, RH12
1EQ.* ☎ (0403) 53126.
Wimblehurst, H, y (Unl), *6 Wimblehurst
Rd, RH12 2ED.* ☎ (0403) 62319. C. ⊨ 14
bedrs, 4 bp, 2 bps, 4 sh, 2 ba, ns. ⓓ CH, TV,
ns, CP 16, CF, 2 BGf, 1 st. Dis. £ BB
£24·50–£29·50, DB £34·50–£39·50, WT
(b) £197, DT (b) £32, ⊞, Bk £3·50, D £7·50.

Repairer: Wilson Purves Ltd, 52 Brighton
Rd. ☎ (0403) 5637 and 61821.
Rescue Service: Elite, S & M Tyres Ltd,
Brighton Rd. ☎ (0403) 64805.

HORSINGTON Somerset. Map 5D
Wincanton 4, London 114, Blandford
Forum 19, Dorchester 25, Shepton Mallet
16, Yeovil 14.
Coombe Cross, G, y (RI), *BA8 0DD.*
☎ Templecombe (0963) 70374. C. ⊨ 5
bedrs, 3 bp, 1 ba, TV, Dgs. ⓓ CH, TV, Dgs,
ns, CP 40, CF, 1 st. £ BB £17·50–£20, DB
£35–£37·50, WT £122·50, DT £26, ⊞.

HORSLEY Northumberland. M. Area 31E
Pop 200. Prudhoe 3½, London 283,
Hexham 12, Newcastle upon Tyne 10.
Golf Prudhoe 18h.

Rescue Service: Northumbrian Land
Roamers, Old Coach Service Station.
☎ Wylam (066 14) 3264.

HORTON-CUM-STUDLEY
Oxfordshire. Map 14F
Pop 458. High Wycombe 26, London 56,
Aylesbury 17, Banbury 26, Bicester 8½,
Chipping Norton 23, Oxford 7½.
Golf North Oxford 18h. **See** Elizabethan
Studley Priory (now hotel).

⚑★★★**Studley Priory,** *OX9 1AZ.*
☎ Stanton St John (086 735) 203. Closed
Jan 1–20. C. ⊨ 19 bedrs, 15 bp, 4 sh, TV.
✗ a l c, mc, at, LD 9.30. ⓓ CH, CP 100, G
3, Ac, con 28, CF, 4 BGf, 1 st. Dis. £ BB
£36, DB fr £55, WB, ⊞, Bk £5·50,
cc 1 2 3 4 5 6

HORTON-IN-RIBBLESDALE
North Yorkshire. Map 27A

Pop 508. Settle 6, London 235, Hawes 16,
Kirkby Lonsdale 18, Lancaster 26.
EC Wed. **See** Craven Caves, Ancient
Church.
ⓘ Pen-y-ghent Cafe. ☎ Horton-in-
Ribblesdale (072 96) 333.

Crown, I, x, *BD24 0HF.* ☎ (072 96) 209.
C. ⊨ 10 bedrs, 6 sh, 2 ba, Dgs. ⓓ ch, TV,
Dgs, CP 15, CF. £ BB £10·95–£11·50, DB
£21·90–£23, WT (b) £115, DT (b) £17·25–
£18, ⊞, Bk £3, D £6·35, cc 5.

HORWICH Greater Manchester
(Lancashire). Maps 20C & 27D
Wigan 6, London 201, M61 Motorway 3,
Bolton 6, Manchester 18, Preston 24.
Swallowfield, H, y (R), *Chorley New Rd,
BL6 6HN.* ☎ (0204) 67914. C. ⊨ 17 bedrs,
9 bp, 5 bps, 1 ba, TV, Dgs. ✗ a l c, mc,
Dgs, CP 25, G 2, CF, 5 BGf, 1 st, Dis. £ BB
£18·40–£21·85, DB £25·30–£29·90, ⊞,
cc 1 2 3.

HOUGHTON-ON-THE-HILL
Leicestershire. M. Area 22F
Pop 1,700. Market Harborough 12,
London 96, Huntingdon 48, Leicester 6½,
Melton Mowbray 13, Peterborough 36,
Stamford 25.
EC Wed. **Golf** Scraptoft 18h. **See** 13th
cent Church.

Repairer: Sunnybrae Motor Co,
Uppingham Rd. ☎ Leicester (0533)
415172.

HOUNSLOW Greater London (Middx.),
Map 7A
Pop 105,000. Brentford and Chiswick 4,
London 10, Ealing 5½, Harrow 8½, Kingston
upon Thames 6, Richmond-upon-Thames
3½, Rickmansworth 14, Slough 11, Staines
7, Uxbridge 8½, Weybridge 9½, Windsor 11.
EC Wed.

★★★**M Master Robert,** *Great West Rd,
TW5 0BA.* ☎ 01-570 6261. C. ⊨ 64 bedrs,
64 bp, TV, Dgs. ✗ a l c, mc, at, LD 11. ⓓ N,
CH, Dgs, CP 80, G 35, Ac, con 100, CF, 30
BGf, 1 st, Dis. £ BB £37·50, DB £47, WB, ⊞,
Bk £2·50, L £7·50, D £7·50, cc 1 2 3 5 6.

Rescue Service: Hounslow (West) Motors
Ltd, 343 Staines Rd. ☎ 01-572 0023.

HOVE East Sussex. Map 7E
See also BRIGHTON.
Pop 84,740. Brighton 1½, London 54,
Arundel 18, Pulborough 21, Worthing 9½.
See Plan of Brighton p. 162.
EC Wed. **P** See Plan for Brighton. **Golf**
West Hove 18h. **See** All Saints' Church,
Floral Clock, Brocke Scented Garden for
the Blind, King Alfred Leisure Centre,
British Engineerium, Hove Museum.
ⓘ Town Hall. ☎ Brighton (0273) 775400.

★★★★**Dudley** (TH), *Lansdowne Pl, BN3
1HQ.* ☎ Brighton (0273) 736266. C. ⊨ 79
bedrs, 79 bp, TV, Dgs. ✗ a l c, mc, at, LD
9.45. ⓓ Lt, N, CH, Dgs, CP 15, G 20, Ac,
con 240, CF, 5 st. £ BB £47, DB £66, WB,
⊞, cc 1 2 3 4 5 6, Dep (Xmas).
★★★**Alexandra,** *42 Brunswick Ter, BN3
1HA,* ☎ Brighton (0273) 202722. C. ⊨ 60
bedrs, 58 bp, 2 bps, TV, Dgs. ✗ a l c, mc, at,
LD 9.30. ⓓ Lt, N, CH, Dgs, Ac, sb, sol, con
60, CF, 4 BGf, 1 st. £ BB £29·50, DB £43,
WT £189, DT £40·50, DBB £35·50, WB, ⊞,
Bk £3·75, L £6, D £7·50, cc 1 2 3 5, Dep b.
★★★**Courtlands,** *The Drive, BN3 3JE.*
☎ Brighton (0273) 731055. C. ⊨ 57
bedrs, 44 bp, 6 bps, 2 ba, TV, Dgs. ✗ a l c,

LD 9.30. ⓓ Lt, N, CH, TV, CP 26, U 4, Ac,
con 35, CF, 8 BGf, 6 st. £ BB £20–£35, DB
£26–£45, DBB £35–£42, WB, ⊞, Bk £4·25,
L £7·50, D £8·50, cc 1 2 3 5 6, Dep b.
★★★**Sackville,** *Kingsway, BN3 4GU.*
☎ Brighton (0273) 736292. C. ⊨ 48
bedrs, 46 bp, 2 bps, TV, Dgs. ✗ a l c, mc, at,
LD 9. ⓓ Lt, N, CH, Dgs, U 4, G 6, Ac, con
80, CF, 10 st. £ BB £35·20–£43·65, DB
£48·50–£65·45, WT £259, DT £51–£59·50,
DBB £44–£52·50, WB, ⊞, Bk £4·25, L
£7·95, D £9·75, cc 1 2 3 5, Dep b.
★★★**St Catherine's Lodge,** *Kingsway,
BN3 2RZ.* ☎ Brighton (0273) 778181.
⊨ 55 bedrs, 36 bp, 6 ba, TV, Dgs. ✗ mc, at,
LD 9. ⓓ Lt, N, CH, TV, G 5, con 40, CF, 8
BGf, 8 st. £ BB £24–£34, DBB £34–£44,
WT £155–£175, DT £32–£34, DBB £32–
£39, ⊞, Bk £4, L £4·50, D £6·95,
cc 1 2 3 5 6.
★★**Imperial,** *First Av, BN3 2GU.*
☎ Brighton (0273) 731121. C. ⊨ 71
bedrs, 33 bp, 16 bps, 2 sh, 11 ba, TV, Dgs.
✗ a l c, mc, at, LD 10. ⓓ Lt, N, CH, Ac, con
150, CF, 8 st. £ BB £22–£32, DB £36–£46,
WT £169, DT £27, DBB £21, WB, ⊞, Bk
£2·95, L £7·50, D £7·50, cc 1 2 3 5.
★★**Langfords,** *Third Av, BN3 2PX.*
☎ Brighton (0273) 738222. C. ⊨ 69
bedrs, 25 bp, 24 bps, TV, Dgs. ✗ mc,
at, LD 10. ⓓ Lt, N, CH, TV, Ac, con 100, CF,
4 st. £ BB £22–£32, DB £36–£46, WT
£169, DT £27, DBB £21, WB, ⊞, Bk £2·95,
L £7·50, D £7·50, cc 1 2 3 5.
Albany, PH, z (RI), *St. Catherine Terr,
BN3 2RR.* ☎ Brighton (0273) 773807. RS
Xmas. C. ⊨ 9 bedrs, 4 bp, 5 bps, TV, Dgs.
ⓓ CH, TV. £ BB £16–£20, DB £23–£26,
WT (c) £99–£140, ⊞, D £4, cc 3.
Cornerways, PH, z (RI), *Caburn Rd,
BN3 6EF.* ☎ Brighton (0273) 731882.
Croft, PH, z (RI), *24 Palmeria Av, BN3
3GB.* ☎ Brighton (0273) 732860. C. ⊨ 11
bedrs, 2 sh, 2 ba, TV, Dgs. ✗ a l c. ⓓ CH,
TV, CF, 3 st. £ BB £12–£13·50, DB £21–
£24, WT (c) £70–£80, ⊞.
Langham, PH, z (RI), *2 York Rd, BN3
1DL.* ☎ Brighton (0273) 722085. C. ⊨ 12
bedrs, 1 sh, 2 ba, TV, Dgs. ⓓ ch, TV, CF.
£ BB £11·50–£15·50, DB £19–£26, WT (b)
£90, DT (b) £16–£21, ⊞, Bk £2, D £5·50,
cc 1 2 3 5.
Tatler, PH, z (RI), *26 Holland Rd, BN3
1JJ.* ☎ Brighton (0273) 736698.
Whitehaven, H, z (R), *34 Wilbury Rd,
BN3 3JP.* ☎ Brighton (0273) 778355. C 8.
⊨ 15 bedrs, 8 bp, 7 bps, TV, Dgs. ⓓ CH, 4
BGf, 1 st, Dis. £ BB £27–£32, DB £40–£42,
WT (c) fr £112, DT (b) fr £27, ⊞, Bk £3, L
£2·50, D £7, cc 1 2 3 5.

Repairers: Harrington Motors, Sussex
House, 270 Old Shoreham Rd. ☎ Brighton
(0273) 737555.
Wadham Stringer (Brighton) Ltd, 154 Old
Shoreham Rd. ☎ Brighton (0273) 26264.
Westbourne Motors, 270 Portland Rd.
☎ Brighton (0273) 731108.
MC Repairer: Tate Bros Ltd (Hangleton
Motors), Hangleton Rd. ☎ Brighton
(0273) 46242.
Rescue Service: Heathcote, W G & Co, 2
Kings Mews, Third Av. ☎ Brighton (0273)
739750.
Tate Bros Ltd (Hangleton Motors),
Hangleton Rd. ☎ Brighton (0273) 46242.

HOVETON Norfolk. Map 16A
Pop 1,784. Norwich 8, London 119,
Cromer 18, Fakenham 30, Gt Yarmouth
19, Potter Heigham 8.

EC Wed. **Golf** Royal Norwich 18h. **See** Clack Horse Pond.

★★Hotel Wroxham, *Broads Centre, NR12 2BJ.* ✆ Wroxham (060 53) 2061.

HOVINGHAM North Yorkshire. Map 25C
Pop 324. York 16, London 214, Boroughbridge 21, Helmsley 7½, Malton 8, Pickering 15, Thirsk 19.
EC Thur. **Golf** Gilling 18h. **See** Parish Church (Saxon tower).

★★Worsley Arms, *High St, YO6 4LA.* ✆ (065 382) 234. Closed Dec 25 & 26. C. ⊷ 14 bedrs, 14 bp, Dgs. ✖ mc, at, LD 8.45. ⊡ CH, Dgs, CP 50, U 4, Ac, con 25, CF, 3 st. £ BB £21–£24, DB £39·50–£44·50, DBB £26·50–£61, WB, ①, Bk £3, L fr £5·50, D £9·50, cc 1 3 6.

Rescue Service: Spa Garage. ✆ (065 382) 296.

HOWDEN Humberside (N. Humberside). Map 25D
Pop 3,215. Goole 4, London 183, M62 Motorway 1, Beverley 19, Hull 23, Market Weighton 12, Selby 10, York 20.
EC Wed. **Golf** Selby 18h. **See** Church of St Peter, Shire Hall.

★★★Bowmans, *Bridgegate, DN14 7JG.* ✆ (0430) 30805. C. ⊷ 13 bedrs, 10 bp, TV, Dgs. ✖ a l c, mc, at, LD 10. ⊡ CH, Dgs, CP 80, Ac, con 15, CF, 1 st. £ BB £21·95, DB £35·95, WB, ①, Bk £4·50, L £4·99, D £6·99, cc 1 3 5.

HOYLAKE Merseyside. Map 19A
Pop 10,740. Chester 20, London 203, Birkenhead 7, Queensferry 18.
EC Wed. **Golf** Royal Liverpool 18h, Hoylake Municipal 18h.

■★★Stanley, *King's Gap, L47 2AH.* ✆ 051-632 3311.
Sandtoft, H, z (RI), *70 Alderley Rd, L47 2BA.* ✆ 051-632 2204. C. ⊷ 9 bedrs, 1 bps, 2 ba, TV, Dgs. ✖ CH, TV, CP 8, U 3, CF, 7 st. £ BB £10·50–£14·50, DB £20·50, WT (b) £100, (c) £70, DT (b) £16·50, ①, D £5.

Repairer: Burnett & Co, 48 Birkenhead Rd. ✆ 051-632 3244.

HUBY North Yorkshire. M. Area 25E
Pop 750. Leeds 10, London 201, Harrogate 5½, Otley 5½.
EC Thur. **Golf** Pannal 18h.

Rescue Service: Huby Garage. ✆ Harrogate (0423) 74253.

HUCKNALL Nottinghamshire. Map 22D
Pop 28,142. Nottingham 7, London 130, Ashbourne 27, Ashby-de-la-Zouch 27, Chesterfield 19, Derby 17, Hinckley 41, Mansfield 9, Matlock 20, Newark 21.
EC Wed. **MD** Fri/Sat. **Golf** Bulwell Common 18h. **See** Parish Church, tombs of the Byron family, Newstead Abbey (ancestral home of Byron) 3 m N.

Repairer: Central Garage (Hucknall) Ltd, Papplewick La. ✆ Nottingham (0602) 641212.

HUDDERSFIELD West Yorkshire. Map 25F and 33C
Pop 124,000. Sheffield 26, London 180, M62 Motorway 2½, Barnsley 17, Bradford 10, Glossop 19, Halifax 7, Leeds 15, Oldham 18, Rochdale 19, Rotherham 27, Stockport 27, Todmorden 17, Wakefield 13.

EC Wed. **MD** Mon, Thur. **Golf** Bradley 18h. **See** Town Hall, Art Gallery, Roman remains, Museum, Castle Hill Tower, Kirklees Hall, New Market Hall, Scammonden Dam.
⑦ 3 Albion St. ✆ Huddersfield (0484) 22133.

★★★George (TH), *St George's Sq, HD1 1JA.* ✆ (0484) 25444. C. ⊷ 62 bedrs, 36 bp, 7 ba, TV, Dgs. ✖ a l c, mc, at, LD 9.45. ⊡ Lt, N, CH, Dgs, CP 12, Ac, con 150, CF, 1 st. £ BB £27·50–£37·50, DB £38–£47, WB, ①, cc 1 2 3 4 5 6.

★★★M Ladbroke, *Ainley Top, HD3 3RH.* ✆ Elland (0422) 75431. C. ⊷ 119 bedrs, 119 bp, TV, Dgs. ✖ a l c, mc, at, LD 10. ⊡ Lt, N, CH, CP 170, Ac, con 300, CF, 16 BGf, 3 st. £ BB £30–£45, DB £40–£65, WB, ①, cc 1 2 3 5 6, Dep b.

Repairers: Adams & Gibbon Ltd, Leeds Rd. ✆ (0484) 23191.
Brockholes, Southgate. ✆ (0484) 29675.
Gee Bros Ltd, The Garage, Outlane. ✆ Elland (0422) 4473.
Specialist Radiator Repairer Serck Radiator Services Ltd, Gledholt Bank, Triangle Paddock. ✆ (0484) 21067.
Rescue Service: Bargate Motors, Bargate, Linthwaite. ✆ Huddersfield (0484) 846056.
Palace Motors (Huddersfield) Ltd, Venn St. ✆ (0484) 20811 and (0484) 30772.
Trinity Garage Co Ltd, Union St. ✆ (0484) 20822.

HULL Humberside (North Humberside). Maps 25B and 24A
Pop 274,000. Lincoln 42, London 175, Beverley 8½, Bridlington 30, Goole 33, Scunthorpe 26, Grimsby 31.
See Plan, p. 236.
EC Thur. **MD** Tue, Fri, Sat. **P** See Plan. **Golf** Springhead 18h, Sutton 18h. **See** Wilberforce House Museum, Holy Trinity Church, St Mary's Church, Burton Constable (interior by Robert Adam) 7½ m NE.
⑦ Central Library, Albion St. ✆ Hull (0482) 223344.

★★★Crest (Hull City), *65 Paragon St, HU1 3JP.* ✆ (0482) 26462. C. ⊷ 125 bedrs, 125 bp, ns, TV, Dgs. ✖ a l c, mc, at, LD 9.45. ⊡ Lt, N, CH, Dgs, Ac, con 230, CF, 1 st. £ B fr £39, BD fr £49·50, WB, ①, Bk £4·95, D £8·95, cc 1 2 3 4 5 6, Dep b.

■★★★Rowley Manor, *Little Weighton, HU20 3XR.* ✆ (0482) 848248.
★★★Willerby Manor (R), *Well La, Willerby, HU10 6ER.* (4½ m W of A164). ✆ (0482) 652616. RS Xmas Day & Bank Holiday Mons. C. ⊷ 41 bedrs, 27 bp, 14 bps, TV, Dgs. ✖ a l c, mc, at, LD 9.30. ⊡ N, CH, TV, CP 200, Ac, con 200, CF, 6 BGf, 1 st. £ BB £17·85–£34·50, DB £28·50–£49, WB, ①, Bk £3·65, L £6·30, D £6·30, cc 1 2 3 5 6, Dep b.

★★Pearson Park (R), *Pearson Park, HU5 2TQ.* ✆ (0482) 43043. Closed Xmas. C. ⊷ 31 bedrs, 17 bp, 6 sh, 2 ba, TV, Dgs. ✖ mc, at, LD 9. ⊡ TV, CP 27, Ac, con 24, CF, 2 BGf, 0 st, Dis. £ BB fr £19, DB fr £29,

DBB fr £25·50, WB, ①, Bk £3, L £3·50, D £6·50, cc 1 3.

Repairer: Armstrong-Massey, 630 Anlaby Rd. ✆ (0482) 506961.
Specialist Radiator Repairer Johnsons Motor Radiators (Hull) Ltd, 8 Madeley St. ✆ (0482) 23019.
MC Repairer: Miles Kingsport Ltd, 353 Anlaby Rd. ✆ (0482) 23529.
Rescue Service: Lex Tillotson Hull, Hedon Rd. ✆ (0482) 795111.

HUNGERFORD Berkshire. Map 6A
Pop 3,900. Newbury 9, London 63; M4 Motorway 3, Amesbury 24, Andover 21, Faringdon 22, Marlborough 10, Pewsey 14, Romsey 37, Salisbury 30, Swindon 17, Wantage 14.
EC Thur. **Golf** Newbury and Chaddleworth 18h. **See** Church, old Bear Inn, Hock-Tide ceremony 2nd Tue after Easter, Littlecote House 2½ m NW.

★★★Bear, *Charnham St, RG17 0EL.* ✆ (0488) 82512. RS Dec 24–27. C. ⊷ 28 bedrs, 24 bp, 2 ba, TV, Dgs. ✖ a l c, mc, LD 9.30. ⊡ CH, CP 75, con 20, CF, 6 BGf. £ BB fr £33·35, DB fr £46·25, WB, ①, Bk £4·25, L £8·50, D £9·50, cc 1 2 3 5, Dep b.

Rescue Service: T E Bell & Co, 31A Charnham St. ✆ (0488) 82641.
Normans of Hungerford, Bath Rd. ✆ (0488) 82033.

HUNMANBY North Yorkshire. Map 25A.
Pop 2,623. Great Driffield 14, London 206, Bridlington 10, Filey 3, Scarborough 10, York 40.
EC Wed. **Golf** Filey 18h. **See** 12th cent Church.

■ ♨ ★★Wrangham House (R), *Stonegate, YO14 0NS.* ✆ Scarborough (0723) 891333. Closed Jan. RS Nov–Feb. C 5. ⊷ 9 bedrs, 2 bp, 5 bps, 1 ba. ✖ LD 7. ⊡ CH, TV, CP 20, con 15. £ BB fr £14, DB fr £28, DBB fr £21·50, WB, ②, Bk £3, D £7·50, cc 1 3.

HUNSTANTON Norfolk. Map 16E
Pop 4,000. King's Lynn 16, London 115, Cromer 37, Fakenham 19, Swaffham 24.
EC Thur. **MD** Wed, Sun. **Golf** Hunstanton 18h. **See** Church of St Mary the Virgin, St Edmunds Chapel ruins, Lighthouse, Sandringham House (grounds only), 9 m S.
⑦ Le Strange Ter. ✆ Hunstanton (048 53) 2610.

★Wash & Tope, *Le Strange Ter, PE36 5AJ.* ✆ (048 53) 2250. C. ⊷ 11 bedrs, 3 ba, TV, Dgs. ✖ a l c, mc, at, LD 10.30. ⊡ CH, TV, Dgs, CP 14, U 4, G, Ac, con 40, CF, 2 st. £ BB £11·50, DB £20–£23, WT £130–£132, DT £17·45, DBB £15·95, WB, ①, Bk £2·50, L £3, D £5·95, cc 1 2 3 6, Dep b.
Caley Hall Motel, x (R), *Old Hunstanton, PE36 6HH.* ✆ (048 53) 33486.
Deepdene, H, z (R & Cl). *29 Avenue Rd, PE36 5BW.* ✆ (048 53) 2460. C. ⊷ 9 bedrs, 1 bp, 4 ba. ⊡ CH, TV, CP 10, CF, 3 st. £ BB £14, DB £28–£31, WT (b) £125, (c) £96, DT (b) £20, ②.
Lincoln Lodge, PH, x (R). *Cliff Par, PE36 6DL.* ✆ (048 53) 2948.
Lodge, H, x, *Old Hunstanton, PE36 6HX.* ✆ (048 53) 2896. C. ⊷ 15 bedrs, 3 bp, 1 bps, 4 ba, TV, Dgs. ✖ a l c. ⊡ Dgs, CP 80, CF, 1 st. £ BB £12·50–£19·50, DB £25–

HULL

0 miles ¼

To Brandesburton 16m.

To Withernsea 20m.
& North Sea Ferry Terminal

RAC

N

Crown copyright reserved

River Humber

Barbs

Williamson St.

Danson Road

Holderness Road A165

A1033

Hedon Road

Garrison Road

Cleveland St.

Scott St.
Bridge

Lane

St. Mark St.

Wincolmlee

St. Durham

Jenning St.

Jarratt St.

New Cleveland St.

North Bridge

Witham

River Hull

High St.

Clarence St.

Gt. Union St.

Union Street

Wilberforce
Museum

Transport &
Archaeological
Museum

Lowgate

Scott St.

Caroline St.

Reform St.

George St.

Worship St.

Police
Station

Guildhall Rd.

Guildhall

Market Pl.

Alfred Gelder St.

G.P.O.

Multi-storey
Car Park

Queen St.

Multi-storey
Car Park

Queen's
Gardens

Trinity
House

Holy Trinity
Church

Ped.
only

C

Bridlington Av.

Norfolk St.

To Beverley 8½m.

Multi-storey
Car Park

A1079

Charles St.

Albion St.

Library

Information
Centre

Theatre

Prospect St.

King Edward St.

Jameson St.

Anne St.

Art
Gallery

City Hall

Car Lane

Multi-storey
Car Park

Castle St.

Ferensway

Osborne St.

Annes St.

Commercial Rd.

Paragon
Sta.

Bus Sta.

Buses Only

Ferensway

To Crematorium 2½m.

Theatre

Park Street

Londesborough St.

Hull
Royal
Infirmary

Argyle Street

Anlaby Road

Pryor Street

Spyvee Street

Regent Street

Rawling Way

Tadman St.

Jackson St.

Hessle Road

William St.

Lister St.

Kingston Street

English Street

Cattle
Market

Albert Dock (Fish Dock)

Riverside Quay

To Howden 23¾m.   To M62

A63

A1105   To M62   To Howden 23¾m.

	Car Park
	Public Conveniences
	Parking Meter Zone
L.C.	Level crossing

236

*For abbreviations see inside back cover—*RAC

£31, WT (b) £133–£161, DT (b) £19–£23,
☐, Bk £2·50, L fr £3·50, D £6·50,▲
Sutton House, PH, z (R), *24 Northgate,
PE36 6AP.* ✆ (048 53) 2552. C 5. ⊨ 10
bedrs, 2 ba. ⊡ CH, TV, CP 6. £ BB £9–£11,
DB £18–£20, WT (b) £75–£105, DT (b)
£14–£17, ☐.
Tolcarne, PH, z (R), *3 Boston Sq.*
✆ (048 53) 2359. Open Mar–Oct. C 2.
⊨ 11 bedrs, 4 bps, 3 sh, 2 ba. ⊡ CH, TV,
CP 8. £ BB £10–£13, DB £20–£26, WT (b)
£100–£110, DT (b) £15·50–£17·50, ☐
10%, Bk £4, D £5·50.

Rescue Service: Mann Egerton & Co Ltd.
12 Lynn Rd. ✆ (048 53) 33435.

HUNTINGDON Cambridgeshire. Map
15B
Pop 17,845 (inc Godmanchester).
Royston 21, London 60, Alconbury 6,
Bedford 21, Biggleswade 20, Cambridge
16, Ely 21, Kettering 26, Northampton 37,
Peterborough 19, Stamford 27, Wisbech
33.
EC Wed. **MD** Sat. **Golf** St Ives (Hunts) 9h.
See Oliver Cromwell born here. All Saints'
Church (register of Cromwell's baptism),
Cromwell Museum, Town Hall, old Inns,
14th cent Bridge, Cowper's House,
Pepys's House (Brampton) 1 m.

★★★Old Bridge, *High St, PE18 6TQ.*
✆ (0480) 52681. RS Xmas. C. ⊨ 21 bedrs,
20 bp, 1 bps, TV, Dgs. ✖ a l c, mc, at, LD
10. ⊡ N, CH, CP 100, Ac, pf, con 30, CF, 2
st. £ BB £37, DB £53, WB, ☐, Bk £4·50, L
£14, D £14, cc 1 2 3 5.
★★George (TH), *George St, PE18 6AB.*
✆ (0480) 53096. C. ⊨ 25 bedrs, 16 bp, 1
bps, 5 ba, TV, Dgs. ✖ a l c, mc, at, LD 9.30.
⊡ CH, Dgs, CP 71, Ac, con 200, CF, 2 st.
£ BB £34–£37, DB £46–£50·50, WB, ☐,
cc 1 2 3 4 5 6, Dep (Xmas).

HURST GREEN East Sussex. Map 10E
Pop 900. Tonbridge 17, London 50,
Eastbourne 23, East Grinstead 27,
Hastings 13, Hawkhurst 3, Lewes 25,
Maidstone 20, Rye 16, Tunbridge Wells
14, Uckfield 18.
Golf Hawkhurst 9h. **See** Bodiam Castle.

Rescue Service: Chartcliff Ltd, The
Garage, London Rd. ✆ (058 086) 267.

HURST GREEN Lancashire. Map 27C
Pop 800. Whalley 4½, London 215,
Blackburn 9, Blackpool 26, Preston 12,
Settle 24, Skipton 23.
Golf Clitheroe 18h. **See** Stonyhurst
School.

▣**★★Shireburn Arms,** *Whalley Rd, BB6
9QJ.* ✆ Stonyhurst (025 486) 208.

HUSBORNE CRAWLEY Bedfordshire.
Map Area 15C
Woburn 2, London 45, M1 Motorway 1,
Aylesbury 15, Bedford 11, Bletchley 6½,
Dunstable 11.

Rescue Service: Guise Motors Ltd, Halt
Garage. ✆ Woburn (052 525) 583242.

HUYTON Merseyside. Map 20F
Pop 57,669. M62 Motorway 2, Warrington
11, London 194, Liverpool 6, St Helens 6.
EC Thur. **Golf** Prescot & Huyton 18h. **See**
Church.
🛈 Municipal Buildings, Archway Rd.
✆ 051 489 6000.

Rescue Service: Robcliffe, Longview
Service Station, Longview Rd.
✆ 051-489 0414.

HYTHE Hampshire. Map 6E
Pop 19,400. Winchester 21, London 85,
M20 Motorway 3, Lymington 11,
Lyndhurst 9, Romsey 13, Salisbury 25,
Southampton 10.
EC Wed. **Golf** Bramshott Hill 18h. **See**
Dibden Parish Church 2 m NW. Scratch
Dial (sundial in churchyard). Beaulieu
Abbey. Palace House and National Motor
Museum 5 m W.

Rescue Service: Berkeley Garages
(Southampton) Ltd, Southampton Rd.
✆ (0703) 843036.
Heath Garage, Dibden Purlieu. ✆ (0703)
842023.

HYTHE Kent. Map 10F
Pop 12,200. Ashford 11, London 66,
Canterbury 17, Folkestone 5, Margate 30,
Rye 21, Tenterden 19.
EC Wed. **Golf** Hythe Imperial 18h. **See** St
Leonard's Church and Crypt (collections
of skulls and other human bones),
Romney, Hythe and Dymchurch Light Rly,
Boating on Royal Military Canal, Port
Lympne Zoo Park and Gardens at Lympne.

★★★★Imperial, *Princess Par, CT21 6AE.*
✆ (0303) 67441. C. ⊨ 83 bedrs, 81 bp, 2
bps, TV. ✖ a l c, mc, at, LD 9. ⊡ Lt, N, CH,
CP 120, U 10, Ac, sp, gc, tc, sc, sb, sol, gym,
con 200, CF, 2 BGf, 1 st, Dis. £ BB £32–
£35, DB £58–£65, WT £280, DT £47–£50,
DBB £43·50–£45, WB, ☐, Bk £5, L £7·50, D
£10·50, cc 1 2 3 5 6, Dep.
★★★Stade Court, *West Par, CT21 6DT.*
✆ (0303) 68263. ⊨ 32 bedrs, 24 bp, 5
bps, 1 ba, TV, Dgs. ✖ a l c, mc, at, LD 9.
⊡ Lt, CH, Dgs, CP 10, U 4, Ac, con 35, CF,
0 st. £ BB £20–£24, DB £36–£43, DBB
£24·50–£29, WB, ☐, Bk £4·50, L £5, D
£8·50, cc 1 2 3 5 6, Dep b.
★Swan, *High St, CT21 5AD.* ✆ (0303)
66236.

IBSTOCK Leicestershire. Map 22F
Pop 5,500. Hinckley 11, London 107,
Ashby-de-la-Zouch 6, Atherstone 13,
Derby 19, Leicester 13, Loughborough 11,
Nottingham 24, Tamworth 15.
EC Wed. **Golf** Willesley Park Ltd 18h. **See**
Singler's Cottage built 1485. 11th cent
Church, Community College, 13th cent
Manor House.

Rescue Service: Fawkes Bros, 116
Melbourne Rd. ✆ (0530) 60273.

ICKENHAM Gtr London (Middlesex).
Map 7A
M40 Motorway 2, London 15, Denham 3,
Harrow, 6, Rickmansworth 7, Uxbridge 3.

Woodlands, G, x (Unl), *84 Long Lane,
UB7 7UG.* ✆ Ruislip (0895) 34830. C 5.
⊨ 9 bedrs, 4 bps, 1 ba. ⊡ CH, TV, CP 10, 3
st. £ BB fr £12·50, DB fr £20.

IDEFORD Devon. Map 3D
Pop 300. Exeter 11, London 179,
Ashburton 12, Newton Abbot 5½,
Okehampton 26.
EC Wed. **Golf** Teignmouth (Haldon) Ltd
18h. **See** Church (15th cent).

Rescue Service: Ideford Garage.
✆ Chudleigh (0626) 852256.

ILCHESTER Somerset. Map 5C
Pop 1,741. Wincanton 13, London 122,
Bridgwater 28, Crewkerne 11, Dorchester
25, Frome 25, Glastonbury 12, Ilminster
12, Shepton Mallet 15, Sherborne 10,
Taunton 22.
EC Sat. **Golf** Yeovil 18h. **See** Roger
Bacon born here, St Mary's EE Church,
17th cent Market Cross, "Falklands
Exhibition", Lytes Cary 2½ m NE, Town Hall
(oldest in England).

★★Northover Manor, *BA22 8LD.*
✆ (0935) 840447.

Rescue Service: Ilchester Garage.
✆ (0935) 840425.

ILFORD Greater London (Essex). Map 7B
Pop 178,024. London 11, Epping 11,
Rainham 7, Romford 5, Woodford 4.
EC Thur. **Golf** Ilford 18h.

Cranbrook, PH, z (RI), *24 Coventry Rd,
IG1 4QR.* ✆ 01-554 6544. C. ⊨ 16 bedrs,
11 bp, 2 ba, TV, Dgs. ✖ a l c. ⊡ CH, TV, CP
11, G 2, CF, 4 BGf, 1 st, Dis. £ BB £14·95–
£21·28, DB £23–£26·45, DT (b) £18·45, Bk
£2·50, L £3·50, D £3·50, cc 2 3 ▲
Park, H, z, *327 Cranbrook Rd, IG1 4UE.*
✆ 01-554 9616. C. ⊨ 21 bedrs, 5 bp, 6
bps, 1 ba, TV, Dgs. ⊡ CH, TV, Dgs, CP 25,
CF, 5 BGf, 2 st, Dis. £ BB £16·50–£20·95,
DB £24–£27·95, WT (b) £140, DT (b) £20,
Bk £2·75, D £6, cc 1 2 3.
Rossmore, PH, z (R), *301 Cranbrook Rd,
IG1 4UA.* ✆ 01-554 3481. C. ⊨ 46 Bedrs,
35 bp, 1 sh, 2 ba, TV. ⊡ CH, CP 45, 6 BGf.
£ BB £17·25–£23, DB £32·20.

Rescue Service: Foxhill, 492 High Rd.
✆ 01-514 3364.
Scott's Garage, 147 Beehive La.
✆ 01-550 9911.
Young's Garage (Ilford) Ltd, 480 Ley St.
✆ 01-554 6093.

ILFRACOMBE Devon. Map 4C
Pop 10,000. Dunster 36, London 201,
Barnstaple 11, Lynmouth 18.
EC Thur. **MD** Sat. **Golf** Ilfracombe 18h.
See Holy Trinity Church, Museum, 14th
cent Chapel of St Nicholas on Lantern Hill,
Torrs Walk, Chambercombe Manor,
Bicclescombe "Pets Village" and Corn
Mill.
🛈 The Promenade. ✆ Ilfracombe
(0271) 63001.

★★Carlton, *Runnacleave Rd, EX34 8AR.*
✆ (0271) 62446. Closed Jan–Mar. C.
⊨ 50 bedrs, 12 bp, 13 bps, 9 ba, Dgs.
✖ mc, at. ⊡ Lt, N, CH, TV, CP 20, Ac,
CF, 4 BGf, 6 st. £ BB £11–£13, DB £22–
£26, WT £119–£131, DT £22–£23, DBB
£18·50–£20·50, WB, ☐, Bk £3·50, L £3·50,
D fr £7·50, cc 1 2, Dep a.
★★Cliffe Hydro, *Hillsborough Rd,
EX34 9NP.* ✆ (0271) 63606. C. ⊨ 37
bedrs, 20 bp, 7 bps, 3 ba. ✖ mc, at, LD 8.
⊡ Lt, ch, TV, CP 6, CF, 5 st. £ BB £13–£15,
DB £30–£34, DBB £15–£17, ☐, Bk £2·75, L
£3, D £5·75, Dep a.
★★Dilkhusa Grand, *Wilder Rd,
EX34 9AH.* ✆ (0271) 63505. Closed Jan &
Feb. C. ⊨ 120 bedrs, 18 bp, 22 bps, 18 ba,
Dgs. ✖ mc, at. ⊡ Lt, N, CH, TV, CP 25, Ac,
con 30, CF. £ BB £11–£14·50, DB £19–
£25·50, WT £79–£99, DT £17–£19, DBB
£15–£19, WB, ☐, Bk £3·50, L £3·50, D £5,
cc 1 3, Dep a.
★★Imperial (RI), *Wilder Rd, EX34 9AL.*
✆ (0271) 62536. Open Apr–Oct. C. ⊨ 100

bedrs, 15 bp, 35 bps, 27 ba, TV, Dgs. ✗ mc, at, LD 8. 🅿 Lt, N, CH, TV, CP 12, Ac, CF, 4 st. **£** BB £12–£16, DB £24–£32, WT £95–£130, DBB £15–£24, ②, Bk £3·75, L £5, D £7·50, cc 6.

🔲★★**St Helier**, *Hillsborough Rd, EX34 9QQ.* ✆ (0271) 63862. Open May–Sep. RS Apr & Oct. C. 🛏 29 bedrs, 7 bp, 6 ba, Dgs. ✗ mc, at, LD 7.30. 🅿 ch, TV, CP 20, G 9, CF, 2 BGf, 2 st. **£** BB £9·30–£9·80, DB £18–£24, DBB £13·50–£18, ①, Bk £2·20, D £6, Dep a.

🔲★★**Tracy House** (R), *Belmont Rd, EX34 8DR.* ✆ (0271) 63933. Closed Nov. C. 🛏 11 bedrs, 4 bp, 4 bps, 1 ba, TV, Dgs. ✗ LD 8. 🅿 CH, TV, Dgs, CP 11, U 1, sol, CF, 1 BGf, 1 st, Dis. **£** BB £12·50–£16·50, DB £22–£31, DBB £16–£21·50, WB, ①, Bk £4, D £7·50, Dep.

🔲★**Hillsborough** (RI), *Larkstone Ter, EX34 9NU.* ✆ (0271) 63946. Closed Nov–Jan. C. 🛏 9 bedrs, 3 bp, 3 ba, Dgs. ✗ mc, at, LD 7.15. 🅿 ch, TV, CF, 3 st. **£** BB £7·50–£10, DB £15–£20, DBB £9·50–£11·50, ①, Bk £2, D £3·50, Dep b.

🔲★**Seven Hills** (Unl), *Torrs Park, EX34 8AY.* ✆ (0271) 62207. Open Apr–Sep. C 3. 🛏 14 bedrs, 5 bp, 3 ba, Dgs. ✗ mc, at, LD 7.30. 🅿 TV, Dgs, CP 12, U 1, CF. **£** BB £8·50–£10, DB £17–£20, WT £90–£95, DT £13–£14, DBB £11–£13, WB, ①, Bk £3, L £3·50, D £4.

🔲★**Torrs** (RI), *Torrs Park, EX34 8AY.* ✆ (0271) 62334. Open Mar–Oct. C 4. 🛏 17 bedrs, 3 bp, 7 bps, 3 ba, Dgs. ✗ mc, at, LD 7.30. 🅿 CH, TV, CP 17, 1 st. **£** BB £12·25–£19, DB £24·50–£31, WT £130–£136, DT £18·75–£21, DBB £15·25–£17·50, WB, ②, Bk £3·50, L £4, D £3·50, cc 1 2 3 4 5, Dep a.

Avenue, PH, z (RI), *Greenclose Rd, EX34 8BT.* ✆ (0271) 63767. Open Mar–Nov. C. 🛏 27 bedrs, 2 bp, 4 ba. 🅿 ch, TV, CP 15, CF, 3 st. **£** BB £9–£13, DB £18–£23·50, WT £86·50–£96, DT £13–£14·50, ②, cc 1 3.

Beaufort, PH, z (RI), *Torrs Park, EX34 8AY.* ✆ (0271) 65483.

Bickleighscombe House, H, y (RI), *41 St Brannock's Rd, EX34 8EH.* ✆ (0271) 63899. C. 🛏 14 bedrs, 1 sh, 3 ba, Dgs. 🅿 ch, TV, Dgs, CP 14, CF. **£** BB £7·50–£9·50, DB £15–£19, WT (b) £63–£75, DT (b) £12·50–£14·50, ①, Bk £2·75, L £3·75, D £5·95, cc 1 2 3.

Briercliffe, PH, z (R), *9 Montpelier Ter, EX34 9HR.* ✆ (0271) 63274. Closed Nov. C. 🛏 10 bedrs, 2 sh, 4 ba, Dgs. 🅿 CH, TV, CP 5, CF. **£** BB £9, DB £18, WT (b) £77–£87·50, DT (b) £13, ①.

Carbis, PH, z (R), *50 St Brannocks Rd, EX34 8EH.* ✆ (0271) 62943.

Cheddar, G, z (Unl), *2 Montpelier Ter, EX34 9HR.* ✆ (0271) 65156.

Collindale, PH, z (R), *Larkstone Ter, EX34 9NU.* ✆ (0271) 63770. Closed Nov & Dec. C. 🛏 11 bedrs, 2 bps, 3 sh, 2 ba. 🅿 ch, TV, CF. **£** BB £9·50–£10, DB £19–£21, WT (b) £75–£80, DT (b) £12–£13, ①, Bk £2·50, D £5.

Cresta, PH, y (RI), *Torrs Pk, EX34 8AY.* ✆ (0271) 63742. Open May–Sept. C. 🛏 25 bedrs, 12 ba, Dgs. 🅿 Lt, ch, TV, Dgs, CP 30, CF, 6 BGf, 0 st, Dis. **£** BB £10·25–£14, DB £20·50–£28, WT (b) £83·25–£111, DT (b) £12–£16, ②.

Doric House, PH, z (RI), *Market St, EX34 9AY.* ✆ (0271) 62082.

Earlsdale, PH, z (R), *51 St Brannocks Rd, EX34 8EQ.* ✆ (0271) 62496. C. 🛏 12 bedrs, 4 bps, 1 ba. 🅿 CH, TV, ns, CP 9, CF.

Earlswood, G, z (Unl), *17 St Brannocks Rd, EX34 8HG.* ✆ (0271) 63170. Open Apr–Oct. C. 🛏 3 bedrs, 1 ba, TV. 🅿 CP, CF. **£** BB £6·50–£7, DB £13–£14, WT (b) £70, (c) £49, DT (b) £10, ①.

Elmfield, PH, y (RI), *Torrs Park, EX34 8AZ.* ✆ (0271) 63377. Open Mar–Nov & Xmas. C 3. 🛏 12 bedrs, 10 bps, 1 ba. 🅿 CH, TV, ns, CP 12, CF, 2 st. **£** BB £13–£17, DB £26–£34, WT (b) £98–£120, DT (b) £16–£20, ①, Bk £2·50, cc 1 2 3.

Gables, PH, xy (RI), *Belmont Rd, EX34 8DR.* ✆ (0271) 62475. Open Mar–Oct, C 2. 🛏 10 bedrs, 2 bp, 2 bps, 6 sh, 3 ba, Dgs. 🅿 ch, TV, CP 13, 2 BGf, 1 st, Dis. **£** BB £7–£10, DB £14–£20, WT £40–£77, DT £10–£11·50, ①.

Glendower, G, z. *Wilder Rd, EX34 9AW.* ✆ (0271) 65711. Open Feb–Nov. C. 🛏 12 bedrs, 2 ba. 🅿 CH, TV, ns, CP 12, CF. **£** BB £9, DB £18, ①, Bk £2.

Gloucester, PH, z (R), *Wilder Rd, EX34 8BS.* ✆ (0271) 63763. Open Mar–Nov. C. 🛏 22 bedrs, 1 bp, 7 bps, 4 sh, 6 ba. 🅿 Lt, CH, TV, CP 12, CF. **£** BB £7–£10, DB £14–£16, WT (b) £65–£84, (c) £49–£56, DT (b) £10–£12, ①.

Goodrest, PH, z (RI), *45 St Brannocks Rd, EX34 8EH.* ✆ (0271) 63865. C. 🛏 9 bedrs, 2 ba. Dgs. 🅿 ch, TV, Dgs, CP 7, CF, 22 st. **£** BB £7–£8, DB £14–£16, WT (b) £69–£79, (c) £47–£54, DT (b) £10·50–£12, ①.

Janda, PH, z (RI), *6 Montpelier Terr.* ✆ (0271) 63213.

Lantern House, PH, z (RI), *62 St Brannocks Rd, EX34 8EQ.* ✆ (0271) 64401. C. 🛏 10 bedrs, 3 ba, Dgs. 🅿 CH, TV, Dgs, CP 8, CF, 1 st. **£** BB £7–£8, DB £14–£16, WT (b) £71–£76, DT (b) £11–£12, ②, D £4, cc 3.

Laston House, H, y (RI), *Hillsborough Rd, EX34 9NT.* ✆ (0271) 62627. C. 🛏 11 bedrs, 5 bp, 1 bps, 2 ba. 🅿 CH, TV, CP 11, CF, 1 BGf, 2 st. **£** BB £10–£16, DB £20–£31, WT (b) £85–£110, DT (b) £12–£18, ①.

Lympstone, PH, z (RI), *Cross Park, EX34 8MJ.* ✆ (0271) 63038. Open Mar–Oct. C. 🛏 16 bedrs, 2 bps, 3 ba, Dgs. 🅿 ch, TV, Dgs, CP 5, CF, 3 st. **£** BB £6·50–£8, DB £13–£17·50, WT (b) £65–£75, (c) £45–£55, DT (b) £9·50–£11, ②, Bk £3, D £3.

Lyncott, G, z (Unl), *56 Brannocks Rd, EX34 8EQ.* ✆ (0271) 62425. Closed Xmas. C. 🛏 10 bedrs, 2 ba, Dgs. 🅿 TV, CP 7, U 1, CF, 13 st. **£** BB £6·50–£7·50, DB £13–£15, WT (b) £58–£65, DT (b) £9–£9·50, ①, Bk £1·50, D £2·50.

Melrose, PH, z (RI), *12 Cross Park, EX34 8BJ.* ✆ (0271) 63409. C. 🛏 6 bedrs, 3 ba, ns, Dgs. 🅿 CH, TV, Dgs, CP 2, CF, 2 st. **£** BB £7·50–£8·50, DB £15–£17, WT (b) £70–£78, (c) £50–£56, ①, Bk £2, D £3.

Merlin Court, PH, z, *Torrs Park, EX34 8AY.* ✆ (0271) 62697.

Norbury, PH, x (RI), *Torrs Park, EX34 8AZ.* ✆ (0271) 63888. Open Apr–Sep. C. 🛏 9 bedrs, 3 bps, 3 sh, 1 ba, Dgs. 🅿 CH, TV, CP 9, CF. **£** BB £7·50–£8·50, DB £15–£17, WT (b) £79·50–£88, WT (b) £12–£13, ①.

Queen's Court, PH (R), *Sea Front, Wilder Rd, EX34 9AJ.* ✆ (0271) 63789. Open Apr–Sep. C. 🛏 16 bedrs, 1 bp, 2 bps, 3 ba, Dgs. 🅿 TV, Dgs, CP 16, CF. **£** BB £8·50–£9·65, DB fr £17, WT (b) £96·60–£104·65, (c) £59·50–£67·55, DT (b) £13·80–£14·95, ②, Bk £1·50, L £1·50, D £5.

Southcliffe, H, z (RI), *Torrs Park, EX34 8AZ.* ✆ (0271) 62958. Open May–Sep. C.

🛏 19 bedrs, 8 bps, 2 sh, 3 ba, Dgs. 🅿 ch, TV, CP 12, CF. **£** BB £8·50–£13·75, DB £17–£23·50, WT (b) £76·76–£84·81, DT (b) £10–£12·25, ①.

South Tor, PH, y (RI), *Torrs Park, EX34 8AZ.* ✆ (0271) 63750. Closed Jan & Feb. C 4. 🛏 15 bedrs, 6 bps, 1 sh, 2 ba, Dgs. 🅿 TV, Dgs, CP 10, G 2. **£** BB £8·50–£9·50, DB £16–£20, WT (b) £80–£89, DT (b) £13–£14·50, ①.

Sunnyhill House, H, x (R), *Lincombe, Lee, EX34 8LL.* ✆ (0271) 62953.

Wentworth House, PH, yz (Unl), *Belmont Rd, EX34 8DR.* ✆ (0271) 63048. Open Apr–Sep. C. 🛏 11 bedrs, 2 ba, Dgs. 🅿 ch, TV, Dgs, CP 11, CF, 8 st. **£** BB £7–£8, DB £13·50–£15·50, WT (b) £57·50–£65, DT (b) £9–£9·75, ①.

Westwell Hall, H, y (R), *Torrs Park Rd, EX34 8AZ.* ✆ (0271) 62792. C. 🛏 16 bedrs, 3 bp, 7 bps, 2 ba, Dgs. 🅿 CH, TV, CP 10, CF, 3 BGf, 2 st. **£** BB £10–£15, DB £20–£30, WT (b) £91–£126, DT (b) £14–£19, ①, Bk £3, L £5, D £6.

Rescue Service: Foxhunters Garage (West Down) Ltd, West Down. ✆ (0271) 63104.
Putts Garage, Northfield Rd. ✆ (0271) 62075.
Robin's Garage, Northfield Rd. ✆ (0271) 62454.

ILKESTON Derbyshire. Map 22D. M1 Motorway 6½, London 129, Derby 10, Loughborough 19, Mansfield 17, Nottingham 7½.

Repairer: Sandicliffe Garage Ltd, Nottingham Rd. ✆ (0602) 302391.

ILKLEY West Yorkshire. Map 25E Pop 13,600. Leeds 16, London 207, Blackburn 34, Bradford 13, Burnley 25, Harrogate 17, Hawes 43, Leyburn 41, Selby 38, Skipton 9½, Todmorden 26, Whalley 31, York 35.
EC Wed. **Golf** Ilkley 18h. **See** Churches, Manor House, Museum, Middleton Woods, Moors, Cow and Calf Rocks, West Wall of Roman Fort, Middleton Lodge (16th cent—now monastery), White Wells, Bolton Abbey 5 m NNE.
🆔 The Library, Station Rd. ✆ Ilkley (0943) 602319.

★★★**Cow & Calf**, *Moor Top, LS29 8BT.* ✆ (0943) 607335. Closed Xmas. C. 🛏 18 bedrs, 9 bp, 3 bps, 4 sh, 2 ba, TV, Dgs. ✗ mc, LD 9.15. 🅿 CH, CP 100, con 30, CF, 2 st. **£** BB £22·50–£27·50, DB £30–£38, WB, ②, Bk £3, D £7·50, cc 1 2 3 4 5 6.

★★★**Craiglands** (TH), *Cowpasture Rd, LS29 8RQ.* ✆ (0943) 607676. C. 🛏 76 bedrs, 47 bp, 5 bps, TV, Dgs. ✗ a l c, mc, at, LD 9.30. 🅿 Lt, N, CH, Dgs, CP 200, G 8, Ac, tc, con 300, CF, 8 st. **£** BB £29–£37·50, DB £42·50–£53·50, WB, ①, cc 1 2 3 4 5 6, Dep (Xmas).

★★**Crescent**, *Brook Street, LS29 8DG.* ✆ (0943) 600012. C. 🛏 20 bedrs, 3 bp, 4 ba. ✗ a l c, mc, LD 8.45. 🅿 ch, TV, CP 50, U 3, Ac, sol, con 100, CF, 0 st. **£** BB £18–£24, DB £24–£28, ①, Bk £2·85, cc 1, Dep b.

★★**Greystones** (R), *1 Ben Rhydding Rd, LS29 8RJ.* ✆ (0943) 607408. RS Dec 24. C. 🛏 10 bedrs, 5 bp, 3 bps, 1 sh, 1 ba, TV, Dgs. ✗ mc, at, LD 9. 🅿 CH, TV, Dgs, CP 15, Ac, CF, 2 st. **£** BB £20·24–£22·14, DB £25·30–£30·36, ②, Bk £3·95, D fr £6·95, cc 1 2 3 5 6.▲

★★**Lister's Arms,** *Skipton Rd, LS29 9EH.*
✆ (0943) 608698. C. 🛏 17 bedrs, 5 bp, 3
ba. ✗ a l c, mc, LD 8·45. 🅿 CH, TV, CP
120, U 1, Ac, con 100, CF, 1 st. £ BB £19–
£25, DB £25–£29, 🔟, Bk £2·95, L £4·80, D
£5·95, cc 1, Dep b.

★★**Troutbeck,** *Crossbeck Rd, LS29 8RQ.*
✆ (0943) 607425.

Repairer: Tunnicliffe's (Ilkley) Ltd, Skipton
Rd. ✆ (0943) 607606.

ILMINSTER Somerset. Map 5E
Pop 4,000. Wincanton 25, London 135,
Axminster 12, Bridgwater 19, Crewkerne
8, Frome 36, Glastonbury 23, Honiton 17,
Shepton Mallet 27, Sherborne 19, Taunton
12.
EC Thur. **MD** Wed. **Golf** Windwhistle 18h.
See Church, 16th cent Grammar School,
Dillington House, Barrington Court 3 m
NE (Nat Trust).
🄿 Shrubbery Hotel Car Park, Station Hill.
✆ Ilminster (046 05) 5294.

★★★**M Horton Cross,** *TA19 9PT.*
✆ (046 05) 2144. C. 🛏 23 bedrs, 23 bp,
TV, Dgs. ✗ a l c, mc, at, LD 9.30. 🅿 N, CH,
TV, Dgs, CP 60, Ac, con 160, CF, 6 BGf, 0
st, Dis. £ BB fr £26·07, DB fr £35·90, WB,
🛂 10%, Bk £3, L £4·45, D £8,
cc 1 2 3 4 5 6, Dep.

Rescue Service: Brakes Motor Works,
Station Rd. ✆ (046 05) 2400.
Ilminster Motor Co, Station Rd.
✆ (046 05) 4331.

IMMINGHAM Humberside (South
Humberside). Maps 24A and 25B.
Pop 11,580. Market Rasen 20, London
169, Gainsborough 34, Grimsby 9½, Hull
22, Louth 22, Scunthorpe 23.
EC Wed, Thur. **MD** Fri. **Golf** Immingham
9h. **See** Pilgrim Fathers' Monument, 13th
cent Church, Museum.

Rescue Service: Pelham Motors Ltd,
Pelham Rd. ✆ (0469) 76276.

INGATESTONE Essex. Map 17F
Pop 5,000. Brentwood 5, London 27,
Bishop's Stortford 23, Chelmsford 6,
Epping 15, Southend-on-Sea 21.
EC Wed. **Golf** Brentwood 18h. **See** 15th
cent Church, Ingatestone Hall.

Rescue Service: Ingatestone Motors, High
St. ✆ (027 75) 3020.

INGLETON North Yorkshire. Map 27A
Pop 1,930. Settle 11, London 240, Hawes
16, Kirkby Lonsdale 6, Lancaster 18.
EC Thur. **MD** Fri. **Golf** Bentham 9h. **See**
Norman Church. Swilla Glen,
Ingleborough Mountain (2,373 ft) with
underground lake, White Scar Cave,
Thornton Force and other waterfalls,
Weathercote Cave
🄿 Community Centre Car Park. ✆ Ingleton
(0468) 41049.

Langber, G, x (Unl), *LA6 3DT.* ✆ (0468)
41587.
Oakroyd, PH, x (RI), *Main St, LA6 3HJ.*
✆ (0468) 41258.
Springfield, PH, x (RI), *Main St, LA6
3HJ.* ✆ (0468) 41280. Closed Nov. C. 🛏 6
bedrs, 2 bps, 1 ba, TV, Dgs. 🅿 CH, TV, Dgs,
CP 12, CF. £ BB £8–£9, DB £16–£18, WT
(b) £77–£84, DT (b) £12·25–£13·25, 🔟, Bk
£1·50, D £4·25.

Rescue Service: William Baines, Imperial
Garage, New Rd, Ingleton, Carnforth,
Lancs. ✆ (0468) 41225.

INGOLDMELLS Lincolnshire. Map 23D
Pop 1,527. Skegness 3½, London 143,
Horncastle 20, Louth 22, Mablethorpe 13.
Golf Skegness 18h (2). **See** 13th cent
Churches, Coronation Park.

Rescue Service: Central Motor Repairs,
Queensway. ✆ Skegness (0754) 73844.

INSTOW Devon. Map 4C.
Pop 721, Barnstaple 6, London 199,
Bideford 3.
EC Wed. **Golf** Royal North Devon 18h.
See Tapeley Park Gardens, Lundy Island.

★★★**Commodore,** *Marine Par,
EX39 4JN.* ✆ (0271) 860347. Closed
Xmas. C. 🛏 21 bedrs, 21 bp, TV. ✗ a l c,
mc, at, LD 9.30. 🅿 N, CH, CP 180, con, CF,
1 st. £ BB £27·50–£34, DB £49·50,
DBB £32·50–£39, WB, 🛂, Bk £3·75, L £6, D £9,
cc 1 2 3

Anchorage, H, x (RI), *The Quay,
EX39 4HX.* ✆ (0271) 860699. Open Mar–
Nov. C. 🛏 11 bedrs, 10 bps, 1 ba. 🅿 CH,
TV, CP 9, CF, 0 st. £ BB £12–£16, DB £24–
£32, WT £124–£131, DT £17·50–£22, 🔟,
Bk £3, D £8, cc 1 2 3

IPPLEPEN Devon. Map 3D
Pop 2,075. Newton Abbot 4, London 187,
Ashburton 6, Torquay 7, Totnes 5½.
EC Sat. **Golf** Newton Abbot (Stover) 18h.
See 12th cent Church.

Rescue Service: David Scrase Ltd, Red
Post Garage. ✆ (0803) 812389.

IPSWICH Suffolk. Map 17C
Pop 122,000. Colchester 18, London 74,
Aldeburgh 24, Clacton-on-Sea 24,
Harwich 22, Saxmundham 21, Scole 23,
Stowmarket 12, Sudbury 21.
MD Tue, Thur, Fri, Sat. **Golf** Ipswich 18h.
See Wolsey's Gate, Christchurch Mansion
and Wolsey Art Gallery, "Great White
Horse" Hotel (Dickens assoc), 16th cent
Ancient House, Old Churches,
Helmingham Hall Gardens 9 m N.
🄿 Town Hall, Princes St. ✆ Ipswich
(0473) 58070.

🛇★★★★**Belstead Brook,** *Belstead Rd,
IP2 9HB.* ✆ (0473) 684241. C. 🛏 32
bedrs, 32 bp, TV. ✗ mc, at, LD 9.30. 🅿 N,
CH, CP 60, Ac, con 30, CF, 18 BGf, 1 st,
Dis. £ BB £43·95, DB £49·95, WT £191·50,
DT £62·95, WB, 🔟, Bk £4·95, L £9·50, D
£9.50, cc 1 2 3 5 6, Dep b.

★★★**M Ipswich Moat House,** *London
Rd, IP8 3JD.* ✆ Copdock (047 386) 444
(3¼ m SW on A12). C. 🛏 47 bedrs, 39 bp, 2
ba, TV, Dgs. ✗ a l c, mc, at, LD 9.20. 🅿 N,
CH, CP 400, Ac, con 500, CF, 16 BGf, 3 st.
£ BB £26–£36·50, DB £36–£50, WB, 🛂, Bk
£5, L £8, D £12, cc 1 2 3 5 6, Dep.

★★★**Marlborough,** *73 Henley Rd,
IP1 3SP.* ✆ (0473) 57677. RS Dec 25. C.
🛏 22 bedrs, 22 bp, TV, Dgs. ✗ a l c, mc, at,
LD 9.15. 🅿 N, CH, Dgs, ns, CP 60, Ac, con
30, CF, 8 BGf, 1 st, Dis. £ BB £18–£39, DB
£36–£48, WB, 🔟, Bk £5·25, L £8·50, D
£8·95, cc 1 2 3 5, Dep b.

★★★**M Post House** (TH), *London Rd,
IP2 0UA.* ✆ (0473) 212313. C. 🛏 118
bedrs, 118 bp, TV, Dgs. ✗ a l c, mc, at, LD
9.45. 🅿 N, CH, Dgs, CP 175, Ac, con
100, CF, 60 BGf, 1 st, Dis. £ BB £42·50, DB
£54·50, WB, 🔟, cc 1 2 3 4 5 6, Dep (Xmas).

★★**Golden Lion,** *Cornhill, IP1 1DP.*
✆ (0473) 56645. C. 🛏 23 bedrs, 20 bp, 3
bps, TV. 🅿 N, CH, CP 18, con 60, CF, 0 st.
£ BB £29·50, DB £39·50, WT £210, DT
£39·50, DBB £37, WB, 🔟, Bk £3·50, L
£3·50, D £7·50, cc 1 2 3 5, Dep b.

★★**Great White Horse** (TH), *Tavern St,
IP1 3AH.* ✆ (0473) 56558. C. 🛏 55 bedrs,
10 bp, 11 ba, TV, Dgs. ✗ a l c, mc, at, LD
9.15. 🅿 N, CH, Dgs, Ac, con 250, CF, 1 st.
£ BB £31–£34, DB £41–£47·50, WB, 🔟,
cc 1 2 3 4 5 6, Dep (Xmas).

Anglesea, PH, z (RI), *Oban St, IP1 3PH.*
✆ (0473) 54278. Closed Xmas. 🛏 7 bedrs,
5 bp, 2 bps, TV. 🅿 CH, CP 9. £ BB fr £21,
DB fr £33, 🔟, Bk £2, cc 1 3.
Graham Court, H, y, *Anglesea Rd, IP1
3PW.* ✆ (0473) 53583. Closed Xmas. C.
🛏 33 bedrs, 6 bp, 12 bps, 3 ba, TV. ✗ a l c.
🅿 CH, TV, CP 60, CF, 3 BGf, 2 st. £ BB
£17·50–£21, DB £27–£30·50, 🔟, Bk £3·75,
L £6·50, D £6·50, cc 1 2 3 5.
Station, H, *Burrell Rd, IP2 8AH.*
✆ (0473) 52664.

Repairer: Boltons (Ipswich) Ltd, Valley
Road Garage, 178 Norwich Rd. ✆ (0473)
53173.
MC Repairer: Revetts (Norwich) Ltd, 53
Norwich Rd. ✆ (0473) 53726.
Rescue Service: Fiveways Garage
(Ipswich) Ltd, Henley Rd, Henley.
✆ (0473) 831284.

IRLAM Greater Manchester
(Lancashire). Maps 19B & 20B
Stockport 13, London 192, M6 Motorway
6, Bolton 11, Liverpool 26, Manchester 9.

Rescue Service: Alan Taylor Ltd, 536A
Liverpool Rd. ✆ 061-775 8454 and 8918.

ISHAM Northamptonshire. Map 15A
Pop 735. Bedford 23, London 73,
Kettering 4, Northampton 13.
Golf Wellingborough 18h.

Rescue Service: Isham Service Station,
Wellingborough Rd. ✆ Burton Latimer
(053 672) 2336.

ISLE OF MAN
See CASTLETOWN, DOUGLAS, PEEL,
PORT ST MARY, RAMSEY.

ISLE OF WIGHT
See BEMBRIDGE, CHALE, COLWELL
BAY, COWES, FRESHWATER,
GODSHILL, NEWPORT, RYDE, ST
LAWRENCE, SANDOWN, SEAVIEW,
SHANKLIN, TOTLAND BAY, VENTNOR,
YARMOUTH.

ISLES OF SCILLY
🄿 Town Hall, St Mary's ✆ Scillonia (0720)
22536.

ST MARY'S
Pop 1,960. Steamer Service to Penzance.
London 281.
EC Wed. **Golf** St Mary's 9h. **See** St Mary's
Church, Flower Farms (Shows Jan and
Mar).

🛇★★**Atlantic,** *TR21 0PL.* ✆ Scillonia
(0720) 22417. Open Apr–Oct. C. 🛏 25
bedrs, 16 bp, 1 bps, 3 ba, TV, Dgs. 🅿 CH,
TV, Dgs, Ac, CF, 0 st. £ BB £16–£23, DB
£30–£44, DBB £19–£27, WB, 🔟, Bk £3·50,
D £8·50, Dep.

🛇★★**Godolphin,** *Church St, Hughtown,
TR21 0JR.* ✆ Scillonia (0720) 22316.
Open Mar–Oct. C. 🛏 31 bedrs, 25 bp, 2
bps, 1 ba, TV. ✗ mc, at, LD 8. 🅿 ch, Dgs,

sb, CF, 8 BGf, 3 st. **£** BB fr £13, DB fr £26, DBB fr £21, ①, Bk £3, D £9.

■★★Tregarthen's, *Hughtown, TR21 0PP.* **℄** Scillonia (0720) 22540. Open Mar–Oct. C. **🛏** 32 bedrs, 24 bp, 2 ba, TV. **✗** mc, at, LD 8. ☎ ch, Ac, con 20, CF, 15 st. **£** DBB £22·50–£38, WB, ①, Bk £5, L £6, D £9·50, cc 1 2 3 5 6, Dep a.

Brantwood, PH, x (Rl), *Rocky Hill, TR21 0NW.* **℄** Scillonia (0720) 22531. Open Apr–Oct. C 10. **🛏** 4 bedrs, 4 bps, TV. ☎ CH, TV. **£** DB £53, WT (b) £177·10–£217, DT (b) £25·30–£31, ②.

TRESCO
Pop 180. Steamer Service, St Mary's to Penzance. London 281.
See Abbey Gardens, Church, castle ruins.
Dogs banned from island.

★★★Island, *TR24 0PU.* **℄** Scillonia (0720) 22883. Open mid Mar–mid Oct. C. **🛏** 35 bedrs, 28 bp, 4 bps, TV. **✗** mc, at, LD 8.15. ☎ CH, TV, sp, pf, CF, 2 st. **£** DBB £36–£68, ②, L £3, D £15, Dep.

ISLEWORTH Greater London (Middlesex). Map 7A.
Brentford & Chiswick 5½, London 12, M3 Motorway 4½, Richmond 5½, Staines 7, Uxbridge 8, Wembley 10.

Kingswood, H, z (Rl), *33 Woodlands Rd, TW7 6NR.* **℄** 01-560 5614. C 5. **🛏** 11 bedrs, 1 sh, 2 ba, TV. ☎ CH, TV, CP 5. **£** BB £13·80, DB £23–£26·45, WT (c) £96·60.

IVINGHOE Buckinghamshire. Map 15E
Pop 1,000. Watford 18, London 35, Aylesbury 9½, Bletchley 13, Buckingham 24, Denham 23, Dunstable 6½, High Wycombe 19, St Albans 17, Slough 26, Wallingford 31.
EC Wed. **Golf** Ivinghoe 9h, Dunstable Downs 18h. **See** 13th–14th cent Church, Ivinghoe Beacon, Windmill (NT).

Rescue Service: Pitstone Engineering Co Ltd, Beacon Garage, Pitstone.
℄ Cheddington (0296) 668263.

IVYBRIDGE Devon. Map 3D.
Pop 5,500. Ashburton 13, London 200, Dartmouth 20, Kingsbridge 13, Plymouth 11, Saltash 14, Tavistock 17, Totnes 12.
EC Wed. **Golf** Elfordleigh, Plympton 9h.
See Flete (Partly Elizabethan) 3 m S.

Repairer: Ivybridge Motors Ltd, Fore St. **℄** (075 54) 2403.
Rescue Service: Bowden, W H & Sons, Erme Valley Garage, Western Rd.
℄ (075 54) 2530.
Westward Garage, Lee Mill. **℄** (075 54) 2926.

KEGWORTH Leicestershire. Map 22F
Pop 3,376. Loughborough 6, London 116, M1 Motorway 1, Ashby-de-la-Zouch 11, Burton-on-Trent 20, Chesterfield 34, Derby 11, Hinckley 26, Mansfield 26, Melton Mowbray 18, Nottingham 11, Uttoxeter 29.
EC Wed. **Golf** Longcliffe, Loughborough 18h. **See** Church.
★★Yew Lodge, (Rl), *DE7 2DF.* **℄** (050 97) 2518. C. **🛏** 39 bedrs, 29 bp, 10 bps, 1 ba, TV, Dgs. **✗** a l c, mc, at, LD 9.30. ☎ Lt, N, CH, Dgs, CP 70, Ac, con 60, CF. **£** BB £28–£30, DB £37–£40, WT £197·50, DBB £35·50, WB, ②, Bk £3·50, L £4, D £7·50, cc 1 2 3.

Repairer: J C S Garages Ltd, Station Rd. **℄** (050 97) 2523.

KEIGHLEY West Yorkshire. Map 27A
Pop 44,346 (Inc Haworth). Halifax 12, London 199, Bradford 10, Harrogate 25, Huddersfield 19, Skipton 9½, Todmorden 14, York 42.
EC Tue. **MD** Wed, Fri, Sat. **Golf** Keighley 18h. **See** Cliffe Castle Museum and Art Gallery, Keighley–Worth Valley Rly, E Rlddlesden Hall (NT) 1 m NE, Brontë Parsonage Museum (Haworth) 3½ m SW.

★★Beeches, *Bradford Rd, BD21 4BB.* **℄** (0535) 607227. C. **🛏** 10 bedrs, 2 bp, 2 ba, annexe 14 bedrs, 9 bps, 1 ba, TV, Dgs. **✗** a l c, mc, LD 8·45, ☎ N, CH, TV, CP 80, G 3, Ac, con 100, CF, 9 BGf, 1 st. **£** BB £12–£20, DB £24–£30, WB, ①, Bk £3, L £5·45, D £5·45, cc 1 2 3, Dep b.

Repairers: Foulds, E (Motor Engineers) Ltd, 25 Cavendish St. **℄** (0535) 604253.
Walter Burgess Ltd, Brewery St. **℄** (0535) 607483.

KELVEDON Essex. Map 17D
Pop 2,400. Chelmsford 13, London 45, Braintree 9, Colchester 10, Haverhill 26, Southend-on-Sea 32.
EC Wed. **Golf** Braintree 18h. **See** Birthplace of Charles Haddon Spurgeon, High St (tablet), Church.

Repairer: Deal, C J Ltd, Railway Garage. **℄** (0376) 70331.

KENDAL Cumbria. Map 26D
Pop 21,596. London 257, M6 Motorway 5½, Ambleside 13, Brough 28, Broughton-in-Furness 30, Hawes 26, Lancaster 22, Kirkby Lonsdale 12, Penrith 25, Ulverston 24.
MD Sat. **Golf** Kendal 18h. **See** 13th cent Parish Church, Castle ruins, Abbot Hall Art Gallery and Museum, 18th cent Sandes Hospital, Sizergh Castle (Nat Trust) 3 m SW.
⛴ Town Hall, Highgate. **℄** Kendal (0539) 25758.

★★★County Thistle, *Station Rd, LA9 6BT.* **℄** (0539) 22461. C. **🛏** 31 bedrs, 24 bp, ns, TV, Dgs. **✗** a l c, mc, LD 9. ☎ Lt, N, CH, TV, Dgs, CP 40, Ac, CF. **£** BB £28·50–£36, DB £38–£42, WB, ②, cc 1 2 3 4 5 6, Dep b.
★★★Woolpack, *Stricklandgate, LA9 4ND.* **℄** (0539) 23852. C. **🛏** 58 bedrs, 58 bp, TV, Dgs. **✗** a l c, mc, at, LD 9.30. ☎ N, CH, TV, Dgs, CP 90, con 120, CF, 1 BGf, 0 st. **£** BB £39, DB £49, DBB £47, WB, ②, Bk £5, L £5, D £8·95, cc 1 2 3 5 6.
★★Gateway (R), *Crook Rd, Plumgarth, LA8 8LX.* **℄** (0539) 20605. Closed Xmas. C. **🛏** 10 bedrs, 4 bp, 2 ba, TV, Dgs. **✗** a l c, mc, LD 9.30. ☎ CH, TV, Dgs, CP 50, Ac, con 20, CF. **£** BB £13·50–£22·50, DB £20–£36, DBB £17·50–£27·50, WB, ②, Bk £3·50, L £3·50, D £6·75, cc 1 2 3, Dep a.
■★★Shenstone Country (R), *Milnthorpe Rd, LA8 8AA.* **℄** (0539) 21023.
Garnett House, F, x (Unl), *Burnside, LA9 5SF.* **℄** (0539) 24542. Closed Xmas & New Year. C. **🛏** 5 bedrs, 2 ba. ☎ TV, CP 6, CF. **£** BB £8, DB £16, DT £11·25, ②.

Repairers: Craghill & Co Ltd, 113 Stricklandgate. **℄** (0539) 20967.
Loxhams Garages (Kendal) Ltd, Westmorland Garage. **℄** (0539) 21732.
Rescue Service: Gardner, J & K, Appleby Rd Service Station. **℄** (0539) 22215.

Tebay Vehicle Repairs Ltd, Killington Lake Garage, M6 Motorway. **℄** Sedbergh (0587) 20971.

KENILWORTH Warwickshire. Map 14B
Pop 19,315. Warwick 4½, London 96, Birmingham 19, Coventry 6, Daventry 22, Lichfield 28, Sutton Coldfield 21, Tamworth 23.
EC Thur. **MD** Thur. **Golf** Kenilworth 18h. **See** Castle ruins, Parish Church of St Nicholas, Old houses, Augustine Priory (remains), National Agricultural Show Centre.
⛴ 11 Smalley Pl. **℄** Kenilworth (0926) 52595.

★★★★De Montfort, *The Square, CV8 1ED.* **℄** (0926) 55944.
★★★Kenilworth Moat House, *Chesford Bridge, CV8 2LN.* **℄** (0926) 58331. C. **🛏** 48 bedrs, 48 bp, TV, Dgs. **✗** a l c, mc, at, LD 10. ☎ N, CH, Dgs, CP 150, Ac, pf, con 120, CF, 20 BGf, 1 st, Dis. **£** BB £34, DB £44, WT £263, DT £47, DBB £41, WB, ①, Bk £4, L £6, D £7·50, cc 1 2 3 5 6, Dep.
★★Clarendon House, *High St, CV8 1LZ.* **℄** (0926) 57668. C. **🛏** 23 bedrs, 9 bp, 9 bps, 5 sh, 2 ba, TV, Dgs. **✗** mc, at, LD 9. ☎ CH, TV, CP 34, Ac, CF, 1 st. **£** BB fr £22, DB £36, WB, ② 10%, Bk £3·75, L £6·50, D £8·50, cc 1 3 6, Dep b.
Enderley, G, z (Rl), *20 Queen's Road, CV8 1JQ.* **℄** (0926) 55388. C. **🛏** 6-bedrs, 2 ba, Dgs. ☎ CH, TV, Dgs. **£** BB £8·50, DB £16, WT (c) £53·55, ①.
Nightingales, H, z (R), *95 Warwick Rd, CV8 1HP.* **℄** (0926) 53594. ▲

KENNFORD Devon. Map 3D
Pop 2,030. M5 Motorway 2, Exeter 5, London 174, Dawlish 9, Newton Abbot 11, Okehampton 25, Sidmouth 16.
EC Wed. **Golf** Dawlish Warren 18h. **See** 14th–15th cent Church.

Rescue Service: Kennford Garage, Main Rd. **℄** Exeter (0392) 832050.

KERNE BRIDGE Hereford & Worcester (Herefordshire). Map 13E
Gloucester 16, London 124, Chepstow 21, Hereford 15, Monmouth 6½, Ross-on-Wye 3½.
Golf Ross 18h. **See** Bridge, Farmhouse (old abbey).
★★Castle View, *HR9 5QT.* **℄** Symonds Yat (0600) 890329. C. **🛏** 8 bedrs, 1 bp, 1 bps, 3 sh, 1 ba, Dgs. **✗** a l c, mc, at, LD 10. ☎ CH, TV, Dgs, CP 60, Ac, con 100, CF, 1 st. **£** BB £15·50–£17·50, DB £26–£29, DBB £36–£39, WB, ①, Bk £3·50, L £6, D £6·50, cc 1 2 3 5, Dep a.

KESSINGLAND Suffolk. Map 16B
Pop 3,500. Saxmundham 19, London 114, Aldeburgh 23, Lowestoft 4½, Norwich 26, Scole 28.
EC Thur. **Golf** Lowestoft 18h. **See** 17th cent Church, Suffolk Wild Life Park.

Rescue Service: Percy C Clarke & Son, 76 High St. **℄** Lowestoft (0502) 740208.

KESWICK Cumbria. Map 26F
See also BASSENTHWAITE, BORROWDALE and THORNTHWAITE.
Pop 4,850. Ambleside 16, London 285, Carlisle 31, Cockermouth 11, Egremont 25, Penrith 16.
EC Wed. **MD** Sat. **Golf** Keswick (Threlkd) 18h. **See** Derwentwater, Friar's Crag (monument to John Ruskin), School

of Industrial Arts, Crosthwaite Parish Church (Southey's grave), Castlerigg prehistoric stone circle.
🆃 Moot Hall, Market Sq. ⬩ Keswick (0596) 72645.

★★★★**Lodore Swiss,** *Borrowdale Rd, CA12 5UX.* ⬩ Borrowdale (059 684) 285. Closed Dec–Feb. C. ⍚ 72 bedrs, 70 bp, 2 bps, 1 ba, TV. ✗ a l c, mc, at, LD 9. 🏠 Lt, N, CH, ns, CP 60, U 24, sp, tc, sc, sb, sol, gym, con 40, CF, 2 st. £ BB £29, DB £58, WT £280, DT £40, DBB £37, ②, L £7, D £9·50, cc 2.

★★★**Derwentwater,** *Portinscale, CA12 5RE.* ⬩ (0596) 72538. C. ⍚ 43 bedrs, 26 bp, 7 bps, 4 ba, Dgs. ✗ mc, at, LD 8.30. 🏠 Lt, N, ch, TV, Dgs, CP 80, Ac, pf, con 100, CF. £ BB £24·50–£29, DB £39–£48, DBB £30·50–£38, WB, ②, Bk £3, D £8, cc 1 2 3 5.

■★★★**Keswick** (TH), *Station Rd, CA12 4NQ.* ⬩ (0596) 72020. C. ⍚ 64 bedrs, 64 bp, TV, Dgs. ✗ a l c, mc, at, LD 8.30. 🏠 Lt, N, CH, Dgs, CP 50, G 50, Ac, con 100, CF, 3 BGf, 3 st. £ BB £33·50, DB £51·50, WB, ②, L 1 2 3 4 5 6, Dep (Xmas).

■★★★**Royal Oak** (TH), *Station St, CA12 5HH.* ⬩ (0596) 72965. C. ⍚ 66 bedrs, 26 bp, 4 bps, 19 ba, TV, Dgs. ✗ a l c, mc, at, LD 9.15. 🏠 Lt, N, CH, Dgs, CP 42, Ac, con 120, CF, 1 st. £ BB £21–£31·50, DB £34–£44·50, WB, ①, cc 1 2 3 4 5 6, Dep (Xmas).

★★★**Skiddaw** (R), *Main St, CA12 5BN.* ⬩ (0596) 72071.

■⬩★★★**Underscar** (R), *Applethwaite, CA12 4PN.* ⬩ (0596) 72469. Closed Dec–Jan. C. ⍚ 12 bedrs, 10 bp, 2 bps, TV. ✗ mc, at, LD 8.15. 🏠 CH, CP 50, CF, 6 BGf, 4 st. £ BB £20–£30, DB £34–£54, DBB £25–£35, WB, ①, Bk £4·50, L £6, D £9, cc 1 3 6.

■★★**Chaucer House** (R), *Derwentwater Pl, CA12 4DR.* ⬩ (0596) 72318. Open Apr–Oct. C. ⍚ 32 bedrs, 3 bp, 6 bps, 4 sh, 9 ba, Dgs. ✗ mc, LD 8. 🏠 ch, TV, Dgs, CP 25, CF. £ BB £10·50–£13·50, DB £19–£25, DBB £14·50–£17·50, ②, Bk £4·50, D £6, cc 1, 2, Dep a.

■★★**Crow Park,** *The Heads, CA12 5ER.* ⬩ (0596) 72208. Closed Dec–Feb. C. ⍚ 27 bedrs, 15 bp, 12 bps, TV, Dgs. ✗ LD 7.30. 🏠 CH, ns, CP 27, CF, 2 st. £ BB £12–£13, DB £24–£26, DBB £17–£19, WB, ②, cc 1 3.

★★**George,** *St John St, CA12 5AZ.* ⬩ (0596) 72076. C. ⍚ 17 bedrs, 5 ba, Dgs. ✗ mc, at, LD 8.30. 🏠 ch, TV, Dgs, CP 4, Ac, CF, 1 st. £ BB £14·30, DB £28·60, WB, ①, cc 1 2 3 5.

■★★**Grange,** *Manor Brow, CA12 4BA.* ⬩ (0596) 72500. C 10. ⍚ 10 bedrs, 3 bp, 5 bps, 1 ba, NS, TV. ✗ mc, at, LD 8.30. 🏠 CH, ns, CP 15, 1 st. £ BB £12–£14, DB £28–£32, WT £192·50–£206·50, DT £27·50–£29·50, DBB £22·50–£24·50, ①, Bk £3·50, L £6, D £8·50.

■★★**Lairbeck** (R), *Vicarage Hill, CA12 5QB.* ⬩ (0596) 73373. C. ⍚ 12 bedrs, 5 bp, 3 ba. ✗ mc, at, LD 8. 🏠 CH, TV, ns, CP 25, CF, 2 st. £ BB £11–£14·50, DB £22–£29, DBB £18·50–£22·50, ②, Bk £3·50, L £3·75, D £7·50.

★★**Lake,** *Lake Rd, CA12 5BZ.* ⬩ (0596) 72069.

★★**Queen's,** *Main St, CA12 5JF.* ⬩ (0596) 73333. Open Mar–Oct. C. ⍚ 30 bedrs, 20 bp, 4 bps, 2 ba, TV. ✗ a l c, mc, LD 8.30. 🏠 Lt, CH, G 18, Ac, CF, 4 st. £ BB

£12–£18, DB £24–£36, ②, Bk £3·50, L £4·25, D £10, cc 1 2 3 5 6, Dep a.

■⬩★★**Red House** (R), *CA12 4QA.* ⬩ (0596) 72211. Open Mar–Oct. C. ⍚ 23 bedrs, 15 bp, 3 ba, Dgs. ✗ mc, at, LD 8. 🏠 ch, TV, Dgs, CP 30, Ac, sp, con 40, CF, 2 BGf, 3 st. £ BB £19–£24, DB £36–£39, WT £140, DT £26, DBB £23–£24·50, WB, ②, Bk £3·50, L £3·50, D £6.

■★★**Tower,** *Portinscale, CA12 5RD.* ⬩ (0596) 73099. C. ⍚ 24 bedrs, 5 bp, 8 bps, 6 ba, TV, Dgs. ✗ mc, at, LD 7.30. 🏠 ch, TV, Dgs, CP 50, Ac, con, CF, 2 st. £ BB £11–£12·50, DB £22–£25, DBB £17–£18·50, WB, ②, Bk £3, L £3·50, D £6·50, Dep.

★**Daleview** (R), *Lake Rd, CA12 5DQ.* ⬩ (0596) 72666. Open Apr–Oct. C. ⍚ 15 bedrs, 7 bp, 2 sh, 2 ba, Dgs. ✗ LD 7. 🏠 CH, TV, CP 15. £ BB £11–£15, DB £20–£24, WT £126–£140, DT £22–£24·50, DBB £16–£18, ①, Bk £4, L £6, D fr £6, Dep.

■★**Linnett Hill** (R), *4 Penrith Rd, CA12 4HF.* ⬩ (0596) 73109. C 4. ⍚ 7 bedrs, 2 bp, 2 ba, Dgs. ✗ a l c, mc, LD 6.30. 🏠 CH, TV, CP 12, 1 st. £ BB £11, DB fr £20, ①, D£5·25, cc 1 3, Dep a.

Acorn House, PH (Rl), *Ambleside Rd, CA12 4DL.* ⬩ (0596) 72553. C. ⍚ 9 bedrs, 4 ba, Dgs. 🏠 CH, TV, Dgs, CP 9, CF, 1 BGf, 1 st, Dis. £ BB £10, DB £18, WT (b) £91·50, (c) £58, DT (b) £13·75, ①.

Allerdale House, G, x (Rt), *1 Eskin St, CA12 4DH.* ⬩ (0596) 73891. Closed Dec. C 3. ⍚ 6 bedrs, 2 bp, 1 bps, 2 sh, 1 ba, Dgs. 🏠 CH, TV, Dgs, CP 3, CF. £ DB £15–£18, WT (b) £161–£182, DT (b) £11–£13, ①.

Burleigh Mead & Hazeldene, PH, x (Rl), *The Heads, CA12 5ER.* ⬩ (0596) 72106. C. ⍚ 23 bedrs, 12 bps, 5 ba, Dgs. 🏠 CH, TV, Dgs, CP 18, CF, 2 st. £ BB £9·30–£12·90, DB £18·60–£25·80, WT (b) £99–£123, DT (b) £14·80–£18·40, ①.

Derwent Lodge, PH, y (Rl), *Portinscale, CA12 5RF.* ⬩ (0596) 72746.

Foye House, G, z (Rl), *23 Eskin St, CA12 4 DG.* ⬩ (0596) 73288. C. ⍚ 6 bedrs, 1 ba, Dgs. 🏠 CH, TV, 1 st. £ BB £7·50, DB £15, WT (b) £80, DT (b) £12, ①.

Highfield, PH, x (Rt), *The Heads, CA12 5ER.* ⬩ (0596) 72508. Open Apr–Oct. C 5. ⍚ 21 bedrs, 12 bps, 3 ba, Dgs. 🏠 CH, TV, CP 20. £ BB fr £9·90, DB fr £19·80, WT (b) fr £115·50, DT (b) £16·50, ②, Bk £3·30, D £6·60.

Lincoln, G, z (Rt), *Stanger St, CA12 5JX.* ⬩ (0596) 72597.

Lynwood, G, x (Rl), *12 Ambleside Rd, CA12 4DL.* ⬩ (0596) 72081.

Melbreak House, G, z (Rl), *29 Church St, CA12 4DX.* ⬩ (0596) 73398. Closed Nov–Dec. C. ⍚ 12 bedrs, 3 ba. 🏠 ch, TV, CF. £ BB £8–£9, DB £16–£18, WT (c) £50–£52, (b) £80–£85.

Richmond House, PH, z (Rl), *37 Eskin St, CA12 4DG.* ⬩ (0596) 73965. C 10. ⍚ 12 bedrs, 3 bps, 3 ba. 🏠 CH, TV 1 st. £ BB £8–£8·75, DB fr £16–£20, WT (b) £80–£93·50, DT (b) £12·25–£14·50, ①, Bk £2·75, L £3·50, D £5, cc 1.

Silverdale, H, z (R), *Blencathra St, CA12 4HT.* ⬩ (0596) 72294. C. ⍚ 13 bedrs, 3 ba, Dgs. 🏠 CH, TV, CP 8, CF, 1 st. £ BB £9·50, DB £19, WT (b) £87·50, DT £14, ①, Bk £2·50, D £4·50.

Squirrel Lodge, G, z (Rl), *43 Eskin St, CA12 4DG.* ⬩ (0596) 73091.

Stonegarth, G, z (Rt), *2 Eskin St, CA12 4DH.* ⬩ (0596) 72436. Open Mar–Oct. C 3. ⍚ 9 bedrs, 4 sh, 1 ba, Dgs. 🏠 CH,

TV, CP 9, 2 st. £ BB £8–£8·50, DB £16–£18, WT (b) fr £84, WT (c) fr £56, DT (b) £12–£12·50, ①.

The Heights, PH, xy, *Rakefoot Lane, CA12 4TE.* ⬩ (0596) 72251. C. ⍚ 14 bedrs, 5 ba, Dgs. 🏠 CH, TV, CP 30, CF, 1 st. £ BB £11–£12, DB £22–£24, WT (b) £110–£115, DT (b) £16–£17, ①.

Repairers: Keswick Motor Co Ltd, Lake Rd. ⬩ (0596) 72064.
Robert Furness & Son (Keswick) Ltd, Royal Oak Garage, Victoria St. ⬩ (0596) 72386.
Specialist Body Repairer Greta Motor Body Works Ltd, Greta Side. ⬩ (0596) 72104.
Rescue Service: Braithwaite, E & Son, Portinscale Garage. ⬩ (0596) 72138.

KETTERING Northamptonshire. Map 15A
Pop 71,000. Bedford 25, London 75, Bletchley 31, Huntingdon 26, Market Harborough 11, Melton Mowbray 29, Northampton 14, Peterborough 28½, Stamford 23.
MD Wed, Fri, Sat. **Golf** Kettering 18h.
See Wicksteed Pleasure Park, Church with 177 ft spire, Art Gallery and Museum, The Mission House, Barton Seagrave Church 1½ m SE, Rockingham Castle 8 m N. Boughton House 3 m N.
🆃 Public Library, Sheep St. ⬩ Kettering (0536) 82143.

★★**George,** *Sheep St, NN16 0AN.* ⬩ (0536) 518620. C. ⍚ 50 bedrs, 21 bp, 11 ba, TV, Dgs. ✗ a l c, mc, at, LD 10.30. 🏠 N, CH, CP 26, con 150, CF, 0 st. £ BB fr £17·50, DB £29·50, ①, Bk £3·45, L £5·95, D £5·95, cc 1 2 3 5.

Repairer: Chrysler Garages (Kettering) Ltd, Bayes St. ⬩ (0536) 512738.▲

KETTLEWELL North Yorkshire. Map 27A
Pop 320. Leeds 37, London 228, Harrogate 32, Hawes 22, Leyburn 20, Settle 19, Skipton 14, York 51.
EC Thur. **Golf** Skipton 18h. **See** Old world village, Caves, 12th cent Church, Moors.

★★**Race Horses,** *BD23 5QZ.* ⬩ (075 676) 233. C. ⍚ 16 bedrs, 3 bp, 2 bps, 4 ba, Dgs. ✗ LD 8.30. 🏠 CH, TV, Dgs, CP 20, Ac, con, CF, 1 st. £ BB £12–£18, DB £24–£38, DBB £15–£27, WB, ②, Bk £4·50, L £6 Sun, D £8, cc 1, Dep a.

★**Bluebell,** *Middle La, BD23 5QX.* ⬩ (075 676) 230. C. ⍚ 7 bedrs, 2 bp, 2 ba, Dgs. ✗ LD 8.45. 🏠 CH, TV, Dgs, CP 6, Ac, CF, 0 st. £ BB £13–£15, DB £26–£29, DBB £19·95–£21·45, WB, ②, Bk £2·50, D £6·95.
Dale House, G, *BD23 5QZ.* ⬩ (075 676) 836.

KEWSTOKE Avon. Map 5A
Pop 1,488. M5 Motorway 3, Bristol 20, London 133, Bath 31, Bridgwater 19, Burnham-on-Sea 13, Wells 19, Weston-super-Mare 2.
Golf Worlebury 18h. **See** Priory, Sand Point, Monks Steps (Both NT), Church.

Owl's Crest, PH, x (Rl), *Kewstoke Rd, BS22 9YE.* ⬩ Weston-super-Mare (0934) 417672. Open Mar–Oct & Xmas. C 6. ⍚ 6 bedrs, 4 bps, 1 ba. 🏠 CH, TV, CP 6, CF. £ BB £9, DB £18–£20, WT (b) £79–£86·80, DT (b) £13·75, ①, Bk £3, L £4, D £4·75.

KEYNSHAM Avon. Map 5A
Pop 20,433 (inc Saltford). Bath 7, London 111, Bristol 5½, Radstock 12, Shepton Mallet 16, Tetbury 30, Wells 17.
EC Wed. **Golf** Saltford 18h. **See** Museum, Roman Villa, St John's Church, Cadbury-Schweppes Factory, Somerdale (by appmt).
■★★**Grange,** *Bath Rd, BS18 1SN.*
℡ (027 56) 2883. C. ⊯ 11 bedrs, 11 bp, TV, Dgs. ✗ a l c, mc, at, LD 9.30. ⬚ CH, TV, CP 36, Ac, con 40, CF, 0 st. £ BB £19–£26, DB £33, WB, ⓘ, Bk fr £3·50, L fr £5·50, D fr £6, cc 1 3, Dep b.
Grasmere, H, z (RI), *22 Bath Rd, BS18 1SN.* ℡ (027 56) 2662.

KIBWORTH Leicestershire. Map 15A
Pop 3,928. Market Harborough 6, London 83, Leicester 9, Melton Mowbray 18, Rugby 19.
EC Thur. **Golf** Kibworth 18h. **See** 14th cent Church, Georgian Houses, Mill dating back to 1711 restored 1972.

Repairer: Regent Autocar Ltd, Harborough Rd. ℡ (053 753) 2303.

KIDDERMINSTER Hereford & Worcester (Worcestershire). Map 13B
See also STONE
Pop 50,603. Bromsgrove 9, London 122, Bromyard 22, Birmingham 17, Bridgnorth 13, Leominster 25, Ludlow 25, Walsall 17, Wolverhampton 15, Worcester 14.
EC Wed. **MD** Tue, Thur, Fri, Sat. **Golf** Kidderminster 18h. **See** St Mary's Church, Statues of Richard Baxter and Sir Rowland Hill, Art Gallery and Museum, 14th cent Caldwell Tower, Harvington Hall 3 m SE, Hartlebury Castle 3 m S.
ⓘ Library, Market St. ℡ Kidderminster (0562) 752832.

★★★**Gainsborough House,** *Bewdley Hill, DY11 6BS.* ℡ (0562) 754041. C.
⊯ 42 bedrs, 42 bp, ns, TV, Dgs. ⬚ N, CH, Dgs, CP 130, Ac, sol, con, CF, 12 BGf, 1 st, Dis. £ BB £29·40–£30·50, DB £39·85–£41·85, DBB £35·50–£36, WB, ⓘ, Bk £3·25, L £4, D £7·40, cc 1 2 3 5, Dep b.

Repairers: Broadwaters Garage, Broadwaters. ℡ (0562) 2006.
Laughton Goodwin & Co Ltd, George St. ℡ (0562) 2255.
Stanley Goodwin Motors Ltd, Worcester Rd. ℡ (0562) 2202.
Rescue Service: Jack Humphries & Co Ltd, Mill Bank Garage, Mill St. ℡ (0562) 3708.
Minster Service Station, 81 Stourport Rd, Foley Park. ℡ (0562) 753319.

KIDLINGTON Oxfordshire. Map 14F
Pop 12,888. Oxford 5, London 63, Banbury 17, Bicester 8, Burford 17, Chipping Norton 14, Towcester 25.
EC Mon, Wed. **MD** Fri. **Golf** North Oxford 18h. **See** Church (spire), Lady Ann Morton's Almshouses.

Black Horse, I, z, *6 Banbury Rd, OX5 2BT.* ℡ (08675) 3154. Closed Xmas. C 5. ⊯ 4 bedrs, 1 ba. ⬚ CH, TV, CP 18, 1 st. £ BB £12, DB £22, ⓘ.
Bowood House, H, z (RI), *238 Oxford Rd, OX5 1EB.* ℡ (08675) 2839. C. ⊯ 9 bedrs, 2 bp, 3 bps, 2 ba, TV. ⬚ CH, TV, CP 12, CF, 1 st. £ BB fr £12, DB fr £22, DT (b) fr £20·50, ⓘ, Bk £4, D £8·50.

Repairer: Hartwells of Oxford Ltd, Oxford Rd. ℡ (08675) 4363.
Specialist Body Repairer Hartwells of Oxford Ltd, Oxford Rd. ℡ (08675) 4363.
Rescue Service: Motor Vehicle Services, Station Approach. ℡ (08675) 2627 and (08675) 2759.

KILDWICK West Yorkshire. Map 27A
Pop 500. Keighley 6, London 211, Burnley 15, Ilkley 8, Skipton 8.
EC Tue. **Golf** Bingley St Ives 18h. **See** Church.

⚑■★★★★**Kildwick Hall,** *BD20 9AE.*
℡ Crosshills (0535) 32244. C. ⊯ 12 bedrs, 10 bp, 2 bps, TV, Dgs. ✗ a l c, mc, at, LD 10. ⬚ CH, TV, Dgs, CP 60, con 20, CF, 10 st. £ BB £30–£42·50, DB £57–£75, WB, ⓘ, Bk £3·75, L £7·95, D £11·95, cc 1 2 3 5.

KILSBY Northamptonshire. Map 14B
Pop 1,280. M1 Motorway 12, London 80, Daventry 5½, Leicester 22, Market Harborough 17, Northampton 15, Rugby 4½.
Golf Rugby 18h. **See** Ashby St Ledgers (Gunpowder Plot assns) 1 m S.

Rescue Service: Beech Autos (Motorway Services) Ltd, Rugby Rd. ℡ Crick (0788) 822347.
Dick Shorton Motors, A5/M1 Link Rd. ℡ Crick (0788) 822040.
Halfway Garage (Rugby) Ltd, Crick Cross Roads. ℡ Crick (0788) 822226.

KINETON Warwickshire. Map 14D
Pop 1,850. Banbury 10, London 83, Daventry 18, Chipping Norton 16, Stratford-upon-Avon 10, Warwick 10.
EC Thur. **Golf** Stratford-on-Avon 18h. **See** Church, Battle of Edgehill assns.

Rescue Service: Station Garage, Warwick Rd. ℡ (0926) 640233.

KINGHAM Oxfordshire. Map 14F
Pop 570. Oxford 23, London 79, Burford 9, Chipping Norton 4½, Moreton-in-Marsh 7½, Stow-on-the-Wold 5½.
EC Wed. **Golf** Chipping Norton 18h. **See** 14th cent Church, Kingham Hill School.

★★**Mill,** *Station Rd, OX7 6UH.*
℡ (060 871) 8188. C 5. ⊯ 17 bedrs, 15 bp, 2 bps, TV, Dgs. ✗ a l c, mc, at, LD 9.30. ⬚ N, CH, CP 50, Ac, pf, con 30, CF, 3 BGf, 2 st. £ BB £20–£22, DB £36–£38, WT £195–£200, DT £29–£30, DBB £24–£26, WB, ⓘ, Bk £4, L £5·50, D £8·75, cc 1 2 3 4 5.

KINGSBRIDGE Devon. Map 3F
Pop 4,236. Totnes 12, London 203, Dartmouth 13, Plymouth 20.
EC Thur. **MD** Wed. **Golf** Thurlestone 18h. **See** St Edmund's Church, St Thomas's Church, Grammar School, The Shambles (16th cent Arcade), Annual Fair in July, Kingsbridge Estuary.
ⓘ The Quay. ℡ Kingsbridge (0548) 3195.

⚑■★★★★**Buckland-Tout-Saints** (R), *Goveton, TQ7 2DS.* ℡ (0548) 3055. Closed Jan. C. ⊯ 10 bedrs, 11 bp, 2 bps, TV, Dgs. ✗ a l c, mc, at, LD 9. ⬚ CH, TV, CP 20, G 2, Ac, con 40, CF, 2 st. £ BB £24–£38, DB £48–£65, WB, ⓘ, Bk £5, L £8·50, D £12, cc 1 2 3 5 6, Dep a.
■★**M Crabshell Motor Lodge,** *Embankment Rd, TQ7 1JZ.* ℡ (0548) 3301. C. ⊯ 24 bedrs, 24 bp, TV, Dgs. ✗ a l c, mc, at, LD 10. ⬚ CH, TV, Dgs, CP 23, G 11, con 25, CF, 2 st. £ BB £21·50, DB

£31–£33·50, WB, ⓘ, Bk £3, L £4·50, D £7·50, cc 1 2 3 5, Dep.
■★**M Kingsbridge** (R), *TQ7 1HN.*
℡ (0548) 2540. C. ⊯ 20 bedrs, 20 bp, TV, Dgs. ✗ LD 9.30. ⬚ N, CH, CP 12, G 8, sp, con 20, CF, 5 BGf, 0 st, Dis. £ BB £20–£21·50, DB £30·50–£33·50, WB, ⓘ, Bk £2·50, D £6·50, cc 1 2 3 5, Dep a.
Ashburton Arms, I, x, *West Charlton, TQ7 2AH.* ℡ Frogmore (054 853) 242. Closed 1st 3 weeks Oct & Xmas. C 7. ⊯ 5 bedrs, 1 ba. ⬚ CH, TV, Dgs, CP 20, 0 st. £ BB £9·66–£10·14, DB £19·32–£20·28, WT (c) £63·60–£67·48, ⓘ.

Repairers: Oke Bros, Bridge St. ℡ (0548) 2350.
Quay Garage Co Ltd, The Quay. ℡ (0548) 2323.
Rescue Service: Michael J Wray, Auto Engineers, 21 Church St. ℡ (0548) 2344.
Wills Garage Ltd, Embankment Rd. ℡ (0548) 2140.

KINGSCLERE Hampshire. Map 6B
Pop 4,450. Basingstoke 8½, London 56, Andover 15, Newbury 7, Reading 16, Wallingford 24, Winchester 21.
EC Thur. **Golf** Bishopswood 9h, Basingstoke 18h. **See** St Mary's Church, Watership Down.

Repairer: T Garrett & Son, Newbury Rd. ℡ (0635) 298325.

KINGSDOWN Kent. Map 10D
Pop 300. Canterbury 18, London 76, Dover 6, Margate 17, Ramsgate 15.
See Church of St Mary's.

Blencathra, PH, x (RI), *Kingsdown Hill, CT14 8EA.* ℡ Deal (0304) 373725. Open Apr–Oct. C 3. ⊯ 5 bedrs, 2 ba. ⬚ CH, TV, CP 7, 0 st. £ BB £9, DB £18, WT (b) £84, (c) £54, DT (b) £14.

KINGSGATE Kent. Map 10D
See also BROADSTAIRS.
Pop 5,000. Margate 3, London 76, Canterbury 19, Dover 23.
EC Wed. **Golf** North Foreland, Broadstairs 9h, 18h.

★★**Fayreness,** *Marine Dr, CT10 3LG.*
℡ Thanet (0843) 61103. C 14. ⊯ 7 bedrs, 3 bp, 1 bps, 1 sh, 2 ba, TV, Dgs. ✗ a l c, mc, LD 9.30. ⬚ CH, TV, Dgs, ns, CP 40, Ac, con 50, 1 BGf, 2 st. £ BB £15–£17·50, DB £25–£30, ⓘ, Bk £3, L £4·75, cc 1 2 3 5 6, Dep a.

KINGSKERSWELL Devon. Map 3D
Pop 5,400 (inc Abbotskerswell). Newton Abbot 2½, London 186, Torquay 4, Totnes 8.
EC Wed. **Golf** Newton Abbot (Stover) 18h. **See** Castle ruins, 14th cent St Mary's Church.

Rescue Service: St Mary's Garage, Fore St. ℡ (080 47) 2236.

KING'S LANGLEY Hertfordshire. Map 15 E
Pop 4,562. Watford 4½, London 21, Aylesbury 19, Dunstable 19, Rickmansworth 8½, St Albans 10.
EC Wed. **Golf** Little Hay 18h. **See** Parish Church (tomb of 1st Duke of York), Palace ruins.

Specialist Body Repairer Pilling (Coachbuilders) Ltd, Rucklers La. ℡ (0928) 651118.

KING'S LYNN Norfolk. Map 16E
Pop 32,698. Ely 29, London 99, Boston 34,
Bury St Edmunds 41, Fakenham 22,
Sleaford 44, Spalding 28, Swaffham 15,
Thetford 27, Wisbech 13.
EC Wed. **MD** Tue, Fri, Sat. **Golf** King's
Lynn 18h. **See** Guildhall of St George, Old
Guildhall, Custom House, Hampton Court,
Thoresby College, St Nicholas' Chapel,
Red Mount Chapel, Museum and Art
Gallery, RC Church (Walsingham Shrine),
Greyfriars Tower, South Gate, St
Margaret's Church, All Saints' Church,
Clifton House (mainly 14th cent), Festival
of Music and the Arts, July, Castle Rising
(12th cent), 4 m NE, Sandringham
Gardens, grounds and Church 8 m NE.
[i] Town Hall, Saturday Market Pl. ℓ King's
Lynn (0553) 63044.

★★★**Duke's Head** (TH), *Tuesday Market
Pl, PE30 1JS.* ℓ (0553) 4996. C. ⊯ 72
bedrs, 72 bp, TV, Dgs. ✗ a l c, mc, at, LD
9.30. [f] Lt, N, CH, Dgs, CP 50, Ac, con 225,
CF, 0 st. £ BB £38, DB £53, WB, [1],
cc 1 2 3 4 5 6, Dep (Xmas).
▣★**Stuart House** (R), *Goodwins Rd,
PE30 5QX.* ℓ (0553) 2169. Closed Xmas-
Jan 2. C. ⊯ 19 bedrs, 11 bp, 3 bps, 1 sh, 2
ba, annexe 2 bedrs, 2 bp, TV, Dgs. ✗ mc, at,
LD 8. [f] CH, TV, CP 23, Ac, con 20, CF, 1
BGf. £ BB £14.50-£19.75, DB £27-£35,
DBB £20.45-£28.55, WB, [1], Bk £3.95, D
£5.95, cc 1 3 6, Dep a.
Runcton House, PH, z (R), *Goodwins
Rd, PE30 5PE.* ℓ (0553) 773098. ⊯ 7
bedrs, 1 bp, 1 bps, 2 ba, TV, Dgs. [f] CH, TV,
CP 12, 1 st. £ BB fr £14.50, DB fr £19, DT fr
£19.50, [1], Bk £3, D £5.

Repairer: Mann Egerton & Co Ltd, Church
St. ℓ (0553) 63133.

KING'S SOMBORNE Hampshire. Map
6C
Pop 1,360. Winchester 9, London 64,
Andover 10, Basingstoke 22, Newbury 26,
Romsey 7½, Salisbury 18.
Golf Ampfield 18h. **See** Church of SS
Peter and Paul, Site of John o' Gaunt's
Palace.

Rescue Service: Somborne Garage,
Romsey Rd. ℓ (079 47) 222.

KINGSTEIGNTON Devon. Map 3D
Pop 6,150. Exeter 14, London 183,
Newton Abbot 2, Okehampton 25.
EC Wed. **Golf** Newton Abbot (Stover)
18h. **See** 15th cent Church, Annual Ram
Roasting (Spring Bank Holiday).

Rescue Service: Bougourds, Exeter Rd
and Newton Rd. ℓ Newton Abbot (0626)
3545.

KINGSTON Devon. Map 3F
Pop 317. Ashburton 20, London 208,
Kingsbridge 8½, Plymouth 14, Tavistock
23, Totnes 17.
Golf Bigbury 18h.

Trebles Cottage, PH, xy, (R) *nr
Kingsbridge. TQ7 4PT.* ℓ Bigbury-on-Sea
(054 881) 268. C. 8. ⊯ 6 bedrs, 3 bp, 1 ba.
[f] CH, TV, CP 10, CF, 1 st. £ BB £10.25,
DB £20.50-£24, WT (b) £98, (c) £70, DT
(b) £15.25, [1], Bk £2.75, D £6.75.

KINGSTON BAGPUIZE Oxfordshire.
Map 14F
Pop 1,925 (inc Southmoor). Wallingford
16, London 62, Burford 14, Faringdon 6,
Oxford 9, Wantage 8½.

EC Thur. **Golf** Frilford Heath 18h (2). **See**
Kingston House (gdns open at times).

Rescue Service: Hale Car Body Repairs,
Rectory La. ℓ Longworth (0865) 820456.

KINGSTON-UPON-HULL
See HULL.

KINGSTON UPON THAMES Greater
London (Surrey). Map 7A.
Pop 140,210. London 10, Croydon 11,
Epsom 6½, Leatherhead 8½, Mitcham 7,
Ripley 12, Staines 9½, Richmond-upon-
Thames 3½, Uxbridge 15, Weybridge 8,
Woking 14.
EC Wed. **MD** Daily. **Golf** Home Park 18h,
Surbiton 18h, Richmond Park 18h (2),
Coombe Wood 18h, Coombe Hill 18h. **See**
Saxon Coronation Stone (Market Pl),
Museum and Art Gallery, All Saints'
Church, Ham House, Hampton Court
Palace 1½ SW.

Antoinette, H, z (R), *26 Beaufort Rd,
KT1 2TQ.* ℓ 01-546 1044. C 10. ⊯ 110
bedrs, 80 bp, 20 bps, 6 ba, TV, Dgs. [f] CH,
TV, Dgs, CP 60, CF, 10 BGf, 3 st. £ BBc
£13.50-£22, DBc £22-£28, [1], Bk £2.75, L
£5, D £5.50, cc 1 2 3.▲
Gay, G, z (Unl), *21 Grange Rd, KT1 2QU.*
ℓ 01-549 1985. Open Mar-Nov. C. ⊯ 3
bedrs, 1 ba, TV. [f] CH, TV, CP 3. £ BB £11-
£12, DB £18-£20, [1].
Hermes, PH, z (R), *1 Portsmouth Rd, KT1
2LU.* ℓ 01-546 5322.
Lingfield House, H, z (Unl), *29 Beaufort
Rd, KT1 2TH.* ℓ 01-546 1988.

Repairers: Bentall's Ltd, Wood St.
ℓ 01-546 1001.
Currie Motors Kingston Ltd, 140A
London Rd. ℓ 01-546 7700.
Reevethorpe Kingston Ltd, Brook St.
ℓ 01-549 9563.
Specialist Body Repairer: Cambridge
Coachworks, 45 Cambridge Rd.
ℓ 01-546 4493.

KINGS SUTTON Oxfordshire
(Northamptonshire). Map 14D
Bicester 12, London 69, Banbury 5, Stow
on the Wold 25, Oxford 23, Towcester 20.

Rescue Service: Cannings Garage, 15
Banbury La. ℓ Banbury (0295) 811382.

KINGSWOOD Buckinghamshire. M.Area
14F
Pop 90, Aylesbury 9, London 49, Bicester
8, Buckingham 12, Bletchley 19.
Golf Ellesborough, Wendover 18h. **See**
Warmley House, 15th cent Church, Nature
Park.

Rescue Service: Lodge Garage, A41
ℓ Grendon Underwood (029 677) 245.

KINGTON Hereford & Worcester
(Herefordshire). Map 13C
Pop 1,951. Hereford 19, London 151,
Brecon 28, Builth Wells 20, Knighton 13,
Leominster 13, Ludlow 20, Rhayader 25.
EC Wed. **MD** Tue. **Golf** Kington 18h. **See**
Parish Church, 15th cent Farmhouse,
Offa's Dyke gardens.
[f] Council Offices, Mill St. ℓ Kington
(0544) 230202.

★★**Burton,** *Mill St, HR5 3BQ.* ℓ (0544)
230323. C. ⊯ 10 bedrs, 3 bp, 2 bps, 2 ba,
Dgs. ✗ a l c, mc, LD 9.30. [f] CH, TV, CP
35, G 3, Ac, CF, 1 st. £ BB £11-70-£14.70,
DB £23.40-£29.40, DBB £16.70-£19.70,
WB, [1], Bk £2.50, D £5, cc 1 3, Dep a.

★**Swan,** *Church St, HR5 3AZ.* ℓ (0544)
230510. Closed Xmas. RS Dec 24. C. ⊯ 6
bedrs, 1 ba, Dgs. ✗ a l c, mc, LD 8.30.
[f] TV, Dgs, CP 18, CF, 1 st. £ BB £12, DB
£20, WT £105, DT £18, DBB £16.50, WB,
[1], Bk £3, D £7, cc 1 6.

Rescue Service: Kington Motors,
Headbrook. ℓ (0544) 230416.

KINTBURY Berkshire. Map 6A
Pop 2,700. Newbury 6½, London 61,
Andover 16, Marlborough 13, Pewsey 15,
Wantage 15.
EC Thur. **Golf** West Berks 18h.
See Pre-Reformation Church, Canal.

Rescue Service: Kintbury Garage Ltd.
ℓ (048 85) 220.

KIRKBY Merseyside. Map 20 E
Pop 51,031. Northwich 25, London 197,
Liverpool 8, Ormskirk 7, St Helens 6½,
Warrington 16.
EC Wed. **MD** Tue, Sat. **Golf** Kirkby 18h.
See Whitefield House, Pigeon House,
Church.
[f] Municipal Buildings, Cherryfield Dr.
ℓ 051-548 6555.

▣★★★**Golden Eagle,** *Cherryfield Dr,
Liverpool, L32 8SB.* ℓ 051-546 4355.
Closed Dec 25 & 26 & Jan 1, RS Dec 24 &
31. C. ⊯ 80 bedrs, 26 bp, 54 bps, TV, Dgs.
✗ a l c, mc, LD 9.15. [f] Lt, N, CH, Dgs, CP
100, G 4, con 35, CF, 1 st. £ B £26, BD £33,
WB, [1], Bk £4.25, L £6, D £6, cc 1 2 3 4 5 6,
Dep b.

KIRKBY-IN-ASHFIELD Notts. Map
22D
Pop 24,467. Nottingham 13, London 136,
Derby 20, Mansfield 5, Matlock 14,
Newark 22.
EC Wed. **MD** Fri, Sat. **Golf** Hollinwell 18h.
See Newstead Abbey 4 m SE, St. Wilfreds
Church.

Rescue Service: Horberry, J E, Kingsway
Garage, Kingsway. ℓ Mansfield (0623)
752244.

KIRKBY-IN-FURNESS Cumbria. Map
26F
M6 Motorway 28, London 275, Barrow-
in-Furness 9½, Broughton 4½, Kendal 30,
Ulverston 8.
Golf Dunnerholme 9h.

Rescue Service: G & E Benson, Grizebeck
Service Station. ℓ (022 989) 259.

KIRKBY LONSDALE Cumbria. Map 27C
Pop 1,506. Settle 16, London 246, Brough
29, Kendal 12, Lancaster 12.
EC Wed. **MD** Thur. **Golf** Kirkby Lonsdale
9h. **See** St Mary's Church (Norman),
Devil's Bridge.
[f] 18 Main St. ℓ Kirkby Lonsdale (0468)
71603.

▣★★★**Royal,** *The Market Sq, LA6 2 AE.*
ℓ (0468) 71217. C. ⊯ 23 bedrs, 14 bp, 3
bps, 3 ba, TV, Dgs. ✗ a l c, mc, at. [f] CH,
TV, CP 30, G 12, Ac, con 60, CF, 0 st. £ BB
£20-£22, DB £30-£35, WB, [2], Bk £3, L
£5.75, D £9.50, cc 1 2 3 5.

Rescue Service: Kirkby Motors, Kendal
Rd. ℓ (0468) 71778.

KIRKBYMOORSIDE North Yorkshire.
Map 24D
Pop 2,293. Pickering 7½, London 231,
Helmsley 6.

EC Thur. **MD** Wed. **Golf** Kirkbymoorside 9h. **See** Tolbooth, restored Church, Market Cross.

★★**George & Dragon,** *Market Pl, YO6 6AA.* ☎ (0751) 31637. RS Dec 24–26. C 8. ⇔ 17 bedrs, 10 bp, 4 bps, 3 sh, 1 ba, TV. ✗ mc, LD 9.30. ⓓ CH, CP 23, CF, 2 BGf, 2 st. £ BB £9–£18, DB £12–£30, WB, ⓩ, Bk £3, L £5, D £12, cc 1 3, Dep a.

Kings Head, H, x, *High Market Pl, YO6 6AT.* ☎ (0751) 31340. C. ⇔ 12 bedrs, 3 ba, TV, Dgs. ✗ a l c. ⓓ CH, TV, Dgs, CP 20, CF. £ BB £11·50–£13·50, DB £23–£37, DT (b) £16–£18·50, ⓵, Bk £2·25, L £4·50, D £6·50, cc 1 2 3 5.

KIRKBY STEPHEN Cumbria. Map 26B Pop 1,557. Hawes 16, London 265, Brough 4, Kendal 24, Kirkby Lonsdale 24. **EC** Thur. **MD** Mon. **Golf** Appleby 18h. **See** 13th cent Church, The Cloister, 15th cent Wharton Hall, Stenkrith Park. ⓘ 22 Market St. ☎ Kirkby Stephen (0930) 71804.

★★**Black Swan,** *Ravenstonedale, CA17 4NG.* ☎ Newbiggin-on-Lune (058 73) 204.

★★**King's Arms,** *Market St, CA17 4QN.* ☎ (0930) 71378. Closed Xmas. C. ⇔ 9 bedrs, 1 bp, 3 ba, Dgs. ✗ a l c, mc, LD 8.30. ⓓ CH, TV, Dgs, CP 3, G 9, Ac, con 15, CF, 1st. £ BB fr £15·25, DB fr £28·50, WB, ⓩ, Bk £4, D £9·25, cc 1 3.

Repairer: Johnstone's Garage, North Rd. ☎ (0930) 71246.

KIRKHAM Lancashire. Map 27D Pop 6,283. Preston 8, London 219, Blackpool 8½, Lancaster 23. **EC** Wed. **MD** Thur. **Golf** Lytham St Annes 18h (4).

Rescue Service: Station Road Garage, 57 Station Rd, Wesham. ☎ (0772) 682404.

KIRK LANGLEY Derbyshire. Map 22C Pop 590. Derby 6½, London 130, Ashbourne 8½, Burton-on-Trent 11, Matlock 16 **EC** Wed. **Golf** Kedleston Park 18h. **See** Church of St Michael, Mapple Well, Village Pond, Langley Hall.

Rescue Service: Howards Engineering (Derby) Ltd, Station Rd, Mickleover. ☎ Derby (0332) 515489.

KIRTON Nottinghamshire. Map 22D Tuxford 3, London 141, Mansfield 12, Newark 15, Worksop 12.

Old Rectory, G (Unl), *Main St, Kirton Nr Ollerton.* ☎ Mansfield (0623) 861540.

KNARESBOROUGH North Yorkshire. Map 25E Pop 12,500. Harrogate 3, London 201, Boroughbridge 7, Leeds 19, York 18. **EC** Thur. **MD** Wed. **P** Disc parking is in operation in High St, York Pl, Market Pl and certain specified side streets between 8 am and 6 pm on each day of the week (S and Pub Hols inc) but excl Wed (Market Day) in respect of the Market Pl. **Golf** Knaresborough 18h. **See** 14th cent Knaresborough Castle ruins, Zoo, 11th cent St Robert's Chapel, The Olde Manor House, Ye Oldest Chymist Shoppe, EE and Perp Church, Dropping Well, Mother Shipton's Cave, Nidderdale. ⓘ Market Pl. ☎ Harrogate (0423) 866886.

⬛★★★**Dower House,** (R), *Bond End, HG5 9AL.* ☎ Harrogate (0423) 863302. RS Dec 25 & 26. C. ⇔ 16 bedrs, 11 bp, 3 bps, 1 ba, TV. ✗ mc, LD 9. ⓓ CH, Dgs, CP 60, con 25, CF, 1 st. £ BB £25–£35, DB £35–£60, DBB £34·50–£44·50, WB, ⓩ, Bk £5, L £6·50, D £9·50, cc 1 3, Dep b.

⬛★★**Mitre,** *Station Rd, HG5 9AA.* ☎ Harrogate (0423) 863589. C. ⇔ 7 bedrs, 1 bp, 5 bps, 1 ba, TV, Dgs. ✗ a l c, mc, at, LD 10. ⓓ CH, TV, Ac, con 50, CF, 1 st. £ BB £21, DB £31, WB, ⓩ, Bk £3·50, L £3, D £7, cc 1 2 3 5 6, Dep.

Ebor Mount, G, z, (Unl), *18 York Pl, HG5 0AA.* ☎ Harrogate (0423) 863315. Closed Dec. C. ⇔ 7 bedrs, 3 sh, 2 ba, Dgs. ⓓ ch, TV, CP 10, CF. £ DB £16–£18, DT (b) £11·25, ⓵.

KNIGHTWICK Hereford & Worcester (Herefordshire). Map 13D Pop 114. Worcester 9, London 123, Bridgnorth 28, Bromyard 5, Kidderminster 16, Ledbury 14. **Golf** Worcester 18h. **See** Knightsford Bridge.

★**Talbot,** *Bromyard Rd, WR6 5PS.* ☎ (0886) 21235.

KNOCK Cumbria. Map 26C Pop 100. Appleby 5, London 277, Brough 12, Kirkby Stephen 15, Penrith 12, Appleby 18. **Golf** Appleby 18h.

Rescue Service: Silverband Garage, nr Appleby. ☎ Kirkby Thore (093 06) 218.

KNOWSLEY Merseyside, Map 20E Pop 3,000. Northwich 23, London 197, Chester 26, Liverpool 16½, Manchester 27, Ormskirk 9½, St Helens 5½, Warrington 13. **Golf** Prescot & Huyton 18h. **See** Knowsley Safari Park and Dolphinarium.

★★★**M Crest,** *East Lancs Rd, L34 9HA.* ☎ 051-546 7531. Closed Xmas. C. ⇔ 50 bedrs, 50 bp, ns, TV, Dgs. ✗ a l c, mc, at, LD 9.30. ⓓ N, CH, Dgs, CP 150, Ac, con 60, CF, 1 st. £ BB fr £37, BD fr £47, WB, ⓵, Bk £4·95, D £7·95, cc 1 2 3 4 5 6, Dep b.

KNUTSFORD Cheshire, Map 19B Pop 13,588. Newcastle-under-Lyme 24, London 173, M6 Motorway 3, Altrincham 7½, Congleton 14, Middlewich 9, Northwich 7, Sandbach 12, Warrington 11, Stockport 14, Macclesfield 11. **EC** Wed. **MD** Fri, Sat. **Golf** Knutsford 9h. **See** 17th cent Unitarian Chapel (grave of Mrs Gaskell), Gaskell Memorial Tower, The Sessions House, Georgian Church (1744), Royal George Hotel, 17th cent Ye Angel Inn, Royal May Day Celebrations, Tatton Park and Gardens, 3½ N. ⓘ Council Offices, Toft Rd. ☎ Knutsford (0565) 2611.

★★★**Royal George,** *King St, WA16 6DT.* ☎ (0565) 4151.

⬛★**Rose & Crown,** *King St, WA16 6DT.* ☎ (0565) 52366. C. ⇔ 11 bedrs, 2 ba, TV, Dgs. ✗ a l c, mc, LD 9.30. ⓓ CH, Dgs, CP 30, Ac, con 10, CF, 1 st. £ BB £15–£20, DB £24–£29, WT £120–£150, DT £20–£28, DBB £18–£26, WB, ⓵, Bk £3, L £3, D £5·50, cc 1 3.

Longview, PH, x (R), *55 Manchester Rd, WA16 0LX.* ☎ (0565) 2119. Closed Xmas. C. ⇔ 14 bedrs, 2 bps, 6 sh, 2 ba, TV, Dgs. ⓓ CH, TV, CP 6, CF, 2 st. £ BB £13·50–£23·50, DB £20–£28, ⓵, Bk £3·75, D £6·25.

Repairers: Phibbs, J A Ltd, Highway Garage, Manchester Rd. ☎ (0565) 2525. Tabley Garage, Over Tabley. ☎ (0565) 3241.

Rescue Service: J Boardman (Garages) Ltd, Knutsford Motorway Services, M6. ☎ Forton (0524) 791666. Brooks, Alcock & Knights, Service Garage. Toft Rd. ☎ (0565) 4294. Top Rank Motorway Service, M6. ☎ (0565) 4439.

LADOCK Cornwall. M. Area 2D Pop 900. St Austell 8, London 240, Fraddon 5, Truro 7. **EC** Wed. **Golf** Truro 18h. **See** Church.

Rescue Service: Brighton Garage, Brighton Cross, nr Truro. ☎ St Austell (0726) 882455.

LAMBOURN Berkshire. Map 6A Pop 3,500. Newbury 13, London 67, Faringdon 15, Swindon 14, Wantage 9. **EC** Thur. **Golf** Chaddleworth 18h. **See** Ashdown House 3½ m NW, Old Church, Almshouses.

Repairer: Lambourn Garages Ltd, High St. ☎ (0488) 71111. *Rescue Service:* Lambourn Motorway Services, M4 Service Area, Membury. ☎ (0488) 71860.

LAMORNA COVE Cornwall. Map 2E Pop 115. Penzance 4, London 285. **EC** Wed. **Golf** West Cornwall Lelant 18h. **See** Lovely rock-bound cove. Lamorna Valley (beauty spot), Old Mill, Pottery.

⬛★★★**Lamorna Cove** (R), *TR19 6XH.* ☎ (0736) 731411. Closed Dec-Jan. C. ⇔ 19 bedrs, 15 bp, 4 bps, TV, Dgs. ✗ a l c, mc, at, LD 9.30. ⓓ Lt, CH, ns, CP 27, sp, sb, sol, con 30, CF. £ BB £21·50–£28·95, DB £39–£55·90, WT £190–£286, DBB £26·50–£34·95, WB, ⓵, Bk £4·75, L £5·95, D £8·95, cc 1 2 3 5 6, Dep a.

LANCASTER Lancashire. Map 27C Pop 45,126. M6 Motorway 4½, London 238, Ambleside 32, Blackpool 24, Broughton-in-Furness 41, Kendal 22, Kirkby Lonsdale 16, Preston 22, Settle 25, Ulverston 34. **EC** Wed. **MD** daily (ex. Wed). **Golf** Lancaster 18h. **See** Castle, RC Cathedral, John of Gaunt's Gateway, Royal Grammar School, St Mary's Church, Town Hall Gardens, old Town Hall (now museum), 18th cent Custom House, Williamson Park (Ashton Memorial). ⓘ 7 Dalton Sq. ☎ Lancaster (0524) 32878.

★★★★**M Post House** (TH), *Waterside Park, Caton Rd, LA1 3RA.* ☎ (0524) 65999. C. ⇔ 121 bedrs, 121 bp, TV, Dgs. ✗ a l c, mc, at, LD 10.30. ⓓ Lt, CH, Dgs, CP 180, Ac, sp, tc, sb, con 100, CF. £ BB £45, DB £60·50, WB, ⓵, cc 1 2 3 4 5 6, Dep (Xmas).

Belle Vue, G (Unl), *1 Belle Vue Ter, Greaves, LA1 4TY.* ☎ (0524) 67751. C. ⇔ 6 bedrs, 1 ba, TV, Dgs. ⓓ Lt, ch, TV, ns, CP 6, CF. £ BB £8·50–£10.

MC Repairer: Wall & Sagar Ltd, 49 North Rd. ☎ (0524) 63817. *Sctr Repairer* Wall & Sagar Ltd, 49 North Rd. ☎ (0524) 63817. *Rescue Service:* Alston, J D & M M Ltd, Wood Cottage Garage, 29 High Rd.

Halton-on-Lune. ℃ Halton-on-Lune (0524) 811345.
Auto Service Recoveries, 40 Braganza Way. ℃ (0524) 33461.
Caton Rd Garage, Caton Rd. ℃ (0524) 65767.
Glanfield Lawrence (Lancaster) Ltd, Penny St. ℃ (0524) 2442 and 2445.
S Marshall & Sons, Reynolds St, off Georges Quay. ℃ (0524) 67298.

LANCHESTER Durham. Maps 31F & 32E
Durham 8, London 268, Corbridge 17, Newcastle upon Tyne 14.

Rescue Service: Chris Turnbull Car Centre, Fenhall Filling Station. ℃ (0207) 521720.

LANCING West Sussex. Map 7E
Pop 17,290. Worthing 2, London 59, Brighton 8½, Crawley 23, Haywards Heath 12, Horsham 20, Pulborough 18.
EC Wed. Golf Worthing 18h (2), Worthing Municipal 18h. See Lancing College, Church, Forge.

Moorings, G, z, 71 Brighton Rd, BN15 8RB. ℃ (0903) 755944. C. ⇔ 5 bedrs, 2 ba, TV, Dgs. ⚙ CH, Dgs, CP 4. £ BB £7·50–£8·50, DB £15–£17, ②, Bk £2·50.

Repairer: Datsun Retail Ltd, T/As Datsun Broadwater Ltd, Churchill Industrial Estate, Peter Rd. ℃ (0903) 63151.

LANEAST Cornwall. Map 3C
Launceston 7, London 218, Bodmin 16, Boscastle 12, Camelford 10, Liskeard 17.

Rescue Service: Moorview Motors, Moorview Garage. ℃ Pipers Pool (056 686) 640.

LANERCOST Cumbria. Map 30F
Brampton 2½, London 301, Bellingham 45, Hexham 31.
Golf Brampton 18h. See Priory, Medieval Bridge, Hadrian's Wall.

◼★★New Bridge, Brampton, CA8 2HG. ℃ Brampton (069 77) 2224. C. ⇔ 6 bedrs, 2 bp, 2 ba, annexe 1 bedr, 1 bps, Dgs. ✗ mc, at, LD 8.30. ⚙ CH, TV, Dgs, CP 20, con 20, 1 st. £ BB £11–£18, DB £22–£35, WB (in winter), ①, Bk £3, D £7·50, Dep a.

LANGFORD Somerset. Map 5A
Bath 22, London 126, Bridgwater 20, Bristol 11, Radstock 17, Shepton Mallet 17, Wells 14, Weston-super-Mare 10.
EC Sat. Golf Weston-super-Mare 18h.

Rescue Service: Cullens (Langford) Ltd. ℃ Churchill (0934) 852041.

LANGHO Lancashire. Map 27B
Pop 2,875. Blackburn 4½, London 212, Preston 11, Whalley 2.
EC Wed. Golf Wilpshire, Blackburn 18h (2).

Rescue Service: Petre Garage Ltd. ℃ Blackburn (0254) 48136.

LANGLEY MILL Derbyshire (Notts). M.
Area 22D
Pop 5,620. Eastwood 1, London 132, Chesterfield 18, Denby 10, Nottingham 9½.
EC Wed. Golf Codnor 18h.

Rescue Service: Langley Mill Garage, 96 Station Rd. Langley Mill, Nottingham. ℃ (077 37) 2056.

LANGLEY MOOR Durham. Map 32E
Pop 1,226. Darlington 18, London 258, Corbridge 26, Durham 2, Hexham 29, Middlesborough 24, Middleton in

Teesdale 26, Newcastle upon Tyne 16, Stockton-on-Tees 20, West Auckland 13.
EC Wed. Golf Durham City 18h, Brancepeth 18h.

Specialist Body Repairer: Ansa Motors Ltd. ℃ Durham (0385) 61155.

LANGPORT Somerset. Map 5C
Pop 940. Wincanton 22, London 130, Bridgwater 12, Crewkerne 15, Glastonbury 14, Ilminster 9½, Shepton Mallet 18, Sherborne 18, Taunton 13.
EC Wed. Golf Taunton 18h. See 15th cent All Saints' Parish Church, Hanging Chapel.

Ashley, G, xy (R), The Avenue, TA10 9SA. ℃ (0458) 250386. C. ⇔ 8 bedrs, 2 ba, Dgs. ⚙ CH, TV, CP 12, CF, 4 st. £ BB £8, DB £16, WT (b) £77, (c) fr £49·50, DT (b) fr £12·25, ②.

Rescue Service: Shire's Garage and Engineering Co Ltd, Premier Garage. ℃ (0458) 250570.

LANIVET Cornwall. Map 2D
Bodmin 3, London 236, Liskeard 15, Newquay 16, Redruth 27, St. Austell 8½.

Rescue Service: R & R Motors, Truro Rd. ℃ (020 883) 831800.

LANREATH Cornwall. Map 3C
Pop 435. Liskeard 9½, London 230, Bodmin 15, Looe 6.
Golf Bin Down, Looe 18h. See Backabarrow Downs, Parish Church dedicated to SS Manacus and Dunstan, Farming Museum (inc. Pets Corner).

◼★★Punch Bowl, PL13 2NX. ℃ (0503) 20218. Open Apr–Oct. C. ⇔ 18 bedrs, 11 bp, 2 sh, 2 ba, TV, Dgs. ✗ a l c, mc, LD 9.30. ⚙ CH, Dgs, CP 50, U 4, CF, 1 st. £ BB £9·45–£15·25, DB £18·90–£30·50, ②, Bk £3, D £7, cc 1 3 6, Dep a.

LANTEGLOS-BY-FOWEY Cornwall.
M. Area 2D
Fowey 1, London 240, Liskeard 14, West Looe 11.

Rescue Service: White Cross Garage, White Cross. ℃ Polruan (072 687) 338.

LAPFORD Devon. Maps 3B & 4F
Pop 875. Crediton 9½, London 187, Barnstaple 23, Okehampton 13, Tiverton 17.
Golf Crediton & Downes 18h. See Church.

Rescue Services: Larters Garage Ltd, T/As Lapford Cross Garage, Crediton Rd. ℃ (036 35) 373 & (036 35) 588.

LARKFIELD Kent. Maps 7B & 10C
M20 Motorway Int. 4, 2, London 34, Maidstone 4, Sevenoaks 12, Tonbridge 11.

★★★Larkfield, London Rd, ME60 6HJ. ℃ West Malling (0732) 846858. C. ⇔ 52 bedrs, 48 bp, 4 bps, TV. ✗ a l c, mc, LD 10. ⚙ N, CH, Dgs, CP 95, Ac, con 100, CF, 10 BGf. £ BB £36, DB £45, WB, ②, Bk £3·50, L £6·95, D £6·95, cc 1 2 3 4 5 6.

LARKHILL Wiltshire. Map 6C
Andover 16, London 81, Amesbury 3½, Devizes 17, Pewsey 13, Romsey 25, Shaftesbury 26, Wantage 40, Warminster 17, Wincanton 31.
Golf High Post, Salisbury 18h. See Garrison.

Rescue Service: Packway Garage Ltd, The Packway. ℃ Durrington Walls (0980) 52214.

LASTINGHAM North Yorkshire. Map 24D
Pop 110. Pickering 9, London 233, Helmsley 11.
Golf Kirkbymoorside 9h. See Parish Church with unique underground Church.

◼#★★Lastingham Grange (R), YO6 6TH. ℃ (075 15) 345. Open Mar–Nov & winter weekends. C. ⇔ 12 bedrs, 12 bp, TV, Dgs. ✗ mc, at, LD 8.30. ⚙ CH, CP 30, U 2, con 20, CF, 4 st. £ WB, Bk £4·50, L £6, D £9·95, cc 2 5.

LAUNCESTON Cornwall. Map 3C
Pop 6,238. Okehampton 19, London 211, Bodmin 22, Bude 18, Camelford 16, Holsworthy 13, Liskeard 15, Saltash 20, Tavistock 13.
EC Thur. MD Tue. Golf Launceston 18h. See Castle ruins, Southgate Arch, Churches, Museum (Nat Trust).

★★Eagle House, (R), 3 Castle St, PL15 8BA. ℃ (0566) 2036. Closed Dec 25 & 26. C. ⇔ 18 bedrs, 5 bp, 3 bps, 4 ba, TV, Dgs.✗ mc, at, LD 9. ⚙ N, ch, TV, CP 60, Ac, con 200, CF, 7 BGf, 0 st. £ BB £9–£11, DB £17–£19, WB, ①, Bk £2, L £3·95, D £4·25, cc 3 5.

★★White Hart, Broad St, PL15 8AA. ℃ (0566) 2013. C. ⇔ 28 bedrs, 14 bp, 4 bps, 5 ba, TV, Dgs. ✗ a l c, mc, at, LD 9.30. ⚙ CH, TV, Dgs, CP 18, Ac, con 150, CF, 4 BGf, 2 st. £ BB £11·50–£14, DB £22–£26, WT fr £22·50, DBB fr £18, WB, ①, Bk £3, D £9, cc 1 2 3 5 6, Dep b.

Hordon Farm, PL15 9LS. ℃ (0566) 2955.

Repairers: Greenaways Garage, Kensey Vale. ℃ (0566) 2222.
Kensey Vale Motor Co, (J & A Moore) 1 Newport Industrial Estate. ℃ (0566) 3500.
S J Broad, Madford Garage, Bounsalls La. ℃ (0566) 2384.
MC Repairer: Wooldridge, J & Son, 4 Southgate. ℃ (0566) 2521.
Sctr Repairer: Wooldridge, J & Son, 4 Southgate. ℃ (0566) 2521.
Rescue Service: Compass Garage, Tregadillett. ℃ (0566) 4557.
Currah, R L, St Stephens Garage. ℃ (0566) 2546.
Truscott Bros (Launceston) Ltd, Western Road Garage. ℃ (0566) 2277.

LAVENHAM Suffolk. Map 17C
Pop 1,725. Sudbury 6½, London 65, Aldeburgh 41, Bury St Edmunds 11, Clacton-on-Sea 33, Harwich 31, Haverhill 19, Ipswich 19, Saxmundham 37, Stowmarket 15.
Golf Newton Green, Sudbury 9h. See 16th cent half-timbered Guildhall (with Museum), mainly Perp Church, Market Cross, old houses.

★★★Swan (TH), High St, CO10 9QA. ℃ (0787) 247477. C. ⇔ 42 bedrs, 42 bp, TV, Dgs. ✗ mc, at, LD 9.45. ⚙ CH, Dgs, CP 60, Ac, con 50, CF, 9 BGf, 0 st, Dis. £ BB £41, DB £58, WB, ①, cc 1 2 3 4 5 6, Dep (Xmas).

LEADENHAM Lincolnshire. Map 23C
Pop 427. Grantham 11, London 123, Horncastle 27, Lincoln 13, Newark 10, Sleaford 9.

EC Wed. **Golf** Sleaford 18h. **See** 13th cent Church, 17th cent George Hotel, Leadenham House, 16th cent The Old Hall, Manor house.

Rescue Service: F Troop & Son. ✆ Loveden (0400) 72232.

LEAMINGTON SPA Warwickshire. Map 14B
Pop 43,000. Banbury 20, London 93, Coventry 8½, Daventry 18, Lichfield 33, Rugby 14, Sutton Coldfield 25, Tamworth 28, Warwick 2.
EC Thur. **MD** Wed, Fri. **Golf** Newbold Comyn 18h. **See** Royal Pump Room, Jephson Gardens, All Saint's Church, Museum and Art Gallery, Guy's Cliffe and Saxon Mill 1½m NW, Warwick Castle 2 m W, Kenilworth Castle 4 m N.
🆔 Jephson Lodge, The Parade.
✆ Leamington Spa (0926) 311470.

★★★**Falstaff**, *20 Warwick New Rd, CV32 5JG.* ✆ (0926) 312044. C. 🛏 53 bedrs, 30 bp, 17 bps, 6 sh, 1 ba, TV, Dgs. ✗ a l c, mc, at, LD 9.15. 🏠 Lt, N, CH, Dgs, CP 85, Ac, sb, con 100, CF, 4 BGf, 5 st. £ BB £27, DB £38, WT £240, DT £39, DBB £34, WB, 🆔, Bk £3, L £5, D £7, cc 1 2 3 4 5 6, Dep b.

★★★**Manor House**, *Avenue Rd, CV31 3NJ.* ✆ (0926) 23251. C. 🛏 54 bedrs, 47 bp, 6 bps, 1 ba, TV, Dgs. ✗ mc, at, LD 10. 🏠 Lt, N, CH, CP 100, Ac, con 100, CF, 0 st. £ BB £37, DB £48, WB, 🆔, cc 1 2 3 4 5 6, Dep b.

★★★**Regent**, *The Parade, CV32 4AX.* ✆ (0926) 27231. 🛏 80 bedrs, 80 bp, TV, Dgs. ✗ a l c, mc, at, LD 10.45. 🏠 Lt, N, CH, TV, CP 70, G 30, Ac, con, CF. £ BB £28–£31, DB £40–£44, WB, 🆔, cc 1 2 3 4 5 6, Dep b.

★★**Abbacourt**, *40 Kenilworth Rd, CV32 6JF.* ✆ (0926) 311188. C. 🛏 19 bedrs, 3 bp, 6 bps, 6 ba, TV, Dgs. ✗ a l c, mc, at, LD 9. 🏠 CH, TV, Dgs, CP 20, Ac, con 30, CF, 2 BGf, 0 st, Dis. £ BB £17·25–£25·30, DB £32·20–£40·25, WT £245·52, DT £51·97, DBB £27·02–£35·07, WB, 🆔, Bk £3, L £6, D £8·50, cc 1 2 3 5 6, Dep b.

★**Amersham**, *34 Kenilworth Rd, CV32 6JE.* ✆ (0926) 21637.

★**Beech Lodge** (Rl), *28 Warwick New Rd, CV32 5JJ.* ✆ (0926) 22227. C 3. 🛏 12 bedrs, 6 bps, 3 sh, 2 ba, TV, Dgs. ✗ at, LD 9. 🏠 CH, TV, Dgs, CP 12, CF, 1 BGf, 0 st, Dis. £ BB £14·50–£17, DB £25–£27·50, WT £182, DBB £22·50, 🆔, Bk £4, D £8.

★**Lansdowne** (R), *Clarendon St, CV32 4PF.* ✆ (0926) 21313. RS Dec 26–Jan 12. C. 🛏 10 bedrs, 4 bp, 2 ba. ✗ mc, LD 8.30. 🏠 CH, TV, CP 8, Ac, con 16, CF, 1 st. £ BB £15·65–£23·95, DB £27·75–£31·50, DBB fr £21·85, 🆔, Bk £3·45, L £6·95, D £8·65, cc 1, Dep a.

★**Park** (Rl), *Avenue Rd, CV31 3PG.* ✆ (0926) 28376.

Buckland Lodge, PH, z (Rl), *35 Avenue Rd, CV31 3PG.* ✆ (0926) 23843. Closed Xmas. C. 🛏 11 bedrs, 1 bp, 3 ba, Dgs. 🏠 CH, TV, CP 12, CF, 0 st. £ BB £9·75–£12, DB £19–£23, DT (b) £15·25, Bk £2·50, D £5·50.

Glendower, G, z (Unl), *8 Warwick Pl, CV32 5BJ.* ✆ (0926) 22784. Closed Dec. C 5. 🛏 8 bedrs, 1 sh, 2 ba, Dgs. 🏠 CH, TV, 0 st. £ BB £8·50–£10, DB £18–£20, WT (c) £59·50–£70, DT (b) £12·50–£14, 🆔.

Poplars, PH, z (R), *1 Milverton Ter, CV32 5BE.* ✆ (0926) 28335. Closed Xmas. C. 🛏 13 bedrs, 4 bp, 1 sh, 2 ba, TV, Dgs.

🏠 CH, TV, Dgs, ns, CP 11, CF, 8 st. £ BB £10·45–£17, DB £19–£29, 🆔, Bk £2, D £5·75.

Westella, PH, z (Unl), *26 Leam Ter, CV31 1BB.* ✆ (0926) 22710. C. 🛏 10 bedrs, 4 sh, 1 ba, Dgs. 🏠 CH, TV, CP 12.

Repairer: Lime Garages (Leamington) Ltd, Lime Av. Lillington. ✆ (0926) 23221.
Rescue Service: Bull Ring Garage, Bull Ring, Harbury. ✆ Harbury (0926) 612275. Midland Autocar Co (Leamington) Ltd, 14 and 24 Russell St. ✆ (0926) 21171. Soans of Leamington Spa, Sydenham Dr. ✆ (0926) 29411.

LEATHERHEAD Surrey. Map 7A
Pop 40,500. Epsom 4, London 18, Dorking 5, Guildford 12, Kingston upon Thames 8½, Reigate 8½, Ripley 9½, Weybridge 9½.
EC Wed. **Golf** Leatherhead 18h. **See** Ancient Parish Church, old 'Running Horse' Inn, Chessington Zoo 3 m N, Mickleham Downs.

Rescue Service: Tudor Motor Engineering, 167 Cobham Rd, Fetcham. ✆ (0372) 76371.

LEDBURY Hereford & Worcester (Herefordshire). Map 13D
Pop 3,911. Tewkesbury 14, London 119, M50 Motorway 4½, Bromyard 13, Cheltenham 22, Evesham 26, Gloucester 16, Hereford 14, Leominster 22, Ross-on-Wye 12, Worcester 16.
EC Wed. **MD** Tue, Wed, Sat. **Golf** Ross 18h. **See** Market Hall, Barrett-Browning Memorial Institute, Church House, St Katherine's Almshouses, old houses and inns, Norman-Gothic Church (detached bell-tower), Eastnor Castle 2 m E.
🆔 St Katherines, High St. ✆ Ledbury (0531) 2641.

★★**Feathers**, *High St, HR8 1DS.* ✆ (0531) 2600. C. 🛏 11 bedrs, 11 bp, TV, Dgs. ✗ a l c, mc, LD 9.30. 🏠 N, CH, Dgs, CP 12, G 8, sc, con 20, CF, 2 st. £ BB £24·75–£28, DB £37·50–£39·50, DBB £25, WB, 🆔, Bk £3·45, L £4·25, D £6·90, cc 1 2 5, Dep b.

■★**Royal Oak**, *Southend, HR8 2EY.* ✆ (0531) 2110. C. 🛏 8 bedrs, 2 ba. 🏠 ch, TV, Dgs, CP 6, U 2, G 6, CF, 4 st. £ BB £12·50–£16, DB £23–£26, WT £140, DT £20, 🆔, Bk £2·75, D £4·75, cc 1 3.

Hope End Country House, PH, xy (R), *Hope End, Wellington Heath, HR8 1JQ.* ✆ (0531) 3613. Closed Dec–Feb. C 12. 🛏 7 bedrs, 7 bp. 🏠 CH, CP 10, 1 BGf. £ BB £29, DB £54, WT (b) £273, DT (b) £42, 🆔, D £15.

Repairers: Brookes, W T & Son, 99 New St. ✆ (0531) 2261.
Hopkins, George & Sons, New St. ✆ (0531) 2333.
Rescue Service: Gittings Bros Motors, Parkway Garage. ✆ (0531) 2320.

LEE Devon. Map 4C
Pop 100. Blackmoor Gate 14, London 205, Barnstaple 13, Croyde 8, Ilfracombe 3½.
Golf Saunton 18h, Ilfracombe 18h. **See** 12th cent Inn, Lee Bay, Cliffs, North Devon Coast Path.

★★★**Lee Bay**, *EX34 8LP.* ✆ Ilfracombe (0271) 63503. C. 🛏 48 bedrs, 47 bp, 1 bps, 1 ba, Dgs. ✗ a l c, mc, at, LD 9.30. 🏠 N, CH, Dgs, CP 200, Ac, sp, sb, sol, con

100, CF. £ DBB £25–£33, WB, 🅱, Bk £4·50, L £5·50, D £9, cc 1 2 3 5, Dep a.▲
■★★★**Lee Manor**, (R), *EX34 8LR.* ✆ (0271) 63920.

LEEDS West Yorkshire. Map 25F
RAC Office, *34 Regent St, Leeds, LS2 7QL* ✆ (General) Leeds (0532) 436091. (Rescue Service only) Leeds (0532) 448556.
Pop 704,885. Pontefract 13, London 191, M1 Motorway 1½, Boroughbridge 25, Bradford 9, Halifax 15, Harrogate 15, Hawes 58, Huddersfield 15, Oldham 32, Selby 21, Skipton 26, Wakefield 9, York 24.
See Plan, p. 247.
EC Wed. **MD** Daily. **P** See Plan. **Golf** Five Municipal Courses and many others. **See** RC Cathedral, University, Town Hall, Art Gallery, Museum, Grammar School, Statues (City Sq), Churches: St Peter's, St John's, St Aidan's, Holy Trinity, Kirkstall Abbey and Abbey House Museum, Roundhay Park, Lotherton Hall (Country House Museum, at Aberford), Temple Newsham House 4 m SE, Harewood House 8 m N.
🆔 Central Library. Calverley St. ✆ Leeds (0532) 462454.

★★★★**Ladbroke Dragonara**, *Neville St, LS1 4BX.* ✆ (0532) 442000. C. 🛏 234 bedrs. 234 bp, ns, TV, Dgs. ✗ a l c, mc, at, LD 10. 🏠 Lt, N, CH, G 70, Ac, con 500, CF, 0 st. £ BB £53·25, DB £68·50, WB, 🆔, Bk £5·25, L £6·95, D £9·25, cc 1 2 3 5, Dep.

★★★★**Queens**, *PO Box 118, City Sq, LS1 1PL.* ✆ (0532) 431323. 🛏 198 bedrs, 198 bp, TV, Dgs. ✗ mc, at, LD 10. 🏠 Lt, N, CH, Dgs, Ac, sb, sol, con 500, CF, 3 st. £ BB £32–£38, DB £58·60, WB, 🅱, cc 1 2 3 4 5 6.

★★★M **Ladbroke**, *Garforth, LS23 1LE.* ✆ (0532) 866556. C. 🛏 147 bedrs, 147 bp, TV, Dgs. ✗ a l c, mc, at, LD 10.30. 🏠 N, CH, CP 250, Ac, con, CF, 1 BGf, 1 st, Dis. £ BB £41·50, DB £55, WB, 🆔, Bk £5·50, L £8·25, D £9·25, cc 1 2 3 5 6.

★★★**Merrion**, *Merrion Centre, LS2 8NH.* ✆ (0532) 439191. C. 🛏 120 bedrs, 120 bp, ns, TV, Dgs. ✗ a l c, mc, at, LD 10.30. 🏠 Lt, N, CH, G 500, Ac, con 80, CF, 0 st. £ BB £25–£42, DB £45–£53, WB, 🆔, Bk £4·50, L £6, D £7, cc 1 2 3 5, Dep a.

★★★**Metropole** (TH), *King St, LS1 2HQ.* ✆ (0532) 450841. C. 🛏 110 bedrs, 68 bp, 6 bps, 18 ba, TV, Dgs. ✗ a l c, mc, LD 10. 🏠 Lt, N, CH, Dgs, CP 28, Ac, con 400, CF, 6 st. £ BB £32·50–£39, DB £43–£52, WB, 🅱, cc 1 2 3 4 5 6.

★★★**Parkway**, *Otley Rd, LS16 8AG.* ✆ (0533) 672551.

★★★M **Stakis Windmill**, *Ring Rd, Seacroft, LS14 5QP.* ✆ (0532) 732323. C. 🛏 40 bedrs, 40 bp, TV, Dgs. ✗ a l c, mc, at, LD 10. 🏠 Lt, N, CH, TV, Dgs, CP 400, Ac, con 350, CF, 1 st. £ D £4·40, cc 1 2 3 4 5 6, Dep b.

■★★★**Golden Lion**, *Lower Briggate, LS1 4AL.* ✆ (0532) 436454. C. 🛏 82 bedrs, 6 bp, 16 ba, TV, Dgs. ✗ mc, at, LD 8.30. 🏠 Lt, N, CH, Dgs, Ac, con 80, CF, 1 st. £ BB £22·55, DB £32·45, WB, 🅱, cc 1 2 3 5.

■★★**Wellesley**, *Wellington St, LS1 4HJ.* ✆ (0532) 430431. C. 🛏 54 bedrs, 22 bp, 8 ba, TV, Dgs. ✗ a l c, mc, at, LD 9.45. 🏠 Lt, N, CH, Dgs, CP 28, Ac, con 250, CF, 0 st. £ BB £30·25, DB £45·25, WB, 🆔, cc 1 2 3 5.

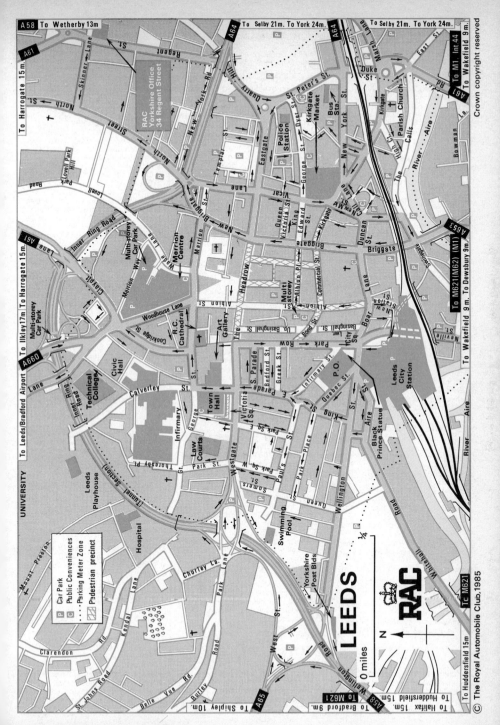

■★**Hartrigg** (Rl), *10 Shire Oak Rd, Headingley, LS6 2DL.* (2 m NW A660). ✆ (0532) 751568. C. ⊷ 28 bedrs, 5 ba, Dgs. ✘ LD 6.15. ▣ ch, TV, CP, con 15, CF, 2 BGf, 1 st, Dis. £ BB £17·25, DB £26·65, ▯, D £4·75, cc 1 2 3.

Ann-Marie House, PH, z (Rl), *47 Cliff Rd, Headingley, LS6 2ET.* ✆ (0532) 758856. Closed Xmas & New Year. C. ⊷ 14 bedrs, 3 ba, TV, Dgs. ▣ CH, TV, CP 10, CF, 4 st. £ BB £10, DB £18, ▯.

Aragon, H, y (Rl), *250 Stainbeck La, LS7 2PS.* ✆ (0532) 759306. Closed Xmas. C. ⊷ 11 bedrs, 3 bp, 2 bps, 2 ba, TV, Dgs. ▣ CH, TV, CP 9, CF, 6 st. £ BB £13·91–£20·12, DB £21·62–£27·60, DT (b) fr £16·67, ▯, Bk £2·30, D £5·86, cc 1 3 5.

Clock, PH, z (R), *317 Roundhay Rd, LS8 4HT.* ✆ (0532) 490304. C. ⊷ 22 bedrs, 1 bp, 2 bps, 4 ba, Dgs. ▣ CH, TV, Dgs, CP 15, CF, 3 BGf, 2 st. £ BB fr £11·70, DB fr £21·28, WT (b) £116·90–£143·50, DT (b) fr £16·70–£20·50, ▢, Bk £1·20, D £5.

Highfield, PH, z (Unl), *79 Cardigan Rd, LS6 1EB.* ✆ (0532) 752193. Closed Dec 25 & 26. C. ⊷ 10 bedrs, 4 ba, Dgs. ▣ CH, TV, Dgs, CP 7, CF, 0 st. £ BB £10·43, DB £19·55, Bk £1·50.

Merevale, PH, z (Unl). *16 Wetherby Rd, LS8 2QD.* ✆ (0532) 658933. C. ⊷ 12 bedrs, 2 ba. ▣ CH, TV, CP 8, 3 st. £ BB £12, DB £21, ▯.

Oak Villa, PH, yz (Unl). *57 Cardigan Rd, Headingley, LS6 1DW.* ✆ (0532) 758439. C. ⊷ 14 bedrs, 4 ba, Dgs. ▣ CH, TV, Dgs, CP 10, CF, 7 st. £ BB £11, DB £20, WT (c) £66, DT (b) £16, ▯.

Pinewood, PH, z (Rl), *78 Potternewton Lane, LS7 3LW.* ✆ (0532) 622561. Closed Xmas–New Year. C. ⊷ 11 bedrs, 1 bps, 5 sh, 1 ba, TV. ▣ ch, TV, ns, CF, 1 BGf, 3 st. £ BB fr £14·50, DB fr £25·50, DT (b) £20·50, ▢, cc 1.

Valley, PH, *337 Roundhay Rd. LS8 4HT.* ✆ (0532) 491863.

Repairers: Appleyard of Leeds Ltd, Roseville Rd. ✆ (0532) 432731.▲

Bristol Street Motors, Water La. ✆ (0532) 38091.

Brown & White (Leeds) Ltd, 98 Roundhay Rd. ✆ (0532) 629301.

P K Motors (Roundhay) Ltd, Street La. ✆ (0532) 661043.

Tate Cars Ltd, New Hunslet Centre, Balm Rd. ✆ (0532) 713981.

Tennant Motor Services (Leeds) Ltd, Swinnow La. ✆ (0532) 563411.

Specialist Body Repairer: Appleyard of Leeds Ltd, Harrogate Rd. ✆ (0532) 32731.

Specialist Radiator Repairers: Northern Radiators Ltd, Sheepscar St. ✆ (0532) 35051.

Serck Radiator Services Ltd, 16 Wortley Moor La, Wortley, 12. ✆ (0532) 636678.

MC Repairers: K P Motor Cycles. No. 1 The Calls. ✆ (0532) 460705.

Watson-Cairns & Co Ltd, 157 Briggate. ✆ (0532) 458081.

Sctr Repairer: Frank Fletcher (Motor Cycles) Ltd, 126 Meadow Rd, 11. ✆ (0532) 444531.

Rescue Service: Commercial Garages Ltd, Tenter La, Swinegate. ✆ (0532) 452677.

Dovener & Routh Ltd, Otley Old Rd, Cookridge, 16. ✆ (0532) 673070.

Naylors Garage, Otley Old Rd. ✆ (0532) 671652.

Ringways Garages (Leeds) Ltd, Whitehall Rd, 12. ✆ (0532) 634222.

LEEK Staffordshire. Map 22C
Pop 19,504, Ashbourne 15, London 154, Buxton 13, Congleton 9½, Macclesfield 13, Matlock 28, Nantwich 25, Newcastle-under-Lyme 11, Sheffield 35, Stoke-on-Trent 11, Stone 16, Uttoxeter 19.
EC Thur. **MD** Wed. **Golf** Leek 18h. **See** Parish Church of St Edward, Nicholson Institute with Museum and Art Gallery, Prince Charlie's House, 17th cent Ash Almshouses, Clock Tower War Memorial, Rudyard Lake 3 m NW, Staffordshire Moorlands (Wallabies).
ℹ️ New Stockwell House, Stockwell St. ✆ Leek (0538) 385181 ext 210.

Repairer: Bode, F & Sons Ltd, Buxton Rd. ✆ (0538) 383442.

Rescue Service: Norbury Motor Garage, Sneyd St. ✆ (0538) 383114.

LEEMING BAR N. Yorkshire. Map 24F
Pop 670. Boroughbridge 16, London 224, Northallerton 6, Scotch Corner 11, Ripon 14.
EC Thur. **Golf** Bedale 18h.
■ Leeming Service Area, A1/A684, Bedale. ✆ Bedale (0677) 23611.

★**White Rose,** *DL7 9AY.* ✆ Bedale (0677) 22707. C. ⊷ 12 bedrs, 2 bp, 8 bps, 1 ba, TV, Dgs. ✘ a l c, mc, at, LD 10.30. ▣ CH, Dgs, CP 30, Ac, con 18, CF, 1 st. £ BB £14, DB £21, DBB £20·25, WB, ▯, Bk £1·95, D £6·25, cc 1 2 3, Dep a.▲

Rescue Service: Don Rose Repair & Recovery, Leeming Bar Industrial Estate. ✆ Bedale (0677) 23773.

LEE-ON-THE-SOLENT Hants. Map 6F
Fareham 4, London 76, Romsey 20, Southampton 13, Winchester 21.
EC Thur. **Golf** Lee-on-the-Solent 18h.

Rescue Service: Skyways Garage, Broomway. ✆ (0705) 551484.

LEICESTER Leicestershire. Map 22F
See also NEWTON LINFORD and ROTHLEY
Pop 279,791. Northampton 31, London 97, M1 Motorway 4, Ashby-de-la-Zouch 17, Coventry 25, Daventry 28, Hinckley 13, Loughborough 11, Market Harborough 15, Melton Mowbray 15, Newark 35, Nottingham 26, Ollerton 44, Peterborough 42, Rugby 20, Stamford 32, Towcester 40.
See Plan, p. 249.
MD Daily. **P** See Plan. **Golf** Leicestershire 18h, Birstall 18h, Rothley Park 18h, Scraptoft 18h, Glen Gorse 18h. **See** Cathedral, St Mary de Castro Church, St Nicholas' and other churches, Jewry Wall Museum, Leicester Castle remains, Guildhall, The Newarke Houses (Local History Museum), De Montfort Hall, Belgrave Hall Museum, Clock Tower, Museum and Art Gallery, Newarke Gateway (with Regimental Museum), Town Hall, Museum of Technology, Kirby Muxloe Castle 4 m W.
ℹ️ 12 Bishop St. ✆ Leicester (0533) 556699.

★★★★**Grand,** *Granby St, LE1 6ES.* ✆ (0533) 555599. Closed Dec 25 & 26. C. ⊷ 93 bedrs, 93 bp, TV, Dgs. ✘ a l c, mc, at, LD 9.30. ▣ Lt, N, CH, Dgs, CP 120, Ac, con 500, CF, 3 st. £ B £40, BD £52, WB, ▯, Bk £4·25, L £6, D £6·6, cc 1 2 3 4 5 6, Dep b.

★★★★**M Holiday Inn,** *St Nicholas Circle, LE1 5LX.* ✆ (0533) 531161. C. ⊷ 190

bedrs, 190 bp, ns, TV, Dgs. ✘ a l c, mc, at, LD 10.15. ▣ Lt, N, CH, ns, CP 20, G 500, Ac, sp, sb, gym, con 300, CF, 1 BGf, 1 st. £ BB fr £43·85, DB fr £54·35, WB, ▯, Bk £4·75, L £6·45, D £10, cc 1 2 3 4 5 6, Dep b.

★★★**Belmont,** *De Montfort St, LE1 7GR.* ✆ (0533) 544773. Closed Dec 25–Jan 2. C. ⊷ 42 bedrs, 33 bp, 3 bps, 2 sh, 2 ba, annexe 19 bedrs, 9 bp, 2 sh, 2 ba, TV, Dgs. ✘ a l c, mc, at, LD 9.45. ▣ Lt, N, CH, CP 45, G 2, Ac, con 60, CF, 3 BGf, 0 st, Dis. £ BB £20–£40, DB £32–£50, WB, ▯, Bk £5, L £5·25, D £6·50, cc 1 2 3 5, Dep b.

★★★**Eaton Bray,** *Abbey St, LE1 3TE.* ✆ (0533) 50666. RS Xmas & New Year. C. ⊷ 73 bedrs, 73 bp, TV, Dgs. ✘ mc, at, LD 10. ▣ Lt, N, CH, Dgs, CP 400, Ac, con 120, CF, 0 st. £ BB £15–£29·95, DB £20–£34·95, DBB £20·95–£36·90, WB, ▯, Bk £3·50, L £5·95, D £6·95, cc 1 2 3 5 6, Dep.

★★★**M Leicester Forest Moat House,** *Hinckley Rd, LE3 3GH.* ✆ (0533) 394661. C. ⊷ 30 bedrs, 30 bp, TV, Dgs. ✘ a l c, mc, LD 9.45. ▣ N, CH, Dgs, CP 150, con 50, CF, 1 st. £ BB £33, DB £38, WB, ▯, Bk £3·95, D £8·50, cc 1 2 3 4 5 6, Dep.

★★★**M Leicester International,** *Humberstone Rd, LE5 3AT.* ✆ (0533) 20471. Closed Xmas. C. ⊷ 218 bedrs, 218 bp, TV, Dgs. ✘ a l c, mc, at, LD 10.15. ▣ Lt, N, CH, Dgs, G 25, Ac, con 700, CF, 1 st. £ BB £32·75, DB £45, WB, ▯, L £5·75, D £5·75, cc 1 2 3 4 5 6, Dep b.

★★★**Leicestershire Moat House,** *Wigston Rd, Oadby, LE2 5QE.* ✆ (0533) 719441. C. ⊷ 29 bedrs, 29 bp, TV, Dgs. ✘ a l c, mc, at, LD 9.45. ▣ Lt, N, CH, TV, Dgs, CP 160, Ac, con 200, CF, 47 BGf, 0 st. £ BB £33, DB £42, WB, ▯, Bk £3·75, L £5·50, D £7·20, cc 1 2 3 5 6, Dep b.

★★★**M Post House** (TH), *Braunstone Lane East, LE3 2FW.* ✆ (0533) 896688. C. ⊷ 179 bedrs, 179 bp, TV, Dgs. ▣ Lt, N, CH, Dgs, CP 102, Ac, con 150, CF, 47 BGf, 0 st. £ BB £40·50, DB £52·50, WB, ▯, cc 1 2 3 4 5 6.

Burlington, PH, z (R), *Elmfield Av, LE2 1RB.* ✆ (0533) 705112. C. ⊷ 17 bedrs, 1 bps, 6 sh, 3 ba, TV. ▣ CH, TV, CP 20, CF, 1 st. £ BB £12·08, DB £19, DT (b) £17·50, ▯, Bk £2·50, D £5·50, cc 1.

Daval, H, z (R), *292 London Rd, Stoneygate, LE2 2AG.* ✆ (0533) 708234. Closed Xmas. C. ⊷ 14 bedrs, 4 sh, 2 ba, TV, Dgs. ▣ CH, TV, CP 20. £ BB £14·50–£17·50, DB £22–£25·50, DT (b) £20·45, ▯, Bk £2·95, D £5·95.

Old Tudor Rectory, PH, y (R), *Main St. Glenfield, LE3 8DG.* ✆ (0533) 312214. C. ⊷ 15 bedrs, 2 bp, 3bps, 4 ba, TV, Dgs. ✘ a l c. ▣ CH, TV, Dgs, CP 40, CF, 1 BGf, 1 st, Dis. £ BB £14·50–£17·50, DB £25·30–£28·75, DT (a) £22–£24, ▯, Bk £2·25, L £3·50, D £6·95, cc 1 3.

Scotia, PH, z (R), *10 Westcotes Dr, LE3 0QR.* ✆ (0533) 549200. Closed Xmas. C. ⊷ 15 bedrs, 5 ba, Dgs. ▣ CH, TV, Dgs, CP 4, CF, 2 st. £ BB £13, DB £22, ▯, Bk £5, D £5·50.

Repairers: Hamshaw H A Ltd, Hamshaw House, Welford Rd. ✆ (0533) 882959.

MC Repairer: Bruce Lewin Ltd, 15 Narborough Rd. ✆ (0533) 541687.

Rescue Service: A1 Autos (Leicester) Ltd, 77 Church Gate. ✆ (0533) 27459.

Albar Motors (Mountsorrell) Ltd. 177 Leicester Rd. Mountsorrel. ✆ (0533) 303055.

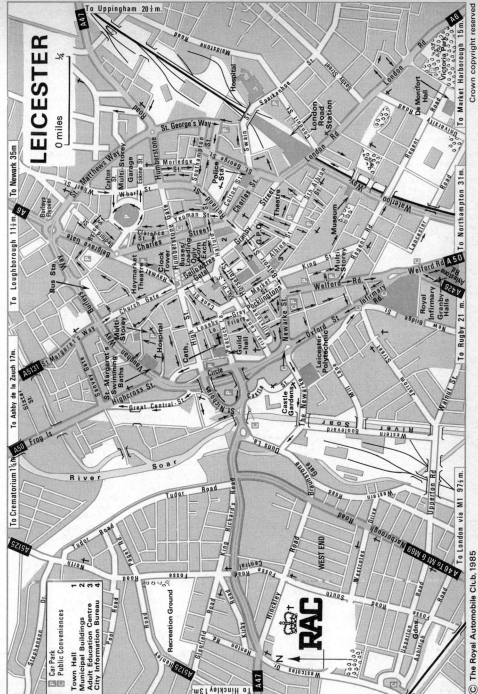

LEICESTER

0 miles ¼

P Car Park
C Public Conveniences

Town Hall 1
Municipal Buildings 2
Adult Education Centre 3
City Information Bureau 4

B M T Motor Engineers, 2 Maidstone Rd.
℡ (0533) 537825.
Castles Stoneygate Garage, Stoneygate
Rd. ℡ (0533) 700521.
Cropston Garage, Station Rd, Cropston.
℡ (0533) 362363.
Jordan Recovery Services, 30–34
Narborough Rd South. ℡ (0533) 895952.

LEIGH Gtr Manchester (Lancashire). Map
27D
Pop 45,626. M6 Motorway 5½, London
194, Bolton 7, Chorley 12, Manchester 12,
St. Helens 10, Warrington 10, Wigan 6.
EC Wed. MD Thur, Fri, Sat. Golf Leigh
18h. See Parish Church with records from
12th cent.

◼★★★M Greyhound, Warrington Rd,
WN7 3XQ. ℡ (0942) 671256. C. ⊯ 56
bedrs, 56 bp, TV, Dgs. ◻ Lt, N, CH, Dgs, CP
250, G 8, Ac, con 60, CF, 1 st. £ B £35·50,
BD £40·50, WB, ◻, Bk £4·25, L £6·95, D
£6·95, cc 1 2 3 5 6, Dep b.

Repairer: F Timms & Co (Leigh) Ltd,
Brown Street North, off Lord St. ℡ (0942)
673401.
Rescue Service: Tamar Motor Co Ltd,
Wigan Rd. ℡ (0942) 676236.

LEIGHTON BUZZARD Beds. Map 15E
Pop 29,648. Dunstable 7½, London 41,
Aylesbury 10, Bedford 18, Bletchley 6½,
Buckingham 17.
MD Tue, Thur, Sat. Golf Leighton Buzzard
10h. See EE Church, Market Cross
(restored), old Inns, St Mary's Church (Old
Linslade), Ascott, nr Wing, Woburn Abbey,
Park and Wild Animal Kingdom (Safari
drive through Game Reserve), 5½ m NE.

★★★Swan, High St, LU7 7EA. ℡ (0525)
372148. RS Xmas. C. ⊯ 35 bedrs, 35 bp,
TV, Dgs. ◻ a l c, mc, at, LD 10. ◻ CH, CP 8,
Ac, con 40, CF, 3 st. £ BB £36–£40, DB
£45–£50, DT £52, DBB £46, WB, ◻, Bk
£4·50, L £6·50, D £10, cc 1 2 3 5 6, Dep b.
★★Hunt, Church Rd, Linslade, LU7 7LR.
℡ (0525) 374692.

Repairer: Camden Motors (Works) Ltd,
Grovebury Rd. ℡ (0525) 372666.
Rescue Service: Mill Motors, Church St,
Wing. ℡ Wing (029 668) 362.

LEINTWARDINE Hereford & Worcester
(Herefordshire). Map 13A
Pop 673. Ludlow 8, London 152, Hereford
24, Knighton 8, Leominster 13, Newton
26, Shrewsbury 26, Welshpool 32.
Golf Ludlow 18h. See Traces of Roman
Station of Bravinium, 11th cent
stonework in Church.

Rescue Service: W & C A Griffiths, The
Garage, High St. ℡ (054 73) 223.

LEISTON Suffolk. Map 17A
Pop 5,133. Ipswich 24, London 98,
Aldeburgh 3½, Lowestoft 21, Norwich 35,
Saxmundham 4.
EC Wed. Golf Thorpeness 18h. See St
Mary's Abbey ruins, Nuclear Power
Station.

MC Repairer: Pat Keeble Motors
(Leiston) Ltd, The Garage, Theberton.
℡ (0728) 830665.
Rescue Service: L B Shotter & Sons,
Waterloo Avenue Service Station.
℡ (0728) 830783.

LENHAM Kent. Map 10C
Pop 2,650. Maidstone 9, London 45,
Ashford 10, Canterbury 18, Rochester 18,
Tenterden 16.
EC Wed. Golf Maidstone 18h. See Old
lock up, St Marys Church, Saxon Warrior.

Harrow Inn, I, x Warren St, ME17 2ED.
℡ Maidstone (0622) 858727. Closed Dec
24–28. C. ⊯ 6 bedrs, 3 bp, 1 bps, 1 ba, TV.
◻ a l c. ◻ CH, TV, CP 30, CF, 0 st. £ BB
£18–£24, DB £28–£34, WT (b) £195, DT
(b) £28, ◻, Bk £4, L £5·75, D £9, cc 1 3.

LENWADE Norfolk. Map Area 16C
Norwich 11, London 122, Cromer 21, East
Dereham 8, Fakenham 15, North Walsham
17.

Rescue Service: D A B Motor Engineers,
Station Rd. ℡ Great Witchingham
(060 544) 367.

LEOMINSTER Hereford & Worcester
(Herefordshire) Map 13C
Pop 9,134. Bromyard 9½, London 148,
Brecon 35, Builth Wells 34, Hereford 12,
Knighton 18, Ledbury 22, Ludlow 11,
Rhayader 38.
EC Thur. MD Fri. Golf Leominster 9h. See
Priory Church, 17th cent Butter Cross,
17th cent Grange Court, many 'black and
white' buildings, Berrington Hall 3 m N,
"Ducking Stool". Museum.
◻ 3 The Grange. ℡ Leominster
(0568) 2951 ext 212.

★★Royal Oak, South St, HR6 8JA.
℡ (0568) 2610. Closed Xmas Day. C.
⊯ 17 bedrs, 14 bp, 4 ba, TV, Dgs. ◻ a l c,
mc, at, LD 9. ◻ ch, Dgs, CP 40, Ac, con
200, CF, 0 st. £ BB £20, DB £29–£32, ◻, Bk
£4, L £6·50, D £6·50, cc 1 2 3.
★★Talbot, West St, HR6 8EP. ℡ (0568)
2121.
Broadward Lodge, G, x (R), Broadward,
HR6 8QG. ℡ (0568) 2914. C. ⊯ 6 bedrs, 1
ba. ◻ CH, TV, ns, CP 16, CF, 2 st. £ BB
£7·50–£9·50, DB £15–£19, WT (b) £72–
£84, DT (b) £11–£13, ◻, Bk £2·35, D £4·50,
cc 1.
Wharton Bank, F, y (Unl). HR6 0NX.
℡ (0568) 2575. Closed Dec. C 7. ⊯ 3
bedrs, 1 bp, 2 ba. ◻ CH, TV, CP. £ BB fr £8,
DB fr £16, WT (c) £56, DT (b) £13, ◻.

Repairer: Henlys (Hereford) Ltd, Borough
Motor Works, South St. ℡ (0568) 2545.

LETCHWORTH Hertfordshire. Map 15D
Pop 31,835. Hatfield 16, London 36,
A1(M) Motorway 2, Baldock 1½, Luton 11.
EC Wed. Golf Letchworth 18h. See
Churches, Museums and Art Gallery.

◼★★★Broadway, The Broadway, SG6
3NZ. ℡ (046 26) 5651. Closed Xmas–New
Year. C. ⊯ 37 bedrs, 22 bp, 3 ba, TV, Dgs.
◻ mc, LD 9.30. ◻ Lt, N, CH, TV, CP 50, Ac,
con, CF, 0 st. £ BB £22–£28, DB £32–£36,
WB, ◻, Bk £2·75, L £5·60, D £5·60,
cc 1 2 3 4 5 6, Dep b.
Specialist Body Repairer: Ensign
Engineering Ltd, 18 Station Rd. ℡ Hitchin
(0462) 59295.
Rescue Service: Vincent Motors, 665
Green La. ℡ (046 26) 74280.

LEVENS Cumbria. Map 26D.
Pop 895. M6 Motorway 5, London 252,
Ambleside 16, Broughton-in-Furness 23,
Kendal 5, Kirkby Lonsdale 10, Lancaster
16, Ulverston 18.

EC Thur. Golf Kendal 18h. See Levens
Hall, Sizergh Castle.

◼₤★★Heaves (Unl). LA8 8EF.
℡ Sedgwick (0448) 60396. Closed Xmas.
C. ⊯ 16 bedrs, 5 bp, 1 bps, 2 ba, TV, Dgs.
◻ a l c, mc, at, LD 8. ◻ ch, TV, CP 30, Ac,
con 30, CF, 3 st. £ BB £13–£16, DB £26–
£32, WT £130–£140, DBB £18–£22, WB,
◻, Bk £2·50, L £4, D £5·50, cc 1 2 3 5.

Rescue Service: Bridge End Garage,
A 590. ℡ Witherslack (044 852) 261.

LEWDOWN Devon. Maps 3C and 4E
Pop 62. Okehampton 10, London 202,
Holsworthy 16, Launceston 8, Tavistock
9½.
EC Thur. Golf Tavistock 18h. See
Lewtrenchard Manor.

◼★★★M Coach House, Lewdown
Service Area, EX20 4DS. ℡ (056 683)
322. C. ⊯ 50 bedrs, 11 bp, 39 bps, TV,
Dgs. ◻ mc, at, LD 8.30. ◻ N, CH, TV, Dgs,
CP 250, Ac, sp, con, CF, 21 BGf, 1 st, Dis.
£ cc 1 2 3 5 6, Dep b.

LEWES East Sussex. Map 7F
Pop 14,725. East Grinstead 21, London
51, Brighton 8½, Eastbourne 16, Hastings
29, Haywards Heath 13, Hurst Green 25,
Uckfield 8.
EC Wed. MD Mon. Golf Lewes 18h. See
Castle and Museum, Anne of Cleves
House, Priory ruins, Southover Grange,
Town Walls, Market Tower, Bull House,
Glynde Place 3 m E, Firle Place 4 m SE.
◻ Lewes House, High St. ℡ Lewes
(079 16) 71600.

★★★Shelleys, High St, BN7 1XS.
℡ (079 16) 2361. C. ⊯ 21 bedrs, 21 bp, 2
ba, TV, Dgs. ◻ a l c, mc, at, LD 9.15. ◻ N,
CH, Dgs, CP 24, Ac, con 60, CF, 0 st. £ BB
£35·75, DB £57·75, WB (in winter), ◻,
cc 1 2 3 5.
★★White Hart, High St, BN7 1XE.
℡ (0273) 474676. C. ⊯ 19 bedrs, 15 bp, 1
ba, TV, Dgs. ◻ a l c, mc, at, LD 10.15. ◻ N,
CH, TV, Dgs, CP 40, Ac, con 40, CF, 7 BGf,
0 st, Dis. £ BB £19–£35, DB £29–£48, WT
£146–£183, DT £29–£31, DBB £25–£41,
WB, ◻, Bk £2·50, L £6, D £6, cc 1 2 3 5,
Dep b.

LEYLAND Lancashire. Map 27D
Pop 26,640. M6 Motorway ½, London 207,
Blackburn 10, Chorley 4½, Ormskirk 13,
Preston 6, Southport 14, Wigan 11.
EC Wed. MD Tue, Fri, Sat. Golf Leyland
18h. See St Mary's (circular) RC Church,
St Andrew Church, Museum.

★★★★M Ladbroke, Junc 28 (M6),
Leyland Way, PR5 2JX. ℡ (077 44) 22922.
C. ⊯ 93 bedrs, 93 bp, TV, Dgs. ◻ a l c, mc,
at, LD 10. ◻ N, CH, Dgs, CP 150, Ac, con
300, CF, 30 BGf, 3 st, Dis. £ BB £38·25, DB
£40·50, DT £53·70, DBB £47·20, WB, ◻,
Bk £5·25, L £6·50, D £8·95, cc 1 2 3 5 6,
Dep b.

Rescue Service: A Tracey, Leyland
Service Stations Ltd, Wigan Rd.
℡ (077 44) 21546.

LICHFIELD Staffordshire. Map 21C
Pop 25,600. Coventry 25, London 116,
Ashbourne 26, Burton-on-Trent 13,
Stafford 16, Stoke-on-Trent 29, Stone 21,
Sutton Coldfield 8, Tamworth 7, Uttoxeter
17, Walsall 9½, Wolverhampton 14.
EC Wed. MD Mon, Fri, Sat. Golf
Whittington Barracks 18h. See Cathedral,

Birthplace of Dr Samuel Johnson (Statue adjacent), Museum, St John's Hospital (Almshouses) with Church adjoining, remains of 13th cent Friary, St Michael's Church, 17th cent Bishop's Palace is now a school.
🆇 9 Breadmarket St. ✆ Lichfield (054 32) 52109.

★★★**George,** *Bird St, WS13 6PR.* ✆ (054 32) 58822. C. 🚄 40 bedrs, 35 bp, 5 bps, TV, Dgs. ✗ a l c, mc, LD 10. 🏵 N, CH, Dgs, CP 50, Ac, con 100, CF, 0 st. £ B £29, BD £38, WB, 🔢, Bk £4·25, L £4·75, D £7·75, cc 1 2 3 4 5 6, Dep b.

★★★**Little Barrow,** *Beacon St, WS13 7AA.* ✆ (054 32) 53311. C. 🚄 26 bedrs, 24 bp, 1 ba, TV. ✗ a l c, mc, LD 10. 🏵 N, CH, TV, CP 70, Ac, con 100, CF, 3 st. £ BB £28·75, DB £36·80, 🔢, Bk £4, L £5·50, D £8, cc 1 2 3 5 6, Dep b.

★★**Angel Croft,** *Beacon St, WS13 7AA.* ✆ (054 32) 23147.

Oakleigh House, H, y (R), *25 St Chad's Rd, WS13 7LZ.* ✆ (054 32) 22688. C. 🚄 11 bedrs, 2 bp, 4 bps, 1 ba, TV, Dgs. 🏵 CH, CP 20, 1 BGf, 1 st, Dis. £ BB £16, DB £22—£25, 🔢, Bk £5, D £10·50.

Repairer: Central Garage, Market Sq. ✆ (054 32) 22826.
MC Repairer: Lichfield Motors Cycle Depot, 37 Tamworth St. ✆ (054 32) 23394.
Rescue Service: Lichfield Motors Ltd, Birmingham Rd. ✆ (054 32) 53566. Ray Acton Motors (Lichfield) Ltd, Burton Rd, Streethay. ✆ (054 32) 23868 & 28059.

LIFTON Devon. Map 3C
Pop 967. Okehampton 14, London 206, Holsworthy 13, Launceston 3½, Tavistock 9½.
EC Tue. **Golf** Tavistock 18h. **See** Church, Cock Pit, Wortham Manor.

★★★**Arundell Arms,** *Fore St, PL16 0AA.* ✆ (056 684) 666. Closed 1 wk Xmas. C. 🚄 23 bedrs, 16 bp, 5 bps, 1 ba, TV, Dgs. ✗ a l c, mc, at, LD 9. 🏵 CH, Dgs, CP 80, pf, con 70, CF, 0 st. £ BB £19—£28, DB £38—£49, DBB £28—£38, WB, 🔢, Bk £3·25, L £7, D £12, cc 1 2 3 6.

▣★★**Lifton Cottage** (R), *PL16 0DR.* ✆ (056 684) 439. C. 🚄 10 bedrs, 4 bps, 2 ba, TV, Dgs. ✗ a l c, mc, at, LD 8.30. 🏵 CH, CP 15, sol, CF, 0 st. £ BB £10·50—£15·50, DB £21—£25, DBB £15·50—£17·50, 🔢, Bk £2·75, L £3·75, D £5·50, cc 1 2 3 5 6, Dep a.

Rescue Service: Fernley Pike, Lifton Down Garage. ✆ (056 684) 447.

LIGHTWATER Surrey. M. Area 7A
1½ m SE of Bagshot. Pop 4,900. London 27, Farnham 12, Guildford 9½, Weybridge 10, Woking 6.
EC Wed. **Golf** Camberley Heath 18h, Wentworth 18h. **See** Country Park, views.

Repairer: Brandon Service Station Ltd, Guildford Rd. ✆ Bagshot (0276) 73060.

LIMPLEY STOKE Wiltshire. Map 5B
Pop 633. Bath 3½, London 108, Devizes 13, Frome 9, Radstock 9½, Warminster 12.
EC Wed. **Golf** Kingsdown, Box 18h. **See** Church.

🏠★★★**Cliffe,** *Limpley Stoke, Bath, Avon, BA3 6HW.* ✆ (022 122) 3226. Closed Dec–Jan. RS Nov–Mar. C. 🚄 9 bedrs, 8 bp, 1 bps, TV. ✗ a l c, mc, at, LD 8.30. 🏵 CH, CP

40, sp, con 3, 3 BGf, 0 st, Dis. £ BB £30, DB £42—£58, WB, ②, L £6·50, D £10·25, cc 1 2 3 5, Dep a.

★★**Limpley Stoke,** *Limpley Stoke, Bath, Avon, BA3 6HZ.* ✆ (022 122) 3333. 🚄 55 bedrs, 43 bp, 12 bps, 1 ba, TV, Dgs. ✗ mc, LD 8.30. 🏵 Lt, CH, TV, Dgs, CP 60, Ac, con 100, CF, 0 st. £ BB £22—£27, DB £34—£40, WB, Bk £3, D £7·50, cc 1 2 3 5 6, Dep a.

LINCOLN Lincolnshire. Map 23C
Pop 78,000. Sleaford 17, London 133, Gainsborough 18, Grantham 25, Horncastle 21, Louth 26, Market Rasen 15, Newark 17, Ollerton 23, Scunthorpe 28, Worksop 28.
EC Wed. **MD** Daily. **Golf** Carholme 18h. **See** Cathedral, Castle (1069) and Court House, Jew's House, The Stonebow (15th–16th cent) with Guildhall above, Newport Arch, Vicar's Court (1300), Churches, ruins of Bishop's Palace, Cardinal's Hat House, 14th cent Cobb Hall, 14th cent Exchequer Gate, Usher Art Gallery, City and County Museum, Doddington Hall 5 m W, Aubourn Hall 6 m SW.
🆇 9 Castle Hill. ✆ Lincoln (0522) 29828.

★★★★**White Hart** (TH), *Bailgate, LN1 3AR.* ✆ (0522) 26222. C. 🚄 57 bedrs, 57 bp, TV, Dgs. ✗ a l c, mc, at, LD 9.45. 🏵 Lt, N, CH, Dgs, CP 25, G 35, Ac, con 90, CF, 3 st. £ BB £44·50, DB £59, WB, 🔢, cc 1 2 3 4 5 6, Dep (Xmas).

★★★M **Eastgate Post House,** (TH), *Eastgate, LN2 1PN.* ✆ (0522) 20341. C. 🚄 71 bedrs, 71 bp, TV, Dgs. ✗ a l c, mc, at, LD 9.45. 🏵 Lt, N, CH, Dgs, CP 110, Ac, sp, con 100, CF, 3 BGf, 1 st. £ BB £43·50, DB £55·50, WB, 🔢, cc 1 2 3 4 5 6, Dep (Xmas).

★★**Bishops,** *Outer Circle Rd, LN2 4HU.* ✆ (0522) 39291. C. 🚄 13 bedrs, 12 bp, 1 bps, TV. ✗ a l c, mc, at, LD 9.30. 🏵 CH, CP 100, Ac, con 50, CF. £ BB £23, DB £30, WB, 🔢, Bk £2·95, L £3·95, D £3·95, cc 1 2 3 5 6, Dep b.

★★**Castle,** *Westgate, LN1 3AS.* ✆ (0522) 38801. C. 🚄 15 bedrs, 15 bp, TV, Dgs. ✗ a l c, mc, LD 9.30. 🏵 CH, CP 20, Ac, 2 BGf, 2 st. £ BB £26·50, DB £35, WB, 🔢, Bk £3·75, L £6, D £6, cc 1 2 3 5 6.

★★**Grand,** *St Mary St, LN5 7EP.* ✆ (0522) 24211. C. 🚄 50 bedrs, 43 bp, 7 bps, TV, Dgs. ✗ a l c, mc, at, LD 10. 🏵 N, CH, CP 40, Ac, con 30, CF, 4 st. £ BB £27, DB £40, WT £210—£259, DT £32—£39, DBB £27—£35, WB, 🔢, Bk £3, L £6, D £7, cc 1 2 3 5, Dep b. ▲

★★**Moor Lodge,** *Branston, LN4 1HU.* ✆ (0522) 791366. (4½ m SE B1188). C. 🚄 34 bedrs, 13 bp, 3 bps, 16 ba, TV, Dgs. ✗ a l c, mc, at, LD 9.30. 🏵 CH, TV, Dgs, CP 150, Ac, con 200, CF, 3 BGf, 0 st, Dis. £ BB fr £21, DB fr £32, DT fr £32·50, DBB fr £23·75, WB, 🔢, Bk £4·25, L £5·50, D £7·25, cc 1 2 3 5.

🏠★★★**Washingborough Hall,** *Church Hill, Washingborough, LN4 1BE.* ✆ (0522) 790340. C. 🚄 12 bedrs, 9 bp, 3 bps, TV, Dgs. ✗ a l c, mc, at, LD 9.30. 🏵 CH, Dgs, CP 50, sp, con 50, CF, 3 st. £ BB £19·50—£25, DB £29—£35, DBB £20·50—£25·50, WB, 🔢, Bk £3·50, L £4·95, D £6, cc 1 2 3 6, Dep a.

Brierley House, PH, z (RI), *54 South Park, LN5 8ER.* ✆ (0522) 26945. Closed Dec. C 5. 🚄 12 bedrs, 5 bp, 6 bps, 1 sh, 2 ba, TV. 🏵 CH, TV, 1 BGf. £ BB £11·50—£14·50, DB £17·50—£21, 🔢, D £4·50.

D'Isney Place, H, yz (Unl), *Eastgate, LN2 4AA.* ✆ (0522) 38881. C. 🚄 14 bedrs, 13 bp, 1 bps, TV, Dgs. 🏵 CH, Dgs, CP 5, CF, 6 BGf, 2 st. £ BB £27·50, DB £37·50, 🔢, cc 1.

Loudor, PH, x (R), *37 Newark Rd, North Hykeham, LN6 8RB* ✆ (0522) 680333.

Rescue Service: Hampsons (Lincoln), Moorland Way, off Tritton Rd. ✆ (0522) 693769.
Specialist Body Repairer: Hartford Motors (Lincolnshire), 186 Wragby Rd. ✆ (0522) 30101.

LINDALE Cumbria. Map 27C
M6 Motorway 11, London 257, Broughton-in-Furness 20, Ambleside 19, Kendal 10, Kirkby Lonsdale 17, Lancaster 22, Ulverston 12.
Golf Grange-over-Sands 18h. **See** Wilkinson Memorial commemorating the 18th cent Ironmaster.

Rescue Service: Hadwin Bros (Lindale) Ltd, Victory Garage. ✆ Grange-over-Sands (044 84) 2937.

LINGFIELD Surrey. Map 7D
Pop 7,430. Godstone 7, London 27, Crawley 9, East Grinstead 3½, Sevenoaks 14, Tunbridge Wells 15, Westerham 9½.
EC Wed. **Golf** Tandridge, Oxted 18h. **See** Church of SS Peter and Paul, St Peter's Cross and Cage, Greathed Manor, Puttenden Manor, Mormon Temple Gardens at Newchapel 2 m SW.

Rescue Service: Lingfield Garage, High St. ✆ (0342) 832022.

LISKEARD Cornwall. Map 3C
Pop 6,305. Tavistock 18, London 214, Bodmin 13, Camelford 20, Fowey 17, Launceston 14, Looe 7½, St Austell 18, Saltash 13.
EC Wed. **MD** Mon. Thur. **Golf** Looe Bin Down 18h. **See** St Martin's Church, Guildhall, Castle Park (Bull Ring), Pipe Well.

🏠★★**Country Castle** (R), *Lamellion Hill, PL14 4EB.* ✆ (0579) 42694. Closed Feb. 🚄 11 bedrs, 5 bp, 2 bps, 1 ba, TV, Dgs. ✗ a l c, mc, at, LD 8.30. 🏵 CH, CP 60, Ac, sp, 1 st. £ WB, D £8·50, cc 1.

★★**Lord Eliot,** *Castle St, PL14 3AU.* ✆ (0579) 42717.

★★**Webb's,** *The Parade, PL14 6AG.* ✆ (0579) 43675. C. 🚄 15 bedrs, 10 bp, 1 ba, TV, Dgs. ✗ a l c, mc, at, LD 8.45. 🏵 ch, TV, Dgs, ns, CP 14, con 120, CF, 2 st.

Badham Farm, G, x (RI), *St. Keyne, PL14 4RW.* ✆ (0579) 43572. C. 🚄 5 bedrs, 1 sh, 1 ba, ns. 🏵 CH, TV, CP 10, CF, 1 BGf, 0 st, Dis. £ BB £9—£10·50, DB £18—£21, WT (b) £84—£90, (c) £54—£60, DT (b) £14—£15, 🔢.

Old Rectory, PH, y (R), *St Keyne, PL14 4RL.* ✆ (0579) 42617. Open Mar–Oct. 🚄 9 bedrs, 1 bp, 2 bps, 2 ba, Dgs. 🏵 CH, TV, CP 20, CF, 1 BGf, 1 st, Dis. £ BB £13, DB £24—£30, WT (b) £136·33—£147·96, 🔢, Bk £4, D £6, cc 1 3.

Sportsman's Arms, I, x, *Menheniot Stn., PL14 3PJ.* ✆ Widegates (050 34) 249.

Repairers: Rowe's Garage, Dobwalls, ✆ Dobwalls (0579) 20218.
Taylors Motors (Liskeard) Ltd, Barras St. ✆ (0579) 45024.
MC Repairer: P H Blee, Motor Cycle Sales & Repairs, Barras Pl. ✆ (0579) 43007.
Rescue Service: Carlyon Garage Ltd, St Neot. ✆ Dobwalls (0579) 20282.

Liskeard Service Centre, Unit 1, Moorswater Industrial Estate. ☎ (0579) 43071.
Reddicliffe Repairs, The Old Coal Yard, Moorswater. ☎ (0579) 44189.

LISS Hampshire. Map 6D
Pop 5,300. Farnham 13, London 52, Alton 8½, Hindhead 9½, Haslemere 9½, Midhurst 9, Petersfield 3½.
EC Wed. **Golf** Liphook 18h. **See** St Peter's Church, St Mary's Church, Bohunt Manor at Liphook 6 m NE, Selborne Village 5 m NW.

Rescue Service: White Rose Engineering Co Ltd, Hill Brow Garage. ☎ (073 082) 2121.

LITTLEBOROUGH Gtr Manchester (Lancashire). Map 27B
Pop 11,976. Rochdale 3, London 195, M62 Motorway 4, Halifax 11, Huddersfield 14, Todmorden 6.
EC Tue. **Golf** Whittaker 9h. **See** Roman Road.

★**Sun,** *Featherstall Rd, OL15 8NY.*
☎ (0706) 78957. C. ➤ 8 bedrs, 6 sh, 2 ba.
✗ mc, LD 9.30. ⓓ CH, TV, CP 6, Ac, CF, 2 st. £ D £3, cc 1 2 3 5 6.

LITTLEHAMPTON West Sussex. Map 7E
See also RUSTINGTON
Pop 21,974. Arundel 3½, London 60, Bognor 6½, Chichester 12, Horsham 22, Worthing 8½.
EC Wed. **MD** Fri, Sat. **Golf** Littlehampton 18h. **See** Miniature Railway, Museum, Mewsbrook Park, Mill and old Church at Clymping.
ⓘ Windmill Theatre Complex, The Green. ☎ Littlehampton (090 64) 3480.

★★**Beach,** *Seafront, BN17 5NT.* ☎ (0903) 717277. C. ➤ 47 bedrs, 30 bp, 7 bps, 6 ba, TV, Dgs. ✗ mc, at, LD 9. ⓓ N, CH, TV, Dgs, CP 100, Ac, sp, con 100, CF, 4 BGf, 1 st, Dis. £ BB £17–£24, DB £26–£34, WT £152–£225, DT £24–£35, DBB £20–£29·50, WB, ①, Bk £2·90, L £5·50, D £6·65, cc 1 5, Dep b.
Braemar, H, z (R), *88 South Terr, BN17 5LJ.* ☎ (090 64) 5487. C. ➤ 8 bedrs, 8 sh, 1 ba, Dgs. ⓓ CH, TV, ns, CF. £ BB £10, DB £20, WT (b) £90, (c) £60, DT (b) £15, ②, Bk £2·40, D £5.
New Inn, z, *5 Norfolk Rd, BN17 5PL.* ☎ (090 64) 3112.
Regency, PH, x (RI), *85 South Terr, BN17 5LJ.* ☎ (0903) 717707. Closed Xmas. C. ➤ 8 bedrs, 8 sh, TV, Dgs. ⓓ CH, TV, Dgs, CF, 10 st. £ BB £9·50–£12, DB £19–£24, WT (c) £56–£65, DT (b) £14·50–£17, ①.
Rowers, H, z (RI), *42 South Terr, BN17 5NU.* ☎ (0903) 713940. C. ➤ 9 bedrs, 1 sh, 3 ba, ns, TV, Dgs. ⓓ ch, TV, Dgs, CP 2, U 2, CF, 4 st. £ BB £8·50–£11·50, DB £17–£23, WT (b) £78–£99, DT (b) £12–£15, ①, D £3·50.

Repairer: Cuff Miller & Co Ltd, Horsham Rd. ☎ (090 64) 4367.
Rescue Service: Rowe's Garage, Terminus Rd. ☎ (090 64) 7271.

LITTLE HAYWOOD Staffs. M. Area 22E
Rugeley 3½, London 126, Burton-on-Trent 18, Derby 28, Stafford 6, Stoke-on-Trent 16, Stone 10, Uttoxeter 11.
EC Wed. **Golf** Brocton 18h. **See** Shrugborough Hall and Museum.

Rescue Service: Little Haywood Garage. ☎ (0889) 881203.

LITTLE KIMBLE Buckinghamshire. Map 15E
Pop 807 (inc Great Kimble), High Wycombe 10, London 40, Aylesbury 4½, Dunstable 17, Oxford 22, Rickmansworth 19, St Albans 23, Wallingford 21, Watford 24.
Golf Ellesborouth 18h, Whiteleaf 9h. **See** Whiteleaf Cross nr Prince's Risborough, 3 m SW.

Rescue Service: Kimble Motors Ltd. ☎ Stoke Mandeville (029 661) 2239.

LITTLEPORT Cambridgeshire. Map 16F
Pop 5,690. Ely 5, London 76, Bury St Edmunds 25, King's Lynn 23, Swaffham 26, Thetford 24, Wisbech 18.
EC Wed. **Golf** Ely 18h. **See** Church

Rescue Service: Littleport Garage Ltd, Wisbech Rd. ☎ Ely (0353) 860576.

LITTLE WEIGHTON Humberside (North Humberside)
See HULL.

LITTLE WYMONDLEY Hertfordshire. M. Area 15D
Hatfield 13, London 33, A1(M) Motorway 1, Baldock 5, Hoddesdon 16, Luton 10, St Albans 15.

★★★**Blakemore,** *Nr Hitchin, SG4 7JJ.*
☎ Stevenage (0438) 355821. C. ➤ 72 bedrs, 72 bp, TV, Dgs. ✗ a l c, mc, at, LD 10. ⓓ Lt, N, CH, TV, Dgs, CP 300, sp, sb, con 200, CF, 8 BGf, 0 st, Dis. £ BB £33·50, DB £45, WT £307·50, DT £48·50, DBB £41, WB, ①, Bk £3·45, L £7·50, D £7·50, cc 1 2 3 5.

LIVERPOOL Merseyside. Map 19A
See also BIRKENHEAD
RAC Office, *Queen's Building, James Street, Liverpool, L2 7NY.* (General) ☎ 051-227 3421. (Rescue Service only) 051-236 2521. (The Liverpool Office may move during 1985).
Pop 503,700. Northwich 26, London 198, M62 Motorway 3½, Birkenhead 1, Ormskirk 13, St Helens 11, Southport 18, Warrington 17, Walkenden 27.
P See Plan, p. 253.
P See Plan. **EC** Wed. **MD** Daily. **Golf** Municipal courses: Allerton Park 18h and 9h, Bowring Park 9h, Liverpool (Kirkby) 18h. **See** Anglican Cathedral, Metropolitan Cathedral, Walker Art Gallery, City Museum, St George's Hall, University, Town Hall, Philharmonic Hall, Building and Design Centre, Planetarium, 18th cent Bluecoat Chambers (Arts Centre), Gladstone's birthplace 62 Rodney St, Royal Liver and Cunard Buildings, Speke Hall 8 m SE, Knowsley Safari Park, Garden Festival Hall and Promenade.
ⓘ 29 Lime St. ☎ 051-709 3631.

■★★★★**M Atlantic Tower Thistle,** *Chapel St, L3 9RE.* ☎ 051-227 4444. C. ➤ 226 bedrs, 226 bp, ns, TV, Dgs. ✗ a l c, mc, at, LD 9.30. ⓓ Lt, N, CH, TV, Dgs, CP 15, Ac, sol, con 100, CF, 0 st. £ BB £50·25–£54·75, DB £65·50–£76·50, WB, ②, Bk £1·20, L £6·90, D £10·50, cc 1 2 3 4 5 6, Dep b.▲

★★★★**M Holiday Inn,** *Paradise St, L1 8JD.* ☎ 051-709 0181. C. ➤ 258 bedrs, 258 bp, TV, Dgs. ✗ a l c, mc, at, LD 10.30.

ⓓ Lt, N, CH, Dgs, sp, sb, sol, gym, con 450, CF, 0 st. £ BB £45, DB £60, WT £402·50, DT £57·50, DBB £52, WB, ①, Bk £5, L £5·50, D £7, cc 1 2 3 4 5 6, Dep b.

★★★★**St George's** (TH), *St John's Precinct, Lime St, L1 1NQ.*
☎ 051-709 7090. C. ➤ 155 bedrs, 155 bp, TV, Dgs. ✗ a l c, mc, at, LD 10.15. ⓓ Lt, N, CH, Dgs, Aо, con 300, CF, 0 st. £ BB £43, DB £59, WB, ①, cc 1 2 3 4 5 6.

★★★**Blundellsands,** *Blundellsands Rd West, L23 6TE.* (Great Crosby 6 m N A565). ☎ 051-924 6515. C. ➤ 43 bedrs, 22 bp, 4 bps, 6 ba, TV, Dgs. ✗ a l c, mc, LD 9. ⓓ Lt, N, CH, TV, Dgs, CP 250, con, CF, 2 st. £ BB fr £22, DB fr £37·50, WB, ①, Bk £4, L £7·50, D £8·50, cc 1 2 3 4 5 6, Dep b.

★★★**Crest,** *Lord Nelson St, L3 5QB.*
☎ 051-709 7050. C. ➤ 160 bedrs, 160 bp, ns, TV, Dgs. ✗ a l c, mc, at, LD 9.45. ⓓ Lt, N, CH, Dgs, CP 200, Ac, con 500, CF, 0 st. £ B fr £40, BD fr £51, WB, ①, Bk £5·25, D £8·95, cc 1 2 3 4 5 6, Dep b.

■★★★**Park,** *Dunnings Bridge Rd, Netherton, L30 3SU.* (5¼ m N A567).
☎ 051-525 7555. C. ➤ 60 bedrs, 60 bp, TV, Dgs. ✗ a l c, mc, at, LD 9.15. ⓓ Lt, N, CH, TV, Dgs, CP 250, G 3, Ac, con 100, CF, 0 st. £ BB £32, DB £44, WB, ①, Bk £3·70, L £4·80, D £4·80, cc 1 2 3 5 6, Dep b.

★★★**Royal,** *Bath St, L22 5PS.*
☎ 051-928 2332.
★★**Green Park** (R), *Greenbank Dr, L17 1AN.* ☎ 051-733 3382. C. ➤ 24 bedrs, 4 bp, 10 bps, 5 ba, TV. ✗ a l c, mc, at, LD 9.30. ⓓ N, CH, TV, CP 25, Ac, con 40, CF, 6 BGf, 3 st. £ BB £18·50–£23·40, DB £27·83–£31·50, WT £175, DT £26·50, DBB £22·50–£29, ①, Bk £1·50, L £2, D £4·50, cc 1 2 3.
★★**Lord Nelson,** *Hotham St, L3 5PD.*
☎ 051-709 4362. C. ➤ 58 bedrs, 20 bp, 10 ba, TV. ✗ a l c, mc, at, LD 9.30. ⓓ Lt, N, CH, TV, U 16, Ac, con 20, CF, 5 st. £ BB £19·50–£27·50, DB £28·50–£37·50, WT £198–£260, DT £28–£38, DBB £25–£33·50, WB, ①, Bk £3·50, L £4·50, D £5·50, cc 1 2 3 5 6, Dep b.
★★**Shaftesbury,** *Mount Pleasant, L3 5SA.* ☎ 051-709 4421. C. ➤ 69 bedrs, 26 bp, 15 ba, TV. ✗ a l c, mc, at, LD 9.30. ⓓ Lt, N, CH, TV, Ac, con 120, CF, 3 st. £ BB fr £19·50, DB fr £28·50, WT £208·25, DT £29·75, DBB fr £25·20, WB, ①, Bk £3·75, L £4·55, D £5·70, cc 1 2 3 5 6.
★**Solna,** *Ullet Rd, L17 3AD.*
☎ 051-733 1943.
Aachen, H, z, *91 Mount Pleasant, L3 5TB.* ☎ 051-709 3477. C. ➤ 17 bedrs, 1 bp, 6 sh, 3 ba, TV. ⓓ CH, TV, Dgs, CP 2, G 3, CF. £ BB £12–£16, DB £20–£27, WT (b) £105, (c) £84, ①, Bk £3, D £3·75, cc 1 2 3 4 5 6.

Repairers: Camerons of Crosby Ltd, Crosby Rd North, Waterloo.
☎ 051-928 6434.
Dudlow Motor Co, Menlove Gardens West. ☎ 051-722 2396.
Jaguar House Ltd, 782–790 Queens Drive. ☎ 051-220 4557.
Rushton Garage, Lark La. ☎ 051-727 1948.
Rescue Service: Altway Service Station Ltd, 136 Altway, Old Roan, 10. ☎ 051-525 3277.
Avenue Service Station, Hunts Cross Av, Woolton. ☎ 051-428 4267.
Calton Motor Co Ltd, 362 Smithdown Rd. ☎ 051-733 7207.

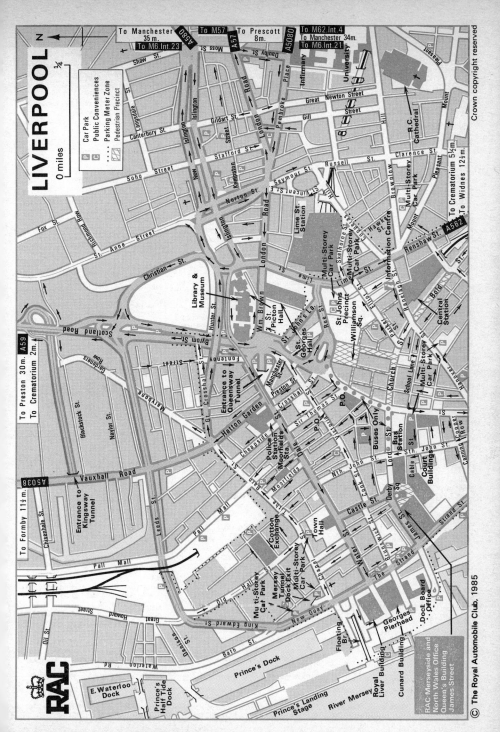

LIVERPOOL

0 miles ¼

N ←

Legend:
- P Car Park
- C Public Conveniences
- ····· Parking Meter Zone
- Pedestrian Precinct

To Manchester 35 m.
To M6.Int.23
A580

To M57
A57

To Prescott 8m.

To M62.Int.4
To Manchester 34m.
To M6.Int.21
A5080

Curphey & Collett, 193a Crosby Rd, South. ☎ 051-928 3921.
Ellison Motors, 1 Cheviot Rd. ☎ 051-228 2911.
Inter-City Recovery Service, 63 Durning Rd. ☎ 051-263 222.▲

LIVERSEDGE West Yorkshire. Map 25F
Wakefield 10, London 192, Bradford 7, Huddersfield 7½, Leeds 10.

Rescue Service: Seagull Motor Company (Cleckheaton) Ltd, 631 Halifax Rd, Hightown. ☎ Cleckheaton (0274) 870231.

LIVERTON Devon. Map 3D
Pop 510. Chudleigh Knighton 3, London 181, Ashburton 5½, Bovey Tracey 2½, Newton Abbot 5.
Golf Newton Abbot (Stover) 18h. **See** Dartmoor, Haytor Rocks.

Rescue Service: W J Stamp & Son, Benedicts Garage & Filling Station. ☎ Bickington (062 682) 338.

LIZARD Cornwall. Map 2E
Pop 810. Helston 11, London 282, Falmouth 19.
Golf Mullion, Helston 18h. **See** Lighthouse, open to public.

■★★**Housel Bay,** *Housel Cove, TR12 7PG.* ☎ (0326) 290417. C 14. ⇔ 27 bedrs, 10 bp, 3 bps, 5 ba, TV, Dgs. ✗ mc, at, LD 8.30. 🅿 CH, TV, ns, CP 30, G 2, 1 st. £ BB £13–£25, DB £16–£44, DBB £14–£28, ②, Bk £4·50, D £8·50, cc 1 2 6, Dep.

■★★**Lizard,** *TR12 7NQ.* ☎ (0326) 290456. Open Mar–Oct. RS Mar & Oct. C. ⇔ 10 bedrs, 1 bp, 2 bps, 3 ba, Dgs. ✗ mc, LD 8. 🅿 TV, Dgs, CP 20, CF, 0 st. £ BB £11·50–£13·50, DB £23–£27, WT £122·50, DT £22, DBB £18·25–£20, ②, Bk £3·50, D £7, Dep a.

■★**Polbrean,** *Sea Front, The Lizard, TR12 7NT.* ☎ (0326) 290418. Open Mar–Oct. C. ⇔ 11 bedrs, 1 bp, 3 bps, 3 ba, TV, Dgs. ✗ a l c, mc, at, LD 9. 🅿 ch, TV, Dgs, CP 25, U 3, Ac, sp, CF, 3 BGf, 2 st. £ BB £13·80–£16·80, DB £27·60–£30·60, WT £98–£102, DT £20·70, WB, ①, Bk £3·50, D £6·90, cc 1 3 6.

Mounts Bay, PH, xy, (R), *Penmenner Rd, TR12 7NP.* ☎ (0326) 290305. Open Mar–Dec (closed Xmas) & New Year. C. ⇔ 10 bedrs, 7 sh, 2 ba, Dgs. 🅿 TV, Dgs, CP 10, CF, 2 BGf, 2 st. £ BB fr £12, DB fr £25, ②, Bk £3, D £6.

Parc Brawse House, PH, x (R), *TR12 7NR.* ☎ (0326) 290466. Open Mar–Oct. C 7. ⇔ 6 bedrs, 1 ba, Dgs. 🅿 ch, TV, Dgs, CP 6, 3 st. £ BB £9–£9·50, DB £18–£19, WT (b) £85–£90, DT (b) £14–£15, ①, D £5·50.

Penmenner House, H, y (RI), *Penmenner Rd, TR12 7NR.* ☎ (0326) 290370. C. ⇔ 8 bedrs, 5 bps, 2 ba, Dgs. 🅿 CH, TV, CP 12, CF, 5 st. £ BB fr £9, DB fr £18, WT £94·50, DT £13·50, ②, Bk £4·75.

Rescue Service: Kynance Garage, Mile End. ☎ (0326) 290368.
Lizard Garage. ☎ (0326) 290216.

LODDON Norfolk, Map 16B
Pop 1,475. Scole 21, London 117, Aldeburgh 30, Great Yarmouth 15, Lowestoft 16, Norwich 10, Saxmundham 26.
EC Wed. **MD** Fri. **Golf** Bungay 18h. **See** Holy Trinity Church.

Repairer: Browne & Son (Loddon) Ltd, The Garage, High St. ☎ (0508) 20315.

LONDON Maps 8 and 9
The information given here is for the London postal districts.
Pop Greater London 7,211,910.
Inner London (former admin county) 3,200,484.
RAC Pall Mall Clubhouse Ltd, *Pall Mall, SW1Y 5HS.* ☎ 01-930 2345.
RAC Motoring Services Ltd, *49 Pall Mall, SW1Y 5JG.* ☎ 01-839 7050.
RAC Motor Sports Association Ltd, *31 Belgrave Square, SW1X 8QH.* ☎ 01-235 8601.
Area Stations with Parking. See p. 51.
Parking Places. See p. 52.
Street Maps. See p. 56.
Theatres and Cinemas. See p. 54.
🆔 London Tourist Board, 26 Grosvenor Gdns, SW1W 0DU. ☎ 01-730 0791.
English Tourist Board, 4 Grosvenor Gdns, SW1W 0DU. ☎ 01-730 3400. Also British Tourist Authority, 64 St James's St, SW1A 1NF. ☎ 01-499 9325.
The London Hotels list is a selection of establishments of all types classified in accordance with a detailed specification, the summarised version of which will be found on page (116). These hotels will be found to conform to the requirements of the classification granted and in some respects may well exceed the minimum requirements of that classification. The tariffs were obtained from the hotels just prior to publication of this Handbook but, of course, are liable to change and should be confirmed if a booking is to be effected. The Club cannot be held responsible for changes in tariff charges which may have occurred.

For London postal districts see the map on pages 8–9 of the atlas section.

E1
★★★★**Tower,** *St Katharine's Way, E1 9LD.* ☎ 01-481 2575. C. ⇔ 834 bedrs, 834 bp, TV. ✗ a l c, mc, at, LD 10.30. 🅿 Lt, N, CH, G 92, CP 40, con 180, CF. £ BB fr £58·25, DB fr £73·50, WB, ②, Bk £5·25, L £7·50, D £9·95, cc 1 2 3 4 5 6, Dep b.

E2
Rescue Service: J & G Motors, Three Colts La, Bethnal Green. ☎ 01-729 2465.

E3
Repairer: O M C Motor Co, 7 Blondin St, Bow. ☎ 01-980 0929

E7
Repairer: Freeman & Co (Stratford) Ltd, 2 Earlham Grove. ☎ 01-534 6842.
MC Repairer: Kaseys Motorcycles, 10 Woodford Rd. ☎ 01-555 3335.
Rescue Service: Leba Motor Services (Valenford Ltd), Forest Service Station, 605 Romford Rd. ☎ 01-472 2932 & 4032.
Lovelock Motors Ltd, 140 Earlham Grove. ☎ 01-534 4101.

E8
Rescue Service: East City Garages (Kingsland) Ltd, 297 Kingsland Rd. ☎ 01-254 7171.
G & W Motors, 1 Dunston St. ☎ 01-254 2416.

E11
Repairer: Eagle Garage (Snaresbrook) Ltd, 74 Hollybush Hill. ☎ 01-989 0041.

Rescue Service: Leytonstone Motors, 725 High Rd. ☎ 01-539 1779 and 7457. Steering lock keys cut.

E12
Repairer: Ferndale Garage, 2 Rectory Rd. ☎ 01-478 1213.

E13
Rescue Service: D & W Motor Repairs, 6 Prince Regent La, Plaistow. ☎ 01-552 8928.

E14
Repairer: Tyler's (London) Ltd, 240 Brunswick Rd. ☎ 01-987 3477.

E16
Rescue Service: Salisbury Garage, 1 Blanche St. ☎ 01-476 2535.

E18
Grove Hill, H, z (RI), *38 Grove Hill, South Woodford, E18 3JG.* ☎ 01-989 3344. C. ⇔ 21 bedrs, 3 bp, 2 bps, 5 sh, 3 ba, TV, Dgs. 🅿 ch, TV, Dgs, CP 8, U 4, CF, 2 BGf, 3 st. £ BB £13·80–£20·12, DB £28·75–£29·90, ②, Bk £2·15, D £6·95.▲

N1
Rescue Service: Santi Sferrino, 184 Pentonville Rd. ☎ 01-837 1376.

N2
Repairer: Arcade Motors Ltd, Lynton Garage, Fortis Green. ☎ 01-883 4036.
Rescue Service: Arcade Motors Ltd, Lynton Garage. ☎ 01-883 4036.

N4
Redland, H, z (Unl), *418 Seven Sisters Rd, N4 2LX.* ☎ 01-800 1826. C. ⇔ 22 bedrs, 2 sh, 6 ba, TV. 🅿 CH, TV, CP 11, CF, 3 BGf, 0 st, Dis. £ BB £13·25, DB £21·85, DT (b) £10·95, ②, Bk £2·50, cc 1 2 3 5.▲
Royal Park, H, yz, *352 Seven Sisters Road, Finsbury Pk, N4 2PQ.* ☎ 01-800 0528.

N6
Repairer: Snelling, E A Ltd, 438 Archway Rd. ☎ 01-340 3456.

N7
Rescue Service: Exan Car Services, 1 Hillmarton Rd. ☎ 01-607 5496.

N8
Aber, G, z (Unl), *89 Crouch Hill, N8 9EG.* ☎ 01-340 2847.
Highgate Lodge, H, z (Unl), *9 Waverley Rd, Crouch Hill, N8 9QS.* ☎ 01-340 5601. C. ⇔ 23 bedrs, 4 ba, Dgs. 🅿 TV, Dgs, CP 4, 2 st. £ BB £11–£12·10, DB £18·60–£20·46, WT (c) £60·53–£66·58, DT (b) £13–£15, ①.
Rescue Service: Kemmys Service Garage, 114a Effingham Rd. ☎ 01-340 2043.

N9
Rescue Service: Enfield Garages Ltd, 38a Bury St. ☎ 01-804 1949 and 5939.

N10
Princes, H, z (Unl), *36 Princes Av, Muswell Hill, N10 3LR.* ☎ 01-883 5676. C. ⇔ 20 bedrs, 4 ba. 🅿 CH, TV, CP 4, CF. £ BB £7–£9, DB £15, WT (c) £42–£54, ①.
Raglan Hall, H, z, *8 Queens Av, Muswell Hill, N10 3NS.* ☎ 01-883 5700. C. ⇔ 42 bedrs, 9 bp, 7 bps, 15 sh, 4 ba, TV, Dgs. 🅿 CH, TV, CF, 2 BGf, 2 st. £ BB £13–£19·50, DB £22–£29, ②, Bk £3, cc 1 2 5.

N13
Rescue Service: K E L Motors, R/O 141 Bowes Rd. ☎ 01-888 9842.

N14

Repairer: Sheborn Motors, 25 Hampden Sq, Southgate. ☎ 01-368 5861.
Rescue Service: Chandos, Hazelwood Garage, Hazelwood La. ☎ 01-886 8644.
Grovelands Park Service Station, Winchmore Hill Rd. ☎ 01-886 2481.

N22

Repairer: Garwood's Garages Ltd, 419 High Rd. ☎ 01-888 6663.

NW1

▣★★★M Kennedy, *Cardington St, NW1 2LP.* ☎ 01-387 4400. C. ⋈ 320 bedrs, 320 bp, TV. ✗ a l c, mc, at, LD 9.30. ▣ Lt, N, CH, Dgs, G 10, Ac, con, CF, 30 BGf. £ BBc fr £38·50, DBc fr £49·50, ⚊, cc 1 2 3 5 6.

Rescue Service: C & S Motors, Somers Town Depot, 89 Midland Rd. ☎ 01-380 1003.

NW2

Clearview House, G, z (Unl), *161 Fordwych Rd, Cricklewood, NW2 3NG.* ☎ 01-452 9773. C 5. ⋈ 6 bedrs, 2 ba, TV. ▣ CH, TV, 2 st. £ BB fr £7, DB fr £14, ⚊.
Garth, H, z (R), *72 Hendon Way, Cricklewood, NW2 2NL.* ☎ 01-455 4742. C. ⋈ 56 bedrs, 25 bp, 15 bps, 9 ba, TV. ▣ CH, TV, CP 36, CF, 20 BGf, 3 st. £ BBc £19·95–£22, DBc £30–£40, ⚊, cc 1 2 3 4 5 6.▲

NW3

★★★★Holiday Inn, *King Henry's Rd, NW3 3ST.* ☎ 01-722 7711. C. ⋈ 291 bedrs, 291 bp, ns, TV, Dgs. ✗ mc, at, LD 10.30. ▣ Lt, CH, Dgs, CP 50, G 75, Ac, sp, sb, sol, gym, con 250, CF, 3 st. £ BB £67·85–£73·43, DB £89·70–£96·73, WB, ⚊, Bk £5·75, L £11·75, D £12, cc 1 2 3 4 5 6, Dep b.
★★★★M Ladbroke Clive, *Primrose Hill Rd, Hampstead, NW3 3MA.* ☎ 01-586 2233. C. ⋈ 84 bedrs, 84 bp, TV, Dgs. ✗ a l c, mc, at, LD 10. ▣ Lt, N, CH, CP 15, ·G 2, Ac, con 300, CF, 2 st. £ BB £47, DB £62, WB, ⚊, Bk £6, L £10, D £10, c 1 2 3 5 6, Dep.
★★★Charles Bernard, *5 Frognall, NW3 6AL.* ☎ 01-794 0101. C. ⋈ 57 bedrs, 57 bp, TV, Dgs. ✗ mc, at, LD 9.30. ▣ Lt, N, CH, TV, Dgs, CP 25, con 25, CF. £ BB fr £36·80, DB fr £48·30, WB, ⚊, D £7·50, cc 1 2 3 5 6, Dep.
★★★M Post House (TH), *Haverstock Hill, NW3 4RB.* ☎ 01-794 8121. C. ⋈ 140 bedrs, 140 bp, TV, Dgs. ✗ a l c, mc, at, LD 10. ▣ Lt, N, CH, Dgs, CP 70, Ac, CF, 1 st. £ BB £46·50, DB £59·50, WB, ⚊, cc 1 2 3 4 5 6, Dep (Xmas).
★★★Swiss Cottage (R), *Adamson Rd, NW3 3HP.* ☎ 01-722 2281. C. ⋈ 65 bedrs, 65 bp, TV. ✗ a l c, mc, at, LD 9. ▣ Lt, N, CH, CP 5, Ac, con, CF. £ BB £30–£54·50, DB £45–£60, WB, ⚊, Bk £5, L £6·50, D £8·50, cc 1 2 3 4 5 6, Dep b.

NW4

★★★★Hendon Hall, *Ashley La, NW4 1HF.* ☎ 01-203 3341. C. ⋈ 52 bedrs, 8 bp, 3 bps, 2 ba, TV, Dgs. ✗ a l c, mc, at, LD 10.30. ▣ Lt, N, CH, Dgs, CP 100, Ac, con 250, CF, 6 BGf, 1 st. £ BB £39, DB £42·50, WB, ⚊, Bk £4·50, L £6·95, D £6·95, cc 1 2 3 5, Dep b.

NW5

Specialist Body Repairer: Metro Coachworks Ltd, Holmes Road Garage, Holmes Rd. ☎ 01-267 1590.

NW6

Dawson House, z (Unl), *72 Canfield Gdns, NW6 3ED.* ☎ 01-624 0079. C 6. ⋈ 15 bedrs, 3 ba. ▣ CH, TV, Dgs. £ BB £9–£10, DB £18–£19, ⚊.▲
McKenna's, G, z (Unl), *8 Burton Rd, NW6 7LW.* ☎ 01-624 6489.

Repairer: Cavendish Motors (Kilburn) Ltd, Cavendish Rd. ☎ 01-459 0046.
Specialist Body Repairer: Cavendish Motors (Kilburn) Ltd, Cavendish Rd. ☎ 01-459 0046.
Rescue Service: A B Dyne (Motors) Ltd, 52 Iverson Rd. ☎ 01-624 9036.
Carlton Garages, 319 West End La. ☎ 01-435 9631.
Central Garage, Canterbury Rd, Kilburn. ☎ 01-286 7766.
Challis's Garage, Kilburn Park Rd. ☎ 01-624 9145.
Maygrove Motors Ltd, Maygrove Rd. ☎ 01-624 0177.
Raybury Motors (Engineers), 28 Malvern Mews. ☎ 01-624 0263.
Wellwin Motors, Broomsleigh St, West Hampstead. ☎ 01-435 8551.

NW7

▣★★★M TraveLodge (TH), (RI), *Scratchwood Service Area, M1 Motorway nr Hendon, NW7 3HB.* ☎ 01-906 0611. C. ⋈ 100 bedrs, 100 bp, TV, Dgs. ✗ mc. ▣ N, CH, Dgs, CP 120, Ac, con 40, CF, 1 st. £ BB £30·50, DB £41, WB, ⚊, cc 1 2 3 4 5 6. Meals are served in the adjacent Motorway Service Area Restaurant.

Repairer: Featherstone Garage, Bunns La. ☎ 01-959 2665.
Rescue Service: Arcade Motors Ltd, Scratchwood Service Area, Ellesmere Av, Mill Hill. ☎ 01-959 2150 & 1293.

NW8

Repairers: Charles Follett Ltd (Service), 6 Hall Rd, St John's Wood. ☎ 01-289 2211.
Volkswagon (North London) Ltd, 46 Lodge Rd. ☎ 01-286 8000.
Rescue Service: Enterprise Garages, Langford Place. ☎ 01-286 1191.
Oslo Court Garage Ltd, Culworth St, Prince Albert Rd, St John's Wood. ☎ 01-722 9782.

NW9

Repairer: Cole & Kirby Ltd, Kingsbury Circle, Kingsbury. ☎ 01-907 8821.

NW10

Repairers: Godfrey Davis (Wembley) Ltd, Neasden La. ☎ 01-450 8000.
V. M. S. Garages Ltd, 63 North Acton Rd. ☎ 01-965 1515.
Specialist Body Repairer: Godfrey Davis (Wembley) Ltd, Neasden La. ☎ 01-450 8000.
Rescue Service: A & S Pegasus Complex Ltd, Pegasus Complex, Trenmar Gardens, Harlesden. ☎ 01-969 4727.
Park Auto Centre Ltd, 62 Park Par, Harlesden. ☎ 01-961 1415.

NW11

Central, PH, z (Unl), *35 Hoop La, Golders Green, NW11 8BS.* ☎ 01-458 5636. C. ⋈ 36 bedrs, 18 bp, 4 ba. ▣ CH, TV, CP 10, CF, 9 BGf. £ BB £20–£30, DB £30–£40, ⚊.
Croft Court, H, z (Unl), *44 Ravenscroft Av, NW11 8AY.* ☎ 01-458 3331. C. ⋈ 18 bedrs, 8 bp, 9 bps, 1 sh, 4 ba, TV, Dgs. ▣ CH, TV, CP 4, CF, 2 BGf, 2 st. £ BB £15–

£24, DB £24–£32, WT (c) £100–£160, DT (b) £21·50–£30·50, ⚊, Bk £2·75, D £6·50.
Hazelwood House, PH, z (Unl), *865 Finchley Rd, Golders Green, NW11 8LX.* ☎ 01-458 8884.▲

Rescue Service: C B Motors, 9 Hoop La. ☎ 01-455 3373.

SE1

Repairer: First Choice Cars (Sales & Service) Ltd, 108–111 Wootton St, Waterloo. ☎ 01-928 1922.▲
Specialist Body Repairer Add-Life Motors, 6 Burrell St, Southwark. ☎ 01-633 0557.
Rescue Service: Carspot, 344 St James Rd. ☎ 01-237 0913.
Southwark Bridge Service Station Ltd, 101 Southwark Bridge Rd. ☎ 01-231 2055 & 01-237 9136.

SE3

Bardon Lodge, PH, z (RI) *15 Stratheden Rd, Blackheath, SE3 7TH.* ☎ 01-853 4051. C. ⋈ 10 bedrs, 10 sh, 3 ba, TV. ▣ CH, TV, CP 10, CF, 10 st. £ BB £17·50–£20, DB £29·50–£34, ⚊.
Stonehall House, PH, (Unl), *35 Westcombe Park Rd, Blackheath, SE3 7RE.* ☎ 01-858 8706. C. ⋈ 22 bedrs, 1 bps, 5 ba, Dgs. ▣ CH, TV, CF, 1 st. £ BB £12, DB £23, WT (c) £72, ⚊, Bk £3, HT £3.

SE8

Rescue Service: Parkside Service Station, Evelyn St. ☎ 01-692 5172.

SE9

Yardley Court, G, z (Unl), *18 Court Yard, SE9 5PZ.* ☎ 01-850 1850. Closed 1 week Xmas. C 3. ⋈ 9 bedrs, 3 bps, 3 ba, TV. ▣ CH, TV, CP 8, 2 st. £ BB £16, DB £24–£32.

Repairer: Scott's (Mottingham) Ltd, Dorset Rd. ☎ 01-857 2231.

SE10

Rescue Service: South Street Service Station, 123 Greenwich South St, Greenwich. ☎ 01-692 4115.

SE11

★★London Park, *Elephant & Castle, SE11 4QU.* ☎ 01-735 9191. C. ⋈ 388 bedrs, 40 bp, 240 bps, TV. ✗ mc, LD 8.45. ▣ Lt, N, CH, Dgs, CP 16, con 120, CF, 1 st. £ BB fr £16·50, DB fr £28, WB, ⚊, L £6·25, D £7, cc 1 2 3 5, Dep b.

SE12

Repairer: Bellamy's (London) Ltd, 2 Burnt Ash Hill. ☎ 01-857 2163.
Rescue Service: Ash Hill Service Station, 155 Burnt Ash Hill, Lee. ☎ 01-857 0022.

SE13

Repairers: Cedars Garage (Lewisham) Ltd, Lee Ter. ☎ 01-852 4616.
Fry's Motor Works Ltd, 104 and 152a Lee High Rd. ☎ 01-862 0111.

SE18

Repairers: Kings Highway Garage Ltd, 43 Kings Highway. ☎ 01-854 1766.
Stormont Engineering Co Ltd, Beresford House, Beresford St. ☎ 01-854 7771.
Rescue Service: Aseco Garage, 154a Sandyhill Rd, Woolwich. ☎ 01-854 0224.

SE19

★★Aucklands (R), *153 Auckland Rd, Upper Norwood, SE19 2RH.* ☎ 01-771 5161. C. ⋈ 35 bedrs, 13 bp, 22 bps, TV, Dgs. ✗ mc, at, LD 9.45. ▣ N, CH, TV, Dgs,

CP 40, Ac, con 70, CF, 1 st. £ BB £25, DB £35, DBB fr £28, WB, ①, Bk £3·25, L £1·75, D £7, cc 1 2 3 5, Dep.
Crystal Palace Tower, PH, z (Unl), *114 Church Rd, SE19 2UB.* ✆ 01-653 0176. C. 🍴 12 bedrs, 4 ba, TV, Dgs. ⓓ CH, TV, CP 10, CF, 4 BGf, 4 st. £ BB £9·50–£10, DB £16–£17, ①.

SE20
Rescue Service: Queens Motors, 89 Maple Rd, Penge. ✆ 01-778 6666 and 01-659 5900.
Southern Panel Co Ltd, Meaford Way, Penge. ✆ 01-778 2281.

SE23
Rutz, G, z (Unl), *16 Vancouver Rd, SE23 2AF.* ✆ 01-699 3071. Closed Xmas. C. 🍴 5 bedrs, 1 bp, 1 sh, 2 ba, ns. ⓓ CH, TV, ns, CP 2, CF, 2 st. £ BB £10–£11, DB £18–£20, WT (b) £91, DT (b) £14, ①, Bk £2, L £2, D £4.

SE24
Rescue Service: Westcourt Services Ltd, 146 Norwood Rd, Tulse Hill. ✆ 01-674 7373.

SE25
Toscana, G, z (RI), *19 South Norwood Hill, SE25 6AA.* ✆ 01-653 3962. Closed Xmas. C. 🍴 8 bedrs, 2 ba, TV. ⓓ CH, TV, CP 8, 12 st. £ BB £13·50–£14·50, DB £21–£22, WT (c) £90, ②.

SW1
★★★★★**Berkeley,** *Wilton Pl, Knightsbridge, SW1X 7RL.* ✆ 01-235 6000. C. 🍴 160 bedrs, 160 bp, TV. ✖ a l c, LD 11.45. ⓓ Lt, N, CH, G 50, sp, sb, CF, 3 st. £ cc 1 2 3.
★★★★★**Hyatt Carlton Tower,** *Cadogan Place, SW1X 9PY.* ✆ 01-235 5411. C. 🍴 212 bedrs, 212 bp, TV. ✖ a l c, mc, at, LD 11.30. ⓓ Lt, N, CH, G, con 150, CF, 1 st. £ BB £155, DB £180, WB, ②, Bk £7·20, L £15·50, D £20, cc 1 2 3 4 5 6, Dep b.
★★★★★**Hyde Park** (TH), *Knightsbridge, SW1Y 7LA.* ✆ 01-235 2000. C. 🍴 179 bedrs, 179 bp, TV, Dgs. ✖ a l c, mc, at, LD 10.30. ⓓ Lt, N, CH, Dgs, con 300, CF, 2 st. £ BB £109·50, DB £131, ①, cc 1 2 3 4 5 6.
★★★★★**Sheraton Park Tower,** *101 Knightsbridge, SW1X 7RN.* ✆ 01-235 8050. RS Jun–Sept. C. 🍴 295 bedrs, 295 bp, 4 ba, TV. ✖ a l c, mc, at, LD 11. ⓓ Lt, N, CH, con 50, CF. £ BB £129·50–£134·50, DB £149·40–£156·30, ②, Bk £8, L £15·50, D £25, cc 1 2 3 4 5 6.
★★★★**Cavendish** (TH), *Jermyn St, SW1Y 6JF.* ✆ 01-930 2111. C. 🍴 253 bedrs, 253 bp, TV, Dgs. ✖ a l c, mc, at, LD 11. ⓓ Lt, N, CH, Dgs, CP 10, G 80, Ac, con 80, CF, 0 st. £ BB £66·50, DB £97, WB, ①, cc 1 2 3 4 5 6.
★★★★**Dukes,** *St James's Place, SW1A 1NY.* ✆ 01-491 4840. C. 🍴 53 bedrs, 53 bp, TV. ✖ a l c, mc, LD 24 hr service. ⓓ N, CH, con, CF. £ BB fr £82, DB fr £123, ②, Bk £7, L £25, D £25, cc 1 2 3 4 5 6, Dep b.
★★★★**Goring,** *Beeston Pl, Grosvenor Gardens, SW1W 0JW.* ✆ 01-834 8211. C. 🍴 100 bedrs, 100 bp, TV. ✖ a l c, mc, at, LD 10.30. ⓓ Lt, N, CH, CP 10, U 4, con 50, CF, 5 st. £ BB fr £62·50, DB fr £93, ①, Bk £6·50, L £12, D £14, cc 1 2 3 4 6, Dep b.
★★★★**Lowndes Thistle,** *Lowndes St, SW1X 9ES.* ✆ 01-235 6020. C. 🍴 80 bedrs, 80 bp, ns, TV. ✖ a l c, LD 9.40. ⓓ Lt,

N, CH, CF, 0 st. £ BB £75–£84, DB £90–£107, WB, ②, Bk £6, cc 1 2 3 4 5 6, Dep b.
🔲★★★★**Royal Westminster Thistle,** *Buckingham Palace Rd, SW1W 0QT.* ✆ 01-834 1821. Closed Dec 25–27. RS Bank Holidays. C. 🍴 136 bedrs, 136 bp, ns, TV. ✖ a l c, mc, at, LD 11.15. ⓓ Lt, N, Dgs, Ac, con 150, CF, 6 st. £ BB £59·50, DB £71, WB, ①, Bk £3·75, L £10, D £10, cc 1 2 3 4 5 6, Dep.
★★★★**St Ermin's,** *Caxton St, SW1H 0QW.* ✆ 01-222 7888. C. 🍴 246 bedrs, 246 bp, 4 ba, TV, Dgs. ✖ a l c, mc, at, LD 10.15. ⓓ Lt, N, CH, Dgs, CP 22, Ac, con 200, CF, 4 st. £ BBc £49, DBc £59, DT £50, WB, ①, Bk £5·75, L £8·75, D £8·75, cc 1 2 3 5, Dep b.
★★★**Royal Horseguards Thistle,** *Whitehall Court, SW1A 2EJ.* ✆ 01-839 3400. C. 🍴 284 bedrs, 284 bp, ns, TV. ✖ a l c, mc, at, LD 10.30. ⓓ Lt, N, CH, con 100, CF, 3 st. £ WB, ①, Bk £3·75, L £12·50, D £12·50, cc 1 2 3 4 5 6, Dep b.
★★★**Rubens,** *Buckingham Palace Rd, SW1W 0PS.* ✆ 01-834 1736.
★**Ebury Court** (Cl and R), *26 Ebury St, SW1W 0LY.* ✆ 01-730 8147. C. 🍴 39 bedrs, 12 bp, 2 sh, 12 ba, Dgs. ✖ a l c, mc, at, LD 9. ⓓ Lt, N, TV, CF. £ BB £28, DB £41·50–£52, WB, ②, cc 1 3, Dep.
Caswell, PH, z (Unl), *25 Gloucester St, SW1V 2DB.* ✆ 01-834 6345. C. 🍴 17 bedrs, 5 ba. ⓓ CH, TV, 5 st. £ BB £12–£15, DB £17–£24, WT (c) £60–£100, ①.
Chesham House, G, z (Unl), *64 Ebury St, Belgravia, SW1W 9QD.* ✆ 01-730 8513.
Diplomat, H, z (Unl), *2 Chesham St, Belgrave Sq, SW1X 8DT.* ✆ 01-235 1544. 🍴 26 bedrs, 16 bp, 10 bps, TV, Dgs. ⓓ Lt, CH, Dgs, 4 st. £ BBc £29·90, DBc £31·05–£39·10, ②, cc 1 2 3 5.
Easton, G, z (RI), *36 Belgrave Rd, SW1V 1RG.* ✆ 01-834 5938. C. 🍴 55 bedrs, 7 bp, 4 bps, 10 ba. ⓓ CH, TV, 4 st. £ BB £12·50–£16, DB £17–£30, ①.
Elizabeth, H, z (Unl), *37 Eccleston Sq, SW1V 1PB.* ✆ 01-828 6812. C. 🍴 24 bedrs, 1 bp, 2 bps, sh, 6 ba, TV. ⓓ CH, TV, ns, CF, 2 BGf, 3 st. £ BB £18–£19, DB £29–£42, ①.
Executive', H, z (RI), *57 Pont St, SW1X 0BD.* ✆ 01-581 2424.
Hamilton House, H, z, *60 Warwick Way, SW1V 1SA.* ✆ 01-821 7113.
Hanover, PH, z (Unl), *30 St George's Dr, SW1V 4BN.* ✆ 01-834 0134.
Stanley House, H, z, *19 Belgrave Rd, SW1V 1RB.* ✆ 01-834 5042.

SW2
Repairer: Hearn Bros Ltd, 94 Brixton Hill. ✆ 01-674 2888.

SW3
★★★★**Capital,** *Basil St, SW3 1AT.* ✆ 01-589 5171. C. 🍴 60 bedrs, 60 bp, TV, Dgs. ✖ a l c, mc, at, LD 10.30. ⓓ Lt, N, CH, Dgs. ns, G 12, CF, 4 st. £ BB fr £85·30, DB fr £104·48, ①, Bk £5·95, L £14·50, cc 1 2 3 4 5, Dep b.
★★★**Basil Street,** *Basil St, SW3 1AH.* ✆ 01-581 3311. C. 🍴 92 bedrs, 67 bp, 10 ba, TV, Dgs. ✖ a l c, mc, at, LD 9.45. ⓓ Lt, N, CH, ns, con, CF, 8 st. £ B £33–£55, BD £52–£75·50, WB, ②, Bk £3·25, L £8·95, D £13·95, cc 1 2 3 4 5, Dep b.
Blair House, H, *34 Draycott Pl, SW3 2SA.* ✆ 01-581 2323. C. 🍴 17 bedrs, 9 bp, 1 sh, 3 ba, TV, Dgs. ⓓ CH, TV, ns, CF, 2 BGf, 5 st. £ BB £22·50–£30·50, DB £35·50–£43·50, ①, cc 1 2 3 5.

Eden House, PH, z (Unl), *111 Old Church St, SW3 6DX.* ✆ 01-352 3403. C. 🍴 14 bedrs, 4 bp, 5 bps, 2 sh, TV, Dgs. ⓓ CH, Dgs, CF, 1 BGf, 5 st. £ BB £15–£35, DB £23–£42, ①, Bk £2·30, cc 1 2 3 5.
Knightsbridge, H, z (RI), *10 Beaufort Gdns, SW3 1PT.* ✆ 01-589 9271. Closed Xmas. C. 🍴 20 bedrs, 4 bp, 5 bps, 4 sh, 4 ba, TV. ⓓ CH, TV, CF, 2 BGf, 6 st. £ BBc £19·50–£26·60, DBc £27·40–£43·80, ①, cc 1 2 3.▲

SW4
Edwards, G, z (Unl), *91 Abbeville Rd, Clapham Common, SW4 9JL.* ✆ 01-622 6347. C 5. 🍴 6 bedrs, 2 ba, TV. ⓓ ch, 3 st. £ BB £8–£10, DB £14–£16, WT (c) £50–£65, ①.
Specialist Body Repairer: Nelsons Motor Body and Radiator Repair Co, 19 Jeffreys Rd. ✆ 01-622 9314.
Rescue Service: Lowood Garage, 12 King's Av, Clapham Park. ✆ 01-622 7174.

SW5
★★★★**M London International,** *147c Cromwell Rd, SW5 0TH.* ✆ 01-370 4200. C. 🍴 415 bedrs, 415 bp, TV, Dgs. ✖ mc, at, LD midnight. ⓓ Lt, N, CH, Dgs, Ac, con 200, CF. £ BB £40·50–£42, DB £50–£52, WB, ①, Bk £5·20, L £5·50, D £10, cc 1 2 3 5 6.
🔲★★★**Barkston,** *Barkston Gdns, Earls Court, SW5 0EW.* ✆ 01-373 7851. C. 🍴 76 bedrs, 76 bp, TV, Dgs. ✖ a l c, mc, LD 9.30. ⓓ Lt, N, CH, Dgs, Ac, con 100, CF, 2 st. £ BB fr £38·75, DB fr £49·50, ②, L £4, D £8, cc 1 2 3 4 5 6, Dep b.
Beaver, H, z (RI), *57 Philbeach Gdns, SW5 9ED.* ✆ 01-373 4553. Closed Xmas. C. 🍴 45 bedrs, 5 bp, 14 ba, Dgs. ⓓ CH, TV, Dgs, CP 20, U 3, CF, 7 BGf, 3 st. £ BB £12–£13, DB £19–£24, ①, Bk £2·50, cc 3.
Merlyn Court, H, z (Unl), *2 Barkston Gdns, SW5 0EN.* ✆ 01-370 1640. C. 🍴 17 bedrs, 2 sh, 6 ba, Dgs. ⓓ CH, TV, Dgs, CF. £ BB £10–£14, DB £16–£22, WT (c) fr £50, ①.

Rescue Service: Earls Court Motors, 12 Wetherby Mews. ✆ 01-993 1600.

SW6
Lindsay, H, z, *422–428 Fulham Rd, SW6 1DU.* ✆ 01-385 8561.

Specialist Body Repairer: J F Motors, Sotheron Rd. ✆ 01-736 8050.

SW7
★★★★**Gloucester,** *4 Harrington Gdns, SW7 4LH.* ✆ 01-373 6030. C. 🍴 531 bedrs, 531 bp, ns, TV, Dgs. ✖ a l c, mc, at, LD 12.30. ⓓ Lt, N, CH, Dgs, G 130, Ac, sb, sol, con 175, CF, 3 st. £ cc 1 2 3 4 5 6, Dep b.
🔲★★★**Forum,** *Cromwell Rd, SW7 4DN.* ✆ 01-370 5757. C. 🍴 908 bedrs, 908 bp, TV, Dgs. ✖ a l c, mc, at, LD 12.30. ⓓ Lt, N, CH, Dgs, G 75, Ac, con 300, CF, 1 st. £ BBc fr £46·50, DBc fr £59, WB, ②, Bk £3, L £5, D £6, cc 1 2 3 4 5 6, Dep b.
★★★**Onslow Court,** *109 Queens Gate, SW7 5LR.* ✆ 01-589 6300. C. 🍴 146 bedrs, 110 bp, 9 ba, TV, Dgs. ✖ a l c, mc, at, LD 10. ⓓ Lt, N, CH, Ac, con 80, CF, 3 st. £ BB £25–£30, DB £35–£45, WB, ①, Bk £3, L £5, D £5, cc 1 2 3 5 6, Dep b.
🔲★★★**Vanderbilt,** *76 Cromwell Rd, SW7 3AN.* ✆ 01-584 0491. C. 🍴 230 bedrs, 200 bp, 30 bps, TV, Dgs. ✖ a l c, mc, at, LD 10. ⓓ Lt, N, CH, Dgs, Ac, con 120, CF, 30 BGf, 10 st. £ BB £40·90, DB £55·90,

WB, ①, Bk £3, L £6·60, D £6·60,
cc 1 2 3 4 5 6, Dep.
Tudor Court, H, z (RI), *58 Cromwell Rd,
SW7 5BY.* ✆ 01-584 8273.

SW8
Repairer: F J Keen & Son Ltd, Queen's
Circus. ✆ 01-622 9922.
Rescue Service: Peter Roland Autos Ltd,
11 Palfrey Pl. ✆ 01-735 4080.

SW9
Rescue Service: Automex Garage, 507
Ridgeway Rd. ✆ 01-733 0554.

SW10
Rescue Service: Stamford Bridge Service
Station, 459 Fulham Rd. ✆ 01-351 4110.

SW11
Rescue Service: Parkgate Service Station
(Battersea) Ltd, 15–25 Parkgate Rd,
Battersea. ✆ 01-223 1926.

SW12
Rex House, H, z (Unl), *45 Endlesham Rd,
SW12 8JX.* ✆ 01-675 0228.

SW13
Arundel, H, z (Unl), *6 Arundel Terrace,
SW13 9DP.* ✆ 01-748 8005.

SW15
Lodge, H, yz, (RI), *52 Upper Richmond
Rd, Putney, SW15 2RR.* ✆ 01-874 1598.
Wilton, G, z (Unl), *2 Ravenna Rd, Putney,
SW15 6AW.* ✆ 01-789 3768.

SW16
Rescue Service: Central Garage, Voss
Court. ✆ 01-764 6054.
Green Lane Motor Co, 1 Hermitage La,
Streatham. ✆ 01-764 9966.

SW17
Repairer: Peacock, F H Ltd, 219 Balham
High Rd. ✆ 01-672 1271.

SW18
Repairers: H L Austin & Son Ltd, 60 West
Hill Rd. ✆ 01-874 6262.
Trinity Cars Ltd, 34 North Side,
Wandsworth Common. ✆ 01-874 1166.
Rescue Service: Naylor & Root Ltd, 25
East Hill, Wandsworth. ✆ 01-870 8711

SW19
Courts, H, z, (Unl), *85 Worple Rd,
SW19 4JH.* ✆ 01-946 0937.
Hatherley, H, z (RI), *87 Worple Rd,
SW19 4JH.* ✆ 01-946 5917.
Trochee, H, z (Unl), *52 Ridgway Pl,
SW19 4QP.* ✆ 01-946 1579. C. ↔ 18
bedrs, 3 bp, 6 bps, 3 ba, TV, Dgs. ⌂ CH, TV,
CP 10, CF, 4 BGf, 4 st. £ BB £15·50–
£18·50, DB £21–£24, ①, Bk £3·50, D £4.
Trochee, H, z (Unl), *21 Malcolm Rd,
Wimbledon, SW19 4AS.* ✆ 01-946 3924.
C. ↔ 17 bedrs, 3 ba, TV, Dgs. ⌂ CH, TV,
CP 6, CF, 2 st. £ BB £15·50, DB £21, ①, Bk
£3·50. ▲
Wimbledon, H (Unl), *78 Worple Rd,
SW19 4HZ.* ✆ 01-946 9265. C. ↔ 12
bedrs, 3 bp, 3 bps, 2 ba, TV, Dgs. ⌂ CH, TV,
CP 12, 1 BGf, 1 st, Dis. £ BB fr £16·95, DB
fr £26·95, ①, cc 1 3.
Worcester House, PH, z (Unl), *38
Alwyne Rd, Wimbledon, SW19 7AE.*
✆ 01-946 1300. C. ↔ 9 bedrs, 9 bps, TV,
CH, CF. £ BB £20·70–£26·45, DB £33·35–
£39·10, ①, D £8·50.

Rescue Service: Fawngrove Ltd, Lyon
House Filling Station, Hartfield Rd.
✆ 01-946 9365.

SW20
Repairer: Fullers of Malden Ltd, Kingston
By-Pass. ✆ 01-949 3331.

W1
★★★★★**Churchill,** *Portman Sq, W1A
4ZX.* ✆ 01-486 5800. C. ↔ 489 bedrs,
489 bp, TV, Dgs. ✗ a l c, mc, at. ⌂ Lt, N,
CH, G 60, con, CF. £ BB fr £119·41, DB fr
£143·60, ①, Bk £4·55, cc 1 2 3 4.
★★★★★**Claridge's,** *PO Box 513, Brook
St, W1Y 2AS.* ✆ 01-629 8860. C. ↔ 205
bedrs, 205 bp, TV. ✗ a l c, mc, at, LD
10.30. ⌂ Lt, N, CH, con 70, CF, 3 st. £ BBc
£85–£105, DBc £120–£145, WB, ①, Bk £5,
cc 1 2 3 6, Dep.
★★★★★**Connaught,** *Carlos Pl, W1Y
6AL.* ✆ 01-499 7070. C. ↔ 90 bedrs, 90
bp, TV. ✗ a l c, mc, at, LD 10.30. ⌂ Lt, N, CH,
CF, 3 st. £ L £17·80, D £17·95, cc 1 6.
★★★★★**Dorchester,** *Park La, W1A 2HJ.*
✆ 01-629 8888. C. ↔ 280 bedrs, 280 bp,
TV. ✗ a l c, mc, at, LD 11. ⌂ Lt, N, CH, G
40, con, CF, 4 st. £ cc 1 2 3 4 5 6, Dep b.
★★★★★**Grosvenor House** (TH), *Park
La, W1A 3AA.* ✆ 01-499 6363. C. ↔ 478
bedrs, 478 bp, TV, Dgs. ✗ a l c, mc, at, LD
10.30. ⌂ Lt, N, CH, Dgs, CP 20, G 100, Ac,
sp, sb, con 1,800, CF, 2 st. £ BB £99, DB
£116, ①, cc 1 2 3 4 5 6.
★★★★★**Inn On The Park,** *Hamilton Pl,
Park La, W1A 1AZ.* ✆ 01-499 0888. C.
↔ 228 bedrs, 228 bp, ns, TV, Dgs. ✗ a l c,
mc, at, LD 12. ⌂ Lt, N, CH, G 80, con 200,
CF. £ BB fr £131·10, DB fr £154·10, ①, Bk
£6·90, L £13·50, D £18, cc 1 2 3 4 5 6,
Dep b.
★★★★★**Ritz,** *PO Box 395, Piccadilly,
W1V 9DG.* ✆ 01-493 8181. C. ↔ 139
bedrs, 139 bp, TV. ✗ a l c, mc, at, LD 11.
⌂ Lt, N, CH, Ac, con, CF, 2 st. £ B fr £88,
BD fr £125, WB, ①, Bk £6·50, L £10·50, D
£21, cc 1 2 3 4 5 6, Dep.
★★★★**Athenaeum,** *Piccadilly, W1V 0BJ.*
✆ 01-499 3464. C. ↔ 112 bedrs, 112 bp,
TV. ✗ a l c, mc, at, LD 10.30. ⌂ Lt, N, CH,
con 45, CF, 3 st. £ BB fr £108, DB fr £130,
WB, ①, L £15·50, D £13, cc 1 2 3 4 5 6.
★★★★**Britannia,** *Grosvenor Sq, W1X
0DX.* ✆ 01-629 9400. C. ↔ 361 bedrs,
361 bp, ns, TV. ✗ a l c, mc, at, LD 10.30
(24 hr room service). ⌂ Lt, N, CH, Dgs, CP
20, G 180, Ac, con 100, CF, 4 st. £ B £92–
£95·45, BD £103·50–£106·95, WB, ①, Bk
£7, L £13·50, D £18, cc 1 2 3 4 5 6, Dep b.
★★★★**Brown's** (TH), *Albemarle St, W1A
4SW.* ✆ 01-493 6020. C. ↔ 130 bedrs,
130 bp, TV, Dgs. ✗ a l c, mc, at, LD 9.30.
⌂ Lt, N, CH, Dgs, con 75, CF, 2 BGf, 1 st,
Dis. £ BB £83·50, DB £115, ①,
cc 1 2 3 4 5 6, Dep (Xmas).
★★★★**Chesterfield,** *Charles St, W1X
8LX.* ✆ 01-491 2622. C. ↔ 85 bedrs, 85
bp, TV. ✗ a l c, mc, at, LD 10.30. ⌂ Lt, N,
CH, con 80, CF, 2 st. £ BB £77–£82, DB
£97–£100, DBB fr £90, ①, Bk £6·25, L £14,
D £14, cc 1 2 3 4 5 6, Dep.
★★★★**Cumberland** (TH), *PO Box 179,
1A Gt Cumberland Pl, W1A 4RF (Marble
Arch).* ✆ 01-262 1234. C. ↔ 910 bedrs,
910 bp, TV, Dgs. ✗ a l c, mc, at, LD 10.30.
⌂ Lt, N, CH, con 180, CF, 2 st. £ BB
£61·50, DB £83·50, WB, ①, cc 1 2 3 4 5 6.
★★★★**Holiday Inn,** *George St, Marble
Arch, W1M 6DM.* ✆ 01-723 1277. C.
↔ 241 bedrs, 241 bp, 2 ba, ns, TV, Dgs.
✗ a l c, mc, at, LD 10.30. ⌂ Lt, N, CH, Dgs,
CP 30, Ac, sp, sb, sol, con 150, CF, 0
st. £ BB fr £84·55, DB fr £101·05, DBB

£94·95, WB, ①, Bk £6·25, L £10·50, D
£10·50, cc 1 2 3 4 5 6, Dep.
★★★★**Hilton International London,**
Park La, W1A 2HH. ✆ 01-493 8000. C.
↔ 503 bedrs, 503 bp, 2 ba, ns, TV, Dgs.
✗ a l c, mc, at, LD 12. ⌂ Lt, N, CH, Dgs, G
300, con 1,200, CF, 3 st. £ BB £101·90–
£120, DB £131·80–£145, ②, Bk £6·90, L
£13·50, D £25, cc 1 2 3 4 5 6, Dep b.
★★★★**London Marriott,** *Grosvenor Sq,
W1A 4AW.* ✆ 01-493 1232. C. ↔ 229
bedrs, 229 bp, 4 ba, ns, TV. ✗ a l c, mc, at,
LD 24 hr service. ⌂ Lt, N, CH, CP 10, G 85,
Ac, con 600, CF, 0 st. £ BB £91·40–
£136·25, DB £112·65–£160·95, WB, ①, Bk
£7·50, L £12, D £15, cc 1 2 3 4 5, Dep.
★★★★**Mayfair,** *Stratton St, W1A 2AN.*
✆ 01-629 7777. C. ↔ 322 bedrs, 322 bp,
ns, TV. ✗ a l c, mc, at, LD 10.30. ⌂ Lt, N,
CH, con 200, CF, 0 st. £ B £108·10, BD
£121·90, ①, Bk £7, L £7·50, D £7·50,
cc 1 2 3 4 5 6.
★★★★**Park Lane,** *Brick St, Piccadilly,
W1A 4UA.* ✆ 01-499 6321. C. ↔ 321
bedrs, 321 bp, TV, Dgs. ✗ a l c, mc, at, LD
10.30. ⌂ Lt, N, CH, Dgs, G 180, Ac, con,
CF, 1 st. £ B £69·95–£76, BD £82·95–£91,
WB, ①, Bk £5, L £12·50, D £14,
cc 1 2 3 5 6, Dep b.
★★★★**Portman Inter-Continental,**
Portman Sq, W1H 9FL. ✆ 01-486 5844. C.
↔ 276 bedrs, 276 bp, TV. ✗ a l c, mc, at,
LD 11. ⌂ Lt, N, CH, G 440, con 350, 1 st.
£ BB fr £104·60, DB fr £122·95, ①, Bk
£6·85, L £8·40, cc 1 2 3 4 5 6.
★★★★**M Regent Crest,** *Carburton St,
W1P 8EE.* ✆ 01-388 2300. C. ↔ 320
bedrs, 320 bp, ns, TV, Dgs. ✗ a l c, mc, at,
LD 10.30. ⌂ Lt, N, CH, Dgs, Ac, con 800,
CF. £ B fr £51, BD fr £62, WB, ①, Bk £5·50,
cc 1 2 3 4 5 6, Dep b.
★★★★**St George's** (TH), *Langham Pl,
W1N 8QS.* ✆ 01-580 0111. C. ↔ 85
bedrs, 85 bp, TV, Dgs. ✗ a l c, mc, at, LD
10. ⌂ Lt, N, CH, Dgs, CP 2, Ac, CF, 0 st.
£ BB £63·50, DB £86, ①, cc 1 2 3 4 5 6.
■★★★★**Selfridge,** *Orchard St, W1H
0JS.* ✆ 01-408 2080. C. ↔ 298 bedrs, 298
bp, 4 ba, ns, TV. ✗ a l c, mc, at, LD 10.30.
⌂ Lt, N, CH, Ac, con 200, CF, 0 st. £ BB
£90·50–£96·50, DB £103–£113, WB, ②, L
£14, D £14, cc 1 2 3 4 5 6, Dep.
★★★★**Westbury** (TH), *PO Box 289, New
Bond St, W1A 4UH.* ✆ 01-629 7755. C.
↔ 256 bedrs, 256 bp, TV, Dgs. ✗ a l c, mc,
at, LD 10.30. ⌂ Lt, N, CH, Dgs, con 120,
CF, 5 BGf, 0 st, Dis. £ BB £82·50, DB £102,
WB, ①, cc 1 2 3 4 5 6.
★★★**Clifton-Ford,** *Welbeck St, W1M
8DN.* ✆ 01-486 6600.
★★★**Flemings,** *7 Half Moon St, W1Y
8BQ.* ✆ 01-499 2964. C. ↔ 140 bedrs,
140 bp, TV. ✗ a l c, mc, at, LD 10.30. ⌂ Lt,
N, CH, Ac, CF, 2 st. £ BB fr £49·90, DB fr
£64·90, ①, Bk £5, L £7·50, D £9·50,
cc 1 2 3 5.
★★★**Londoner,** *57 Welbeck St, W1M
8HS.* ✆ 01-935 4442. C. ↔ 142 bedrs,
142 bp, ns, TV, Dgs. ✗ a l c, mc, at, LD
9.45. ⌂ Lt, N, CH, Ac, CF. £ WB, Bk £2·50,
L £7·50, D £7·50, cc 1 2 3 5 6, Dep.
★★★**Mount Royal,** *Bryanston St, W1A
4UR (Marble Arch).* ✆ 01-629 8040. C.
↔ 700 bedrs, 700 bp, TV. ✗ a l c, mc, at.
⌂ Lt, N, CH, Dgs, Ac, con, CF, 50 BGf. £ B
fr £46·50, BD fr £56·50, WB, ①,
cc 1 2 3 5 6.
★★★**New Piccadilly,** *Piccadilly, W1A
0BH.* ✆ 01-734 8000. C. ↔ 318 bedrs,
318 bp, TV. ✗ a l c, mc, at, LD 24 hr

service. ⚐ Lt, N, CH, ns, Ac, sp, sc, sb, sol, gym, con 300, CF, 0 st. £ BB £109, DB £128, WB, ⊡, cc 1 2 3 4 5 6, Dep b.

■★★★Stratford Court, 350 Oxford St, W1N 0BY. ✆01-629 7474. C. ⋈ 139 bedrs, 139 bp, TV. ✘ a l c, mc, at, LD 10.30. ⚐ Lt, N, CH, con 30, CF. £ WB, Bk £5, L £8·25, D £8·25, cc 1 2 3 5, Dep.

■★★Green Park, Half Moon St, W1Y 8BP. ✆01-629 7522.

★★Mostyn, Bryanston St, W1H 0DE. ✆01-935 2361. C. ⋈ 125 bedrs, 114 bp, 5 ba, TV, Dgs. ✘ a l c, mc, at, LD 9.30. ⚐ Lt, N, CH, con 150, CF, 6 st. £ BBc fr £42, DBc fr £52, ⊡, Bk £5·50, L £8·50, D £8·50, cc 1 2 3 4 5 6, Dep.

★★Regent Palace (TH), Piccadilly Circus, W1A 4BZ. ✆01-734 7000. C. ⋈ 1,032 bedrs, 123 ba, TV. ✘ a l c, mc, at, LD 9. ⚐ Lt, N, ch, Dgs, Ac, con 120, CF, 0 st. £ BB £22·50, DB £36·50, WB, ⊡, cc 1 2 3 4 5 6, Dep (Xmas).

★★Royal Angus Thistle, 39 Coventry St, W1V 8EL. ✆01-930 4033. C. ⋈ 92 bedrs, 90 bp, 2 bps, ns, TV, Dgs. ✘ a l c, mc, at, LD 10. ⚐ Lt, N, CH, Dgs, Ac, CF, 2 st. £ BB £44–£52, DB £57–£64, WB, ⊡, Bk £3·75, L £7, D £7, cc 1 2 3 4 5 6, Dep b.

Bentinck House, PH, z (Unl), 20 Bentinck St, W1M 5RL. ✆01-935 9141.

Bickenhall House, H, z (R), 119 Gloucester Pl, W1H 3PJ. ✆01-935 3401.

Georgian House, H, z (Rl), 87 Gloucester Pl, W1H 3PG. ✆01-935 2211. C 5. ⋈ 19 bedrs, 14 bp, 5 bps, TV. ⚐ Lt, CH, TV, 3 BGf, 3 st. £ BBc £18–£22, DB £26–£32, ⊡, cc 2 3.

Glynne Court, H, z (Unl), 41 Gt Cumberland Pl, W1H 7LG. ✆01-262 4344. C. ⋈ 11 bedrs, 4 ba. ⚐ ch, TV, 3 st. £ BBc £12·50–£16, DBc £16–£22, ⊡.

Hart House, PH, z (Unl), 51 Gloucester Pl, W1H 3PE. ✆01-935 2288. C. ⋈ 15 bedrs, 7 bp, 3 ba, TV. ⚐ CH, TV, CF, 3 BGf, 3 st. £ BB £17·25–£18·50, DB £27·60–£34·50, ⊡, cc 1 3.

Milford House, G, z (Unl), 31 York St, W1H 1PX. ✆01-935 1935. C. ⋈ 6 bedrs, 1 bp, 3 ba, TV. ⚐ CH, TV, CF. £ BB £13–£22, DB £18–£28, ⊡.

Montagu House, PH, z (Unl), 3 Montagu Pl, W1H 1RG. ✆01-935 4632.

Portman Court, PH, z (Unl), 30 Seymour St, W1H 5WD. ✆01-402 5401. C. ⋈ 30 bedrs, 5 bp, 6 sh, 7 ba, TV, Dgs. ⚐ ch, TV, 3 BGf, 1 st, Dis. £ BBc £18–£22, DBc £28–£35, ⊡, cc 1 2 3 5.

W2

★★★★M London Embassy, 150 Bayswater Rd, W2 4RT. ✆01-229 1212. C. ⋈ 192 bedrs, 192 bp, TV, Dgs. ✘ a l c, mc, at, LD 10.15. ⚐ Lt, N, CH, Dgs, CP 10, G 23, Ac, con 120, CF, 10 BGf, 0 st, Dis. £ BBc fr £48, DBc fr £58, WB, ⊡, L £7·75, D £8·75, cc 1 2 3 4 5 6.

★★★★Royal Lancaster, Lancaster Terrace, W2 2TY. ✆01-262 6737. C. ⋈ 435 bedrs, 435 bp, TV, Dgs (guide dgs only). ✘ a l c, mc, at, LD 10.45. ⚐ Lt, N, CH, CP 120, con 1,000, CF, 1 st. £ BB fr £74·50, DB fr £105, WB, ⊡, Bk £4·50, L £9·50, D £13·95, cc 1 2 3 4 5 6, Dep b.

★★★★White's, Lancaster Gate, W2 3NR. ✆01-262 2711. C. ⋈ 61 bedrs, 61 bp, TV. ✘ a l c, mc, at, LD 11.30. ⚐ Lt, N, CH, Dgs, CP 15, con, CF. £ B fr £49·50, BD fr £61·50, WB, ⊡, cc 1 2 3 5 6.

★★★Coburg, Bayswater Rd, W2 4RJ. ✆01-229 3654. RS Xmas. C. ⋈ 125 bedrs, 70 bp, 8 bps, 18 ba, TV, Dgs. ✘ a l c, LD 9.30. ⚐ Lt, N, CH, con 100, CF, 0 st. £ cc 1 2 3 4 5 6, Dep b.

★★★Hospitality Inn, Bayswater Rd, W2 3HL. ✆01-402 5060. C. ⋈ 175 bedrs, 175 bp, TV. ✘ a l c, mc, at, LD 9.30. ⚐ Lt, N, CH, Dgs, CP 15, G 40, Ac, con, CF. £ B fr £43·50, BD £57·50, WB, ⊡, cc 1 2 3 5 6.

★★★Park Court, Lancaster Gate, W2 3NN. ✆01-402 4272. C. ⋈ 442 bedrs, 442 bp, TV. ✘ a l c, mc, at, LD 9.30. ⚐ Lt, N, CH, Dgs, con, CF, 60 BGf. £ BB fr £39·50, DB fr £49·50, WB, ⊡, cc 1 2 3 5 6.

Ashley, PH, z (Unl), 15 Norfolk Sq, Hyde Park, W2 1RU. ✆01-723 3375. Closed Xmas. C. ⋈ 16 bedrs, 2 bps, 3 sh, 2 ba, TV. ⚐ CH, TV, 3 BGf, 5 st. £ BB £9·90–£10·50, DB £18–£22·80, ⊡.

Camelot, G, z (Unl), 45 Norfolk Sq, W2. ✆01-723 9118. C. ⋈ 19 bedrs, 2 bp, 1 bps, 8 sh, 4 ba. ⚐ CH, TV, CP 2, CF, 3 BGf. £ BB £16·65–£26·50, DB £24·85–£38, ⊡, Bk £2·50, cc 1 2 3 5.

Darlington House, PH, z (Unl), 111 Sussex Gdns, W2 2RU. ✆01-723 5131.

Dylan, PH, z (Unl), 14 Devonshire Ter, W2 3DW. ✆01-723 3280.

Garden Court, H, z, (Cl), 30 Kensington Gardens Sq, W2 4BG. ✆01-727 8304. C. ⋈ 37 bedrs, 6 bp, 4 bps, 6 ba. ⚐ CH, TV, Dgs, 2 BGf. £ BB £11–£16, DB £21–£25, ⊡.

Hotel Edward, H, z, 1A Spring St, Hyde Park, W2 3RA. ✆01-262 2671.

Kings, H, z (Rl), 60 Queensborough Ter, Paddington, W2. ✆01-229 7055. C. ⋈ 27 bedrs, 9 bp, 15 bps, 2 ba, TV, Dgs. ⚐ CH, TV, Dgs, 2 st. £ BB £21–£27, DB £31–£37, ⊡, cc 1 2 3 5.

Lancaster Gate, H, z, 105 Lancaster Gate, W2 3NU. ✆01-723 8501.

Nayland, G, z, 134 Sussex Gdns, W2 1UB. ✆01-723 9118.

Park House, H, z (Unl), 110 Sussex Gdns, W2 1PR. ✆01-723 3386.

Pembridge Court, H, z (R), 34 Pembridge Gdns, W2 4DX. ✆01-229 9977. C. ⋈ 35 bedrs, 20 bp, 14 bps, 1 sh, TV, Dgs. ⚐ CH, TV, Dgs, ns, G 2, CF, 7 st. £ BB £30–£33, DB £40–£45, ⊡, Bk £4, D £9, cc 1 2 3 4 5.

Slavia, H, z, 2 Pembridge Sq, W2 4EW. ✆01-727 1316. C. ⋈ 31 bedrs, 31 bps, Dgs. ⚐ Lt, CH, TV, CP 2, CF, 4 BGf, 10 st. £ BB £13–£20, DB £20–£30, WT (c) £80–£120, ⊡, Bk £2·50, D £7·50, cc 1 2 3 5.

Tregaron, PH, z (Unl), 17 Norfolk Sq, Hyde Park, W2 1RU. ✆01-723 9966. Closed Xmas. C. ⋈ 17 bedrs, 5 bps, 1 sh, 3 ba, TV. ⚐ CH, TV, 3 BGf, 5 st. £ BB £9·90–£10·50, DB £18–£22·80, ⊡.

Warwick House, PH, z (Unl), 6–8 Norfolk Sq, Lancaster Gate, W2 1RS. ✆01-723 3386. C. ⋈ 33 bedrs, 6 ba, TV, Dgs. ⚐ ch, TV, Dgs, CP 2, CF, 3 BGf, 10 st. £ BB £14–£16, DB £24–£26, ⊡, cc 1 2 3 5.

Westland, H, z (R), 154 Bayswater Rd, W2 4HP. ✆01-229 9191. C. ⋈ 30 bedrs, 28 bp, 1 ba, TV. ⚐ Lt, CH, TV, ns, CP 6, CF, 3 st. £ BB £28, DB £35·75, ②, Bk £4, D £6·50, cc 1 2 3 5.

W3

Acton Park, H, z, 116 The Vale, W3 7JT. ✆01-743 9417. C. ⋈ 18 bedrs, 9 bp, 8 bps, 1 sh, TV, Dgs. ✘ a l c, LD 9. ⚐ Lt, CH, Dgs, ns, CP 6, CF, 0 st. £ BB fr £15·18, DB fr

£29·09, DT (b) £27·14, ⊡, Bk £2·50, L £3·50, D £6, cc 2 3 5.

Rescue Service: Vehicle Maintenance, Mill Hill Ter, Crown St. ✆01-993 1600.

W4

Repairer: Hogarth Garage, 120 Cranbrook Rd. ✆01-994 1356 and 7865.
Rescue Service: Shrimpton Garage, Chiswick High St. ✆01-994 2065.

W5

■★★★M Carnarvon, Ealing Common, W5 3HN. ✆01-992 5399. RS Xmas & New Year. C. ⋈ 145 bedrs, 145 bp, TV. ✘ a l c, mc, at, LD 9.30. ⚐ Lt, N, CH, CP 150, Ac, con 200, CF. £ BBc £42·50, DBc £51·50, WB, ⊡, Bk £6·45, L £7·50, D £7·50, cc 1 2 3 5 6, Dep.

Christines, G, z (Unl), 26 Kenilworth Rd, Ealing, W5 3OH. ✆01-579 5569. Closed Xmas & Easter. C. ⋈ 10 bedrs, 2 ba. ⚐ CH, TV, CP 2. £ BB £9–£10, DB £18, WT (c) £65, ⊡.

Grange Lodge, PH, z (Rl), 50 Grange Rd, Ealing, W5 5BX. ✆01-567 1049. C. ⋈ 14 bedrs, 4 bps, 2 ba. ⚐ CH, TV, Dgs, CP 11, CF, 2 BGf, 2 st. £ BB fr £12, DB fr £18, DT (b) £9–£12, ⊡, Bk £2·50.

Granville Garden, PH, z (Unl), 8 Granville Gdns, W5 3PA. ✆01-992 1646.

Rescue Service: B & C Autos, 18 The Mall, Ealing. ✆01-567 3560.

W6

Rescue Service: Shrimptons Garage, 141 Stamford Brook Arches, Ravenscourt Park. ✆01-741 3329.
S.T.S. 6 Stamford Brook Rd. ✆01-748 9595.

W8

★★★★★Royal Garden, Kensington High St, W8 4PT. ✆01-937 8000. C. ⋈ 411 bedrs, 411 bp, TV. ✘ a l c, mc, at, LD 11.30. ⚐ Lt, N, CH, Dgs (guide dogs only), G 160, Ac, con 900, CF. £ BB £75·75–£83·75, DB £91·25–£93·75, WB, ②, Bk £6·25, L £8·90, D £20, cc 1 2 3 4 5 6, Dep b.

★★★★Kensington Close (TH), Wrights La, Kensington, W8 5SP. ✆01-937 8170. C. ⋈ 530 bedrs, 530 bp, TV, Dgs. ✘ a l c, mc, at, LD 10. ⚐ Lt, N, CH, Dgs, G 100, Ac, sp, sc, sb, con 100, CF, 5 st. £ BB £45·50, DB £60, WB, ⊡, cc 1 2 3 4 5 6, Dep (Xmas). Being refurbished.

★★Lexham (Unl), 32 Lexham Gdns, W8 5JU. ✆01-373 6471. Closed Xmas week. C. ⋈ 61 bedrs, 13 bp, 7 bps, 14 ba. ✘ mc, at, LD 8. ⚐ Lt, N, CH, TV, Ac, con 20, CF, 6 st. £ BB £16–£21, DB £24–£33, WT £119–£150, DT £20–£29, WB, ⊡, Bk £3·25, L £3, D £5·50, cc 1 3, Dep.

Apollo, H, z, 18 Lexham Gdns, W8 5JE. ✆01-373 3236. C. ⋈ 59 bedrs, 40 bp, 1 bps, 6 ba. ⚐ CH, TV, Dgs, CF, 6 BGf, 6 st. £ BBc fr £13·50, DBc £24, WT £84–£105, ⊡, Bk £2·50, D £4·50, cc 1 2 3 4 6.

Atlas, H, z, 24 Lexham Gdns, W8 5JE. ✆01-373 7873.

W9

Colonnade, H, z (Rt), 2 Warrington Cres, W9 1ER. ✆01-286 1052. C. ⋈ 53 bedrs, 43 bp, 10 bps, 4 ba, TV, Dgs. ⚐ Lt, CH, Dgs, ns, CP 4, CF, 7 BGf, 3 st. £ BB £23·50–£40, DB £33–£55, ⊡, Bk £4, D £6·95, cc 1 2.

Rescue Service: Olympic Breakdown &
Recovery Services, 32A Goldney Rd.
☎ 01-286 8282.

W10
MC Repairer: Hamrax Motors, 329
Ladbroke Grove. ☎ 01-969 5380.

W11
Repairer: Automobile Tuning Centre, 32
Holland Park Mews. ☎ 01-727 7111.
Rescue Service: Chapman's London
Garage Ltd, 12 Codrington Mews,
Blenheim Cres. ☎ 01-727 9864.

W14
Lautrec, H, z (Unl), *5 Russell Rd,
Kensington, W14 8JA.* ☎ 01-603 3114. C.
☞ 20 bedrs, 1 ba, Dgs. ▣ CH, TV, 8 st.
£ BB £11·50–£16·10, DB £19·90–£24·75,
②

Repairer: Lion Automobile Engineers, 17
Netherwood Rd, Shepherds Bush.
☎ 01-743 9621.

WC1
★★★★**Russell** (TH), *Russell Sq, WC1B
5BE.* ☎ 01-837 6470. C. ☞ 318 bedrs, 318
bp, TV, Dgs. ✘ a l c, mc, at, LD 10. ▣ Lt, N,
CH, Dgs, Ac, con 400, CF, 9 st. £ BB
£50·50, DB £66·50, WB, ①, cc 1 2 3 4 5 6,
Dep (Xmas).
★★★**Bloomsbury Crest,** *Coram St,
Russell Sq, WC1N 1HT.* ☎ 01-837 1200.
C. ☞ 250 bedrs, 250 bp, ns, TV, Dgs.
✘ a l c, mc, at, LD 11. ▣ Lt, N, CH, Ac, con
1,200, CF, 0 st. £ B fr £46·50, DB fr £56·50,
WB, ①, Bk £5·50, D £9·25, cc 1 2 3 4 5 6,
Dep b.
★★★**Kingsley** (TH), *Bloomsbury Way,
WC1A 2SD.* ☎ 01-242 5881. C. ☞ 146
bedrs, 146 bp, TV. ✘ a l c, mc, at. ▣ Lt, N,
CH, TV, Ac, con, CF. £ BBc fr £38·50, DBc
fr £49·50, ①, cc 1 2 3 5 6.
★★★**London Ryan,** *Gwynne Pl, WC1X
9QB.* ☎ 01-278 2480. C. ☞ 213 bedrs,
213 bp, TV. ✘ a l c, mc, at, LD 9.30. ▣ Lt,
N, CH, Dgs, CP 20, Ac, con, CF, 0 st. £ BB fr
£37·50, DB fr £47·50, WB, ①, cc 1 2 3 5 6.
★★★**Royal Scot Thistle,** *Kings Cross
Rd, WC1X 9DT.* ☎ 01-278 2434. C. ☞ 349
bedrs, 349 bp, ns, TV, Dgs. ✘ a l c. ▣ Lt, N,
CH, TV, Dgs, CP 35, Ac, sb, sol, gym, CF, 0
st. £ BBc £42·45, DBc £55·30, WB, ②, Bk
£4·95, L £8·50, D £8·50, cc 1 2 3 4 5 6,
Dep b.
★★**Cora,** *Upper Woburn Pl, WC1H 0HT.*
☎ 01-387 5111.
★★**Ivanhoe,** *Bloomsbury St, WC1B 3QD.*
☎ 01-636 5601.
Crescent, PH, z (Unl), *49 Cartwright
Gdns, WC1H 9EL.* ☎ 01-387 1515. C.
☞ 29 bedrs, 6 ba, Dgs. ▣ CH, TV, Dgs.
£ BB £12–£14, DB £22–£24, ①▲
Haddon Hall, PH, z (Unl), *39 Bedford Pl,
WC1B 5JT.* ☎ 01-636 2474. C. ☞ 33
bedrs, 1 bp, 5 bps, 7 ba ▣ CH, TV, 1 RGf
£ BB £13–£20, DB £22–£32, ①, Bk £1·50.
Mount Pleasant, H, z, *53 Calthorpe St,
WC1X 0HL.* ☎ 01-837 9781.

Rescue Service: W Godleman and Son,
21a King's Mews. ☎ 01-405 5641.
Store Street Service Station, Store St.
☎ 01-286 8282.

WC2
★★★★★**Savoy,** *Strand, WC2R 0EU.*
☎ 01-836 4343. C. ☞ 200 bedrs, 200 bp,
TV. ✘ a l c, mc, at, LD 10.30. ▣ Lt, N, CH,
TV, CP 90, con 500, CF. £ B £80–£90, BD

£110–£120, WB, ①, Bk £4·80, L £15, D
£18·50, cc 1 2 3 5 6.
★★★★**M Drury Lane,** *10 Drury Lane,
High Holborn, WC2B 5RE.*
☎ 01-836 6666. C. ☞ 127 bedrs, 127 bp,
TV, Dgs. ✘ a l c, mc, LD 10. ▣ Lt, N, CH,
CP 11, con, CF. £ cc 1 2 3 4 5 6, Dep b.
★★★★**Waldorf** (TH), *Aldwych, WC2B
4DD.* ☎ 01-836 2400. C. ☞ 310 bedrs,
310 bp, TV, Dgs. ✘ a l c, mc, LD 10. ▣ Lt,
N, CH, Dgs, Ac, con 500, CF, 8 st. £ BB
£63·50, DB £86, WB, ①, cc 1 2 3 4 5 6,
Dep (Xmas).
▣★★★**Royal Trafalgar Thistle,**
*Whitcomb St, Trafalgar Square, WC2H
7HG.* ☎ 01-930 4477. C. ☞ 107 bedrs,
107 bp, ns, TV. ✘ a l c, mc, at, LD 10.30.
▣ Lt, N, CH, CF, 0 st. £ BB £57–£64, DB
£69·50–£76, WB, ①, Bk £3·75, L £7·50, D
£7·50, cc 1 2 3 4 5 6, Dep.
★★★**Strand Palace** (TH), *Strand, WC2R
0JJ.* ☎ 01-836 8080. C. ☞ 761 bedrs, 761
bp, TV. ✘ a l c, mc, at, LD 10.45. ▣ Lt, N,
CH, Ac, con 200, CF, 3 st. £ BB £46, DB
£59, WB, ①, cc 1 2 3 4 5 6, Dep (Xmas).

LONDON AIRPORT Greater London.
Map 7A
See also CRANFORD.
Brentford and Chiswick 8, London 14, M4
Motorway ¾, Ealing 8½, Harrow 9½,
Kingston upon Thames 9½, Richmond-
upon-Thames 8, Slough 7, Staines 5½,
Watford 16, Windsor 7½, Uxbridge 5½.
See Spectators' facilities including
Cafeterias, Licensed Bars, Shops, etc.
Leaflet giving particulars of facilities at
and in the vicinity of the Airport is
available from any RAC Office.
⑦ Heathrow Central Station.
☎ 01-730 0791.

★★★★**M Excelsior** (TH), *Bath Rd, West
Drayton, UB7 0DU.* ☎ 01-759 6611. C.
☞ 662 bedrs, 662 bp, TV, Dgs. ✘ a l c, mc,
at, LD 10.45. ▣ Lt, N, CH, Dgs, con 500,
Ac, sp, con 700, CF, 56 BGf, 0 st, Dis. £ BB
£55, DB £68, ①, cc 1 2 3 4 5 6.
★★★★**M Holiday Inn,** *Stockley Rd, West
Drayton, UB7 9NA.* ☎ West Drayton
(0894) 445555. C. ☞ 400 bedrs, 400 bp,
TV, Dgs. ✘ a l c, mc, at, LD 10.30. ▣ Lt, N,
CH, Dgs, CP 400, Ac, sp, gc, tc, sb, sol,
gym, con 140, CF, 1 BGf, 0 st, Dis. £ BB fr
£49·90, DB fr £61·85, WB, ①, Bk £3·90, L
£7·95, D £7·95, cc 1 2 3 4 5 6, Dep.
★★★**M Ariel** (TH), *Bath Rd, Hayes, UB3
5AJ.* ☎ 01-759 2552. C. ☞ 178 bedrs, 178
bp, TV, Dgs. ✘ a l c, mc, at, LD 10.30. ▣ Lt,
N, CH, Dgs, CP 100, Ac, con 70, CF, 0 st.
£ BB £47·50, DB £60, ①, cc 1 2 3 4 5 6.
★★★**Berkeley Arms,** *Bath Rd, Cranford,
TW5 9QE.* ☎ 01-897 2121. C. ☞ 41 bedrs,
41 bp, TV, Dgs. ✘ a l c, mc, at, LD 10. ▣ Lt,
N, CH, Dgs, CP 120, Ac, con 70, CF, 0 st.
£ B £40, BD £50, ①, Bk £4·25, L £7·50, D
£7·50, cc 1 2 3 4 5 6, Dep b.
★★★**M Heathrow Crest,** *Bath Rd, West
Drayton, UB7 0EQ.* ☎ 01-759 2400. C.
☞ 360 bedrs, 360 bp, ns, TV, Dgs. ✘ a l c,
mc, at, LD 10.30. ▣ Lt, N, CH, Dgs, CP
800, Ac, sp, tc, con 700, CF. £ B fr £45, BD
fr £54·50, WB, ①, Bk £5·25, D £9·25,
cc 1 2 3 4 5 6.
★★★**M Post House** (TH), *Sipson Rd,
West Drayton, UB7 0JU.* ☎ 01-759 2323.
C. ☞ 594 bedrs, 594 bp, TV, Dgs. ✘ a l c,
mc, at, LD 10.30. ▣ Lt, N, CH, Dgs, CP
400, Ac, con 200, CF, 1 st. £ BB £50·50,
DB £63, WB, ①, cc 1 2 3 4 5 6.

★★★**M Skyway** (TH), *Bath Rd, Hayes,
UB3 5AW.* ☎ 01-759 6311. C. ☞ 445
bedrs, 445 bp, TV, Dgs. ✘ a l c, mc, at, LD
10. ▣ Lt, N, CH, Dgs, CP 230, Ac, sp, con
300, CF, 63 BGf, 0 st, Dis. £ BB £45·50, DB
£58·50, WB, ①, cc 1 2 3 4 5 6.

LONG BUCKBY Northants. M. Area 14B
Pop 3,100. Towcester 14, London 75,
Atherstone 30, Daventry 5½, Hinckley 23,
Leicester 28, Market Harborough 16,
Northampton 10, Nuneaton 25, Rugby 10.
Golf Cold Ashby 18h. **See** 13th cent
Church (restored).

Rescue Service: Beach Autos (Motor
Services) Ltd, M1 Service Area, Watford
Gap. ☎ Daventry (025 16) 5181.
Station Garage, Station Rd. ☎ (0327)
842311.

LONGDOWN Devon. M. Areas 4F & 3B
Pop 592. 4 m WSW of Exeter, London
173, M5 Motorway 5½, Ashburton 20,
Crediton 7½, Newton Abbot 15,
Okehampton 21.
Golf Exeter 18h.

Rescue Service: Longdown Garage.
☎ (039 281) 274.

LONG EATON Derbyshire. Map 22F
Pop 33,000. M1 Motorway 5, London 121,
Ashby-de-la-Zouch 15, Chesterfield 28,
Derby 9½, Hinckley 29, Loughborough 12,
Mansfield 20, Matlock 26, Nottingham 7.
EC Thur. **MD** Wed, Fri, Sat. **Golf** Chilwell
Manor 18h. **See** Church, Trent Lock.
⑦ Central Library, Tamworth Rd. ☎ Long
Eaton (060 76) 5426.

★★★**M Novotel,** *Bostock La, NG10 4EP.*
☎ (060 76) 60106. C. ☞ 112 bedrs, 112
bp, TV, Dgs. ✘ a l c, mc, at, LD 12. ▣ Lt, N,
Dgs, CP 160, Ac, sp, sol, con 300, CF, 2
BGf, 0 st, Dis. £ cc 1 2 3 4 5 6, Dep.
★**Europa,** *Derby Rd, NG10 1LW.*
☎ Nottingham (0602) 728481. C. ☞ 18
bedrs, 6 bp, 1 bps, 7 sh, 1 ba, TV, Dgs.
✘ a l c, mc, at, LD 9. ▣ CH, TV, Dgs, CP 25,
Ac, con 15, CF, 1 st. £ BB fr £17, DB fr £26,
DBB fr £23, WB, ①, Bk £3·50, L £4·50, D
£6, cc 1 2 3 5 6.

Rescue Service: Cue & Jones Ltd,
Chatsworth Av. ☎ (0602) 2666.
Junction Service Station, Wiltshire Rd.
☎ (0602) 3139.

LONGHAM Dorset. Maps 5F & 6E
Ringwood 7, London 100, Bournemouth
5½, Christchurch 8, Wimborne Minster 4,
Poole 6.
See Stapehill Abbey (1½ m NW).

★★★**Bridge House,** *2 Ringwood Rd,
BH22 9AN.* ☎ Bournemouth (0202)
578828. C. ☞ 26 bedrs, 22 bp, 4 bps, TV.
▣ CH, TV, CP 200, CF, 6 BGf, 3 st. £ BBc
£24, DBc £35, ①, Bk £4, L £3·50, D £7·50,
cc 1 2 3 6.

LONGHORSLEY Northumberland. Map
31D
Morpeth 7, London 295, Alnwick 14,
Hexham 31, Newcastle-upon-Tyne 21,
Rothbury 8½, Wooler 25.

⬛★★★★**Linden Hall,** *Longhorsley,
Morpeth, Northumberland.* ☎ Morpeth
(0670) 56611. C. ☞ 45 bedrs, 45 bp, TV,
Dgs. ✘ a l c, mc, at, LD 9.30. ▣ Lt, N, CH,
TV, Dgs, CP 180, tc, sb, sol, con 120, CF,
10 BGf, 0 st, Dis. £ BB £41·50–£44·50, DB
£49·50–£58·50, WT £250, WB, ①, Bk

£5·50, L £6·50, D £15·50, cc 1 2 3 4 5, Dep b.

LONG MELFORD Suffolk. Map 17C
Pop 3,267. Sudbury 3, London 61, Aldeburgh 45, Bury St Edmunds 13, Haverhill 14, Newmarket 23, Saxmundham 41, Stowmarket 19.
Golf Newton Green 9h. **See** 15th cent Bull Hotel, Church with detached 15th cent Lady Chapel, Melford Hall.

★★★**Bull** (TH), *CO10 9JG*. ✆ Sudbury (0787) 78494. C. ⚑ 27 bedrs, 27 bp, TV, Dgs. ✗ a l c, mc, at, LD 10. ⓗ CH, Dgs, CP 40, G 4, Ac, con 130, CF, 1 st. £ BB £40, DB £58, WB, ⓣ, cc 1 2 3 4 5 6, Dep (Xmas).
★**Crown Inn,** *Hall St, CO10 9JL*.
✆ Sudbury (0787) 77666. RS Xmas. C. ⚑ 8 bedrs, 2 bp, 2 ba, TV, Dgs. ✗ a l c, mc, LD 9.30. ⓗ CH, Dgs, CP 10, Ac, CF, 3 BGf, 1 st. £ BB £17–£22, DB £28–£34, DBB £22·95–£27·95, WB, ⓩ, Bk £3·15, L £4·95, D £5·95, cc 1 2 3 5 6.

Rescue Service: W D Gardiner (Motors) Ltd, Little St Mary's. ✆ Sudbury (0787) 75703.

LONGNOR Staffordshire. Map 22C
Pop 375. Ashbourne 16, London 155, Buxton 6½, Chesterfield 21, Congleton 18, Leek 10, Macclesfield 15, Matlock 17, Sheffield 25.
Golf Buxton and High Peak 18h. **See** St Bartholomew's Church.

★**Crewe & Harpur,** *SK17 0NS*.
✆ (029 883) 205.

Rescue Service: Golden Green Garage.
✆ (029 883) 274.

LONGRIDGE Lancashire. Map 27D
Pop 17,151. Preston 7½. London 218, Blackburn 10, Blackpool 22, Lancaster 23, Settle 29, Skipton 29, Whalley 10.
EC Wed. **MD** Thur. **Golf** Longridge 18h.

Rescue Service: Irelands Garage, 60 Inglewhite Rd. ✆ (077 478) 3723.

LONG STRATTON Norfolk. Map 16D
Pop 2,382. Scole 9½, London 105, Aldeburgh 37, East Dereham 22, Great Yarmouth 29, Lowestoft 26, Norwich 11, Saxmundham 30, Thetford 26.
EC Wed. **Golf** Diss 9h, Norwich 18h. **See** St Mary's Church (Sexton's Wheel), Old Ice House.

Rescue Service: Stratton Motor Co, Ipswich Rd. ✆ (0508) 30491 & (0508) 31101.

LONG SUTTON Lincolnshire. Map 23F
Pop 2,863. Wisbech 9, London 103, Boston 21, King's Lynn 13, Spalding 13.
EC Wed. **MD** Thur, Sat. **Golf** Sutton Bridge 9h. **See** Church.

Rescue Service: Long Sutton Motors Ltd, 94 London Rd. ✆ Holbeach (0406) 363282.

LONGTON Staffordshire. Map 19D.
See STOKE-ON-TRENT.

LONGTOWN Cumbria. Map 30F
Pop 2,200. M6 Motorway 6, Carlisle 8, London 302, Brampton 11, Canonbie 6, Gretna 5.
EC Wed. **Golf** Carlisle 18h. **See** Arthuret Church, St Michael's Well
ⓘ 21 Swan St. ✆ Longtown (0228) 791201.

★★**Graham Arms,** *English St, CA6 5SE*.
✆ (0228) 791213. C. ⚑ 15 bedrs, 2 bp, 4 ba. ✗ a l c, mc, at, LD 8.30. ⓗ CH, TV, CP 15, Ac, pf, CF, 2 st. £ Bk £3, L £3, D £5, cc 1.
⚑✦**Marchbank** (R), *CA6 5XP*. (3 m N of Longtown) ✆ (0228) 791325. C. ⚑ 7 bedrs, 1 bp, 1 sh, 1 ba. ✗ at, LD 8.30. ⓗ CH, TV, Dgs, ns, CP 25, pf, con, CF, 1 BGf, 1 st, Dis. £ BB £15–£25, DB £28–£36, DBB fr £26, ⓩ, 10%, Bk £5·50, L £6, D £11.

LOOE Cornwall. Map 3C
Pop 4,340. Saltash 15, London 227, Bodmin 13, Fowey 19 (Fy 10), Liskeard 7½, Plymouth (Fy) 18, St Austell 24.
EC Thur. **Golf** Looe Bin Down 18h. **See** 14th cent Church (W Looe), 16th cent Old Guildhall (Museum) (E Looe), Cornish Museum (local history, arts, crafts etc), Venue of the Int. Deep Sea and Shark Angling Festival.
ⓘ The Guildhall, Fore St. ✆ Looe (050 36) 2072.

◼★★★**Hannafore Point** *Marine Dr, PL13 2DQ*. ✆ (050 36) 3273. Open Mar–Oct & Xmas. C. ⚑ 40 bedrs, 38 bp, 2 bps, TV, Dgs. ✗ mc, at, LD 9. ⓗ Lt, CH, CP 40, U 5, G 3, sp, con 80, CF, 17 st. £ BB £26·50–£29·50, DB £44–£61, DBB £26·50–£35, WB, ⓣ, Bk £5, L £3, D £9·25, cc 1 2 3 5, Dep b.
◼⚑★★★**Talland Bay** (R), *Talland Bay, nr Looe, PL13 2JB*. ✆ Polperro (0503) 72667. Closed Jan. C. ⚑ 19 bedrs, 17 bp, 1 ba, ns, TV, Dgs. ✗ a l c, mc, at. ⓗ CH, ns, CP 30, sp, sol, con 20, CF. £ BB £20–£34, DB £44–£75, DBB £28–£40, ⓩ, Bk £3, D £9·50, cc 1 2 3 5 6.
◼⚑★★**Klymiarven** (R), *Barbican Hill, PL13 1BH*. ✆ (050 36) 2333. Open Mar–Nov. C 10. ⚑ 14 bedrs, 6 bp, 1 bps, 1 sh, 2 ba, TV, Dgs. ✗ mc, at, LD 8. ⓗ CH, Dgs, CP 30, Ac, sp, 0 st. £ BB £5–£15·50, DB £10–£31, DBB £10–£23, ⓩ, Bk £3·50, D £7·50, Dep a.
★★**Rock Towers** (R), *Marine Dr, PL13 2DQ*. ✆ (050 36) 2140. C. ⚑ 20 bedrs, 11 bp, 5 bps, 4 ba, TV. ✗ a l c, mc, at, LD 9.15. ⓗ N, CH, TV, CP 14, G 8, Ac, pf, CF, 1 BGf, 12 st. £ WB, Bk £3·50, L £3·50, D £6·25, cc 3, Dep.
Beechcroft, G, x (Unl), *Marine Drive, Hannafore, West Looe*. ✆ (050 36) 2995. Open Apr–Sep. C. ⚑ 5 bedrs, 1 sh, 1 ba. ⓗ CH, TV, CP 3, CF. £ BB £6·50–£8, DB fr £13, ⓣ.
Bodrigan, H, x (R), *Hannafore Rd, PL13 2DD*. ✆ (050 36) 2065. Open Mar–Oct & Xmas. C. ⚑ 22 bedrs, 4 bps, 3 ba. ⓗ ch, TV. £ BB £8·62, DB £17–£34, DBB (b) £80·50, DT (b) £11·50, ⓣ, Bk £3, L £3·50 D £4, cc 1.
Commonwood Manor, PH, y (R), *St Martin's Rd, East Looe, PL13 1LP*.
✆ (050 36) 2929.
Coombe Farm, G, xy (R), *Widegates, PL13 1QN*. ✆ Widegates (050 34) 223. Open Mar–Oct. C. ⚑ 8 bedrs, 2 ba. ⓗ CH, TV, CP 12, CF, 2 BGf, 1 st, Dis. £ BB £10·35–£13·50, DB £14·50–£20·50, WT £89–£110, DT £14·25–£17, ⓣ, Bk £2·50, D £7·50.
Deganwy, PH, x (RI), *Station Rd, PL13 1HL*. ✆ (050 36) 2984. C. ⚑ 10 bedrs, 1 sh, 2 ba, Dgs. ⓗ TV, CP 6, CF. £ BB £6–£9, DB £12–£18, WT (b) £63–£84, (c) £42–£63, DT £9–£12, ⓣ.
Fieldhead, H, yz (R), *Portuan Rd, Hannafore, West Looe, PL13 2DR*.

✆ (050 36) 2689. Open Mar–Nov. C. ⚑ 14 bedrs, 5 bp, 8 sh, 1 ba, TV. ⓗ ch, TV, CP 11, U 3, G 4, CF. £ BB £15–£19, DB £31–£38, WT (c) £98–£126, ⓣ, D £3·50, cc 1 2 3 5.
Hillingdon, PH, z (RI), *Portuan Rd, Hannafore, West Looe, PL13 2DW*.
✆ (050 36) 2906. Open Mar–Oct. C. ⚑ 8 bedrs, 3 ba, TV. ⓗ ch, TV, G 5, CF. £ BB £7–£9, DB £14–£18, WT (b) £87·50–£98, (c) £45·50–£59·50, DT (b) £13·50–£15·50, ⓩ.
Killarney, PH, z (RI), *Shutta Rd, East Looe, PL13 1HW*. ✆ (050 36) 2307.
Closed Nov, Xmas & New Year. C. ⚑ 8 bedrs, 6 bps, 1 ba, TV. ⓗ CH, TV, CF. £ BB £5–£10, DB £12–£20, DT (b) £11–£15, ⓣ, Bk £1·75, D £5, cc 1 3.
Leeward, G, y (Unl), *Shutta, East Looe, PL13 1LT*. ✆ (050 36) 2032. Open Mar–Oct. C 8. ⚑ 4 bedrs, 1 ba. ⓗ CH, TV, CP 8. £ DB £12–£15, ⓣ.
Ogunquit, G, x (Unl), *Portuan Rd, PL13 2DW*. ✆ (050 36) 3105. Open Mar–Nov. C. ⚑ 6 bedrs, 1 bps, 1 ba, Dgs. ⓗ CH, TV, Dgs. £ BB £7·50–£8·50, DB £15–£17·50, WT (b) £72·50–£81·50, (c) £48·50–£55·50, DT (b) £12–£13, ⓣ.
Panorama (late **Rockwell**), **H, x** (R), *Hannafore Rd, West Looe, PL13 2DE*.
✆ (050 36) 2123.
Pixies Holt, PH, y (RI), *Shutta, East Looe, PL13 1JD*. ✆ (050 36) 2726. Open Apr–Oct. C 5. ⚑ 5 bedrs, 2 bp, 1 ba, TV. ⓗ CH, TV, CP 8. £ BB £7·50–£11, DB £15–£22, WT (b) £87·50–£112, DT (b) £12·50–£16, ⓣ, D £6, cc 1 3.
Polraen, PH, xy (R), *Sandplace, PL13 1PJ*. ✆ (050 36) 3956. Closed Jan. C. ⚑ 6 bedrs, 1 bp, 5 bps, 1 ba, TV. ⓗ ch, TV, Dgs, CP 12, CF, 1 BGf, 0 st, Dis. £ DB £25–£30, WT (b) £120–£140, DT (b) £18·50–£21, ⓩ, Bk £3·50, L £2·25, D £7·50.
Riverside, PH, z (RI), *Station Rd, East Looe, PL13 1HN*. ✆ (050 36) 2100. Open Apr–Oct. C. ⚑ 13 bedrs, 3 ba. ⓗ TV, CF. £ BB £7·50, DB £15, ⓣ.
Trelaske Lodge, H, xy (R), *Polperro Rd, Trelaske, PL13 2JS*. ✆ (050 36) 2159.

Repairers: Looe Motor Co, Fore St.
✆ (050 36) 2377 and (050 36) 2412.
Martins Garage (Looe) Ltd, Fore St.
✆ (050 36) 2161.
Rescue Service: Barbican Motor Co, Barbican Rd, East Looe. ✆ (050 36) 2498.

LOSTWITHIEL Cornwall. Map 2D
Pop. 2,212. Liskeard 11, London 232, Bodmin 5½, Fowey 7½, Launceston 24, Looe 16, St Austell 8½.
EC Wed. **Golf** Carlyon Bay 18h. **See** St Bartholomew's Church, Guildhall, Duchy Hall (Gt Hall of Lostwithiel), 14th cent bridge, Museum, Restormel Castle ruins 1 m N, Lanhydrock 3 m N.

◼★★**M Carotel** (R), *6 Edgcumbe Rd, PL22 0DW*. ✆ Bodmin (0208) 872223.

Repairer: Four Way Auto Services Ltd, North St. ✆ Bodmin (0208) 872503.
Rescue Service: Bridgend Garage.
✆ Bodmin (0208) 872308.
Downend Garage & Motor Co. ✆ Bodmin (0208) 872363.
Rose Garage (Lostwithiel) Ltd, Edgcumbe Rd. ✆ Bodmin (0208) 872416.

LOUGHBOROUGH Leics. Map 22F
Pop 49,081. Leicester 11, London 109, M1 Motorway 3, Ashby-de-la-Zouch 12, Derby 16, Hinckley 22, Melton Mowbray 15, Newark 31, Nottingham 15.

EC Wed. **MD** Thur. **Golf** Longscliffe 18h.
See War Memorial with Carillon Tower
(47 bells), restored remains of 13th cent
Rectory, University of Technology, Parish
Church, Great Central Railway (steam
trains), Charnwood Forest (4 m SW),
Mount St Bernard's Abbey (6 m W).
🛈 John Storer House, Wards End.
📞 Loughborough (0509) 230131.

★★★**Cedars,** *Cedars Rd, LE11 2AB.*
📞 (0509) 21449.
★★★**King's Head,** *High St, LE11 2QL.*
📞 (0509) 214893. C. 🛏 83 bedrs, 59 bp, 6
sh, 4 ba, TV, Dgs. ✗ a l c, mc, at, LD 9.15.
📶 Lt, N, CH, TV, Dgs, CP 80, Ac, con 100,
CF, 2 st. £ B fr £32, BD fr £38, WB, 🛈, Bk
£4·25, L £6·50, D £6·95, cc 1 2 3 4 5 6,
Dep b.
★★**Great Central,** *Gt Central Rd, LE11
1RW.* 📞 (0509) 263405. C. 🛏 19 bedrs, 7
bp, 9 bps, 1 ba, TV, Dgs. ✗ a l c, mc, LD 9.
📶 CH, Dgs, CP 20, G 3, Ac, con 80, CF, 0
st. £ BB £15–£25, DB £20–£30, DBB £20–
£30, WB, 🛈, L £2·45, D £4·95, cc 1 2 3 5 6,
Dep b.
De Montfort, PH, z (Rl), *88 Leicester Rd,
LE11 2AH.* 📞 (0509) 216061. C. 🛏 9
bedrs, 2 ba, TV, Dgs. 📶 CH, TV, Dgs, CF, 4
st. £ BB £11·50, DB £21, WB (b) £93, DT
(b) £15·50, 🛈, Bk £2·50, D £4, cc 1 3.
Sunnyside, H, z (Unl), *The Coneries,
LE11 1DZ.* 📞 (0509) 216217. Closed Dec
24–Jan 2. C 5. 🛏 11 bedrs, 2 ba, Dgs.
📶 CH, TV, CP 8, G 3, CF, 1 st. £ BB
£10·50–£11, DB £18–£19, WT (b) £94·50–
£99·25, DT (b) £15–£15·75, 🛈, D £4·50,
cc 3.

Repairers: Latham's (Loughborough) Ltd,
Woodgate. 📞 (0509) 266771.
Moss, Archie E Ltd, Woodgate. 📞 (0509)
213030.
Sandicliffe of Loughborough, Derby Rd.
📞 (0509) 267721.
Specialist Body Repairer: Farmer &
Carlisle Bodyworks Ltd, Clarence St.
📞 (0509) 266236.
Specialist Spring Repairer: Jonas
Woodhead Ltd, Unit 28, Kernan Dr.
📞 (0509) 231558.
Rescue Service: Arthur Prince's Garages
Ltd, Market St. 📞 (0509) 263244.
Shreeve & Mardell, Limehurst Av.
📞 (0509) 263644.
Yeates of Loughborough Ltd, Derby Rd.
📞 (0509) 217777.

LOUGHTON Buckinghamshire. Map 15C
Pop 514. Bletchley 4½, London 50,
Bedford 18, Buckingham 12, Kettering 30,
Northampton 18, Peterborough 53,
Towcester 12.
EC Thur. **Golf** Windmill, Bletchley 18h.
See Church, Manor House.

Repairer: Cowley & Wilson Ltd, Crown
Hill Garage, London Rd. 📞 Shenley Church
End (090 853) 335.

LOUGHTON Essex. Map 15F
Pop 28,918. Woodford 4, London 12,
Enfield 9, Epping 5, Hoddesdon 12,
Romford 9.
EC Thur. **Golf** Chigwell 18h. **See** Epping
Forest (Loughton Camp, Queen
Elizabeth's Hunting Lodge).

Repairer: Brown's Garage (Loughton)
Ltd, Brown's Corner, 250 High Rd.
📞 01-508 6262.

Specialist Body Repairer: Dawkins
Coachworks, Oakwood Hill Industrial
Estate, Debden. 📞 01-502 0431.

LOUTH Lincolnshire. Map 23B
Pop 13,296. Horncastle 13, London 148,
Boston 30, Hull (Fy) 32, Lincoln 26,
Grimsby 16, Market Rasen 14, Skegness
23.
EC Thur. **MD** Wed, Fri, Sat. **Golf** Louth
18h. **See** 16th cent St James's Church
(300 ft spire), Town Hall, Market Hall.
🛈 Town Hall, Eastgate. 📞 (0507) 602391.

Priory, PH, yz (R), *Eastgate.* 📞 (0507)
602930. RS Xmas. C. 🛏 12 bedrs, 6 bp, 2
bps, 4 sh, 1 ba, TV. 📶 CH, TV, CP 24, CF, 0
st. £ BB £21·55–£26·55, DB £34·05–£38,
DT (b) £32·75, 🛈, Bk £3·50, D £6·50,
cc 1 3.

Rescue Service: N T Shaw, 59 James St.
📞 (0507) 603382.

LOWDHAM Nottinghamshire. Map 22D
Pop 2,005. Leicester 29, London 126,
Grantham 19, Mansfield 14, Matlock 29,
Melton Mowbray 22, Newark 13,
Nottingham 8, Ollerton 15.
See Church, Gonalston Mill. **Golf** Oxton
18h.

Rescue Service: Morley, T C & Son, The
Garage, Main St. 📞 (060 745) 2241.

LOWER DICKER East Sussex. Map 7F
Pop 5,070. Uckfield 9½, London 53,
Eastbourne 10, Hailsham 1½, Lewes 11.

◼★★★**Boship Farm,** *Lower Dicker,
Hailsham, BN2 4AT (on A22 at Hailsham
Roundabout).* 📞 Hailsham (0323) 844826.
C. 🛏 47 bedrs, 47 bp, TV, Dgs. ✗ a l c, mc,
at, LD 9.30. 📶 N, CH, TV, CP 100, Ac, sp,
tc, pf, sb, sol, con 50, CF, 6 BGf, 2 st. £ BB
£22·50–£25, DB £30–£38, WB, 🛈, Bk
£3·50, L £5·50, D £7·50, cc 1 2 3 4 5 6,
Dep.

LOWER SLAUGHTER Gloucestershire.
Map 14E
Pop 206. Stow-on-the-Wold 3, London
87, Burford 11, Cheltenham 15,
Cirencester 17, Evesham 18.
Golf Burford 18h. **See** Brick Mill,
Cotswold stone cottages, attractive
riverside setting.

◼♨★★★**Manor,** *GL5 2HP.* 📞 Bourton-on-
the-Water (0451) 20456. C 8. 🛏 11
bedrs, 11 bp, TV. ✗ mc, at, LD 9. 📶 CH, CP
50, sp, con 20, 4 BGf, 6 st. £ BB £44, DB
£57, WB, 🛈, Bk £6, L £7, D £11,
cc 1 2 3 5 6, Dep a.

LOWER STOKE Kent. Map 10A
4 m NE Hoo. Pop 150. Dartford 21,
London 37, Dartford Tunnel 22, Rochester
8½.
EC Wed. **Golf** Deansgate Ridge 18h.

Rescue Service: Stoke Garage Ltd, High
St. 📞 Medway (0634) 270261.

LOWER UPHAM Hampshire. Map 6D
Winchester 8½, London 74, Alton 22,
Fareham 11, Portsmouth 18, Salisbury 27,
Southampton 10.

Rescue Service: Marquis Motors/Lower
Upham Garage, Winchester Rd. 📞 Durley
(048 96) 219, 497 & 559.

LOWESTOFT Suffolk. Map 16B
Pop 58,000. Saxmundham 23, London
117, Aldeburgh 27, Great Yarmouth 10,
Norwich 27, Scole 29, Stowmarket 45.

EC Thur. **MD** Fri, Sat. **Golf** Lowestoft
18h. **See** St Margaret's Church, Sparrow's
Nest, Lighthouse, Somerleyton Hall 4½ m
NW.
🛈 Esplanade. 📞 Lowestoft (0502) 65989.

★★★**Hedley House Park,** *Chapel Rd,
NR33 8BL.* 📞 (0502) 60772. C. 🛏 17
bedrs, 11 bp, 3 bps, 2 sh, 1 ba, TV, Dgs.
✗ a l c, mc, at, LD 10.30. 📶 N, CH, CP 220,
Ac, pf, con 200, CF. £ BB £22–£29, DB
£32–£38, WB, 🛈, Bk £4, L £3·50, D £5,
cc 1 2 3 5 6.

◼★★★**Victoria,** *Kirkley Cliff, NR33 0BZ.*
📞 (0502) 4433. C. 🛏 46 bedrs, 27 bp, 5
bps, 8 ba, TV, Dgs. ✗ mc, LD 9. 📶 Lt, N,
CH, TV, Dgs, CP 70, Ac, con 50, CF, 0 st.
£ BB £29·50–£33, DB £40–£45, DBB
£37·25–£40·95, WB, 🛈, Bk £4·75, L £5, D
£7·75, cc 1 2 3 4 5 6.

Ascot House, G, z (Unl), *537 London Rd
South, NR33 0PD.* 📞 (0502) 61251.
Closed Dec. C 5. 🛏 6 bedrs, 1 ba. 📶 CH,
TV, CP 10, 2 st. £ BB £9·50–£9, DB £17–
£18, WT (c) £56–£59·50, 🛈.
Denes, H, z, *Corton Rd, NR32 4PL.*
📞 (0502) 64616. Closed Xmas. C. 🛏 11
bedrs, 11 bps, TV, Dgs. 📶 CH, CP 22, 1 st.
£ BB £16, DB £24, WT (c) £77, 🛈, L £3·99,
D £3·99, cc 1 2 3.
Hotel Katherine, H, z (R), *49 Kirkley Cliff
Rd, NR33 0DF.* 📞 (0502) 67858.
Kingsleigh, G, z (Unl), *44 Marine Parade,
NR33 0QN.* 📞 (0502) 2513.
Seavilla, G, z (Unl), *43 Kirkley Cliff Rd,
NR33 0DF.* 📞 (0502) 4657. Closed Xmas.
C 3. 🛏 9 bedrs, 2 ba. 📶 CH, TV, CP 2, CF, 2
st. £ BB £7–£8, DB £14–£16, DT (b) £10–
£12, 🛈, D £3.

Repairer: Day's Garages Ltd, Whapload
Rd. 📞 (0502) 2042.

LOWESWATER Cumbria. Map 26F
Pop 180. Keswick 11, London 296,
Cockermouth 11, Egremont 13,
Workington 10.
EC Mon. **Golf** Embleton Cockermouth
18h. **See** Loweswater, Crummock Water,
Scale Force—120 ft waterfall.

◼★★**Scale Hill,** *CA13 9UX.* 📞 Lorton
(090 085) 232. Closed Jan. C. 🛏 12
bedrs, 10 bp, 1 bps, 1 ba, Dgs. ✗ mc, at, LD
7.45. 📶 ch, ns, CP 25, CF, 2 BGf, 0 st, Dis.
£ BB £14–£21·50, DB £24–£39, WT £130–
£202, DBB £20–£31, 🛈, Bk £3, D £8.
◼★**Grange** (Rl), *CA13 0SU.* 📞 Lamplugh
(0946) 861211. Closed Xmas & Jan–Feb
14. C. 🛏 7 bedrs, 1 bp, 3 sh, 3 ba, annexe 8
bedrs, 4 bp, 2 sh, 1 ba, Dgs. ✗ mc, at, LD 8.
📶 CH, TV, Dgs, ns, CP 20, U 2, CF, 2 BGf, 2
st. £ BB £14–£15·50, DB £28–£31, WT
£144–£154, DT £23·50–£25, 🛈, Bk £3, L
£2, D £7·50.

LOW WORSALL North Yorkshire. Map
24F
Pop 360. Northallerton 13, London 240,
Darlington 14, Stockton on Tees 8½, Thirsk
22, Whitby 36.
Golf Eaglescliffe 18h.

Rescue Service: Ship Service Station,
Richmond Rd. 📞 Eaglescliffe (0642)
780456.

LUDLOW Shropshire. Map 13A
Pop 7,500. Worcester 29, London 143,
Bridgnorth 19, Bromyard 21,
Kidderminster 25, Knighton 15,
Leominster 11, Newtown 32, Shrewsbury
27, Welshpool 32.

EC Thur. **MD** Mon, Fri, Sat. **Golf** Ludlow 18h. **See** Castle ruins, remains of Norman circular chapel, St Laurence's Church, Old Inns, Reader's House, Butter Cross, Broad Gate, Museum, The White House and Country Life Museum (Aston Munslow) 9 m N, Burford House Gardens 6 m SE. ⒢ Castle St. ✆ Ludlow (0584) 3857.

★★★**Feathers,** Bull Ring, SY8 1AA. ✆ (0584) 5261. C. ✉ 35 bedrs, 35 bp, TV. ✖ a l c, mc, at, LD 9. ⒟ N, CH, Dgs, CP 35, Ac, con 80, CF, 3 st. £ BB £33–£35, DB £48–£58, WT £250–£300, DT £40–£50, WB, ⒤, Bk £5, L £5, D £10, cc 1 2 3 4 5 6.

★★**Angel,** Broad St, SY8 1NG. ✆ (0584) 2581. C. ✉ 16 bedrs, 4 bp, 4 ba. ✖ a l c, mc, LD 9. ⒟ CH, TV, CP 30, G 7, Ac, con 100, CF, 6 st.

⧫★★**Overton Grange,** SY8 4AD. (1½ m S on A49). ✆ (0584) 3500. C. ✉ 17 bedrs, 4 bp, 2 bps, 5 ba, TV, Dgs. ✖ a l c, mc, at, LD 9.30. ⒟ CH, CP 80, G 2, Ac, con 150, CF, 0 st. £ BB £13·50–£21·50, DB £26·50–£39·50, WB, ⒤, Bk £3·50, L £6·75, D £7·50, cc 1 2 3 4 5.

◪★**Cliff,** Dinham, SY8 2JE. ✆ (0584) 2063. C. ✉ 11 bedrs, 1 sh, 3 ba. ✖ mc, at, LD 9.30. ⒟ CH, TV, Ac, pf, con 30, CF. £ BB £10–£12, DB £20–£24, DBB £16–£18, WB, ⒤, L £5, D £5, ⒉, Dep a.

Rescue Service: Feathers Motors Ltd, Bromfield Rd· ✆ (0584) 5249 & (0584) 5240.

LULWORTH Dorset. Map 5F
Wareham 8½, London 120, Blandford Forum 18, Dorchester 16, Weymouth 14. **Golf** Wareham 9h, Lakey Hill 18h. **See** Cove, Durdle Door, Fossil Forest. (The Fossil Forest is within the Firing Ranges and not always accessible.)

★★**Lulworth Cove,** Lulworth Cove, BH20 5RQ. ✆ West Lulworth (092 941) 333. C. ✉ 17 bedrs, 3 bp, 6 bps, 5 sh, 1 ba, TV, Dgs. ✖ a l c, mc, at, LD 10.30. ⒟ CH, TV, Dgs, CP 20, Ac, con 20, CF, 1 st. £ BB £15–£18, DB £24–£26, WT £125, DT fr £17, WB, ⒉, Bk £2·50, L £3·30, D £5·50, cc 1 2 3 4 5 6, Dep a.

★**Bishop's Cottage** (R), West Lulworth, BH20 5RQ. ✆ West Lulworth (092 941) 261. Open Mar–Oct. C. ✉ 11 bedrs, 1 bp, 3 ba, annexe 3 bedrs, 2 bp, 1 ba, Dgs. ✖ a l c, mc, at, LD 10. ⒟ ch, TV, CP 6, sp, CF. £ BB £9·50–£10·50, DB £19–£21, DBB £15·50–£16·50, WB, ⒉, 10%, Bk £2·50, L £3, D £6, cc 1 3 6, Dep a.

Lulworth, H, x (Rl), West Lulworth, BH20 5RJ. ✆ West Lulworth (092 941) 230.
Shirley, H, x (R), Main Rd, West Lulworth, BH20 5RL. ✆ West Lulworth (092 941) 358. Open Mar–Oct. C. ✉ 17 bedrs, 10 bp, 7 bps, 5 ba, TV, Dgs. ⒟ CH, Dgs, CP 20, CF, 2 BGf, 2 st. £ BB £11·50–£12·50, DB £23–£25, WT £109·90–£119, DT £15·70–£17, ⒉, Bk £3·30, D £4·50, cc 1 3.

Rescue Service: Central Garage, Main St, West Lulworth. ✆ West Lulworth (092 941) 346.
Lulworth Garage, East Lulworth. ✆ West Lulworth (092 941) 283 and Bindon Abbey (0929) 462294.

LUTON Bedfordshire. Map 15E
Pop 165,000. St Albans 10, London 31, M1 Motorway 1½, Baldock 13, Bedford 19, Biggleswade 19, Dunstable 5, Hatfield 13.

MD Daily. **Golf** Stockwood Park 18h. **See** Church of St Mary, Museum (Wardown Park), Luton Hoo (Fabergé collection), Airport (spectator area), Whipsnade Zoo, Safari Park, Woburn Abbey. ⒢ Central Library, St George Sq. ✆ Luton (0582) 32629.

★★★**M Chiltern** Dunstable Rd, LU4 9RU. ✆ (0582) 575911. C. ✉ 99 bedrs, 99 bp, ns, TV, Dgs. ✖ a l c, mc, at. ⒟ Lt, N, ch, Dgs, CP 190, Ac, con 250, CF, 1 st. £ B fr £45, BD fr £53·50, WB, ⒤, Bk £5·50, D £9·25, cc 1 2 3 4 5 6, Dep b.

★★★**M Luton Crest,** Dunstable Rd, LU4 8RQ. ✆ (0582) 575955. Closed 1 week Xmas. C. ✉ 139 bedrs, 139 bp, ns, TV, Dgs. ✖ a l c, mc, LD 10. ⒟ Lt, N, CH, Dgs, CP 120, Ac, con 75, CF. £ B fr £40·50, BD fr £49, WB, ⒤, Bk £5·25, D £9·25, cc 1 2 3 4 5 6.

★★★**Strathmore Thistle,** Arndale Centre, LU1 2PR. ✆ (0582) 34199. C. ✉ 151 bedrs, 151 bp, ns, TV. ✖ a l c, mc, at, LD 9.30. ⒟ Lt, N, CH, TV, CP 18, con 200, CF, 0 st. £ BB £43·95–£50·95, DB £55·90–£57·90, WB, ⒉, Bk £4·95, L £8·75, D £9·50, cc 1 2 3 4 5 6, Dep a.

★★**Leaside,** 72 New Bedford Rd, LU13 1BT. ✆ (0582) 417643. Closed Xmas. C. ✉ 12 bedrs, 1 bp, 11 bps, TV. ✖ a l c, mc, at, LD 9.30. ⒟ CH, TV, Dgs, CP 30, CF, 2 st. £ BB £25·30–£29·90, DB £31·05–£36·80, ⒤, B £3·50, L £9·95, D £9·95, cc 1 2 3 5 6, Dep a.

Lansdowne Lodge, PH, z (R), 31 Lansdowne Rd. LU3 1EE. ✆ (0582) 31411. C. ✉ 14 bedrs, 9 bps, 1 ba, TV, Dgs. ✖ a l c. ⒟ CH, TV, CP 20, CF, 1 BGf, 1 st, Dis. £ BB £20–£32·20, DB £30–£40, ⒤, D £6·50.

Rescue Service: Trimoco Cars (Luton) Ltd, 326 Dunstable Rd. ✆ (0582) 31133.

LUTTERWORTH Leicestershire. Map 14B
Pop 6,758. M1 Motorway ½, London 89, Coventry 14, Daventry 15, Hinckley 10, Leicester 13, Market Harborough 12, Northampton 22, Nuneaton 13, Rugby 7. **EC** Wed. **MD** Thur. **Golf** Coventry Road 9h. **See** St Mary's Church, Stanford Hall.

★★**M Moorbarns,** A5 Trunk Rd, LE17 4HU. ✆ (045 55) 2237. Closed Xmas Day–New Year's Eve. C 1–16. ✉ 11 bedrs, 6 bp, 5 bps, TV. ✖ a l c, mc, LD 10. ⒟ CH, CP 40, sp, con 20, 11 BGf, 2 st. £ BB £26, DB £38, DBB £33·50, ⒉, 10%, Bk £3·50, L £5·25, D £7·50, cc 1 2 5.

Rescue Service: Broughton Astley Motors Ltd, The Oaks Industrial Estate, Gilmorton Rd. ✆ (045 55) 56453.

LYDFORD Devon. Maps 3C and 4E
Pop 321. Okehampton 8½, London 200, Launceston 12, Tavistock 8½. **Golf** Tavistock 18h. **See** Gorge, St Petroc's Church, Waterfall in grounds of Manor Hotel, Kit's Steps (cascade), Castle ruins.

⧫★★**Lydford House,** EX20 4AU. ✆ (082 282) 347. Closed Xmas. C 5. ✉ 11 bedrs, 4 bp, 1 bps, 3 ba, Dgs. ✖ a l c, mc, LD 8.30. ⒟ CH, TV, CP 30, Dgs. £ BB £12–£13·50, DB £24–£27, DBB £18–£19·50, WB, ⒤, Bk £3, L £5·50, D £6, cc 1 2 5 6.

◪★**The Manor,** Lydford Gorge, EX20 4BC. ✆ (082 282) 208. Open Apr–Oct. C 10. ✉ 6 bedrs, 2 bp, 2 bps, 2 sh, Dgs. ✖ a l c, mc, LD 7.30. ⒟ CH, TV, Dgs, CP 20, Ac, 1 st. £ BB £14–£18, DB £25–£30, DBB £19–£22, ⒉, Bk £2·75, L £4, D £7, cc 1 2 3 5, Dep a.

LYDFORD-ON-FOSSE Somerset. Map 5C
Pop 306. Wincanton 10, London 118, Glastonbury 8½, Ilminster 17, Shepton Mallet 8½, Taunton 22.
EC Wed. **Golf** Bruton 9h.

Repairer: Maggs, R G, Central Garage. ✆ Wheathill (096 324) 237.

LYDNEY Gloucestershire. Map 13E
Pop 7,246. Gloucester 18, London 123, Chepstow 8½, Monmouth 10, Ross-on-Wye 15.
EC Thur. **Golf** Lydney 9h & 18h. **See** Church, 14th cent Cross (restored), Lydney Park Grounds (site of Roman Villa).

★★**Feathers,** High St, GL15 5DN. ✆ Dean (0594) 42826.

Rescue Service: Hardacres Garage Ltd, Forest Rd. ✆ Dean (0594) 42447.
Watts of Lydney, High St. ✆ Dean (0594) 42481.

LYE West Midlands. Map 21F
Pop 7,668. Birmingham 10, London 121, Bridgnorth 15, Bromsgrove 9½, Kidderminster 7½, Walsall 11, Wolverhampton 11.
EC Thur. **Golf** Stourbridge 18h.

Repairer: Gallie's Garage Ltd, Stourbridge Rd. ✆ (038 482) 2788 and (038 482) 2755.
Rescue Service: Barley Bros Ltd, Folkes Rd. ✆ (038 482) 4431.

LYME REGIS Dorset. Map 5F
Pop 3,447. Dorchester 26, London 147, Axminster 5, Crewkerne 15, Exeter 28, Weymouth 28.
EC Thur. **Golf** Lyme Regis 18h. **See** Parish Church, The Cobb (Harbour) Museum, 250-year-old Umbrella Cottage. ⒢ Guildhall, Bridge St. ✆ Lyme Regis (029 74) 2138.

★★★**Alexandra,** Pound St, DT7 3HZ. ✆ (029 74) 2101. Open Feb–Nov. C. ✉ 26 bedrs, 14 bp, 5 bps, 3 ba, TV, Dgs. ✖ a l c, mc, at, LD 8.30. ⒟ CH, CP 17, con 80, CF, 3 BGf, 3 st. £ BB £14·50–£23, DB £29–£56, DBB £24–£33, WB, ⒉, Bk £3·50, L £5·75, D £8·50, cc 1 2 3 4 5 6.

★★★**Devon** (Rl), Uplyme, DT7 3TQ. ✆ (029 74) 3231.

★★★**High Cliff,** Sidmouth Rd, DT7 3EH. ✆ (029 74) 2300. Open Mar–Dec (closed Xmas). C. ✉ 11 bedrs, 4 bp, 3 bps, 3 ba, TV, Dgs. ✖ a l c, mc, at, LD 8.30. ⒟ CH, TV, CP 25, G 4, con 12, CF, 2 st. £ BB fr £19·90, DB fr £33, WT fr £165, DBB fr £25, WB, ⒉, Bk £4, D £8, Dep a.

★★★**Mariners** (R), Silver St, DT7 3HS. ✆ (029 74) 2753. Open Mar–Oct. C. ✉ 16 bedrs, 8 bp, 4 bps, 1 ba, TV. ✖ mc, at, LD 8.15. ⒟ TV, CP 22, CF, 2 BGf, 3 st. £ BB £19–£26, DB £32–£46, DBB fr £25–£30, WB, ⒉, Bk £3·50, D £11, cc 1 2 3 4 5 6, Dep.

◪★★**Bay,** Marine Par, DT7 3JQ. ✆ (029 74) 2059. Open Mar–Oct. C. ✉ 25 bedrs, 5 bp, 2 bps, 6 ba, Dgs. ✖ mc, at, LD

8. ⚑ CH, TV, Dgs, G 20, CF, 1 st. ⚐ BB
£15–£17, DB £30–£34, DBB £20–£23, WB,
🅻, Bk £3·50, L £3·50, D £7·50, Dep a.

★★**Buena Vista** (R), *Pound St, DT7 3HZ*.
✆ (029 74) 2494. Open Mar–Nov. RS Mar
& Nov. C. ⚐ 20 bedrs, 8 bp, 4 ba, TV, Dgs.
✗ mc, at, LD 8. ⚑ ch, TV, CP 17, U 2, CF.
£ BB £17·50–£22, DB £31–£50, DBB
£22·50–£32, WB, 🅶, 10%, Bk £4·50, L £4, D
£8·50, cc 1 2 3 5 6.

★★**Dower**, *Rousdon, DT7 3RB*. ✆ Seaton
(0297) 21047. Closed Jan. C 10. ⚐ 9
bedrs, 2 bp, 4 bps, 2 ba, Dgs. ✗ a l c, LD
8.30. ⚑ ch, TV, CP 45. £ BB £16–£24, DB
£28–£40, WT £136–£164, DT £22–£28,
WB, 🅶, Bk £3·50, L £6·50, D £7·95,
cc 1 2 3 5.

◼★★**Royal Lion**, *Broad St, DT7 3QF*.
✆ (029 74) 2768. C. ⚐ 22 bedrs, 8 bedrs,
7 bp, 2 ba, TV, Dgs. ✗ a l c, mc, at, LD 8.30.
⚑ CH, TV, Dgs, CP 25, Ac, con 20, CF.
£ BB £14–£18·50, DB £30–£37, WT £154–
£168, DBB £21–£25, WB, 🅶, Bk £3·50, D
£7·50, cc 1 3, Dep b.

◼★★**St Michaels** (R), *Pound St, DT7
3HZ*. ✆ (029 74) 2503. C. ⚐ 13 bedrs, 4
bp, 2 sh, 2 ba, Dgs. ✗ LD 7.30. ⚑ ch, TV,
Dgs, CP 10, CF. £ BB £12·75–£14·75, DB
£25·50–£29·50, DBB £18·25–£20·75, 🅻, D
£5·50, cc 1, Dep a.

★★**Three Cups**, *Broad St, DT7 3QE*.
✆ (029 74) 2732. C. ⚐ 19 bedrs, 7 bp, 1
sh, 3 ba, TV, Dgs. ✗ a l c, mc, LD 9.30.
⚑ CH, TV, CP 40, Ac, con 20, CF.
£ BB£15·50–£19, DB £31·10–£39·10,
DBB £23·05–£27·05, Bk £2·50, L £4, D
£7·50, cc 1 2 3 5 6, Dep a.

◼★**Dorset** (R), *Silver St, DT7 3HR*.
✆ (029 74) 2482. Open Mar–Oct. C. ⚐ 13
bedrs, 5 bps, 3 ba, Dgs. ✗ a l c, mc, LD
7.30. ⚑ ch, TV, Dgs, CP 14, CF. £ BB £10–
£12, DB £20–£24, DBB £14·50–£17·80,
WB, 🅻, Bk £2·10, D £5·95.

★**Stile House** (R), *Stile La, DT7 3JD*.
✆ (029 74) 2052. Open Feb–Oct. C. ⚐ 16
bedrs, 3 ba, TV. ✗ mc, at, LD 7. ⚑ CH, TV,
ns, CF. £ BB £14–£15·50, DB £30·50, WB,
🅻, Bk £3·75, D £5·95.

◼★**Tudor House** (R), *Church St, DT7
3BU*. ✆ (029 74) 2472. Open Mar–Oct. C.
⚐ 17 bedrs, 4 bp, 3 ba, Dgs. ✗ mc, LD
7.30. ⚑ TV, Dgs, CP 12, Ac, CF, 2 st. £ BB
£9–£14, DB £18–£28, DBB £80–£105, 🅻,
Bk £4, D £5·50.

Coverdale, G, x (Unl), *Woodmead Rd,
DT7 3AB*. ✆ (029 74) 2882. Open Mar–
Oct. C. ⚐ 9 bedrs, 2 ba. ⚑ CH, TV, CP 10,
CF. £ BB £7·50–£9, DB £15–£18, WT £72–
£82, DT (b) £11–£12·50, 🅻, D £3·75.

Kent House, H, *Silver St, DT7 3HT*.
✆ (029 74) 2020. Open Feb–Oct. C. ⚐ 7
bedrs, 4 bp, 2 sh, 1 ba. ⚑ CH, TV, ns, CP 8,
CF, 2 BGf, 3 st. £ BB £11·50–£14, DB
£21–£26, WT £112–£119, DT (b) £17–£18,
🅻, Bk £3, D £6·50.

Kersbrook, PH, y (R), *Pound Rd, DT7
3JIX*. ✆ (029 74) 2596. Open Mar–Nov. C.
⚐ 14 bedrs, 2 bp, 5 bps, 1 ba, Dgs. ⚑ CH,
TV, Dgs, CP 14, CF. £ BB £13–£14, DB
£25–£28, WT £135–£145, DT (b) £20–£23,
🅶, DB £5·50, cc 1 2 3.

Old Monmouth, H, z (R), *Church St, DT7
3BS*. ✆ (029 74) 2456.

Rotherfield, G, z (RI), *View Rd, DT7 3AA*.
✆ (029 74) 2811. C. ⚐ 7 bedrs, 2 ba, Dgs.
⚑ CH, TV, CP 10, CF. £ BB £7·50–£8·50, DB
£15–£17, WT (c) £49–£56, DT (b) £74–
£81, 🅻, D £4·25.

White House, G, z (RI), *47 Silver St, DT7
3HR*. ✆ (029 74) 3420.

LYMINGTON Hampshire. Map 6E
Pop 12,500. Lyndhurst 8, London 92,
Bournemouth 16, Ringwood 13.
EC Wed. **MD** Sat. **Golf** Barton-on-Sea
18h. **See** Parish Church of St Thomas the
Apostle, Buckland Rings 1 m N, Beaulieu
Abbey, Palace House and National Motor
Museum 5½ m NE, Buckler's Hard Museum
(maritime) 6 m NE.

◼⚑★★**Passford House,** *Mount Pleasant,
SO4 8LS*. ✆ (0890) 682398. C. ⚐ 53
bedrs, 53 bp, 3 ba, ns, TV, Dgs. ✗ a l c, mc,
at, LD 8.30. ⚑ CH, TV, Dgs, CP 80, U 3, sp,
tc, sb, con 50, CF, 14 BGf, 0 st, Dis. £ BB
£31, DB £50, DT £36, WB, 🅶, Bk £5, L
£6·60, D £9·95, cc 2, Dep a.

★★**Stanwell House** (R), *15 High St, SO4
9AA*. ✆ (0890) 77123.

LYMM Cheshire. Map 20B
Pop 11,000. M6 Motorway 2, London 181,
Altrincham 6½, Bolton 17, Manchester 13,
Northwich 11, Warrington 4½.
EC Wed. **Golf** Lymm 18h. **See** Parish
Church, Stocks, Market Cross.

◼★★★**Lymm**, *Whitbarrow Rd, WA13
9AQ*. ✆ (092 575) 2233. C. ⚐ 23 bedrs, 7
bp, 16 bps, 1 ba, TV, Dgs. ✗ a l c, mc, at,
LD 10. ⚑ N, CH, Dgs, CP 160, Ac, con, CF,
8 BGf, 2 st. £ BB £42, DB £42, WB, 🅶, 10%,
Bk £3·80, L £6, D £7, cc 1 2 3 5 6, Dep b.

Repairer: Avenue Motor Services (Lymm)
Ltd, Park Garage, Agden. ✆ (092 575)
2447.
Rescue Service: Station Garage (Heatley)
Ltd, 47 Mill La, Heatley. ✆ (092 575)
2231.

LYMPSHAM Somerset. Map 5A
Pop 686. M5 Motorway 4, Axbridge 7,
London 139, Bridgwater 13, Wells 18,
Weston-super-Mare 6.
Golf Burnham 18h. **See** Perp Church.

◼⚑★★**Batch Farm**, *Batch La, BS24
0EX*. ✆ Edingworth (093 472) 371. Open
Mar–Oct. C 4. ⚐ 10 bedrs, 4 bp, 2 ba, ns,
TV. ✗ mc, at, LD 8. ⚑ CH, TV, ns, CP 50, G
1, pf, con 20, CF. £ BB fr £14, DB fr £26,
DBB fr £17, WB, 🅶, Bk £3, L £2·50, D £5,
cc 1 3.▲

LYNDHURST Hampshire. Map 6E
Pop 2,900. Winchester 19, London 84,
M27 Motorway 3, Bournemouth 19,
Lymington 8, Ringwood 14, Romsey 9½,
Salisbury 19, Southampton 9½.
EC Wed. **Golf** Lyndhurst 18h. **See**
Church, 14th cent Queen's House.
🅿 Main Car Park. ✆ Lyndhurst (042 128)
2269.

★★★**Crown**, *High St, SO4 7NF*.
✆ (042 128) 2722. C. ⚐ 42 bedrs, 42 bp,
TV, Dgs. ✗ a l c, mc, at, LD 9.45. ⚑ Lt, N,
CH, TV, Dgs, CP 50, U 9, Ac, con 70, CF, 2
st. £ BB fr £31, DB fr £44, DBB fr £35, WB,
🅻, Bk £5, L £7·50, D £0·50, cc 1 2 3 5,
Dep b.

★★★**Lyndhurst Park**, *High St, SO4 7BJ*.
✆ (042 128) 2823. C. ⚐ 59 bedrs, 59 bp,
TV, Dgs. ✗ mc, at, LD 9.45 (9.15 Sun).
⚑ Lt, N, CH, Dgs, CP 100, Ac, sp, tc, con
150, CF, 2 st. £ BB £28, DB £38, WB, 🅻, Bk
£2·50, L £7, D £8·95, cc 1 2 3 4 5 6, Dep a.

★★★**Evergreens** (R), *Romsey Rd, SO4
7AR*. ✆ (042 128) 2175. C. ⚐ 17 bedrs, 1
bp, 10 bps, 6 sh, 2 ba, TV, Dgs. ✗ a l c, mc,
at, LD 9.30. ⚑ CH, TV, CP 34, Ac, sp, con,
CF, 3 BGf, 2 st. £ BB fr £18, DB fr £30, DBB
fr £22·25, WB, 🅻, Bk £3, D £7·25.

★★**Pikes Hill Forest Lodge** (R), *Romsey
Rd, SO4 7AS*. ✆ (042 128) 3677.

◼★**Forest Point** (R), *Romsey Rd, SO4
7AR*. ✆ (042 128) 2420. Closed Jan, RS
Feb. C. ⚐ 10 bedrs, 1 bp, 1 sh, 3 ba, TV,
Dgs. ✗ mc, at, LD 10. ⚑ CH, TV, CP 20, U
2, Ac, con 20, CF, 1 BGf, 0 st, Dis. £ BB
£12·50–£23, DB £25–£39, DBB £19·25–
£29·75, WB, 🅶, Bk £2·50, L £6, D £6·75,
cc 1 2 3 5 6, Dep a.

Bench View, H, x (Unl), *Southampton
Rd*, ✆ (042 128) 2502. Closed Dec. C.
⚐ 8 bedrs, 2 ba, TV, Dgs. ⚑ ch, TV, Dgs,
CP 10, CF. £ BB £8–£14, DB £17–£19, WT
£55–£60, 🅻.

Ormonde House, H, x (R), *Southampton
Rd, SO4 7BT*. ✆ (042 128) 2806. C. ⚐ 14
bedrs, 2 bp, 5 bps, 3 ba, TV, Dgs. ⚑ CH, TV,
CP 20, CF. £ BB £11·80–£12·80, DB
£23·80–£31, WT (b) £109·50–£116·50, DT
(b) £17·30–£18·30, 🅶, Bk £2·50, D £6·50,
cc 1 2 3.▲

Repairer: New Forest Services
(Lyndhurst) Ltd, High St. ✆ (042 128)
2861.
Pat's Garage (Lyndhurst) Ltd, Romsey Rd.
✆ (042 128) 2609 & (042 128) 2255.

LYNEHAM Wiltshire. Maps 5B and 6A
Pop 4,681. Swindon 10, London 88,
Chippenham 9½, Cirencester 19, Devizes
14, Frome 29, Marlborough 16, Tetbury
14, Warminster 28.
EC Wed. **Golf** Chippenham 18h. **See** 15th
cent Parish Church, Medieval Cross and
prehistoric earthworks on Clack Hill,
Ancient Yew.

Rescue Service: G & K Barnes Ltd, T/A
Edmonds Garage, 81 The Green.
✆ Bradenstoke (0249) 890331.

LYNG Norfolk. Map 16C
Pop 700. Norwich 13, London 125,
Cromer 23, Dereham 7½, Fakenham 13.
EC Wed. **Golf** Dereham 9h, Barnham
Broom 18h, Norwich 18h.

Rescue Service: Lyng Garage. ✆ Great
Witchingham (060 544) 229.

LYNMOUTH Devon. Map 4C
Pop 1,600 (inc Lynton and Woody Bay).
Minehead 16, London 184, Barnstaple 17,
Ilfracombe 17, South Molton 20.
Golf Ilfracombe 18h. **See** Valley of Rocks,
Watersmeet, Glen Lyn, Doone Valley and
Oare Church, Shelley's Cottage,
Countisbury Church (16th cent), Exmoor,
Culbone Church (16th cent), reputed
smallest in England.
🅿 Lee Rd, Lynton. ✆ Lynton (059 85)
2225.

★★★**Tors**, *EX35 6NA*. ✆ Lynton (0598)
53236. Closed 2nd week Nov–Feb. C.
⚐ 39 bedrs, 32 bp, 2 ba, TV, Dgs. ✗ a l c,
mc, at, LD 9. ⚑ Lt, ch, TV, Dgs, CP 35, Ac,
sp, con, CF, 0 st. £ BB £16–£23, DB £32–
£46, DBB £21–£30, WB, 🅻, Bk f 4 l f 4·75
D £8·75, cc 1 2 3 6.▲

★★**Bath**, *Sea Front, EX35 6EL*. ✆ Lynton
(059 85) 2235. Open Apr–Oct. RS Mar. C.
⚐ 24 bedrs, 12 bp, 1 bps, 3 ba, TV, Dgs.
✗ mc, at, LD 8.30. ⚑ CH, TV, Dgs, CP 12,
U 4, Ac, CF, 3 st. £ BB £10–£18, DB £20–
£36, WT £131–£182, DT £19–£25, WB, 🅻,
Bk £3·75, L £4, D £7·50, cc 1 2 3 5 6.

◼⚑★★**Beacon** (R), *Countisbury Hill, EX35
6ND*. ✆ Lynton (059 85) 3268. Open Feb–
Nov. C 12. ⚐ 7 bedrs, 2 bp, 3 bps, 1 ba, TV.
✗ a l c, mc, at, LD 8. ⚑ CH, CP 10, 1 st.
£ BB £13·25–£14·75, DB £23·50–£31·50,

DBB £18·25–£22·50, WB, 🅟, Bk £3·25, L
£4·95, D £6·85.

★**Rising Sun,** *Sea Front, Mars Hill, EX35
6EQ.* ✆ Lynton (059 85) 3223.

■★**Shelley's Cottage** (R), *Watersmeet
Rd, EX35 6EP.* ✆ Lynton (059 85) 3219.
Open Mar–Oct. C 4. 🛏 14 bedrs, 1 sh, 3
ba, Dgs. ✗ mc, at, LD 6. 🄰 TV, Dgs, Ac, 3
st. £ BB £9·50–£11·50, DB £19–£23, DBB
£79–£92, WB, 🄰, Bk £3, D £7·50, cc 1, Dep.

Countisbury Lodge, H, x (R), *Tors Park,
EX35 6NB.* ✆ Lynton (059 85) 2388. C.
🛏 8 bedrs, 2 bp, 1 ba, ns, Dgs. 🄰 CH, TV,
Dgs, CP 10, CF. £ BB £10·50–£11·50, DB
£19–£23, DT (b) £15–£16, 🄰, D £5·50.

East Lynn, G, x (Rl), *17 Watersmeet Rd,
EX35 6EP.* ✆ Lynton (059 85) 2540.

Glenville, PH, x (Rl), *Tors Rd.* ✆ Lynton
(059 85) 2202. C 5. 🛏 7 bedrs, 2 ba, Dgs.
🄰 TV, CF. £ BB £7·50–£8·50, DB £15–£17,
DT (b) £12·25–£12·50, 🄰.

Heatherville, PH, x (Rl), *Tors Park,
EX35 6NB.* ✆ Lynton (059 85) 2327.
Open Feb–Nov. C. 🛏 8 bedrs, 3 bps, 2 ba.
🄰 CH, TV, ns, CP 8, CF. £ BB £10·50–£12,
DB £21–£24, WT £94, DT £15, 🄰, D £4·50.

LYNTON Devon. Map 4C
Pop 1,600 (inc Lynmouth). Lynmouth ½,
London 185, Barnstaple 16, Ilfracombe
16, South Molton 20.
EC Sat (win). **Golf** Ilfracombe 18h. **See**
Valley of Rocks, St Mary's Church, Lyn
and Exmoor Museum, Watersmeet, Glen
Lyn, Doone Valley and Oare Church,
Countisbury Church (16th cent), Exmoor,
Culbone Church (16th cent), reputed
smallest in England.
🛈 Lee Rd. ✆ Lynton (059 85) 2225.

★★★**Lynton Cottage,** *North Walk, EX35
6ED.* ✆ (059 85) 2342. Open Mar–Oct. C.
🛏 21 bedrs, 9 bp, 5 bps, 3 ba, Dgs. ✗ a l c,
mc, at, LD 8.30. 🄽 CH, TV, CP 26, con,
CF, 1 st. £ BB £13–£18·50, DB £26–
£36·50, DBB £20–£25·50, WB, 🄰, Bk
£3·50, L £4·50, D £7·75, cc 1 3 6, Dep a.

■★★**Combe Park** (R), *Hillsford Bridge,
EX35 6LF.* ✆ (059 85) 2356.

■★★**Crown,** *Market, Sinai Hill, EX35
6AG.* ✆ (059 85) 2253. C. 🛏 16 bedrs, 15
bp, 1 bps, TV, Dgs. ✗ mc, LD 8.15. 🄰 CH,
TV, Dgs, CP 24, CF, 1 st. £ BB £18·75–
£20·25, DB £31·50–£34·50, DBB £22·50–
£24·50, WB, 🄰, Bk £4·50, D £7·50,
cc 1 2 3 5.

■★★**Sandrock,** *Longmead, EX35 6DH.*
✆ (059 85) 3307. Open Feb–Nov. 🛏 10
bedrs, 4 bp, 1 bps, 1 ba, TV, Dgs. ✗ mc, at,
LD 8. 🄰 CH, Dgs, CP 9, CF, 2 st. £ BB
£9·50–£13, DB £19–£25, DBB £16–£19,
WB, 🄰, Bk £2, D £6·50, cc 1 2, Dep.

★★**Valley of Rocks,** *EX35 6HS.*
✆ (059 85) 2349. Open Apr–Oct & Xmas.
C. 🛏 78 bedrs, 35 bp, 1 bps, 14 ba, Dgs.
✗ mc, at, LD 8.30. 🄰 Lt, N, ch, TV, Dgs, CP
35, Ac, con 250, CF, 1 st. £ BB fr £24·75,
DB fr £35·75, WB, 🄰, cc 1 2 3 5 6.

■★**Chough's Nest,** *North Walk,
EX35 6HJ.* ✆ (0598) 53315. Open Mar–
Oct. C. 🛏 11 bedrs, 6 bp, 3 bps, 1 ba.
✗ mc, LD 10.30. 🄰 CH, ns, CF, 7 st. £ BB
£11–£11·50, DB £22–£23, WT £127, DBB
£17·25–£18·50, WB, 🄰, Bk £4, D £5·25,
Dep.

■★**Conway** (R), *Castle Hill, EX35 6JA,*
✆ (059 85) 2291. Open Apr–Oct. C. 🛏 9
bedrs, 2 bp, 1 bps, 3 sh, 1 ba. ✗ LD 6.
🄰 CH, TV, CF, 5 st. £ BB £8·75–£11·75, DB
£17·50–£21, DBB £13·25–£15, 🄰, Bk
£2·25, D £5, cc 1 3, Dep a.

■★**Neubia House** (Rt), *Lydiate Lane,
EX35 6AH.* ✆ (059 85) 2309. Open Feb–
Nov & Xmas. C. 🛏 12 bedrs, 9 bp, 3 bps,
Dgs. ✗ LD 7.30. 🄰 CH, TV, Dgs, CP 14,
CF, 1 st. £ BB £12·15–£13·25, DB £24·30–
£26·50, DBB £19·40–£20, WB, 🄰, Bk
£3·50, L £3·50, D £7.

■★**Rockvale** (R), *EX35 6HW.* ✆ (059 85)
2279.

■★**Seawood** (Rt), *North Walk, EX35
6HJ.* ✆ (059 85) 2272. Open Mar–Nov. C.
🛏 11 bedrs, 8 bps, 2 ba, Dgs. ✗ mc, at, LD
7.30. 🄰 CH, TV, CP 11, CF, 2 st. £ BB £9–
£12·50, DB £18–£25, DBB £14–£19·50,
WB, 🄰, Bk £2·20, L £2·20, D £6.

Alford House, PH, z (Rl), *3 Alford Ter,
EX35 6AT.* ✆ (0598) 52359. Open Mar–
Oct. C 5. 🛏 8 bedrs, 2 bps, 3 sh, 1 ba, Dgs.
🄰 CH, TV, CF, 12 st. £ BB £16·45–£17·25,
DB £29·90–£39·10, WT (c) £89·70–£115,
🄰.

Gable Lodge, H, x (Rt), *Lee Rd, EX35
6BS.* ✆ (0598) 52367. C. 🛏 9 bedrs, 2 bp,
4 bps, 1 ba, Dgs. 🄰 CH, TV, Dgs, CP 7, CF,
2 st. £ BB £9·50–£10·50, DB £19–£23·40,
WT (b) £89·50–£106·50, DT (b) £14–
£16·70, 🄰, Bk £1·50, L £3, D £5.

Hazeldene, G, z (Rt), *27 Lee Rd, EX35
6BP.* ✆ (059 85) 2364. Open Mar–Oct. C
5. 🛏 8 bedrs, 2 bp, 4 ba. 🄰 CH, TV, CP
8, 3 st. £ BB £7·50–£8·50, DB £14–£19,
WT (b) £75–£85, DT (b) £12–£13, 🄰,
cc 1 3.

Horwood House, G, z (Rl), *Lydiate Lane,
EX35 6HE.* ✆ (059 85) 2334. Open Apr–
Oct. C. 🛏 5 bedrs, 2 ba, Dgs. 🄰 ch, TV, CP
4, G 1, CF. £ BB £7–£8, DBB £15–£17, WT
(b) £72–£78, DT (b) £12·50–£13·50, 🄰.

Ingleside, PH, x (Rl) *Lee Road,
EX35 6HW.* ✆ (059 85) 2223. Open Mar–
Oct. C. 🛏 7 bedrs, 4 bp, 3 bps, TV. 🄰 CH,
TV, CP 13, CF, 1 BGf, 1 st. £ BB £13·50–
£15·50, DB £24–£46, WT £126–£140, DT
(b) £19–£21, 🄰, Bk £4, D £7, cc 1.

Kingford House, PH, x (Rl), *Longmead,
EX35 6DQ.* ✆ (059 85) 2361. Open Mar–
Sep. C 5. 🛏 8 bedrs, 3 bps, 2 ba. 🄰 ch, TV,
ns, CP 8, 1 st. £ BB £7·50–£8·50, DB £15–
£19, WT (b) £79·50–£87, DT (b) £12–£14,
🄰.

Longmead House, PH, x (Rl),
Longmead, EX35 6DQ. ✆ (059 85) 2523.
Open Apr–Oct. C 5. 🛏 9 bedrs, 2 ba. 🄰 CP
9. £ BB £7·50–£8, DB £15–£16, WT
£82·25–£85·75, DT £12–£12·50, 🄰, D
£4·50.

Lyn Crest, G, x (Unl), *22 Lee Rd, EX35
6BP.* ✆ (059 85) 3269. C 5. 🛏 6 bedrs, 2
ba, Dgs. 🄰 CH, TV, Dgs, CP 4. £ BB £7·50–
£8·50, DB £15–£17, WT £80–£85, DT £12–
£13, 🄰.

Lynhurst, PH, xy (Rt), *Lynway, EX35
6AX.* ✆ (059 85) 2241. C. 🛏 7 bedrs, 5 bp,
2 sh, 1 ba, TV, Dgs. 🄰 CH, TV, Dgs, CP 7,
12 st. £ BB £8–£9·50, DB £16–£17, DT
£10, 🄰.

Mayfair, PH, xy (Rl) *Lynway, EX35 6AX.*
✆ (059 85) 3227. C. 🛏 12 bedrs, 2 bp, 1
sh, 2 ba, Dgs. 🄰 CH, TV, Dgs, CP 12, CF.
£ BB £6·50–£8, DB £19–£24, WT (b) £60–
£72, DT (b) £9·50–£11, 🄰.

Pine Lodge, PH, xy (Unl), *Lynway, EX35
6AX.* ✆ (059 85) 3230. Open Apr–Sep. C
5. 🛏 9 bedrs, 3 ba, Dgs. 🄰 CH, TV, CP 8, 3
BGf. £ BB £8·75–£9·50, DB £17·50–£19,
WT (b) £91–£95, DT (b) £13·50–£14·50,
🄰.

Southcliffe, PH, z (Rl), *Lee Rd,
EX35 6BS.* ✆ (059 85) 3328. Closed Jan–
Feb. C 5. 🛏 8 bedrs, 1 bp, 2 bps, 2 ba, Dgs.

🄰 CH, TV, CP 8, U 1, 0 st. £ BB £8–£11·50,
DB £16–£23, WT (b) £85–£95, DT (b)
£13–£15·50.

South View, G, x (Unl), *23 Lee Rd, EX35
6BP.* ✆ (059 85) 2289.

Turret, G, z (Unl), *Lee Rd, EX35 6BS.*
✆ (059 85) 3284.

Valley House, PH, y (Rl), *Lynbridge Rd.*
✆ (059 85) 2285. C 3. 🛏 8 bedrs, 5 sh, 2
ba, ns, CP 8. £ BB £9·80–£12·40, DB
£19·60–£24·80, WT (b) £80–£105·80, DT
(b) £13·22–£14·95, 🄰, cc 1 3.▲

Waterloo House, PH, z (Rl), *Lydiate
Lane, EX35 6AJ.* (059 85) 3391. C. 🛏 12
bedrs, 2 bps, 2 ba, Dgs. 🄰 ch, TV, Dgs, CP
2, CF. £ BB £7·50–£9·50, DB £15–£19, WT
(b) £75–£88, DT (b) £11·50–£14, 🄰.

Woodlands, PH, x (R), *Lynbridge, EX35
6AX.* ✆ (059 85) 2324. C 16. 🛏 9 bedrs, 4
bps, 2 ba. 🄰 CH, TV, CP 10, 1 st. £ BB £10–
£14, DB £20–£60, WT (b) £95–£150, DT
(b) £15–£20, 🄰, cc 1 3.

Repairer: Prideaux Garage, Lee Rd.
✆ (059 85) 3338.
Rescue Service: Granville Garages, 41 Lee
Rd. ✆ (059 85) 2513.

LYTCHETT MATRAVERS Dorset.
Map 5F
Pop 1,876. Wimborne Minster 6, London
109, Blandford Forum 9, Bournemouth 10,
Lyndhurst 26, Salisbury 28, Wareham 6.
EC Wed. **Golf** Broadstone 18h.

Rescue Service: Allan Davis (Lytchett)
Ltd, Yucca Villa, Middle Rd. ✆ Lytchett
Minster (0202) 622491.

LYTHAM ST ANNES Lancs. Map 27D
Pop 39,607. Preston 14, London 224,
Blackpool 4½.
EC Wed. **Golf** Fairhaven 18h. Royal
Lytham and St Annes 18h, Lytham (Green
Drive) 18h, St Annes Old Links 18h.
See Parish Church, Carnegie Library, St
Annes Pier, Lifeboat Memorial, Lowther
Gardens, Ashton Gardens, Motive Power
Museum, Fairhaven Lake, Lytham
Windmill, Green Drive (wooded avenue–
no cars).
🛈 St Annes Square. ✆ Lytham (0253)
725610.

★★★★**Clifton Arms,** *West Beach, FY8
5QJ.* ✆ Lytham (0253) 739898. C. 🛏 46
bedrs, 42 bp, 4 bps, TV, Dgs. ✗ mc, at, LD
10 (9 Sun). 🄰 Lt, N, CH, TV, Dgs, CP 60,
Ac, con, CF, 5 st. £ WB, cc 1 2 3 4 5 6,
Dep b.

★★★**Grand Crest,** *South Prom, FY8
1NB.* ✆ St Annes (0253) 721288. C. 🛏 40
bedrs, 40 bp, ns, TV, Dgs. ✗ a l c, mc, at,
LD 9.45. 🄰 Lt, N, CH, Dgs, CP 150, Ac, con
85, CF, 3 st. £ B fr £36·50, BD fr £50, WB,
🄰, Bk £4·95, D £9·25, cc 1 2 3 4 5 6, Dep.

★★**Chadwick,** *South Prom, FY8 1NP.*
✆ St Annes (0253) 720061. C. 🛏 70
bedrs, 60 bp, 10 bps, TV, Dgs. ✗ mc, at, LD
8.15. 🄰 Lt, N, CH, TV, ns, CP 45, U 1, Ac,
sol, con 70, CF, 12 BGf, 0 st. Dis. £ BB
£14·50–£15·50, DB £24–£26·50, WT
£131–£143·50, DT £18·80–£20·80, WB, 🄰,
Bk £2·50, D £7, cc 1 2 3 5.

★★**Fernlea** (Rl), *15 South Prom, FY8 1LU.*
✆ St Annes (0253) 726726. C. 🛏 91
bedrs 91 bp, TV. ✗ mc, at, LD 8. 🄰 Lt, N,
CH, TV, CP 60, Ac, sp, sc, sb, sol, gym, con
200, CF, 5 BGf. £ BB £18, DB £36, DBB
£23–£27, WB, 🄰, Bk £4·50, L £7, D £8·50,
cc 1.

★★Glendower, *North Prom, FY8 2NQ.*
✆ St Annes (0253) 723241.
★★St Ives (R), *7 South Prom, FY8 1LS.*
✆ St Annes (0253) 720011. C. 🛏 76
bedrs, 71 bp, 3 ba, TV. ✗ a l c, mc, at, LD
9.30. 🅿 N, CH, TV, CP 80, Ac, sp, sb, sol,
con 150, CF, 10 BGf, 2 st. £ BB fr £19, DB
fr £32, ①, Bk £3·25, L £4·75, D £7·50,
cc 1 2 3 5 6, Dep a.
★Lindum (Rl), *63 South Prom, FY8 1LZ.*
✆ St Annes (0253) 721534. C. 🛏 80
bedrs, 54 bp, 6 bps, 20 sh, 7 ba, TV, Dgs.
✗ mc, at, LD 7. 🅿 Lt, N, ch, TV, CP 25, Ac,
sb, sol, con 80, CF, 6 st. £ BB £12·50–
£14·50, DB £25–£29, WB, ②, Bk £2·85, D
£5·95, cc 1 3 5, Dep a.
Beaumont, PH, z (Rl), *11 All Saints Rd,
FY8 1PL.* ✆ St Annes (0253) 723958.
Endsleigh, PH, z (Rt), *315 Clifton Drive
South, FY8 3HN.* ✆ St Annes (0253)
725622. C. 🛏 11 bedrs, 6 bps, 2 ba, ns, TV.
🅿 CH, TV, CP 6, CF, 2 st. £ BB £9·75–
£11·75, DB £19·50–£23·50, WT £78–£88,
DT £14–£15·50, ①.
Gables, H, z (Rl), *35 Orchard Rd, FY8
1PG.* ✆ St Annes (0253) 729851.
Harcourt, PH, z (Rl), *21 Richmond Rd,
FY8 1PE.* ✆ St Annes (0253) 722299.
Closed Xmas & New Year. C. 🛏 10 bedrs,
2 ba, Dgs. ✗ a l c. 🅿 CH, TV, CP 6, CF, 3 st.
£ BB £8·33–£8·62, DB £16·67–£17·25, WT
(b) £76·47–£80·50, DT £10·92–£11·50, ②,
D £3·45.
Lyndhurst, G, z (Unl), *338 Clifton Drive
North, FY8 2PB.* ✆ St Annes (0253)
724343. Closed Xmas. C. 🛏 12 bedrs, 1
bp, 3 ba, Dgs. 🅿 ch, TV, CP 11, CF, 7 st.
£ BB £10·50–£11·50, DB £15–£19, WT (b)
£59–£71, DT (b) £11–£12·50, ①, Bk £2, D
£3·50.
Queens, H, z, *Central Beach, FY8 5LB.*
✆ (0253) 737316.

Rescue Service: Boulevard Motors, Lord
St. ✆ St Annes (0253) 726166.
Lytham Garages Ltd, Freckleton St.
✆ Lytham (0253) 733900.

MABLETHORPE Lincolnshire. Map 23B
Pop 7,456. (inc Sutton-on-Sea), Skegness
17, London 156, Boston 33, Grimsby 28,
Horncastle 21, Louth 14.
EC Wed. (win). **MD** Thur. **Golf** Sandilands
18h. **See** St Mary's Church.
ℹ️ Foreshore Office, Central Promenade.
✆ Mablethorpe (052 13) 2496.

Auralee, PH, z (Rl), *72 The Boulevard,
LN12 2AD.* ✆ (0521) 77660. Closed
Xmas. C 3. 🛏 10 bedrs, 3 ba. 🅿 CH, TV,
CF. £ BB £10·50, DB £18, WT £70, DT (b)
£12·50, ①.

Rescue Service: Seacroft Garage Ltd,
Seacroft Rd. ✆ (0521) 2333.

MACCLESFIELD Cheshire. Map 19B
See also BOLLINGTON and WINCLE.
Pop 45,000, Leek 12, London 167,
Altrincham 14, Buxton 11, Chapel-en-le-
Frith 12, Congleton 8, Knutsford 11,
Middlewich 15, Stockport 11.
EC Wed. **MD** Tue, Fri, Sat. **P** Disc Parking
is in operation from 8 am to 6 pm. Sundays
and Bank Hols are exempt. Vehicles using
the authorised parking places within the
zone must display a disc set to indicate
the time of arrival. The maximum period of
waiting is two hours. PARKING DISCS are
obtainable free from Town Hall, public
library, police station and traffic wardens.
PARKING MUST NOT TAKE PLACE

WHERE THERE IS A SINGLE YELLOW
LINE ALONG THE ROAD. **Golf**
Macclesfield 9h. **See** Museum (silk
industry), Glacial Stone, Market Stone, St
Michael's Church, Unitarian Chapel,
Capesthorne Hall 5 m W, Adlington Hall 5
m N, Gawsworth Hall 3 m SW, Jodrell
Bank (the 25ft radio telescope may be
operated by visitors) 8 m W.
ℹ️ Town Hall, Market Pl. ✆ Macclesfield
(0625) 21955 ext 115.

★★Ellesmere (R), *Buxton Rd, SK11 7ES.*
✆ (0625) 23791. C. 🛏 8 bedrs, 1 bp, 2
bps. 2 ba, TV, Dgs. ✗ a l c, mc, at, LD 9.
🅿 CH, TV, CP 25, Ac, con 12, CF, 1 BGf, 0
st, Dis. £ BB £17–£24·75, DB £27·50–£33,
WT £150, DT £24, WB, ①, Bk £2·75, L
£3·50, D £6·75, cc 1 3 5.

Repairers: Cookson, J J Ltd, Central
Garage, Waters Green. ✆ (0625) 22226.
G H Horn & Co (Macclesfield) Ltd, 98
Chestergate. ✆ (0625) 22909.
Lookers of Macclesfield Ltd, Hobson St.
✆ (0625) 27759.
T Simister Ltd, Hibel Rd and Station St.
✆ (0625) 27766.
Rescue Service: Park Garages
(Macclesfield) Ltd, Rodney St. ✆ (0625)
23533.
S Houghton Ltd, Buxton Rd. ✆ (0625)
23923.

MAENPORTH Cornwall. Map 2F
Pop 75. Truro 12, London 258, Falmouth 3,
Helston 10, Redruth 11.
Golf Falmouth 18h. **See** Coastal walks.
🔲★★**Trelawne** (R), *TR11 5HS.*
✆ Falmouth (0326) 250226. Open Mar–
Nov. C. 🛏 16 bedrs, 10 bp, 2 bps, 2 sh, 2
ba, TV, Dgs. ✗ mc, at, LD 8.30. 🅿 CH, ns,
CP 25, sp, CF, 4 BGf, 2 st. £ BB £19–£25,
DB £38–£50, ②, Bk £3·90, L £3·50, D
£6·90, cc 1 3 4 5.

MAGHULL Merseyside. Maps 19A & 20E
M57 Motorway 2, London 202, Liverpool
8, St Helens 12, Ormskirk 5.

Rescue Service: Cowie-Kirkby Ltd,
Northway. ✆ 051-531 9020.
Maghull Motor Co, Northway.
✆ 051-526 4242.

MAIDENCOMBE Devon.
See listing at end of entries under
TORQUAY.

MAIDENHEAD Berkshire. Map 7A
Pop 50,000. Slough 6, London 26,
A308(M) Motorway 1½, Bagshot 13,
Basingstoke 29, Henley-on-Thames 8½,
High Wycombe 9½, Oxford 32, Reading 12,
Windsor 6½.
EC Thur. **MD** Fri, Sat. **Golf** Maidenhead
18h. **See** Brunel's Viaduct, Oldfield House
(Henry Reitlinger bequest), 18th cent
Bridge, Cliveden 3 m NE, Courage Shire
Horse Centre 1½ m W, Stanley Spencer
Gallery (Cookham).
ℹ️ Central Library, St Ives Rd.
✆ Maidenhead (0628) 25657.

★★★M Crest, *Manor La, SL6 2RA.*
✆ (0628) 23444. C. 🛏 190 bedrs, 190 bp,
ns, TV, Dgs. ✗ a l c, mc, at, LD 9.45. 🅿 Lt,
N, CH, Dgs, CP 300, Ac, con 585, CF, 52
BGf, 0 st, Dis. £ B fr £47·50, BD fr £57, WB,
①, Bk £5·50, D £9·95, cc 1 2 3 4 5 6,
Dep b.
★★Bear, *High St, SL6 1QJ.* ✆ (0628)
25183.

🔲♨★★**Taplow House,** *Berry H..!,
Taplow, SL6 0DA.* ✆ (0628) 70056.
Closed Dec. C. 🛏 25 bedrs, 12 bp, 13 bps,
TV, Dgs. ✗ a l c, LD 9.30. 🅿 N, CH, CP 80,
Ac, con, CF, 1 st. £ WB, ①, Bk £3·75, L £7,
D £7·50, cc 1 3 4 5 6, Dep b.
🔲★★**Thames,** *Ray Mead Rd, SL6 8NR.*
✆ (0628) 28721. C. 🛏 31 bedrs, 1 bp, 30
bps, 1 ba, TV, Dgs. ✗ a l c, mc, at, LD 10.
🅿 N, CH, Dgs, CP 150, Ac, con 70, CF, 4 st.
£ BB £28, DB £41, WB, ①, Bk £4, L £6, D
£9·90, cc 1 3 4 5 6, Dep b.
Clifton, G, z (Unl), *21 Craufurd Rise, SL6
7LR.* ✆ (0628) 23572. C. 🛏 10 bedrs, 2
bps, 3 ba, TV. 🅿 CH, TV, CP 8, CF. £ BB
£10–£11·50, DB £16–£23, ①.

Repairer: Lex Mead Ltd, 128 Bridge Rd.
✆ (0628) 33188.

MAIDEN NEWTON Dorset. Map 5E
Pop 763. Dorchester 8, London 130,
Axminster 21, Crewkerne 13, Lyme Regis
19, Sherborne 15.
Golf Came Down 18h. **See** Church
Norman Chancel, Ancient Market Town,
Mosaic Pavement.

Rescue Service: Maiden Newton Service
Station, Dorchester Rd. ✆ (0300) 289 &
(0300) 330.

MAIDSTONE Kent. Map 10C
See also HOLLINGBOURNE
Pop 72,100. Sidcup 22, London 36, M20
Motorway 2, Ashford 18, Canterbury 27,
Hurst Green 20, Rochester 8½, Sevenoaks
16, Tenterden 18, Tonbridge 13,
Tunbridge Wells 16.
EC Wed. **MD** Mon, Tue, Fri. **Golf** Bearsted
18h. **See** Archbishop's Palace, All Saints'
Church, St Peter's Church, Town Hall,
Medieval houses in Bank St, Carriage
Museum, Art Gallery and Museum,
Stoneacre (15th cent yeoman's house) at
Otham 3m SE, The Friary (at Aylesford—
sculpture, ceramics, pottery) 3 m NW,
Leeds Castle 4 m E, Cobtree Manor
Country Park.
ℹ️ The Gatehouse, Old Palace Gardens.
✆ Maidstone (0622) 671361.

★★M Emma, (Rl), *136 Boxley Rd, ME14
2AH.* ✆ (0622) 677523.
★★Royal Star, *High St, ME14 1JA.*
✆ (0622) 55721. C. 🛏 32 bedrs, 8 bp, 6
bps, 6 ba, TV, Dgs. ✗ a l c, mc, at, LD 9.30.
🅿 N, ch, Dgs, CP 50, G 70, Ac, con 80, CF,
1 st. £ BB fr £25, DB fr £34, WB, ①, Bk
£4·25, L £4·75, D £4·75, cc 1 2 3 4 5 6,
Dep b.
Carval, PH, z (Rl), *56 London Rd, ME16
8QL.* ✆ (0622) 62100. C. 🛏 8 bedrs, 2 ba.
✗ a l c. 🅿 CH, TV, CP 8, CF. £ BB £11, DB
£18, WT (c) £77, ①, Bk £1·50, cc 1 3 4 5.
Howard, H, z (R), *22 London Rd,
ME16 8QL.* ✆ (0622) 58778. C. 🛏 16
bedrs, 2 sh, 1 ba, Dgs. ✗ a l c. 🅿 CH, TV,
CP 17, CF, 1 st. £ BB £12, DB £20·50, WT
(b) £119, DT (b) £17, ①, Bk £2·50, L £3·50,
D £5.
Tanyard, PH, xy, (Rl), *Wierton Hill,
Boughton Monchelsea, ME17 4JT.*
✆ (0622) 44705. C 5. 🛏 5 bedrs, 4 bp, 1
bps. 🅿 CH, TV, CP 6. £ BB £27·60, DB
£36·80, WT (b) £213·33–£277·73, DT (b)
£30·48–£39·68, ①, cc 1 2 3 5.▲

Repairer: Haynes Bros Ltd, 21 Ashford
Rd. ✆ (0622) 56781.
Specialist Body Repairer: Haynes Bros
Ltd, 21 Ashford Rd. ✆ (0622) 56781.

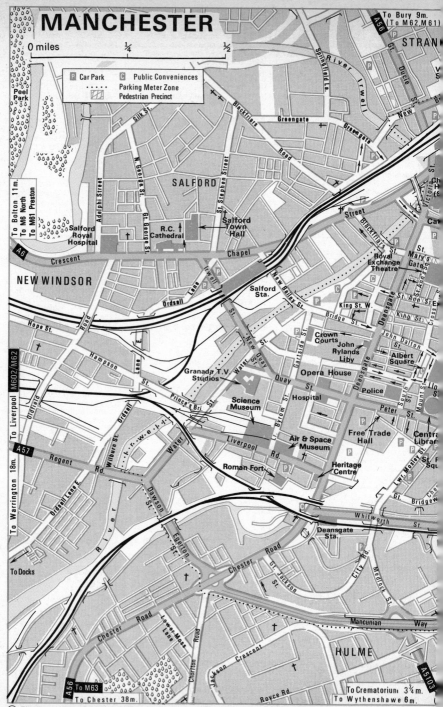

MANCHESTER

0 miles   ¼   ½

To Bury 9m.
(To M62,M61)

STRAN

P Car Park   **C** Public Conveniences
         Parking Meter Zone
         Pedestrian Precinct

Peel
Park

River Irwell

Springfield La.

Silk St.

Blackfriars Road

Greengate

Greengate

N. George St.

SALFORD

St. Stephen Street

Gt. George St.

Adelphi Street

To Bolton 11m.
To M6 North
To M61 Preston

Salford
Royal
Hospital

R.C.
Cathedral

Salford
Town
Hall

Chapel Street

Victoria

A6   Crescent

Blackfriars St.

St. Mary's Gate

Royal
Exchange
Theatre

NEW WINDSOR

Irwell

Ordsall Lane

Salford
Sta.

New Bailey St.

St. Ann St.

C

Deansgate

King St. W.

King St.

Hope St.

Road

Lane E.

Hampson St.

Bridge St.

John Dalton

Crown
Courts

John
Rylands
Liby

Albert
Square

M602/M62

To Liverpool

Granada T.V.
Studios

Water St.

New Quay St.

Garside St.

Quay St.

Opera House

Deansgate

Prince's Bri.

Science
Museum

Broom St.

Hospital

Police

Peter St.

Ordsall

Wilburn St.

Irwell

Liverpool Rd.

Air & Space
Museum

Free Trade
Hall

Central
Library

St. P
Squ

A57   Regent Rd.

Water

Roman Fort

Heritage
Centre

To Warrington 18m.

Ordsall Lane E.

River

Dawson St.

Egerton St.

Deansgate
Sta.

Whitworth St.

Gt. Bridgew

To Docks

Chester Road

Gt. Jackson St.

City Rd.

Medlock St.

Chester Road

Lower Mass Lane

Chorlton Road

Jackson Crescent

Mancunian Way

HULME

A56   To M63
To Chester 38m.

Royce Rd.

To Crematoriun 3¾ m.
To Wythenshawe 6m.

A5103

© The Royal Automobile Club,1985

For abbreviations see inside back cover-

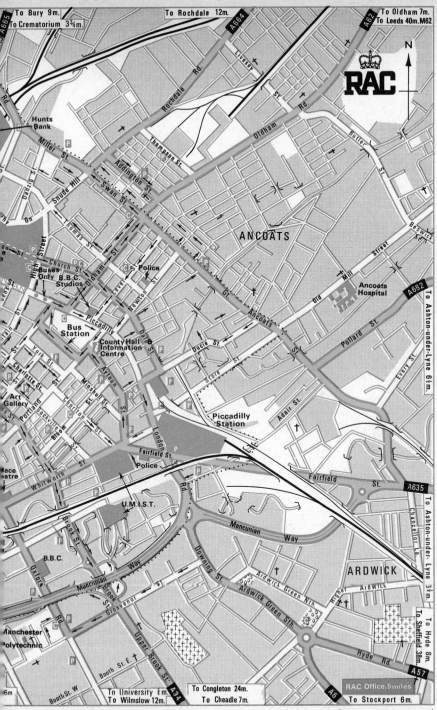

To Bury 9m.
To Crematorium 3¾m.
To Rochdale 12m.
To Oldham 7m.
To Leeds 40m. M62

A665
A664
A62

N

RAC

Hunts Bank

Miller St.

Addington St.

Thompson St.

Rochdale Rd.

Oldham Rd.

Livesay St.

Butler St.

Beswick St.

Snade Hill

Danzig St.

Swan St.

Thomas St.

ANCOATS

Mill Street

Church St.
Buses Only
B.B.C. Studios

Police

Oldham St.

Newton St.

Level St.

Gt. Ancoats St.

Ancoats Hospital

A662

To Ashton-under-Lyne 6½m.

Piccadilly

Bus Station

Dale St.

County Hall
Information
Centre

Ducie St.

Store St.

Pollard St.

Every St.

York St.

Charlotte St.

Minshull St.

Chorlton St.

Aytoun St.

Art Gallery

Portland St.

Sackville St.

Broom

London Rd.

Piccadilly
Station

Adair St.

Fairfield St.

Police

Whitworth St.

Fairfield St.

A635

To Ashton-under-Lyne 3¾m.

lace eatre

U.M.I.S.T.

Brook St.

Downing St.

Mancunian Way

ARDWICK

Ardwick Green Nth.

Ardwick Green Sth.

Higher Ardwick

B.B.C.

Oxford Rd.

Mancunian Way

Grosvenor St.

Upper Brook St.

Chancellor La.

To Hyde 8m.

To Sheffield 38m.

Manchester Polytechnic

Booth St. E.

Booth St. W.

A34

Hyde Rd.

A57

6m.
To University ¾m.
To Wilmslow 12m.
To Congleton 24m.
To Cheadle 7m.
A6
RAC Office,5miles
To Stockport 6m.

Crown copyright reserved

For Explanatory Notes to Directory see page 116

Rescue Service: Gatward (Maidstone) Ltd, Chatham Road Service Station, Chatham Rd. ☎ (0622) 55545.

MALBOROUGH Devon. Map 3F
Pop 500. Kingsbridge 3½, London 208, Plymouth 21.
Golf Thurlestone 18h. **See** Bolt Head, Bolt Tail, Bolberry (Nat Trust), All Saints' Church.

▣★★**Soar Mill Cove** (R), *Soar Mill Cove, Salcombe, TQ7 3DS.* ☎ Kingsbridge (0548) 561566. Open Mar–Sept. C. 🛏 14 bedrs, 13 bp, 1 bps, TV, Dgs. ✕ mc, at, LD 9.30. 🏠 CH, CP 20, sp, tc, CF, 3 BGf, 0 st, Dis. **£** BB £28–£32, DB £50–£60, WT £180–£230, WB [1], Bk £5, L £3, D £14, cc 1 3 4 5.

Repairer: Salcombe Road Garage Ltd. ☎ Galmpton (0548) 561333 & (0548) 561366.

MALDON Essex. Map 17D
Pop 15,500. Chelmsford 10, London 43, Braintree 13, Colchester 16, Southend 20.
EC Wed. **MD** Thur, Sat. **Golf** Maldon 9h, Warren 18h. **See** All Saints' Church, St Peter's Church, Plume Library, old Inns, Moot Hall, Beeleigh Abbey, Chelmer & Blackwater Navigation.
[i] Oakwood Arts Centre. ☎ Maldon (0621) 56503.

★★**Blue Boar** (TH), *Silver St, CM9 7QE.* ☎ (0621) 52681. C. 🛏 26 bedrs, 26 bp, TV, Dgs. ✕ a l c, mc, at, LD 9.30. 🏠 CH, Dgs, CP 43, Ac, con 40, CF, 3 BGf, 0 st, Dis. **£** BB £34, DB £50·50, WB, [1], cc 1 2 3 4 5 6, Dep (Xmas).
Swan, H, z, *73 High St, CM9 7EP.* ☎ (0621) 53170. C. 🛏 6 bedrs, 2 bp, 4 bps, 2 ba, TV. ✕ a l c. 🏠 CH, CP 20, U 3, CF, 1 st. **£** BB fr £12, DB fr £20, WT (c) fr £84, DT fr £17, [1], cc 1 2 3 4 5 6.

Repairers: Bates Motors (Belcher) Ltd, Spital Rd. ☎ (0621) 52131.

MALMESBURY Wiltshire. Maps 5B and 14E
Pop 2,593. Swindon 15, London 92, M4 Motorway 5½, Bath 24, Bristol 26, Chepstow 32, Chippenham 9, Cirencester 11, Faringdon 25, Tetbury 4½.
EC Thur. **Golf** Westonbirt 18h. **See** Abbey, Market Cross, St John's Almshouses, Old Bell Museum.
[i] Town Hall, Cross Hayes. ☎ Malmesbury (066 62) 2143.

★★★**Old Bell,** *Abbey Row, SN16 0BW.* ☎ (066 62) 2344. Closed 25th Dec–1 st Jan. C. 🛏 18 bedrs, 10 bp, 2 bps, 6 sh, 3 ba, TV, Dgs. ✕ a l c, mc, at, LD 9.30. 🏠 CH, Dgs, CP 25, G 2, con 20, CF, 1 st. **£** BB £20–£35, DB £34–£50, WB, [2], Bk £4·50, L £7, D £10, cc 1 3 4 5 6.
♣★★★**Whatley Manor** (R), *Easton Grey, SN16 0RB* (2½ W on B4040). ☎ (066 62) 2888. C. 🛏 15 bedrs, 15 bp, 3 bedrs annexe 3 bp, TV, Dgs. ✕ mc, at, LD 9. 🏠 N, CH, sp, tc, pf, rf, con, CF. **£** BB £32–£42, DB £47·50–£57·50, WB, Bk £4·50, L £6·50, D £12·95, [2], cc 1 3 4 5 6, Dep b.

MALTON North Yorkshire. Map 25C
Pop 4,300. Beverley 26, London 205, Bridlington 28, Helmsley 16, Market Weighton 28, Pickering 8, Scarborough 24, Thirsk 25, York 17.
EC Thur. **MD** Tue, Fri, Sat. **Golf** Malton and Norton 18h. **See** Relic of Gilbertine Priory, Town Hall, 17th cent Malton Lodge, St Michael's Church, Roman Museum, Castle Howard 6 m W, Howsham Hall, 8 m SW, Kirkham Priory 5 m SW, North York Moor Nat Park.

★★**Green Man,** *Market St, YO17 0LY.* ☎ (0653) 2662. Closed Dec. C. 🛏 23 bedrs, 3 bp, 11 bps, 1 sh, 4 ba, Dgs. ✕ a l c, mc, at, LD 8.30. 🏠 CH, TV, Dgs, CP 30, U 1, Ac, con 80, CF, 10 st, cc 1 3 5.
★★**Talbot** (TH), *Yorkersgate, YO17 0AA.* ☎ (0653) 4031. C. 🛏 24 bedrs, 7 bp, 6 ba, TV, Dgs. ✕ a l c, mc, at, LD 9. 🏠 CH, Dgs, CP 20, G 10, Ac, con 50, CF, 0 st. **£** BB £31–£36, DB £41–£48, WB, [1], cc 1 2 3 4 5 6.
★**Wentworth Arms,** *Town St, Old Malton, YO17 0HD.* ☎ (0653) 2618. RS Xmas. C 6. 🛏 7 bedrs, 2 ba, ✕ a l c, mc, at, LD 8.45. 🏠 CH, Dgs, CP 30, 1st. **£** BB £11·50–£12·50, DB £23–£25, [2], Bk £2·50, L £3·50, D £6, cc 5.

MC Repairer: Bower's Motor Exchange, Church St, Norton. ☎ (0653) 2176.
Rescue Service: Robsons Motor Services Ltd, Welham Rd, Norton. ☎ (0653) 2165.

MALVERN Hereford & Worcester (Worcestershire). Map 13D
Pop 31,000. Tewkesbury 13, London 118, Bromyard 10, Evesham 20, Gloucester 20, Hereford 19, Ledbury 7, Worcester 8
EC Wed. **MD** Fri. **Golf** Worcestershire 18h. **See** College, Priory Church and Gateway, St Anne's Well, Priory remains and St Wulstan's Church, Little Malvern (grave of Sir Edward Elgar), Malvern Hills (views).
[i] Winter Gardens, Grange Rd. ☎ Malvern (068 45) 4700.

★★★**Abbey,** *Abbey Rd, WR14 3ET.* ☎ (068 45) 3325. C. 🛏 106 bedrs, 81 bp, 15 bps, 2 ba, TV, Dgs. ✕ a l c, LD 8.30. 🏠 Lt, N, CH, CP 120, Ac, con 300, CF, 19 BGf, 7 st. **£** BB £38, DB £54, WB, [1], Bk £4, L £7, D £8, cc 1 2 3 5 6, Dep b.
★★★**Foley Arms,** *14 Worcester Rd, WR14 4QS.* ☎ (068 45) 3397. C. 🛏 26 bedrs, 19 bp, 7 bps, ns, TV, Dgs. ✕ a l c, mc, at, LD 9.15. 🏠 N, CH, ns, CP 45, U 4, Ac, con 120, CF, 0 st. **£** BB fr £29·50, DB fr £44, DT fr £32, WB, Bk £3·75, L £6·95, D £7·50, [1], cc 1 2 3 4 5 6, Dep b.
★★**Montrose** (RI), *Graham Rd, WR14 2HU.* ☎ (068 45) 2335. C. 🛏 14 bedrs, 1 bp, 5 bps, 1 sh, 2 ba, ns, TV. ✕ mc, at, LD 7.30. 🏠 CH, TV, Dgs, CP 16, CF. **£** BB £13·50–£26, DB £22–£26, WB, Bk £1·50, L £3·50, D £6, [1], cc 1 5, Dep a.
★★**Thornbury,** (R), *Avenue Rd, WR14 3AR.* ☎ (068 45) 2278.
Sidney House, PH, z (R), *40 Worcester Rd, WR14 4AA.* ☎ (068 45) 4994. C. 🛏 6 bedrs, 2 ba, TV, Dgs. 🏠 CH, TV, Dgs, CP 8, CF, 0 st. **£** BB £10–£13, DB £17–£20, WT (b) £79–£88, (c) £51–£60, DT £12·50–£14, [1], Bk £3, D £5, cc 1.

Repairer: Rothwell & Millbourne Ltd, Central Garage. ☎ (068 45) 3301.

COLWALL
★★**Colwall Park,** *WR13 6QG.* ☎ Colwall (0684) 40206. C. 🛏 14 bedrs, 10 bp, 4 bps, TV, Dgs. ✕ a l c, mc, at, LD 9. 🏠 CH, CP 40, Ac, con 100, CF, 1 st. **£** BB £25·75, DB £42·50, WB, [2], Bk £3·50, L £4·50, D £8·50, cc 15, Dep a.
Horse & Jockey, H, y *Walwyn Rd, WR13 6QX.* ☎ Colwall (0684) 40247.

MALVERN WELLS
▣★★**Essington,** *Holywell Rd, WR14 4LQ.* ☎ Malvern (068 45) 61177. C. 🛏 10 bedrs, 3 bp, 1 bps, 3 ba, TV, Dgs. ✕ mc, LD 8.15. 🏠 CH, Dgs, CP 30, CF, 2 st. **£** BB £14–£20, DB £28–£36, WB, [2], Bk £4·50, L £3, D £8, cc 1 5.

WELLAND
♣★★**Holdfast Cottage** (R), *Nr. Malvern, WR13 6NA.* ☎ Hanley Swan (0684) 310288. C. 🛏 9 bedrs, 4 bp, 2 bps, 1 ba, Dgs. ✕ mc, at, LD 8.45. 🏠 CH, TV, Dgs, CP 15, CF, 2 st. **£** BB £17–£19, DB £30–£36, DBB £24–£28, WB, [2], D £9·50, Dep a.

WEST MALVERN
★★**Broomhill** (RI), *West Malvern, WR14 4AY.* (2 m W B4232). ☎ Malvern (068 45) 64367. Open Mar–Oct. C 5. 🛏 10 bedrs, 3 bp, 2 bps, 1 ba, Dgs. ✕ mc, at, LD 8. 🏠 CH, TV, ns, CP 10. **£** BB fr £13·50, DB fr £23, WT £81–£113, WB, [2], Bk £4, L £1·50, D £6·80, Dep a.

WYNDS POINT
★★**Malvern Hills,** *WR13 6DW.* ☎ Colwall (0684) 40237. C. 🛏 15 bedrs, 10 bp, 2 ba, TV, Dgs. ✕ a l c, mc, at, LD 9.45. 🏠 CH, TV, Dgs, CP 40, Ac, CF, 2 BGf, 1 st, Dis. **£** BB fr £18, DB fr £29·50, WB, [1], Bk £3·75, L £6·45, D £6·95, cc 1 3 4.

MANCHESTER Gtr Manchester. Map 20A
See also ALTRINCHAM, ASHTON-UNDER-LYNE, AUDENSHAW, CHADDERTON, SALFORD and STOCKPORT.
Pop 458,600. Stockport 6, London 184, M602 Motorway 6, Altrincham 8, Barnsley 36, Bolton 11, Bury 8, Congleton 24, Glossop 14, Liverpool 34, Oldham 7, Rochdale 10, St Helens 22, Walkden 7, Warrington 16, Wigan 17.
See Plan, pp 266 and 267.
P See Plan. **Golf** Bramhall 18h, Ringway 18h, Heaton Park Municipal 18h, Northenden 18h etc. **See** Cathedral, John Ryland's Library, City Art Gallery, Museum, Heaton Hall, Platt Hall Gallery of English Costume, Museum of Science and Technology, Wythenshawe Hall, St Mary's RC Church, Belle Vue (Gardens, etc).
[i] Magnum House, Portland St, Piccadilly. ☎ 061-247 3694.

★★★★★**Hotel Piccadilly,** *PO Box 107, Piccadilly, M60 1QR.* ☎ 061-236 8414. Closed 25th–28th Dec. RS 1st & 2nd Jan. C. 🛏 250 bedrs, 250 bp, ns, TV, Dgs. ✕ a l c, mc, at, LD 10.30. 🏠 Lt, N, CH, Dgs, CP 80, Ac, con 700, CF, 3 st. **£** B fr £49, BD fr £65, WB, [1], Bk £5·25, L £3·05, D £3·05, cc 1 2 3 4 5 6, Dep b.
★★★★**Grand** (TH), *Aytoun St, M1 3DR.* ☎ 061-236 9559. C. 🛏 146 bedrs, 131 bp, 15 bps, TV, Dgs. ✕ a l c, mc, at, LD 10. 🏠 Lt, N, CH, Dgs, Ac, con 450, CF, 12 st. **£** BB £47·50, DB £61·50, WB, [1], cc 1 2 3 4 5 6.
★★★★**Portland Thistle,** *Portland St, M1 6DP.* ☎ 061-228 3567. C. 🛏 221 bedrs, 221 bp, 3 ba, ns, TV. ✕ a l c, mc, at, LD 9.30. 🏠 Lt, N, CH, TV, Dgs, CP 34, sp, sb, sol, gym, con 350, CF, 0 st. **£** BB £50·50–£60·50, DB £66–£76, WB, [2], Bk

£5·50, L £8·50, D £8·50, cc 1 2 3 4 5 6,
Dep b.
★★★M Post House (TH), *Palatine Rd,
Northenden, M22 4FH.* ✆061-998 7090.
C. ⋈ 201 bedrs, 201 bp, TV, Dgs. ✗ a l c,
mc, at, LD 10.30. ⓑ Lt, N, CH, Dgs, CP
243, Ac, con 150, CF, 0 st. £ BB £44·50,
DB £57, WB, ⬜, cc 1 2 3 4 5 6.
★★★Willow Bank (R), *340 Wilmslow
Rd, Fallowfield, M14 6AF.*
✆061-224 0461. RS Bank Hols. C. ⋈ 123
bedrs, 99 bp, 12 bps, 3 ba, TV, Dgs. ✗ a l c,
mc, at, LD 10.15. ⓑ N, CH, TV, CP 100, G
40, con 50, CF, 7 st. £ BB £22–£31, DB
£42, DT fr £35, WB, ⬜, Bk £4, L £4, D £7,
cc 1 3 4 5 6, Dep b.
▣★★**Brookhouse,** *393 Wilmslow Rd,
M20 9WA.* ✆061-224 2015. RS Sat &
Sun. C. ⋈ 38 bedrs, 31 bps, 2 ba, TV, Dgs.
✗ a l c, mc, at, LD 10, N, CH, TV,
Dgs, CP 60, con 30, CF, 8 st. £ WB, Bk
£2·50, L £4, D £6, cc 1 3 4 5 6.
★★Simpson's (R), *122 Withington Rd,
M16 8FB* (Whalley Range). ✆061-226
2235.
Imperial, PH, z (RI), *157 Hathersage Rd,
M13 0HY.* ✆061-225 6500. C 5. ⋈ 20
bedrs, 1 bp, 5 ba, Dgs. ✗ a l c,
ⓑ CH, TV, CP 40, CF, 3 BGf, 6 st. £ BB
£15–£18, DB £25–£30, WT (c) £80–£98,
DT £17·50–£21, ⓶, cc 1 3 5.
New Central, *144–146 Heywood St, M8
7PD.* ✆061-205 2169.

Repairers: Blakes Motors Ltd, Blackfriars
Rd. ✆061-834 8200.
Cascade Motors, 51 Barton Rd.
✆061-748 5531.
G E Sparkes & Co Ltd, Chorlton Green
Garage, Chorlton Green. ✆061-881 4414.
J Cotton & Co, 126 Great Ancoats St.
✆061-236 9931.
Knibbs (Manchester) Ltd, Upper Brook
St. ✆061-273 1343.
Syd Abrams Ltd, 141 Waterloo Rd.
✆061-792 4321.
Williams Motor Co (Manchester) Ltd, 325
Deansgate. ✆061-832 8781.
Specialist Body Repairers: Blakes Motors
Ltd, Blackfriars Rd. ✆061-834 8200.
Specialist Radiator Repairer: Serck
Radiator Services Ltd, Nutsford Vale
Works, Pink Bank La. ✆061-223 3777,
and at 1 Commercial St, Knott Mill.
✆061-834 4637.
MC Repairers: B & C Auto Ltd, 198
Oldham Rd. ✆061-832 3328.
Horner, R W & Sons Ltd, 35 Ayres Rd, Old
Trafford. ✆061-226 2882.
Hunts Cycle & Motor Stores, 257
Kingsway, Levenshulme.
✆061-432 1303.
Rescue Service: Ardwick Cars (Repairs),
129 Stockport Rd, Ardwick. ✆061-273
2574.
A Euthors (Motor Engineers), 70
Cornbrook Rd. ✆061-872 4642.
Billington Bros, Birch Services, M62
(Eastbound). ✆061-643 6153.
Housley's Ltd, 38 and 121 Ashton Old Rd,
Ardwick. ✆061-273 3133.
Junction Garage (W Hume), Greenhill Rd,
Middleton Junction. ✆061-643 8174.
McGuire Motors Ltd, 213 Upper Chorlton
Rd. ✆061-840 4618.
Rapaport & Tonge Ltd, 119 Wilmslow Rd.
✆061-224 7282.
Schenk Motors (Firswood) Ltd, Warwick
Rd South, Old Trafford. ✆061-881 9112.

Viscount Group Services, Viscount
Service Station, Chapman St. ✆061-
223 0516.▲
MANCHESTER AIRPORT Gtr
Manchester (Lancashire). Map 20B
See also WILMSLOW.
Congleton 16, London 177, M56
Motorway ½, Altrincham 5, Macclesfield
12, Manchester 9½, Stockport 6½.
★★★★Excelsior (TH), *Ring Road,
Wythenshawe, M22 5NS.*
✆061-437 5811. C. ⋈ 304 bedrs, 304 bp,
TV, Dgs. ✗ a l c, mc, at, LD 10.15. ⓑ Lt, N,
CH, Dgs, CP 350, Ac, sp, con 220, CF, 56
BGf, 0 st, Dis. £ BB £51, DB £65, WB, ⬜,
cc 1 2 3 4 5 6.
Rescue Service: A K Motors Ltd, Hanger
7, Central Rd. ✆061-489 3153.
MANNINGTREE Essex. Map 17C
Pop 331. Colchester 9, London 65,
Clacton 15, Harwich 11, Ipswich 10,
Sudbury 17.
EC Wed. **MD** Wed, Sat. **Golf** Harwich 9h.
See Swannery, Mistley Towers, Dedham
Vale (Constable Country) 3 m W, Stour
Estuary.

Thorn, H, x, *High St, Mistley.*
✆Colchester (0206) 392821. Closed
Xmas. C. ⋈ 5 bedrs, 2 ba. ✗ a l c. ⓑ CH,
TV, CP 5, CF, 1 st. £ BB £11·50–£12·50,
DB £23–£25, ⓶, Bk £3·50, L £4·50, D
£4·50, cc 1 5.

MANSFIELD Nottinghamshire. Map 22D
Pop 100,000. Nottingham 14, London
138, M1 Motorway 6½, Chesterfield 12,
Derby 23, Matlock 16, Newark 18,
Ollerton 8½, Rotherham 23, Sheffield 22,
Worksop 13.
EC Wed. **MD** Mon, Thur, Fri, Sat. **Golf**
Mansfield 18h. **See** Parish Church of SS
Peter and Paul, Moot Hall, Bentinck
Memorial, Clumber Park, Thoresby Hall, 8½
m NE, Newstead Abbey 4½ m S, Sherwood
Forest and "Major Oak", Hardwick Hall 6½
m NW.

▣★★**Midland,** *Midland Pl, NG18 1DP.*
✆(0623) 24668.
MC Repairer: W Henstock's, 126
Chesterfield Rd North. ✆(0623) 25311.
Rescue Service: Neville, G E & Son Ltd,
Nottingham Rd. ✆(0623) 26101.
Sherwood Hall Garage (Forest Town) Ltd,
Clipstone Rd West, Forest Town.
✆(0623) 27661.
MANSTON Kent. M. Area 10D
3 m W of Ramsgate. Pop 150. Canterbury
16, London 74, Dover 17, Margate 3½,
Rochester 42.
Golf St Augustines, Ramsgate 18h.
Rescue Service: Manston Court Garage
Ltd. ✆(084 380) 236 (breakdown)
✆Thanet (0843) 295896).
MAPPERLEY Nottinghamshire
See NOTTINGHAM.
MARAZANVOSE Cornwall. Map 2D
Fraddon 9, London 254, Falmouth 15,
Newquay 9, Penzance 25, St Austell 16.
Rescue Service: Solways Garage. ✆Zelah
(087 254) 330.
MARAZION Cornwall. Map 2E
Pop 1,385. Helston 9, London 280,
Penzance 4, Redruth 15, St Ives 8.

EC Wed. **Golf** Praa Sands 18h & Lelant
18h. **See** St Michaels Mount, Castle, Age
of Steam (steam engines).

Chymorvah-Tolgarrick, H, xy (RI),
TR18 0DG. ✆Penzance (0736) 710497.
C. ⋈ 9 bedrs, 2 sh, 2 ba, Dgs. ⓑ CH, TV,
CP 9, CF, 2 BGf. £ BB £6·50–£10·50, DB
£13–£21, WT £65–£96, DT £11·50–
£15·50, ⬜, Bk £1·75, D £5, cc 1 5.

MARCH Cambridgeshire. Map 15B
Pop 15,000. Cambridge 30, London 85,
Ely 18, Huntingdon 23, Peterborough 16,
Wisbech 11.
EC Tue. **MD** Wed, Sat. **Golf** March 9h.
See St Wendreda's Church, The Stone
Cross Monument, Town Hall, Statute Fair
4th Wed. in Sept.

Rescue Service: Station Road Garage
(Cambs) Ltd, 132 Station Rd. ✆(035 42)
2455.

MARDEN Kent. Map 10C
Pop 2,485. Maidstone 8, London 44,
Ashford 23, Hurst Green 12, Tenterden 15,
Tonbridge 16, Tunbridge Wells 14.
EC Wed. **Golf** Cranbrook 18h. **See** Parish
Church, old stocks, mounting blocks.

Rescue Service: Collier Street Garage Ltd,
Collier St. ✆Collier Street (089 273) 321.

MARGARETTING Essex. Map 10A
Pop 859. Brentwood 7, London 29,
Bishop's Stortford 20, Chelmsford 3½.
Golf Chelmsford 18h. **See** 15th cent
Church.

Rescue Service: Speedwell Service
Station, Roman Rd. ✆Ingatestone
(027 75) 3261.
Weaver, E & Sons, The Oaks, Wantz Rd.
✆Ingatestone (027 75) 3224.

MARGATE Kent. Map 10D
See also CLIFTONVILLE and
WESTGATE-ON-SEA.
Pop 50,347. Rochester 42, London 69,
Canterbury 15, Dover 20.
EC Thur. **Golf** North Foreland, Broadstairs
18h, Westgate and Birchington 18h. **See**
The Grotto (shell mosaics), Powell-
Cotton Big Game Museum (Birchington),
St John's Church, Caves, Tudor Cottage
(Hosking Memorial Museum) in King St,
Safari Park.
ⓘ Marine Ter. ✆Thanet (0843) 20241.

Alice Springs, PH, z (RI), *6 Carfield Rd,
CT9 5AR.* ✆Thanet (0843) 23543. C 6.
⋈ 18 bedrs, 9 sh, 2 ba, TV. ✗ a l c. ⓑ CH.
£ BB £7–£8, DB £14–£16, WT £40–£48, ⬜
Beachcomber, PH, z (R), *3 Royal Espl.
Westbrook, CT9 5DL.* ✆Thanet (0843)
21616. Open Apr–Sept. C. ⋈ 5 bedrs, 5
sh, 2 ba, ⓑ ch, TV, CF, 1 st. £ BB £9·20–
£10, DB £18·40–£20, WT (b) £63·25–
£80·50, DT (b) £12·65–£13·80, ⓶, L £1, D
£4·50.
Charnwood, PH, z (RI), *20 Canterbury
Rd, CT9 5BW.* ✆Thanet (0843) 224158.
Closed Nov & Dec. C. ⋈ 15 bedrs, 4 sh, 2
ba. ⓑ ch, TV, Dgs, CP 4, CF, 2 st.
£ BB £6·50–£8·50, DB £13–£16, WT (b)
£46–£56, (c) £34–£42, DT £8·50–£10, ⬜,
Bk £1·50, D £3.

Tyrella, PH, z (RI), *19 Canterbury Rd, Westbrook, CT9 5AW.* ✆ Thanet (0843) 292746. Closed Xmas & New Year. C 6. ⇔ 8 bedrs, 7 sh, 1 ba. ⒟ CH, TV, 10 st. **£** BB £7–£7·50, DB £14–£15, WT (b) £50–£60, DT (b) £10–£10·50, ▯.

MARK Somerset. Map 5C
Pop 1,090. Wells 11, London 132, Bridgwater 11, Bristol 21, Glastonbury 12, Weston-super-Mare 11.
Golf Wells 18h. **See** 13th cent Parish Church.

Rescue Service: Foundry Garage Co, Mark Causeway. ✆ Mark Moor (027 864) 203.

MARKET DRAYTON Shropshire. Map 19F
Pop 8,247. Newport 11, London 153, Nantwich 14, Newcastle-under-Lyme 13, Shrewsbury 19, Stafford 18, Stone 17, Wellington 16, Whitchurch 13.
EC Thur. **MD** Wed, Fri. **Golf** Market Drayton 11h. **See** Parish Church (Norman west door), Grammar School (assoc Robert Clive), Hodnet Hall Gardens 5½ m SW.

★★Corbet Arms, *High St, TF9 1PY.*
✆ (0630) 2037. C. ⇔ 10 bedrs, 8 bp, 2 bps, TV, Dgs. ✗ a l c, mc, at, LD 9 (9.30 Sat). ⒟ CH, TV, Dgs, CP 40, U 2, Ac, con 120, CF. **£** BB £18–£20, DB £26–£32, WT fr £120, DT fr £21, WB, ▯, Bk £3·50, L £4·50, D £5·50, cc 1 3 4 5 6, Dep b.

★★★Tern Hill Hall, *Tern Hill, TF9 3PU* (2 m SW A53). ✆ Tern Hill (063 083) 310. RS Xmas Day. C. ⇔ 11 bedrs, 8 bp, 3 sh, 2 ba, TV. ✗ a l c, mc, LD 9.30. ⒟ CH, CP 120, U 6, con 60, CF, 1 st. **£** BB fr £18, DB fr £26, WB, ▯, Bk £4, L £4·50, D £7, cc 1 3 4 5 6, Dep b.

Repairer: Arnolds Auto Sales & Services, Shrewsbury Rd. ✆ (0630) 2027.

MARKET HARBOROUGH
Leicestershire. Map 15A
See also MARSTON TRUSSELL.
Pop 15,965. Northampton 17, London 82, Coventry 28, Daventry 21, Kettering 11, Leicester 15, Melton Mowbray 22, Peterborough 33, Rugby 18, Stamford 25.
EC Wed. **MD** Tue, Sat. **Golf** Market Harborough 9h. **See** Grammar School (17th cent), Church of St Dionysius, old houses and inns, Town Hall.
⒤ Pen Lloyd Library, Adam and Eve St. ✆ Market Harborough (0858) 62649.

★★Angel, *High St, LE16 7NL.* ✆ (0858) 63123. Closed Xmas. C. ⇔ 18 bedrs, 4 ba, TV, Dgs. ✗ a l c, mc, at, LD 9.15. ⒟ TV, CP 40, G 4, Ac, con 40, CF, 0 st. **£** BB fr £14, DB fr £28, WB, ▯, Bk £2·75, D £7·50, cc 1 3 4 5 6, Dep b.

★★M Grove, *66 Northampton Rd, LE16 9HA.* ✆ (0858) 64082.
★★Three Swans, *High St, LE16 7NJ.*
✆ (0858) 66644. RS Sun. C. ⇔ 18 bedrs, 10 bp, 8 bps, TV, Dgs. ✗ a l c, mc, LD 9.30. ⒟ CH, Dgs, CP 60, G 8, con 60, CF, 1 st. **£** BB £20–£28, DB £28–£40, ② 10%, Bk £3·75, L £6, cc 1 2 3 4 5 6.

Repairer: Regent Autocar Co Ltd, Leicester Rd. ✆ (0858) 67664.
Rescue Service: Badger Bros, 109 Main St, Lubenham. ✆ (0858) 66964. Homestead Garage (Medbourne) Ltd, Ashley Rd. ✆ Medbourne Green (085 883) 810.

Marand Motors, Marand House, Springfield St. ✆ (0858) 67177.

MARKET RASEN Lincolnshire. Map 23A
Pop 2,786. Lincoln 16, London 149, Gainsborough 19, Grimsby 20, Horncastle 18, Hull (Fy) 25, Louth 14, Scunthorpe 22, Sleaford 32.
EC Thur. **MD** Tue, Wed. **Golf** Market Rasen 18h. **See** St Thomas's Church, Racecourse.

❦★★★Limes, *Gainsborough Rd, LN8 3JW.* ✆ (0673) 842357. C. ⇔ 10 bedrs, 10 bp, 3 bps, annexe 4 bedrs, 4 bp, TV, Dgs. ✗ a l c, mc, at, LD 9.30. ⒟ CH, Dgs, CP 30, Ac, tc, sc, con 70, CF, 2 BGf, 1st, Dis. **£** BB £28–£30, DB £35–£38, WT £176, DT £41·25–£43, WB, ▯, Bk £3, L £5·75, D £7·50, cc 1 3 5 6, Dep b.
White Hart, l, *Magna Mile, Ludford, LN3 6AD.* ✆ Burgh-on-Bain (050 781) 664.

MARKET WEIGHTON Humberside (North Humberside). Map 25A
Pop 3,775. Lincoln 52, London 185, Beverley 10, Bridlington 28, Malton 28, Scarborough 36, Selby 18, York 19.
EC Thur. **Golf** Beverley 18h. **See** Ancient Church, Home of Giant Bradley (tablet in Church).

★★Londesborough Arms, *High St, YO4 3AH.* ✆ (069 62) 2219.

Repairer: Armstrong-Massey, High St and Beverley Rd. ✆ (069 62) 2361.

MARKSBURY Avon. Map 5B
Pop 350. Bath 6½, London 111, Bristol 9, Radstock 6, Shepton Mallet 13, Wells 14, Weston-super-Mare 25.
Golf Saltford 18h. **See** Church.

Rescue Service: L R Bence & Co Ltd, Westways Garage. ✆ Timsbury (0761) 70391.

MARKS TEY Essex. Map 17C
Pop 2,700. Chelmsford 17, London 61, Braintree 10, Colchester 5, Haverhill 24, Southend 36.
Golf Kings Ford 9h. **See** St Andrew's Church (rare wood font).

MC Repairer: R W Parkinson Motor Cycles, London Rd. ✆ Colchester (0206) 210467.

MARKYATE Hertfordshire. Map 15E
Pop 2,750. London 30, M1 Motorway 2, Dunstable 4, Luton 4, St Albans 8, Watford 13.
EC Wed. **Golf** Stockwood Park 18h. **See** Original Benedictine Nunnery, Markyate Cell, Church.

★★★M Hertfordshire Moat House, *London Rd, AL3 8HH.* ✆ Luton (0582) 840840. C. ⇔ 97 bedrs, 97 bp, TV, Dgs. ✗ a l c, mc, at, LD 10. ⒟ N, CH, Dgs, CP 250, Ac, gc, rf, con 300, CF, 40 BGf, Dis. **£** BB £33–£37, DB £38·£43, WB, ▯, Bk £4·50, L £6·25, D £7·25, cc 1 3 4 5, Dep b.
Parking facility available for patrons using Luton Airport.

Rescue Service: Shaw Bros, Hicks Rd. ✆ Luton (0582) 840662.

MARLBOROUGH Wiltshire. Map 6A
Pop 6,839. Newbury 19, London 72, M4 Motorway 8, Andover 21, Burford 32, Chippenham 18, Devizes 14, Faringdon

21, Pewsey 6, Romsey 36, Swindon 11, Wantage 23.
EC Wed. **MD** Wed. **Golf** Marlborough 18h. **See** College (apply porter, main gateway), St Mary's Church, St Peter's Church, Elizabethan houses and old inns, ancient remains in vicinity, Avebury Manor 7 m W, Avebury Stone Circle and Museum 5½ m W, Savernake Forest.
⒤ St Peter's Church, High St.
✆ Marlborough (0672) 53989.

★★Ailesbury Arms, *High St, SN8 1AB.* ✆ (0672) 53451. C. ⇔ 30 bedrs, 7 bp, 8 bps, 4 ba, TV, Dgs. ✗ a l c, mc, at, LD 10. ⒟ CH, TV, Dgs, CP 30, G 8, Ac, con 40, CF, 5 st. **£** BB fr £18·50, DB fr £34·60, DT fr £33·55, WB, ② 10%, Bk £3, L £5, D £7, cc 1 3 4 5 6, Dep b.

★★Castle and Ball (TH), *High St, SN8 1LZ.* ✆ (0672) 52002. C. ⇔ 30 bedrs, 6 bp, 10 ba, TV, Dgs. ✗ a l c, mc, at, LD 9.30. ⒟ CH, Dgs, CP 50, Ac, CF, 2 st. **£** BB £34–£37, DB £44–£50·50, WB, ▯, cc 1 2 3 4 5 6, Dep (Xmas).

Rescue Service: RWS Motors, London Rd. ✆ (0672) 52564 & (0672) 53911.

MARLBROOK Hereford & Worcester (Worcestershire) M. Area 13B
Bromsgrove 2½, London 115, M5 Motorway 1½, Birmingham 10, Kidderminster 11, Stratford-upon-Avon 22.

Specialist Body Repairer Clarks Motor Services, Belle Vue Garage, 492 Birmingham Rd. ✆ 021-445 4268.

MARLOW Bucks. Maps 6B and 15E
Pop 13,600. Slough 11, London 31, M40 Motorway 3, Bagshot 18, Denham 15, Henley-on-Thames 7½, High Wycombe 4½, Oxford 27, Reading 13, Windsor 11.
EC Wed. **Golf** Temple 18h. **See** RC Church by Pugin, Marlow Pl, Bisham Abbey, Suspension Bridge, Shelley's House.

★★★★Compleat Angler (TH), *Marlow Bridge, SL7 1RG.* ✆ (062 84) 4444. C. ⇔ 42 bedrs, 42 bp, TV, Dgs. ✗ a l c, mc, at, LD 10. ⒟ N, CH, Dgs, CP 100, G 4, Ac, tc, con 100, CF, 2 st. **£** BB £64·50, DB £82, ▯, cc 1 2 3 4 5 6, Dep (Xmas).

Repairer: Platt's Garage, West St and Oxford Rd. ✆ (062 84) 2215.

MARNHULL Dorset. M. Area 5D
3 m N of Sturminster Newton. Pop 1,894. Shaftesbury 8, London 111, Sherborne 13.
Golf Ashley Wood 9h. **See** Church, Crown Inn, assoc with Thomas Hardy.

Rescue Service: Guys Automobile Engineers, Phillips Hill. ✆ (0258) 820244.

MARSTON TRUSSELL Northants. Map 15A
Pop 135. Northampton 18, London 84, Coventry 24, Leicester 15, Market Harborough 3, Rugby 15.
Golf Market Harborough 9h. **See** Church of St Nicholas.

★★Sun Inn, *LE16 9TY.* ✆ Market Harborough (0858) 65531. C. ⇔ 10 bedrs, 9 bp, 1 bps, 2 ba, TV. ✗ a l c, mc, at, LD 10. ⒟ CH, ns, CP 100, G 2, Ac, con 50, CF, 4 BGf. **£** BB fr £21, DB fr £28, WB, ▯, Bk £2·50, L 75p, D £5·95, cc 1 3 4 5 6, Dep a.

MARTHAM Norfolk. Map 16A
Pop 2,210. Norwich 18, London 129,
Cromer 24, Gt Yarmouth 10.
EC Wed. Golf Gt Yarmouth and Caister
18h. See Church.

Rescue Service: Martham Motors, 2
Rollesby Rd. ✆ Gt Yarmouth (0493)
740247.

MARTINHOE Devon. Map 4C
Pop 110. Lynmouth 5, London 189,
Barnstaple 15, Ilfracombe 11, South
Molton 19.
Golf Ilfracombe 18h. See 11th cent
Church.

⚑★★★Heddon's Gate (R), Heddon's
Mouth, EX31 4PZ. ✆ Parracombe
(059 83) 313. Open Apr–Oct. C 10. ⊨ 13
bedrs, 11 bp, 2 bps, TV, Dgs. ✗ mc, at, LD
8.15. ⓕ CH, Dgs, ns, CP 20, 1 st. £ BB
£11·30–£18·95, DB £22·60–£37·90, DBB
£18·50–£28·15, ②, Bk £5, D £7·20, cc 1 2.
◨⚑★Old Rectory (RI), EX31 3QJ.
✆ Parracombe (059 83) 368. Open Apr–
Oct. C 6. ⊨ 11 bedrs, 6 bp, 1 bps, 3 ba, TV,
Dgs. ✗ LD 7.30. ⓕ CH, ns, CP 14, gc, 2
BGf. £ BB £9–£15, DB £18–£34, WT £100–
£130, DT £22–£25, WB, ②, Bk £3·50, L
£4·50, D £9·50, cc 5.

MARTOCK Somerset. Map 5C
Pop 3,723. Wincanton 18, London 126,
Bridgwater 18, Crewkerne 7, Dorchester
27, Glastonbury 14, Ilminster 8½, Shepton
Mallet 20, Sherborne 10, Taunton 21.
EC Thur. Golf Yeovil 18h. See All Saints'
Church believed to be one of finest in
England, Treasurer's House (NT) viewing
by arrangement, 17th cent Church House.
★White Hart, TA12 6JQ. ✆ (093 582)
822005. C. ⊨ 9 bedrs, 9 sh, 3 ba, TV, Dgs.
✗ a l c, mc, at, LD 10. ⓕ TV, Dgs, CP 18, G
2, Ac, con, CF, 1 st. £ BB fr £14, DB fr £28,
WT fr £115, DT fr £20, WB, Bk £2·50, L
£4·50, D £4·50, ①, cc 5.

Repairer: Brooks & Son (Martock) Ltd,
Bridge Garage. ✆ (093 582) 822547.
Rescue Service: Yandle's Garage Ltd,
Station Garage. ✆ (093 582) 822504.

MARYPORT Cumbria. Map 26E
Pop 11,300. Cockermouth 6½, London
305, Carlisle 27, Workington 5½.
EC Wed. MD Fri. Golf Maryport 9h. See
Christ Church, Maritime Museum.
ⓘ Maritime Museum, 1 Senhouse St.
✆ Maryport (090 081) 3738.
★★Waverley, Curzon St, CA15 6LW.
✆ (0900) 812115. C. ⊨ 20 bedrs, 1 bp, 10
sh, 4 ba, TV, Dgs. ✗ a l c, mc, at, LD 8.
ⓕ CH, TV, Dgs, CP 20, Ac, con 50, CF, 2 st.
£ BB £12–£18, DB £21–£25, WB, Bk
£2·50, L £2, D £6·50, ②, cc 1 5 6.

MARY TAVY Devon. Map 3C
Pop 731. Okehampton 12, London 204,
Exeter 34, Launceston 17, Plymouth 17,
Tavistock 4½. See Wheal Betsy (Cornish
beam engine house).
◨⚑★★Moorland Hall, (R), Brentor Rd,
PL19 9PY. ✆ (0822 81) 466. Open Mar–
Nov. C. ⊨ 10 bedrs, 4 bp, 2 bps, 2 ba, Dgs.
✗ at, LD 8. ⓕ N, CH, TV, Dgs, CP 15, CF, 2
st. £ BB £16–£20, DB £26–£30, WB, ②, Bk
£2·50, D £8·50, cc 1 5, Dep a.

MASHAM North Yorkshire. Map 25E
Pop 1,000. Harrogate 17, London 222,
Boroughbridge 13, Darlington 26,
Leyburn 9½, Northallerton 23, Thirsk 13.

EC Thur. MD Tue, Wed. Golf Masham 9h.
See Jervaulx Abbey 4 m NW, Norman
Church with Saxon Cross.

★★King's Head, Market Pl, HG4 4EF.
✆ Ripon (0765) 89295. C. ⊨ 14 bedrs, 6
bp, 9 bps, 3 ba, TV, Dgs. ✗ a l c, mc, LD
9.30. ⓕ CH, CP 100, CF. £ BB £13·95–
£17·50, DB £22·50–£32·50, WB, ①, Bk £3,
L £5·50, D £8·25, cc 1 3 4 5.
Bank Villa, G, x (RI), HG4 4DB. ✆ Ripon
(0765) 89605. Open Mar–Oct. C 5. ⊨ 7
bedrs, 4 sh, 1 ba, Dgs. ⓕ CH, TV, CP 7.
£ BB £12, DB £20, WT (b) £107·50–£125,
(c) £62·50–£75, DT (b) £17–£19, ①, D £7.

Rescue Service: Brownless, J A, Bank
Foot Garage. ✆ Ripon (0765) 89349.

MATLOCK Derbyshire. Map 22C
See also MATLOCK BATH.
Pop 10,776. Derby 18, London 144,
Ashbourne 13, Buxton 20, Chesterfield 10,
Leek 28, Mansfield 18, Nottingham 24.
EC Thur. MD Tue, Fri. Golf Matlock 18h.
See High Tor (673ft), Hall Leys Park,
Riber Castle, Fauna Reserve, Artists
Corner, Tramway Museum at Crich 4½ m
SE, Haddon Hall 5 m NW. Chatsworth 8 m
N, Hardwick Hall 10 m E.
⚑★★★Riber Hall, (R), DE4 5JU.
✆ (0629) 2795. C 10. ⊨ 11 bedrs, 11 bp, 1
ba, TV. ✗ a l c, mc, at, LD 9.30. ⓕ CH, CP
50, G 1, con 12, CF, 4 BGf, 12 st. £ BBc
£38–£40, DBc £52–£55, WB, ①, Bk £3·75,
L £7, cc 1 2 3 4 5 6, Dep b.
◨★High Tor, Dale Rd, DE4 3PS.
✆ (0629) 2031. C. ⊨ 18 bedrs, 5 sh, 3 ba,
TV, Dgs, LD 8. ⓕ CH, TV, Dgs, CP 20, G 3,
Ac, con 20, 1 st. £ BB £14–£20, DB £20–
£34, WT £140–£189, DT £20–£27, ②, Bk
£3·95, L £5, D £5, Dep a.
Packhorse, F, y. ✆ (0629) 2781. C 3.
⊨ 5 bedrs, 1 ba. ⓕ CH, TV, CP 5. £ BB fr
£6·50, DB fr £13, WT (c) fr £45·50.

Repairers: Matlock Green Garage Ltd,
Matlock Green. ✆ (0629) 3668.
Slater's Garage (Matlock) Ltd, 50
Smedley St. ✆ (0629) 2101.

MATLOCK BATH Derbyshire. Map 22C
See also MATLOCK.
Pop 3,566. Derby 17, London 143,
Ashbourne 12, Leek 27, Matlock 1,
Nottingham 23.
EC Thur. Golf Matlock 18h. See
Petrifying Well, Heights of Abraham
(Rutland and Masson Caverns), Aquarium,
Lovers' Walks, Illuminations and Venetian
Fête Nights (Sept).
ⓘ The Pavilion. ✆ Matlock (0629) 55082.

★★★New Bath (TH), New Bath Rd,
DE4 3PX. ✆ (0629) 3275. C. ⊨ 56 bedrs,
56 bp, TV, Dgs. ✗ a l c, mc, at, LD 9.30.
ⓕ N, CH, Dgs, CP 250, Ac, sp, tc, sb, con
200, CF, 9 BGf, 3 st. £ BB £36·50, DB
£53·50, WB, ①, cc 1 2 3 4 5 0 Dep (Xmas).
★★Temple, Temple Walk, DE4 3PG.
✆ (0629) 3911. C. ⊨ 13 bedrs, 1 bp, 2
bps, 4 sh, 3 ba, TV, Dgs. ✗ a l c, mc, at, LD
9.30. ⓕ TV, Dgs, CP 30, Ac, con 50, CF.
£ BB £18·50–£26·50, DB £26·50–£34, ①,
Bk £3, L £3·50, D £3·50, cc 1 2 3 4 5 6.

MATTINGLEY Hampshire. M. Area 6B
Pop 600. Bagshot 14, London 41, Alton
12, Basingstoke 8, Farnham 12, Reading
11.
Golf Tylney Park, Rotherwick 18h. See
15th cent Church.

Rescue Service: U-Hire Ltd, Hound Green
Garage. ✆ Heckfield (073 583) 242.

MAWGAN PORTH Cornwall. Map 2D
Pop 1,208 (inc St Mawgan-in-Pydar).
Bodmin 18, London 251, Newquay 5, St
Austell 18, Wadebridge 13.
Golf Newquay 18h.

◨★★Tredragon (R), TR8 4DQ. ✆ St
Mawgan (0637) 860213. Open April–Oct,
Easter & Xmas. C. ⊨ 30 bedrs, 13 bp, 11
bps, 2 ba, Dgs. ✗ mc, at, LD 8. ⓕ ch, TV,
CP 25, Ac, sp, sb, sol, con 60, CF, 8 st. £ BB
£12–£20, DB £24–£36, WT £95–£170, ②,
Bk £4, L £1, D £6·50, cc 1, Dep.

Seavista, H, x (RI), TR8 4AL. ✆ St
Mawgan (0637) 276. C. ⊨ 10 bedrs, 2 ba,
Dgs. ✗ a l c. ⓕ ch, TV, CP 8, CF, 3 st. £ BB
£7·50–£8·50, DB fr £15, WT (b) £65–£70.

MAWNAN SMITH Cornwall. M Area 2F
Pop 1,185. Truro 13, London 259,
Falmouth 5, Helston 8, Redruth 12.
Golf Falmouth 18h.

Rescue Service: Alanco Motor Services
Ltd, Goldmartin Garage. ✆ (0326)
250394.

MAYFIELD Derbyshire (Staffordshire).
Map 22C.
Ashbourne 1½, London 140, Leek 13,
Stoke on Trent 19, Uttoxeter 9½.

Rescue Service: Seatons of Mayfield,
Main Rd. ✆ Ashbourne (0335) 42930.

MAYFIELD East Sussex. Map 7D
Pop 3,242. Tunbridge Wells 8½, London
45, Ashford 36, Eastbourne 20, Hastings
21, Haywards Heath 19, Hurst Green 12,
Lewes 16, Maidstone 27, Tenterden 24,
Uckfield 9½.
EC Wed. Golf Crowborough Beacon 18h.
See Argos Hill Windmill (not open to
public at present), Church, Convent
Chapel.

★★Middle House, High St, TN20 6AB.
✆ Tunbridge Wells (0435) 872146. C. ⊨ 8
bedrs, 6 bp, 2 sh, 1 ba, TV, Dgs. ✗ a l c, mc,
at, LD 9. ⓕ CH, Dgs, CP 20, Ac, con, CF, 2
st. £ BB £15–£17·50, DB £30, ①, Bk £2·50,
D £6, cc 1 3 4 5 6, Dep a.

MEALSGATE Cumbria. Map 26E
Keswick 14, London 299, Carlisle 15,
Cockermouth 9, Maryport 12, Penrith 22.
◨★★Pink House (R), CA5 1JP. ✆ Low
Ireby (096 57) 229.

MEARS ASHBY Northants. M. Area 15A
3½ m SW of Wellingborough. Pop 462. M1
Motorway 19, London 69, Bedford 22,
Bletchley 24, Cambridge 44, Huntingdon
30, Kettering 9, Market Harborough 17,
Northampton 7½, Peterborough 34.
Golf Wellingborough 18h. See Griffin's
Head (old Inn), Parish Church, Jacobean
Hall.

Rescue Service: Peter Britton, Mears
Ashby Service Station. ✆ Northampton
(0604) 810394.

MEASHAM Leicestershire. Map 22F
Pop 4,220. Hinckley 15, London 114,
Ashby-de-la-Zouch 12, Atherstone 9,
Burton-on-Trent 9½, Leicester 17,
Nuneaton 13, Tamworth 10.
EC Wed. MD Fri. Golf Willesley Park,
Ashby-de-la-Zouch 18h. See 14th cent
Parish Church.

★★**M Measham Inn,** *Tamworth Rd,*
DE12 7DU. ✆ (0530) 70095. RS Xmas &
Bank Hols. C. ⊯ 32 bedrs, 32 bp, TV, Dgs.
✗ a l c, mc, at, LD 9.30. ⌂ CH, Dgs, CP
100, Ac, con 100, CF, 16 BGf, Dis. £ BB
£18–£24·75, DB £23·40–£30·50, WB, ⬜,
Bk £3, L £4·25, D £5·50, cc 1 3 5 6.

MEIR Staffordshire.
See STOKE-ON-TRENT.

MELKSHAM Wiltshire. Map 5B
Pop 10,000. Marlborough 20, London 93,
Bath 12, Chepstow 36, Chippenham 7,
Devizes 7½, Frome 14, Radstock 17,
Swindon 25, Warminster 13.
EC Wed. **MD** Sat. **Golf** Kingsdown Box
18h. **See** Parish Church, Georgian houses,
Lacock Abbey 3 m N (Nat Trust), Great
Chalfield Manor 3 m SW.
⊠ The Round House, Church St.
✆ Melksham (0225) 707424.

⚑★★★**Beechfield House,** *Beanacre,*
SN12 7PU. ✆ (0225) 703700. C. ⊯ 16
bedrs, 16 bp, TV. ✗ a l c, mc, at, LD 7.
⌂ CH, CP 40, sp, tc, pf, con 12, CF, 4 BGf,
2 st. £ BB £33–£60, DB £50–£65, WB, ②
10%, Bk £5·25, L £7·95, cc 1 3 4 5 6, Dep.
★★**King's Arms,** *Market Pl, SN12 6EX.*
✆ Bath (0225) 707272. C. ⊯ 13 bedrs, 5
bp, 2 ba, TV, Dgs. ✗ a l c, mc, at, LD 9.
⌂ CH, Dgs, CP 50, Ac, con 20, CF, 1 st.
£ BB fr £16·50, DB fr £24, WT fr £171·50,
DT fr £24·50, WB, ⬜, Bk £3, L £6, D £6·50,
cc 1 3 5.
★**Conigre Farm,** *Semington Rd, SN12*
6BZ. ✆ (0255) 702229. C. ⊯ 9 bedrs, 2
bp, 4 bps, 1 ba, TV. ✗ a l c. ⌂ CH, CP 12, G
2, CF, 5 BGf, 0 st, Dis. £ BB £15–£20, DB
£21–£25, WT £147–£182, DT £21–£26, ②,
Bk £3·25, L £4·95, D £8·95, cc 1 2 3 5.▲
Longhope, G, y (Unl), *9 Beanacre Rd,*
SN12 8AG. ✆ (0225) 706737. Closed
Xmas. C. ⊯ 8 bedrs, 2 bp, 1 bps, 3 sh, 1 ba,
TV, Dgs. ⌂ CH, TV, CP 8, CF, 2 BGf, 2 st.
£ BB £10–£12, DB £20–£22, WT (c) £70,
DT £10, ⬜, D £4.
Regency, PH, z (Rl), *10 Spa Rd,*
SN12 7NS. ✆ (0225) 702971. C. ⊯ 12
bedrs, 6 sh, 2 ba, TV, Dgs. ⌂ CH, TV, Dgs,
CP, CF, 1 st. £ BB fr £11, DB fr £22, WT (b)
fr £126, DT (b) fr £18, ⬜, Bk £3, D £8.
Shaw Farm, G, xy (R), *Shaw, SN12 8EF.*
✆ (0225) 702836. Closed Xmas. C. ⊯ 12
bedrs, 1 bp, 5 bps, 2 ba. ⌂ CH, TV, CP 15,
CF, 1 st. £ BB £13–£16·50, DB £24–
£27·50, ⬜, D £6·50, D £6·50.
York, G, z (Unl), *Church Walk, SN12 6LY.*
✆ (0225) 702063. C. ⊯ 10 bedrs, 2 ba,
Dgs. ⌂ CH, TV, Dgs, CP, CF £ BB £6–
£8·50, DB £16–£17, DT (b) fr £13·50, ⬜.

Repairer: Wadham Stringer (Melksham)
Ltd, Market Pl. ✆ (0225) 702256.
MC Repairer: Bob Missen, Church St.
✆ (0225) 702325.
Rescue Service: Bransons Motor Works
Ltd, 9 Market Pl. ✆ (0225) 703296.
Normans of Melksham (Diagan Motors
Ltd), Semington Rd. ✆ (0225) 702182.
Turnpike Garage (Melksham) Ltd, Devizes
Rd. ✆ (0225) 702166.

MELLOR Lancashire. Map 27D
Pop 2,249. Blackburn 3, London 211,
Clitheroe 10, Longridge 8, M6 Motorway
4½, Preston 8.
EC Wed. **Golf** Blackburn 18h.

★★**Millstone,** *Church Lane, Mellor, nr*
Blackburn, BB2 7JR. ✆ (025 481) 3333.

MELLS Somerset. M. Area 5D
Pop 669. 3 m W of Frome. London 108,
Bath 14, Wells 15.
Golf West Wilts 18h. **See** Perp Church,
15th cent Tithe Barn, War Memorial.

Rescue Service: Talbot Inn Garage.
✆ (0373) 812439.

MELTHAM W Yorkshire. Map 22A/33C
Pop 7,000. Sheffield 24, London 184,
Barnsley 16, Huddersfield 4½, Oldham 14.
EC Wed. **Golf** Meltham 18h.

★★★**Durker Roods,** *Huddersfield Rd,*
HD7 3AG. ✆ Huddersfield (0484)
851413. RS Closed Xmas Day. C. ⊯ 14
bedrs, 7 bp, 7 bps, TV, Dgs. ✗ a l c, LD
9.30. ⌂ N, CH, CP 75, Ac, con 100, CF, 9
BGf, 4 st. £ BB £25–£30, DB £30–£35, DT
£38·50–£43·50, WB, ⬜, L £5·50, D £8,
cc 1 3 4 5 6.

MELTON MOWBRAY Leics. Map 23E
Pop 23,500. Kettering 29, London 104,
Grantham 16, Leicester 15,
Loughborough 15, Market Harborough
22, Nottingham 18, Spalding 36, Stamford
20.
MD Tue, Sat. **Golf** Melton Mowbray 9h.
See Church (13th cent enlarged 1550),
17th cent Bede House, Anne of Cleves
House.
ⓘ Carnegie Museum, Thorpe End.
✆ Melton Mowbray (0664) 69946.

★★★**George,** *High St, LE13 0TR.*
✆ (0664) 62112.
★★★**Harboro',** *Burton St, LE13 1AF.*
✆ (0664) 60121 C. ⊯ 27 bedrs, 23 bp, 4
bps, TV, Dgs. ✗ a l c, mc, at, LD 10. ⌂ N,
CH, TV, Dgs, CP 40, Ac, con 95, CF, 0 st.
£ BB fr £33, DB fr £44, WB, ⬜, Bk £3, L
£4·35, D £7·95, cc 1 2 3 4 5 6, Dep b.
Sysonby Knoll, H, y (R), *Ashfordby Rd,*
LE13 0HP. ✆ (0664) 63563. Closed Xmas.
C. ⊯ 18 bedrs, 7 bp, 4 bps, 1 ba, TV, Dgs.
✗ a l c. ⌂ CH, TV, Dgs, CP 20, CF, 3 BGf,
£ BB £15–£22, DB £25–£30, ⬜, Bk £2·25,
L £3, D £4·25, cc 1 5.
Westbourne, PH, z (Unl), *11A*
Nottingham Rd, LE13 0NP. ✆ (0664)
69456. C. ⊯ 16 bedrs, 3 ba, Dgs. ✗ a l c.
⌂ CH, TV, ns, CP 18, CF £ BB £9–£9·50,
DB £18–£19, ⬜.

Repairers: Sharman & Ladbury Ltd, High
St. ✆ (0664) 63423.

MENDHAM Suffolk. Map 16B.
Scole 9, London 105, East Dereham 32,
Great Yarmouth 25, Lowestoft 20,
Norwich 21, Saxmondham 20, Swaffham
39.

★**Sir Alfred Munnings,** *Studio Corner.*
✆ Harleston (0379) 852358. C. ⊯ 14
bedrs, 1 bp, 6 bps, 2 ba, Dgs. ✗ a l c, mc,
at, LD 9.30. ⌂ CH, TV, Dgs, CP 40, Ac, sp,
con 30, CF, 7 st. £ BB fr £18·50, DB fr £25,
WB, ②, Bk £2·95, L £4·50, D £4·95,
cc 1 3 4 5 6.

MEOLE BRACE Shropshire. Map 19E
Wellington 11, London 155, Bala 44,
Bridgnorth 20, Knighton 35, Llangollen
29, Ludlow 27, Newton 31, Shrewsbury
1½, Welshpool 19.
Golf Meole Brace Municipal 9h. **See** Holy
Trinity Church.

Rescue Service: Downes, E A & Sons, The
Garage. ✆ Shrewsbury (0743) 62754.

MERE Wiltshire. Map 5D
Pop 1,800. Amesbury 24, London 103,
Frome 12, Salisbury 22, Shaftesbury 9,
Shepton Mallet 18, Warminster 10,
Wincanton 7½.
EC Wed. **Golf** West Wilts Warminster
18h, Bruton 9h. **See** Mainly Perp Church,
medieval Chantry House, Inn signs at 'Old
Ship', Castle Hill (views), Stourhead 3 m
NW.
ⓘ The Square, Church St. ✆ Mere (0747)
860341.

★★**Old Ship,** *Castle St, BA12 6JE.*
✆ (0747) 860258. C. ⊯ 25 bedrs, 15 bp, 2
bps, 8 sh, 4 ba, TV, Dgs. ✗ a l c, mc, at, LD
9.30. ⌂ CH, Dgs, CP 50, G 3, Ac, con 50,
CF, 5 BGf, 0 st. £ BB £15–£23, DB £25–
£36, WT £140–£160, DT £29·50, WB, ⬜,
Bk £3·50, L £7, D £7·50, cc 1 5 6.
★**Talbot,** *The Square, BA12 6DR.*
✆ (0747) 860427. C. ⊯ 8 bedrs, 4 bp, 2
bps, 1 ba, TV, Dgs. ✗ a l c, mc, at, LD 9.
⌂ CH, Dgs, CP 25, Ac, CF, 0 st. £ BB £17,
DB £26–£30, WT £125, DT fr £28, WB, ⬜,
Bk £4, L £5·50, D £7·50, cc 1.

Rescue Service: Griffin's Garage, No 4,
Unit F Quarry Fields, Industrial Estate.
✆ (0747) 860060.

MERIDEN West Midlands. Map 21B
Pop 2,432. Coventry 6, London 100,
Atherstone 14, Birmingham 12, Evesham
33, Lichfield 21, Nuneaton 11, Sutton
Coldfield 13, Tamworth 16, Warwick 13.
EC Wed. **Golf** North Warwickshire,
Hampton in Arden 9h. **See** St Lawrence's
Church, Cross (reputedly marking centre
of England), Cyclists War Memorial.
★★★**Manor,** *Birmingham Rd, CV7 7NH.*
✆ (0676) 22735.

MERRIOTT Somerset. M. Area 5E
Pop 1,871. 2 m N Crewkerne. Wincanton
22, London 132, Bridgwater 25, Frome 33,
Glastonbury 20, Ilminster 6½, Shepton
Mallet 24, Sherborne 13.
Golf Windwhistle, Chard 12h. **See**
Church 15th cent.

Rescue Service: P L Warry, Merriott
Service Station. ✆ Crewkerne (0460)
73411.

MEVAGISSEY Cornwall. Map 2F
Pop 2,173. St Austell 5½, London 244,
Truro 14.
Golf Carlyon Bay 18h. **See** Harbour,
Aquarium, Local History Museum, Model
Rly, old Church.

⬛★★**Spa,** (R), *Polkirk Hill, PL 26 6UY.*
✆ (0726) 842244. C 5. ⊯ 10 bedrs, 5 bp, 2
ba. ✗ mc, at, LD 8. ⌂ CH, TV, CP 10, G 2,
Ac, tc, CF, 14 st. £ BB £12·50–£16·50, DB
£25–£33, WT £105·90–£117·45, DT £22–
£24, WB, ⬜, Bk £2·50, L £3, D £7·10,
cc 1 3 4 5, Dep a.
⬛★★**Tremarne** (Rl), *Polkirt Hill,*
PL 26 6UY. ✆ (0726) 842213. Open Apr–
Oct. C 5. ⊯ 14 bedrs, 4 bp, 10 bps, 2 ba,
TV. ✗ mc, at, LD 8. ⌂ CH, Dgs, CP 14, sp,
14 st. £ BB £14–£16, DB £22–£30, WT
£105–£140, WB, ②, Bk £4·50, D £8·50,
cc 1 5, Dep a.
★★**Trevalsa Court,** *School Hill,*
PL26 6TH. ✆ (0726) 842468. Closed Dec.
C. ⊯ 10 bedrs, 3 bp, 2 bps, 3 ba, TV, Dgs.
✗ a l c, mc, LD 9. ⌂ CH, TV, Dgs, CP 45,
CF, 1 BGf, 0 st, Dis. £ BB £15·50–£19, DB
£36–£40, WT £109–£116, WB, ②, Bk
£3·50, L £3·50, D £6, cc 1 3 4 5, Dep.

Headlands, PH, x (RI), *Polkirt Hill,*
PL26 6UX. ✆ (0726) 843453. Open Mar–
Oct & Xmas. C. ⊷ 14 bedrs, 6 bps, 3 ba,
Dgs. ✗ a l c. ⓕ CH, TV, Dgs, CP 11, CF, 4
BGf, 25 st. £ BB £9·75–£10·90, DB
£19·50–£24·70, WT (b) £96–£104, DT (b)
£13·70–£14·90, ⬚, Bk £2·30, L £2·30, D
£3·97.
Ship Inn, I, x, *PL26 6TU.* ✆ (0726) 3324.
Treleaven, F, x (RI), *PL26 6RZ.* ✆ (0726)
842413. Closed Xmas & New Year. C. ⊷ 5
bedrs, 1 ba, TV. ✗ a l c. ⓕ CH, TV, CP 6, CF
2 st. £ DB £14–£18, WT (b) £75–£86, ⬚.
Valley Park, PH, y (RI), *Tregony Hill,*
PL26 6RS. ✆ (0726) 842347. C. ⊷ 8
bedrs, 3 bps, 3 ba. ⓕ TV, ns, CP 11, CF, 1
BGf, Dis. £ BB £11·50–£12·50, DB
£34·50–£36·60, WT £103·50–£110, DT
£37·50–£39·75, ⬚.▲

Rescue Service: Ava Motors, Valley Rd.
✆ (0726) 843339.

MICHELDEVER Hampshire. Map 6D
Pop 575. Basingstoke 11, London 58,
Andover 12, Alton 19, Newbury 21,
Salisbury 26, Winchester 7.
See Old Church, old thatched cottages.

Rescue Service: P F & W A Mullins Ltd,
Ideal Garage, London Rd. ✆ (096 289)
313.

MICKLETON Gloucestershire. Map 14C
Pop 1,343. Moreton-in-Marsh 9½, London
93, Banbury 25, Cheltenham 22, Evesham
9½, Stratford-upon-Avon 9, Stow-on-the-
Wold 3, Tewkesbury 21.
Golf Broadway 18h. **See** Church, Hidcote
Manor Gardens 4 m.

■★★★**Three Ways,** *Chapel La,*
GL55 6SB. ✆ (038 677) 231429. C. ⊷ 39
bedrs, 34 bp, 3 bps, 3 ba, TV, Dgs. ✗ mc,
at, LD 9 (9.30 Fri & Sat). ⓕ N, CH, TV, Dgs,
CP 70, Ac, con 60, CF, 14 BGf, Dis. £ BB fr
£19·50, DB fr £32·50, WB, ②, Bk £4·50, L
£7, D £8·50, cc 1 3 4 5 6.

MIDDLEHAM North Yorkshire. Map 24F
Pop 800. Masham 7½, London 230, Bedale
10, Hawes 17, Leyburn 2, Richmond 12,
Ripon 17.
EC Thur. **Golf** Catterick 18h. **See** 12th
cent Church, Keep, Castle ruins, St.
Alkeda's Well.

★★**Millers House** (R), *Market Pl,*
DL8 4NR. ✆ Wensleydale (0969) 22630.
C. ⊷ 6 bedrs, 5 bp, 1 sh, TV. ✗ a l c, mc,
LD 8.30. ⓕ CH, CP 8, CF, 1 st. £ BB £17,
DB £34, WB, ⬚, L £2·50, D £8.

MIDDLE HERRINGTON Tyne & Wear.
M. Area 32E
3 m SW of Sunderland. A1 (M) Motorway
7, London 268, Durham 9, Middlesbrough
26, Newcastle upon Tyne 12, Stockton-
on-Tees 25.
EC Wed. **Golf** Houghton-le-Spring 11h.

Rescue Service: Parkside Garage,
Silksworth Rd. ✆ Sunderland (0783)
281110.

MIDDLESBROUGH Cleveland. Map
24D
See also THORNABY-ON-TEES
Pop 150,000. Stockton-on-Tees 4,
London 247, Helmsley 28, Pickering 38,
Sunderland 27, Whitby 30.
MD Daily. **Golf** Middlesbrough 18h. **See**
Municipal Art Gallery, Dorman Museum,
Parks, Bridges, RC Cathedral, Ormesby
Hall 3 m SE, Newham Grange (farm

museum), Captain Cook's Birthplace
Museum, Preston Hall Museum and
Stockton Transport Museum (4 m W).
⬚ 125 Albert Rd. ✆ Middlesbrough
(0642) 245750.

★★★★**M Ladbroke Dragonara,** *Fry St,*
TS1 1JH. ✆ (0642) 248133. RS Xmas. C.
⊷ 140 bedrs, 136 bp, 13 bps, TV, Dgs.
✗ a l c, mc, LD 10. ⓕ Lt, N, CH, G 40, Ac,
con 400, CF. £ BB fr £41·50, DB fr £57,
WB, ⬚, Bk £5·50, L £6·75, D £9·50,
cc 1 2 3 4 5 6, Dep b.
★★★**M Blue Bell,** *Acklam, TS5 7HL.*
✆ (0642) 593939. C. ⊷ 60 bedrs, 60 bp,
ns, TV, Dgs. ✗ mc, at. ⓕ Lt, N, CH, CP 200,
con 25, CF, 10 BGf, 2 st. £ BB £32, DB £46,
DBB £40, WB, ⬚, Bk £5·50, D £8,
cc 1 2 3 5, Dep b.
★★★**Marton,** *Stokesley Rd, Marton,*
TS7 8DS. ✆ (0642) 317141. C. ⊷ 52
bedrs, 52 bp, TV, Dgs. ✗ a l c, mc, at, LD
9.15. ⓕ N, CH, TV, CP 200, Ac, con 600,
CF. £ BB £21–£25, DB £30–£36, WT £252,
DT £36, WB, ⬚, Bk £4·75, L £4·75, D £7·50,
cc 1 3 4 5 6, Dep b.
★★★**M Marton Way** (late **Crest**),
Marton, TS4 3BS. ✆ (0642) 817651.
Closed Xmas night. C. ⊷ 53 bedrs, 53 bp,
ns, TV, Dgs. ✗ a l c, mc, at, LD 9.45. ⓕ N,
CH, CP 200, G 2, Ac, con 100, CF, 25 BGf,
2 st. £ BB £16·50–£25, DB £23–£32, WB,
⬚, Bk £3·50, L £4·25, D £4·75, cc 1 3 4 5,
Dep.
Chadwick, PH, z (Unl), *27 Clairville Rd,*
TS4 2HN. ✆ (0642) 245340.
Longlands, PH, z (RI), *295 Marton Rd,*
TS4 2HF. ✆ (0642) 244900. C. ⊷ 8 bedrs,
2 bp, 3 ba, ns. ⓕ CH, TV, CP 2, G 2, CF, 1 st.
£ BB £13·80, DB £20·70, WT (c) £64·40,
DT (b) £13·85, ⬚.

Rescue Service: H Stephenson Autotune
Ltd, Lamport St. ✆ (0642) 244634.

MIDDLETON Gtr Manchester
(Lancashire). Map 20A
Pop 51,505. Oldham 3½, London 189, Bury
6½, Manchester 5½, Rochdale 5½, St Helens
26, Walkden 10, Warrington 22.
EC Tue. **MD** Fri, Sat. **Golf** Manchester
18h, North Manchester 18h. **See** Church
with 12th cent tower arch, Old Boar's
Head Inn.

Repairer: C C McRea, Rochdale Rd.
✆ 061-643 4317.
Rescue Service: John Murphy C/G
Engineering, John Lee Fold Garage, John
Lee Fold. ✆ 061-643 5277.

MIDDLETON CHENEY
Northamptonshire. Map 14D
Pop 3,106. Buckingham 14, London 70,
Banbury 3, Bicester 17, Daventry 15,
Northampton 22, Towcester 15.
Golf Farthingstone 18h. **See** 14th cent
Church.

Rescue Service: Farthinghoe Garage Ltd,
Brackley. ✆ Banbury (0295) 710358.

MIDDLETON IN TEESDALE Durham.
Map 26A
Pop 1,200. Boroughbridge 43, London
258, Alston 22, Brough 14, Darlington 24,
Durham 28, Harrogate 61, Hexham 31,
Leyburn 35, Northallerton 42, Newcastle
upon Tyne 37, Thirsk 48, West Auckland
17.
EC Wed. **MD** alt Tue. **Golf** Barnard Castle
18h. **See** Church with detached bell

tower, Old Clock Tower, High Force (17 ft
fall) 5 m NW, Winch Bridge (WNW).
⬚ 1 Market Pl. ✆ Teesdale (0833) 40806.

★★**Teesdale,** *Market Pl, DL12 0QG.*
✆ Teesdale (0833) 40264. C. ⊷ 14 bedrs,
7 bp, 2 ba, TV, Dgs. ✗ a l c, mc, at, LD 8.30.
ⓕ CH, TV, Dgs, CP, Ac, con, CF, 2 st. £ BB
fr £11·95, DB fr £23·90, WB, ②, D £7·50,
cc 5, Dep a.▲

MIDDLETON-ON-SEA West Sussex.
Map 7E
Pop 3,070. Pulborough 15, London 62,
Arundel 7½, Bognor Regis 3, Littlehampton
4½, Petworth 17.
EC Wed. **Golf** Bognor Regis 18h. **See**
Early registers in Parish Church.

Ancton, PH, xy (R), *Ancton La,*
PO22 6NH. ✆ (024 369) 2482. C. ⊷ 9
bedrs, 2 bp, 1 bps, 1 ba, Dgs. ✗ a l c.
ⓕ CH, TV, CP 5, G 5, CF, 1 BGf, 1 st, Dis.
£ BB £12–£14, DB £24–£28, WT (b) £95,
DT (b) £16·50, ⬚, L £3·95, D £6, cc 5.

Rescue Service: Centurion Garage
(Bognor Regis) Ltd, Elmer Rd.
✆ (024 369) 2432.
Middleton Service Station. ✆ (024 369)
2092.

MIDDLE WALLOP Hampshire. Map 6C
Andover 7, London 72, Amesbury 10,
Salisbury 12, Stockbridge 5½.
See Museum of Army Flying.

◫★★★**Fifehead Manor,** *SO20 8EG.*
✆ Andover (0264) 781565. Closed 2
weeks Xmas, New Year. C. ⊷ 12 bedrs, 7
bp, 5 bps, TV, Dgs. ✗ a l c, mc, at, LD 9.30.
ⓕ CH, CP 50, U 2, con 15, CF, 2 st. £ BBc
£32, DBc £45–£55, WB, ⬚, Bk £3·50, L
£12, D £12, cc 1 3 4 5 6.

MIDDLEWICH Cheshire. Map 19D
Pop 8,209. Sandbach 5, London 166,
Altrincham 16, Chester 20, Congleton 10,
Knutsford 9, Macclesfield 15, Nantwich
10, Northwich 6, Stockport 23.
EC Wed. **Golf** Sandbach 9h. **See** Church
of St Michael and All Saints, Museum
(Roman period).

Rescue Service: F Cash Ltd, Ashfield
Garage, Lewin St. ✆ (060 684) 2357.

MIDHURST West Sussex. Map 7C
Pop 4,148. Haslemere 8, London 49, Alton
18, Chichester 12, Cosham 21, Hindhead
10, Petersfield 10, Petworth 6½.
EC Wed. **Golf** Cowdray Park 18h. **See**
Cowdray Park and Tudor Mansion ruins,
St Margaret's Church, Grammar School,
old houses and inns, Petworth House
5½ m E, Woolbeding Common (3 m NW).

★★★**Spread Eagle,** *South St, GU29 9NH.*
✆ (073 081) 2211. C. ⊷ 27 bedrs, 23 bp,
2 ba, TV, Dgs. ✗ a l c, mc, at, LD 9.30. ⓕ N,
CH, Dgs, CP 100, Ac, con 100, CF. £ BB
£37·50, DB fr £39, ⬚, Bk £5·50, L £8·25, D
£11·50, cc 1 3 4 5 6, Dep b.

Repairer: Midhurst Engineering and
Motor Co Ltd, Rumbolds Hill (Works),
Service Station, North St. ✆ (073 081)
2162.

MIDSOMER NORTON Avon. M. Area
5B
Pop 10,000 (inc Radstock), Radstock 1½,
London 111, Bristol 15, Shepton Mallet
8½, Wells 10, Weston-super-Mare 26.

EC Wed. **Golf** Mendip 18h. **See** 15th cent Tithe Barn (incorp RC Church of the Holy Ghost), St John's Parish Church.

Rescue Service: Norton Hill Garage, Fosseway. ✆ (0761) 413377.

MILBORNE ST ANDREW Dorset. Map 5F
Blandford Forum 8, London 113, Bournemouth 20, Dorchester 8½, Ringwood 25, Sherborne 22, Wareham 10, Wincanton 30.

Rescue Service: Bourne Valley Service Station. ✆ (025 887) 353.

MILDENHALL Suffolk. Map 16F
Pop 11,958. Newmarket 9, London 71, Bury St Edmunds 12, Dereham 34, Ely 15, Huntingdon 34, King's Lynn 35, Thetford 11, Swaffham 25, Wisbech 32.
EC Thur. **MD** Fri. **Golf** Royal Worlington 9h, Newmarket 18h. **See** St Mary's Church, 15th cent Market Cross.

★★**Bell,** *High St, IP28 7EA.* ✆ (0638) 712134. C. ◢ 18 bedrs, 12 bp, 1 bps, 2 ba, TV, Dgs. ✗ a l c, mc, at, LD 9. ⊞ CH, Dgs, CP 25, Ac, con 60, CF, 1 st. £ BB £21–£28, DB £31–£34, WT £180–£250, DT £30–£40, WB, ⊡, Bk £2·50, L £1·60, D £8, cc 1 3 4 5 6, Dep.

★★**M Smoke House Inn,** *Beck Row, IP28 8DH.* ✆ (0638) 713223. C. ◢ 59 bedrs, 59 bp, TV. ✗ a l c, mc, at, LD 10. ⊞ N, CH, CP 200, Ac, sp, CF, 59 BGf, 2 st. £ BB £33·50, DB £38·50, WB, ⊡, Bk £4·50, L £6·50, D £7·50, cc 1 3 5 6, Dep.

MILFORD ON SEA Hampshire. Map 6E
Pop 4,350. Lymington 4½, London 96, Blandford Forum 30, Bournemouth 14, Ringwood 15.
Golf Barton-on-Sea 18h. **See** Norman Parish Church, Hurst Castle 3 m SE.

Rescue Service: Moore's Central Garage Ltd, 1 High St. ✆ (059 069) 2161.

MILLOM Cumbria. Map 27E
Pop 6,956. Broughton-in-Furness 7½, London 284, Egremont 26.
EC Wed. **Golf** Silecroft 9h. **See** Castle ruins now farmhouse, Holy Trinity Church, Muncaster Castle 11½ m NW, Folk Museum.
🛈 St George's Rd. ✆ Millom (0657) 2555.
Repairers: J H Bennett, Central Garage, 32 Duke St. ✆ (0657) 2241.
Rescue Service: Valley End Motors, Valley End Garage, Silecroft. ✆ (0657) 2407.

MILNTHORPE Cumbria. Map 27C
Pop 1,635. M6 Motorway 4, London 248, Ambleside 19, Broughton-in-Furness 29, Kendal 8, Kirkby Lonsdale 9½, Lancaster 14, Ulverston 23.
EC Thur. **MD** Fri. **Golf** Silverdale 9h. **See** Dallam Tower Park (fallow deer), Levens Hall 2½ m.

Rescue Service: Coultert, J A, Sandside Garage. ✆ (044 82) 2289.

MILTON Hampshire
See NEW MILTON.

MILTON ABBAS Dorset. Map 5F
Pop 732. 2½ m NW of Winterbourne Whitechurch. Blandford Forum 8, London 113, Bournemouth 21, Dorchester 11, Ringwood 26, Sandbanks 21, Shaftesbury 16, Sherborne 17, Wareham 13, Wincanton 22.

Golf Keyneston 18h. **See** Milton Abbey Church, picturesque street.

▣◢★★**Milton Manor,** (Rl) *Blandford Forum, DT11 0AZ.* ✆ (0258) 880254. Open Mar–Oct. C 12. ◢ 12 bedrs, 4 bp, 3 bps, 1 sh, 3 ba. ✗ mc, at, LD 7.30. ⊞ ch, TV, CP 20, 0 st. £ BB fr £18, DB fr £28, WT fr £159, DT fr £26, ⊡, Bk £4, L £3, D £7.

MILTON COMMON Oxfordshire. Map 14F
London 46, M40 Motorway ½, Aylesbury 13, High Wycombe 16, Oxford 10, Wallingford 18.

★★**Belfry,** *Brimpton Grange, OX9 2JW.* ✆ Gt Milton (084 46) 381. Closed 25th–28th Dec incl. C. ◢ 43 bedrs, 31 bp, 7 bps, 2 ba. ✗ a l c, mc, at, LD 9.30. ⊞ N, CH, CP 200, Ac, sp, con 200, CF, 6 st. £ BB £28–£34, DB £37–£44·50, WB, ⊡, Bk £5, L £7, D £9·25, cc 1 3 4 5, Dep b▲.

Rescue Service: Lantern Service Station. ✆ Gt Milton (084 46) 336.

MILTON DAMEREL Devon. Maps 3A and 4E
Pop 450. South Molton 30, London 211, Bideford 13, Bude 12, Holsworthy 6.
Golf Holsworthy 18h. **See** 11th cent Parish Church.

★★★**Woodford Bridge,** *EX22 7LL* (A 388). ✆ (040 926) 481. C. ◢ 32 bedrs, 28 bp, 3 bps, 1 sh, 4 ba, TV, Dgs. ✗ a l c, mc, at, LD 8.45. ⊞ CH, TV, CP 200, sp, tc, pf, sc, rf, sb, sol, con 100, CF. £ BB £17·80–£30, DB £34·50–£58, WT £160·50–£214, DT £25·50–£34, WB, ⊡, Bk £6, L £6·75, D £12, Dep a.

Rescue Service: W Sanders & Sons, Horrelsford Garage. ✆ (040 926) 212.

MILTON KEYNES Buckinghamshire. Map 15C
Pop 148,080 (inc New City). London 56, M1 Motorway 1, Bedford 13, Bletchley 5½, Buckingham 13, Newport Pagnell 4, Towcester 13.
MD Tue, Sat. **Golf** Bletchley & Abbey Hill 18h. **See** Modern town centre, Broughton Church, Bradwell Abbey, Stacey Hill Collection of Industry and Rural Life.
🛈 300 Saxon Gate West. ✆ Milton Keynes (0908) 678361.

★★**Cock,** *Watling St, MK11 1AH.* ✆ (0908) 562109. Closed Xmas. C. ◢ 19 bedrs, 1 bp, 4 bps, 4 ba, TV, Dgs. ✗ a l c, mc, LD 9. ⊞ ch, TV, Dgs, CP, Ac, con 20, CF. £ BB £18–£29, DB £24–£42, WB, ⊡, Bk £3·50, cc 1 3 4 5.

★★**Swan Revived,** *High St, Newport Pagnell MK16 8AR.* ✆ (0908) 610565. Closed 10 days after Xmas. C. ◢ 31 bedrs, 12 bp, 19 bps, TV, Dgs. ✗ a l c, mc, at, LD 9.45. ⊞ Lt, N, CH, Dgs, CP 15, 9 3, Ac, con 80, CF, 2 BGf, 1 st, Dis. £ BB £20–£32, DB £26–£40, WT £272, DT £32–£44, WB, ⊡, Bk £2·50, L £6, D £6·50, cc 1 3 4 5 6, Dep b.

Linford, H, y (Rt). *Great Linford, MK14 5AZ.* ✆ (0908) 605879. C 5. ◢ 4 bedrs, 4 bp, TV. ✗ a l c. ⊞ CH, CP 60, CF. £ BB £27–£32, DB £39–£44, DT (a) fr £42, ⊡, Bk £3·50, L £8·50, D £8·50, cc 1 3 4 5.

MILTON-ON-STOUR Dorset. Map 5D
Pop 146. Amesbury 27, London 110, Salisbury 25, Shaftesbury 5½, Shepton Mallet 17, Warminster 13, Wincanton 6½.

▣◢★★★**Milton Lodge,** *Gillingham, SP8 4PR.* ✆ Gillingham (074 76) 2262. C. ◢ 12 bedrs, 9 bp, 1 bps, TV, Dgs. ✗ a l c, mc, at, LD 9.30. ⊞ CH, CP 50, Ac, sp, pf, rf, sol, con 80, CF, 1 st. £ BB £20–£27, DB £36–£50, WB, ⊡ 10%, Bk £3·50, L £3·50, D £8·50, cc 1 6, Dep a.

MINEHEAD Somerset. Map 4D
Pop 8,722. Taunton 24, London 167, Bridgwater 26, Dunster 2, Lynmouth 16.
EC Wed. **Golf** Minehead and West Somerset 18h. **See** Parish Church (14th cent), 17th cent Quirke's Almshouses, 14th cent Fishermen's Chapel, Model Village and Mini Rly, old houses, Dunster Village and Castle, Cleeve Abbey (Washford), Exmoor National Park, West Somerset Rly (Steam Engines).
🛈 Market House, The Parade. ✆ Minehead (0643) 2624.

★★★**Beach** (TH), *The Avenue, TA24 5AP.* ✆ (0643) 2193. C. ◢ 35 bedrs, 35 bp, TV, Dgs. ✗ a l c, mc, at, LD 8.45. ⊞ CH, Dgs, CP 40, Ac, sp, con 40, CF, 0 st. £ BB £35·50, DB £48, WB, ⊡, cc 1 2 3 4 5 6.

★★★**Benares** (R), *Northfield Rd, TA24 5PT.* ✆ (0643) 2340. C. ◢ 21 bedrs, 16 bp, 1 bps, 2 ba, TV, Dgs. ✗ a l c, mc, at, LD 8.15. ⊞ CH, TV, CP 24, Ac, CF, 3 st. £ BB £19–£21·50, DB £33·65–£36·05, WB, ☒, Bk £3·50, D £7·50, cc 1 3 4 5 6, Dep a.

★★★**Northfield** (R), *Northfield Rd, TA24 5PU.* ✆ (0643) 5155. Open Mid Feb–Mid Nov & Xmas. C. ◢ 27 bedrs, 21 bp, 3 bps, 1 ba, TV, Dgs. ✗ a l c, mc, at, LD 8.15. ⊞ Lt, CH, CP 24, U 3, sp, gc, tc, con 16, CF, 0 st, Dis. £ BB £24·25–£31·25, DB £45–£63·50, WT £203–£266, DT £32–£36, WB, ⊡, Bk £2·95, L £5·50, D £8·25, cc 1 3 4 5.

▣★★**Beaconwood** (R), *Church Rd, North Hill, TA24 5SB.* ✆ (0643) 2032. Closed Nov. C. ◢ 16 bedrs, 5 bp, 1 bps, 1 sh, 4 ba, TV, Dgs. ✗ a l c, at, LD 8. ⊞ CH, TV, Dgs, CP 30, Ac, sp, con 20, CF, 1 st. £ BB £12·50–£14, DB £25–£28, WT £144–£150, DT £22·50, WB, ⊡, Bk £3, L £4, D £7, cc 1 5, Dep a.

▣★★**Merton** (R), *Western La, The Parks, TA24 8BZ.* ✆ (0643) 2375. Open Apr–Oct. C. ◢ 12 bedrs, 3 bp, 3 bps, 3 ba, Dgs. ✗ mc, at, LD 8. ⊞ TV, CP 14, CF, 1 BGf, 0 st, Dis. £ BB £9·95–£12·15, DB £19·90–£27·40, Bk £2·35, L £3·50, D £7·50, ⊡, cc 1 6, Dep b.

▣★★**Remuera,** (R), *Northfield Rd, TA24 5QH.* ✆ (0643) 2611. C. ◢ 10 bedrs, 3 bp, 1 sh, 2 ba, TV, Dgs. ✗ a l c, mc, at, LD 8. ⊞ CP 10, Ac, con 25, CF, 1 st. £ BB fr £15, DB fr £26, WT £115–£132, WB, Bk £4·15, L 70p, D £7·35, cc 5, Dep a.

★★**Winsor** (Rl), *The Avenue, TA24 5AW.* ✆ (0643) 2171. Open Apr–Oct. C. ◢ 38 bedrs, 9 bp, 1 bps, 3 sh, 7 ba, ns, TV, Dgs. ✗ a l c, mc, at, LD 8. ⊞ TV, CP 26, CF, 2 BGf, Dis. £ BB £11–£13, DB £22–£26, WT £110, DT £15·72, ⊡, Bk £2·75, L £3, D £5·75, cc 1 3 5, Dep a.

▣★★**York,** *The Avenue, TA24 5AN.* ✆ (0643) 5151. C. ◢ 22 bedrs, 5 bp, 4 bps, 3 ba, TV. ✗ a l c, mc, at, LD 9.30. ⊞ CH, TV, CP 18, Ac, con 30, 2 st. £ BB £12–£17·50, DB £24–£35, WB, ⊡, Bk £2·50, L £3, D £7·50, cc 1 3 4 5 6, Dep a.

▣★**Glen Rock** (R), *The Avenue, TA24 5AY.* ✆ (0643) 2245. Open Mar–Nov. C 3. ◢ 14 bedrs, 3 ba, ns, Dgs. ✗ a l c, mc, at, LD 7.30. ⊞ ch, TV, CP 10, U

1, Ac, CF, 4 BGf, Dis. £ BB £8·50–£9·50, DB £16–£18, WT £74–£80, DT £14·50–£16, WB, ⊡, Bk £2·50, L £3·50, D £5, Dep a.

★Kingsway (R), *Ponsford Rd, TA24 5DY.* ✆ (0643) 2313. Open Apr–Oct. C 5, ⋈ 10 bedrs, 2 ba, TV, Dgs. ✗ LD 7. ⬠ CH, TV, Dgs, CP 10, 2 st. £ BB £12, DB £24, WT £112, WB, ⊡, Bk £3, L £5, D £7, cc 1 5.

Bilbrook Lawns, H, xy (R), *Bilbrook, TA24 6HE.* ✆ Washford (0984) 40331. C. ⋈ 14 bedrs, 2 ba, 3 bps, 3 ba, TV, Dgs. ✗ a l c. ⬠ CH, CP 15, G 2, 4 BGf, 1 st, Dis. £ BB £15–£16, DB £27–£30, WT (b) £125, DT (b) £23·50, ⊡, D £8·50.

Carbery, G, x (Rl), *Western Lane, The Parks, TA24 8BZ.* ✆ (0643) 2941.

Gascony, PH, z (R), *50 The Avenue, TA24 5BB.* ✆ (0643) 2817. Open Mar–Oct. C. ⋈ 15 bedrs, 2 bp, 6 bps, 1 sh, 2 ba. ⬠ CH, TV, ns, CP 10, CF, 1 Bgf, Dis. £ BB £9–£12, DB £18–£22, WT (b) £72–£79, DT (b) £13·50–£14·50, ⊡, Bk £2·50, D £4·50, cc 1 5.

Harley House, PH, z (Unl) *Irnham Rd, TA24 5DL.* ✆ (0648) 2850. Open Apr–Oct & Easter. C. ⋈ 10 bedrs, 2 ba, Dgs. ✗ a l c. ⬠ ch, TV, CP 10, CF, 1 st. £ BB £8·70, DB £17·40, WT (b) £77·70, DT (b) £12·20, ⊡.

Marston Lodge, PH, y (R), *St Michaels Rd, TA24 5JP.* ✆ (0643) 2510. C. ⋈ 12 bedrs, 1 sh, 2 ba, Dgs. ⬠ TV, CP 9, G 2. £ BB fr £7·50, DB fr £15, WT (b) fr £74·75, DT (b) fr £11·50, ⊡.

Mayfair, PH, z (Rt), *The Avenue, TA24 5AY.* ✆ (0643) 2719. Open Mar–Oct. C. ⋈ 18 bedrs, 3 ba, Dgs. ⬠ CH, TV, CP 14, CF, 1 Bgf, 2 st. £ BB £9·50–£10·50, DB £18–£19·50, WT (b) £72–£77, DT (b) £13–£15, Bk £2, L £4·50, D £4·50.

Woodbridge, PH, z (R), *12 The Parks, TA24 8BS.* ✆ (0643) 4860. C. ⋈ 10 bedrs, 1 bp, 2 bps, na, Dgs. ⬠ CH, TV, CP 5, U 2, 1 BGf, 2 st. £ BB fr £8·80, DB fr £15, WT (b) fr £62·50, DT (b) fr £12·50, ⊇, D £5, cc 1 3 5.

Repairer: Staddons Garage (1937) Ltd, Brampton St. ✆ (0643) 3461.
Rescue Service: Minehead Service Station, Townsend Rd. ✆ (0643) 3379. P G Hayes, Pollards Garages, Bampton St. ✆ (0643) 3461. Premier Garage (Alcombe) Ltd, 71 Alcombe Rd. ✆ (0643) 3458.

MINSTERWORTH Gloucestershire. Map 13F
Gloucester 5, London 109, Chepstow 24, Leominster 36, Monmouth 21, Ross-on-Wye 14, Tewkesbury 14.

Severn Bank, G (Rl), *GL2 8JH.* ✆ (045 275) 357. Closed Xmas Day. C 5. ⋈ 6 bedrs, 2 ba, ns. ⬠ CH, TV, ns, CP 15, 3 st. £ BB £8·50, DB £17, WT (c) £59·50, DT (b) £14.

MIRFIELD West Yorkshire. M. Area 25F and 33C
Pop 18,599. Wakefield 9, London 191, Bradford 11, Halifax 9, Leeds 11, Oldham 23, Rochdale 23, Skipton 28, Todmorden 20.
EC Tue. **MD** Wed, Fri. **Golf** Dewsbury and District 18h. **See** House and College of Resurrection, Peter Claver College.

Rescue Service: Newgate Garage Ltd, Newgate. ✆ (0924) 492105.

MITCHAM Greater London (Surrey). Map 7B

Pop 63,690. London 8, Croydon 4, Epsom 7½, Kingston upon Thames 7, Purley 6, Redhill 12, Reigate 12, Richmond-upon-Thames 9, Thornton Heath 3½.
EC Wed. **Golf** Mitcham 18h.

Repairer: Gresham Motors Ltd, 263 London Rd. ✆ 01-648 8181.

MITCHELDEAN Gloucestershire. Map 13F
Pop 2,741. Gloucester 11, London 116, Chepstow 21, Hereford 18, Ledbury 15, Monmouth 13, Ross-on-Wye 6½.
Golf Ross-on-Wye 18h. **See** Interesting old Church, timbered houses.

Rescue Service: Mitcheldean Garage. ✆ Dean (0594) 542228.

MITCHELL Cornwall. Map 2D
Summercourt 2, London 249, Bodmin 16, Newquay 7, Redruth 12, St Austell 11, Truro 7.
See Raleigh House.

Rescue Service: Abbewind Ltd, Mitchell Garage. ✆ (087 251) 688.

MOBBERLEY Cheshire. Map 19B
Pop 2,515. Knutsford 2½, London 175, Altrincham 6½, Congleton 15, Macclesfield 10, Stockport 13.
Golf Wilmslow 18h. **See** Parish Church, Mobberley Old Hall.

Rescue Service: Rectory Garage. ✆ (056 587) 2130.

MOCKBEGGAR Hampshire. Map Area 6E
Fordingbridge 3½, London 94, Bournemouth 15, Lymington 17, Ringwood 3, Southampton 21.

Rescue Service: Ibsley Service Station Ltd, Gorley Rd. ✆ Ringwood (042 54) 3283.

MODBURY Devon. Map 3D
Pop 1,259. Ashburton 14, London 202, Dartmouth 17, Kingsbridge 8, Plymouth 12, Tavistock 22, Totnes 11.
Golf Bigbury on Sea 18h. **See** 13th cent Church, quaint old conduits.

★Modbury Inn, *Brownston St, PL21 0RQ.* ✆ (0548) 830275. C 5. ⋈ 6 bedrs, 1 bp, 1 ba, TV. ✗ a l c, mc. LD 9.30. ⬠ CH, TV, CP 20, Ac, con 20, £ BB fr £11·50, DB fr £23, WB, Bk £2·50, L £3·50, D £3·50, Dep a.

Rescue Service: Stevens Garage, Broad St. ✆ (0548) 830211. Walters Garage, New Rd. ✆ (0548) 830235.

MONK FRYSTON North Yorkshire. Map 25D
Pop 737. Doncaster 20, London 184, Castleford 7, Selby 7, Tadcaster 9, Leeds 14.
Golf Selby 18h. **See** Tudor houses thatched cottage, Church.

⬚★★★Monk Fryston Hall, *Selby Rd, LS25 5DU.* ✆ South Milford (0977) 682369. C. ⋈ 24 bedrs, 24 bp, TV, Dgs. ✗ a l c, mc, at, LD 9.30. ⬠ N, CH, Dgs, CP 60, U 2, con 60, CF, 5 BGf, 0 st, Dis. £ BB £32–£36, DB £43–£46, WB, ⊡, Bk £4, L £6·30, D £9·50, cc 1 3 5, Dep b.

MONKSEATON Tyne & Wear. Map 32B
Pop 38,400. Tyne Tunnel 5, London 282, Alnwick 34, Coldstream 61, Hawick 70,

Jedburgh 65, Newcastle upon Tyne 9½, Sunderland 14.
EC Wed. **Golf** Whitley Bay 18h.

Rescue Service: Taylor's Garage (Monkseaton) Ltd, Earsdon Rd. ✆ Whitley Bay (0632) 523355.

MONKTON COMBE Avon. Map 5B
Pop 339. Bath 2½, London 107, M4 Motorway 13, Bristol 15, Devizes 16, Frome 11, Wells 19.
EC Wed. **Golf** Lansdown, Mendip, Saltford all 18h.

Rescue Service: Monkton Combe Garage, Warminster Rd. ✆ Limpley Stoke (022 122) 3295.

MONTACUTE Somerset. Map 5C
Yeovil 4, London 129, Bridport 19, Bristol 40, Honiton 26, Lyme Regis 23, Weymouth 32.

★★Kings Arms, *Bishopston, TA15 6UU.* ✆ Hartock (0935) 822513. Closed Xmas Day. C. ⋈ 10 bedrs, 10 bp, TV. ✗ a l c, mc, at, LD 10. ⬠ CH, ns, CP 24, Ac, CF, 4 BGf, 0 st, Dis. £ BB £27·50–£30, DB £35–£40, WT £192·50, WB, ⊇, Bk £2·95, L £3·25, D £8·95, cc 1 2 3 5, Dep a.

MOORGREEN Nottinghamshire. M. Area 22D
1½ m NE of Eastwood. Pop 8,875. M1 Motorway 3½, London 131, Ashbourne 22, Chesterfield 18, Derby 13, Loughborough 21, Mansfield 11, Matlock 17, Newark on Trent 25, Nottingham 7½.
Golf Bulwell Forest 18h. **See** Remains of Greasley Castle and Beauvale Priory.

Rescue Service: Moorgreen Garage, Church Rd. ✆ Langley Mill (077 37) 3150.

MORCOTT Leicestershire. Maps 23F and 15A
Pop 568. Kettering 16, London 91, Leicester 23, Market Harborough 16, Melton Mowbray 16, Stamford 8.
Golf Luffenham Heath 18h. **See** Norman and 13th cent Church, Windmill (Recon).

Rescue Service: Morcott Service Station, Uppingham Rd. ✆ (057 287) 878.

MORECAMBE Lancashire. Map 27C
See also HEYSHAM.
Pop 40,661 (inc. Heysham). Lancaster 3½, London 242, Ambleside 33, Broughton-in-Furness 42, Kendal 22, Kirkby Lonsdale 17, Ulverston 37.
EC Wed. **MD** Tue, Sat. **Golf** Morecambe 18h, Heysham 18h. **See** Marineland, Illuminations in autumn, Heysham Head Entertainment Centre (inc Kart Racing Circuit).
🛈 Marine Road Central. ✆ Morecambe (0524) 414110.

★★★Elms, *Elms Rd, LA4 6DD.* ✆ (0524) 411501. C. ⋈ 39 bedrs, 29 bp, 3 bps, 3 ba. ✗ a l c, mc, at, LD 9. ⬠ Lt, N, CH, TV, CP 80, U 11, Ac, con 120, CF, 3 st. WB, ⊡, Bk £3·50, L £3·50, D £7, cc 1 3 5.

★★★Headway, *East Promenade, LA4 5AN.* ✆ (0524) 412525.

★★★Midland, *Marine Rd West, LA4 4BZ.* ✆ (0524) 417180. C. ⋈ 46 bedrs, 40 bp, 6 bps, 4 ba, TV, Dgs. ✗ a l c, mc, at, LD 8.45. ⬠ Lt, N, CH, Dgs, CP 60, Ac, con, CF, Dis. £ BB £31, DB £46, WB, ⊡, cc 1 3 4 5, Dep b.▲

★★★Strathmore, *Marine Rd East, LA4 5AP.* ✆ (0524) 411314. C. ⋈ 55 bedrs, 30

bp, 11 bps, 5 ba, TV. ✗ a l c, mc, at, LD 10, (10.30 Sat). ⓓ Lt, N, CH, CP 30, G 12, Ac, con 150, CF, 0 st, Dis. £ BB £13·75–£27·50, DB £27·50–£40, WT £118–£135, WB, ⑦, Bk £4, L £4·50, D £5·50, cc 1 3 4 5 6, Dep b.

★★Clarendon, *Marine Rd West, LA4 5EP.* ✆ (0524) 410180. C. ⊶ 31 bedrs, 19 bp, 4 bps, 2 sh, 7 ba, TV, Dgs. ✗ a l c, LD 9. ⓓ Lt, N, CH, TV, Dgs, Ac, sb, sol, con 70, CF, 3 st. £ BB £13–£18·50, DB £23–£27, WB, ⑦, Bk £3, D £4, cc 1 3 4 5, Dep b.

★★Grovesnor, *Sandylands Promenade, LA3 1DR.* ✆ (0524) 412606. C. ⊶ 45 bedrs, 24 bp, 7 bps, 6 ba, TV, Dgs. ✗ a l c, mc, at, LD 10. ⓓ Lt, N, CH, TV, Dgs, CP 30, Ac, sb, sol, con 200, CF, 8 st. £ BB fr £17·50, DB fr £33, WT fr £150·50, WB, ⑦, Bk £2·50, L £4·25, D £5·50, cc 1 3 4 5 6, Dep a.

Ashley, PH, x (RI), *371 Marine Rd East, LA4 5AH.* ✆ (0524) 412034. C. ⊶ 14 bedrs, 3 ba, TV, Dgs. £ BB £9–£9·50, DB £18–£19, ⑦.

Balmoral, PH, z (RI), *34 Marine Rd, LA3 1BZ.* ✆ (0524) 418526.

Beach Mount, PH, z (RI), *395 Marine Rd East, LA4 5AN.* ✆ (0524) 420753. Open Mar–Oct & Xmas. ⊶ 27 bedrs, 20 bp, 2 bps, 5 sh, 3 ba, TV, Dgs. ⓓ CH, TV, CP 6, CF, 5 st. £ BB £9–£11, DB £18–£22·50, WT (b) £84·50–£89, DT £14·75–£15·50, ②, Bk £3·25, L £5, D £6·25, cc 1 5.

Carr Garth, G, yz (Unl), *18 Bailey La, Heysham Village, LA3 2PS.* ✆ Heysham (0524) 51175. Open Apr–Oct. C. ⊶ 10 bedrs, 2 ba, Dgs. ✗ a l c. ⓓ TV, Dgs, CP 7, CF. £ BB fr £7·75, DB fr £14·50, WT (b) fr £59·50, DT (b) fr £9·25, ②.

Ellesmere, PH, z (Unl), *44 Westminster Rd, LA4 4JD.* ✆ (0524) 411881. Open Apr–Oct. C. ⊶ 5 bedrs, 1 ba. ⓓ Lt, ch, TV, CF, 1 st, Dis. £ BB £6·50–£7·50, DB £13–£15, WT (b) £52–£54, DT (b) £8–£9, ②.

Elstead, PH, z (RI), *72 Regent Rd, LA3 1TF.* ✆ (0524) 412260. C. ⊶ 12 bedrs, 2 ba. ⓓ CH, TV, CF

Headway, H, z (R) Marine Rd, East, LA4 5AN. ✆ (0524) 412525. Closed Xmas & New Year, RS Nov–Mar. C. ⊶ 51 bedrs, 47 bp, 4 bps, 1 ba, TV. ✗ a l c. ⓓ Lt, CH, CP 20, CF. £ BB £19–£20, DB £36–£38, WT £150–£155, DT (b) £24–£26, ②, Bk £3·25, L £5, D £6·25, cc 1 5.

New Hazelmere, PH, z (RI), *391 Marine Rd West, LA4 5AN.* ✆ (0524) 417876. Open Apr–Nov. C. ⊶ 21 bedrs, 4 ba, Dgs. ⓓ TV, Dgs, CF, 4 BGf, 3 st. £ BB £9·20, DB £18·40, WT (b) £74·75–£86·25, DT (b) £12·65–£13·80, ⑦.

Prospect, PH, z (RI), *363 Marine Rd, LA4 5AQ.* ✆ (0524) 417819. Open Apr–Oct. C. ⊶ 15 bedrs, 8 bp, 2 ba, TV, Dgs. ⓓ CH, TV, CP 6, CF, 3 BGf, 2 st. £ BB fr £8·05, DB fr £16·10, WT (b) fr £77·05, DT (b) fr £11·50, ⑦.

Romney, PH, z (RI), *21 Sea View Parade, LA4 4DL.* ✆ (0524) 413015. Open Apr–Oct. C. ⊶ 25 bedrs, 4 sh, 4 ba. ⓓ ch, TV, CP 10, CF, 4 BGf, 8 st. £ BB £7·50–£11, DB £15–£22, WT (b) fr £72·50, DT (b) fr £10·50, ②, Bk £2, L £3, D £4, cc 1 5.

Rydal Mount, PH, z (RI), *391 Marine Rd East, LA4 5AQ.* ✆ (0524) 411858. Open Apr–Oct. C. ⊶ 14 bedrs, 3 bps, 3 ba, Dgs. ⓓ ch, TV, Dgs, CP 12, 2 st. £ BB £9·78–£11·35, DB £20–£24, WT (b) £75·90–£78·20, (c) fr £62, ⑦.

Warwick, PH, z (RI), *394 Marine Rd East, LA4 5AN.* ✆ (0524) 418151. C. ⊶ 23 bedrs, 3 bp, 9 bps, 4 ba, TV, Dgs.

ⓓ Lt, ch, TV, CF, 5 BGf, 5 st. £ BB fr £8·60, WT (a) fr £78, ⑦, cc 1 3 5.

Wilmslow, PH, z (RI), *374 Marine Rd East, LA4 5AH.* ✆ (0524) 417804. Open Mar–Oct & Xmas. C. ⊶ 15 bedrs, 3 bps, 3 ba. ⓓ CH, TV, ns, CP 9, CF, cc 1 5.

York, H, *Lancaster Rd, LA4 5QR.* ✆ (0524) 418226.

Repairer: Bare Motor Co Ltd, Bare La. ✆ (0524) 410205.

Rescue Service: Whitehouse Motors, Westgate. ✆ (0524) 413329.

MORETON Dorset. Map 5F
Pop 286. Ringwood 28, London 121, Blandford Forum 14, Dorchester 8, Sherborne 24, Wareham 9, Weymouth 12, Wincanton 32.
Golf Wareham 9h, Lakey Hill 18h. **See** Grave of Lawrence of Arabia in village cemetery, Church of St Nicholas, 'Lawrence's cottage' Clouds Hill 3 m NE.

Rescue Service: Hurst Garage. ✆ Bindon Abbey (0929) 462754.

MORETON Wirral, Merseyside. Map 19A
Pop 19,745. Birkenhead 4, London 201, Chester 18, Queensferry 17.
EC Wed. **Golf** Wallasey 9h. **See** Lighthouse, Castle.

★★★Leasowe Castle, *Leasowe, L46 3RF.* ✆ 051-606 9191.▲

Rescue Service: Highway Rescue Services, Unit 1, Tarran Way West, Tarran Way Industrial Estate, Pasture Rd. ✆ (051 678) 8151 & 8743.

MORETONHAMPSTEAD Devon. Maps 3D and 4E
Pop 1,610. Exeter 13, London 182, Ashburton 13, Crediton 11, Newton Abbot 12, Okehampton 13, Plymouth 29, Saltash 30, Tavistock 21.
EC Thur. **Golf** Manor House Hotel Course 18h. **See** Base of Old Cross marking site of celebrated 'Dancing Tree', St Andrew's Church, Almshouses (Nat Trust).

◼★★**White Hart**, *The Square, TQ13 8NF.* ✆ (0647) 40406. C 10. ⊶ 18 bedrs, 14 bp, 2 bps, 2 sh, 2 ba, TV, Dgs. ✗ a l c, mc, at, LD 8·30. ⓓ CH, TV, Dgs, ns, CP 6, con 30, CF. £ BB £15·50–£19, DB £28–£34, WB, ⑦, Bk £3, L £1, D £7, cc 1 3 4 5 6.

Cookshayes, G, xy (RI), *33 Court St, TQ13 8LG.* ✆ (0647) 40374. Open Mar–Oct. C 8. ⊶ 8 bedrs, 1 bp, 4 bps, 2 ba, Dgs. ✗ a l c, mc. ⓓ CH, TV, CP 15, CF, 2 BGf, 2 st. £ BB £9–£11, DB £18–£24, WT (b) £98–£110, DT £15·50–£17, ⑦, D £6, cc 1 5.

Rescue Service: Central Garage, 17 The Square. ✆ (064 74) 324.
Court Street Garage. ✆ (064 74) 225.

MORETON-IN-MARSH Gloucestershire. Map 14C
Pop 2,572. Chipping Norton 8½, London 83, Banbury 19, Evesham 14, Rugby 36, Stow-on-the-Wold 4½, Stratford-upon-Avon 16, Tewkesbury 24, Warwick 22.
EC Wed. **Golf** Broadway 18h. **See** White Hart Royal Hotel (assoc Charles I), Redesdale Hall, Old Curfew Tower, old houses, Chastleton House 3½ m SE.
ⓘ Council Offices, High St. ✆ Moreton-in-Marsh (0608) 50881.

★★★Manor House, *High St, GL56 0LJ.* ✆ (0608) 50501. C 10. ⊶ 41 bedrs, 34 bp, 7 bps, 3 ba, TV. ✗ mc, at, LD 9. ⓓ Lt, N,

CH, CP 30, U 3, Ac, sp, rf, sb, con, CF, 2 BGf, 0 st, Dis. £ BB £19·50–£35, DB £34–£49, WB, ⑦, Bk £4, L £5·75, D £11, cc 1 2 3 4 5 6.

★★Redesdale Arms, *High St, GL56 0AW.* ✆ (0608) 50308. C. ⊶ 8 bedrs, 3 bp, 3 ba, annexe 6 bedrs, 2 bp, 1 ba, TV, Dgs (annexe). ✗ a l c, LD 9.30. ⓓ CH, TV, CP 22, Ac, con 30, CF, 6 BGf, 0 st, Dis. £ BB £20, DB £36–£40, WB, ②, Bk £4·75, L £7·50, D £10·75, cc 1 3 4 5 6, Dep.

★★White Hart Royal (TH), *High St, GL56 0BA.* ✆ (0608) 50731. C. ⊶ 21 bedrs, 6 bp, 5 ba, TV, Dgs. ✗ a l c, mc, at, LD 9.30. ⓓ ch, Dgs, CP 10, Ac, con 70, CF, 0 st. £ BB £34–£37, DB £46·50–£50·50, WB, ⑦, cc 1 2 3 4 5 6, Dep (Xmas).

Repairer: Curfew Garages Ltd, High St and Worcester Road Garage. ✆ (0608) 50323.
Rescue Service: Oil Well Garage, Little Compton. ✆ (0608) 74202.
Troopers Lodge Service Station, Bourton-on-the-Hill. ✆ Blockley (0386) 700328.

MORETON VALENCE Gloucestershire. Map 13F
M5 Motorway 3, London 108, Stroud 8, Bath 34, Bristol 29, Gloucester 7.

Rescue Service: Moreton Valence Garage, A 38 Bristol Rd, ✆ Gloucester (0452) 720201.

MORLEY West Yorkshire. Map 25F/33B
Pop 48,000. Wakefield 6½, London 188, Bradford 8, Goole 34, Halifax 12, Huddersfield 11, Leeds 4½, Oldham 29, Pontefract 15, Rochdale 28, Thorne 35.
EC Tue. **MD** Fri, Sat. **Golf** Howley Hall 18h. **See** Howley Hall 1589, Woodkirk Church, Tong Church.

Rescue Service: Carr of Morley Ltd, Victoria Garage, Wakefield Rd. ✆ (0532) 534921.

MORPETH Northumberland. Map 31D
Pop 16,000. Newcastle upon Tyne 15, London 288, Alnwick 19, Bellingham 26, Coldstream 46, Corbridge 25, Hawick 56, Jedburgh 51.
EC Thur. **MD** Wed. **Golf** Morpeth 18h. **See** 19th cent Court House, 14th cent Parish Church, 17th cent Clock Tower, Newminster Abbey ruins, Town Hall, Castle (Carlisle Park), 14th cent Chantry Chapel, new Northumberland County Hall, Wallington (17th–18th cent house at Combo—Nat Trust) 10½ m W.

★★Queen's Head, *Bridge St, NE61 1NB.* ✆ (0670) 512083. Closed Xmas Day. C. ⊶ 23 bedrs, 10 bp, 8 bps, 5 sh, 4 ba, TV. ✗ a l c, mc, at, LD 9.30. ⓓ N, CH, G 25, Ac, con 12, CF. £ BB fr £16, DB fr £26·50, ⑦, cc 1 3 4 5 6, Dep b.

Repairer: S Jennings Ltd, 55 Bridge St. ✆ (0670) 519611.
Rescue Service: F B Rutherford Ltd, Scots Gap. ✆ Scots Gap (067 074) 231.
G K Jackson & Sons (Recovery Services) Ltd, Priestbridge Service Station. ✆ Felton (067 087) 387.

MORTEHOE Devon. Map 4C
Pop 500. Dunster 39, London 204, Barnstaple 13, Ilfracombe 6, Lynmouth 21.
EC Wed (win). **Golf** Ilfracombe 18h. **See** Parish Church, Morte Stone, Morte Point.

◼★**Glenhaven** (RI), *EX34 7DZ.* ✆ Woolacombe (0271) 870376. C. ⊶ 12

bedrs, 1 bp, 4 bps, 2 ba, Dgs. ✗ mc, at, LD 7.30. ⌂ CH, TV, CP 10, Ac, CF, 1 BGf. **£** BB £8–£10·75, DB £16–£23·80, WT £98–£117·50, DT £14–£16·78, WB, Ⅰ, Bk £2·50, D £6, Dep a.

Baycliffe, PH, x (Rl) *Chapel Hill, EX34 7DZ.* ✆ Woolacombe (0271) 870393. C. ⇔ 11 bedrs, 1 bp, 2 ba, Dgs. ⌂ ch, TV, Dgs, CP 9, CF, 22 st. **£** BB £7·50–£10, DB £15–£22, WT (b) £85–£98, DT (b) £12·50–£15, Ⅰ.

Rescue Service: Mortehoe Garages Ltd. ✆ Woolacombe (0271) 870354.

MOSTERTON Dorset. Map 5E
3 m NW of Beaminster. Pop 360.
Sherborne 16, London 136, Crewkerne 4, Dorchester 20, Lyme Regis 16.
Golf Bridport 18h.

Rescue Service: Mosterton Garage. ✆ Broadwindsor (0308) 451.

MOTTRAM ST ANDREW Cheshire.
Map 19B
Pop 500. Prestbury 2½, London 73, Buxton 16, Congleton 13, Knutsford 10, Macclesfield 5½, Stockport 10.
Golf Prestbury 18h, Alderley Edge 9h.

★★★Mottram Hall. ✆ Prestbury (0625) 828135. C. 72 bedrs, 72 bp, TV, Dgs. ✗ a l c, mc, at, LD 10. ⌂ N, CH, CP 200, Ac, tc, con, CF, 6 BGf, 0 st, Dis. **£** BB fr £43·50, DB fr £54, WB, Ⅰ, Bk £4, L £6·75, D £9, cc 1 3 4 5, Dep b.

MOULSFORD-ON-THAMES
Oxfordshire. Map 6B
Reading 11, London 49, Henley-on-Thames 12, Newbury 14, Wallingford 4, Wantage 15.

★Beetle & Wedge, *Ferry La, OX10 9JF.* ✆ Cholsey (0491) 651381. C. ⇔ 10 bedrs, 8 bp, 1 bps, 1 sh, 1 ba, TV, Dgs. ✗ a l c, mc, at, LD 10. ⌂ CH, Dgs, CP 40, G 2, Ac, pf, con 10, CF, 1 BGf, 0 st, Dis. **£** BB £21·50, DB £42, WT £255·50, DT £37, WB, Ⅰ, Bk £2, L £7·75, D £7·75, cc 1 2 3 5 6.

MOULDSWORTH Cheshire. Map 19C
Nantwich 17, London 179, Chester 8½, Macclesfield 31, Runcorn 10, Whitchurch 21.

Rescue Service: H Taylor & Son, Smith Garage. ✆ Manley (092 84) 286.

MOUNTSORREL Leicestershire. Map 22F
Pop 4,009. M1 Motorway 8, Leicester 7, London 116, Ashby-de-la-Zouch 17, Loughborough 5, Melton Mowbray 13.
Golf Rothley 18h. **See** Market Cross, Castle Hill, Site of Norman Castle.

Rescue Service: Albar Autos (Mountsorrel), 177 Leicester Rd. ✆ Leicester (0533) 303055.

MOUSEHOLE Cornwall. Map 2E
Pop 2,000. Penzance 3, London 284.
EC Wed. **Golf** West Cornwall, Lelant 18h.
See Harbour, Bird Sanctuary and Hospital.

■★★Carn Du (R) *Raginnis Hill, TR19 6SS.* ✆ Penzance (0736) 731233. Closed Nov. C 12. ⇔ 7 bedrs, 2 bp, 5 bps. ✗ mc, at, LD 8·30. ⌂ CH, TV, CP 12, 2 st. **£** BB £16–£20, DB £28–£36, WB, Ⅰ, Bk £2·50, D £6, cc 1 3 4 5, Dep a.

★★The Lobster Pot (R) *South Cliff, TR19 6QX.* ✆ Penzance (0736) 731251. Closed Jan, Feb. C. ⇔ 14 bedrs, 11 bp, 1 bps, 2 sh, annexe 10 bedrs, 6 bp, 1 bps, 2 ba, Dgs. ✗ a l c, mc, at, LD 9·45. ⌂ CH, TV, CP 10, Ac, CF, 1 BGf. **£** BB £8–£10·75, DB £16–£23·80, WT £98–£41·80, WT £149·80–£269·50, DT £21·40–£38·50, Ⅰ, Bk £4·50, L £3·50, D £8·50, Dep.

Tavis Vor, PH, y (Rl) *The Parade, TR19 6PR.* ✆ Penzance (0736) 731306. Open Mar–Oct. C. ⇔ 7 bedrs, 3 bps, 1 ba. ⌂ CH, TV, CP 7. **£** BB £9·50–£10·50, DB £19–£25, WT (b) £96·25–£103·25, DT (b) £14·50–£15·50, Ⅰ.

Rescue Service: R C Harding, Parade Garage. ✆ Penzance (0736) 731217.

MUCH BIRCH Hereford and Worcester (Herefordshire). Map 13C
Ross-on-Wye 8½, London 129, Abergavenny 20, Hereford 6½, Ledbury 18.

★★★Pilgrim, *HR2 8HJ.* ✆ Golden Valley (0981) 540742. Closed 1st 2 weeks Jan. C. ⇔ 18 bedrs, 16 bp, 2 bps, TV, Dgs. ✗ a l c, mc, at, LD 9·45. ⌂ CH, CP 50, con 40, CF, 7 BGf, 3 st. **£** BB £26·50, DB £37·50, WT £185·50, DT £26·50–£34·50, WB, Ⅰ, Bk £4, L £7, D £9, cc 1 2 3 5 6, Dep b.▲

MUCH MARCLE Hereford & Worcester (Herefordshire). Map 13C
Pop 605. Gloucester 16, London 120, Hereford 15, Ledbury 5, Leominster 22, Ross-on-Wye 7½.
Golf Ross-on-Wye 18h. **See** 13th cent Church, Hellen's Fortified House, Hall Court.

Repairer: Weston's Garage & Service Depot. ✆ (053 184) 232.

MUDDIFORD Devon. Map 4C
Pop 60. Barnstaple 3, London 196, Dunster 31, Ilfracombe 7½, Lynmouth 16.
Golf Ilfracombe 18h. **See** Marwood Hill Gdns (2m).

Home Farm, F, xy (Unl) *Lower Blakewell, EX31 4ET.* ✆ Barnstaple (0271) 42955. Open Mar–Oct. C. ⇔ 4 bedrs, 1 ba, Dgs. ⌂ ch, TV, Dgs, CP 4, CF. **£** BB £7, DB £14–£16, WT (b) fr £65, DT (b) £10–£12, Ⅰ.▲

MUDEFORD Dorset. Map 6E
Pop 3,846. Lyndhurst 13, London 97, Bournemouth 7, Christchurch 2, Lymington 10, Ringwood 9½.
EC Wed. **Golf** Highcliffe Castle 18h. **See** The Quay.

★★★Avonmouth (TH) *Christchurch, BH23 3NT.* ✆ Bournemouth (0202) 483434. C. ⇔ 27 bedrs, 27 bp, TV, Dgs. ✗ mc, at, LD 8·45. ⌂ CH, Dgs, CP 66, Ac, sp, con 60, CF, 1 st. **£** BB £36, DB £60, WB, Ⅰ, cc 1 2 3 4 5 6, Dep (Xmas).

★★Waterford Lodge (R) *Friars Cliff, BH23 4DN.* ✆ Highcliffe (042 52) 72948. C. ⇔ 20 bedrs, 11 bp, 1 bps, 2 ba, TV, Dgs. ✗ a l c, mc, at, LD 8·50. con 30, CF, 2 BGf, 3 st. **£** BB £14·95–£24·15, DB £28·75–£34·50, WT £163·45, DT £27·30, WB, Ⅱ, Bk £4·60, L £5·75, D £6·60, cc 1 5, Dep a.

MULLION Cornwall. Map 2E
Pop 1,995. Helston 6½, London 277, Falmouth 15.
EC Wed. **Golf** Mullion 18h. **See** Mullion Cove (beauty spot), 16th cent Church, Marconi Memorial commem first morse signal Poldhu to St Johns, Newfoundland, Dec 1901.

★★★Polurrian, *Polurrian Rd, TR12 7EN.* ✆ (0326) 240421. Open Apr–Oct. C. ⇔ 43 bedrs, 39 bp, 1 ba, TV, Dgs. ✗ a l c, mc, at, LD 9.30. ⌂ N, ch, TV, CP 60, U 3, G 3, sp, tc, sc, sol, con 100, CF, 2 BGf, 0 st, Dis. **£** BB £14·50–£29·50, DB £29–£62, WB, Ⅰ, Bk £4·50, L £4·50, D £9, cc 1 3 4 5 6, Dep.▲

★★Mullion Cove, *TR12 7EP.* ✆ (0326) 240328.

Belle Vue, G, x (Unl) *Nansmellion Rd, TR12 7DH.* ✆ (0326) 240483. Open Apr–Sept. C. ⇔ 8 bedrs, 1 ba. ⌂ ch, TV, CP 10, CF, 6 st. **£** BB £7–£8, DB £14–£16, WT £75–£80, DT £11–£12, Ⅰ.

Henscath House, G, xy (Rl) *Mullion Cove, TR12 7EP.* ✆ (0326) 240537. Closed Xmas & New Year. C. ⇔ 6 bedrs, 2 bp, 2 bps, 1 ba. ⌂ CH, TV, CP 8, CF, 4 BGf, 0 st, Dis. **£** BB fr £9, DB fr £18, WT (b) £97–£104, DT (b) £14·50–£15·50, Ⅰ.

Rescue Service: Mullion Garage Ltd. ✆ (0326) 240332.

MUNDESLEY Norfolk. Map 16A
Pop 1,556. Norwich 19, London 130, Cromer 6½, Fakenham 29, Great Yarmouth 26.
EC Wed. **Golf** Mundesley 9h. **See** 15th cent All Saints' Church, Paston Windmill, St Margaret's Church (Paston tombs), 16th cent barn.

★★★Continental, *NR11 3YY.* ✆ (0263) 720271. Open Apr–Oct. C. ⇔ 44 bedrs, 26 bp, 1 bps, 4 ba, Dgs. ✗ a l c, mc, at, LD 9.30. ⌂ L t, N, TV, CP 100, Ac, sp, tc, con 100, CF. **£** BB fr £24·20, DB fr £48·40, WB, Ⅰ, cc 1 3 4 5.

★★Manor, *NR11 3YY.* ✆ (0263) 720309. Closed 2–15 Jan. C. ⇔ 26 bedrs, 9 bp, 10 bps, 2 ba, TV, Dgs. ✗ a l c, mc, at, LD 8.50. ⌂ CH, TV, Dgs, CP 50, Ac, sp, con 50, CF, 3 st. **£** BB £16–£19·50, DB £28–£31·50, WT £100–£110, WB, Ⅰ, Bk £2·50, L £4, D £5, Dep a.

Rescue Service: Coastline Motors (Coredale) Ltd, Cromer Rd. ✆ (0263) 720404.

MUNDFORD Norfolk. Map 16F
Pop 1,000. Newmarket 23, London 85, Ely 23, King's Lynn 21, Swaffham 10, Thetford 7½.
EC Wed. **Golf** Swaffham 9h. **See** Grimes Graves (Flint Mines), Museum, Forest with Arboretum, Church, "Cherry Tree" Inn.

Rescue Service: Seletar Garage Ltd, Fir Close. ✆ (084 287) 226.

MUNGRISDALE Cumbria. Map 26C
M6 Motorway 12, Windermere 24, London 288, Ambleside 20, Kendal 38, Keswick 9½, Penrith 13.

■★The Mill (R) *CA11 0XR.* ✆ Threlkeld (059 683) 659. Open Mar–Oct. C. ⇔ 12 bedrs, 2 bp, 3 ba, TV. ✗ mc, at, LD 6. ⌂ ch, TV, CP 12, G 2, CF, 6 st. **£** BB £12–£14, DB £20–£30, WT £105–£133, Ⅱ, D £7, Dep a.▲

Mill Inn, I, x *CA11 0XR.* ✆ Threlkeld (0596 83) 632. Closed Xmas. C. ⇔ 6 bedrs, 1 ba, Dgs. ✗ a l c. ⌂ ch, TV, Dgs, ns, CP 25, CF, 0 st. **£** BB £8·50, DB £17, WT (c) £59·50, Ⅱ, Bk £4, L £3·50, D £4·50.

MURTON Durham. Maps 31F and 32F
Pop 8,954. Easington 3, London 263,
Chester-le-Street 9, Durham 9, Stockton-
on-Tees 21, Sunderland 8.
EC Wed. **Golf** Seaham 18h.

Rescue Service: Murton Car Sprays,
Church St. ☎ Hetton-le-Hole (0783)
263035.▲

MUSBURY Devon. Map 5E.
Axminster 3, London 150, Exeter 25,
Honiton 10, Lyme Regis 6½.

Rescue Service: Musbury Garage.
☎ Colyton (0297) 52292.

NAILSWORTH Gloucestershire. Map
13F
Pop 5,329. Tetbury 6, London 103, Bath
23, Bristol 25, Cheltenham 17, Chepstow
27, Cirencester 12, Gloucester 13.
EC Thur. **Golf** Minchinhampton 18h. **See**
Old Mills, 17th cent Friends' Meeting
House, Baptist Graveyard 1715.

★★**George,** *George St, GL6 0AG.*
☎ (045 383) 2070.
Gables, H, x (R), *Tiltups End, Bath Rd,
GL6 0QE.* ☎ (045 383) 2265. Open Mar-
Nov. C. ⚘ 6 bedrs, 2 ba, Dgs. ✗ a l c.
🅿 ch, TV, Dgs, CP 8, CF, 3 st. £ BB £9·50,
DB £19, 🔟 Bk £2, D £5.

NANTWICH Cheshire. Map 19D
Pop 11,500. Stone 20, London 162,
Chester 18, Middlewich 9½, Newcastle-
under-Lyme 13, Newport 24, Sandbach
9½, Stafford 22, Whitchurch 10, Wrexham
18.
EC Wed. **MD** Thur, Sat. **Golf** Crewe 18h.
See Church, timbered houses, Churche's
Mansion, Sweet Briar Hall, 17th cent
Crown Hotel.
ℹ️ Council Offices, Beam St. ☎ Nantwich
(0270) 623914.

♨★★★**Rookery Hall,** *Worleston, CW5
6DJ.* ☎ (0270) 626866. C 10. ⚘ 10 bedrs,
10 bp, annexe 2 bedrs, 2 bp, TV. ✗ a l c,
mc, at, LD 9.15 (9.45 Sat).🅿 Lt, CH, TV,
CP 40, tc, pf, con, 2 BGf, 2 st. £ DBB £60,
WB, 🔟, Bk £6·95, L £12·95, D £19·95,
cc 1 2 3 4 5 6, Dep.
★★**Lamb,** *Hospital St, CW5 5RH.*
☎ (0270) 625286.

NARBOROUGH Leicestershire. Map
14B
Pop 6,333. M1 Motorway 3, Daventry 27,
London 101, Coventry 19, Leicester 6,
Lutterworth 11, Market Harborough 18.
EC Wed. **Golf** Kirby Muxloe 18h.

★★**Charnwood,** (R), *48 Leicester Rd,
LE9 5DF.* ☎ Leicester (0533) 862218.
Closed 26 Dec (1 wk). C. ⚘ 23 bedrs, 8
bp, 2 bps, 3 sh, 4 ba, TV. ✗ a l c, mc, at, LD
9.30. 🅿 CH, CP 40, con 20, CF, 4 BGf, 4 st.
£ BB fr £17·50, DB fr £26·50, 🔟, Bk £3, L
£2·95, D £5·65, cc 1 6.

NAYLAND Suffolk. Map 17C
Pop 1,200 (inc Wissington). Colchester 6,
London 62, Harwich 20, Ipswich 15,
Sudbury 8½.
EC Wed. **Golf** Newton Green, Sudbury 9h.
See St James's Church (altar piece by
Constable). 15th cent Alston Court, White
Hart Inn, Norman Church with 13th cent
frescoes at Wissington.

Rescue Service: Garnett Automobiles Ltd,
1 Stoke Rd. ☎ (0206) 262334.

NEAR SAWREY Cumbria Map 26D
M6 Motorway 29, London 269, Coniston
5½, Windermere 10 (Fy 3½).

High Green Gate, G, x (Unl),*LA22 0LF.*
☎ Hawkshead (096 66) 296. Open Mar-
Oct, Xmas & New Year. C. ⚘ 7 bedrs, 1
bps, 1 ba, Dgs. 🅿 CH, TV, CP 7, CF. £ BB
£9–£10·50, DB £18–£21, WT (b) £88–£95,
DT (b) £13·50–£14·25, 🔟, Bk £3·50, D
£5·50.
Sawrey House, H, xy (R), *LA22 0LF.*
☎ Hawkshead (096 66) 387. Closed Dec.
C. ⚘ 11 bedrs, 3 bp, 1 bps, 3 ba, Dgs.
🅿 CH, TV, CP 20, CF, 1 BGf, 3 st. £ BB fr
£10·50, DB fr £21, WT (b) £115–£134, DT
(b) £17–£19·75, 🔟, D £6·50.

NEEDHAM MARKET Suffolk. Map 17C
Pop 3,420. Colchester 23, London 79,
Aldeburgh 28, Ipswich 8, Saxmundham
22, Stowmarket 4, Sudbury 18.
EC Tue. **Golf** Stowmarket 18h. **See**
Parish Church, Shrubland Hall.

Rescue Service: Kerridges (Needham
Market) Ltd, The Hall Garage. ☎ (0449)
720222.

NELSON Lancashire. Map 27B
Pop 30,000. Burnley 4, London 210, Settle
17, Skipton 13.
EC Tue. **MD** Wed, Fri, Sat. **Golf** Nelson
18h. **See** St Mary's Church, Roughlee Hall,
packhorse bridge, Museum.
ℹ️ 19 Leeds Rd. ☎ Nelson (0282) 67731.

★★**Great Marsden,** *Barkerhouse Rd,
BB9 9NL.* ☎ (0282) 64749. C. ⚘ 14 bedrs,
3 bp, 3 bps, 6 sh, 3 ba, TV. ✗ a l c, mc, at,
LD 9. 🅿 Lt, CH, TV, CP 150, Ac, gc, con 80,
CF, 1 st, Dis. £ BB £12·65, DB £25·30, WT
£157·15, DT £22·45, 🔟, Bk £3, L £3·80, D
£6.

Repairer: Ratcliffe & Thornton Bros Ltd,
Manchester Rd. ☎ (0282) 62276.
Rescue Service: Park Engineering Co
(Nelson) Ltd, 133 and 148 Scotland Rd.
☎ (0282) 62441.

NETHER POPPLETON North Yorkshire.
Map 25C
York 4, London 197, Harrogate 18, Malton
22, Thirsk 27, Wetherby 13.

Repairer: Forsselius Ltd, Millfield La.
☎ York (0904) 793231.

NETHER WASDALE Cumbria Map 26F
Pop 218. Ravenglass 7, London 304,
Broughton-in-Furness 16, Whitehaven 16.
Golf Seascale 18h. **See** Wastwater Lake.

Low Wood Hall, PH, x (R), *CA20 1ET.*
☎ Wasdale (094 06) 289. C. ⚘ 10 bedrs, 1
bp, 1 bps, 3 ba, Dgs. ✗ a l c. 🅿 ch, TV, CP
8, G 2, CF. £ £11·50–£13, DB £22–£25, WT
£69–£74·75, 🔟 D £4·50.

NETLEY MARSH Hampshire. Map 6E
Winchester 16, London 81, Lyndhurst 5,
Ringwood 14, Salisbury 19, Southampton
5.

Rescue Service: Netley Marsh Garage,
Ringwood Rd. ☎ Totton (0703) 866544.

NEW ALRESFORD Hampshire. Map 6D
Alton 10, London 58, Basingstoke 15, M3
Motorway 13, Petersfield 14, Winchester
8.

See Church, Pond, attractive tree-lined
main street.

★★**Swan,** *11 West St, SO24 9AD.*
☎ Alresford (096 273) 2302.

NEWARK ON TRENT Notts. Map 23C
Pop 24,135. Grantham 15, London 126,
Doncaster 37, Leicester 35, Lincoln 17,
Mansfield 18, Nottingham 19, Ollerton 13,
Sleaford 18, Worksop 25.
EC Thur. **MD** Wed, Fri, Sat. **Golf** Newark
18h. **See** Castle ruins, Church of St Mary
Magdalene (14th cent), Beaumond Cross,
Town Hall, Museum and Art Gallery,
Governor's House, old inns, interesting old
buildings in Market Square.
ℹ️ The Ossington, Castlegate. ☎ Newark
(0636) 78962.

■★★**Grange** (R), *73 London Rd,
NG24 1RZ.* ☎ (0636) 703399. Closed
Xmas. C 12. ⚘ 6 bedrs, 2 bp, 2 ba, TV.
✗ a l c. 🅿 CH, TV, CP 7. £ BB £15·95–£22,
DB £25·95–£29·95, 🔟, Bk £2·75, L £4·50,
D £6·50, cc 1 5.
★★**Ram,** *Castle Gate, NG24 1AZ.*
☎ (0636) 702255.
★★**Robin Hood,** *Lombard St, NG24 1XB.*
☎ (0636) 703858. Closed Xmas Night. C.
⚘ 20 bedrs, 20 bp, 1 ba, TV, Dgs. ✗ a l c,
mc, at, LD 10. 🅿 N, CH, Dgs, CP 50, U 2,
Ac, con 180, CF.£ BB £31, DB £42, WB, 🔟,
Bk £4·50, L £8·20, D £8·20, cc 1 2 3 4 5 6,
Dep b.
Edgefield, H, *Vicarage La, NG23.*
☎ (0636) 700313.

Repairers: Cowies of Newark Ltd,
Farndon Rd. ☎ (0636) 704131.
Elliots (Newark) Ltd, Sleaford Rd.
☎ (0636) 703406.
John Heron, Northern Rd. ☎ (0636)
704484. (24 hr breakdown/recovery
☎ (0636) 71872 or (0636) 704921.)
T C Harrison (Newark) Ltd, 69 Northgate.
☎ (0636) 703413.
MC Repairer: Northgate Garage, 17
Northgate. ☎ (0636) 704346.
Rescue Service: Hampsons Motor
Repairers, Unit 3, Northern Rd. ☎ (0636)
79080
Lewis Abdy 3 Forest Rd, New Ollerton.
☎ Mansfield (0623) 860316.
Milnes, S V, North Rd Garage, North Rd,
North Muskham. ☎ (0636) 703232.

NEW BRIGHTON Merseyside.
See WALLASEY.

NEWBURN-ON-TYNE Tyne & Wear.
Map 32C
1½ m SE of Throckley. Pop 9,761 (inc
Walbottle). Newcastle upon Tyne 5½,
London 279, Corbridge 10.
EC Wed. **Golf** Westerhope Municipal
Newcastle 18h. **See** Early Norman Parish
Church, Motor Museum.

MC Repairer: Andrew Barton Ltd, The
Garage ☎ Lemington (0632) 674449.
Rescue Service: Andrew Barton Ltd, The
Garage ☎ Lemington (0632) 674449.

NEWBURY Berkshire. Map 6B
Pop 26,199. Reading 15, London 54, M4
Motorway 3½, Andover 16, Basingstoke
16, Marlborough 19, Oxford 26, Pewsey
22, Swindon 25, Wallingford 18, Wantage
14, Winchester 24.
EC Wed. **MD** Thur, Sat. **Golf** Newbury
18h. **See** Church (1510), with Jacobean
pulpit and ancient brasses, 16th cent
Cloth Hall (now museum). St
Bartholomew's Hospital (almshouses),
Sandleford Priory, 18th cent bridge, old
Weavers' Cottages, Racecourse, remains
of 14th cent Donnington Castle 1½ m NW.
ℹ️ Wharf Rd. ☎ Newbury (0635) 30267.

★★★**Chequers** (TH), *Oxford St, RG13 1J.* ✆ (0635) 43666. C. ⊨ 58 bedrs, 35 bp, 5 bps, 5 ba, TV, Dgs. ✖ a l c, mc, at, LD 9.30. ⊡ N, CH, Dgs, CP 60, Ac, con 70, CF, 6 BGf, 3 st. £ BB £34–£40·50, DB £44–£56, WB, ⊡, cc 1 2 3 4 5 6, Dep (Xmas).

Repairer: Wheelers (Newbury) Ltd, London Rd. ✆ (0635) 41020. *Specialist Battery and Car Lighting and Ignition Repairer:* Boreham's Car Electrical Services Ltd, West Mills St. ✆ (0635) 40644. *Rescue Service:* Auto Centre, Ampere Rd, London Rd Industrial Estate. ✆ (0635) 44519. Edwards Garage, Faraday Rd. ✆ (0635) 49624. Gowrings of Newbury Ltd, 256 London Rd. ✆ (0635) 45100. Nias of Newbury, Kings Rd. ✆ (0635) 41100.

NEWBY BRIDGE Cumbria. Map 26D M6 Motorway 16, London 262, Ambleside 12, Broughton-in-Furness 13, Kendal 15, Kirkby Lonsdale 22, Lancaster 26, Penrith 35, Ulverston 7½. **Golf** Ulverston 18h. **See** Lake Windermere, 'Swan' (ancient Coaching Inn), Lakeside–Haverthwaite Rly (steam, standard gauge).

▣★★★**Lakeside,** *nr Ulverston, LA12 8AT.* ✆ (0448) 31207. ★★★**White Water,** *The Lakeland Village, nr Ulverston, LA12 8PX.* ✆ (0448) 31133.

Rescue Service: Newby Bridge Service Station. ✆ (0448) 31253.

NEWCASTLE-UNDER-LYME Staffordshire. Map 19D Pop 120,100. Stone 8½, London 149, M6 Motorway 2½, Congleton 12, Leek 11, Nantwich 13, Newport 20, Sandbach 11, Shrewsbury 32, Stoke-on-Trent 2. **EC** Thur. **MD** Mon, Fri, Sat. **Golf** Newcastle 18h. **See** Museum, Guildhall, Castle Mound, Art Gallery. ⛫ Area Reference Library, Ironmarket. ✆ Newcastle (0782) 618125.

★★★**Clayton Lodge,** *Newcastle Rd, Clayton, ST5 4AF.* ✆ (0782) 613093. C. ⊨ 50 bedrs, 50 bp, TV, Dgs. ✖ a l c, mc, at, LD 10. ⊡ N, CH, Dgs, CP 400, Ac, con 370, CF, 3 st. £ B fr £21·50, BD fr £33·75, WB, ⊡, Bk £4·25, L £4·75, D £6·75, cc 1 2 3 4 5 6, Dep b. ★★★**M Crest,** *Liverpool Rd, ST5 9DX.* ✆ (0782) 612431. RS Xmas–New Year. C. ⊨ 75 bedrs, 75 bp, ns, TV, Dgs. ✖ a l c, mc. ⊡ N, CH, CP 150, Ac, con 130, CF, 6 BGf, 0 st, Dis. £ B fr £37·50, BD fr £44·50, WB, ⊡, Bk £5·25, D £8·95, cc 1 2 3 4 5 6, Dep b. ★★★**M Post House** (TH), *Clayton Rd, ST5 4DL.* ✆ (0782) 625151. C. ⊨ 126 hedrs, 126 bp, TV, Dgs. ✖ a l c, mc, at, LD 10.15. ⊡ N, CH, Dgs, CP 128, Ac, con 800, CF, 0 st. £ BB £40·50, DB £53, WB, ⊡, cc 1 2 3 4 5 6. ★★**Borough Arms,** *King St, ST5 1HX.* ✆ (0782) 629421. C. ⊨ 23 bedrs, 9 bp, 4 ba, annexe 15 bedrs, 15 bp, ns, TV. ✖ a l c, mc, at, LD 10.30. ⊡ ch, CP 40, Ac, con, CF, 11 BGf, 1 st, Dis. £ BB fr £21, DB fr £31, DBB fr £35·75, WB, ⊡, Bk £4·25, L £5·75, D £7·50, cc 1 2 3 4 5 6. ★**The Deansfield** (RI), *98 Lancaster Rd, ST5 1DS.* ✆ (0782) 619040. C. ⊨ 9 bedrs, 9 bps, 1 ba, TV, Dgs. ✖ a l c, mc, at, LD

8.30. ⊡ CH, TV, Dgs, ns, CP 12, U 1, con 12, CF, 3 BGf, 1 st. £ BB £15·80, DB £26, WT fr £130, WB, ⊇, Bk £2, L £3, D £4, cc 1 3 4 5.

Grove Court, PH, y (RI), *100 Lancaster Rd, ST5 1DS.* ✆ (0782) 614406. C. ⊨ 11 bedrs, 3 bp, 6 bps, 2 sh, 1 ba, TV, Dgs. ⊡ CH, TV, CP 12, CF, 3 BGf, 3 st. £ BB £9·20–£14·95, DB £18·40–£23, DT (b) £17·25–£20·70, ⊇, cc 1 5.

Specialist Repairer: Chas F Wilson & Sons Ltd, Wayside Av, May Bank. ✆ (0782) 561251. *Specialist Radiator Repairer:* Serck Radiator Services Ltd, Stonewall Industrial Estate, Silverdale. ✆ Silverdale (0524) 451. *Rescue Service:* Crossheath Service Station, Liverpool Rd. ✆ (0782) 617280. Higherland Garage Ltd. ✆ (0782) 615585. Keele Motorway Recovery Service, M6 Service Area, Keele, ✆ (0782) 628241 and (0782) 620307. Priory Garage, Clayton Rd. ✆ (0782) 617571.

NEWCASTLE UPON TYNE Tyne & Wear. Maps 24E and 31F *See also* GATESHEAD, GOSFORTH and WALLSEND. RAC Office, *2 Granville Rd, Jesmond Rd, Newcastle upon Tyne, NE2 1UB.* ✆ (General) Newcastle (0632) 815714, (Rescue Service only) Newcastle (0632) 814271. Pop 267,600. Durham 14, London 273, Alnwick 34, Coldstream 60, Corbridge 17, Hawick 62, Jedburgh 57, Sunderland 12. See Plan p. 280. **EC** Wed (suburbs) **MD** Tue, Thur, Sat, Sun. **P** See Plan. **Golf** Newcastle United 18h. **See** St Nicholas' Cathedral, St Mary's RC Cathedral, Castle, Civic Centre, Laing Art Gallery, Hancock Museum, Museum of Science and Engineering, John George Joicey Period Museum, Guildhall, Scotswood Bridge, Airport, Jesmond Dene. ⛫ Central Library, Princess Sq. ✆ Newcastle upon Tyne (0632) 610691.

★★★★**M Holiday Inn,** *Gt North Rd, Seaton Burn, NE13 6BP.* ✆ (0632) 365432. C. ⊨ 150 bedrs, 150 bp, ns, TV, Dgs. ✖ a l c, mc, at, LD 10.30. ⊡ N, CH, Dgs, CP 280, Ac, sp, sb, sol, gym, CP 400, CF, 1 BGf, 1 st. £ WB, ⊡, Bk £5·65, L £10·25, D £10·25, cc 1 2 3 4 5 6, Dep b. ★★★**M Stakis Airport,** *Woolsington, NE13 8DJ.* ✆ Ponteland (0661) 24911. C. ⊨ 100 bedrs, 100 bp, TV, Dgs. ✖ a l c, mc, at, LD 10. ⊡ Lt, N, CH, Dgs, CP 100, Ac, con 600, CF, 30 BGf, 1 st, Dis. £ WB, Bk £3·50, L £3·75, D £7·50, cc 1 2 3 4 5 6, Dep b. ★★★**County Thistle,** *Neville St, NE99 1AH.* ✆ (0632) 322471. C. ⊨ 115 bedrs, 115 bp, 2 ba, ns, TV, Dgs. ✖ a l c, mo, at, LD 9. ⊡ Lt, N, CH, TV, Dgs, CP 50, Ac, con 120, CF, 2 st. £ BB £37·25–£42·75, DB £47·50–£52·50, WB, ⊇, Bk £4·75, cc 1 2 3 4 5 6, Dep b. ★★★**Crest,** *New Bridge St, NE1 8BS.* ✆ (0632) 326191. Closed Dec 24–31. C. ⊨ 180 bedrs, 180 bp, ns, TV, Dgs. ✖ a l c, mc, at, LD 10. ⊡ Lt, N, CH, Ac, sb, sol, con 600, CF, 0 st. £ B fr £42, BD fr £51, WB, ⊡, Bk £5·25, D £8·95, cc 1 2 3 4 5 6, Dep b. ★★★**Imperial,** *Jesmond Rd, Jesmond, NE2 1PR.* ✆ (0632) 815511. RS Xmas. C.

⊨ 131 bedrs, 131 bp, TV, Dgs. ✖ a l c, mc, at, LD 10. ⊡ Lt, N, CH, Dgs, CP 30, G 90, Ac, sp, sb, sol, gym, con 150, CF, 6 BGf, 3 st. £ BB £21–£36, DB £32–£45, WB, ⊡, Bk £6·05, L £5·25, D £8, cc 1 2 3 5 6, Dep. ▣★★★**Northumbria,** *Osborne Rd, NE2 2BR.* ✆ (0632) 814961. C. ⊨ 71 bedrs, 23 bp, 32 bps, 7 ba, TV, Dgs. ✖ a l c, mc, at, LD 9.45. ⊡ Lt, N, CH, CP 30, Ac, sb, sol, con 60, CF, 4 BGf, 2 st. £ BB fr £32·45, DB fr £38·50, WB, ⊡, cc 1 3 4 5 6. ★★★**Royal Station,** *Neville St, NE99 1DW.* ✆ (0632) 320781. Closed Xmas. C. ⊨ 126 bedrs, 95 bp, 6 bps, 25 sh, 7 ba, TV, Dgs. ✖ a l c, mc, at, LD 10. ⊡ N, CH, Dgs, CP 9, Ac, con 250, CF. £ BB £19–£38, DB £33–£46, WB, ⊡, Bk £5, D £7, cc 1 2 3 4 5 6, Dep b. ★★★**Swallow,** *Newgate Arcade, NE1 5SX.* ✆ (0632) 325025. C. ⊨ 92 bedrs, 92 bp, TV, Dgs. ✖ a l c, mc, at, LD 9.30. ⊡ Lt, N, CH, Dgs, CP 120, Ac, con 50, CF, 0 st. £ BB £10–£23, DB £20–£31, DBB £15·50–£28·50, WB, ⊡, Bk £3·50, L £4·50, D £5·50, cc 1 5. **Chirton House, PH, y** (RI), *46 Clifton Rd, NE4 6XH.* ✆ (0632) 730407. C. ⊨ 11 bedrs, 3 bps, 2 ba, Dgs. ✖ a l c. ⊡ CH, TV, Dgs, CP 12, 8 st. £ BB fr £13·80, DB fr £23, WT (c) fr £90, DT (b) fr £20·70, ⊡, D £6·90. **Morrach, H, z** (RI), *84 Osborne Rd, NE2 2AP.* ✆ (0632) 813361. C. ⊨ 34 bedrs, 8 bp, 4 bps, 7 ba, TV, Dgs. ✖ a l c. ⊡ CH, TV, Dgs, CP 27, U 2, G 2, CF, 2 st. £ BB £11·50–£21·85, DB £20·70–£32·20, WT (c) fr £86·25, ⊡, Bk £2, L £2·50, D £5.

Repairers: Dutton-Forshaw (North-East) Ltd, Westgate Rd. ✆ (0632) 737901. Minories Garages Ltd, Benton Rd. ✆ (0632) 666361. Patterson, R H & Co Ltd (Ford Products), Scotswood Rd. ✆ (0632) 739161. *Specialist Body Repairer:* Barron & Rollings, Heaton Park Rd. ✆ (0632) 656443. *Specialist Radiator Repairer:* Serck Services Ltd, Skinnerburn Rd. ✆ (0632) 731131. *MC Repairer:* H Wood Ltd, 221 Westgate Rd. ✆ (0632) 610121. *Rescue Service:* Buist Manor Ltd, T/As Buist Motors, Etherstone Av. ✆ (0632) 663311. Clousden Hill Service Station, Gt Lime Rd, Forest Hall. ✆ (0632) 681525. Henlys (Newcastle) Ltd, Melbourne St. ✆ (0632) 611471. H G Block & Son Ltd, High Cross Garage, 26 Benwell La. ✆ (0632) 733178. Joseph Scott & Son (Heaton) Ltd, The Garage, Gt North Rd. ✆ Wideopen (0632) 364620. Lyles Garage, Diana St. ✆ (0632) 322314. Northern Brakes Ltd, 133 Sandyford Rd. ✆ (0632) 813810. North East Garages Ltd, Ponteland Rd. ✆ (0632) 860999.

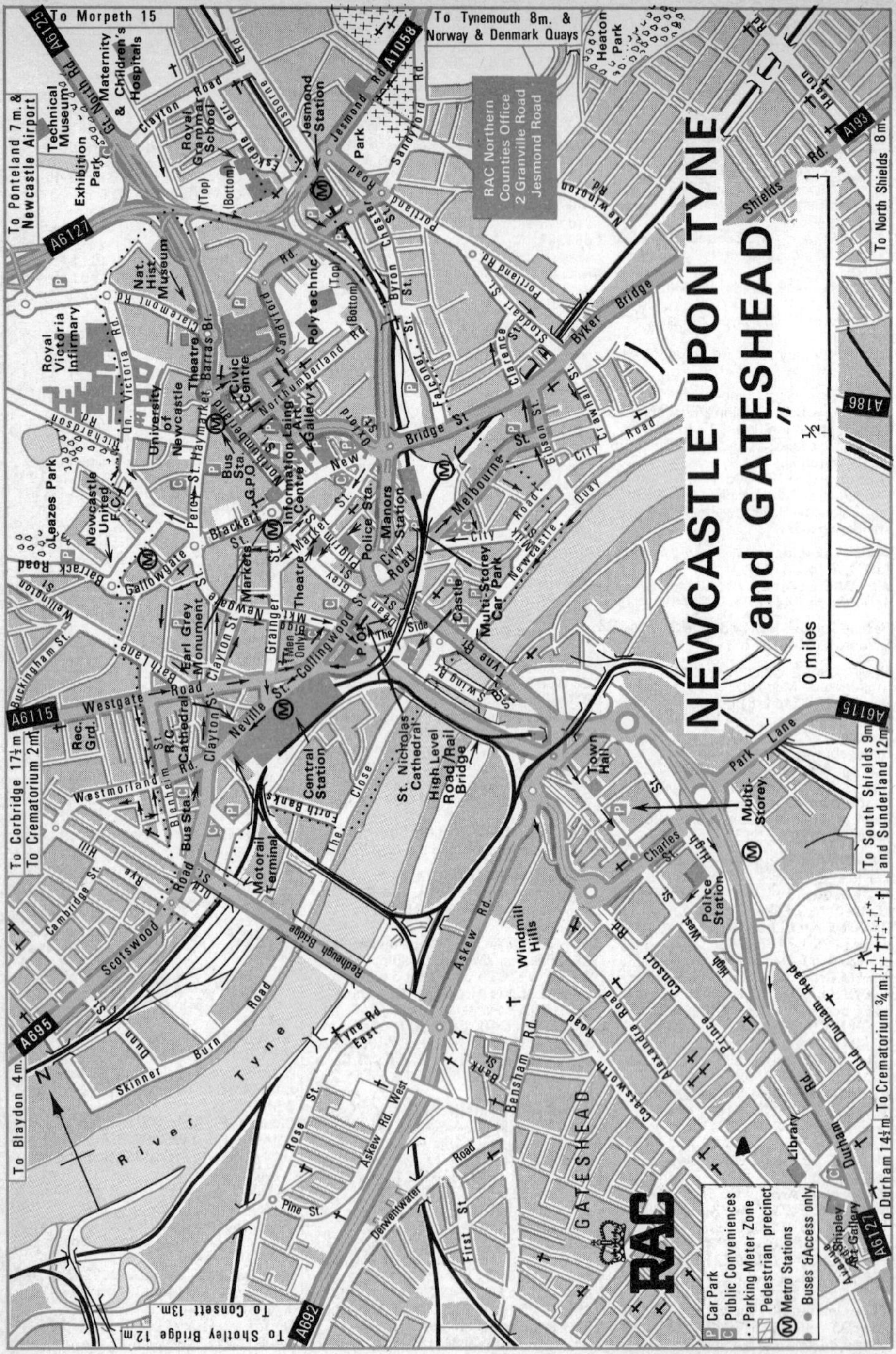

NEWCASTLE UPON TYNE
and GATESHEAD
0 miles
½
1
RAC
Car Park
Public Conveniences
Parking Meter Zone
Pedestrian precinct
Metro Stations
Buses &Access only
RAC Northern Counties Office
2 Granville Road
Jesmond Road
To Morpeth 15
To Tynemouth 8m. &
Norway & Denmark Quays
To Ponteland 7m. &
Newcastle Airport
To Corbridge 17½ m
To Crematorium 2m
To Blaydon 4m.
To Shotley Bridge 12m.
To Consett 13m.
To Durham 14½ m
To Crematorium ¾ m.
To South Shields 9m
and Sunderland 12m
To North Shields 8m
A6125
A1058
A6127
A6115
A695
A692
A186
A193
River Tyne
GATESHEAD
Central Station
St. Nicholas Cathedral
High Level Road/Rail Bridge
Redheugh Bridge
Tyne Bridge
Byker Bridge
Civic Centre
Polytechnic
University of Newcastle
Royal Victoria Infirmary
Nat. Hist. Museum
Leazes Park
Newcastle United F.C.
Exhibition Park
Technical Museum
Maternity & Children's Hospitals
Royal Grammar School
Jesmond Station
Manors Station
Heaton Park
Town Hall
Police Station
Library
Windmill Hills
Shipley Art Gallery
Earl Grey Monument
R.C. Cathedral
Motorail Terminal
Bus Sta.
Multi-Storey Car Park
Laing Art Gallery
Information Centre
Theatre
Castle

North Jesmond Garage, Lodare Rd.
☎ (0632) 842440.
Self, W H Ltd, Thorntree Garage, Denton
Burn. ☎ (0632) 744044.
Shieldfield Service Station, Stoddart St.
☎ (0632) 326736.
Tulip's Garage, Harlow Hill, Horsley.
☎ Wylam (066 14) 2126.
Wideopen Service Station, Gt North Rd.
☎ Wideopen (0632) 365904.

NEW EASTWOOD Nottinghamshire
See EASTWOOD.

NEWENDEN Kent. Map 10E
Hawkhurst 5½, London 56, Ashford 18,
Hastings 14, Rye 8½.

Rescue Service: Rother Valley Motors,
Rye Rd. ☎ Northiam (079 74) 3103.

NEWENT Gloucestershire. Map 13D
Pop 4,832. Gloucester 9, London 113,
Hereford 19, Ledbury 8, Leominster 28,
Ross-on-Wye 9.
EC Wed. **Golf** Ross-on-Wye 18h. **See** St
Mary's Church, 16th cent Market House.

Rescue Service: W E Bennion & Sons Ltd,
Central Garage, Broad St. ☎ (0531)
820333.

NEWGATE STREET Herts. Map 15F.
Pop 350. London 18, Enfield 6½, Epping 12,
Hatfield 7, Harlow 15, Potters Bar 4½.
EC Thur. **Golf** Brookham Park 18h.

⭐⭐⭐**Ponsbourne,** Ponsbourne Pk,
SG13 8QZ. ☎ Cuffley (0707) 875221. C.
🚗 32 bedrs, 26 bp, 6 bps, TV, Dgs. ✗ a l c,
LD 9.30 (10.30 Sat). 🅿 N, CH, Dgs, CP
200, Ac, sp, tc, con 100, CF, 1 st. £ BB
£36·30–£39·60, DB £44–£77, WT
£350·35–£373·45, DT £63·75–£66·05, ⊔,
Bk £3, L £11·50, D £13·75, cc 1 3 4 5 6,
Dep b.

NEWHAVEN East Sussex. Map 7F
See also PEACEHAVEN and SEAFORD
RAC Port Office, Newhaven Harbour, BN9
0DB. ☎ Newhaven (0273) 514068.
Pop 11,000. Lewes 6½, London 58,
Brighton 8, Eastbourne 12.
EC Wed. **Golf** Peacehaven 9h, Seaford
Head 18h, Seaford 18h. **See** 12th cent St
Michael's Parish Church, St Leonard's
Church, Denton, Fort (inc Museum), Cliffs.
🚹 Car Ferry Terminal Car Park, The
Harbour. ☎ Newhaven (0273) 517450.

Rescue Service: Le Forte' Vehicles Ltd,
Unit 8, New Rd, ☎ (0273) 513571 and
(0273) 517751.

NEWINGREEN Kent. Map 10D
Ashford 8½, London 64, M20 Motorway 1,
Canterbury 14, Folkestone 6½, Rye 20,
Tenterden 16.
Golf Sene Valley 18h, Hythe 9h.

▣⭐⭐**M Royal Oak,** Ashford Rd, CT21
4JA. ☎ Hythe (0303) 66580.

NEWLYN Cornwall
See PENZANCE

NEW MALDEN Greater London
(Surrey). M. Area 7A
Pop 46,472 (inc Coombe), London 10,
Croydon 8½, Epsom 5½, Kingston upon
Thames 2½, Mitcham 4½, Purley 9½, Reigate
12, Weybridge 9½.
EC Wed. **Golf** Malden 18h, Coombe Hill
18h, Coombe Wood 18h.

Repairer: Laidler Motor Co Ltd, 89
Kingston Rd. ☎ 01-942 1941.

Rescue Service: Fawngrove Service
Station, 159 Kingston Rd. ☎ 01-942 0112.
Ned's Motor Repairs Ltd, rear of 92 High
St. ☎ 01-397 7221.

NEW MALTON North Yorkshire.
See MALTON.

NEWMARKET Suffolk. Map 17E
See also SIX MILE BOTTOM.
Pop 16,546 (inc Exning). Bishop's
Stortford 32, London 63, Bury St
Edmunds 14, Cambridge 13, Ely 13,
Haverhill 14, Royston 24, Swaffham 33,
Thetford 18.
EC Wed. **MD** Tue, Sat. **Golf** Newmarket
18h. **See** 'Devil's Dyke' (prehistoric
earthworks), Churches of St Mary and St
Agnes, Cooper Memorial, Nell Gwynne's
House, Cleveland House, two
Racecourses.

⭐⭐⭐**Newmarket Moat House,**
Moulton Rd, CB8 8DY. ☎ (0638) 667171.
RS Sat lunch. C. 🚗 45 bedrs, 45 bp, TV,
Dgs. ✗ a l c, mc, at, LD 9.45. 🅿 Lt, N, CH,
Dgs, CP 50, U 5, G 10, Ac, con 120, CF, 1
BGf, 1 st. £ BB fr £32, DB fr £62, WB, ⊔, Bk
£4, L £7·95, D £7·95, cc 1 3 4 5 6, Dep.

▣⭐⭐**Bedford Lodge,** Bury Rd, CB8 7BX.
☎ (0638) 663175. C. 🚗 14 bedrs, 5 bp, 5
bps, 1 ba, TV, Dgs. ✗ a l c, mc, at, LD 10.
🅿 N, CH, TV, Dgs, CP 100, Ac, con 60, CF,
1 BGf, 0 st, Dis. £ BB £22–£35, DB £37–
£50, WT £262–£322, DT £36–£46, WB, ⊔,
Bk £4, L £6·75, D £7·50, cc 1 3 4 5 6,
Dep a.

⭐⭐**Rutland Arms,** High St, CB8 8NB.
☎ (0638) 664251. C. 🚗 49 bedrs, 43 bp, 2
ba, TV, Dgs. ✗ a l c, mc, at, LD 9. 🅿 N, CH,
TV, CP 26, G 8, CF, 0 st. £ BB fr £17·50, DB
fr £29·50, WB, ⊔, Bk £3·45, L £5·95, D
£5·95, cc 1 2 3 5.

⭐⭐**White Hart,** High St, CB8 8JT.
☎ (0638) 663051. C. 🚗 21 bedrs, 10 bp,
TV, Dgs. ✗ a l c, mc, at, LD 9.30. 🅿 CH,
Dgs, CP 25, Ac, con 100, 1 st. £ BB £31–
£34·50, DB £42·50–£49, WB, ⊔,
cc 1 2 3 4 5 6.

Rescue Service: Exning Garage Ltd,
Church St, Exning. ☎ Exning (063 877)
258.

NEW MILTON Hampshire. Map 6E
Pop 18,300. Lyndhurst 10, London 94,
Bournemouth 11, Lymington 6, Ringwood
13.
EC Wed. **Golf** Barton-on-Sea 18h. **See**
16th cent Parish Church.

▣⭐⭐⭐⭐**Chewton Glen,** Christchurch
Rd, BH25 6QS. ☎ Highcliffe (042 52)
5341. C 7. 🚗 44 bedrs, 44 bp, TV. ✗ a l c,
mc, at, LD 9.30. 🅿 N, CH, CP 100, sp, tc,
con 45, 6 BGf, 0 st, Dis. £ BB £50–£96, DB
£82–£96, WB, ⊔, Bk £7, L £9·75, D £19·50,
cc 1 2 3 4 5 6.

Repairer: Coopers (New Milton) Garages
Ltd, Fernhill La. ☎ (042 52) 612121.
MC Repairer: Ian Mansfield Motorcycles,
4 Ashley Par. ☎ (042 52) 619194.

NEWPORT Gloucestershire. Map 13E
Pop 250. Tetbury 14, London 112, M5
Motorway 3½, Bristol 19, Gloucester 16.
Golf Stinchcombe Hill 18h. **See**
Dissenters Chapel.

⭐⭐**M Newport Towers,** GL13 9PX.
☎ Dursley (0453) 810575.

NEWPORT Isle of Wight. Map 6F
Pop 22,957. Portsmouth (Fy) 5, London
76, Cowes 4½, Ryde 7, Sandown 8½,
Shanklin 8½, Ventnor 9½, Yarmouth 9½.
EC Thur. **MD** Tue, Fri. **Golf** Newport 9h.
See Guildhall, old Grammar School
building, Gods Providence House,
Carisbrooke Castle and Priory 1 m SW,
Arreton Manor 2½ m SE.
🚹 21 High St. ☎ Isle of Wight (0983)
524343.

Rescue Service: Blackwater Service
Station, Blackwater. ☎ Isle of Wight
(0983) 523684.
Hunnyhill Garage Ltd, 12 Parkhurst Rd.
☎ Isle of Wight (0983) 522555.
Premier Motors (Solent) Ltd, 4 St James
St. ☎ Isle of Wight (0983) 523441.
Town Garages, Unit 3, Chain La. ☎ Isle of
Wight (0983) 529843.

NEWPORT Shropshire. Map 19F
Pop 9,000. Wolverhampton 18, London
142, Bridgnorth 18, Nantwich 24,
Newcastle-under-Lyme 20, Shrewsbury
18, Stafford 12, Stoke-on-Trent 21, Stone
14, Tamworth 33, Wellington 8,
Whitchurch 21.
EC Thur. **MD** Mon, Fri, Sat. **Golf** Lilleshall
18h. **See** 12th cent St Nicholas Church,
Adams' Grammar School and Almshouses,
13th cent Pulestone Cross, Old Guildhall.
🚹 9 St Mary's St. ☎ Newport (0952)
814109.

⭐⭐**Royal Victoria,** St Marys St, TF10
7AB. ☎ (0952) 810831. C. 🚗 21 bedrs, 10
bp, 5 bps, 3 ba, TV, Dgs. ✗ a l c, mc, at, LD
9.30. 🅿 CH, TV, Dgs, CP 100, Ac, con 140,
CF. £ BB fr £17, DB fr £22, WB, ⊔, Bk £3, L
£5·75, D £6·75, cc 1 5.

Repairer: Aston, N & Son Ltd, Station Rd.
☎ (0952) 811285.
Rescue Service: Waverley Garage
(Newport Salop) Ltd, Wolverhampton Rd.
☎ (0952) 810234.

NEWPORT PAGNELL
Buckinghamshire. Map 15C
See also MILTON KEYNES.
Pop 11,590, London 52, M1 Motorway 2½,
Bedford 12, Bletchley 6½, Buckingham 14,
Kettering 23, Northampton 15, Towcester
14.
EC Thur. **Golf** Stony Stratford 18h. **See**
EE and Perp Church, Chicheley Hall 4 m
from M1 Junc. 14.

⭐⭐⭐**M TraveLodge** (TH) (RI), Service
Area 3, M1, MK16 8DS. ☎ (0908) 610878.
C. 🚗 100 bedrs, 100 bp, TV, Dgs. ✗ mc.
🅿 N, CH, Dgs, CP 120, Ac, CF, 30 BGf, 0 st.
£ BBc £27, DBc £37·50, WB, ⊔,
cc 1 2 3 4 5 6. Meals are served in the
adjacent Motorway Service Area
Restaurant.
Cannon, I, z, 50 High St, MK16 2AP.
☎ (0908) 610042. Closed Xmas & New
Year C. 🚗 5 bedrs, 2 ba. 🅿 ch, TV, CP 15,
0 st. £ BB £15, DB £20, DT (b) £18·95, ⊔,
D £3·95, cc 1 5.

Rescue Service: Cowan Recovery Ltd,
Motorway Service Area, M1 Motorway.
☎ (0908) 610568.

NEWQUAY Cornwall. Map 2D
Pop 15,251. Bodmin 18, London 252,
Redruth 15, St Austell 14, Truro 18,
Wadebridge 14.
EC Wed (win). **Golf** Newquay 18h. **See**
Zoo, Huer's Hut, Trerice (Elizabethan) 3 m

SE, 15th cent church (St Columb Minor), 12th cent church and stocks at Crantock, Bedruthan Steps 7 m N. 16th cent Packhorse Bridge at Trevempa.
🅟 Cliff Rd. ✆ Newquay (063 73) 71345.

★★★**Atlantic,** *Dane Rd, TR7 1EN.*
✆ (063 73) 2244. Open Apr–Oct. C. ⋈ 80 bedrs, 63 bp, 6 ba, TV, Dgs. ✗ a l c, mc, at, LD 8.45. 🅟 Lt, N, CH, TV, CP 100, U 6, sp, gc, sc, sb, sol, gym, con 200, CF, 3 st. £ BB £20–£26, DB £40–£52, WT £172·50–£230, DT £28·75–£35·70, ②, Bk £2·87, L £5·10, D £7·95, cc 1 3 4 5 6.▲

★★★**Barrowfield,** *Hilgrove Rd, TR7 2QY.* ✆ (063 73) 2560. C. ⋈ 74 bedrs, 68 bp, 2 bps, 4 sh, 2 ba, ns, TV. ✗ a l c, mc, at, LD 8.30. 🅟 Lt, N, CH, TV, Dgs, CP 43, G 16, Ac, sp, sb, sol, gym, con 300, CF, 3 BGf, 2 st. £ BB £16·10–£20·70, DB £32·20–£41·40, WT £73·60–£147·20, DT £23–£25·50, WB, ①, Bk £4·89, L £0·30, D £7·50, cc 5, Dep a.▲

★★★**Bay,** *Esplanade Rd, TR7 1PT.*
✆ (063 73) 2988. Open Mar–Oct, & Xmas. C. ⋈ 104 bedrs, 48 bp, 1 bps, 6 sh, 13 ba, Dgs. ✗ a l c, mc, at, LD 8. 🅟 Lt, N, CH, TV, CP 80, Ac, sp, CF, 6 BGf, 3 st. £ BB £10–£14, DB £20–£28, WT £82–£127, DT £12–£18, WB, ①, Bk £2·50, L £2·50, D £6, cc 1, Dep.

★★★**Bristol,** *Narrowcliff, TR7 2PQ.*
✆ (063 73) 5181. C. ⋈ 110 bedrs, 63 bp, 17 ba, TV, Dgs. ✗ a l c, mc, at, LD 8.30. 🅟 Lt, N, CH, TV, CP 100, U 5, Ac, sp, CP 150, CF, 2 st. £ BB £19–£26, DB £36–£48, WT £206–£229·45, DT £31–£34·50, WB, ①, Bk £4·50, L £6, D £8·25, cc 1 3 4 5, Dep b.

★★★**Edgcumbe** (R). *Narrowcliff, TR7 2RR.* ✆ (063 73) 2061. Open Mar–Nov. C. ⋈ 86 bedrs, 61 bp, 25 bps, TV, Dgs. ✗ a l c, mc, at, LD 8.30. 🅟 Lt, N, CH, TV, CP 70, Ac, sp, sb, sol, CF, 12 BGf, Dis. £ BB £14·26, DB £28·52–£49·52–£190, DT £13·45–£31, WB, ②, Bk £3, L £5·75, D £8·50, Dep a.

★★★**Kilbirnie** (R). *Narrowcliff, TR7 2RS.* ✆ (063 73) 5155. Closed Xmas. C. ⋈ 73 bedrs, 53 bp, 8 ba, TV, Dgs. ✗ a l c, mc, LD 8.15. 🅟 N, CH, TV, CP 60, sp, sb, sol con 100, CF, 3 BGf, 5 st. £ BB £12–£21, DB £24–£42, DT £16–£22·50, WB, ①, Bk £4, D £8, cc 1 5.

■★★★**Riviera,** *Lusty Glaze Rd, TR7 3AA.* ✆ (063 73) 4251. Closed Xmas. C. ⋈ 50 bedrs, 31 bp, 9 bps, 4 ba, TV, Dgs. ✗ a l c, mc, at, LD 10. 🅟 Lt, N, CH, TV, CP 50, Ac, sp, con 100, CF. £ BB £21–£27, DB £42–£54, WT £115–£190, WB, ①, Bk £3·75, L £4·50, D £8·75, cc 1 3 5 6, Dep.

★★★**St Brannocks** (R). *Narrowcliff, TR7 2PN.* ✆ (063 73) 2038. Closed Jan & 1st week Feb. C. ⋈ 51 bedrs, 42 bp, 9 bps, 3 ba. ✗ a l c, mc, at, LD 8.30. 🅟 Lt, N, ch, TV, CP 8, U 5, 8, Ac, sp, sb, sol, con 40, CF, 1 st. £ BB £13·50–£20, DB £27–£36, WT £122–£157, DT £22·65–£27·80, WB, ②, Bk £4, L £5, D £7, cc 1 3 5 6, Dep.

★★★**St Rumon's,** *Esplanade Rd, TR7 1PS.* ✆ (063 73) 2978. Open Apr–Oct. C. ⋈ 77 bedrs, 69 bp, 2 bps, 4 sh, 3 ba, TV, Dgs. ✗ a l c, mc, at, LD 8.30. 🅟 Lt, N, CH, TV, CP 55, sp, sb, sol, gym, CF, 8 st. £ WT £136·39–£156·86, DT £22·14–£24·67, ①, Bk £5·17, L £7·46, D £10·35, cc 3 4 5, Dep.

■★★★**Trebarwith** (R). *Trebarwith Cres, TR7 1BZ.* ✆ (063 73) 2288. Open Apr–Sept. C. ⋈ 46 bedrs, 29 bp, 6 bps, 6 ba, TV,

✗ mc, at, LD 8.30. 🅟 N, ch, CP 40, sp, sb, sol, CF, 5 st. £ BB £14·50–£27·50, DB £25–£55, WT £83–£162, ①, Bk £4, L £1, D £9, cc 1 5, Dep.

■★★★**Windsor** (R). *Mount Wise, TR7 2AY.* ✆ (063 73) 5188. Open Mar–Oct. C. ⋈ 45 bedrs, 33 bp, 3 bps, 4 ba, TV. ✗ a l c, mc, at, LD 8.30. 🅟 CH, CP 40, sp, sb, sol, gym, con 80, CF, 2 st. £ BB £12–£26, DB £24–£52, WB, ①, Bk £4·50, D £8, cc 1 5, Dep b.

■★★**Beachcroft,** *Cliff Rd, TR7 1SW.*
✆ (063 73) 3022. C. ⋈ 69 bedrs, 23 bp, 13 bps, 14 sh, 9 ba, TV, Dgs. ✗ mc, at, LD 7.55. 🅟 LT, N, CH, TV, Dgs, CP 40, sp, gc, tc, sb, con 125, CF, 2 BGf, Dis. £ BB £8·75–£13·50, DB £17·50–£27, WT £86·50–£132·50, ①, D £3·50.

★★**Bewdley** (RI). *Pentire Rd, TR7 1NX.*
✆ (063 73) 2883. Open Mar–Oct. C. ⋈ 31 bedrs, 4 bp, 13 bps, 4 sh, 6 ba, Dgs. ✗ mc, at, LD 7.30. 🅟 N, CH, TV, Dgs, CP 40, Ac, sp, con 90, CF, 1 BGf, 2 st. £ BB £9–£13·50, DB £18–£27, WT £82–£135, DT £18–£22, WB, ①, Bk £2·75, L £3·50, D £6, cc 1 5, Dep a.

■★★**Corisande Manor** (R). *Riverside Av, Pentire, TR7 1PL.* ✆ (063 73) 2042. Open May–Nov. C 3. ⋈ 11 bedrs, 7 bps, 3 ba, annexe 8 bedrs, 4 bp, 2 ba, Dgs. ✗ mc, at, LD 8. 🅟 CH, TV, CP 19, CF. £ BB £10·50–£16·50, DB £21–£33, WB, ②, Bk £3, L £3, D £6.

■★★**Cross Mount** (R). *Church St, St Columb West, TR7 3EX.* ✆ (063 73) 2669. Closed Jan, Feb, Nov. C. ⋈ 12 bedrs, 4 bp, 3 bps, 5 sh, 2 ba. ✗ a l c, mc, at, LD 9.45. 🅟 ch, TV, CP 10, CF, 2 st. £ BB £7–£14·50, DB £14–£29, WB, ①, Bk £3, L £1, D £7·50, cc 1 5, Dep.

★★**Great Western,** *Cliff Rd, TR7 2PT.*
✆ (063 73) 2010. RS Nov–Mar. C. ⋈ 45 bedrs, 25 bp, 20 bps, 4 ba. ✗ LD 10. 🅟 Lt, N, CH, TV, Dgs, CP 30, U 20, con 150, CF. £ BB £19–£26, DB £36–£48, WT £206–£229·45, DT £31–£34·50 WB, ①, Bk £4·50, L £6, D £8·25, cc 1 3 4 5, Dep a.

■★★**Hotel Mordros** (R). *Pentire Av, TR7 1PA.* ✆ (063 73) 6700.

■★★**Minto House** (Rt). *38 Pentire Cres, TR7 1PU.* ✆ (063 73) 3227. C. ⋈ 28 bedrs, 10 bp, 18 bps, 2 ba, annexe 3 bedrs, 3 bp, TV, Dgs. ✗ mc, at, LD 8. 🅟 CH, CP 16, Ac, sb, sol, gym, CF, 3 BGf, 0 st. Dis. £ BB £10·50–£16, DB £23–£32, WT £75–£110, WB ②, Bk £4·50, D £7·50, cc 1 3 4 5 6, Dep a.

■★★**Pine Lodge** (R). *91 Henver Rd, TR7 3DJ.* ✆ (063 73) 2549. Closed Dec. C. ⋈ 10 bedrs, 2 bp, 1 bps, 2 ba, annexe 5 bedrs, 1 bp, 4 bps, TV. ✗ a l c, mc, at, LD 8. 🅟 CH, ns, CP 20, sp, CF, 5 BGf, 1 st, Dis. £ BB £12–£18, DB £24–£34, WB, ①, Bk £2·75, L £3, D £5·75, cc 1 3 5 6, Dep.

★★**Porth Veor Manor** (R). *Porth Way, St Columb Porth, TR7 3LW.* ✆ (063 73) 3274. Closed Nov & Xmas. C. ⋈ 14 bedrs, 11 bp, 3 bps, 1 ba, TV, Dgs. ✗ a l c, mc, at, LD 9. 🅟 CH, Dgs, CP 30, con 50, CF, 2 st. £ BB £16·50–£21·50, DB £33–£41, WB, ②, Bk £3·25, L £4·50, D £6·50, cc 1 3 5, Dep a.

■★★**Sandy Lodge** (R). *Hilgrove Rd, TR7 2QY.* ✆ (063 73) 2851. Open Apr–Oct. C. ⋈ 46 bedrs, 10 bp, 12 bps, 8 ba, Dgs. ✗ mc, at, LD 8. 🅟 ch, TV, ns, CP 50, Ac, sb, sol, gym, con 150, CF, 3 BGf, 1 st, Dis. £ BB £9·20–£12·65, DB £18·40–£25·30, WT £96·60–£138, WB, ①, Bk £2·85, L £2·30, D £6·90, Dep.

■★★**Tregurrian** (R). *Watergate Bay, TR8 4AB.* ✆ St Mawgan (0637) 860280. Open May–Sept. C 2. ⋈ 28 bedrs, 15 bps, 2 sh, 3

ba, Dgs. ✗ mc, at, LD 7.30. 🅟 ch, TV, Dgs, CP 22, sp, sol, CF, 1 st. £ BB £9·50–£18·25, DB £19–£34, WT £75–£120, WB, ①, Bk £2·85, D £4·75, Dep a.

■★★**Waters Edge** (RI). *Esplanade Rd, TR7 1QA.* ✆ (063 73) 2048. Open May–Oct & Easter. C. ⋈ 20 bedrs, 12 bp, 4 bps, 2 ba. ✗ mc, at, LD 8.15. 🅟 ch, TV, CP 18, U 1, CF, 7 BGf, 2 st. £ BB £8·90–£16·10, DB £17·80–£35·65, DB £11·50–£20·70, WB, ①, Bk £3·25, D £7·95, Dep b.

■★**Cleavelands** (R). *Watergate Bay, TR8 4AB.* ✆ St Mawgan (0637) 860273. Open Apr–Sep. C. ⋈ 27 bedrs, 7 bp, 3 bps, 6 ba. ✗ mc, at, LD 8.30. 🅟 N, ch, TV, ns, CP 40, CF, 2 st. £ BB £11–£18, DB £22–£36, WB, ②, Bk £3, D £6·50.

Arundell, H, z (RI). *86 Mount Wise, TR7 2BS.* ✆ (063 73) 2481. Open May–Sept. C. ⋈ 40 bedrs, 8 bp, 10 bps, 5 ba. 🅟 ch, TV, CP 30, CF, 3 BGf, 0 st, Dis. £ BB £5·75–£10·85, DB £11·50–£21·70, WT (b) £56·35–£88·55, DT (b) £8·05–£12·65, ①, Bk £1·75, D £4.

Barrowcliff, PH, z (RI). *Henver Rd, TR7 3BJ.* ✆ (063 73) 3492. Open May–Sept. C 3. ⋈ 23 bedrs, 1 bp, 2 bps, 3 ba. 🅟 CH, TV, CP 20, CF, 4 BGf, 2 st. £ BB £8·05–£10·35, DB £16·10–£22·70, WT (b) £65·55–£86·25, (c) £52·90–£70, DT (b) £10·35–£13·23, ①, Bk £3, D £4·60, cc 5.

Brakespear, H, z (RI). *44 Edgcumbe Av, TR7 2NJ.* ✆ (063 73) 4771. C. ⋈ 10 bedrs, 1 bps, 1 ba. 🅟 ch, TV, CP 7, CF, 1 BGf, 1 st, Dis. £ BB £7–£9, DB £14–£19, WT (b) £55–£77, DT (b) £9–£11.

Cherington, H, z (RI). *7 Pentire Av. TR7 1NZ.* ✆ (063 73) 3363. Open Apr–Sept. C. ⋈ 22 bedrs, 2 bp, 4 bps, 7 sh, 4 ba, Dgs. 🅟 ch, TV, CP 14, CF, 1 st. £ BB £7–£9, DB £14–£17, WT (b) £57–£75, DT (b) £10·50–£14, ②.

Cliffside, H, z (RI). *The Crescent, TR7 1DT.* ✆ (063 73) 2897. C. ⋈ 36 bedrs, 1 bp, 11 bps, 3 sh, 3 ba, Dgs. 🅟 ch, TV, Dgs, ns, CP 7, CF.

Copper Beech, PH, z (Rt). *70 Edgcumbe Av, TR7 2NN.* ✆ (063 73) 3376. Open Apr–Oct. C. ⋈ 16 bedrs, 3 bps, 2 sh, 2 ba, Dgs. 🅟 CH, TV, Dgs, CP 16, CF, 5 BGf, 2 st. £ BB £6·90–£8·05, DB £13·80–£16·10, WT (b) £67·85–£85·10, DT (b) £9·78–£12·35, ①, cc 5.

Fistral Beach, PH, z (RI). *Esplanade Rd, Pentire, TR7 1QA.* ✆ (063 73) 3993. Open Mar–Oct & Xmas. C. ⋈ 15 bedrs, 5 bps, 3 ba, Dgs. ✗ a l c. 🅟 CH, TV, CP 12, CF, 3 BGf, 5 st. £ BB £8·50–£12, DB £17–£24, WT (b) £70–£99·80, DT (b) £10·80–£14·30, ②, Bk £2·50, D £5·50.

Gluvian Park, PH, z (RI). *12 Edgcumbe Gdns, TR7 2QD.* ✆ (063 73) 3133. Open Mar–Oct & Xmas. C. ⋈ 23 bedrs, 1 bp, 10 bps, 2 ba. 🅟 CH, TV, ns, CP 12, CF, 7 st. £ BB £7·50–£11·50, DB fr £23, WT (b) £73·50–£106·75, DT (b) £12·25–£16·50, ②, Bk £2·50, D £5·50.

Homestake, F, y (Unl). *Black Cross, TR8 4LU.* ✆ St Austell (0726) 860423.

Jonel, PH (RI). *88–90 Crantock St, TR7 1JW.* ✆ (063 73) 5084. Open Apr–Oct. C. ⋈ 12 bedrs, 1 sh, 2 ba. 🅟 CH, TV, CP 7, CF, 4 st. £ BB £7–£10·90, DB £14–£21·80, WT (b) £63–£85, DT (b) £10–£13, ①, Bk £1·50, D £3.

Kellsboro, H, z (R). *12 Henver Rd, TR7 3BJ.* ✆ (063 73) 4620. Open Apr–Oct. C. ⋈ 14 bedrs, 5 bp, 3 bps, 6 sh, 2 ba, ns, Dgs. 🅟 CH, TV, CP 20, CF, 1 st. £ BB £10·35–

£13·80, DB £20·70–£34·50, WT (b) £80·50–£97·75, DT (b) £11·50–£14·95, [2].

Links, PH, z (RI), *Headland Rd, TR7 1HN.* ☎ (063 73) 3211. Open Mar–Oct. C. ⊨ 15 bedrs, 12 bp, 1 sh, 2 ba, TV. ⊞ CH, TV, CF, 1st. £ BB £9·20–£12·88, DB £16·10–£23·46, WT (b) £70–£95, [1].

Michelle, G, z (RI), *3 Manewas Way, TR7 3AH.* ☎ (063 73) 4521. Open Easter–Sept. C 3. ⊨ 5 bedrs, 1 bp, 1ba, Dgs. ⊞ CH, TV, CP 6, CF, 1 BGf, 1 st. £ BB £5·75–£7, DB £11·50–£15·50, WT (b) £53–£68, DT (b) £7·75–£9·75, [1].

Pendeen, PH, z (RI), *7 Alexandra Rd, TR7 3ND.* ☎ (063 73) 3521. Open Feb–Oct. C. ⊨ 15 bedrs, 6 bp, 4 bps, 2 ba, TV. ⊞ CH, TV, CP 15, CF, 6 st. £ BB £8–£11, DB £16–£22, WT (b) £69–£89, DT (b) £12–£16, [1], Bk £2, L £3·25, D £5·25.

Pensalda, G, z (RI), *98 Henver Rd, TR7 3BL.* ☎ (063 73) 4601.

Philema, H, x (R), *Esplanade Rd, TR7 1PY.* ☎ (063 73) 2571. C. ⊨ 14 bp, 7 bps, 3 sh, 3 ba, TV, Dgs. ⊞ CH, TV, CP 33, CF. £ BB £12–18·50, DB £24–£37, WT (b) £75–£112, DT (b) £15–£20, [1], Bk £2, L £3, D £4, cc 1 5.

Priory Lodge, H, y (R), *30 Mount Wise, TR2 2BH.* ☎ (063 73) 4111. C. ⊨ 21 bedrs, 5 bp, 11 bps, 2 ba. ✗ a l c. ⊞ CH, TV, CP 30, CF, 1 BGf, 2 st. £ BB £11·50–£17·83, DB £23–£32·20, WT £79·35–£113·85, DT (b) £8·50–£11·28, [1].

Riverside, G, y (Unl), *Tregunnel Hill, TR7 2QT.* ☎ (063 73) 3547. Open Mar–Oct. C. ⊨ 11 bedrs, 1 bps, 2 ba, Dgs. ⊞ CH, TV, CP 11, CF. £ BB £5·50–£10, DB £11–£18·50, WT (b) £52·50–£80·50, (c) £38·50–£59·50, DT (b) £7·50–£11·50, [2].

Rolling Waves, PH, x (RI), *Alexandra Rd, TR7 3NB.* ☎ (063 73) 3236. Open Mid Mar–Oct & Xmas. C. ⊨ 9 bedrs, 1 bps, 1 sh, 2 ba. ⊞ ch, TV, CP 11, CF, 1 BGf, 5 st. £ BB £7·50–£8·50, DB £15–£19, WT (b) £60–£68, (c) £54–£58, DT (b) £8·50–£10, [1], Bk £1·50, D £2·50.

Rumours (late *Viewpoint*), **H, z** (R), *89 Henver Rd, TR7 3DJ.* ☎ (063 73) 2170. Closed Nov. C. ⊨ 15 bedrs, 9 bp, 6 bps, 1 ba, TV. ✗ a l c. ⊞ CH, CP 18, 1 st. £ BB £15–£19, DB £30–£38, DT (b) £22–£24, [1], Bk £2·50, L £2·50, D £5, cc 1 3 4 5.

Stanford, G, z (Unl), *91a Henver Rd, TR7 3DJ.* ☎ (063 73) 5474.

Sutherland, H, x, *29 Mount Wise, TR7 2BH.* ☎ (063 73) 4470. Open May–Sept. C. ⊨ 36 bedrs, 4 bps, 10 sh, 4 ba, Dgs. ⊞ CH, TV, CP 40, CF, 12 st. £ BB £8–£12, DB £16–£32, WT £64–£90, DT (b) £12–£16, [2], Bk £1·75, L £3·50, D £6·50.

Toppers, PH, x (RI), *73 Mount Wise, TR7 2BP.* ☎ (063 73) 6693. Open Apr–Oct. C. ⊨ 14 bedrs, 8 sh, 2 ba. ⊞ ch, TV, CP 4, CF, 12 st. £ BB fr £6·95, DB fr £13·90, WT (b) fr £83·90, DT (b) fr £12, [2], Bk £2·85, D £3·45, cc 5.

Tregenna House, G, y (RI), *TR8 5RZ.* ☎ Crantock (063 73) 830381.

Trelissick, PH, z (RI), *19 Eliot Gardens, TR7 2QE.* ☎ (063 73) 6764. Open Apr–Sept. C 3. ⊨ 7 bedrs, 1 ba. ⊞ ch, TV, CP 10, CF, 4 st. £ BB £6–£7, DB £12–£14, WT (b) £63–£70, DT (b) £9–£10, [1].

Trenance Farm House, G, x (Unl), *Trenance, Mawgan Porth.* ☎ St Mawgan (063 74) 515.

Wheal Treasure, PH, x (RI), *72 Edgcumbe Av, TR7 2NN.* ☎ (063 73) 4136. Open May–Sept. C 4. ⊨ 10 bedrs, 2 bp, 1ba. ⊞ CH, TV, ns, CP 10, 2 BGf, 3 st.

£ BB £7–£8·50, DB £14–£19, WT (b) £74–£85, DT (b) £10–£14, [1].

Windward, G, x (RI), *Alexandra Rd, TR7 3NB.* ☎ (063 73) 3185. Open Apr–Oct. C. ⊨ 7 bedrs, 2 bp, 1 sh, 1 ba, Dgs. ⊞ CH, TV, Dgs, CP 10, CF, 1 BGf, Dis. £ BB £50–£12·25, DB £15–£24·50, WT (b) £55–£72, (c) £47–£61, [1].

Yonder Towan, PH, z (RI), *4 Beachfield Av, TR7 1DR.* ☎ (063 73) 2756. Open Mar–Nov. C. ⊨ 10 bedrs, 10 sh, 2 ba, TV, Dgs. ⊞ CH, TV, CP 2, CF. £ BB £6–£7·50, DB £12–£15, WT (b) fr £53, (c) fr £42, DT (b) £9·50, [2], cc 1.

Rescue Service: Chris Perry, Narrow La, Summercourt. ☎ St Austell (0726) 860574.

Globe Garage, Quintrell Downs. ☎ (063 73) 2410.

Numoplus Ltd, The Clock Garage, Summercourt. ☎ Mitchell (087 251) 232.

Phoenix (Self-Drive) Hire & Auto Repairs, Eliot Gdns. ☎ (063 73) 4884.

Polkinghornes Garage, Marcus Hill. ☎ (063 73) 2029.

Treglown's Garage Ltd, Albany Rd. ☎ (063 73) 3865.

NEWTHORPE Nottinghamshire. Map 22D
M1 Motorway 3½, London 131, Nottingham 8½.

Rescue Service: Cliff Lacey Motors, 88 Newthorpe Common. ☎ Langley Mill (0773) 719698.

NEWTON ABBOT Devon. Map 3D
Pop 20,350. Honiton 30, London 183, Ashburton 7½, Exeter 15, Okehampton 26, Torquay 6, Totnes 8.
EC Thur. **MD** Wed, Sat. **Golf** Newton Abbot (Stover) 18h. **See** Forde House, St Leonard's Tower, Wolborough Church.
[i] 8 Sherborne Rd. ☎ Newton Abbot (0626) 67494.

■⚤★★Netherton House (R), *Combe-in-Teignhead, TQ12 4RN.* ☎ Shaldon (062 687) 3251. C 10. ⊨ 10 bedrs, 5 bp, 1 bps, 2 ba, TV, Dgs. ✗ mc, at, LD 8.30. ⊞ CH, ns, CP, sp, pf, con 12, 2 st. £ BB £14–£20, DB £27–£44, WB, [2], Bk £3·75, D £8·95, cc 1 3 5, Dep a.

★★Queen's, *Queen St, TQ12 2EZ.* ☎ (0626) 63133. C. ⊨ 26 bedrs, 15 bp, 1 bps, 2 ba, TV, Dgs. ✗ a l c, mc, at, con 150, CF, 2 st. £ BB £18–£23, DB £27–£34, WT £120, DT £29, WB, [1], Bk £3·75, L £5, D £6, cc 1 4 5.

Hazelwood House (late *Berwyn*), **H, z** (R), *33a Torquay Rd, TQ12 2LW.* ☎ (0626) 66130. C. ⊨ 6 bedrs, 3 bps, 1 ba, TV. ✗ a l c. ⊞ CH, TV, CP 6, CF, 1 BGf, 2 st. £ BB £12–£16, DB £22–£28, WT (b) fr £108, (c) fr £80, DT (b) fr £16·50, [1], Bk £3·50, L £4·50, D £4·50, cc 1.

Lamorna, G, x (RI), *Coombe Cross, Sandygate, TQ13 0AR.* ☎ (0626) 65627. C. ⊨ 7 bedrs, 2 ba. ✗ a l c. ⊞ CH, TV, CP 20, U 1, CF, 2 BGf, 2 st. £ BB fr £9, DB fr £16, WT (c) fr £63, DT (b) fr £15·50, [1].

Repairers: Newton Abbot Motors Ltd, 74 Wolborough St. ☎ (0626) 5081.

Quay Garage (Freddie Hawken Ltd), The Avenue. ☎ (0626) 2525.

Renwicks Garage (Vickring) Ltd, The Avenue. ☎ (0626) 2641.▲

Wadham Stringer (Newton Abbot) Ltd, 64 Wolborough St. ☎ (0626) 4141.

MC Repairer: South Devon Motor Cycles, The Avenue. ☎ (0626) 2317.

Tower Motor Cycles & Bicycles Ltd, 13 Wolborough St. ☎ (0626) 2942.

Sctr Repairer: South Devon Motor Cycles, The Avenue. ☎ (0626) 2317.

Rescue Service: Torbay Motor Cycles (Newton Abbot), 128 Ashburton Rd. ☎ (0626) 2527.

NEWTON AYCLIFFE Durham. Map 24F
Pop 21,000. Darlington 7, London 251, Durham 12, Stockton-on-Tees 12, West Auckland 8.
EC Wed. **Golf** Darlington 18h. **See** St Andrew's Church (Saxon) at Aycliffe.

Rescue Service: Harold Taylor, Newton Aycliffe Service Station, Shafto Way. ☎ Aycliffe (0325) 312794.

NEWTON FERRERS Devon. Map 3E
Pop 1609. Ashburton 21, London 208, Dartmouth 18, Kingsbridge 16, Plymouth 10, Totnes 19.
Golf Staddon Heights 18h.

■⚤★★Court House, *PL8 1AQ.* ☎ Plymouth (0752) 872324. C 8. 12 bedrs, 5 bp, 4 ba, Dgs. ✗ at, LD 9. ⊞ ch, TV, ns, CP 25, sp, con 75. £ BB £20–£25, DB £30–£42, WB, [2] 10%, Bk £4·50, L £4·50, D £9·50, cc 5.

■★★River Yealm, *Yealm Rd, PL8 1BL.* ☎ Plymouth (0752) 872419. C. ⊨ 19 bedrs, 3 bp, 4 sh, 3 ba, Dgs. ✗ a l c, mc, at, LD 8.30. ⊞ CH, TV, Dgs, CP 60, G 1, Ac, pf, con 50, CF, 4 BGf, 12 st. £ BB fr £15, DB fr £30, WB, [1], Bk £3, L £2, D £7·50.

NEWTON FLOTMAN Norfolk. M. Area 16B
Pop 958. Scole 13, London 108, Aldeburgh 40, East Dereham 22, Great Yarmouth 29, Lowestoft 26, Norwich 7, Saxmundham 33, Thetford 29.
Golf Eaton 18h, Royal Norwich 18h.
Rescue Service: Brighton Bros, Main Rd. ☎ Swainsthorpe (0508) 470620.

NEWTON-LE-WILLOWS Merseyside. Map 20C
Pop 22,180. M6 Motorway 3, London 190, Altrincham 16, Bolton 13, Liverpool 15, Manchester 18, St Helens 4, Warrington 5, Wigan 7.
EC Thur. **MD** Fri. **Golf** Haydock Park 18h.

Rescue Service: Three Ways Garage, Market St. ☎ (092 52) 5977.

NEWTON SOLNEY Derbyshire.
See BURTON-ON-TRENT

NEWTOWN LINFORD Leicestershire. Map 22F
Pop 1200. M1 Motorway 3, Leicester 6½, London 104, Burton-on-Trent 26, Nottingham 25, Peterborough 47.
Golf Nanpantan 18h, Rothley 18h. **See** Bradgate Park, All Saints Church.

★★Johnscliffe, *73 Main St, LE6 0AF.* ☎ Markfield (0530) 242228. RS Xmas-New Year. C. ⊨ 8 bedrs, 2 bp, 3 bps, 1 ba, TV, Dgs. ✗ a l c, mc, at, LD 9.45. ⊞ CH, TV, Dgs, CP 25, Ac, con 10, 2 st. £ BB £15–£22·50, DB £28–£35, WT £170, DT £27·50, DBB £22·50–£33, WB, [2] 10%, Bk £3, L £4·95, D £6·95, cc 1 3 5 6.

NO-MANS-HEATH Warwickshire. M. Area 21A.

Pop 75. Atherstone 9, London 113,
Burton-on-Trent 11, Nottingham 28,
Tamworth 9.

Rescue Service: L Arrowsmith & Sons,
Main Rd. ✆ Tamworth (0827) 830280.

NORMAN CROSS Cambridgeshire.
Map 15B
Pop 12,000. Alconbury 8, London 77,
Kettering 22, Market Harborough 27,
Northampton 36, Peterborough 5½,
Stamford 13.
Golf Peterborough 18h. **See** Elton Hall,
Iron Post in Holme Fen.

■★★★**M Crest,** *Gt North Rd, PE7 3TB,*
✆ Peterborough (0733) 240209. RS Bank
Holidays, Sun. C. ◪ 97 bedrs, 97 bp, ns,
TV, Dgs. ✗ a l c, mc, at, LD 9.45. ⓑ N, CH,
Dgs, CP 200, Ac, con 50, CF, 39 BGf, 0 st.
£ B fr £38·50, BD fr £49·50, WB, ①, Bk
£4·95, D £8·95, cc 1 2 3 4 5 6, Dep b.

NORTHALLERTON North Yorkshire.
Map 24F
Pop 10,300. Boroughbridge 19, London
227, Brought 44, Darlington 16, Leyburn
18, Middleton-in-Teesdale 42, Stockton-
on-Tees 19, Thirsk 9½.
EC Thur. **MD** Wed, Sat. **Golf** Thirsk and
Northallerton 9h. **See** Church (12th–14th
cent), Porch House (1584), Market Cross,
Old Inns, Monument commem. Battle of
the Standard, Mount Grace Priory 6 m NE.

■♣★★★**Solberge Hall,** *Newly Wiske, DL7
9ER.* ✆ (0609) 779191. Closed Jan. C.
◪ 15 bedrs, 14 bp, 1 bps, TV, Dgs. ✗ a l c,
mc, at, LD 9.30. ⓑ CH, Dgs, CP 40, G 4, Ac,
con 24, CF, 3 st. £ BB £28, DB £40–£52,
WT £224–£248, DT £32–£39, WB, ①, Bk
£5, L £5·50, D £10·50, cc 1 2 3 4 5 6.
★★**Golden Lion** (TH), *High St, DL7 8PP.*
✆ (0609) 2404. C. ◪ 29 bedrs, 10 bp, 5
ba, TV, Dgs. ✗ a l c, mc, at, LD 9. ⓑ CH,
Dgs, CP 60, Ac, con 200, CF, 0 st. £ BB
£33·50–£36, DB £44–£48, WB, ①,
cc 1 2 3 4 5 6, Dep (Xmas).
Buck, H, x, *237 High St, DL7 8LU.*
✆ (0609) 3636.
Windsor, G, z (Unl). *56 South Par, DL7
8SL.* ✆ (0609) 774100. Closed 2 wks Oct
& 14 Dec–2 Jan. C. ◪ 8 bedrs, 1 ba, Dgs.
ⓑ CH, TV, CF, 1 st. £ BB fr £10, DB fr £19,
①

Repairer: Motor Delivery Co
(Northallerton) Ltd, Brompton Rd.
✆ (0609) 3891.
Rescue Service: Morton Service Station,
Morton on Swale. ✆ (0609) 2339.

NORTHAM Devon. Map 4C
Pop 4,700. Bideford 2, London 204.
EC Wed. **Golf** Royal North Devon 18h.
See Bloody Corner, burial place of King
Hubba 892 A.D.

Sonnenheim, H, xy (Rl), *Heywood Rd,
EX39 2QA.* ✆ Bideford (023 72) 4989.
Tadworthy House, PH, x (Rl),
Tadworthy Rd, EX39 1JN. ✆ Bideford
(023 72) 4721. C. ◪ 6 bedrs, 1 bps, 4 sh, 1
ba, TV, Dgs. ✗ a l c. ⓑ TV, Dgs, CP 12, CF.
£ BB £9–£10·50, DB £18–£21, WT (b)
£105–£115·50, DT (b) £15–£16·50, ①

NORTHAMPTON Northamptonshire.
Map 15C
Pop 162,200 (inc Weston Favell). M1
Motorway 4, London 66, Bedford 22,
Bletchley 21, Buckingham 21, Daventry
12, Huntingdon 37, Kettering 14,

Leicester 31, Market Harborough 17,
Peterborough 37, Rugby 20, Towcester
8½.
EC Thur. **MD** Wed, Fri, Sat. **Golf**
Northampton 18h. **See** Abingdon Park
Museum, Church of Holy Sepulchre (12th
cent interior, one of four round churches in
England), St Peter's Church (Norman), All
Saints' Church, 12th cent St John's
Church (former medieval Hospital),
Museum and Art Gallery, County Hall,
Guildhall, RC Cathedral, Delapre Abbey,
Lamport Hall and Garden, Hazelrigg
House (Tudor), Queen Eleanor Cross
2 m S, Castle Ashby House 7 m E, Althorp
House 5 m NW.
🛈 21 St Giles St. ✆ Northampton (0604)
22677.

★★★**Grand,** *Gold St, NN1 1RE.* ✆ (0604)
34416. C. ◪ 59 bedrs, 41 bp, 4 ba, TV,
Dgs. ✗ a l c, mc, at, LD 10. ⓑ Lt, N, ch, CP
16, Ac, con 170, CF, 1st. £ BB £22–£28·50,
DB £32·50–£38·50, WB, ①, Bk £3·80, L
£5·25, D £5·25, cc 1 4 5 6, Dep b.
★★★**Moat House** (late **Saxon Inn**)
Silver St, NN1 2TA. ✆ (0604) 22441. C.
◪ 135 bedrs, 135 bp, TV, Dgs. ✗ a l c, mc,
at, LD 10.30. ⓑ Lt, N, CH, Dgs, CP 250, Ac,
con 500, CF, 1 st. £ WB, ①, Bk £4·50, L
£4·95, D £6·95, cc 1 3 4 5 6, Dep.
★★★**Westone Moat House,** *Ashley
Way, NN3 3EA.* (Weston Favell 3 m E
A45). ✆ (0604) 406262. Closed Xmas &
New Year. C. ◪ 65 bedrs, 65 bp, TV, Dgs.
✗ a l c, mc, at, LD 9.45. ⓑ Lt, N, CH, TV,
CP 100, U 2, G 2, Ac, sb, sol, gym, con 200,
CF, 19 BGf, 1 st, Dis. £ BB fr £33, DB fr
£42, WT fr £238, DT fr £34·50, ①, Bk £4, L
£6, D £7, cc 1 2 3 4 5 6, Dep b.
★★**Angel,** *21 Bridge St, NN1 1NA.*
✆ (0604) 21661. C. ◪ 46 bedrs, 17 bp, 6
ba, TV, Dgs. ✗ a l c, mc, LD 9.30. ⓑ Lt, N,
ch, TV, Dgs, ns, CP 24, G 6, Ac, sp, gc, tc,
con 100, CF, 1 st. £ BB fr £19·25, DB fr
£27·95, WB, ①, Bk £3·50, L £3·95, D £5·95,
cc 1 2 3 4 5 6, Dep.

Repairers: Airflow Streamlines Ltd,
Hopping Hill, New Duston. ✆ (0604)
581121.
Alexanders of Northampton Ltd, Weston
Favell Centre. ✆ (0604) 404211.
Douglas Garage Ltd, 46 Sheep St.
✆ (0604) 35471.
Grose Ltd, Queens Park Parade. ✆ (0604)
712525.
Kingsthorpe Garage Ltd, 50 Harborough
Rd. ✆ (0604) 22911.
Wadham Stringer (Westonia) Ltd,
Westonia Garage, Wellingborough Rd,
Weston Favell. ✆ (0604) 41141.
Specialist Radiator Repairer: Serck
Radiator Services Ltd, St Michael's Rd.
✆ (0604) 37276.
Specialist Spring Repairer: Jonas
Woodhead Ltd, Factory Unit No 1,
Kingsfield Cl, Kings Heath. ✆ (0604)
52056.
MC Repairers: Glanfield Baldet Ltd, 30
Campbell St. ✆ (0604) 37551.
John Burbidge Motor Cycles, 2 Chinton
Rd, Far Cotton. ✆ (0604) 61701.
Mick Berrill Motor Cycles, Henry St.
✆ (0604) 36760.
Tony Clark Motorcycles, 8 St Michaels
Rd. ✆ (0604) 35634.
Sctr Repairer: Glanfield Baldet Ltd,
30 Campbell St. ✆ (0604) 37551.

Rescue Service: Blue Cars Repairs
(Bugbrook) Ltd, Litchborough Rd,
Bugbrook. ✆ (0604) 830010.
Gerald White (Northampton) Ltd, Total
Service Centre, Weedon Rd, Kislingbury.
✆ (0604) 830770.
Westbridge Motors (Northampton) Ltd,
St James Rd. ✆ (0604) 54444.

NORTH BENFLEET Essex. M. Area 10A
Pop 300. Romford 17, London 33,
Brentwood 13, Chelmsford 14, Colchester
32, Dartford 19, Rainham 18, Southend-
on-Sea 8.
Golf Basildon 18h. **See** Church.

Rescue Service: Victor Service Station,
Arterial Rd. ✆ Basildon (0268) 726545.

NORTH BOARHUNT Hampshire. Map
6F
Cosham 5, London 71, Chichester 18,
Fareham 1, Portsmouth 9, Winchester 17.

Rescue Service: Boarhunt Garage,
Southwick Rd. ✆ Wickham (0329)
833270.

NORTHBOURNE Dorset.
See BOURNEMOUTH.

NORTH BOVEY Devon. Map 4F
Pop 600. Moretonhampstead 1½, London
184, Bovey Tracey 7½, Exeter 14, Newton
Abbot 12, Okehampton 14, Plymouth 27,
Princetown 12.
Golf Manor House Hotel 18h. **See** 15c
Clock.

Blackaller House, PH, xy (R). *TQ13
8QY.* ✆ Moretonhampstead (0647)
40322. Open Mar–Nov. C 10. ◪ 8 bedrs, 6
bp, 1 bps, 1 sh, 1 ba, TV, Dgs. ⓑ CH, TV, CP
14, CF, 1 BGf, 3 st. £ BB fr £15, DB fr £30,
WT (b) fr £158, DT (b) fr £25, ②, Bk £3, D
£10, cc 1 3 5.

NORTH CURRY Somerset. Map 5C
Pop 1,256. Wincanton 27, London 137,
Bridgwater 10, Glastonbury 16, Ilminster
9½, Sherborne 26, Taunton 6½.
Golf Vivary Park 18h. **See** 14th cent
Church whose scene of 'Reeves Feast',
village noted for basket-making.

Rescue Service: Queens Square Garage,
Queens Sq. ✆ (0823) 215.

NORTHENDEN Gtr Manchester
(Lancashire). Map 20B
Congleton 16, London 180, Altrincham 4,
Macclesfield 13, Manchester 5, Stockport
4½, Walkden 10.

Rescue Service: Barrow Motor Co Ltd,
391 Palatine Rd. ✆ 061-998 3427.

NORTHFLEET Kent.
See GRAVESEND.

NORTH HUISH Devon. Map 3D
Totnes 7, London 198, Buckfastleigh 8,
Dartmouth 11, Kingsbridge 9, Plymouth
16.

■♣★★**Brookdale** (R), *TQ10 9NR.*
✆ Gara Bridge (054 882) 402. Closed Jan.
C. ◪ 6 bedrs, 2 bp, 1 bps, 1 ba, TV, Dgs.
✗ mc, at, LD 9.15. ⓑ CH, CP 30, con 12,
CF. £ BB £17–£20, DB £28–£31, WT £148,
DT £26, ②, Bk £4, L £6·50, D £7, cc 1 3 4 5.

NORTH KILWORTH Leicester. Map
14B
Pop 512. M1 Motorway 4½, London 93,
Coventry 19, Daventry 17, Hinckley 14,
Leicester 13, Market Harborough 8,
Northampton 18, Nuneaton 18, Rugby 10.

EC Wed. **Golf** Lutterworth 9h. **See** St Andrew's Church, Tudor Cottages, Medieval Fish Ponds

Rescue Service: Sambrook Service Station Ltd, Station Rd. ✆ Market Harborough (0858) 880243.

NORTHLEACH Gloucestershire. Map 14E
Pop 1,043. Burford 9, London 75, Cheltenham 13. Cirencester 10, Gloucester 20, Stow-on-the-Wold 9.
EC Wed. **Golf** Burford 18h. **See** Church (15th cent brasses), old houses, Blind House (agric Museum).
ⓘ Cotswold Countryside Collection. ✆ Northleach (045 16) 715.

★**Wheatsheaf,** *West End, GL54 3EZ.* ✆ (045 16) 244. RS Xmas. C. ⇄ 8 bedrs, 2 ba, Dgs. ✗ a l c, mc, LD 8.30. ⓑ CH, TV, Dgs, CP 20, G 3, Ac, con 20, CF, 1 st. £ BB fr £12, DB fr £20, WB, ② 10%, Bk £2·50, D £4·50.

Rescue Service: Clifford & Webb Ltd, Service Station. ✆ (045 16) 388. Stratford & Tea, The Garage. ✆ (045 16) 248.

NORTH PETHERTON Somerset. Map 5C
See BRIDGWATER

NORTH SHIELDS Tyne & Wear. Map 31F
See also TYNEMOUTH.
Pop 68,740. Tyne Tunnel 2. London 279, Alnwick 37, Coldstream 58, Newcastle upon Tyne 7½, Sunderland 11.
EC Wed. **Golf** Tynemouth 18h. **See** at Tynemouth: Ancient Gatehouse and ruins of 11th cent Priory, Pier, Lighthouse, Tynemouth Park, Monument to Admiral Lord Collingwood, Fish Quay and Market (N. Shields), Cullercoats Harbour.
ⓘ Tyne Commission Quay. ✆ North Shields (0632) 579800.

Repairer: Monk Car Sales Ltd, Waterville Rd. ✆ (0632) 573232.
Rescue Service: Coast Road Motor Co, Queen Alexandra Rd. ✆ (0632) 571355. Turnballs Garage, Albion Rd. ✆ (0632) 571201.

NORTH SKELTON Cleveland. Map 24D
Pop 7,100. Thirsk 29, London 250, Middlesbrough 12, Northallerton 25, Stockton-on-Tees 16, Whitby 18.
Golf Saltburn-by-the-Sea 18h.

Rescue Service: G Boocock & Sons, Holmbeck Garage. ✆ Skelton (085 34) 50247.

NORTH STIFFORD Essex. Map 17F
Pop 395. Rainham 6, London 21, Brentwood 10, Chelmsford 21, Dartford Tunnel 3, Romford 11, Southend-on-Sea 20.
EC Wed. **Golf** Belhus Park 18h. **See** St Mary's Church.

★★★**M Stifford Moat House,** *High Rd, RM16 1UE.* ✆ Grays Thurrock (0375) 71451. Closed Dec, Jan. C. ⇄ 64 bedrs. 64 bp, TV, Dgs. ✗ a l c, mc, at, LD 9.30. ⓑ N, CH, Dgs, CP 100, Ac, tc, con 100, CF, 20 BGf, 3 st. £ BB £18·50–£36, DB £18·50–£43, WB, ①, Bk £4, L £8, D £8, cc 1 3 4 5 6, Dep b.

NORTH STOKE Oxon. Map 6B
Henley-on-Thames 13, London 48, Newbury 19, Oxford 16, Reading 14

⬧⊞★★★**Springs,** *Wallingford Rd, OX9 6BE.* ✆ Wallingford (0491) 36687.

NORTH TAWTON Devon. Maps 3B and 4E
Pop 1,182. Crediton 11, London 186, Barnstaple 29, Bideford 24, Holsworthy 22, Newton Abbot 25, Okehampton 7.
Golf Okehampton 18h. **See** 11th cent Church, Broad Hall, Manor House.

Rescue Service: Blogg's Garage, The Square. ✆ (083 782) 232.

NORTH TUDDENHAM Norfolk. M. Area 16C
Pop 250. East Dereham 4, London 109, Cromer 26, Norwich 8, Scole 28.
Golf Dereham 9h. **See** Church.

Specialist Car Lighting and Ignition Repairer: Bowden Auto Electrical Ltd, North Tuddenham Garage. ✆ Swanton Morley (036 283) 644.
Rescue Service: North Tuddenham Garage Ltd, A47. ✆ Swanton Morley (036 283) 343.

NORTH WALSHAM Norfolk. Map 16A
Pop 7,944. Norwich 14, London 126, Cromer 8½, East Dereham 23, Fakenham 24, Great Yarmouth 24.
EC Wed. **MD** Thur. **Golf** Mundesley 9h. **See** Perp Church, Market Cross, 17th cent Paston School (assoc Nelson).

Felmingham Hall, PH, xy (Rt), *NR28 0LP.* ✆ Swanton Abbot (069 269) 228. C 12. ⇄ 12 bedrs, 7 bp, 1 ba, ns, TV. ⓑ CH, ns, CP 100. £ BB £11–£15·30, DB £22–£29·20, WT £105–£150·50, DT £15–£21·50, ②, Bk £2·50, L £5, D £8, cc 1 3 4.
Scarborough Hill House, H, xy, *Yarmouth Rd, NR28 9NA.* ✆ Walcott (0692) 402151. C. ⇄ 14 bedrs, 14 sh, 3 ba, Dgs. ⓑ TV, CP 100, CF. £ BB £15·81, DB £25·93, ①, L £1·50, cc 1 3 4 5.
Witton Old Rectory, PH, xy, (R) *Witton, NR28 9TR.* ✆ Walcott (0692) 650370. C. ⇄ 10 bedrs, 3 bp, 1 bps, 2 ba, TV, Dgs. ⓑ ch, TV, Dgs, CP 20, CF, 2 st. £ BB £8–£13, DB £16–£26, WT £89–£99, DT £13–£15, ①, Bk £3, L £5, D £5.

Rescue Service: Gleave & Key (Norfolk) Ltd, Happisburgh Rd. ✆ (0692) 402281. Harmer & Scott Ltd, 7 Norwich Rd. ✆ (0692) 402171.

NORTHWICH Cheshire. Map 19B
Pop 20,000. Middlewich 6, London 173, M6 Motorway 6, Altrincham 13, Chester 18, Knutsford 7, Liverpool 26, St Helens 20, Warrington 11, Whitchurch 24.
EC Wed. **MD** Tue, Fri, Sat. **Golf** Sandiway 18h. **See** Parish Church, Memorial Hall, Anderton Lift (connecting R Weaver to the Trent and Mersey Canal) 2½ m, Marbury Country Park 2½ m, Budworth Mere.

★★★**M Hartford Hall,** *School La, CW8 1PW.* ✆ (0606) 75711. C. ⇄ 21 bedrs, 21 bp, TV. ✗ a l c, mc, at. ⓑ N, CH, TV, CP 50, Ac, con 30, CF, 7 BGf, 1 st. £ BB £31, DB £41, WB, ①, Bk £3, L £9·50, D £9·50, cc 1 3 4 5 6, Dep b.
★★**Woodpecker,** *London Rd, Leftwich, CW8 7EQ.* ✆ (0606) 45524. RS Xmas. C. ⇄ 34 bedrs, 28 bp, 1 bps, 2 ba, TV, Dgs. ✗ a l c, mc, LD 10. ⓑ N, CH, CP 100, Ac,

con 30, CF, 11 BGf, 1 st, Dis. £ BB fr £31·50, DB fr £40, WB, ② 10%, Bk £3·30, L £6, D £6, cc 1 3 4 5, Dep b.

Repairers: Charles Barber & Sons Ltd, Station Rd. ✆ (0606) 6061. Knutsford Motors Ltd, Chester Way. ✆ (0606) 6141. Lookers of Northwich Ltd, Castle Garage, Castle St. ✆ (0606) 75333.
Rescue Service: Birtwisle & Co Ltd, Chester. ✆ (0606) 74361. Willows Garage, Runcorn Rd, Barton. ✆ (0606) 74976.

NORTHWOOD Greater London. M. Area 15E
2 m NNW of Pinner. Pop 72,791 (inc Ruislip). Harrow 8½, London 14, Denham 6½, Rickmansworth 4, Uxbridge 6, Watford 5½.
EC Wed. **Golf** Haste Hill 18h, Pinner Hill 18h.

Rescue Service: Sandy Lodge Service Station Ltd, Sandy La. ✆ (092 74) 24355 and (092 74) 23808.

NORWICH Norfolk. Map 16B
See also BUNWELL.
RAC Office, *Norvic House, Chapel Field Road, Norwich, NR2 1RS.* ✆ Norwich (0603) 28255.
Pop 121,000. Scole 19, London 111, Cromer 23, East Dereham 16, Fakenham 26, Great Yarmouth 18, Lowestoft 25, Saxmundham 32, Thetford 28.
See Plan, p. 286.
EC Thur. **MD** Daily. **P** See Plan. **Golf** Royal Norwich 18h. Eaton 18h. **See** Cathedral, mainly Norman, entire length 461 ft with many notable items, 40 City Churches, King Edward VI School, Erpingham Gate with archway built 1420, St Peter Hungate Church built 1460 now Ecclesiastical Museum, Guildhall, Museum, Library, RC Cathedral, remains of city wall, many interesting old buildings and streets.
ⓘ Augustine Steward House, 14 Tombland. ✆ Norwich (0603) 20679.

★★★★**Maid's Head,** *Tombland, NR3 1LB.* ✆ (0603) 28821. C. ⇄ 82 bedrs, 67 bp, 11 bps, 2 ba, TV, Dgs. ✗ a l c, mc, at, LD 9.45. ⓑ Lt, N, CH, Dgs, ns, CP 80, G 20, Ac, con 100, CF, 0 st. £ BB fr £27·30, DB fr £48·75, WT fr £76, DT fr £45·25, WB, ②, Bk £3·75, L £4·50, D £7·75, cc 1 3 4 5 6.
★★★**Castle,** *Castle Meadow, NR1 3PZ.* ✆ (0603) 611511. C. ⇄ 79 bedrs, 26 bp, 12 ba, TV, Dgs. ✗ a l c, mc, at, LD 9.30 (9 Sun). ⓑ Lt, N, ch, Dgs, Ac, con 120, CF, 2 st. £ BB fr £21·50, DB fr £32, WB, ①, Bk £4·75, L £7·50, D £7·50, cc 1 2 3 5 6, Dep b.
★★★**M Hotel Nelson,** *Prince of Wales Rd, NR1 1DX.* ✆ (0603) 28612. C. ⇄ 94 bedrs, 94 bp, ns, TV. ✗ a l c, mc, LD 9·45. ⓜ l t, N, CH, CP 96, G 32, Ac, sb, con 70, CF, 18 BGf, 0 st, Dis. £ BB fr £39, DB fr £46·50, WB, ①, L £3·75, D £8, cc 1 3 4 5 6, Dep b.
★★★**M Hotel Norwich,** *121 Boundary Rd, NR3 2BA.* ✆ (0603) 410431. C. ⇄ 102 bedrs, 102 bp, ns, TV. ✗ a l c, mc, at, LD 10. ⓑ N, CH, CP 225, Ac, con 300, CF, 22 BGf, 0 st, Dis. £ BB fr £36·50, DB fr £44, WB, ①, L £3·75, D £8, cc 1 3 4 5, Dep b.
★★★**M Post House** (TH), *Ipswich Rd, NR4 6EP.* ✆ (0603) 56431. C. ⇄ 120

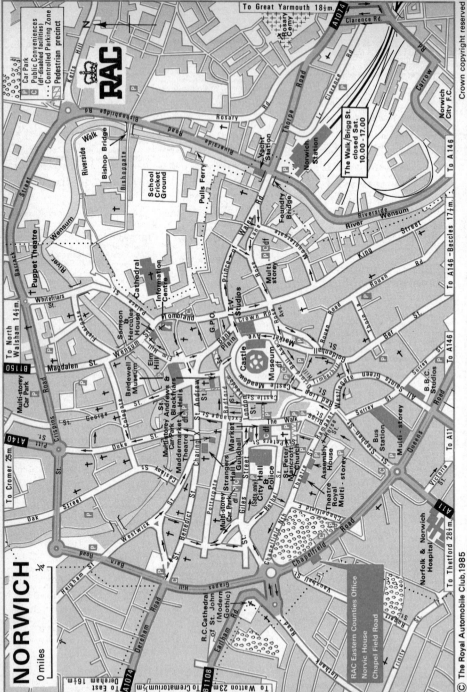

NORWICH

0 miles ¼

RAC

Car Park
Public Conveniences
(d-disabled facilities)
Controlled Parking Zone
Pedestrian precinct

To Great Yarmouth 18½m.
A1074
Clarence Rd.

The Walk/Brigg St.
closed Sat.
10.00 - 17.00

Rosary Cemy.

Norwich City F.C.

To North Walsham 14½m.

B1150

Multi-storey Car Park

A140
Pill St.

To Cromer 25m.

Riverside Walk
Bishop Bridge
Bishopbridge Rd
Bishopgate
Riverside Rd

School Cricket Ground

Pulls Ferry

Yacht Station

Thorpe Road

Norwich Station

Clarence Rd

Carrow Rd

Whitefriars St.
Puppet Theatre

River Wensum

Magdalen St.

Cathedral

Information Centre

Tombland

G.P.O.

T.V. Studios

Prince of Wales Rd

Rose Lane

Foundry Bridge

River Wensum

King Street

To A146 – Beccles 17½m.

To A146

Bank Plain

Samson & Hercules House
Elm Hill

Bridewell Museum
St. Andrews & Blackfriars Halls

St. Andrew St.
Exchange St.
London St.

Castle

Museum

Castle Meadow

Crown Rd
Market

Rouen Road

Golden Ball St.

Ber Street

B.B.C. Studios

To A146

Maddermarket Theatre

Multi-storey Car Park

St. Georges St.
Colegate St.
Duke St.
St. Benedict St.
Charing X
Pottergate
Bethel St.
Giles Street
Westwick Street
Barn Road
Heigham St.
Oak Street
Crispins Rd

Theatre Royal
Multi-storey

St. Peter Mancroft Church

The Walk
City Hall
Guildhall
Strangers Hall
Police

Assembly House

Multi-storey

Timberhill
Westlegate
All Saints Green

Bus Station

Surrey St.
Stepping Lane

Multi-storey

Queens Road

Victoria St.

A11
To A11

R.C. Cathedral of St. John (Modern Gothic)

Chapelfield

Chapelfield Road

Norfolk & Norwich Hospital

To Thetford 28½m.

A1074
To East Dereham 16½m.

B1108
To Watton 23m.

To Crematorium ½m.

Earlham Road
Chapelfield

Vauxhall St
Trinity St
Rupert St

RAC Eastern Counties Office
Norvic House
Chapel Field Road

286

For abbreviations see inside back cover—**RAC**

bedrs, 120 bp, TV, Dgs. ✗ a l c, mc, at, LD 9·45. ℗ N, CH, Dgs, CP 200, Ac, sp, con 120, CF, 40 BGf, 1 st, Dis. £ BB £40, DB £53·50, WB, ☐, cc 1 2 3 4 5 6, Dep (Xmas).

★★**Arlington**, *Arlington La, Newmarket Rd, NR2 2DA.* ✆ (0603) 617841. C. ✉ 42 bedrs, 37 bp, 5 sh, 2 ba, TV, Dgs. ✗ a l c, mc, at, LD 10. ℗ N, CH, TV, CP 60, Ac, con 120, CF, 0 st. £ BB £20–£26, DB £40, WB, ☑, Bk £4, L £2·95, D £7·95, cc 1 3 4 5 6.

★★**Lansdowne**, *Thorpe Rd, NR1 1RU.* ✆ (0603) 20302. Closed Xmas. C. ✉ 44 bedrs, 24 bp, 3 bps, 4 ba, TV, Dgs. ✗ a l c, mc, at, LD 9.15. ℗ Lt, N, CH, TV, Dgs, CP 60, Ac, con 150, CF, 2 st. £ B fr £22, BD fr £36, WB, ☐, Bk £4·25, L £6·25, D £6·25, cc 1 2 3 4 5 6, Dep b.

★★**Oaklands**, (R & Cl), *89 Yarmouth Rd, Thorpe St Andrew, NR7 0HH.* ✆ (0603) 34471. Closed Xmas. C. ✉ 42 bedrs, 23 bp, 3 bps, 4 ba, TV, Dgs. ✗ a l c, mc, at, LD 10. ℗ CH, TV, Dgs, CP 90, Ac, con 70, CF. £ BB fr £17·50, DB fr £26·50, WT fr £175, DT fr £31·50, WB, ☐, Bk £3, L £4·25, D £6·25, cc 1 5 6, Dep b.

Cavalier, H, z (R & Cl), *244 Thorpe Rd, NR1 1TP.* ✆ (0603) 34291.

Grey Gables, G, *Norwich Rd, Cawston, NR10 4EY.* ✆ (0603) 871259.▲

Windsor, H, x (R), *2 Yarmouth Rd, Thorpe, NR7 0EB.* ✆ (0603) 35193.

Repairers: Howes & Sons (Norwich) Ltd, 79 Mile Cross La. ✆ (0603) 410661.
Mann Egerton & Co Ltd, 5 Prince of Wales Rd. ✆ (0603) 29011.
Norwich Motor Co Ltd, 118 Prince of Wales Rd. ✆ (0603) 28811.
Pointer Motor Co Ltd, The Garage, Aylsham Rd. ✆ (0603) 45345.
Robinson, R & Co (Motor Services) Ltd, Riverside Rd. ✆ (0603) 27134.
Specialist Body Repairer: East Anglian Motor & Sheet Metal Co Ltd, 10 Garden St. ✆ (0603) 25664 and (0603) 27791.
MC Repairers: Clark, R O Ltd, 93 Ber St. ✆ (0603) 28805.
Pointer Motor Co Ltd, Aylsham Rd. ✆ (0603) 45345.
Sctr Repairer: Pointer Motor Co Ltd, Aylsham Rd. ✆ (0603) 45345.
Rescue Service: Delmonte Garage (Racing), 96A Angel Rd. ✆ (0603) 46746.
Roys Motor Co, Normans Building, Rouen Rd. ✆ (0603) 21629.
St Benedicts Garage Ltd, St Benedicts Gates. ✆ (0603) 20545.

NOTTINGHAM Nottinghamshire. Map 22D
See also BEESTON, RUDDINGTON and TOTON.
RAC Office. *21 Gregory Boulevard, Nottingham, NG7 6NY.* ✆ (General) Nottingham (0602) 623331. (Rescue Service only) Nottingham (0602) 626200. Pop 271,080. Leicester 26, London 123, M1 Motorway 5, Ashby-de-la-Zouch 21, Chesterfield 20, Derby 15, Grantham 24, Loughborough 15, Mansfield 14, Matlock 24, Melton Mowbray 18, Newark 19, Ollerton 18.
See Plan, p 288.
MD Daily. **P** See Plan. **Golf** Bulwell 18h, Wollaton 18h. **See** Parish Church (15th cent), Castle (now art gallery and museum), Statue of Robin Hood, Council House, Willoughby House, Bromley House, Newdigate House, four interesting churches, Unitarian Chapel, RC Cathedral, Arboretum, Wollaton Hall (Natural History

and Industrial Museum), 12th cent Trip to Jerusalem Inn, 13th cent Salutation Inn, Playhouse Theatre, Annual Goose Fair, Newstead Abbey 9 m N. Underground Caves.
☐ 18, Milton St. ✆ Nottingham (0602) 40661.

★★★★**Albany** (TH), *St James's St, NG1 6BN.* ✆ (0602) 470131. C. ✉ 160 bedrs, 160 bp, TV, Dgs. ✗ a l c, mc, at, LD 10.30. ℗ Lt, N, CH, Dgs, Ac, con 600, CF, 3 st. £ BB £46·50, DB £62·50, WB, ☐, cc 1 2 3 4 5 6, Dep (Xmas).

★★★★**M Victoria**, *Milton St, NG1 0DR.* ✆ (0602) 419561. C. ✉ 167 bedrs, 167 bp, TV, Dgs. ✗ a l c, mc, at, LD 10. ℗ Lt, N, CH, Dgs, CP 15, Ac, con 130, CF. £ WB, Bk £4·50, L £2, D £9, cc 1 3 4 5 6, Dep b.

★★★**Savoy**, *Mansfield Rd, NG5 2BT.* ✆ (0602) 602621. Closed Xmas Day. C. ✉ 125 bedrs, 125 bp, TV. ✗ a l c, mc, at, LD 11.30. ℗ Lt, N, CH, CP 170, Ac, con 40, CF, 1 st. £ BB fr £31·50, DB fr £43, ☐, Bk £3·25, L £3·40, D £3·70, cc 1 3 4 5 6.

■★★★**Strathdon Thistle**, *Derby Rd, NG2 5ST.* ✆ (0602) 377185. C. ✉ 64 bedrs, 20 bp, 44 bps, 2 ba, ns, TV, Dgs. ✗ a l c, mc, at, LD 9·30. ℗ Lt, N, CH, Dgs, Ac, con 120, CF, 6 st. £ BB £36·75–£39·75, DB £49–£52, WB, ☑, Bk £4·75, L £6·10, D £8·60, cc 1 2 3 4 5 6, Dep b.

★★**Edwalton Hall**, *Village St, Edwalton, NG12 4AE.* (3½ m S A606). ✆ (0602) 231116.

★★**Sherwood**, *Gregory Boulevard, NG7 6LB.* ✆ (0602) 603261. C. ✉ 69 bedrs, 30 bps, 4 sh, 9 ba, TV, Dgs. ✗ mc, at, LD 8·30. ℗ N, CH, TV, Dgs, CP 50, con 30, CF, 3 BGf, Dis. £ BB fr £15, DB fr £24, WB, ☐, L £4·50, D £6, cc 1 5, Dep b.

Crantock, H, z (Rl), *480 Mansfield Rd, Sherwood, NG5 2EL.* ✆ (0602) 623294.

Forest Hills, PH, z (R), *102 Mapperley Rd, West Bridgford NG2 7PS.* ✆ (0602) 811133.

Rufford, PH, z (R), *53 Melton Rd, (A606), West Bridgford, NG2 7NE.* ✆ (0602) 814202. Closed Xmas. C. ✉ 31 bedrs, 31 bps, TV. ✗ a l c, mc. ℗ N, CH, TV, Dgs, CP 35, CF, 7 BGf, 4 st. £ BB £18·40–£20·70, DB £27·60–£32·20, DT (b) £25·30–£28·18, ☐, Bk £4, D £7·48, cc 1 6.

Windsor Lodge, H, z (R), *116 Radcliffe Rd, West Bridgford, NG2 5HG.* ✆ (0602) 813773. C. ✉ 43 bedrs, 3 bp, 23 bps, 13 sh, 2 ba, TV. ✗ a l c. ℗ CH, TV, CP 48, CF, 1 BGf, 2 st. £ BB fr £16·10, DB fr £23, DT (b) fr £23, ☐, Bk £2·85, D £6·90, cc 1 5.

Repairers: Challands, Ross & Co Ltd, 38 Canal St. ✆ (0602) 50095.
Jack F Hopewell Ltd, Edward Rd, West Bridgford. ✆ (0602) 813660.
Slaney, H V Ltd, Teesdale Garage, Hucknall Rd. ✆ (0602) 65146.
Specialist Body Repairer: N C V of Nottingham Ltd, Bulwell Forest Works, Hucknall Rd, Bulwell. ✆ (0602) 272915.
Specialist Radiator Repairer: Serck Radiator Services Ltd, Lambourne Dr, Wollaton. ✆ (0602) 282211.
MC Repairers: Downtown Motorcycles, 48 Lilac Cres, Beeston. ✆ (0602) 256641.
Rescue Service: Hooley's Garage Ltd, Derby Rd. ✆ (0602) 46111.
Rod Blanchard Motors, Main Road Garage, Watnall. ✆ (0602) 382781.
Sheppards Wood Service Station, Bracebridge Drive, Billborough Estate. ✆ (0602) 293454.

NUNEATON Warwickshire Map 14B
Pop 71,600. London 99, M6 Motorway 5, Ashby-de-la-Zouch 16, Atherstone 5, Birmingham 21, Burton-on-Trent 23, Coventry 8½, Hinckley 4½, Rugby 16.
MD Sat. **Golf** Nuneaton 18h. **See** EE and Perp Church of St Nicolas, St Mary's Church, 13 cent All Saints Church, Council House, Art Gallery and Museum, George Eliot's birthplace (South Farm), Arbury Hall 2½ m SW. Astley Castle (now hotel) 3 m.
☐ Library, Church St. ✆ Nuneaton (0203) 384027.

★★**M Longshoot**, *Watling St, CV11 6JH.* ✆ (0203) 329711. C. ✉ 47 bedrs, 47 bp, TV, Dgs. ✗ mc, LD 10·30. ℗ N, CH, CP 47, con 30, CF, 2 BGf, 1 st, Dis. £ BB £15·50–£26·50, DB £23–£33·50, ☑, Bk £4, L £4·75, D £4·75, cc 1 3 5, Dep b.

Longshoot Motel: *Under construction.*

Rescue Service: Dudley Bedford Ltd, County Garage, Leicester Rd, Hinckley. ✆ Hinckley (0455) 637310.

NUTBOURNE West Sussex. M. Area 7C
2 m E of Pulborough. Dorking 23, London 46, Brighton 22, Guildford 22, Haywards Heath 19, Horsham 12, Pulborough 2, Worthing 13.
Golf West Sussex 18h. **See** West Chiltington Mill.

Rescue Service: Nutbourne Garage (1972) Ltd, High St. ✆ West Chiltington (079 83) 2194.

OAKHAM Leicestershire. Map 23D
Pop 8,859. Kettering 20, London 95, Grantham 20, Leicester 19, Market Harborough 18, Melton Mowbray 9, Stamford 10.
EC Thur. **MD** Wed, Sat. **Golf** Luffenham Heath 18h. **See** Castle ruins with fine Norman banqueting hall, unique collection of horseshoes, Rutland County Museum, Butter Cross, Stocks, Parish Church, 13th cent Flore's House.
☐ Oakham Library, Catmos St. ✆ Oakham (0572) 2918.

★★★**Crown**, *High St, LE15 6AP.* ✆ (0572) 3631. C. ✉ 25 bedrs, 23 bp, TV, Dgs. ✗ a l c, mc, at, LD 10. ℗ N, CH, TV, Dgs, CP 30, Ac, con 120, CF, 0 st. £ BB £22–£31, DB £30–£39, DBB £22·50–£27, WB, ☑, Bk £3·50, L £4·75, D £6·95, cc 1 2 3 5 6, Dep b.

★★**George**, *Market Pl, LE15 6DT.* ✆ (0572) 56971. C. ✉ 19 bedrs, 8 bp, 3 sh, 3 ba, TV. ✗ a l c, mc. ℗ CH, TV, Dgs, CP 10, Ac, con 50, CF, 1 BGf. £ BB fr £19, DB fr £27·50, WB, ☑, Bk £3, L £4, D £8, cc 1 2 3 5 6.
Repairer: Victor Wood of Oakham Ltd, Burley Rd. ✆ (0572) 2657.

OAKLEY Bedfordshire. M. Area 15C
4 m NW of Bedford. Pop 1,400. London 54, Bletchley 18, Buckingham 26, Kettering 22, Northampton 20.
Golf Bedford and County 18h. **See** Oakley Arms, ancient bridge, EE church.

Repairer: Oakley Garage (Bedford) Ltd, Station Rd. ✆ (023 02) 3118.

ODIHAM Hampshire. Map 6D
Pop 4,333. London 41, London 41, M3 Motorway 2, Alton 8, Basingstoke 7½, Farnham 7, Guildford 17, Reading 15, Woking 19.

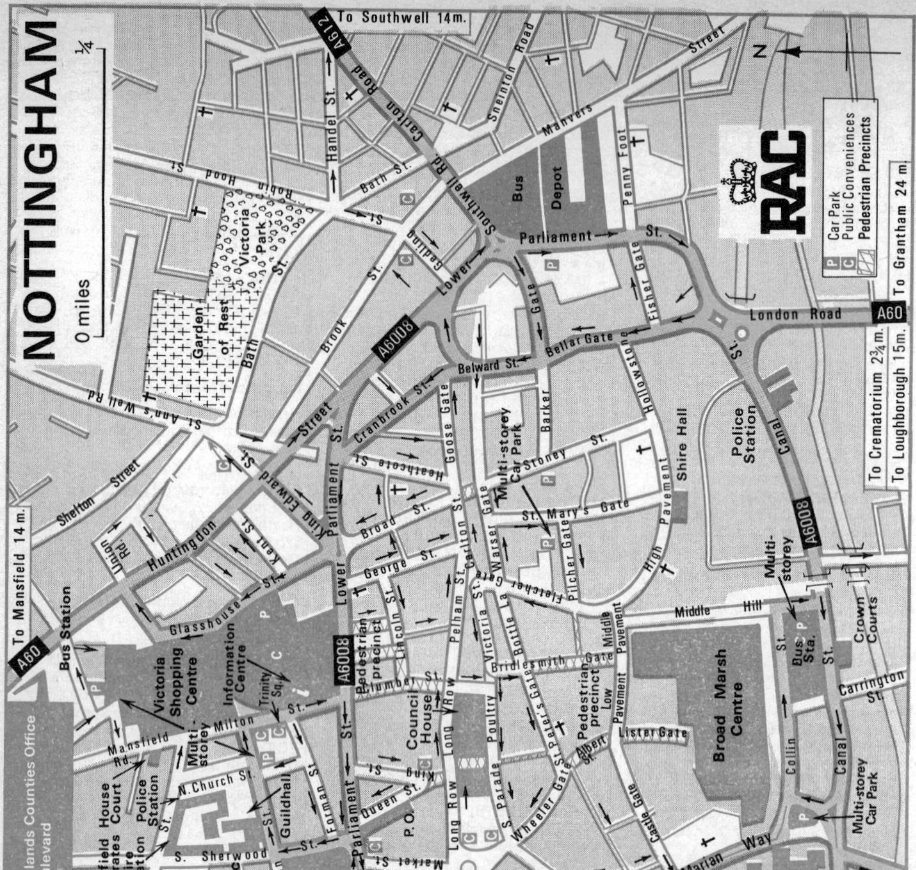

NOTTINGHAM
0 miles ¼
RAC
Car Park
Public Conveniences
Pedestrian Precincts
N
Crown copyright reserved
© The Royal Automobile Club, 1985
RAC North Midlands Counties Office
21 Gregory Boulevard
To Southwell 14m.
To Mansfield 14 m.
To Grantham 24 m.
To Crematorium 2¾ m.
To Loughborough 15m.
To Ashby de la Zouch 21 m.
To Derby 16 m.
To Ilkeston 7 m.
To Ripley 14m.
To M1. Int. 25 Southbound
To M1. Int. 26 Northbound
A60
A612
A6008
A453
A6005
A6200
A609
A610
Bus Station
Victoria Shopping Centre
Information Centre
Trinity Sq.
Council House
Broad Marsh Centre
Shire Hall
Police Station
Bus Depot
Garden of Rest
Victoria Park
Multi-storey Car Park
Guildhall
Sandfield House Court
Magistrates Court
Fire Station
Trent Polytechnic
Royal Centre
Theatre
Playhouse Theatre
R.C. Cathedral
Eye Hospital
Hospital
Nottingham Castle
People's College
Post Office
Mus.
P.O.
Crown Courts
College of Art
Pedestrian precinct
Parliament St.
Lower Parliament St.
Upper Parliament St.
Huntingdon St.
Glasshouse St.
Milton St.
Mansfield Rd.
Shakespeare St.
Goldsmith St.
Clarendon St.
Chaucer St.
Talbot St.
Wollaton St.
Derby Road
The Ropewalk
Maid Marian Way
Castle Boulevard
Canal St.
Middle Hill
Carrington St.
Collin St.
London Road
Manvers Street
Sneinton Road
Carlton Road
Southwell Rd.
Bellar Gate
Belward St.
Hollowstone
Fisher Gate
Penny Foot St.
Stoney St.
St. Mary's Gate
High Pavement
Fletcher Gate
Bridlesmith Gate
Low Pavement
Middle Pavement
Lister Gate
Castle Gate
Castle Rd.
Friar Lane
Wheeler Gate
St. Peter's Gate
Albert St.
Long Row
Angel Row
Market St.
Queen St.
King St.
Pelham St.
Victoria St.
Carlton St.
Goose Gate
Cranbrook St.
Heathcote St.
Broad St.
George St.
Lincoln St.
Clumber St.
Poultry
S. Parade
Chapel Bar
Mount St.
Park Row
Peveril Drive
Park Drive
Lenton Road
Fishpond Drive
Cromwell Street
Shelton Street
St. Ann's Well Rd.
Robin Hood St.
Bath St.
Brook St.
Handel St.
Kent St.
Union Rd.
King Edward St.
Burton St.
Sherwood St.
N. Church St.
Forman St.
Barker Gate
Warser Gate
Pilcher Gate
Bottle La.
James's St.
Gedling St.
Parliament St.

For abbreviations see inside back cover—**RAC**

Golf Hartley Wintney 9h. **See** Castle ruins, EE Church, old George Hotel, 17th cent Almshouses, stocks, whipping post.

Repairer: Oast Garage, King St.
☎ (025 671) 2259.

OKEHAMPTON Devon. Maps 3A and 4E
Pop 4,000. Exeter 22, London 192,
Ashburton 27, Barnstaple 28, Bideford 26,
Crediton 17, Holsworthy 20, Newton
Abbot 26, Launceston 19, Tavistock 16,
South Molton 27.
EC Wed. **MD** Sat. **Golf** Okehampton 18h.
See Castle ruins. 17th cent Town Hall, All
Saints Parish Church, Fitz Well, St James's
Church (14th cent tower).
🛈 White Hart Yard, West St.
☎ Okehampton (0837) 3020.

MC Repairer: Young's Motorcycles,
School Way, Market St. ☎ (0837) 2517
Rescue Service: Downings Motor & Body
Works, 88 North St. ☎ (0837) 2494.
F. J. Glass & Co (1981) Ltd, School Rd.
☎ (0837) 2255.
I G MacCulloch & Sons, Yes Tor Service
Station, East St. ☎ (0837) 2163.

OLDBURY Warley, West Midlands. M.
Area 21F
Pop 53,948. Birmingham 6, London 117,
Bridgnorth 21, Bromsgrove 12,
Kidderminster 13, Walsall 7,
Wolverhampton 8.
EC Thur. **MD** Tue, Sat. **Golf** Dudley 18h.

MC Repairer: Bob Joyner & Son, 816
Wolverhampton Rd. ☎ 021-552 2577.
Rescue Service: Jackson & Lawley, 9
Brades Rd, Rounds Green.
☎ 021-552 1737.

OLDHAM Gtr Manchester (Lancashire).
Map 27B
See also CHADDERTON
Pop 103,690. Glossop 12, London 186,
A 627(M) Motorway 1½, Barnsley 29, Bury
10, Halifax 19, Huddersfield 18,
Manchester 7, Rochdale 5½, Stockport 10,
Walkden 13.
EC Tue. **MD** Mon, Fri, Sat. **Golf** Oldham
18h. **See** Art Gallery, Parish Church
(crypt), Town Hall, Bluecoat School,
Tommyfield Market.
🛈 Greaves St. ☎ 061-620 8930.

★★★Belgrade, *Manchester St, OL8 1UZ.*
☎ 061-624 0555. C. 🛏 130 bedrs, 130 bp,
TV. ✗ a l c, mc, at, LD 10. 🄯 Lt, N, CH, CP
150, Ac, con 350, CF, 4 st. £ BB fr £29, DB
fr £35, 🛈, Bk £3·50, L £5·50, D £9,
cc 1 2 3 4 5 6.
★★★Bower, *Hollingwood Av,
Chadderton, OL9 8DE.* ☎ 061-682 7259.
RS Dec 29–Jan 1. C. 🛏 66 bedrs, 41 bp,
25 bps, TV, Dgs. ✗ a l c, mc, at, LD 9.30.
🄯 N, CH, Dgs, ns, CP 150, Ac, con 200, CF,
19 BGf, 0 st. Dis. £ BB fr37·50, DB f45,
WB, 🛈, Bk £3·50, L £6, D £6·50,
cc 1 2 3 5 6, Dep b.

Repairers: Martins Wellington Ltd,
Wellington St. ☎ 061-633 1331.
Oldham Motor Co Ltd, 2 Manchester Rd.
☎ 061-652 2411.
Springhead Garage, Oldham Rd.
☎ 061-624 2725.
Specialist Body Repairers: Oldham Motor
Co Ltd, 2 Manchester Rd.
☎ 061-624 3401.
Supertune Motors Ltd, Derker St.
☎ 061-624 8789.

Specialist Radiator Repairer: Serck
Radiator Services, Marshland Industrial
Est, Green St, Werneth. ☎ 061-652 2034.
Rescue Service: Alpine Service Station,
Hollins Rd. ☎ 061-624 7172.
Central Garage (Saddleworth) Ltd, High
St, Uppermill. ☎ Saddleworth (045 77)
2178.
Kershaws of Springhead Ltd, Oldham Rd,
Springhead. ☎ 061-624 3042.
Moorside Garages, Ripponden Rd,
Moorside. ☎ 061-624 4400.
Supertune Motors Ltd, inc Supertune
Motor Bodies, Derker St.
☎ 061-624 8789.

OLD SODBURY Avon. Map 5B
Pop 400. Swindon 27, London 104, M4
Motorway 3, Bristol 13, Tetbury 10.
EC Thur. **Golf** Chipping Sodbury 18h. **See**
Church.

🄯 **★★Cross Hands,** *Tetbury Rd, BS17
6RJ.* ☎ Chipping Sodbury (0454) 313000.
C. 🛏 15 bedrs, 2 bp, 2 bps, 3 ba, TV, Dgs.
✗ a l c, mc. 🄯 CH, Dgs, CP 150, Ac, con
20, CF. £ BBc £15–£22, DBc £26·50–
£33·50, WB, 🄯, Bk £3·95, L £3·75, D £3·75,
cc 1 2 3 5, Dep b.

Rescue Service: Roman Camp Garage,
A46 Stroud Rd. ☎ Chipping Sodbury
(0454) 314202.

OLD STRATFORD Northants Map 15C
See also STONY STRATFORD.
Pop 1,074. Bletchley 8, London 54,
Aylesbury 19, Bedford 19, Buckingham 7½,
Northampton 13, Towcester 7.
EC Wed. **Golf** Milton Keynes 18h.

Rescue Service: River Garage Ltd, 14
London Rd. ☎ Milton Keynes (0908)
562194.

OLLERTON Nottinghamshire. Map 22D
Pop 7,255. Newark 13, London 139,
Chesterfield 19, Doncaster 25,
Gainsborough 22, Leicester 44, Lincoln
23, Mansfield 8½, Nottingham 18, Worksop
9.
EC Wed. **MD** Fri, Sat. **Golf** Sherwood
Forest 18h. **See** Sherwood Forest, Major
Oak, Ollerton Hall, Thoresby Hall 2 m N.

★Hop Pole, *NG22 9AB.* ☎ Mansfield
(0623) 822573. C. 🛏 12 bedrs, 1 bp, 5 sh,
3 ba. ✗ mc, at, LD 10. 🄯 CH, TV, Dgs, CP
30, Ac, sb, sol, gym, con 12, 0 st. £ BB £14–
£19, DB fr £22, 🄯, 10%, Bk £3·50, L £3·95,
D £5·20, cc 1 3.
Old Rectory, G, xy (Unl), *Main St, Kirton,
NG22 9LP.* ☎ Mansfield (0623) 861540.
Closed Dec 22. C. 🛏 10 bedrs, 3 ba. 🄯 CH,
TV, CP 18, CF, 3 st. £ BB fr £11, DB fr £21,
WT (b) fr £99, DT (b) fr £16, 🄯, Bk £3·75, D
£5·50.

OLNEY Buckinghamshire. Map 15C
Pop 3,690. M1 Motorway 7, London 57,
Bedford 11, Bletchley 11, Kettering 18,
Northampton 11.
EC Wed. **MD** Thur. **Golf** Bedford and
County 18h. **See** Mainly 14th cent Church
of SS Peter and Paul (Cowper Memorial
Chapel), Cowper Museum (orig the poet's
home), Transatlantic Pancake Race
Shrove Tue (with Liberal, Kansas, USA),
Emberton Park.

Repairer: Hilary Brock Ltd, High St.
☎ Bedford (0234) 711280.

OMBERSLEY Hereford & Worcs. Map
13B

Pop 2,043. Droitwich 4, London 118,
Kidderminster 8½, Stourport on Severn 6,
Tenbury Wells 18, Worcester 5½.
Golf Droitwich 18h, Fladbury 18h. **See**
18th cent Parish Church, Telford's Severn
Bridge.

Rescue Service: Old School House
Garage, Church La. ☎ Worcester (0905)
620367.

ORFORD Suffolk. Map 17A
Pop 662. Ipswich 20, London 94,
Aldeburgh 11, Saxmundham 9, Scole 30,
Stowmarket 29.
Golf Woodbridge 18h. **See** Castle, 14th
cent Church, forest and river walks.

★★Crown & Castle (TH), *IP12 2LJ.*
☎ (039 45) 205. C. 🛏 10 bedrs, 1 bp, 2 ba,
TV, Dgs. ✗ a l c, mc, at, LD 9. 🄯 CH, Dgs,
CP 20, Ac, CF, 1 st. £ BB £30–£34, DB
£43–£49·50, WB, 🛈, cc 1 2 3 4 5 6, Dep
(Xmas).
King's Head, l, x, *Front St, IL12 2LW.*
☎ (039 45) 271. Closed Jan. C. 🛏 5 bedrs,
2 ba. ✗ a l c. 🄯 ch, Dgs, CP 100, G 1, CF, 1
st. £ BB £13·20, DB £26·40, 🛈, Bk £4, L £8,
D £8, cc 5.

ORMESBY ST MARGARET Norfolk.
Map 16A
Pop 3,000. Norwich 18, London 129,
Caister 3, Cromer 27, Great Yarmouth 4½,
North Walsham 19.
EC Wed. **Golf** Caister 18h. **See** Church

🄯 🅫★★**Ormesby Lodge,** *Decoy Rd.* ☎ Gt
Yarmouth (0493) 730910. C. 🛏 8 bedrs, 7
bp, 1 sh, TV. ✗ LD 10.30. 🄯 CH, Dgs, CP 40, sp,
con 30, CF. £ BB £22–£25, DB £35, DBB
£34–£37, WB, 🄯, 10%, Bk £4·50, L £6·40, D
£12, cc 1 2 3 5, Dep.

ORPINGTON Greater London (Kent).
Map 7B
Pop 87,925. London 14, Bromley 5½,
Croydon 9½, Dartford 9, Maidstone 24,
Purley 11, Sevenoaks 9, Sidcup 4½,
Westerham 11.
EC Thur. **Golf** Chislehurst 18h, Langley
Park 18h. **See** All Saints' Church (Saxon
work).

Repairer: Burton & Deakin Ltd, 1 Crofton
Rd. ☎ (0959) 31661.
Fox's Garages (Badgers Mount) Ltd,
Orpington-by-pass. ☎ Knockholt (0959)
34218.
Rescue Service: Maxwell Garage Co
(Orpington) Ltd, Station App. ☎ (0959)
20009.

ORSETT Essex. Maps 10A & 17F
Pop 1,430. London 20, London 25,
Brentwood 9, Dartford Tunnel 4, Tilbury 5.
EC Wed. **Golf** Orsett 18h. **See** Lock up,
Earthworks, Churches, Stone Age Camp
¾m N.E.

Rescue Service: Orsett Garage Ltd,
Stanford Rd. ☎ Grays Thurrock (0375)
891208.

OSMINGTON Dorset. Map 5F
Pop 428. Ringwood 34, London 127,
Axminster 33, Blandford Forum 20,
Dorchester 8, Lyme Regis 30, Wareham
14, Weymouth 4½.
Golf Dorchester 18h. **See** Chalk figure
(George III on horse), on Downs.

Rescue Service: St Christophers Garage,
Grove Hill. ☎ Preston (0772) 832210.

OSSETT West Yorkshire. Map 25F/33B
See also WAKEFIELD.
Pop 17,183, Wakefield 4, London 186, M1
Motorway 1, Barnsley 12, Bradford 12,
Halifax 14, Huddersfield 11, Leeds 9½.
EC Mon, Wed. **MD** Tue, Fri. **Golf** Low
Laithes 18h. **See** Parish Church.

★★★**M Post House** (TH), Queens Dr,
WF5 9BE. ✆ Wakefield (0924) 276388. C.
⊨ 96 bedrs, 96 bp, TV, Dgs. ✗ a l c, mc, at,
LD 10.15. ⊞ Lt, N, CH, Dgs, CP 140, Ac
con 140, CF, 37 BGf, 0 st, Dis. £ BB £44,
DB £56·50, WB, ⊡, cc 1 2 3 4 5 6,
Dep (Xmas).

OSWESTRY Shropshire. Map 19E
Pop 12,400. Shrewsbury 17, London 173,
Aberdovey 59, Aberystwyth 67, Bala 32,
Dolgellau 49, Llangollen 12, Welshpool
15, Whitchurch 19, Wrexham 16.
EC Thur. **MD** Wed. **Golf** Oswestry 18h,
Llanymynech 18h. **See** Parish Church of
St Oswald, King Oswald's Well, Llwyd
Mansion, 16th cent Croeswylan Stone,
Castle Bank (traces of ancient castle),
Offa's Dyke, Iron Age earthworks at Old
Oswestry.
🛈 The Library, Arthur St. ✆ Oswestry
(0691) 662753.

★★★**Wynnstay** (TH), Church St, SY11
2SZ. ✆ (0691) 655261. C. ⊨ 31 bedrs, 16
bp, 2 bps, 8 ba, TV, Dgs. ✗ a l c, mc, LD
9.30. ⊞ CH, Dgs, CP 70, Ac, CF, 0 st. £ BB
£31–£34, DB £41–£47·50, WB, ⊡,
cc 1 2 3 4 5 6, Dep (Xmas).

⊯★★**Sweeney Hall**, SY10 9EU.
✆ (0691) 652450. C. ⊨ 8 bedrs, 5 bp, 3
ba, Dgs. ✗ a l c, mc, at, LD 9.30. ⊞ CH, TV,
CP 50, Ac, con 50, CF, 4 st. £ BB £15–£21,
DB £22–£34, DT £28–£31, ⊡, Bk £3, L £6,
D £7, cc 3.

Repairer: Roy Evans (Garages) Ltd,
Willow St. ✆ (0691) 652301.
Rescue Service: Morda Garage, Morda.
✆ (0691) 652037.

OTTERBOURNE Hampshire. Map 6D
Pop 1,000. Winchester 4, London 68,
Cosham 19, Fareham 16, Romsey 8½,
Southampton 8.
EC Sat. **Golf** Winchester 18h, Twyford
18h. **See** Old Coaching Inn.

Repairer: Williams' Garages (LJW) Ltd,
Otterbourne Garage. ✆ Twyford (0734)
713150.

OTTERBURN Northumberland. Map
31C
Pop 300. Corbridge 22, London 299,
Alnwick 27, Alston 43, Bellingham 8½,
Berwick-upon-Tweed 52, Brampton 45,
Hawick 31, Hexham 23, Jedburgh 27,
Newcastle-upon-Tyne 32.
Golf Bellingham 18h. **See** Otterburn
Tower, Battle of Otterburn Memorial.

◼★★★**Percy Arms**, NE19 1NR.
✆ (0830) 20261. RS Jan. C. ⊨ 31 bedrs,
26 bp, 4 bps, 1 sh, 1 ba, ns, TV, Dgs. ✗ mc,
at, LD 9.30. ⊞ CH, TV, ns, CP 40, U 4, Ac, pf,
con 100, CF, 2 st. £ BB £18·50–£23, DB
£36–£44, DBB £25–£30, WB, ⊡, Bk £4·50,
L £4·50, D £10, cc 1 2 3 5, Dep.

OTTERTON Devon. Map 4F
Pop 700. Ottery St Mary 6½, London 164,
Budleigh Salterton 3, Exeter 12, Exmouth
6½, Sidmouth 3½.
EC Sat. **Golf** Budleigh Salterton 18h,
Sidmouth 18h. **See** Parish Church,

Working Mill with water wheels, South
Devon Coast Path, Bicton Gardens (1 m
W).

Rescue Service: Cross Tree Garage,
✆ Colaton Raleigh (0395) 68265.

OTTERY ST MARY Devon. Map 4F
Pop 7,069. Honiton 5½, London 158,
Exeter 12, Lyme Regis 18, Tiverton 19.
EC Wed. **Golf** Honiton 18h. **See** St Mary's
Church (14th cent clock), Cadhay (16th
cent manor house) 1 m NW, Circular
Tumbling Weir.

⊯★★★**Salston**, EX11 1RQ. ✆ (040 481)
2310. C. ⊨ 33 bedrs, 15 bp, 3 ba, ns, TV,
Dgs. ✗ a l c, mc, at, LD 9.30. ⊞ CH, Dgs,
ns, CP 100, Ac, sp, sc, sb, sol, con 50, CF, 6
BGf, 2 st. £ BB £25–£42, DB £30–£48,
DBB £34–£41, WB, ⊡, Bk £3·50, L £6, D
£8·50, cc 1 2 3 4 5 6.

Venn Ottery Barton, H, xy (RI), EX11
1RZ. ✆ (040 481) 2733. Open Mar–Oct. C.
⊨ 13 bedrs, 4 bp, 4 bps, 2 ba, Dgs. ⊞ CH,
TV, Dgs, ns, CP 16, CF. £ BB £12·50–
£16·50, DB £22–£30, WT (b) £91–£106,
DT (b) £14–£16, ⊡, D £6.

Rescue Service: Riverside Motors, Exeter
Rd. ✆ (040 481) 3016.

OULTON West Yorkshire. Map 25F
Pop 4,500. Pontefract 8½, London 186,
M62 Motorway 1, Boroughbridge 28,
Goole 27, Halifax 19, Huddersfield 18,
Leeds 5, Oldham 35, Rochdale 35, Selby
18, Thorne 28, Wakefield 5½, York 23.
EC Mon, Wed. **Golf** Temple Newsam 18h
(2). **See** St John's Church, The Nookin
(17th cent house).

★★★**M Crest**, The Grove, LS26 8EJ.
✆ Leeds (0532) 826201. C. ⊨ 40 bedrs,
40 bp, ns, TV, Dgs. ✗ a l c, mc, LD 10. ⊞ N,
CH, CP 200, Ac, CF, 24 BGf, 3 st. £ B fr
£42, BD fr £53, WB, ⊡, Bk £5·25, D £9·60,
cc 1 2 3 4 5 6, Dep b.

Rescue Service: Frank Cooper & Sons
(Oulton) Ltd, Regency Garage, Aberford
Rd. ✆ Leeds (0532) 822382.

OULTON BROAD Suffolk. Map 16B
Saxmundham 23, London 118, Aldeburgh
27, Great Yarmouth 10, Lowestoft 2,
Norwich 25, Scole 27, Stowmarket 45.
EC Thur. **Golf** Lowestoft 18h. **See** Oulton
Broad.

★★★**Wherry**, Bridge Rd, NR32 3LN.
✆ Lowestoft (0502) 3521.
★★**M Oulton Broad**, Bridge Rd, NR32
2LR. ✆ Lowestoft (0502) 2157.

OUNDLE Northamptonshire. Map 15A
Pop 3,223. Biggleswade 35, London 80,
Bedford 30, Bletchley 41, Huntingdon 23,
Kettering 17, Market Harborough 21,
Melton Mowbray 34, Northampton 28,
Peterborough 13, Stamford 15.
EC Wed. **MD** Thur. **Golf** Oundle 18h. **See**
Oundle Public School (founded in 1556),
St Peter's Church (200 ft spire), 17th cent
Talbot Inn, Paines Almshouses, Oundle
Marina 1 m.

★★★**Talbot**, New St, PE8 4EA. ✆ (0832)
73621. C. ⊨ 38 bedrs, 38 bp, TV, Dgs.
✗ a l c, mc. ⊞ N, CH, Dgs, CP 50, Ac, con
100, CF, 1 BGf, 2 st. £ BB £36, DB £48,
WB, ⊡, Bk £4·50, L £6·20, D £9,
cc 1 2 3 5 6, Dep b.

Rescue Service: Oundle Motors Ltd,
Station Rd. ✆ (0832) 73542.

OUTWELL Norfolk (Cambs). Map 16F
Pop 1,243. Littleport 14, London 90,
Downham Market 7, March 11, Wisbech
5½.
EC Wed. **Golf** Denver 9h.

Rescue Service: Lawrence Buck, Wisbech
Rd, Outwell, Wisbech. ✆ Upwell
(094 571) 2310.

OVERTON Hampshire. Map 6D
Pop 3,700. Basingstoke 8, London 54,
Andover 11, Newbury 14, Reading 23,
Wallingford 31, Winchester 14.
EC Wed. **Golf** Overton 9h. **See** Old
Cottages, Tudor Inn, Church, 14th cent
Arches.

Rescue Service: Berry Down Garage,
London Rd. ✆ Basingstoke (0256)
770580.

OWER Hampshire. Map 6C
Pop 500. Romsey 3½, London 79,
Lyndhurst 6, Ringwood 14, Salisbury 15,
Southampton 7.
Golf Lyndhurst 18h, Bramshaw 18h (2).

★★★**M New Forest Moat House**, SO5
0ZJ. ✆ Southampton (0703) 814333. C.
⊨ 43 bedrs, 43 bp, TV, Dgs. ✗ a l c, mc,
LD 9.30. ⊞ N, CH, Dgs, CP 200, G 6, Ac,
con 50, CF, 24 BGf, 0 st, Dis. £ BB £33–
£36, DB £43–£48, WB, ⊡, Bk £4·20, L
£5·50, D £8, cc 1 2 3 4 5 6, Dep b.

OXFORD Oxfordshire. Map 14F
See also HEADINGTON.
RAC Office, 226 Banbury Road, Oxford,
OX2 7DN. ✆ (General) Oxford (0865)
53443 (Rescue Service only) Oxford
(0865) 53333.
Pop 116,400. High Wycombe 26, London
56, M40 Motorway 8½, Aylesbury 22,
Banbury 23, Bicester 12, Burford 20,
Chipping Norton 20, Faringdon 17,
Newbury 26, Stratford-upon-Avon 39,
Swindon 29, Towcester 33, Wallingford
12, Wantage 15.
See Plan, p. 291.
EC Thur. **MD** Wed. **P** See Plan. **Golf** North
Oxford 18h, Southfield 18h. **See** Colleges,
Cathedral, Bodleian Library, Sheldonian
Theatre, Ashmolean, History of Science
and University Museums, Botanic Garden,
many churches, Martyrs Memorial, Carfax
Tower (interesting clock), old inns,
towpath walks (Isis and Cherwell),
Blenheim Palace and Garden Centre,
Woodstock 8 m N, Bladon Church (grave
of Sir Winston Churchill), Rousham House
11½ m N.
🛈 St Aldates Chambers. ✆ Oxford (0865)
726871.

★★★★**Randolph** (TH), Beaumont St,
OX1 2LN. ✆ (0865) 247481. C. ⊨ 109
bedrs, 109 bp, TV, Dgs. ✗ a l c, mc, at, LD
10.15. ⊞ Lt, N, CH, Dgs, G 60, Ac, con 350,
CF, 3 st. £ BB £47·50, DB £63·50, WB, ⊡,
cc 1 2 3 4 5 6, Dep (Xmas).

★★★**Linton Lodge**, Linton Rd, OX2 6UJ.
✆ (0865) 53461. C. ⊨ 72 bedrs, 66 bp, 6
bps, 3 ba, TV, Dgs. ✗ mc, at, LD 9.30. ⊞ Lt,
N, CH, Dgs, CP 40, Ac, con 120, CF, 1 st.
£ BB £35–£45, DB £48–£62·50, DT £60–
£62, DBB £48–£54, WB, ⊡, Bk £5·25, L
£7·50, D £9, cc 1 2 3 4 5 6, Dep b.

★★★**M Oxford Moat House**,
Wolvercote Roundabout, OX2 8AL.
✆ (0865) 59933. C. ⊨ 155 bedrs, 155 bp,
TV, Dgs. ✗ mc, at, LD 9.30. ⊞ N, CH, Dgs,
CP 250, G 8, Ac, gc, con 120, CF, 30 BGf, 2

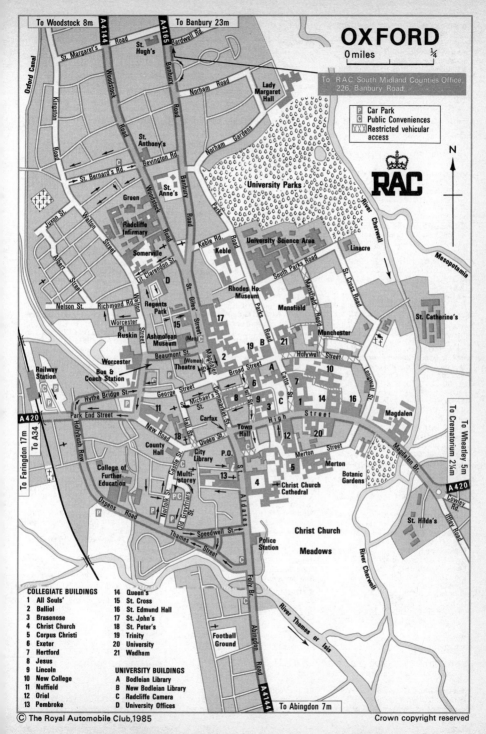

OXFORD

0 miles ¼

To R.A.C. South Midland Counties Office, 226, Banbury Road.

P	Car Park
C	Public Conveniences
XXX	Restricted vehicular access

N

RAC

COLLEGIATE BUILDINGS
1 All Souls'
2 Balliol
3 Brasenose
4 Christ Church
5 Corpus Christi
6 Exeter
7 Hertford
8 Jesus
9 Lincoln
10 New College
11 Nuffield
12 Oriel
13 Pembroke
14 Queen's
15 St. Cross
16 St. Edmund Hall
17 St. John's
18 St. Peter's
19 Trinity
20 University
21 Wadham

UNIVERSITY BUILDINGS
A Bodleian Library
B New Bodleian Library
C Radcliffe Camera
D University Offices

st. **£** BB fr £38, DB fr £48, WT fr £164, WB, ▣, Bk £3·75, L £4·95, D fr £6·75, cc 1 2 3 4 5 6, Dep b.

★★★M TraveLodge (TH), *Peartree Roundabout, Woodstock Rd, OX2 8JZ.* ✆ (0865) 54301. C. ⊯ 102 bedrs, 102 bp, TV, Dgs. ✖ mc. ▣ N, CH, Dgs, CP 102, Ac, sp, con 50, CF, 51 BGf, 2 st. **£** BB £31·50, DB £42, WB, ▣, cc 1 2 3 4 5 6. Meals are served in the adjacent Service Area Restaurant.

★★Cotswold Lodge, *Banbury Rd, OX2 6JP.* ✆ (0865) 512120. C. ⊯ 52 bedrs, 52 ba. ▣ N, CH, CP 60, Ac, CF, 18 BGf, 4 st. **£** BB £35–£38·50, DB £45–£48·50, DBB £45–£60·50, ▣, Bk £5·50, L £7·50, D £8·50, cc 1 2 3 5 6.

★★Eastgate, *The High, OX1 4BE.* ✆ (0865) 248244. C. ⊯ 42 bedrs, 38 bp, 4 bps, TV, Dgs. ✖ mc, at, LD 10. ▣ Lt, N, CH, CP 42, Ac, CF, 4 st. **£** BB £40·50, DB £48, ·WB, ▣, Bk £4, L £6·95, D £6·95, cc 1 2 3 4 5 6, Dep.

▣★★Isis (R), *Iffley Rd, OX4 1ED.* ✆ (0865) 248894. C. ⊯ 33 bedrs, 5 bp, 6 ba, annexe 5 bedrs, 1 ba, TV, Dgs. ✖ mc, at, LD 9. ▣ CH, TV, CP 13, G 8, Ac, con 12, CF, 2 BGf, 6 st. **£** BB £19·50–£28·50, DB £32–£40, WT £171–£190, DT £27·25–£29, WB, ▢, B £3·25, L £1·25, D £6·50, cc 1 2 3 5 6, Dep b.

★★Royal Oxford, *Park End St, OX1 1HR.* ✆ (0865) 248432. C. ⊯ 25 bedrs, 12 bp, 4 ba, TV, Dgs. ✖ mc, LD 9.30. ▣ N, CH, Dgs, CP 12, Ac, con 45, CF, 1 st. **£** B fr £23, BD fr £33, WB, ▣, Bk £4·25, D £6·75, cc 1 2 3 4 5 6, Dep b.

★★Victoria (Rt), *180 Abington Rd, OX1 4RA.* ✆ (0865) 724536. C. ⊯ 15 bedrs, 5 bp, 2 ba, ns, TV, Dgs. ✖ a l c, mc, at, LD 9.30. ▣ CH, Dgs, ns, CP 20, Ac, CF £ BB £17·50–£24·50, DB £28–£35, WB, ▣, Bk £3·75, L £4·50, D £7·50, cc 1 6, Dep a.

Ascot, G, z (Unl), *283 Iffley Rd, OX4 4AQ.* ✆ (0865) 240259. C. ⊯ 6 bedrs, 1 bp, 1 ba, TV. ▣ CH, TV, CP 2. **£** BB £9·50–£10·50, DB £16–£21, ▣.

Brown's, G, x (Unl), *281 Iffley Rd, OX4 4AQ.* ✆ (0865) 246822.

Earlmount, G, z (Unl), *322 Cowley Rd, OX4 2AF.* ✆ (0865) 240236. Closed Xmas. C. ⊯ 12 bedrs, 2 sh, 4 ba, TV. ▣ CH, TV, ns, CP 10, G 1, CF, 3 BGf, 1 st. **£** BB £8·50–£9·50, DB £17–£18, ▣.

Galaxie, PH, z (Unl), *180 Banbury Rd, OX2 7BT.* ✆ (0865) 55688.

Kings, G, z (Unl), *363 Iffley Rd, OX4 4DP.* ✆ (0865) 241363. C 5. ⊯ 5 bedrs, 3 sh, 1 ba. ▣ CH, TV, CP 6. **£** BB fr £10·50, DB fr £20, WT (c) £63, ▣.

Melcombe House, G, z (Unl), *227 Iffley Rd, OX4 1SE.* ✆ (0865) 249520. C 3. ⊯ 7 bedrs, 2 ba, Dgs. ▣ CH, TV, Dgs, CP 6, 4 st. **£** BB £8·50–£9·10, DB £17–£18, ▣.

Pine Castle, G, z (Unl), *290 Iffley Rd, OX4 1AE.* ✆ (0865) 241497. C. ⊯ 7 bedrs, 1 sh, 1 ba, TV, Dgs. ▣ CH, TV, CP 4, CF. **£** BB £8–£11, DB £15–£24, WT (a) fr £89, (b) fr £75, (c) fr £55, DT £11–£15, ▣, Bk £2, D £4.

River, H, z (R), *17 Botley Rd, OX2 0AA.* ✆ (0865) 243475. Closed Xmas and New Year. C. ⊯ 17 bedrs, 6 bp, 5 bps, 6 sh, 2 ba, TV, Dgs. ▣ CH, TV, ns, CP 20, CF, 3 BGf, 8 st. **£** BB fr £15, DB fr £25, ▢, Bk £3, L £3, D £3·50.

Tilbury Lodge, G (Unl), *5 Tilbury Lane, Botley, OX2 9NB.* ✆ (0865) 862138. Closed Xmas. C. ⊯ 7 bedrs, 2 bp, 2 bps, 1

ba, TV, Dgs. ▣ CH, TV, CP 7, G 2, CF. **£** BB £10–£11, DB £20–£25, ▣,▲

Westgate, H, z (R), *1 Botley Rd, OX2 0AA.* ✆ (0865) 726721. Closed Xmas. C. ⊯ 13 bedrs, 5 sh, 3 ba, TV, Dgs. ▣ CH, TV, CP 12, CF. **£** BB fr £15, DB fr £27, ▣, cc 1 2 3 5.▲

Westwood Country, H, xy (R), *Hinksey Hill Top, OX1 5BG.* ✆ (0865) 735408. C. ⊯ 18 bedrs, 10 bp, 8 bps, 1 ba, TV. ▣ Lt, CH, TV, ns, CP 26, CF, 4 BGf, 0 st, Dis. **£** BB £23–£26, DB £30–£45, ▣, Bk £3·50, D £7·50, cc 1 2 3.▲

White House View, G, z (Unl), *9 Whitehouse Rd, OX1 4PA.* ✆ (0865) 721626. C. ⊯ 9 bedrs, 1 bps, 1 ba, Dgs. ▣ CH, TV, Dgs, 1 st. **£** BB £8, DB £15–£17, ▣, Bk £2·50.

Willow Reaches, PH, z (Rl). *1 Wytham Street, OX1 4SU.* ✆ (0865) 721545. C. ⊯ 8 bedrs, 2 bp, 1 bps, 3 ba, TV. ▣ CH, TV, G 4, CF, 3 st. **£** BB £11·50–£23, DB £19·50–£26, ▣, D £6, cc 2 3 5.

Windrush, G, z, (Unl), *11 Iffley Rd, OX4 1EA.* ✆ (0865) 247933. Closed Xmas. C. 5. ⊯ 8 bedrs, 2 ba, Dgs. ▣ TV, 2 BGf, 4 st. **£** BB £10–£12, DB £16–£20, ▣.

Repairers: City Motor Co (Oxford) Ltd, The Roundabout, Woodstock Rd. ✆ (0865) 59955.
Groom & Hornsby, 496 Cowley Rd. ✆ (0865) 778282.
Hartford Motors (Oxford) Ltd, Seacourt Tower, West Way. ✆ (0865) 249966.
Hartwell's of Oxford Ltd, Botley Rd. ✆ (0865) 244833.
Magdalen Service Garage, 60 Magdalen Rd, Iffley Rd. ✆ (0865) 247307.
North Oxford Garage Ltd, 280 Banbury Rd. ✆ (0865) 511461.
Oxford Motors Ltd, 370 Iffley Rd. ✆ (0865) 776161.
Specialist Battery and Car Lighting and Ignition Repairer: Boreham's Car Electrical Service Ltd, St Thomas St. ✆ (0865) 244582.
Specialist Body Repairer: City Motor Co (Oxford) Ltd, Iffley Rd. ✆ (0865) 777629.
Specialist Radiator Repairer: Serck Radiator Services Ltd, 9 Botley Works, North Hinksey La. ✆ (0865) 249051.
MC Repairer: Faulkner & Son Ltd, 55 Walton St. ✆ (0865) 57279.
Rescue Service: J T Motors, Worcester Pl. ✆ (0865) 59078.
Oxford Motors Ltd, 370 Iffley Rd. ✆ (0865) 776161.
St Clements Garage, Dawson St. ✆ (0865) 244554.

OXTED Surrey. Map 7D
Purley 9½, London 21, M25 Motorway 3, Crawley 17, East Grinstead 10, Redhill 8, Westerham 3½.
See Detillens (1 m E).

★★Hoskins Hotel, *Station Rd West, RH8 9EE.* ✆ (0883) 2338. C. ⊯ 10 bedrs, 10 bp, 1 ba, TV, Dgs. ✖ a l c, mc, at, LD 9.30. ▣ CH, TV, CP 30, con 30, CF, 3 st. **£** BB £30, DB £37·50, DBB £43·50–£45, ▣, Bk £2·25, L £5, D £5, cc 1 2 3 5 6, Dep b.

PADIHAM Lancashire. Map 27B
Pop 10,075. Burnley 3, London 209, Accrington 4, Blackburn 8½, Bolton 20, Bradford 30, Settle 24, Skipton 19, Whalley 4½.
EC Tue. **Golf** Accrington 18h, Burnley 18h, Whalley 9h. **See** Gawthorpe Hall (Nat Trust), Pendle Hill (6 m N).

★★Higher Trapp, *Trapp La, Simonstone, BB12 7QW.* ✆ (0282) 72781. C. ⊯ 17 bedrs, 17 bp, TV. ✖ a l c, mc, at, LD 10. ▣ CH, CP 150, Ac, con 100, CF, 1 st. **£** BB fr £27·50, DB fr £39, Bk £2·50, L £7·50, D £7·50, cc 1 2 3 5 6, Dep b.

PADSTOW Cornwall. Map 2D
See also CONSTANTINE BAY.
Pop 3,000. Wadebridge 7½, London 246, Newquay 14, St Austell 18, Truro 23.
EC Wed. **MD** Thur. **Golf** Trevose Gold and CC 18h. **See** 13th–15th cent St Petroc's Church, Tropical Bird and Butterfly Garden, Hobby Horse Festival on May Day, Trevose Head.

★★★Metropole (TH), *Station Rd, PL28 8DB.* ✆ (0841) 532486. Open Mar–Oct. C. ⊯ 44 bedrs, 44 bp, TV, Dgs. ✖ a l c, mc, at, LD 8.30. ▣ Lt, CH, Dgs, CP 40, Ac, sp, con 35, CF, 2 BGf, 0 st, Dis. **£** BB £34·50, DB £56·50, WB, ▣, cc 1 2 3 4 5 6.

▣★★Old Custom House, *South Quay, PL28 8BY.* ✆ (0841) 532359. Open Apr–Oct. C. ⊯ 14 bedrs, 14 bp, TV, Dgs. ✖ mc, LD 9. ▣ CH, TV, Dgs, con 25, CF. **£** BB £17–£20, DB £30–£36, DBB £22·50–£25·50, ▢, Bk £2·50, L £3·80, D £7·50, cc 1 3, Dep b.▲

▣★Dinas (R), *Sarahs La, PL28 8EL.* ✆ (0841) 532326.

▣★Trevone Bay (Rl), *Dobbin Close, Trevone, PL28 8QS.* ✆ (0841) 520243. Open May–Oct. C. ⊯ 15 bedrs, 5 ba, Dgs. ✖ mc, at, LD 7.30. ▣ ch, TV, CP 12, CF, 2 st. **£** BB £8·60–£9·20, DB £17·20–£40, WT £88·55–£97·75, DBB £13·22–£14·95, ▢, Bk £3·45, L £4, D £6·90, Dep a.

Bay House, H, x (Rt), *Harlyn Bay, PL28 8LW.* ✆ (0841) 520472. Open Apr–Oct. C. ⊯ 17 bedrs, 4 ba, Dgs. ▣ ch, TV, CP 17, CF, 1 st. **£** Bk £2·70, D £5·70.

Cross House, G, z (Unl), *Church St, PL28 8BG.* ✆ (0841) 532391.

Duke House, G, z (Unl), *48 Duke St, PL28 8AD.* ✆ (0841) 532372. C. ⊯ 8 bedrs, 2 ba, Dgs. ▣ TV, 1 st. **£** BB £8–£9·50, DB £13–£17, WT £45–£55, ▣.

Green Waves, PH, xy (Rl), *Trevone Bay, PL28 8RD.* ✆ (0841) 520114.▲

The Nook, PH, x (Rl), *Fentonluna La, PL28 8BA.* ✆ (0841) 532317. C. ⊯ 10 bedrs, 2 ba, Dgs. ▣ CH, TV, CP 10. **£** BB £12·07–£16·67, DB £24·14–£28·74, WT (c) £58·65–£71·32, DT (b) £17·82–£20·12, ▣.

Tregea, G, x (Unl), *High St, PL28 8BB.* ✆ (0841) 532455. Open Feb–Nov. C. ⊯ 8 bedrs, 3 ba, Dgs. ▣ CH, TV, Dgs, CP 8, CF, 1 st. **£** BB £11·50–£13, DB £18·50–£19·50, WT (b) £84·50–£94·50, DT (b) £13·50–£14·50, ▣, Bk £2·50, D £6·50.

Woodlands, G, xy (Rl), *Treator, PL28 8RU.* ✆ (0841) 532426. C. ⊯ 9 bedrs, 9 bps, 1 ba, Dgs. ▣ CH, TV, Dgs, CP 15, CF, 2 st. **£** BB £8·62–£10, DB £17·24–£18·40, WT (b) £91·35–£98, (c) £56·35–£60·34, DT (b) £13·62, ▣, D £5.

Rescue Service: St Merryn Garage, St Merryn. ✆ (0841) 520255.
Tregoning, J C & Son, Trecerus Industrial Estate ✆ (0841) 532669.

PAGHAM West Sussex. Map 7E
Bognor Regis 4, London 67, Chichester 7.
See Harbour (bird sanctuary).

King's Beach, H, *PO21 4UW.* ✆ (024 32) 2006.

PAIGNTON Torbay. Devon. Map 3D
Pop 35,100. Torquay 3, London 191,
Dartmouth (Fy) 7½, Totnes 6.
EC Wed. **Golf** Churston 18h. **See**
Paignton Zoological & Botanical Gardens,
Oldway Mansion, Kirkham House,
Compton Castle, Aquarium, Illuminations,
Torbay and Dartmouth Rly (Paignton-
Kingswear), Torbay Aircraft Museum,
Dart Valley Rly (Buckfastleigh–Totnes).
⊺ Festival Hall, Esplanade Rd. ☎ Paignton
(0803) 558383.

★★★Palace (TH), *Esplanade Rd, TQ4
6BJ.* ☎ (0803) 555121. C. ⊨ 54 bedrs, 54
bp, TV, Dgs. ✗ a l c, mc, at, LD 8.45. ⓓ Lt,
N, CH, Dgs, CP 60, Ac, sp, tc, sc, sb, con
150, CF, 1 BGf, 7 st. £ BB £35·50, DB
£57·50, WB, ⓵, cc 1 2 3 4 5 6, Dep (Xmas).

★★★Redcliffe, *Marine Drive, TQ3 2NL.*
☎ (0803) 526397. C. ⊨ 63 bedrs, 56 bp, 7
bps, TV, Dgs. ✗ a l c, mc, at, LD 8.30. ⓓ Lt,
N, CH, TV, CP 100, Ac, sp, pf, con 150, CF,
6 st. £ BB £19–£28, DB £38–£56, DBB
£22–£32, WB, ⓶, Bk £4, L £5, D £7·25,
cc 1 2 3, Dep b.

★★Alta Vista (R), *10 Alta Vista Rd, TQ4
6BY.* (Roundham.) ☎ (0803) 551496.

★★Hunter's Lodge, (RI), *Roundham Rd,
Goodrington, TQ4 6DN.* ☎ (0803)
557034.

◻★★St Ann's, *6 Alta Vista Rd, TQ4 6BZ.*
☎ (0803) 557360. Open Apr–Oct. RS Apr
& Oct. C. ⊨ 28 bedrs, 28 bp, TV, Dgs.
✗ mc, at, LD 8. ⓓ CH, TV, CP 31, Ac, sp,
sb, sol, con 75, CF, 3 BGf, 0 st, Dis. £ BB
£12·50–£20, DB £25–£38, DBB £17·50–
£48, ⓵, Bk £3·50, D £7·50, cc 1 6, Dep.

★★M Torbay, *Totnes Rd, TQ4 7PP.*
☎ (0803) 558226.▲

Amaryllis, PH, xy (Unl), *Sands Rd, TQ4
6EG.* ☎ (0803) 559552.

Bayview, PH, z (R), *6 Cleveland Rd, TQ4
6EN.* ☎ (0803) 557400.Open Nov–Dec. C.
⊨ 10 bedrs, 2 ba. ⓓ CH, TV, CP 10, CF, 4
st. £ BB £6·50–£8·50, DB £13·50–£17, WT
(b) £65–£77, DT (b) fr £9, ⓵, Bk £1·50, D
£3.

Blue Dolphin, G, x (Unl), *131 Torquay
Rd, TQ3 2SG.* ☎ (0803) 556727.

Blue Seas, PH, z (RI), *4 St Andrews Rd,
TQ4 6HA.* ☎ (0803) 558348. C. ⊨ 12
bedrs, 1 bps, 2 ba. ⓓ CH, TV, CP 8, CF, 1
BGf, 2 st. £ BB fr £6, DB fr £12, WT (b) fr
£58, (c) fr £38, DT (b) fr £9, ⓵.

Braemar, PH, z (RI), *38 Seaway Rd,
Preston.* ☎ (0803) 558752. Open Feb–
Nov. C. ⊨ 10 bedrs, 2 ba. ⓓ CH, TV, CP
10, CF, 2 st. £ BB fr £7, DB fr £14, WT (a) fr
£80·50, (c) fr £49, DT (b) fr £11·50, ⓵.

Briars, PH, z (RI), *26 Sands Rd, TQ4 6EJ.*
☎ (0803) 557729. C 5. ⊨ 15 bedrs, 8 bps,
2 ba, Dgs. ⓓ CH, TV, ns, CP 9. £ BB £8–
£11·50, DB £16–23, WT fr £77–£86, DT
(b) £11·50–£12·50, ⓵, Bk £3, D £4.

Cambria Hotel, H (RI), *Sea Front, TQ4
6BL.* ☎ (0803) 559256. Closed Jan. C.
⊨ 24 bedrs, 2 ba, Dgs. ⓓ CH, TV, CF. £ BB
£10–£14, DB £18–£24, WT £56–£104, DT
£18–£24, ⓵.

Channel View, PH, z (RI), *8 Marine
Parade, TQ3 2NU.* ☎ (0803) 522432.

Clennon Valley, H, z (RI), *1 Clennon
Rise, TQ4 5HG.* ☎ (0803) 550304. C.
⊨ 11 bedrs, 1 bp, 8 bps, 2 ba, TV,
Dgs. ⓓ CH, TV, Dgs, CP 12, CF, 8 st. £ BB
£8·50–£12, DB £15–£24, WT £75–£95,
DT (b) £13–£15, WB, ⓵, Bk £2, D £6.

Commodore, H, z, (RI), *14 Esplanade
Rd, TQ4 6EB.* ☎ (0803) 553107. Open

Feb–Nov. C. ⊨ 15 bedrs, 1 bps, 1 sh, 3 ba,
Dgs. ⓓ ch, TV, CP 8, CF, 6 st. £ BB £8·05–
£11·50, DB £16·10–£23, WT (b) £76·47–
£96·60, DT (b) £10·92–£13·92, ⓵.

Cove Bungalow, PH (Unl), *43 Seaway
Rd. TQ3 2NX.* ☎ (0803) 523311. C. ⊨ 8
bedrs, 2 ba. ⓓ CH, TV, Dgs, CP, CF.
£ BB £5·50–£8·50, DB £11–£17, WT (b)
£50–£75, (c) £36–£57, DT (b) £8–£11·50,
WB, ⓵, Bk £2·50, D £3·50.

Dainton House, PH, z (R), *Dartmouth
Rd, TQ4 6NA.* ☎ (0803) 550067. C. ⊨ 12
bedrs, 1 bps, 3 sh, 2 ba, TV. ✗ a l c. ⓓ CH,
TV, CP 20, CF, 5 BGf, 0 st, Dis. £ BB
£10·25–£10·75, DB £20·50–£21·50, WT
(b) £99–£100, DT (b) £15·25–£15·75, ⓵, L
£4·25, D £5·85.▲

Dalveen, PH, z (RI), *15 Manor Rd, TQ3
2HT.* ☎ (0803) 551131.

Florida, G, z (Unl), *9 Colin Rd, TQ3 2NR.*
☎ (0803) 551447. Open Mar–Oct. C. ⊨ 9
bedrs, 2 ba, Dgs. ⓓ ch, TV, Dgs, CP 2, CF.
£ BB £6·50–£8, DB £13–£16, WT (b)
£59·50–£77, DT (b) £8·50–£11, ⓵.

Haven, PH, z (RI), *14 Grosvenor Rd, TQ4
5AY.* ☎ (0803) 559483.

Lookout, PH, (RI), *14 Marine Par, TQ3
2NU.* ☎ (0803) 525638. C. ⊨ 12 bedrs, 1
bps, 1 sh, 3 ba, Dgs. ⓓ CH, TV, Dgs, CP 8,
CF, 1 BGf, 1 st, Dis. £ BB £7–£10, DB £14–
£20, WT (b) £69–£89, DT (b) £11–£14, ⓵,
Bk £2, D £4·50, cc 2 3.

Nevada, PH, z (Rt), *61 Dartmouth Rd,
TQ4 5AE.* ☎ (0803) 558317.

Palm Sands, PH, z (RI), *21 Morin Rd,
Preston. TQ3 2PL.* ☎ (0803) 523226.

Pendarry, PH, z (RI), *35 Dartmouth Rd.
TQ4 5AE.* ☎ (0803) 551077.

Preston Sands, H, z (RI), *Marine Par,
TQ3 2NU.* ☎ (0803) 558718. Open Mar–
Nov. C. ⊨ 15 bedrs, 6 bps, 3 sh, 3 ba, TV,
Dgs. ⓓ CH, TV, CP 10, CF, 2 BGf, 2 st.
£ BB £7–£10·50, DB £14–£20, WT (b) fr
£70, (c) fr £49, DT (b) fr £11·50, ⓵.

Priory Towers, PH, z, (RI), *21
Esplanade Rd, TQ4 6AE.* ☎ (0803)
551032. Open Mar–Oct. C. ⊨ 21 bedrs, 6
bps, 3 ba, Dgs. ⓓ CH, TV, CP 15, CF, 4 BGf,
1 st.

Radford, PH, z (Rt), *28 Youngs Park Rd,
TQ4 6BU.* ☎ (0803) 559671. C. ⊨ 14
bedrs, 4 ba, Dgs. ⓓ CH, TV, CP 4, CF, 4
BGf. £ BB £6·45–£8·30, DB £12·90–
£16·60, WT (b) £65, WT£5, ⓶, Bk £2, D £6.

Redcliffe Lodge, PH, z (RI), *1 Marine
Drive, TQ3 2NJ.* ☎ (0803) 551394. Open
Mar–Nov. C. ⊨ 19 bedrs, 7 bp, 6 bps, 2 ba,
TV. ⓓ CH, TV, CP 20, CF, 3 BGf, 1 st, Dis.
£ BB fr £10·50, DB fr £21, WT (b) £95–
£130, Bk £2·50, D £5.

Rockview, G, z (Unl), *13 Queens Rd,
TQ4 6AT.* ☎ (0803) 556702. Closed Nov–
Dec. C. ⊨ 6 bedrs, 1 sh, 1 ba. ⓓ CH, TV, CF,
4 st. £ BB £6·75–£8·45, DB £13·50–
£16·90, WT (b) £56–£69, DT (b) £8·50–
£10.25, ⓵, cc 3.

Romford Lodge, PH, z (RI), *19 Marine
Drive, TQ3 2NY.* ☎ (0803) 550315. C.
⊨ 10 bedrs, 3 bps, 2 ba, Dgs. ⓓ CH, TV,
CP 12, CF, 1 BGf, 2 st. £ BB £10·50–
£15·50, DB £15–£25, WT (b) £80–£100,
(c) £50–£70, DT (b) £12–£15, ⓵,
cc 1 2 3 5.

Rosslyn, PH, x (RI), *16 Colin Rd, TQ3
2NR.* ☎ (0803) 525578. C. ⊨ 9 bedrs, 2
ba, Dgs. ⓓ ch, TV, Dgs, CP 8, CF, 1 st. £ BB
£7·50–£9, DB £15–£18, WT (b) £60–£85,
DT (b) £10·50–£13, ⓵.

Rozel, H, y (R), *25–27 St Andrews Rd,
TQ4 6HA.* ☎ (0803) 553238. C. ⊨ 23

bedrs, 1 bps, 3 ba, Dgs. ⓓ CH, TV, Dgs, CP
23, CF. £ BB £7–£10, DB £14–£22, WT (b)
£50–£82, DT (b) £8–£12.

St. Weonards, PH, z (RI), *12 Kernou Rd,
TQ4 6BA.* ☎ (0803) 558842. Open Feb–
Nov. C. ⊨ 9 bedrs, 2 ba. ⓓ ch, TV, CP 2,
CF, 0 st. £ BB £6–£9, DB £12–£18, DT
£10–£12, ⓵.

San Remo, PH, z (R), *35 Totnes Rd, TQ4
5LA.* ☎ (0803) 557855.

Sattva, PH, z (RI), *Esplanade, TQ4 6BL.*
☎ (0803) 557820. C. ⊨ 24 bedrs, 3 bp, 9
bps, 2 ba, TV. ⓓ CH, TV, CP 6, CF, 2 BGf, 2
st. £ BB £11–£15, DB £20–£30, WT (b)
£85–£115, DT (b) £14·50–£17, ⓶, Bk
£2·50, D £5.

Sealawn, PH, z (RI), *20 Esplanade, TQ4
6BE.* ☎ (0803) 559031.

Sea Verge, PH, z (RI), *Marine Dr, TQ3
2NJ.* ☎ (0803) 557795. Closed Xmas. C.
⊨ 12 bedrs, ⅝ sh, 2 ba, TV, Dgs. ⓓ CH, TV,
Dgs, CP 12, 2 BGf. £ BB £7·50–£9·50, DB
£15–£23, WT (b) £84–£98, (c) £52·50–
£66·50, DT (b) £12–£14, ⓵.

Shorton House, PH, z (RI), *17
Roundham Rd, TQ4 6DN.* ☎ (0803)
557722.

Southlawn, G, z (Unl), *68 Upper Manor
Rd, TQ3 2TJ.* ☎ (0803) 551305. C 5. ⊨ 8
bedrs, 2 ba. ⓓ CH, TV, CP 8, 5 BGf, 1 st,
Dis. £ BB £4·95–£7·50, DB £9·90–£15, WT
(b) £59·50–£73·50, (c) £38·50–£52·50, DT
(b) £8·50–£10·50, ⓵.

South Sands, H (R), *Alta Vista Rd,
Goodrington, TQ4 6BZ.* ☎ (0803) 557231.
Open Mar–Oct & Xmas. C. ⊨ 26 bedrs, 1
bp, 4 ba, Dgs. ⓓ ch, TV, Dgs, CP 17, CF. 3
BGf, 2 st. £ BB £7·50–£10, DB £15–£20, ⓶.

Sundale, PH, z (Unl), *10 Queens Rd, TQ4
6AT.* ☎ (0803) 557431. Closed Dec. C.
⊨ 11 bedrs, 2 ba. ⓓ CH, TV, Dgs, CF, 0 st.
£ BB £7–£9·50, DB £14–£18, WT (b) £63–
£75, (c) £49·50–£59, DT (b) £9·25–£11·50, ⓵.

Sunnybank, PH, z (RI), *2 Cleveland Rd,
TQ4 6EN.* ☎ (0803) 525540. C. ⊨ 12
bedrs, 2 sh, 3 ba, TV, Dgs. ⓓ ch, TV, Dgs,
CP 8, CF, 3 BGf, 2 st. £ BB £7·50–£9·50,
DB £15–£19, WT £57·50–£87·50, DT
£11·50–£14, ⓵, Bk £, L £2, D £3·50, cc 1.

Torbay Sands, PH, z (RI), *16 Marine Par.*
☎ (0803) 525568. Closed Nov. C. ⊨ 12
bedrs, 2 sh, 2 ba, Dgs. ⓓ CH, TV, Dgs, CP
5, CF, 2 BGf, 0 st, Dis. £ BB £7·50–£11·50,
DB £15–£23, WT (b) £66–£90, DT (b)
£11–£15.

Tor Sands, H, y (RI), *8 Sands Rd, TQ4
6EH.* ☎ (0803) 559695.

Victoria Park, H, (RI), *24 Polsham Park,
TQ3 2AD.* ☎ (0803) 557701.

Wulfruna, PH, z (Unl), *8 Esplanade Rd,
TQ4 6EB.* ☎ (0803) 555567. Open Apr–
Oct. C. ⊨ 12 bedrs, 3 ba, Dgs. ⓓ ch, TV,
Dgs, CP 9, CF. £ BB £7–£10, DB £14–£20,
WT (b) £64·80–£83·50, (c) £43·80–£56,
DT £10·50–£13, ⓶.

Repairer: Roger's Garages (Paignton) Ltd,
Bishops Pl. ☎ (0803) 556234.
Rescue Service: Marldon Service Station
Ltd, Marldon. ☎ (0803) 558860.
Norman Snowdon & Sons, Totnes Rd.
☎ (0803) 559362.
Perrys Ltd, 288 Torquay Rd, Preston.
☎ (0803) 522146.
Torbay Motors, 45 Totnes Rd. ☎ (0803)
554484.
Waterside Garage, Dartmouth Rd.

PAINSWICK Gloucestershire. Map 13F
Pop 3,172. Stroud 3½, London 103,
Cheltenham 10, Gloucester 6.

EC Wed. **MD** Fri. **Golf** Painswick 18h.
See 14th cent Church with 99 clipped yew trees in churchyard, iron stocks, Painswick House, Falcon Inn.
🛈 The Library, Stroud Rd. ✆ Painswick (0452) 812569.

■★★★**Painswick,** (R), *Kemps La, GL6 6YB.* ✆ (0452) 812160. C. 🛏 15 bedrs, 14 bp, 1 ba, TV, Dgs. ✗ mc, at, LD 9.30. 🅿 CH, Dgs, CP 25, Ac, con 60, CF, 10 st. £ BB £26–£32, DB £36–£46, WB, 🖻, Bk £3·50, D £12, cc 1 2 3 5 6.
★★**Falcon,** *New Street GL6 6YB.* ✆ (0452) 812189.

PANGBOURNE Berkshire, Map 6B
Pop 2,460. Reading 6, London 45, M4 Motorway 5, Basingstoke 18, Newbury 13, Wallingford 10, Wantage 18.
Golf Calcot Park 18h. **See** Church, Timbered cottages, Bere Court, old inns.

★★★**Copper Inn,** *RG8 7AR.* ✆ (073 57) 2244. C. 🛏 21 bedrs, 21 bp, TV. ✗ a l c, mc, LD 9.30. 🅿 CH, Dgs, CP 16, con 50, CF, 3 BGf, 1 st, Dis. £ BB £40·50, DB £53, WB, 🖻, Bk £4·25, L £7, cc 1 2 3 5, Dep b.

Rescue Service: Pangbourne Service Station, Reading Rd. ✆ (073 57) 2456.

PAPPLEWICK Nottinghamshire. Map 22D
2½ m NE of Hucknall. Nottingham 7½, London 130, Buxton 43, Derby 20, Mansfield 7, Newark on Trent 19.

Rescue Service: Crossroads Garage (Papplewick) Ltd, 1–3 Main St. ✆ Nottingham (0602) 636223.

PAR Cornwall. Map 2D
Pop 1,127. Liskeard 16, London 237, Bodmin 9½, Fowey 3½, Launceston 30, St Austell 4½.
EC Thur. **Golf** Carlyon Bay 18h, St Austell 18h. **See** 10th cent monolith in churchyard.

Elmswood, G, x (Rl), *73 Tehidy Rd.* ✆ (072 681) 4221. Closed Oct & Dec. C. 🛏 7 bedrs, 1 sh, 2 ba, Dgs. 🅿 CH, TV, Dgs, CP 7, CF, 6 st. £ BB £7·50–£8, DB £14–£16, WT (b) £75–£78, DT £11–£11·50, 🛈.

Rescue Service: Collins Motors (St Austell), Fore St, Tywardreath.
✆ (072 681) 2524.
Highway Garage, Tywardreath Highway. ✆ (072 681) 2781.
St Andrews Road Garage, St Andrews Rd. ✆ (072 681) 2318.
Walkers of Par, Eastcliffe Rd. ✆ (072 681) 4000.

PARBOLD Lancashire. Map 20C
Pop 4,236. M6 Motorway (27) 3, London 199, Ormskirk 6½, Preston 15, Skelmersdale 4½, Southport 13, Wigan 8.
Golf Beacon Park 18h. **See** Churches, Parbold House.

■★★**Lindley** (Rt), *Lancaster Lane, WN8 7AB.* ✆ (025 76) 2804. C. 🛏 10 bedrs, 2 bp, 8 bps, TV, Dgs. ✗ a l c, mc, LD 10. 🅿 CH, CP, DB fr £28, 🖻, 10%, Bk £3·50, L £7·35, cc 1 2 3.

PARKGATE Cheshire. Map 19A
12 m NW of Chester. London 195, Birkenhead 10, Northwich 23 Queensferry 10, Warrington 28.

★★**Parkgate,** *Boathouse La, L64 6RD.* ✆ 051-336 5101. C. 🛏 26 bedrs, 26 bp,

TV. ✗ a l c, mc, LD 9.30. 🅿 N, CH, CP 100, CP, CF, 2 st. £ BB £26–£31, DB £42–£52, WB, 🖻, Bk £4·60, D £7, cc 1 2 3 5, Dep b.
★★**Ship,** *The Parade, L64 6SA.* ✆ 051-336 3931.

PARKSTONE Dorset
See POOLE

PARRACOMBE Devon. Map 4C
Dunster 24, London 188, Barnstaple 12, Ilfracombe 11, Lynmouth 5, South Molton 15.

Heddon Hall, G, xy (R), *Nr Barnstaple, EX31 4PE.* ✆ (059 83) 332. Open Apr–Oct. C. 🛏 7 bedrs, 2 bp, 1 bps, 2 ba. 🅿 CH, TV, CP 2, CF, 1 BGf, 3 st. £ BB £10–£13, DB £20–£29, WT £90–£100, DT £18·50, 🖻.
Hunters Inn, I, xy, *Heddons Mouth, Nr Barnstaple, EX31 4PY.* ✆ (059 83) 230. C 5. 🛏 10 bedrs, 5 bp, 5 sh, 3 ba, Dgs. ✗ a l c. 🅿 CH, TV, Dgs, CP 400, 0 st. £ BB £15–£16·50, DB £30–£33, WT (b) £86, 🛈, D £7, cc 1 3 5.

Rescue Service: Blackmoor Gate Garage, The Drive. ✆ (059 83) 284.

PATELEY BRIDGE North Yorkshire. Maps 27A and 25E
Pop 1,900. Harrogate 14, London 217, Hawes 40, Leeds 27, Leyburn 31, Northallerton 29, Skipton 20, York 33.
EC Thur. **MD** alt Sat. **Golf** Ripon 9h. **See** Bronze Age remains, Caverns W 4 miles.

♨★★**Harefield Hall,** *HG3 5QE.* ✆ Harrogate (0423) 711429.C. 🛏 15 bedrs, 3 bp, 9 bps, 2 ba, ns, Dgs. ✗ mc, at, LD 11. 🅿 CH, Dgs, CP 60, Ac, pf, con 60, CF, 3 st. £ WB, Bk £3, D £7·50, cc 1 2 3 5, Dep.
Talbot, PH, *High St, HG3 5AL.* ✆ (0423) 711597.

PATSHULL PARK Staffordshire. Maps 13B & 19F
Wolverhampton 7½, London 132, Bridgnorth 7, Shrewsbury 23, Telford 12.

♨★★★★**Lakeside Lodge,** *Patshull Park, Burnhill Green, nr Wolverhampton, WV6 7HR.* ✆ Pattingham (0902) 700100.

PATTERDALE Cumbria. Map 26D
Pop 599. M6 Motorway 28, London 276, Ambleside 8, Kendal 20, Keswick 17, Lancaster 40, Penrith 14, Ulverston 25.
Golf Penrith 18h. **See** Quaint Church, old Spinning Gallery, Aira Force, Ullswater, Helvellyn 3,118 ft.

■★★**Patterdale,** *CA11 0NN.* ✆ Glenridding (085 32) 231. Open Apr–Oct. C. 🛏 53 bedrs, 28 bp, 8 ba, Dgs. ✗ mc, at, LD 8. 🅿 CH, TV, CP 50, U 1, Ac, pf, CF. £ BB £14–£17, DB £28–£34, DBB fr £20, WB, 🖻, Bk £4, D £6·50.

PEACEHAVEN East Sussex. M. Area 7F
Pop 10,000. Brighton 6½, London 59, Newhaven 2½.
EC Wed. **Golf** Peacehaven 9h. **See** King George V Memorial, The Warren.
🛈 Meridian Centre, Roderick Av. ✆ Peacehaven (079 14) 2600.

★★**Peacehaven,** *South Coast Rd, BN9 7HX.* ✆ (079 14) 4555. C. 🛏 12 bedrs, 3 bp, 1 sh, 3 ba, Dgs. ✗ a l c, mc, LD 10. 🅿 CH, TV, Dgs, CP 50, Ac, CF. £ BB £10–£14, DB £20–£35, 🛈, Bk £3, L £4·90, D £5·90, cc 1 2 3 5 6, Dep a.

PEASLAKE Surrey, Map 7C
Pop 1,241. Leatherhead 10, London 29, Dorking 6½, Guildford 8½, Haslemere 19, Hindhead 19, Horsham 12, Petworth 22, Pulborough 18, Ripley 6½, Woking 12.
Golf Merrow 18h. **See** Old Cottages.

★★**Hurtwood Inn** (TH). *Walking Bottom, GU5 9RR.* ✆ Dorking (0306) 730851. C. 🛏 12 bedrs, 1 bps, 2 ba, TV, Dgs. ✗ a l c, mc, at, LD 10. 🅿 ch, Dgs, CP 50, Ac, con 40, CF, 2 st. £ BB £31–£34, DB £46–£50·50, WB, 🛈, cc 1 2 3 4 5 6, Dep (Xmas).

Rescue Service: Peaslake Garage. ✆ Dorking (0306) 730731.

PEASMARSH East Sussex. Map 10E
Pop 890. Hawkhurst 10, London 60, Eastbourne 28, Lewes 38, Rye 3½, Tenterden 9.
EC Wed. **Golf** Rye 18h. **See** Norman Church.

Repairer: Farley & Son, Main Rd. ✆ (079 721) 213.

PEEL Isle of Man. Map 27F
Pop 3,500. Douglas 11 (Steamer Service to Liverpool), London 209, Castletown 10, Ramsey 16.
EC Thur. **Golf** Peel 18h. **See** St Germain's Cathedral ruins and present Cathedral, Tynwald Hill (site of Open Air Parliament), Castle remains, Viking Festival.
🛈 Town Hall, Derby Rd. ✆ Peel (0624) 842341.

Rescue Service: Empire Garage Ltd, Marine Par. ✆ (0624) 2666.

PEGWELL BAY Kent.
See RAMSGATE.

PELYNT Cornwall, Map 3C
Pop 1,075. Looe 4, London 231, Bodmin 16, Fowey 19 (Fy 6), Launceston 25, Liskeard 11, St Austell 20.
EC Wed. **Golf** Looe Bin Down 18h. **See** 15th cent Church, (Trelawney's Grave), St Nun's Well.

★★**Jubilee Inn,** *Jubilee Hill, PL13 2JZ.* ✆ Lanreath (0503) 20312.

Rescue Service: Wesley Garage. ✆ Lanreath (0503) 20326.

PEMBERTON Grtr Manchester (Lancashire). Maps 19B and 20C
M6 Motorway 1½, Ashton-in-Makerfield 4, London 195, St Helens 7½, Skelmersdale 4½, Wigan 2.
EC Wed. **Golf** Haigh Hall 18h.

Rescue Service Trevor Jones, Delph Garage, Billinge Rd. ✆ Wigan (0942) 214312.

PENCRAIG Hereford & Worcester (Herefordshire). Map 13E
Ross-on-Wye 4, London 125, M50 Motorway 5, Monmouth 7.
Golf Monmouth 18h. Ross 18h.

■♨★★**Pencraig Court** (R), *HR9 6HR.* ✆ Llangarron (098 984) 306. Open Apr–Oct. C. 🛏 11 bedrs, 5 bp, 2 ba, TV. ✗ mc, at, LD 8. 🅿 CH, TV, CP 25, Ac, con 35, CF, 1 st. £ BB £13·50–£17·50, DB £24–£32, DBB £19–£23, WB, 🛈, Bk £3·50, L £2·25, D £7, cc 1 2 3, Dep a.
Harbour, G, x (Unl), *HR9 6HR.* ✆ Llangarron (098 984) 359. C. 🛏 4 bedrs, 2 ba. 🅿 CH, TV, CP 8, G 4, CF. £ BB £9·50, DB £16, WT £80, DT £12·40, 🛈, £4·40.

PENDEEN Cornwall. Map 2E
Penzance 6, London 287, Land's End 8, St. Ives 11.

Rescue Service: Trewellard Garage. ☎ Penzance (0736) 788468.

PENDOGGETT Cornwall. M. Area 2D
Camelford 6½, London 234, Bodmin 10, Wadebridge 6½.
EC Thur. **Golf** St Endoc, Rock 18h.

▣★★**Cornish Arms,** *PL30 3HH.* ☎ Port Isaac (020 888) 263.

Rescue Service: Mewtons Garage Ltd, The Garage. ☎ Port Isaac (020 888) 221.

PENN Buckinghamshire. M.Area 15E
Pop 4,532 (Inc Penn St). Denham 10, London 28, Aylesbury 16, Dunstable 25, High Wycombe 4, Rickmansworth 13, St Albans 23, Slough 11.
Golf Flackwell Heath 18h. **See** 11th cent Penn Church, Village has assns with William Penn, founder of Pennsylvania.

Rescue Service: George Slade, Slade's Garage. ☎ (049 481) 2115.

PENPILLICK Cornwall. Map 2D
Pop 352. Liskeard 14, London 235, Bodmin 7, Fowey 6, Launceston 28, St Austell 5½.
EC Thur. **Golf** Carlyon Bay 18h.

▣★★**Penpillick House,** *PL24 2RU.* ☎ Par (072 681) 2742.

PENRITH Cumbria. Map 26C
See also EDENHALL.
Pop 12,395. Kendal 25, London 276, M6 Motorway ½, Alston 19, Ambleside 22, Brampton 23, Brough 21, Carlisle 18, Hawes 40, Keswick 16, Ulverston 43.
EC Wed. **MD** Tue. **Golf** Penrith 18h. **See** Castle ruins, St Andrews Church (Giant's Grave and Giant's Thumb—monuments), earthworks, ancient inns, Brougham Castle 1½ m SE, Acornbank Gardens (Temple Sowerby Manor) 6½ m SW.
ⓘ Robinson's School, Middlegate. ☎ Penrith (0768).

★★★**George,** *Devonshire St, CA11 7SU.* ☎ (0768) 62696. Closed Xmas & New Year. C. 🛏 31 bedrs, 11 bp, 19 bps, 1 ba, TV, Dgs. ✕ mc, at, LD 8.30. 🏠 N, CH, TV, Dgs, CP 40, Ac, con 30, CF, 1 st. **£** BB fr £21·50, DB fr £34, DT fr £31·50, WB, [2], Bk £2·75, L £4·40, D £7·25, cc 1, Dep b.
★★**Abbotsford,** *Wordsworth St, CA11 7QY.* ☎ (0768) 63940. C. 🛏 11 bedrs, 9 bp, 2 bps, TV, Dgs. ✕ a l c, mc, at, LD 10. 🏠 CH, TV, Dgs, G 4, Ac, con, CF. **£** BB fr £17·50, DB fr £33, WT fr £181·50, DT fr £30·50, WB, [2], L £5, D £8, cc 1 2 3 5 6, Dep a.
★★**M Clifton Hill,** *Clifton, CA10 2EJ.* (2¾ m S A6). ☎ (0768) 62717. C. 🛏 24 bedrs, 23 bp, 1 bps, TV, Dgs. ✕ a l c, mc, at, LD 8.30. 🏠 CH, TV, Dgs, CP 200, G 25, Ac, con 80, CF. **£** BB £17·50, DB £24·25, WT fr £126·50, DBB £24·60, [2], Bk £3·50, L £3·75, D £7·10.
★★**Glen Cottage** (R), *Corney Sq, CA11 7PX.* ☎ (0768) 62221. Closed Xmas. C. 🛏 7 bedrs, 3 bp, 1 ba, TV, Dgs. ✕ mc, LD 9.30. 🏠 CH, U 3, CF, 0 st. **£** BB £12·50, DB £23–£26·50, WB, [2], Bk £3, L £3, D £4, cc 1 2 3 4 5.
★★**Strickland** (R), *Corney Sq, CA11 7PX.* ☎ (0768) 62262.
▣★**Station,** *Castlegate, CA11 7PX.* ☎ (0768) 62072.
Barco, G (Unl), *Carleton Rd, CA11 8LR.* ☎ (0768) 63176. C. 🛏 5 bedrs, 1 sh, 2 ba, Dgs. 🏠 CH, TV, CP 8, CF, 6 st. **£** DB £14–£15, [1].
Limes Country Hotel, PH, xy (Unl), *Redhills, Stainton, CA11 0DT.* ☎ (0768) 63343. Closed Nov & Xmas. C. 🛏 8 bedrs, 2 ba. 🏠 CH, TV, CP 12, 6 st. **£** BB £8·50–£10, DB £15–£18, WT £84–£95, DT (b) £12·50–£14, [2].
Pategill Villas, PH, y (R), *Carlton Rd, CA11 8JW.* ☎ (0768) 63153. C. 🛏 12 bedrs, 2 ba, TV. 🏠 CH, TV, Dgs, CP 18, CF, 1 BGf, 1 st, Dis. **£** BB £7·50–£8, DB £13–£15, [1], Bk £3, L £3, D £4·50.
Woodland House, PH, z (Rt), *Wordsworth St, CA11 7QY.* ☎ (0768) 64177.

Repairer: Armstrong & Fleming Ltd, Roper St. ☎ (0768) 62371.
Rescue Service: County Garage Co Ltd, Old London Rd. ☎ (0768) 64571.
MacDavidson, Regent Garage, Tynefield Bridge La. ☎ (0768) 62594.
Tebay Vehicle Repairs, M6 Interchange 38, Tebay. ☎ Orton (058 74) 341.
Two 'M' Services, Woodland Garage, Catterlen. ☎ (0768) 64019.
Ullswater Road Garage Ltd, Ullswater Rd. ☎ (0768) 64545.

PENRYN Cornwall. Map 2F
Pop 5,135. Truro 8½, London 263, Falmouth 2, Helston 10, Redruth 8.
EC Thur. **Golf** Falmouth 18h. **See** St Gluvias' Church, 13th cent Glasney College remains, Museum, Town Hall, Queen Ann Cottage (St Thomas St), Seven Stars Inn.

Rescue Service: Arnold's (Penryn) Ltd, Park Garage. ☎ (0326) 72363.
Cornish Landrover Services, The Old Brewery, Treluswell. ☎ Falmouth (0326) 72511.
Four Cross Garage, Treluswell. ☎ (0326) 72556.
Lewis Motors (Cornwall) Ltd, Falmouth Rd. ☎ (0326) 72641.
Trenoweth Garage, Antron Hill, Mabe. ☎ (0326) 73351.

PENSHURST Kent. Map 7D
Pop1,550. Westerham 9, London 32, East Grinstead 10, Sevenoaks 8, Tonbridge 5, Tunbridge Wells 5.
Golf Tunbridge Wells, Knole Park 18h.
See Penshurst Place, Church, Old houses.

★★**Leicester Arms,** *TN11 8BT.* ☎ (0892) 870551.

PENSILVA Cornwall. M. Area 3C
Pop 1,600. Tavistock 15, London 218, Camelford 20, Launceston 12, Liskeard 4½, Saltash 13.
Golf St Mellion 18h. **See** Caradon Hills.

Specialist Body Repairer: Marsh's Motor Bodyworks. ☎ Rilla Mill (0579) 62595.
Rescue Service: Daniel Motors Ltd. ☎ Rilla Mill (0579) 62222.

PENZANCE Cornwall. Map 2E
See also ROSUDGEON.
Pop 19,145. Redruth 17, London 281, Helston 13, St Ives 8.
EC Wed. **MD** Tue, Thur, Sat. **Golf** West Cornwall Lelant 18h. **See** Penlee Memorial Park, with Museum, Market Cross, Nautical Museum, Geological Museum, Gulval Church, Madron Church, Boat and helicopter service to the Scilly Isles, Chysauster Ancient Village 3 m N, Trengwainton Gardens 2 m NW Newlyn, St Peter's Church, Penlee Park.
ⓘ Alverton St. ☎ Penzance (0736) 2341, ext 292.

★★★**Mount Prospect** (R), *Britons Hill, TR18 3AE.* ☎ (0736) 3117. C. 🛏 26 bedrs, 24 bp, 2 bps, 1 ba, TV, Dgs. ✕ a l c, mc, at, LD 9. 🏠 N, CH, Dgs, CP 14, Ac, sp, con 80, CF, 2 BGf, 2 st. **£** WB, cc 1 2 3 5 6.
▣★★★**Queen's** *Promenade, TR18 4HG.* ☎ (0736) 2371.
▣★**Yacht Inn,** *Coinagehall Pl, TR18 4LU.* ☎ (0736) 2787. Open Feb–Oct. C 5. 🛏 8 bedrs, 3 ba, Dgs. ✕ mc, LD 8. 🏠 TV, Dgs, CP 8, CF, 5 st. 🏠 BB £9·50–£11·50, DB £18·40–£23, WT £95–£110, DT £14–£15·50, [1], Bk £1·50, D £5.
Beachfield, H, z (R), *The Promenade, TR18 4NW.* ☎ (0736) 2067. Open Mar–Oct. C. 🛏 32 bedrs, 12 bps, 8 ba, Dgs. 🏠 CH, TV, Dgs, CF, 2 BGf, 3 st. **£** BB £10·03–£12·18, DB £20·06–£28·68, WT (b) £97·52–£110·45, DT (b) £14·67–£16·82, [2].
Bella Vista, PH, z (Unl), *7 Alexandra Ter, TR18 4NX.* ☎ (0736) 62409. Open Apr–Oct. C 3. 🛏 10 bedrs, 3 ba. 🏠 TV, CP 8, 6 st. **£** BB £7–£12, DB £13–£17, WT (b) £65–£87, DT (b) £10·50–£12·50, [1].
Camilla House, PH, z (Unl), *Regent Ter, TR18 4DE.* ☎ (0736) 3771. Open Feb–Nov. C 6. 🛏 10 bedrs, 3 ba, Dgs. 🏠 ch, TV, Dgs, CF, 9 st. **£** BB fr £6·50–£7·50, DB £13–£15, WT £65–£70, DT £10–£10·50, [1].
Carlton, PH, z (Rt), *Promenade, TR18 4NW.* ☎ (0736) 2081. Open March–Oct. C 10. 🛏 12 bedrs, 3 bps, 3 sh, 2 ba, TV. 🏠 ch, TV, 20 st. **£** BB £8·50–£9·50, DB £17–£18, WT (b) £80–£90, (c) £59·50–£66·50, DT (b) £14–£16, [1], Bk £3, D £5·50.
Carnson, PH, z (Rl), *2 East Terrace, TR18 2TD.* ☎ (0736) 65589. Closed Xmas. C 4. 🛏 6 bedrs, 1 ba. 🏠 CH, TV, 1 st. **£** BB £8·50–£9·50, DB £17–£19, WT (b) £80–£90, (c) £53–£60, DT (b) £13·50–£14·50, [1], Bk £2·75, D £5, cc 1 3.
Dunedin, PH, z (Rl), *Alexandra Rd, TR18 4LZ.* ☎ (0736) 2652. Open Feb–Nov. C. 🛏 9 bedrs, 3 ba, TV, Dgs. 🏠 CH, TV, Dgs, CF, 6 st. **£** BB £7–£8·50, DB £14–£17, WT (b) £70–£85, DT (b) £10–£13, [1], Bk £2·50, D £3·50.
Estoril, H, z (Rl), *46 Morrab Rd, TR18 4EX.* ☎ (0736) 2468. Closed Nov–Dec. C. 🛏 10 bedrs, 5 bp, 5 bps, TV, Dgs. 🏠 CH, Dgs, ns, CP 4, CF, 1 BGf, 5 st. **£** BB £13–£14, DB £26–£28, WT £120–£133, [1], cc 1 3. ▲
Glencree, PH, z (Unl), *2 Mennaye Rd, TR18 4NG.* ☎ (0736) 2026. C. 🛏 9 bedrs, 2 ba. 🏠 TV, CF, 2st. 🛏 BB £6·50–£7·50, DB £13–£15, WT (b) £75–£82, DT (b) £11–£12, [1], D £4·50.
Kilindini, PH, z (Rl), *Regent Ter, TR18 4DW.* ☎ (0736) 4744. Closed Xmas. C 3. 🛏 12 bedrs, 1 bp, 3 bps, 2 ba, TV. 🏠 CH, TV, CP 10, 3 BGf, 9 st. **£** BB £8·50–£12·50, DB £17–£25, WT (b) £82·50–£110·50, DT (b) £12–£16, [1].
Kimberley House, G, z (Rl), *10 Morrab Rd, TR18 4EZ.* ☎ (0736) 2727. C 5. 🛏 9 bedrs, 3 ba. 🏠 CH, TV, CP 4, 3 st. **£** BB £7·50–£8·50, DB £15–£17, WT (b) £80–£85, DT (b) £12–£13, [1], Bk £1·50, D £4·50, cc 1 3.
Mount Royal, H, z (Unl), *Chyandour Cliff, TR18 3LQ.* ☎ (0736) 2233. Open Mar–Oct. C. 🛏 8 bedrs, 3 bp, 2 ba, Dgs.

🏠 ch, TV, CP 8, U 4, CF, 1 BGf, 4 st. £ BB £10·50–£12, DB £21–£28, WT (c) £70–£80·50, ⬜, Bk £3, D £7·50.

Old Manor House, PH, z (RI), *Regent Ter, TR18 4DW*. 📞 (0736) 3742. Closed Xmas. C 3. 🍴 12 bedrs, 7 bps, 5 sh, 4 ba, TV. 🏠 CH, ns, CP 10, CF, 1 BGf, 5st. £ BB £12–£15, DB £23–£26, WT £130–£140, DT (b) £20–£25, ⬜, Bk £2·50, D £5·50.

Panorama, G, z (RI), *Chywoone Hill, Newlyn, TR18 5AR*. 📞 (0736) 68498. C. 🍴 8 bedrs, 2 ba, TV, Dgs. 🏠 ch, TV, CP 10, CF, 0 st. £ BB £8·50, DB £17, WT (b) £87, DT (b) £13, ⬜.

Penmorvah, PH, z (R), *Alexandra Rd, TR18 4LZ*. 📞 (0736) 60100. C. 🍴 11 bedrs, 5 bp, 6 bps, TV, Dgs. 🏠 CH, Dgs, CP 2, CF, 1 BGf, 6 st. £ BB £12–£13, DB £24–£26, WT (b) £108–£115, (c) £80–£88, DT (b) £18–£19, ⬜, Bk £3·50, L £3·50, D £6, cc 1 2 3.

Sea and Horses, PH, z (RI), *6 Alexandra Ter, TR18 4NX*. 📞 (0736) 61961. C. 🍴 11 bedrs, 1 bp, 4 bps, 4 sh, 1 ba. 🏠 CH, TV, CP 10, U 1, CF, 6 st. £ BB £9·50–£10·50, DB £19–£23, WT (c) £63·20–£70, DT (b) £15·35–£16·35, ⬜, Bk £2·50, D £5·85.

Southern Comfort, H, z *Alexandra Ter, Sea Front, TR18 4NX*. 📞 (0736) 66333. Open Mar–Oct. C. 🍴 12 bedrs, 1 bp, 6 bps, 2 ba. 🏠 CH, TV, CP 6, G 1, CF. £ BB £9–£14·50, DB £18–£25, DT (b) £14–£16, ⬜, Bk £2·50, L £2·50, D £5.

Tarbert, PH, z (RI), *11 Clarence St, TR1 2NU*. 📞 (0736) 3758. Closed Xmas. C. 🍴 14 bedrs, 7 bps, 7 sh, 3 ba, Dgs. 🏠 CH, TV, CP 4, CF. £ BB £10·50–£14, DB £21–£28, WT (b) £91–£123, DT (b) £16–£19·50, ⬜, Bk £3, L £4·50, D £5·50, cc 1 2 3.

Trevelyan, G, x (RI), *16 Chapel St, TR18 4AW*. 📞 (0736) 2494. Open Feb–Nov. C. 🍴 8 bedrs, 1 bps, 2 ba. 🏠 TV, CP 9, CF, 3 st. £ BB £7–£8, DB £14–£16, WT fr £77, (c) fr £49, DT (b) fr £11, ⬜, Bk £2, D £4.

Trewella, G, z (RI), *18 Mennaye Rd, TR18 4NG*. 📞 (0736) 3818. Open Apr–Oct. C 3. 🍴 8 bedrs, 2 sh, 1 ba, Dgs. 🏠 TV. £ BB £7–£8, DB £14–£16, WT (b) £66–£73, DT (b) £10–£11, ⬜, D £3.

Willows, PH, z (Unl), *Cornwall Ter, TR18 4HL*. 📞 (0736) 3744. Closed Oct. C 5. 🍴 7 bedrs, 3 sh, 1 ba, Dgs. 🏠 CH, TV, Dgs, CP 6, 2 st. £ BB £10, DB £17–£19, WT (b) fr £83·50, DT (b) fr £13·50, ⬜.

Repairers: Mumfords of Penzance Ltd, Long Rock. 📞 (0736) 2307.
Penzance Garage Ltd, East Ter. 📞 (0736) 3358.
MC Repairer: Blewett & Pender, Albert St. 📞 (0736) 4157.
Rescue Service: Brookside Garage, Riverside, Relubbus. 📞 Germoe (073 676) 2530.
Buryas Bridge Garage, Buryas Bridge. 📞 (0736) 5464.
Mill Service Station, Nancledra. 📞 Cockwells (0736) 740428.
Sheffield Garage, Sheffield. 📞 (0736) 731350.
Trelawny Garage, Morrab Rd. 📞 (0736) 2717.
Truro Garages Ltd, The Cliff. 📞 (0736) 3334.

PERRANPORTH Cornwall. Map 2D
Pop 1,750. Bodmin 24, London 257, Newquay 8, Redruth 10, St Austell 18, Truro 9.

Golf Perranporth 18h. **See** Remains of 6th cent Church, Piran Round (open air theatre), Perran Bay, Trevaunance Cove (5 m SW), St Agnes Head, St Agnes Beacon, Wheal Cote's Engine House (6 m SW).

Beach Dunes, H, xy (RI), *Ramoth Way, Reen Sands, TR7 0BY*. 📞 (087 257) 2263. Closed Nov–Dec. C. 🍴 10 bedrs, 5 bp, 1 bps, 1 ba, TV, Dgs. 🏠 CH, TV, CP 16, CF, 3 BGf, 3 st. £ BB £10–£18. DB £20–£36, WT (b) £105–£150·50, DT (b) £15–£21·50, ⬜, Bk £3, L £4, D £6·50, cc 1 3.

Cellar Cove, H, xy (RI), *Droskyn Point, TR6 0DS*. 📞 (087 257) 2110. Closed Nov. C. 🍴 16 bedrs, 2 bps, 4 ba, Dgs. 🏠 CH, TV, ns, CP 18, CF, 1 BGf, 3 st. £ BB £10–£12, DB £20–£24, WT (b) £90–£120, DT (b) £18, ⬜, D £5·50.

Fairview, PH, x (R), *Tywarnhayle Rd, TR6 0DX*. 📞 (087 257) 2278. Open Mar–Oct. C. 🍴 15 bedrs, 1 bps, 1 sh, 2 ba, Dgs. 🏠 CH, TV, Dgs, CP 4, CF, 5 st.

Lake House, PH, x (RI), *Perrancombe, TR6 0HT*. 📞 (087 257) 3202. Open late Mar–start Oct. C. 🍴 10 bedrs, 3 ba. 🏠 CH, TV, CP 7, U 1, CF, 2 BGf. £ BB £8–£10·35, DB £16–£20·70, WT (b) £66–£85, DT (b) £10–£12·50, ⬜, cc 1 3.

Lamorna, PH, x (RI), *Tywarnhayle Rd, TR6 0DX*. 📞 (087 257) 3398. Closed Xmas. C. 🍴 10 bedrs, 3 ba, Dgs. 🏠 TV, Dgs, CF, 10 st. £ BB £10·50, DB £21, WT (b) £85, DT (b) £14, ⬜.

Lynton, G, z (RI), *Cliff Rd, TR6 0DR*. 📞 (087 257) 3457.

Park View, G, z (RI), *42 Tywarnhayle Rd, TR6 0DX*. 📞 (087 257) 3009. Open Apr–Sep. C. 🍴 5 bedrs, 1 ba, Dgs. 🏠 CH, TV, Dgs, CP 5, CF, 20 st.

Perrancourt, PH, z (RI), *27 Tywarnhayle Rd, TR6 0DX*. 📞 (087 257) 2151. Open Apr–Sept. C. 🍴 11 bedrs, 2 bp, 3 bps, 2 ba, Dgs. 🏠 ch, TV, CP 6, CF. £ BB £6–£10, DB £12–£22, ⬜.

Villa Margarita, PH, xy, (RI), *Bone Mill Rd, Bolingsy, TR6 0AS*. 📞 (087 257) 2063. C 8. 🍴 7 bedrs, 4 bps, 3 sh, 1 ba. 🏠 ch, TV, CP 8, 3 BGf, 6 st. £ BB £10·85–£12, DB £21·70–£24, WB (b) £110–£118, (c) £65–£72, DT (b) £17·85–£19, ⬜.

PERRANUTHNOE Cornwall. Map 2E
Pop 1,555. Helston 8, London 279, Penzance 5½, Redruth 18, St Ives 10.
Golf Praa Sands 9h. **See** Perran Sands.

Ednovean House, PH, xy (RI), *TR20 9LZ*. 📞 Penzance (0736) 711071. C 7. 🍴 8 bedrs, 5 bps, 1 ba, Dgs. 🗶 a l c. 🏠 CH, TV, ns, CP 12, CF, 1 st. £ BB £14–£23, DB £26–£40, WT (c) £86–£110, DT (b) £21–£30, ⬜, Bk £3·50, L £4·80, D £7.

PERSHORE Hereford & Worcester (Worcestershire). Map 14C
Pop 5,767. Evesham 6½, London 104, M5 Motorway 6, Cheltenham 17, Droitwich 13, Ledbury 19, Stratford-upon-Avon 20, Tewkesbury 10, Worcester 9½.
EC Thur. **Golf** Evesham (Hadbury) 9h. **See** Abbey Church, old bridge, St Andrew's Church, large orchards nearby.
ⓘ Council Offices, 37 High St. 📞 Pershore (0386) 554711.

★★Angel Inn, *High St, WR10 1AF*. 📞 (0386) 552046. Closed Xmas. C. 🍴 17 bedrs, 15 bp, 1 ba, TV, Dgs. 🗶 mc, at, LD 9. 🏠 CH, Dgs CP 50, pf, CF, 3 st. £ BB £21–

£24, DB £30–£40, WB, ②, Bk £2·50, D £7·50, cc 1 2 3 5.
★★Manor House, *Bridge St, WR10 1AX*. 📞 (0386) 552713. Closed Dec 25. C. 🍴 8 bedrs, 3 sh, 2 ba, Dgs. 🗶 a l c, mc, LD 9.30. 🏠 CH, TV, CP 40, Ac, 1 st. £ BB £12·65–£16·10, DB £24·15–£29·90, DBB £19·40–£22·85, Bk £2·50, L £4·50, D £6·75, cc 1 2 3 5 6, Dep b.

Rescue Service: Central Garage (Pershore) Ltd, Worcester Rd. 📞 (0386) 552056.
Cox's Garage, New Rd. 📞 (0386) 2843.

PETERBOROUGH Cambridgeshire. Maps 15B and 23F
See also NORMAN CROSS
Pop 110,000. Alconbury 13, London 83, Ely 32, Kettering 28, Leicester 42, Market Harborough 33, Northampton 37, Sleaford 33, Spalding 17, Stamford 14, Wisbech 20.
EC Thur. **MD** Wed, Fri, Sat. **Golf** New Milton, Peterborough 18h. **See** Cathedral, Bishop's Palace, Museum, Old Guildhall, 15th cent St John's Church, Peakirk Waterfowl Gardens 7 m N.
ⓘ Town Hall, Bridge St. 📞 Peterborough (0733) 63141.

★★★Bull, *Westgate, PE1 1RB*. 📞 (0733) 61364. C. 🍴 114 bedrs, 107 bp, 3 ba, TV, Dgs. 🗶 a l c, mc, at, LD 10.30. 🏠 N, CH, CP 100, gym, con 170, CF, 2 st. £ BB fr £32·50, DB fr £42, WB, ⬜, Bk £3·45, L £6·15, D £6·15, cc 1 2 3 5.
★★★Peterborough Moat House (late Saxon Inn), *Thorpe Wood, PE3 6SG*. 📞 (0733) 260000. C. 🍴 84 bedrs, 98 bp, TV, Dgs. 🗶 a l c, mc, at, LD 10. 🏠 Lt, N, CH, TV, Dgs, CP 230, Ac, con 400, CF, 17 BGf, 0 st, Dis. £ BB £40, DB £53·35, WB, ⬜, Bk £4·45, L £7·10, D £8·15, cc 1 2 3 5 6, Dep b.

Repairer: Marshalls (Cambridge) Ltd, 7 Oundle Rd. 📞 (0733) 66011.
Specialist Body Repairer: Werrington Green Garage, Chapel La, Werrington. 📞 (0733) 71144.
Rescue Service: Parker Fry Garages, Whittlesey Rd, Stanground. 📞 (0733) 66551.

PETERLEE Durham. Map 32F
Pop 24,168. Stockton-on-Tees 17, London 260, Darlington 23, Durham 11, Middlesbrough 18, Newcastle upon Tyne 20, Sunderland 11, West Auckland 23.
EC Wed. **Golf** Castle Eden 18h. **See** Nature Reserve.
ⓘ The Upper Chase. 📞 Peterlee (0783) 864450.

★★★Norseman, *Bede Way, SR8 1BU*. 📞 Sunderland (0783) 862161. RS Xmas & New Year. C. 🍴 26 bedrs, 26 bp, TV, Dgs. 🗶 a l c, mc, LD 9.30. 🏠 Lt, N, CH, ns, CP 50, Ac, con 120, CF, 1 st. £ BB £25, DB £35, DT £38, ⬜, Bk £2·60, L £2·95, D £5, cc 1 2 3 5 6, Dep b.

Rescue Service: Peterlee Motor Co Ltd, Shotton Rd. 📞 (0783) 867516.

PETERSFIELD Hampshire. Map 6D
Pop 10,500. Hindhead 12, London 53, Alton 12, Chichester 18, Cosham 13, Farnham 17, Haslemere 12, Midhurst 10, Winchester 19.
EC Thur. **MD** Wed, Sat. **Golf** Petersfield 18h. **See** Statue of William III in Market Sq, Norman Church, Dragon House, Old

College, Spain House, Uppark 5 m S (Nat Trust). Butser Hill (Iron Age model farm).

Station, G, z (Unl), *7 Charles St, GU32 3EJ.* ✆ (0730) 3714.

Rescue Service: Stroud Garages Ltd, 60 Winchester Rd, Stroud. ✆ (0730) 66241.

PETTS WOOD Greater London (Kent). M. Area 7B
2½ m NW of Orpington, Bromley 3½, London 15, Croydon 9, Sevenoaks 10, Sidcup 3½, Westerham 10.
EC Wed. **Golf** West Kent 18h.

Rescue Service: Dunstonian Garage Ltd, 52 Queensway. ✆ Orpington (0689) 24232.

PETTY FRANCE Avon. Map 5B
Pop 30. Chippenham 14, London 105, M4 Motorway 5, Bath 15, Bristol 16, Cheltenham 27, Chepstow 21, Gloucester 23, Tetbury 8.
Golf Chipping Sodbury 18h.

★★★Petty France (R), *Dunkirk, Badminton, GL9 1AF.* (A46). ✆ Didmarton (045 423) 361. C. ➡ 8 bedrs, 7 bp, 1 bps, annexe 8 bedrs, 7 bp, 1 bps, TV, Dgs.
✗ a l c, mc, at, LD 9·45. ⌂ CH, Dgs, CP 50, con 20, CF, 2 st. £ BB £30–£32, DB £43–£50, WT £200, DT £43, DBB £33, WB, ⊡, Bk £4, L £10, D £10, cc 1 2 3 5 6.

PETWORTH West Sussex. Map 7C
Pop 2,920. Guildford 20, London 48, Arundel 11, Bognor Regis 16, Chichester 14, Dorking 26, Haslemere 10, Haywards Heath 27, Horsham 16, Midhurst 6½, Pulborough 5.
EC Wed. **Golf** Cowdray Park 18h. **See** Petworth House and Deer Park (Nat Trust), Church, South Lodge, Roman Villa at Bignor 5 m S.

Rescue Service: Harwoods Garage (Pulborough) Ltd, North St. ✆ (0798) 42232.

PEVENSEY BAY East Sussex. Map 10E
Pop 2,656 (Pevensey), Uckfield 19, London 65, Eastbourne 4, Hastings 12, Hurst Green 18, Lewes 17, Tunbridge Wells 30.
EC Thur. **Golf** Royal Eastbourne 18h and 9h. **See** Castle ruins, 14th cent Old Mint House (now shop), Parish Church, Old Court House, Martello Towers.
⒫ Castle Car Park, High St, Eastbourne.
✆ Eastbourne (0323) 761444.

⬩★★★★Glyndley Manor, *Hailsham Rd, Stone Cross, BN24 5BS.* 1½ m NW of Stone Cross on B2104. ✆ Eastbourne (0323) 843737. C. ➡ 21 bedrs, 18 bp, 3 bps, 1 ba, TV, Dgs. ✗ a l c, mc, at, LD 9·30. ⌂ CH, Dgs, CP 100, Ac, sp, tc, pf, con 40, 2 RGf. 1 st, Dis. £ BB £28, DB £50, DBB £50, WB, ⊡ 10%, Bk £4·50, L £7·50, D £8·50, cc 1 2 3 4 5 6.

★★Priory Court, *BN24 5LG.*
✆ Eastbourne (0323) 763150. C. ➡ 8 bedrs, 8 bp, annexe 4 bedrs, 1 ba, TV.
✗ a l c, mc, at, LD 9.30. ⌂ N, CH, TV, ns, CP 40, Ac, con 15, CF, 3 BGf, 1 st, Dis.
£ BB £19–£24, DB £29–£39, WT fr £190, DT fr £26, DBB fr £26·50, WB, ⊡, Bk £4·50, L £4·95, D £7·50, cc 1 2 3 5, Dep.

PEWSEY Wiltshire. Map 6A
Pop 2,000. Newbury 22, London 76, Amesbury 13, Andover 18, Devizes 12, Marlborough 6, Wantage 28.

EC Wed, Sat. **MD** Tue. **Golf** Marlborough 18h. **See** Statue of King Alfred in Market Place, old Church, White Horse turf-cutting on Downs.

Rescue Service: Pewsey (Wilts) Motors Ltd, The Market Pl. ✆ (067 26) 2371.

PICKERING North Yorkshire. Map 24D
Pop 6,200. Malton 8, London 213, Bridlington 31, Helmsley 13, Scarborough 16, Whitby 20.
EC Wed. **MD** Mon. **Golf** Malton & Norton 18h. **See** Castle ruins, Beck Isle Museum, Church (12th cent mural paintings), Flamingo Land 3 m SW, Steam Railway.
⒫ The Station, Park St. ✆ Pickering (0751) 73791.

★★Forest & Vale, *Malton Rd, YO18 7DL.*
✆ (0751) 72722. Closed Xmas. C. ➡ 17 bedrs, 7 bp, 5 bps, 3 ba, annexe 6 beds, 5 bp, 1 bps, TV, Dgs. ✗ a l c, mc, LD 9. ⌂ CH, TV, Dgs, CP 70, Ac, con 80, CF, 6 BGf, 2 st. £ BB £16–£17, DB £32–£38, WT £187–£194, DT £27·50–£30, WB, ⊡, Bk £3·50, L £5·50, D £9, cc 1 2 3 5.

Repairer: North Riding Garages Ltd, Eastgate. ✆ (0751) 72251.

PIDDLETRENTHIDE Dorset. Map 5F
Pop 594. Blandford Forum 15, Dorchester 7, Wareham 18, Sherborne 13.
Golf Came Down 18h. **See** 12th cent Norman Church, 700 yr old Font.

▣★★Old Bakehouse (Rt), *DT2 7QR.*
✆ (030 04) 305. C 12. ➡ 9 bedrs, 9 bp, TV, Dgs. ✗ LD 9. ⌂ CH, CP 25, sp, sb, sol, 5 BGf, 1 st, Dis. £ BB £16–£18, DB £26–£32, WB, ⊡, Bk £3·50, D £7, cc 1 3,▲

PILNING Avon. Map 5A
Pop 2,500. Chippenham 28, London 119, Bristol 9, Avonmouth 5½, Aust 3.
Golf Filton 18h.

Rescue Service: Pilning Garage, Cross Hands Rd. ✆ (045 45) 2909.

PILTON Somerset Map 5C
Pop 722. Shepton Mallet 2, London 119, Glastonbury 6, Sherborne 19, Wells 5½, Wincanton 14.
Golf Mendip 18h. **See** Pilton Vineyard, Manor House, Tithe Barn, Parish Church.

Long House, PH, x (R), *BA4 4BP.*
✆ (074 989) 283. C 6. ➡ 7 bedrs, 3 bp, 3 bps, 1 ba, Dgs. ⌂ CH, ns, CP 8, CF, 1 st.
£ BB £14–£19·50, DB £28, WT (b) £115, DT (b) £20·50, ⊡, Bk £3, D £6·65, cc 1 2 3 5.

Rescue Service: Gould, E W, Pilton Garage, ✆ (074 989) 231.

PINNER Greater London (Middx). Maps 7A and 15E
Harrow 4, London 13, Edgware 6, Rickmansworth 8, Uxbridge 8, Watford 8.

Repairer: Lancefields Autos Ltd, T/As Whittington Service Station, 74 Whittington Way. ✆ 01-866 5203.

PINXTON Derbyshire. M. Area 22D
8 m SW of Mansfield. Pop 4,470. M1 Motorway 1, London 139, Ashbourne 23, Chesterfield 14, Derby 17, Loughborough 28, Matlock 13, Nottingham 15.
EC Wed. **Golf** Coxmoor 18h. **See** Old Church, Elizabethan Brookhill Hall.

Rescue Service: Four Ways Garage, Kirby La. ✆ Ripley (0773) 810694.

PITY ME Durham. Map 32E
A1 (M) Motorway 4½, Durham 2½, London 263, Lanchester 7, Newcastle upon Tyne 13, Sunderland 14.

Rescue Service: K A M Services (Durham) Ltd, T/As Kamshaft, Abbey Rd. ✆ Durham (0385) 44000.

PLEASLEY Derbyshire. Map 22
See also Mansfield 3, London 141, Chesterfield 9, Matlock 15, Ollerton 9, Rotherham 20, Sheffield 19, Worksop 13.
Golf Sherwood Forest 18h. **See** St Michael's Church.

Rescue Service: Reg Morgan, The Garage, Pleasley Cross. ✆ Mansfield (0623) 810330.

PLYMOUTH Devon. Map 3C
See also WEMBURY.
RAC Office, *RAC House, 15–17 Union St, Plymouth, PL1 2SZ.* ✆ (General) Plymouth (0752) 669301. (Rescue Service only) Plymouth (0752) 21411.
Pop 256,400. Ashburton 24, London 211, Kingsbridge 20, Saltash 4, Tavistock 14, Totnes 22.
See Plan, p. 298.
P See Plan. **Golf** Yelverton 18h. **See** Citadel, The Hoe (Drake's Statue), Elizabethan House, Museum and Art Gallery, Smeaton's Tower (Aquarium), RC Cathedral, Brunel's Rly Bridge, Tamar Road Bridge, Barbican (city's oldest quarter—curio shops, tiny alleys), St Andrew's Church, Civic Centre, Guildhall, Devonport Dockyard, Saltram House 3 m E, Antony House 5 m W, Buckland Abbey (Drake Museum), 8½ m N.
⒫ Civic Centre, Royal Par. ✆ Plymouth (0752) 264849.

★★★★Holiday Inn, *Armada Way, PL1 2HJ.* ✆ (0752) 662866. C. ➡ 218 bedrs, 218 bp, ns, TV, Dgs. ✗ mc, at, LD 11. ⌂ Lt, N, CH, CP 20, G 110, Ac, sp, sb, sol, gym, con, CF, 10 BGf, 2 st. £ B fr £45·42, BD fr £52·32, WB, ⊡, Bk £5·60, L £9, D £8·45, cc 1 2 3 4 5 6, Dep b.

★★★Astor, *Elliot St, PL1 2PS.* ✆ (0752) 25511. Closed Xmas. C. ➡ 58 bedrs, 54 bp, 4 bps, TV. ✗ a l c, mc, LD 9.30. ⌂ Lt, N, CH, Dgs, Ac, con 60, CF, 3 st. £ BB £31·50, DB £45·50, WB, ⊡, Bk £4·50, L £5, D £7·50, cc 1 2 3 5, Dep b.

★★★Duke of Cornwall, *Millbay Rd, PL1 3LG.* ✆ (0752) 266256. Closed Xmas. C. ➡ 67 bedrs, 50 bp, 17 bps, TV, Dgs.
✗ a l c, mc, LD 9.30. ⌂ Lt, N, CH, TV, CP 60, Ac, con 275, CF, 11 st. £ BB fr £28, DB fr £38, DT fr £41, WB, ⊡, Bk £3·75, L £5, D £7·50, cc 1 2 3 5, Dep b.

★★★Mayflower Post House (TH), *The Hoe, PL1 3DL.* ✆ (0752) 662828. C.
➡ 104 bedrs, 104 bp, TV, Dgs. ✗ a l c, mc, at, LD 10·30. ⌂ Lt, N, CH, TV, Dgs, CP 149, Ac, sp, con 70, CF, 1 st. £ BB £44, DB £57·50, WB, ⊡, cc 1 2 3 4 5 6, Dep (Xmas).

★★★M Novotel, *Marsh Mills Roundabout, 270 Plymouth Rd, PL6 8NH.*
✆ (0752) 21422. C. ➡ 100 bedrs, 100 bp, 2 ba, TV, Dgs. ✗ a l c, mc, at, LD midnight.
⌂ Lt, N, CH, Dgs, CP 140, Ac, sp, con 350, CF, 2 BGf, 0 st, Dis. £ BB £34–£36, DB £45, WB, ⊡, Bk £4, D £8·25, cc 1 2 3 4 5 6, Dep.

★★★Strathmore House, *Elliot St, The Hoe, PL1 2SP.* ✆ (0752) 662101. C. ➡ 59 bedrs, 43 bp, 16 bps, TV. ✗ a l c, mc, at, LD 10. ⌂ Lt, N, CH, TV, CP 6, Ac, con 100, CF, 10 st. £ BB £23, DB £35, WT £225, DT £34,

0 miles ¼ ½

To Crematorium 1½ m.

To Exeter 42m. A374
To Yealmpton 7m. A379

To Liskeard 17m.
To Yelverton 9m.
To Saltash 4m.
To Airport
A386

To Crematorium 1½ m.

To Devonport 1m. A374

RAC

MOUNT GOULD
ST JUDE'S
PRINCE ROCK
CATTEDOWN
COXSIDE
PENNYCOMEQUICK
STOKE
STONEHOUSE
MILLBAY

Mount Gould Hospital
Freedom Fields Hospital
Beaumont Park
Greenbank Hospital
Fire Station
Mutley Plain
Railway Station
Cemetery
Central Park
Polytechnic
Charles Church
Library
Museum
Drake Circus
Eastlake St.
Guildhall
Royal Theatre
Civic Centre
T.S.W. Studio
Law Courts
Bus Station
St. Andrew's Church
Sutton Harbour
Piers
Fisher's Nose
The Citadel
Aquarium
Bathing Pool
Drake's Statue
The Hoe
The Promenade
Smeaton Lighthouse
West Hoe Pier
R.C. Cathedral
R.N. Hospital
R.M. Barracks
Ferry Terminal
Ferry Port
Inner Basin
West Wharf
Eastern King Point
Outer Basin

Esso Wharf
Cattewater
Clovelly Bay
Mount Batten Breakwater
The Sound
Firestone Bay
Western King Point

Ashford Road
Alexandra Road
Isson Grove
Beaumont Road
Mount Gould Road
Mount Gould Road
Faringdon Road
Prior Road
Lanhydrock Road
Grenville Road
Embankment Road
Laira Bridge Road
Laira Bridge
Mainstone Ave.
Elliott Road
Cattedown Rd.
Clovelly Rd.
Madeira Road
Hoe Road
Cliff Road
West Hoe Rd.
Grand Parade
Millbay Road
Union St.
Stonehouse St.
East St.
Martin St.
King St.
Cecil Street
Wyndham St.
North Road
Wilton Road
Wingfield Road
Stuart Rd.
Whittington St.
Alma Road
Beechwood Ave.
Ford Park Road
Houndiscombe Rd.
Greenbank Road
North Hill
Clifton Place
Camden St.
Seymour Road
Queen's Road
Tothill Ave.
Exeter Street
Sutton Road
Ebrington Street
Breton Side
Vauxhall St.
Southside St.
Notte St.
Looe St.
New Street
Buckwell St.
Princess St.
Royal Parade
Armada Way
New George St.
Cornwall St.
Mayflower St.
Western Approach
Sydney St.
Oxford St.
West St.
Caroline Pl.
Durnford Street
Cremyll Street
King's Road
Manor St.
Clarence Place
Wolsdon St.

Molesworth Road
Paradise Rd.
Devonport Rd.
Collingwood Rd.
Fitzroy Rd.
Portland Rd.
Church St.

Car Park P
Public Conveniences C

RAC Western Counties Office
RAC House
15-17 Union Street

N

WB, ☐, Bk £3, L £4·50, D £6·50, cc 1 2 3 5,
Dep b.

★★**Grosvenor,** *9 Elliott St, PL1 2PP.*
✆ (0752) 260411. RS Xmas. C. ⊯ 13
bedrs, 7 bp, 6 bps, 2 ba, TV. ✗ a l c, mc, at,
LD 9.45. ⏢ CH, TV, CP 2, Ac, con 25, CF.
£ cc 1 3 6, Dep b.▲

◨♨★★**Langdon Court,** *Down Thomas,
PL9 0DY.* ✆ (0752) 862358. C 5. ⊯ 14
bedrs, 14 bp, TV, Dgs. ✗ mc, LD 9. ⏢ ch,
Dgs, CP 50, con 30, CF. £ BB £24·75, DB
£36·85, ☒, Bk £3·50, cc 1 2 4 5 6.

◨★**Drake** (Rt), *1 Windsor Villas, Lockyer
St, The Hoe, PL1 2QD.* ✆ (0752) 29730.
Closed Xmas. C. ⊯ 16 bedrs, 3 bps, 4 sh, 3
ba, TV, Dgs. ✗ mc, at, LD 9. ⏢ CH, TV, Dgs,
CP 10, con 30, CF, 2 st. £ BB £16–£18, DB
£26–£28, DBB £24–£26, WB ☐, Bk £3, D
£5·50, cc 1 2 3.

Akabo, G, z (RI), *20 Woodland Ter,
Greenbank, PL4 8NL.* ✆ (0752) 663247.

Benvenuto, G, z (RI), *69 Hermitage Rd,
Mannamead, PL3 4RZ.* ✆ (0752) 667030.
C. ⊯ 7 bedrs, 1 sh, 2 ba, Dgs. ⏢ CH, TV,
CF. £ BB fr £8, DB fr £15, WT (b) fr £77, ☐,
Bk £2, D £4.

Camelot, H, z (RI), *Elliott St, PL1 2PP.*
✆ (0752) 21255. RS Xmas. C. ⊯ 15 bedrs,
6 bp, 9 bps, TV, Dgs. ✗ a l c, mc, at, LD 9.
⏢ CH, TV, CP 3, Ac, con 30, CF, 8 st. £ BB
fr £18, DB fr £30·50, WT £182, DT fr
£28·90, WB, ☒, Bk £3·75, L £4·95, D £5·95,
cc 1 2 3 6, Dep b.

Carnegie, PH, z (Rt), *172 Citadel Rd, The
Hoe, PL1 3BD.* ✆ (0752) 25158. Closed
Xmas week. C. ⊯ 9 bedrs, 2 sh, 2 ba, Dgs.
⏢ CH, TV, CF, 5 st. £ BB £10·50–£11, DB
£21–£24, WT (b) £108·50–£112, (c) £70–
£73·50, DT (b) £16–£16·50, ☐, cc 1 2 3.

Chester, GH, z (Unl), *54 Stuart Rd,
Pennycomequick.* ✆ (0752) 663706.

Cranbourne, H, z (Unl), *282 Citadel Rd,
The Hoe, PL1 2PZ.* ✆ (0752) 263858.
Closed last week Dec. C. ⊯ 10 bedrs. 2
sh, 1 ba, Dgs. ⏢ CH, TV, CF, 6 st. £ BB £7–
£9, DB £14–£20, ☐.

Drakes View, PH, z (RI), *33 Grand
Parade, PL1 3DQ.* ✆ (0752) 21500.
Closed Xmas. C. ⊯ 6 bedrs, 2 ba, TV, Dgs.
⏢ CH, TV, CF. £ BB £10–£15, DB £20–£22,
☐, D £5.

Dudley, G, z (Unl), *42 Sutherland Rd,
Mutley, PL4 6BN.* ✆ (0752) 668322. C.
⊯ 6 bedrs, 1 ba, Dgs. ⏢ CH, TV, Dgs, CF.
£ BB £7–£9·50, DB £14–£19, WT (c) £45,
DT (b) £12–£14·50, ☐, Bk £2·50, D £5,
cc 1 3.

Dunheved, H, z (R), *33 Beaumont Rd, St
Judes, PL4 9BJ.* ✆ (0752) 23696. Closed
Xmas. C. ⊯ 15 bedrs, 3 ba. ⏢ CH, TV, CP
6, G 4, CF, 3 st.

Gables Hotel, G, z (Unl), *29 Sutherland
Rd, Mutley, PL4 6BW.* ✆ (0752) 20803. C.
⊯ 7 bedrs, 2 ba. ⏢ CH, TV, U 2, CF, 3 st.
£ BB £10·35, DB £20·70, WT (c) £69, ☐.

Georgian House, H, z (RI), *51 Citadel Rd,
The Hoe PL1 5AQ.* ✆ (0752) 663237. C.
⊯ 10 bedrs, 4 bp, 6 bps, 1 ba, TV, Dgs.
⏢ CH, TV, CP 2, CF. £ Bk £2·75, D £7·50,
cc 1 2 3.▲

Glendevon, H, z (RI), *20 Ford Park Rd,
Mutley, PL4 6RB.* ✆ (0752) 663655.

Headland H, z (R & Cl), *1a Radford Rd,
West Hoe, PL1 3BY.* ✆ (0752) 660866.

Imperial, H, z (Rt), *3 Windsor Villas,
Lockyer St, PL1 2QD.* ✆ (0752) 27311.
Closed Xmas. C. ⊯ 22 bedrs, 2 bp, 11 bps,
4 ba, TV, Dgs. ⏢ CH, TV, CP 20, CF, 5 BGf,
3 st. £ BB £15–£23, DB £30–£35, WT (b)

£127–£148, ☐, Bk £3·50, D £6·50,
cc 1 2 3.

Lockyer House, H, z (RI), *2 Alfred St, The
Hoe, PL1 2RP.* ✆ (0752) 665755. Closed
Xmas. C. ⊯ 6 bedrs, 1 ba, Dgs. ⏢ CH, TV,
Dgs, 3 st. £ BB £9·90, DB £17·60, DT (b)
£15·90, ☐, Bk £2·75, D £6.

Merlin, H, z (R), *2 Windsor Villas,
Lockyer St, The Hoe, PL1 2QD.* ✆ (0752)
28133. Closed Dec 24–Jan 2. C. ⊯ 24
bedrs, 11 bps, 6 sh, 4 ba, TV, Dgs. ✗ a l c.
⏢ CH, TV, CP 14, G 3, CF, 3 st. £ BB
£13·75–£18·25, DB £27·50–£29·50, ☐, Bk
£3·25, L £4·95, D £5·50, cc 1 2 3 5.

Merville, PH, z (RI), *75 Citadel Rd, PL1
3AX.* ✆ (0752) 667595. Closed Xmas. C.
⊯ 10 bedrs, 2 ba, TV, Dgs. ⏢ ch, TV, CP 2,
CF, 1 st. £ BB £9–£10, DB £16–£18, WT
(b) £88–£95, DT (b) £13·95–£14·95, ☐, Bk
£2·95, D £4·95, cc 1 3.

Phantele, G, z (RI), *176 Devonport Rd,
PL1 5RD.* ✆ (0752) 51506.

Riviera, PH, z (RI), *8 Elliott St, PL1 2PP.*
✆ (0752) 662329. C. ⊯ 10 bedrs, 6 bp, 1
ba, TV, Dgs. ⏢ CH, TV, CF, 5 st. £ BB £10–
£12, DB £26–£28, WT (c) £70–£98, DT (b)
£15–£20, ☐, Bk £2, D £5, cc 1 2 3.

St James, H, z (RI), *49 Citadel Rd, The
Hoe, PL1 3AU.* ✆ (0752) 661950. Open
Feb–Nov. C 6. ⊯ 9 bedrs, 9 bps, 1 ba, TV,
Dgs. ⏢ CH, TV, 2 st. £ BB fr £13·50, DB
£23, WT fr £75, DT fr £17·45, ☐,
D £5·95.

San Remo, H, z (R), *Addison Rd, PL4
8LL.* ✆ (0752) 665839. C. ⊯ 13 bedrs, 1
bp, 2 sh, 3 ba. ⏢ ch, TV, CF, 2 st. £ BB fr
£13, DB fr £21·50, ☐, Bk £1·95, D £5·25,
cc 1 3.

Smeatons Tower, G, z (RI) *44 Grand
Par, PL2 4LR.* ✆ (0752) 21007. C. ⊯ 6
bedrs, 2 sh, 1 ba, ns, TV. ✗ a l c. ⏢ CH, TV,
CF. £ BB £6·55–£7·50, DB £13–£15, WT
(b) £70–£77, (c) £45–£50, DT (b) £10–
£11.

The Yorkshireman, PH, z (Unl), *64
North Rd East, PL4 6AL.* ✆ (0752)
668133. Closed Xmas. C. ⊯ 12 bedrs, 2
ba. ⏢ ch, TV, ns, CP 7, CF. £ BB £7–£7·50,
DB £14–£15, ☐.

Trenant, PH, z (RI), *Queens Rd, Lipson,
PL4 7PJ.* ✆ (0752) 663879. Closed Xmas.
C. ⊯ 21 bedrs, 4 ba, Dgs. ⏢ CH, TV, ns, CP
24, CF. £ BB £10·50, DB £21, WT (c) fr
£63, DT (b) fr £15, ☐.

Trillium, G, z (RI), *4 Alfred St, The Hoe,
PL1 2RP.* ✆ (0752) 670452. C 5. ⊯ 6
bedrs, 4 bps, 1 ba. ⏢ CH, TV, CP 3. £ BB
£12·25–£13·58, DB £24·50–£27·16, DT fr
£19·25, ☐, Bk £4, D £7, cc 1 2 3.

Repairers: Allens (Plymouth) Ltd,
Cobourg St. ✆ (0752) 668886.
Chapman, Frank (Plymouth) Ltd, Lipson
Vale Garage. ✆ (0752) 667325, and at
Compton Service Station, Eggbuckland
Rd. ✆ (0752) 774514.
Harper, R Ltd, Woodlands Garage,
Crownhill Rd. ✆ (0752) 361222.
Haskell & Son (Plymouth) Ltd, The
Crescent. ✆ (0752) 668332.
Plymouth Automobile Engineering Co Ltd,
Davis Garage, Marshead Rd. ✆ (0752)
771124.
Turnbull's of Plymouth, Breton Side.
✆ (0752) 667111.
Vospers Motor House (Plymouth) Ltd,
Millbay Rd. ✆ (0752) 668040.
Wadham Stringer (Plymouth) Ltd,
Leyland House, Union St. ✆ (0752)
263355.

M C Repairer: E & E Motor Cycles, Bath
Place West. ✆ (0752) 665141.
Terry Hobbs Motorcycles, 2 Camden St.
✆ (0752) 662429.
Specialist Body Repairers: Haskell & Son
(Plymouth) Ltd, The Crescent. ✆ (0752)
668332.
Turnbull's of Plymouth, Breton Side.
✆ (0752) 667111.
Wadham Stringer (Plymouth) Ltd,
Leyland House, Union St. ✆ (0752)
263355.
Waterfields Crash Repair Centre, Sugar
Mill Industrial Estate, Billacombe Rd.
✆ (0752) 492110.
Specialist Radiator Repairer: Serck
Radiator Services Ltd, Stonehouse St.
✆ (0752) 669373.
Rescue Service: Grenville Garage,
Cromwell Rd, St Judes. ✆ (0752) 664916.
Hay's (Plymouth) Ltd, Stirling Rd, St
Budeaux. ✆ (0752) 361251.
Laira Bridge Service Station, Laira Bridge
Rd. ✆ (0752) 665028.
McMullin Motors, Lakeside Garage, Hooe
Rd. ✆ (0752) 41804.
Oakden's Garage, Wilesley Rd, Milehouse.
✆ (0752) 53009.
Rees Motors, 62 Church Rd, Plymstock.
✆ (0752) 43109.
St Mary's Bridge Garage, Plymouth Rd,
Plympton. ✆ (0752) 339715.
Waterfield Garages Ltd, Old Laira Rd.
✆ (0752) 664389.
White's Auto-Care, Elm Road Garage,
Mannamead. ✆ (0752) 662741 & (0752)
667999.

PLYMPTON
◨♨★★**Elfordleigh,** *PL7 5EB.*
✆ Plymouth (0752) 336428. RS Xmas.
⊯ 15 bedrs, 2 bp, 7 bps, 3 ba, Dgs. ✗ mc,
at, LD 8. ⏢ CH, TV, Dgs, CP 50, sp, gc, tc,
sc, sb, sol, con, CF. £ BB fr £21, DB £26·50,
DBB £27·80, WB, ☐, Bk £2, D £7, Dep.

Rescue Service: Chaddlewood Garages
Ltd, Main Exeter Rd. ✆ Plymouth (0752)
338487.
Hall, Graves & Lee, 27 Market Rd.
✆ Plymouth (0752) 339598.
K G Haskell & Son (Plymouth) Ltd,
Newnham Rd, Colebrook. ✆ Plymouth
(0752) 336462.
Kastner of Plymouth Ltd, Valley Rd.
✆ Plymouth (0752) 338306.
Dave Reed Motors, 22 Church Rd, St
Maurice. ✆ (0752) 332221.

PLYMSTOCK
★★**Highlands** (R). *Dean Cross Rd, PL9
7AZ.* ✆ Plymouth (0752) 43643. C. ⊯ 9
bedrs, 4 bp, 2 bps, 1 ba, annexe 6 bedrs, 6
bps, TV, Dgs. ✗ a l c, mc, LD 9. ⏢ CH, Dgs,
CP 24, sp, con 90, CF, 7 BGf, 1 st, Dis. £ BB
fr £17, DB fr £24·50, WB, ☐, Bk £2·25, L
£5·70, D £5·70.

Rescue Service: Warren Bros (Plymstock)
Ltd, Dean Cross. ✆ Plymouth (0752)
42297.

POCKLINGTON Humberside. Map 25C
Pop 5,051. Market Weighton 6, London
191, Bridlington 28, York 13.
EC Wed. **Golf** Fulford (York) 18h. **See**
Burnby Hall Gardens Famous Water Lily
Ponds and Museum.

★★M Feathers, *Market Pl, YO4 2AH.*
✆ (075 92) 3155. C. ⇔ 6 bedrs, 5 bp, 1 bps, annexe 6 bedrs, 6 bp, TV. ✗ a l c, mc, at, LD 9. ⓓ CH, TV, CP 60, G 6, Ac, con 20, CF, 6 BGf, 1 st, Dis. **£** BB £17–£19, DB £30, WB, ②, Bk £3·50, L £4·25, D £5·75, cc 1 2 3 5 6.

POLBATHIC Cornwall. Map 3C.
Pop 660. St Germans 1½, London 219, Liskeard 9, Looe 8, Saltash 7½, Seaton 3½, Torpoint 8.

Old Mill House, G, x (Rl), *Torpoint, PL11 3HA.* ✆ St Germans (0503) 30596.

POLEGATE East Sussex. Map 7F
Pop 6,777. Uckfield 14, London 58, Eastbourne 5, Hastings 15, Hurst Green 21, Lewes 11, Tunbridge Wells 26.
EC Wed, Thur. **Golf** Willingdon 18h, Eastbourne 18h. **See** Restored working windmill.

Repairer: Polegate Motor Co Ltd, Eastbourne Rd. ✆ (032 12) 2666.

POLPERRO Cornwall. Map 3E
Pop 920. Looe 4, London 231, Fowey (Fy) 9.
EC Sat. **Golf** Looe Bin Down 18h. **See** Museum of Smuggling, 'The House on the Props', Chapel Cliff (Nat Trust).

▣**Ap Claremont** (Unl), *The Coombes, PL13 3RG.* ✆ (0503) 72241. Open Mar–Oct. C. ⇔ 9 bedrs, 4 bps, 2 ba, Dgs. ⓓ ch, TV, Dgs, CP 16, CF. **£** BB fr £12, DB fr £23, DBB fr £15, WB, ②, D £6, Dep.
Landaviddy Manor, G, xy (Rl), *Landaviddy Lane, PL13 2RT.* ✆ (0503) 72210. Open Apr–Oct. C 10. ⇔ 9 bedrs, 3 bps, 3 ba. ⓓ CH, TV, CP 12, 3 st. **£** BB £10–£11, DB £20–£25, WT (b) £96–£120, DT (b) £17–£20, ①.
Lanhael House, G, xy (Unl), *PL13 2PW.* ✆ (0503) 72428. Open Mar–Oct. C. ⇔ 7 bedrs, 2 bps, 1 sh, 1 ba. ⓓ CH, TV, CP 7, U 1, 1 BGf. **£** BB £12·50–£15, DB £19–£21, ②.
Mill House, H, z, *Mill Hill, PL13 2RP.* ✆ (0503) 73262. C. ⇔ 11 bedrs, 9 sh, 2 ba, ns, TV, Dgs. ⓓ CH, TV, Dgs, ns, CP 5, CF, 0 st. **£** BB £9–£10, DB £18–£20, WT (b) £88–£92·50, DT (b) £13–£14, ①, Bk £2, D £4, cc 1.
Penryn House, H, z (Rl), *The Coombes, PL13 2RG.* ✆ (0503) 72157. C. ⇔ 12 bedrs, 5 bp, 3 ba, Dgs. ⓓ CH, TV, Dgs, CP 15, CF, 1 st. **£** BB £7–£9, DB £14–£20, WT £70–£91, DT (b) £10–£13, ①, Bk £2·50, D £3·50.▲
Rainbows End, G, x (Unl), *Brentfield, PL13 2JJ.* ✆ (0503) 72510. Open May–Oct. C 10. ⇔ 4 bedrs, 1 bps, 1 ba. ⓓ ch, CP 4, 2 BGf, 2 st. **£** BB £8–£10, DB £12–£15, WT (b) £57–£68, DT (b) £8·50–£10, ①.
Sleepy Hollow, PH, x (Unl), *Brentfields, PL13 2JJ.* ✆ (0503) 722258. Open Mar–Sep. C 12. ⇔ 6 bedrs, 2 bps, 1 ba. ⓓ ch, TV, CP 7. **£** BB £6–£7·50, DB £12–£15, WT (b) £63–£73·50, DT (b) £9–£10·50, ①.

Rescue Service: Granthurst Ltd, Central Garage, The Coombes. ✆ (0503) 72341.

POLZEATH Cornwall. Map 2D
Pop 250. Camelford 12, London 240, Wadebridge 6.
Golf St Endoc Rock 18h. **See** Pentire Head, The Rumps.

▣**★★Atlantic House,** *PL27 6TG.* ✆ (020 886) 2208. Open Apr–Sep. C. ⇔ 27 bedrs, 2 bp, 7 ba, Dgs. ✗ mc, at, LD 9. ⓓ TV, CF, 8 st. **£** BB £8·50–£10·50, DB £17–£22, WT £95–£110, DBB £14–£19, WB, 10% ②, Bk £3, D £7, Dep.
White Lodge, PH, x (Rl), *near Wadebridge, PL27 6TJ.* ✆ Trebetherick (020 886) 2370.

PONTEFRACT West Yorkshire. Map 25D
Pop 29,655. Doncaster 14, London 177, Barnsley 14, Boroughbridge 31, Goole 20, Harrogate 27, Leeds 13, Rotherham 20, Selby 13, Thorne 20, Wakefield 9, York 25.
EC Thur. **MD** Sat. **Golf** Pontefract & District 18h, **See** Castle ruins (1069), All Saints' Church, Butter Cross, Old Pump, 14th cent Arcade, St Giles' Church. Racecourse.

Rescue Service: New Quarry Service Station, Wakefield Rd. ✆ (0977) 702468.

PONTELAND Northumberland. Map 31E
Pop 12,000. Newcastle upon Tyne 7½, London 281, Alnwick 29, Coldstream 48, Corbridge 14, Hawick 50, Jedburgh 49.
EC Thur. **Golf** Ponteland 18h. **See** Norman Church, old Pele Tower, remains of medieval castle.

Rescue Service: J S Robinson (Ponteland) Ltd, Belle Villa Garage. ✆ (0661) 22382.
R H Patterson (Ponteland) Ltd, Main St. ✆ (0661) 24261.

POOLE Dorset. Map 5F
Pop 115,500. Ringwood 12, London 106, Blandford Forum 13, Bournemouth 4, Dorchester 23, Salisbury 32, Sandbanks 4½, Wareham 9.
EC Wed. **MD** Tue, Sat. **Golf** Broadstone (Dorset) 18h, Parkstone 18h. **See** Old Town House (orig Guildhall), Pottery, 14th cent Gateway and walls, Guildhall (1761), now Museum, Poole Park (Zoo, Miniature Rly, boating, etc), Old Wool House, Georgian Customs House and Harbour Office, Almshouses, Merley Tropical Bird Gardens, Illuminations, Compton Acres Gdns (Canford Cliffs), Brownsea Island (heronry, woodlands, lakes, reconstructed castle, daily boat service in summer) (Nat Trust).
🛈 Poole Quay. ✆ Poole (0202) 675151.

★★★★M Hospitality Inn, *The Quay, BH15 1HD.* ✆ (0202) 671200. C. ⇔ 68 bedrs, 65 bp, 3 bps, TV, Dgs. ✗ a l c, mc, at, LD 10. ⓓ Lt, N, CH, CP 120, Ac, con 40, CF, 22 BGf, 0 st. **£** BB fr £41·25, DB fr £49·50, WB, ①, cc 1 2 3 5.
★★★Dolphin, *High St, BH15 1DU.* ✆ (0202) 673612. C. ⇔ 71 bedrs, 49 bp, 13 bps, 1 ba, TV, Dgs. ✗ mc, at, LD 9.30. ⓓ Lt, N, CH, CP 30, Ac, con 60, CF, 0 st. **£** BB £19–£30, DB £29–£39, WB, ②, Bk £4, L £6, D £9, cc 1 2 3 5 6, Dep b.
★★★Harbour Heights, *Haven Rd, BH13 7LW.* ✆ Canford Cliffs (0202) 707272. C. ⇔ 35 bedrs, 19 bp, 14 bps, 1 ba, TV, Dgs. ✗ mc, at, LD 9.30. ⓓ Lt, N, CH, Dgs, CP 70, con 50, CF, 0 st. **£** BB £18·50–£24·50, DB £41–£49, WB, ①, Bk £3·50, D £8, cc 1 2 3 5 6, Dep b.
★★★Sandbanks, *BH13 7PS.* ✆ Canford Cliffs (0202) 707377. Open Apr–Oct. C. ⇔ 120 bedrs, 82 bp, 11 bps, 10 ba, TV.

✗ mc, at, LD 8.30. ⓓ Lt, N, CH, TV, CP 250, Ac, sp, sb, sol, con 100, CF, 10 BGf. **£** BB £21–£29, DB £42–£58, WT £198–£242, DT £28·50–£35, DBB £27–£35, WB, ②, Bk £4, L £6, D £7, cc 1 3 6, Dep.
★★Haven, *Sandbanks, BH13 7QL.* ✆ Canford Cliffs (0202) 707333. C. ⇔ 100 bedrs, 72 bp, 3 bps, 13 ba, TV. ✗ mc, at, LD 8.30. ⓓ Lt, N, CH, ns, CP 200, sp, con 200, CF, 4 st. **£** BB £15·50–£23, DB £31–£46, WT £140–£200, DT £22·50–£28·50, DBB £21–£28·50, WB, ①, Bk £3·50, L £5·50, D £6·50, cc 1 3 5, Dep b.
★★Quarterdeck (R), *2 Sandbanks Rd, BH14 8AQ.* ✆ Parkstone (0202) 740066. C 6. ⇔ 15 bedrs, 3 bp, 9 bps, 2 ba, TV. ✗ a l c, mc, at, LD 9.30. ⓓ TV, CP 30, CF, 5 BGf, 3 st. **£** BB fr £16·50, DB fr £28, WB, ①, Bk £3·75, L £5·50, D £7·50, cc 1 2, Dep.
★★Sea-Witch (Rt), *47 Haven Rd, Canford Cliffs, BH13 7LH.* ✆ Canford Cliffs (0202) 707697.
Avalon, PH, z (Rl), *14 Pinewood Rd, Branksome Park, BH13 6JS.* ✆ Bournemouth (0202) 760917. Closed Xmas. C. ⇔ 14 bedrs, 3 bps, 3 sh, 4 ba, Dgs. ⓓ CH, TV, Dgs, CP 14. **£** BB £9·78–£14·49, DB £19·56–£28·98, WT (b) £74·75–£100·62, DT (b) £13·22–£18·51, ①.
Bays, G, z (Unl), *82 Bournemouth Rd, Parkstone, BH14 0HA.* ✆ Parkstone (0202) 740116. C. ⇔ 5 bedrs, 1 sh, 2 ba, TV, Dgs. ⓓ CH, TV, CP 6, CF, 1 BGf, 1 st. **£** BB £11–£12·50, DB £22–£27, ①.
Dene, PH, z (Rl), *16 Pinewood Rd, Branksome Park, BH13 6JS.* ✆ Bournemouth (0202) 761143. Closed Xmas. C. ⇔ 18 bedrs, 1 bp, 7 bps, 2 sh, 2 ba, TV. ⓓ CH, TV, CP 20, CF, 2 BGf, 2 st. **£** BB £14–£19·50, DB £24–£38, WT £78·20–£120·20, DT £19·50–£24, ①, Bk £3·75, L £5·50, D £6·50, cc 1 2 3 5.
Gables, PH, y (Rl), *19 Forest Rd, Branksome Park, BH13 6DQ.* ✆ Bournemouth (0202) 760949. Open Apr–Sep. C 5. ⇔ 10 bedrs, 4 bp, 1 sh, 2 ba. ⓓ ch, TV, Dgs, CP 20. **£** BB £10–£12, DB £20–£27, WT (c) £70–£84, DT (b) £15–£17.
Grovefield, PH, y (Rl), *18 Pinewood Rd, Branksome Park, BH13 6JS.* ✆ (0202) 766798. C. 2 ⇔ 13 bedrs, 6 bp, 7 sh, 2 ba, TV, Dgs. ⓓ CH, TV, CP 14. **£** BB fr £11, DB fr £22, WT fr £74, DT (b) fr £16, ①.
Inglewood, PH, yz (Rl), *54 Bournemouth Rd, Parkstone, BH14 0EY.* ✆ Parkstone (0202) 740012. C. ⇔ 8 bedrs, 3 bp, 1 bps, 2 ba, TV. ⓓ ch, TV, CP 20, CF, 1 st. **£** BB fr £11·50, DB fr £19, cc 2.
Lewina, G, z (Unl), *225 Bournemouth Rd, Parkstone, BH14 9HU.* ✆ Parkstone (0202) 742295. C. ⇔ 7 bedrs, 1 bps, 1 ba, Dgs. ⓓ ch, TV, Dgs, CP 6, CF. **£** BB £7–£8, DB £14–£16, WT (c) £47–£54, DT (b) £10·74–£11·75, ①.
Norfolk Lodge, H, *1 Flaghead Rd, Canford Cliffs, BH13 7JL.* ✆ Bournemouth (0202) 708614. C. ⇔ 12 bedrs, 2 bp, 1 bps, 6 sh, 3 ba, TV, Dgs. ⓓ CH, TV, Dgs, CP 2, CF, 2 BGf, 2 st. **£** BB £11–£14, DB £22–£32, WT (b) fr £65, (c) fr £55, DT (b) £15–£18, ①, Bk £2, L £5, D £6·50.
Pinewood Lodge, PH, y (Rl), *24 Pinewood Rd, Branksome Park, BH13 6JS.* ✆ Bournemouth (0202) 761165. Open Feb–Nov. C. ⇔ 10 bedrs, 2 bps, 4 ba, Dgs. ⓓ CH, TV, CP 12, CF, 1 st. **£** BB £9–

£10, DB £18–£20, WT (b) £75–£90, DT (b) £13–£15, ⬚.
Redcroft, H, z (RI), *20 Pinewood Rd, Branksome Park, BH13 6JS.* ✆ Bournemouth (0202) 763959. C 5. ⇔ 10 bedrs, 3 bp, 1 bps, 3 ba, TV. ⓓ CH, TV, CP 12, CF, 2 st. £ BB £12·65–£13·91, DB £25·30–£27·83, WT (b) £88·55–£101·20, (c) £75·90–£79·20, DT (b) £18·37, ⬚, Bk £3·50, D £5·70.
Rosemount, H, z (Unl), *167 Bournemouth Rd, Parkstone, BH14 9HT.* ✆ Parkstone (0202) 732138. Closed Xmas. C. ⇔ 6 bedrs, 2 ba, TV, Dgs. ⓓ CH, TV, Dgs, ns, CP 6, CF, 1 BGf, 2 st. £ BB £7·50–£8, DB £15–£16, WT (b) £60–£70, DT (b) £10–£10·50, ⬚.
Sandbourne, PH, z (Unl), *1 Sandcotes Rd, Parkstone. BH14 8NT.* ✆ Parkstone (0202) 747704.
Sheldon Lodge, PH, z (RI), *22 Forest Rd, Branksome Park, BH13 6DH.* ✆ Bournemouth (0202) 761186. C. ⇔ 14 bedrs, 7 bp, 4 bps, 1 ba, Dgs. ⓓ CH, TV, ns, CP 3, CF, 1 BGf, 1 st, Dis. £ BB £12–£15·50, DB £24–£31, WT (b) £95–£120, DT (b) £15–£18, ⬚.
Wayside Lodge, H, z (RI), *179 Bournemouth Rd, Parkstone, BH14 9HT.* ✆ Parkstone (0202) 732328. C. ⇔ 12 bedrs, 2 bp, 4 bps, 2 ba, TV, Dgs. ⓓ CH, TV, Dgs, ns, CP 15, CF, 2 BGf, 2 st. £ BB £11·50–£13·80, DB £18·40–£21·85, WT (b) £86·25, DT (b) £13·23, ⬚, cc 1 2 3.

Repairer: Parkstone Motor Co Ltd, Station Rd, Parkstone. ✆ Parkstone (0202) 745000.
Rescue Service: Brown Motors, Kinson Pottery Industrial Estate, 75 Ringwood Rd, Parkstone. ✆ Parkstone (0202) 742049.
Browns Garage, 417 Wimborne Rd. ✆ (0202) 673822.
Castle Hill Garage (Simmonds Auto Services), 22 Bournemouth Rd, Parkstone. ✆ Parkstone (0202) 746087.
J F & A Coupland (Motor Services) Ltd, T/ As Castle Hill Garage, 22 Bournemouth Rd. ✆ Parkstone (0202) 733232.
Fernside Road Service Station, Fernside Rd. ✆ (0202) 675516.
Grand Parade Motors Ltd, 400 Poole Rd, Branksome. ✆ Bournemouth (0202) 763361.

POOLEY BRIDGE Cumbria. Map 26C
Pop 300. Kendal 28, London 285, Ambleside 16, Keswick 19, Penrith 5½, Ulverston 35.
Golf Penrith 18h. **See** Ullswater.
ⓘ Eusemere Car Park. ✆ Pooley Bridge (085 36) 530.

⬛★★★**Sharrow Bay** (R), *Sharrow Bay, CA10 2LZ.* (1½ m S, unclass). ✆ (085 36) 301. Open Mar–Nov. C 13. ⇔ 12 bedrs, 8 bp, 1 ba, annexe 17 bedrs, 15 bp, 2 bps, ns, TV. ✗ mc, at, LD 8.45. ⓓ CH, ns, CP 30, G 2, con 12, 5 BGf, 1 st, Dis. £ DBB £42–£70, ⬚, Bk £7·50, L £16·50, D £22·50.

PORLOCK Somerset. Map 4D
Pop 1,374. Minehead 5½, London 173, Lynmouth 11.
EC Wed. **Golf** Minehead and West Somerset 18h. **See** Ship Inn, 13th cent Church, Porlock Hill (gradient in 4). Culbone Church (reputed smallest in England).

⬛★★**Castle,** *High St, TA24 8PY.* ✆ (0643) 862504.
⬛★**Ship Inn,** *High St, TA24 8QD.* ✆ (0643) 862577. RS Nov–Feb except Xmas. C. ⇔ 11 bedrs, 5 bp, 1 bps, 2 ba, TV, Dgs. ✗ mc, LD 8.30. ⓓ CH, Dgs, CP 22, G 2, Ac, con 50, CF, 1 st. £ BB £13·03–£14·42, DB £26·06–£28·84, DBB £20·03–£21·42, WB, ⬚, Bk £2·50, D £7, Dep a.
Lorna Doone, PH, x (RI), *TA24 8PS.* ✆ (0643) 862404. C. ⇔ 12 bedrs, 2 bp, 1 bps, 2 ba. ✗ a l c. ⓓ CH, TV, CP 8, CF, 1 BGf, 0 st, Dis. £ BB £9·75, DB £18–£21, WT (b) £99·75, (c) £64·75, DT (b) £14·75, ⬚, L £2·75, D £5.

Rescue Service: P. G. Hayes, Pollard's Garage. ✆ (0643) 862334.

PORLOCK WEIR Somerset. Map 4D
Minehead 7½, London 175, Lynmouth 13.

★★**Anchor & Ship,** *TA24 8PB.* ✆ (0643) 862753. C. ⇔ 23 bedrs, 15 bp, TV, Dgs. ✗ a l c, mc, at, LD 9. ⓓ CH, CP 20, Ac, con 25, CF, 1 st. £ BB £17·70–£43·20, DB £35·40–£48·50, DT £36, DBB £26·45–£33·95, WB, ⬚, Bk £3·50, L £5·50, D £9·75, cc 1 3 6, Dep a.▲

PORTH Cornwall
See NEWQUAY.

PORTHCURNO Cornwall. Map 2E
Pop 60. 8½ m SW of Penzance, London 289.
Golf West Cornwall 18h. **See** Minack open-air theatre.
Rescue Service: Porthcurno Service Station. ✆ St Buryan (073 672) 345. St Levan Garage. ✆ Sennen (073 687) 300.

PORTHLEVEN Cornwall. Map 2E
Pop 3,200. Helston 2½, London 274, Lizard 14, Penzance 13, Redruth 13, St Ives 14.
EC Wed. **Golf** Mullion 18h, Praa Sands 9h.
★**Tye Rock** (R), *Loe Bar Rd, Helston, TR13 9EW.* ✆ Helston (032 65) 2695.

PORTHTOWAN Cornwall. Map 2E
Pop 250. Bodmin 30, London 263, Newquay 16, Redruth 4, St Austell 24, Truro 10, Wadebridge 29.
Golf Tehidy Park 18h.
Rescue Service: Porthtowan Garage. ✆ (0209) 215 and (0209) 331.

PORT ISAAC Cornwall. Map 2D
Pop 800. Camelford 7½, London 235, Wadebridge 10.
Golf St Enodoc Rock 18h (2). **See** Harbour, Smugglers' caves, 17th cent Golden Lion.

⬛★★**Castle Rock** (R), *4 New Rd, PL29 3SB.* ✆ (020 888) 300. Open Apr–Oct. C. ⇔ 20 bedrs, 7 bp, 2 bps, 5 ba, TV, Dgs. ✗ mc, at, LD 8.30. ⓓ ch, TV, CP 20, CF, 5 BGf. £ BB £11·70–£16·40, DB £23·40–£32·40, DBB £19·70–£24·40, WB, ⬚, Bk £3·50, D £8, cc 1 5 6.
Bay, H, z (R), *1 The Terrace, PL29 3SG.* ✆ (020 888) 380. C. ⇔ 11 bedrs, 2 sh, 2 ba, Dgs. ⓓ ch, TV, Dgs, CP 10, CF, 4 st. £ BB £8·50–£11·50, DB £17–£23, WT (b) £76–£96, (c) £52–£68, DT £13–£16, ⬚, Bk £3·50, D £6.
Fairholme, G, x (Unl), *30 Trewetha Lane, PL29 3RW.* ✆ (020 888) 397. C. ⇔ 6 bedrs, 1 ba. ⓓ CH, TV, CP 8, CF. £ DB £13–£14, WT (b) fr £70, (c) fr £42, DT fr £11·50, ⬚.

Trethoway, H, x (RI), *98 Fore St, PL29 3RF.* ✆ (020 888) 214. Open Apr–Oct. C. ⇔ 9 bedrs, 2 ba, Dgs. ⓓ TV, CP 6, CF, 2 st.
Rescue Service: Central Garage. ✆ (020 888) 334.

PORTISHEAD Avon. Map 5A
Pop 11,331. Bristol 9, London 122, Weston-super-Mare 20.
EC Thur. **MD** Fri. **Golf** Clevedon 18h. **See** St Peter's Church (14th–15th cent Cross), Tudor House, Court House, The Grange.
Rescue Service: Auto Distress 9135, Cab Stand. ✆ Freephone 9135.

PORTLAND Dorset. Map 5E
Pop 12,000. Weymouth 6, London 137.
EC Wed. **Golf** Weymouth 18h. **See** Portland Castle, Museum, Portland Bill and Lighthouse, Quarry Sculpture Park, St George's Church, Chesil Bank (11 m breakwater of graded pebbles), Bird Observatory.

★★**Pennsylvania Castle,** *Pennsylvania Rd, DT5 1HZ.* ✆ (0305) 820561. C. ⇔ 13 bedrs, 5 bps, 6 bp, 1 ba, TV, Dgs. ✗ a l c, mc, at, LD 10. ⓓ N, CH, Dgs, ns, CP 100, con 40, CF, 0 st. £ BB £23, DB £36–£37, WB, ⬚, Bk £2·50, L £6·35, D £6·35, cc 1 2 3 5 6, Dep.
Rescue Service: Auto-Repairs, 181A Brandy Row. ✆ (0305) 826611. Easton Motor Services, 26 Easton Sq. ✆ (0305) 820084 & (0305) 820259.

PORTLOE Cornwall. Map 2F
Pop 150. St Austell 11, London 251, Newquay 24, Truro 14.
Golf Truro 18h.

⬛★★**Lugger** (R), *TR2 5RD.* ✆ Truro (0872) 501322. Open Mar–Nov. C 12. ⇔ 6 bedrs, 1 ba, annexe 14 bedrs, 14 bp, TV. ✗ mc, at, LD 9. ⓓ CH, TV, CP 20, sb, sol, 1 st. £ BB £18–£25, DB £36–£50, WT £175–£224, DBB £27–£33·50, WB, ⬚, Bk £4·50, L £5·50, D £9·50, cc 1 2 3 5 6.

PORT ST MARY Isle of Man. Map 27F
Pop 1,572. Douglas 14 (Steamer Service to Liverpool). London 212, Peel 14.
EC Thur. **Golf** Port St Mary 9h. **See** Cregneash Folk Museum 1 m SW.
ⓘ Town Hall, Promenade. ✆ Port St Mary (0624) 832101.
Repairer: Island Garages (Shore) Ltd, Shore Garage. ✆ (0624) 832021.

PORTSCATHO Cornwall. Map 2F
Pop 500. St Austell 15, London 255, Falmouth (Fy) 14, Newquay 25, Truro (Fy) 10.
Golf Truro 18h.

⬛⬛★★★**Rosevine,** *Porthcurnick Beach, TR2 5EW.* ✆ (087 258) 203. Open Apr–Sep. C. ⇔ 16 bedrs, 10 bp, 1 bps, 2 ba, TV, Dgs. ✗ mc, at, LD 8.45. ⓓ N, CH, TV, CP 45, Ac, con, CF, 2 st. £ BB £15–£19·50, DB £30–£39, DBB £23–£27·50, ⬚, 10%, Bk £4·50, D £9, cc 1 2 3 5.
⬛★★**Gerrans Bay** (R), *Gerrans, TR2 5ED.* ✆ (087 258) 338. Open Apr–Oct & Xmas. C. ⇔ 15 bedrs, 12 bp, 1 ba, Dgs. ✗ a l c, mc, at, LD 8. ⓓ ch, TV, CP 16, CF, 4 BGf, 3 st. £ BB £13–£14·50, DB £26–£29, DBB £17·50–£24, ⬚, Bk £2·75, D £7·50, cc 1 2 3, Dep a.
⬛⬛★★**Roseland House** (RI), *Rosevine, TR2 5EW.* ✆ (087 258) 644. Closed Dec–

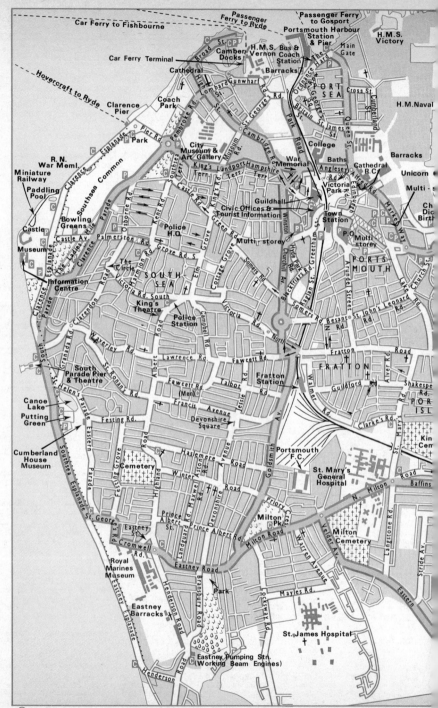

For abbreviations see inside back cov

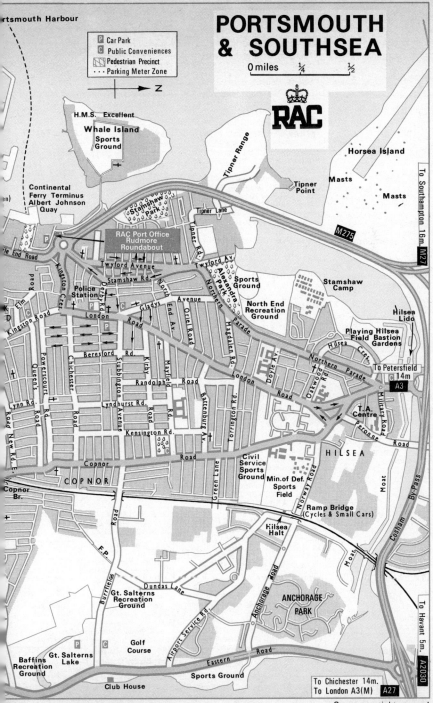

PORTSMOUTH & SOUTHSEA

P Car Park
C Public Conveniences
Pedestrian Precinct
... Parking Meter Zone

0 miles   ¼   ½

RAC

Portsmouth Harbour

H.M.S. Excellent
Whale Island
Sports Ground

Tipner Range

Horsea Island

Tipner Point
Masts
Masts

Continental Ferry Terminus
Albert Johnson Quay

Stamshaw Park
Tipner Lane

To Southampton 16m. M27

M275

RAC Port Office
Rudmore Roundabout

le End Road

Twyford Avenue
Tipner Rd.
Twyford Av.

Kingston Road

Stamshaw Rd.
Alexandra
Sports Ground
Sports Ground

Stamshaw Camp

Police Station

Gladys
Avenue
Northern

North End Recreation Ground

Hilsea Lido

London
Road

Oxtel Road
North End Av.

Magdalen Rd.

Parade

Hilsea Cres.

Playing Hilsea Field Bastion Gardens

Elm

Derd Rd.

To Petersfield

Beresford Rd.
Kirby
Mayfield Rd.

London

Dove Av.

Northern Parade

Oakwood Rd.

A3 14m.

Powerscourt Rd.

Chichester

Stubbington Avenue

Road

Randolph Road

Battenburg Av.

Road

Lyndhurst Rd.

Torrington Rd.

Road

T.A. Centre

Military Road

Queen's Road

Road

Kensington Rd.

Peronne
Road

Lynn Rd.

Copnor

Road

Civil Service Sports Ground

HILSEA

New Rd. E.

COPNOR

Green Lane

Min. of Def. Sports Field

Norway Road

Moat

Coshan By-Pass

Copnor Br.

Ramp Bridge (Cycles & Small Cars)

F.P.

Hilsea Halt

Moat

Burrfields

Dundas Lane

Gt. Salterns Recreation Ground

Airport Service Rd.

ANCHORAGE PARK

To Havant 5m. A2030

P C
Baffins Recreation Ground

Gt. Salterns Lake

Golf Course

Anchorage Road

Eastern
Road

Sports Ground

To Chichester 14m.
To London A3(M)   A27

Club House

Crown copyright reserved

Jan. C 5. ✉ 20 bedrs, 8 bp, 3 ba. ✗ a l c,
mc, at, LD 7.30. ⓓ CH, TV, CP 25, G 3, pf,
CF, 6 BGf. £ BB £12–£22, DB £24–£44,
WB, ②, D £7·50, Dep.

PORTSLADE East Sussex. M. Area 7E
Pop 17,000. Crawley 21, London 52,
Brighton 3, Haywards Heath 14, Horsham
21, Pulborough 14, Worthing 7.
EC Wed. **Golf** West Hove 18h. **See** St
Nicolas Church.

Repairer: Tates, 28 Church Rd. ✆ Brighton
(0273) 411020.

PORTSMOUTH AND SOUTHSEA
Hampshire. Map 6F
RAC Port Office, Rudmore Roundabout,
PO2 8DN. ✆ Portsmouth (0705) 697713.
Pop 175,000. Cosham 4, London 71,
M275 Motorway 1½.
See Plan, pp. 302 and 303.
MD Thur, Fri, Sat. **P** See Plan. **Golf** Gt
Salterns 18h. **See** Cathedral, Dickens's
Birthplace and Museum, Dockyard
(Nelson's flagship 'Victory' and Museum),
HMS 'Mary Rose' War Memorial, RC
Cathedral, Cumberland House Museum,
City Museum and Art Gallery, restored
Garrison Church, Square Tower, Point
Battery and Round Tower, Southsea:
D-Day Memorial, Castle and Museum,
Town Fortifications, Forts on Portsdown
Hills, Royal Naval Museum, Royal Marines
Museum.
ⓘ Civic Offices, Guildhall Sq.
✆ Portsmouth (0705) 826722.

★★★★**M Holiday Inn,** *North Harbour,*
PO6 4SH. ✆ (0705) 383151. C. ✉ 170
bedrs, 170 bp, ns, TV, Dgs. ✗ a l c, mc, at,
LD 10.30. ⓓ Lt, N, CH, CP 200, Ac, sp, sc,
sb, sol, gym, con 300, CF. £ WB,
cc 1 2 3 4 5 6, Dep b.

★★★**Crest,** *Pembroke Rd, PO1 2NS.*
✆ (0705) 827651. C. ✉ 169 bedrs, 169
bp, ns, TV, Dgs. ✗ a l c, mc, at, LD 9.45.
ⓓ Lt, N, CH, CP 124, Ac, con 600, CF, 9
BGf, 1 st. £ B fr £43·50, BD fr £52·50, WB,
①, Bk £5·25, D £8·95, cc 1 2 3 4 5 6,
Dep b.

★★★**Pendragon** (TH), *Clarendon Par,*
Southsea, PO5 2HY. ✆ (0705) 823201. C.
✉ 58 bedrs, 37 bp, 8 ba, TV, Dgs. ✗ a l c,
mc, at, LD 9. ⓓ Lt, N, CH, Dgs, U 2, G 6, Ac,
con 450, CF, 10 st. £ BB £30·50–£34·50,
DB £42·50–£50, WB, ①, cc 1 2 3 4 5 6,
Dep (Xmas).

★★★**Hospitality Inn** (late **Royal**
Beach), *St Helen's Par, Southsea, PO4*
0RN. ✆ (0705) 731281. C. ✉ 108 bedrs,
108 bp, TV, Dgs. ✗ a l c, mc, at, LD 9.45.
ⓓ Lt, N, CH, CP 40, Ac, con 250, CF, 0 st.
£ BB fr £35·75, DB fr £44, WB, ①,
cc 1 2 3 4 5.

★★**Berkeley** (R), *South Par, Southsea,*
PO4 0SH. ✆ (0705) 735059. Open Apr–
Oct. C. ✉ 44 bedrs, 20 bp, 7 ba, TV, Dgs.
✗ mc, at, LD 8. ⓓ Lt, TV, Dgs, CP 3, U 6,
Ac, CF, 3 BGf, 0 st, Dis. £ BB £17–£27, DB
£32–£50, WF £148–£190, DT £29–£38, ①,
Bk £5·50, L £6·50, D £8, cc 1 3 6.

★★**Keppels Head,** *24 The Hard, PO1*
3DT. ✆ (0705) 833231. C. ✉ 24 bedrs, 17
bp, 7 bps, TV, Dgs. ✗ a l c, mc, at, LD 10.
ⓓ Lt, N, CH, Dgs, CP 20, Ac, CF, 5 BGf.
£39, DB £49, WB, ②, Bk £4·75, L £6·95, D
£6·95, cc 1 2 3 4 5 6, Dep b.

★**Upper Mount House** (RI), *The Vale,*
Clarendon Rd, Southsea, PO5 2EQ.
✆ (0705) 820456. C. ✉ 9 bedrs, 2 bp, 4
bps, 1 sh, 1 ba, TV, Dgs. ✗ LD 7. ⓓ CH,

Dgs, CP 7, CF, 2 BGf, 4 st. £ BB fr £13·50,
DB fr £27, ②, D £5·95, cc 1 3.

Abbeville, PH (RI), *26 Nettlecombe Ave,*
PO4 0QW. ✆ (0705) 826209. C. ✉ 12
bedrs, 2 ba, TV, Dgs. ⓓ CH, TV, Dgs, ns, CP
6, CF, 1 BGf, 2 st. ✉ BB £9·50–£10, DB
£19–£20, WT (b) £85–£90, DT (b) £13·50–
£14, ①.

Amberley Court, G, z (Unl), *97 Waverley*
Rd, PO5 2PL. ✆ (0705) 735419. C. ✉ 9
bedrs, 1 sh, 3 ba. ⓓ CH, TV, Dgs, CF, 1 st.
£ BB £9, DB £18, WT (b) £68, DT (b) £15,
①.

Birchwood, G, z (Unl), *44 Waverley Rd,*
PO5 2PP. ✆ (0705) 811337. C 6. ✉ 6
bedrs, 2 ba. ⓓ CH, TV, 0 st. £ BB £9, DB
£18, WT (b) £68–£75, DT (b) fr £13, ①.

Bristol, H, z (RI), *55 Clarence Par, PO5*
2HX. ✆ (0705) 821815.

Canterbury Bell, G, z (Unl), *29 St*
Simons Rd, PO5 2PE. ✆ (0705) 826917.
Closed Dec. C. ✉ 10 bedrs, 1 ba. ⓓ CH,
TV, ns, CP 8, CF, 12 st. £ BB £8, DB £15,
WT (c) £49, ①.

Dolphins, H, z (R), *10 Western Par,*
PO5 3JF. ✆ (0705) 820833. C. ✉ 30
bedrs, 6 sh, 8 ba, TV, Dgs. ⓓ CH, TV, Dgs,
CF. £ BB £17–£20, DB £28–£34, WT
£149–£168, ①, Bk £2·50, D £6·80,
cc 1 2 3 5.

Gainsborough House, G, z (Unl), *9*
Malvern Rd. PO5 2LZ. ✆ (0705) 822604.
Closed Xmas. C 3. ✉ 7 bedrs, 2 ba, Dgs.
ⓓ CH, TV. £ BB £7–£8, DB £14–£15, WT
(b) £63–£67, DT (b) £10·50–£11·50, ①.

Goodwood, G, z (Unl), *1 Taswell Rd,*
Southsea, PO5 2RG. ✆ (0705) 824734.
Closed 24 Dec–3 Jan. C 2. ✉ 8 bedrs, 4
sh, 2 ba, TV, CP 1, 1 st. £ BB £8·50–
£10·50, DB £17–£20, DT £14–£15, ①.

Salisbury, H, *57 Festing Rd, PO4 0NQ.*
✆ (0705) 823606. C. ✉ 26 bedrs, 1 bp, 5
sh, 8 ba, Dgs. ⓓ CH, TV, CP 17, CF, 10 st.
£ BB £13·50–£23, DB £23–£37, WT (b)
£110·40–£128·50, DT (b) £17·25–£19·50,
①, D £6·50, cc 1 3 ▲.

Saville, H, z (RI), *Clarence Par, PO5 2ER.*
✆ (0705) 812526. Open Apr–Oct. C 2.
✉ 45 bedrs, 6 bp, 2 bps, 6 ba, Dgs. ⓓ Lt,
CH, TV, CF, 2 BGf, 14 st. £ BB £12–£30, DB
£24–£45, WT (b) £99–£125, DT (b) £17–
£35, ②, Bk £3, L £4, D £5.

Tudor Court, PH, z (RI), *1 Queen's*
Grove, Southsea, PO5 3HW. ✆ (0705)
820174. C. ✉ 11 bedrs, 2 bp, 2 sh, 3 ba,
TV, Dgs. ⓓ CH, TV, CP 9, CF. £ BB £24, DB
£20–£36, WT (b) £90–£95, DT (b) £17–
£17·50, ①, Bk £2, D £5·50.

White Heather, PH, z (R). *1 Redcliffe*
Gdns, Clarendon Rd, Southsea. ✆ (0705)
823090. C. ✉ 10 bedrs, 4 bps, 3 sh, 1 ba,
TV. ⓓ CH, TV, CF. £ BB £13·50–£15·50,
DB £26–£30, WT (b) fr £105, (c) fr £85, DT
(b) fr £17, ①, Bk £1·50, L £3, D £4·50.

Specialist Radiator Repairer: Serck
Radiator Services Ltd, London Rd.
✆ (0705) 667641.
Rescue Service: Bunny's, 249 Goldsmith
Av, Fratton. ✆ (0705) 818855.
Central Garage, Florence Rd. ✆ (0705)
812198.
Cromwell Garage, 60 Cromwell Rd.
✆ (0705) 733247.
Wadham Stringer (Southsea) Ltd, Austin
House, Granada Rd. ✆ (0705) 735311.

POSTCOMBE Oxfordshire. M. Area 15E
2 m NW of Aston Rowant, High Wycombe
11, London 41, Aylesbury 13, Bicester 19,

Henley-on-Thames 13, Oxford 14, Reading
18, Wallingford 11.
Golf Princes Risborough 9h.

Rescue Service: Postcombe Service
Station. ✆ Tetsworth (084 428) 222.

POTTO North Yorkshire. Map 24D
Thirsk 16, London 236, Northallerton 11,
Stokesley 5.

★★★**Potto Hall,** *DL6 3EU.* ✆ Stokesley
(0642) 700186.

POUNDSGATE Devon. Map 3D
Ashburton 4, London 191, Tavistock 15.
Golf Newton Abbot (Stover) 18h. **See**
Dartmoor Nat. Park.

Lower Aish, G, x (Unl), *TQ13 7NY.*
✆ (036 43) 229. Open Easter–Sep. C. ✉ 5
bedrs, 1 ba, Dgs. ⓓ CH, TV, CP 10. £ BB fr
£8, DB fr £16, ①.

Rescue Service: Lower Aish Garage.
✆ (036 43) 229.

POULTON-LE-FYLDE
Lancashire. Map 27C
Preston 14, London 225, Blackpool 3,
Lancaster 18.
See Blackpool Zoo 3 W (3 m S).

Rescue Service: Specialised Breakdown &
Recovery Services, Unit C, Furness Drive.
✆ (0253) 892094.

POWBURN Northumberland. M. Area
31C
Pop 231. Newcastle upon Tyne 37,
London 310, Alnwick 9, Berwick-upon-
Tweed 24, Coldstream 22.
Golf Wooler 9h.

★★★★**Breamish House** (R), *NE66 4LL.*
✆ (066 578) 266. Closed Jan. C 12. ✉ 10
bedrs, 8 bp, 2 bps, TV. ✗ mc, at, LD 9.
ⓓ CH, ns, CP 40, G 2, 1 st. £ BB £20–£25,
DB £30–£40, DBB £26–£36, WB, ②, L
£3·95, D £11, Dep a.

PRAA SANDS Cornwall. Map 2E
Pop 785. Helston 6, London 277,
Penzance 7½, St Ives 13.
Golf Praa Sands 9h. **See** Restored 16th
cent Pengersick Castle, Prussia Cove
(once smugglers' haunt), St Germoe
Church, St Michael's Mount, 'Furry Dance'
at Helston in May.

★★**Prah Sands** (R), *TR20 9SY.* ✆ Germoe
(073 676) 2438. Open Mar–Oct. C. ✉ 22
bedrs, 10 bp, 3 ba, TV, Dgs. ✗ a l c, mc, at,
LD 9. ⓓ ch, TV, CP 40, tc, CF, 6 BGf, 1 st,
Dis. £ BB £13·25–£17·50, DB £26–£35,
WT £127–£140, DT £25–£27·25, WB, ①,
Bk £3, L £3·75, D £7, cc 1 3, Dep a.

PRESTON Lancashire. Map 27D
Pop 126,000. M6 Motorway 4, London
211, Blackburn 10, Blackpool 16, Bolton
19, Chorley 9, Lancaster 22, Ormskirk 17,
Southport 17, Whalley 15, Wigan 17.
MD Daily (exc. Thur). **Golf** Preston 18h.
See Museum and Art Gallery, St
Walburge's RC Church, Crown Court Hall
(Renaissance style, 180 ft tower), Parish
Church, Harris Public Library, Museum of
Roman Antiquities (Ribchester).
ⓘ Town Hall, Lancaster Rd. ✆ Preston
(0772) 53731.

★★★**Barton Grange,** *Garstang Rd,*
Barton, PR3 5AA. (5½m to m on A6).
✆ (0772) 862551. C. ✉ 60 bedrs, 53 bp, 7
bps, TV, Dgs. ✗ mc, at, LD 10. ⓓ Lt, N, CH,
CP 300, Ac, sp, tc, con 300, CF, 0 st. £ BB

fr £20, DB fr £30, WT £200, WB, ⏣, Bk £4, L
£5·50, D £7·50, cc 1 2 3 5, Dep b.

★★★**Broughton Park** (R), *Garstang Rd,
Broughton PR3 5JB, Junction 32 M6/
M55.* ✆ (0772) 864087. C. 🚗 61 bedrs, 54
bp, 7 bps, 1 ba, TV, Dgs. ✗ a l c, mc, at, LD
10. 🅿 N, CH, CP 220, Ac, sp, sb, sol, gym,
con 250, CF, 25 BGf, 1 st, Dis. £ BB fr £32,
DB fr £38, WB, ②, Bk £3·50, L £5·50, D
£8·50, cc 1 2 3 5 6, Dep b.

★★★**M Crest,** *The Ringway, PR1 3AU.*
✆ (0772) 59411. C. 🚗 132 bedrs, 132 ba,
ns, TV, Dgs. ✗ a l c, mc, at, LD 9.45. 🅿 Lt,
N, CH, Dgs, CP 30, Ac, con 100, CF, 0 st.
£ B fr £42, BD fr £52, WB, ⏣, D £9·25,
cc 1 2 3 4 5 6, Dep b.

★★★**M Tickled Trout** (Rt), *Preston New
Rd, Samlesbury, PR5 0UJ.* (M6).
✆ Samlesbury (077 477) 671. Closed
Xmas. C. 🚗 66 bedrs, 66 bp, TV, Dgs.
✗ a l c, mc, at, LD 10. 🅿 N, CH, Dgs, CP
200, Ac, pf, con 100, CF, 4 BGf, 0 st. £ BB
£20·50–£35, WB, ⏣, Bk £4·50, L £2·90, D
£7·80, cc 1 2 3 5 6, Dep.▲

★★★**M Trafalgar,** *Preston New Rd,
Samlesbury, PR5 0UL.* ✆ Samlesbury
(077 477) 351. RS Xmas Day. C. 🚗 50
bedrs, 54 bp, 26 bps, ns, TV, Dgs. ✗ a l c,
mc, at, LD 10.30. 🅿 N, CH, CP 300, Ac, sp,
sc, sol, con 200, CF, 0 st. £ BB £35–£38,
DB £48–£51, WB, ⏣, Bk £3·50, L £5·50, D
£10·50, cc 1 2 3 4 5, Dep.

Fulwood Park, H, z (R), *49 Watling St,
Fulwood, PR2 4EA.* ✆ (0772) 718067. C.
🚗 25 bedrs, 7 bp, 9 bps, 2 ba, TV, guide
Dgs only. ✗ a l c. 🅿 CH, TV, Dgs, CP 25,
CF, 1 BGf, 0 st, Dis. £ BB £15–£20·75, DB
£26–£33, WT (b) £106·75–£178·50, (c)
£77–£150, ⏣, Bk £2·50, L £2·60, D £6·50,
cc 1 2 3 5.

Lauderdale, PH, z (Rl), *29 Fishergate
Hill, PR1 8DN.* ✆ (0772) 555460.

Tulketh, PH, y (R), *209 Tulketh Rd,*
✆ (0772) 728096. C. 🚗 7 bedrs, 1 bps, 1
ba, TV. ✗ a l c. 🅿 CH, TV, CP 20, CF. £ BB
£18·40–£21·27, DB £31, WT (b) £185·15,
DT (b) £26·45, ⏣, Bk £4, D £8.

Repairers: Cuerdon Motors Ltd,
Manchester Rd. ✆ (0772) 58384.
Devonshire Garage, Devonshire Pl.
✆ (0772) 700959.
Dutton-Forshaw (Preston) Ltd, Moor La.
✆ (0772) 22901.
Specialist Body Repairer: J S
Ramsbottom (Preston) Ltd, Brook St.
✆ (0772) 57834.
Specialist Radiator Repairer: Serck
Radiator Services Ltd, Kay St. ✆ (0772)
53016.
Rescue Service: Cann Bridge Service
Station, Cann Bridge St, High Walton.
✆ (0772) 35235.

PRIDDY Somerset. Map 5C
Pop 400. Wells 5, London 127, Bristol 16,
Radstock 12, Weston-super-Mare 17.
Golf Wells 18h. **See** Church, Roman lead
mines.

Rescue Service: Mendip Garages. ✆ Wells
(0749) 73019.

PRINCES RISBOROUGH Buckingham-
shire. Map 15E
Pop 8,270. High Wycombe 8, London 38,
Aylesbury 8, Bicester 22, Denham 21,
Dunstable 18, Oxford 20, Rickmansworth
18, Wallingford 17.
EC Wed. **MD** Sat. **Golf** Whiteleaf 9h. **See**
Parish Church, 17th cent cottages, 17th

cent Princes Risborough Manor, Market
House, Cross turf-cutting on hillside.

Repairer: Risboro Garage Ltd, Wycombe
Rd. ✆ (084 44) 5222.
Rescue Service: High Street Garage, High
St. ✆ (084 44) 4893.
G Jacobs Ltd, High St. ✆ (084 44) 3026.

PRINCETHORPE Warwickshire. Map
14B
Pop 556. Daventry 12, London 86,
Banbury 20, Coventry 6½, Rugby 7,
Warwick 7½.
Golf Rugby 18h. **See** 16th cent Manor
House.

★★**Woodhouse,** *Leamington Rd, CV23
0PZ.* ✆ Marton (0926) 632303. Closed
Xmas Day. C. 🚗 24 bedrs, 6 bp, 12 bps, 4
ba, TV, Dgs. ✗ a l c, mc, at, LD 10.30.
🅿 CH, Dgs, CP 50, Ac, sp, tc, con 100, CF,
10 BGf, 6 st. £ BB fr £21·50, DB fr £32, ⏣,
Bk £4·50, L £6·50, D £7·50, cc 1 2 5.

PRUDHOE Northumberland. Map 31E
Pop 11,500. West Auckland 32, London
280, Corbridge 9, Durham 23, Hexham 11,
Middleton-in-Teesdale 32, Newcastle
upon Tyne 9½.
EC Wed. **Golf** Eastwoods Park 18h. **See**
Castle, Ovingham Church.

Rescue Service: Glendinning Bros, The
Garage, Princess Way. ✆ (0661) 32468
and (0661) 32255.

PUDDLETOWN Dorset. Map 5F
Pop 949. Blandford Forum 12, London
118, Dorchester 5, Poole 17.
Golf Came Down 18h. **See** Perp Church,
Athelhampton House (15th cent
dovecote), Rhododendron Mile.

Rescue Service: Olds & Sons, Blandford
Rd. ✆ (030 584) 456.

PULBOROUGH West Sussex. Map 7C
Billingshurst 5½, London 47, Arundel 8½,
Bognor Regis 16, Petworth 5, Worthing
14.
Golf West Sussex 18h. **See** Church,
medieval Stopham Bridge, Hardham
Church (wall paintings).

★**Chequers** (R), *Church Place, RH20
1AD.* ✆ (079 82) 2486. C. 🚗 9 bedrs, 6 bp,
1 bps, 1 ba, Dgs. ✗ mc, at, LD 8. 🅿 CH, TV,
Dgs, CP 12, CF, 5 st. £ BB £17·75–£18·75,
DB £29–£31, WT £126, DT £25·50, WB, ⏣,
Bk £3·50, L £4·50, D £7·95, cc 1 2 3 5 6.

PURFLEET Essex. Map 7B
Pop 1,270. Rainham 3½, London 21,
Dartford Tunnel 2½, Southend 22.
EC Wed. **Golf** Belhus Park 18h.

★★**Royal,** *High St, RM16 1QA.*
✆ (040 26) 5432. C. 🚗 9 bedrs, 9 bp,
annexe 22 bedrs, 22 bp, TV, Dgs. ✗ a l c,
mc, at, LD 10.30. 🅿 N, CH, Dgs, CP 40, Ac,
pf, con 50, CF, 6 BGf, 1 st. £ BB £22, DB
£44, WB, ②, Bk £2·50, L £4·40, D £4·40,
cc 1 2 3 4 5 6, Dep b.

Rescue Service: D Tongue (Auto
Mechanical Engineers), Long Reach
Station, London Rd (A13). ✆ (040 26)
3702.

PURLEY Greater London (Surrey). Map
7B
Pop 16,010. Thornton Heath 4, London
12, Croydon 2½, Dartford 18, Dartford
Tunnel 21, Epsom 7, Godstone 7, Kingston
upon Thames 12, Mitcham 6, Redhill 7½,
Reigate 8½, Westerham 10.

EC Wed. **Golf** Purley Downs 18h.

Specialist Body Repairer: Fawngrove
Coachworks Ltd, 47 Imperial Way.
✆ 01-680 0600.
Rescue Service: Surrey Breakdown Ltd,
53 Whytecliffe Rd. ✆ 01-668 2456.

PUTSBOROUGH Devon. Map 4C
Pop 18. Barnstaple 10, London 203,
Ilfracombe 9.
Golf Saunton 36h.

★★★**Putsborough Sands,** *EX33 1LB.*
✆ Croyde (0271) 890555. Open Apr–Sep.
C. 🚗 61 bedrs, 30 bp, 2 bps, 6 ba, ns.
✗ mc, at, LD 8.30. 🅿 N, CH, TV, ns, CP 50,
sp, sc, sb, sol, con 30, CF. £ BB £12–£23,
DB £24–£46, DBB £18–£26, WB, ②, Bk
£3·30, D £8·80, cc 1 2 3, Dep.

QUORN or **QUORNDON**
Leicestershire. Map 22F
Leicester 8½, London 107, Coalville 10,
Loughborough 2½, Melton Mowbray 14.

★★★★**Quorn Country,** *Chornwood
House, 66 Leicester Rd, LE12 8BB.*
✆ (0509) 415050. C. 🚗 19 bedrs, 19 bp,
TV, Dgs. ✗ a l c, mc, at, LD 10. 🅿 N, CH,
Dgs, CP 100, pf, con 50, CF, 7 BGf, 1 st,
Dis. £ BB £41, DB £52, WB, ⏣, Bk £4, L
£7·50, D £9·95, cc 1 2 3 5 6.

RADCLIFFE Greater Manchester
(Lancashire). Map 20A
Pop 29,000. Manchester 6, London 190,
Bolton 5, Bury 3, Oldham 11, Walkden 5.
EC Wed. **MD** Tue, Fri, Sat. **Golf** Stand
18h, Bury 18h. **See** Parish Church, 17th
cent Tithe Barn, Radcliffe Tower ruins,
18th cent Knowsley Cottages.

MC Repairer: Will Lord (Motor Cycles)
Ltd, 115 Blackburn St. ✆ 061-723 2002.
Sctr Repairer: Will Lord (Motor Cycles)
Ltd, 115 Blackburn St. ✆ 061-723 2002.

RADCLIFFE-ON-TRENT Notts. Map
22D
Pop 8,050. Leicester 24, London 121,
Grantham 18, Melton Mowbray 17,
Newark 18, Nottingham 5½, Ollerton 21.
EC Wed. **Golf** Radcliffe-on-Trent 18h.
See Rockley Memorial Park.

Repairer: Lamcote Motors Ltd, 49 Main
Rd. ✆ (060 73) 2075.

RADFORD Avon. Map 5A
Radstock 2, London 112, Bath 8, Bristol
12, Wells 12.

Old Malt House, H, x (R), *BA3 1QF.*
✆ Timsbury (0761) 70106. C 3. 🚗 8 bedrs,
3 bp, 5 bps, TV. ✗ a l c. 🅿 CH, CP 23, 1 st.
£ BB £21–£22, DB £32–£34, ②, L £5·50, D
£8·50, cc 1 2 3 5.

RADLETT Hertfordshire. Map 15F
Pop 9,300. Barnet 6½, London 14, M1
Motorway 3, Harrow 8, Hatfield 7, St
Albans 5, Watford 4½.
EC Wed. **Golf** Porters Park 18h. **See**
Roman Kilns nearby.

■★★**Red Lion,** *Watling St, WD7 7NP.*
✆ (092 76) 5341. C. 🚗 17 bedrs, 7 bp, 1
bps, 3 ba, TV, Dgs. ✗ a l c, mc, at, LD
10.15. 🅿 CH, Dgs, CP 20, Ac, con 20, CF, 1
st. £ BB £25–£32, DB £35–£44, WB, ⏣,
cc 1 2 3 4 5 6, Dep b.

Repairer: L A P Motors (Radlett) Ltd, 203
Watling St. ✆ (092 76) 4851.

RAINHAM Kent. Map 10C
Rochester 5½, London 36, M2 Motorway
3½, Ashford 21, Canterbury 22, Maidstone
8, Margate 36.

Rescue Service: Petrol Supermarkets Ltd,
Greens Garage, London Rd. ✆ Medway
(0634) 31242.

RAINHILL Merseyside. Map 20D
Pop 12,000. Northwich 17, London 189,
M62 Motorway 1½, Chester 21, Liverpool
10, St Helens 3, Warrington 7½.
EC Thur. **Golf** Huyton 18h.

★**Rockland** (R), *View Rd, L35 OLG.*
✆ 051-426 4603. C. ⊷ 12 bedrs, 2 bp, 3
ba, annexe 10 bedrs, 4 bp, 6 bps, TV, Dgs.
✗ a l c, mc, at, LD 8.15. ⊡ CH, TV, Dgs, CP
30, Ac, con 50, CF, 7 BGf, 3 st. £ BB £16–
£19·50, DB £28–£32·50, WB, ②, Bk £3, L
£4, D £6·50.

Rescue Service: D J Motors, 375
Warrington Rd. ✆ 051-426 4234.
Pierpoint & Shearon, Tasker Ter, Rainhill
Rd. ✆ 051-426 4271 and 3000.

RAME Cornwall. M. Area 2E
Truro 10, London 256, Falmouth 7,
Helston 6, Redruth 10.
Golf Falmouth 18h.

Rescue Service: Edgcumbe Service
Station, Edgcumbe. ✆ Stithians (0209)
860289.

RAMPISHAM Dorset. M. Area 5E
Yeovil 10, London 135, Beaminster 6,
Weymouth 21.

Rescue Service: Rampisham Garage.
✆ Evershot (093 583) 611.

RAMSBOTTOM Greater Manchester
(Lancashire). Map 27B
Pop 16,000. Bury 4½, London 196, M66
Motorway 1, Blackburn 11, Bolton 7½,
Burnley 10, Rochdale 8, Todmorden 12,
Whalley 13.
EC Wed. **MD** Sat. **Golf** Greenmount 9h.
See Peel Tower on Holcombe Hill, ruins of
16th cent New Hall (Edenfield), Grant's
Tower (remains), Waugh's Well.

★★**Old Mill,** *Springwood St, BL0 9DS.*
✆ (070 682) 2991. Closed Dec 25 night.
C. ⊷ 17 bedrs, 17 bp, TV. ✗ a l c, mc, LD
9.45. ⊡ N, CH, TV, CP 100, con 50, CF, 4
BGf. £ BB £29·90, DB £39·90. ②, Bk £2, L
£4·50, D £8·50, cc 1 2 3 5.

Rescue Service: Oakdene Service Station,
Stubbins La. ✆ (070 682) 3418.

RAMSEY Isle of Man. Map 27E
Pop 6,000. Douglas 15 (Steamer Service
to Liverpool), London 213, Peel 16.
EC Wed. **MD** Mon, Fri. **Golf** Ramsey 18h.
See St Mary's Church, Albert Tower,
Mooragh Park, Grove Rural Life Museum,
Maughold Church 3 m (oldest in island),
Wildlife Park 5½ m W, Snae Fell.
🛈 Town Hall, Parliament Sq. ✆ Ramsey
(0624) 812228.

Rescue Service: Raymotors Ltd,
Parliament Sq. ✆ (0624) 813000.

RAMSGATE Kent. Map 10D
RAC Port Office, *Ferry Terminal, Military
Rd, Ramsgate, CT11 9LG.* ✆ Thanet
(0843) 588452.
Pop 39,561. Canterbury 16, London 74,
Dover 18, Margate 4.
EC Thur. **MD** Fri. **Golf** St Augustine's 18h,
North Foreland, Broadstairs 18h & 9h. **See**

St Augustine's RC Church, St Laurence's
Church, Model Tudor Village, replica of
Viking Ship 'Hugin' on clifftop, St
Augustine's Cross (Ebbsfleet), Harbour
and Yachting Marina.
🛈 Argyle Centre, Queen St. ✆ Thanet
(0843) 51086.

★★**San Clu,** *Victoria Par, East Cliff, CT11
8DT.* ✆ Thanet (0843) 592345. C. ⊷ 53
bedrs, 21 bp, 8 ba, TV, Dgs. ✗ a l c, mc, at,
LD 9. ⊡ Lt, N, ch, TV, CP 12, Ac, con 60,
CF, 1st. £ BB £15–£24, DB £22–£32, WT
£133–£175, DBB £22–£31, ①, Bk £4, L £6,
D £8, cc 1 2 3 6, Dep.

★★**Savoy** (R), *Grange Rd, CT11 9NA.*
✆ Thanet (0843) 592637. Closed Feb, C.
⊷ 14 bedrs, 1 bp, 2 bps, 5 sh, 1 ba, annexe,
11 bedrs, 2 bp, 9 bps, TV, Dgs. ✗ a l c, mc,
at, LD 10. ⊡ N, CH, Dgs, CP 20, CF, 1 BGf,
5 st. £ BB £13–£20, DB £20–£26, WT
£94·50–£125, ①, Bk £2·50, L £4·50, D
£6·50, cc 1 2 3 6.

Abbeygail, G, z (Unl), *17 Penshurst Rd,
CT11 8EG.* ✆ Thanet (0843) 594154.
Closed Xmas, C. ⊷ 10 bedrs, 2 ba. ⊡ TV,
U1, 1 st. £ BB £7·50–£8·50, DB £15–£17,
WT(b) £55–£70, DT(b) £10–£12, ①, , Bk
£2, D £3.

★★**Allandale, PH, z** (RI), *20 North Av,
CT11 9BT.* ✆ Thanet (0843) 592385.
Open Jan–Oct & Xmas. C. ⊷ 12 bedrs, 2
ba, ns, Dgs. ⊡ ch, TV, CP 5, CF, 2 BGf, 8 st.
£ BB £7–£9, DB £14–£18, WT (b) £56–
£65, DT (b) £9·50–£12, ①.

Beverley, PH, z (R), *10 Nelson Cres,
CT11 9JF.* ✆ Thanet (0843) 591514. C.
⊷ 26 bedrs, 2 bps, 1 sh, 5 ba. ⊡ CH, TV,
CF, 4 st. £ BB £9·78–£12·08, DB £19·56–
£24·15, WT (c) £60–£75, ①

Jalna, PH, z (RI), *49 Vale Sq, CT11 9DA.*
✆ Thanet (0843) 593848. Open Mar–Dec.
C. ⊷ 9 bedrs, 3 bp, 2 sh, 2 ba. ⊡ ch, TV,
CP3, CF, 6 st. £ BB £7·50–£10·50, DB
£15–£21, WT £60–£70, DT (b) £11·50–
£12·50, ①.

Malvern Mini, M, y (Unl), *Truro Rd,
CT11 8DH.* ✆ Thanet (0843) 53155.
Piper Lodge, PH, z (RI), *Victoria Rd.*
✆ Thanet (0843) 51661.
St Hilary, PH, z (RI), *21 Crescent Rd,
CT11 9QU.* ✆ Thanet (0843) 591427. C 4.
⊷ 7 bedrs, 3 sh, 1 ba. ⊡ ch, TV, 5 st. £ BB
£7·50–£8·50, DB £15–£17, WT (b)
£59·50–£65, DT (b) £10·50–£11·50, ①, Bk
£2, D £3, cc 1.

Sylvan, H, z (R), *160 High St, CT11 9TT.*
✆ Thanet (0843) 593026. C. ⊷ 16 bedrs,
4 ba, Dgs. ⊡ ch, TV, Dgs. CP 10, CF. £ BB
£9·20–£9·78, DB £18·40–£19·56, WT (b)
£69–£75·90, (c) £51·75–£56·93, DT
£12·65–£13·23, ①, cc 13.

Westbourne, H, *3 The Paragon, CT11
9JX.* ✆ Thanet (0843) 593118. C. ⊷ 18
bedrs, 7 ba, ns, Dgs. ⊡ ch, TV, Dgs, ns, CF,
6 st. £ BB £9·20–£12·65, DB £18·40–
£25·30, WT (b) £75–£85, DT (b) £12–£15,
①, Bk £2, L £2·45, D £4·50, cc 1 2 3 5.

Westcliff, PH, z (RI), *9 Grange Rd, CT11
9NG.* ✆ Thanet (0843) 581222.

Repairer: Caffyns Plc, Grange Rd.
✆ Thanet (0843) 583541.
Rescue Service: Invicta Motors Ltd,
Boundary Rd. ✆ Thanet (0843) 53784.

RANGEWORTHY Avon. Map 5B
Pop 320. Chippenham 20, London 111,
M4 Motorway 9½, Bath 19, Bristol 11,
Cirencester 29, Gloucester 27, Severn
Road Bridge 10.

Golf Cotswold Edge 18h. **See** Church.

■⇟★★**Rangeworthy Court,** *BS17
5ND.* ✆ (045 422) 347. Closed 24 Dec–7
Jan. C. ⊷ 14 bedrs, 1 bp, 6 bps, 1 sh, 2 ba,
Dgs. ✗ mc, at, LD 9. ⊡ CH, TV, CP 60, sp,
con 50, CF, 1 st. £ BB £18–£20·50, DB
£26·35–£29, WT £145, DT £28·50, WB, ①,
Bk £3·50, D £7·60, cc 3.

RAVENGLASS Cumbria. Map 26F
Pop 266. Broughton-in-Furness 20,
London 297, Egremont 11.
EC Sat. **Golf** Seascale 18h. **See**
Muncaster Castle and Gardens, Nature
Reserve, Roman Villa ruins, Ravenglass
and Eskdale Narrow Gauge Rly, Museum.
🛈 Ravenglass & Eskdale Railway Stn.
✆ Ravenglass (065 77) 278.

★**Pennington Arms,** *Main St, CA18
1SD.* ✆ (065 77) 222. C. ⊷ 17 bedrs, 4 bp,
1 sh, 4 ba, annexe 19 bedrs, 6 ba, Dgs.
✗ a l c, mc, at, LD 8·30. ⊡ CH, TV, Dgs, CP
50, U 1, G 1, Ac, con 50, CF, 3 BGf, 0 st, Dis.
£ BB £11·90–£16·90, DB £23·80–£33·80,
WT £125·30–£140, DT £22–£24, DBB
£17–£22, WB, ②, Bk £3, L £4, D £5, Dep a

RAVENSCAR North Yorkshire. Map 24B
Pop 250. Scarborough 9½, London 222,
Whitby 14.
Golf Raven Hall Hotel 9h & 18h.

⇟★★★**Raven Hall,** *YO13 OET.*
✆ Scarborough (0723) 870353. Open
Mar–Dec. C. ⊷ 57 bedrs, 37 bp, 5 ba, TV,
Dgs. ✗ a l c, mc, at, LD 8·45. ⊡ N, ch, TV,
CP 200, U 2, Ac, sp, gc, tc, sol, con 100, CF,
4 BGf, 2 st. £ WB, Bk £3, D £7·50,
cc 1 2 3 5 6, Dep a.

Smugglers Rock, G, x (Unl), *YO13 PBT.*
✆ Scarborough (0723) 870044. Open
Mar–Nov, C. ⊷ 8 bedrs, 4 ba, Dgs. ⊡ CH,
TV, CP 8, CF, 0 st. £ BB £8·75, DB £17·50,
WT (b) £85, (c) £60, DT (b) £12·50, ①.

RAWTENSTALL Lancs. Map 27B
Pop 22,230. Bury 8½, London 201,
Blackburn 10, Bolton 11, Burnley 6½,
Rochdale 9, Todmorden 9, Whalley 10.
EC Tue. **MD** Thur, Sat. **Golf** Rossendale
18h. **See** Whitaker Park, Art Gallery,
Friends Meeting House
(Crawshawbooth), Artificial ski slope at
Oakenhead Wood.

Repairers: Holmefield Garage Ltd,
Burnley Rd. ✆ Rossendale (0706) 215940.
Lords of Rossendale Ltd, Sandy Bank
Garage, Bacup Rd, Waterfoot.
✆ Rossendale (0706) 214641.
Motor Services (Rossendale) Ltd,
Brookside Garage, Burnley Rd.
✆ Rossendale (0706) 229096.
Rescue Service: Laneside Garage Ltd,
Hall Carr Mill, Fallbarn Rd. ✆ Rossendale
(0706) 216320.

READ Lancashire. M. Area 27B
Pop 1,522. Bury 17, London 209,
Blackburn 8½, Bolton 20, Burnley 5,
Skipton 21, Whalley 2½.
Golf Whalley 9h.

Rescue Service: Pollard Bros, Friendship
Garage, Church St. ✆ Padiham (0282)
71740.

READING Berkshire. Map 6B
See also TILEHURST.
Pop 137,000. Slough 18, London 38, A329
(M) Motorway 1½, Alton 23, Aylesbury 32,
Bagshot 16, Basingstoke 16, Farnham 25,
Henley-on-Thames 8, High Wycombe 18,

Newbury 15, Staines 22, Wallingford 14, Wantage 23, Windsor 17.
MD Mon, Wed, Fri, Sat. **Golf** Calcott 18h, Emmer Green 18h. **See** Art Gallery and Museum (Roman collection from Silchester). University (apply Bursar), Town Hall, remains of Norman Abbey, Churches—St Laurence's, St Mary's, St Matthew's, St Giles, Greyfriars, Elizabethan Mapledurham House, 6 m NW, Swallowfield Park 5 m S, Stratfield Saye House and Wellington County Park 7 m S. ⑦ Civic Offices, Civic Centre. ☎ Reading (0734) 55911.

★★★★**M Ramada,** *Oxford Rd, RG1 7RH.* ☎ (0734) 586222. C. ⊠ 200 bedrs, 200 bp, ns, TV, Dgs. ✗ a l c, mc, at, LD 11.30. ⓓ Lt, N, CH, Dgs, G 75, Ac, sp, sb, sol, con 200, CF, 0 st. £ BB £51·35, DB £62·20, WB, ①, Bk £4·25, L £6·25, D £10, cc 1 2 3 4 5 6, Dep.

★★★**M Post House** (TH), *Basingstoke Rd, RG2 0SL.* ☎ (0734) 875485, C. ⊠ 143 bedrs, 143 bp, TV, Dgs. ✗ a l c, mc, at, LD 10.15. ⓓ N, CH, Dgs, CP 240, sp, sb, con 30, CF, 74 BGf, 0 st, Dis. £ BB £48, DB £60·50, WB, ①, cc 1 2 3 4 5 6, Dep (Xmas).

★★**Ship,** *4 Duke St, RG1 4RY.* ☎ (0734) 583455. C. ⊠ 32 bedrs, 20 bp, 2 bps, 4 ba, TV, Dgs. ✗ a l c, mc, at, LD 10. ⓓ N, CH, TV, Dgs, CP 15, G 6, Ac, con 100, CF, 1 st. £ BB £24·50–£37, DB £43, WB, ②, Bk £4·50, L £8·20, D £8·20, cc 1 2 3 4 5 6, Dep b.

Repairers: Horncastle Garage Ltd, Bath Rd. ☎ (0734) 412021.
David Ruskin Ltd, 660 Wokingham Rd. ☎ (0734) 669621.
Specialist Body Repairer: Zenith (Reading) Trucks, Body Shop Dept, Commercial Rd. ☎ (0734) 868511.
Specialist Radiator Repairer: Serck Radiator Services Ltd, Unit 15, Deacon Way. ☎ (0734) 415252.
Rescue Service: Autocity (Reading) Ltd, T/AS Autocentre (Reading), 20–22 Queen's Rd. ☎ (0734) 597162.
Julians of Reading Ltd, Portman Rd. ☎ (0734) 585011.
Mike Spence (Reading) Ltd, Shinfield Green. ☎ (0734) 883312.
Paddock Coachworks Co, Unit 32, Forbury Industrial Park, Kenavon Drive. ☎ (0734) 589747.
Reading Garage Co, Penta House, Basingstoke Rd. ☎ (0734) 85151.

REDBOURN Hertfordshire. Map 15E
Pop 5,000. St Albans 4½, London 25, M1 Motorway 2, Aylesbury 22, Dunstable 8½, High Wycombe 24, Luton 6.
EC Wed. **Golf** Redbourn 18h & 9h. **See** 12th cent St Mary's Parish Church, The Aubreys Camp, Plateau Fort.

★★★**M Aubrey Park,** *Hemel Hempstead Rd, AL3 7AF.* ☎ (058 285) 2105. C. ⊠ 80 bedrs, 80 bp, TV, Dgs. ✗ a l c, mc, at, LD 10. ⓓ N, CH, CP 120, Ac, sp, con 60, CF, 32 BGf, 2 st. £ BB £28–£45, DB £40–£55, WB, ①, cc 1 2 3 4 5 6, Dep b.

REDCAR Cleveland. Map 24C
Pop 36,700, Thirsk 35, London 254, Helmsley 34, Middlesbrough 8½, Northallerton 31, Pickering 36, Whitby 22.
EC Wed. **Golf** Redcar 18h. **See** Red Barnes House, Kirkleatham (2 m), Sir William Turner's Hosp, Chapel attrib. Sir Christopher Wren (open to public).

⑦ Zetland Museum, Esplanade. ☎ Redcar (0642) 471921.

★★★**Hotel Royal York,** *Coatham Rd, TS10 1RP.* ☎ (0642) 486221. C. ⊠ 51 bedrs, 51 bp, TV. ✗ a l c, mc, at, LD 10. ⓓ Lt, N, CH, CP 300, Ac, con 600, CF, 1st. £ BB £15·50–£21·50, DB £22·50–£29·50, WT fr £175·35, DT fr £25·05, WB, ②, Bk £4, L £3·60, D £5·95, cc 1 2 3 5 6, Dep b.

★★**Park,** *Granville Ter, TS10 3AR.* ☎ (0642) 482341.

★★**Swan,** *High St, TS10 3DR.* ☎ (0642) 483678. C. ⊠ 36 bedrs, 18 bp, 5 ba, TV. ✗ a l c, mc, at, LD 10. ⓓ N, CH, TV, Dgs, G 12, Ac, con 250, CF. £ BB £17–£21, DB £25–£34, WT fr £177·90, DT fr £26·40, WB, ①, Bk £3·65, L £2·45, D £6·95, cc 1 2 3 5, Dep b.

REDDITCH Hereford & Worcester (Worcestershire). Map 14A
Pop 72,500. Stratford-upon-Avon 15, London 108, Bromsgrove 6, Birmingham 13, Evesham 16.
EC Wed. **MD** Tue, Wed, Thur, Fri, Sat. **Golf** Redditch 18h. **See** Bordesley Abbey, Forge Mill, now National Needle Museum. ⑦ Royal Sq. ☎ Redditch (0527) 60806.

★★★**Southcrest,** *Mount Pleasant, B97 4JG.* ☎ (0527) 41511. RS Sun evenings, C. ⊠ 31 bedrs, 26 bp, 5 ba, TV. ✗ a l c, LD 9.15. ⓓ N, CH, CP 100, Ac, con 50, CF, 10 BGf, 3 st. £ BB £32, DB £40, DT fr £47, WB, ②, Bk £4, L £7·50, D £8, cc 1 2 3 5 6, Dep.

Rescue Service: Bordesley Garage Ltd, Birmingham Rd. ☎ (0527) 63636.

REDHILL Avon. Map 5A
Pop 654. Bristol 8, London 121, Bath 23, Bridgwater 22, Radstock 18, Shepton Mallet 18, Wells 16, Weston-super-Mare 12.
Golf Weston Super Mare 18h.

★★**M Paradise,** *Cowslip Green, BS18 7RB.* ☎ Wrington (0934) 862277.

REDHILL Nottinghamshire. M. Area 22D
4 m N of Nottingham. London 127, Mansfield 9½, Newark 16, Ollerton 14.
EC Wed.

Rescue Service: Hutchinson Bros (Motors) Ltd, Mansfield Rd. ☎ Nottingham (0602) 267806.

REDHILL Surrey. Map 7C
Pop 21,450. Purley 7½, London 20, Crawley 9½, East Grinstead 13, Godstone 4½, Haywards Heath 18, Mitcham 12, Reigate 1½.
EC Wed. **Golf** Earlswood Common 18h. **See** Gatton Hall and Lakes.

★★**M Mill House,** *Brighton Rd, Salfords, RH1 5BT.* (2½ m S A23). ☎ (0737) 67277. Closed Dec 27–29. C. ⊠ 28 bedrs, 8 bp, 16 bps, 4 sh, 2 ba, TV. ✗ mc, LD 10. ⓓ N, CH, TV, CP 100, con 30, CF, 3 st. ⊠ BB £21–£28, DB £31·50–£37·50, ①, Bk £3·50, L £9·50, D £9·50, cc 1 2 3 5 6, Dep.

Ashleigh House, G, x (Unl) *39 Redstone Hill, RH1 4BG.* ☎ (0737) 64763. Closed Xmas. C. ⊠ 9 bedrs, 1 bps, 2 sh, 3 ba. ⓓ CH, TV, CP 9. £ BB £14·50, DB £24–£26, ①.

Hunters Lodge (late **Ivy House**), **H, y** (Rl), *Nutfield Rd, RH1 4ED.* ☎ (0737) 66701. C. ⊠ 24 bedrs, 13 bp, 4 ba, TV, Dgs. ✗ a l c. ⓓ CH, TV, Dgs, CP 40, U 2,

CF, 3 BGf, 0 st, Dis. £ BB £10–£13, DB £27–£29, WT (b) £135, DT (b) fr £19, ②, 10%, Bk £3, L £4, D £8.

REDLYNCH Wiltshire. M. Area 6C
Pop 2,800. Romsey 11, London 87, Blandford Forum 28, Lyndhurst 12, Ringwood 12, Salisbury 7½, Southampton 17.
Golf Bramshaw 18h (2).

Repairer: August Motors. ☎ Downton (0725) 20340.

REDMILE Leicestershire. Map 23C
Pop 279. Melton Mowbray 13, London 117, Grantham 9, Mansfield 25, Newark 13, Nottingham 16, Ollerton 26.
Golf Melton Mowbray 18h. **See** 13th cent Church, Belvoir Castle nearby.

Ye Olde Mill House, G, x (Unl), *NG8 5LH.* ☎ Bottesford (0949) 42460.

Rescue Service: Hall Bros. ☎ Bottesford (0949) 42358.

REDRUTH Cornwall. Map 2E
Pop 10,180. Bodmin 30, London 263, Falmouth 10, Helston 10, Newquay 15, Penzance 17, St Ives 14, Truro 9.
EC Thur. **MD** Fri. **Golf** Tehidy Park 18h. **See** Wm Murdoch's House (pioneer of gas lighting), Cam Brea Castle (hill fort), de Dunstanville monument views.

★★★**Penventon,** *TR15 1TS.* ☎ (0209) 214141. C. ⊠ 55 bedrs, 35 bp, 9 bps, 5 ba, ns, TV, Dgs. ✗ a l c, mc, at, LD 9.30. ⓓ N, CH, CP 300, Ac, sp, sb, sol, gym, con 250, CF, 2 st. £ BB £9·50–£26, DB £17·50–£49, WT £99–£250, DT £20–£40, WB, ①, Bk £3·50, L £5·50, D £8·50, cc 1 2 3, Dep.

■★★**M Crossroads,** *Scorrier, TR16 5BP.* ☎ St Day (0209) 820551. C. ⊠ 30 bedrs, 25 bp, 5 bps, TV, Dgs. ✗ a l c, mc, LD 10. ⓓ CH, Dgs, CP 143, Ac, con 120, CF, 7 BGf, 1st, Dis. £ BB £21·50–£23, DB £28·50–£33, DBB £28–£29·50, WB, ①, Bk £3, L £4, D £6, cc 1 2 3 5 6.

Lyndhurst, G, z (Unl), *80 Agar Rd, TR15 3NB.* ☎ (0209) 215146.

Rescue Service: Central Garage, Four Lanes. ☎ (0209) 216492.
Hillside Garage Ltd, Bucketts Hill. ☎ (0209) 215854.
Park Bottom Service Station, Illogan. ☎ (0209) 215696.
P Williams Motors, Lanner Hill. ☎ (0209) 215841.
Reg Williams's, Treruffe Hill. ☎ (0209) 216425.
Volks Engineering, Wesley St. ☎ (0209) 217161 & (0209) 218325.

REEPHAM Norfolk. Map 16C
East Dereham 10, London 115, Cromer 18, Fakenham 15, Norwich 15,

★★**Old Brewery House,** *Market Place, NR10 4JJ.* ☎ Norwich (0603) 870881. C. ⊠ 21 bedrs, 15 bp, 2 ba, TV, Dgs. ✗ a l c, mc, at, LD 9.30. ⓓ CH, TV, Dgs, CP 150, Ac, sp, sc, sb, sol, gym, con 400, CF, 7 BGf, 2 st. £ BB £18–£20, DB £28–£30, WT £120, DB £32, WB, ②, Bk £2·50, L £6, D £7·50, cc 1 2 3.

REETH North Yorkshire. Map 26B
Pop 800 (inc Fremington and Healaugh). Leyburn 11, London 247, Brough 21, Darlington 18, Hawes 16, Middleton-in-Teesdale 24, West Auckland 26.

Golf Richmond 18h. **See** Remains of old lead mines, Wesleyan Church (1796), 11th cent Church at Grinton, Folk Museum. 🛈 Swaledale Folk Museum. ✆ Richmond (0748) 84373.

Arkleside, PH, x (R), *DL11 6SG.* ✆ Richmond (0748) 84200. Open Mar–Oct. C. ⌘ 8 bedrs, 4 bps, 1 sh, 1 ba, ns, Dgs. ⊡ CH, TV, CP 6, G 2, CF, 1 BGf, 4 st. £ BB £10·50–£14, DB £21–£22·50, WT (b) £108·50, DT (b) £16·50, ②, D £6·50.
Bridge, I, x, *Grinton-in-Swaledale, DL11 6HH.* ✆ Richmond (0748) 84224. Open April–Oct, C. ⌘ 10 bedrs, 3 bp, 2 ba, Dgs. ⊡ CH, TV, Dgs, CP 25, CF, 0 st. £ BB fr £11, DB fr £22, DT fr £16·50, ②, 10%.

Rescue Service: Reeth Garage, Grinton-in-Swaledale. ✆ Richmond (0748) 84243. Weighills Garage. ✆ Richmond (0748) 84245.

REIGATE Surrey. Map 7C
Pop 21,460. Purley 8½, London 21, M25 Motorway 2, Crawley 10, Dorking 6, East Grinstead 14, Epsom 9, Haywards Heath 18, Leatherhead 8½, Mitcham 12, Redhill 1½.
EC Wed. **Golf** Reigate Heath 9h. Redhill & Reigate 18h. **See** Castle grounds and Baron's Cave, St Mary's Church, Market House (1728), Windmill (now church), Gatton Park estate.

★★★**M Bridge House,** *Reigate Hill, RH2 9RP.* ✆ (07372) 46801. Closed Dec 27–30. C. ⌘ 30 bedrs, 28 bp, 2 bps, TV, Dgs. ✗ a l c, LD 8·30. ⊡ N, CH, CP 160, con 40, CF, 1 st. £ BB £35·50, DB £51, WB, ①, Bk £5·50, L £7·50, D £11·50, cc 1 2 3 5 6, Dep b.
Cranleigh, H, x (R), *41 West St, RH2 9BL.* ✆ (07372) 40600. C. ⌘ 12 bedrs, 4 bp, 2 ba, TV. ⊡ CH, TV, CP 5, CF. £ BB £18–£26, DB £26–£34, ①, Bk £3, D £7.

RENISHAW Derbyshire. Map 22B
Mansfield 13, London 151, M1 Motorway 2, Chesterfield 7, Doncaster 22, Sheffield 9, Worksop 9.

★★★**Sitwell Arms,** *Renishaw Village, S31 9WE.* (1½ m W of Junction 30 (M1) on A616.) ✆ Eckington (0246) 435226. Closed Dec 25 evening. RS Sat. C. ⌘ 30 bedrs, 23 bp, 7 bps, TV, Dgs. ✗ a l c, mc, at, LD 9·30. ⊡ N, CH, CP 120, Ac, con 150, CF, 1 st. £ BB £26·95–£32·85, DB £44·90, DBB £35·90–£41·80, WB, ②, 10%, Bk £2·95, L £8·10, D £8·95, cc 1 2 3 5 6, Dep b.

REPTON Derbyshire. Map 22E
Pop 2,240. Ashby-de-la-Zouch 7½, London 120, Ashbourne 20, Burton-on-Trent 4, Derby 7½, Uttoxeter 15.
EC Wed. **Golf** Bretby 18h. **See** Repton Public School, Dec Church, restored Market Cross, old houses and thatched cottages, Repton Shrubs, Dawson's Rock.

Rescue Service: Tom Goodall (Repton) Ltd, High St. ✆ Burton-on-Trent (0283) 702141.

RETFORD Nottinghamshire. Map 22B
Pop 18,402. Newark 20, London 146, Doncaster 16, Gainsborough 10, Ollerton 11, Rotherham 19, Worksop 8.
EC Wed. **MD** Thur, Sat. **Golf** Retford 9h. **See** St Swithin's Church.

Repairer: Central Garage (Retford) Ltd, Grove St. ✆ (0777) 703754.

Rescue Service: Century Road (International) Recovery Ltd, Century Rd. ✆ (0777) 706483.
E Hodgson & Son Ltd, Regent Garage, London Rd. ✆ (0777) 702266.

RICHMOND North Yorkshire. Map 24F
Pop 7,245. Boroughbridge 25, London 233, Brough 32, Darlington 12, Leyburn 10, Middleton-in-Teesdale 28, Northallerton 14, West Auckland 18.
EC Wed. **MD** Sat. **P** Disc Parking affects highways throughout the town—discs can be obtained either from the District Council Offices, Swale House, Frenchgate or through most shopkeepers. Permitted parking and re-parking times are indicated by signs. **Golf** Richmond (Yks) 18h. **See** Holy Trinity Church, St Mary's Church, Green Howards' Museum, Castle ruins, St Martin's Priory ruins, Grey Friars Tower, Georgian Theatre, Culloden Tower, Middleham Castle 9 m SW.
🛈 Friary Garden, Queens Rd. ✆ Richmond (0748) 3525.

★★**Frenchgate** (R), *DL10 7AE.* ✆ (0748) 3596. Closed mid Dec–mid Feb. C 7. ⌘ 12 bedrs, 3 bp, 3 bps, 3 ba, TV, Dgs. ✗ a l c, mc, LD 8·30. ⊡ CH, Dgs, CP 6, con 12, 3 BGf, 2 st. £ BB £18·50–£23, DB £33–£35, DBB £24–£25, WB, ②, Bk £3·75, D £7·50, cc 1 2 3.
★★**King's Head,** *Market Pl, DL10 4HS.* ✆ (0748) 2311.
West End, G, z (Rl), *45 Reeth Rd, DL10 4EX.* ✆ (0748) 4783. Closed Nov. C. ⌘ 5 bedrs, 2 ba. ⊡ CH, TV, CP 6, U 2, G 2. £ BB £12, DB £17–£18, WT (b) £86·45–£109·75, DT (b) £13–£16·50, ①.

Rescue Service: Scotch Corner Garage, Richmond Rd, Eastside. ✆ (0748) 4831.

RICHMOND-UPON-THAMES Greater London (Surrey). Map 7A
Pop 41,024. Brentford and Chiswick 2½, London 8½, Kingston upon Thames 3½, Mitcham 9, Slough 13, Staines 16, Weybridge 10.
EC Wed. **Golf** Richmond 18h, Royal Mid Surrey 18h. **See** Remains of Palace on the Green, Maids of Honour Row, Almshouses, Terrace Gardens (view), Richmond Park (White Lodge now The Royal Ballet School), Kew Gardens, Ham House 1 m S.

★★★**Richmond Gate,** *Richmond Hill, TW10 6RP.* ✆ 01-940 0061. C. ⌘ 49 bedrs, 49 bp, TV. ✗ a l c, mc, at, LD 9·30. ⊡ N, CH, CP 60, G 2, con 28, CF, 14 BGf, 6 st. £ BB £42, DB £53, DBB £52, WB, ①, Bk £4·75, L £4, D £10, cc 1 2 6.

Rescue Service: Bells Breakdown Services Ltd, 1 North Rd. ✆ 01-876 6201. Empire Service Station, 2 Lower Mortlake Rd. ✆ 01-940 1750.

RICKMANSWORTH Hertfordshire. Maps 8A and 15F
Pop 30,000. Harrow 7½, London 18, Denham 6½, High Wycombe 15, Watford 3.
EC Wed. **Golf** Moor Park 18h. **See** Aquadrome, Moor Park Mansion (reconstructed 1727) and grounds (inc three golf courses—one open to public).

Rescue Service: T A J Motors, R/O 33 Station Rd. ✆ (092 37) 73384.▲

RINGWOOD Hampshire. Map 6E
Pop 11,900. Romsey 17, London 93, Bournemouth 12, Dorchester 32,

Lymington 13, Lyndhurst 14, Salisbury 16, Sandbanks 15, Shaftesbury 24, Southampton 18, Wareham 21.
EC Thur. **MD** Wed. **Golf** Burley 9h. **See** Parish Church, thatched cottages, New Forest.

★★**Struan,** *Horton Rd, Ashley Heath, BH24 2EG.* ✆ (042 54) 3553. ⌘ 10 bedrs, 2 bps, 6 sh, 2 ba. ✗ a l c, mc, LD 9.30. ⊡ CH, TV, Dgs, CP 75, Ac, con 20, CF, 1 st. £ BB fr £20, DB fr £35, ①, Bk £3·50, L £4·95, D £10, cc 1 2 3 5 6, Dep b.
Little Forest Lodge, G, xy (Unl), *Poulner Hill, BH24 3HR.* ✆ (042 54) 78848. Open Mar–Oct & Xmas. C. ⌘ 4 bedrs, 2 bp, 2 bps, TV. ⊡ CH, TV, CP 10, G 2, CF. £ BB £10–£14, DB £20–£28, WT (b) £98–£123. DT (b) £15–£19, ①, cc 1 3.
Little Moortown House, PH, x (R), *244 Christchurch Rd, BH24 3AS.* ✆ (042 54) 3325. C 12. ⌘ 6 bedrs, 4 bps, 1 ba, TV, Dgs. ⊡ CH, TV, CP 6. £ BB £13–£17, DB £21–£26, DT (b) fr £19, Bk £4·50, D £6·50, cc 1 3.

Repairers: Robin Payne (Motor Engineers) Ltd, Unit 5, Millstream Trading Estate, Christchurch Rd. ✆ (042 54) 5588 and (042 54) 78520.
J W Wells (Salisbury Rd Garage) Ltd, Salisbury Rd. ✆ (042 54) 6111.

RIPLEY Derbyshire. Map 22D
Pop 18,691. M1 Motorway 13, London 135, Ashbourne 16, Chesterfield 10, Derby 12, Mansfield 12, Matlock 10, Nottingham 13.
EC Wed. **MD** Fri, Sat. **Golf** Codnor 18h. **See** Padley Hall.
Britannia, G, x (Unl), *243 Church St, DE5 9TF.* ✆ (0773) 43708. ⌘ 6 bedrs, 1 bps, 2 ba. ⊡ CH, TV, CP 10, CF, 2 BGf, 1st, Dis. £ BB £11, DB £22, ①.

Rescue Service: Clifton Motors (Derby) Ltd, Church St. ✆ (0773) 42019. Fountain Garage (Merebrook) Ltd, Peasehill Rd. ✆ (0773) 42000.

RIPLEY Surrey. Map 7A
Pop 2,000. Kingston upon Thames 12, London 21, Guildford 6, Leatherhead 9, Staines 11, Weybridge 6½, Woking 5.
EC Wed. **Golf** West Byfleet 18h. **See** St Mary's Church, old houses and inns, 18th cent Cricket Club House, Wisley Gardens (R.H.S.).

Rescue Service: Methold Engineering Ltd, Portsmouth Rd. ✆ (048 643) 3373.

RIPON North Yorkshire. Map 25E
Pop 12,500. Harrogate 11, London 216, Boroughbridge 6, Darlington 35, Leyburn 20, Middleton-in-Teesdale 50, Northallerton 18, Skipton 29, Thirsk 11, West Auckland 41.
EC Wed. **MD** Thur. **P** Disc Parking is in operation on weekdays from 8 am–6 pm. Sundays and Bank Holidays are exempt. PARKING IS FREE where indicated on the carriageways by L-shaped white markings at the termination points of the parking places which will be connected by broken white lines. PARKING DISCS must be displayed on the nearside front of the vehicle and can be obtained from the Council's Parking Attendants, hotels, shops, garages and police stations. PARKING MUST NOT TAKE PLACE WHERE THERE ARE YELLOW LINES ALONG THE ROAD. **Golf** Ripon 18h. **See**

For abbreviations see inside back cover—**RAC**

Cathedral, St Wilfrid's Church, Wakeman's House (13th cent), Wakeman's Horn blown nightly at 9 pm, St Anne's and St Mary's Hospitals (both Almshouses), 18th cent Obelisk, Town Hall, Markenfield Hall (not open to public), Racecourse, Fountains Abbey 3 m SW, Newby Hall, 3½ m SE.
🛈 Wakeman's House, Market Pl. ℓ Ripon (0765) 4625.

★★★Ripon Spa, *Park St, HG4 2BU.*
ℓ (0765) 2172. C. 🛏 41 bedrs, 35 bp, 6 bps, TV, Dgs. ✗ mc, at, LD 9. 🄳 Lt, N, CH, TV, Dgs, CP 100, Ac, con 100, CF, 3 BGf, 1 st, Dis. £ BB £25–£26·50, DB £39–£52, DBB fr £30, WB, 🄸, Bk £4, L £5, D £8·50, cc 1 2 3 5 6, Dep b.
Crescent Lodge, G, z (Unl). *42 North St, HG4 1EN.* ℓ (0765) 2331. Closed Dec. C. 🛏 12 bedrs, 2 ba, Dgs. 🄳 ch, TV, Dgs, CP 10, CF, 2 BGf, 5 st. £ BB fr £8·50, DB fr £16, DT (b) fr £14, 🄸, D £5·75.

Repairers: Croft & Blackburn Ltd, Harvester House, Kirkby Rd. ℓ (0765) 4491.
Glovers of Ripon Ltd, Morris House, Borrage Bridge. ℓ (0765) 2371.

RISHWORTH West Yorkshire. Map 27B
Pop 1,400. Huddersfield 7, London 193, M62 Motorway 4, Halifax 6, Leeds 22, Oldham 12, Rochdale 11.
EC Wed. **Golf** Sowerby Bridge 9h.

★★Royal, *Oldham Rd, HX6 4QB.*
ℓ Halifax (0422) 822382. C. 🛏 9 bedrs, 3 bp, 6 bps, TV, Dgs. ✗ a l c, mc, at, LD 10. 🄳 CH, Dgs, CP 80, Ac, con 60, CF, 3 BGf, 2 st. £ BB fr £20, DB £30, WT £220, DT £35, DBB fr £28, WB, Bk £3·50, L £8, D £10, cc 1 2 3 5 6, Dep b.

RISLEY Derbyshire. Map 22D
Pop 705. M1 Motorway 1, London 116, Ashby-de-la-Zouch 16, Derby 6, Loughborough 13, Mansfield 19, Nottingham 8.
Golf Erewash Valley 18h. **See** 16th cent Church.

Rescue Service: Risley Garage, 81 Derby Rd. ℓ Sandiacre (0602) 398472.

ROBERTSBRIDGE East Sussex. Map 10E
Pop 1,850. Hurst Green 2½, London 52, Eastbourne 19, Hastings 11, Lewes 25, Rye 12.
EC Wed. **Golf** Hastings 18h. **See** 13th cent Church, Bodiam Castle 3 m ENE.

Repairer: Silverhill Garage, Northbridge St. ℓ (0580) 880277.

ROBIN HOOD'S BAY North Yorkshire. Map 24B
Pop 200. Scarborough 16, London 220, Whitby 5½.
EC Wed. **Golf** Whitby 18h. **See** Picturesque fishing village, steep narrow streets.

★★Grosvenor (R), *Station Rd, YO22 4RA.* ℓ Whitby (0947) 880320. C. 🛏 14 bedrs, 1 sh, 4 ba. ✗ mc, at, LD 8.30. 🄳 ch, TV, CP 10, Ac, CF, 10 st. £, BB £10–£13, DB £20–£28, WT £100–£120, DT £18–£19·50, WB, 🄲, Bk £3·95, L £5·95, D £7·50, cc 1 3.
★Victoria, *Station Rd, YO22 4RL.* ℓ Whitby (0947) 880205.

ROCHDALE Greater Manchester (Lancashire). Map 27B
Pop 94,119. Oldham 5½, London 192, A627(M) Motorway 2, Blackburn 18, Burnley 14, Bury 6, Halifax 17, Huddersfield 19, Manchester 10, Todmorden 7½, Walkden 14, Whalley 20.
EC Tue. **MD** Daily (exc Tue). **Golf** Rochdale 18h, Springfield Park 18h. **See** St Chad's Church, Town Hall, Art Gallery and Museum, John Bright's grave (Friends' Graveyard), original Co-op Shop in Toad Lane (now Co-op Museum).

★★Midway, *Manchester Rd, OL11 2XX.* ℓ (0706) 32881. C. 🛏 29 bedrs, 2 bp, 19 bps, TV. ✗ a l c, mc, LD 11. 🄳 N, CH, CP 120, con 120, CF, 0 st. £ BB £21–£26, DB £36, DBB £28–£33, WB, 🄲, Bk £3, L £3·50, D £6·95, cc 1 2 3 5 6, Dep b.

Repairer: Clarke's Motors (Rochdale) Ltd, Roch Valley Way. ℓ (0706) 32012.
Sctr Repairer: Jeff Shepherd Ltd, 246 Yorkshire St. ℓ (0706) 33426.
Rescue Service: Exmouth Street Garage. ℓ (0706) 43222.
Ratcliffe Bros (Rochdale) Ltd, Mount Green Garage, Halifax Rd. ℓ Littleborough (0706) 73021.
Waggon Garage (Milnrow), New St, Milnrow. ℓ (0706) 33342.

ROCHE Cornwall. Map 2D.
Bodmin 7½, London 241, Falmouth 28, Newquay 13, Penzance 41, Plymouth 38, St Austell 6, Wadebridge 9.

Greystones Country House, G, y (RI). *Mount Pleasant, PL26 8LH.* ℓ (0726) 890863. C. 🛏 7 bedrs, 2 bp, 3 bps, 2 ba, ns. 🄳 CH, TV, Dgs, ns, CP 10, U 1, CF, 1 BGf, 2 st. £ BB £8·50–£13·50, DB £17–£25, WT (b) £70–£80, DT (b) £11–£15, 🄸, D £5.

ROCHESTER Kent. Map 10C
Pop 144,700. London 30, Canterbury 26, Maidstone 8, Tonbridge 19.
EC Wed. **MD** Fri. **Golf** Deangate Ridge 18h. **See** Castle (open to public), Cathedral, 11th cent Guildhall, Corn Exchange, Eastgate House Museum, Upnor Castle, 16th cent blockhouse.
🛈 Eastgate Cottage, Eastgate High St. ℓ Medway (0634) 43666.

★★Royal Victoria and Bull, *High St, ME1 1PT.* ℓ Medway (0634). 46266. C. 🛏 TV, Dgs. ✗ a l c, mc, at, LD 11. 🄳 N, CH, Dgs, CP 16, Ac, con 100, CF, 2 st. £ BB £20·90–£23·10, DB £31·90–£34·10, WB, 🄸, Bk £3, L £5·50, D £5·50, cc 1 2 3 5, Dep a.

Rescue Service: W J F Motors, 2 Dunnings La. ℓ Medway (0634) 409288.

ROCHESTER Northumberland. Map 31C
Pop 150. Corbridge 25, London 308, Alnwick 32, Bellingham 12, Hawick 24, Jedburgh 21, Newcastle upon Tyne 35.
Golf Bellingham 18h. **See** Roman Fort with Pele Tower.

▓★Redesdale Arms, *NE19 1TA.* ℓ Otterburn (0830) 20668. Closed Xmas. C. 🛏 10 bedrs, 2 sh, 3 ba. ✗ mc, LD 9.45. 🄳 CH, TV, CP 20, CF, 1 st. £ BB £11–£13, DB £22–£30, WB, 🄸, Bk £3, D £4, cc 1 2 6.

Rescue Service: R Parker, The Garage. ℓ Otterburn (0830) 20220.

ROCHFORD Essex. Map 10A
Pop 9,500. Romford 26, London 42, Brentwood 21, Chelmsford 18, Colchester 36, Dartford Tunnel 26, Rainham 29, Southend-on-Sea 3.
EC Wed. **MD** Tue. **Golf** Rochford 18h.
See Church, remains of Rochford Hall (birthplace of Anne Boleyn).

Repairer: W H Whittingham & Sons Ltd, West St. ℓ Southend (0702) 544146.

ROCK Cornwall. Map 2D
Pop 350. Camelford 14, London 241, Wadebridge 6½.
EC Sat. **Golf** St Enodoc 18h (2). **See** Parish Church, St Enodoc Church at Daymer Bay once buried in sand dunes.

★★Roskarnon House (R), *PL27 6LD.* ℓ Trebetherick (020 886) 2785. Open Mar–Oct. C. 🛏 16 bedrs, 4 bp, 1 bps, 2 sh, 3 ba, TV. ✗ mc, at, LD 8.30. 🄳 TV, CP 14, G 2, CF, 2 BGf, 0 st. £ BB £10–£18, DB £20–£40, WT fr £140, DT fr £18, WB, 🄲, Bk £3·75, L £3·75, D £6·75, Dep.

ROCK FERRY Merseyside.
See BIRKENHEAD.

ROLLESBY Norfolk. Map 16A
Pop 1,169. Acle 5, London 127, Beccles 21, Cromer 25, Great Yarmouth 9, Norwich 16.
EC Wed. **Golf** Caister 18h.

Rescue Service: Becks Garage, Martham Rd. ℓ Gt Yarmouth (0493) 740274.

ROMALDKIRK Durham. Map 26B
Pop 180. Boroughbridge 47, London 254, Brough 16, Darlington 21, Durham 26, Harrogate 56, Hexham 35, Leyburn 35, Middleton-in-Teesdale 4, Newcastle upon Tyne 38, Northallerton 27, Thirsk 44, West Auckland 14.
Golf Barnard Castle 18h. **See** Bowes Museum, 12th–14th cent Cathedral of the Dales, Market Cross, Barnard Castle.

★Rose and Crown, *DL12 9EB.* ℓ Teesdale (0833) 50213. C. 🛏 9 bedrs, 4 bp, 2 bps, 2 ba, TV, Dgs. ✗ a l c, mc, at, LD 10. 🄳 N, CH, TV, Dgs, CP 60, Ac, con, CF, 0 st. £ BB £13–£24, DB £25–£37, DBB £22·50–£33·50, WB, 🄸, Bk £3, L £3, D £9·50, cc 1 2 3 5.

ROMFORD Greater London (Essex). Maps 7B and 17F
Pop 78,000. London 16, Brentwood 6, Epping 12, Rainham 5, Southend-on-Sea 25, Woodford 8.
EC Thur. **MD** Wed, Fri, Sat. **Golf** Romford 18h.

Repairer: Romford Market Garage, 2 Market Link. ℓ (0708) 40584.
Specialist Body Repairer: Charles H Allen (Bodies) Ltd, Jutsums La. ℓ (0708) 46001.
Rescue Service: Alpha Autos, 161 Victoria Rd. ℓ (0708) 23392.
Mawney Service Station, Mawney Rd, Eastern Av. ℓ (0708) 44842.

ROMSEY Hampshire. Map 6C
Pop 13,180. Winchester 10, London 75, M27 Motorway 3, Andover 17, Fareham 20, Hungerford 37, Lyndhurst 9½, Marlborough 36, Ringwood 17, Salisbury 15, Southampton 8.
EC Wed. **Golf** Romsey 18h. **See** Abbey Church, Palmerston's Statue, King John's House (13th cent), 16th cent White Horse

Hotel, War Memorial Park, Mottisfont
Abbey 4½ m NW, Broadlands (open to
public) home of late Earl Mountbatten of
Burma.

★★★**White Horse** (TH), *Market Pl, SO5
8ZJ.* ✆ (0794) 512431. C. ⊯ 33 bedrs, 33
bp, TV, Dgs. ✗ a l c, mc, at, LD 9.30. ⌂ CH,
TV, Dgs, CP 60, Ac, con 40, CF, 7 BGf, 0 st,
Dis. £ BB £40·50, DB £56, WB, ⬜,
cc 1 2 3 4 5 6, Dep (Xmas).
Adelaide House, G, z (Unl), *45
Winchester Rd, SO5 8AB.* ✆ (0794)
512322. Closed Xmas. C. ⊯ 5 bedrs, 1 ba,
⌂ CH, TV, CP 5. £ BB £8·25–£9·25, DB
£15·50–£16·50, ⬜.

Repairers: Mitchell Bros (Romsey) Ltd,
24 Middlebridge St. ✆ (0794) 513806.
Wrynams Ltd, Winchester Rd. ✆ (0794)
512850.
Rescue Service: Testwood Motors
(Romsey) Ltd, By-Pass Filling Station.
✆ (0794) 512576.

ROOKSBRIDGE Somerset. Map 5C.
Pop 945. M5 Motorway 3, Axbridge 4,
London 136, Highbridge 4½, Wells 15,
Weston-super-Mare 8.
Golf Enmore Park, Berrow 18h.

Rescue Service: Rooksbridge Garage.
✆ Edingworth (093 472) 229.

ROPLEY Hampshire. Map 6D
Pop 1,500. Alton 7, London 55,
Basingstoke 15, Cosham 21, Fareham 19,
Petersfield 10, Winchester 11.
Golf Tichborne Down, Alresford 18h.
See 13th–14th cent church.

Rescue Service: Ropley Garage, The Dene.
✆ (096 277) 2444.

ROSEDALE ABBEY North Yorkshire.
Map 24D
Pickering 10, London 233, Helmsley 13,
Stokesley 18, Whitby 14.

★★**Blacksmith's Arms,** *Hartoft End,
YO18 8EN.* ✆ Lastingham (075 15) 331.
C. ⊯ 12 bedrs, 7 bps, 2 ba, TV, Dgs. ✗ mc,
at, LD 9.15. ⌂ CH, Dgs, CP 80, con 24, CF,
0 st. £ BB £15–£20, DB £29–£36, DBB
£20–£26·50, WB, ②, Bk £3·50, D £8·50,
cc 3, Dep a.
★★**Milburn Arms,** *YO18 8RA.*
✆ Lastingham (075 15) 312.
★★**White Horse Farm,** *YO18 8SE.*
✆ Lastingham (075 15) 239. C. ⊯ 15
bedrs, 7 bp, 8 bps, 1 ba, TV, Dgs. ✗ mc, at,
LD 9.30. ⌂ CH, CP 50, con 20, CF, 8 st.
£ BB £23·50–£25, DB £35–£37, DBB £44–
£47, WB, ②, Bk £5, L £5, D £9, cc 2 5,
Dep a.▲

ROSS-ON-WYE Hereford & Worcester
(Herefordshire). Map 13C
See also PENCRAIG and WALFORD
Pop 8,000. Gloucester 16, London 121,
M50 Motorway 1½, Abergavenny 22,
Builth Wells 49, Chepstow 24, Hereford
14, Ledbury 12, Monmouth 10,
Tewkesbury 24.
EC Wed. **MD** Thur, Fri, Sat. **Golf** Ross-on-
Wye 18h. **See** 'Man of Ross' House, 17th
cent Market Hall, St Mary's Church and
Prospect Walk, Grave of John Kyrle (the
'Man of Ross'), Plague Cross, Royal Hotel
frequented by Dickens, Goodrich Castle
3½ m SW.
ℹ 20 Broad St. ✆ Ross-on-Wye (0989)
62768.

★★★**Chase,** *Gloucester Rd, HR9 5LH.*
✆ (0989) 63161. C. ⊯ 39 bedrs, 39 bp, TV,
Dgs. ✗ a l c, mc, at, LD 9.45. ⌂ N, CH, TV,
CP 200, Ac, con 175, CF, 0 st. £ BB
£39·50, DB £55, WB, ⬜, Bk £5·50, L £9, D
£9·50, cc 1 2 3 5 6.▲
★★★**Pengethley,** *HR9 6LL.* (4 m W of
A49). ✆ Harewood End (098 987) 211. C.
⊯ 13 bedrs, 11 bp, 2 bps, 1 ba, TV, Dgs. ✗
a l c, mc, at, LD 9.15. ⌂ CH, TV, CP 70, U 2,
sp, pf, con 120, CF, 1 BGf. £ BB £35–£56,
DB £70–£92, WT £321–£397, WB, ⬜, Bk
£4·50, L £8·95, D £14·50, cc 1 2 3 5 6,
Dep a.▲
★★★**Royal** (TH), *Palace Pound, HR9
5HZ.* ✆ (0989) 65105. C. ⊯ 31 bedrs, 31
bp, TV, Dgs. ✗ a l c, mc, at, LD 9·15. ⌂ CH,
TV, Dgs, CP 20, Ac, con 40, CF, 5 st. £ BB
£40·50, DB £54, WB, ⬜, cc 1 2 3 4 5 6,
Dep (Xmas).
★★★**Wye,** *Weston-under-Penyard,
HR9 7NT.* (2 m E of A40). ✆ (0989) 63541.
C. ⊯ 43 bedrs, 36 bp, 4 ba, TV, Dgs. ✗ mc,
at, LD 9.15. ⌂ N, CH, CP 150, G 10, Ac, sc,
con 150, CF, 3 st. £ BB fr £24·50, DB fr
£36·50, DBB fr £25·25, WB, ⬜, Bk £4, D
£9·50, cc 1 2 3 5.
★★★**Chasedale,** *Walford Rd, HR9 5PQ.*
✆ (0989) 62423. C. ⊯ 12 bedrs, 6 bp, 3
ba, TV, Dgs. ✗ a l c, mc, at, LD 9. ⌂ CH, TV,
Dgs, CP 15, con 50, CF, 2 BGf, 3 st. £ BB
£16·50–£20·50, DB £26·50–£34, DBB
£18·50–£26, WB, ⬜, Bk £3·25, L £5, D £7,
cc 1 2 3.
★**Brookfield House** (R), *Over Ross. HR9
7AT.* ✆ (0989) 62188. Closed Nov & Jan.
C. ⊯ 8 bedrs, 1 bp, 2 bps, 2 ba, Dgs. ✗ LD
7. ⌂ CH, TV, Dgs, CP 10, U 5, CF, 3 st. £
WB, cc 1 3.
★**Rosswyn,** *High St, HR9 5BZ.* ✆ (0989)
62733. C. ⊯ 9 bedrs, 3 bp, 1 bps, 1 sh, 2
ba, Dgs. ⌂ CH, TV, Dgs, CF. £ BB £12–£16,
DB £24–£32, WB, ⬜, Bk £2·50, L £2·50, D
£8·50, cc 1 3, Dep a.
★**Wilton Court,** *Wilton, HR9 6AQ.*
✆ (0989) 62569. Closed Xmas Day. C.
⊯ 8 bedrs, 3 bp, 3bps, 1 ba, TV, Dgs.
✗ mc, LD 9.30. ⌂ CH, Dgs, CP 25, pf, CF,
1 st. £ BB £18·50–£19·50, DB £32·50–
£34·50, DBB £22·30–£23·20, WB, ⬜, Bk
£2·95, D £5·95, cc 1 2 6.
Arches Country House, G, y, (R),
Walford Rd, HR9 5PT. ✆ (0989) 63348.
Closed Xmas & New Year. C. ⊯ 6 bedrs, 1
bp, 2 ba, ns. ⌂ CH, TV, Dgs, CP 8, CF, 1 st.
£ BB £8–£10·50, DB £16–£21, WT (b) fr
£50·50, (c) fr £54·70, DT (b) £12·90, ⬜, D
£4·90.
Bridge House, H, x (R). *Wilton, HR9
6AA.* ✆ (0989) 62655. Closed Xmas. C.
⊯ 9 bedrs, 1 bp, 1 bps, 2 ba. ⌂ ch, TV, CP
15, CF, 3 st. £ BB £12·50, DB £20·50–£26,
WT (b) £120–£125, DT (b) £18–£18·50, ⬜,
Bk £3, D £6.
Castle Lodge, H, x (R) (late **Tulip Tree**).
Wilton, HR9 6AD. ✆ (0989) 62234.
Closed Xmas. C. ⊯ 9 bedrs, 8 bp, 1 bps,
TV. ✗ a l c. ⌂ CH, CP 50, CF, 0 st. £ BB
£16·50–£18, DB £30–£33, ②, Bk £3·50, L
£3·50, D £6, cc 1 2 3.
Radcliffe, G, x, *Wye St, HR9 7BS.*
✆ (0989) 63895. Closed Xmas. C. ⊯ 6
bedrs, 1 bp, 2 ba. ⌂ ch, TV, CF, 1 BGf, 2 st.
£ BB £7·50–£7·95, DB £15–£15·90, ⬜.
Ryefield House, PH, x (Rl), *Gloucester
Rd, HR9 5NA.* ✆ (0989) 63030. Open Jan–
Oct. C. ⊯ 7 bedrs, 1 bp, 1 ba, Dgs.
⌂ ch, TV, CP 8, CF, 1 BGf, 2 st. £ BB
£9·75–£10·25, DB £16–£20·50, WT (b)

£160–£165, (c) £98–£104, DT (b) £12·80–
£13·40, ⬜.
Repairers: Butcher, W & Sons (Ross) Ltd,
The Motor House, Brookend St. ✆ (0989)
62440.
T C Longford Ltd, Ross Motor Works,
Cantilupe Rd. ✆ (0989) 62400 and (0989)
62492.
MC Repairer: Lucas Motor Cycles, 28
Broad St. ✆ (0989) 63261.
Rescue Service: C F Lerego, Castle
Garage, Wilton Rd. ✆ (0989) 62447.
Overross Garage Ltd. ✆ (0989) 63666
and (0989) 63222.

ROSUDGEON Cornwall. Map 2E
Helston 7, London 278, Penzance 6,
Redruth 14, St Ives 10.
Golf Prah Sands 9h. **See** Perran Sands,
Prussia Cove, Cudden Point, Praa Sands.

◼★★**Rosudgeon** (late **Courtlands**) (R),
Penzance, TR20 9PN. ✆ Penzance (0736)
710476.

Rescue Service: Hodges Motor Works,
✆ Germoe (073 676) 3701.

ROTHBURY Northumberland. Map 31C
Pop 1,694. Newcastle upon Tyne 30,
London 303, Alnwick 12, Alston 52,
Bellingham 23, Berwick-on-Tweed 37,
Brampton 54, Coldstream 34, Corbridge
31, Hawick 47, Hexham 32, Jedburgh 42.
EC Wed. **Golf** Rothbury 9h. **See** Cragside
grounds, Brinkburn Priory, Church, old
bridge, Callaby Castle.

★**Coquet Vale,** *Station Rd, NE65 7QN.*
✆ (0669) 20305. C. ⊯ 10 bedrs, 5 bps, 2
ba, TV, Dgs. ✗ mc, LD 8.30. ⌂ CH, Dgs,
CP 30, Ac, con 60, CF, 20 st. £ BB fr £14,
DB fr £28, WT fr £190, DT fr £27, DBB fr
£21·95, WB, ⬜, Bk £3·50, L £5·25, D £6·95,
cc 1 3, Dep a.

Rescue Service: County Garage, West
End. ✆ (0669) 20400.

ROTHERFIELD East Sussex. M. Area 7D
Pop 1,572. Tunbridge Wells 7, London 43,
Eastbourne 22, East Grinstead 15,
Hastings 24, Hawkhurst 14, Haywards
Heath 20, Hurst Green 13, Uckfield 8½,
Westerham 20.
EC Wed. **Golf** Crowborough Beacon 18h.
See Mainly EE Church (fine pulpit,
superbly carved font cover).

Rescue Service: Kennedy Bros
(Engineers) Ltd, North St. ✆ (089 285)
2286.

ROTHERHAM South Yorkshire. Map
22B and 33F
Pop 84,770. Mansfield 23, London 161,
M1 Motorway 2½, Barnsley 11,
Chesterfield 16, Doncaster 11,
Gainsborough 27, Huddersfield 27,
Pontefract 20, Sheffield 5½, Worksop 14.
EC Thur. **MD** Mon, Sat. **Golf** Rotherham
18h. **See** Ancient Bridge with Chapel, All
Saints' Church, Museum and Art Gallery in
Clifton Pk.

★★★★**M Carlton Park,** *102 Moorgate
Rd, S60 2BG.* ✆ (0709) 64902. C. ⊯ 62
bedrs, 62 bp, TV. ✗ a l c, mc, at, LD 10
(9.30 Sun). ⌂ Lt, N, CH, Dgs, CP 90, sb,
con 180, CF, 18 BGf, 2 st. £ Bk £4·25, L
£5·25, D £7·95, cc 1 2 3 4 5, Dep a.
★★**Brentwood,** *Moorgate Rd, S60 2TY.*
✆ (0709) 382772. RS Xmas. C. ⊯ 24
bedrs, 12 bp, 6 bps, 2 ba, TV, Dgs. ✗ a l c,

mc, LD 9.30. ⒟ CH, TV, CP 50, Ac, con 30, CF, 9 BGf, 2 st. **£** BB £15–£27, DB £20–£33, DBB £28–£35, WB, L £3·25, D £7·95, cc 1 2 3 5 6, Dep a.

★★Elton, *Main St, Bramley, S66 0SF.*
✆ (0709) 545681. C. ⇄ 14 bedrs, 2 bp, 3 bps, 2 sh, 3 ba, TV, Dgs. ✖ a l c, mc, at, LD 9.30. ⒟ N, Dgs, CP 20, Ac, con 60, CF, 3 BGf, 1 st, Dis. **£** BB £13·75–£20·75, DB £23·75–£29·75, WT £192·15, DT £27·45, DBB £21·70–£28·70, ⏢, Bk £3·50, L £5·75, D £7·95, cc 1 2 3, Dep b.

Repairer: Kirkby Central Ltd, 128 Wellgate. ✆ (0709) 75571.
Rescue Service: Eastwood Recovery Service, Eastwood Service Station, 174 Fitzwilliam Rd. ✆ (0709) 63845. Moorhouse & Alstead, Reliance Garage, Fitzwilliam Rd. ✆ (0709) 2213.

ROTHLEY Leicestershire. Map 22F
M1 Motorway 6½, Leicester 6, London 115, Ashby-de-la-Zouch 18, Loughborough 6, Melton Mowbray 13.
EC Wed. **Golf** Rothley Park 18h. **See** Ancient Temple, Church, Main Line Steam Trust.

♨★★★Rothley Court, *Westfield La, LE7 7LG.* ✆ Leicester (0533) 374141. RS. Bank Hols. C. ⇄ 14 bedrs, 12 bp, 2 bps, TV, Dgs. ✖ a l c, mc, at, LD 9.30. ⒟ N, CH, Dgs, CP 100, Ac con 100, CF, 10 BGf, 0 st, Dis. **£** BB £29·90–£46, DB £35·65–£53, WT £324–£371, DT £60–£68·50, DBB £51·06–£58·72, WB, ⏢, Bk £3, L £8·53, D £11·38, cc 1 2 3 5, Dep b.

ROTTINGDEAN East Sussex. Map 7F
Brighton 3½, London 56, Lewes 8½, Newhaven 4½.
EC Wed. **Golf** East Brighton Ltd 18h. **See** Burne-Jones grave, Windmill, Cliffs.

★★Olde Place (R), *High St, BN2 7HE.*
✆ Brighton (0273) 31051. C. ⇄ 21 bedrs, 14 bp, 3 ba, TV, Dgs. ✖ a l c, mc, at. ⒟ CH, TV, Dgs, CP 8, G 12, Ac, CF, 1 BGf, 0 st, Dis. **£** BB £20–£27, DB £27·50–£38·50, DBB £26·50–£34, WB, ⏢, Bk £3·75, L £6·50, D £6·50, cc 1 2 3 6, Dep b.
★★White Horse, *Marine Dr, BN2 7HB.*
✆ Brighton (0273) 31955. C. ⇄ 18 bedrs, 18 bp, TV, Dgs. ✖ a l c, mc, LD 10. ⒟ Lt, N, CH, CP 60, Ac, con 25, CF, 1 st. **£** WB (winter), cc 1 2 3 5 6, Dep.
Braemar House, G, z (Unl), *Steyning Rd, BN2 7GA.* ✆ Brighton (0273) 34263. C. ⇄ 14 bedrs, 3 sh, 3 ba, Dgs. ⒟ CH, TV, Dgs, CF, 1 BGf, 2 st. **£** BB £8–£9, DB £16–£18, WT (c) £56, ⏢.

Repairer: Denes Motors, High St. ✆ Brighton (0273) 31969.

ROUGHTON Norfolk. Map 16A
Pop 728. Norwich 19, London 130, Cromer 3½, North Walsham 6½.
EC Wed. **Golf** Cromer 18h.

Rescue Service: W Davison & Son, Shell Garage. ✆ Hanworth (026 376) 293.

ROUSDON Devon. Map 5E
See also LYME REGIS.
Pop 485. Lyme Regis 3, London 150, Axminster 6, Exeter 26, Honiton 13.
Golf Axe Cliff, Axmouth 18h. **See** Interesting Church at Comboyne.

★★Orchard (R), *DT7 3XW.* ✆ Lyme Regis (029 74) 2972.

ROWLANDS CASTLE Hampshire.
Map 6F
Petersfield 10, London 63, Chichester 10, Cosham 7, Midhurst 12.
Golf Rowlands Castle 18h.

Rescue Service: H E Hall (Rowlands) Ltd, The Green. ✆ (070 541) 2244.

ROWLANDS GILL Tyne & Wear. Map 32C
Pop 7,834. Durham 17, London 277, Alston 38, Corbridge 15, Hexham 18, Middleton-in-Teesdale 31, Newcastle upon Tyne 7½, West Auckland 25.
EC Wed. **Golf** Garesfield 18h. **See** Gibside Chapel.

Rescue Service: Hamsterley Mill Garage. ✆ Ebchester (0207) 560338. Thompson, A & Co, Townley Garage, Station Rd. ✆ (020 74) 2230.

ROWLEY REGIS Warley, West Midlands. Maps 14A & 21F.
Birmingham 7½, London 118, Bridgnorth 19, Bromsgrove 11, Kidderminster 12, Sutton Coldfield 13, Walsall 9, Wolverhampton 8.
EC Thur. **MD** Wed, Sat. **Golf** Dudley 18h.

Highfield House, PH, z, *Waterfall La, B65 0BH.* ✆ 021-559 1066. C. ⇄ 12 bedrs, 2 ba. ⒟ CH, TV, CP 12, 3 st. **£** BB fr £11, DB fr £22, WT (b) fr £108·50, DT (b) £15·50, ⏢

Repairer: Webster Garage, Penncricket La. ✆ 021-559 3205.
Rescue Service: Kissane & Jeffries, Station Rd. ✆ 021-559 1085.

ROWSLEY Derbyshire. Map 22C
Pop 200. Matlock 4, London 148, Buxton 14, Chapel-en-le-Frith 16, Chesterfield 16, Glossop 29, Sheffield 16.
Golf Bakewell 9h, Matlock 18h. **See** 17th cent Peacock Hotel, Haddon Hall 1½ m NW, Chatsworth House, (Garden and Theatre Gallery) 4½ m N.

★★★Peacock, *DE4 2EB.* ✆ Matlock (0629) 733518. C. ⇄ 14 bedrs, 10 bp, 4 bps, TV, Dgs. ✖ mc, at, LD 9. ⒟ N, CH, Dgs, CP 45, U 5, pf, CF, 2 BGf, 1 st, Dis. **£** B fr £23, BD fr £35, WB, ⏢, Bk £4·25, L £4·50, D £14·50, cc 1 2 3 4 5 6, Dep b.

ROWSTOCK Oxfordshire. M. Areas 6B and 14F
Pop 60. Wallingford 9, London 55, Newbury 14, Oxford 12, Reading 17, Wantage 5.
Golf Frilford Heath 18h (2).

Rescue Service: Rowstock Service Station Ltd, Rowstock Cross Roads. ✆ Abingdon (0235) 834336 and (0235) 834286.

ROYAL LEAMINGTON SPA *See* LEAMINGTON SPA

ROYAL TUNBRIDGE WELLS *See* TUNBRIDGE WELLS

ROYDON Essex. Map 15F
Pop 2,516. Hoddesdon 3½, London 23, Bishop's Stortford 10, Epping 6½, Royston 22.
EC Wed. **Golf** Royal Epping Forest 18h. **See** 13th cent Church, Ancient Lock-up & Stocks.

Repairer: Roydon Garage, High St. ✆ (027 979) 2266.

RUAN HIGH LANES Cornwall. Map 2F
Pop 215. St Austell 11, London 243, Falmouth (Fy) 14, Newquay 21, Truro 11, Wadebridge 28.
Golf Truro 18h. **See** 13th cent Church, 12th cent Lamorran Church.

■★★Hundred House (R), *TR2 5JR.*
✆ Truro (0872) 501336. Open March–Oct & Xmas. C 5. ⇄ 9 bedrs, 2 bp, 3 bps, 1 sh, 2 ba, TV, Dgs. ✖ mc, at, LD 9. ⒟ CH, ns, CP 20, pf, con 8, 0 st. **£** BB £12–£16, DB £25–£32, WB, ⏢, Bk fr £2·50, D £8·50, cc 1 2 3 6, Dep a.

■★★Pendower Beach House (R), *TR2 5LW.* ✆ Truro (0872) 501241. Open Mar–Oct. C 6. ⇄ 15 bedrs, 1 bp, 5 ba, Dgs. ✖ mc, at, LD 7.30. ⒟ TV, CP 50, tc, 1 BGf, 0 st, Dis. **£** BB £12–£20, DB £24–£40, WT £125–£133, DBB £17–£22, WB, Bk £4, L £6, D £9·50, cc 3 6, Dep a.

■♨★★Polsue Manor (R), *TR2 5LU.*
✆ Truro (0872) 501270. C. ⇄ 13 bedrs, 9 bp, 2 ba, Dgs. ✖ mc, at, LD 8.15. ⒟ TV, CP 20, con 20, CF, 3 st. **£** BB £14–£17, DB £28–£38, DBB £20–£25, WB, ⏢, L £3·75, D £7, Dep a.

Rescue Service: J J Harris & Son (Engrs) Ltd, Treworran Garage. ✆ Tregony (087 253) 304.

RUDDINGTON Notts. Map 22F
Pop 6,494. Leicester 18, London 117, Loughborough 9, Melton Mowbray 15, Nottingham 4½.
EC Wed. **Golf** Edwalton 9h. **See** Village Museum.

Rescue Service: W H Dolman & Co Ltd, Distillery St. ✆ Nottingham (0602) 212044.

RUGBY Warwickshire. Map 14B
Pop 60,380. London 81, M1 Motorway 2½, Banbury 25, Coventry 12, Daventry 10, Hinckley 15, Leicester 20, Market Harborough 13, Northampton 20, Nuneaton 16, Warwick 14.
MD Mon, Fri, Sat. **Golf** Rugby 18h. **See** Rugby School, Art Gallery, Percival Guildhouse, Town Hall, Roman Catholic Church of St Marie, St Andrew's Church, Frescoes at Church (origin probably Saxon) of Ashby St Ledgers 7m SE, Stanford Hall 6 m NE.
⏢ Library, St Matthews St. ✆ Rugby (0788) 2687.

★★★★M Post House (TH), *Crick, NN6 7XR.* ✆ Crick (0788) 822101. C. ⇄ 96 bedrs, 96 bp, TV, Dgs. ✖ a l c, mc, at, LD 10. ⒟ N, CH, Dgs, CP 150, Ac, con 70, CF, 48 BGf, 1 st, Dis. **£** BB £43·50, DB £55·50, WB, ⏢, cc 1 2 3 4 5 6.
♨★★★Clifton Court, *CV23 0BB.*
✆ (0788) 65033. RS 26–31 Dec. C. ⇄ 14 bedrs, 10 bp, 4 bps, TV, ✖ a l c, mc, at, LD 9.30. ⒟ N, ch, TV, CP 200, Ac, con 200, CF, 1 st. **£** BB £39·50, DB £53, WB, ⏢, Bk £4, L £5·95, D £7·45, cc 1 3 6, Dep b.
★★★Three Horse Shoes, *Sheep St, CV21 3BX.* ✆ (0788) 4585. C. ⇄ 32 bedrs, 18 bp, 14 bps, TV, Dgs. ✖ a l c, mc, at, LD 10.30. ⒟ N, CH, Dgs, AC, con 40, CF, 1 st. **£** BBc £38·50–£40·42, DBc £49–£51·45, WT £210–£231, DT £54·40–£58·12, DBB £47·45–£51·17, WB, ⏢, cc 1 2 3 5 6, Dep a.

Repairer: Grove of Rugby Ltd, Forum Dr, Leicester Rd. ✆ (0788) 62731.

Specialist Body Repairer: Grove of Rugby Ltd, Forum Dr, Leicester Rd. ✆ (0788) 62371.
Rescue Service: Lawford Garage, Main St, Long Lawford. ✆ (0788) 65381.
S Woodcock & Son (Rugby) Ltd, 339 Hillmorton Rd. ✆ (0788) 73671.

RUGELEY Staffordshire. Map 22E
Pop 24,400. Lichfield 7, London 123, Burton-on-Trent 15, Stafford 8½, Stone 14, Uttoxeter 11, Walsall 15, Wolverhampton 15.
EC Wed. **MD** Tue, Thur, Fri, Sat. **Golf** Beau Desert 18h. **See** Remains of 12th cent Parish Church, Market Hall, Garden of Remembrance, Cannock Chase.

★★**Eaton Lodge,** *Wolseley Rd, WF15 2ET.* ✆ (088 94) 3454. C. 🛏 12 bedrs, 1 bp, 6 sh, 3 ba, TV, Dgs. ✕ a l c, mc, at, LD 9.15. ⌂ CH, Dgs, CP 200, Ac, con 200, CF. **£** BB fr £16, DB fr £22, WB, ①, Bk £3, L £3·95, D £7·50, cc 1 3, Dep b.

Rescue Service: Bradbury & Brown (Rugeley) Ltd, Armitage Rd. ✆ (088 94) 3156.
J Edwards & Son Garages (Rugeley) Ltd, Brereton Road Garage. ✆ (088 94) 2248.

RUISLIP Greater London (Middx). Maps 15E and 7A
Pop 72,791 (inc Northwood). London 13, Denham 4, Ealing 7, Harrow 3½, Rickmansworth 6, Uxbridge 3.
EC Wed. **Golf** Ruislip 18h, Northwood 18h, Haste Hill 18h, Pinner Hill 18h, Hillingdon 9h. **See** Priory and Parish Church of St Martin, Manor Farm, Ruislip Lido, Swakeley's at Ickenham nearby, Grand Union Canal 1½m W.

The Barn, H, yz (R), *West End Rd, HA4 6JD.* ✆ (089 56) 36057. Closed 23 Dec–2 Jan. C. 🛏 56 bedrs, 40 bp, 8 ba, TV, Dgs. ✕ a l c. ⌂ CH, TV, CP 70, CF, 22 BGf, 1 st, Dis. **£** BB £28·50–£34·50, DB £36·50–£42, ①, L £7·50, D £7·50, cc 1 2 3.

Rescue Service: A F Silver (Recovery Service), Breakspeare Autopoint, Breakspeare Rd. ✆ (089 56) 76074.

RUNCORN Cheshire. Map 20D
Pop 64,600 (inc Halton Village). Northwich 11, London 184, M56 Motorway 5, Chester 14, Liverpool 13, Nantwich 23, St Helens 8½, Warrington 8½, Whitchurch 27.
EC Wed. **MD** Tue, Thur, Sat. **Golf** Runcorn 18h. **See** Rebuilt All Saints' Church, Castle Inn, Runcorn–Widnes High Level Road Bridge, Norton Priory & Museum open to public (excavation).
ⓘ 57 Church St. ✆ Runcorn (092 85) 76776.

★★★**M Crest,** *Wood La, Beechwood, WA7 3HA.* (at Junction 12, M56). ✆ (0928) 714000. RS Bank Holidays. C. 🛏 130 bedrs, 130 bp, ns, TV, Dgs. ✕ a l c, mc, at, LD 9.45. ⌂ Lt, N, CH, Dgs, CP 250, Ac, con 450, CF, 24 BGf. **£** B fr £42, BD fr £51, WB, ①, Bk £5·25, D £9·25, cc 1 2 3 4 5 6, Dep b.

Rescue Service: Bikers Corner, 65A Church St. ✆ (092 85) 75851.
Halton Brow Service Station Ltd, Halton Brow. ✆ (092 85) 64433.
Sutton Weaver Service Station, Sutton Weaver. ✆ Aston (092 86) 633.

RUSHDEN Northamptonshire. Map 15A
Pop 22,230. Bedford 14, London 64, Bletchley 25, Cambridge 35, Huntingdon 23, Kettering 11, Northampton 15, Peterborough 28, Stamford 29.
EC Thur. **MD** Sat. **Golf** Rushden 9h. **See** 13th cent Church, Rushden Hall, Hinwick House nearby.

★**Queen Victoria,** *High St, NN10 9BT.* ✆ (0933) 312189.
▣★**Westward** (R), *Shirley Rd, NN10 9BY.* ✆ (0933) 312376. Closed Dec 23–Jan 1. C. 🛏 18 bedrs, 8 sh, 3 ba, TV. ✕ LD 8. ⌂ CH, TV, CP 16, Ac, sp, con 20, CF, 7 BGf, 1 st, Dis. **£** BB £15–£20, DB £22·50–£30, DBB £21–£26, ①, Bk £3·50, D £6.

Repairer: Townsends (Garages) Ltd, 58 High St South. ✆ (0933) 59111.

RUSHYFORD Durham. Map 24E
Pop 226. Darlington 9, London 253, A1(M) Motorway 2, Alston 41, Durham 8½, Middleton-in-Teesdale 14, West Auckland 7½.
Golf Bishop Auckland 18h. **See** Auckland Castle and Auckland Castle Deer House (4½m W).

★★★**Eden Arms,** *DL17 0LL.* ✆ (0388) 720541. C. 🛏 51 bedrs, 51 bp, TV, Dgs. ✕ a l c, mc, at, LD 9.30. ⌂ N, CH, TV, CP 150, U 6, Ac, con 60, CF, 6 BGf, 2 st. **£** BB £17·50–£29, DB £26–£40, DBB £23–£35, WB, ①, Bk £4, L £4·75, D £6·95, cc 1 2 3 5 6, Dep b.

RUSTINGTON West Sussex. Map 7E
Pop 8,650. Horsham 21, London 57, Arundel 4½, Littlehampton 2, Worthing 6½.
EC Wed. **Golf** Littlehampton 18h. **See** Parish Church.

▣★**Mayday** (R), *Broadmark La, BN16 2HH.* ✆ (090 62) 71198. Closed Oct. C 6. 🛏 8 bedrs, 4 bps, 2 ba, TV. ✕ mc, at, LD 7.15. ⌂ CH, TV, CP 12, 4 st. **£** BB £14–£16, DB £28–£34, WB, ②, Bk £3·50, D £7·50, Dep.
Kenmore, G, z (Unl), *Claigmar Rd, BN16 2NL.* ✆ (090 62) 4634. C. 🛏 5 bedrs, 1 bp, 2 ba, TV, Dgs. ⌂ CH, TV, Dgs, CP 6, CF, 1 BGf, 0 st, Dis. **£** BB £7·20–£10·20, DB £17·90–£20·40, ①, Bk £1·95.

Repairer: Rustington Service Station, Station Rd. ✆ (090 62) 72222.

RYDAL Cumbria. Map 26D
M6 Motorway 27, Ambleside 1½, London 271, Broughton-in-Furness 18, Kendal 15, Keswick 15, Penrith 24, Windermere 6½.
See Nab Cottage, Rydal Mount, Rydal Fell, Dove Cottage and Wordsworth Museum at Grasmere, Rydal Water Loughrigg Fell and Tarn.

▣★★**Glen Rothay,** *LA22 9LR.* ✆ Ambleside (0966) 32524. C. 🛏 11 bedrs, 4 bp, 7 bps, 1 ba, Dgs. ✕ mc, LD 7.30. ⌂ CH, TV, Dgs, CP 40, CF. **£** BB £20–£23, DB £34–£46, WT £140–£195, DBB £20–£30·95, ②, Bk £4, D £7·50, cc 1 2 3 5.
▣★**Rydal Lodge** (Rt), *LA22 9LR.* ✆ Ambleside (0966) 33208. Closed Jan except New Year. C. 🛏 8 bedrs, 3 ba, Dgs. ✕ mc, at, LD 6.30. ⌂ ch, TV, Dgs, CP 12, CF, 1 BGf, 1 st, Dis. **£** BB £17, DB £26, DBB £20, ①, Bk £3·50, D £8·70, cc 1 3, Dep a.

RYDE Isle of Wight. Map 6F
See also SEAVIEW.
Pop 19,969. London (Fy) 74, Cowes 8, Newport 7, Sandown 5½.
EC Thur. **Golf** Ryde 9h. **See** Shell Museum and Albert Cottage, Binstead, long pier, St Helen's Abbey, Quarr Abbey nearby, Flamingo Park Bird Sanctuary, Isle of Wight Steam Railway at Haven Street, Spithead.
ⓘ Esplanade. ✆ Isle of Wight (0983) 62581.

★★**Ryde Castle,** *Esplanade, PO33 1JA.* ✆ Isle of Wight (0983) 63755. C. 🛏 17 bedrs, 10 bp, 7 bps, TV, Dgs. ✕ a l c, mc, at, LD 10. ⌂ CH, Dgs, CP 60. **£** BB £18·40, DB £36·80, DBB £22·50, ②, Bk £3, L £4·50, D fr £4, cc 1 3, Dep.
★★**Yelf's** (TH), *Union St, PO33 2LG.* ✆ Isle of Wight (0983) 64062. C. 🛏 21 bedrs, 21 bp, TV, Dgs. ✕ a l c, mc, LD 8.45. ⌂ CH, Dgs, Ac, con 50, CF, 2 st. **£** BB £35·50, DB £51·50, WB, ①, cc 1 2 3 4 5 6.
★**Wellington Lodge,** (R), *Augusta Rd (off Spencer Rd), PO33 3AT.* ✆ Isle of Wight (0983) 68844. Open Feb–Nov, C. 🛏 19 bedrs, 19 bp, 2 ba, TV, Dgs. ✕ a l c. ⌂ ch, TV, Dgs, CF, 6 BGf, 1 st. **£** BB £11·95–£18·60, DB £23·90–£37·20, DBB £17·75–£27·90, ①, Bk £3, L £4·50, D £6·40, cc 2 5.
Dorset, H, z (R), *Dover Rd, PO33 2BW.* ✆ Isle of Wight (0983) 64327. C 5. 🛏 25 bedrs, 1 bp, 6 bps, 4 ba. ⌂ TV, CP 20, 12 st. **£** BB £10–£14, DB £19–£26, WT fr £65, DT fr £25, ①, Bk £2, L £3·75, D £5.
Georgian, PH, *22 George St, PO33 2EW.* ✆ Isle of Wight (0983) 63989.

Rescue Service: Downing & Donovan Ltd, Ryde Garage, Victoria St. ✆ Isle of Wight (0983) 63661.
Westridge Garage (Ryde) Ltd, 200 Great Preston Rd. ✆ Isle of Wight (0983) 62717.
Wight Motors (Ryde) Ltd, Theatre Royal Garage, 186 High St. ✆ Isle of Wight (0983) 62281.

RYE East Sussex. Map 10E
Pop 5,000. Hawkhurst 13, London 63, Folkestone 25, Hastings 11, Hurst Green 16, Tenterden 10.
EC Tue. **MD** Wed, Thur. **Golf** Rye 18h. **See** Cinque Port, 12th cent Ypres Tower (museum), Flushing Inn (15th cent), Mermaid Inn (15th cent), Land Gate, Town Hall, St Mary's Church (quarter-boys clock), George Hotel, Lamb House (Nat Trust), Great Dixter 7 m NW, Royal Military Canal, The Salts, Gun Gardens, Martello Tower at Rye Harbour.
ⓘ Council Offices, Ferry Rd. ✆ Rye (079 73) 222293.

★★★**George** (TH), *High St, TN31 7JP.* ✆ (0797) 222114. C. 🛏 20 bedrs, 12 bp, 8 bps, TV, Dgs. ✕ a l c, mc, LD 9. ⌂ CH, Dgs, CP 9, G 8, Ac, con 160, CF, 1 BGf, 2 st. **£** BB £37, DB £54, WB, ①, cc 1 2 3 4 5 6, Dep (Xmas).
★★★**Mermaid,** *Mermaid St, TN31 7EY.* ✆ (0797) 223065. RS late Jan & Feb. C 8. 🛏 29 bedrs, 16 bp, 6 bps, 2 ba. ✕ a l c, LD 9.15. ⌂ N, CH, TV, Dgs, ns, CP 25, Ac, con 75, CF, 4 st. **£** BB £20–£26, DB £33–£40, DBB £28·25–£34·25, WB, ②, Bk £4·50, L £6·25, D £8·25, cc 2 3 4 5.
★★**Hope Anchor,** *Watchbell St, TN31 7HA.* ✆ (0797) 222216.
★★**Saltings,** *Hilders Cliff, High St, TN31 7LD.* ✆ (0797) 223838. C. 🛏 15 bedrs, 2 bp, 6 bps, 5 sh, 1 ba, TV, Dgs. ✕ a l c, mc, at, LD 9.45. ⌂ CH, TV, Dgs, CP 35, Ac, con

60, CF, 1 st. **£** BB £15–£22, DB £27–£38, DT fr £28, DBB fr £23, Bk £3·50, L £5, D £8, cc 1 2 3 5 6, Dep b.

★★Ship Inn, *The Strand, TN31 7DB.* ✆ (0797) 222233. RS mid week, mid winter. C. ⊷ 12 bedrs, 4 bp, 3 ba, TV. ✗ a l c, LD 9.30. 🅿 CH, Dgs, Ac, 1 st. **£** BB £16–£20, DB £25–£31·50, DBB £22·50–£26·50, WB, ②, 10%, Bk £4, L £5, D £6·50, cc 2 3 5.

Durrant House, H, z, (Rt), *Market St, TN31 7LA.* ✆ (0797) 223182. C 5. ⊷ 8 bedrs, 3 bps, 2 sh, 2 ba, TV. Dgs. ✗ a l c. 🅿 CH, TV, Dgs, 2 st. **£** BB £10·50–£20, DB £20–£34, WT £95–£120, DT £15–£22, ②, L £5, D £6·50.

Little Saltcote, G, x (Unl), *22 Military Rd, TN31 7NY.* ✆ (0797) 223210. Closed Xmas, C. ⊷ 6 bedrs, 1 bp, 1 ba, TV. 🅿 CH, CP 3, CF, 1 BGf, 1 st. **£** BB £10–£18, DB £16–£18, ①.

Mariners, PH, z (R), *High St, TN31 7JF.* ✆ (0797) 223480. C. ⊷ 12 bedrs, 11 bp, 1 bps, 2 ba, TV, Dgs. ✗ a l c. 🅿 CH, TV, Dgs, CF, 2 BGf, 0 st. **£** BB £19·25–£28, DB £36·50–£42·50, WT (a) £204, (b) £184, DT (a) £34·50–£44·50, (b) £30–£38·25, ①, Bk £5, L £8·95, D £10, cc 1 2 3 4 5.

Monastery, H, z (R), *6 High St, TN31 7JE.* ✆ (0797) 223272. Closed Xmas Day & Tuesdays throughout year. C 5. ⊷ 8 bedrs, 1 bp, 6 sh, 2 ba, Dgs. ✗ a l c. 🅿 CH, TV, 0st. **£** DB £22–£30, ①, L £10·25, D £10·25.

Old Borough Arms, H, z, *The Strand, TN31 7DB.* ✆ (0797) 222128. Open Mar–Dec. C. ⊷ 9 bedrs, 9 bps, TV, Dgs. 🅿 CH, Dgs, CP 2, G 2, CF, 4 BGf, 0 st. **£** BB £15·50–£16·50, DB £25–£27, ①.

Repairer: Skinners of Rye, Fishmarket Rd. ✆ (0797) 223334.

RYTON Tyne & Wear. Map 32C
Pop 8,553. West Auckland 29, London 278, Corbridge 11, Durham 19, Hexham 14, Newcastle upon Tyne 7.
EC Wed. **Golf** Ryton 18h, Tyneside 18h.
See Floral Village, Ryton Willows (Riverside).

Rescue Service: D Loughhead, Barmoor Garage, Main Rd. ✆ (089 422) 2323.

SAFFRON WALDEN Essex. Map 17E
Pop 9,971. Bishop's Stortford 11, London 43, M11 Motorway 4½, Braintree 19, Cambridge 15, Dunmow 13, Haverhill 12, Newmarket 19, Royston 13.
EC Thur. **MD** Tue, Sat. **Golf** Saffron Walden 18h. **See** Castle ruins, Museum, St Mary's Church, Audley End Mansion, Timbered houses, Mole Hall Wildlife Park 4 m S.
🛈 Corn Exchange, Market Sq. ✆ Saffron Walden (0799) 24282.

★★Saffron, *10 High St, CB10 1AY.* ✆ (0789) 22676. RS Xmas & Sun, C. ⊷ 18 bedrs, 4 bp, 2 ba, 6 sh, 4 ba, TV, Dgs. ✗ a l c, LD 9.30. 🅿 ch, TV, Dgs, CP 12, Ac, con 70, CF, 1 st. **£** BBc £13·50–£22·50, DBc £21–£34, WB, ①, Bk £3·85, L £6·50, D £6·50, cc 1 3 6.

ST AGNES Cornwall. Map 2C
Pop 2,000. Bodmin 26, London 269, Newquay 11, Redruth 7½, St Austell 20, Truro 8.
Golf Truro 18h. **See** Church, Ancient Cross, St Agnes Head, Beacon, Harbour, Trevaunance Cove.

🅱🆕★★**Rose-in-Vale** (R), *Mithian, TR5 0QD.* ✆ (087 255) 2202. C 5. ⊷ 15 bedrs, 6 bp, 2 bps, 2 ba, Dgs. ✗ mc, at, LD 8. 🅿 ch, TV, ns, CP 40, Ac, sp, sol, con 40, CF, 3 BGf, 1 st, Dis. **£** BB £8·20–£18·40, DB £16·40–£36·80, DBB £14·90–£25, WB, ①, D £5·75, Dep a.

🅱★★**Rosemundy House** (R), *8 Rosemundy, TR5 0UF.* ✆ (087 255) 2101. Open Apr–Oct. C. ⊷ 42 bedrs, 23 bp, 9 bps, 10 sh, 3 ba, TV, Dgs. ✗ mc, at, LD 8. 🅿 ch, TV, Dgs, CP 50, sp, CF, 9 BGf, 1 st, Dis. **£** BB £8–£16, DB £16–£32, DBB £12–£21, ②, Bk £3·50, D £6, cc 3, Dep.

🅱★**Lamorna House** (R), *Goonvrea, TR5 0NG.* ✆ (087 255) 2670. Open Apr–Oct. C. ⊷ 10 bedrs, 3 ba, Dgs. ✗ mc, at, LD 7.30. 🅿 TV, CP 12, CF, 5 BGf, 2 st. **£** BB £8·60–£11·30, DB £17·20–£22·60, DBB £14·20–£17, ①, Bk £2·65, D £6·60.

Mount Pleasant, F, xy (Unl), *Rosemundy, TR5 0UD.* ✆ (087 255) 2387. Open May–Oct. C. ⊷ 11 bedrs, 3 ba, Dgs. 🅿 TV, CP 12, CF.

Penkerris, G, x (Unl), *Penwinnick Rd, TR5 0PA.* ✆ (087 255) 2262. C. ⊷ 5 bedrs, 2 ba, TV, Dgs. 🅿 ch, TV, CP 12, CF. **£** BB £5–£10, DB £10–£16, WT (b) £50–£80, (c) £35–£52·50, DT £8–£12, ①, Bk £1·95, L £3, D £4.▲

Rescue Service: Peterville & Dales Garage. ✆ (087 255) 2296.
Stris Motors, Wheal Kitty. ✆ (087 255) 2102.

ST ALBANS Herts. Map 15F
Pop 50,888. London 19, M10 Motorway 1½, Aylesbury 23, Baldock 20, Barnet 9½, Dunstable 13, Hatfield 6, High Wycombe 24, Luton 10, Watford 7.
EC Thur. **MD** Wed, Sat. **Golf** Batchwood Hall 18h. **See** 11th cent Cathedral with massive tower faced with Roman tiles, Abbey Gateway (now part of St Albans School), St Michael's Church (effigy of Sir Francis Bacon), 'Fighting Cocks' Inn (one of the oldest inhabited houses), 'Verulamium'—Roman excavations, Museum, Hypocaust (in Verulamium Park), Bleak House, Romeland House, 15th cent Clock Tower, Gorhambury 2 m W, Salisbury Hall 4 m SE.
🛈 37 Chequer St. ✆ St Albans (0727) 64511.

★★★M Noke Thistle, *Watford Rd, AL2 3DS.* (2⅓ m S at junc of A412/A405). ✆ (0727) 54252. C. ⊷ 57 bedrs, 57 bp, ns, TV, Dgs. ✗ a l c. 🅿 CH, TV, Dgs, CP 200, Ac, con 75, CF, 1 st. **£** BB £42·95–£49·95, DB £54·90–£61·90, WB, ②, Bk £4·95, cc 1 2 3 4 5 6, Dep b.

★★★St Michael's Manor, *Fishpool St, AL3 4RY.* ✆ (0727) 64444.
🅱★★★**Sopwell House,** *Cottonmill La, AL1 2HQ.* ✆ (0727) 64477. RS Sun. C. ⊷ 27 bedrs, 26 bp, 1 bps, annexe 3 bedrs, 3 bp, TV. ✗ a l c, mc, at, LD 9.30. 🅿 N, CH, CP 100, Ac, con 80, CF, 3 BGf, 1 st, Dis. **£** BB £29·70–£41·80, DB £43·45–£56·65, DBB £40·42–£52·52, WB, ②, 10%, Bk £4·50, L £7·50, D £9·75, cc 1 2 3 5.

Ardmore House, PH, z (Unl), *54 Lemsford Rd.* ✆ (0727) 59313. C. ⊷ 14 bedrs, 5 bps, 3 ba, TV. 🅿 CH, TV, Dgs, CP 15, CF, 2 BGf, 1 st, Dis. **£** BB fr £16·10, DB fr £25·30, ①.

Glenmore, G, z (Unl), *16 Woodstock Rd North, AL1 4QQ.* ✆ (0727) 53794. C. ⊷ 8 bedrs, 1 ba, TV. 🅿 CH, TV, Dgs, CP 5, CF, 1

BGf, 1 st. **£** BB £12·50–£15·50, DB £21–£25, ①.

Haven, H, *234 London Rd, AL1 1JQ.* ✆ (0727) 62750. Closed Xmas Day. C. ⊷ 44 bedrs, 2 bp, 27 bps, 5 ba, TV, Dgs. ✗ a l c. 🅿 CH, TV, Dgs, CP 100, CF, 9 BGf, 4 st. **£** BB £17·50–£25, DB £25–£33, ①, Bk £5, L £5, D £5·22, cc 1 3.

Melford, G, z (Rl), *24 Woodstock Rd North, AL1 4QQ.* ✆ (0727) 53642. C. ⊷ 12 bedrs, 4 bps, 3 ba, Dgs. 🅿 CH, TV, CP 12, CF, 1 BGf, 1 st, Dis. **£** BB £14·95–£25·30, DB £24·15–£29·90, WT £89·90, ②.

Repairers: Autoport (St Albans) Ltd, 2 Beech Rd. ✆ (0727) 50871.
Frogmore Garage, Park St. ✆ Park St. (0727) 72676.
Marlbro Motors (St Albans) Ltd, 100 London Rd. ✆ (0727) 50601.

ST ANNES ON SEA Lancashire.
See LYTHAM ST ANNES.

ST AUSTELL Cornwall. Map 2D
Pop 19,693. Liskeard 18, London 232, Bodmin 11, Fowey 7½, Newquay 14, Truro 14.
EC Thur. **Golf** St Austell 18h, Carlyon Bay 18h. **See** Church (12th–15th cent), White Hart Hotel (old inn), China Clay quarries (tours of the Blackpool China Clay Works by arrangement with the Information Officer, John Keay House, St Austell), Market House (1791), Mengu Stone.

★★★Carlyon Bay, *PL25 3RD.* ✆ Par (072 681) 2304. C. ⊷ 72 bedrs, 67 bp, 2 ba, TV, Dgs. ✗ a l c, mc, at, LD 9. 🅿 Lt, N, CH, CP 100, U 8, sp, gc, tc, sb, sol, gym, con, CF, 2 st. **£** WB, Bk £4·03, L £7·59, D £10·12, cc 1 2 3 5 6.

★★★Porth Avallen (R), *Sea Rd, Carlyon Bay, PL25 3SG.* ✆ Par (072 681) 2802. RS late Dec–early Jan. C. ⊷ 25 bedrs, 19 bp, 2 bps, 2 ba, TV. ✗ mc, at, LD 8.30. 🅿 CH, TV, CP 50, Ac, con 100, CF, 2 st. **£** BB £17·50–£27, DB £29–£40·50, WT £160–£195, DT £27·50–£30·50, DBB £24·50–£34·50, ①, Bk £3·50, L £4, D £7, cc 1 2 3 5 6.

🅱🆕★★**Boscundle Manor** (R), *Tregrehan, PL25 3 RL.* ✆ Par (072 681) 3557. Closed Dec 22–Feb 7, RS Sun & Bank Hols. C. ⊷ 7 bedrs, 2 bp, 4 bps, 1 sh, TV, Dgs. ✗ LD 9. 🅿 CH, CP 12, sp, con 8, CF, 9 st. **£** BB £30, DB £45, ①, D £13·50, cc 1 2 3.

🅱★★**Cliff Head,** *Carlyon Bay, PL25 3RB.* ✆ Par (072 681) 2125. Open Apr–Oct. C. ⊷ 50 bedrs, 14 bp, 14 ba, ns, TV, Dgs. ✗ mc, LD 8. 🅿 CH, TV, CP 60, Ac, sp, con 50, CF, 10 BGf, 2 st. **£** BB £13·80–£18·40, DB £25·30–£29·90, ①, Bk £3, D £6·90, cc 1 3, Dep.

★★White Hart, *Church St, PL25 4AT.* ✆ (0726) 2100. C. ⊷ 20 bedrs, 4 bp, 7 sh, 4 ba, TV, Dgs. ✗ mc, at, LD 8.30. 🅿 CH, con 50, CF, 2 st. **£** BB £17·50–£22·50, DB £27·50–£31·50, WT £225–£275, WB, ①, Bk £3·20, L £2·35, D £6, cc 1 2 3 5.

Alexandra, H, z (Rl), *52 Alexandra Rd, PL25 4QN.* ✆ (0726) 4242. Closed Xmas. C. ⊷ 14 bedrs, 4 bps, 2 ba, Dgs. 🅿 CH, TV, CP 16, CF. **£** BB fr £7·50, DB £15–£17, WT (b) £74·75–£79·35, DT (b) £11·50–£12·50, ①.

Lynton, H, x (Rl), *48 Bodmin Rd, PL25 5AF.* ✆ (0726) 3787. C. ⊷ 6 bedrs, 1 ba. 🅿 ch, TV, CP 6, 5 st. **£** BB £7·50–£8·50, DB £15–£17, WT (b) £70·24–£77·86, DT (b) £11–£12, ①.

Selwood House, PH, z (R),
60 Alexandra Rd, PL25 4QN. ✆ (0726)
65707. C. 🚶 12 bedrs, 6 sh, 1 ba, Dgs.
🅿 CH, TV, CP 8, G 2, CF, 0 st. £ BB £7–
£8·50, DB £15–£17, WT £70–£75, DT
£11·50–£12·50, ⅂, D £4.
Treskillon, G, x (Rl), *26 Woodland Rd,
PL25 4QY.* ✆ (0726) 2920. C. 🚶 10 bedrs,
2 ba. 🅿 CH, TV, CP 10, CF. £ BB £8–£10,
DB £16–£20, WT (b) £66–£78, (c) £48–
£60, DT (b) £11–£13, ⅂.
Winchmore, G, z (Unl), *72 Alexandra
Rd, PL25 4QN.* ✆ (0726) 4585. C. 🚶 6
bedrs, 1 ba, Dgs. 🅿 CH, TV, Dgs, CP 3, CF,
2 st. £ BB £6·50–£7, DB £13–£14, WT (b)
£63–£70, DT (b) £9·50–£10·50, ⅂.

Specialist Radiator Repairer: Serck
Radiator Services Ltd, Mount Charles.
✆ (0726) 2484.
MC Repairer: R S Damerell & Son Ltd,
Whitemoor. ✆ (0726) 822402.
Sctr Repairer: R S Damerell & Son Ltd,
Whitemoor. ✆ (0726) 822402.
Rescue Service: Beech Motors (St
Austell) Ltd, Beech La. ✆ (0726) 4743.
Carlyon Bay Garages Ltd, Carlyon Bay.
✆ Par (072 681) 2451.
Ochre (Roche) Ltd, Central Garage, Trinity
St. ✆ (0726) 66233.
Pentewan-Valley-Motors, London
Apprentice. ✆ (0726) 4056.
U B M Motors Ltd, Slades Rd. ✆ (0726)
2333.

ST BLAZEY Cornwall. Map 2D
Pop 3,371. Liskeard 16, London 230,
Bodmin 8, Fowey 4, St Austell 4.
Golf Carlyon Bay 18h, St Austell 18h. **See**
Church.

Moorshill House, PH, y (R), *73 Rosehill,
PL24 2LQ.* ✆ Par (072 681) 2368. C. 🚶 5
bedrs, 1 ba, Dgs. 🅿 CH, TV, Dgs, CP 6, CF, 4 st.
£ BB £6·50, DB £13, WT (b) £60–£65, DT
(b) £10, ⅂, D £5·50.

ST BRIAVELS Gloucestershire. M. Area
13E
Pop 1,305. Gloucester 24, London 129,
Chepstow 8, Monmouth 8½, Ross-on-Wye
15.
EC Thur. **Golf** Coleford 18h. **See** 12th
cent Castle, interesting 12th cent Church
(Old Custom, Whit Sunday, "Bread and
Cheese" Ceremony dating from 13th
cent), Views of Wye Valley, Tintern Abbey
4 m SW.

Rescue Service: W Parry & Sons, The
Garage. ✆ Dean (0594) 530331.

ST BURYAN Cornwall. Map 2E
Pop 1,000. Penzance 5, London 286.
Golf West Cornwall Lelant 18h. **See**
Market Cross, 15th cent Church, Bronze
Age Stone Circle.

Rescue Service: St Buryan Garage,
Church Town. ✆ (073 672) 322.

ST COLUMB MAJOR Cornwall. Map
2D
Pop 2,749. Wadebridge 8, London 247,
Bodmin 12, Newquay 6½, St Austell 10,
Truro 14.
EC Wed. **MD** Mon. **Golf** Newquay 18h.
See Parish Church (Monuments) Old
Glebe House, Hurling game Shrove Tue
(old custom).

St Margaret's, PH, *Fraddon, TR9 6LX.*
✆ St Austell (0726) 860375.

Rescue Service: Enterprise Garage (St
Columb) Ltd, Trekenning Rd. ✆ St Columb
(0637) 880488.
St Columb Motors, Station Rd. ✆ (0637)
880312.

ST EVAL Cornwall. M. Area 2D
Pop 1,280. Wadebridge 9½, London 248,
Newquay 10, St Austell 18, Truro 24.
Golf St Enodoc 18h. Trevose 18h.

Rescue Service: Tonkins Garage.
✆ Rumford (084 14) 231.

ST GENNYS Cornwall. M. Area 2B
Pop 554. Launceston 20, London 231,
Bude 10, Camelford 11, Holsworthy 18.

Rescue Service: W G Cox, The Garage,
Wainhouse Corner. ✆ (084 03) 385.

ST HELENS Merseyside. Map 20C
Pop 189,251. Warrington 9½, London 192,
Liverpool 11, Manchester 22, Northwich
20, Ormskirk 10, Walkden 17, Wigan 8½.
EC Thur. **MD** Daily. **Golf** Sherdley Park
18h. **See** Windleshaw Abbey ruins,
Seddon's Cottage, Sherdley Park and
Ornamental Gardens, Glass Museum.

★★★**Fleece,** *Church St, WA10 1AB.*
✆ (0744) 26546. C. 🚶 73 bedrs, 70 bp, 2
bps, 1 sh, 3 ba, TV, Dgs. ✗ mc, LD 9.15.
🅿 Lt, N, CH, Dgs, CP 60, Ac, con 250, CF,
1 st. £ BB £33·50, DB £44, WB, ⅂, Bk
£3·50, L £3·50, D £7, cc 1 2 3 5 6, Dep b.

Rescue Service: Fisher Street Motors, 23
Fisher St, Sutton. ✆ Marshalls Cross
(0744) 821401.
W Hancock & Son, Parkside Garage,
Jubits La, Sutton Manor. ✆ Marshalls
Cross (0744) 815588.

ST IVES Cambridgeshire. Map 15B
Pop 12,845. Royston 20, London 61,
Biggleswade 19, Cambridge 13, Ely 18,
Huntingdon 5½, Peterborough 23,
Wisbech 33.
EC Thur. **MD** Mon. **Golf** St Ives (Hunts),
9h. **See** All Saints' Church, Stone Bridge
(with Chapel), Norris Museum and Library,
Oliver Cromwell statue, Old Custom
(1675), dicing for Bibles on Spring Bank
Hol.

★★★**Slepe Hall,** *Ramsey Rd, PE17 4RB.*
✆ (0480) 63122. Closed Xmas. C. 🚶 14
bedrs, 10 bp, 3 ba, TV, Dgs. ✗ a l c, mc, at,
LD 10. 🅿 CH, CP 120, U 1, Ac, con 200,
CF, 1 st. £ BB fr £25, DB fr £36, WB, ⅂, Bk
£5, L £9·95, D £9·95, cc 1 2 3 5 6.
★★**M St Ives,** *London Rd, PE17 4EX.*
✆ (0480) 63857. Closed Dec 25 & 26. C.
🚶 16 bedrs, 16 bp, TV, Dgs. ✗ a l c, mc, at,
LD 9.30. 🅿 CH, CP 80, con 50, CF, 16 BGf,
1 st, Dis. £ BB £24·75, DB £36, WB, ⅂, Bk
£3·75, L £7, D £8·50, cc 1 2 3 5.

Rescue Service: St Ives Motors (Hunts)
Ltd, The Quadrant. ✆ (0480) 62871.

ST IVES Cornwall. Map 2E
See also CARBIS BAY
Pop 6,750. Redruth 14, London 277,
Helston 15, Penzance 8.
EC Thur (Win.). **Golf** West Cornwall
Lelant 18h. **See** Oldest house (plaque),
Art Galleries, Chysauster Ancient Village
(1st cent BC), The Island (St Nicholas'
Chapel), St Leonard's Chapel, 15th cent
Church, picturesque harbour, Museum.
🇹 Guildhall, Street-an-Pol. ✆ Penzance
(0736) 796297.

🔲★★★**Chy-an-Drea** (R), *The Terrace,
TR26 2BP.* ✆ Penzance (0736) 795076.
Open Mar–Nov. C 4. 🚶 33 bedrs, 22 bp,
11 bps, TV, Dgs. ✗ mc, LD 8.30. 🅿 CH,
Dgs, CP 5, G 20, Ac, CF, 2 BGf, 12 st. £ BB
£17–£21, DB £34–£42, DBB £22–£26, ②,
Bk £4, L £2·50, D £7·50, cc 1 2 3 5 6,
Dep a.
★★★**Porthminster,** *The Terrace, TR26
2BN.* ✆ Penzance (0736) 795221. RS mid
Dec–mid Jan. C. 🚶 50 bedrs, 25 bp, 25
bps, TV, Dgs. ✗ a l c, mc, at, LD 8.30. 🅿 Lt,
N, ch, TV, Dgs, CP 32, G 10, Ac, sp, sb, sol,
CF, 3 st. £ BB £21–£24·50, DB £42–£49,
DBB £24–£31, WB, ②, Bk £3·50, L £4·50, D
£8, cc 1 2 3 4 5 6.
⬛★★★★**Tregenna Castle,** *TR26 2DE.*
✆ Penzance (0736) 795254. C. 🚶 80
bedrs, 69 bp, 11 bps, 9 ba, TV, Dgs. ✗ mc,
at, LD 9. 🅿 Lt, N, CH, TV, CP 100, U 4, G
12, Ac, sp, gc, tc, sc, rf, con 150, CF, 2 st.
£ BB £15–£36, DB £28–£68, DBB £25–
£46, WB, ⅂, Bk £5, L £6·50, D £11,
cc 1 2 3 4 5 6, Dep b.
🔲★★**Chy-an-Albany** (R), *Albany Ter,
TR26 2BS.* ✆ Penzance (0736) 796759.
Open Mar–Oct & Xmas. C. 🚶 35 bedrs, 9
bps, 7 ba, TV, Dgs. ✗ mc, at, LD 7.45.
🅿 ch, TV, CP 35, Ac, CF, 20 st. £ BB
£10·50–£16, DB £21–£32, DBB £13·50–
£19, WB, ⅂, Bk £3, D £5·50, cc 1 2 3 5 6,
Dep a.
★★**Chy-an-Dour** (Rl) *Trelyon Ave,
TR26 2AD.* ✆ Penzance (0736) 796436.
RS Nov–Feb. C. 🚶 20 bedrs, 12 bp, 2 bps,
4 ba, TV, Dgs. ✗ LD 8. 🅿 Lt, N, CH, TV, CP
22, Ac, con 21, CF, 3 BGf, 0 st, Dis. £ BB
£14·95, DB £29·90, WB, ⅂, Bk £3·45, D
£6·90, cc 1 3, Dep a.
★★**Chy Morvah,** *The Belyars, TR26 2DB.*
✆ Penzance (0736) 796314. Open Apr–
Nov. C. 🚶 40 bedrs, 11 bp, 4 bps, 6 sh, 6
ba. ✗ mc, at, LD 8. 🅿 ch, TV, CP 25, Ac, sp,
CF, 10 BGf, 4 st. £ BB £11·50–£20, DB
£23–£40, DBB £14·50–£23, WB, ⅂, Bk
£3·25, D £5·25, cc 1 3, Dep.
🔲★★**Pedn Olva** (R), *Porthminster Beach,
TR26 2EA.* ✆ Penzance (0736) 796222.
Open Apr–Sep. RS Oct–Mar except Xmas.
C. 🚶 33 bedrs, 14 bp, 16 bps, 2 ba, TV,
Dgs. ✗ mc, at, LD 8. 🅿 ch, TV, Ac, con 50,
CF, 2 BGf, 1 st, Dis. £ BB £15–£24, DB
£28–£44, WB, ⅂, Bk £3·50, D £6·50, Dep.
🔲★**Ocean Breezes** (R), *West Pl,
Barnoon, TR26 1JD.* ✆ Penzance (0736)
795587. Closed Nov. C. 🚶 20 bedrs, 5
bps, 4 sh, 3 ba, TV. ✗ mc, at, LD 7. 🅿 CH,
TV, sol, CF, 2 BGf, 1 st, Dis. £ BB £9·50–
£11, DB £19–£23, ②, cc 1 2 3 5, Dep a.
🔲★**Trecarrell** (R), *Carthew Ter, TR26
1EB.* ✆ Penzance (0736) 795707. Open
Mar–Oct. C. 🚶 14 bedrs, 1 bp, 7 bps, 1 sh,
2 ba. ✗ a l c, mc, at, LD 7.45. 🅿 CH, CP 14,
CF, 7 st. £ BB £10·35–£13·11, DB £18·08–
£24·84, ②, L £4·50, D £5·25, cc 1 2 3 5,
Dep a.
Chy-an-Creet, H, x (R), *Higher
Stennack, TR26 2HA.* ✆ Penzance (0736)
796559. Open Mar–Oct. C. 🚶 13 bedrs, 1
bps, 3 ba, Dgs. 🅿 CH, TV, CP 17, CF, 3 BGf,
1 st. £ BB £7·95–£11·95, DB £15·90–
£25·90, WT (b) £75–£105, DT (b) £11·50–
£15·50, ⅂, Bk £3, D £4·50, cc 1 3.
Dean Court, PH, z (Rl), *Trelyon Av, TR26
2AD.* ✆ Penzance (0736) 796023. Open
Mar–Oct. 🚶 12 bedrs, 5 bp, 7 bps, 1 ba,
TV. 🅿 CH, TV, CP 12, 0 st, P. £ BB £15–
£20, DB £30–£40, WT (b) £111–£130, DT
(b) £19–£25, ⅂.

Dunmar, H, z (R), *Pednolver Ter, TR26 2EL.* ✆ Penzance (0736) 796117. Open Mar–Oct. C. ⇥ 18 bedrs, 1 bp, 4 bps, 6 ba, Dgs. 🏠 Lt, TV, Dgs, CP 20, CF, 1 BGf, 14 st. £ BB £8–£15·75, DB £16–£31·50, WT (b) £79–£115, DT (b) £11–£15, ①, Bk £2·50, D £5.

Hollies, PH, z (Rl), *Talland Rd, TR26 2DF.* ✆ Penzance (0736) 796605. C. ⇥ 12 bedrs, 4 ba. 🏠 CH, TV, CP 12, CF. £ BB £8–£13, DB £16–£26, DT £13–£16, ①, Bk £1·75, D £3.

Longships, PH, z (R), *2 Talland Rd, TR26 2DF.* ✆ Penzance (0736) 798180. Open Mar–Oct. C. ⇥ 24 bedrs, 3 bp, 12 bps, 3 ba, TV, Dgs. 🏠 ch, TV, Dgs, CP 15, CF, 2 BGf, 3 st. £ BB £8–£13, DB £16–£26, WT (b) £75–£112, ①, Bk £2·50, L £2, D £4, cc 1 3.

Pondarosa, G, z (Unl), *10 Porthminster Ter, TR26 2DQ.* ✆ Penzance (0736) 795875. Open Apr–Oct. C 5. ⇥ 10 bedrs, 1 bp, 2 ba. 🏠 CH, TV, CP 8, 3 st. £ BB £7·50–£9·50, DB £15–£22, WT (b) £75–£90, DT (b) £12–£14·50, ①.

Primrose Valley, PH, x (R), *Primrose Valley, TR26 2ED.* ✆ Penzance (0736) 794939. Open Apr–Oct. C. ⇥ 11 bedrs, 5 bp, 1 bps, 2 ba, Dgs. 🏠 ch, TV, CP 11, CF, 0 st. £ BB £8·37–£14·57, DB £16·74–£29·14, WT (b) £86·25–£112·70, DT (b) £13·37–£17·68, ①, Bk £3, D £5.

Rosemorran, PH, y (Rl), *The Belyars, TR26 2AD.* ✆ Penzance (0736) 796359.

St Margaret's, G, z (Rl), *3 Parc Av, TR26 2DN.* ✆ Penzance (0736) 795785.

St Merryn, PH, x (Rl), *Trelyon, TR26 2PF.* ✆ Penzance (0736) 795767. Open Mar–Nov. C. ⇥ 15 bedrs, 3 bp, 1 bps, 4 ba. 🏠 CH, TV, CF, 1 BGf, 1 st. £ BB £7·80–£11·35, DB £15·60–£22·70, WT £63·25–£97·75, DT £11·80–£14·40, ①.

Trelissick, PH, x (Rl), *Bishops Rd, TR26 2BY.* ✆ Penzance (0736) 795035. Open Apr–Oct. C. ⇥ 15 bedrs, 3 bp, 1 bps, 3 ba, Dgs. 🏠 ch, TV, Dgs, CP 10, CF. £ cc 1 3.

Rescue Service: Parc-an-Creet Garage, The Stennack. ✆ Penzance (0736) 795442.
St Ives Motor Co, The Stennack. ✆ Penzance (0736) 795156.

ST JUST-IN-PENWITH Cornwall. Map 2E
Pop 4,020. Penzance 7, London 288, St Ives 12.
EC Thur. **Golf** West Cornwall, Lelant 18h. **See** 15th cent Church, Cape Cornwall, Tin Mining Museum.

Boscean Country, H, y (Rl), *TR19 7QP.* ✆ (0736) 788748. C. ⇥ 10 bedrs, 6 bp, 3 sh, 2 ba. 🏠 CH, TV, CP 12, G 2, CF, 3 st. £ BB £9·75–£11·75, DB £19·50–£23·50, WT (b) £95–£112, DT (b) £15–£17, ①.

Rescue Service: Carn Bosavern Garage, Carn Bosavern. ✆ Penzance (0736) 788336.
Trelew Garage, Nancherrow Hill. ✆ Penzance (0736) 788787.

ST JUST-IN-ROSELAND Cornwall. Map 2F
Pop 1,200. St Austell 17, London 249, Newquay 22, Truro 8.
Golf Truro 18h. **See** 13th cent Church, favourite centre for Artists.

Rose-da-Mar, PH, x (R), *TR2 5JB.* ✆ St Mawes (0326) 270450. Open Apr–Oct, C 7. ⇥ 9 bedrs, 4 bp, 1 bps, 2 ba, Dgs. 🏠 CH,

TV, CP 9, 4 BGf, 1 st, Dis. £ BB £14–£15·50, DB £26–£31, WT (b) £160·40, DT (b) £23·50, ②, Bk £4, L £4, D £8.

ST KEVERNE Cornwall. Map 2F
Pop 1,690. Truro 23, London 278, Falmouth 7½, Helston 11, Redruth 23.
EC Wed. **Golf** Mullion 18h. **See** 13th–15th cent Church, Telstar PO satellite tracking station on Goonhilly Downs.

Three Tuns, I, x, *Village Square, TR12 6NA.* ✆ (0326) 280348. C. ⇥ 5 bedrs, 2 ba, Dgs. 🏠 TV, Dgs, CF. £ BB £10–£13, DB £16–£19, WT (b) £82–£99·50, DT (b) £13–£14·50, ②, Bk £2·50, D £5.

Rescue Service: J H Moore, Zoar Garage. ✆ (0326) 280235.

ST KEW HIGHWAY Cornwall. Map 2D
Pop 285. Camelford 7, London 234, Bodmin 7, Launceston 26, Liskeard 20, Wadebridge 3.
EC Thur. **Golf** St Enodoc 18h.

Kelly Green Farm, F, x (Unl), *Bodmin, PL30 3DT.* ✆ Bodmin (0208) 850275. C. ⇥ 5 bedrs, 2 ba. 🏠 Lt, ch, TV, CP5, CF. £ BB £6·50–£7, DB £13–£14, WT fr £73·50, ①.

ST LAWRENCE Isle of Wight. Map 6F
Pop 700. Ventnor 2, London (Fy) 88, Newport 9.
EC Wed. **Golf** Ventnor 9h. **See** St Lawrence Old Church, St Lawrence Well, Woolverton Manor and ruins (Dean Farm House), Lisle Coombe was the home of the poet Alfred Noyes.

★★**Old Park** (R), *Nr. Ventnor, PO38 1XS.* ✆ Isle of Wight (0983) 852583. Open Mar–Oct & Xmas. C. ⇥ 39 bedrs, 30 bp, 2 ba, Dgs. ✗ mc, at, LD 8.30. 🏠 CH, TV, Dgs, ns, CP 80, sb, sol, CP 180, CF, 6 BGf, 2 st. £ BB £10·50–£19·50, DB £21–£39, DBB £16·50–£25·50, WB, ①, , Bk £3·50, D £6, cc 1 3 6, Dep b.

▣⬛★★**Rocklands,** *PO38 1XH.* ✆ Isle of Wight (0983) 852964. Open May–Sept. C. ⇥ 16 bedrs, 9 bp, 2 bps, 1 sh, 3 ba, annexe 6 bedrs, 2 ba, TV. ✗ a l c, mc, at, LD 6.30. 🏠 CH, TV, CP 20, sp, sb, sol, CF. £ BB fr £16·10, DB fr £29·90, DBB fr £24·73, ②, Bk £2·75, D £11·50.

Woody Bank, PH, x (Rl), *Undercliff Dr, PO38 1XF.* ✆ Isle of Wight (0983) 852610. Open March–Oct. C 5. ⇥ 9 bedrs, 4 bps, 2 ba, Dgs. 🏠 CH, TV, CP 8. £ BB £12–£13, DB £26–£28, WT (b) £122–£129, DT (b) £17·50–£19·50, ①.

ST LAWRENCE-IN-THANET Kent
See RAMSGATE.

ST LEONARDS-ON-SEA East Sussex
See HASTINGS.

ST MABYN Cornwall. Map 2D
Launceston 23, London 234, Bodmin 6½, Wadebridge 4½.

Rescue Service: Longshore Filling Station. ✆ (020 884) 300.

ST MARGARET'S BAY Kent. Map 10D
Pop 2,240. Dover 4, London 78, Margate 20.
EC Wed. **Golf** Kingsdown 18h. **See** 12th cent Church, Dover Patrol Memorial, St Margaret's Bay Trust Garden (statue of Sir Winston Churchill by Oscar Vernon).

Rescue Service: St Margaret's Motors, Reach Rd, St Margaret's at Cliffe. ✆ Dover (0304) 852411.

ST MAWES Cornwall. Map 2F
Pop 1,200. St Austell 18, London 251, Falmouth (Fy) 15, Truro 18 (Fy 9½).
Golf Truro 18h. **See** Castle (16th cent).

★★★**Hotel Tresanton** (R), *Lower Castle Rd, TR2 5DR.* ✆ (0326) 270544. C 10. ⇥ 21 bedrs, 6 bp, 15 bps, TV, Dgs. ✗ LD 9. 🏠 CH, TV, CP 58, con 20. £ WB, L £6·50, D £12·50, cc 2 3 5, Dep a.

▣★★★**Idle Rocks** (R), *Sea Front, TR2 5AN.* ✆ (0326) 270771. Open Mar–Oct. C 6. ⇥ 15 bedrs, 13 bp, 2 bps, 1 ba, TV, Dgs. ✗ mc, at, LD 9.30. 🏠 CH, TV, Ac, con 25, CF, 1 st. £ BB £18–£25, DB £36–£50, WT £175–£224, DBB £27–£33·50, WB, ②, Bk £4·50, L (Sun) £5·50, D £9·50, cc 1 2 3 5 6.

▣★★**Green Lantern** (R), *Marine Par, TR2 5DW.* ✆ (0326) 270502.

▣★★**Rising Sun,** *The Square, TR2 5DJ.* ✆ (0326) 270233.

Rescue Service: Tresanton Co Ltd, T/A St Mawes Garage. ✆ (0326) 270200.

ST MAWGAN Cornwall. Map 2D
Pop 1,245. Wadebridge 11, London 249, Bodmin 15, Newquay 6, St Austell 15.
EC Wed. **Golf** Newquay 18h. **See** 13th cent Church.

▣⬛★**Dalswinton** (R), *TR8 4EZ.* ✆ (0677) 860385. Closed Xmas. C. ⇥ 10 bedrs, 3 bp, 2 bps, 1 sh, 1 ba, Dgs. ✗ mc, at, LD 7.30. 🏠 CH, TV, Dgs, CP 15, sp, CF, 1 BGf. £ BB £9·78–£16·68, DB £19·55–£29·90, DBB £15·33–£22·43, WB, ①, Bk £2·90, D £5·90, cc 1, Dep a.

Pen-y-Morfa H, x, *TR8 4EF.* ✆ (06374) 363. C. ⇥ 11 bedrs, 2 ba, TV, Dgs. ✗ a l c. 🏠 ch, TV, Dgs, CP 45, CF. £ BB £13·20–£17·10, DB £26·40–£34·20, WT £86·25–£130·50, DT £21·25–£25·75, ①, Bk £3·50, L £5, D £8·50.

ST MELLION Cornwall. Map 3C
Saltash 5, London 217, Callington 4, Liskeard 10, Tavistock 12.

★★★**M St Mellion,** *Saltash, PL12 6RN.* ✆ St Dominick (0579) 50101.

ST MICHAELS-ON-WYRE Lancashire. Map 27C
Pop 310. Preston 12, London 223, Lancaster 14, Blackpool 10.
EC Wed. **Golf** Lancaster 9h. **See** 13th cent Church.

Rescue Service: St Michaels Garage (Lancashire) Ltd. ✆ (099 58) 254.

ST MINVER Cornwall. Map 2D
Pop 900. Camelford 10, London 238, Wadebridge 4.
Golf St Enodoc Rock 18h (2). **See** Church.

Rescue Service: S H Lander & Son, Rock Rd. ✆ Trebetherick (020 886) 2351.

ST NEOT Cornwall. Map 3C
Pop 824. Liskeard 5, London 219, Bodmin 9, Launceston 20, St Austell 18, Saltash 18.
EC Thur. **Golf** Looe, Bin Down 18h. **See** Church, Slate Caverns.

Rescue Service: Carlyon Garage. ✆ Dobwalls (0579) 20282.

ST NEOTS Cambridgeshire. Map 15D
Pop 21,595. Biggleswade 11, London 57, Alconbury 10, Bedford 10, Cambridge 19, Huntingdon 10, Kettering 27, Royston 22.

EC Thur. **MD** Thur. **Golf** St Neots 18h.
See Church of St Mary (15th cent), The
Cage (Eaton Socon), 13th cent Church at
Eynesbury.

Rescue Service: D A B Autos, Windmill
Row, High St. ✆ Huntingdon 216490 &
(weekends) Huntingdon 73419.

ST WENN Cornwall. Map 2D
Pop 311. Bodmin 8, London 241,
Newquay 11, St Austell 10, Truro 19.
Golf Newquay 18h, Wadebridge 9h.

■⚑★**Wenn Manor** (Rl), *PL30 5PS.*
✆ Roche (0726) 890240. C. ⇒ 9 bedrs, 6
bp, 1 bps, 1 ba, Dgs. ✗ mc, at, LD 8.30.
⬚ CH, TV, Dgs, CP 20, G 1, sp, CF, 1 st.
£ BB £11–£14, DB £22–£28, DBB £16.50–
£19.50, WB, ②. Bk £2.50, D £5.50, cc 1 3.

SALCOMBE Devon. Map 3F
Pop 2,451. Kingsbridge 6½, London 211,
Plymouth 22.
Golf Thurlestone 18h. **See** Fort Charles
(Castle ruins), Sharpitor Rocks,
Overbecks (Sharpitor—Gardens and small
museum) 1½ m SW, Bolt Head.
ⓘ Market St. ✆ Salcombe (054 884)
2736.

■★★★**Bolt Head,** *Cliff Rd, TQ8 8LL.*
✆ (054 884) 2780. Open Apr–Oct & Xmas.
C. ⇒ 29 bedrs, 27 bp, 2 bps, TV, Dgs.
✗ a l c, mc, at, LD 9. ⬚ CH, CP 41, sp, con,
CF, 2 BGf, 4 st. £ DBB £25–£32, WB, ②, Bk
£4.50, L £5, D £12.50, cc 1 2 3 5, Dep b.
■★★★**St Elmo,** *Sandhills Rd, TQ8 8JP.*
✆ (054 884) 2233. Open Apr–Oct. C.
⇒ 25 bedrs, 21 bp, 4 bps, TV, Dgs. ✗ mc,
at, LD 8.30. ⬚ CH, CP 40, Ac, con 45, CF, 3
st. £ BB £20.12–£24.15, DB £40.24–
£48.30, DBB £23–£32.20, WB, ②. Bk £4, D
£10.85, cc 1 3.
■★★★**Tides Reach,** *Cliff Rd, TQ8 8LJ.*
✆ (054 884) 3466. Closed Dec–Feb.
⇒ 40 bedrs, 36 bp, 4 bps, TV, Dgs. ✗ a l c,
mc, at, LD 10. ⬚ Lt, N, CH, CP 100, sp, sc,
sb, sol, con 30, 4 st. £ BB £27.40 (low
season), DB £54.80 (low season only),
DBB £32–£48, WB, ②. Bk £4.50, D £12.50,
cc 1 2 3 5, Dep a.
■★★**Castle Point** (R), *Sandhills Rd, TQ8
8JP.* ✆ (054 884) 2167. Open Easter–Oct.
C 6. ⇒ 20 bedrs, 7 bp, 46ps, 1 sh, 4 ba, TV.
✗ mc, at, LD 8. ⬚ ch, TV, CP 40, U 3, con
30, 1 st. £ BB £12–£19, DB £24–£40, DBB
£16–£27, WB, ②. Bk £3.50, D £8, cc 1 3 5,
Dep a.
■★**Grafton Towers** (R), *Moult Rd,
TQ8 8LG.* ✆ (054 884) 2882. Open Apr 1–
early Oct. C. ⇒ 15 bedrs, 7 bp, 2 bps, 3 ba,
TV, Dgs. ✗ mc, at, LD 8.30 (9.30 Fri, Sat).
⬚ ch, CP 10, CF, 22 st. £ BB £10.50–£20,
DB £21–£40, DBB £15–£26, WB, ②. Bk
£2.50, L £3, D £8, cc 1 3 6, Dep a.
■★**Melbury,** (R), *Devon Rd, TQ8 8HJ.*
✆ (054 884) 2883. Open Apr–Sep, C 5.
⇒ 14 bedrs, 4 bp, 5 bps, 2 ba. ✗ mc, LD
7.30. ⬚ ch, TV, CP 18, CF. £ BB fr £10.50,
DB fr £21, DBB £14–£18, WB, ②. Bk £2.50,
D £5.80.
■★**Sunny Cliff** (R), *Cliff Rd, TQ8 8JX.*
✆ (054 884) 2207. Open Apr–Oct C.
⇒ 15 bedrs, bp, 4 sh, 4 ba, annexe 3
bedrs, 1 ba, Dgs. ✗ mc, at, LD 8. ⬚ TV, CP
14, G 1, Ac, sp, pf, CF, 6 st. £ BB £14–£18,
DB £28–£36, WT £117.50–£150, DBB
£18.50–£23.50, WB, ①, Bk £3, D £6.90,
Dep a.
■★**Wells,** *Herbert Rd, TQ8 8HU.*
✆ (054 884) 3484. C 5. ⇒ 14 bedrs, 6 bp,

6 bps, 1 ba, TV, Dgs. ✗ a l c, mc, at, LD 8.
⬚ CH, TV, CP 20, 3 BGf, 3 st. £ BB £12–
£14, DB £24–£28, DBB £18.95–£20.95,
WB, ①, Bk £2.50, D £6.95, cc 1 2 3 4 5 6,
Dep a.
Charborough House, PH, z (R), *Devon
Rd, TQ8 8HB.* ✆ (054 884) 2260. Open
Mar–Oct. C. ⇒ 9 bedrs, 1 bp, 5 bps, 2 sh, 1
ba, TV. ✗ a l c. ⬚ CH, TV, CP 9. CF, 1 BGf,
0 st. £ BB £11.50–£17.50, DB £23–£30,
WT £98–£135, DT £18.50–£22, ②, Bk
£3.25, L £4, D £7.
Lyndhurst, H, z (R), *Bonaventure Rd,
TQ8 8BG.* ✆ (054 884) 2481. Closed
Xmas. C 7. ⇒ 8 bedrs,4 bps, 2 sh, 1 ba, ns,
TV. ⬚ CH, TV, ns, CP 8. £ BB £11.25, DB
£19–£20, WT (b) £93, DT (b) £15, ①, Bk
£2.75, D £5.50, cc 1 3.
Old Porch House, G, x (R),
Shadycombe Rd, TQ8 8DJ. ✆ (054 884)
2157.
Penn Torr, H, x (R), *Herbert Rd, TQ8
8HN.* ✆ (054 884) 2234. Open Mar–Oct. C
4. ⇒ 10 bedrs, 2 bp, 3 bps. ⬚ TV, CP 9, 1
st. £ BB £11.50, DB £23–£27, WT (b)
£80.50, DT (b) £14.95, ②, Bk £2.50, D
£5.50.
Stoneycroft, PH, z (R), *Devon Rd, TQ8
8HJ.* ✆ (054 884) 2218. Closed Dec. C 5.
⇒ 10 bedrs, 9 bps, 1 ba. ⬚ CH, TV, ns, CP
15, U 1, CF, 2 BGf, 2 st. £ BB £10–£12, DB
£20–£24, WT £87.50–£101.50, DT
£15.50–£17.50, ①, Bk £2, L £3.50, D £5.50.
Trennels, PH, y (Unl), *Herbert Rd, TQ8
8HR.* ✆ (054 884) 2500. Open Mar–Nov. C
12. ⇒ 11 bedrs, 2 ba. ⬚ CH, TV, CP 8, G 1.
£ BB £8.50–£9.50, DB £17–£19, WT (b)
£73–£77, (c) £48–£52, DT (b) £12.50–
£13.50.

SALE Greater Manchester (Cheshire).
Map 20B
Pop 57,824. Altrincham 3, London 183,
Macclesfield 17, Manchester 5, Stockport
8, Walkden 8.
EC Wed. **Golf** Altrincham 18h. **See** St
Martin's Church, founded 1304, rebuilt
1703.

Repairer: Gordon Stewart Motors Ltd,
Morris House, 77 Cross St.
✆ 061-969 1421.
Specialist Body Repairer: Gordon Stewart
Motors Ltd, Cross St. ✆ 061-973 2241.
Rescue Service: Robroy Garages Ltd,
Cottage Garage, 375 Northenden Rd.
✆ 061-973 0534.

SALFORD Greater Manchester
(Lancashire). Map 20A
See also MANCHESTER.
Pop 246,400. Manchester 2, London 186,
M602 Motorway 4, Altrincham 7, St
Helens 21, Walkden 6½, Warrington 15,
Wigan 16.
EC Wed. **MD** Mon, Wed, Fri, Sat. **Golf**
Swinton Park 18h. **See** RC Cathedral,
Royal Museum and Art Gallery, Natural
History and Mining Museum, 15th cent
Ordsall Hall (Period Museum).

■★★**Racecourse,** *Littleton Rd, M7 0TN.*
✆ 061-792 1420.
■★**Beaucliffe** (R), *254 Eccles Old Rd,
M6 8ES.* ✆ 061-789 5092. C 6. ⇒ 23
bedrs, 1 bp, 19 bps, 3 sh, 1 ba, Dgs. ✗ mc,
at, LD 8. ⬚ CH, TV, CP 40, G 2, CF, 3 BGf, 2
st. £ BB fr £18, DB fr £25, DBB fr £22, ②,
Bk £3.50, L £5.50, D £5.50, cc 1 2 3 4 5 6.
Hazeldean, H, z, (R), *467 Bury New Rd,
Kersal Bar, M7 0NX.* ✆ 061-792 6667. C.
⇒ 21 bedrs, 11 bp, 6 bps, 2 ba, TV, Dgs.

⬚ CH, TV, Dgs, CP 21, U 1, CF. £ BB
£21.51–£26.57, DB £35.42–£40.48, ①, Bk
£4.50, L £3.50, D £6, cc 1 2 3 5.

SALHOUSE Norfolk. M. Area 16A
Norwich 6, London 117, Aylsham 13,
Beccles 23, Cromer 23, Great Yarmouth
15.

Rescue Service: Salhouse Service Station,
Mill Rd. ✆ Norwich (0603) 720447.

SALISBURY Wiltshire. Map 6C
Pop 36,000. Basingstoke 36, London 83,
Amesbury 8, Andover 18, Blandford
Forum 23, Devizes 25, Lyndhurst 19,
Ringwood 16, Romsey 15, Shaftesbury
20, Southampton 22, Wantage 42,
Warminster 20, Wincanton 24, Winchester
23.
See Plan, p. 317.
EC Wed. **MD** Tue, Sat. **P** See Plan. **Golf**
High Post 18h, South Wilts 18h. **See**
Cathedral (404 ft spire), the North
Canonry, Bishop's Palace (now Choir
School), Mompesson House (Nat Trust),
Malmesbury House, Old Castle
(monument), Guildhall and War Memorial,
Ye Halle of John Halle, Salisbury and S
Wilts Museum, 16th cent Joiners Hall,
Churches, Old Inns, House of John a'Port,
Old Sarum 2 m N, Wilton House 3 m W,
Wilton Royal Carpet Factory at Wilton,
Breamore House 7 m S, Stonehenge 10 m
NNW.
ⓘ 10 Endless St. ✆ Salisbury (0722) 4956.

★★★**Red Lion,** *Milford St, SP1 2AN.*
✆ (0722) 23334. C. ⇒ 52 bedrs, 40 bp, 1
sh, 2 ba, TV, Dgs. ✗ a l c, mc, at, LD 8.45.
⬚ N, ch, Dgs, CP 6, G 10, Ac, con 150, CF,
0 st. £ BB £22.50–£31, DB £45–£48.50,
DT fr £36, DBB £30, WB ①, Bk £4.50, L
£4.50, D £8.50, cc 1 2 3 4 5 6, Dep.
★★★**White Hart** (TH), *St John St, SP1
2SD.* ✆ (0722) 27476. C. ⇒ 72 bedrs, 56
bp, 4 ba, TV, Dgs. ✗ a l c, mc, at, LD 9.30.
⬚ N, CH, Dgs, CP 85, Ac, con 80, CF, 0 st.
£ BB £31.50–£37, DB £46.50–£53, WB, ①,
cc 1 2 3 4 5 6, Dep (Xmas).
■★★**Cathedral,** *7 Milford St, SP1 2AJ.*
✆ (0722) 20144. RS Dec 25, C. ⇒ 30
bedrs, 11 bp, 4 sh, 5 ba, TV. ✗ a l c, mc, LD
9. ⬚ Lt, N, CH, Ac, con 20, CF, 2 st. £ BB
£16.50–£25.50, DB £26.50–£39.50, DBB
£20.50–£27.50, WB, ②, Bk £3.50, L fr
£3.25, D fr £5, cc 1 3.
★**King's Arms,** *St Johns St, SP1 2SB.*
✆ (0722) 27629. C. ⇒ 13 bedrs, 5 bp, 3
sh, 4 ba, annexe 3 bedrs, 1 sh, 1 ba, TV,
Dgs. ✗ a l c, mc, LD 9. ⬚ CH, TV, Dgs, CP
30, Ac, con 25, CF, 1 st. ⬚ WB, Bk £4, L
£5.50, D £6.50, cc 1 2 3 4 5 6.
★**White Horse,** *Castle St, SP1 1BN.*
✆ (0722) 27844. C. ⇒ 12 bedrs, 4 bp, 8
bps, 2 ba, Dgs. ✗ a l c. ⬚ CH, TV. £ BB
£12–£17, DB £27–£35, ①, Bk £3.50, L
£2.50, D £5.95, cc 1 3 5.
Byways House, G, z (Unl), *31 Fowler's
Rd, SP1 2QP.* ✆ (0722) 28364. C. ⇒ 17
bedrs, 6 bps, 4 ba. ⬚ CH, TV, CP 12, U 1,
CF, 6 BGf, 2 st. ✗ mc. £ BB £9–£11.50, DB
£23, WT £73.50–£80.50, ①, Bk £3.
Hayburn Wyke, G, z (Unl), *72 Castle Rd,
SP1 2PX.* ✆ (0722) 24141. C 6. ⇒ 6
bedrs, 1 bps, 1 ba, Dgs. ⬚ TV, CP 5, G 1, 3
st. £ DB £17–£24, ①.
Holmhurst, G, z (Unl), *Downton Rd, SP2
8AR.* ✆ (0722) 23164. C 5. ⇒ 8 bedrs, 3
bps, 1 ba, Dgs. ⬚ CH, TV, ns, CP 8, 2 BGf, 1
st. £ DB £8–£9, DB £15–£19, ①, Bk £3.

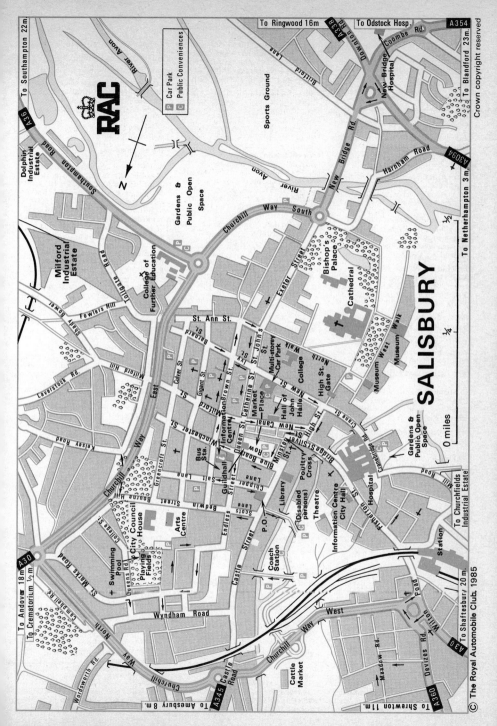

SALISBURY

To Ringwood 16m   To Odstock Hosp.

A354

To Blandford 23m.

New Bridge Hospital

Downton Rd.

Coombe Rd.

A3094

To Netherhampton 3m.

Harnham Road

Sports Ground

Bishop's Palace

Cathedral

Museum West Walk

Museum Walk

Gardens & Public Open Space

Churchill Way South

River Avon

New Bridge Rd.

Exeter Street

P Car Park
C Public Conveniences

RAC

River Avon

Dolphin Industrial Estate

A36 To Southampton 22m

Milford Industrial Estate

Southampton Road

College of Further Education

Fowlers Hill

Milford Hill

St. Ann St.

Barnard St.

Gigant St.

Brown St.

Catherine St.

St. John's St.

Multi-storey Car Park

College

High St. Gate

Gardens & Public Open Space

0 miles

¼

½

½

Leverstock Rd.

Kelsey Road

Milford Hill

Culver St.

St. Edmund's Church St.

Market Place

Hall of John Halle

New St.

High St.

Crane St.

St. Ann's

Information Centre

New Canal

Minster St.

Queen St.

Blue Boar Row

Poultry Cross

Bridge St.

Silver St.

Mill Road

Crane Bridge Rd.

Churchill Way East

Winchester St.

Salt Lane

Chipper Lane

Endless Street

Scots Lane

Bedwin Street

Greencroft St.

Bourne Hill

College St.

Guildhall

Library

Theatre

Information Centre
City Hall

Fisherton Hospital

To Churchfields Industrial Estate

Bus Sta.

Arts Centre

City Council House

Swimming Pool

Queens Rd.

St. Marks Road

Playing Fields

Disabled persons

P.O.

Coach Station

Castle Street

Wyndham Road

A30 To Andover 18m

To Crematorium ½ m.

North Street

Scamblers Rd.

Wordsworth Rd.

Devizes Rd.

A345 To Amesbury 8m.

Castle Road

Churchill Way West

Cattle Market

A360 To Shrewton 11m.

Wilton Road

A30 To Shaftesbury 20m.

Station

The Warren, G, z (Unl), *High St,*
Downton, SP5 3PG. ✆ Downton (0725)
20263.

Repairers: Collets-Avon Motors Ltd,
Brunel Rd, Church Fields. ✆ (0722) 23131.
W Goddard & Co Ltd, 41 Winchester St.
✆ (0722) 336681.
Henleys (West) Ltd, Southampton Rd.
✆ (0722) 33525.
Rescue Service: Graham Dimmer Motors,
Newton Rd, Churchfield Trading Estate.
✆ (0722) 20193 and (0722) 29274.
Wheels Automobile Service, Stephenson
Rd, Churchfields. ✆ (0722) 333666.
Wood Motors, Middleton Rd. ✆ (0722)
24343.

SALTASH Cornwall. Map 3C.
Pop 12,960. Exeter 42, London 212,
Ashburton 27, Launceston 20, Liskeard
13, Looe 15, Plymouth 4, Tavistock 14,
Totnes 23.
EC Thur. **Golf** St Mellion 18h. **See** Tamar
Road Bridge, Royal Albert Rly Bridge
(designed by Brunel), Ince Castle, remains
of Tremanton Castle, Mary Newman's
cottage.

Holland Inn, M, *Hatt, PL12 6PJ.*
✆ (075 55) 3635. Closed Xmas. C. ✉ 30
bedrs, 30 bp, TV, Dgs. ✗ a l c ⌂ Dgs, CP
30, CF, 1 st. £ BB £22, DB £35, ▯, Bk £4, L
£8, D £10, cc 1 3.

Rescue Service: Carkeel Motors Ltd,
Saltash Trading Estate. ✆ (075 55) 2297.
Rogers Garage, Moorlands La, Burraton.
✆ (075 55) 5222.
Westward Engineering, Moorlands View
Industrial Estate. ✆ (075 55) 7480.

SALTBURN-BY-THE-SEA Cleveland.
Map 24D
Guisborough 6, London 252, Darlington
29, Middlesbrough 12, Scarborough 35.
See Guisborough Priory, Chapel Beck
Gallery Guisborough.

⬛★★★**Grinkle Park,** *Grinkle Lane,*
Easington, TS13 4UB. ✆ Guisborough
(0287) 40515. C. ✉ 20 bedrs, 16 bp, 2 ba,
TV, Dgs. ✗ mc, at, LD 9. ⌂ CH, TV, CP 70,
CF, 1 st. £ BB £15·45–£32·15, DB £29·30–
£42·75, WB, ▯, Bk £3·85, L £6·40, D
£10·95, cc 1 3.

SALTFORD Avon. M. Area 5B
Pop 18,995. Bath 4½, London 109, Bristol
7, Radstock 13, Shepton Mallet 23, Wells
19.
EC Wed. **Golf** Saltford 18h.

Rescue Service: Saltford Motor Services
Ltd, 491 Bath Rd. ✆ (022 17) 3172.

SAMPFORD PEVERELL Devon. Map 4F
Pop 937. M5 Motorway 1, London 157,
Exeter 19, Honiton 15, Taunton 15,
Tiverton 5.
Golf Tiverton 18h. **See** 12th cent Church.

Green Headland, H, y (R), *EX16 7BJ.*
✆ Tiverton (0884) 820255. C. ✉ 6 bedrs,
1 sh, 1 ba, Dgs. ✗ a l c ⌂ CH, TV, Dgs, CP
100, CF, 2 st. £ BB £10–£12, DB £19–£23,
DT (b) £15–£28, ▣, Bk £3, L £4·50, D
£4·75, cc 1.

SANDBACH Cheshire. Map 19D
Pop 14,806. London 161, M6 Motorway 1,
Congleton 2, Knutsford 12, Middlewich 5,
Nantwich 9½, Newcastle-under-Lyme 11,
Stoke-on-Trent 13.

EC Tue. **MD** Thur. **Golf** Sandbach 9h,
Malkins Bank 18h. **See** Remarkable
sculptured Saxon Crosses in Market Pl,
17th cent Old Hall, now hotel, 17th cent
'Black Bear' Inn, St Mary's Parish Church.
▯ Sandbach Service Area M6.
✆ Sandbach (093 67) 60460.

★★★**Chimney House,** *Congleton Rd,*
CW11 0ST. ✆ (093 67) 4141. C. ✉ 20
bedrs, 20 bp, TV, Dgs. ✗ a l c, mc, at, LD
10. ⌂ N, CH, CP 80, con 20, CF, 4 BGf, 0 st,
Dis. £ BB £35–£40, DB £45–£50, WB, ▯,
Bk £4·50, L £5·50, D £8·50, cc 1 2 3 5,
Dep b.

★★★**M Saxon Cross** (R), *Holmes Chapel*
Rd, CW11 9SE. (M6 Junction 17).
✆ (093 67) 3281. Closed Dec 24–26. C.
✉ 52 bedrs, 52 bp, TV, Dgs. ✗ a l c, mc,
LD 9.30. ⌂ N, CH, CP 200, Ac, con 60, CF,
52 BGf, 1 st, Dis. £ BB £29·50, DB £37,
WB, ▯, Bk £4, L 4·50, D £8, cc 1 2 3 5 6,
Dep b.

⬛★★**Old Hall,** *Newcastle Rd, CW11 0AJ.*
✆ (093 67) 61221.

Rescue Service: A & D Beech, Common
Mill, Congleton Rd. ✆ (093 67) 61176.
Ettiley Heath Garage, Elton Rd.
✆ (093 67) 60625.
Sandbach Service Station Co Ltd,
Bradwell Rd. ✆ (093 67) 3395.

SANDBANKS Dorset
See POOLE.

SANDFORD Avon. M. Area 5A
Pop 1,500. Bath 25, London 129,
Bridgwater 21, Bristol 14, Radstock 19,
Wells 16, Weston-super-Mare 7.
Golf Worlebury 18h.

Rescue Service: Sandford Service Station.
✆ Churchill (0934) 852380.

SANDIACRE Derbyshire. Map 22D
Pop 8,065. 1 m W of Stapleford. M1
Motorway 1, London 123, Ashby-de-la-
Zouch 17, Chesterfield 26, Derby 8,
Loughborough 12, Mansfield 20, Matlock
25, Nottingham 6½.
Golf Erewash, Stanton 18h. **See** Parish
Church.

★★★**M Post House** (TH), *Bostocks La,*
NG10 5NJ. ✆ Nottingham (0602)
397800. C. ✉ 106 bedrs, 106 bp, TV, Dgs.
✗ a l c, mc, at, LD 10. ⌂ N, CH, Dgs, CP
180, Ac, con 70, CF, 53 BGf, 0 st, Dis. £ BB
£44, DB £56·50, WB, ▯, cc 1 2 3 4 5 6.

SANDIWAY Cheshire. Map 19D
Pop 5,516 (Inc Cuddington). Middlewich
7½, London 173, Chester 13, Nantwich 12,
Northwich 3½, Warrington 11, Whitchurch
17.
Golf Sandiway 18h. **See** Cheshire Hunt
Kennels.

MC Repairer: Spanns Garage, Daleford
La. ✆ (0606) 882219.
Rescue Service: J P Moores & Co
(Sandiway) Ltd, Blue Cap Garage, Chester
Rd. ✆ (0606) 883288.
Spanns Garage, Daleford La. ✆ (0606)
882219.

SANDON Essex. M. Area 17F
Pop 1,447. Chelmsford 2½, London 35,
Southend 18.
Golf Chelmsford 18h. **See** Church with
massive 16th cent tower.

Rescue Service: J Barr & Son (Engineers)
Ltd, Southend Rd, nr Chelmsford.
✆ Chelmsford (0245) 71113.

SANDOWN Isle of Wight. Map 6F
Pop 8,050. Ryde 6, London (Fy) 80,
Newport 8½, Shanklin 2.
EC Wed. **MD** Mon. **Golf** Sandown and
Shanklin 18h. **See** Geological Museum,
Yaverland Church and Manor House, Zoo,
Brading Roman Villa, Robin Hill Country
Park.
▯ Esplanade. ✆ Isle of Wight
(0983) 403886.

⬛★★★**Broadway Park,** *Melville St,*
PO36 9DJ. ✆ Isle of Wight (0983)
402007. Open June–Aug. RS May & Sep.
C. ✉ 53 bedrs, 39 bp, 1 bps, 3 ba, TV.
✗ mc, at, LD 8.30. ⌂ Lt, N, CH, TV, ns, CP
100, Ac, sp, tc, con 200, CF, 3 BGf, 5 st.
£ BB £15–£21, DB £30–£42, DBB £20–
£29, ▣, L £3·50, D £7·50, cc 1 2 3 6, Dep b.
★★★**Melville Hall,** *Melville St, PO36*
9DH. ✆ Isle of Wight (0983) 403794. C 3.
✉ 37 bedrs, 21 bp, 3 bps, 3 ba, TV. ✗ mc,
at, LD 8.30. ⌂ N, ch, TV, CP 30, Ac, sp, CF
5 st. £ BB £13–£23, DB £26–£46, WT
£135–£195, DT £22·50–£32·50, DBB £17–
£27, ▣, Bk £4·50, L £5·50, D fr £6·50,
cc 1 2 3, Dep.
⬛★**Rose Bank,** *High St, PO36 8DA.*
✆ Isle of Wight (0983) 403854. Closed
Xmas wk. C 6. ✉ 1 bedrs, 3 sh, 1 ba, Dgs.
✗ mc, at, LD 7.30. ⌂ CH, TV, Dgs, 4 BGf, 2
st. £ BB £10–£12, DB £20–£24, DBB £14–
£16, ▣, Bk £3, L £4·25, D £6·50, Dep a.
Cherry Trees, PH, x (Rl), *Nunwell St,*
PO36 9DE. ✆ Isle of Wight (0983)
402504. Open Feb–Oct. C. ✉ 12 bedrs, 2
bp, 3 bps, 2 ba. ⌂ CH, TV, CP 5, CF. £ BB
£9·50–£15, DB £18·40–£32·30, WT (b)
£69–£94·30, (c) £11·50–£16, ▯.
Chester Lodge, H, y (Unl), *7 Beachfield*
Rd, PO36 8NA. ✆ Isle of Wight (0983)
402773. Open Feb–Nov. C 3. ✉ 17 bedrs,
4 ba, Dgs. ⌂ CH, TV, Dgs, ns, CP 15, CF, 3
BGf, 2 st. £ BB £8·05–£8·63, DB £16·10–
£17·26, WT (b) £74·75–£80·05, (c)
£11·50–£12·65, ▣, Bk £2·30, D £3·45. ▲
Rostrevor, PH, z (Rl), *96 Sandown Rd,*
PO36 9JX. ✆ Isle of Wight (0983)
402775.
St Catherine's, H, x (R), *1 Winchester*
Park Rd. PO36 8HJ. ✆ Isle of Wight
(0983) 402392. Closed Dec. C. ✉ 18
bedrs, 5 bp, 4 bps, 2 sh, 2 ba, TV. ⌂ CH, TV,
CP 8, CF, 4 BGf, 1 st, Dis. £ BB £13·50–
£16·25, DB £27–£32·50, ▯, Bk £2·50, D
£5·50, cc 1 3 6.
Trevallyn, PH, z (R), *32 Broadway, PO36*
9BY. ✆ Isle of Wight (0983) 402373.

Rescue Service: Lake Motors, Louis Rd,
Lake. ✆ Isle of Wight (0983) 402900.
Manor House Auto Services, Lake Hill,
Lake. ✆ Isle of Wight (0983) 405347.
Sandown Garage Co Ltd, Avenue Rd.
✆ Isle of Wight (0983) 402581.

SANDWICH Kent. Map 10D
Pop 4,500. Canterbury 12, London 70,
Dover 10, Folkestone 15, Margate 8½.
EC Wed. **MD** Thur. **Golf** Prince's 27h. **See**
Cinque Port, The Barbican (Tudor),
Guildhall (paintings), Fisher Gate, old
houses, old Town Walls, Richborough
Castle 1½ m NW, Richborough Roman fort.

★★★**Bell,** *The Quay, CT13 9EF.* ✆ (0304)
613388. C. ✉ 33 bedrs, 16 bp, 1 bps, 9 ba,
TV, Dgs. ✗ a l c, mc, at, LD 10. ⌂ N, CH,

Dgs, CP 10, Ac, con 120, CF, 1 st. **£** BB
£22–£24·50, DB £35–£39·50, WT £195–
£227·50, DT £29·50–£39, DBB £24–
£33·85, WB, ①, Bk £3·50, L £5, D £8·50,
cc 1 2 3 5 6, Dep b.

SANDY Bedfordshire. Map 15D
Pop 8,345. Biggleswade 4, London 49,
Alconbury 18, Bedford 8, Cambridge 22,
Huntingdon 16, Luton 22, Royston 17.
EC Thur. **MD** Fri. **Golf** John o'Gaunt 18h.
See Parish Church.

Rescue Service: Sandy Auto Services,
No 1 Unit, London Rd, Industrial Estate.
✆ (0767) 80929.

SAUL Gloucestershire. M. Area 13F
Pop 250. Cirencester 21, London 109,
Bath 35, Bristol 27, Chepstow 26,
Gloucester 9, Tetbury 17.
EC Sat. **Golf** Gloucester CC 18h. **See**
Church (Lychgate).

Repairer: Silvey Bros, Saul & District
Garage. **✆** Gloucester (0452) 740227.

SAUNTON Devon. Map 4C
Barnstaple 7, London 200, Dunster 39,
Ilfracombe 10, Lynmouth 23.
Golf Saunton 18h. **See** Five miles of
excellent sands.

★★★★Saunton Sands, *EX33 1LQ.*
✆ (0271) 890212. C. **☞** 90 bedrs, 89 bp, 1
bps, 3 ba, TV. **✗** a l c, mc, at, LD 9.30. ⓗ Lt,
N, CH, TV, CP 200, G 4, sp, tc, sc, sb, sol,
con 200, CF, 12 BGf, 3 st. **£** BB £27–£33,
DB £44·85–£66, DBB £63–£85, WB, ②, Bk
£3·75, L £6·90, D £10·20, cc 1 2 3 5 6,
Dep.▲

SAVERNAKE Wiltshire. Map 6A
Pop 240. Newbury 18, London 72,
Amesbury 20, Andover 18, Marlborough 5,
Pewsey 7, Romsey 32, Salisbury 26,
Wantage 23.
EC Wed. **MD** Wed & Sat. **Golf**
Marlborough 18h. **See** Forest 4,000 acres,
4 m avenue of beech trees.

★★Savernake Forest, *Marlborough,
SN8 3AY.* **✆** Marlborough (0672) 810206.
C. **☞** 12 bedrs, 12 bp, Dgs. **✗** mc, at, LD 9.
ⓗ CH, TV, CP 80, pf, con 30, CF, 1 st. **£** BB
£22–£28, DB £38–£44, DT £37·50–£43·50,
DBB £32·50–£38·50, WB, ①, Bk £3·50, D
£10·50, cc 1 2 3 5 6, Dep a.

SAWBRIDGEWORTH Herts. Maps 15F
and 17F
Pop 7,777. Epping 8, London 26, Bishop's
Stortford 4, Brentwood 18, Chelmsford
16, Hoddesdon 9½.
EC Thur. **Golf** Bishop's Stortford 18h. **See**
Great St Mary's Parish Church.

Rescue Service: Fullers Motors, 94
London Rd. **✆** Bishop's Stortford (0270)
724191.
White's Garage (Sawbridgeworth) Ltd,
London Rd. **✆** Bishop's Stortford (0279)
723401.

SAWSTON Cambridgeshire. Maps 15D
& 17E
Bishop's Stortford 20, London 51, M11
Motorway 4, Cambridge 6½, Newmarket
15, Royston 12.

Rescue Service: E F G Moule (D & L
Motors), The Garage, Cambridge Rd.
✆ Cambridge (0223) 833116.

SAXMUNDHAM Suffolk. Map 17A
Pop 2,371. Ipswich 20, London 94,
Aldeburgh 7, Framlingham 7, Lowestoft
23
EC Thur. **MD** Alt Wed. **Golf** Aldeburgh
18h. **See** Church.

Rescue Service: Samkins of Saxmundham
Ltd, Chantry Rd. **✆** (0728) 2071.

SCALBY North Yorkshire. Map 24B
Pop 9,138. Scarborough 2½, London 216,
Bridlington 20, Pickering 18, Whitby 17,
York 43.
Golf North & South Cliff 18h (2). **See**
Church, Nature Walks.

♨★★Wrea Head, *YO13 0PB.*
✆ Scarborough (0723) 378211.

SCARBOROUGH North Yorkshire. Map
24B
Pop 41,770. Driffield 21, London 213,
Beverley 33, Bridlington 17, Malton 24,
Pickering 16, Whitby 18.
See Plan, p. 322.
EC Wed. **MD** Thur. **P** See Plan. **Golf** North
Cliff 18h, South Cliff 18h. **See** Spa with
Ballroom, Theatre and Concert Hall, Castle
ruins, St Mary's Church (Anne Brontë's
grave), Art Gallery, Natural History,
Archaeological Museums, Zoo and
Marineland, Oliver's Mount (War Memorial
and Motor Cycle Racing Circuit),
Miniature Rly.
⑦ St Nicholas Cliff. **✆** Scarborough
(0723) 72261.

★★★★Crown, *Esplanade, YO11 2AG.*
✆ (0723) 373491. C. **☞** 80 bedrs, 80 bp,
TV. **✗** mc, at, LD 9. ⓗ Lt, N, CH, TV, CP 50,
U 5, Ac, sol, con CF. **£** BB £21–£25,
DB £41–£48·50, WB, ②, Bk £4·50, L (Sun)
£6·50, D £7·50, cc 1 2 3 5 6.

★★★★Holbeck Hall, *Seacliff Rd, South
Cliff, YO11 2XX.* **✆** (0723) 374374. Closed
Jan–Feb. C. **☞** 30 bedrs, 30 bp, TV. **✗** a l c,
mc, at, LD 9.30. ⓗ N, CH, TV, CP 50, Ac, con
100, CF, 1 st. **£** BB £25–£30, DB £50–£60,
WT £260–£310, DT £45–£50, DBB £40–
£45, WB, ①, Bk £5, L £5·75, D £9·95,
cc 1 2 3 5▲

★★★★Royal, *St Nicholas St, YO11 2HE.*
✆ (0723) 364333. C. **☞** 137 bedrs, 137
bp, 2 ba, TV. **✗** a l c, mc, at, LD 9.
ⓗ Lt, N, CH, TV, Dgs, Ac, sp, sb, sol, gym,
con 250, CF, 4 st. **£** BB £25–£30, DB £42–
£50, WT £245–£280, DT £38–£40, DBB
£32–£34, WB, ①, Bk £4, L £4, D £8·50,
cc 1 2 3 4 5 6, Dep a.

★★★Palm Court (R), *St Nicholas Cliff,
YO11 2ES.* **✆** (0723) 368161. C. **☞** 51
bedrs, 51 bp, TV. **✗** mc, at, LD 9. ⓗ Lt, N,
CH, CP 6, sp, con 120, CF, 6 st. **£** BB £23,
DB £46, DT £33, DBB £29, WB, ②, Bk £4, L
fr £4, D £6, cc 2 3, Dep a.

★★Brooklands (R), *Esplanade Gdns,
YO11 2AW.* **✆** (0723) 376576. Open Apr–
Oct. C. **☞** 53 bedrs, 34 bp, 4 ba, IV. **✗** mc,
at, LD 6.30. ⓗ Lt, N, CH, TV, Ac, con 150,
CF, 9 st. **£** BB £13·80–£15·80, DB £25·60–
£29·60, WT £149·80–£156·80, DT
£21·40–£22·40, DBB £19·20–£21·20, WB,
②, Bk £2·75, L £3, D £7, cc 1 3, Dep a.

★★Carlton, *Belmont Rd, YO11 2AA.*
✆ (0723) 60938.

★★Clifton, *Queens Parade, YO12 7HX.*
✆ (0723) 375691. Closed Xmas, RS lunch
Oct–May. C. **☞** 70 bedrs, 36 bp, 34 bps, 2
ba. **✗** mc, at, LD 8. ⓗ Lt, N, CH, TV, CP 50,
Ac, con 120, CF, 0 st. **£** BB £14–£14·75,
DB £28–£29·50, WT £163–£170, DT

£24·35–£25·75, DBB £19·85–£21, WB, ①,
Bk £3·30, L £4·50, D £5·85, Dep b.

★★Crescent, *The Crescent, YO11 2PP.*
✆ (0723) 360929. C. **☞** 24 bedrs, 4 bp, 3
sh, 4 ba, TV. **✗** mc, LD 9. ⓗ Lt, CH, TV, CP
6, Ac, con 40, CF, 3 st. **£** BB £12·50–
£17·50, DB £25–£35, DBB £17·50–£22·50,
WB, ①, Bk £2·50, L £4·75, D £5, cc 1 3,
Dep.

★★Esplanade, *Belmont Rd, YO11 2AD.*
✆ (0723) 360382. Open Feb–Nov & Xmas.
C. **☞** 78 bedrs, 49 bp, 12 bps, 7 ba, TV,
Dgs. **✗** a l c, mc, at, LD 9. ⓗ Lt, N, CH, TV,
CP 20, Ac, con 120, CF, 2 st. **£** BB fr £17,
DB fr £32, DBB fr £23, WB, ①, Bk £3·50, L
£4·95, D £6·95, cc 1 2 3 5, Dep b.

★★Southlands, *15 West St, YO11 2QW.*
✆ (0723) 361461. Open Apr–Oct & Xmas.
C. **☞** 60 bedrs, 43 bp, 10 bps, 3 ba, TV,
Dgs. **✗** a l c, mc, at, LD 8.30. ⓗ Lt, N, CH,
Dgs, CP 45, Ac, con 100, CF, 10 st. **£** BB
£20–£24, DB £36–£40, WB, ②, Bk £3·50, L
£4·75, D £7·50, cc 1 2 3 5 6, Dep b.▲

★Dorchester (Unl), *Filey Rd, YO11 2SE.*
✆ (0723) 361668. Open May–Sep. C.
☞ 40 bedrs, 14 bp, 6 ba, Dgs. **✗** mc, at, LD
7.15. ⓗ Lt, ch, TV, CP 20, CF, 0 st. **£** BB
£8–£12, DB £16–£24, WT £121·80, DT
£17·40, DBB £16·65, ①, Bk £3, L £3·96, D
£6, Dep b.

Almora, PH, z (RI), *12 Esplanade Gdns,
South Cliff, YO11 2AW.* **✆** (0723) 61800.

Bay, H, z (R), *67 Esplanade, YO11 2UZ.*
✆ (0723) 373926. C. **☞** 18 bedrs, 12 bps,
3 ba, TV, Dgs. ⓗ CH, TV, mc, CP 12, CF, 10 st.
£ BB £16–£21, DB £28–£34, WT (b) £126–
£140, DT (b) £20–£21, ①, Bk £3, L £5, D
£5.

Church Hills, PH, z (RI), *St Martin's Av,
South Cliff, YO11 2DE.* **✆** (0723) 63148.

East Ayton Lodge, H, xy (RI), *Moor
Lane, East Ayton, YO13 9EW.* **✆** (0723)
864227. C. **☞** 6 bedrs, 6 bp, TV, Dgs.
✗ a l c. ⓗ CH, Dgs, CP 50, CF, 1 st. **£** BB
£17·50–£21·50, DB £25–£33, WT (c) £80–
£105, ①, L £5, cc 3.

Foxholm, PH, x (RI), *Ebberston, YO13
9NJ.* **✆** (0723) 85550. Open Mar–Oct &
Xmas. C. **☞** 10 bedrs, 1 bp, 3 bps, 2 sh, 3
ba, Dgs. ⓗ CH, TV, Dgs, CP 12, U 2, 4 BGf,
2 st. **£** BB £11–£15, DB £22–£30, WT (b)
£100–£125, DT (b) £16–£20, ②, D £5.

Gainsborough, PH, z (RI), *23 Prince of
Wales Ter, YO11 2AN.* **✆** (0723) 73692.

Geldenhuis, PH, z (RI), *146 Queen's Par,
YO12 7HU.* **✆** (0723) 361677. Open Mar–
Oct & Xmas. C. **☞** 23 bedrs, 5 ba, Dgs.
ⓗ CH, TV, CP 18, CF, 1 st. **£** BB £6·65–£10·35,
DB £17·30–£20·70, WT (c) £60·55–
£72·45, (b) £76·30–£92·40, ①.

Glenville, PH, z (Unl), *8 Blenheim St,
North Bay, YO12 7HB.* **✆** (0723) 72681.

Lynwood, PH, y (Unl), *2 Lyndle Cres,
Northstead Manor Dr, YO12 6AQ.*
✆ (0723) 72997.

Parade, H (R), *29 Esplanade, YO11 2AQ.*
✆ (0723) 361285. C. **☞** 20 bedrs, 12 bps,
2 ba, TV. ⓗ CH, TV, CF, 4 st. **£** BB £9–£12,
DB £18–£36, ①, Bk £3, L £3, D £4·50.

Park, PH, z (R), *21 Victoria Park,
YO12 7TS.* **✆** (0723) 375580. Open Mar–
Oct. C. **☞** 16 bedrs, 1 bp, 3 bps, 2 ba, ns.
ⓗ CH, TV, CF, 5 st. **£** BB £7–£9·50, DB
£14–£19, WT (b) £58–£75, (c) £49–
£59·50, DT (b) £8·50–£11, ②, Bk £2·50, D
£3.

Reads, PH, z (RI), *111 Queens Par, YO12
7HT.* **✆** (0723) 361071. Open Apr–Oct. C.
☞ 23 bedrs, 1 bps, 4 ba, Dgs. ⓗ ch, TV,
CF, 1 BGf. **£** BB £10–£10·50, DB £20–£26,

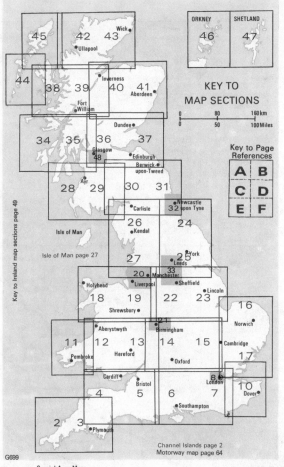

KEY TO
MAP SECTIONS

0   80   160 km
0   50   100 Miles

Key to Page
References

A	B
C	D
E	F

Isle of Man page 27

Key to Ireland map sections page 49

G699

Channel Islands page 2
Motorway map page 64

ROAD MAP OF
GREAT BRITAIN
AND IRELAND

Specially prepared for
THE ROYAL AUTOMOBILE CLUB
by John Bartholomew & Son Ltd

EXPLANATION

RAC Office

RAC Office with RAC
Appointed Hotel or Listed
Establishment (see Directory)

Place of popular interest with RAC
Appointed Hotel or Listed
Establishment (see Directory)

Town/Village with RAC Appointed
Hotel or Listed Establishment
(see Directory)

RAC/AA Telephone Boxes

RAC Service Centre

Special Area Maps

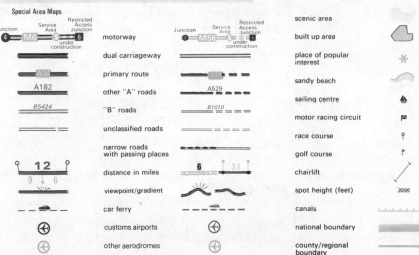

Special Area Maps

Junction 4	Service Area M6	Restricted Access Junction 6 under construction	motorway	Junction 3	Service Area M56	Restricted Access Junction 5 under construction
		dual carriageway			
A34		primary route			
A182		other "A" roads	A529		
B5424		"B" roads	B1010		
		unclassified roads			
		narrow roads with passing places			
12 9 6		distance in miles	6 3 1		
		viewpoint/gradient			
		car ferry			
		customs airports			
		other aerodromes			

scenic area

built up area

place of popular
interest

sandy beach

sailing centre

motor racing circuit

race course

golf course

chairlift

spot height (feet)   3095

canals

national boundary

county/regional
boundary

All maps in this 64 page Atlas Section are © John Bartholomew & Son Ltd

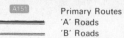

Junction / M56 / Service Area	Motorways	
	Dual Carriageways	
A151	Primary Routes	
	'A' Roads	
	'B' Roads	

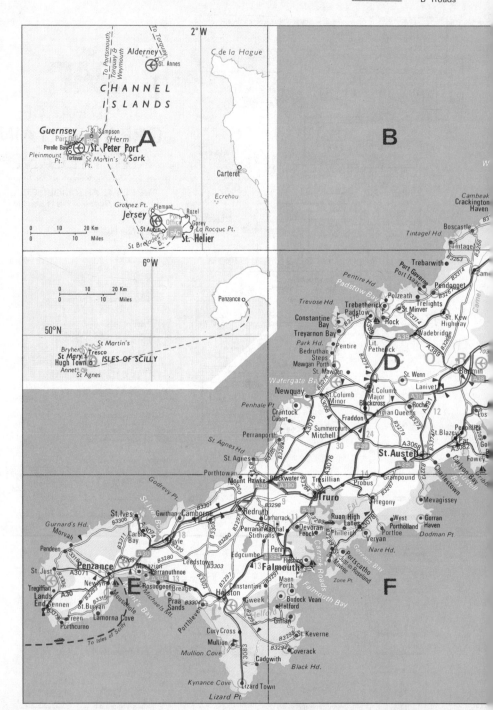

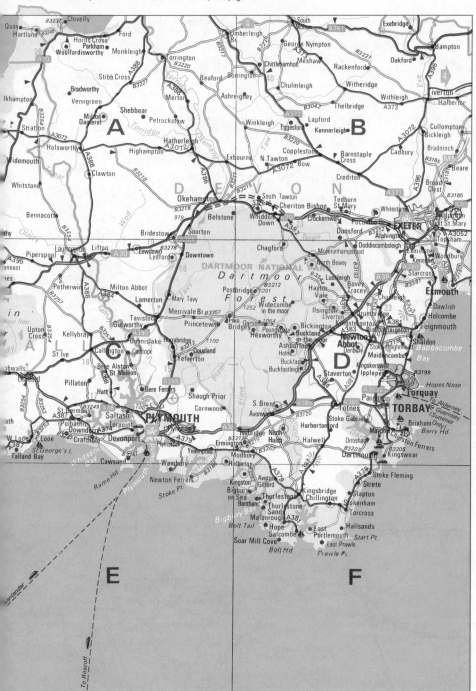

Unclassified Roads

▲ RAC and AA Boxes

'See article Motorway Junctions with Restricted Access', text page 40

Miles 0 · 5 · 10 · 15
Km 0 · 4 · 8 · 16 · 24

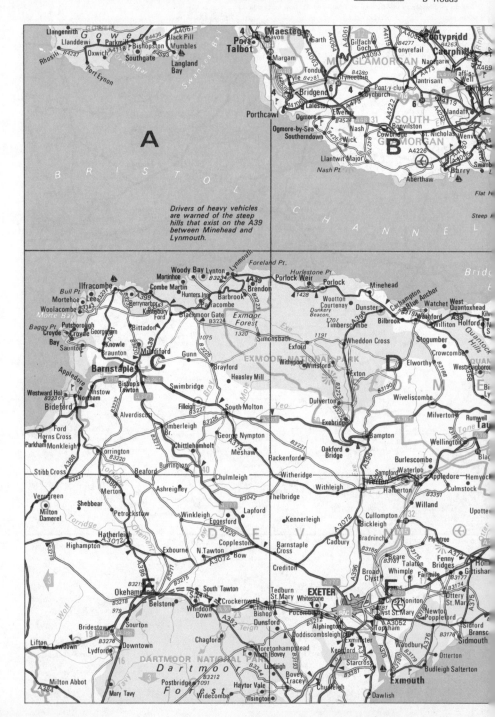

Junction ⑰ **M56** Ⓢ **Service Area**
Motorways
Dual Carriageways

A151
Primary Routes
'A' Roads
'B' Roads

Drivers of heavy vehicles
are warned of the steep
hills that exist on the A39
between Minehead and
Lynmouth.

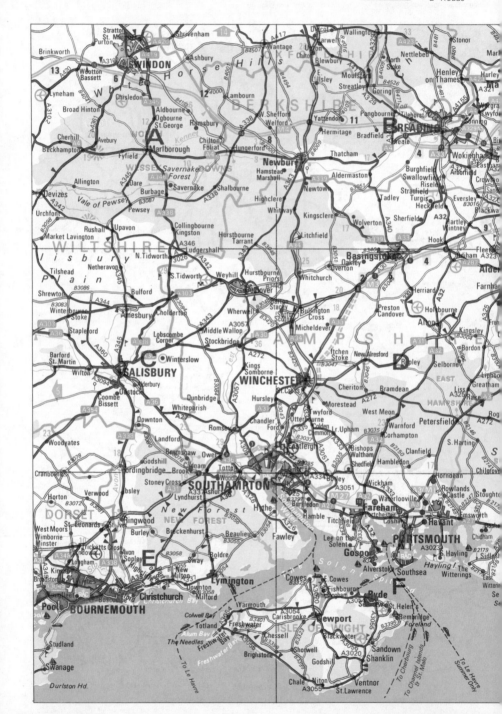

Junction · Service Area — M56 — Motorways / Dual Carriageways — A151 — Primary Routes / 'A' Roads / 'B' Roads

Unclassified Roads

▲   RAC and AA Boxes

See article Motorway Junctions with Restricted Access, text page 40

0	5	10	15 Miles
0	4	8	16	24 Km

8

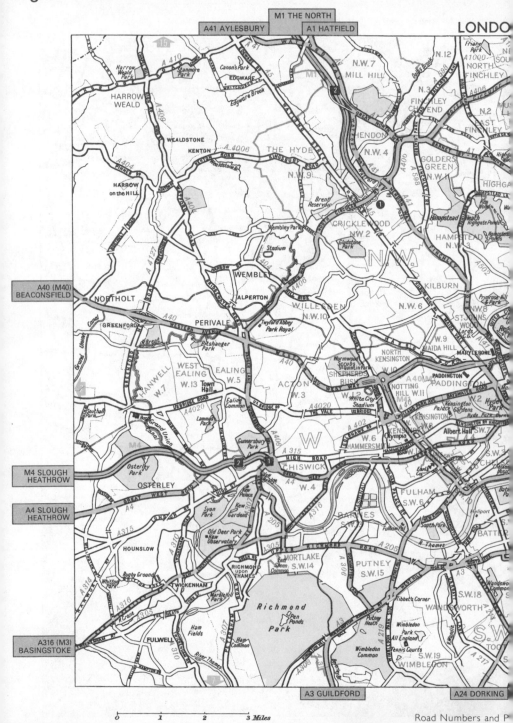

M1 THE NORTH

A41 AYLESBURY | A1 HATFIELD

A40 (M40) BEACONSFIELD

M4 SLOUGH HEATHROW

A4 SLOUGH HEATHROW

A316 (M3) BASINGSTOKE

A3 GUILDFORD | A24 DORKING

Road Numbers and P

0   1   2   3 Miles

EA MAP A10 CAMBRIDGE   M11 CAMBRIDGE

A12 CHELMSFORD

A13 SOUTHEND

A2 DOVER

A20 SWANLEY

A23 BRIGHTON   © – John Bartholomew & Son, Ltd. Edinburgh

icts Shown in Red   Motorway   Primary Route

Junction Service Area Motorways

Dual Carriageways

A151 Primary Routes
'A' Roads
'B' Roads

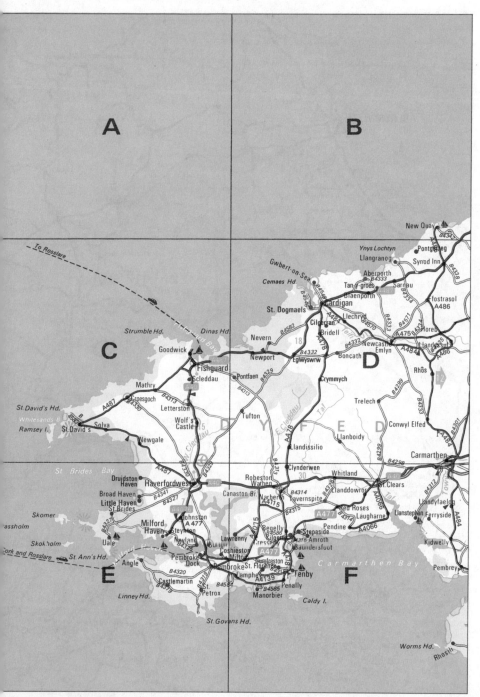

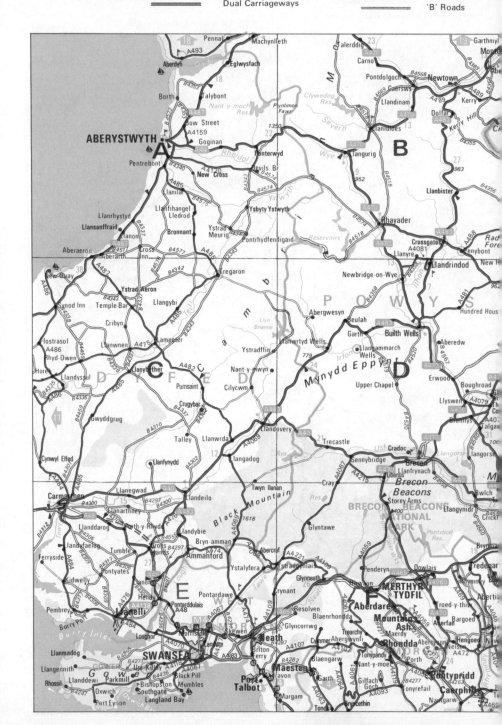

Unclassified Roads

▲ RAC and AA Boxes

See article Motorway Junctions with Restricted Access, text page 40

Miles
Km

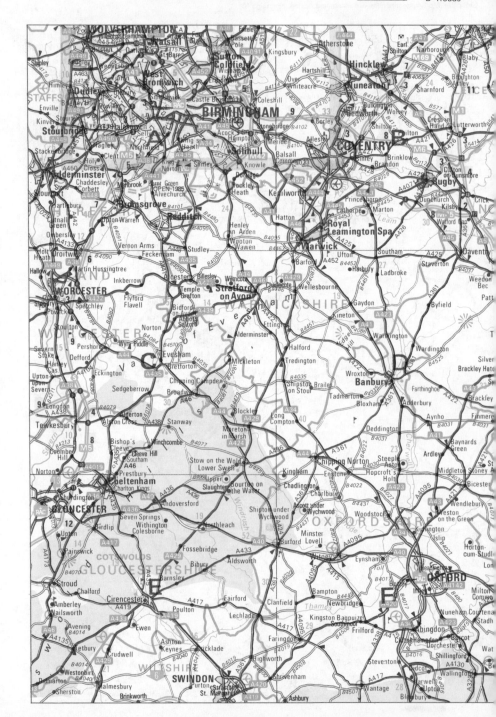

Unclassified Roads

▲ RAC and AA Boxes

See article Motorway Junctions with Restricted Access, text page 40

0 ___ 5 ___ 10 ___ 15 Miles

0 ___ 4 ___ 8 ___ 16 ___ 24 Km

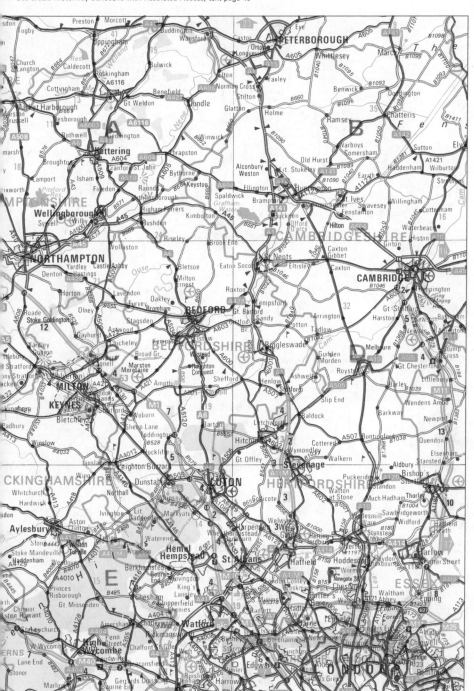

Junction — Service Area
⑩ M56 Ⓢ   Motorways
Dual Carriageways

A151   Primary Routes
'A' Roads
'B' Roads

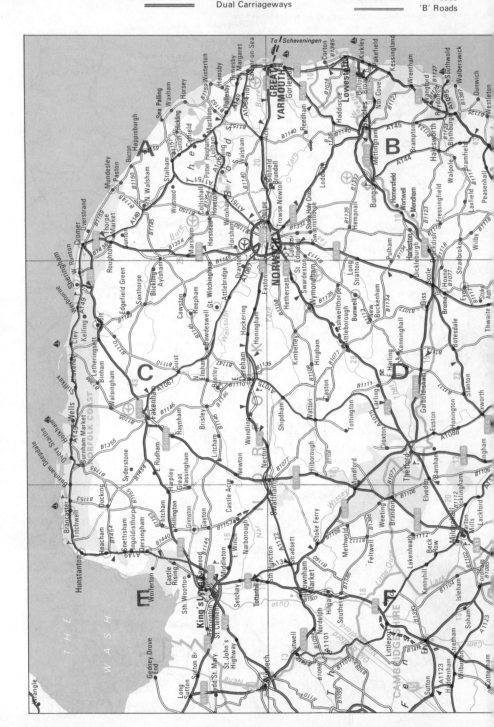

Unclassified Roads

▲ RAC and AA Boxes

0 ____ 5 ____ 10 ____ 15 Miles
0 ____ 4 ____ 8 ____ 16 ____ 24 Km

'See article Motorway Junctions with Restricted Access', text page 40

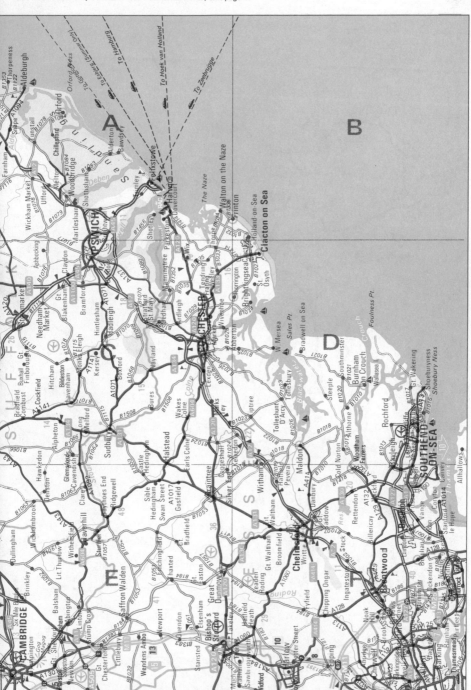

Junction   Service Area
M56
Motorways
Dual Carriageways

A151
Primary Routes
'A' Roads
'B' Roads

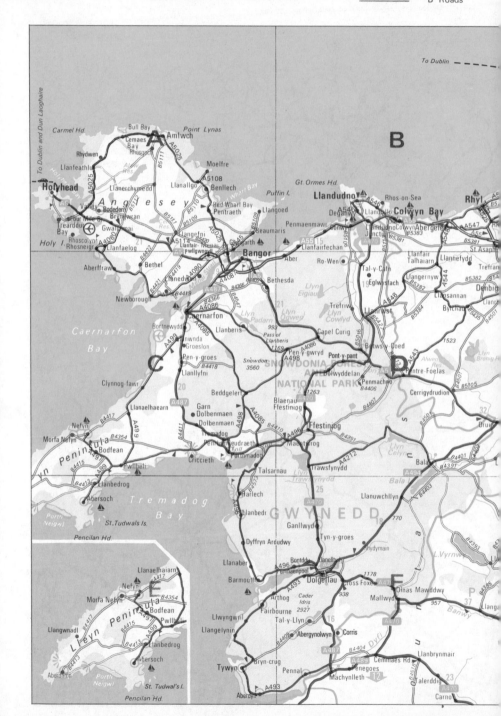

Unclassified Roads

▲ RAC and AA Boxes

Miles
Km

See article Motorway Junctions with Restricted Access, text page 40

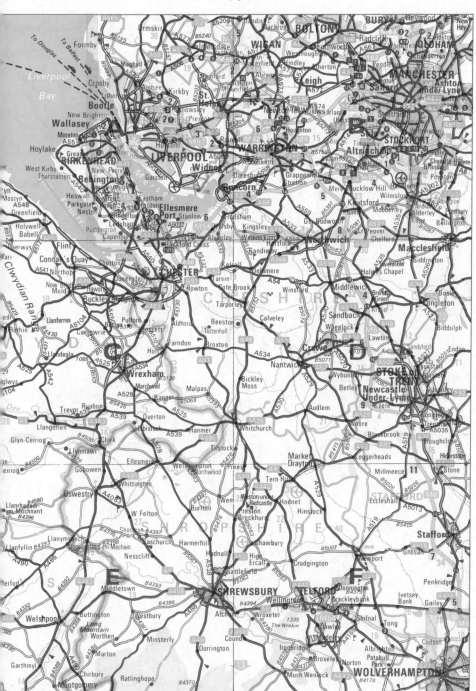

Junction   Service Area

Motorways

Dual Carriageways

Primary Routes
'A' Roads
'B' Roads

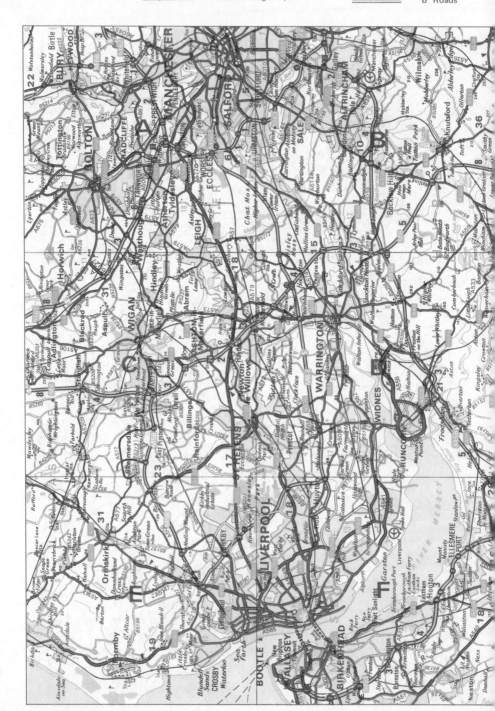

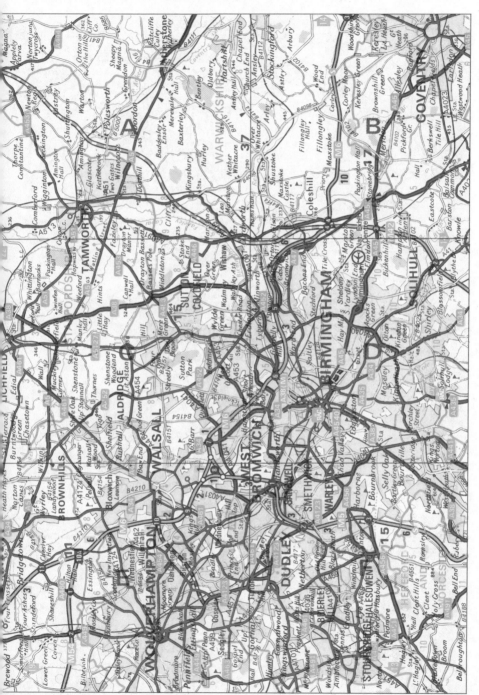

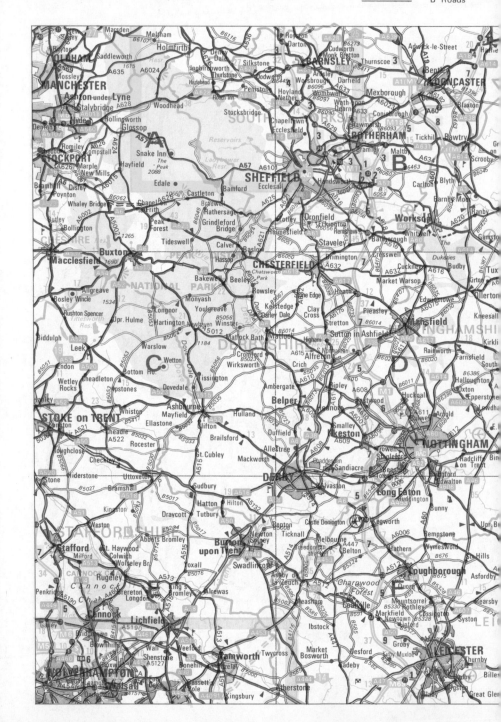

Junction ⑲ M56 Ⓢ Service Area

Motorways

Dual Carriageways

Primary Routes

'A' Roads

'B' Roads

Unclassified Roads

▲ RAC and AA Boxes

0 ... 5 ... 10 ... 15 Miles
0 ... 4 ... 8 ... 16 ... 24 Km

'See article Motorway Junctions with Restricted Access', text page 40

Junction | Service Area
⑦ M56 Ⓢ | Motorways
Dual Carriageways
A151 | Primary Routes
'A' Roads
'B' Roads

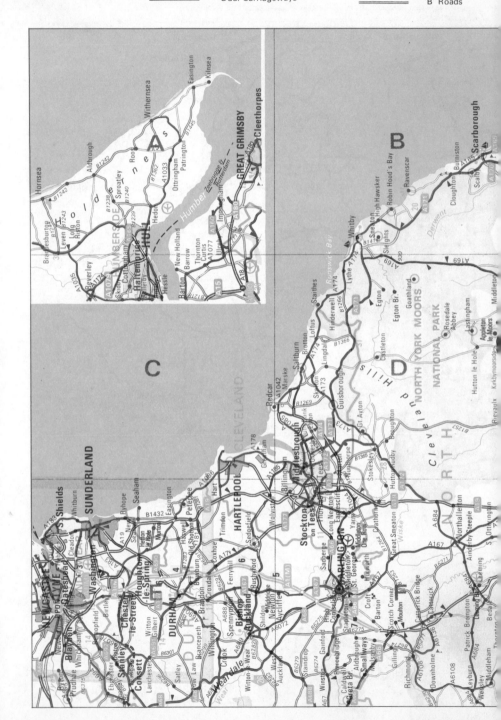

Unclassified Roads

▲ RAC and AA Boxes

'See article Motorway Junctions with Restricted Access', text page 40

0   5   10   15 Miles
0   4   8   16   24 Km

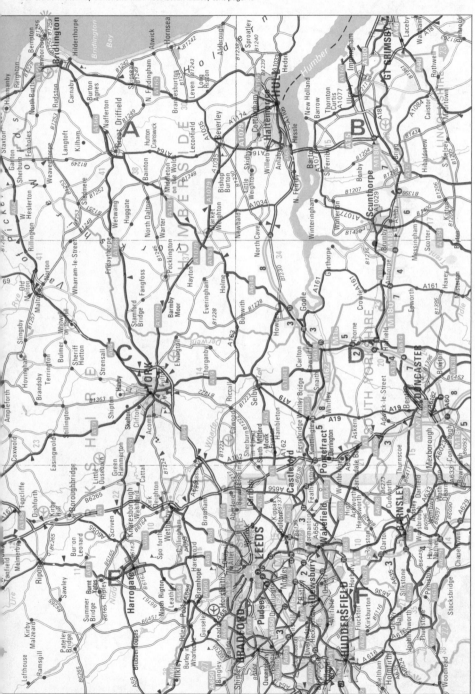

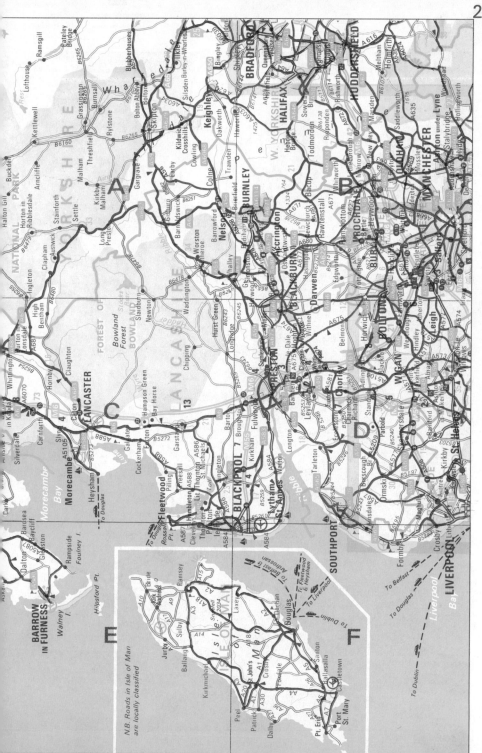

N.B. Roads in Isle of Man are locally classified

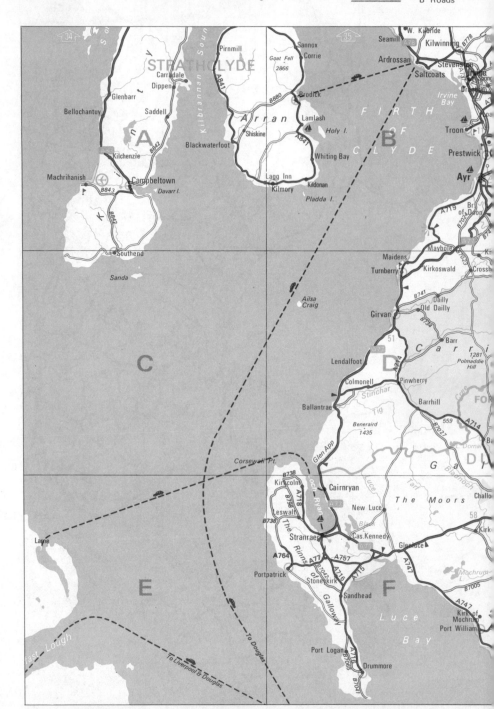

Junction ⑰ M56 Ⓢ Service Area — Motorways — Dual Carriageways

A151 — Primary Routes — 'A' Roads — 'B' Roads

STRATHCLYDE

34

Carradale
Dippen
Glenbarr
Bellochantuy
Saddell
Kilchenzie
Machrihanish
Campbeltown
Davarr I.
Southend
Sanda

Pirnmill
Goat Fell 2866
Arran
Shiskine
Blackwaterfoot
Lagg Inn
Kilmory

Sannox
Corrie
Brodick
Lamlash
Holy I.
Whiting Bay
Kildonan
Pladda I.

35

Seamill
Ardrossan
Saltcoats
FIRTH
OF
CLYDE
Troon
Prestwick
Ayr

W. Kilbride
Kilwinning
Stevenston
Irvine Bay

Maidens
Turnberry
Girvan

Maybole
Kirkoswald
Crossh
B741
Dailly
Old Dailly

Ailsa Craig

Lendalfoot
Colmonell
Ballantrae

Pinwherry
Stinchar
Tig
Beneraird 1435

Carri
1281
Polmaddie Hill
Barr
Barrhill
559
B7027
A714
FO
Ba

Corsewall Pt.
Glen App
Ga
DI

Larne

Kirkcolm
Leswalt
Stranraer
Portpatrick
Stonykirk
A764
A716
Sandhead
Galloway
Port Logan
Drummore

Cairnryan
New Luce
Cas.Kennedy
A77
A757
A715
Glenluce

The Moors
Challo
Kirk
Machrum L.
A747
B7005

Luce Bay
Kirk of Mochru
Port William

To Douglas
To Liverpool & Douglas
fast Lough

A
B
C
D
E
F

Unclassified Roads

▲ RAC and AA Boxes

'See article Motorway Junctions with Restricted Access, text page 40

0 ___ 5 ___ 10 ___ 15 Miles
0 __ 4 __ 8 __ 16 __ 24 Km

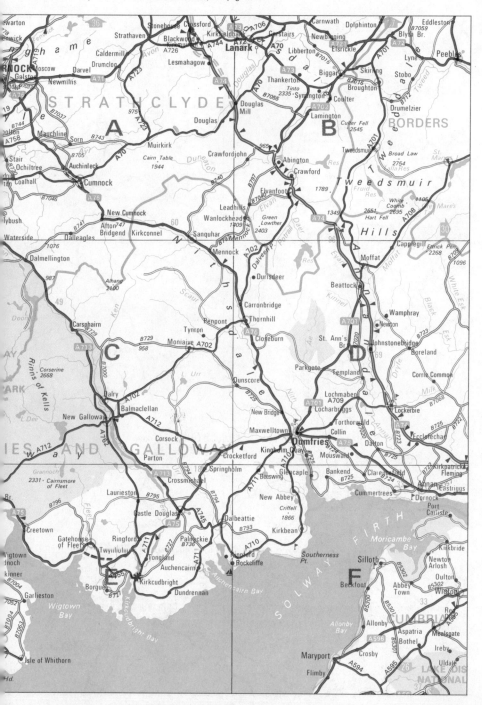

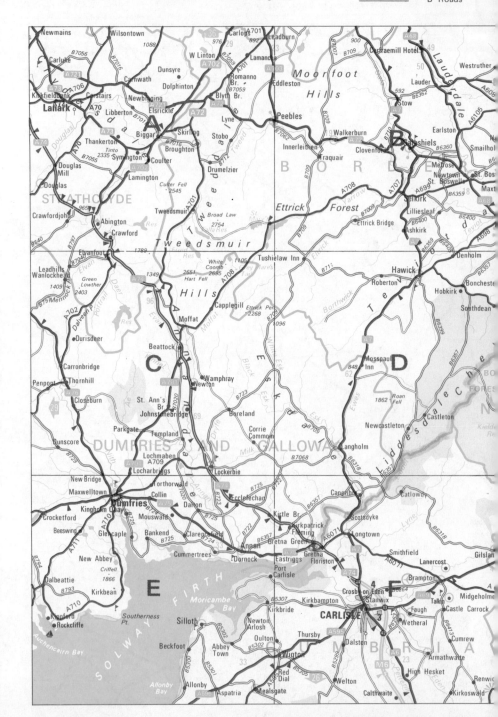

Junction Service Area
M56
Motorways
Dual Carriageways

A151
Primary Routes
'A' Roads
'B' Roads

Unclassified Roads

▲ RAC and AA Boxes

0 ____ 5 ____ 10 ____ 15 Miles
0 ___ 4 ___ 8 ___ 16 ___ 24 Km

See article Motorway Junctions with Restricted Access, text page 40

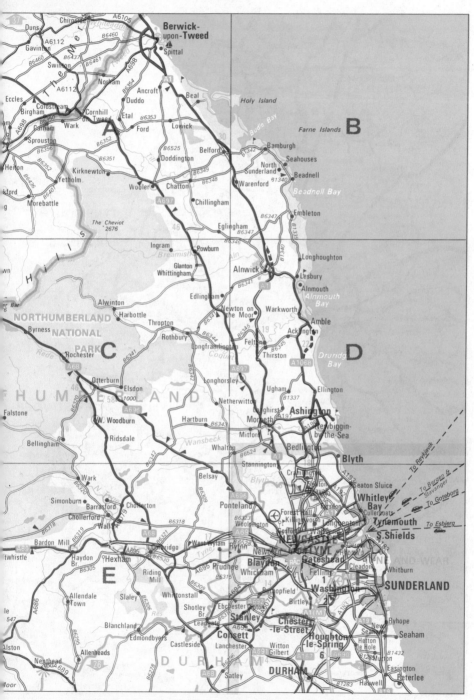

Junction   Service Area
M6   Motorways
'Dual Carriageways
A60   Primary Routes
'A' Roads
'B' Roads

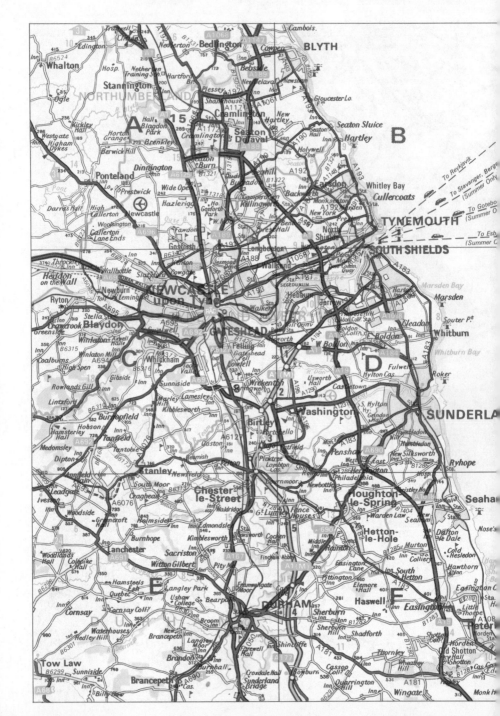

Unclassified Roads

RAC and AA Boxes

See article Motorway Junctions with Restricted Access, text page 40

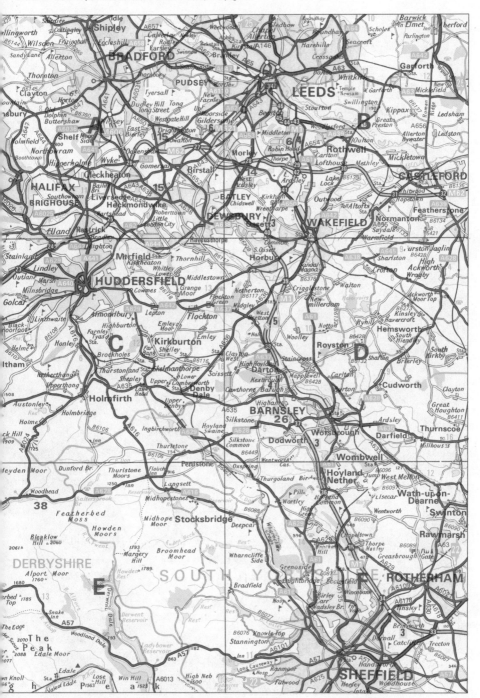

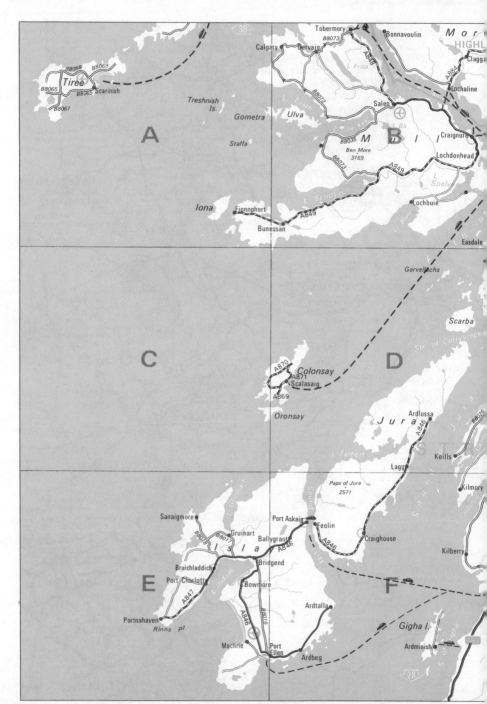

Tobermory
Bonnavoulin
M o r
HIGHL

Calgary   Dervaig
B8073
Clagga

B8068   B8069
A884

Tiree
L Frisa
Lochaline

B8065   Scarinish
B8072

B8065
Salen

B8067
Treshnish Is.
Craignure

Gometra   Ulva
L Ba

A
L na Keal
M   **B**   **I**

Staffa
B8035
Lochdonhead

Ben More 3169
L. Spelv

B8073

A849

Iona   Fionnphort
Lochbuie

Bunessan
A849
L Buie

Easdale

Garvellachs

Scarba

C
A870   **Colonsay**
D
Str. of Corryvrecka

A871

Scalasaig
A869

Oronsay
Ardlussa

J u r a
A846
S T

L Tarbert
Keills

Lagg
B8025

Paps of Jura 2571
Kilmory

Sanaigmore
Port Askaig

Gruinart
Feolin

B8018   B8017
Ballygrant

I s l a
A846
Craighouse

Bridgend
A846

Bruichladdich
Kilberry

Port Charlotte

E
Bowmore
F

A847
L Indaal

Portnahaven
B8016
Ardtalla

Rinns Pt
A846
Gigha I.

Machrie
Ardminish

Port Ellen

Ardbeg

Unclassified Roads

▲ RAC and AA Boxes

0 ... 5 ... 10 ... 15 Miles
0 ... 4 ... 8 ... 16 ... 24 Km

See article Motorway Junctions with Restricted Access, text page 40

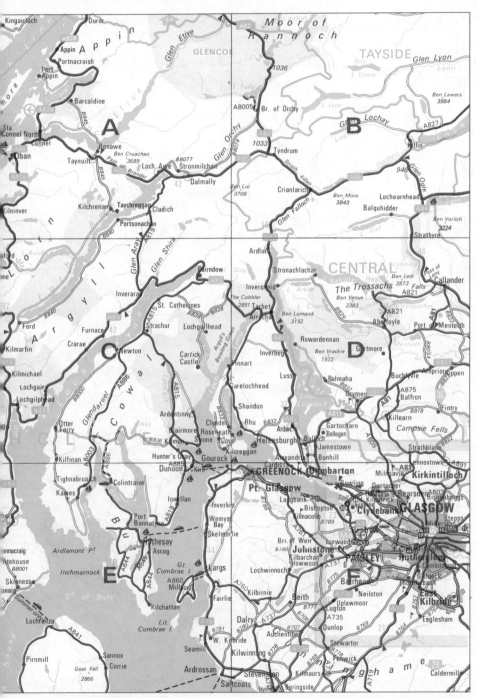

Junction   Service Area

M56 Motorways

Dual Carriageways

A151 Primary Routes
'A' Roads
'B' Roads

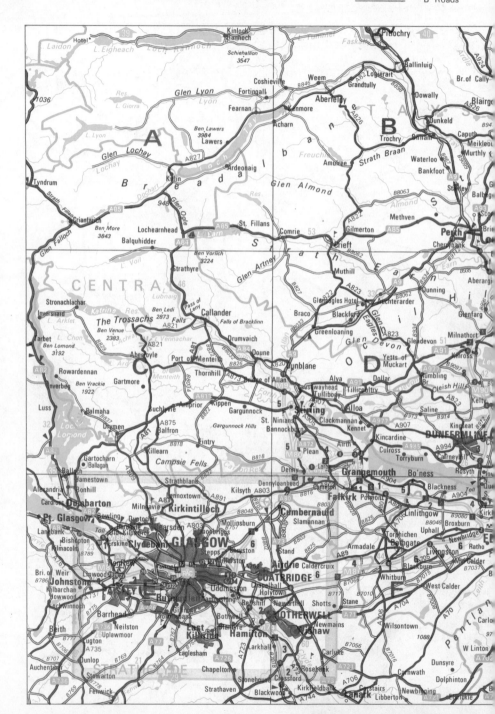

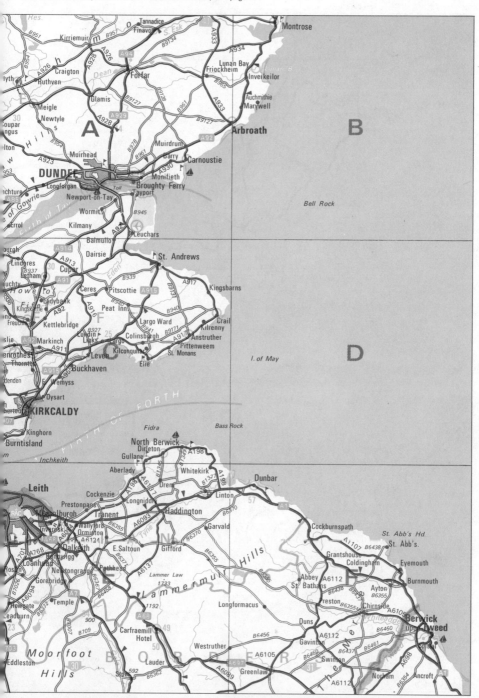

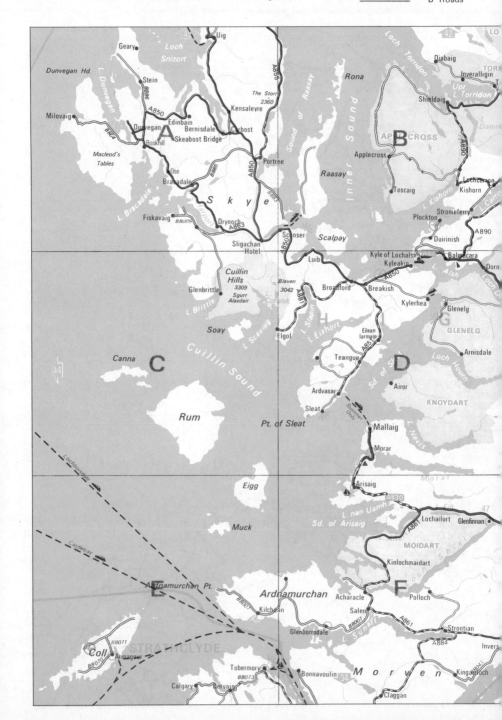

Junction
Service Area
Motorways
Dual Carriageways
Primary Routes
'A' Roads
'B' Roads

Unclassified Roads

RAC and AA Boxes

See article Motorway Junctions with Restricted Access, text page 40

0 5 10 15 Miles
0 4 8 16 24 Km

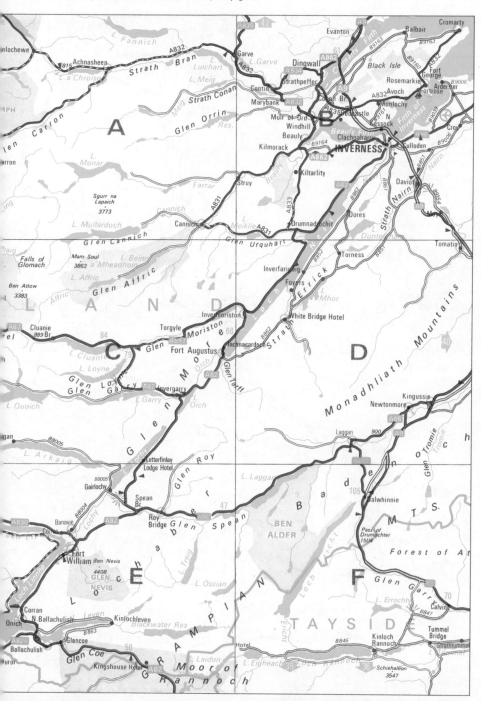

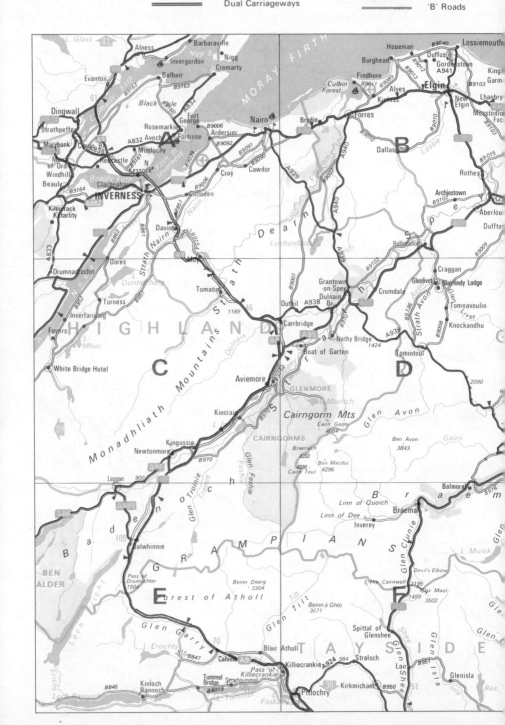

Junction Service Area
17 M56 S Motorways
Dual Carriageways

A151
Primary Routes
'A' Roads
'B' Roads

Unclassified Roads

RAC and AA Boxes

See article Motorway Junctions with Restricted Access, text page 40

0 5 10 15 Miles
0 4 8 16 24 Km

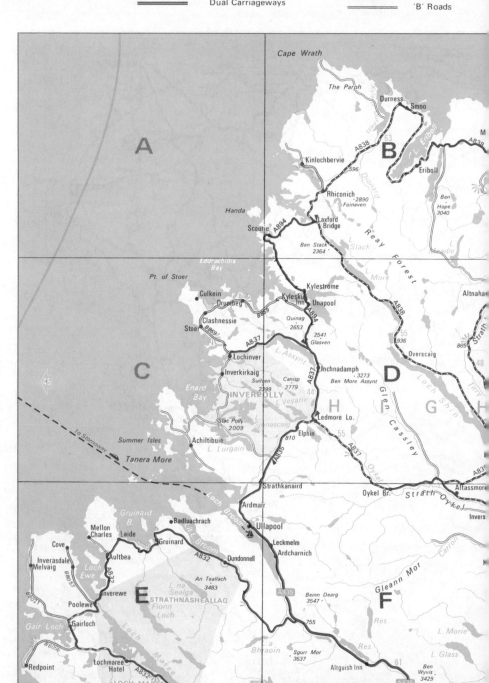

Junction   Service
Area

Motorways

Dual Carriageways

A151

Primary Routes
'A' Roads
'B' Roads

Cape Wrath

The Parph

Durness
Smoo

L. Eriboll

A838

A838

B

M

Kinlochbervie

A838

596

Eriboll

Dionard

Rhiconich
·2890
Foinaven

Ben
Hope
3040

Handa

Scourie

A894

Laxford
Bridge

Reay

L.
Stack

Forest

Ben Stack
2364 ·

Meadie

Eddrachillis
Bay

Pt. of Stoer

Kylestrome

L. More

Altnahar

Culkein
Drumbeg

B869

Kylesku
Inn

Unapool

A838

Strath

Clashnessie

Stoer

B869

Quinag
2653

A894

2541
Glasven

55
936

869

Overscaig

Lochinver

A837

L. Assynt

48

C

Inverkirkaig

Suilven
2399

Canisp
2779

Inchnadamph
·3273
Ben More Assynt

D

Glen

Loch

Shin

Enard
Bay

INVERPOLLY

44

L. Veyatie

H

H

G

H

Stac Polly
2009

Strionascaig

Ledmore Lo.

Cassley

Summer Isles

L. Lurgain

Achiltibuie

Elphin
810

55

A837

Oykel

A835

Tanera More

To Stornoway

Loch Broom

Strathkanaird

Oykel Br.

Strath Oykel

Altassmor

A835

Ardmair

Invers

Gruinaid
B.

Badluachrach

Ullapool

Leckmelm

Mellon
Charles

Laide

Gruinard

L. Broom

Ardcharnich

Gleann

Mor

Carron

Cove

Aultbea

A832

Dundonnell

Inverasdale
Melvaig

B8057

Loch
Ewe

A832

An Teallach
3483

Beinn Dearg
3547 ·

A835

Res.

Inverewe

E

STRATHNASHEALLAG

F

Poolewe

B8021

Fionn
Loch

755

Gleann Mor

Gair Loch

Gairloch

L. Morie

L Glass

B8056

a
Bhraoin

Sgurr Mor
· 3637

Res.

Redpoint

Lochmaree
Hotel

A832

Loch

Maree

Altguish Inn

61

A835

Ben
Wyvis ·
3429

LOCH MAREE

49

L. Fannich

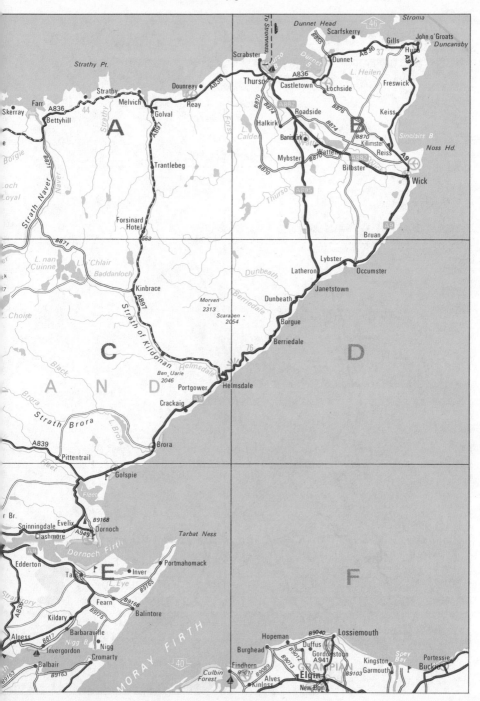

Unclassified Roads

▲ RAC and AA Boxes

See article Motorway Junctions with Restricted Access, text page 40

0 5 10 15 Miles
0 4 8 16 24 Km

Stroma

Dunnet Head
To Stromness
Scarfskerry
46
Scrabster
Gills
John o'Groats
Duncansby
B855
Dunnet
A836 37
Huna
Thurso
A836
L. Heilen
Freswick
Castletown
Lochside
Strathy Pt.
Strathy
A9
A836
B870
B874
Roadside
B876
Keiss
Dounreay
Reay
B882
Melvich
Golval
Halkirk
B874
B
Killimster
Sinclairs B.
Skerray
Farr
A836 44
Banskirk
Reiss
A9
Noss Hd.
Bettyhill
A897
A
Mybster
B870
Watten
A882
Trantlebeg
Biloster
B870
Wick
Strath Naver
A895
B871
Thurso
Naver
Bruan
A9
Forsinard
Hotel
563
Lybster
L. nan
Cuinne
Latheron
Occumster
Lu'Chlair
Baddanloch
Dunbeath
Janetstown
Kinbrace
Dunbeath
A897
Berriedale
Morven
2313
Scaraben
2054
Borgue
Strath of Kildonan
C
A N D
Berriedale
76
D
Black
Helmsdale
Ben Uarie
2046
Strath Brora
Portgower
Helmsdale
A9
Crackaig
Brora
L.Brora
A839
Brora
Pittentrail
Golspie
Fleet
E
F
r Br.
Spinningdale
Evelix
B9168
Dornoch
A949
Clashmore
A9
Tarbat Ness
Edderton
Dornoch Firth
Tain
Inver
Portmahomack
E
L.Eye
B9165
Fearn
B9166
Balintore
B9175
Kildary
Alness
B817
Barbaraville
Nigg
B9040
Lossiemouth
Invergordon
Nigg B.
Cromarty
Hopeman
Duffus
Portessie
Balblair
Burghead
Gordonstoun
Kingston
Spey
Bay
Buckie
B9163
A941
Garmouth
B9103
MORAY FIRTH
40
Findhorn
B9089
B9013
Elgin
GRAMPIAN
Culbin
Forest
B9011
Alves
Kinloss
New Elgin

Junction Service Area

Motorways

Dual Carriageways

Primary Routes
'A' Roads
'B' Roads

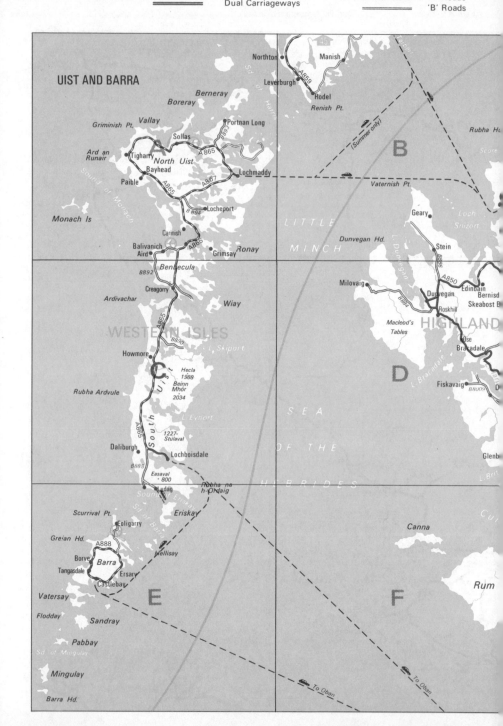

UIST AND BARRA

Northton • • Manish
Leverburgh •
A859
Berneray • Rodel
Boreray Renish Pt.

Griminish Pt. Vallay
Sollas (Summer only) Rubha Hu
• Portnan Long Score
Ard an North Uist A865
Runair Tigharry
Bayhead B
Paible Lochmaddy
A865 A867 Vaternish Pt.

Lochport
Monach Is B894 Geary Loch
Snizort
LITTLE
Carinish Dunvegan Hd. Stein
Balivanich MINCH
Aird • A865 Ronay A850
Grimsay A895

B892 Benbecula Edinbain
Creagorry Milovaig Dunvegan Bernisd
Ardivachar Wiay Roskhill Skeabost B
A865 Macleod's HIGHLAND
WESTERN ISLES B890 Tables Ose
L. Skiport Bracadale

Howmore Hecla
1988 D
Rubha Ardvule Beinn
Mhór Fiskavaig B8009
2034
L. Eynort SEA
South Uist 1227-
Stulaval OF THE
Daliburgh HEBRIDES
B888 Lochboisdale Glenb
Easaval
• 800
Ludag Rubha na
h-Ordaig

Scurrival Pt. Eriskay Canna
Eoligarry
Greian Hd. A888
Borve Barra
Tangasdale Hellisay E F Rum
Ersary
Castlebay
Vatersay
Flodday Sandray
Pabbay
Sd. of Mingulay
Mingulay
Barra Hd. To Oban To Oban

─────── Unclassified Roads

▲ RAC and AA Boxes

See article Motorway Junctions with Restricted Access, text page 40

| 0 | 5 | 10 | 15 | Miles |
| 0 | 4 | 8 | 16 | 24 | Km |

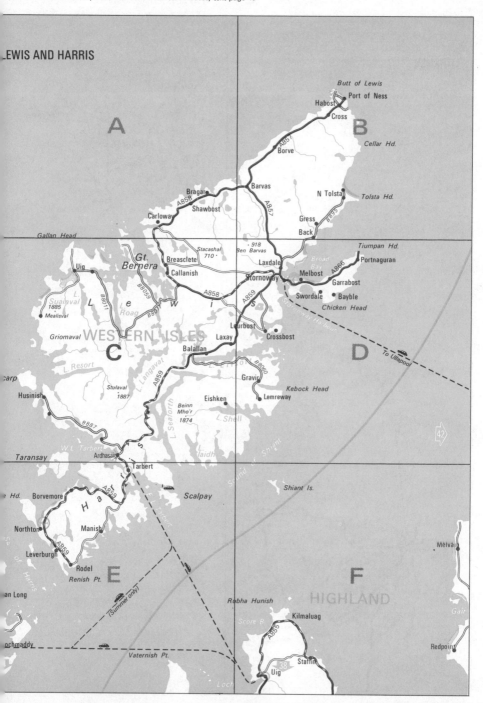

LEWIS AND HARRIS

A

B

Butt of Lewis
Port of Ness
Habost
Cross
Cellar Hd.
Borve
Barvas
N Tolsta
Tolsta Hd.
Bragar
Shawbost
Carloway
Gress
Back
Gallan Head
·918
Stacashal Ben Barvas
710·
Tiumpan Hd.
Gt.
Bernera
Breasclete
Laxdale
Portnaguran
Uig
Callanish
Stornoway
Melbost
Garrabost
L
Suainaval
1885
·Mealisval
L
Le
Roag
W
I
S
Swordale
Bayble
Chicken Head
Griomaval
WESTERN ISLES
Leurbost
Laxay
Crossbost
C
Balallan
D
To Ullapool
carp
Gravir
Husinish
Stulaval
·1887
Eishken
Lemreway
Kebock Head
Beinn
Mho'r
1874
L. Shell
42
Taransay
W.L. Tarbert
Ardhasaig
Tarbert
Hd.
Borvemore
H a
Scalpay
Shiant Is.
Northton
Manish
Leverburgh
Melval
Rodel
Renish Pt.
E
F
HIGHLAND
an Long
Gair
(Summer only)
Robha Hunish
ochmaddy
Vaternish Pt.
Kilmaluag
Redpoint
Uig
Staffin

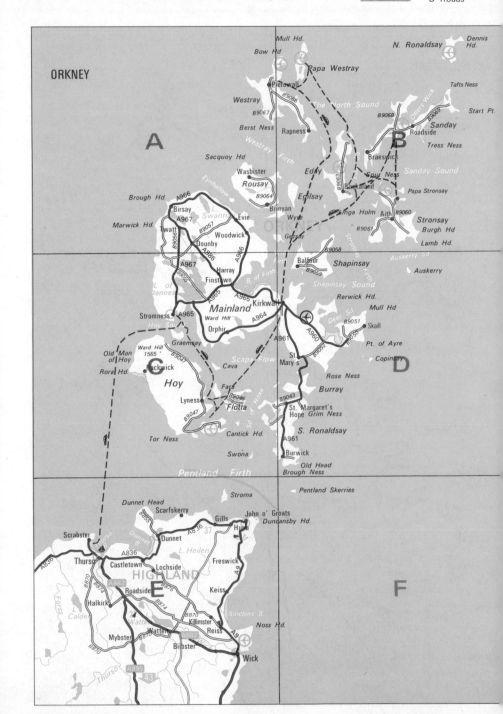

Junction — Service Area
M56 — Motorways
Dual Carriageways
A151 — Primary Routes
'A' Roads
'B' Roads

ORKNEY

Mull Hd.
Bow Hd.
Papa Westray
N. Ronaldsay
Dennis Hd.
Pierowall
Westray
B9066
The North Sound
Tafts Ness
Otters Wick
Start Pt.
B9067
B9068
B9069
Berst Ness
Rapness
Sanday
Roadside
Tress Ness
Sacquoy Hd.
Braeswick
Wasbister
Eday
Spur Ness
Sanday Sound
Rousay
B9064
Egilsay
B9063
Brekkland
Papa Stronsay
Brinyan
Wyre
Linga Holm
Aith
B9060
Evie
A966
Birsay
A967
L. Swanny
B9057
Woodwick
Garsay
Stronsay
Burgh Hd.
B9061
Marwick Hd.
Brough Hd.
Twatt
A966
B9055
Dounby
A986
A966
B9058
Lamb Hd.
B9059
Auskerry Sd.
A967
Harray
Balfour
Shapinsay
B9056
Finstown
B. of Firth
Auskerry
L. of Stenness
A985
Kirkwall
Mainland
A965
Rerwick Hd.
Mull Hd.
Stromness
A965
Ward Hill
A964
A960
Skaill
B9051
B9050
Pt. of Ayre
Orphir
A961
B9052
Ward Hill 1565
Graemsay
A947
St. Mary's
Copinsay
Old Man of Hoy
Rackwick
Cava
Rose Ness
Roral Hd.
Hoy
Fara
Burray
B9046
Lyness
Flotta
B9043
St. Margaret's Hope
Grim Ness
B9047
S. Ronaldsay
Tor Ness
Cantick Hd.
A961
Swona
Burwick
Old Head
Brough Ness

Pentland Firth

Stroma
Pentland Skerries
Dunnet Head
Scarfskerry
Gills
John o' Groats
Duncansby Hd.
B9055
Dunnet
A836
Huna
Scrabster
Thurso
Castletown
Lochside
L. Heilen
Freswick
A9
A836
HIGHLAND
B9070
Roadside
B9076
Keiss
Halkirk
B9074
Mybster
Watten
Killimster
Reiss
Noss Hd.
B9070
B9882
Sinclairs B
B880
Bilbster
A9
Wick
A895

Unclassified Roads

RAC and AA Boxes

See article Motorway Junctions with Restricted Access, text page 40

0 ___ 5 ___ 10 ___ 15 Miles
0 __ 4 __ 8 ___ 16 ___ 24 Km

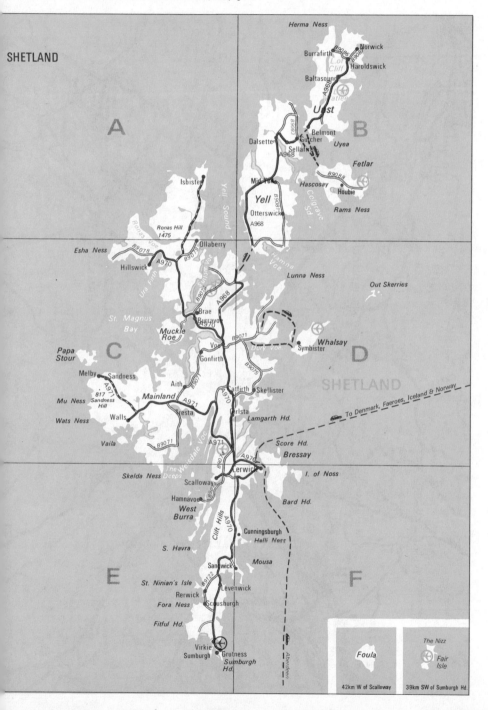

SHETLAND

Herma Ness

Burrafirth
Norwick
B9086 B9089
Lon.
Cliff
Haroldswick
Baltasound
A968
Catlee
Uist

A

B

Belmont
Dalsetter
Gutcher
Sellafirth
A968
Uyea

B9083

Mid Yell
Fetlar
B9088
Hascosay
Houbie

Isbister
Yell
B9081
Otterswick
A968
Rams Ness

Yell Sound

Ronas Hill
1475
Ollaberry
Coigrave Sd.

Esha Ness
B9078
Hillswick
A970
B9079
Ronas Voe
Ura Frth

Lunna Ness

Out Skerries

Hamna Voe

Brae
A968
Burravoe
B9070
A970
Muckle
Roe

Whalsay
B9071
Voe
Symbister

St. Magnus
Bay

Papa
Stour

C

D

SHETLAND

Gonfirth
Dury Voe

Melby
Sandness
B9075
Aith

To Denmark, Faeroes, Iceland & Norway

Mu Ness
817
Sandness
Hill
Mainland
B9071
Catfirth
Skellister

Wats Ness
Walls
A971
Nesta
A970
Girlsta
Lamgarth Hd.

Vaila
B9071
A971
Score Hd.
Bressay

The Weisdale Voe
B9074

Skelda Ness
Lerwick
I. of Noss

Scalloway
A970

Hamnavoe
West
Burra
Bard Hd.

S. Havra
Clift Hills
A970
Cunningsburgh
Hølli Ness

Mousa

St. Ninian's Isle
Sandwick
A972

E

F

Rerwick
Levenwick
Fora Ness
Scousburgh

Fitful Hd.

Aberdeen

Virkie
Sumburgh
Grutness
Sumburgh
Hd.

The Nizz

Foula

Fair
Isle

42km W of Scalloway
39km SW of Sumburgh Hd.

48

Junction Service Area

Motorways

Dual Carriageways

0 1 2 3 4 5 6 Miles
0 2 4 6 8 10 Km

See article Motorway Junctions with Restricted Access, text page 40

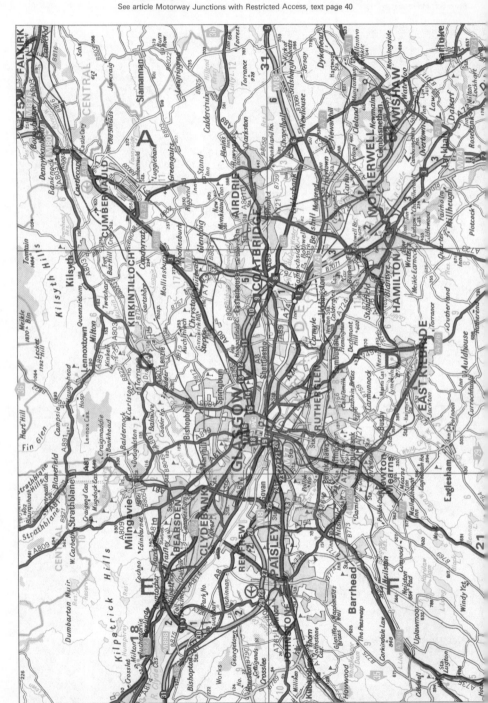

N2	National primary route
N19	National secondary route

See article Motorway Junctions with Restricted Access, text page 40

0 5 10 15 Miles
0 4 8 16 24 Km

R501 Regional Road

KEY TO IRELAND MAP SECTIONS

49	50	51	
52	53	54	55
56	57	58	59
	62	63	
60	61		

Londonderry
Larne
Belfast
Galway
Athlone
Dublin
Limerick
Waterford
Cork

Key to Page References

B
D
F

80 160km
50 100Miles

EXPLANATION

Port Office
RAC — RAC County or Port Office

○ Town/Village with RAC Appointed Hotel/Restaurant etc. - excluding RAC Appointed Garages (See Directory)

▲ RAC/AA Telephone Boxes
▲ RAC Service Centre

Border Customs Post
Republic of Ireland
Northern Ireland

te:
her map symbols, may be found on the key at the front of
p section. Key to roads in the Republic of Ireland, shown
head of relevant pages.

Map labels

B

Tory Island
Horn Head
Tory Sound
Inishbofin
Bloody Foreland
Dunfanaghy
N56
Falcarragh
Clochaneely
Creeslough
Gortahork
Muckish Mt. 2197
R257
Gola I.
Gweedore
R245
Derrybeg
Owey I.
Bunbeg
N258
Gweedore
Errigal 2466
R251
828
L. Beagh
Rosses Bay
R259
The Rosses
Annagry
L. Nacung
Derryveagh Mts
GLENVEAGH NATIONAL PARK
L. Gartan
Burtonport
R261
L. Anure
2240
Slieve Snacht
800
R254
Crohy Hd.
Dungloe
R252
N56
Doochary
780
R250
Gweebarra Bay
D
1257
Doghleheen
Fintown
R252
Lettermacaward
L. Finn
Aghla Mt. 1961
Clogham
Portnoo
Naran
Maas
R253
800
DONEGAL
Rosbeg
Glenties
Gaugin Mt. 1865
Loughros More Bay
R261
Owena
C
1515
Slievetooey
N56
Ardara
Blue Stack Mts.
50
Glen Bay
Glencolumbkille
900
Blue Stack 2219
499
Rossan Point
R262
18
Malin Bay
Malin More
R263
Meentullynagarn
Esko
Rathlin O'Birne I.
Slieve League 1972
Carrick
Crownarad 1621
Inver
N56
Mountcharles
N15
Killybegs
Donegal
Kilcar
Killaghy
Dunkineely
Laghey
Muckross Head
Doorin Pt.
R232
St. John's Pt.
Ballintra
Rossnowlagh
R231
E
Coolmore
N15
Donegal Bay
F
Ballyshannon
R230
A47
Bundoran
Belleek
446
FERMANAGH
Inishmurray
40
Kinlough
R52
Cliffoney
Lough Melvin
Garrison
N15
Grange
SLIGO
Benbulbin 1722
Dartry Mts. 2113 Truskmore
LEITRIM
Rossinver
53
R280
B52
Carney
Glencar L.
Kiltyclogher
R292
Glenade L.

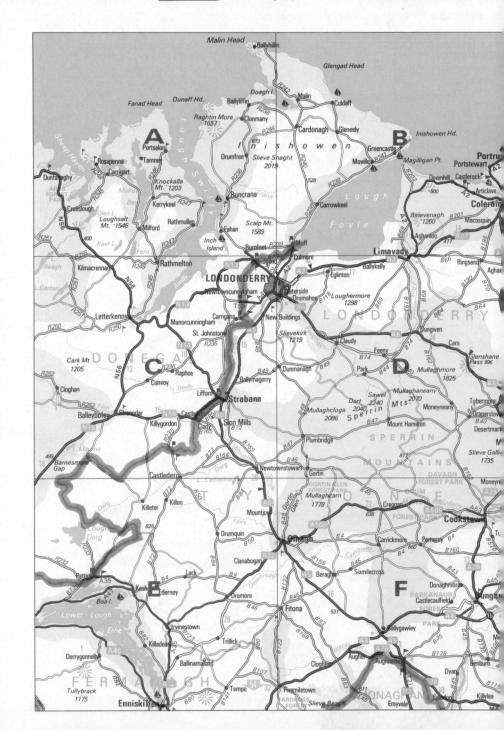

Unclassified Road

See article Motorway Junctions with Restricted Access, text page 40

0   5   10   15 Miles
0   4   8   16   24 Km

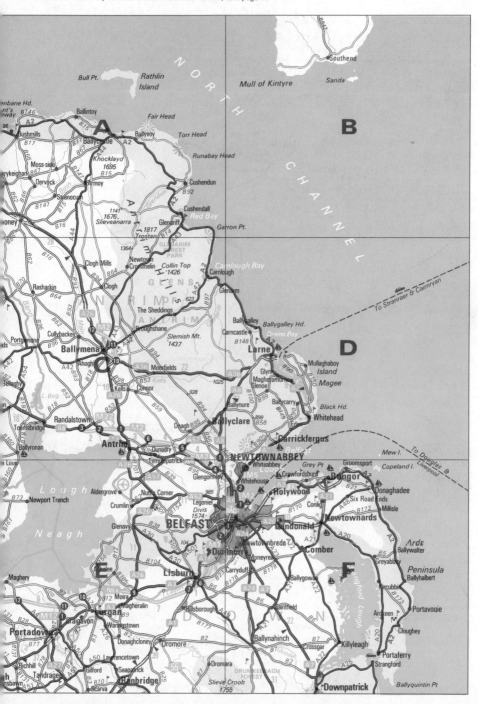

National primary route

National secondary route

R501   Regional Road

N2

N19

See article Motorway Junctions with Restricted Access, text page 40

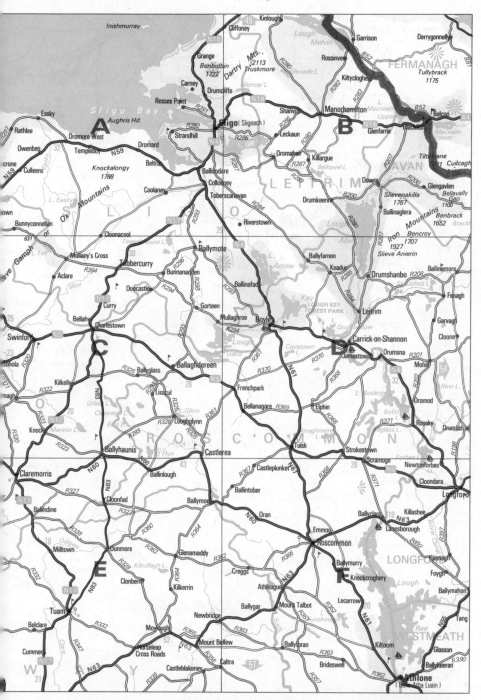

N. Ireland | Primary route | Republic of Ireland
Motorways | 'A' Roads | National primary route
Dual Carriageways | 'B' Roads | National secondary route

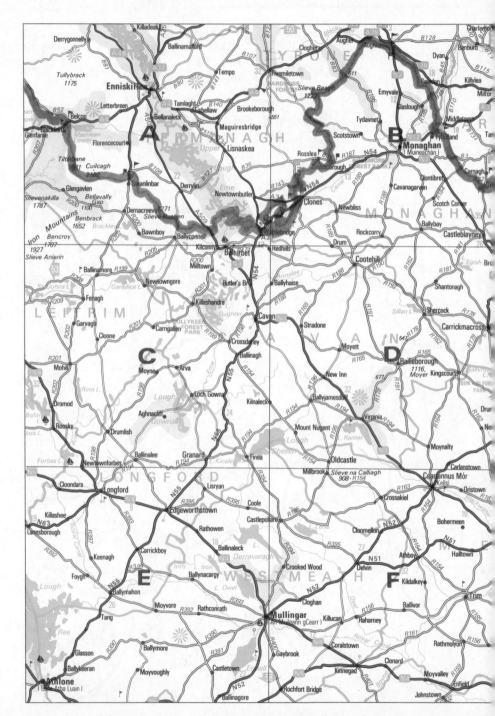

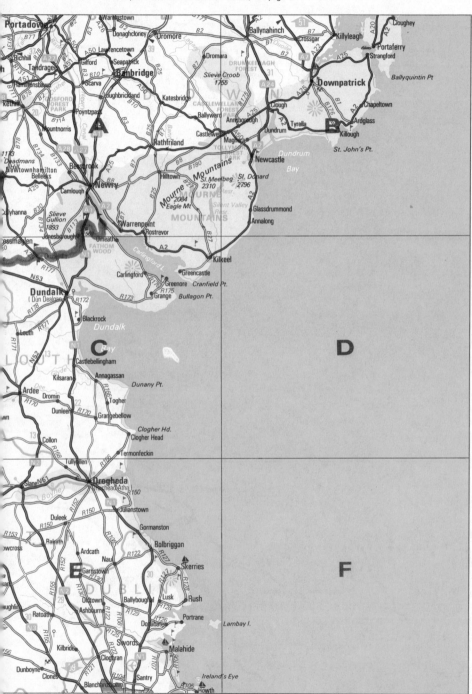

R501 Regional Road

0   5   10   15   Miles
0 4 8   16   24 Km

See article Motorway Junctions with Restricted Access, text page 40

National primary route

National secondary route

Regional Road

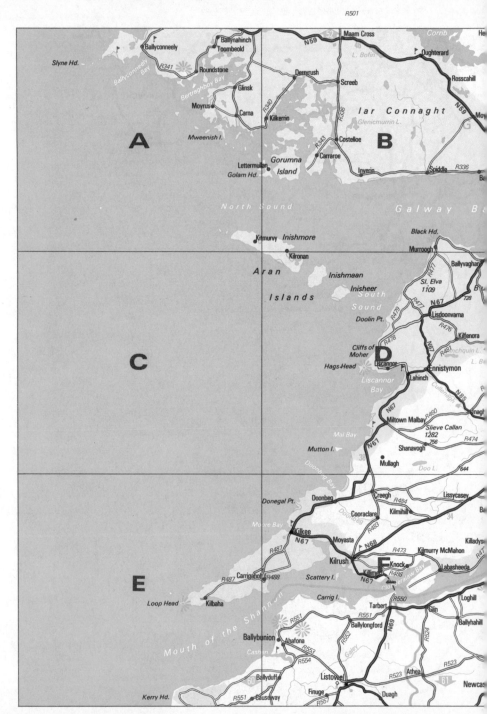

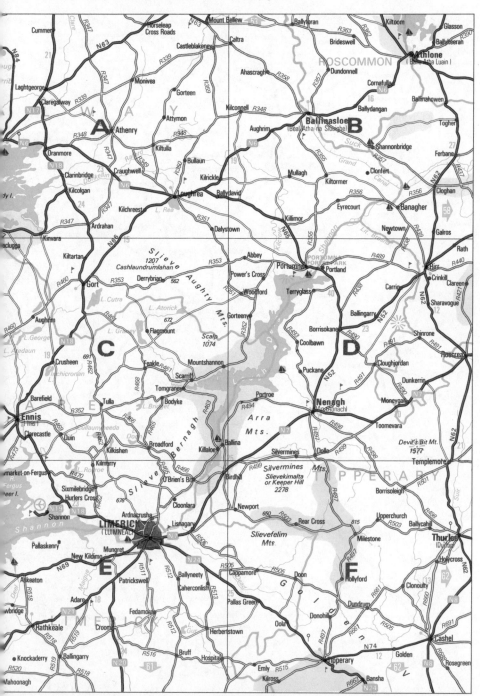

See article Motorway Junctions with Restricted Access, text page 40

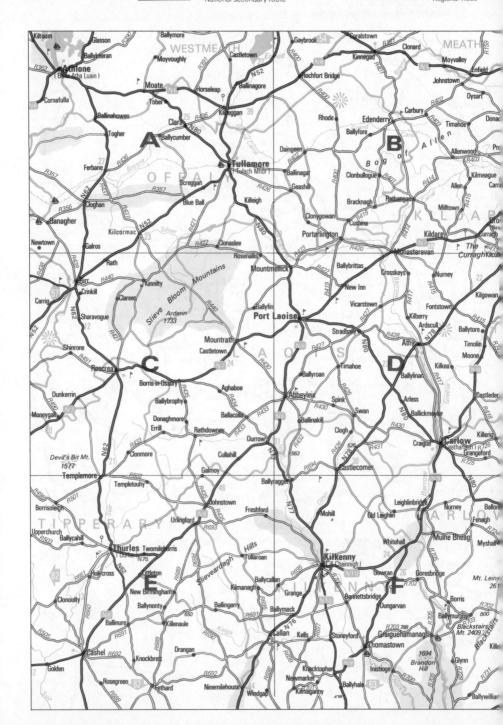

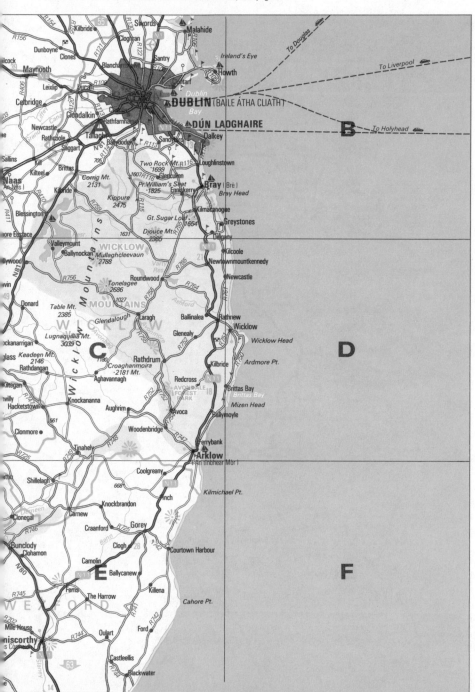

Unclassified Road ━━━━━

'See article Motorway Junctions with Restricted Access, text page 40

| 0 | | 5 | 10 | 15 Miles |
| 0 | 4 | 8 | 16 | 24 Km |

A

Kilbride
Swords
Malahide
R154
R156
R130
Cloghran
R121
Dunboyne
Clones
Santry
ilcock
Maynooth
Blanchard
Ireland's Eye
Howth
To Douglas
To Liverpool
R406
Leixlip
Lucan
R109
Celbridge
Clondalkin
Rathfarnham
DUBLIN [BAILE ÁTHA CLIATH]
Dublin Bay
Newcastle
Rathcoole
Tallaght
Ballyboden
Sandyford
DÚN LAOGHAIRE
Dalkey
To Holyhead

B

Saggart
N81
R113
Sallins
Kill
Kilteel
Brittas
Two Rock Mt. R116
'1699
Loughlinstown
Naas
An Nás)
Corrig Mt.
2131
1607
Glencullen
Pr.William's Seat
·1825
Enniskerry
Bray (Brè)
Bray Head
Kilbride
Kippure
2475
Gt. Sugar Loaf
1654
Kilmacanogue
Blessington
Djouce Mt.
2385
Delgany
Greystones
ore Eustace
Valleymount
1631
Ballynockan
Mullaghcleevaun
2788
Kilcoole
Newtownmountkennedy
R756
Roundwood
R765
Newcastle
R764
lwood
Tonelagee
2686
R755
Ashford
vin
Donard
Table Mt.
2385
1027
MOUNTAINS
Glendalough
Laragh
Ballinalea
Rathnew
Glenealy
Wicklow
Wicklow Head

C

Lugnaquillia Mt.
3039
Keadeen Mt.
2146
Rathdangan
Rathdrum
Croaghanmoira
·2181 Mt.
Kilbride
Ardmore Pt.
Aghavannagh
Redcross
ickanarrigan
glass
Kiltegan
Knockananna
Aughrim
Avoca
Brittas Bay
Mizen Head
wily
Hacketstown
561
Ballymoyle
Clonmore
Woodenbridge
R747
Tinahely
Ferrybank
R725
Arklow
[An tinbhear Mór]

D

E

Coolgreany
Shillelagh
668
Inch
Kilmichael Pt.
attin
Knockbrandon
Clonegal
Carnew
Craanford
R725
Gorey
Bunclody
Clohamon
Clogh
Courtown Harbour
Camolin
Ballycanew
N80
Ferns
The Harrow
Killena
Cahore Pt.
R745
WEXFORD
R702
Mile House
niscorthy
s Corbaid
Oulart
Ford
R744
63
Castleellis
14
Blackwater

F

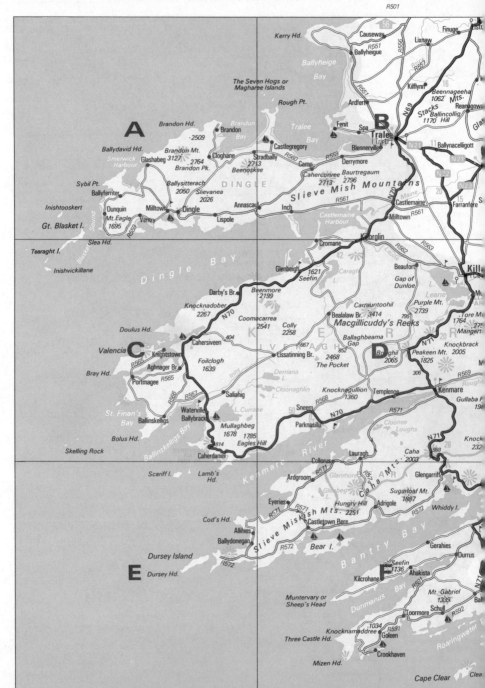

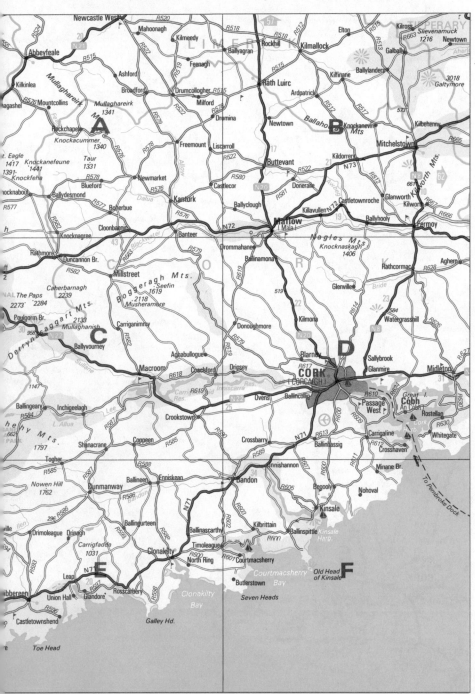

Unclassified Road ───────

0   5   10   15 Miles
0   4   8   16   24 Km

See article Motorway Junctions with Restricted Access, text page 40

Unclassified Road

0 ... 5 ... 10 ... 15 **Miles**
0 ... 4 ... 8 ... 16 ... 24 **Km**

See article Motorway Junctions with Restricted Access, text page 40

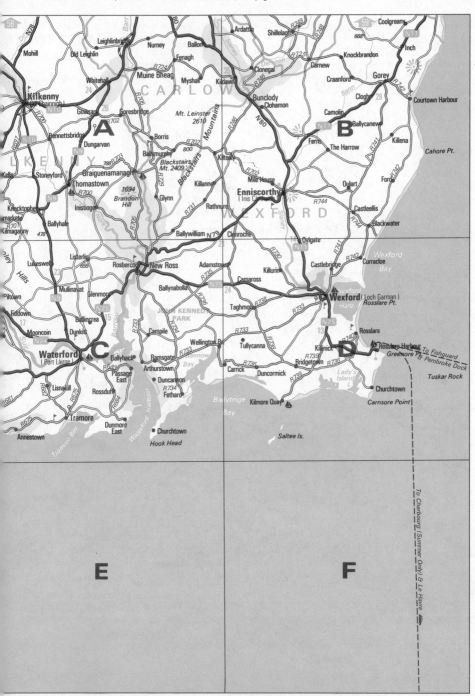

PRINCIPAL MOTORWAYS

Motorways

Motorways under construction

Selected Trunk Roads

| 0 | Miles | 10 |
| 0 | Kilometres | 16 |

ALL THE BEST IN TYRES, BATTERIES AND EXHAUSTS.

Tremendous value and top brands together with free fitting and safety checks to the highest standards. All backed by powerful guarantees.

ALL PART OF THE SERVICE.

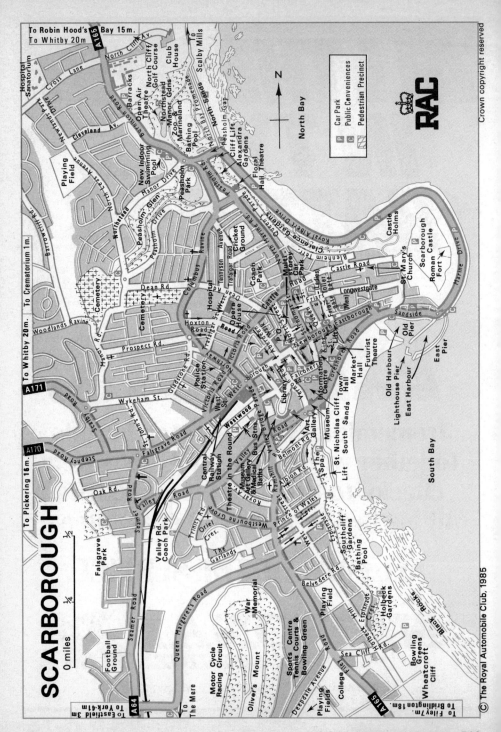

WT (b) £91, (c) £66, DT (b) £13·50, ②, Bk
£2·50, D £5.
Roseleigh, PH, *33 Valley Rd, YO11 2LY.*
✆ (0723) 361998.
Savoy, H, z (Rl), *24 Prince of Wales Ter,
Southcliff, YO11 2AN.* ✆ (0723) 367178.
Open Apr–Nov. C. ⊯ 44 bedrs, 12 ba.
⌂ Lt, CH, TV, CF, 10 st.
Sefton, PH, z, *18 Prince of Wales Ter,
YO11 2AL.* ✆ (0723) 372310. Closed
Jan–Feb. C 5. ⊯ 16 bedrs, 3 bp, 5 ba, Dgs.
⌂ Lt, CH, TV. £ BB £8·20–£8·78, DB
£16·40–£19·86, WT (a) £88–£98, (b) £76–
£80, DT (a) £13·23–£13·80, ①.
Valley Lodge, H, z, *51 Valley Rd, YO11
2LX.* ✆ (0723) 75311.
Wave Crest, H, z (Rl), *34 Prince of Wales
Ter, YO11 2AN.* ✆ (0723) 373129. Open
Mar–Oct & Xmas. C. ⊯ 15 bedrs, 4 ba,
Dgs. ⌂ ch, TV, CP 2, CF, 2 st. £ BB £9·75,
DB £19·50, WT (b) £82·50, DT (b) £12·75,
②, Bk £2·50, L £3·50, D £4·75.
Weydale, H, z (Rl), *Weydale Av, YO12
6BA.* ✆ (0723) 373393. Open Apr–Oct.
C 3. ⊯ 30 bedrs, 2 bp, 8 bps, 4 ba, ns, Dgs.
⌂ CH, TV, CP 16, ① BB £9–£12·50,
DB £18–£25, WT £71·70–£89·70, DT
£11·95–£14·95, ①, D £4·50.

Repairers: Arundale of Scarborough Ltd,
Northway. ✆ (0723) 363533.
Thompson of Scarborough Ltd,
Westborough. ✆ (0723) 360333.
Rescue Services: Pavilion Garage,
Pavilion Ter. ✆ (0723) 373259.
Quarry Garage, Crossgates. ✆ (0723)
862268.
Robsons Motors, Wrea La. ✆ (0723)
370207.
Scarborough Filling Station, Crossgates.
✆ (0723) 862277.▲

SCILLY ISLES
See ISLES OF SCILLY

SCOLE Norfolk. Map 16D
Pop 1,134. Colchester 40, London 96,
Bury St Edmunds 22, East Dereham 28,
Great Yarmouth 34, Ipswich 23,
Lowestoft 29, Norwich 19, Saxmundham
24, Stowmarket 18, Thetford 18.
EC Wed. **Golf** Diss 9h. **See** Scole Inn,
Church with stained glass window by
Patrick Reyntiens, 'Crossways' (Tudor
House—now restaurant), Old Mill at
Billingford 1 m.

★Scole Inn, *Diss, IP21 4DR.* ✆ Diss
(0379) 740481. C. ⊯ 8 bedrs, 2 bp, 3 ba,
annexe 12 bedrs, 12 bp, TV, Dgs. ✗ a l c,
mc, LD 10. ⌂ CH, TV, CP 60, Ac, con 40,
CF, 7 BGf, 1 st. £ BB £20·50–£26, DB £29–
£36, WB, ②, Bk £3·50, L £6·50, D £6·50,
cc 1 2 3 5 6.

SCOPWICK Lincolnshire M Area 23C
Pop 627 (inc Kirby Green), Sleaford 8½,
London 123, Grantham 21, Horncastle 20,
Lincoln 10, Market Rasen 20, Newark 22.
Golf Blankney 18h. **See** Water mill
(disused), old Church.

Rescue Service: Leonard Brackenbury,
The Garage, Camp Rd. ✆ Metheringham
(0526) 20238.

SCOTCH CORNER North Yorkshire.
Map 24F
Boroughbridge 28, London 236, A1 (M)
Motorway 1½, Brough 24, Darlington 7½,
Leyburn 15, Middleton-in-Teesdale 21,
West Auckland 14.

EC Wed. **Golf** Richmond 18h. **See**
Barnard Castle ruins 12½ m NW, Richmond
Castle, ruins of Easby Abbey, Stanwick
fort (all nearby).

★★★Scotch Corner, *Gt North Rd, DL10
6NR.* ✆ Richmond (N. Yorks) (0748)
2943. C. ⊯ 45 bedrs, 37 bp, 4 ba, TV, Dgs.
✗ a l c, mc, at, LD 10. ⌂ Lt, N, CH, Dgs, CP
150, G 15, Ac, con 350, CF, 3 st. £ BB £25–
£28, DB £40–£46, DBB £22–£36, WB, ①,
Bk £4·25, L £5, D £7·50, cc 1 2 3 4 5 6,
Dep b.

SCUNTHORPE Humberside (South
Humberside). Map 25B
Pop 66,047. Lincoln 28, London 161,
M181 Motorway 2, Doncaster 22,
Gainsborough 16, Goole 21, Grimsby 30,
Hull 26, Market Rasen 22, Thorne 14.
MD Fri, Sat. **Golf** Scunthorpe 18h. **See**
Church of St Laurence (Norman with
12th–13th cent additions), Normandy Hall
and Gardens, Borough Museum and Art
Gallery, Roman mosaic in Civic Centre,
Parish Church of St John, 13th cent St
Peter's Church.

★★★Wortley, *Rowland Rd, DN16 1SU.*
✆ (0724) 842223. C. ⊯ 26 bedrs, 23 bp, 3
ba, TV, Dgs. ✗ a l c, mc, at, LD 9.30. ⌂ N,
CH, TV, Dgs, ns, CP 200, Ac, con 300, CF, 1
st. £ BB £22–£33·50, DB £35–£40, WB, ①,
Bk £3·50, L £4·50, D £5·50, cc 1 2 3 5.
★★★Royal, *Doncaster Rd, DN15 7DE.*
✆ (0724) 868181. C. ⊯ 33 bedrs, 33 bp,
TV, Dgs. ✗ mc, at, LD 9.45. ⌂ N, CH, TV,
CP 36, Ac, con 240, CF, 2 st. £ BB £33, DB
£41, WB, ②, Bk £3·50, L £8·65, D £8·65,
cc 1 2 3 4 5 6, Dep b.

Rescue Services: Dolphin Motors,
Moorwell Rd Industrial Estate. ✆ (0724)
867526.
Rainton of Ashby Ltd, Collum Av.
✆ (0724) 844146.
Turners (Berkeley Services) Ltd,
Doncaster Rd. ✆ (0724) 860212.

SEAFORD East Sussex. Map 7F
Pop 18,000. Lewes 10, London 61,
Eastbourne 8½, Hastings 24, Newhaven 3½.
EC Wed. **MD** Thur. **Golf** Seaford Head
18h. **See** Parish Church (Norman origin),
Martello Tower, Seaford Head, Cuckmere
Haven (birdlife).
⎚ The Downs, Sutton Rd. ✆ Seaford
(0323) 892224.

★★M Ladbroke, *On A259 at Newhaven,
BN25 2RB.* ✆ (0323) 891055.
Avondale, PH, z (Unl), *5 Avondale Rd,
BN25 1RJ.* ✆ (0323) 890008. Closed
Xmas. C. ⊯ 6 bedrs, 6 sh, 2 ba. ⌂ CH, TV, 3
st. £ BB £8–£9·25, DB £16–£18·50, WT (b)
£77–£87·75, DT £12·50–£13·75, ①.
Redriff, G, z (l lnl) *96 Claremont Rd,
BN25 2QA.* ✆ (0323) 891981. C 9. ⊯ 4
bedrs, 1 ba, Dgs. ⌂ CH, TV, CP 4, 1 st.
£ BB £8–£8·50, DB £16–£17, WT (b)
£73·50–£77, (c) £49–£52·50, DT £11·50–
£12, ①.

MC Repairer Eric Kennard & Co, Seaford
Motorcycles, Steyne Road Filling Station,
Steyne Rd. ✆ (0323) 903669.
Rescue Service: Brooklyn Motors
(Seaford), 8 Richmond Rd. ✆ (0323)
893040.

SEAHAM Durham. Map 24E
Pop 22,033. A1 (M) Motorway 10,
Stockton-on-Tees 22, London 265,

Durham 13, Tyne Tunnel 13, Newcastle
upon Tyne 19, Sunderland 5.
EC Wed. **Golf** Seaham Harbour 18h. **See**
St Marys Church.

Rescue Service: W W & A Padgett, New
Seaham Service Station, Mount Pleasant,
Stockton Rd. ✆ (0783) 813091.

SEAHOUSES Northumberland. Map 31B
Pop 1,709. Alnwick 14, London 321,
Berwick-upon-Tweed 22, Coldstream 29.
EC Wed. **Golf** Seahouses 18h. **See**
Bamburgh Castle, Sand Dunes, Farne
Islands—Bird Sanctuary and Seal Colony.
⎚ 16 Main St. ✆ Seahouses (0665)
720424.

★★Olde Ship, *9 Main St, NE68 7RD.*
✆ (0665) 720200. Open Apr–mid Oct. C.
⊯ 10 bedrs, 2 bp, 5 bps, 2 ba, TV. ✗ mc, at,
LD 7·45. ⌂ CH, TV, CP 10, U 2, CF, 1 BGf,
1 st, Dis. £ BB fr £12·50, DB fr £25, WT
£130–£140, DBB fr £19, ①, Bk £3, L £3, D
£6·50, Dep a.
▣★Beach House (R), *Seafront, NE68
7SR.* ✆ (0665) 720337. Open Mar–Oct. C.
⊯ 14 bedrs, 7 bp, 7 bps, 3 ba, TV, Dgs.
✗ mc, LD 8. ⌂ CH, CP 16, CF, 2 BGf, 0 st,
Dis. £ BB £13–£19, DB £26–£34, WB, ②, D
£7·50, cc 1 3.
Bamburgh Castle, H, x (Rl), *NE68 7SQ.*
✆ (0665) 720283. Closed Dec. C. ⊯ 22
bedrs, 5 ba, Dgs. ⌂ CH, TV, Dgs, CP 34,
CF, 4 st. £ BB £12·50, DB £24, WT (b)
£120, DT (b) £17·50, ①, Bk £2·50, L £3·50,
D £5.▲

SEASCALE Cumbria. Map 26F
Pop 1,585. Broughton-in-Furness 37,
London 314, Egremont 5.
EC Wed. **Golf** Seascale 18h. **See** Calder
Abbey ruins 2 m N.

▣★Sea Field (R), *Drigg Rd, CA20 1NS.*
✆ (0940) 28298. Closed Sep, Xmas & New
Year. C 7. ⊯ 9 bedrs, 4 bps, 2 ba, Dgs.
✗ LD 8. ⌂ CH, TV, Dgs, CP 9, 2 st. £ BB
£12·50–£15, DB £20–£23, DBB £18·50–
£21, ①, Bk £2·50, L £3·50, D £6·50.

SEATON Cornwall. Map Area 3C
Plymouth 17, London 228, Liskeard 9,
West Looe 5½.

Blue Haven, PH, x (Rl), *Looe Hill, PL11
3JQ.* ✆ (050 35) 310. C. ⊯ 6 bedrs, 2 bps,
2 ba, Dgs. ⌂ ch, TV, Dgs, CP 6, CF, 3 BGf.
£ BB £8–£9·50, DB £16–£21·50, WT (b)
£78–£83, (c) £50–£55, DT (b) £12·25–
£13·75, ①, D £4·25.

SEATON Devon. Map 5E
Pop 5,000. Axminster 6½, London 153,
Exeter 22, Honiton 11, Lyme Regis 7½.
EC Thur. **MD** Mon. **Golf** Axecliffe 18h.
See Church, Site of Roman buildings—
Moridunum Seaton Down Rd, Site of
Roman Villa off Homer La.
⎚ The Esplanade. ✆ Seaton (0297)
21660.

★★Bay, *East Walk, EX12 2NP.*
✆ (050 35) 20073.
Check House, G, yz (Unl), *Beer Rd,
EX12 2 PR.* ✆ (0297) 21858. Open Apr–
Sep. C 8. ⊯ 9 bedrs, 2 bp, 1 bps, 2 ba.
⌂ CH, TV, CP 10, U 1, 1 BGf. £ BB £9·50–
£14, DB £19–£27, WT (b) £88–£102, DT
(b) £14–£15·50, ①.
Glendare, G, z (Rl), *46 Fore St, EX12
2AD.* ✆ (0297) 20542. Closed Dec. C 5.
⊯ 6 bedrs, 1 ba. ⌂ CH, TV, ns, 1 st. £ DB

£16–£18, WT (c) £52·50–£60, DT (b) £12–£13, ⬚.

Mariners Homestead, PH, z (R), *East Walk, Esplanade, EX12 2NP.* ✆ (0297) 20560. Open Feb–Oct. C 3. ⬚ 11 bedrs, 1 bp, 3 bps, 2 ba, TV, Dgs. ⬚ CH, TV, Dgs, CP 8, CF, 1 BGf, 2 st. £ BB £11–£15, DB £22–£27, WT (b) £105–£115, DT (b) £17–£18, ⬚, D £6, cc 3.

St Margarets, PH, z (Rl), *5 Seafield Rd, EX12 2QS.* ✆ (0297) 20462. Open Mar–Oct. C. ⬚ 9 bedrs, 5 bps, 1 sh, 2 ba, TV, Dgs. ✘ a l c. ⬚ CH, CP 6, CF, 1 BGf, 2 st. £ BB £9·50–£10·50, DB £15–£20, WT (b) £73·50–£89·50, DT (b) £12·25–£13·25, ⬚, Bk £1·50, L £2, D £4·75.

Thornfield, PH, y (R), *87 Scalwell Lane, EX12 2ST.* ✆ (0297) 20039. C. ⬚ 8 bedrs, 2 ba, Dgs. ⬚ CH, TV, CP 10, CF, 2 BGf, 3 st. £ BB £9–£11, DB £18–£22, WT (b) £94·50–£108·50, DT (b) £13·50–£15·50, ⬚, Bk £2, L £4, D £4·50.

SEATON SLUICE Northumberland. Map 32B
Newcastle upon Tyne 10, London 284, Alnwick 32, Coldstream 58, Sunderland (Fy) 14.
See Seaton Delaval Hall.

Rescue Service: Astley Garage, Links Rd. ✆ Seaton Delaval (0632) 371844.
Wilson & Young, Boundary Way. ✆ Seaton Delaval (0632) 371683.

SEAVIEW Isle of Wight. Map 6F
Pop 3,537 (inc St Helens). Ryde 2½, London (FY) 77, Newport 9, Sandown 6.
EC Thur. **Golf** Ryde 9h. **See** Flamingo Park.

★★**Seaview,** *High St, PO34 5EX.* ✆ (098 371) 2711. RS Sun. C. ⬚ 13 bedrs, 10 bp, 2 ba, Dgs. ✘ mc at, LD 9.30. ⬚ CH, TV, Dgs, CP 12, con 60, CF. £ BB £15–£20, DB £27–£34, DBB £22–£27, WB, ⬚, Bk £2·95, L £5·95, D £6·95, cc 1 2 3, Dep b.

SEDBERGH Cumbria. Map 26D
Pop 2,741. Kirkby Lonsdale 10, London 256, Brough 19, Hawes 15, Kendal 9½.
EC Thur. **MD** Wed. **Golf** Sedbergh 9h. **See** Well known Public School (to view apply in writing to Bursar), 12th cent Church, Friends Meeting House, 15th cent Middleton Hall, Cautley Scout Waterfall 4 m NE.
⬚ National Park Centre, 72 Main St. ✆ Sedbergh (0587) 20125

Rescue Service: R S Morphet Ltd, Central Garage, Bainbridge Rd. ✆ (0587) 20336.
Sedbergh Motor Co Ltd, Station Rd. ✆ (0587) 20678.

SEDGEBERROW Hereford & Worcester (Worcestershire). Map 14C
Pop 600. Stow-on-the-Wold 16, London 100, Cheltenham 13, Evesham 3½, Tewkesbury 9½.
EC Mon. **Golf** Evesham 18h. **See** Church of St Mary the Virgin, Thatched Cottages.

Rescue Service: Sedgeberrow Garages Ltd, Cheltenham Rd. ✆ Evesham (0386) 881208.

SEDGEBROOK Lincolnshire. M. Area 23C
Pop 289. 4 m W of Grantham, London 115, Melton Mowbray 15, Newark 12, Nottingham 19.
Golf Belton 18h. **See** Parish Church.

Rescue Service: Barrowby View Garage (Sedgebrook) Ltd. ✆ Bottesford (0949) 42990.

SEDGEFIELD Cleveland. Map 24E
Pop 6,072. Stockton-on-Tees 8, London 252, A1 (M) Motorway 2½, Durham 9, Darlington 13.
EC Wed. **MD** Tue. **Golf** Castle Eden 18h. **See** Church.

★★★**Hardwick Hall,** *TS21 2EH.* ✆ (0740) 20253. C. ⬚ 17 bedrs, 17 bp, TV. ✘ a l c, mc, LD 10. ⬚ CH, CP 300, Ac, con, CF, 0 st. £ BB £29, DB £37, DT £46, WB, ⬚, Bk £5·50, L £5·15, D £8·50, cc 1 2 3 5 6, Dep b.

★**Crosshill** (R), *TS21 2AB.* ✆ (0740) 20153. C. ⬚ 9 bedrs, 2 ba, TV, Dgs. ✘ a l c, mc, at, LD 10. ⬚ CH, CP 9, Ac, con 35, CF, 2 st. £ BB £16·50–£17·50, DB £22–£24, WT £147–£161, DT £21–£25, DBB £17·50–£23, WB, ⬚, Bk £2·50, L £5·50, D £7·50, Dep b.

Rescue Service: Anthony Turner, Rectory Row. ✆ (0740) 20338.

SEDLESCOMBE East Sussex. Map 10E
Pop 1,400. Hurst Green 6½, London 56, Eastbourne 15, Hastings 7, Hawkhurst 7½, Lewes 21, Rye 10.
EC Wed. **Golf** Beauport Park 18h. **See** Church, old houses, 17th cent Tithe Barn (now restaurant), Oaklands—English Pestalozzi Children's Village.

★★**Brickwall,** *The Green, TN33 0QA.* ✆ (042 487) 253. C. ⬚ 19 bedrs, 15 bp, 2 ba, TV, Dgs. ✘ at, LD 8.45. ⬚ CH, Dgs, CP 20, U 2, sp, con 20, CF, 9 BGf, 2 st. £ BB £20–£26, DB £30–£36, WT £189–£211·50, DT £28–£35, DBB £23–£32, WB, ⬚, Bk £3, L £5·50, D £8·25, cc 1 2 5, Dep a.

SELBORNE Hampshire. Map 6D
Pop 1,100. Alton 4½, London 52, Haslemere 12, Hindhead 11, Midhurst 13, Petersfield 7½.
EC Wed. **Golf** Blackmoor 18h. **See** 'The Wakes' (home of the naturalist the Rev Gilbert White, also housing the Oates Memorial Library and Museum), Old Church with memorial window to Rev Gilbert White, Selborne Hanger (Nat Trust).

★**Queens,** *High St, GU34 3JJ.* ✆ (042 050) 272. RS Dec 25 & 26. C. ⬚ 4 bedrs, 2 bps, 2 ba, annexe 5 bedrs, 4 bps, 1 ba, Dgs. ✘ a l c, mc, at, LD 9. ⬚ ch, Dgs, CP 40, Ac, con 30, CF, 2 BGf, 1 st. £ BB £11·50–£16·50, DB £21–£26, WT £126–£154, DT £18, DBB £24, WB, ⬚, Bk £2·60, L £4·10, D £6·30, cc 1 2 3 4 6.

SELBY North Yorkshire. Map 25D
See also SOUTH MILFORD
Pop 10,715. Thorne 12, London 180, Doncaster 20, Goole 12, Harrogate 29, Hull 34, Leeds 21, Market Weighton 18, Pontefract 13, York 13.
EC Thur. **MD** Mon, Fri. **Golf** Selby 18h. **See** Abbey Church, 18th cent Market Cross, old wooden Toll Bridge.

★★**Londesborough Arms,** *Market Pl, YO8 0NS.* ✆ (0757) 707355. C. ⬚ 34 bedrs, 12 bp, 8 sh, 4 ba, TV, Dgs. ✘ a l c, mc, at, LD 9.30. ⬚ N, CH, Dgs, CP 20, G 7, Ac, con 30, CF. £ BB fr £19, DB fr £29, WB, ⬚, Bk £2·75, L £4·25, D £6·50, cc 1 2 3 5, Dep b.

Hazeldene, G, z (Unl), *34 Brook St, YO8 0AR.* ✆ (0757) 704809. Closed Xmas. C. ⬚ 7 bedrs, 2 ba. ⬚ TV, CP 6. £ BB £9–£10, DB £17–£18, ⬚, Bk £1·75.

Repairer: Mackays of Selby Ltd, Central Garage, Gowthorpe. ✆ (0757) 702323.

SELLINDGE Kent. Map 10D
Pop 1,300. Ashford 6, London 62, Canterbury 14, Folkestone 10, Rye 20, Tenterden 15.
EC Wed. **Golf** Sene Valley 18h. **See** Parish Church.

Rescue Service: Norrington's (Sellindge) Ltd, Main A20 Rd. ✆ (030 381) 2120.

SENNEN Cornwall. Map 2E.
Penzance 9½, London 291.

■★★**Tregiffian Hotel** (R), *TR19 7BE.* ✆ (073 687) 408. C. ⬚ 11 bedrs, 3 bp, 8 bps, TV, Dgs. ✘ mc, at, LD 8.30. ⬚ CH, TV, CP 20, CF, 2 BGf, 1 st, Dis. £ BB £14–£17, DB £27–£33, DBB £17·50–£24, WB, ⬚, Bk £2·50, D £7·50, cc 1 3 5 6, Dep a.

Sunny Bank, H, x (R), *Seaview Hill, TR19 7AR.* ✆ (073 687) 278. C. ⬚ 12 bedrs, 2 bps, 10 sh, 2 ba, Dgs. ⬚ CH, TV, Dgs, CP 12, CF. £ BB £7·50–£8·50, DB £15–£19, WT £75–£84, ⬚.

SETTLE North Yorkshire. Map 27A
Pop 2,270. Burnley 23, London 229, Hawes 22, Kirkby Lonsdale 16, Skipton 16, Whalley 23.
EC Wed. **MD** Tue. **Golf** Settle 9h. **See** The Folly. The Shambles, Pig Yard Club Museum, Scaleber Foss, Giggleswick School Chapel, Ebbing and Flowing Well (Giggleswick), Stainforth Foss and Caterigg Foss at Stainforth, Victoria and Attermire Caves (for pot-holers).
⬚ Town Hall, Cheapside. ✆ Settle (072 92) 3617.

★★★**Falcon Manor,** *Skipton Rd, BD24 9BD.* ✆ (072 92) 3814. C. ⬚ 16 bedrs, 13 bp, 2 bps, 1 ba, TV, Dgs. ✘ mc, at, LD 9.30. ⬚ CH, CP 80, Ac, sol, con 60, CF, 1 st. £ BB fr £25, DB fr £38, DBB fr £28, WB, ⬚, Bk £4, D £7·90, cc 1 3 5.

★★**Royal Oak,** *Market Pl, BD24 9ED.* ✆ (072 92) 2561. C 5. ⬚ 6 bedrs, 5 bp, 1 bps, TV. ✘ a l c, mc, at, LD 10. ⬚ CH, CP 20, Ac, pf, CF, 2 st. £ BB £20, DB £35, DT fr £30, ⬚, Bk £4, L £3·50, D £6·50, Dep b.

Close House, F, xy (R), *Giggleswick, BD24 0EA.* ✆ (072 92) 3540. Open May–Sep. ⬚ 4 bedrs, 1 ba. ⬚ ch, ns, CP 6. £ BB £15–£16, DB £30–£32, WT (c) £94·50, DT (b) £24·50, ⬚, D £10.▲

Repairer: F H Ellis, West Yorkshire Garages. ✆ (072 92) 2529.

SEVENOAKS Kent. Map 7B
See also DUNTON GREEN.
Pop 20,000. Bromley 14, London 25, M25 Motorway 3½, Dartford 14, Dartford Tunnel 16, East Grinstead 17, Maidstone 16, Tonbridge 7, Westerham 6.
EC Wed. **MD** Mon, Wed. **Golf** Knole Park 18h. **See** Parish Church, Knole (Nat Trust), Ightam Mote 3½ m SE, Lullingstone Roman Villa 5 m N, Old Soar Manor 5 m .
⬚ Car Park, Buckhurst La. ✆ Sevenoaks (0732) 450305.

■★★**Sevenoaks Park** (R), *4 Seal Hollow Rd, TN13 3PH.* ✆ (0732) 454245. C. ⬚ 16 bedrs, 3 bp, 3 bps, 3 ba, TV. ✘ a l c, mc, at, LD 9.30. ⬚ CH, TV, CP 26, Ac, sp, con, CF,

1 BGf, 2 st. £ BB £20–£26, DB £23–£30, ②,
Bk £2·95, L £5·50, D £5·50, cc 1 2 3 5 6.
Moorings, PH, z (Rl), *97 Hitchen Hatch
La, TN13 3BE.* ✆ (0732) 452589. C. ⇔ 11
bedrs, 3 bps, 4 sh, 2 ba, TV. ⓓ CH, CP 25,
CF, 10 st. £ BB fr £17·25, DB fr £21·85, ①,
Bk £3·45, cc 1 3.

Repairers: Star Motors (Sevenoaks) Ltd,
128 Seal Rd. ✆ (0732) 451337.
Stormont Engineering Co (Sevenoaks)
Ltd, The Vine. ✆ (0732) 452341.
Specialist Body Repairer: Stormont
Engineering Co (Sevenoaks) Ltd, The
Vine. ✆ (0732) 452341.

SHAFTESBURY Dorset. Map 5D
Pop 5,213. Salisbury 20, London 103,
Blandford Forum 11, Frome 19, Ringwood
24, Shepton Mallet 20, Sherborne 16,
Warminster 15, Wincanton 11.
EC Wed. **MD** Thur. **Golf** Ashley Wood 9h.
See Abbey ruins, St Peter's Church,
Museum, Castle Hill, Gold Hill (medieval
wall, old cottages, viewpoint), Pyt House
4½ m NE, Wardour Castle 5 m NE.
[i] County Library, Bell St. ✆ Shaftesbury
(0747) 2256.

★★★**Grosvenor** (TH), *The Commons,
SP7 8JA.* ✆ (0747) 2282. C. ⇔ 48 bedrs,
40 bp, 2 bps, 3 ba, TV, Dgs. ✖ a l c, mc, at,
LD 9. ⓓ N, CH, Dgs, Ac, con 200, CF, 1 st.
£ BB £34, DB £41–£50·50, WB, ①,
cc 1 2 3 4 5 6, Dep (Xmas).
★★★**Royal Chase,** *Royal Chase
Roundabout, SP7 8DB.* ✆ (0747) 3355. C.
⇔ 18 bedrs, 11 bp, 3 bps, 2 sh, 2 ba, TV,
Dgs. ✖ a l c, mc, at. ⓓ CH, TV, Dgs, CP
200, Ac, con 40, CF. £ BB £14–£39, DB
£28–£56, WB, ①, Bk £4·50, L £8, D £8,
cc 1 2 3 5 6.
★**Grove House** (R), *Ludwell, SP7 9ND.*
✆ Donhead (074 788) 365. C 5. ⇔ 12
bedrs, 1 bp, 6 bps, 2 ba. ✖ LD 7.30. ⓓ CH,
TV, Dgs, ns, CP 12, 2 st. £ D £6·75, cc 1 3.

Rescue Service: Causeway Garage,
Sherborne Causeway (A30). ✆ (0747)
2479.
Five Square Motors, Salisbury Rd.
✆ (0747) 2295.

SHALDON Devon. Map 3D
Pop 2,000. Exeter 16, London 183,
Newton Abbot 5, Torquay 6.
EC Thur. **Golf** Teignmouth 18h. **See**
Tunnel through Cliffs to Beach. Children's
Zoo.

◪★**Glenside** (R), *Ringmore Rd, TQ14
0EP.* ✆ (062 687) 2448. Open Mar–Oct. C.
⇔ 12 bedrs, 3 bp, 4 bps, 2 ba, TV, Dgs.
ⓓ ch, Dgs, CP 12, U 1, CF, 1 BGf, 4 st.
£ BB £8·50–£9·50, DB £17–£22, WT (b)
£79·50–£96, (c) £58–£66·50, DT (b) £13–
£15, ①, Bk £3·50, L £4·50, D £5·50, cc 1 3.

SHANKLIN Isle of Wight. Map 6F
Pop 7,400. Sandown 2, London (Fy) 82,
Newport 9, Ventnor 3½.
EC Wed. **Golf** Sandown and Shanklin
18h. **See** The Chine, Old cottages, 12th
cent Church, thatched Crab Inn,
Luccombe Common and Chine.
[i] 67 High St. ✆ Shanklin (098 386) 2942.

★★★**Cliff Tops,** *Park Rd, PO37 6BB.*
✆ Isle of Wight (0983) 3262.
★★★**Shanklin,** *1 East Mount Rd, PO37
6DL.* ✆ I.O.W. (0983) 862286. Open Apr–
Sep. C. ⇔ 69 bedrs, 47 bp, TV, Dgs. ✖ mc,
at, LD 8.30. ⓓ Lt, N, CH, TV, CP 40, U 1, G
1, Ac, con 150, CF, 2 BGf, 1 st, Dis. £ Dep.

◪★★**Brunswick House** (Rl), *Queen's
Rd, PO37 6AN.* ✆ Isle of Wight (0983)
3245.
★★**Luccombe Hall** (R), *Luccombe Rd,
PO37 6RL.* ✆ Isle of Wight (0983)
862719. Open Apr–Oct. RS Feb, Mar &
Nov. C. ⇔ 32 bedrs, 22 bp, 3 bps, 2 ba, TV,
Dgs. ✖ LD 8.30. ⓓ N, CH, TV, Dgs, CP 26,
Ac, sp, tc, CF, 7 BGf, 1 st, Dis. £ BB
£13·50–£24, DB £24–£38, WT £110–£165,
DT £22·50–£31·50, DBB £18–£27, WB, ②,
Bk £4·50, L £4·50, D £9·50, cc 1 3, Dep a.
★★**Melbourne-Ardenlea** (R), *Queens
Rd, PO37 6AP.* ✆ Isle of Wight (0983)
862283. Open Mar–Oct. C. ⇔ 47 bedrs,
17 bp, 2 bps, 4 ba, TV, Dgs. ✖ LD 8. ⓓ CH,
TV, Dgs, CP 12, Ac, con 30, CF, 8 BGf, 0 st,
Dis. £ BB £10–£15, DB £20–£30, WT
£133–£161, DT £19–£23, DBB £15–£20,
WB, ①, Bk £3·45, L £4·60, D £5·75.
◪★★**Monteagle** (Rl), *Priory Rd, PO37
6RJ.* ✆ Isle of Wight (0983) 862854.
Closed mid Oct–mid Mar. C 5. ⇔ 40
bedrs, 21 bp, 9 bps, 1 sh, 4 ba, ns, TV, Dgs.
✖ mc, at, LD 8. ⓓ N, CH, CP 30, Ac, sp,
con, CF. £ BB £10–£16, DB £20–£36, WB,
①, Bk £3·50, L £4, D £7, Dep a.
◪★★**Ocean View** (R), *Esplanade, PO37
6BL.* ✆ Isle of Wight (0983) 862602. Open
Mar–Oct. C. ⇔ 36 bedrs, 4 bp, 13 bps, 8
sh, 4 ba, Dgs. ✖ mc, at, LD 8. ⓓ CH, TV,
Dgs, CP 25, CF, 2 st. £ BB £10·25–£15, DB
£20·50–£30, DBB £15·75–£20·75, WB, ②,
Bk £3·70, D £6·25, cc 1 2 3.
◪★**Fern Bank** (Rl), *6 Highfield Rd, PO37
6PP.* ✆ Isle of Wight (0983) 862790. Open
Jan 15–Dec 24. C 7. ⇔ 20 bedrs, 7 bp, 8
bps, 4 ba, TV, Dgs. ⓓ CH, TV, ns, CP 16, 1
BGf. £ BB £10·10–£13·15, DB £20·20–
£26·30, DBB £15·60–£17·15, ②, Bk £1·50,
D £4, cc 1 3.
Afton, H, z (R), *Clarence Gdns, PO37
6HA.* ✆ Isle of Wight (0983) 863075.
Open Feb–Nov. C 5. ⇔ 9 bedrs, 6 bps, 2
ba, TV. ⓓ CH, TV, CP 4, 1 BGf, 8 st. £ WT
(b) £113·34–£124·67, DT (b) £18·75–
£20·62, ②, D £6·50. ▲
Alleyn, G, z (Unl), *16 Victoria Av, PO37
6PN.* ✆ Isle of Wight (0983) 866435.
Open Feb–Nov. C ⇔ 5 bedrs, 1 ba, Dgs.
ⓓ CH, TV, Dgs, CP 3, CF. £ BB £7–£8, DB
£14–£16, WT (b) £60–£68, DT (b) £9·50–
£10·50, ①, Bk £2, D £2·50.
Aqua, H (Rl), *Esplanade, PO37 6BN.*
✆ Isle of Wight (0983) 863024. Open
Mar–Nov. C. ⇔ 24 bedrs, 2 bp, 4 ba. ⓓ ch,
TV, CP 2, CF, 1 st. £ BB £6·50–£15, DB
£13–£30, WT (b) £57·50–£110, DT (b)
£8·50–£16, ①, Bk £3·50, L £3·50, D £5,
cc 1 3.
Avenue, PH, z (Rl), *35 Victoria Av, PO37
6LT.* ✆ Isle of Wight (0983) 862386. Open
Apr–Sep. C ⇔ 10 bedrs, 2 bps, 6 sh, 1 ba.
ⓓ ch, TV, CP 10, CF, 1 st.
Bay House, H, x (Rl), *0 Chine Av, Keats
Green, PO36 6AN.* ✆ Isle of Wight (0983)
3180. C. ⇔ 20 bedrs, 16 bp, 4 sh, 2 ba, TV,
Dgs. ⓓ CH, TV, Dgs, CP 25, G 2, CF, 8 BGf,
1 st. £ BB £11–£16, DB £22–£32, WT £98–
£115, DT £15–£17·50, ①.
Berry Brow, PH, y (R), *Popham Rd,
PO37 6RE.* ✆ Isle of Wight (0983)
862825.
Culver, PH, z (Rl), *Culver Rd, PO37 6ER.*
✆ Isle of Wight (0983) 863515. Open
Mar–Nov. C 10. ⇔ 8 bedrs, 2 bp, 6 bps, 1
ba, TV, Dgs. ⓓ CH, CP 7, 6 st. £ BB £10–
£14, DB £20–£28, WT (b) £98–£126, (c)
£70–£98, DT (b) £14–£18, ①, Bk £2, L
D £2·50, D £5.

Fawley, H, z (Rl), *12 Hope Rd,
PO37 6EA.* ✆ Isle of Wight (0983)
862190. Open Apr–Oct. C 5. ⇔ 13 bedrs,
2 ba. ⓓ TV, ns, CP 12, 3 st. £ BB £9·50–
£10·50, DB £19–£21, WT (b) £75–£85, DT
£11·50–£13·50, ①, Bk £2, D £4.
Hambledon, H, z (Rl), *11 Queens Rd,
PO37 6AW.* ✆ Isle of Wight (0983)
862403.
La Turbie, PH (R), *Culver Rd, PO37 6ER.*
✆ Isle of Wight (0983) 862767. C. ⇔ 15
bedrs, 1 bp, 6 bps. ⓓ TV, CP 8, CF. £ BB
£6–£8, DB £24·40–£33·60.
Osborne House, PH, z (R), *Esplanade,
PO37 6BN.* ✆ Isle of Wight (0983)
862501. Closed Dec. C 5. ⇔ 15 bedrs, 1
bp, 9 bps, 2 ba. ⓓ CH, TV, 7 st. £ BB fr
£10·35, DB fr £20·70, ②, Bk £3, D £5·75.
Overstrand, PH, y (R), *Howard Rd,
PO37 6HD.* ✆ Isle of Wight (0983)
862100. Open Mar–Oct. C. ⇔ 15 bedrs, 5
bp, 6 bps, 3 ba, TV. ⓓ CH, TV, CP 20, CF, 2
st. £ BB £10–£14·50, DB £18–£27, DT
£86–£114, ②, Bk £2, D £5, cc 1.
Perran Lodge, PH, z (Rl), *2 Crescent Rd,
PO37 6DH.* ✆ Isle of Wight (0983)
862816.
Pulboro, H, z (Rl), *6 Park Rd, PO37 2DT.*
✆ Isle of Wight (0983) 862740. Open Apr–
Oct. C. ⇔ 14 bedrs, 4 bps, 1 sh, 2 ba. ⓓ ch,
TV, CF. £ BB £9–£12, DB £18–£27, WT (b)
£75–£98, DT (b) £12–£15, ①.
Royson, PH (Rl), *Littlestairs Rd, PO37
6HS.* ✆ Isle of Wight (0983) 862163.
Open Mar–Sep. C 1. ⇔ 9 bedrs, 1 sh, 1 ba.
ⓓ ch, TV, CP 8, CF, 1 st. £ BB £8·50, DB
£17, WT £69–£75, DT £11, ①.
Somerton Lodge, PH (R), *43 Victoria Av,
PO37 6LT.* ✆ Isle of Wight (0983)
862710. Closed Dec. C ⇔ 20 bedrs, 10
bps, 1 sh, 2 ba. ⓓ CH, TV, CP 11, CF, 5 BGf,
1 st, Dis. £ BB £9–£12, DB £18–£24, WT
(b) £76–£87, DT (b) £11–£12·50, ①.
Victoria Lodge, PH, y (Rl) *Alexandra
Rd, PO37 6AF.* ✆ Isle of Wight (0983)
862361. Open Apr–Oct. C. ⇔ 22 bedrs, 6
bp, 5 bps, 2 ba. ⓓ CH, TV, CP 20, CF. £ BB
£9–£14, DB £18–£32, WT (b) £79–£118,
DT £15–£19, ①, cc 1 3.

Repairer: Davies Garage (Shanklin) Ltd,
Sandown Rd. ✆ Isle of Wight (0983)
862744.

SHAP Cumbria. Map 26D
Pop 1,343. Kendal 16, London 273, M6
Motorway 3, Penrith 9.
EC Thur. **Golf** Appleby 18h. **See** Abbey
ruins, Parish Church, Keld Chapel, old
Market Cross, Stone Circles (Druidical
remains).

★★**Shap Wells,** *CA10 3QU.* ✆ (093 16)
628. Closed Jan–mid Feb. C. ⇔ 73 bedrs,
45 bp, 3 bps, 7 ba, Dgs. ✖ a l c, mc, at, LD
9. ⓓ N, CH, TV, Dgs, CP 200, Ac, tc, pf, con
100, CF, 7 BGf, U st, Dis. £ BB £13–£20, DB
£24–£35, DBB £18·75–£22, WB, ①, Bk £3,
L £4, D £7·50, cc 1 2 3 5 6.

Rescue Service: T Simpson & Sons, Shap
Garage, Main St. ✆ (093 16) 212.

SHAPWICK Somerset. Map 5C
Pop 420. Street 4, London 132,
Bridgwater 9, Bristol 32, Dorchester 38,
Ilminster 21, Taunton 18.
Golf Enmore Park 18h.

◪⬛★★**Shapwick House,** *TA7 9NL.*
✆ Ashcott (0458) 210321. C. ⇔ 12 bedrs,
6 bp, 6 bps, Dgs. ✖ mc, at, LD 9. ⓓ CH, TV,
Dgs, CP 98, U 2, con 30, CF, 0 st. £ BB fr

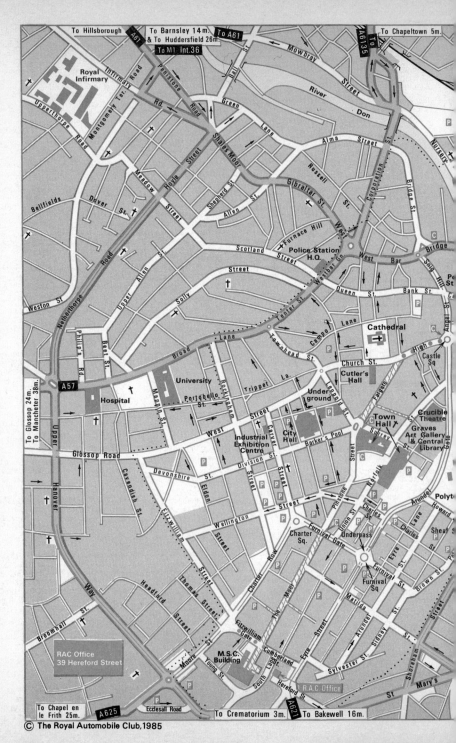

For abbreviations see inside back cover-

To Chapeltown 5m

A6135

Carlisle St.

Spital Hill

A6109 To Rotherham 6m
To M1. Int. 34

Street

Attercliffe Road

A6178

To M1 Int. 34

Savile

Station

Station St.

River Don Street
Effingham

Foley St.

Effingham Road

B6107

Sussex Street

Sheffield Canal Street

Lumley

Wicker

P

Furnival Rd.

P

P

Blonk St.

legate

C

stle rket

C

hange St.
Sheaf Market

Bernard

To Worksop 18m.
To M1 Int. 34

A57 A630 To M1. Int. 33

Cricket Inn Road

Park Square

P

Broad St.

Maltravers

Road

ercial St.

P

P

ow St.

Reed St.

Bernard Street

N

).

d Hill

South Street

Granville Street

Duke Street

Oaks Road

Manor

Park Hill Lane

RAC

Sheaf Baths

La.

Sheaf Street

PARK
HILL

• • Buses only
P Car Park
C Public Conveniences
· · · · Parking Meter Zone
⊠ Pedestrian Precinct

Bungay St.

Talbot St.

Blagden St.

SHEFFIELD

and on

Almshouses

Gleadcoe Road

0 miles ¼

Shrewsbury Road

Granville Street

Norfolk Road

Fitzwalter Rd.

Stafford Rd.

City Road

Granville Road

A6134

Granville Road

A616 To M1 Int. 30

Norfolk Park

To Chesterfield 12 m.

To Eckington 9m. & Newark

Crown copyright reserved

£25, DB fr £38, DBB fr £29, WB, ②, Bk £4,
D £10, cc 1 2 3 5 6, Dep a.

SHAW Greater Manchester. M. Area 27B
Pop 17,500. Oldham 3, London 189,
Halifax 16, Huddersfield 16, Manchester
10, Rochdale 4.
EC Tue. **MD** Thur. **Golf** Crompton and
Royton 18h.

Rescue Service: Queen Anne Garage Ltd,
Church Rd. ✆ (0706) 47472.

SHAWELL Leicestershire. Map Area 14B.
Intersection 18 M1 6, London 86,
Coventry 15, Leicester 17, Market
Harborough 14, Northampton 20.

Rescue Service: Gibbetts Cross Garage,
Watling St. ✆ Swinford (078 885) 457.

SHEDFIELD Hampshire. Map 6D.
Wickham 1½, London 69, Portsmouth 13,
Southampton 10, Winchester 14.

★★★M Meon Valley, *Sandy La, SO3
2HQ.* ✆ Wickham (0329) 833455. C. ⊯ 54
bedrs, 54 bp, TV, Dgs. ✗ a l c, mc, at, LD
9.45. ⓕ N, CH, TV, CP 250, Ac, sp, gc, tc,
sc, sb, sol, con 120, CF, 5 BGf, 1 st. £ BB
£35, DB £42, WB, ①, Bk £4·20, L £6·25, D
£8·25, cc 1 2 3 5 6, Dep b.

SHEERNESS Kent. Map 10A.
Pop 13,141. Rochester 18, London 50,
Ashford 29, Canterbury 25, Maidstone 18,
Margate 41.
EC Wed. **MD** Tue. **Golf** Sheerness 18h.

Rescue Services: Deltunes, Swale Auto
Point, Halfway Rd. ✆ (0795) 667578.

SHEFFIELD South Yorkshire. Map 22B
RAC Office, *39 Hereford St, Sheffield,
S1 4PP.* ✆ (General) Sheffield (0742)
737944 (Rescue Service only), Sheffield
(0742) 25882.
Pop 544,200. Mansfield 22, London 154,
M1 Motorway Int. 30, 10, Barnsley 14,
Buxton 25, Chapel-en-le-Frith 23,
Chesterfield 12, Glossop 24, Huddersfield
26, Rotherham 5½, Worksop 18.
See Plan, pp. 326 and 327.
EC Thur. **MD** Daily exc Thur. **P** See Plan.
Golf Abbeydale 18h, Beauchief 18h, Dore
and Totley 18h, etc. **See** Cathedral,
University, City Museum and Mappin Art
Gallery, Graves Art Gallery, Cutlers Hall,
RC Cathedral, City Hall, New Crucible
Theatre, 17th cent Oakes Park, Abbeydale
18th cent Industrial Hamlet, Kelham
Industrial Museum.
ⓘ Central Library, Surrey St. ✆ Sheffield
(0742) 734760.

★★★★Grosvenor House (TH), *Charter
Sq, S1 3EH.* ✆ (0742) 20041. C. ⊯ 121
bedrs, 103 bp, 6 ba, TV, Dgs. ✗ a l c, mc, at,
LD 9.45. ⓕ Lt N, CH, Dgs, G 82, Ac, con
600, CF, 0 st. £ BB £45·50, DB £57, WB, ①,
cc 1 2 3 4 5 6.
★★★★Hallam Tower Post House (TH),
Manchester Rd, S10 5DX. ✆ (0742)
686031. C. ⊯ 135 bedrs, 135 bp, TV, Dgs.
✗ a l c, mc, LD 9.30. ⓕ Lt, N, CH, Dgs, CP
120, Ac, con 300, CF, 0 st. £ BB £43, DB
£55, WB, ①, cc 1 2 3 4 5 6, Dep (Xmas).
★★★★St George, *Kenwood Rd, S7 1NQ.*
✆ (0742) 583811. C. ⊯ 119 bedrs, 108
bp, 8 bps, 3 ba, TV, Dgs. ✗ a l c, mc, at, LD
10. ⓕ Lt, N, CH, CP 160, Ac, pf, con 100,
CF, 30 BGf, 1 st. Dis. £ BB £19·50–£38·50,
DB £37·50–£51·50, DBB £27–£46, WB, ①,
Bk £5·50, L £5·50, D £7·50, cc 1 2 3 5 6,
Dep b.

★★★Kenwood (R), *Kenwood Rd, S7
1NQ.* ✆ (0742) 583691.
■★★★Roslyn Court, *180 Psalter La, S11
8US.* ✆ (0742) 666188. C. ⊯ 31 bedrs, 20
bp, 11 bps, TV, Dgs. ✗ mc, at, LD 8.45.
ⓕ N, CH, Dgs, CP 40, Ac, con 15, CF, 5
BGf, 3 st. £ BB £22, DB £34, WT £175·50,
DT £29·50, DBB £27, ①, Bk £3, D £5,
cc 1 2 5, Dep b.
★★Rutland, *452 Glossop Rd, S10 2PY.*
✆ (0742) 665215. RS Dec 25 & 26. C.
⊯ 73 bedrs, 67 bp, 2 bps, 4 sh, 7 ba,
annexe 17 bedrs, 16 bp, 1 bps, TV, Dgs.
✗ a l c, mc, at, LD 9.30. ⓕ N, CH, TV,
CP 80, Ac, con 70, CF, 1 st. £ BB £19–
£27·50, DB £36, WB, ①, Bk £3·50, L £3·95,
D £6·25, cc 1 2 3 5 6, Dep b.
■★★St. Andrews, *46 Kenwood Road,
S7 1NQ.* ✆ (0742) 550309. C. ⊯ 41
bedrs, 9 bp, 21 bps, 3 ba, TV, Dgs. ✗ a l c,
mc, LD 8.45. ⓕ N, CH, TV, Dgs, CP 100, Ac,
con 30, CF, 2 st. £ BB £20, DB fr £30, DT
£40·70, DBB fr £25·95, WB, ②, Bk £3·56, L
£4·75, D £5·95, cc 1 2 3 5 6, Dep b.
Millingtons, G, z (Unl), *70 Broomgrove
Rd, S10 2NA.* ✆ (0742) 669549. C 12.
⊯ 7 bedrs, 3 bp, 1 bps, 3 sh, 2 ba, TV.
ⓕ CH, TV, Dgs, CP 4, 3 st. £ BB £10–£11,
DB £20, WT (c) £70.
Sharrow View, H (R), *13 Sharrow View,
S7 1ND.* ✆ (0742) 51542. C. ⊯ 26 bedrs,
7 bp, 7 ba, ns, TV, Dgs. ✗ a l c. ⓕ CH, TV,
CP 34, CF, 3 BGf. £ BB £14·50–£20, DB
£24·50–£34, WT £90, DT £19·45, ①, Bk
£2·50, L £3·60, D £4·95.
Valley View, G (Unl), *715 Manchester
Rd, S10 5PS.* ✆ (0742) 302885. C. ⊯ 4
bedrs, 3 ba. ⓕ CP 6, G 2, 4 st. £ BB £10,
DB £18, WT (b) £80·50, DT (b) £12·50, ②.

Repairers: Bramall of Sheffield, 1 Savile
St. ✆ (0742) 751565.
Ernest W Hatfield Ltd, 100 Corporation
St. ✆ (0742) 730291.
Millhouses Engineering Co Ltd, 968
Abbeydale Rd. ✆ (0742) 362292.
Turret Motor Co, 245 Eccleshall Rd.
✆ (0742) 685922.
Rescue Service: Arundel Motors Ltd, 296
Middlewood Rd. ✆ (0742) 343444.
Heeley Bridge Garage Ltd, Broadfield Rd.
✆ (0742) 588121.
Hoggs, S B (Garages) Ltd, Toll Bar Garage,
187 Burngreave Rd. ✆ (0742) 22902.
Meersbrook Garage, 1 Meersbrook Rd.
✆ (0742) 57315.
Park Garage (Swallownest) Ltd, Park Hill,
Swallownest. ✆ (0742) 692411.
Richardson Motorcycles, Intake Service
Station, 21 Mansfield Rd. ✆ (0742)
396001.
Sandygate Motor Services Ltd,
Sandygate Rd. ✆ (0742) 302021.

SHEFFORD Bedfordshire. Map 15D
Pop 3,225. Hatfield 20, London 40,
Baldock 7½, Bedford 9½, Biggleswade 5,
Bletchley 15, Dunstable 17, Luton 14.
EC Wed, Sat. **MD** Fri. **Golf** Beadlow
Manor 18h and 9h.

Repairer: John R Ford & Sons Ltd,
Ampthill Rd. ✆ Hitchin (0462) 813242.

SHELDWICH Kent. M. Area 10C
2½ m S of Faversham. Pop 450. Rochester
20, London 52, Ashford 10, Canterbury 11,
Hawkhurst 26, Maidstone 20, Margate 26,
Tunbridge Wells 35.
Golf Belmont 18h. **See** Church, Lees
Court.

Rescue Service: Stocks Garage, Ashford
Rd. ✆ Faversham (079 582) 2404.

SHEPLEY West Yorkshire. M. Area 25F
and 33C
Pop 2,300. Sheffield 20, London 180,
Barnsley 12, Glossop 16, Huddersfield 6½,
Oldham 18, Stockport 22, Wakefield 20.
EC Tue. **Golf** Woodsome Hall 18h.

Repairer: Gill of Sovereign Ltd.
✆ Huddersfield (0484) 606666.
Rescue Service: Shepley Coachworks
Ltd, Abbey Rd. ✆ Huddersfield (0484)
602780.

SHEPSHED Leicestershire. M. Area 22F
Pop 10,129. M1 Motorway 1½, Leicester
13, London 110, Burton-on-Trent 17,
Derby 16, Loughborough 5.
EC Wed. **MD** Fri. **Golf** Longcliffe 18h.
See Church, Monastery, Windmill.

Rescue Service: Poyser & Rutherford
(Armetts Garage), Brook St. ✆ (050 95)
3207.

SHEPTON MALLET Somerset. Map 5C
Pop 6,600. Frome 11, London 118, Bristol
20, Crewkerne 26, Glastonbury 9,
Ilminster 27, Radstock 9, Shaftesbury 20,
Sherborne 25, Wells 5½, Wincanton 12.
EC Wed. **MD** Fri. **Golf** Mendip 9h. **See**
Rebuilt Church (12th cent nave), 16th
cent Market Cross, 17th cent
Almshouses, Museum.

★★★Charlton House (R), *Charlton Rd,
BA4 4PR.* ✆ (0749) 2008. Closed Xmas &
1st 2 weeks Jan. C. ⊯ 12 bedrs, 12 bp, 2
ba, TV. ✗ a l c, mc, at, LD 9. ⓕ N, CH, CP
40, G 4, sp, tc, sb, sol, con 35, CF, 3 st. £ BB
£26–£33, DB £38–£40, WB, ①, Bk £3·50, L
£8·50, D £11.50, cc 1 2 3 5 6.
★★Shrubbery (R), *Commercial Rd, BA4
5BU.* ✆ (0749) 2555.

Rescue Service: Moff Motors Ltd,
Allhampton Ditcheat. ✆ Castle Cary
(0963) 310.
Shepton Mallet Motors, Townsend Rd.
✆ (0749) 2864.
Williams, G & Son, Charlton Garage.
✆ (0749) 2517.

SHERBORNE Dorset. Map 5C
Pop 7,572. Shaftesbury 16, London 120,
Blandford Forum 20, Crewkerne 14,
Dorchester 18, Frome 22, Glastonbury 20,
Shepton Mallet 25, Wincanton 9.
EC Wed. **MD** Mon. **Golf** Sherborne 18h.
See Abbey Church, Sherborne School
(incorp Abbey remains), 16th cent Chapel,
ruins of Sherborne Old Castle, Sherborne
Castle, Museum, Almshouses.
ⓘ Hound St. ✆ Sherborne (0935) 815341.

★★★M Post House (TH), *Horsecastles
La, DT9 6BB.* ✆ (0935) 813191. C. ⊯ 60
bedrs, 60 bp, TV, Dgs. ✗ a l c, mc, ac, LD
10. ⓕ N, CH, Dgs, CP 100, Ac, con 80, CF,
30 BGf, 3 st. £ BB £38·50, DB £51, WB, ①,
cc 1 2 3 4 5 6, Dep (Xmas).
★★Eastbury (R), *Long St, DT9 3BY.*
✆ (0935) 813387. C. ⊯ 15 bedrs, 5 bp, 3
ba, Dgs. ✗ a l c, mc, at, LD 8.15. ⓕ ch, CP
20, G 3, Ac, con 60, CF, 0 st. £ BB £15–£18,
DB £27–£33, WT £144–£162, DT £24–£27,
DBB £20–£25, WB, ①, Bk £3·25, L £4, D
£6·50.
■★★Saffron House (R), *The Avenue,
DT9 3AH.* ✆ (0935) 812734. Closed Dec
24–Jan 1. C. ⊯ 6 bedrs, 5 bp, 1 bps, Dgs.
✗ LD 8.45. ⓕ CH, TV, CP 20, con 60, CF, 3 st.

£ BB £18·50, DB £37, WT £190, DT £32·25, DBB £25·50, ②, Bk £2·50, L £6·75, D £7.

Repairer: F W B Saunders Ltd, Digby Rd. ☎ (0935) 812436.
Rescue Service: Westbury Garage, Lower Acreman St. ☎ (0935) 4781.

SHERFIELD-ON-LODDON Hampshire. Map 6B
Pop 1,600. Bagshot 18, London 44, Basingstoke 4½, Farnham 15, Reading 11.
Golf Hartley Wintney 9h. **See** NT Tudor Mansion.

Repairer: Dodd's Garage. ☎ Basingstoke (0256) 882271.

SHERINGHAM Norfolk. Map 16C
Pop 5,515. Cromer 4, London 137, Fakenham 18.
EC Wed. **MD** Sat. **Golf** Sheringham 18h. **See** Upper Sheringham Church, Beeston Priory ruins at Beeston Regis, North Norfolk Railway (Preserved Steam Trains).
🅟 Station Car Park. ☎ Sheringham (0263) 824329.

■★★**Southlands** (R), *South St, NR26 8LL.* ☎ (0263) 822679. C. ⇔ 21 bedrs, 9 bp, 3 ba, TV, Dgs. ✕ mc, at, LD 8. 🅓 CH, CP 20, con 100, CF, 1 st. **£** BB fr £17·50, DB fr £35, DBB fr £26·50, ②, Bk £5·50, D £8·60.

Beacon, H (RI), *1 Nelson Rd, NR26 8BT.* ☎ (0263) 822019. Open Apr–Oct. C 12. ⇔ 8 bedrs, 3 ba. 🅓 CH, TV, CP 8, 2 st. **£** BB £12, DB £24, WT (b) £95, DT (b) £16, ①, D £5·50, cc 1 3.

Melrose, PH, z (Unl), *9 Holway Rd, NR26 8HN.* ☎ (0263) 823299. C 5. ⇔ 9 bedrs, 2 ba. 🅓 CH, TV, CP 10, 0 st. **£** BB £7·50–£9, DB £15–£18, WT (b) £69·50–£79·50, DT (b) £11–£13, ①.

Rescue Service: Central Garage (Sheringham) Ltd, High St. ☎ (0263) 823168.▲
Sheringham Garage (Coredale) Ltd, 46 Cromer Rd. ☎ (0263) 822022.

SHERINGTON Buckinghamshire. M. Area 15C.
Newport Pagnell 2, London 54, M1 Motorway 4, Bedford 12, Buckingham 16, Milton Keynes 7, Northampton 16.

Rescue Service: Dorrill Auto Services, Water La. ☎ Newport Pagnell (0908) 612615.

SHERSTON Wiltshire. Map 5B
Pop 1,410. Swindon 20, London 98, Bath 18, Bristol 21, Chippenham 11, Tetbury 5½.
EC Wed. **Golf** Westonbirt 18h. **See** 17th & 18th cent buildings.

Rescue Service: Gray's Garage. ☎ (066 649) 302.

SHIFNAL Salop. Map 19F
Pop 6,045. Wolverhampton 12, London 136, M54 Motorway 3, Bridgnorth 10, Lichfield 24, Newport 8, Wellington 6.
EC Thur. **Golf** Shifnal 18h. **See** 12th cent Parish Church, 19th cent RC Church, old houses, Tong Church and Castle 2½ m E, Boscobel House 5½ m E, Weston Park (1671) 4 m NW.

★★★**Park House,** *Park St, TF11 9BA.* ☎ Telford (0952) 460128. RS 24–30 Dec. C. ⇔ 21 bedrs, 13 bp, 8 bps, TV, Dgs. ✕ a l c, mc, at, LD 9·45. 🅓 N, CH, Dgs, CP

80, Ac, sp, con 20, CF, 2 st. **£** BB £20–£40, DB £35–£55, WT £350–£450, DT £50–£65, WB, ②, Bk £3, L £10, D £18, cc 1 2 3 5, Dep b.
Old Bell, I, *Church St.* ☎ Telford (0952) 460475.

Rescue Service: George Oakley & Co, (Ag. Div), W & S, Ltd, Park St. ☎ Telford (0952) 460631.
Paton's (Shifnal) Ltd, Cheapside. ☎ Telford (0952) 460412.
Repairer: George Oakley & Co (Ag Div) W & S Ltd, Park St. ☎ Telford (0952) 460631.

SHIPHAM Somerset. Map 5A
Pop 1,050. M5 Motorway 7, Axbridge 3, London 135, Bath 24, Bristol 15, Bridgwater 18, Wells 11, Weston-super-Mare 9.
Golf Wells 18h.

★**Penscot Farmhouse** (R), *BS25 1TW.* ☎ Winscombe (093 484) 2659. Open Feb–Nov & Xmas. C. ⇔ 18 bedrs, 6 bp, 3 ba, Dgs. ✕ a l c, mc, at, LD 9. 🅓 CH, TV, Dgs, CP 20, Ac, sp, con 30, CF, 2 BGf, 5 st. **£** BB £13·50, DB fr £22, DBB fr £16·50, WB, ②, Bk £1·50, D £3·50, cc 1 2 3 5, Dep a.

SHIPLEY West Yorkshire. Map 25F and 33A
Pop 31,700. Bradford 3, London 199, Harrogate 15, Leeds 10, Skipton 16.
EC Wed. **MD** Fri, Sat. **Golf** Northcliffe 18h. **See** Saltaire Village, built 1851–76.

MC Repairer: Jefferies (Saltaire) Motor Co, 206 Saltaire Rd. ☎ Bradford (0274) 587451.

SHIPSTON-ON-STOUR Warwickshire. Map 14D
Pop 3,136. Oxford 28, London 87, Banbury 14, Chipping Norton 10, Moreton-in-Marsh 7, Stratford-upon-Avon 10, Warwick 16.
EC Thur. **Golf** Stratford 18h. **See** Compton Wynyates 5 m E.

Bell, I, z, *Sheep St, CV36 4AF.* ☎ (0608) 61443. C. ⇔ 8 bedrs, 2 bp, 3 ba, TV, Dgs. ✕ a l c. 🅓 CH, TV, Dgs, CP 25, CF, 0 st. **£** BB £15·53–£24·73, DB £21·28–£30·48, WT (c) fr £105 (b) fr £126, (a) fr £154, ①, Bk £2·95, L £3·50, D £6·25, cc 1 2 3 5.

Rescue Service: Charles Osborne Motor Repairs, 24 Stratford Rd. ☎ (0608) 61871.

SHIPTON-UNDER-WYCHWOOD Oxfordshire. Map 14F
Pop 1,100. Burford 4, London 79, Chipping Norton 6½, Stow-on-the-Wold 9½.
Golf Burford 18h. **See** Church, Old Inn (15th cent Hospice).

Rescue Service: D J Johnson, Station Rd Garage. ☎ (0993) 830249.

SHIREMOOR Tyne & Wear. M. Area 32B
Pop 8,969. Newcastle upon Tyne 6, London 279, Whitley Bay 3½, Seaton Delaval 3.
EC Wed. **Golf** Backworth 9h.

Rescue Service: Webster & Kidd Auto Services, Algernon Industrial Estate. ☎ Whitley Bay (0632) 521222.

SHIRLEY West Midlands. Map 21D
Pop 30,400. Warwick 15, London 108, Birmingham 6, Bromsgrove 16, Coventry

15, Evesham 24, Stratford-upon-Avon 17, Sutton Coldfield 12.
EC Wed. **Golf** Shirley 18h.

Repairer: Archer's (Shirley) Ltd, Stratford Rd. ☎ 021-744 1710.
Specialist Body Repairer: John Fitzpatrick Motors Ltd, 17 Stratford Rd. ☎ 021-745 5811.
Rescue Service: Cranmore Garage (Shirley) Ltd, Drayton Rd, Cranmore Industrial Estate. ☎ 021-704 1181.
Streetsbrook Service Station, Streetsbrook Rd. ☎ 021-744 1251.

SHOEBURYNESS Essex. Maps 10A and 17D
See also SOUTHEND-ON-SEA
Southend-on-Sea 4½, London 46.
EC Wed.

Rescue Service: Wakefield & Sage Ltd, Ness Rd. ☎ (037 08) 2616.

SHOREHAM BY SEA West Sussex. Map 7E
Pop 20,935. Crawley 22, London 52, Brighton 6, Horsham 18, Pulborough 15, Worthing 4½.
EC Wed. **Golf** West Hove 18h. **See** 10th cent St Nicholas Church, Marlipins 12th cent stone and flint toll house now museum, Parish Church of St Mary.

Pende-Shore, PH, z (RI), *416 Upper Shoreham Rd, BN4 5NE.* ☎ (07917) 452905. Closed 2 weeks Xmas. C. ⇔ 18 bedrs, 2 bp, 3 ba, TV. 🅓 CH, TV, CP 8, CF, 2 st. **£** BB £15·64–£22, DB £27·95–£33·52, WT (c) £97·80–£117, DT (b) £22·44–£24·40, ①, Bk £2·25, D £6·80.

Repairers: Endeavour Motor Co (Hove) Ltd, Old Shoreham Garage, 434 Upper Shoreham Rd. ☎ (079 17) 4971.
Riverside Motors, 25 Shoreham Rd. ☎ (079 17) 3195.
Rescue Service: Frost's (Cars) Ltd, 398 Brighton Rd. ☎ (079 17) 61411.
Southwick Garage Service Centre, 161 Old Shoreham Rd, Southwick. ☎ Southwick (038 778) 592460.

SHOTTISHAM Suffolk. Map 17A
Pop 179. Ipswich 14, London 88, Saxmundham 16, Scole 31.
Golf Woodbridge 18h. **See** Church with 13th cent Priests' doorway.

■▲♣★★**Wood Hall,** *Wood Hall Dr, IP12 3EG.* ☎ (0394) 411283.

SHREWSBURY Shropshire. Map 19E
Pop 87,300. Wellington 11, London 154, Bridgnorth 21, Knighton 34, Llangollen 29, Ludlow 27, Newcastle-under-Lyme 32, Newport 18, Stone 34, Welshpool 18, Whitchurch 18, Wrexham 29.
EC Thur. **MD** Tue, Wed, Fri, Sat. **Golf** Meole Brace 9h. **See** Castle, Council House, Abbey Church, Public School (old school buildings now Museum and Free Library), Ireland's Mansion, St Chad's Church, St Mary's Church, St Alkmund's Church, 16th cent Rowley's House Museum, RC Cathedral, old Market Hall, Statue of Charles Darwin, Natural History Museum and Art Gallery, Owens Mansions, Butcher Row (15th cent buildings), Clive House Museum, remains of Town Walls, Attingham Park 4 m SE, Wroxeter Roman City remains 5 m SE.
🅟 The Square. ☎ Shrewsbury (0743) 52019.

★★★**Ainsworth's Radbrook Hall,**
Radbrook Rd, SY3 9BQ. ✆ (0743) 4861. C.
🛏 43 bedrs, 35 bp, 8 bps, 1 ba, TV, Dgs.
✗ a l c, mc, at, LD 9.30. 🅿 N, CH, TV, Dgs,
CP 200, Ac, sc, sb, sol, con 350, 5 BGf, 0 st,
Dis. £ BB £25, DB £36, DT £39, DBB £32,
WB, ②, Bk £3·50, L £6, D £7, cc 1 2 3 5.▲
★★★**Lion** (5H), *Wyle Cop, SY1 1UY.*
✆ (0745) 53107. C. 🛏 60 bedrs, 60 bp, TV,
Dgs. ✗ a l c, mc, LD 10. 🅿 Lt, N, CH, Dgs,
CP 32, G 40, Ac, con 250, CF, 0 st. £ BB
£35·50, DB £53·50, WB ①, cc 1 2 3 4 5 6,
Dep (Xmas).
★★★**Lord Hill,** *Abbey Foregate, SY2
6AX.* ✆ (0743) 52601. C. 🛏 22 bedrs, 15
bp, 7 bps, annexe 24 bedrs, 24 bp, TV, Dgs.
✗ a l c, mc, at, LD 9.15. 🅿 N, CH, Dgs, CP
200, Ac, con 200, CF, 8 BGf, 1 st, Dis. £ BB
£30·50, DB £42, WB, ②, 10%, Bk £3·50, L
£5·25, D £5·75, cc 1 2 3 5 6, Dep b.
★★★**Prince Rupert,** *Butcher Row, SY1
1UQ.* ✆ (0743) 52461. C. 🛏 70 bedrs, 46
bp, 8 bps, sh, 4 ba, TV, Dgs. ✗ a l c, mc,
at, LD 10.15. 🅿 Lt, N, CH, TV, CP 50, Ac,
con 60, CF, 1 st. £ BB fr £28, DB fr £38, DT
fr £34, DBB fr £27·50, WB, Bk £3·50, L
£6·50, D £8·50, cc 1 2 3 5 6, Dep b.▲
★★**Beauchamp,** *The Mount, SY3 8PJ.*
✆ (0743) 3230. RS Sun, C. 🛏 24 bedrs, 7
bp, 4 bps, 4 ba, TV, Dgs. ✗ mc, at, LD 9.
🅿 CH, TV, Dgs, CP 150, Ac, con, CF, 5 BGf,
0 st, Dis. £ BB fr £18, DB fr £29, DBB
£24·50, WB, ①, Bk £2·50, L £4·75, D £6·50,
cc 1 2 3 5.
▥★★**Britannia,** *Mardol, SY1 1PU.*
✆ (0743) 61246. RS Dec 24–Jan 4. C.
🛏 25 bedrs, 12 bp, 5 ba, TV, Dgs. ✗ mc, LD
9. 🅿 N, ch, TV, CP 30, G 3, Ac, con 70, CF,
1 st. £ BB £25, DB £35, WB, ② 10%, Bk
£3·30, L £2·50, D £7·60, cc 1 2 3 5 6,
Dep b.
▥▲★★**Shelton Hall,** *Shelton, SY3 8BH.*
✆ (0743) 3982. C. 🛏 11 bedrs, 2 bp, 4
bps, 1 sh, 1 ba, TV. ✗ LD 9. 🅿 CH, TV, CP
70, pf, con 40, CF, 1 BGf, 1 st, Dis. £ BB
£17·50–£26, DB £26–£30, WT £192–£297,
DT £27·50–£42·50, DBB £21·50–£34·50,
①, Bk £4·50, L £6, D £8·50, cc 1 3.
★**Abbey Gardens** (Rl), *Whitehall St, SY2
5AB.* ✆ (0743) 56538.

Repairers: Charles Clark & Son Ltd, 6
Chester St. ✆ (0743) 57231.
Frank Painter & Sons, Service Garage,
Ditherington. ✆ (0743) 62023.
Rescue Service: Belle Vue Service Station,
Belle Vue Rd. ✆ (0743) 56295.
Diamond Motor Services, Amoco Service
Station, St Michael's St. ✆ (0743) 65980.
Furrows Ltd, Mobil Station, Whitchurch
Rd. ✆ (0743) 52174.
T W Morris & Sons (Recovery), Walford
Garage, Bomere Heath. ✆ Bomere Heath
(0939) 290380.

SHREWTON Wiltshire. Maps 5D and 6C
Pop 2,000. Amesbury 6, London 85,
Devizes 13, Salisbury 11, Warminster 13,
Wincanton 27.
EC Wed. **Golf** High Post, Salisbury 18h.
See Church.

Rescue Service: Bridge Garage (Repairs),
Maddington St. ✆ (0980) 620349.

SHRIVENHAM Oxon (Wilts). Map 6A
Pop 2,152. M4 Motorway 7½, London 76,
Lambourn 9, Faringdon 5, Highworth 3½,
Marlborough 15, Swindon 5½.
EC Thur. Sat. **Golf** Bremhill 18h. **See**
15th–17th cent Church, Memorial Hall.

Rescue Service: Swan Hill Garage,
Townsend Rd. ✆ Swindon (0793)
783323.

SHURDINGTON Gloucestershire. Map
14E
Cheltenham 3½, London 100,
Andoversford 7, Gloucester 7, Stroud 10.

Rescue Service: Wren Car Sales,
Twynings Service Station, Shurdington
Rd. ✆ Cheltenham (0242) 862510.

SIDFORD Devon. Map 4F
Pop 1,990. Honiton 7½, London 160,
Axminster 12, Exeter 14, Lyme Regis 14.
EC Thur. **Golf** Sidmouth 18h.

★**Applegarth** (Rt), *Church St, EX10 9QP.*
✆ Sidmouth (039 55) 3174. Closed mid
Oct–mid Nov & Dec 27–30. RS Dec 25–26
also Tues & Sun. C 10. 🛏 8 bedrs, 2 ba,
Dgs. ✗ a l c, mc, LD 9.30. 🅿 ch, TV, Dgs,
ns, CP 15, Ac, 2 BGf, 1 st. £ BB £10–£12,
DB £20–£24, DBB £16–£20, WB, ①, Bk £3,
L £3·75, D £6, cc 2 3 6 , Dep a.

Rescue Service: Hamilton Garage, Church
St. ✆ Sidmouth (039 55) 3334.

SIDMOUTH Devon. Map 4F
Pop 12,446 Honiton 9½, London 162,
Axminster 14, Exeter 16, Lyme Regis 16.
EC Thur. **Golf** Sidmouth 18h. **See** Norman
Lockyer Observatory, Museum at Hope
Cottage, ancient Sidbury Church.
🛈 The Esplanade. ✆ Sidmouth (039 55)
6441.

★★★★**Victoria,** *Esplanade, EX10 8RY.*
✆ (039 55) 2651. C. 🛏 62 bedrs, 62 bp,
TV, Dgs. ✗ a l c, mc, at, LD 9. 🅿 Lt, N, CH,
TV, CP 90, U 6, G 4, sp, tc, sb, con 110,
CF, 1 st. £ BB £21–£36, DB £44–£65, WT
£184–£320, DT £26–£46, DBB £23–£43,
WB, ②, Bk £5, L £8, D £11·50, cc 1 2 3 5 6,
Dep b.▲
▥★★★**Bedford,** *Esplanade, EX10 8NR.*
✆ (039 55) 3047. Open Mar–Oct. C. 🛏 40
bedrs, 22 bp, 5 bps, 3 ba, TV, Dgs. ✗ mc,
at, LD 8.30. 🅿 Lt, N, CH, TV, CF, 4 BGf, 4 st.
£ BB £15–£23, DB £16–£24, DT £23–£34,
DBB £20–£32, WB, ①, Bk £3·50, D £8,
cc 2 3, Dep a.
★★★**Belmont,** *Esplanade, EX10 8RX.*
✆ (039 55) 2555. Closed Jan 1–Feb 15.
C 2. 🛏 50 bedrs, 50 bp, 3 ba, TV, Dgs.
✗ a l c, mc, at, LD 8.30. 🅿 Lt, N, CH, TV, CP
32, Ac, CF, 1 BGf, 2 st. £ BB £25–£30, DB
£50–£60, DT £27–£34, WB, ①, Bk £5, L £7,
D £8, cc 1 2 3 5.
★★★**Fortfield,** *Fortfield Pl, EX10 8NU.*
✆ (039 55) 2403. C. 🛏 55 bedrs, 31 bp, 3
bps, 6 ba, TV, Dgs. ✗ mc, at, LD 8.30. 🅿 Lt,
N, CH, TV, CP 60, sp, sb, sol, con 30, CF, 2
BGf, 2 st. £ BB £21–£28, DB £36–£56,
DBB £21–£31, WB, ②, Bk £3·50, D £6·50,
cc 1 3 5 6, Dep a.
★★★**Riviera,** *Esplanade, EX10 8AY.*
✆ (039 55) 5201. C. 🛏 34 bedrs, 22 bp, 4
bps, 5 ba, TV, Dgs. ✗ a l c, mc, at, LD 9.
🅿 Lt, N, CH, TV, Dgs, CP 12, G 9, Ac, con
80, CF, 1 st. £ BB £18·50–£29·50, DB £37–
£58·50, DBB £35–£33, WB, ①, Bk £5, L
£8, D £10, cc 2 5.▲
★★★**Royal Glen,** *Glen Rd, EX10
8RW.* ✆ (039 55) 3221. C 8. 🛏 37 bedrs,
18 bp, 9 bps, 3 ba, TV, Dgs. ✗ a l c, mc, at,
LD 7.30. 🅿 CH, TV, CP 16, Ac, 1 BGf, 1 st.
£ BB £11·45–£21·55, DB £22·90–£45·48, WT
£99·80–£175·30, DT £14·26–£27·56, DBB
£13–£25·72, WB, ②, Bk £3·25, L £4·75, D
£5, cc 2 3.

★★★**Royal York,** *Esplanade, EX10 8AZ.*
✆ (039 55) 3043. C. 🛏 40 bedrs, 14 bp, 2
bps, 8 ba, TV, Dgs. ✗ mc, at, LD 8. 🅿 Lt,
CH, TV, CP 5, Ac, con 50, CF, 2 st. £ BB
£13·80–£19·90, DB £27·60–£39·80, WT
£129·15–£194, DT £18·75–£28·50, DBB
£14·75–£24·50, WB, ①, Bk £3·50, L £4·80,
D £6·50, cc 1 3.
★★★**Salcombe Hill House,** *Beatlands
Rd, EX10 8JQ.* ✆ (039 55) 4697. Open
Mar–Oct. C 3. 🛏 33 bedrs, 22 bp, 3 bps, 5
ba, TV, Dgs. ✗ mc, at, LD 8. 🅿 Lt, N, CH,
TV, CP 35, U 5, sp, tc, con 25, CF, 2 BGf, 1
st, Dis. £ BB £17–£25, DB £34–£50, WT
£145–£198, DT £21–£32, DBB £19–£30,
WB, ①, Bk £4, L fr £4·50, D fr £6, cc 1 3,
Dep a.▲
★★★**Westcliff,** *Manor Rd, EX10 8RU.*
✆ (039 55) 3252. Closed Jan. RS Nov–
Dec & Feb–Mar. C. 🛏 38 bedrs, 29 bp, 1
bps, 3 ba, TV. ✗ mc, at, LD 8.30. 🅿 Lt, CH,
TV, Dgs, ns, CP 50, sp, con 50, CF, 5 BGf, 2
st. £ BB £11·65–£24, DB £23·30–£48, WT
£122–£199·50, DBB £19–£32, WB, ①, Bk
£3·85, D £8·50, cc 1 3, Dep a.
▣★★**Abbeydale** (R), *Manor Rd, EX10
8RP.* ✆ (039 55) 2060. Open Mar–Oct. C
4. 🛏 17 bedrs, 16 bp, 1 bps, TV. ✗ mc, at,
LD 8.30. 🅿 CH, CP 24, CF, 1 BGf, 1 st.
£ BB £16–£20, DB £32–£40, DBB £22–
£26, WB, ②, Bk £3, D £6·50, Dep a.
▲▣★★**Brownlands,** *Sid Rd, EX10 9AG.*
✆ (039 55) 3053. C. 🛏 17 bedrs, 4 bp, 5
bps, 2 ba, Dgs. ✗ mc, at, LD 8. 🅿 CH, TV,
ns, CP 30, U 2, Ac, con 25, CF, 4 BGf, 2 st.
£ DBB fr £18, WB, ①, D £5·50, Dep a.▲
★★**Byes Links** (R), *Sid Rd, EX10 9AA.*
✆ (039 55) 3129.
★★**Faulkner,** *Esplanade, EX10 8BA.*
✆ (039 55) 3043. C. 🛏 24 bedrs, 16 bp, 8
ba, TV, Dgs. ✗ mc, at, LD 8. 🅿 Lt, CH, TV,
CP 5, Ac, con 50, CF, 4 BGf, 2 st. £ BB
£13·80–£19·90, DB £27·60–£39·80, WT
£129·15–£194, DT £18·75–£28·50, DBB
£14·75–£24·50, WB, ①, Bk £3·50, L £4·80,
D £6·50, cc 1 3.
★★**Little Court** (R), *Seafield Rd, EX10
8HF.* ✆ (039 55) 5279. Open Mar–Nov &
Xmas. C. 🛏 21 bedrs, 12 bp, 4 bps, 2 ba,
TV, Dgs. ✗ mc, at, LD 8. 🅿 CH, TV, CP 14,
sp, CF, 5 BGf, 0 st, Dis. £ BB £15–£25, DB
£30–£50, WB, ②, Bk £4·50, D £7·50, Dep.
★★**Torbay** (R), *Station Rd, EX10 8NW.*
✆ (039 55) 3456. C. 🛏 24 bedrs, 16 bp, 4
bps, 4 ba, TV, Dgs. ✗ a l c, mc, at, LD 7.30.
🅿 Lt, CH, TV, CP 9, CF, 0 st. £ WB, ②, cc 3
Dep.
★★**Westbourne** (Rl), *Manor Rd, EX10
8RR.* ✆ (039 55) 3774. C. 🛏 13 bedrs, 7
bp, 6 sh, 2 ba, Dgs. ✗ mc, at, LD 7.15.
🅿 CH, TV, CP 14, CF, 2 BGf, 2 st. £ BB
£14–£16, DB £28–£36, DBB £18–£24, WB,
②, Bk £3·50, D £6·50, Dep a.
★★**Woodlands** (Rt), *Cotmaton Cross,
EX10 8HG.* ✆ (039 55) 3120. C 3. 🛏 30
bedrs, 15 bp, 4 ba, Dgs. ✗ LD 8. 🅿 CH, CP
25, 4 BGf, 1 st. £ BB £11·50–£15·50, DB
£23–£31, WB, ②, Bk £2, L £3·25, D £4·25,
Dep b.
Canterbury House, G, z (Unl),
Salcombe Rd, EX10 8PR. ✆ (039 55)
3373. Open Apr–Oct. C. 🛏 7 bedrs, 1 bp, 4
bps, 1 ba, Dgs. ch, TV, CP 6, CF, 2 BGf.
£ DB £19–£27, WT (b) £87–£94·30, (c)
£62·50–£73, DT (b) £13–£16·50, ①,
D £13·25.
Roehurst, PH, x (Unl) *Bickwell Valley,
EX10 8SG.* ✆ (039 55) 2147. C 7. 🛏 6
bedrs, 1 ba. 🅿 ch, TV, CP 6, 2 st. £ DB

£21–£25, WT (b) £80–£90, (c) £65–£75,
DT (b) £13–£15, ①.
Royal London, H, z, *Fore St, EX10 8NW.*
✆ (039 55) 3931.
Willow Bridge, PH (Rl), *Milford Rd,*
EX10 8DR. ✆ (039 55) 3599. C. ⊷ 8
bedrs, 2 sh, 1 ba, Dgs. ✿ CH, TV, CP 7, 1
BGf, 1 st. £ BB £11–£13, DB £22–£29, WT
(b) £87·50–£95, DT (b) £14–£16, ①.

Repairers: F R Northcott, Mill Street
Garage. ✆ (039 55) 3433.
Reed Motors (Sidmouth), Vicarage Rd.
✆ (039 55) 2433.
Woolbrook Garage, Woolbrook Rd.
✆ (039 55) 2931.

SILKSWORTH Tyne & Wear. M. Area
32D
Stockton-on-Tees 22, London 265,
Sunderland 4, Washington 6, Seaham 6.

Rescue Service: Warwick Garage,
Warwick Ter. ✆ Sunderland (0783)
210838.

SILLOTH Cumbria. Map 26E
Pop 2,585. Penrith 33, London 309,
Cockermouth 17, Maryport 13.
EC Tue. **Golf** Silloth 18h. **See** Lakes,
Hadrian's Wall.
ℹ Council Offices, Eden St. ✆ Silloth
(0965) 31944.

■**★★Golf,** *Criffel St, CA5 4AB.* ✆ (0965)
31438. C. ⊷ 24 bedrs, 13 bp, 3 bps, 4 ba,
TV, Dgs. ✿ a l c, mc, at, LD 9.15. ✿ CH, TV,
Dgs, Ac, con 150, CF, 7 st. £ BB £16–£25,
DB £26–£35, WB, ②, Bk £3·50, L £4·50, D
£7, cc 1 2 5 6.

SILVERSTONE Northamptonshire. Map
14D
Pop 1,360. Buckingham 7½, London 63,
Banbury 15, Brackley 7, Oxford 28,
Towcester 4.

Rescue Service: Circuit Motors
Silverstone, 3 Brackley Rd. ✆ (0327)
857206.

SITTINGBOURNE Kent. Map 10C
Pop 53,250 (inc. Milton). Rochester 11,
London 42, M2 Motorway 3½, Ashford 20,
Canterbury 17, Maidstone 13, Margate 31.
EC Wed. **MD** Fri. **Golf** Sittingbourne 18h.
See St Michael's Church (Easter
Sepulchre), Dolphin Sailing Barge
Museum, 15th cent Old Court Hall
(Milton).

★★★**Coniston,** *London Rd, ME10 1NT.*
✆ (0795) 72907. C. ⊷ 50 bedrs, 36 bp, 4
bps, 4 ba, TV, Dgs. ✿ a l c, mc, at, LD 10.30.
✿ N, CH, TV, CP 100, U 7, Ac, tc, con 150,
CF, 3 st. £ BB fr £20·50, DB fr £32, DBB fr
£25·50, ☎ Bk £4, L £4·05, D £4·06,
cc 1 2 3 5 6.
♨★★★**Newington Manor,** Rl, *Callaways*
La, Newington, ME9 7LU. ✆ (0795)
842053. Closed Dec 26–Jan 1. C. ⊷ 11
bedrs, 11 bp, TV, Dgs. ✿ a l c, mc, LD 10.
✿ ch, TV, ns, CP 25, Ac, con 35, CF, 8 BGf,
2 st. £ BB £28, DB £28–£40, ②, Bk £4·50, L
£6·50, D £12, cc 1 2 3 5.
Hillcroft, PH, z (Rl), *94 London Rd,*
ME10 1WS. ✆ (0795) 71501.

Repairer: Swale Motors Ltd, Crown Quay
La. ✆ (0795) 70711.

SIX MILE BOTTOM Cambridgeshire.
Map 17E

Bishop's Stortford 25, London 56,
Cambridge 9, Haverhill 17, Newmarket 6,
Saffron Walden 14.

♨★★★**Swynford Paddocks,**
Newmarket, CB8 0UQ. ✆ (063 870) 234.
C. ⊷ 12 bedrs, 12 bp, TV, Dgs. ✿ a l c, mc,
LD 9. ✿ CH, CP 30, tc, con 16, CF, 0 st.
£ BB fr £38, DB fr £53, WB, ②, Bk £4,
cc 1 3 5, Dep b.

SKEGNESS Lincolnshire. Map 23D.
Pop 14,553. Boston 21, London 139,
Horncastle 21, Louth 23, Sleaford 38.
EC Thur (Oct–May). **MD** Daily (sum).
Golf North Shore 18h, Seacroft 18h. **See**
St Clement's Church, Natureland
(Aquarium and marine Zoo).
ℹ Embassy Centre, Grand Par.
✆ Skegness (0754) 68333.

★★**County,** *North Par, PE25 2UB.*
✆ (0754) 2461. C. ⊷ 44 bedrs, 33 bp, 11
bps, TV, Dgs. ✿ a l c, mc, at, LD 9.30. ✿ Lt,
N, CH, TV, Dgs, CP 40, G 8, Ac, sb, con 100,
CF, 2 st. £ BB £23, DB £36, WB, ①, L £6·10,
D £6·10, cc 1 2 3 5.
★★**Links,** *Drummond Rd, PE25 3BT.*
✆ (0754) 3605. C. ⊷ 21 bedrs, 2 bp, 2
bps, 4 ba, Dgs. ✿ mc, at, LD 9. ✿ ch, TV,
Dgs, CP 40, Ac, con 30, CF, 1 st. £ BB
£12·50–£16·50, DB £25–£33, DBB
£17·50–£20·50, WB, ②, Bk £2·75, L £3·25,
D £5·75, cc 1 3, Dep a.
★★**Vine,** *Vine Rd, PE25 3DB.* ✆ (0754)
3018. C. ⊷ 20 bedrs, 17 bp, 2 ba, TV, Dgs.
✿ a l c, mc, at, LD 9.15. ✿ CH, TV, Dgs, CP
100, Ac, con 100, CF, 1 st. £ BB fr £16, DB
fr £30, WB, ②, 10%, Bk £2·50, L fr £3·50, D
fr £4, cc 1 2 3 5, Dep a.
★**Chatsworth,** *North Par, PE25 2UB.*
✆ (0754) 4177. Open Mar–Oct. C. ⊷ 22
bedrs, 8 bp, 5 bps, 2 ba, Dgs. ✿ mc, at, LD
7.30. ✿ ch, TV, CP 12, G 4, Ac, CF, 2 st.
£ BB fr £18·50, DB fr £31, WB, ①, Bk
£2·75, D £4.
★**Crawford** (R), *South Par, PE25 3HR.*
✆ (0754) 4215. Open Mar–Oct & Xmas. C.
⊷ 20 bedrs, 9 bps, 1 sh, 2 ba, Dgs.
✿ mc, at, LD 5. ✿ Lt, CH, TV, Dgs, Ac, sp,
sol, con 40, CF, 1 st. £ BB £12–£16, DB
£24–£30, DBB £16–£19·50, WB, ②, Bk
£2·50, D £4·50, Dep a.
Belle View, PH, z (Rl), *12 South Par,*
PE25 3NW. ✆ (0754) 5274. C. ⊷ 12
bedrs, 4 bps, 5 sh, 1 ba, TV, Dgs. ✿ CH, TV,
Dgs, CF. £ BB £7·85–£11·47, DB £15·70–
£22·94, WT (b) £63·39–£94·18, DT (b)
£9·05–£14·49, ①.
George, PH, z, *98 South Par, PE25 3HR.*
✆ (0754) 3991. Closed Jan & Nov. C.
⊷ 18 bedrs, 3 ba, ns, TV, Dgs. ✿ CH, TV,
Dgs, CP 6, CF, 1 st. £ BB £8·88–£10·08,
DB £17·76–£20·16, WT (b) £99·82–
£103·67, DT (b) £14·26–£14·81, ①, Bk £3,
D £6.

Rescue Service: Holland Bros Ltd, Roman
Bank. ✆ (0754) 3671.
Roman Bank Filling Station, Roman Bank.
✆ (0754) 4154.
Seacroft Garage, 1 Clifton Grove.
✆ (0754) 3589.

SKELLOW South Yorkshire. Map Areas
22B & 25D
Doncaster 6, London 170, A1(M)
Motorway ½, Barnsley 14, Leeds 23, Selby
18, Wakefield 14, York 32.

Rescue Service: Skellow Garage Services
Ltd, Great North Rd. ✆ Doncaster (0302)
722380.

SKELWITH BRIDGE Cumbria
See AMBLESIDE.

SKIPSEA North Humberside. Map 25A
Pop 478. M62 Motorway 28, Beverley 16,
London 218, Bridlington 9, Gt Driffield 11,
Hornsea 6, Kingston-upon-Hull 21.
EC Wed. **Golf** Hornsea 18h.

Rescue Service: Skipsea Service Station,
Hornsea Rd, Driffield. ✆ (026 286) 234.

SKIPTON North Yorkshire. Map 27A
Pop 13,000. Halifax 17, London 204,
Bradford 19, Burnley 18, Harrogate 22,
Leeds 26, Leyburn 34, Settle 16,
Todmorden 26, Whalley 22.
EC Tue. **MD** Mon, Wed, Fri, Sat. **Golf**
Skipton 18h. **See** Castle, Church (tombs
of Cliffords), 13th cent Corn Mill, Craven
Museum, Bolton Abbey 6 m E.
ℹ High St Car Park. ✆ Skipton (0756)
2809.

★**Midland,** *Broughton Rd, BD23 1RT.*
✆ (0756) 2781. C. ⊷ 10 bedrs, 2 sh, 2 ba.
✿ mc, LD 8.30. ✿ CH, TV, CP 30, Ac, CF, 0
st. £ BB £12·50, DB £24, ①, Bk £2·75, L
£4·25, D £5, cc 2 3 , Dep a.
Fairleigh, G, z (Unl), *24 Belle Vue Ter,*
BD23 1RU. ✆ (0756) 4153. C. ⊷ 5 bedrs,
1 ba. ✿ ch, TV, CF, 9 st. £ BB £7·50–£8·50,
DB £15–£17, WT (c) £52·50–£59·50, DT
(b) £12–£14, ①.
Highfield, H, z (R), *58 Keighley Rd, BD23*
2NB. ✆ (0756) 3182. Closed Xmas & New
Year. C. ⊷ 10 bedrs, 3 bp, 2 sh, 2 ba, Dgs.
✿ ch, TV, 5 st. £ BB fr £10·65, DB fr
£20·50, WT (b) £104, DT (b) £16·50.
Kirk Skye, PH, x (R), *High St, Gargrave,*
BD23 1BR. ✆ Gargrave (075 678) 356.
Open Mar–Oct & Xmas. C. ⊷ 9 bedrs, 5 bp,
2 ba. ✿ CH, TV, Dgs, CP 4, 0 st.
Dis. £ BB £9–£10, DB £18–£20, WT (b)
£91, DT £14, ①, D £5.
Tudor, G, y (Rl), *Bell Busk, BD23 4DT.*
✆ Airton (07293) 301. C. 5. ⊷ 4 bedrs, 2
ba, ns, TV. ✿ CH, TV, ns, CP 8. £ BB £8·50,
DB £15, DT £12, ①.

Rescue Service: Parklands (Teeside) Ltd,
Carlton Garage, Otley Rd. ✆ (0756) 2807.

SKIPTON-ON-SWALE North Yorkshire.
Map 25E
Boroughbridge 9½, London 218, Ripon 7,
Scotch Corner 21, Thirsk 4½.

Skipton Hall, PH, x (Unl) *YO7 4SB.* C.
⊷ 7 bedrs, 2 ba, Dgs. ✿ TV, CP 12.
£ BB fr £10, DB fr £18, cc 1 3.

SLAIDBURN Lancashire. Map 27A
Pop 318. Clitheroe 9, London 223, Kirkby
Lonsdale 21, Preston 22, Settle 14.
See 'Hark to Bounty' Inn, Church.

Parrock Head Farm, Γ, x (Rl),
Woodhouse La, BB7 3AH. ✆ (020 06) 614.
Closed Xmas. C. ⊷ 10 bedrs, 10 bp, 2 ba,
TV, Dgs. ✿ a l c, mc. ✿ CH, CP 10, CF, 2 BGf, 2
st. £ BB £15, DB £30, ①, Bk £3·50, L £5, D
£7, cc 2.

SLEAFORD Lincolnshire. Map 23C
Pop 8,591. Peterborough 33, London 116,
Boston 17, Grantham 14, Horncastle 23,
King's Lynn 44, Lincoln 17, Newark 18,
Skegness 38, Spalding 19, Stamford 28.
EC Thur. **MD** Mon, Fri, Sat. **Golf** Sleaford
18h. **See** Gothic Church of St Denys,
Carre's Hospital (Bedehouses), Handley
Monument, Black Bull Inn sign.

★**Carre Arms,** *Mareham La, NG34 7JP.*
✆ (0529) 303156. C. ⇔ 15 bedrs, 1 bps, 3 ba, TV, Dgs. ✗ a l c, mc, LD 10. ⌂ CH, TV, Dgs, CP 50, Ac, CF, 2 st. £ BB £15, DB £25·50, DBB £19·50, WB, ⎕, Bk £2·75, L £3·95, D £4·50, cc 1 5.

★**Lion,** *Northgate, NG34 7BH.* ✆ (0529) 302127. Closed Xmas. C. ⇔ 10 bedrs, 3 ba, TV, Dgs. ✗ mc, LD 8. ⌂ CH, TV, CP 15, G 10, Ac, con 100, CF, 1 st. £ BB £14·78, DB £24·15, DT £24, DBB £20·13, ⎕, Bk £2·50, D £5·75, Dep a.

Whichcote Arms, I, x, *Osbournby, NG34 0DG.* ✆ Culverthorpe (052 95) 239. C. ⇔ 6 bedrs, 4 bp, 1 ba, TV. ✗ a l c. ⌂ CH, Dgs, CP 20, CF, 1 st. £ BB fr £10, DB fr £18, ⎕, L £5, D £6, cc 1 3.

Repairers: Holdingham Garage, Holdingham. ✆ (0529) 302545.
Holland Bros Ltd, Carre St. ✆ (0529) 303034.
Rescue Service: Eric D Bland, Black Bull Garage, Southgate. ✆ (0529) 302135.

SLOUGH Berkshire. Map 7A
Pop 98,900. Brentford and Chiswick 13, London 20, M4 Motorway 2½, Denham 6½, Henley-on-Thames 14, High Wycombe 13, Reading 18, Richmond-upon-Thames 13, Uxbridge 6, Windsor 2.
EC Wed. **MD** Daily except Wed. **Golf**
Stoke Poges 18h. **See** 12th cent Church of St Laurence, 17th cent Bayliss House, Herschel Park, 16th cent Red Cow Inn, Stoke Poges Church (Gray's 'Elegy') 3 m.

★★★★**M Holiday Inn,** *Ditton Rd, SL3 8PT.* ✆ (0753) 44244. C. ⇔ 224 bedrs, 224 bp, 2 ba, ns, TV, Dgs. ✗ a l c, mc, at, LD 10.30. ⌂ Lt, CH, Dgs, CP 250, Ac, sp, tc, sb, sol, gym, con 300, CF, 21 BGf, 0 st. Dis. £ BB £56·25, DB £75·12, WT £533·75, DBB £65·75, WB, ⎕, Bk £5·65, L £9·50, D £9·50, cc 1 2 3 4 5 6, Dep.
Francis House, PH, z (RI), *21 London Road, SL3 7RL.* ✆ (0753) 22286.
Parkside, PH (Rt), *1 Upton Court Rd.* ✆ (0753) 22533.

Repairer: Normans of Slough, 383 Bath Rd. ✆ Burnham (062 86) 3121.
Windrush Garage Ltd, 57 Farnham Rd. ✆ (0753) 33914.
Specialist Battery Repairer: Speedwell Batteries (London) Ltd, 98 Uxbridge Rd. ✆ (0753) 24681.
Rescue Service: Upton Court Service Station, 80 London Rd. ✆ (0753) 27296.

SMALLWAYS North Yorkshire. Map 24F
Boroughbridge 35, London 242, Brough 21, Darlington 14, Harrogate 45, Leyburn 21, Middleton-in-Teesdale 15, Northallerton 23, Thirsk 32, West Auckland 13.
Golf Richmond 18h.

★**A66,** *Barningham, DL11 7QW.*
✆ Teesdale (0833) 27334. C. ⇔ 6 bedrs, 1 bp, 1 ba, TV, Dgs. ✗ a l c, mc, at. ⌂ Dgs, CP 50, Ac, con 50, CF, 6 st, 1 Dis. £ BB £15–£20, DB £20–£22, DT £23·50, DBB £20–£25, ⎕, Bk £2·50, L £3·50, D £5, cc 1 3 5 6.

SMEETH Kent. M. Area 10D
Pop 950. Ashford 4½, London 60, Canterbury 15, Folkestone 11, Rye 19, Tenterden 14.
Golf Ashford 18h. **See** St Mary's Church.

Rescue Service: John Childs, Anchor Garage, Brabourne Lees. ✆ Sellindge (030 381) 3118.

SMETHWICK Warley, West Midlands. Map 21F
See also ROWLEY REGIS.
Pop 68,390. Birmingham 3, London 114, Bridgnorth 21, Bromsgrove 13, Kidderminster 17, Walsall 6½, Wolverhampton 10.
EC Wed. **MD** Thur, Fri, Sat. **Golf** Dudley 18h.

Specialist Body Repairers: Richmond Motors, Middlemore Industrial Estate, Middlemore Rd. ✆ 021-558 3042.
Rydale Cars (Bodyshop), Ruskin Pl, Oldbury Rd. ✆ 021-558 0646 & 3882.

SMITHFIELD Cumbria. Map 26C
Carlisle 7½, London 302, Beattock 38, Brampton 6½, Dumfries 33, Langholm 17.
Golf Brampton 18h.

Rescue Service: Thompson Motors, Smithfield Garage. ✆ Kirklinton (022 875) 467.

SNAINTON North Yorkshire. Maps 25A and 24B
Pop 744. Market Weighton 28, London 222 (Fy 217), Beverley 31, Bridlington 23, Malton 11, Pickering 7½, Scarborough 9.
Golf Ganton 18h. **See** Allerston and Wykeham Forests, Moors.

★★**Coachman Inn,** *Pickering Rd West, YO13 9PL.* ✆ Scarborough (0723) 85231. C. ⇔ 10 bedrs, 5 bp, 3 bps, 1 ba, Dgs. ✗ mc, LD 9. ⌂ CH, TV, Dgs, CP 50, Ac, CF. £ BB £16·50–£18, DB £33–£36, DBB £25·25–£26·75, WB, ⏁, Bk £4·50 D £8·75, cc 1 2 3 5, Dep a.

Rescue Service: Station Garages, Station Rd. ✆ Scarborough (0723) 85491.

SNAPE Suffolk. Map 17A
Pop 536. Ipswich 19, London 93, Aldeburgh 4½, Saxmundham 3.
EC Wed. **Golf** Aldeburgh 18h. **See** The Maltings (Concert Hall).

Rescue Service: P M Balls, Church Garage, Farnham–Aldeburgh Rd. ✆ (072 888) 327.

SNODLAND Kent. Map 10C.
Pop 5,500. M20 Motorway 2, London 34, Maidstone 7, Rochester 6, Sevenoaks 14, Tonbridge 13.
EC Wed. **Golf** West Malling 18h.

Rescue Service: Sparkdrill Garages Ltd, Ham Hill Service Station, Malling Rd. ✆ Medway (0634) 242404.

SOHAM Cambridgeshire. Map 16F
Pop 6,610. Newmarket 7½, London 70, Cambridge 21, Ely 6, Mildenhall 8.
EC Wed. **MD** Fri. **Golf** Ely 18h. **See** 12th cent Church.

Rescue Service: K & E Parsons (Garage) Ltd, Fordham Rd. ✆ Ely (0353) 720551.

SOLIHULL West Midlands. Map 21D
Pop 107,095. Warwick 13, London 105, Birmingham 7½, Bromsgrove 18, Coventry 12, Evesham 27, Stratford-upon-Avon 19, Sutton Coldfield 10.
EC Wed. **Golf** Olton Ltd 18h. **See** Church, timbered houses.
⏍ Central Library, Homer Rd. ✆ 021-705 4917 ext 504.

★★★**George,** *The Square, B91 3RF.*
✆ 021-704 1241. C. ⇔ 47 bedrs, 41 bp, 4

ba, TV, Dgs. ✗ a l c, mc, at, LD 9.15. ⌂ N, CH, Dgs, CP 200, G 100, Ac, con 200, CF, 3 st. £ B fr £24, BD fr £34, WB, ⎕, Bk £4·25, L £6·75, D £7·25, cc 1 2 3 4 5 6, Dep b.

★★★**St John's,** *Warwick Rd, B91 1AT.*
✆ 021-705 6777. C. ⇔ 213 bedrs, 192 bp, 21 sh, 5 ba, TV, Dgs. ✗ mc, at, LD 9.45. ⌂ Lt, N, CH, TV, Dgs, CP 350, Ac, con 750, CF, 0 st. £ BB £21–£32, DB £29–£44, DBB fr £36·95, WB, ⎕, Bk £3·60, L £5·95, D £7·95, cc 1 2 3 4 5 6, Dep b.

★★**Arden,** *Coventry Rd, Bickenhill, B92 0EH.* ✆ Hampton-in-Arden (067 55) 3221. C. ⇔ 46 bedrs, 46 bp, TV, Dgs. ✗ mc, LD 11. ⌂ Lt, N, CH, TV, Dgs, ns, CP 150, Ac, con 100, CF. £ BB £25·50–£38·50, DB £42–£45·50, WB, ⎕, Bk £3·50, L £6·95, D £8, cc 1 2 3 5 6.

Rescue Service: Cornyx Lane Motor Engineers, 65 Cornyx La. ✆ 021-705 1320.

SOMERTON Somerset. Map 5C
Pop 4,376. Wincanton 16, London 126, Bridgwater 16, Crewkerne 14, Dorchester 29, Glastonbury 8, Ilminster 14, Shepton Mallet 15, Sherborne 13, Taunton 18.
EC Wed. **Golf** Yeovil 18h. **See** Dec Church, 17th cent Market Cross, old houses.

Church Farm, G, x (RI), *School Lane, Compton Dundon, TA11 6PE.* ✆ (0458) 72927. C 4. ⇔ 6 bedrs, 1 bp, 1 bps, 1 ba, TV, Dgs. ⌂ ch, CP 6, G 2, CF, 2 BGf, 1 st, Dis. £ BB £9·50–£11, DB £18–£21, WT £99–£111, DT (b) £16·50–£18, ⎕.

SONNING COMMON Oxfordshire. M. Area 6B
5 m SW of Henley-on-Thames. Pop 3,850. London 40, Aylesbury 27, Wallingford 10.
EC Wed. **Golf** Reading 18h. **See** Chiltern Hills.

Rescue Service: Sonning Common Garage, Peppard Rd. ✆ Kidmore End (0734) 3127.
Swan & Sons, Peppard Rd. ✆ Kidmore End (0734) 2254.

SONNING-ON-THAMES Berkshire. Map 6B
Pop 1,750. Slough 14, London 35, A423 (M) Motorway 7½, Bagshot 14, Farnham 23, Henley-on-Thames 6, Reading 3, Windsor 13.
Golf Sonning 18h. **See** EE Church, ancient Bridge.

★★★**White Hart,** *Thames St, RG4 0UT.*
✆ Reading (0734) 692277.

SOUTHAM Gloucestershire. Maps 13D and 14C
Pop 699. Cheltenham 3, London 100, Evesham 15, Gloucester 11, Stow-on-the-Wold 16.
Golf Cleeve Hill 18h. **See** Manor House, Church.

★★★**De la Bere,** *GL52 3NH.*
✆ Cheltenham (0242) 37771. C. ⇔ 22 bedrs, 21 bp, 1 bps, annexe 11 bedrs, 10 bp, 1 bps, TV, Dgs. ✗ mc, LD 9.45. ⌂ N, CH, CP 250, Ac, sp, tc, sb, sol, gym, con 200, CF, 2 st. £ BB £33–£40, DB £57–£70, WB, ⎕, Bk £3·50, L £5·75, D £11, cc 1 2 3 5 6, Dep b.

SOUTHAMPTON Hampshire. Map 6E
See also BOTLEY.

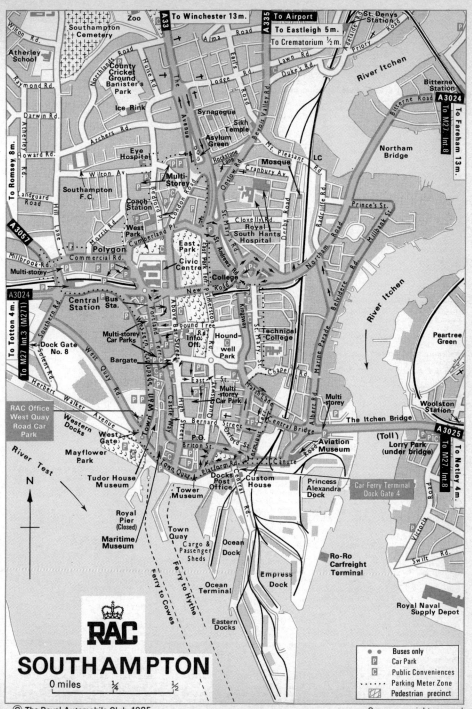

RAC Office, *West Quay Road Car Park, Southampton, SO1 0NY.* ☎ Southampton (0703) 24244.
Pop 204,406. Winchester 12, London 77, M271 Motorway 3, Fareham 12, Lyndhurst 9½, Ringwood 18, Romsey 8, Salisbury 22.
See Plan p. 333.
MD Thur, Fri, Sat. **P** See Plan. **Golf** Municipal 18h. **See** Old Gates, Towers and Town Walls, Docks (passes from Chief Docks Manager), Museums: Tudor House, Bargate, God's House Tower (Archaeology), Maritime, Pilgrim Fathers' (Mayflower) Memorial, Churches: St Mary's, St Michael's, St Nicholas, Holy Rood, Chapel of St Julian. King John's Palace, old inns, Netley Abbey 2 m SE.
ⓘ Above Bar Precinct. ☎ Southampton (0703) 23855 ext 615.

★★★★**Polygon** (TH), *Cumberland Pl, SO9 4GD.* ☎ (0703) 26401. C. ⊷ 119 bedrs, 119 bp, TV, Dgs. ✗ a l c, mc, at, LD 9.45. ⓓ Lt, N, CH, Dgs, CP 120, U 4, CP 16, Ac, con 500, CF, 0 st. **£** BB £46·50, DB £60·50, WB, ⓣ, cc 1 2 3 4 5 6, Dep (Xmas).

★★★**Dolphin** (TH), *High St, SO9 2DS.* ☎ (0703) 26178. C. ⊷ 72 bedrs, 72 bp, TV, Dgs. ✗ a l c, mc, at, LD 9.45. ⓓ Lt, N, CH, Dgs, CP 70, Ac, con 70, CF, 13 BGf, 0 st. **£** BB £36·50, DB £50·50, WB, ⓣ, cc 1 2 3 4 5 6, Dep (Xmas).

★★★**M Post House** (TH), *Herbert Walker Av, SO1 0HJ.* ☎ (0703) 28081. C. ⊷ 132 bedrs, 132 bp, TV, Dgs. ✗ a l c, mc, at, LD 10. ⓓ Lt, N, CH, Dgs, CP 250, Ac, sp, con 250, CF, 1 st. **£** BB £43·50, DB £56, WB, ⓣ, cc 1 2 3 4 5 6.

★★★**Southampton Park,** *Cumberland Pl, SO9 4NY.* ☎ (0703) 23467. Closed Dec 25 & 26. C. ⊷ 77 bedrs, 77 bp, TV, Dgs. ✗ a l c, mc, at, LD 11. ⓓ Lt, N, CH, Ac, con 50, CF, 5 st. **£** BB £32·50, DB £39·75, DBB £38·50, WB, ⓣ, Bk £3·50, D £8·25, cc 1 2 3 5 6, Dep b.

★★**Albany,** *Winn Rd, SO9 1PR.* ☎ (0703) 554553. RS Bank Holidays & Xmas. C. ⊷ 32 bedrs, 11 bp, 21 bps, 1 ba, TV, Dgs. ✗ a l c, mc, at, LD 9.15. ⓓ Lt, N, CH, Dgs, CP 50, Ac, con 100, CF, 3 BGf, 1 st, Dis. **£** BB £24·50–£28, DB £35–£37, WT £210–£230, DT £36·50–£38, WB, ⓩ, Bk £3, L £5·75, D £5·75, cc 1 2 3, Dep b.

Anglesea Road, H, z, *30 Anglesea Rd, Shirley, SO1 5QS.* ☎ (0703) 789297.

Atlantic, PH, z (RI), *28 Hill La, SO1 5AY.* ☎ (0703) 24612.

Claremont, G, z (Unl), *33 The Polygon, SO1 2BP.* ☎ (0703) 23112. C. ⊷ 14 bedrs, 3 bps, 2 ba. ⓓ CH, TV, Dgs, CP 10, 5 BGf, 1 st, Dis. **£** BB £7–£9·50, DB £14–£18, WT (b) £45–£50, ⓣ, Bk £2.▲

Cliffden, G, z, *43 The Polygon, SO1 2BP.* ☎ (0703) 24003. C. ⊷ 8 bedrs, 2 ba. ⓓ CH, TV, CP 3, CF, 1 BGf, 1 st, Dis. **£** BB fr £7·50, DB fr £14·50, WT (b) fr £66, DT fr £10·50, ⓣ.

Dormy, G, x (Unl), *21 Barnes La, Sarisbury Green, SO3 6DA.* ☎ Locks Heath (048 95) 2626. C. ⊷ 7 bedrs, 2 bp, 2 bps, 3 sh, 1 ba, TV, Dgs. ⓓ CH, TV, Dgs, CP 10, CF, 2 st. **£** BB £8·50, DB £17–£21, ⓣ, Bk £2.

Earley House, H, yz (R), *46 Pear Tree Av, Bitterne, SO2 7JP.* ☎ (0703) 448117. C. ⊷ 9 bedrs, 5 bp, 4 bps, 1 ba. ⓓ CH, TV, CP 25, CF, 0 st. **£** BB £14–£16, DB £26–£30, WT £120–£180, DT £19–£20, ⓣ, Bk £2·50, D £5.

Eaton Court, PH, z (R), *32 Hill La, SO1 5AY.* ☎ (0703) 23081. Closed Xmas week. C. ⊷ 12 bedrs, 2 bp, 2 ba. ⓓ CH, TV, CP 12, 2 st. **£** BB £10·75–£12·75, DB £20–£22·50, ⓣ, Bk £2·50, D £3·75, cc 1 3.

Eden Court, PH, z (Unl), *29 The Polygon, SO1 2BP.* ☎ (0703) 20540. C. ⊷ 18 bedrs, 2 bps, 1 sh, 3 ba, Dgs. ⓓ CH, TV, Dgs, CP 15, CF. **£** BB £7·50–£9·50, DB £15–£21, WT (b) £70–£90, DT (b) £11–£13·50, ⓣ.

Elizabeth House, PH, z (RI), *43 The Avenue, SO1 2SX.* ☎ (0703) 24327.

Hunters Lodge, PH, z (RI), *25 Landguard Rd, Shirley, SO1 5DL.* ☎ (0703) 27919. Closed Dec 18–Jan 5. C. ⊷ 17 bedrs, 2 bp, 1 sh, 3 ba, TV. ⓓ CH, TV, CP 17, U 4, CF, 1 BGf, 2 st. **£** BB £11·50, DB £19·55–£20·70, WT (b) £115, (c) £80·50, DT (b) £16·10, Bk £2, D £4·60, cc 3.

La Valle, G, z (Unl), *111 Millbrook Rd, SO1 0HP.* ☎ (0703) 27821. C. ⊷ 6 bedrs, 2 ba, TV, Dgs. ⓓ CH, Dgs, ns, CP 6, CF. **£** BB fr £6, DB fr £12, WT (c) fr £42, ⓣ.

Linden, G, z (Unl), *51 The Polygon, SO1 2BP.* ☎ (0703) 25653. C. ⊷ 12 bedrs, 2 ba. ⓓ CH, TV, Dgs, ns, CP 7, CF. **£** BB £7·50–£8·50, DB £15–£17, ⓣ.

Nirvana, H, z (R), *386 Winchester Rd, Bassett.* ☎ (0703) 760474. C. 2. ⊷ 23 bedrs, 14 bp, 5 ba, TV, Dgs. ⓓ CH, TV, CP 26. **£** BB £15·50, DB £26·90, DT (b) £22, ⓣ, D £6·50.

Repairer: Bristol Street Motors (Soton) Ltd, 362 Shirley Rd, Shirley. ☎ (0703) 775331.
Wadham Stringer (Southampton) Ltd, 73 The Avenue. ☎ (0703) 28811.
Specialist Car Lighting and Ignition Repairer: Squirrel Auto Services, 144 Avenue Rd. ☎ (0703) 553770.
Rescue Service: Andrews (Shipside Services) Ltd, No. 10 Gate, Western Dock. ☎ (0703) 28001.
Oakmount Recovery, The Workshop, Rownhams Services. ☎ (0703) 738672.
Pete Spacagna Motor Cycles, 63a Northam Rd. ☎ (0703) 29767.
Polygon Service Station (Loveland) Ltd, Polygon House, Commercial Rd. ☎ (0703) 37055.
R F Seward & Co Ltd, 234 Winchester Rd. ☎ (0703) 785111.
Sheriff Motors, High St, Shirrell Heath. ☎ Wickham (0329) 832161.
Warsash Motors, 90 Warsash Rd. ☎ Locks Heath (048 95) 5188.
"Wheelbase", Thornhill Service Station, 30 Thornhill Park Rd. ☎ (0703) 462266.

SOUTHBOROUGH Kent. Map 7D
Pop 9,994. Tonbridge 2½, London 35, Godstone 18, Tunbridge Wells 2, Westerham 14.
EC Wed. **Golf** Tunbridge Wells 9h. **See** 16th cent 'The Weavers' now restaurant, Penshurst Place 3 m WNW, St Peter's Church.

★★**Sceptre,** *London Rd, TN4 0RL.* ☎ Tunbridge Wells (0892) 37055. C. ⊷ 26 bedrs, 26 bp, TV. ✗ a l c, mc, at, LD 9. ⓓ CH, Dgs, CP 40, Ac, con 60, CF, 0 st.

£ BB £21–£23·50, DB £29–£32·50, DBB £28·10–£30·60, WB, ⓣ, Bk £3, L £4·50, D £7·10, cc 1 2 3 5.

SOUTHBOURNE Dorset
See BOURNEMOUTH.

SOUTH BRENT Devon. Map 3D
Pop 2,166. Ashburton 8, London 195, Kingsbridge 11, Plymouth 15, Totnes 7.
Golf Wrangaton 18h. **See** Old Toll House, Parish Church, Avon Dam, Brent Hill (views).

▲★★Glazebrook House (R), *TQ10 9JE.* ☎ (036 47) 3322. C. ⊷ 12 bedrs, 8 bp, 1 ba, TV. ✗ a l c, mc, at. ⓓ CH, ns, CP 50, Ac, sp, pf, con 75, CF, 1 st. **£** cc 1 2 3.

Coombe House, PH, xy (RI), *North Huish, TQ10 9NJ.* ☎ Gara Bridge (054 882) 277. Open Mar–Dec. C 4. ⊷ 4 bedrs, 3 bp, 1 bps, 1 ba. ⓓ ch, TV, CP 10, 2 st. **£** BB £14·50, DB £25, WT (b) £115–£130, DT (b) £18–£20, ⓣ, D £8·50.

Rescue Service: Sopers of South Brent Ltd, Manor Garage. ☎ (054 882) 3335.

SOUTHEND-ON-SEA Essex. Maps 10A and 17D
See also WESTCLIFF-ON-SEA.
Pop 156,700. Romford 25, London 42, Brentwood 21, Chelmsford 19, Colchester 37, Dartford Tunnel 21, Rainham 26.
MD Thur, Fri, Sat. **Golf** Belfairs 18h. **See** Pier—over 1¼ m long, Civic House (formerly 16th cent Manor House), 13th cent Southchurch Hall, Kursaal and Amusement Gardens, Beecroft Art Gallery, Airport, 12th cent Prittlewell Priory and Museum, Flower Festival in May, Carnival Week in mid Aug.
ⓘ High Street Precinct. ☎ Southend-on-Sea (0702) 355120.

★★★**M Airport Moat House,** *Aviation Way, SS2 6UL.* ☎ (0702) 546344. RS Xmas & New Year. C. ⊷ 65 bedrs, 65 bp, TV, Dgs. ✗ mc, LD 9.50. ⓓ N, CH, Dgs, CP 300, Ac, sc, sb, sol, gym, con 200, CF, 65 BGf, 1 st. **£** BB £15–£32, DB £20–£35, WB, ⓩ, Bk £4, D £7, cc 1 2 3 5 6, Dep.

Argyle, H, z (R), *12 Clifftown Par, SS1 1DP.* ☎ (0702) 339483. C. ⊷ 10 bedrs, 3 ba, TV, Dgs. ⓓ CH, TV, Dgs, CF, 2 st. **£** Bk £2, L £3, D £4·25.

Ferndown, H, z, *136 York Rd, SS1 2EA.* ☎ (0702) 68614. C. ⊷ 13 bedrs, 4 ba, TV. ⓓ CH, TV, CP 10, CF, 3 BGf, 2 st. **£** BB £12·65, DB £20·24, WT (c) £88·55, DT (b) £17·25, ⓣ.

Gladstone, H, z (RI), *40 Hartington Rd, SS1 2HS.* ☎ (0702) 62776. C 3. ⊷ 7 bedrs, 2 ba, ns, TV, Dgs, CF, 3 st. **£** BB £9·50, DB £17–£18, WT (b) £81–£84·50, DT (b) £12–£13, ⓣ, D £3·50.

Regency, PH, z (RI), *18 Royal Ter, SS1 1DU.* ☎ (0702) 40747. C. ⊷ 11 bedrs, 1 bp, 3 ba, TV, Dgs. ⓓ CH, TV, CP 1, G 1, 1 st. **£** BB £13–£15, DB £23–£25, WT (b) £115–£120, DT £18–£20, ⓣ, Bk £3, L £2·50, D £5.

Terrace, PH, z (RI), *8 Royal Ter, SS1 1DY.* ☎ (0702) 348143. Closed mid Dec–mid Jan. C 10. ⊷ 9 bedrs, 2 ba, Dgs. ⓓ CH, TV, 1 st. **£** BB fr £10, DB fr £18, ⓣ.

Tower, H, z (RI), *146 Alexandra Rd, SS1 1HE.* ☎ (0702) 348635. C. ⊷ 15 bedrs, 2 bps, 11 sh, 1 ba, TV, Dgs. ✗ a l c. ⓓ CH, TV, Dgs, CF, 2 st. **£** BB £10–£20, DB £24–£28, WT (b) £105–£182, DT (b) £15–£25, ⓣ, Bk £1·50, L £2·50, D £4·50, cc 1 2 3 5.

Repairers: Oasis Garage Ltd, 654 Sutton Rd. ☎ (0702) 66670.
Southend Motor & Aero Co Ltd, Priory Cres. ☎ (0702) 48222.
Specialist Body Repairer: Kent Elms Coach Works Ltd, Kent Elms Corner, Prince Av. ☎ (0702) 525438.
Rescue Service: Inverness Garage, Inverness Av, Westcliff-on-Sea. ☎ (0702) 333333.

SOUTHERY Norfolk. Map 16F
Pop 1,177. Ely 11, London 82, King's Lynn 17, Swaffham 21, Thetford 6, Wisbech 19.
EC Wed. **Golf** Denver, nr Downham Market 9h.

Rescue Service: Lyndale Garage (Southery) Ltd, Feltwell Rd. ☎ (036 66) 305–6 & (036 66) 653 (after hours).

SOUTH GODSTONE Surrey. Map 7D
Godstone 2½, London 22, East Grinstead 7, Edenbridge 8, Horley 8, Lingfield 4, Redhill 6.

Rescue Service: South Godstone Garage Ltd, Eastbourne Rd. ☎ (034 285) 3434.

SOUTH HOLMWOOD Surrey. M. Area 7C
Pop 1,140. Dorking 2½, London 26, Horsham 9½, Petworth 21, Pulborough 18.
EC Wed. **Golf** Dorking 9h.

Rescue Service: Holmwood Garage. ☎ Dorking (0306) 6373.

SOUTH MILFORD North Yorkshire. Map 25D
Pop 1,589. Doncaster 20, London 184, Leeds 13, York 17.
Golf Selby 18h. **See** Steeton Gateway.

★★★**Selby Fork**, *Junction A1/A63, Lumby, LS25 5LF.* ☎ (0977) 682711. C. ⊷ 109 bedrs, 59 bp, 50 bps, TV, Dgs. ✕ a l c, mc, at, LD 10. 🅟 N, CH, CP 220, Ac, sp, gc, tc, sb, con 200, CF, 50 BGf, 1 st, Dis. £ BB £20–£35, DB £30–£42, WT £184·20, WB, 🆔, Bk £3, L £6·45, D £6·45, cc 1 2 3 4 5 6, Dep b.

SOUTH MIMMS Hertfordshire. Map 15F
Barnet 3½, London 15, A1 (M) Motorway 1, Brentford and Chiswick 17, Ealing 15, Enfield 8, Harrow 11, Hatfield 7, Hoddesdon 14, St Albans 8, Watford 9½.
EC Thur. **Golf** Potters Bar 18h. **See** Mimms Hall 16th cent house, Church of St Giles.

★★★**M Crest**, *Barnet By-Pass, EN6 3NH.* ☎ Potters Bar (0707) 43311. RS Xmas. C. ⊷ bedrs, 120 bps, ns, TV, Dgs. ✕ a l c, mc, at, LD 10. 🅟 N, CH, Dgs, CP 150, con 200, CF, 40 BGf, 1 st, Dis. £ B fr £43·50, BD fr £53·50, WB, 🆔, Bk £5·25, D £9·60, cc 1 2 3 4 5 6, Dep b.

Rescue Service: Lantern Service Station, A1, Barnet By-Pass. ☎ Potters Bar (0707) 43180.

SOUTHMINSTER Essex. Maps 17D and 10A
Romford 20, London 45, Braintree 25, Brentwood 24, Chelmsford 20, Colchester 28, Dartford Tunnel 31, Southend-on-Sea 24.

Rescue Service: Steeple Road Garage, 7 Steeple Rd. ☎ Maldon (0621) 773269.

SOUTH MOLTON Devon. Map 4C
Pop 3,600. Tiverton 17, London 180, Barnstaple 11, Crediton 26, Great Torrington 15, Okehampton 29.
EC Wed. **MD** Thur. **Golf** Saunton 18h (2). **See** Church of St Mary Magdalene.

★★**Goose & Gander**, *Queen St, EX36 3BJ.* ☎ (076 95) 2526. C. ⊷ 12 bedrs, 2 ba, Dgs. ✕ a l c, mc, at, LD 8.30 (winter), 9.45 (summer). 🅟 CH, TV, Dgs, CP 50, Ac, con 200, CF, 0 st. £ BB £10–£12, DB £20–£24, WT £125–£150, DT £17·50–£20, DBB £13–£15, WB, 🆔, 10%, Bk £3·50, L £4·25, D £6, cc 3.

Heasley House, H, x (R), *Heasley Mill, EX36 3LE.* ☎ North Molton (059 84) 213. C. ⊷ 10 bedrs, 1 bp, 3 ba, Dgs. 🅟 CH, TV, CP 11, CF, 1 BGf, 2 st. £ BB £7·80–£9·80, DB £15·60–£17·60, WT (b) £88, DT (b) £13·20, 🆔, Bk £2, D £6.

MC Repairer: Phil Rycroft Motorcycles, Market St. ☎ (076 95) 3313.
Rescue Service: Central Park Garage Ltd, 135 East St. ☎ (076 95) 2135.

SOUTHMOOR Oxfordshire. Map 14F
Wallingford 16, London 62, Burford 14, Faringdon 8, Oxford 9, Wantage 8½.

Repairer: Crossroads Garage (Southmoor) Ltd, nr Kingston Bagpuize. ☎ Oxford (0865) 820273.

SOUTH NORMANTON Derbyshire. Map 22D
Pop 7,130. M1 Motorway 1¼, London 140, Ashbourne 19, Chesterfield 12, Derby 16, Loughborough 31, Mansfield 7, Matlock 12, Nottingham 14.
EC Wed. **Golf** Coxmoor 18h.

★★★★**M Swallow**, *DE55 2EH.* ☎ (0773) 812000. C. ⊷ 123 bedrs, 123 bp, TV, Dgs. ✕ a l c, mc, at, LD 10. 🅟 N, CH, TV, CP 200, Ac, sp, sb, sol, gym, con 100, CF, 40 BGf, 0 st, Dis. £ BB £28–£41·50, DB £36–£52, WB, 🆔, Bk £5·50, L £7, D £7·50, cc 1 2 3 4 5 6, Dep b.

Repairer: Arthur Kettle & Son Ltd, Carnfield Garage, 113 Alfreton Rd. ☎ Ripley (0773) 811251.
Rescue Service: T Coleman, Mansfield Road Garage, Mansfield Rd. ☎ Ripley (0773) 811542.

SOUTH OCKENDON Essex. Map 7B
Upminster 5, London 22, M25 Motorway 4, Brentwood 9, Tilbury 6½.

Rescue Service: Arisdale Motor Centre, Arisdale Av. ☎ (040 25) 7335.

SOUTH PETHERTON Somerset. Map 5C
Pop 2,761. Wincanton 19, London 129, Bridgwater 20, Crewkerne 5, Frome 20, Glastonbury 16, Ilminster 6.
Golf Yeovil 18h. **See** Parish Church dating back to 1080, Ina's Palace, East Lambrook Manor.

Rescue Service: B D & C A Giles, Harp Road Garage. ☎ (0460) 40249.
J & P Motors, 47 St James St. ☎ (0460) 40553.

SOUTHPORT Merseyside. Map 27D
Pop 86,858. Ormskirk 8, London 211, Chorley 19, Liverpool 18, Preston 17.
EC Tue. **Golf** Royal Birkdale 18h. Southport and Ainsdale 18h. **See** St Cuthbert's Church, Atkinson Art Gallery, Floral Hall and Gardens, Zoo.

🅸 Tourism Dept, Cambridge Arcade. ☎ Southport (0704) 33133.

★★★★**Prince of Wales**, *Lord St, PR8 1JS.* ☎ (0704) 36688. C. ⊷ 96 bedrs, 96 bp, 3 ba, TV, Dgs. ✕ a l c, mc, at, LD 10. 🅟 Lt, N, CH, Dgs, ns, CP 90, Ac, con 450, CF, 1 BGf, 4 st. £ BB £39·50, DB £54, WB, 🅰, Bk £3·50, L £6·50, D £8, cc 1 2 3 4 5 6, Dep b.

★★★**Royal Clifton**, *Promenade, PR8 1RB.* ☎ (0704) 33771. C. ⊷ 115 bedrs, 69 bp, 13 ba, TV, Dgs. ✕ mc, at, LD 9.15. 🅟 Lt, N, CH, Dgs, CP 50, Ac, con, CF, 7 BGf, 5 st. £ BB £16·50–£28·50, DB £26·50–£47, DBB £15·50–£29·50, WB, 🅰, Bk £4·25, L £4·95, D £6·95, cc 1 2 3 5, Dep.

★★**Balmoral Lodge** (R), *41 Queens Rd, PR9 9EX.* ☎ (0704) 44298. Closed Xmas. C. ⊷ 12 bedrs, 4 bp, 8 bps, 1 ba, ns, TV. ✕ a l c, LD 8.30. 🅟 CH, TV, CP 8, sol, CF, 1 BGf, 8 st. £ BB £14–£19, DB £25, WT £135, DT £23, DBB £20, 🆔, Bk £3·50, L £3, D £6, cc 1 3 5.

★★**Bold**, *583 Lord St, PR9 0BE.* ☎ (0704) 32578. C. ⊷ 26 bedrs, 12 bp, 3 bps, 3 ba, TV, Dgs. ✕ a l c, mc, at, LD 10. 🅟 N, CH, TV, Dgs, CP 16, con 250, CF, 1 st. £ BB £20–£25, DB £30–£35, WT £210, DT £31–£36, 🆔, Bk £3, L £4·80, D £6·50, cc 1 2 3 5 6, Dep b.

★★**Carlton** (late Red Rum), *86–88 Lord St, PR8 1JT.* ☎ (0704) 35111. C. ⊷ 25 bedrs, 9 bp, 4 bps, 3 ba, TV, Dgs. ✕ a l c, mc, at, LD 9.45. 🅟 Lt, N, CH, Dgs, CP 17, Ac, con 35, CF, 12 st. £ BB £19·50–£24, DB £29–£38·50, WT £247, DT £37, WB, 🆔, Bk £2·50, D £7, cc 1 2 3 6, Dep b.

★★**Metropole**, *Portland St, PR8 1LL.* ☎ (0704) 36836. C. ⊷ 27 bedrs, 8 bp, 7 bps, 4 ba, TV, Dgs. ✕ mc, at. 🅟 CH, TV, Dgs, CP 12, Ac, con 20, CF, 3 st. £ BB £15–£18·50, DB £27–£34, WT £140, DT £22, WB, 🆔, Bk £2·50, L £3·25, D £5·50, cc 1 2 3, Dep b.

★★**Scarisbrick**, *239 Lord St, PR9 1NZ.* ☎ (0704) 38321. C. ⊷ 52 bedrs, 46 bp, 6 sh, 5 ba, TV, Dgs. ✕ mc, LD 9.30. 🅟 Lt, N, CH, TV, Dgs, CP 26, G 16, Ac, con 200, CF, 1 st. £ BB £20·50–£25, DB £29–£35, WT £157, DBB £19·50–£22·50, WB, 🅰, Bk £3·50, L £3·95, D £7·50, cc 1 2 3 4 5, Dep b.

Belvedere, G (Rl), *15 Seabank Rd, PR9 0EW.* ☎ (0704) 38744. ⊷ 5 bedrs, 1 ba. 🅟 TV, ns, CP 6, CF. £ BB £8·25–£8·50, DB £16·50–£17, D £3.

Crimond, PH, z (R), *28 Knowsley Rd, PR9 0HN.* ☎ (0704) 36456. C. ⊷ 12 bedrs, 4 bps, 2 sh, 2 ba, TV, Dgs. 🅟 CH, TV, Dgs, CP 15, CF, 3 st. £ BB £11–£14, DB £21–£27, WT (b) £108–£120, (c) £75–£85, DT (b) £17–£20, 🆔, Bk £3·25, L £1·50, D £6·60, cc 1 3.

Elsinore, G, z (Rl) *43 King St, PR8 1LG.* ☎ (0704) 32766.

Fairways, PH, z (Rl), *106 Leyland Rd, PR9 0DQ.* ☎ (0704) 42069. C. ⊷ 9 bedrs, 2 bps, 3 ba. 🅟 CH, TV, CP 20, CF. £ BB fr £10, DB fr £20, DT fr £13, D £3.

Fernley, PH, x (Rl), *69 Promenade, PR9 0JB.* ☎ (0704) 35610.

Franklyn, PH, x (R), *65 Promenade, PR9 0JB.* ☎ (0704) 40290.

Fulwood, PH, z (Rl), *82 Leyland Rd, PR9 0NJ.* ☎ (0704) 30993. C. ⊷ 11 bedrs, 1 sh, Dgs. 🅟 CH, TV, CP 9, CF, 7 st. £ BB £9·50, DB fr £19, WT (b) fr £86, DT (b) fr £13, 🆔, Bk £3, D £4·50.

Golf Links, H, z (RI), *85 Promenade, PR9 0JB.* ✆ (0704) 30405.

Hollies, H, z (Unl), *7 Mornington Rd, PR9 0TS.* ✆ (0704) 30054. C. ⊨ 15 bedrs, 3 bp, 3 bps, 3 ba, TV. ⊞ CH, CP 15, CF, 1 BGf, 8 st. £ BB £9·50–£12·50, DB £17–£22, WT (b) £78–£86·50, DT (b) £12–£13·50, ⏢. Bk £2·25, L £2·25, D £3·75.

Knowsley, H, y (RI), *2 Knowsley Rd, PR9 0HG.* ✆ (0704) 30190. Closed Oct. C. ⊨ 12 bedrs, 2 ba, Dgs. ⊞ CH, TV, Dgs, CP 10, CF, 3 st. £ BB £9–£9·50, DB £18–£19, WT (b) £77·50–£81, (c) £60–£63·50, ⏢.

Merlwood, PH, z (Unl), *22 Portland St, PR8 1HU.* ✆ (0704) 31247. Open Apr–Oct. C 2. ⊨ 6 bedrs, 1 ba. ⊞ TV, CP 6, 4 st. £ BB £10–£12, DB £20–£24, WT (b) £80–£85, (c) £63–£70, DT (b) £13–£15, ⏢.

Newholme, G, z (Unl), *51 King St, PR8 1DA.* ✆ (0704) 30425.

Sandpiper, PH, z (Unl), *8 Alexandra Rd, PR9 0NB.* ✆ (0704) 30327. Closed Xmas. C. ⊨ 4 bedrs, 1 ba, Dgs. ⊞ CH, TV, CP 4, 4 st. £ BB fr £7·50, DB fr £14, WT (b) fr £65, (c) fr £50, DT (b) fr £9·50, ⏢.

Sidbrook, PH, z (RI), *14 Talbot St, PR8 1HP.* ✆ (0704) 30608. C. ⊨ 9 bedrs, 2 ba, Dgs. ⊞ Ch, TV, CP 10, CF, 3 st.

Singleton Arms, H, z *16 Portland St, PR8 1LJ.* ✆ (0704) 34424. C 3. ⊨ 12 bedrs, 4 bps, 8 sh, 3 ba. ⊞ CH, TV, CP 40, CF, 8 st. £ BB fr £13·80, DB fr £24·80, WT (b) fr £109·75, DT (b) fr £17·25, ②, Bk £3, cc 1 3.

Stutelea, H, y (R), *Alexandra Rd, PR9 0NB.* ✆ (0704) 30080. C. ⊨ 15 bedrs, 4 bp, 1 bps, 4 ba, TV. ⊞ CH, CP 8, CF, 5 st. £ BB £11·50–£12·50, DB £23–£25, WT (a) fr £110, (b) fr £90, (c) fr £70, DT £11·50–£18·50, ②, Bk £2, L £3·50, D £3·50, cc 1 3.

Sunningdale, PH, z (RI), *85 Leyland Rd, PR9 0NJ.* ✆ (0704) 38673. C. ⊨ 15 bedrs, 5 bps, 7 sh, 2 ba. ⊞ CH, TV, CP 10, CF, 4 BGf, 7 st. £ BB £12·50–£13·25, DB £24·50–£26, WT £106–£115, DT (b) £17–£18·25, ⏢, D £5·50.

Talbot, H, z (R), *Portland St, PR8 1LR.* ✆ (0704) 33975.

White Lodge, PH, z (RI) *12 Talbot St, PR8 1HP.* ✆ (0704) 36320. C. ⊨ 10 bedrs, 2 ba. ⊞ ch, TV, CP 6, CF, 6 st. £ BB £8–£10, DB £16–£20, WT (b) £70–£85, (c) £11–£13, ⏢.

Whitworth Fall, PH, z (R), *16 Lathom Rd, PR9 0JL.* ✆ (0704) 30074. C. ⊨ 14 bedrs, 2 bps, 3 ba, Dgs. ⊞ ch, TV, Dgs, CP 14, CF, 1 BGf, 4 st. £ BB £9·20–£9·78, DB £18·40–£19·56, WT (b) £79·35–£82·80, DT (b) £13·22–£13·80, ⏢, Bk £2, D £4.

Windsor Lodge, H (R), *37 Saunders St, PR9 0HJ.* ✆ (0704) 30070. C. ⊨ 12 bedrs, 1 bp, 3 ba. ⊞ CH, TV, CP 12, CF, 2 BGf, 2 st. £ BB £9·50–£12·50, DB £19–£25, WT (b) £79·50–£85·50, DT (b) £13·25–£14·25, ②, Bk £2·50, D £4·75.

Body Repair Specialists: Bill Sheil Refinishers, 111A Boundary St. ✆ (0704) 32646.
Repairers: Goulder, John Ltd, Weld Rd and Palace Garages. ✆ (0704) 66613. Hattons (Southport) Ltd, 6–16 Roe Lane. ✆ (0704) 33555. Hollands Motors Ltd, 4 Virginia St. ✆ (0704) 31550.
Rescue Service: Walmayne Motors, 32 Linaker St. ✆ (0704) 32663.

SOUTHSEA Hampshire.
See PORTSMOUTH and SOUTHSEA.

SOUTH SHIELDS Tyne & Wear. Map 31F
Pop 86,400. Sunderland 7, London 277, Durham 19, Newcastle upon Tyne 9½.
EC Wed. **MD** Mon, Sat. **Golf** South Shields 18h. **See** Roman Fort and Museum, old Lifeboat and Memorial, Marsden Rock Bird Sanctuary.
🛈 South Foreshore. ✆ South Shields (0632) 557411.

★★**New Crown,** *Mowbray Rd, NE33 3NG.* ✆ (0632) 553472. C. ⊨ 11 bedrs, 3 bp, 2 ba, TV, Dgs. ✗ a l c, mc, at, LD 9. ⊞ CH, Ac, CF. £ BB £14–£16, DB £20·50–£22·50, ⏢, L £4, D £4, cc 1 2 3 5, Dep a.

★★**Sea,** *Sea Rd, NE33 2LD.* ✆ (0632) 566227.

Rescue Service: Baulard & Fosters Ltd, 36 Sunderland Rd. ✆ (0632) 552101.
Dean Garages (South Shields) Ltd, Dean Rd. ✆ (0632) 553312.
G & B Garages, 183 Sunderland Rd. ✆ (0632) 555241.
Highfield Service Station, 99 Highfield Rd. ✆ (0632) 541860.
Lynch & Berry Motors, Wilson St. ✆ (0632) 564665.
Selwood Garages Ltd, Commercial Rd. ✆ (0632) 552227.

SOUTHWELL Nottinghamshire. Map 22D
Pop 6,395. Leicester 33, London 131, Mansfield 11, Melton Mowbray 25, Newark 7, Nottingham 12, Ollerton 12.
EC Wed. **MD** Sat. **Golf** Oxton 18h. **See** Minster (earliest part 12th cent), Bishop's Manor, Prebend's Walk, Saracen's Head, Banqueting Hall, Grammar School, Water Gardens (Fiskerton Rd).

★★★**Saracen's Head,** *Market Place, NG25 0HE.* ✆ (0636) 812701. C. ⊨ 23 bedrs, 23 bp, TV, Dgs. ✗ a l c, mc, LD 8.30. ⊞ N, CH, TV, Dgs, CP 73, G 2, Ac, con 100, CF, 3 st. £ BB £34·50, DB £45, WB, ②, Bk £3, L £4·25, D £7·95, cc 1 2 3 4 5 6, Dep b.

Rescue Service: Minster Garage Ltd, King St. ✆ (0636) 812146.

SOUTHWOLD Suffolk. Map 16B
Pop 1,795. Saxmundham 14, London 109, Aldeburgh 17, Lowestoft 11, Norwich 29, Scole 25, Stowmarket 36.
EC Wed. **MD** Mon, Thur. **Golf** Southwold 9h. **See** St Edmund's Church, Museum, Town Hall, Lighthouse, 17th cent Sutherland House, note ships' figureheads in front of some houses.
🛈 Town Hall, Market Pl. ✆ Southwold (0502) 722366.

★**Pier Avenue,** *Station Rd, IP18 6LB.* ✆ (0502) 722632. C. ⊨ 13 bedrs, 5 bp, 3 bps, 1 sh, 2 ba, TV. ✗ a l c, mc, LD 8.30. ⊞ CH, TV, Dgs, CP 10, Ac, CF, 2 st. £ BB £13·50–£19·25, DB £27–£35·50, WT £136–£161, DT £22–£26, WB, ⏢, Bk £3·50, L £4·50, D £7·50, cc 3, Dep a.

Randolph, *Wangford Rd, Reydon, IP18 6PZ.* (2 m NW B1126). ✆ (0502) 723603. Closed Dec. C. ⊨ 12 bedrs, 2 bp, 3 ba, TV, Dgs. ⊞ ch, TV, Dgs, CP 15, U 2, CF, 4 st. £ BB £13·50–£17·50, DB £24–£31, WT (b) £120–£134, ⏢.

Rescue Service: Belcher's Garage (Southwold) Ltd, Station Rd. ✆ (0502) 723140 and (0502) 723310.

SOUTH WOODHAM FERRERS Essex.
Maps 10A and 17F
Woodham Ferrers 1, London 38, Brentwood 16, Chelmsford 12, Colchester 26, Dartford Tunnel 24, Southend-on-Sea 14.

★★**Oakland,** *Merchant St,* ✆ Chelmsford (0245) 322811.

Rescue Service: D & H Motors, Unit 8, Plot 1, Saltcoats Industrial Estate. ✆ Chelmsford (0245) 321971.

SOUTH ZEAL Devon. Maps 3B and 4E
Exeter 18, London 188, Ashburton 19, Crediton 14, Newton Abbot 21, Okehampton 5.
EC Wed. **Golf** Okehampton 18h.

★★**Oxenham Arms,** *EX20 2JT.* ✆ Sticklepath (083 784) 244. RS Xmas. C. ⊨ 8 bedrs, 6 bp, 1 ba, TV, Dgs. ✗ a l c, mc, at, LD 9. ⊞ ch, TV, Dgs, CP 8, rf, CF, 2 st. £ BB £18–£22, DB £28–£35, WT £156–£170, DT £30–£32, WB, ②, Bk £1·75, L £4·25, D £8·50, cc 1 2 3 5 6.

SPALDING Lincolnshire. Map 23F
Pop 18,223. Peterborough 17, London 101, Boston 16, Grantham 30, King's Lynn 28, Melton Mowbray 36, Sleaford 19, Stamford 19, Wisbech 20.
EC Thur. **MD** Tue, Sat. **Golf** Surfleet 18h. **See** Church (13th cent), Ayscoughfee Hall with Bird Museum and Public Gdns, RC Church, White Horse Inn, Bulb Fields (April–May), Springfields.
🛈 Ayscoughfee Hall, Churchgate. ✆ Spalding (0775) 5468.

★★**White Hart** (TH), *Market Pl, PE11 1SU.* ✆ (0775) 5668. C. ⊨ 29 bedrs, 4 bp, 4 ba, TV, Dgs. ✗ a l c, mc, at, LD 10. ⊞ CH, Dgs, CP 40, Ac, con 70, CF, 2 st. £ BB £31–£34, DB £43·50–£47·50, WB, ⏢, cc 1 2 3 4 5 6.

Cley Hall, H, *22 High St, PE11 1TX.* ✆ (0775) 5157. C. ⊨ 4 bedrs, 4 bp, TV, Dgs. ✗ a l c. ⊞ CH, CP 20, CF, 3 st. £ B fr £25, BD fr £35, ⏢, , Bk £4, L £6·50, D £6·50, cc 1 2 3 5.

Repairers: Holland Bros Ltd, Pinchbeck Rd. ✆ (0775) 3651.
R C Edmondson (Spalding) Ltd, St Johns Rd. ✆ (0775) 3671.
Specialist Radiator Repairer: Serck Radiator Services Ltd, Willows Walk, Commercial Rd. ✆ (0775) 4747 and at Cradge Bank Rd. ✆ (0775) 3942.
Specialist Spring Repairer: Jonas Woodhead Ltd, Le Boeuf Yard, Pinchbeck Rd. ✆ (0775) 3660.
Rescue Service: Little London Service Station, Little London. ✆ (0775) 66661. Sanderson's Garage, 65 High Rd, Moulton. ✆ Holbeach (0406) 370307.

SPARKFORD Somerset. Map 5C
Pop 477. Wincanton 7, London 117, Bridgwater 25, Crewkerne 16, Frome 18, Glastonbury 22, Ilminster 18, Shepton Mallet 12, Sherborne 8, Taunton 25.
Golf Yeovil 18h. **See** 13th cent Church.

Repairer: Windsor & Partners, London Road Garage. ✆ North Cadbury (0963) 241.
Rescue Service: Wake's Services (Sparkford) Ltd, Northfield Garage. ✆ Marston Magna (0935) 409.

SPARSHOLT Hampshire. Map 6D
See WINCHESTER.

SPEKE Merseyside. Map 20F
Runcorn 7, London 191, Birkenhead 10, St
Helens 12, Warrington 13.

Repairer: Horsmans Ltd, Speke Hall Lane.
✆ 051-486 8846.
Body Repair Service: Horsmans Ltd,
Speke Hall Lane. ✆ 051-486 8846.

SPILSBY Lincolnshire. Map 23D
Pop 1,632. Boston 16, London 133,
Horncastle 9½, Louth 18, Skegness 14,
Sleaford 26.
EC Tue. **MD** Mon. **Golf** Northshore,
Skegness 18h.
See St James' Church (monuments), Sir
John Franklin Memorial, 14th cent Butter
Cross.
🛈 41B High St. ✆ Spilsby (0790) 52301.

MC Repairer: A E Wildman, Halton Rd.
✆ (0790) 53219.

STAFFORD Staffordshire. Map 22E
Pop 54,530. Lichfield 16, London 132, M6
Motorway 2, Burton-on-Trent 26,
Nantwich 22, Newport 12, Stone 7½,
Uttoxeter 14, Walsall 17, Whitchurch 32,
Wolverhampton 15.
EC Wed. **MD** Tue, Fri, Sat. **Golf** Stafford
Castle 9h. **See** Izaak Walton born here
1593 (plaque in Eastgate St.), Churches of
St Mary and St Chad, Art Gallery and
Museum, ancient High House ('black and
white'), Sir Martin Noel's Almshouses (The
College), old inns, Izaak Walton cottage at
Shallowford, Shugborough Hall 5½ m E.
🛈 Civic Offices, Riverside. ✆ Stafford
(0785) 3181.

★★★**Tillington Hall,** *Eccleshall Rd,
ST16 1JJ.* ✆ (0785) 53531. C. ➡ 93
bedrs, 90 bp, 3 bps, TV, Dgs. ✗ a l c, mc, at,
LD 10. 🅰 Lt, N, CH, CP 200, U 1, Ac, con
200, CF, 0 st, Dis. £ BB £38, DB
£48, WB, 🔢, L £6, D £6·50, cc 1 2 3 5 6,
Dep b.
★★**Garth,** *Moss Pit, ST17 9JB.* ✆ (0785)
56124. C. ➡ 32 bedrs, 24 bp, 2 ba, TV,
Dgs. ✗ a l c, mc, at, LD 10. 🅰 N, CH, Dgs,
CP 150, Ac, con 40, CF, 12 BGf, 0 st, Dis.
£ BB fr £20, DB fr £25, WB, 🔢, Bk £3, L
£4·50, D £6·95, cc 1 3, Dep b.
◼★★**Swan,** *Greengate St, ST16 2JA.*
✆ (0785) 58142. Closed Xmas. C. ➡ 31
bedrs, 31 bp, TV. ✗ a l c, mc, at, LD 10.30.
🅰 N, CH, CP 70, Ac. £ BB fr
£23·10, DB fr £40·95, WB, 🔢, Bk £2·42, L
£5, D £5, cc 1 2 3 5.
◼★**Vine,** *Salter St, ST16 2JU.* ✆ (0785)
51071. C. ➡ 26 bedrs, 8 ba, TV, Dgs.
✗ a l c, mc, at, LD 9.30. 🅰 Dgs, CP 10, Ac,
CF. £ BB £15·50, DB £23, WB, 🔢, Bk £3, L
£2·95, D £5·75, cc 1 3.
Abbey, G, z (Unl), *65 Lichfield Rd, ST17
4LW.* ✆ (0785) 51881. Closed Xmas–New
Year. C. ➡ 21 bedrs, 7 bps, 4 ba. 🅰 CH, TV,
CP 20, U 7, CF, 3 BGf. £ BB £12–£16, DB
£20–£26, 🔢, D £3·50, ▲
Leonards Croft, G, z (Unl), *80 Lichfield
Rd, ST17 4LP.* ✆ (0785) 3676. Closed
Xmas. C. ➡ 18 bedrs, 5 ba, Dgs. 🅰 CH, TV,
CP 12, 5 BGf, 3 st. £ BB £7·48, DB £13·80,
🔢, Bk £2·50.

Repairers: Attwood Garages Ltd,
Lichfield Rd. ✆ (0785) 42366.
S Weaver & Son (Stafford) Ltd, Lichfield
Rd. ✆ (0785) 52324.
Specialist Body Repairer: Lloyds Garage
Ltd, Stone Rd. ✆ (0785) 51331.
Rescue Service: Brocton Service Station,
Cannock Rd, Brocton. ✆ (0785) 61311.

Lloyds Garage Ltd, Stone Rd. ✆ (0785)
51331.
Moss Pit Garage Ltd, Wolverhampton Rd.
✆ (0785) 52119.
Pasturefields Recovery Services,
Drummond Rd, Astonfields Industrial
Estate. ✆ (0785) 54495.
Sandon Road Motors (Stafford) Ltd,
Sandon Rd. ✆ (0785) 45299.
Walton Garage (Stafford) Ltd, Walton.
✆ (0785) 61293.

STAINES Surrey. Map 7A
Pop 19,000. Brentford and Chiswick 10,
London 17, M25 Motorway 1, Bagshot
10, Ealing 12, Kingston upon Thames 9½,
Reading 22, Richmond-upon-Thames 10,
Slough 7, Uxbridge 11, Weybridge 6,
Windsor 6, Woking 9.
EC Thur. **MD** Wed & Sat. **Golf** Ashford
Manor 18h.
See St Mary's Church (tower by Inigo
Jones), London Stone in Lammas
Recreation Ground, Bridge built by Rennie
in 1832, Magna Carta Island 2 m NE.
★★**Thames Lodge,** *Thames St, TW18
4SJ.* ✆ (0784) 54221. C. ➡ 48 bedrs, 48
bp, TV, Dgs. ✗ a l c, mc. 🅰 N, CH, TV, Dgs,
CP 60, Ac, con 20, CF, 8 BGf, 1 st, Dis.
£ BB fr £41·50, DB fr £49, WB, 🔢, Bk
£4·50, L £6·95, D £6·95, cc 1 2 3 5 6, Dep.
★★**Stanwell Hall,** *Town La, TW19 7PW*
(Stanwell 2½ m E B378). ✗ Ashford
(Middx) (078 42) 52292. C. ➡ 27 bedrs, 6
bp, 6 ba, TV. ✗ a l c, mc, at. 🅰 CH, TV, CP
50, G 3, Ac, con, 1 st. £ BB fr £19, DB fr
£35, 🔢, Bk £5·25, D £7, cc 1 2 3 6, Dep b.
Angel, H, z, *24 High St, TW19 5NT.*
✆ (0784) 52509.

STAINLAND West Yorkshire. M. Area
25F and 33C
Huddersfield 5, London 191, Bradford 12,
Halifax 6, Leeds 17, Oldham 17, Rochdale
14, Wakefield 16.
EC Tue. **Golf** Halifax Bradley Hall Ltd 18h.
See Stainland Cross.

Rescue Service: Black Horse Garage Ltd.
✆ Elland (0422) 74826.

STALYBRIDGE Greater Manchester
(Cheshire). Maps 22A and 27B
Pop 26,237. Glossop 6, London 180,
Barnsley 27, Huddersfield 19, Manchester
8, Oldham 5½, Stockport 8½.
EC Tue. **MD** Daily exc Tue. **Golf** Windy
Harbour 9h. **See** St Paul's Church, Art
Gallery.

MC Repairer: Sellars Garage Ltd, Feroden
Works, Leech St. ✆ 061-338 2447.
Rescue Service: Sellars Garage Ltd,
Feroden Works, Leech St. ✆ 061-338
2447.

STAMFORD Lincolnshire. Map 23E
Pop 16,656. Alconbury 24, London 91,
Grantham 21, Kettering 23, Leicester 32,
Melton Mowbray 20, Peterborough 14,
Sleaford 28, Spalding 19.
EC Thur. **MD** Mon, Sat. **Golf** North
Luffenham 18h. **See** Browne's Hospital
(15th cent almshouses), Town Hall,
Stamford School, Castle remains, George
Hotel (gallows inn sign), old churches and
inns, Burghley House 1½ m SE.
🛈 Council Offices, St Mary's Hill.
✆ Stamford (0780) 64444.

★★★**George of Stamford,** *St Martins,
PE9 2LB.* ✆ (0780) 55171. C. ➡ 44 bedrs,
38 bp, 2 ba, TV, Dgs. ✗ a l c, mc, at, LD

10.30. 🅰 N, CH, Dgs, CP 100, U 2, Ac, con
50, CF, 0 st. £ BB £27·50–£40, DB £42–
£54, WB, 🔢, Bk £4·50, L £15, D £15,
cc 1 2 3 4 5 6.
★★**Crown,** *All Saints Pl, PE9 2AG.*
✆ (0780) 63136. RS Dec 25. C. ➡ 18
bedrs, 6 bp, 3 bps, 4 ba, TV, Dgs. ✗ a l c,
mc, at, LD 9.30. 🅰 CH, TV, Dgs, CP 40, Ac,
con 40, CF, 1 st. £ BB £20–£24, DB £28–
£34, WB, 🔢, Bk £2·75, L £5·95, D £6·95,
cc 1 2 3 5 6.
★★**Lady Annes's,** *37–38 High St, St
Martins, PE9 2LJ.* ✆ (0780) 53175. C.
➡ 30 bedrs, 14 bp, 7 bps, 5 sh, 2 ba, TV,
Dgs. ✗ a l c, mc. 🅰 CH, TV, Dgs, CP
200, Ac, con 150, CF, 3 BGf, 0 st, Dis. £ BB
£12–£30, DB £28–£50, DBB fr £18·95, WB,
🔢, cc 1 2 3 5 6.
◼★**St Martins Garden House,** (R), *42
High St, St Martins, PE9 2LJ.* ✆ (0780)
63359. C. ➡ 10 bedrs, 2 ba, TV, Dgs.
✗ mc, at, LD 9.30. 🅰 CH, Dgs, CP 3, G 5,
Ac, con 20, CF, 0 st. £ BB fr £17, DB fr £28,
WB, 🔢, Bk £3, D £8, cc 1 3.

Repairer: Mill View Motors, Porters Lane,
Easton-on-the-Hill. ✆ (0780) 63943.
Marshall of Stamford Ltd, 36 St Pauls St.
✆ (0780) 3174.
Rescue Service: St George's Garage, St
George's Sq. ✆ (0780) 3374.
Uffington Motors, Bertia La, Uffington.
✆ (0780) 3936.

STANDISH Greater Manchester
(Lancashire). Map 20C
Pop 12,317. Wigan 3, London 198, M6
Motorway 1½, Chorley 5, Ormskirk 10,
Preston 14.
EC Wed. **Golf** Haigh Hall Municipal 18h.
See 16th cent St Wilfrid's Church, Stocks
and Ancient Cross in Market Place, Old
Boars Head Inn.

★★★**M Cassinellis Almond Brook,**
Almond Brook Rd, WN6 0SR. ✆ (0257)
425588. C. ➡ 64 bedrs, 64 bp, TV. ✗ a l c,
mc, at, LD 10. 🅰 N, CH, CP 200, Ac, con
100, CF, 25 BGf, 3 st. £ BB £35–£29·75,
DB £24–£35, WB, 🔢, Bk £3·50, cc 1 2 3 5.
Beeches, H, y (R), *School La, Wigan,
WN6 0AB.* ✆ (0257) 426432. C. ➡ 7
bedrs, 5 bp, 2 bps, TV. ✗ a l c. 🅰 CH, CP
70, CF, 3 st. £ BBc £20, DBc £21–£26, 🔢,
Bk £3, L £3·50, D £7·50, cc 1 2 3 5.

Rescue Service: Standish Service Station,
Preston Rd. ✆ (0257) 422899.

STANDLAKE Oxfordshire. M. Area 14F
Pop 1,257. Wallingford 19, London 66,
Burford 13, Faringdon 11, Wantage 12.
Golf Frilford Heath 18h (2). **See** Church.

Rescue Service: W K Saxel, Standlake
Garage. ✆ (086 731) 203.

STANLEY Durham. Map 32C
Pop 17,900. Durham 11, London 271,
Alston 38, Corbridge 19, Hexham 22,
Middleton-in-Teesdale 31, Newcastle
upon Tyne 8½, Sunderland 14, West
Auckland 21.
EC Wed. **MD** Thur. **Golf** Hobson 18h.
See Causey Arch (18th cent, single span),
2 m N, Beamish open air Museum.

Rescue Service: Fultons Stanley Ltd, Kip
Hill Garage. ✆ (0207) 38311.

STANNINGTON Northumberland. Map
31F
Pop 1,500. Newcastle upon Tyne 9,
London 282, Alnwick 25, Bellingham 32,

Coldstream 52, Corbridge 31, Hawick 62, Jedburgh 57.
EC Wed. **Golf** Morpeth 18h. **See** Blagdon Hall, Parish Church, Bellasis Bridge.

Rescue Service: Stannington Service Station, Gt North Rd. ✆ (067 089) 221.

STANSTEAD ABBOTTS Hertfordshire. Map 15F.
Hoddesdon 2½, London 23, Bishops Stortford 11, Chelmsford 24, Harlow 5½, Hatfield 12, Royston 23.
Golf East Herts 18h. **See** Marina.

⚕★★★★Briggens House, *Ware, SG12 8LD.* ✆ Roydon (027 979) 2416. C. 📧 26 bedrs, 22 bp, 4 bps, TV. ✗ a l c, mc, at, LD 10. 🅿 Lt, N, CH, CP 200, sp, gc, tc, pf, con 120, CF, 11 BGf, 4 st. £ BB £29–£32, DB £45–£60, WB, 2. Bk £3, L £8·25, D £10, cc 1 2 3 5 6, Dep.

STANSTED Essex. Maps 15D and 17E
Pop 4,974. Bishop's Stortford 2½, London 34, Cambridge 24, Dunmow 9, Haverhill 22, Newmarket 29.
EC Wed. **Golf** Bishop's Stortford 18h.
See Stansted Mountfitchet Windmill (built 1787, restored 1966), 12th cent Church. Castle.

Rescue Service: Concord Motor Services (Stansted) Ltd, 1 Cambridge Rd. ✆ Bishop's Stortford (0279) 813608.

STANTON Suffolk. Map 16D
Pop 2,297. Bury St Edmunds 9, London 83, Ipswich 24, Norwich 29, Scole 12, Thetford 9½.
EC Wed. **Golf** Bury St Edmunds 18h.

Rescue Service: Baker's Garage. ✆ (0359) 50210.

STANTON ST QUINTON Wiltshire. M. Area 5B
Pop 430. Swindon 18, London 96, Chippenham 4½, Cirencester 17, Tetbury 10.
Golf Chippenham 18h. **See** St Giles Church, Saxon Village.

Rescue Service: A Smith & Sons (Stanton) Ltd. ✆ Hullavington (066 63) 223.

STANWAY Essex. M. Area 17C
Pop 5,400. Chelmsford 18, London 62, Braintree 11, Colchester 3½, Haverhill 25, Southend-on-Sea 37.
EC Thur. **Golf** Colchester 18h. **See** 14th cent Stanway Hall and Zoo, Stanway Rose Gardens.

Rescue Service: Stanway Garage, London Rd. ✆ Colchester (0206) 74254.

STAPLEFORD Nottinghamshire. Map 22D
Pop 18,095. M1 Motorway 7½, London 123, Ashby-de-la-Zouch 16, Chesterfield 26, Derby 9, Hinckley 31, Loughborough 14, Mansfield 18, Matlock 24, Nottingham 5½.
Golf Beeston Fields 18h. **See** Saxon Market Cross shaft, Ancient Hemlock Stone, St Helen's Church.

Repairer: Sandcliffe Garage Ltd, Nottingham Rd. ✆ Sandiacre (0602) 395000.

STAPLEHURST Kent. Map 10C
Pop 5,500. Maidstone 9, London 45, Ashford 19, Canterbury 28, Hawkhurst 9, Tenterden 12, Tonbridge 18, Tunbridge Wells 17.

EC Wed. **Golf** Cranbrook 9h. **See** Perp Church, Tudor Manor House.

Rescue Service: J R & M E Sayner, Staplehurst Service Station, High St. ✆ (0580) 891318.
Ottermount Ltd, T/As Iden Park Motor Co, Cranbrook Rd. ✆ (0580) 892093

STARCROSS Devon. Map 3D
Pop 2,000. M5 Motorway 7, Exeter 9, London 178, Dawlish 3, Exminster 5.
EC Wed. **Golf** Dawlish Warren 18h.

Rescue Service: Cowton & Western, Cockwood Service Station. ✆ (0626) 315.

STATHERN Leicestershire. M. Area 23E
Pop 480. Melton Mowbray 9½, London 114, Grantham 22, Nottingham 15.
Golf Melton Mowbray 9h. **See** Church (mainly 14th–15th cent).

Rescue Service: Wood & Cooke, Main St. ✆ Harby (0949) 60205.

STAVELEY Derbyshire. Map 22B
Pop 17,644. Mansfield 12, London 150, Chesterfield 4½, Ollerton 16, Rotherham 13, Sheffield 11, Worksop 10.
EC Mon. **MD** Fri. **Golf** Renishaw Park, nr Sheffield 18h. **See** St John's Church, historic Staveley Hall (former Rectory), Netherthorpe Grammar School, The Hagge, The Chantry.

Repairer: John Turner, High St.
✆ Chesterfield (0246) 472224 & (0246) 472281.

STAVERTON Devon. Map 3D
Pop 100. Newton Abbot 8, London 217, Ashburton 5, Plymouth 23, Totnes 3.

★Sea Trout Inn, *TQ9 6PA.* ✆ (080 426) 274.

STAWELL Somerset. Map 5C
Pop 280. Glastonbury 10, London 136, Bridgwater 5, Wells 15, Weston-super-Mare 17. **Golf** Enmore 18h.

Fruit & Honey, F, xy (Unl), *Innsmead La, TA7 9AN.* ✆ Chilton Polden (0278) 722459.

STEEPLE ASTON Oxfordshire. Map 14D
Pop 872. Bicester 9, London 66, Banbury 10, Brackley 14, Chipping Norton 12, Oxford 13½, Witney 15.
Golf North Oxford 18h. **See** Perp Church, Dormers Folly.

★★Hopcrofts Holt, *Banbury Rd, OX5 3QQ.* ✆ (0869) 40259. C. 📧 23 bedrs, 20 bp, 3 bps, 1 sh, 2 ba, TV. ✗ mc, at, LD 9.30. 🅿 CH, Dgs, CP 100, Ac, con 55, CF, 1 st. £ BB £21–£25, DB £27–£32, DBB £20·50–£28, WB, 1. Bk £3, L £6·95, D £6·95, cc 1 2 3 5, Dep b.

Westfield Farm Riding Centre, F, x (RI), *The Fenway, OX5 3SS.* ✆ (0869) 40591. Closed Xmas. C. 📧 7 bedrs, 7 bps, TV, Dgs. 🅿 CH, TV, CP 15, CF, 1 st. £ BB fr £15, DB fr £26, 1. Bk £2, D £5.

Rescue Service: Hopcroft Holt Service Station. ✆ (0869) 47401.

STEVENAGE Hertfordshire. Map 15D
See also LITTLE WYMONDLEY.
Pop 75,000. Hatfield 10, London 31, A1(M) Motorway 1½, Baldock 6, Bedford 20, Bishop's Stortford 21, Hoddesdon 15, Luton 12.
EC Wed. **MD** Thur, Fri, Sat. **Golf** Stevenage 18h. **See** Early 12th cent St Nicholas' Church, Museum, Annual Fair

(first held 1281) in Sept, Knebworth House 3 m S.
🅸 Central Library, Southgate. ✆ Stevenage (0438) 69441.

★★★Grampian, *SG1 1EJ.* ✆ (0438) 350661. C. 📧 100 bedrs, 100 bp, TV, Dgs. ✗ mc, at, LD 9.30. 🅿 Lt, N, CH, Dgs, Ac, con 150, CF, 0 st. £ BB £34–£36, DB £40–£42, DT £46·50–£48·50, DBB £41·50–£43·50, WB, 2. Bk £4·75, L £5·50, D £7·50, cc 1 2 3 5 6, Dep b.

★★★M Roebuck (TH), *Old London Rd, Broadwater, SG2 8DS.* ✆ (0438) 65444. C. 📧 54 bedrs, 54 bp, TV, Dgs. ✗ a l c, mc, LD 9.45. 🅿 N, CH, Dgs, CP 80, Ac, con 50, CF, 17 BGf, 4 st. £ BB £38, DB £49·50, WB, 1. cc 1 2 3 4 5 6, Dep (Xmas).

Rescue Service: Clem Motor Repairers, Crompton Rd. ✆ (0438) 51785.

STEYNING West Sussex. Map 7E
Pop 4,155. Crawley 20, London 50, Brighton 11, Haywards Heath 18, Horsham 16, Pulborough 11, Worthing 7.
EC Thur. **Golf** Hill Barn, Worthing 18h.
See Church of St Andrew's (12th cent), Grammar School, 'House of Pipes' (in Bramber), Bramber Castle ruins and St Mary's at Bramber 1 m SE.

★★Springwells (R), *High St, BN4 3GG.* ✆ (0903) 812446. C. 📧 10 bedrs, 6 bp, 2 ba, TV. ✗ a l c, LD 9.30. 🅿 N, CH, CP 6, sp, sb, con 20, CF, 0 st. £ BB fr £18, DB £38, WB, 1. Bk £3·50, L £6·50, D £12, cc 1 2 3 5,▲
Lands Down, G, x (Unl), *Laines Rd, BN4 3LL.* ✆ (0903) 812065.

STIBBINGTON Cambridgeshire.
M. Areas 23E and 15A
1½ m W of Wansford. Pop 465. Alconbury 15, London 83, Bedford 38, Kettering 25, Leicester 34, Northampton 36, Peterborough 8, Stamford 7.
Golf New Milton, Peterborough 18h. **See** 17th cent Stibbington Hall, Haycock Hotel, old coaching inn.

Rescue Service: D Collier Ltd, Peterborough Rd, Wansford. ✆ Stamford (0780) 782229.

STICKLEPATH Devon. M. Area 3B.
Whiddon Down 3½, London 189, Exeter 19, M5 Motorway 21, Moretonhampstead 9½, Okehampton 4.

Rescue Service Owlsfoot Garage. ✆ (083 784) 304.

STINCHCOMBE Gloucestershire. Map 13F
Tetbury 11, London 109, M5 Motorway 7, Bath 26, Bristol 22, Cheltenham 23, Chepstow 23, Gloucester 14.

⚕★★★★Stinchcombe Manor, *GL11 6BQ.* ✆ Dursley (0453) 2538.

STOCKBRIDGE Hampshire. Map 6C
Pop 520. Basingstoke 21, London 68, Amesbury 16, Andover 7½, Romsey 10, Salisbury 15, Winchester 9.
EC Wed. **Golf** Leckford 9h. **See** Tudor Buildings, Church.

★★Grosvenor, *High St, SO20 6EU.* ✆ Andover (0264) 810606. C. 📧 14 bedrs, 1 bp, 4 ba, TV. ✗ a l c, mc, at, LD 9.30. 🅿 CH, TV, Dgs, CP 30, Ac, con 20, CF, 1 st. £ BB DB fr £30, WB, 2. Bk £4, L £6, D £8, cc 1 2 3 5.
Carbery, G, x (RI), *Salisbury Hill, SO20 6EZ.* ✆ Andover (0264) 810771. Closed

Xmas. C. ♨ 11 bedrs, 3 ba. ⓓ CH, TV, CP 12, CF, 2 st. £ BB £10·92, DB £21·85, WT (b) £110, ①.

The Old Three Cups, PH, x (R), *High St, SO20 6HB*. ✆ Andover (0264) 810527. Closed Jan. C. ♨ 8 bedrs, 3 bp, 1 ba, TV. ✗ a l c. ⓓ CH, CP 12, 2 st. £ BB £13·80–£23, DB £25·30–£34·50, ②, Bk £3, L £4·20, D £5·50, cc 1 3.

Repairer: Fenning's Garage, High St. ✆ Andover (0264) 810711.
Rescue Service: G P Motors, The Garage, Queenswood Rd, Broughton. ✆ Broughton (079 430) 440.

STOCKPORT Greater Manchester (Cheshire). Maps 19B and 22A
See also BRAMHALL.
RAC Office, *65–81 St Petersgate, Stockport, SK1 1DS*. ✆ (General) 061-477 6500. (Rescue Service only) 061-477 7000.
Pop 291,000. Buxton 18, London 179, M63 Motorway ½, Altrincham 8½, Barnsley 33, Chapel-en-le-Frith 14, Glossop 11, Huddersfield 27, Knutsford 14, Macclesfield 12, Manchester 6, Oldham 11, Wakefield 39.
See Plan pp. 340 and 341.
MD Tue, Fri, Sat. **P** See Plan. **Golf** Stockport 18h. **See** Art Gallery, Museum, Bramall Hall, Bramall 2½ m S, Lyme Park 6½ m SE.
ⓣ 9 Princes St. ✆ 061-480 0315.

★★★Alma Lodge, *149 Buxton Rd, SK2 6EL*. ✆ 061-483 4431. C. ♨ 70 bedrs, 54 bp, 3 ba, TV, Dgs. ⓓ N, CH, Dgs, CP 250, Ac, con 250, CF, 1 st. £ B £23–£30, BD fr £36, WB, ①, Bk £4·25, L £3·75, D £6·75, cc 1 2 3 4 5 6, Dep.

★★★Belgrade, *Dialstone La, SK2 6AG*. ✆ 061-483 3851. C. ♨ 162 bedrs, 162 bp, TV. ✗ a l c, mc, at, LD 10.30. ⓓ CH, CP 400, Ac, con 400, CF, 54 BGf, 3 st. £ BB £31, DB £36, WB, ①, Bk £3·75, L £5·50, D £9, cc 1 2 3 5, Dep b.

■★**Acton Court** (Rt), *187 Buxton Rd, SK2 7AA*. ✆ 061-483 6172.

Appleton Lodge, PH, z (Rl). *15 Brownsville Rd, Heaton Moor, SK4 4PE*. ✆ 061-432 8198. C. ♨ 13 bedrs, 2 bp, 4 bps, 2 ba, TV, Dgs. ⓓ CH, TV, CP 12, U 3, G 1, CF, 2 BGf. £ BB £12·07–£16·67, DB £18·40–£23, WT (c) fr £84·49, DT (b) fr £16·38, ①, Bk £1·50, D £4·30.

Ascot House, z (R), *195 Wellington Rd North, SK4 2PB*. ✆ 061-432 2380. Closed 1 week Xmas. C. ♨ 14 bedrs, 6 bp, 4 ba, TV. ⓓ CH, TV, CP 15, CF, 2 BGf, 0 st, Dis. £ BB £14·95–£20, DB £23–£28, ①, cc 1 2.

Repairers: Heron Motor Group, Town Hall Sq. ✆ 061-480 7966.
Lex Cockshoot Ltd, Wellington Rd North. ✆ 061-432 6201.
Stockport Motor House Ltd, Buxton Rd, Heaviley. ✆ 061-480 4244.
Specialist Body Repairers: F Lindsay & Sons Ltd, Richardson St. ✆ 061-480 5360.
Rescue Service: Autoton (Stockport) Ltd, New Beech Garage, Broadstone Rd, Reddish. ✆ 061-430 3977.
Lookers Garage, 91 Heaton Moor Rd, Heaton Moor. ✆ 061-432 9416.
Motor Move (UK) Ltd, Banks Lane Service Station, Banks La. ✆ 061-429 6055.

M S R Recovery Service, 22 Compstall Rd, Marple Bridge. ✆ 061-427 5133.

STOCKSFIELD-ON-TYNE Northumberland. M. Area 31E
Pop 2,000 (inc Broomley). West Auckland 28, London 227, Corbridge 5, Durham 21, Hexham 8, Newcastle upon Tyne 14.
EC Thur. **Golf** Stocksfield 18h. **See** Bywell Castle. Churches, Prudhoe Castle 3 m E.

Rescue Service: Fewsters (Garages) Ltd, ✆ (066 15) 2283.

STOCKTON-ON-TEES Teesside, Cleveland. Map 24F
Pop 172,470. Thirsk 22, London 243, Darlington 11, Durham 19, Middlesbrough 4, Northallerton 19, Sunderland 26.
EC Thur. **MD** Wed, Sat. **Golf** Eaglescliffe 18h. **See** 18th cent Town Hall, Preston Hall Museum of Social History, Darlington and Stockton Rly Museum, interesting Parish Churches at Stockton and Norton Parks.

■★★★**Swallow,** *10 John Walker Sq, TS18 1AQ*. ✆ (0632) 679721. C. ♨ 127 bedrs, 127 bp, TV, Dgs. ✗ a l c, mc, at, LD 11. ⓓ Lt, N, CH, G 400, Ac, con 300, CF, 0 st. £ BB £21–£38, DB £31·50–£50, WB, ①, Bk £4, L £7·75, D £8·95, cc 1 2 3 5, Dep b.
Claireville, PH, y (Rl), *519 Yarm Rd, Eaglescliffe, TS16 9BG*. ✆ Eaglescliffe (0642) 780378. Closed Xmas Day & New Years Day. C. ♨ 21 bedrs, 4 ba, Dgs. ⓓ CH, TV, Dgs, CP 20, CF, 0 st. £ BB fr £12·75, DB fr £22, WT (c) fr £89·25, DT (b) fr £17, ①, Bk £2·50, D £4·25.
Grange, H, *91 Yarm Rd, TS18 3PS*. ✆ (0632) 675908.
Sctr Repairer: T Cowie Ltd, Norton Rd. ✆ (0632) 65361.
Rescue Service: Fairfield Service Station, Bishopton Rd West. ✆ (0632) 65007.
Hartburn Garage Ltd, Darlington Rd, Hartburn. ✆ (0632) 582102.
Minories Garage Ltd, Church Rd. ✆ (0632) 612621.

STOGURSEY Somerset. M. Area 4D
Pop 1,199. Bridgwater 9, London 150, Dunster 15.
EC Wed. **Golf** Minehead. 18h. **See** Priory Church of St Andrew, St Andrew's Well, Castle ruins.

Rescue Service: Stogursey Motors, 7 High St. ✆ Nether Stowey (0278) 732237.

STOKE BY NAYLAND Suffolk. M. Area 17C
Pop 737. Colchester 7½, London 63, Harwich 21, Ipswich 14, Scole 35, Stowmarket 18, Sudbury 9.
Golf Stoke by Nayland 18h (2). **See** 15th cent Church, Medieval Guildhall, Old Maltings and other old houses.

Rescue Service: L S Eaves Ltd, Alde Garage, Polstead St. ✆ Nayland (0206) 262123.

STOKE FLEMING Devon. Map 3F
Pop 963. Dartmouth 3, London 208 (Fy 202), Kingsbridge 12.
Golf Churston 18h. **See** 13th cent St Petroc's Church.

★★Stoke Lodge (R), *TQ6 0QF*. ✆ (0803) 770523. C. ♨ 14 bedrs, 2 bp, 8 bps, 1 ba, TV, Dgs. ✗ a l c, mc, at, LD 9.30. ⓓ CH, TV, CP 40, sp, con 30, CF, 1 BGf, 4 st. £ BB

£12–£20·50, DB £24–£33, DBB £17·25–£22, WB, ②, Bk £2·95, L £4·50, D £6·50.

Repairer: Premier Garage (Dartmouth) Ltd. ✆ (080 427) 324.

STOKE GABRIEL Devon. Map 3D
Pop 1,000. Torquay 6, London 221, Dartmouth 7, Totnes 4.
Golf Churston 18h. **See** Perp Church, Lotus Pottery.

▮■★★★Gabriel Court (R), *Stoke Hill, TQ9 6SF*. ✆ (080 428) 206. C. ♨ 24 bedrs, 17 bp, 5 bps, 2 ba, Dgs. ✗ mc, at, LD 8.30. ⓓ CH, TV, Dgs, CP 14, G 6, sp, tc, con 50, CF, 1 BGf, 1 st, Dis. £ BB fr £19·50, DB fr £40, WT fr £235, DT fr £35, ①, Bk £5, L £5·50, D £10, cc 1 2 3 5 6.

STOKE GOLDINGTON Bucks. Map 15C.
Newport Pagnell 5, London 57, M1 Motorway 6, Bedford 16, Northampton 11, Wellingborough 16.

Rescue Service: Gardner & White, Stoke Goldington, Newport Pagnell, Milton Keynes. ✆ (090 855) 387.

STOKE MANDEVILLE Bucks. Map 15E
Pop 2,139. Watford 22, London 39, Aylesbury 2½, Denham 22, Dunstable 14, Henley-on-Thames 25, High Wycombe 14, Reading 30, St Albans 22, Wallingford 23.
Golf Ellesborough 18h. **See** Church.

Belmore, H, x (Rl), *Risborough Rd, HP22 5UT*. ✆ (029 661) 2258. Closed Xmas. C. ♨ 17 bedrs, 15 bp, 2 bps, TV, Dgs. ⓓ CH, CP 20, CF, 13 BGf, 0 st, Dis. £ BB £26·20–£34·27, DB £35·40–£46·69, WT (b) £211–£246·60, DT (b) £33·40–£41·40, ①, cc 1 2 3 5.

Repairer: Brook End Motors & Engineering Co Ltd, Weston Turville. ✆ (029 661) 2400 and (029 661) 2567.

STOKENCHURCH Bucks. Map 15E
Pop 4,060. High Wycombe 7, London 37, Aylesbury 16, Bicester 25, Henley-on-Thames 14, Oxford 18, Reading 19, Wallingford 13.
Golf Whiteleaf 9h. **See** Church (11th cent and later).

Rescue Service: Five Alls' Service Station, Oxford Rd, Studley Green. ✆ Radnage (024 026) 3200 and (024 026) 2066. Tower Garage, Oxford Rd. ✆ Radnage (024 026) 3355.

STOKE-ON-TRENT Staffordshire. Map 19D and 22C
Comprising BURSLEM, FENTON, HANLEY, LONGTON, STOKE-UPON-TRENT and TUNSTALL and *including* BUCKNALL, CORBRIDGE, HANFORD, MEIR and TRENTHAM.
See also NEWCASTLE-UNDER-LYME.
Pop 252,000. Lichfield 29, London 152, M6 Motorway 3, Ashbourne 22, Congleton 13, Leek 11, Newcastle-under-Lyme 2, Newport 21, Sandbach 13, Stone 8, Uttoxeter 15.
See Plan, p. 342.
EC Thur. **MD** Wed, Fri, Sat. **Golf** Burslem 9h, Trentham Park 18h. **See** STOKE-ON-TRENT: Josiah Wedgwood and Colin Minton Monuments, St Peter's Church, Town Hall.
BURSLEM: St John's Church part 16th cent, Royal Doulton Works (viewable by appt). CORBRIDGE: Arnold Bennett Museum. HANLEY: Birthplace of Arnold

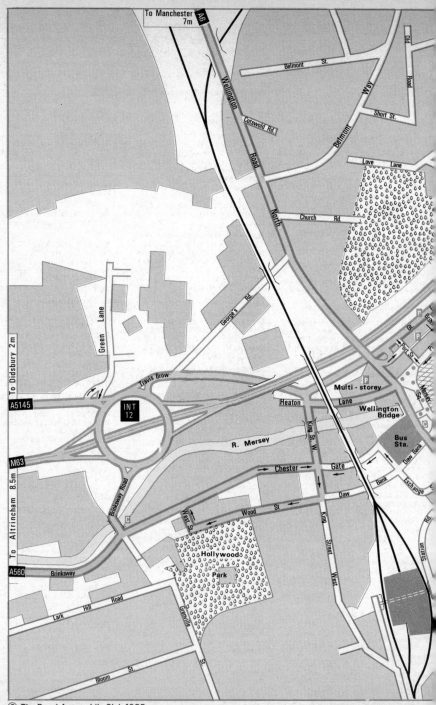

For abbreviations see inside back cover

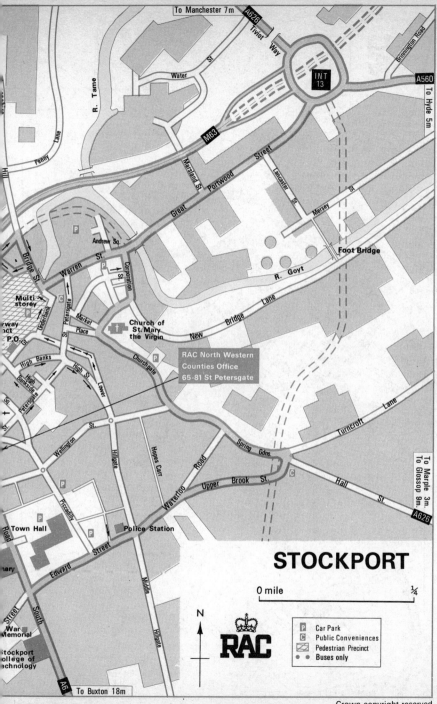

STOCKPORT

0 mile   ¼

N

RAC

P Car Park
C Public Conveniences
⬚ Pedestrian Precinct
●● Buses only

Crown copyright reserved

STOKE-UPON-TRENT

N

RAC

P	Car Park
C	Public Conveniences
	Pedestrian Precincts

To Ashbourne 22 m.
To Crematorium 3m.
A52

To Fenton 1m.
A5007
To Blurton 1m.

To Hanley 1m.
A5006

To M6 (North) Int.16
A500 Queensway

A500
To M6 (South) Int 15
To Birmingham 40 m.

Boundary Road
Leek Road
Wintonfield St.
P.O.
Thornton Rd.
Ashford Street
College Rd.
North Staffordshire Polytechnic
Station Road
Station

Lytton Street
City Road
Queensway
Whieldon Road

Queensway
Copeland Street
Glebe St.
Street
Bow peal St.
Woolrhoter St.
Cornwallis St.
Selwin St.
Stoke City F.C.
Lonsdale

King's Hall & Town Hall
Spode Pottery
Market Hall
Church St.
Minton Pottery
Fleming Rd.
Boothen Road
Police Station
Booth St.
Fletcher Road

Liverpool Road
France Road
Yale St.
Hill St.
P.O.
Library
Bath St.
Bilton St.
London Road
B5041
To Stone 8 m.

Charlton St.
Stratheden Rd.
Swan St.
Hartshill Road
Honeywall
Spark Ter.
Goan Av.
New Road

North Street
Queensway
Hartshill

Recn. Ground

Richmond Street
Oxford St.
Westland St.
Stone St.
Penkhull Ter.
Mill St.
Penkhull

Quarry Ave.
Watson Ave.
West Avenue
Harris St.
Fradrick Ave.
Prince's Road
Stone Road
Honeywall
St. Thomas Pl.
Chamberlain Ave.
Trent Valley Rd.
Rothwell St.
Garden St.

Hartshill Road
Quarry Rd.
Yoxall Av.
Prince's
N. Staffs Royal Infirmary
Queens Road
Newcastle Lane

0 miles ¼

To Newcastle 2 m.
A52

To Newcastle 2 m.

© The Royal Automobile Club 1985

342

For abbreviations see inside back cover—RAC

Bennett, Museum and Art Gallery.
TRENTHAM: Trentham Gdns, 1,000 acres, open to public.
🏛 Central Library, Bethesda St, Hanley.
✆ Stoke-on-Trent (0782) 21242.

■★★★★North Stafford (TH), *Station Rd, ST4 2AE.* ✆ (0782) 48501. C. ✉ 70 bedrs, 42 bp, 28 bps, TV, Dgs. ✘ a l c, mc, at, LD 9.45. 🅿 Lt, N, CH, Dgs, CP 120, Ac, con 450, CF, 1 st. £ BB £43, DB £57, WB, ①, cc 1 2 3 4 5 6, Dep (Xmas).

Repairers: A R Chatfield (Stoke-on-Trent) Ltd, Clough St, Hanley. ✆ (0782) 29591.
Bailey's Garage Ltd, Leek Rd, Hanley.
✆ (0782) 24371.
B & S (Bucknall) Ltd, Werrington Rd, Bucknall. ✆ (0782) 25406.
Hanley Garage Ltd, 105 Broad St, Hanley.
✆ (0782) 25523.
Platts Garage (Longton) Ltd, Lightwood Rd, Longton. ✆ (0782) 319212.
MC Repairer: Lawton Garage (S-O-T) Ltd, Church Lawton. ✆ Alsager (093 63) 3716.
Sctr Repairer: Stoke Motor Cycles Sales Ltd, Liverpool Rd. ✆ (0782) 47747.
Rescue Services: Ash Green Garage Ltd, Longton Rd, Trentham. ✆ (0782) 57348.
Bell, W T (Burslem) Ltd, Sandbach Rd, Corbridge. ✆ (0782) 85257.
Burton, L & A & Son, Moorland Rd, Burslem. ✆ (0782) 87702.
Hanford Motor Engineers, Hanford Roundabout, Trentham. ✆ (0782) 657037.
North Stafford Motors (Tunstall) Ltd, High St, Tunstall. ✆ (0782) 84172.
P & H Motors, Norton Test Centre, Ford Green Rd, Norton. ✆ (0782) 542646.
Podmore's Garage Ltd, Clayton La.
✆ Newcastle (Staffs) (0782) 613061.
Scholar Green Service Station, 131 Congleton Rd, Scholar Green.
✆ Kidsgrove (078 16) 2002.
V G Vehicles (Hanley) Ltd, Victoria Rd, Hanley. ✆ (0782) 22875.

STOKE POGES Buckinghamshire.
M. Area 7A
Pop 4,900. Slough 3, London 23, Aylesbury 25, Denham 6½, Dunstable 28, High Wycombe 11, Uxbridge 5½.
EC Wed. **Golf** Stoke Poges 18h. **See** Mainly 14th cent Church immortalized in Gray's 'Elegy', Gray's Monument Field (Nat Trust), Nature Reserve.

Rescue Service: Stoke Poges Motors Co Ltd, Bells Hill. ✆ Farnham Common (028 14) 2365.
Wexham Street Service Station, Wexham St. ✆ Fulmer (028 16) 2501.

STOKE-UNDER-HAM Somerset.
M. Area 5C
Pop 1,001. Wincanton 18, London 127, Crewkerne 6, Frome 29, Glastonbury 16, Ilminster 8, Shepton Mallet 20, Sherborne 11.
See Church (Norman details), The Priory, Ham Hill, limestone quarries and viewpoint.

Rescue Service: Cartage Garage.
✆ Martock (0935) 3213.

STONE Hereford & Worcester. Maps 13B & 14A
Pop 609. Bromsgrove 7, London 120, Kidderminster 2½, Stourbridge 8.
Golf Kidderminster 18h. **See** Church.

⚑★★★★★**Stone Manor,** *DY10 4PJ.*
✆ Chaddesley Corbett (056 283) 555. C.
✉ 23 bedrs, 23 bp, TV. ✘ a l c, mc, at, LD 10. 🅿 N, CH, CP 400, Ac, sp, tc, con 300, CF, 5 BGf, 2 st. £ BB £39·50, DB £56, Bkc £2·50, L £6, cc 1 2 3 5 6, Dep b.

STONE Staffordshire. Maps 19F and 22E
Pop 10,985. Lichfield 21, London 138, Ashbourne 23, Leek 16, Nantwich 20, Newcastle-under-Lyme 8½, Newport 14, Stafford 7½, Stoke-on-Trent 8, Uttoxeter 13, Whitchurch 24.
EC Wed. **MD** Tue, Thur. **Golf** Stone 9h.

⚑★★★★**Stone House** (late **Brooms**), *ST15 0BQ.* ✆ (0785) 815531. RS Dec 25–27 & Jan 1. C. ✉ 16 bedrs, 12 bp, 1 ba, TV.
✘ mc, at, LD 9.45. 🅿 CH, TV, CP 40, Ac, con 40, CF. £ BB £15–£27, DB £27·50–£38·50, WB, ②, Bk £3·50, L £5·95, D £9·25, cc 1 2 3 5,▲.

★★★**Crown,** *High St, ST15 8AS.*
✆ (0785) 813535. C. ✉ 13 bedrs, 13 bp, TV, Dgs. ✘ a l c, mc, LD 9.30. 🅿 N, CH, CP 150, Ac, con 100, CF, 6 BGf, 1 st, Dis.
£ WB, Bk £4, L £4·25, D £6·25, cc 1 2 3 5, Dep a.

Rescue Service: Aston Garage. ✆ (0785) 813035.
Kibblestone Garage, Kibblestone Rd, Oulton. ✆ (0785) 812560.
Robert Simcock & Son Ltd, Norton Bridge Garage, Norton Bridge. ✆ Stafford (0785) 760281.
Stone Motorists Centre, Crown St.
✆ (0785) 815897.

STONEHOUSE Gloucestershire. Map 13F
Pop 6,493. Cirencester 16, London 103, Bath 30, Bristol 27, Cheltenham 16, Chepstow 27, Gloucester 9½, Tetbury 11.
EC Thur. **Golf** Painswick 18h. **See** Wycliffe College.

Rescue Service: J A Gordon & Son Ltd, Ebley Rd. ✆ (045 382) 2139.

STONEY CROSS Hampshire. Map 6E
Pop 50. Romsey 8½, London 84, Lyndhurst 4, Ringwood 9, Salisbury 16, Southampton 11.
Golf Bramshaw 18h. **See** Rufus Stone.

■★★**Compton Arms,** *Ringwood Rd, SO4 7GN.* ✆ Southampton (0703) 812134.

STONY STRATFORD Buckinghamshire.
Map 15C
Pop 5,660. Bletchley 7½, London 54, Aylesbury 18, Bedford 19, Buckingham 8, Northampton 14, Towcester 7½.
EC Thur. **MD** Sat. **Golf** Stony Stratford 18h.

Rescue Service: Caves Stony Stratford (Garages) Ltd, 0 London Rd. ✆ Milton Keynes (0908) 562361.

STORRINGTON West Sussex. Map 7E
Pop 5,000. Horsham 15, London 51, Arundel 8½, Bognor Regis 15, Brighton 17, Chichester 16, Haywards Heath 19, Pulborough 5, Worthing 9½.
EC Wed. **Golf** West Sussex 18h. **See** Church, RC Priory, Sullington Warren, Rackham Hill (view), Parham Park 2 m N, Church, Parham House.

⚑★★★★**Little Thakeham,** *Merrywood La, RH20 3HE.* ✆ (090 66) 4416. Closed Xmas & New Year. C. 7. ✉ 10 bedrs, 9 bp, 1

bps, 3 ba, TV. ✘ a l c. 🅿 CH, Dgs, CP 30, sp, tc, 1 BGf, 7 st. £ Bk £5, L £15, D £15, cc 1 2 5.

Rescue Service: Storrington Motors Ltd, Corner Garage. ✆ (090 66) 2400.

STOTFOLD Bedfordshire. Map 15D
Pop 6,772. Baldock 3, London 41, Bedford 8, Bletchley 24, Huntingdon 26.
Golf Beadlow Manor 18h & 9h. **See** 12th cent Church.

Rescue Service: Stotfold Motor Centre, 28 Astwick Rd. ✆ Hitchin (0462) 730222.

STOURBRIDGE West Midlands. Maps 14A and 13B
Pop 60,000. Birmingham 11, London 122, Bridgnorth 13, Bromsgrove 9½, Kidderminster 7, Walsall 11, Wolverhampton 10.
EC Thur. **MD** Daily. **Golf** Stourbridge 18h. **See** Noted glass making centre (Exhibition of Stourbridge Glass at Council House), Mary Stevens Park.

★★**Bell,** *Market St, DY8 1DW.* ✆ (0384) 396783. C. ✉ 20 bedrs, 1 bp, 14 sh, 3 ba, TV, Dgs. ✘ a l c, mc, at, LD 8.45. 🅿 CH, Dgs, CP 100, Ac, con 40, CF, 1 st. £ BB fr £16, DB fr £22, WB, ①, Bk £3, L £3, D £4·75, cc 1 3, Dep b.

★★**Talbot,** *High St, DY8 1DW.* ✆ (0384) 394350. C. ✉ 21 bedrs, 6 bp, 1 bps, 1 sh, 4 ba, TV, Dgs. ✘ a l c, mc, at, LD 9.15. 🅿 CH, TV, Dgs, CP 30, Ac, con 130, CF. £ BB fr £19, DB fr £26, WB, ①, Bk £3, L £4·75, D £5·25, cc 1 3.

Limes, PH, z (Unl), *260 Hagley Rd, Pedmore, DY9 0RW.* ✆ Hagley (0562) 882689. Closed Xmas. C. ✉ 10 bedrs, 2 ba, Dgs. 🅿 CH, TV, CP 3, CF, 3 BGf, 2 st. £ BB fr £12·50, DB fr £20, ①.

Repairer: Lex Mead (Stourbridge) Ltd, Hagley Rd. ✆ Hagley (0562) 393022.
North Worcestershire Motors Ltd, Oldswinford. ✆ (0384) 3031.
Specialist Body Repairer: F J Fildes Ltd, Park St. ✆ (0384) 3108.
Rescue Service: Queensway Recovery Service, Gauden Rd, Pedmore. ✆ Hagley (0562) 882929.

STOURPORT-ON-SEVERN Hereford & Worcester (Worcestershire). Map 13B
Pop 19,054. Bromsgrove 11, London 124, Birmingham 20, Bromyard 17, Kidderminster 3½, Leominster 31, Ludlow 21, Worcester 11.
EC Wed. **MD** Fri. **Golf** Littlelakes 9h. **See** Canal Basin and Locks, Harvington Hall 5 m E.
🏛 Library. County Buildings, Worcester St. ✆ Stourport (029 93) 2866.

★★★**Mount Olympus,** *35 Hartlebury Rd, DY13 9LT.* ✆ (029 93) 77333. C. ✉ 37 bedrs, 37 bp, TV. ✘ a l c, mc, at, LD 10. 🅿 N, CH, TV, CP 350, Ac, sp, tc, sc, rf, con 90, CF, 18 BGf, 3 st. £ BB £12–£29·50, DB £24–£39, WT £200–£245, DT £22–£41, WB, ①, Bk £3·50, L £3·50, D £7·25, cc 1 2 3 5 6, Dep b.

Rescue Service: Lloyds Garage, 8 Bridge St. ✆ (029 93) 2053.

STOWMARKET Suffolk. Map 17C
Pop 10,832. Sudbury 18, London 76, Bury St Edmunds 14, Colchester 27, Ipswich 12, Saxmundham 25, Scole 18, Thetford 21.

EC Tue. **MD** Thur, Sat. **Golf** Finborough Park 18h. **See** Dec-Perp Church ('Father Smith' organ), Museum of East Anglian Life.

★**Cedars,** *Needham Rd, IP14 2AJ.*
✆ (0449) 612668. Closed Xmas. C. ⇄ 15 bedrs, 9 bp, 3 bps, 3 sh, 2 ba, TV, Dgs.
✗ a l c, mc, at, LD 9 (10 Sat & Sun). ⊕ CH, Dgs, CP 60, Ac, con 20, CF, 5 BGf. £ BB £20–£22, DB £30–£34, WB, ②, 10%, Bk £2·25, L £6, D £6, cc 1 3.

MC Repairer: Revetts (Stowmarket) Ltd, 59 Ipswich St. ✆ (0449) 612651.
Rescue Service: W H Pike & Sons Ltd, Bridge Garage. ✆ (0449) 613296.

STOW-ON-THE-WOLD Gloucestershire. Map 14C
Pop 1,681. Chipping Norton 9, London 84, Burford 10, Cheltenham 18, Cirencester 19, Evesham 16, Moreton-in-Marsh 4½, Tewkesbury 20.
EC Wed. **Golf** Broadway 18h. **See** Town Hall, St Edward's Church, St Edward's Hall, Museum, 14th cent Market Cross, Stocks, Porch House, Enoch's Tower.
⚏ Public Library, St Edward's Hall. ✆ Stow-on-the-Wold (0451) 30352.

★★**Fosse Manor,** *Fosseway, GL54 1JX.*
✆ Cotswold (0451) 30354. Closed 1 wk Xmas. C. ⇄ 24 bedrs, 8 bp, 8 bps, 4 ba, TV, Dgs. ✗ a l c, mc, at, LD 9.30. ⊕ CH, TV, Dgs, CP 40, Ac, con 40, CF, 4 BGf, 1 st, Dis. £ BB £10–£21·50, DB £20–£43, WT fr £170, WB, ①, Bk £4·50, L £8·50, D £8·50, cc 1 2 3 5, Dep a.

★★**Royalist,** *Digbeth St, GL54 1BN.*
✆ Cotswold (0451) 30670. Closed Xmas. C 5. ⇄ 8 bedrs, 5 bp, 2 sh, 2 ba, annexe 4 bedrs, 1 bp, bps, TV. ✗ mc, LD 9. ⊕ CH, TV, Dgs, CP 10, Ac, 2 BGf, 2 st. £ BB £16, DB £32–£35, WB, Bk £4, D £10, cc 1 2 3 5, Dep b.

★★**Stow Lodge,** *The Square, GL54 1AB.*
✆ Cotswold (0451) 30485. Closed Dec 16–Jan. C 5. ⇄ 11 bedrs, 10 bp, 1 ba, annexe 10 bedrs, 10 bp, TV. ✗ mc, at, LD 9 (9.30 Sat). ⊕ CH, CP 30, 2 st. £ DB £35–£39, DBB £22·75–£26·50, WB, ②, Bk £4·75, L £6, D £8·50, cc 2 5.

★★**Talbot,** *The Square, GL54 1BQ.*
✆ (0451) 30631.

★★**Unicorn Crest,** *Sheep St, GL54 1HQ.*
✆ Cotswold (0451) 30257. C. ⇄ 20 bedrs, 20 bp, ns, TV, Dgs. ✗ a l c, mc, LD 9.30. ⊕ CH, CP 50, con 40, CF, 2 st. £ B fr £36, BD fr £47, WB, ①, Bk £4·95, D £8·95, cc 1 2 3 4 5 6, Dep.

★**Grapevine** (formerly **Parkdene**) (R), *Sheep St, GL54 1AU.* ✆ Cotswold (0451) 30344. Closed Jan. C. ⇄ 15 bedrs, 8 bp, 2 bps, 1 sh, 1 ba, TV, Dgs. ✗ a l c, mc, at, LD 9.30. ⊕ CH, TV, Ac, con 20, CF, 1 BGf, 1 st, Dis. £ BB £9·75–£13, DB £19·50–£33, WT £108·50–£161, DT £15·50–£23, DBB £12–£19·50, WB, ②, Bk £3·50, L £3·50, D £5·95, cc 1 3, Dep.

Limes, G, x (Unl), *Tewkesbury Rd, GL54 1EN.* ✆ Cotswold (0451) 30034. C. ⇄ 5 bedrs, 2 ba, TV, Dgs. ⊕ CH, TV, Dgs, CP 6, 1 BGf, 1 st, Dis. £ BB £8–£8·50, DB £16–£17, WT (c) fr £56, ②, Bk £3.

Rescue Service: Stow Service Station Ltd, Fosseway. ✆ (0451) 31009.

STRATFIELD TURGIS Hampshire. Map 6B

Pop 90. Bagshot 15, London 42, Alton 16, Basingstoke 7, Farnham 15, Guildford 23, Reading 9½, Windsor 23, Woking 22.
Golf Tylney Hall 18h. **See** Church, Stratfield Saye House & Museum.

■★★**Wellington Arms,** *RG27 0AS.*
✆ Basingstoke (0256) 882214.

STRATFORD-UPON-AVON Warwickshire. Map 14C
See also CHARLECOTE and WILMCOTE.
Pop 21,220. Oxford 39, London 93, Banbury 20, Birmingham 23, Bromsgrove 20, Cheltenham 30, Chipping Norton 21, Droitwich 21, Evesham 14, Moreton-in-Marsh 16, Warwick 8, Worcester 27.
See Plan, p. 345.
EC Thur. **MD** Tue, Fri. **P** See Plan. **Golf** Stratford-upon-Avon 18h. **See** Shakespeare's birthplace (Henley St), (tomb in Holy Trinity Church), Royal Shakespeare Theatre and Museum, New Place (foundations of Shakespeare's last home preserved in an Elizabethan garden, Nash's House, New Place Museum, adj), Hall's Croft, Elizabethan Garrick Inn and other old inns, Town Hall, Grammar School (in Guildhall), Lofty Shrieves House, Enions Court, Alveston Manor, Almshouses, Judith Quiney's House, Harvard House, American Fountain, Mop Fair Oct, Mary Arden's House at Wilmcote 3 m NW, Anne Hathaway's Cottage (Shottery), Charlecote Park, 4 m E.
⚏ Judith Shakespeare House, 1 High St.
✆ Stratford-upon-Avon (0789) 293127.

★★★★**Moat House International** (late **Hilton International**), *Bridgefoot, CV37 6YR.* ✆ (0789) 67511. C. ⇄ 249 bedrs, 249 bp, TV, Dgs. ✗ mc, at, LD 11.30. ⊕ Lt, N, CH, Dgs, ns, CP 350, Ac, con 400, CF, 0 st. £ B £44·10–£47·35, BD £55·10–£61·10, WB, ②, Bk £5·10, L £7·20, D £8·40, cc 1 2 3 4 5 6.

★★★★**Shakespeare** (TH), *Chapel St, CV37 6ER.* ✆ (0789) 294771. C. ⇄ 66 bedrs, 66 bp, TV, Dgs. ✗ a l c, mc, at, LD 9.30. ⊕ Lt, N, CH, Dgs, CP 35, Ac, con 100, CF, 1 st. £ BB £47, DB £67, WB, ①, cc 1 2 3 4 5 6, Dep (Xmas).

★★★**Alveston Manor** (TH), *Clopton Bridge, CV37 7HP.* ✆ (0789) 204581. C. ⇄ 112 bedrs, 112 bp, TV, Dgs. ✗ a l c, mc, LD 9.15. ⊕ N, CH, Dgs, CP 200, Ac, con 100, CF, 45 BGf, 1 st, Dis. £ BB £41, DB £57, WB, ①, cc 1 2 3 4 5 6, Dep (Xmas).

★★★**Arden,** *44 Waterside, CV37 6BA.*
✆ (0789) 294949. C. ⇄ 59 bedrs, 42 bp, 14 bps, 2 ba, TV, Dgs. ✗ a l c, mc, at, LD 9. ⊕ N, CH, TV, Dgs, CP 40, Ac, con 40, CF, 5 st. £ BB £20·50–£28, DB £43, WB, ①, Bk £4·50, L £6·25, D £7·75, cc 1 2 3 4 5 6, Dep b.

★★★**Falcon,** *Chapel St, CV37 6HA.*
✆ (0789) 205777. C. ⇄ 73 bedrs, 73 bp, TV, Dgs. ✗ a l c, mc, at, LD 9. ⊕ Lt, N, CH, Dgs, CP 100, G 20, Ac, con 200, CF. £ BB £30–£38, DB £49–£54, WT £239·75–£292·25, DT £34·25–£41·75, WB, ①, Bk £4·75, L £6·75, D £8·50, Dep b.

★★★**Grosvenor House,** *Warwick Rd, CV37 6YT.* ✆ (0789) 69213. Closed Xmas. C. ⇄ 57 bedrs, 53 bp, 4 bps, 4 ba, TV.

✗ a l c, mc, at, LD 8.45. ⊕ N, CH, TV, ns, CP 50, Ac, sb, sol, gym, con 30, CF, 1 BGf, 0 st, Dis. £ BB £17·50–£24, DB £27·50–£39, WB, ①, cc 1 2 3 5, Dep b

★★★**Swan's Nest** (TH), *Bridgefoot, CV37 7LT.* ✆ (0789) 66761. C. ⇄ 70 bedrs, 44 bp, 8 bps, 7 ba, TV, Dgs. ✗ a l c, mc, at, LD 9.30. ⊕ N, CH, Dgs, CP 100, Ac, con 150, CF, 2 BGf, 3 st. £ BB £34–£37, DB £46·50–£54, WB, ①, cc 1 2 3 4 5 6, Dep (Xmas).

★★★**White Swan** (TH), *Rother St, CV37 6NH.* ✆ (0789) 297022. C. ⇄ 55 bedrs, 22 bp, 2 bps, 6 ba, TV, Dgs. ✗ a l c, mc, LD 8.30. ⊕ N, CH, Dgs, Ac, con 70, CF, 0 st. £ BB £31–£34, DB £43·50–£50·50, WB, ①, cc 1 2 3 4 5 6, Dep (Xmas).

★★**Bancroft Garden** (RI), *Waterside, CV37 6EF.* ✆ (0789) 69196.

★**Ravenhurst** (R), *Broad Walk, CV37 6HS.* ✆ (0789) 292515. C. ⇄ 7 bedrs, 2 ba, TV, Dgs. ✗ a l c, mc, at, LD 10.30. ⊕ CH, TV, con 20, CF, 3 st. £ BB £9–£10·50, DB £15–£16·50, DBB £13–£20, WB, ①, Bk £1·50, L £3·50, D £5, cc 1 3.

Albany, G, z (Unl), *9 Alcester Rd, CV37 6PN.* ✆ (0789) 292840. C. ⇄ 8 bedrs, 3 ba, TV. ⊕ CH, TV, ns, CP 8, CF. £ BB £8·50–£9·50, DB £16–£19, WT (b) £65–£78, DT (b) £10·50–£12·50, ①, Bk £2·50, D £3, cc 1 3.

Ambleside, G, z (Unl), *41 Grove Rd, CV37 6PB.* ✆ (0789) 297239. C. ⇄ 6 bedrs, 2 sh, 1 ba, TV, Dgs. ⊕ CH, TV, CF, 1 st. £ BB £7–£9, DB £14–£20, ①, Bk £3·50, cc 1 3.

Coach House, PH, z (Unl), *17 Warwick Rd, CV37 6YW.* ✆ (0789) 204109. C. ⇄ 11 bedrs, 4 bp, 7 sh, 2 ba, TV. ⊕ CH, CP 11, CF. £ BB £10·50–£24, DB £19·50–£25, WT (b) £94·75–£110·50, DT (b) £14·75–£17·50, ①, Bk £2, D £5.

Glenavon, PH, z (Unl), *6 Chestnut Walk, CV37 6HG.* ✆ (0789) 292588.

Hardwick House, G, z (Unl), *1 Avenue Rd, CV37 6UY.* ✆ (0789) 204307. Closed Xmas. C. ⇄ 12 bedrs, 2 bps, 5 ba, TV. ⊕ CH, ns, CH, 1 BGf, 2 st. £ BB £7–£10, DB £14–£25, WT (c) £45–£70, ①.

Hylands, PH, z (R), *Warwick Rd, CV37 6YW.* ✆ (0789) 297962. Closed Xmas. C. ⇄ 17 bedrs, 1 bp, 16 bps, TV. ⊕ CH, CP 15, CF, 4 BGf, 1 st, Dis. £ BB £20–£24, DB £26–£32, ①, Bk £3, cc 3.▲

Marlyn, PH, z (Unl), *3 Chestnut Walk, CV37 6HG.* ✆ (0789) 293752. Closed Xmas. C. ⇄ 8 bedrs, 2 ba. ⊕ CH, TV, 1 BGf, 1 st, Dis. £ BB £8·50–£9·95, DB £17–£19·90, ①.

Melita, PH, z (RI), *37 Shipston Rd, CV37 7LN.* ✆ (0789) 292432. Closed Xmas–New Year. C. ⇄ 13 bedrs, 6 bp, 1 bps, 3 ba, TV. ⊕ CH, TV, CP 12, U 2, CF, 3 BGf, 2 st. £ BB £12–£18, DB £22–£32, ①, Bk £3.

Nando's, G, z (Unl), *18 Evesham Pl, CV37 6HT.* ✆ (0789) 204907. C. ⇄ 14 bedrs, 2 bp, 4 ba, TV, Dgs. ⊕ CH, TV, CP 8, CF, 2 BGf, 1 st. £ BB £8·50–£10·50, DB £16–£23, DT £11–£13·50, ①, Bk £2, D £3·50.

Penshurst, G, z (RI), *34 Evesham Pl, CV37 6HT.* ✆ (0789) 205259. Open Apr–Dec. C. ⇄ 9 bedrs, 1 sh, 2 ba. ⊕ CH, TV, CF. £ BB £7·50–£8·50, DB £15–£17, ①.

Virginia Lodge, G, z (RI), *12 Evesham Pl, CV37 6HT.* ✆ (0789) 292157. Closed Dec 23–Jan 4. C. ⇄ 7 bedrs, 2 ba, Dgs. ⊕ CH, TV, ns, CP 7. £ BB £7–£8, DB £14–£16, ①.

Woodburn House, PH, z (Unl), *89 Shipston Rd, CV37 7LW.* ✆ (0789)

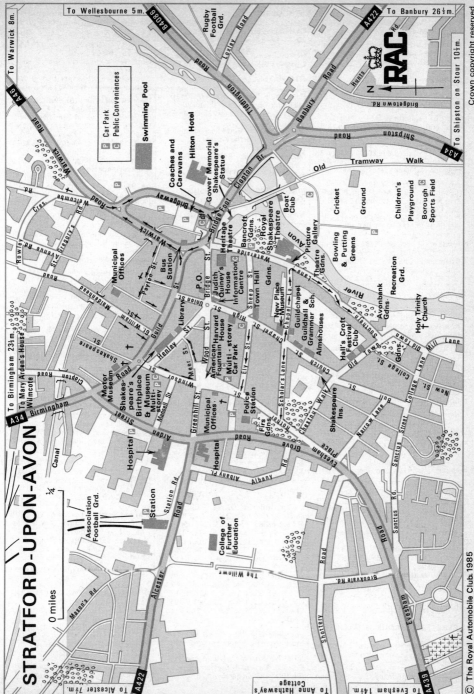

STRATFORD-UPON-AVON

204453. Closed Xmas. C 5. ⇔ 7 bedrs, 3 bps, 2 ba, TV. ⓟ CH, CP 10, 2 st. £ BB £10–£18, DB £24–£36, ①.

Repairers: Arden Garages Ltd, Arden St. ☎ (0789) 67446.
F Guyver & Sons Ltd, Rother St. ☎ (0789) 66254.
Heron, Saville Motors Ltd, Birmingham Rd. ☎ (0789) 68121.
Shaylor Motors (Stratford) Ltd, 23 Western Rd. ☎ (0789) 293577.

STREET Somerset. Map 5C
Pop 8,800. Glastonbury 2, London 128, Bridgwater 13, Crewkerne 23, Dorchester 36, Ilminster 21, Sherborne 21, Taunton 20, Weston-super-Mare 26, Wincanton 23.
EC Wed. **Golf** Wells (Somerset) 18h. **See** Holy Trinity Church, Geological Museum.

★★★**Wessex,** *High St, BA16 0EA.*
☎ (0458) 43383. C. ⇔ 50 bedrs, 50 bp, TV, Dgs. ✗ a l c, mc, at, LD 9.45. ⓟ Lt, N, CH, Dgs, CP 40, G 20, Ac, con 250, CF, 1 st. £ BB £16·80–£25·80, DB £25·80–£35·80, WB, ①, Bk £2·50, L £2·65, D £5·80, cc 1 2 3 5 6. ▲

★★**Bear** (R), *High St, BA16 0EF.* ☎ (0458) 42021. C. ⇔ 10 bedrs, 8 bp, 2 bps, annexe 6 bedrs, 1 bp, 2 ba, TV, Dgs. ✗ mc, at, LD 10. ⓟ CH, CP 16, Ac, con 100, CF, 2 BGf, 3 st. £ BB £21–£33, DB £32–£43, WT £230–£275, DT £34–£40, WB, ②, 10%, Bk £4·50, L £5·50, D £7·50, cc 1 2 3, Dep b.

Rescue Service: Foundry Garage, Leigh Rd. ☎ (0458) 42013.
North Park Garage, North Side Car Park, High St. ☎ (0458) 45332.

STRENSHAM Hereford & Worcester (Worcestershire). Map 13D
Pop 161. (M5 Motorway Services), Evesham 15, London 113, Tewkesbury 6, Worcester 12.
EC Thur. **Golf** Evesham 18h. **See** Perp. Church, brasses and monuments.

Repairer: Kenning Motor Group, M5 Service Area. ☎ Tewkesbury (0684) 293004.

STRETE Devon. Map 3F
Pop 442. Dartmouth 4, London 209, Kingsbridge 10, Totnes 11.
Golf Churston 18h. **See** Slapton Ley (NT).

Highcliff, G, xy (R), *TQ6 0RU.* ☎ Stoke Fleming (0803) 770307. Open Apr–Oct. ⇔ 10 bedrs, 1 bp, 2 ba, TV, Dgs. ⓟ CP 10, CF, 1 BGf, 3 st. £ BB £9, DB £18, WT (b) £83, DT (b) £12, ①, Bk £2, L £3, D £4.

STRETFORD Greater Manchester (Lancashire). Map 20A
Pop 47,600. Altrincham 4, London 186, Congleton 23, Macclesfield 17, Manchester 2, Stockport 7½, Walkden 6½.
EC Wed. **Golf** Urmston 18h.

Repairers: Graham Bros (Motors) Ltd, 799 Chester Rd. ☎ 061-872 3311.
Lookers Ltd, 776/778 Chester Rd. ☎ 061-865 4433.

STRETTON-ON-DUNSMORE
Warwicks. Map 14B
M45 Motorway 3½, Daventry 13, London 87, Coventry 6½, Leamington Spa 7½, Rugby 6½.

Rescue Service: Edgenay Service Station, London Rd (A45), nr Rugby. ☎ Wolston (0203) 543373.

STROOD Kent. Map 10C
Dartford 13, London 30, M2 Motorway 1½, Canterbury 28, Maidstone 10, Sevenoaks 20.

Rescue Service: N E Lane Motor Services, Dongola Rd. ☎ Medway (0634) 723159.

STROUD Gloucestershire. Maps 13F and 14E
Pop 20,628. Cirencester 12, London 100, M5 Motorway 5, Bath 27, Bristol 30, Cheltenham 13, Chepstow 29, Gloucester 9, Tetbury 8½.
EC Thur. **MD** Sat. **Golf** Minchinhampton 18h. **See** Home of the West of England cloth industry, 16th cent Town Hall, Museum, Art Gallery, St Lawrence's Church, Festival of Drama, Music and the Arts in Oct. Wildfowl Trust at Slimbridge 8 m W.
ⓣ Council Offices, High St. ☎ Stroud (045 36) 4252.

★★★**Bear of Rodborough,** *Rodborough Common, GL5 5DE.* ☎ Amberley (045 387) 3522. C. ⇔ 30 bedrs, 27 bp, 3 bps, TV, Dgs. ✗ a l c, LD 9.15 (Fri & Sat 9.45). ⓟ N, CH, Dgs, CP 100, Ac, con 50, CF, 9 BGf, 0 st, Dis. £ BB £38, DB fr £48, WB, ①, Bk £4·50, L (Sun) £6·85, D £9·50, cc 1 2 3 5 6, Dep b.

▮★★★**Stonehouse Court,** *Bristol Rd, Stonehouse, GL10 3RA.* (2 miles W on A419.) ☎ (045 382) 5155. Closed 2 weeks after Xmas. C 11. ⇔ 10 bedrs, 7 bp, 2 bps, TV. ✗ a l c, mc, LD 9.30. ⓟ CH, CP 100, tc, pf, sb, sol, gym, con 30, 1 BGf, 4 st. £ BB £35, DB £48, WB, ②, 10%, Bk £4·50, L £12, D £14, cc 1 2 3 4 5 6, Dep b.

★★**Alpine Lodge,** *67 Stratford Rd, GL5 4AJ.* ☎ (045 36) 4949. C. ⇔ 10 bedrs, 8 bp, 2 bps, TV, Dgs. ✗ a l c, mc, at, LD 9.30. ⓟ CH, Dgs, CP 30, Ac, con 20, CF, 1 st. £ BB £15–£17·50, DB £26, DBB £22·50, ①, Bk £2, L £3, D £5, Dep b.

▮★★**Burleigh Court** (R), *Brimscombe, GL5 2PF.* (2½ m SE off A419.) ☎ Brimscombe (0453) 883804. Closed Dec 24–30. C. ⇔ 11 bedrs, 8 bp, 3 bps, TV. ✗ a l c, mc, at, LD 8.30. ⓟ CH, TV, CP 40, U 1, sp, con 20, CF, 0 st. £ BB £30, DB £40–£45, WB, ①, Bk £5, L £2·50, D £9·95, cc 1 2 3.

Downfield, PH, z (R), *134 Cainscross Rd, GL5 4HN.* ☎ (045 36) 4496. C. ⇔ 23 bedrs, 3 bp, 3 bps, 2 ba, Dgs. ⓟ CH, TV, Dgs, CP 26, CF, 5 BGf, 1 st, Dis. £ BB £11–£14, DB £20–£24, WT (c) £50–£60, ①, Bk £2, D £6. ▲

Rescue Service: Poole Bros & Jackson Ltd, London Rd. ☎ (045 36) 4203.

STRUMPSHAW Norfolk. M. Area 16B
Pop 436. Norwich 8½, London 120, Beccles 16, Great Yarmouth 13, Lowestoft 21.
EC Sat.

Rescue Service Page (Strumpshaw), Norwich Rd. ☎ Norwich (0603) 712010.

STUDLAND Dorset. Maps 5F and 6E
Pop 373. Wareham 9½, London 126 (Fy 111), Sandbanks (Fy) 3.
Golf Isle of Purbeck 18h. **See** Norman Church, Agglestone Rock (reputed Druids worship stone), Brownsea Island (Poole Harbour—daily boat service April–Sept).

▮▯★★★**Knoll House** (R), *Swanage Rd, BH19 3AH.* ☎ (092 944) 251. C. ⇔ 104 bedrs, 83 bp, 10 ba, annexe 7 bedrs, 2 ba, Dgs. ✗ mc, at, LD 8.20. ⓟ N, ch, TV, Dgs, CP 100, sp, gc, tc, sol, con 20, CF, 6 BGf. £ BB £22–£37, DB £44–£74, WT £182–£287, DT £31–£40, DBB £26–£41, ①, Bk £3, L £7·20, D £8·20. ▲

▮▯★★★**Manor House** (R), *BH19 3AU.* ☎ (092 944) 288. Open Mar–Oct. C 5. ⇔ 19 bedrs, 10 bp, 8 bps, 1 ba, TV, Dgs. ✗ mc, at, LD 8.30. ⓟ CH, CP 40, 10 st. £ BB £12·50–£23, DB £25–£48, DBB £18–£31, WB, ②, Bk £4, D £9·75.

SUDBURY Derbyshire. Map 22E.
Pop 827. Burton-on-Trent 9½, London 132, Ashbourne 10, Derby 14, Lichfield 17, Uttoxeter 5.
See Sudbury Hall (open to public).

★**M Boars Head,** *Lichfield Rd, DE6 5GX.* ☎ Burton-on-Trent (0283) 820344. C. ⇔ 12 bedrs, 7 bp, 5 bps, TV, Dgs. ✗ a l c, mc, LD 9.30. ⓟ CH, Dgs, CP 100, Ac, con 20, 12 BGf 1 st. £ BB £19, DB £30, ①, Bk £2, L £4·95, D £7·50, cc 1 2 3 6.

SUDBURY Suffolk. Map 17C
Pop 10,067. Braintree 14, London 60, Bury St. Edmunds 16, Colchester 14, Harwich 30, Haverhill 16, Ipswich 21, Stowmarket 18.
EC Wed. **MD** Thur, Sat **Golf** Newton Green 9h. **See** Church of St Gregory (skull of Simon Sudbury), St Peter's Church (Gainsborough statue), All Saints' Church, restored Corn Exchange, Gainsborough's House (birthplace of the painter), Old Moot Hall, Town Hall, Salter's Hall, Hedingham Castle Keep 6½ m SW.
ⓣ Sudbury Library, Market Hill. ☎ Sudbury (0787) 72092.

★★★**Mill,** *Walnut Tree Lane, CO10 6BD.* ☎ (0787) 75544. C. ⇔ 50 bedrs, 50 bp, TV, Dgs. ✗ a l c, mc, at, LD 9.30. ⓟ N, CH, TV, Dgs, ns, CP 100, Ac, pf, con 60, CF, 8 BGf, 1st, Dis. £ WB, Bk £3·75, L £6·20, D £8·20, cc 1 2 3 4 5 6, Dep b.

★★**Four Swans,** *12 North St, CO10 6RB.* ☎ (0787) 78103. RS Xmas. C. ⇔ 5 bedrs, 2 ba, annexe, 12 bedrs, 12 bp, TV, Dgs. ✗ a l c, mc, LD 9.30. ⓟ CH, TV, Dgs, CP 20, Ac, CF, 6 BGf, 1 st, Dis. £ WB, ①, Bk £2·50, L £2·75, D £6, cc 1 2 3 5 6, Dep a.

Rescue Service: D J Molkenthin, Bull Yard, Cross St. ☎ (0787) 74840.

SUNDERLAND Tyne & Wear. Map 32D
Pop 210,000. Stockton-on-Tees 26, London 269, Durham 13, Middlesbrough 27, Newcastle upon Tyne 12.
Golf Wearside 18h. **See** St Peter's Church, St Andrew's Church, Wearmouth Bridge, Docks, Town Hall and Civic Centre, Museum and Art Gallery.

★★★**Mowbray Park,** *Borough Rd, SR1 1PR.* ☎ (0783) 78221. C. ⇔ 58 bedrs, 33 bp, 1 bps, 6 ba, ns, TV, Dgs. ✗ a l c, mc, at, LD 10.30. ⓟ Lt, N, CH, TV, Dgs, CP30, Ac,

con 60, CF, 3 st. **£** BB £17·25–£28·75, DB £32·20–£40·25, DBB £27·20–£35·25, WB, ⬜, Bk £3·75, L £4·50, D £6·50, cc 1 2 3 4 5 6, Dep b.

★★★**Seaburn,** *Queen's Par, SR6 8DB.* ✆ (0783) 292041. C. 📧 82 bedrs, 79 bp, 3 bps, TV, Dgs. ✗ a l c, mc, at, LD 9.30. 🅿 Lt, N, CH, TV, CP 200, U 2, Ac, con 200, CF, 1 st. **£** BB £18·50–£35, DB £26·50–£42, WB, ⬜,Bk £5·50, L £5, D £6·50, cc 1 2 3 5 6, Dep b.

★**Gelt House** (R), *23 St. Bedes Ter, Christchurch, SR2 8HS.* ✆ (0783) 672990. C. 📧 15 bedrs, 3 bp, 1 bps, 2 sh, 2 ba, TV. ✗ LD 8.30. 🅿 CH, TV, CP 14, sb, CF, 2 BGf, 6 st. **£** BB £15–£20, DB £23–£28, DBB £20·70–£25·70, ②, Bk £2·50, L £4·95, D £5·70.

Specialist Body Repairer: Dutton-Forshaw (North-East) Ltd, Roker Av. ✆ (0783) 56221.
Specialist Radiator Repairer: Serck Services Ltd, East Cross St. ✆ (0783) 57545.

SUNNINGDALE Berkshire. M. Area 7A Pop 3,500. Staines 6, London 23, Bagshot 4, Reading 16, Weybridge 9, Windsor 7, Woking 7½.
EC Wed. **Golf** Sunningdale 18h (2), Wentworth 18h (2).

Rescue Service: P I R A Autos, 40 High St. ✆ Ascot (0990) 24866.

SURBITON Greater London (Surrey). Map 7A
See also KINGSTON UPON THAMES. Pop 63,150. Kingston upon Thames 1½, London 11, Croydon 10, Epsom 5, Leatherhead 7, Mitcham 7, Purley 11, Ripley 11, Weybridge 7½, Woking 14.
EC Wed. **Golf** Home Park, Hampton Wick 18h, Surbiton 18h. **See** St Mark's Church, Hampton Court Palace.

Holmdene, G, z (Unl), *23 Cranes Dr, KT5 8AJ.* ✆ 01-399 9992. Closed Dec. C 5. 📧 5 bedrs, 2 ba, Dgs. 🅿 CH, TV, Dgs. 1 st. **£** BB £10–£12, DB £19–£22, WT (c) £56–£70, ⬜.

Pembroke Lodge, G, y (Unl) *35 Cranes Park, KT6 9AF.* ✆ 01-390 0731. C. 📧 10 bedrs, 3 bp, 2 ba, TV, Dgs. 🅿 CH, CP 6, U 2, CF, 3 BGf. **£** BB £13·80–£16·10, DB £20·70–£23, ②.

Warwick, G, z (Unl), *321 Ewell Rd, KT6 7BX.* ✆ 01-399 5837.

Rescue Service: Maypole Motors (Surbiton) Ltd, 7 Hook Rd. ✆ 01-399 4314 and 4051.
Surbiton Hill Garage & Coachworks, The Avenue. ✆ 01-399 1939.

SUTTON Greater London (Surrey) Map 7A
Pop 170,000. Mitcham 3½, London 11 Croydon 4, Epsom 4½, Kingston upon Thames 6½, Purley 5, Reigate 9½.
EC Wed. **Golf** Banstead Downs 18h.

Dene, H, z (Unl) *39 Cheam Rd, SM1 2AT.* ✆ 01-642 3170. C 5. 📧 18 bedrs, 4 bp, 2 bps, 1 sh, 3 ba, TV. 🅿 CH, CP 9, CF, 2 BGf, 1 st. **£** BB £12·65–£27·60, DB £27·60–£34·50, ②, Bk £3·45.

Eaton Court, PH, z (R), *49 Eaton Rd, SM2 5DN.* ✆ 01-643 6766. C. 📧 13 bedrs, 2 bps, 2 ba, TV, Dgs. 🅿 CH, TV, CP6, 4 st. **£** BB fr £15, DB fr £25, ⬜, cc 1 2.

Thatched House, H, z (R), *135 Cheam Rd, SM1 2BD.* ✆ 01-642 3131. C. 📧 18

bedrs, 6 bps, 3 sh, 2 ba, TV. 🅿 CH, TV, CP 12, CF, 9 BGf, 2 st. **£** BB £19–£25, DB £30–£35, ⬜, Bk £4, D £8, cc 3.

Repairer: Phoenix Motor Co (Surrey) Ltd, 315 High St. ✆ 01-642 0161.
Rescue Service: Fawngrove (Sutton) Ltd, Tonfield Service Station, 400 Sutton Common Rd. ✆ 01-644 6702.

SUTTON BRIDGE Lincolnshire. Map 16E
Pop 2,344. King's Lynn 10, London 110, Boston 20, Sleaford 33, Spalding 16, Wisbech 10.
EC Wed. **MD** Thur. **Golf** Sutton Bridge 9h.
See Old lighthouse on East and West banks of R Nene, Church of St Matthew.

Repairer: Leeson's Garage Ltd, Railway La. ✆ Lincoln (0522) 752654.

SUTTON COLDFIELD West Midlands. Map 21C
Pop 83,550. Coventry 19, London 113, M6 Motorway 4, Birmingham 7, Lichfield 8½, Newport 31, Stafford 21, Tamworth 7, Walsall 9, Warwick 23.
Golf Sutton Coldfield 18h. **See** Parish Church, Sutton Park, Vesey Memorial Gardens, Boddington Gardens.

★★★★**Belfry,** *Lichfield Rd, Wishaw, B76 8BR.* ✆ Curdworth (0675) 70301. C. 📧 116 bedrs, 116 bp, TV, Dgs. ✗ a l c, mc, at, LD 10.30. 🅿 Lt, N, CH, CP 500, Ac, sp, gc, tc, sc, sb, sol, gym, con 600, CF, 4 BGf, 0 st, Dis. **£** BB £39·50, DB £49·50, WB, ⬜, Bk £3·75, L £6·95, D £9·95, cc 1 2 3 5 6, Dep.

★★★★**Penns Hall,** *Penns La, Walmley, B76 8LH.* ✆ 021-351 3111. C. 📧 121 bedrs, 114 bp, 7 bps, TV, Dgs. ✗ a l c, mc, at, LD 9.45. 🅿 Lt, N, CH, Dgs, CP 600, Ac, pf, con 600, CF, 2 st. **£** B £22–£40, BD £33–£49, ⬜, Bk £4·25, cc 1 2 3 4 5 6, Dep b.

★★★**Moor Hall,** *Moor Hall Dr, B75 6LW.* ✆ 021-308 3751. C. 📧 50 bedrs, 50 bp, TV, Dgs. ✗ a l c, mc, at, LD 10.30. 🅿 N, CH, CP 200, Ac, gc, sb, sol, gym, con 150, CF, 15 BGf, 3 st. **£** BB £36, DB £44, WB, ②, Bk £4, L £7·50, D £12·95, cc 1 2 3 4 5 6, Dep b.

■★★**Sutton Court** (R), *66 Lichfield Rd, B74 2NA.* ✆ 021-355 2135. C. 📧 20 bedrs, 6 bp, 14 bps, TV, Dgs. ✗ a l c, mc, at, LD 9·30. 🅿 CH, TV, CP 70, U 5, Ac, con, CF, 1 BGf, 2 st. **£** BB £25·85–£29·15, DB £35·75, WT £245, DBB £33·85–£37·15, WB, ⬜, Bk £2·95, L £5·95, D £10·95, cc 1 2 3 5 6, Dep b.

Repairer: Eastcroft Garage Ltd, 11 Coleshill Rd. ✆ 021-354 6283.
Specialist Body Repairer: Eastcroft Garage Ltd, Coleshill Rd. ✆ 021-354 9846.
Rescue Service: Forge Motor Body Specialists, Forge La, Four Oaks. ✆ 021-353 4172.

SUTTON-IN-ASHFIELD Notts. M. Area 22D
Pop 41,270. Nottingham 14, London 137, Ashbourne 22, Chesterfield 12, Derby 19, Mansfield 2½, Matlock 15.
EC Wed. **MD** Fri, Sat. **Golf** Coxmoor 18h.
See Parish Church of St Mary, Skegby Church, Teversal Manor, Hardwick Hall.

Rescue Service: Forest Road Garage, Skegby. ✆ Mansfield (0623) 53048. Texacar, Alfreton Rd. ✆ Mansfield (0623) 57355.

SUTTON-ON-SEA Lincolnshire. Map 23B
Pop 6,156 (inc Mablethorpe). Skegness 15, London 154, Boston 32, Grimsby 30, Horncastle 22, Louth 16.
EC Thur. **Golf** Sandilands 18h.

★★**Bacchus,** *High St, LN12 2ET.* ✆ (0521) 41204.
★★**Grange & Links,** *Sea Lane, Sandilands.* ✆ (0521) 41334. C. 📧 16 bedrs, 11 bp, 3 bps, 3 ba, TV, Dgs. ✗ mc, LD 8.30. 🅿 CH, TV, Dgs, CP 100, Ac, tc, sol, con 200, CF. **£** BB £20·70, DB £31·05, WT £110–£130, WB, ②, Bk £3, L £3·50, D £8, cc 1 2 3 5.

Rescue Service: Steve Wood Motors, High St. ✆ (0521) 41215.

SUTTON-ON-TRENT Notts. M. Area 23C
Pop 1,030. Newark 7½, London 133, Doncaster 29, Gainsborough 24, Lincoln 22, Ollerton 11, Worksop 17.
Golf Newark 18h. **See** All Saints' Church, 16th cent.

Rescue Service: Major's Garage Ltd, Gt North Rd. ✆ Newark (0636) 821200.

SUTTON SCOTNEY Hampshire. Map 6D
Pop 2,500. Basingstoke 13, London 61, Alton 19, Andover 7, Newbury 18, Romsey 17, Salisbury 22, Winchester 6½.
EC Sat. **Golf** Royal Winchester 18h. **See** Stoke Charity Church, Hunton Church.

Rescue Service: Hill Farm Garage, Hill Farm Crossroads. ✆ (096 276) 665. Scotney Service Station, Newbury Rd. ✆ (096 276) 351.

SUTTON VENY Wiltshire. M. Area 5D
3 m SE of Warminster. Pop 466. Amesbury 18, London 98, Salisbury 20, Shaftesbury 13, Wincanton 17.
EC Wed. **See** Iron Age earthwork. Churches.

Rescue Service: T Griffin-Agricultural & Plant Repairs, Haycombe Hill. ✆ (098 54) 406 & (098 54) 237.

SWAFFHAM Norfolk. Map 16C
Pop 1,776. Newmarket 33, London 96, East Dereham 12, Ely 26, Fakenham 16, King's Lynn 15, Thetford 18, Wisbech 26.
EC Thur. **MD** Sat. **Golf** Swaffham 9h. **See** Church (15th cent), Market Cross, Swaffham Pedlar Sign, Oxburgh Hall 7 m SW.

★★**George,** *Station St, PE37 7LJ.* ✆ (0760) 21238.
Lydney House, H, y, *Norwich Rd, PE37 7QS.* ✆ (0760) 24108. C. 📧 10 bedrs, 8 bp, 2 bps, 2 ba, TV. ✗ a l c 🅿 CH, TV, CP 40, CF, 3 st. **£** BB £15–£21, DB £20–£30, ②, 15%, BK £3, L £4·50, D £5·50, cc 1 3.

SWALWELL Tyne & Wear. Map 32C
Pop 3,007. Durham 16, London 276, Corbridge 15, Hexham 17, Middleton-in-Teesdale 35, Newcastle upon Tyne 4, Sunderland 14, West Auckland 30.
EC Wed. **Golf** Whickham 18h.**See** Derwent Walk.

Rescue Service: Garden House Service Station, Market La. ✆ Whickham (0632) 887074.

SWANAGE Dorset. Maps 5F and 6E
Pop 6,704. Wareham 9½, London 126 (Fy
115), Sandbanks (Fy) 6½.
EC Thur (win). **Golf** Isle of Purbeck 18h.
See Parish Church and old mill pond,
Clock Tower, Town Hall (facade by Wren,
quaint lock-up at rear), Quarries, Tilly
Whim Caves and Great Globe, Corfe
Castle 5 m NW, Durlston Country Park.
🛈 The White House, Shore Rd. ✆ Swanage
(0929) 422885.

★★★**Corrie** (R), *De Moulham Rd, BH19
1NS.* ✆ (0929) 423104.
★★★**Grosvenor,** *BH19 2AR.* ✆ (0929)
422292. Open Apr–Oct. C. ⋈ 95 bedrs, 56
bp, 1 bps, 10 ba, ns. ✗ mc, at, LD 8.30.
🅿 Lt, N, ch, TV, ns, CP 300, Ac, sp, tc, sb,
sol, con 200, CF, 5 BGf, 0 st, Dis. £ BB
18.50–£26, DB £37–£52, WT £168–£217,
DT £25.50–£31.50, WB 🛈, Bk £3, L £5.50,
D £7.50, cc 1 3, Dep b.
★★★**Pines,** *Burlington Rd, BH19 1LT.*
✆ (0929) 425211. C. ⋈ 51 bedrs, 46 bp, 3
bps, 1 ba, TV, Dgs. ✗ mc, at, LD 9. 🅿 Lt, N,
CH, CP 60, con 60, CF, 7 BGf, 1 st, Dis. £
BB £17.25–£23, DB £34.50–£46, WT
£159.85–£227.70, DT £32.20–£37.95,
DBB £27.03–£32.75, WB (Oct–May), 🛈,
Bk £3.50, L £5.75, D £8.63, cc 1 3 6.▲
🔳★★**Clifftop,** *8 Burlington Rd, BH19
1LR.* ✆ (0929) 422091.
★★**Grand,** *Burlington Rd, BH19 1LU.*
✆ (0929) 423353. C. ⋈ 26 bedrs, 9 bp, 9
ba, Dgs. ✗ a l c, LD 8.45. 🅿 Lt, N,
ch, TV, Dgs, CP 12, Ac, con 40, CF, 3 st.
£ BB £13–£17, DB £26–£34, DBB £19–
£21, WB, 🛈, L £1.80, D £6.50, cc 1 2 3 5,
Dep b.
🔳★**Suncliffe** (RI), *Burlington Rd, BH19
1LR.* ✆ (0929) 423299.
Ap. York (RI), *Cauldon Av, BH19 1PQ.*
✆ (0929) 422704. Open Apr–Oct. C ⋈ 22
bedrs, 4 bp, 5 ba, Dgs. ✗ mc, at, LD 8.
🅿 ch, TV, CP 15, U 4, Ac, CF, 1 BGf, 2 st.
£ BB £10.50–£12.50, DB £17–£21, DBB
£14–£21.50, 🛈, 10%, Bk £3, L £2, D £6,
Dep a.

Byways, G, z (Unl), *5 Ulwell Rd, BH19
1LE.* ✆ (0929) 422322. Open May–Sep. C
5. ⋈ 11 bedrs, 2 ba, Dgs. 🅿 ch, TV, Dgs,
CP 4, 1 st. £ BB £9.50–£10.50, DB £19–
£21, WT (b) £72–£77, DT (b) £12.50–
£13.50, 🛈.
Castleton, PH, z (RI), *1 Highcliffe Rd,
BH19 1LW.* ✆ (0929) 423972. Open Feb–
Oct. C 3. ⋈ 12 bedrs, 1 bp, 3 bps, 1 sh, 2
ba. 🅿 CH, TV, CP 12, CF, 1 st. £ BB £8.05–
£10.93, DB £16.10–£21.85, WT (b),
£73.60–£89.70, (c) £52.90–£64.40, DT (b)
£11.50–£13.80, 🛈.
Danesfort, PH, z (RI), *Highcliffe Rd,
BH19 1LW.* ✆ (0929) 422551. Open Mar–
Oct, C 4. ⋈ 8 bedrs, 4 bps, 1 ba. 🅿 CH, TV,
CP 7, 4 st. £ BB £7.50–£10.50, DB £15–
£21, WT (b) £75–£90, (c) £50–£60, DT (b)
£12–£15, D £6, D £4.50.
Eversden, PH, z (RI), *5 Victoria Rd, BH19
1LY.* ✆ (0929) 423276. C. ⋈ 12 bedrs, 2
bp, 3 bps, 2 ba. 🅿 CH, TV, Dgs, ns, CP 12,
CF, 1 st. £ BB fr £8, DB fr £16, 🛈, D £4.
Firswood, G, z (Unl), *29 Kings Rd, BH19
9HF.* ✆ (0929) 422306. Closed Dec. C 5.
⋈ 7 bedrs, 2 ba. 🅿 CH, TV, CP 7. £ BB £8–
£10, DB £16–£18, WT £70–£80, DT £13–
£15, 🛈, cc 1 3.
Glen Roy, G, z (Unl), *18 Park Rd, BH19
2AD.* ✆ (0929) 423102. Open Mar–Oct.
⋈ 6 bedrs, 2 sh, 1 ba, Dgs. 🅿 CH, TV, CF.
£ BB £7–£7.50, DB £14–£15, WT (b) £71–

£74, (c) £49–£52.35, DT (b) £10.50–
£11.50, 🛈.
Golden Sands, H, (RI), *10 Ulwell Rd,
BH19 1LH.* ✆ (0929) 422093. Open Mar–
Nov, C. ⋈ 13 bedrs, 10 bp, 2 bps, 1 ba, TV.
🅿 CH, TV, CP 14, CF. £ BB £8.50–£12.75,
DB £17–£25.50, WT (b) £80–£105, DT (b)
£11.50–£15.50.
Havenhurst, PH, z (RI), *3 Cranborne Rd,
BH19 1EA.* ✆ (0929) 424224. Open Mar–
Oct. C. ⋈ 16 bedrs, 1 bp, 6 bps, 3 ba.
🅿 CH, TV, CP 16, CF, 1 BGf, 4 st. £ BB
£10–£13, DB £20–£26, WT (b) £88–£105,
DT £15–£17, 🛈, D £5.
Ingleston, H, z (RI), *2 Victoria Rd, BH19
1LY.* ✆ (0929) 422391. Open Mar–Oct. C.
⋈ 8 bedrs, 2 ba. 🅿 CH, TV, ns, CP 10, CF.
£ BB £9.20–£11.60, DB £18.40–£23.20,
WT (b) £86.25–£92, DT (b) £12.65–
£14.95, 🛈.
Malverns, H, z (R), *38 Park Rd,
BH19 2AD.* ✆ (0929) 422575. C 3. ⋈ 19
bedrs, 1 bp, 3 bps, 4 ba, Dgs. 🅿 CH, TV, CP
12. £ BB £9–£15.25, DB £18–£27.75, WT
(b) £83–£106, DT (b) £13–£17, 🛈, Bk
£3.50, D £5, cc 1 2 3 5.
Millbrook, G, z (RI), *56 Kings Rd, BH19
1HR.* ✆ (0929) 423443.
Nethercourt, PH, z (RI), *62 Park Rd,
BH19 2AE.* ✆ (0929) 423518. Open Mar–
Oct, C 10. ⋈ 6 bedrs, 4 sh, 2 ba. 🅿 CH, TV,
CP 6. £ BB £9–£12, DB £17–£22, WT (b)
£90–£110, DT (b) £14–£17, 🛈, cc 1 2 3.
Oxford, PH, z (RI), *Park Rd, BH19 2AA.*
✆ (0929) 422527.
St Michaels, G, z (RI), *31 Kings Rd,
BH19 1HF.* ✆ (0929) 422064.
Stafford Court, H, z (RI), *Stafford Rd,
BH19 2BQ.* ✆ (0929) 423700.
Tower Lodge, PH, (RI), *17 Ulwell Rd,
BH19 1LF.* ✆ (0929) 422887. Open Mar–
Oct. C. ⋈ 11 bedrs, 6 bps, 2 ba. 🅿 ch, TV,
ns, CP 9, CF, 2 BGf, 0 st. £ BB £12.14, DB
£24.28–£27.15, WT (b) £105.22, DT (b)
£15.03, 🛈.

Repairer: Brook Garage (Swanage) Ltd,
King's Rd. ✆ (0929) 422266.
Rescue Service: St Michael's Garage,
Valley Rd. ✆ Corfe Castle (0929) 480221.
Foley's Garage, Valley Rd, Harmans Cross.
✆ Corfe Castle (0929) 480215.

SWANLEY Kent. M. Area 7B
Pop 19,500. Sidcup 4, London 18, Bromley
7½, Dartford 4½, Dartford Tunnel 7½,
Maidstone 14, Sevenoaks 10, Westerham
15.
EC Wed. **MD** Wed, Sat. **Golf** Lullingstone
Park 18h.

Rescue Service: Birchwood Motor Works,
Birchwood Corner. ✆ (0322) 63448 and
(0322) 65925.
Dawes of Swanley Ltd, Station Rd.
✆ (0322) 62211.

SWAY Hampshire. Map 6E
Pop 3,200. Lyndhurst 7, London 91,
Bournemouth 14, Lymington 3½,
Ringwood 10.
Golf Barton-on-Sea 18h. **See** Peterson's
Folly (220 ft Tower), no admission.

★★★**White Rose,** *Station Rd, SO4 0BA.*
✆ Lymington (0590) 682754. C. ⋈ 13
bedrs, 9 bp, 2 ba, TV, Dgs. ✗ a l c, mc, at,
LD 8.45. 🅿 Lt, CH, Dgs, CP 50, Ac, sp, CF,
1 st. £ BB £14–£19, DB £28–£42, DBB
£19–£27, WB, 🛈, Bk £2.75, L £5.50, D
£6.50, cc 1 3, Dep b.

SWAYTHLING Hampshire. M. Area 6D
Winchester 9½, London 75, Fareham 12,
Romsey 6½, Southampton 3.

Rescue Service: F Halfpenny & Son Ltd,
102 High Rd. ✆ Southampton (0703)
554346.

SWILLINGTON West Yorkshire. M. Area
25F and 33B
Wakefield 7, London 189, M62 Motorway
3½, Castleford 4½, Garforth 1½, Leeds 6.

Rescue Service: G Wagstaff, Goody Cross
Garage, Goody Cross La. ✆ Leeds (0532)
871963.

SWINDON Wiltshire. Map 6A
Pop 130,000. Wantage 17, London 77, M4
Motorway 4½, Burford 19, Chepstow 48,
Chippenham 20, Cirencester 15, Devizes
15, Faringdon 12, Marlborough 11,
Newbury 25, Oxford 29, Tetbury 19.
EC Wed. **MD** Mon, Wed, Sat. **Golf** Brome
Manor 18h. **See** BR (W Reg) Works, Rly
Museum, Richard Jeffries Museum and Art
Gallery, Christ Church, Coate Water,
Lydiard Park and Mansion 4 m W.
🛈 32 The Arcade. ✆ Swindon (0793)
30328.

★★★★**Blunsdon House,** *The Ridge,
Blunsdon, SN2 4AD* (4 m N A419).
✆ (0793) 721701. C. ⋈ 93 bedrs, 91 bp, 2
bps, TV, Dgs. ✗ a l c, mc, at, LD 10. 🅿 Lt,
N, CH, Dgs, CP 250, Ac, con 200, CF, 1
BGf, 0 st, Dis. £ BB £35–£42.50, DB £44–
£49, WB, 🛈, Bk £4, L £6.50, D £8,
cc 1 2 3 4 5 6.
★★★**M Crest,** *Oxford St, Stratton St
Margaret, SN3 4TL.* ✆ (0793) 822921. C.
⋈ 98 bedrs, 98 bp, ns, TV, Dgs. ✗ a l c,
mc, at, LD 9.45. 🅿 N, CH, Dgs, CP 150, Ac,
con 80, CF, 48 BGf, 0 st, Dis. £ B fr £42, BD
fr £53, WB, 🛈, Bk £5.25, D £9.25,
cc 1 2 3 4 5 6, Dep a.
★★★**M Goddard Arms,** *High St, SN1
3EW.* ✆ (0793) 692313.
★★★**M Post House** (TH), *Marlborough
Rd, Coate, SN3 6AQ.* ✆ (0793) 24601. C.
⋈ 103 bedrs, 103 bp, TV, Dgs. ✗ a l c, mc,
at, LD 10. 🅿 N, CH, Dgs, CP 200, Ac, sp,
con 90, CF, 53 BGf, 0 st, Dis. £ BB £44, DB
£55.50, WB, 🛈, cc 1 2 3 4 5 6, Dep (Xmas).
★★★**Wiltshire,** *Fleming Way, SN1 1TN.*
✆ (0793) 28282. C. ⋈ 85 bedrs, 85 bp, TV,
Dgs. ✗ a l c, mc, at, LD 10.30. 🅿 Lt, N, CH,
Dgs, CP 600, Ac, con 230, CF, 0 st. £ BB
£39, DB £50, WB, 🛈, Bk £4, L £7.55, D
£7.55, cc 1 2 3 5, Dep b.

Repairer: Lex Motor Co (Swindon) Ltd,
Drove Rd. ✆ (0793) 34035.
MC Repairer: Swindon Motor Co Ltd, 34
Wood St. ✆ (0793) 22065.
Sctr Repairers: Alston & Young, 123
Cricklade Rd. ✆ (0793) 36671.
Swindon Motor Co Ltd, 34 Wood St.
✆ (0793) 22065.
Rescue Service: County Garages
(Swindon) Ltd, Units 4 & 5, Hawksworth
Trading Estate. ✆ (0793) 31464 and
(0793) 615222.▲
Days Garage Breakdown & Recovery
Service, Cambria Bridge Rd. ✆ (0793)
21465.
Edwin H Bradley & Sons Ltd, Okus Rd.
✆ (0793) 28131.
Greens of Swindon, 5 Marlborough Rd.
✆ (0793) 27251.
Titcombe Garages, off Sheppard St.
✆ (0793) 41643.▲

Whitbourne Service Station, Whitbourne Av. ✆ (0793) 27678.

SWINTON Greater Manchester (Lancashire). Map 20A
Pop 40,000 (inc Pendlebury), Manchester 4½, London 188, Altrincham 9½, Walkden 2½, Warrington 15.
EC Wed. **MD** Tue, Fri, Sat. **Golf** Swinton Park 18h. **See** Churches, Clifton Marina.

Rescue Service: Wesley Garage, Wesley St. ✆ 061-794 4916.

SYMONDS YAT Hereford & Worcester (Herefordshire). Map 13E
Pop 350. Gloucester 20, London 125, Chepstow 17, Hereford 17, Monmouth 7, Ross-on-Wye 6½.
Golf Monmouth 9h. **See** Symonds Yat, famous beauty spot and viewpoint on River Wye.

★★Old Court, *Whitchurch, HR9 6DA.*
✆ (0600) 890207. C. ✉ 17 bedrs, 10 bp, 2 ba, TV, Dgs. ✗ a l c, at, LD 9. 🏠 ch, Dgs, CP 50, Ac, sp, CF, 0 st. £ BB £17·50–£21, DB £27·50–£32, WB, 🄳, Bk £3·50, D £9, cc 1 2 3 5.

★★Paddocks, *HR9 6BL.* ✆ (0600) 890246. Open Apr–Oct & Xmas–New Year. C. ✉ 27 bedrs, 10 bp, 2 bps, 5 ba, Dgs. ✗ mc, at, LD 8. 🏠 CH, TV, Dgs, CP 200, Ac, tc, con 200, CF, 1 st. £ BB £13·50–£19, DB £27–£30, WT £135–£145, DT £21.50, WB, 🄳, Bk £3·50, L £4·50, D £8.

♨★★Royal, *Symonds Yat East, HR9 6JL.* ✆ (0600) 890238. C 4. ✉ 23 bedrs, 11 bp, 5 ba. ✗ a l c, mc, at, LD 8. 🏠 CH, TV, CP 40, Ac, sp, con 50, CF, 0 st. £ BB £17·50–£24, DB £35–£48, WT £196, DT £40·54, WB, 🄳, Bk £4·50, L £6·50, D £10, cc 1 2 3, Dep.

▣♨★★Wye Rapids (R), *HR9 6BL.* ✆ (0600) 890366. C. ✉ 16 bedrs, 4 bp, 3 bps, 3 ba, Dgs. ✗ a l c, mc, at, LD 8.30. 🏠 CH, TV, CP 30, con 12, CF, 2 st. £ BB £18–£25, DB £26–£35 WT £145, WB, 🄳, Bk £3·50, D £7·95, cc 1 2 3 5, Dep a.

Garth Cottage, H, x (R), *Symonds Yat East, HR9 6JL.* ✆ (0600) 890364. Open Feb–Oct. C 7. ✉ 7 bedrs, 3 bps, 2 ba. 🏠 CH, TV, CP 9. £ BB £10–£11, DB £20–£25, WT (b) £105–£110. DT (b) £16–£17, 🄳, Bk £2·25, D £6, cc 1.

Saracens Head, l, x, *Symonds Yat East, HR9 6JL.* ✆ (0600) 890435. C. ✉ 6 bedrs, 3 bps, 1 ba. ✗ a l c. 🏠 CH, TV, Dgs, CP. £ DB £20–£35, WT (b) £115–£168. DT (b) £16·50–£24, 🄳, Bk £4·50, L £5·50, D £6·50, cc 1 2.

Woodlea, G, x (RI), *HR9 6BL.* ✆ (0600) 890206. Closed Xmas. C. ✉ 10 bedrs, 3 bps, 2 ba, Dgs. 🏠 CH, TV, Dgs, CP, CF. £ BB £11·50, DB £20·50–£23·50, WT (b) £105, DT (b) £16, 🄳.

SYSTON Leicestershire. Map 22F
Pop 8,833. Leicester 5½, London 103, Loughborough 8, Melton Mowbray 9½, Newark 29, Nottingham 20, Ollerton 39.
Golf Birstall 18h. **See** 13th cent Church.

Rescue Service: Jones Garage (Syston) Ltd, 1369 Melton Rd. ✆ Leicester (0533) 608663.

SYWELL Northamptonshire. Map 15A
Pop 823. M1 Motorway 20, London 69, Bedford 23, Bletchley 25, Cambridge 45, Huntingdon 31, Kettering 9, Market Harborough 16, Northampton 6, Peterborough 35, Rugby 22.

Golf Northampton 18h. **See** Aerodrome.

★M Sywell, *Sywell Airport, NN6 0BT.* ✆ Northampton (0604) 491594. C. ✉ 56 bedrs, 32 bp, 24 bps, TV, Dgs. ✗ a l c, mc, at, LD 9.30. 🏠 CH, TV, Dgs, CP 100, Ac, con 80, 23 BGf, 1 st, Dis. £ BB £17·30–£20·30, DB £26·60–£29·60, WB, 🄳, Bk £2·80, L £5, D £6·50, cc 1 2 3 5.

TADLEY Hampshire. Map 6B
Reading 14, London 52, Andover 20, Basingstoke 6½, Newbury 13, Oxford 35.

Rescue Service: Mendem Motor, Unit 14, Stacey Industrial Estate. ✆ (073 56) 2392.

TADWORTH Surrey. Map 7A
Mitcham 9½, London 16, Epsom 3, Purley 7, Reigate 5.

Rescue Service: Tattenham Corner Motor Co Ltd, Ashurst Rd. ✆ (073 781) 2900.

TALKIN Cumbria. Maps 26C and 30F
Penrith 22, London 298, Brampton 3, Carlisle 9½.
EC Wed. **Golf** Brampton 18h. **See** Talkin Tarn.

♨★★Tarn End, *Talkin Tarn, CA8 1LS.* ✆ Brampton (069 76) 2340. Closed Nov & Dec 25. C 14. ✉ 6 bedrs, 3 bp, 2 ba. ✗ a l c, mc, at, LD 9. 🏠 CH, TV, CP 70, pf, 4 st. £ BB fr £15·75, DB fr £30, WB, 🄳, Bk £5·25, L £6·95, D £12·65, cc 1 2 5, Dep a.

TAMWORTH Staffordshire. Map 22E
Pop 65,000. Atherstone 8, London 112, Ashby-de-la-Zouch 13, Burton-on-Trent 15, Coventry 19, Lichfield 7, Newport 33, Sutton Coldfield 7, Uttoxeter 24, Walsall 11, Warwick 27.
EC Wed. **MD** Tue, Sat. **Golf** Tamworth 18h. **See** Castle with Museum and Pleasure Grounds, St Editha's Church, Old Town Hall, 17th cent Guy's Almshouses, 16th cent Moat House.
🄸 Municipal Offices, Marmion House, Lichfield St. ✆ Tamworth (0827) 4222 ext 387.

★★Castle, *Ladybank, B79 7NB.* ✆ (0827) 57181. C. ✉ 16 bedrs, 2 bp, 14 bps, TV, Dgs. ✗ a l c, mc, at, LD 10. 🏠 N, CH, TV, Dgs, Ac, con 200, CF, 0 st. £ BB £18·50–£22·50, DB £24–£30, WT £233, DT £31–£35, DBB £25·25–£29·25, WB, 🄳, Bk £3, L £5·75, D £6·75, cc 1 2 3, Dep b.

Repairer: Rose Bros (Tamworth) Ltd, Central Garage. ✆ (0827) 60331.
MC Repairer: Motor Cycle Shop, 5 Aldergate. ✆ (0827) 62711.
Rescue Service: Bole Bridge Garage Ltd, Bole Bridge St. ✆ (0827) 3535. Hopleys Farm Service Station, Argyle St, Glascote. ✆ (0827) 3896. Warton Garage, Church Rd, Warton. ✆ (0827) 804260.

TANKERTON Kent. Map 10D
See also WHITSTABLE.
Pop 3,686. Rochester 26, London 56, Canterbury 7, Margate 15.
EC Wed. **Golf** Seasalter 9h.

★★Marine, *Marine Par, CT5 2BE.* ✆ Whitstable (0227) 272672. C. ✉ 18 bedrs, 4 bp, 10 bps, 3 ba, Dgs. ✗ a l c, mc, at, LD 8.15 (Fri & Sat 9). 🏠 ch, TV, Dgs, CP 12, U 3, Con 100, CF 0 st. £ BB £24·50–£29, DB £44–£48, WT £210–£227·50, DT £30–£32·50, DBB £28·50–£31, WB, 🄳, Bk £3, L £5, D £7, cc 1 3, Dep b.

TAPLOW Buckinghamshire. M. Area 7A
Pop 2,270. Slough 4½, London 24, Bagshot 17, Henley-on-Thames 10, High Wycombe 9, Reading 14.
EC Wed. **Golf** Burnham Beeches 18h. **See** Cliveden 2 m N, Taplow Court Woods (Nat Trust).

Repairer: Maidenhead Autos & Stevensons Ltd, Bath Rd. ✆ Maidenhead (0628) 25131.
MC Repairer: S.G.T. Superbiking, Station Rd. ✆ Burnham (062 86) 5353.

TARNOCK Somerset. M. Area 5C
Pop 430. Wells 13, London 135, Bath 18, Bridgwater 12, Bristol 19, Radstock 17, Weston-super-Mare 8½.
EC Tue. **Golf** Weston-super-Mare 18h.

Rescue Service: Tarnock Garage Ltd. ✆ Edingworth (093 472) 320.

TARPORLEY Cheshire. Map 19D
Pop 1,859. Nantwich 10, London 172, Chester 11, Middlewich 13, Northwich 11, Warrington 19, Whitchurch 14
EC Wed. **Golf** Vicars Cross, Chester 18h. **See** Medieval Church, Castle ruins, Ancient Coaching House.

★Swan, *50 High St, CW6 0AG.* ✆ (082 93) 2411. Closed Dec 24 & 25. C. ✉ 9 bedrs, 2 ba, TV. ✗ a l c, mc, LD 9.15. 🏠 CH, TV, CP 40, Ac, con 80, CF, 1 st. £ BB £18, DB £29, WT £220·50, DT £31·50, DBB £25·25, WB, 🄳, Bk £4, L £6·25, D £7·25, cc 1 2 3 5, Dep b.

Willington Hall, H, xy, *Willington, CW6 0NB.* ✆ Kelsall (0829) 52321. Closed Xmas. C 5. ✉ 5 bedrs, 5 bp, TV, Dgs. ✗ a l c. 🏠 CH, Dgs, CP 60, CF, 2 st. £ BB £25, DB £40, 🄳, Bk £3, L £9·50, D £9·50, cc 1 2 3 5.

Rescue Service: P & P Recovery (Smithy Garage), Huxley La, Tiverton. ✆ (0884) 2272.

TAUNTON Somerset. Map 4D
Pop 37,444. Wincanton 33, London 143, M5 Motorway 1½, Bridgwater 10, Dunster 22, Exeter 33, Glastonbury 22, Honiton 18, Ilminster 12, South Molton 36, Tiverton 20.
Golf Vivary Park 18h. Pickeridge 18h. **See** Castle (Norman Keep, County Museum, Judge Jeffrey's Hall), Taunton Public School, Almshouses, St Mary Magdalene Church, St James's Church, Priory Gatehouse, West Somerset Rly.
🄸 Central Library, Corporation St. ✆ Taunton (0823) 74785.

★★★★Castle, *Castle Green, TA1 1NF.* ✆ (0823) 72671. C. ✉ 40 bedrs, 40 bp, TV, Dgs. ✗ a l c, mc, at, LD 9. 🏠 Lt, N, CH, CP 30, G 10, Ac, con 40, CF, 1 st. £ BB £44·50 £61, DB £77 £07, WB, 🄳, Bk £3·90, L £6·90, D £14·90, cc 1 2 3 4 5 6, Dep b.

★★★County (TH), *East St, TA1 3LT.* ✆ (0823) 87651. C. ✉ 72 bedrs, 60 bp, 12 ba, TV, Dgs. ✗ a l c, mc, LD 9.30. 🏠 Lt, N, CH, Dgs, CP 100, U 8, Ac, con 500, CF, 1 st. £ BB £30·50–£36·50, DB £43–£52·50, WB, 🄳, cc 1 2 3 4 5 6, Dep (Xmas).

★★Corner House, *Park St, TA1 4DQ.* ✆ (0823) 84683. C. ✉ 22 bedrs, 5 bp, 5 ba, TV. ✗ a l c, mc, at, LD 9·45. 🏠 CH, TV, CP 32, G 2, Ac, con 20, CF, 1 st. £ BB £19·55–£24·55, DB £34·50–£39·50, WB, 🄳, Bk £3·50, L £6, D £9, cc 1 2 3 5 6.

■★★**Falcon** (R), *Henlade, TA3 0DM.*
✆ Henlade (0823) 442502. Closed Dec
19–Jan 14. C 5. ⋈ 9 bedrs, 7 bp, 2 bps, TV.
✗ mc, at, LD 8. ⓓ CH, TV, CP 25, sb, sol,
gym, 2 st. £ BB £24·75, DB £38·50, WB, ⛨,
Bk £3·50, D £6·75, cc 1 3.

■★★**St Quintin** (R), *Bridgwater Rd,
Bathpool, TA2 8BG.* ✆ (0823) 73016. C.
⋈ 6 bedrs, 2 ba, annexe 4 bedrs, 1 ba, TV.
✗ a l c, mc, at, LD 9.30. ⓓ CH, TV, CP 30,
Ac, con 25, CF, 0 st. £ BB £16·75–£19·50,
DB £29·50–£33·50, WT £95–£140, DT
£26·50–£30, DBB £22·75–£26·50, WB, ⛨,
Bk £3·45, L £2·50, D £4·50, cc 1 2 3 5.

Brookfield, G, z (RI), *16 Wellington Rd,
TA1 4EQ.* ✆ (0823) 72786. C. ⋈ 8 bedrs,
2 ba. ⓓ CH, TV, CP 8, CF, 0 st. £ BB
£11·50, DB £20·70, DBB £16·50, ⛨, D
£3·75, cc 1 3.

Meare Green, G, x (R), *Stoke St Gregory,
TA3 6HZ.* ✆ North Curry (0823) 490250.
C 10. ⋈ 6 bedrs, 2 ba. ⓓ CH, TV, CP 20, 2
st.▲

Meryan House, PH, x (R), *Bishops Hull,
TA1 5EG.* ✆ (0823) 87445.

Wey House, G, xy (Unl), *Norton
Fitzwarren, TA4 1BT.* ✆ (0823) 87391.

White Lodge, PH, y (RI), *81 Bridgwater
Rd, TA1 2DU.* ✆ (0823) 73287. C. ⋈ 10
bedrs, 6 bps, 2 ba, TV. ⓓ CH, TV, Dgs, CP
12, 0 st. £ BB £50–£21, DB £28·50–
£32, WT (b) £150, DT (b) £25, Bk £2, D £6,
cc 1 2 3.

Repairers: Marshalsea Motors Ltd, 30
Wellington Rd. ✆ (0823) 81081.
Wadham Stringer (Taunton) Ltd, Austin
House, South St, off East St. ✆ (0823)
88991.
Rescue Service: Creech Motors, Creech
St Michael. ✆ (0823) 442480.
C S Motors, Yarde Pl, Wood St. ✆ (0823)
74203.
Dunn's Motors Ltd, East St and Silver St.
✆ (0823) 72607.
Jubilee Service Station, East Lyng.
✆ Burrowbridge (082 369) 202.
Lyng Motors, Locketts Cottage, East
Lyng. ✆ Burrowbridge (082 369) 278.
Silver Street Motors, Silver St. ✆ (0823)
88371.
South West Motor Services, Cornishway
North, Galminton Trading Estate.
✆ (0823) 77805.▲
Trull Garage, Trull. ✆ (0823) 76021.
Valley Motors, Bridgwater Rd, Bathpool,
West Monkton. ✆ (0823) 81221.

TAVISTOCK Devon. Map 3C
Pop 9,188. Exeter 33, London 202,
Ashburton 20, Launceston 13, Liskeard
18, Okehampton 16, Plymouth 14, Saltash
14.
EC Wed. **MD** Fri. **Golf** Tavistock 18h. **See**
Abbey ruins (10th cent), Parish Church of
St Eustachius (mainly 15th cent),
Gatehouse ruins (Betsy Grimbal's Tower),
Drake Statue, Brent Tor 4 m N, Morwell
Rocks 3 m SW, Buckland Abbey (museum
with relics of Sir Francis Drake) 6 m S,
Cotehele (15th cent) 8 m SW.
ⓘ Dartmoor National Park Centre,
Bedford Sq. ✆ Tavistock (0822) 2938.

★★★**Bedford** (TH), *Plymouth Rd, PL19
8BB.* ✆ (0822) 3221. C. ⋈ 32 bedrs, 30
bp, 2 bps, TV, Dgs. ✗ a l c, mc, at, LD
9.ⓓ CH, Dgs, G 12, Ac, CF, 6 BGf, 5 st.
£ BB £37, DB £54, WB, ⛨, cc 1 2 3 4 5 6,
Dep (Xmas).

Cherry Trees, G, z (Unl), *40 Plymouth
Rd, PL19 8BU.* ✆ (0822) 3070.

Rescue Service: Carr's Garage (Tavistock)
Ltd, Plymouth Rd. ✆ (0822) 2301.
B.S. & J.S. Williams, Plymouth Rd
Industrial Estate. ✆ (0822) 4587.

TEBAY Cumbria. Map 26D
Pop 595. Kirkby Lonsdale 18, London
264, Brough 16, Hawes 25, Kendal 12,
Penrith 18.
Golf Appleby 18h.

★★★**M Tebay Mountain Lodge** (R),
Orton, CA10 3SB. ✆ Orton (058 74) 351.
C. ⋈ 30 bedrs, 30 bp, TV, Dgs. ✗ a l c, mc,
at, LD 9.30. ⓓ N, CH, TV, Dgs, CP 40, Ac,
con 25, CF, 14 BGf, 0 st, Dis. £ BBc £23–
£25·50, DBc £33–£37, WT £168, DBBc
£28–£30, WB, ⛨, Bk £2·50, L £2·50, D £6,
cc 1 2 3 5 6, Dep a.

Rescue Service: Ian Grant, Woodend
Garage. ✆ Orton (058 74) 213.
Tebay Vehicle Repairs Ltd, M6,
Interchange 38. ✆ Orton (058 74) 341.

TEDBURN ST MARY Devon. Maps 3B
and 4F
Pop 675. Exeter 7, London 176,
Ashburton 21, Crediton 4, Newton Abbot
16, Okehampton 15.
EC Thur. **Golf** Exeter 18h. **See** Church.

★★**King's Arms**, *EX6 6EG.* ✆ (064 76)
224. C. ⋈ 9 bedrs, 1 bp, 2 sh, 2 ba, TV, Dgs.
✗ mc, LD 9·15. ⓓ CH, TV, Dgs, CP 50, U 2,
CF, 2 BGf, 1 st. £ BB fr £13, DB fr £20, ⛨,
Bk £3·50, L £4·65, D £7·50, Dep a.▲

Rescue Service: Frys Garage. ✆ (064 76)
220.

TEDDINGTON Greater London
(Middlesex). M. Area 7A
2 m S of Twickenham, Richmond-upon-
Thames 2½, London 11, Kingston upon
Thames 1½, Slough 14, Staines 9, Uxbridge
13.
EC Wed. **Golf** Fulwell 18h, Strawberry Hill
9h. **See** St Mary's Church, modern Church
of St Alban the Martyr, Bushy Park.

Rescue Service: Brian H Gillett Ltd, 2
Watts La. ✆ 01-977 7800.

TEESSIDE Map 24C
See BILLINGHAM, MIDDLESBROUGH,
REDCAR, STOCKTON-ON-TEES,
THORNABY-ON-TEES.

TEIGNMOUTH Devon. Map 3D
Pop 14,000 (inc Shaldon). Exeter 15,
London 184, Newton Abbot 6.
EC Thur. **Golf** Teignmouth (Haldon) Ltd
18h. **See** Bridge.
ⓘ The Den. ✆ Teignmouth (062 67) 6271.
Ext 207.

★★★**London**, *Bank St, TQ14 8AW.*
✆ (062 67) 2776. C. ⋈ 26 bedrs, 21 bp, 5
bps, TV, Dgs. ✗ a l c, mc, at, LD 10. ⓓ L, N,
CH, TV, Dgs, Ac, sp, sb, sol, gym, con 150,
CF, 0 st. £ BB £17–£21, DB £30–£36, WT
£120–£150, DT £25–£32, DBB £21–£27,
WB, ⛨, Bk £3·50, L £4·75, D £7·50,
cc 1 2 3 6.

■★★**Glendaragh** (R), *Barnpark Rd,
TQ14 8PN.* ✆ (062 67) 2881. Open Apr–
Oct. C. ⋈ 10 bedrs, 8 bp, 1 ba, TV, Dgs.
✗ mc, at, LD 8. ⓓ CH, CP 10, U 2, CF.
£ BB £14·95–£17·25, DB £29·90–£34·50,
WB, ⛨, Bk £3·75, D £8, cc 1 3, Dep a.

♨★★**Venn Farm**, *Higher Exeter Rd,
TQ14 9PB.* ✆ (062 67) 2196. Closed

Xmas–New Year. C. ⋈ 10 bedrs, 7 bp, 2
bps, 1 ba, TV. ✗ a l c, mc, LD 9. ⓓ ch, CP
50, con 25, CF. £ BB £22–£25, DB £30–
£44, WT £145–£155, DBB £29·50–£32,
WB, ⛨, Bk £3, L £5·50, D £8·50, cc 1 2 3 5.

■★**Belvedere** (R), *Barnpark Rd, TQ14
8PJ.* ✆ (062 67) 4561.

■★**Coombe Bank** (RI) *Landscore Rd,
TQ14 9JL.* ✆ (062 67) 2369.

■★**Portland** (RI), *Sea Front, TQ14 8BQ.*
✆ (062 67) 2761. Open Apr–Oct, Xmas &
Easter. C. ⋈ 28 bedrs, 2 sh, 5 ba, Dgs.
✗ mc, at, LD 7.30. ⓓ Lt, CH, TV, Dgs, Ac,
con 68, CF, 0 st. £ BB £10·50–£11·50, DB
£20–£22, DT £22, DBB £17·50, WB, ⛨,
cc 1, Dep b.

Baveno, PH, y (RI), *40 Higher Brimley
Rd, TQ14 8JU.* ✆ (062 67) 3102. C. ⋈ 15
bedrs, 4 ba, Dgs. ⓓ CH, TV, Dgs, CP 10,
CF. £ BB £6·50–£8·75, DB £13–£17·50, DT
(b) £8·50–£15·50, ⛨.

Cotteswold, PH, y (RI), *Second Drive,
Landscore Rd, TQ14 9JS.* ✆ (062 67)
4662. Closed Jan–Feb. C. ⋈ 17 bedrs, 16
bps, 2 sh, 3 ba, Dgs. ⓓ CH, TV, Dgs, CP 16,
CF, 8 BGf, 4 st.

Glen Devon, H, z (RI), *3 Carlton Pl, TQ14
8AB.* ✆ (062 67) 2895. C. ⋈ 8 bedrs, 2
bps, 1 sh, 2 ba, TV, Dgs, CP 6, CF, 1
st. £ BB £7·50–£9, DB £15–£22, WT (b)
£75–£89, DT (b) £11–£13, ⛨, Bk £2, D
£3·75.

Glenkealey, PH (R), *Upper Hermosa Rd,
TQ14 9JW.* ✆ (026 27) 4214. Open May–
Sep & Xmas. C. ⋈ 18 bedrs, 2 bp, 4 bps, 3
ba, TV. ⓓ CH, TV, CP 20, CF, 1 BGf, 4 st.
£ BB fr £9·45, DB £18·90–£22·90, WT (b)
£77·25–£86·66, DT (b) £14·59, ⛨, Bk £3, L
£3·60, D £4.

Hillrise, H, y (RI), *1 Winterbourne Rd,
TQ14 6JT.* ✆ (062 67) 3108. C. ⋈ 9
bedrs, 2 sh, 2 ba, Dgs. ⓓ CH, TV, Dgs, CP
6, CF. £ BB £6–£7·50, DB £12–£15, WT (b)
£45–£68, DT (b) £8·50–£9·50, ⛨.

Knoll, H, z (Rt), *5 Winterbourne Rd,
TQ14 8JT.* ✆ (062 67) 4241. C. ⋈ 19
bedrs, 3 ba, Dgs. ⓓ CH, TV, Dgs, CP 19,
CF, 3 BGf, 3 st. £ BB £8–£9·50, DB £16–
£19, WT (b) £63·25–£83, DT (b) £10·50–
£13·50, ⛨.

Thornhill, PH, z (RI), *Sea Front, TQ14
8TA.* ✆ (062 67) 3460. Open Apr–Oct. C.
⋈ 12 bedrs, 2 ba. ⓓ ch, CH, CP 2, BGf,
2 st. £ BB £9·20–£10·35, DB £18·40–
£20·70, WT (b) £69–£89·70, DT (b) £11–
£12, ⛨, Bk £2, D £4.

Repairer: Central Garage (Teignmouth)
Ltd, Northumberland Pl. ✆ (062 67) 2535.
Rescue Service: Bobbetts Garage, 27
Brunswick St. ✆ (062 67) 4220.
Motorway Tyres & Wheels Ltd, Bitton
Park Rd. ✆ (062 67) 2166.

TELFORD Shropshire. Map 19F
See also DONNINGTON and
WELLINGTON.
Pop 103,000. Wolverhampton 17, London
167, M54 Motorway 1, Wellington 3,
Bridgnorth 12, Shrewsbury 14.
Golf Wrekin 18h. **See** Ironbridge Gorge
(complex of Museums), Iron Bridge, The
Wrekin hill.

Rescue Service: Greenhous (Telford) Ltd,
Holyhead Rd. ✆ (0952) 618081.
Telford Recovery, Trench Lock Industrial
Estate, Trench. ✆ (0952) 55387.
Telford Service Station, Finger Rd,
Dawley. ✆ (0952) 595567.

TEMPLE CLOUD Avon. M. Area 5A
Pop 939. Radstock 5, London 115, Bath
11, Bristol 11, Shepton Mallet 10, Wells 9½,
Weston-super-Mare 22.
EC Wed. **Golf** Mendip, nr Shepton Mallet
18h. **See** St James's Church.

Rescue Service: Temple Cloud Garage.
☎ (0761) 52229.

TEMPLECOMBE Somerset. Map 5D
Pop 1,138. Wincanton 4½, London 115,
Blandford Forum 18, Shaftesbury 11,
Shepton Mallet 16, Sherborne 8.
EC Sat. **Golf** Sherborne 18h. **See** Village
Stocks, Church.

MC Repairer: Raymond, Eric A, Bridge
House, Throop Rd. ☎ (0963) 368.
Sctr Repairer: Raymond, Eric A, Bridge
House, Throop Rd. ☎ (0963) 368.

TENBURY WELLS Hereford &
Worcester (Worcestershire). Map 13A
Pop 2,472. Worcester 20, London 134,
Bridgnorth 23, Bromsgrove 10, Droitwich
20, Kidderminster 18, Leominster 9½,
Ludlow 8.
EC Thur. **MD** Tue, Fri. **Golf** Ludlow 18h.
See St Mary's Church, 16th cent Royal
Oak Hotel, 16th cent Fountain Inn, St
Michael's College, Teme Bridge (rebuilt by
Telford).

★**Royal Oak,** *WR15 8BQ.* ☎ (0584)
810417. C. ⋈ 6 bedrs, 4 sh, 2 ba, TV, Dgs.
✗ mc, LD 10. ⓓ Lt, CH, TV, CP 100, con
90, CF, 2 st.
Crow, *Teme St, WR15 8BA.* ☎ (0584)
810503.

Rescue Service: Swan Garage. ☎ (0584)
810466.

TENDRING Essex. Map 17C
Pop 765. Colchester 10, London 66,
Clacton 8, Harwich 11, Ipswich 16.
EC Thur. **Golf** Frinton 9h & 18h.

Repairer: Demaid, E L & Sons Ltd,
Halfway Garage, Colchester Rd. ☎ Weeley
(0255) 380364.

TENTERDEN Kent. Map 10E
Pop 6,250. Maidstone 18, London 54,
Ashford 12, Folkestone 23, Hastings 20,
Hawkhurst 10, Rye 10, Tonbridge 24.
EC Wed. **MD** Fri. **Golf** Tenterden 18h.
See St Mildred's Church, Smallhythe
Place 2 m S, Great Maytham Hall 3 m SW,
Steam Railway.
ⓘ Town Hall, High St. ☎ Tenterden
(058 06) 3572.

★★**White Lion,** *High St, TN30 6BD.*
☎ (058 06) 2921.

Rescue Service: CB Motors, Rolvendon
Rd. ☎ (058 06) 3353.
Major Minor Garage, rear of 1 East Cross.
☎ (058 06) 2543.

TETBURY Gloucestershire. Maps 13F
and 14E
Pop 4,186. Swindon 19, London 96, Bath
23, Bristol 26, Cheltenham 24, Chepstow
29, Chippenham 14, Cirencester 10,
Gloucester 19.
EC Thur. **Golf** Cirencester 18h.
Minchinhampton 18h. **See** 'Chipping
Steps', Market Hall, St Mary's Church,
Jacobean and Georgian Houses in Long
St, Westonbirt Arboretum 3½ m SW.
ⓘ The Old Court House, Long St.
☎ Tetbury (0666) 53552.

★★★**Close** (R), *Long St, GL8 8AQ.*
☎ (0666) 52272. C. ⋈ 11 bedrs, 10 bp, 1
bps, TV. ✗ mc, at, LD 9.45. ⓓ CH, CP 14,
con 22, CF, 3 st. £ BBc £28·50–£36, DBc
£44–£64, WT £199–£249, DT £35–£42·50,
DBBc £29·50–£37, WB, ⓘ, Bk £5, L £5·50,
D £12·50, cc 1 2 3 5.
■★★★**Snooty Fox,** *Market Pl, GL8 8ES.*
☎ (0666) 52436. C. ⋈ 12 bedrs, 12 bp, ns,
TV. ✗ a l c, mc, at, LD 10. ⓓ CH, con 20,
CF, 2 st. £ BBc £32–£35, DBc £45–£60, ⓶,
Bk £3·50, L £5·50, D £9·50, cc 1 2 3 4 5 6.

TEWKESBURY Gloucestershire. Maps
13D and 14C.
Pop 9,554. Stow-on-the-Wold 20, London
104, M5 Motorway 1½, Cheltenham 9,
Evesham 13, Gloucester 10, Ledbury 14,
Ross-on-Wye 24, Worcester 15.
EC Thur. **MD** Wed, Sat. **Golf** Tewkesbury
Park 18h. **See** Fine Norman Abbey with
massive Tower, Abbey Mill, House of
Nodding Gables, Museum, old Baptist
Chapel, King John's Bridge, Cross House,
The Old Hat Shop, old Inns and Hotels,
row of medieval merchants' houses
(restored 1970–71).
ⓘ Tewkesbury Museum, 64 Barton St.
☎ Tewkesbury (0684) 295027.

★★★**Bell,** *Church St, GL20 5SA.*
☎ (0684) 293293. C. ⋈ 25 bedrs, 25 bps,
ns, TV, Dgs. ✗ a l c, mc, at, LD 9.15. ⓓ N,
CH, TV, Dgs, ns, CP 90, U 7, G 20, Ac, con
70, CF, 4 BGf, 1 st, Dis. £ BB £20–£35, DB
£30–£45, WT £200–£259, DT £37–£52,
DBB £33–£48, WB, ⓘ, Bk £4·50, L £2, D £4,
cc 1 2 3 4 6.
★★★**Royal Hop Pole Crest,** *Church St,
GL20 5RT.* ☎ (0684) 293236. C. ⋈ 29
bedrs, 29 ba, ns, TV, Dgs. ✗ a l c, mc, at,
LD 9.30. ⓓ N, CH, Dgs, CP 20, Ac, con 70,
CF, 5 BGf, 2 st. £ BB fr £40, BD fr £53, WB,
ⓘ, Bk £5·25, D £9·25, cc 1 2 3 4 5 6,
Dep b.
★★★**Tewkesbury Park,** *Lincoln Green
Lane, GL20 7DN.* ☎ (0684) 295405. C.
⋈ 52 bedrs, 52 bp, ns, TV, Dgs. ✗ mc, at,
LD 9·30. ⓓ N, CH, TV, Dgs, CP 200, Ac, sp,
gc, sc, sb, sol, con 150, CF. £ BB fr £33, DB
fr £42, WB, ⓘ, L £5·25, D £7·95,
cc 1 2 3 4 5 6.
★**Tudor House** (R), *High St, GL20 5BH.*
☎ (0684) 297755.
Ancient Grudge, H, z (Rt), *15 High St,
GL20 5AL.* ☎ (0684) 292204. Closed 2
weeks Jan. C. ⋈ 4 bedrs, 4 sh, Dgs.
✗ a l c. ⓓ CH, TV, CP 4, CF. £ BB £19, DB
£28, ⓶, Bk £2·50, L £4·40, D £7, cc 1 2 3 5.

Repairer: Ledbury Road Motors, Ledbury
Rd, Bushley. ☎ (0684) 292361.
Rescue Service: Eriksons Garages,
Shuthonger. ☎ (0684) 293448.
Graham Wright Motors, Ashchurch Rd,
Newtown. ☎ (0684) 292398.
Stratford Bridge Garage, Ripple. ☎ Upton-
on-Severn (068 46) 2657.

THAME Oxfordshire. Map 15E
Pop 10,000. High Wycombe 15, London
45, M40 Motorway 4, Aylesbury 9,
Bicester 13, Henley-on-Thames 18,
Oxford 13, Reading 23, Rickmansworth
25, Wallingford 17.
EC Wed. **MD** Tue. **Golf** Princes
Risborough 9h. **See** Parish Church, Old
Grammar School (John Hampden
educated here), Spread Eagle Hotel,
Birdcage Inn.
ⓘ Town Hall. ☎ Thame (084 421) 2036.

★★★**Spread Eagle,** *16 Cornmarket, OX9
2BR.* ☎ (084 421) 3661. Closed 29th–
30th Dec. C. ⋈ 26 bedrs, 26 bp, TV. ✗ mc,
at, LD 9.30 (10 Sat, 9 Sun). ⓓ N, CH, Dgs,
CP 100, Ac, con 200, CF. £ BBd £36·75–
£40·25, DBc £47·25–£51·55, WT (c)
£449·75–£494·72, DT (c) £55–£60, WB, ⓘ,
Bk £4·75, L £8·20, D £9·85, cc 1 3 4 5 6,
Dep b.

Essex House, G, z (Unl), *Chinnor Rd,
OX9 3LS.* ☎ (084 421) 5145. C. ⋈ 4
bedrs, 1 bp, 2 bps, 1 ba. ⓓ CF, TV, CP 8,
CF. £ BB £14·50–£18, DB £23·50–£27, DB
(b) £22·95–£26·45, ⓘ.

THATCHAM Berkshire. Map 6B
Pop 17,540. Reading 13, London 52,
Basingstoke 15, Newbury 3, Wallingford
17.
EC Wed. **Golf** Newbury and Crookham
18h. **See** 17th and 18th cent houses and
inns, Tudor Thatcham Grange, 14th cent
chapel which, in 1707, became Bluecoat
School, parish church with Norman
doorway.

Repairers: C G Brown & Co Ltd, 58 The
Broadway. ☎ (0635) 64333.
Keene Bros Ltd, Bath Rd. ☎ (0635) 63389.

THEALE Berkshire. M. Area 6B
Pop 6,700. Reading 4½, London 43,
Basingstoke 14, Newbury 12, Wallingford
13, Wantage 22.
EC Wed. **Golf** Calcot Park 18h. **See** 16th
cent Old Lamb (now tea-house), Holy
Trinity Church.

Repairer: Theale Motor Works Ltd, 22
High St. ☎ Reading (0734) 302422.

THETFORD Norfolk. Map 16D
Pop 19,500. Newmarket 18, London 81,
Bury St Edmunds 12, East Dereham 24,
King's Lynn 27, Norwich 28, Scole 18,
Stowmarket 21, Swaffham 18.
EC Wed. **MD** Tue, Sat. **Golf** Thetford 18h.
See Cluniac Priory ruins, St Peter's, St
Mary the Less and St Cuthbert's
Churches, Guildhall Art Gallery, King's
House, old Bell Hotel, old lock up and
stocks, The Ancient House (Museum),
Euston Hall 3½ m SE, Grime's Graves 7 m
NW (Neolithic flint mines), Thetford
Forest.
ⓘ Ancient House Museum, White Hart St.
☎ Thetford (0842) 2599.

★★★**Bell** (TH), *King St, IP24 2AZ.*
☎ (0842) 4455. C. ⋈ 42 bedrs, 42 bp, TV,
Dgs. ✗ a l c, mc, at, LD 9.15. ⓓ N, CH, Dgs,
CP 65, Ac, con 30, CF, 1 st. £ BB £45, DB
£65, WB, ⓘ, cc 1 2 3 4 5 6.
Wereham, G, z (Unl), *24 White Hart St,
IP24 1AD.* ☎ (0842) 61956. ⋈ 8 bedrs, 2
ba, TV. ⓓ CH, CP 20, CF. £ BB £11–
£12, DB £18–£20, WT (b) £101·50–£112,
DT (b) £14·50–£16, ⓘ.

Rescue Service: Carbrooke Service
Station, Church St, Carbrooke. ☎ Watton
(0953) 881448.
Cunningham Motors, Station La. ☎ (0842)
61709.

THEYDON BOIS Essex. M. Area 15F
Pop 4,116. Woodford 7½, London 17,
Enfield 8½, Epping 2, Romford 10.
EC Wed. **Golf** Theydon Bois 18h. **See**
17th cent Bull Inn, Theydon Hall (18th
cent), nr site Med Church.

Repairer: Wood & Krailing Ltd, High Rd.
☎ (037 881) 3831.

Rescue Service: J J Tidd Ltd, Station Garage, Station Approach. ☎ (037 881) 2451.

THIRSK North Yorkshire. Map 25E
Pop 6,830. Boroughbridge 12, London 220, Helmsley 14, Leyburn 24, Malton 25, Northallerton 8½, Stockton-on-Tees 22, York 23.
EC Wed. **MD** Mon, Thur, Sat. **Golf** Thirsk and Northallerton 9h. **See** Church (ancient statue of Madonna and Child), 18th cent Thirsk Hall, Golden Fleece Inn, Byland Abbey ruins.
ℹ️ Museum, 16 Kirkgate. ☎ Thirsk (0845) 22755.

★★**Golden Fleece** (TH), *Market Pl, YO7 1LL.* ☎ (0845) 23108. C. ✉ 22 bedrs, 6 bp, 5 ba, TV, Dgs. ✗ a l c, mc, at, LD 9. 🅿 ch, Dgs, CP 50, U 2, Ac, con 100, CF, 0 st. £ BB £34–£36·50, DB £44–£46, WB, 🅣, cc 1 2 3 4 5 6, Dep (Xmas).
★★**Three Tuns,** *Market Pl, YO7 1LH.* ☎ (0845) 23124. C. ✉ 12 bedrs, 8 bp, 4 sh, 2 ba, TV, Dgs. ✗ mc, LD 9.30. 🅿 N, CH, Dgs, CP 25, U 2, Ac, con 20, CF, 1 st. £ BB £25–£29, DB £33–£38, WT £135–£145, WB, 🅣, Bk £4·25, L £5·20, D £7·50, cc 1 2 3 4 5 6.

MC Repairer: Moss's Motors, 8 Finkle St. ☎ (0845) 23248.
Sctr Repairer: Moss's Motors, 8 Finkle St. ☎ (0845) 23248.

THORNABY-ON-TEES Teesside, Cleveland. Map 24F
Pop 23,270. Thirsk 20, London 242, Middlesbrough 3, Northallerton 17, Stockton-on-Tees 1½.
EC Mon, Wed. **MD** Thur. **Golf** Teesside 18h. **See** Church of St Peter ad Vincula.

★★★**Golden Eagle Thistle,** *Trenchard Av, TS17 0DA.* ☎ Stockton-on-Tees (0642) 766511. C. ✉ 54 bedrs, 54 bp, ns, TV, Dgs. ✗ a l c, mc, LD 9. 🅿 Lt, N, CH, TV, Dgs, CP 80, Ac, con 300, CF, 2 st. £ BB £31·75–£35·25, DB £44·50–£51·50, WB, 🅣, Bk £4·75, L £6·50, D £8, cc 1 2 3 4 5 6, Dep b.
★★★**M Post House** (TH), *Low La, Stainton Village, TS17 9LW.* ☎ Middlesbrough (0642) 591213. C. ✉ 136 bedrs, 136 bp, TV, Dgs. ✗ a l c, at, LD 10.15. 🅿 N, CH, Dgs, CP 250, Ac, con 120, CF, 70 BGf, 0 st. Dis. £ BB £37, DB £49·50, WB, 🅣, cc 1 2 3 4 5 6.

THORNBURY Avon. Maps 5A and 13E
Pop 12,000. Chippenham 25, London 117, Bath 23, Bristol 12, Chepstow 10, Gloucester 23, Tetbury 20.
EC Thur. **MD** Thur. **Golf** Filton 18h. **See** Castle (begun 1511, never completed), Church.

🏩★★★**Thornbury Castle** (R), *BS12 1HH.* ☎ (0454) 412647. Closed 5 days Xmas. C 14. ✉ 12 bedrs, 12 bp, TV. ✗ LD 9.30. 🅿 CH, CP 30, con 15, 0 st. £ BBc £45, DBc £70, DBBc £67, 🅣, L £17·50, D £22, cc 1 2 3 4 5 6, Dep b.

Rescue Service: MAAR International Supplies Ltd, Gloucester Rd, Grovesend. ☎ (0454) 413752.
Tockington Service & Repair Station, Camp La, Elberton, nr Pilning. ☎ (0454) 414670.

THORNE South Yorkshire. Map 25D
Pop 11,741. Newark 40, London 166, M18 Motorway 1, Doncaster 9½, Gainsborough 26, Goole 11, Pontefract 20, Scunthorpe 14, Selby 12.
EC Thur. **MD** Tue, Fri, Sat. **Golf** Doncaster 18h. **See** Parish Church.

★★**Belmont** (R), *Horse Fair Green, DN8 5EE.* ☎ (0405) 812320. C. ✉ 25 bedrs, 8 bp, 5 sh, 3 ba, TV. ✗ a l c, mc, at, LD 9.30. 🅿 CH, TV, Dgs, CP 25, Ac, con 30, CF, 5 BGf, 0 st, Dis. £ BB fr £15, DB fr £26, DT fr £25, DBB £20, 🄯, Bk £3·20, L £5, cc 1.

Rescue Service: Adams (Fairfield Garages) Ltd, Fieldside. ☎ (0405) 812345.

THORNTHWAITE Cumbria. Map 26E
Pop 150. Keswick 3½, London 289, Carlisle 27, Cockermouth 8.
Golf Cockermouth 18h.

★★**Swan,** *CA12 5SQ.* ☎ Braithwaite (059 682) 256. Closed Dec–Feb. C. ✉ 15 bedrs, 3 bp, 3 bps, 2 ba, TV, Dgs. ✗ a l c, mc, at, LD 8.30. 🅿 CH, TV, Dgs, CP 60, CF, 0 st. £ BB £10·85–£12·65, DB £21·70–£31·70, DBB £18·20–£23·20, WB, 🅣, Bk £4·25, D £8·50, cc 1 3.
Ladstock Country House, H, xy (R), *CA12 5RZ.* ☎ Braithwaite (059 682) 210. C. ✉ 17 bedrs, 2 bp, 12 sh, 5 ba. 🅿 CH, TV, CP 20, CF, 5 BGf, 3 st. £ BB £11·50, DB fr £22, WT (b) fr £102, DB fr £17, 🄯, Bk £3, L £5, D £7.

Rescue Service: G W Mayhew & Son, The Garage. ☎ Braithwaite (059 682) 238.

THORNTON CLEVELEYS Lancashire. Map 27C
Pop 27,250. Preston 19, London 230, Blackpool 4½, Lancaster 22.
EC Wed. **Golf** Fleetwood 18h. **See** Windmill.
ℹ️ Victoria Sq. ☎ Cleveleys (0253) 853378.

Rescue Service: Cooper Garages, St George's La. ☎ Cleveleys (0253) 853038 & (0253) 869409.

THORNTON DALE North Yorkshire. Map 24D
Pop 1,720. Malton 8, London 213, Scarborough 14, Whitby 19, Pickering 2.
EC Wed. **Golf** Malton & Norton 18h. **See** Church, old Market Cross and stocks, 17th cent Almshouses, Grammar School.

★**New Inn,** *The Square, YO18 7LF.* ☎ Pickering (0751) 74226.

THORNTON HEATH Greater London (Surrey). Map 7B
Pop 14,500. Bromley 6½, London 8½, Croydon 1½, Mitcham 3, Purley 4.
EC Wed. **Golf** See Croydon.

Cresta House, PH, z (Unl) *601 London Rd, CR4 6AY.* ☎ 01-684 3947. C 3. ✉ 12 bedrs, 3 ba. 🅿 CH, TV, ns, CP 6, 3 st. £ BB £13–£14, DB £23–£24, 🄯.
Dunheved, H, z (Rl) *639 London Rd, CR4 6AZ.* ☎ 01-684 2009. ✉ 15 bedrs, 4 ba, TV. 🅿 CH, TV, CP 8, 2 st. £ BB fr £15, DB fr £24, 🅣.
Norfolk House, H, z (Rl) *587 London Rd, CR4 6AY.* ☎ 01-684 1632. C. ✉ 74 bedrs, 8 bp, 46 bps, 5 sh, 4 ba, TV, Dgs. ✗ a l c. 🅿 CH, TV, CP 50, CF. £ BB £15–£25, DB £25–£32, 🅣, Bk £3·25, L £6·65, D £6·65, cc 1 2 3 5.

Repairers: Frank Watson (Croydon) Ltd, 160 Thornton Rd. ☎ 01-684 4221.
Specialist Body Repairer: Frank Watson (Croydon) Ltd, Thornton Rd. ☎ 01-684 4221.
Rescue Service: Falcon Motors (F K Roberts) Ltd, 949 London Rd. ☎ 01-684 5252.

THORNTON HOUGH Merseyside (Cheshire). Map 20F
Pop 935. M53 Motorway 2, Chester 16, London 199, Birkenhead 8, Ellesmere Port 8.
EC Thur. **Golf** Heswall 18h. **See** Thornton Hall & Smithy.

★★★**Thornton Hall,** *Neston Road, L63 1JF.* ☎ 051-336 3938. C. ✉ 11 bedrs, 11 bp, annexe 27 bedrs, 27 bp, TV. ✗ a l c, mc, LD 10. 🅿 N, CH, CP 200, con 150, CF, 11 BGf, 1 st, Dis. £ BB £24·35–£30·65, DB £30·65–£43, WB, 🅣, L £7·50, D £7·50, cc 1 2 3 4 5 6.

THORNTON-LE-STREET North Yorkshire. M. Area 24F
Pop 100. Thirsk 3, London 223, Northallerton 5½, Stockton-on-Tees 22.
Golf Thirsk and Northallerton 9h. **See** Old Church, remains Roman Settlement.

Rescue Service: Metcalf, J C & Sons, Fairview Garage. ☎ Thirsk (0845) 23274.

THORNTON WATLASS North Yorkshire. Map 24F
Pop 155. Boroughbridge 18, London 226, Brough 44, Darlington 24, Harrogate 23, Leyburn 10, Middleton in Teesdale 39, Northallerton 11, Thirsk 16, West Auckland 30.
Golf Bedale 18h. **See** Parish Church.

★**Buck Inn,** *HG4 4AH.* ☎ Bedale (0677) 22461.

THORRINGTON Essex. Map 17D
Pop 1,005. Colchester 6½, London 62, Clacton 7½, Harwich 16, Ipswich 21.
EC Wed. **Golf** Clacton on Sea 9h & 18h. **See** 14th cent Church, disused Watermill, 17th cent Inn.

Silver Springs Motel, y (R), *CO7 8JG.* ☎ Colchester (0206) 250366. Closed Dec 25–26. C. ✉ 35 bedrs, 35 bp, TV, Dgs. 🅿 ch, CP, CF, 35 BGf, 0 st. £ BB fr £18, DB fr £26, DT (b) fr £24·50, 🄯, Bk £2·50, L £3·50, D £6·50, cc 1 2 3 5.▲

THROCKLEY Tyne & Wear. Map 32C
Pop 5,836. Newcastle upon Tyne 6, London 279, Alnwick 33, Coldstream 52, Corbridge 11, Hawick 54, Jedburgh 53.
EC Wed. **Golf** Westerhope Municipal 18h.

Repairer: Humble, A H Ltd, The Garage, Hexham Rd. ☎ Lemington (0632) 674496.
Rescue Service: Dickson's of Throckley, Hexham Rd. ☎ Lemington (0632) 672327.

THROPTON Northumberland. Map 31C
Rothbury 2, London 305, Alnwick 14, Hexham 34, Morpeth 18, Otterburn 13.

Rescue Service: Thropton Motors, Masons Yard, Thropton. ☎ Rothbury (0669) 20856.

THROWLEIGH Devon. M. Area 3B
Pop 121. Exeter 17, London 186, Ashburton 18, Crediton 14, Newton Abbot 20, Okehampton 6, Plymouth 30, Saltash 31, Tavistock 20.
Golf Okehampton 18h. **See** Church, 15th cent Shilstone Farmhouse, Ancient Cross.

PERSONAL LOANS AT REDUCED RATES

Lombard
RAC FINANCE

With a Lombard loan, you could soon have many of the things you have always wanted.

CAR FINANCE MADE SIMPLE

RAC
MOTORLOAN

PLEASE SEND ME FURTHER DETAILS

Name ....

Address ....

....

....

I am interested in the following (please tick)

Motorloan ☐   Lombard RAC Finance ☐

* Motorloan is available to RAC Members aged 18 or over who are bank current account holders

* Lombard RAC Finance is available to RAC Members aged 18 or over

Lombard North Central PLC, Registered in England, No. 33704.
Registered Office: Lombard House, Curzon Street, London W1A 1EU.

♻ **A member of the National Westminster Bank Group**

SEND THIS CARD NOW (postage paid) TO RECEIVE FULL WRITTEN DETAILS

Lombard ❖ RAC FINANCE

SPECIAL PERSONAL LOAN RATES FOR RAC MEMBERS

RAC
MOTORLOAN

CAR FINANCE MADE SIMPLE

Postage
will be
paid by
licensee

Do not affix Postage Stamps if posted in Gt. Britain,
Channel Islands, N. Ireland or the Isle of Man

BUSINESS REPLY SERVICE
Licence No. CN 921

RAC Finance Manager
Lombard North Central PLC
320 Purley Way
CROYDON CR9 9ER

Rescue Service: L Wadman & Son.
☎ Whiddon Down (064 723) 303.

THUNDERSLEY Essex. M. Areas 10A and 17F
6 m W of Southend-on-Sea, Romford 20, London 36, Brentwood 16, Chelmsford 15, Colchester 34, Dartford Tunnel 17, Rainham 20.
EC Thur. **Golf** Boyce Hill 18h. **See** Church of St Peter (1200).

Rescue Service: T G Motors, 14 Fulton Rd, Manor Trading Estate. ☎ South Benfleet (037 45) 58386.

THURCASTON Leicestershire. M. Area 22F
2 m S of Rothley. Pop 1,951. Leicester 5, London 102, Loughborough 6½, Melton Mowbray 14, Newark 33.
Golf Rothley 18h. **See** All Saints' Church (Anstey La), Latymer House (16th cent).

Rescue Service: Hilltop Garage (Thurcaston) Ltd, Leicester Rd.
☎ Leicester (0533) 362773.

THURLESTONE Devon. Map 3F
Pop 827. Kingsbridge 3½, London 207, Plymouth 20.
Golf Thurlestone 18h. **See** Perp Church (Norman font).

★★★Thurlestone, *TQ7 3NN.*
☎ Kingsbridge (0548) 560382. Closed Jan. C. ⋈ 74 bedrs, 62 bp, 5 ba, TV, Dgs. ✗ a l c, mc, at, LD 9. ⊞ Lt, N, CH, ns, CP 100, G 25, sp, gc, tc, sc, sb, sol, gym, con 120, CF, 0 st. £ BB £22–£40, DB £44–£80, WT £199·50–£283·50, DT £30·50–£39·50, DBB £27–£41, WB, ①, Bk £3·50, L £3·25, D £9·50, cc 1 2 3 5.

▣★**Charnwood,** (RI), *Thurlestone, TQ7 3LY.* ☎ Kingsbridge (0548) 560824. C. ⋈ 10 bedrs, 1 sh, 3 ba, Dgs. ✗ mc, at, LD 7·30. ⊞ CH, TV, CP 12, con 15, CF, 2 BGf, 1 st, Dis. £ BB £10·50–£11·50, DB £21–£23, DBB £15–£16, WB, ①, L £3·75, D £5, cc 1 3.

Rescue Service: Blight Engineering, Bantham Garage. ☎ Thurlestone (054 857) 220.

TIDDINGTON Oxfordshire. M. Area 14F
Pop 550. High Wycombe 16, London 46, Aylesbury 12, Bicester 17, Henley-on-Thames 19, Oxford 9½, Reading 23, Rickmansworth 28, Wallingford 17.
Golf North Oxford 18h.

Rescue Service: Maule's Garage.
☎ Ickford (084 47) 210.

TIDEFORD Cornwall. M. Area 3C
Pop 2,275. Saltash 6, London 218, Liskeard 8, Looe 10.
Golf Bin Down Looe 18h.
⑦ Heskyn Hill, nr Saltash. ☎ Landrake (075 538) 397.

Rescue Service: D W & S M K Welch & M C Roberts, Riverside Garage, Quay Rd, ☎ Landrake (075 538) 276.

TILEHURST Berkshire. Map 6B
Pop 9,825. Reading 3, London 41, Abingdon 22, Basingstoke 20, Newbury 16, Oxford 26.
EC Wed. **Golf** Calcot 18h. **See** Church, Calcot Park.

Aeron, PH, z (RI), *191 Kentwood Hill, RG3 6JE.* ☎ Reading (0734) 24119. Closed 2 weeks Xmas–New Year. ⋈ 19 bedrs, 1 sh, 5 ba, TV, Dgs. ⊞ CH, Dgs, ns,

CP 15, 5 BGf, 6 st. £ BB fr £14, DB £22–£24, ①, D £4, cc 1 3.

TINTAGEL Cornwall. Map 2B
Pop 1,600. Launceston 19, London 230, Bude 17, Camelford 5.
EC Wed. **MD** Thur. **Golf** St Enodoc Rock 18h and 9h. **See** 'King Arthur's Castle', 'King Arthur's Hall', Saxon Church (Roman milestone in transept), Old Post Office, St Nectan's Glen and waterfall 1 m NE. Trebarwith Strand (surfing).

▣★★**Atlantic View** (RI), *Treknow, PL34 0EJ.* ☎ Camelford (0840) 770221. Open Apr–Oct. C 6. ⋈ 10 bedrs, 8 bp, 2 bps, Dgs. ✗ mc, at, LD 8.15. ⊞ CH, TV, CP 16, sp, sol, CF, 3 st. £ BB £16–£20, DB £26–£32, DBB £20·50–£24·50, WB, ①, Bk £3·50, D £8·50, cc 1 2 3 5, Dep a.

★★**Bossiney House** (R), *Bossiney, PL34 0AX.* ☎ Camelford (0840) 770240. Open Apr–Oct. C. ⋈ 20 bedrs, 11 bp, 6 bps, 1 ba, Dgs. ✗ mc, at, LD 8. ⊞ CH, TV, CP 30, sp, sb, sol, CF, 2 BGf, 1 st, Dis. £ BB £13·65–£16·50, DB £27·30–£33·50, WT £139, DBB £19·65–£22·80, WB, ①, Bk £2·30, D £6·80, cc 2 5.▲

Belvoir House, G, x (RI), *Tregatta, PL34 0DY.* ☎ Camelford (0840) 770265. Closed Xmas. C. ⋈ 7 bedrs, 1 bps, 2 ba, Dgs. ⊞ ch, TV, CP 12, CF, 1 BGf, 0 st, Dis. £ BB £6·75–£7·75, DB £13·50–£17·50, WT (b) £66·75–£79·75, DT (b) £11–£13, ①.

Willapark Manor, H, xy (R), *Bossiney, PL34 0BA.* ☎ Camelford (0840) 770782. C. ⋈ 9 bedrs, 5 bp, 1 bps, 2 ba, TV, Dgs. ⊞ ch, TV, Dgs, CP 20, CF, 1 BGf, 2 st. £ BB £10·50–£12·50, DB £21–£25, WT (b) £105–£115, DT (b) £16–£17, ①, Bk £2·50, L £3, D £5·50.

Rescue Service: Tonkin's Garage, Bossiney Rd. ☎ Camelford (0840) 770259.

TINTINHULL Somerset. M. Area 5C
Pop 979. Wincanton 15, London 129, Crewkerne 8, Dorchester 22, Frome 25, Glastonbury 15, Ilminster 9½.
EC Sat. **Golf** Yeovil 18h. **See** 17th cent Tintinhull House (Nat Trust), 13th cent Church, Stocks.

Rescue Service: Taylor, E R, Townsend Garage. ☎ Martock (0935) 2636.

TIPTON West Midlands. Map 21F
Dudley 1, London 121, Birmingham 10, Wolverhampton 5.
EC Wed. **MD** Tue, Sat.

Specialist Body Repairer: Sutton Motor Panels (Tipton) Ltd, Bloomfield Rd.
☎ 021-557 5371.

TIPTON ST JOHN Devon. M. Area 4F
Honiton 7½, London 160, Budleigh Salterton 8, Exeter 13, Lyme Regis 18, Sidmouth 4, Tiverton 21.

Rescue Service: Tipton Garage. ☎ Ottery St. Mary (040 481) 2091.

TISBURY Wiltshire. M. Area 5D
Pop 1,900. 13 m W of Salisbury. London 96, Shaftesbury 7½, Wincanton 17.
EC Wed. **Golf** High Post 18h.
See Church, Ancient Yew, Tithe Barn.

Rescue Service: Wells Motor Works, High St. ☎ (0747) 870258.

TITCHFIELD Hampshire. Map 6F
Fareham 2½, London 74, Southampton 9½, Winchester 18.

EC Wed. **Golf** Lee-on-the-Solent 18h.
See Church, Abbey remains, St Margaret's Priory.

Rescue Service: R E Morton, Beaumont Garage, Hunts Pond Rd, Titchfield Common. ☎ Locks Heath (048 95) 3368.
Priory Garage. Southampton Rd.
☎ (048 95) 43167.

TITCHWELL Norfolk. Map 16E
Pop 94. King's Lynn 22, London 119, Cromer 31, Fakenham 15, Swaffham 24.
Golf Hunstanton 18h. **See** Church, RSPB Rescue at Titwell Marsh.

★★**Manor,** *Main Rd, PE31 8BB.*
☎ Brancaster (0485) 210221. Closed Dec 24–30. C. ⋈ 7 bedrs, 4 bp, 1 bps, 2 ba, TV, Dgs. ✗ a l c, mc, at, LD 9.15. ⊞ CH, TV, CP 30, Ac, con 20, CF, 3 BGf. £ BB £17·25–£23, DB £30·50–£39·40, WB, ②, Bk £4, D £9, cc 1 2 3 5, Dep a.

TIVERTON Devon. Maps 3B and 4F
Pop 16,539. Taunton 20, London 163, Crediton 12, Dunster 26, Exeter 15, Honiton 19, South Molton 21.
EC Thur. **MD** Tue, Fri, Sat. **Golf** Tiverton 18h. **See** Castle remains, 17th cent Blundells School, Great House of St George (now Council Offices), St Peter's Church, Museum, Almshouses, Knighthayes Court Gardens 1½ m N.
⑦ Museum, St Andrews St. ☎ Tiverton (0884) 256295.

★★★**M Tiverton,** *Blundells Rd. EX16 4DB.* ☎ (0884) 256120. C. ⋈ 29 bedrs, 29 bp, TV, Dgs. ✗ mc, at, LD 9·15. ⊞ N, ch, TV, CP 100, Ac, con 300, CF, 14 BGf, 1 st, Dis. £ BB £30–£42, DBB £19–£38·50, WB, ①, Bk £3·75, L £5·25, D £7·50, cc 1 2 3 5 6, Dep.▲

★★**Hartnoll,** *Bolham, EX16 7RA.*
☎ (0884) 252777.
Bridge, G, z (R), *23 Angel Hill, EX16 6PE.* ☎ (0884) 252804. C. ⋈ 11 bedrs, 2 ba, TV, Dgs. ⊞ CH, TV, Dgs, ns, CP 5, G 1, CF. £ BB £8–£9, DB £15–£18, WT (b) £77–£84, (c) £55–£60, DT (b) £12–£13, ①, Bk £2, D £4.

Rescue Service: Bolham Road Garage, Bolham Rd. ☎ (0884) 254842.
Devco M.V.S. Ltd, Twyford House, Kennedy Way. ☎ (0884) 254318.
R & M Cars, Bolham Road Garage
☎ (0884) 254842.

TOLPUDDLE Dorset. M. Area 5F
Pop 275. Ringwood 25, London 118, Blandford Forum 11, Bournemouth 20, Dorchester 7, Sherborne 19, Wareham 10, Weymouth 14.
Golf Came Down, Dorchester 18h. **See** Village of the Tolpuddle Martyrs, Martyrs' Tree on the green, Six cottages erected by the TUC in 1934 (centenary year) in memory of the six men.

Rescue Service: Wayside Garage.
☎ Puddletown (030 584) 329.

TONBRIDGE Kent. Map 7D
Pop 30,000. Sevenoaks 7, London 32, Hawkhurst 16, Hurst Green 17, Maidstone 13, Rochester 19, Tenterden 24, Tunbridge Wells 4, Westerham 14.
EC Wed. **MD** Sat. **Golf** Poult Wood 18h.
See Tonbridge School (apply Porter's Lodge), 16th cent Chequers Inn, Port Reeve's House, remains of 12th cent castle, Chiddingstone Castle 5½ m W.

★★★**Rose & Crown** (TH), *High St, TN9 1DD.* ☎(0732) 357966. C. ⍻ 52 bedrs, 52 bp, TV, Dgs. ✗ a l c, mc, at, LD 10. ⊞ N, CH, Dgs, CP 62, Ac, con 130, CF, 10 BGf, 1 st, Dis. £ BB £37, DB £54, WB, ⬚, cc 1 2 3 4 5 6, Dep (Xmas).

Rescue Service: Rawson's Eurocars Ltd, Vale Rd. ☎(0732) 355822.
Repairer: Dutton-Forshaw Kent, Cannon La. ☎(0732) 364444.

TOPSHAM Devon. Map 4F
Pop 3,963. Honiton 17, London 170, Ashburton 19, Axminster 28, Exeter 4, Lyme Regis 27, Newton Abbot 16.
EC Wed. **See** Rebuilt Church, Tudor Houses, Local interest Museum, old inns.

Rescue Service: Station Garage (Topsham) Ltd. ☎(039 287) 3129.

TORCROSS Devon. Map 3F
Pop 100. Kingsbridge 6, London 211 (Fy 207), Dartmouth 7½.
Golf Thurlestone 18h.

⊞★**Greyhomes** (R), *TQ7 2TH.*
☎Kingsbridge (0548) 580220. Open Apr–Oct. C. ⍻ 6 bedrs, 3 bp, 1 ba, Dgs. ✗ mc, at, LD 7. ⊞ CH, TV, Dgs, CP 15, G 3, CF, 3 st. £ BB £13–£17, DB £26–£34, DBB £17·20–£21·20, WB, ⬚ 10%, Bk £3, D £7, Dep a.

TORMARTON Avon. Map 5B
M4 Motorway 1½, London 102, Bath 11, Bristol 15, Chippenham 11, Stroud 20.

⊞★**Compass Inn**, *nr Badminton, BL9 1JB.* ☎Badminton (045 421) 242. C. ⍻ 11 bedrs, 7 bp, 4 sh, 2 ba, TV, Dgs. ✗ a l c, mc, LD 9.30. ⊞ CH, Dgs, CP 160, con 60, CF. £ BB £23·50–£29·95, DB £33·95–£42·95, WB, ⬚, Bk £3·90, L £5, D £5, cc 1 2 3 5.

TORPOINT Cornwall. Map 3C
See also CRAFTHOLE.
Pop 8,490. Saltash 17, London 229 (Fy 212), Liskeard 15, Looe 14, Plymouth (Fy) 12.
EC Wed. **Golf** Whitsand Bay 18h. **See** Antony House (Nat Trust), Plymouth Sound.

Ap. Whitsand Bay, *Portwrinkle, Crafthole, P11 3BU.* ☎St. Germans (0503) 30276.

Rescue Services: Clifford Motors, 12 Antony Rd. ☎Plymouth (0752) 812568.
Pete's Garage, The Parade, Millbrook. ☎Plymouth (0752) 822534.
Ranchway Car Sales Ltd, Venture Garage, Polbathic. ☎St Germans (0503) 30576.

TORQUAY Torbay, Devon. Map 3D
Pop 100,000. Newton Abbot 6, London 189, Dartmouth (Fy) 10, Totnes 8.
See Plan, p. 355.
EC Wed. **P** See Plan. **Golf** Torquay 18h. **See** Torre Abbey monastic ruins (conducted tours), Torre Abbey Mansion House (Art Gallery), Artificial outdoor ski-run, illuminations, remains of 12th cent St Michael's Chapel, 'Kent's Cavern' (stalactites and stalagmites), Model Village, Oddicombe Beach, Anstey's Cove, Cockington Village, Babbacombe Pottery, Museums, Torbay and Dartmouth Rly, Dart Valley Rly, Compton Castle 3½ m NW. ⓘ Vaughan Par. ☎Torquay (0803) 27428.

★★★★★**Imperial** (TH), *Parkhill Rd, TQ1 2DG.* ☎(0803) 24301. C. ⍻ 164 bedrs, 164 bp, TV, Dgs. ✗ a l c, mc, at, LD 9.30. ⊞ Lt, N, CH, Dgs, CP 200, U 46, G 14, Ac, sp, tc, sc, sb, con 500, CF, 4 BGf, 0 st, Dis. £ BB £49·50–£61·50, DB £87–£98·50, WB, ⬚, cc 1 2 3 4 5 6, Dep (Xmas).

★★★★**Grand**, *Sea Front, TQ2 6NT.* ☎(0803) 25234. C. ⍻ 109 bedrs, 109 bp, TV, Dgs. ✗ a l c, mc, at, LD 9.30. ⊞ Lt, N, CH, G 50, Ac, sp, tc, sb, sol, gym, con 300, CF, 1 BGf, 10 st. £ BB £22–£39, DB £44–£78, WT £221–£316, DT £35–£52, DBB £28–£45, WB, ⬚, Bk £4, L £7, D £9·50, cc 1 2 3 5 6, Dep b.▲

★★★★**Palace**, *Babbacombe Rd, TQ1 37G.* ☎(0803) 22271. C. ⍻ 141 bedrs, 112 bp, 29 bps, TV, Dgs. ✗ a l c, mc, at, LD 9.15. ⊞ Lt, N, CH, TV, CP 100, G 40, Ac, sp, gc, tc, sc, sb, con 350, CF, 2 st. £ BB £30–£33, DB £60–£66, WT £240–£260, DBB £39–£42, WB, ⬚, L £6, D £11, cc 1 2 3 5 6, Dep b.▲

★★★**Belgrave**, *Belgrave Rd, TQ2 5HE.* ☎(0803) 28566. C. ⍻ 54 bedrs, 50 bp, 4 bps, TV, Dgs. ✗ mc, at, LD 8.30. ⊞ Lt, N, CH, CP 80, U 6, sp, con 150, CF, 8 BGf, 5 st. £ BB £18·50–£24·50, DB £37–£49, DBB £25–£31, WB, ⬚, Bk £2·50, D £6·50, cc 1 2 3 5, Dep.

★★★**Corbyn Head**, *Torbay Rd, TQ2 6RH.* ☎(0803) 213611. C. ⍻ 46 bedrs, 37 bp, 6 bps, 3 ba, TV, Dgs. ✗ a l c, mc, at, LD 10. ⊞ N, CH, CP 60, sp, con 120, CF, 1 BGf, 0 st, Dis. £ BB £15–£23, DB £30–£46, DBB £20–£29, WB, ⬚, Bk £3·50, L £5, D £8, cc 1 2 3 5 6, Dep.

★★★**Devonshire** (R), *Parkhill Rd, TQ1 2DY.* ☎(0803) 24850. C. ⍻ 54 bedrs, 27 bp, 6 bps, 6 ba, TV, Dgs. ✗ a l c, mc, at, LD 8.45. ⊞ N, CH, TV, ns, CP 50, G 3, Ac, sp, tc, con 120, CF, 3 st. £ BB £12·50–£21·50, DB £25–£43, WT £101·50–£140, DT £15·90–£20, DBB £13·40–£21·50, WB, ⬚, Bk £2·95, L £4·80, D £6·70, cc 1 2 3 4 5 6.▲

★★★**Gleneagles**, *Asheldon Rd, TQ1 2QS.* ☎(0803) 23637. Open Apr–Oct. C. ⍻ 41 bedrs, 38 bp, 3 bps, TV, Dgs. ✗ mc, at, LD 8. ⊞ ch, TV, CP 30, Ac, sp, sol, con 40, CF, 0 st. £ BB £17–£25, DB £34–£50, DBB £21–£26, WB, Bk £4·50, D £7·50, cc 2 3 5, Dep a.

★★★**Homer's** (R), *Warren Rd, TQ2 5TN.* ☎(0803) 213456. Closed Jan & Feb. C. 7. ⍻ 14 bedrs, 11 bp, 3 bps, 4 ba, TV, Dgs. ✗ mc, at, LD 8.30. ⊞ CH, CP 5, 1 BGf, 0 st. £ WB, Bk £4·50, D £11·95, cc 1 2 3 5 6.

★★★**Kistor**, *Belgrave Rd, TQ2 5HF.* ☎(0803) 23219. C. ⍻ 52 bedrs, 51 bp, 1 bps, TV, Dgs. ✗ mc, at, LD 8.30. ⊞ Lt, CH, TV, CP 40, Ac, sp, sol, gym, con 80, CF. £ BB £16–£28, DB £32–£48, WT £140–£196, DT £20–£30, DBB £18–£28, WB, ⬚, Bk £4·25, L £4·50, D £7·75, cc 1 2 3 5, Dep.

★★★**Lincombe Hall**, *Meadfoot Rd, TQ1 2JX.* ☎(0803) 213361. C. ⍻ 44 bedrs, 29 bp, 2 bps, 4 ba, TV, Dgs. ✗ a l c, mc, at, LD 9. ⊞ N, CH, CP 200, con 50, CF, 2 BGf, 1 st, Dis. £ BB fr £17, DB fr £29, DBB fr £23, WB, ⬚, Bk £3·50, L £4·95, D £6·95, cc 1 2 3 5, Dep b.

★★★**Livermead Cliff**, *Sea Front, TQ2 6RQ.* ☎(0803) 22881. C. ⍻ 64 bedrs, 53 bp, 7 bps, 4 ba, TV, Dgs. ✗ a l c, mc, at, LD 8.30. ⊞ Lt, N, CH, TV, CP 65, G 20, Ac, sp, pf, con 80, CF 1 st. £ BB £17–£27, DB £31–£53, WT £147–£245, DT £23·50–£36·50, DBB £21·50–£37, WB, ⬚, Bk £4·50, L £5·50, D £7·75, cc 1 2 3.

★★★**Livermead House**, *Sea Front, TQ2 6QJ.* ☎(0803) 24361. C. ⍻ 70 bedrs, 52 bp, 8 bps, 6 ba, annexe 2 bedrs, 2 bp, TV, Dgs. ✗ a l c, mc, at, LD 8.30. ⊞ Lt, N, CH, TV, CP 100, G 10, Ac, sp, tc, pf, sc, sb, sol, gym, con 85, CF, 4 BGf, 0 st, Dis. £ BB £16·50–£26, DB £30–£52, WT £147–£231, DT £22·50–£35, DBB £21–£36, WB, ⬚, Bk £4·50, L £5·35, D £7·50, cc 1 2 3 6.

★★★**Maidencombe House**, *Teignmouth Rd, TQ1 4SF.* ☎(0803) 36611. C. ⍻ 21 bedrs, 14 bp, 2 ba, TV, Dgs. ✗ a l c, mc, at, LD 8.15. ⊞ N, CH, CP 100, Ac, sp, con 200, CF, 3 st. £ BB £15–£17·75, DB £24–£27·50, DBB £18–£20·75, WB, ⬚, Bk £2·50, L £4·25, D £6, cc 1 3, Dep.

★★★**Nepaul**, *27 Croft Rd, TQ2 5UB.* ☎(0803) 28457. C. ⍻ 41 bedrs, 36 bp, 5 bps, TV, Dgs. ✗ mc, at, LD 8.30. ⊞ Lt, N, CH, TV, CP 17, G 5, sp, tc, CF, 3 BGf, 2 st. £ BB £16·50–£22, DB £33–£44, WT £150·50–£189, DT £26–£31·50, DBB £21·50–£27, WB, Bk £3, L £4·50, D £8·50, cc 1 3, Dep a.▲

★★★**Oswalds**, *Palermo Rd, TQ1 3NW.* ☎(0803) 39292. C. ⍻ 55 bedrs, 19 bp, 4 bps, 10 ba, TV, Dgs. ✗ mc, at, LD 8. ⊞ Lt, N, CH, TV, Dgs, CP 30, Ac, con 100, CF. £ cc 1 3, Dep a.

★★★**Overmead** (R), *Daddyhole Rd, TQ1 2EF.* ☎(0803) 27633. Open Mar–Oct & Xmas. C. ⍻ 61 bedrs, 37 bp, 10 bps, 7 ba, TV, Dgs. ✗ a l c, mc, at, LD 8.30. ⊞ Lt, N, CH, TV, CP 7, G 20, Ac, sp, con 100, CF, 2 BGf, 0 st, Dis. £ BB £14·50–£19·50, DB £27–£39, WB, ⬚, Bk £3·50, D £7, cc 1 2 3 5 6, Dep a.

★★★**Palm Court**, *Torbay Rd, TQ2 5HD.* ☎(0803) 24881. C. ⍻ 72 bedrs, 40 bp, 8 ba, TV, Dgs. ✗ a l c, mc, at, LD 9. ⊞ Lt, N, CH, TV, Dgs, CP 15, Ac, con 150, CF, 8 st. £ BB £12–£18·50, DB £24–£37, WT £157·50–£203, DT £22·50–£29, DBB £18–£24·50, WB, ⬚, Bk £3·25, L £4·25, D £8, cc 1 2 3 5 6, Dep b.

★★★**Princes** (R), *Parkhill Rd, TQ1 2DU.* ☎(0803) 25678. Open Mar–Oct & Xmas. C. ⍻ 57 bedrs, 25 bp, 2 bps, 6 ba, TV, Dgs. ✗ a l c, mc, at, LD 8.30. ⊞ N, CH, TV, ns, CP 40, Ac, sp, con 100, CF, 2 st. £ BB £9–£17·50, DB £18–£35, WT £80·50–£115·50, WB, ⬚, Bk £2·95, L £4·80, D £6·70, cc 1 2 3 4 5 6.

★★★**Rainbow House**, *Belgrave Rd, TQ2 5HJ.* ☎(0803) 213232.

★★★**Toorak** (R), *Chestnut Av, TQ2 5JS.* ☎(0803) 211866.

⊞★★**Ansteys Lea** (RI), *Barrington Rd, TQ1 2QJ.* ☎(0803) 24843. Open Apr–mid Oct & Xmas. C. ⍻ 27 bedrs, 5 bp, 4 bps, 4 ba, TV, Dgs. ✗ mc, at, LD 7.30. ⊞ CH, TV, CP 20, sp, sol, CF, 1 BGf, 0 st, Dis. £ BB £10·50–£14·50, WB, ⬚, D £5·50, Dep a.

⊞★★**Ardmore** (R), *Asheldon, Wellswood, TQ1 2QN.* ☎(0803) 24792. Open Mar–Oct, Xmas & by arrangement in winter. C. ⍻ 29 bedrs, 9 bp, 20 bps, 5 ba, Dgs. ✗ mc, at, LD 8. ⊞ CH, TV, CP 40, Ac, sp, CF, 4 BGf, 2 st. £ BB £8·62–£12·65, DB £17·34–£25·30, ⬚, Bk £2·30, D £5·75.

⊞★★**Balmoral**, *Meadfoot Beach, TQ1 2LQ.* ☎(0803) 23381. Closed Nov. C. ⍻ 23 bedrs, 7 bps, 5 ba, TV, Dgs. ✗ a l c, mc, at, LD 9.30. ⊞ CH, Dgs, CP 18, Ac, CF, 2 st. £ BB £10·50–£16·50, DB £21–£33, WT £120–£140, DT £17·25–£21, WB, ⬚, Bk £3·75, L £4·60, D £6·50, cc 1 2 3, Dep a.

TORQUAY

0 miles ¼ ½

P Car Park
C Public Conveniences

RAC

N

Anstey's Cove

Ilsham Marine Dri.

Ilsham Rd.

Kent's Cavern

Meadfoot Beach

Oddicombe Beach

Babbacombe Beach

Concert Hall

Anstey Cove Rd.

Ilsham Rd.

WELLSWOOD

Babbacombe

Museum

Meadfoot Rd.

Meadfoot

Coral Island

BABBACOMBE

Babbacombe Rd.

Reddenhill Rd.

Cedars Rd.

Pleasure Ground

ELLACOMBE

Rosehill Children's Hosp.

Haldon Pier

ST. MARYCHURCH

Warbro Rd.

Torquay U.F.C.

Carlton Rd.

Ellacombe Church Rd.

Princess Gardens

Inner Harbour

Outer Harbour

Victoria Rd.

P.O.

Fleet St.

Princess Theatres

Princess Pier

To Teignmouth 8 m.

Manor Rd.

Hatfield Rd.

St. Marychurch Rd.

Market St.

Union St.

Pavilion

Information Bureau

Torbay Rd.

Fore St.

St. Margarets Av.

Steps

Town Hall & Library

St. Marychurch Rd.

Law Courts

Abbey Rd.

Abbey Park

A379 To Paignton 3 m.

Barewell Rd.

UPTON

Lymington Rd.

Upton Hill

Union St.

Torr Hill Rd.

Art Gallery

Torre Rd.

Corbyn Hd.

The Kings Dri.

A379

Westhill Rd.

Parkfield Rd.

Teignmouth Rd.

Brunswick Sq.

South St.

Police Station

Belgrave Rd.

Chestnut Av.

Rathmore Rd.

Torquay Station (W.R.)

Hele Rd.

Cricketfield Rd.

Avenue

Rampyde Rd.

Falkland Rd.

Rec. Grnd.

CHELSTON

TORRE

Barton Rd.

Torre Station

Old Mill Rd.

Huxtable Hill

Walnut Rd.

Nut Bush La.

Barton Hill Road

Crematorium

Shiphay Lane

Newton Road

Torbay Hospital

A380

To Exeter B

M5

To Newton Abbot 6 m.

■★★**Bancourt** (R) *Avenue Rd, TQ2 5LG.* ✆ (0803) 25077. C. ⊷ 47 bedrs, 20 bp, 5 ba, TV, Dgs. ✗ mc, at, LD 7.45. ⒟ N, CH, TV, Ac, sp, con 40, CF. £ BB £10·50–£17, DB £21–£34, DBB £16·45–£22·95, WB, ②, Bk £2·75, D £5·95, cc 1 3 6.

★★**Brigatine Motor** (R), *56 Marldon Rd, TQ2 7EJ.* ✆ (0803) 63162.▲

■★★**Burlington** (R), *462–466 Babbacombe Rd, TQ1 1HN.* ✆ (0803) 24374. Open Apr–Oct & Xmas. C. ⊷ 45 bedrs, 4 bp, 11 bps, 1 sh, 8 ba, Dgs. ✗ mc, at. ⒟ N, ch, TV, CP 30, Ac, con 80, CF, 6 BGf, 7 st. £ BB £8·50–£17·50, DB £17– £29, DBB £12·50–£20, WB, ①, Bk £3·50, D £6, cc 1 3 6, Dep a.

★★**Bute Court** (R), *Belgrave Rd, TQ2 5HQ.* ✆ (0803) 23771. C. ⊷ 47 bedrs, 28 bp, 3 bps, 7 ba, TV, Dgs. ✗ mc, at. ⒟ Lt, N, CH, TV, Dgs, CP 32, G 5, Ac, sp, con 60, CF, 16 BGf, 2 st. £ BB £10– £18·50, DB £20–£37, WT £115–£150, DT £16·70–£21·50, DBB £14–£23·50, ①, Bk £3, L £4, D £5, cc 1 2 3 5 6.

★★**Cavendish** (R), *Belgrave Rd, TQ2 5HN.* ✆ (0803) 23682. Open Apr–Oct & by arrangement winter. C 5. ⊷ 59 bedrs, 8 bp, 5 bps, 4 sh, 10 ba. ✗ a l c, mc, at, LD 8. ⒟ N, CH, TV, CP 24, Ac, sp, sb, sol, gym, con 50, 10 st. £ BB £16–£23·50, DB £28– £43, WT £135–£160, DT £22·50–£27, DBB £18–£25·50, WB, ②, Bk £3·75, L £4·90, D £6·25, cc 1 2 3 5, Dep.

■★★**Chelston Towers** (R), *Rawlyn Rd, TQ2 6PQ.* ✆ (0803) 607351. Open Feb– Nov. & Dec 29–Jan 2. C. ⊷ 22 bedrs, 7 bp, 2 bps, 4 ba, Dgs. ✗ mc, at, LD 8. ⒟ ch, Dgs, CP 40, Ac, sp, con 30, CF, 6 BGf, 2 st. £ BB £14–£17, DB £28–£34, DBB £16– £19, WB, ①, Bk £3·30, D £6·50.

★★**Conway Court**, *Warren Rd, TQ2 5TS.* ✆ (0803) 25363. Open Mar– Oct. C. ⊷ 40 bedrs, 14 bp, 17 bps, 3 ba, TV, Dgs. ✗ a l c, mc, at, LD 8. ⒟ CH, TV, Ac, con 80, CF, 5 BGf, 1 st. £ BB £15–£21, DB £29–£41, WT £150·50–£169·50, DT £21·50–£26·50, DBB £170·50–£25·50, WB, ②, Bk £4, L £6·50, D £12·25, Dep a.

★★**Coppice** (R), *Barrington Rd, TQ2 2QJ.* ✆ (0803) 27786. C. ⊷ 29 bedrs, 23 bp, 4 ba. ✗ a l c, mc, at, LD 8. ⒟ CH, TV, Dgs, CP 30, G 2, Ac, sp, con, CF, 10 BGf, 1 st, Dis. £ BB £6·50–£11·50, DB £15–£26, DBB £10·50–£15·50, WB, Dep a.

■★★**Elmington** (RI), *St Agnes La, TQ2 6QE.* ✆ (0803) 605192. C. ⊷ 22 bedrs, 7 bp, 5 bps, 5 ba, Dgs. ✗ mc, at, LD 7.30. ⒟ N, ch, Dgs, CP15, Ac, sp, CF, 2 BGf, 0 st, Dis. £ Dep.

■★★**Forest** (Cl), *Haldon Rd, TQ1 2LY.* ✆ (0803) 24842. Open Mar–Oct. C. ⊷ 34 bedrs, 9 bp, 1 bps, 10 sh, 5 ba, TV, Dgs. ✗ mc, at, LD 7. ⒟ ch, TV, Dgs, CP 20, Ac, sp, con, CF, 3 BGf, 2 st. £ BB £9·20– £12·30, DB £18·40–£24·60, DBB £9·90– £16·26, WB, ②, Dep a.

■★★**Gresham Court** (R), *Babbacombe Rd, TQ1 1HG.* ✆ (0803) 23007. Open Mar–Nov. C. ⊷ 34 bedrs, 7 bp, 6 bps, 5 ba. ✗ LD 8. ⒟ Lt, CH, TV, CP 4, Ac, CF. £ BB £8·60–£13·90, DB £17·20–£27·80, WT £97–£123, DT £13–£16·75, DBB £11– £16·35, ②, Bk £2, L £2, D £3·25, cc 1 3, Dep a.

★★**Howden Court** (R), *Croft Rd, TQ2 5UD.* ✆ (0803) 24844. Open Apr–Sep & Xmas. C. ⊷ 32 bedrs, 12 bp, 20 bps, Dgs. ✗ mc, at, LD 7.30. ⒟ ch, TV, CP 25, Ac, con, CF, 5 BGf, 0 st, Dis. £ BB 10·35–

£12·65, DB £18·40–£23, ①, Bk £1·65, D £5, Dep a.

■★★**Hunsdon Lea** (RI), *Hunsdon Rd, TQ1 1QB.* ✆ (0803) 26538. Open Mar– Oct & Xmas. C. ⊷ 18 bedrs, 8 bp, 1 bps, 9 sh, 2 ba, TV, Dgs. ✗ mc, at, LD 8.30. ⒟ CH, TV, ns, CP 12, sp, sol, con 32, CF, 5 BGf, 3 st. £ BB £11–£19·50, DB £22–£39, WT £106–£153, DT £17–£23·50, DBB £13·50– £22, WB, ①, Bk £2·50, D £4·50, Dep a.

■★★**Lansdowne** (R), *Babbacombe Rd, TQ1 1PW.* ✆ (0803) 22822. Open Apr– Oct & Xmas. C. ⊷ 32 bedrs, 26 bp, 2 bps, 2 ba, TV, Dgs. ✗ mc, at, LD 8. ⒟ CH, TV, Dgs, CP 32, Ac, sp, sol, con, CF, 10 BGf, 3 st. £ BB £10·50–£12·50, DB £21–£25, WT £104–£129, DBB £14–£19, WB, ①, Bk £3·50, D £6·50, Dep a.

★★**Meadfoot Bay**, *Meadfoot Sea Rd, TQ1 2LQ.* ✆ (0803) 24722. Open Mar–Oct & Xmas. C. ⊷ 26 bedrs, 9 bp, 2 bps, 4 ba, TV, Dgs. ✗ a l c, LD 8. ⒟ CH, TV, CP 20, Ac, con 25, CF, 1 BGf, 0 st, Dis. £ BB £11– £16, DB £18–£33, WT £101·50–£132·50, DT £16·95–£21·95, WB, ②, cc 1 3.

■★★**Nethway** (R), *Falkland Rd, TQ2 5JR.* ✆ (0803) 27630. Open Apr–Nov, Xmas & Easter. C. ⊷ 46 bedrs, 12 bp, 12 bps, 1 ba, TV, Dgs. ✗ mc, at, LD 8. ⒟ N, CH, TV, CP 20, sp, con 50, CF, 4 BGf, 1 st, Dis. £ BB £13·85–£18, DB £25–£35, DBB £18·10–£25, WB, ②, Bk £3·50, D £5·95, cc 3, Dep b.

■★★**Regina**, *Victoria Par, TQ1 2BE.* ✆ (0803) 22904. Closed Nov & Feb. C. ⊷ 70 bedrs, 22 bp, 27 bps, 2 sh, 5 ba, TV, Dgs. ✗ a l c, mc, at, LD 8. ⒟ N, CH, TV, Dgs, CP 1, G 16, Ac, con 30, CF, 2 st. £ BB £9–£17, DB £18–£34, DBB £11–£24, WB, ①, Bk £2, L £2·50, D £3·95, cc 1 2 3 5, Dep.

■★★**Rock Walk** (R), *Warren Rd, TQ2 5TN.* ✆ (0803) 28775. Open Mar–Oct & Xmas. C. ⊷ 34 bedrs, 10 bp, 11 bps, 5 ba, Dgs. ✗ mc, at, LD 7.30. ⒟ CH, TV, Dgs, CP 10, Ac, con 65, CF, 2 BGf, 2 st. £ BB £10·50–£18, DB £19–£30·70, WT fr £105, ①, Bk £2·50, L £5·50, D £6·50.

■★★**Roseland** (R), *Warren Rd, TQ2 5TT.* ✆ (0803) 24614. Open Mar–Oct & Dec. C 2. ⊷ 29 bedrs, 20 bp, 5 ba, TV. ✗ mc, at, LD 7.30. ⒟ N, CH, TV, G 3, Ac, con 20, CF, 1 BGf. £ WB, cc 1 2 3, Dep.

■★★**Shedden Hall** (R), *TQ2 5TX.* ✆ (0803) 22964. Open Apr–Oct. C. ⊷ 27 bedrs, 16 bp, 5 bps, 2 ba, TV, Dgs. ✗ mc, at, LD 8. ⒟ CH, TV, CP 27, Ac, sp, con 100, CF, 0 st. £ BB £10·72–£17·85, DB £25·50– £38·99, DBB £12·75–£19·50, ②, Bk £3, D £7, cc 1 2 3, Dep b.

★★**Sydore** (R), *Meadfoot Rd, TQ1 2JP.* ✆ (0803) 24758. C. ⊷ 14 bedrs, 4 bp, 7 sh, 2 ba, TV, Dgs. ✗ mc, at, LD 7.30. ⒟ ch, TV, CP 20, con 25, CF, 1 BGf, 2 st. £ BB £7–£10, DB £14–£20, WT £94·50–£119, DT £13·50–£17, DBB £10–£14, WB, ②, Bk £2·50, L £3·50, D £5.

★★**Templestowe** (RI), *Tor Church Rd, TQ2 5UU.* ✆ (0803) 25145. Open Mar– Nov. C. ⊷ 91 bedrs, 45 bp, 2 bps, 15 ba, TV, Dgs. ✗ mc. ⒟ Lt, N, ch, TV, CP 60, Ac, sp, tc, con 150, CF, 9 BGf, 0 st. £ BB £12·50–£18·50, DB £25–£37, WT £101– £149, DT £16·50–£20·50, DBB £12·50– £21·65, ①, Bk £3·50, L £4·50, D £6·50, cc 1 3 6, Dep a.▲

■★★**Vernon Court** (R), *Warren Rd, TQ2 5TR.* ✆ (0803) 22676. C 3. ⊷ 19 bedrs, 12 bp, 2 bps, 2 ba. ✗ mc, at, LD 8. ⒟ CH, TV, CP 9, Ac, 2 BGf, 0 st, Dis. £ BB £10–£18,

DB £20–£36, DBB £12–£22, WB, ①, Bk £4, D £6.

■★★**Westleigh** (R), *Ash Hill Rd, TQ1 3JB.* ✆ (0803) 23895. C. ⊷ 23 bedrs, 9 bp, 4 ba. ✗ a l c, mc, at, LD 7.45. ⒟ ch, ns, CP 24, Ac, sp, sb, sol, gym, con 50, CF, 5 BGf, 8 st. £ BB £15·50–£18, DB £23–£34, WB, ②, cc 1 5, Dep.

■★★**Windsor** (R), *Abbey Rd, TQ2 5NR.* ✆ (0803) 23757. Open Mar–Oct & Xmas. C. ⊷ 43 bedrs, 5 bp, 8 ba, Dgs. ✗ mc, at, LD 7.30. ⒟ CH, TV, CP 20, Ac, sp, CF, 0 st. £ DBB £11·50–£18·75, WB, ②, Bk £1·50, L £2, D £4·25, Dep.

■★★**Woodhaye**, *Old Torwood Rd, TQ1 1PP.* ✆ (0803) 26046. Open Mar–Oct & Xmas. C. ⊷ 40 bedrs, 12 bp, 28 sh, 6 ba, TV, Dgs. ✗ mc, at. ⒟ CH, TV, CP 25, Ac, CF, 6 BGf, 2 st. £ BB £12–£16·50, DB £24– £33, DBB £15–£19·50, WB, ①, Bk £2·50, D £4·50, cc 1 3, Dep.▲

■★**Ashley Rise** (R), *Babbacombe Rd, TQ1 3SJ.* ✆ (0803) 37282.

■★**Audrey Court**, *Lower Warberry Rd, TQ1 1QS.* ✆ (0803) 24563.

■★**Carlton**, *Falkland Rd, TQ2 5JJ.* ✆ (0803) 27666. Open Mar–Oct & Xmas. C. ⊷ 34 bedrs, 14 bp, 1 bps, 19 sh, 4 ba, Dgs. ✗ mc, at, LD 7.30. ⒟ Lt, CH, TV, Dgs, CP 26, Ac, sp, con 100, CF, 1 st. £ BB £8·50–£13·75, DB £17–£27·50, DBB £12– £26·50, WB, ②, Bk £3, L £3·45, D £4·75, cc 1 3, Dep a.

■★**Clevedon** (RI), *Meadfoot Sea Rd, TQ1 2LQ.* ✆ (0803) 24260. Open Apr–Oct & Xmas. C 6. ⊷ 15 bedrs, 1 bp, 3 ba, ns, Dgs. ✗ mc, at, LD 7.30. ⒟ ch, TV, CP 10, CF, 3 BGf, 2 st. £ BB £8·75–£10, DB £17·50–£22, WB, ①, Bk £1·75, D £4·50, Dep a.

■★**Fairmount House** (Unl), *Herbert Rd, TQ2 6RW.* ✆ (0803) 605446. Open Mar– Oct. C. ⊷ 7 bedrs, 2 bp, 3 bps, 2 ba, Dgs. ✗ mc, LD 7.30. ⒟ TV, Dgs, ns, CP 7, CF, 2 BGf, 0 st, Dis. £ BB £9·50–£12, DB £19– £24, DBB £14·75–£17·25, WB, ②, Bk £3, L £3·50, D £5, cc 2 3.

★**Palm Grove** (R), *Meadfoot Sea Rd, TQ1 2LQ.* ✆ (0803) 23027. Closed Dec–Feb. C. ⊷ 24 bedrs, 4 bp, 5 bps, 4 ba, Dgs. ✗ mc, at. ⒟ CH, TV, CP 16, Ac, sp, sb, CF, 5 BGf, 2 st. £ BB £9–£12·25, DB £18–£24·50, DBB £13·50–£16·75, ①, Bk £2·50, D £4·50, cc 2 3, Dep.

■★**Protea** (R), *Seaway Lane, TQ2 6PW.* ✆ (0803) 607722. C. ⊷ 22 bedrs, 3 bp, 7 bps, 2 ba, Dgs. ✗ mc, at, LD 7. ⒟ CH, TV, CP 20, Ac, sp, CF. £ BB £8·50–£13, DB £17–£27, DBB £12–£17·50, WB, ②, Bk £2, L £4, D £6, cc 1, Dep a.

■★**Shelley Court** (R), *Croft Rd, TQ2 5UD.* ✆ (0803) 25642. Open Apr–Sep & Dec. C. ⊷ 29 bedrs, 2 bp, 14 bps, 3 ba, Dgs. ✗ mc, at, LD 7.30. ⒟ CH, TV, CP 18, Ac, sol, con 30, CF, 4 BGf, 0 st, Dis. £ BB £9·20–£13·60, DB £18·40–£27·20, DBB £15·80–£20·20, WB, ①, Bk £3·45, D £6·90, Dep a.

■★**Tormohun** (RI), *Newton Rd, TQ2 5BZ.* ✆ (0803) 23681. C. ⊷ 23 bedrs, 12 bp, 10 bps, 1 sh, 2 ba, TV, Dgs. ✗ a l c, mc, at, LD 7.30. ⒟ CH, TV, CP 23, Ac, sp, con, CF, 2 BGf, 2 st. £ BB £6·90–£8·62, DB £13·80–£17·24, WB, ①, Bk £1·90, L £1·20, D £3·50, cc 1 2 6, Dep.

★**Windsurfer**, *St Agnes La, TQ2 6QE.* ✆ (0803) 606550.

Anstey's Lodge, G, z (Unl), *307 Babbacombe Rd, TQ1 3TB.* ✆ (0803) 27261.

Arundale, PH, z (Unl), *48 Bampfylde Rd, TQ2 5AY.* ✆ (0803) 27402. Open Apr–Oct. C 5. ⇔ 9 bedrs, 2 ba, Dgs. ⓓ TV, CP 5. £ BB fr £7, DB fr £14, DT (b) fr £69, ①, Bk £2, D £3·50.

Ashwood, PH, z (RI), *2 St Margaret's Rd, St Marychurch, TQ1 4NM.* ✆ (0803) 38173. Open May–Oct. C. ⇔ 9 bedrs, 2 ba, Dgs. ⓓ ch, TV, Dgs, CP 10, U 1, CF, 1 BGf, 1 st, Dis. £ BB £8·50–£9, DB £17–£18, WT (b) £84–£89, ①.

Avron, H, z (Unl), *70 Windsor Rd, TQ1 1SZ.* ✆ (0803) 24182. Open May–Sep. C. ⇔ 14 bedrs, 6 bp, 2 bps, 6 sh, 2 ba, TV, Dgs. ⓓ TV, Dgs, CP 6, CF, 2 BGf, 0 st, Dis. £ WT (b) £72–£79, ①, Bk £2, D £3·50.

Beechmoor, PH, z (R), *Vansittart Rd, TQ2 5BW.* ✆ (0803) 22471. Open Apr–Oct. C. ⇔ 16 bedrs, 2 bp, 5 ba, ns. ⓓ CH, TV, CP 20, CF. £ BB £6·50–£7·50, DB £14–£22, WT (b) £55–£80, DT (b) £8–£11·50, Bk £2·75, D £3·75.

Braddon Hall, PH, z (R), *Braddons Hill Rd East, TQ1 1HF.* ✆ (0803) 23908. Closed Nov. C. ⇔ 13 bedrs, 1 bp, 2 ba, Dgs. ⓓ CH, TV, Dgs, CP 10, CF, 1 BGf, 4 st. £ BB £6·75–£9·50, DB £13·50–£19, WT (b) £60–£85, DT (b) £9·10–£12·50, ①

Burleigh House, G, y, z (Unl), *25 Newton Rd, TQ2 5BZ.* ✆ (0803) 23431. C 2. ⇔ 8 bedrs, 2 ba. ⓓ CH, TV, CP 8, 2 BGf, 1 st, Dis. £ BB £5·50–£9, DB £11–£18, WT (b) £63–£87·50, DT (b) £9–£12·50, ①.

Carn Brea, H, y (RI), *21 Avenue Rd, TQ2 5LB.* ✆ (0803) 22002. Closed Dec. C. ⇔ 20 bedrs, 7 bps, 3 ba, ns. ⓓ ch, CP 16, G 2, CF, 1 BGf, 1 st, Dis. £ BB £7·50–£9·95, DB £15–£19·90, WT (b) £75–£92, DT (b) £13–£13·50, ①.

Carysfort, G, z (Unl), *13 Warren Rd, TQ2 5TQ.* ✆ (0803) 24160. C. ⇔ 6 bedrs, 2 ba. ⓓ CH, TV, ns, CP 3, U 1, CF, 2 st. £ BB £5·50–£7·50, DB £9–£15, ①.

Casey's Court Motel, z (Unl), *127 Newton Rd, TQ2 7AJ.* ✆ (0803) 63909. Open Apr–Oct. ⇔ 6 bedrs, 2 ba. ⓓ CH, CP 6, G 1, CF. £ BB £7–£7·50, DB £12–£15, WT (c) £40–£48, ①, Bk £2·75.

Castle Mount, PH, z (Unl), *7 Castle Rd, TQ1 3BB.* ✆ (0803) 22130. Open Mar–Nov. C 7. ⇔ 9 bedrs, 1 bp, 2 ba, Dgs. ⓓ ch, TV, CP 6. £ BB £6·50–£7·50, DB £13–£16·50, WT (b) £77, (c) £49, ①, D £4·50.

Castleton, PH, z (RI), *Castle Rd, TQ1 3BB.* ✆ (0803) 24976. C. ⇔ 15 bedrs, 3 ba, ns. ⓓ CH, TV, ns, CP 7, CF. £ BB £6·33–£8·05, DB £12·66–£16·10, WT (b) £69–£86·25, DT (b) £9·89–£12·36, ①.

Chelston Banks, H (Unl), *Chelston Sq, Old Mill Rd, TQ2 6HW.* ✆ (0803) 607129.

Cheltenham, H, y (RI), *Rousdown Rd, TQ2 6PB.* ✆ (0803) 605488.

Cherry Trees, PH, z (Rt), *29 Crownhill Park, TQ2 5LW.* ✆ (0803) 24895.

Colindale, PH, z (Rt), *20 Rathmore Rd, TQ2 6NY.* ✆ (0803) 23947. Open Mar–Oct. C 5. ⇔ 9 bedrs, 5 bps, 2 ba. ⓓ ch, TV, ns, CP 6, 1 BGf, 2 st. £ BB £7·95–£8·95, DB £15·90–£17·90, WT (b) £79·95–£85·95, DT (b) £11·50–£12·50, ①, Bk £2·50, D £4·50.

Concorde, H, z (RI), *26 Newton Rd, TQ2 5BZ.* ✆ (0803) 22330. Open Apr–Oct. C. ⇔ 16 bedrs, 5 bps, 5 ba, Dgs. ⓓ ch, TV, CP 16, CF, 2 BGf, 2 st, Dis. £ BB £8–£11, DB £16–£22, ①.

Courthouse, PH, x (RI), *Rock House Lane, Maidencombe, TQ1 4SU.* ✆ (0803) 38335. Open Apr–Oct. C. ⇔ 15 bedrs, 3 bp, 2 bps, 3 ba, Dgs. ⓓ TV, CP 10, CF, 3 st.

£ BB £7–£9, DB £14–£18, WT (b) £80–£94, DT (b) £11·50–£14·50, ①, cc 1 2 3 5.

Craig Court, H, z (RI), *10 Ash Hill Rd, TQ1 3HZ.* ✆ (0803) 24400. Open Apr–Oct. C. ⇔ 10 bedrs, 4 bps, 3 ba. ⓓ ch, CP 10, CF, 2 BGf, 0 st, Dis. £ DB £12·50–£22·50, WT (b) £64·75–£89·25, DT (b) £9·25,–£12·75, ①, D £3.

Cranborne, PH, z (Unl), *58 Belgrave Rd, TQ2 5HY.* ✆ (0803) 28046. C. ⇔ 15 bedrs, 5 bp, 3 sh, 2 ba. ⓓ ch, TV, CP 3, CF, 6 st. £ BB £7–£9·50, DB £14–£23, WT (c) £45–£63·50, DT (b) £11·50–£14, ①.

Crowndale, PH, z (RI), *18 Bridge Rd, TQ2 5BA.* ✆ (0803) 23068. C. ⇔ 10 bedrs, 2 ba. ⓓ CH, TV, CP 6, CF. £ BB £7·50–£9, DB £15–£18, WT (b) £65–£78, DT (b) £9·50–£12, ①.

Danby Lodge, PH, y (RI), *Lincombe Dr, TQ1 2HQ.* ✆ (0803) 25570. C. ⇔ 10 bedrs, 1 bp, 1 bps, 2 sh, 3 ba, Dgs. ⓓ CH, TV, CP 10, CF. £ BB £8·50–£9·50, DB £17–£21, WT (b) £70–£84, DT (b) £13–£15, ①, Bk £1·90, L £2·50, D £4·50.

Daphne Court, PH, y (RI), *Lower Warberry Rd, TQ1 1QS.* ✆ (0803) 212011. C. ⇔ 15 bedrs, 7 bp, 1 bps, 2 ba, Dgs. ⓓ CH, TV, Dgs, CP 14, CF, 2 BGf, 1 st, Dis. £ BB £8·50–£10·75, DB £17–£21·50, WT (b) £63–£103, DT (b) £13–£15·25, ①.

Devon Court, PH, z (RI), *Croft Rd, TQ2 5UE.* ✆ (0803) 23603. Closed Dec & Jan. C. ⇔ 14 bedrs, 1 bps, 2 sh, 2 ba. ⓓ CH, TV, CP 15, CF, 1 st. £ BB £5–£14, DB £10–£28, WT (b) £56–£119, DT (b) £8–£17, ①.

Elmdene, PH, *Rathmore Rd, TQ2 6NZ.* ✆ (0803) 24940. Open Mar–Oct & Xmas. C 5. ⇔ 13 bedrs, 2 bp, 3 bps, 2 ba, Dgs. ⓓ CH, TV, CP 12, 1 BGf, 3 st. £ BB £9–£13·25, DB £18–£26·50, WT (b) £80–£100, DT (b) £13–£17, ①, Bk £2, L £3·50, D £5·50, cc 1 3 6.

Erin, H, z (RI), *84 Avenue Rd, TQ2 5LF.* ✆ (0803) 27844.

Fretherne, PH, y (Rt), *St Luke's Rd South, TQ2 5NZ.* ✆ (0803) 22594. Open Apr–Oct. C. ⇔ 24 bedrs, 7 sh, 3 ba. ⓓ ch, TV, Dgs, CP 24, CF, 6 BGf, 1 st, Dis. £ BB £7·50–£9, DB £15–£18, WT (b) £84, DT (b) £13·50–£15, ②, Bk £3, D £6·50.

Glenorleigh, PH (RI), *26 Cleveland Rd, TQ2 5BE.* ✆ (0803) 22135. C. ⇔ 16 bedrs, 7 bp, 3 ba. ⓓ CH, TV, CP 12, CF, 3 BGf, 0 st, Dis. £ BB £8·05–£12·10, DB £16·10–£24·70, WT (b) £74·75–£119·60, DT (b) £11·50–£17·25, ①.

Glenwood, H, z (RI), *Rowdens Rd, TQ2 5AZ.* ✆ (0803) 26318. C. ⇔ 10 bedrs, 2 ba. ⓓ CH, TV, CP 9, CF, 0 st. £ BB £7·50–£9, DB £15–£18, WT (b) £79–£88, DT (b) £13–£15, ①.

Hart Lea, G, z (Unl), *81 St Marychurch Rd, TQ1 3HG.* ✆ (0803) 312527. C. ⇔ 6 bedrs, 2 ba. ⓓ CH, TV, CF. £ BB £6·50–£7, DB £11–£14, WT (b) £49–£70, (c) £35–£48, DT (b) £7·50–£10·50, ①.

Hatherleigh, PH, yz (RI), *56 St Marychurch Rd, TQ1 3JE.* ✆ (0803) 25762.

Hendon, H, x (RI), *1 Lisburne Cres, TQ1 2LA.* ✆ (0803) 23363.

Hind, PH, z (RI), *29 Bampfylde Rd, TQ2 5AY.* ✆ (0803) 27212. Open Apr–Oct, Xmas & Easter. C. ⇔ 12 bedrs, 2 ba. ⓓ CH, TV, CP 10, CF, 3 BGf, 1 st, Dis. £ BB fr £7, DB fr £14, WT (b) fr £70, DT (b) fr £10, ①.

Hotel Howard, H, y (RI), *373 Babbacombe Rd, TQ1 3TB.* ✆ (0803) 25944. C. ⇔ 10 bedrs, 1 bps, 4 sh, 2 ba, Dgs. ⓓ CH, TV, Dgs, CP 8, CF, 2 BGf. £ BB

£7–£10, DB £14–£18·50, WT (b) £65–£82, (c) £47–£58, DT (b) £10–£12, ①.

Ilsham Valley, PH (R), *Ilsham Close, off Marine Dr, TQ1 2JA.* ✆ (0803) 22075. Open Mar–Oct. C. ⇔ 19 bedrs, 3 ba, Dgs. ⓓ CH, TV, Dgs, CP 18, U 2, CF, 4 BGf, 8 st. £ BB £9–£9·50, DB £18–£19, ①, Bk £2·50, D £6·50.

Ingoldsby, H, y (RI), *1 Chelston Rd, TQ2 6PT.* ✆ (0803) 607497. Open Mar–Oct. C. ⇔ 16 bedrs, 3 sh, 2 ba, Dgs. ⓓ ch, TV, CP 14, CF, 4 BGf, 1 st, Dis.

Lindum, PH (RI), *Abbey Rd, TQ2 5NP.* ✆ (0803) 22795.

Mapleton, PH, z (R), *St Luke's Rd North, TQ2 5PD.* ✆ (0803) 22389. Open Apr–Oct & Easter. C. ⇔ 9 bedrs, 3 ba. ⓓ ch, TV, CP 8, CF, 1 BGf, 1 st. £ BB £7·50–£9·50, DB £15–£19, WT (b) £69–£89, DT (b) £10–£13, ①, Bk £2, D £3·50, ▲

Melba House, PH, z (Unl), *62 Bampfylde Rd, TQ2 5AY.* ✆ (0803) 22331.

Mount Nessing, PH, z (RI), *St Luke's Rd North, TQ2 5PD.* ✆ (0803) 22970.

Norwood, H, z (Unl), *60 Belgrave Rd, TQ2 5HY.* ✆ (0803) 24236. Open Apr–Sep & Easter. C. ⇔ 12 bedrs, 4 ba. ⓓ TV, ns, CP 12, CF, 5 st. £ BB £7–£9, DB £14–£18, WT (b) £70–£87, DT (b) £10–£13, ①.

Pembroke, PH, x (RI), *Meadfoot Sea Rd, TQ1 2LQ.* ✆ (0803) 22837.

Pencarrow, PH, z (RI), *64 Windsor Rd, TQ1 1SZ.* ✆ (0803) 23080. Open May–Sep. C 5. ⇔ 13 bedrs, 8 bps, 5 sh, 1 ba, TV, Dgs. ⓓ TV, Dgs, CP 8, CF, 1 BGf, 3 st. £ BB £6·75–£9·25, DB £13·50–£18·50, WT (b) £68·50–£85, DT (b) £10–£12·50, ①.

Pines, PH, y (RI), *St Marychurch Rd, TQ1 3HG.* ✆ (0803) 38384. C. ⇔ 22 bedrs, 1 bp, 5 ba, TV. ⓓ ch, TV, CP 15, CF, 12 BGf, 1 st. £ BB £7·25–£9, DB £15–£19·50, WT (b) £77–£90, DT (b) £11–£13·75, ①, Bk £2·50, D £3·75.

Rawlyn House, PH, y (RI), *Rawlyn Rd, Chelston, TQ2 6PL.* ✆ (0803) 605208. Open Mar–Oct & Xmas. ⇔ 17 bedrs, 5 bp, 12 bps, 2 ba. ⓓ CH, TV, ns, CP 15, CF, 2 BGf, 1 st, Dis. £ BB £8–£13·75, DB £16–£27·50, WT (b) £70–£97, DT (b) £10–£14, ①, Bk £2, D £4·25.

Red Squirrel Lodge, H, y (RI), *Chelston Rd, TQ2 6PU.* ✆ (0803) 605496. Open Mar–Nov & Xmas. C. ⇔ 17 bedrs, 4 ba, Dgs. ⓓ CH, TV, Dgs, CP 10, CF, 4 BGf, 4 st. £ BB £7·50–£11·50, DB £15–£23, WT (b) £65–£96, DT (b) £11–£15, ①, Bk £2·50, D £4·50.

Richwood, PH, z (R), *20 Newton Rd, TQ2 5QN.* ✆ (0803) 23729.

Riva Lodge, PH, z (RI), *Croft Rd, TQ2 5UE.* ✆ (0803) 22614. Open Mar–Oct & Dec. C. ⇔ 20 bedrs, 3 bp, 8 bps, 2 ba, Dgs. ⓓ CH, TV, Dgs, CP 20, CF, 1 st. £ BB £8·50–£10·50, DB £17–£25, WT (b) £12·45–£113·40, DT (b) £12–£14, ①, cc 1 3.

St Bernard's, H, z (RI), *Castle Rd, TQ1 3BB.* ✆ (0803) 22508. Closed Xmas. C. ⇔ 14 bedrs, 3 bps, 2 ba. ⓓ CH, TV, CP 8, CF. £ BB £6–£10·50, DB £12–£23, WT (b) £60–£91, DT (b) £9·50–£14, ①.

St Kilda, PH, y (RI), *49 Babbacombe Rd, TQ1 3SJ.* ✆ (0803) 37238. Open Apr–Oct. C. ⇔ 26 bedrs, 2 bp, 13 bps, 3 ba, Dgs. ⓓ ch, TV, Dgs, CP 30, CF, 3 BGf, 4 st. £ BB £7·50–£9·25, DB £15–£18·50, WT (b) £85, DT (b) £11·30–£12·30, ①.

St Lawrence, G, z (Unl), *Lansdowne Rd, TQ2 5BP.* ✆ (0803) 27006. C 5. ⇔ 9 bedrs, 2 ba. ⓓ TV, ns, CP 8, 2 BGf, 2 st.

£ BB £6–£7·50, DB £12–£15, WT (b) £55–£65, DT (b) £9–£9·50, ②.

Sandpiper, PH, z (Rl), *Rowdens Rd.* ✆ (0803) 22779.

Seaway, PH, yz (R), *46 Newton Rd, TQ2 6AA.* ✆ (0803) 25326.

Seaway, H, y (Rl), *Chelston Rd, TQ2 6PU.* ✆ (0803) 605320.

Sherwood, PH, z (Rl), *Belgrave Road, TQ2 5HP.* ✆ (0803) 24534.

Silverlands, H, z (Unl), *27 Newton Rd, TQ2 5DB.* ✆ (0803) 22013. Closed Dec & Jan. C 3. ⋈ 12 bedrs, 2 ba, Dgs. ⓣ CH, TV, Dgs, CP 12, 2 BGf. £ BB £6–£7, DB £12–£14, WT (c) £42–£49, ②.

Silvermead, PH, z (Rl), *30 Castle Rd, TQ1 3BQ.* ✆ (0803) 23239. C. ⋈ 10 bedrs, 2 ba. ⓣ CH, TV, ns, CP 9, CF. £ BB £5·50–£7·50, DB £14–£16, WT (b) £50–£60, cc 3.

Skerries, PH, z (Unl), *25 Morgan Av, TQ2 5RR.* ✆ (0803) 23618. C. ⋈ 12 bedrs, 2 ba, Dgs. ⓣ CH, TV, Dgs, CP 7, CF, 0 st. £ BB £6·50–£8·50, DB £13–£17, WT (b) £63–£77, DT (b) £9·50–£11·50, ①.

Southbourne, H, y (R), *9 Cleveland Rd, TQ2 5BD.* ✆ (0803) 27609.

Springfield House, G, z (Unl), *St Luke's Rd North, TQ2 5PD.* ✆ (0803) 27596. C. ⋈ 6 bedrs, 2 ba. ⓣ CH, TV, CP 6, CF. £ BB £7–£8, DB £14–£16, WT (b) £60–£73, DT (b) £9·50–£11, ①.

Sun Court, PH, z (Rl), *Rowden Rd, TQ2 5AZ.* ✆ (0803) 27242. Open Mar–Oct. C 7. ⋈ 12 bedrs, 2 ba, Dgs. ⓣ ch, TV, Dgs, CP 12, 3 BGf. £ BB £6·50–£8, DB £13–£16, WT (b) £70–£85, DT (b) £10·50–£12·50, ①, cc 1 3.

Sunleigh, H, y (R), *Livermead Hill, TQ2 6QY.* ✆ (0803) 607137. Open Apr–Sep & Xmas. C. ⋈ 23 bedrs, 12 bps, 2 sh, 3 ba. ⓣ CH, TV, CP 20, CF, 2 BGf, 3 st. £ BB £8·75–£11·25, DB £17·50–£22·50, WT (b) £72·21–£92·63, DT (b) £12·25–£14·50, ①.

Torbay Rise, H, y (Rl), *Old Mill Rd, TQ2 6HL.* ✆ (0803) 605541. Open Apr–Oct & Xmas. C. ⋈ 16 bedrs, 2 bps, 1 sh, 3 ba, Dgs. ⓣ ch, TV, CP 12, CF. £ BB £8·50–£12·50, DB £17–£28, WT (b) £70–£105, DT (b) £12–£16, ①, cc 1 3.

Torcroft, PH, y (Rl), *28 Croft Rd, TQ2 5UE.* ✆ (0803) 28292. Open Mar–Oct. C. ⋈ 21 bedrs, 6 bps, 2 ba. ⓣ TV, CP 15, CF, 3 BGf, 0 st. £ BB £7·50–£11·50, DB £15–£23, WT (b) £65–£92, DT (b) £10–£14, ①, Bk £2·50, D £4.

Trafalgar House, PH, z (Rl), *30 Bridge Rd, TQ2 5BA.* ✆ (0803) 22486. C. ⋈ 12 bedrs, 2 bps, 2 ba, Dgs. ⓣ CH, TV, CP 7, CF, 2 BGf, 1 st, Dis. £ BB £7–£9·50, DB £14–£19, WT (b) £56–£75, DT (b) £10–£11·50, ②.

Tregenna, PH, y (Rl), *20 Cleveland Rd, TQ2 5BE.* ✆ (0803) 23578. Open Mar–Oct. C. ⋈ 11 bedrs, 3 ba, Dgs. ⓣ ch, TV, CP 8, CF, 1 st. £ Bk £1·50, D £5.

Victoria Lodge, PH (R), *16 Newton Rd, TQ2 5BZ.* ✆ (0803) 211580. C 4. ⋈ 10 bedrs, 1 bps, 1 sh, 2 ba. ⓣ ch, TV, CP 10, CF, 2 BGf, 2 st. £ BB £7–£9, DB £14–£18, WT (b) £75–£95, DT (b) £11–£14, ①, Bk £3·50, D £5.

Villa Marina, H (Unl), *Cockington Lane, Livermead, TQ2 6QU.* ✆ (0803) 605440. Open May–Sep. C. ⋈ 26 bedrs, 18 bp, 2 bps, 2 ba, Dgs. ⓣ CH, TV, CP 23, CF, 4 BGf, 5 st. £ BB £8·50–£11·50, DB £17–£23, WT (b) £99–£104, DT (b) £14·50–£15, ②.

Westowe, H, y (Rt), *Chelston Rd, TQ2 6PU.* ✆ (0803) 605207. Open Apr–Oct. C 5. NS. ⋈ 12 bedrs, 2 sh, 3 ba, ns, TV.

ⓣ CH, TV, ns, CP 8. £ BB £10·50–£12·50, DB £21–£27, WT (b) £80·50–£94·50, DT (b) £11·50–£13·50, ①.

White Gables, H, y (R) *Rawlyn Rd.* ✆ (0803) 605233. C. ⋈ 10 bedrs, 3 ba. ⓣ CH, TV, CP 10, CF, 1 BGf, 0 st, Dis. £ BB £6–£10, DB £12, WT (b) £60–£90, DT (b) £9–£13, ①, Bk £2, D £4.

Woodgrange, PH, z (Rl), *18 Newton Road, TQ2 5BZ.* ✆ (0803) 212619. Closed Xmas. C 3. ⋈ 12 bedrs, 2 ba. ⓣ ch, TV, CP 10, CF, 1 st. £ BB £6–£8·50, DB £12–£17, WT (b) £64–£75, (c) £42–£52, DT (b) £9·50–£11, ①, Bk £2, D £4.

Woodley Grange, H, y (Rt) *34 Petitor Rd, TQ1 4QF.* ✆ (0803) 37899. C 5. ⋈ 9 bedrs, 3 bp, 1 bps, 5 sh, 2 ba, ns, Dgs. ⓣ CH, ns, CP 9, CF, 0 st. £ BB £6·50–£8·50, DB £13–£19, WT (b) £70–£88.

Repairer: Tom Brown & Son (Torquay) Ltd, Brunswick Garage, Brunswick Sq. ✆ (0803) 22287.

Dutton-Forshaw (Torbay), Hele Rd. ✆ (0803) 62781.

Specialist Car Lighting and Ignition and Battery Repairer: Auto Maintenance Ltd, 10 Newton Rd. ✆ (0803) 23268. Lucas authorised service.

Specialist Body Repairer: Reed & Co (Torquay) Ltd, Lawes Bridge, Hele Rd. ✆ (0803) 64269 and (0803) 64812.

MC Repairer: Torre Motor Cycles, 254 Union St. ✆ (0803) 24184.

Sctr Repairer: Torre Motor Cycles, 254 Union St. ✆ (0803) 24184.

Rescue Service: Ashleigh Garage, Potters Hill. ✆ (0803) 24864.

Chelston Garage (Torquay) Ltd, Walnut Rd. ✆ (0803) 65858.

Conway Autos, R/O 78 Princes Rd. ✆ (0803) 212314.

D S P Auto Repairs, Higher Union La. ✆ (0803) 212326.

Enoch & Co (Torbay) Ltd, Imperial Garages, 50 Torwood St. ✆ (0803) 28555.

Forest Road Garage (Torquay) Ltd, Forest Rd. ✆ (0803) 39143.

Kenbern Garage, rear of 35 Princes Rd, Ellacombe. ✆ (0803) 22914.

Moores Motors (Torquay) Ltd, 230 Lymington Rd. ✆ (0803) 37369.

Peter G Gillard, 20 Hoxton Rd, Ellacombe. ✆ (0803) 23938.

Sherwell Garage Ltd, 1 Avenue Rd. ✆ (0803) 24002.

Thomas, G H (Belgrave Garage) Ltd, Tor Church Rd. ✆ (0803) 22851.

Westhill Garage, Chatto Rd. ✆ (0803) 38351.

Wilkins (Torbay) Ltd, Alexandra Garage, Alexandra La. ✆ (0803) 27914.

BABBACOMBE

★★★Anchorage (Rl), *Cary Av, TQ1 3NQ.* ✆ (0803) 36175. C. ⋈ 49 bedrs, 26 bp, 2 bps, 22 sh, 5 ba, TV, Dgs. ✗ mc, at, LD 8.30. ⓝ N, CH, TV, ns, CP 49, Ac, CF, 14 BGf, 2 st. £ BB £12–£16, DB £23–£30, WT £84–£112, DT £12–£18, DBB £11–£18, WB, ①, Bk £3·50, L £3·50, D £6, Dep b.

⬛★★Morningside (Rt), *St Albans Rd, Babbacombe Downs, TQ1 3LG.* ✆ (0803) 37025. Open Mar–Oct & Xmas. ⋈ 18 bedrs, 1 bps, 5 sh, 2 ba, TV. ✗ mc, at, LD 7. ⓣ ch, TV, CP 14, 4 BGf, 1 st, Dis. £ BB £11–£12, DB £22–£28, DBB £26–£38, ②, Bk £2·50, L £2·50, D £6·50, Dep a.

⬛★★Norcliffe (R), *Babbacombe Downs Rd, TQ1 3LF.* ✆ (0803) 38456. C. ⋈ 22

bedrs, 9 bp, 1 bps, 4 sh, 4 ba, TV, Dgs. ✗ mc, at, LD 8. ⓣ CH, Dgs, CP 17, CF, 1 BGf, 2 st. £ BB £10–£16·50, DB £20–£40, DBB £15–£21·50, ①, Bk £2·10, D £6·50, cc 1 3, Dep b.▲

⬛★★Penrhyn (R), *Cary Park, TQ1 3NH.* ✆ (0803) 37385. Closed Dec & Jan. C. ⋈ 20 bedrs, 5 bp, 8 bps, 2 ba, Dgs. ✗ mc, at, LD 8. ⓣ CH, TV, Dgs, CP 19, Ac, con, CF, 5 BGf, 0 st, Dis. £ BB £9·50–£15, DB £19–£30, WT £94–£114, DT £14·50–£18·50, DBB £12·50–£18, WB, ①, Bk £3, L £2, D £6, Dep a.

⬛★★Sunray (Rl), *Aveland Rd, Cary Park, TQ1 3PT.* ✆ (0803) 38285. C. ⋈ 24 bedrs, 12 bp, 6 bps, 3 ba, TV, Dgs. ✗ mc, at, LD 8. ⓣ CH, TV, Dgs, CP 15, G 1, CF, 2 BGf, 0 st, Dis. £ BB £11·30–£13, DB £12–£26, DBB £14·25–£16, WB, ①, Bk £2, D £5·50, cc 1 3, Dep a.

⬛★Viscount (Rt), *St Albans Rd, TQ1 3NP.* ✆ (0803) 37444. Open Mar–Oct. C. ⋈ 20 bedrs, 7 bp, 3 ba, TV, Dgs. ✗ mc, at, LD 7·30. ⓣ ch, TV, Dgs, CP 20, Ac, sp, CF, 5 BGf, 1 st, Dis. £ BB £11·16–£18·50, DB £22·32–£41, WT £82·50–£126·50, DBB £13·75–£23·08, WB, ①, Bk £4, L £2·50, D £5·50, Dep.

Devonshire House, H, y (Rl), *47 Babbacombe Rd, TQ1 3SJ.* ✆ (0803) 37935. C. ⋈ 28 bedrs, 2 bp, 3 bps, 5 ba. ⓣ ch, TV, CP 30, CF, 6 BGf, 5 st. £ BB £10, WT (b) £85, DT (b) £14.

Exmouth View, PH, z (Rl), *St. Albans Rd. TQ1 3LJ.* ✆ (0803) 37307. Open Apr–Oct & Xmas. C. ⋈ 36 bedrs, 6 bps, 3 sh, 5 ba, Dgs. ⓣ CH, TV, CP 25, CF, 2 BGf, 1 st, Dis. £ BB £8–£11·50, DB £16–£25·50, WT (b) £78·75–£105, DT (b) £11·25–£15, ①.

Rescue Service: Dutton Foreshaw, 55 Babbacombe Rd. ✆ (0803) 27571.

MAIDENCOMBE

⬛★★Bowden Close (R), *Teignmouth Rd, Maidencombe, TQ1 4TJ.* ✆ (0803) 38029. Closed Jan & Feb. C. ⋈ 21 bedrs, 1 bp, 10 bps, 2 sh, 2 ba, TV. ✗ mc, at, LD 7.30. ⓣ CH, TV, CP 50, U 1, G 1, con 45, CF, 3 st. £ BB £9·25–£13·55, DB £17–£22·60, WT £83–£92, DBB £12·50–£15·15, WB, ①, Bk £2·50, D £5·50, cc 3.

⬛★★Orestone House (R), *Rockhouse La, TQ1 4SX.* ✆ (0803) 38099. Open Mar–Oct & Xmas. ⋈ 15 bedrs, 6 bp, 7 bps, 2 ba, TV, Dgs. ✗ a l c, mc, at, LD 8·30. ⓣ ch, CP 28, sp, con 25, CF, 1 st. £ BB £20–£25, DB £38–£43, DBB £24·50–£30, WB, ②, Bk £3·50, L £4, D £7·25, cc 1 2 3 5 6, Dep a.

Cleveland Country House, H, x (Rl), *Steep Hill, TQ1 4TS.* ✆ (0803) 38577. C 3. ⋈ 6 bedrs, 2 ba, Dgs. ⓣ CH, TV, Dgs, CP 6, 2 BGf, 3 st. £ BB £6·50–£8·50, DB £13–£24, WT (b) £63–£84, DT (b) £9–£12, ①.

Higher Commons, G, y (Rl), *Teignmouth Rd, TQ1 4TP.* ✆ (0803) 38441. C ⋈ 10 bedrs, 2 ba, Dgs. ⓣ CH, TV, ns, CP 10, 1 st. £ BB £6·50–£7·50, DB £13–£15, WT (b) £71·50–£75, DT (b) £10·50–£11, ①, Bk £2, D £3·50.

Parkfield, H, x, y (R), *Cladden La, TQ1 4TB.* ✆ (0803) 38952. Open Apr–Oct. C. ⋈ 13 bedrs, 3 ba, Dgs. ⓣ ch, TV, CP 20, CF, 4 st. £ BB £7·50–£9·50, DB £15–£21·40, WT (b) £78–£93, (c) £46·50–£61·50, DT (b) £12–£14, ①, Bk £2·75, D £4·50.

Rosewood, G, xy (Unl), *Teignmouth Rd, TQ1 4SF.* ✆ (0803) 38178. C. ⋈ 8 bedrs,

2 bps, 2 ba. ⒟ CH, TV, CP 14, CF, 2 BGf, 3 st. £ Bk £2·25, D £3·95.

TORRINGTON Devon. Maps 3A and 4C
Pop 7,509. South Molton 15, London 196, Barnstaple 11, Bideford 7, Holsworthy 14, Okehampton 19.
Golf Torrington 9h. **See** Four-arm Cross at Windy Corner, Rosemoor, Charitable Garden

★★Castle Hill, *South St. EX38 8AA.*
✆ (0805) 22339. C. ⇄ 10 bedrs, 8 bp, 1 bps, 1 sh, 1 ba, TV. ✖ a l c, mc, at, LD 8.45. ⒟ CH, TV, CP 40, Ac, con 150, CF, 4 BGf, 2 st. £ BB £12·73–£14·70, DB £18·70–£21·70, WB, Ⓐ️, Bk £1·75, L £2·75, D £4·50, cc 1 3 4 5.
Smytham, G, y (Rl), *EX38 8PU.* ✆ (0805) 22110. C. ⇄ 12 bedrs, 3 ba, Dgs. ⒟ TV, Dgs, CP 12, CF. £ BB £6·50, DB £13, WT (b) £70, DT (b) £10.

Repairer: Heard's Garage Ltd, 39 Well St. ✆ (0805) 2229.

TORVER Cumbria. Map 26F
Pop 182. Ambleside 9½, London 278, Broughton-in-Furness 7, Ulverston 10.
Golf Ulverston 18h.

Rescue Service: Hadwin, J F & E, The Garage. ✆ Coniston (096 64) 317.

TOTLAND BAY Isle of Wight. Map 6E
Pop 2,230. Portsmouth (Fy) 17, London 78, Newport 10, Ventnor 18, Yarmouth 2½.
EC Wed. **Golf** Freshwater Bay 18h. **See** Tennyson Down, Alum Bay.

★★★Country Gardens (R), *Church Hill, PO39 0GT.* ✆ Isle of Wight (0983) 4521. Closed Xmas. C 14. ⇄ 16 bedrs, 16 bp, TV, Dgs. ✖ a l c, mc, at, LD 9.30. ⒟ N, CH, CP 20, Ac, 4 BGf, 2 st. £ BB £18–£20, DB £38–£40, WT £155–£165, WB, Ⓐ️, Bk £3, L £5, D £7·50, cc 1 3 4 5 6, Dep a.
■★★**Sentry Mead** (R), *Madeira Rd, PO39 0BJ.* ✆ Isle of Wight (0983) 753212.
Garrow, PH, xy (Rl), *Church Hill, PO39 0EU.* ✆ Isle of Wight (0983) 753174. Open May–Sep. C 3. ⇄ 16 bedrs, 6 bps, 10 sh, 3 ba. ⒟ ch, TV, CP 16, 2 BGf, 1 st, Dis. £ BB £10–£12, DB £20–£24, WT (b) £84, DT (b) £13, Ⓐ️.
Hermitage, PH, xy (R), *Cliff Rd, PO39 0EW.* ✆ Isle of Wight (0983) 752518. C. ⇄ 12 bedrs, 2 bp, 2 bps, 6 sh, 2 ba, Dgs. ⒟ ch, TV, Dgs, ns, CP 12, CF. £ BB £10·50–£17, DB £21–£29, WT (b) £97–£146, DT (b) £16–£23, Ⓐ️, Bk £2, L (Sun) £6, D £6, cc 1 3 ▲.
Hilton House, PH, x (Rl), *Granville Rd, PO39 9AZ.* ✆ Isle of Wight (0983) 754768. Open Mar–Oct. C. ⇄ 6 bedrs, 1 bps, 1 bp, TV, Dgs. ⒟ CH, TV, Dgs, ns, CP 1, BGf, 4 st. £ BB £7·50–£8, DB £15–£17 WT (b) £75–£80, DT (b) £12·50–£15, Ⓐ️, Bk £2·50, D £5·50.
Nodes Country, H, x, y (R), *Alum Bay Old Rd, PO39 9HZ.* ✆ Isle of Wight (0983) 752859. C. ⇄ 11 bedrs, 2 bp, 6 bps, 2 ba, Dgs. ⒟ CH, TV, Dgs ns, CP 16, CF, 5 BGf. £ BB £10–£15, DB £20–£30, WT (b) £96–£120, DT (b) £15–£19, Ⓐ️, Bk £3, D £6.

TOTNES Devon. Map 3D
Pop 6,500. Newton Abbot 8, London 191, Ashburton 8, Dartmouth 13 (Fy 11), Kingsbridge 12, Plymouth 22, Saltash 23, Torquay 8.
EC Thur. **MD** Tue, Fri. **Golf** Churston 18h. **See** Church (15th cent), Castle ruins,

Butterwalk, Guildhall (16th cent) and Museum, Totnes Museum, restored 15th cent East Gate, Brutus Stone, Buckfast Abbey 5 m NW, Dart Valley Rly (standard gauge steam engine) Buckfast to Totnes.
🛈 The Plains. ✆ Totnes (0803) 863168.

★★Royal Seven Stars, *The Plains, TQ9 5DD.* ✆ (0803) 862125. C. ⇄ 18 bedrs, 10 bp, 5 ba, TV, Dgs. ✖ a l c, mc, LD 9.30. ⒟ ch, TV, Dgs, ns, CP 25, Ac, con 60, CF. £ BB £20–£28, DB £30–£38, WT fr £129, DT £27–£32, WB, Ⓐ️, Bk £3·50, L £5·75, D £8·75, cc 1 4 5.
Buckyette Farm, F, x (Unl), *Buckyette, Little Hempston, TQ9 6ND.* ✆ Staverton (080 426) 638. C. ⇄ 6 bedrs, 2 ba. ⒟ TV, CP 8, CF, 6 st. £ BB £8·40, DB £16·80, WT (b) £77·70–£84, (c) £57·75, DT (b) £12·60, Ⓐ️.
Four Seasons, G, *13 Bridgetown, TQ9 5AB.* ✆ (0803) 862091.
Stanborough Hundred, PH, y (Rl), *Halwell, TQ9 7JG.* ✆ East Allington (054 852) 236. Closed Jan & Feb. C. ⇄ 8 bedrs, 2 bp, 1 ba, ns, TV, Dgs. ⒟ CH, TV, CP 10, CF, 1 BGf, 0 st, Dis. £ BB £10–£13·50, DB £20–£31, WT (b) £85–£97, DT (b) £18–£19·50, Ⓐ️, Bk £1·75, D £8.

Repairer: Evans & Cutler Ltd, North St. ✆ (0803) 862466.
Rescue Service: Moorland Garages Ltd, Station Rd. ✆ (0803) 862404.
MC Repairer: Totnes Motorcycles, Station Bridge. ✆ (0803) 866097.

TOTON Nottinghamshire. Map 22F
M1 Motorway 3, London 119, Ashby-de-la-Zouch 14, Derby 10, Loughborough 13, Nottingham 6.

Manor, PH, x (R), *Nottingham Rd, NG9 6EF.* ✆ Nottingham (0602) 733487. Closed Xmas. C. ⇄ 18 bedrs, 2 bp, 5 sh, 4 ba, TV, Dgs. ⒟ CH, Dgs, CP 18, CF, 1 BGf, 2 st. £ BB £16·50–£19·55, DB £26·45–£28·75, Ⓐ️.

TOTTENHILL Norfolk. Map 16E
Downham Market 6, London 94, King's Lynn 6½, Swaffham 14, Thetford 25, Wisbech 13.

Oakwood House, H, x, y (R), *PE33 0RH.* ✆ King's Lynn (0553) 810256. Closed Xmas. C. ⇄ 12 bedrs, 3 bp, 1 bps, 1 sh, 1 ba, TV. ✖ a l c, mc, CP 20, CF, 3 BGf, 1 st, Dis. £ BB £11·50–£16, DB £21–£26, WT (b) fr £98, Ⓐ️, Bk £2·75, L £3·70, D £6·50.

TOYNTON-ALL-SAINTS Lincolnshire. M. Area 23D
1½m South of Spilsby. Boston 16, London 133, Grimsby 34, Lincoln 32, Mablethorpe 18, Skegness 14.

Rescue Service: Fendyke Garage, Fenside. ✆ Spilsby (0790) 53647.

TREBETHERICK Cornwall. Map 2D
Pop 500. Camelford 12, London 240, Wadebridge 8.
Golf St Enodoc Rock 9h & 18h. **See** St Enodoc's Church.

Rescue Service: Fore Dore Garage. ✆ (020 866) 2355.

TREGONY Cornwall. Map 2F
Pop 450. St Austell 8, London 240, Bodmin 19, Newquay 6, Truro 8.
Golf St Austell 18h. **See** Almshouses, 17th cent.

Tregony House, G, z (R), *TR2 5RN.* ✆ (087 253) 671. Open Mar–Oct. C 5. ⇄ 6 bedrs, 2 ba, Dgs. ⒟ ch, TV, CP 6, 2 st. WT (b) £103, DT (b) £15·95, Ⓐ️, D £7.

Rescue Service: J J Harris & Son (Eng) Ltd, Treworran Garage, Ruan High Lanes. ✆ (087 253) 304.

TREYARNON BAY Cornwall. Map 2D
Pop 50. Wadebridge 11, London 250, Newquay 11, Truro 23, St Austell 21.
Golf Trevose Head 27h.

★★Waterbeach (R), *PL28 8JW.* ✆ Padstow (0841) 520292. Open May–Sept. C. ⇄ 16 bedrs, 7 bp, 2 sh, 3 ba. ✖ a l c, mc, at, LD 8.30. ⒟ ch, TV, CP 35, tc, CF, 2 st. £ BB £15–£19, DB £30–£40, WT £170–£180, Ⓐ️, Bk £4·75, D £9, cc 1 5, Dep.

TRING Hertfordshire. Map 15E
Pop 11,774. Watford 16, London 32, Aylesbury 7, Denham 19, Dunstable 10, High Wycombe 16, Rickmansworth 15, St Albans 15, Wallingford 26.
EC Wed. **MD** Mon, Fri. **Golf** Wendover 9h. **See** Perp Church, Natural History Museum.

■★★**Rose & Crown** (TH), *High St, HP23 5AH.* ✆ (044 282) 4071.

TROWBRIDGE Wiltshire. Map 5B
Pop 24,000. Devizes 7, London 103, Bath 11, Chippenham 12, Frome 8, Radstock 11, Warminster 9.
EC Wed. **MD** Tue, Fri, Sat. **Golf** West Wilts 18h. **See** Fine Parish Church, Town Hall (tablet, bust of Sir Isaac Pitman), 18th cent Lock-up (Blind House), The Courts, Holt 3 m N, Tropical Bird Gardens, Rode 4 m W.

■★**Hilbury Court** (R), *Hilperton Rd, BA14 7JW.* ✆ (022 14) 2949. Closed Xmas. C. ⇄ 12 bedrs, 3 bp, 2 ba. TV. ⒟ CH, TV, CP 20, CF, 6 st. £ BB £17–£20, DB £27–£29, Ⓐ️, Bk £3, L £3, D £6, cc 1 3.
★Polebarn, *Polebarn Rd, BA14 7EW.* ✆ (022 14) 65624. C. ⇄ 11 bedrs, 5 bps, 4 sh, 2 ba, TV. ✖ a l c, mc, at, LD 9. ⒟ CH, TV, CP 12, Ac, con 100, CF, 2 st. £ BB fr £18·50, DB fr £24·50, Ⓐ️, Bk £2·50, L £1·85, D £1·85, cc 1 3 5 6.

Rescue Service: Lesters Garages Ltd, Duke St. ✆ (022 14) 2077.
Riverway Motors, Riverway. ✆ (022 14) 62631.
Williams & Williams (Westbury) Ltd, Yarnbrook Garage. ✆ (022 14) 63081.

TROWELL Nottinghamshire. Map 22D
Pop 1,835. M1 Motorway 3, Stapleford 2, London 125, Derby 11, Ilkeston 1½, Mansfield 16, Nottingham 6.
See St Helen's Church.

Rescue Service: Riseley Garage Granada Services, Motorway Service Area. ✆ Ilkeston (0602) 324733.

TRURO Cornwall. Map 2F
Pop 16,500. St Austell 14, London 246, Bodmin 24, Falmouth 11, Helston 16, Newquay 18, Redruth 8, Wadebridge 23.
MD Wed. **Golf** Truro 18h. **See** Cathedral, County Museum and Art Gallery, Trelissick Gdns 4 m S.
🛈 Municipal Buildings, Boscawen St. ✆ Truro (0872) 74555.

★★Brookdale (R), *Tregolls Rd, TR1 1JZ.* ✆ (0872) 73513. Closed Xmas. C. ⇄ 25

bedrs, 12 bp, 4 bps, 6 sh, 6 ba, annexe 18 bedrs, 5 bp, 2 bps, 4 ba, TV, Dgs. ✘ mc, at, LD 8.45. ◫ ch, CP 50, G 10, Ac, con 35, CF, 0 st. £ BB fr £21·10, DB fr £38, DBB fr £30·30, WB, ①, Bk £3·50, L £3·50, D £8, cc 1 2 3 5.

▣★★Carlton (RI), *Falmouth Rd, TR1 2HL.* ✆ (0872) 72450. Closed 20 Dec–5 Jan. C. ⊯ 25 bedrs, 5 bp, 16 bps, 2 sh, 3 ba, TV, Dgs. ✘ a l c, mc, at, LD 8. ◫ CH, Dgs, CP 30, con, CF, 7 BGf, 1 st, Dis. £ cc 1 5.

★★Royal, *Lemon St, TR1 2QB.* ✆ (0872) 70345. RS Xmas. C. ⊯ 34 bedrs, 34 bp, TV, Dgs. ✘ a l c, mc, at, LD 9.30. ◫ N, CH, CP 20, G 14, Ac, con 50, CF, 2 st. £ BB £19·75–£24·75, DB £37·50–£38·50, WB, ①, Bk £3·50, L £4·50, D £4·50, cc 1 3, Dep b.

Farley, H, z (Unl), *12 Falmouth Rd, TR1 2HX.* ✆ (0872) 73680.

Laurel Cottage, G, x (Unl), *St Erme Rd, Trispen, TR4 9BJ.* ✆ (0872) 79632. Open May–Sep. C. ⊯ 5 bedrs, 2 ba. ◫ ch, TV, CP 6, CF, 1 BGf. £ BB £8·50, DB £15, WT (b) £56, DT (b) £13, ①.

Midway, I, x, *Grampound Rd Village, TR2 4EE.* ✆ St Austell (0726) 882343. Open Apr–Sep. C. ⊯ 4 bedrs, 2 sh, 2 ba. ◫ ch, TV, CP 4, CF. £ BB £9·25–£9·75, DB £18·50–£19·50, DT (b) £13·50–£14, ①.

Pengelly, F, y (Unl), *St Erme, TR4 9BG.* ✆ Mitchell (087 251) 245. Open Mar–Sep. C 10. ⊯ 4 bedrs, 1 ba. ◫ TV, CP 4. £ BB £6·50–£7, DB £12–£14, WT (c) £42–£49, ②

Repairer: Mumfords of Truro Ltd, Newquay Rd. ✆ (0872) 2581.
MC Repairer: Collins W H & Son (Motors) Ltd, Kenwyn St. ✆ (0872) 74334.
Sctr Repairer: Collins W H & Son (Motors) Ltd, Kenwyn St. ✆ (0872) 74334.
Rescue Service: Brian Ferris, incorporating Ferris Recovery Services, The Garage, Feock. ✆ Devoran (0872) 862218.
Penhaligon, R C, Kenwyn Hill Garage, Bissoe. ✆ Devoran (0872) 863073.
Richards, L J & Sons, Point Mills Garage, Bissoe. ✆ Devoran (0872) 863073.
S Hicks & Sons Ltd, T/As Hicks of Truro, Lemon Quay. ✆ (0872) 74321.

TUNBRIDGE WELLS Kent. Map 7D
See also SOUTHBOROUGH.
Pop 44,821. Tonbridge 4, London 36, Eastbourne 29, East Grinstead 13, Hawkhurst 18, Hurst Green 14, Maidstone 16, Uckfield 16.
EC Wed. **MD** Wed. **Golf** Nevill 18h. **See** The Pantiles, 17th cent King Charles the Martyr Church, Holy Trinity Church (designed by Decimus Burton), Museum at Civic Centre, Toad Rock 1 m N, High Rocks 1½ m SW, Penshurst Place 4½ m NW, The Owl House Gardens 5 m SE, Scotney Castle Gardens 7 m SE.
ℹ Town Hall. ✆ Tunbridge Wells (0892) 26121.

★★★Calverley, *Crescent Rd, TN1 2LY.* ✆ (0892) 26455.

★★★Spa, *Mount Ephraim, TN4 8XJ.* ✆ (0892) 20331. C. ⊯ 70 bedrs, 66 bp, 3 bps, 2 ba, TV, Dgs. ✘ a l c, mc, at LD 9.30. ◫ Lt, N, CH, Dgs, CP 120, Ac, sp, tc, sc, sb, sol, gym, con 250, CF, 2 BGf, 1 st, Dis. £ BB £30–£38·50, DB £54–£60, WB, ①, Bk £5·50, L £8·80, D £9·90, cc 1 2 3 4 5 6, Dep b.

█★★Beacon, *Tea Garden La, TN3 9JH.* ✆ (0892) 24252.

★★Royal Wells Inn, *Mount Ephraim, TN4 8BE.* ✆ (0892) 23414.

★★Russell, *80 London Rd, TN4 0PP.* ✆ (8092) 44833. C. ⊯ 21 bedrs, 11 bp, 10 bps, TV. ✘ mc, at, LD 9.30. ◫ CH, TV, CP 20, Ac, con 20, CF, 4 st. £ BB £29–£30, DB £38–£44, DBB £28–£38, WB, ②, Bk £3·50, L £7, D £9, cc 1 2 3 5, Dep.

★★Wellington, *Mount Ephraim, TN4 8BU.* ✆ (0892) 42911. C. ⊯ 66 bedrs, 28 bp, 6 bps, 8 ba, TV, Dgs. ✘ a l c, mc, at, LD 7.30. ◫ Lt, N, CH, TV, Dgs, CP 25, Ac, sb, sol, gym, con 110, CF, 3 BGf. £ BB fr £15, DB fr £30, DT fr £25, DBB fr £22, WB, ①, Bk £3, L £3·50, D £7, cc 1 2 3 5.

Firwood, G, z (Unl), *89 Frant Rd, TN2 5LP.* ✆ (0892) 25596. Closed Dec 20–Jan 14. C. ⊯ 10 bedrs, 7 bp, 3 bps, 1 ba, TV. ◫ CH, TV, CP 12, CF. £ BB £20, DB £30, ②, Bk £5·50, D £7, cc 1 2 3 5.

Marlborough, PH, x (RI), *57 Mount Ephraim, TN4 8BB.* ✆ (0892) 21328.

Repairers: Cundell A A Ltd, Calverley Garage, Crescent Rd. ✆ (0892) 25266.
Rawson, J & Sons Ltd, Mount Pleasant. ✆ (0892) 27202.
Silverdale Showrooms Ltd, Upper Grosvenor Rd. ✆ (0892) 27174.
Stormont Engineering Co Ltd, 3 Mount Ephraim. ✆ (0892) 20323.
G E Tunbridge Ltd, 323 St John's Rd. ✆ (0892) 26416.
Specialist Body Repairer: Classified Development, Ltd, T/As P K Motors, 1 North Farm Rd. ✆ (0892) 32886.

TURVEY Bedfordshire. Map 15C
Pop 950. Bedford 7, London 57, Buckingham 21, Huntingdon 25, Kettering 19, Northampton 13.
EC Tue. **Golf** Bedford 18h. **See** Church Cross, 17th cent Three Fyshes Inn, Abbey.

★★The Laws At Turvey, *High St, MK43 8DB.* ✆ (023 064) 213. Closed Xmas week, RS Sun, Mon, Sat. C 8. ⊯ 5 bedrs, 4 bp, 1 bps, TV. ✘ a l c, LD 9 (10 Sat, Sun). ◫ CH, CP 50, con 14, 2 st. £ BB fr £29·50, DB fr £34, ①, cc 1 5, Dep b.

TUTBURY Staffordshire. Map 22E
Pop 3,089. Burton-on-Trent 4, London 125, Ashbourne 15. Derby 11, Uttoxeter 10.
EC Wed. **Golf** Burton-on-Trent 18h. **See** 15th cent Castle, Norman Church, Ye Olde Dog and Partridge Inn, Glassworks, N. Staffs Traction Engines.

★★★Ye Olde Dog & Partridge, *High St, DE13 9LS.* ✆ Burton-on-Trent (0283) 813030.

TUTSHILL Gloucestershire. M. Area 13E
Pop 4,773, Chepstow 1, London 124, Gloucester 27, Ross-on-Wye 23.
Golf Chepstow 18h.

Rescue Service: Bowens Garage Ltd. ✆ Chepstow (029 12) 3131.

TUXFORD Nottinghamshire. Map 22D
Pop 2,690. Newark 13, London 138, Doncaster 24, Gainsborough 17, Lincoln 18, Ollerton 6, Thorne 29, Worksop 12.
EC Wed. **Golf** Retford 9h. **See** Parish Church, old Grammar School, old lock-up.

★★Newcastle Arms, *Market Place, NG22 0LA.* ✆ (0777) 870208. C. ⊯ 13 bedrs, 7 bp, 2 sh, 1 ba, TV, Dgs. ✘ a l c, mc,

at, LD 9.30 (10 Fri & Sat). ◫ CH, Dgs, CP 100, U 4, Ac, con 50, CF. £ BB fr £25, DB fr £30, WB, ①, Bk £2·50, L £5·25, D £7·50, cc 1 3 4 5.▲

Rescue Service: Sanderson's Garage, Market Pl. ✆ (0777) 870207.

TWICKENHAM Greater London (Middx). Maps 7A and 8
Pop 100,971. Richmond-upon-Thames 2, London 9, Brentford and Chiswick 4½, Kingston upon Thames 3, Slough 13, Staines 9, Uxbridge 11.
EC Wed. **Golf** Fulwell 18h, Strawberry Hill 9h. **See** Marble Hill House.

Repairers: Ferden-Birch Motors Ltd, 92 Cross Deep. ✆ 01-892 3379.
M & J Autos (Brentford), 1 Haliburton Rd. ✆ 01-892 6812.
MC Repairer: Blays of Twickenham, 192 Heath Rd. ✆ 01-892 2103.

TWO BRIDGES Devon. Map 3C
Exeter 24, London 193, Ashburton 11, Okehampton 9, Plymouth 17, Tavistock 9.

Cherrybrook, PH, x (R), *PL20 6SP.* ✆ Tavistock (0822) 88260. Closed Xmas–New Year. C. ⊯ 8 bedrs, 5 bps, 1 ba, Dgs. ◫ CH, Dgs, CP 12, CF. £ BB £11–£12·50, DB £25, WT (b) £122·50, DT (b) £17·50, ①, Bk £2·50, D £6·50.

TWYFORD Berkshire. Map 6B
Pop 5,175. Slough 13, London 33, Bagshot 13, Farnham 21, Henley-on-Thames 5, High Wycombe 12, Reading 5.
EC Wed. **Golf** Sonning 18h. **See** Almshouses.

Rescue Service: Knowl Hill Garage, Bath Rd. ✆ Littlewick Green (062 882) 2715. Twyford Service Garage, New Bath Rd. ✆ (0734) 345777.

TWYFORD Hampshire. Map 6D
Pop 1,443. Winchester 4, London 69, Fareham 15, Romsey 9, Southampton 10.
Golf Hockley 18h. **See** Twyford House (Georgian).

Rescue Service: G E Ivan Stacey, The Garage. ✆ (0962) 712148.
Prince Bros. Grove Service Station, London Road. ✆ (0892) 340309.

TYNEMOUTH Tyne & Wear. Map 32B
Pop 50,014. Tyne Tunnel 2½, London 280, Alnwick 36, Coldstream 54, Newcastle upon Tyne 8, Sunderland 11.
EC Wed. **Golf** Tynemouth 18h. **See** Ancient Gatehouse and ruins of 11th cent Priory. Watch House (collection of relics), Collingwood Monument, Lighthouse.

★★★Grand, *Grand Parade, NE30 4ER.* ✆ North Shields (0632) 572106.

★★★Park, *Grand Parade, NE30 4JQ.* ✆ North Shields (0632) 571406. RS Bank Holidays. C. ⊯ 27 bedrs, 16 bp, 2 bps, 5 ba, TV, Dgs. ✘ a l c, LD 9.30. ◫ N, CH, Dgs, CP 400, Ac, con, CF, 1 st. £ BB £13·50–£31·50, DB £27–£37·50, WT £195–£280, DT £28·50–£45·50, DBB £22·50–£39·50, WB, ①, Bk £3·75, L £4·25, D £5·75, cc 1 2 3 4 5 6, Dep b.

Rescue Service: Mariners Garage, Tynemouth Rd. ✆ North Shields (0632) 572442.

UBLEY Avon. M. Area 5A
Pop 320. Radstock 13, London 121, Bath 17, Bridgwater 25, Bristol 11, Wells 9, Weston-super-Mare 14.

Golf Mendip 18h. **See** 13th cent Church.

Rescue Service: Ubley Motor Services (1968) Ltd, Cleeve Hill Garage. ✆ Blagdon (0761) 62275.

UCKFIELD East Sussex. Map 7D
Pop 9,200. East Grinstead 13, London 43, Eastbourne 19, Hastings 26, Haywards Heath 12, Hurst Green 18, Lewes 8, Tunbridge Wells 16, Westerham 22.
EC Wed. **Golf** Piltdown 18h. **See** Church (15th cent Tower), Maiden's Head Inn (formerly King's Arms), Beeches Farm Gardens 1½ m W, Bluebell Rly from Sheffield Park to Horsted Keynes, Bentley Wild Fowl Collection 3 m S, Sheffield Park Gardens 5 m NW.

★★Ye Maiden's Head, *High St, TN22 1RJ.* ✆ (0825) 2019. C. ⊷ 13 bedrs, 6 bp, 3 ba, TV. ✗ a l c, mc, LD 9.30. ⌂ CH, Dgs, CP 40, Ac, con 60, 2 st. £ BB £16–£20, DB £25–£31·50, DBB £22·50–£26·50, WB, ⊉ 10%, Bk £4, L £5, D £6·50, cc 2 3 5.

Repairer: Tressler Trailer Coachworks Ltd, Unit 3, Bellbrook Industrial Estate. ✆ (0825) 2262.

ULCEBY Humberside (South Humberside). M. Area 24A
Pop 1,309. Lincoln 33, London 167, Grimsby 14, Hull 16, Market Rasen 18, Scunthorpe 17.
Golf Elsham 18h.

Rescue Service: John Morris Motors, Wootton. ✆ Wootton (046 95) 512.

ULLESTHORPE Leicestershire. M. Area 14B
Pop 866. M1 Motorway 3½, London 92, Coventry 14, Hinckley 7, Leicester 12, Market Harborough 15, Nuneaton 10, Rugby 10.
EC Wed. **Golf** Ullesthorpe Court 18h. **See** Windmill.

Rescue Service: Wrights Garages (Ullesthorpe) Ltd, Claybrooke Rd. ✆ Leire (0455) 209171.

ULLSWATER Cumbria
See GLENRIDDING, PATTERDALE, POOLEY BRIDGE, WATERMILLOCK.

ULVERSTON Cumbria. Map 27E
Pop 11,907. M6 Motorway 24, London 270, Ambleside 21, Broughton-in-Furness 9½, Kendal 24, Lancaster 34, Penrith 43.
EC Wed. **MD** Thur. **Golf** Ulverston 18h. **See** Swarthmoor Hall, 12th cent Parish Church, Sir John Barrow Monument.
🄸 Renaissance Centre, 17 Fountain St. ✆ Ulverston (0229) 52299.

◼★★Lonsdale House (Rl), *Daltongate, LA12 7BD.* ✆ (0229) 52598.▲
▲ ▲ **Sefton House** (R), *34 Queen St, LA12 7AF.* ✆ (0229) 52190. Closed Xmas & New Year. C. ⊷ 11 bedrs, 2 bp, 5 bps, 2 ba, TV. ✗ a l c, mc, LD 9. ⌂ CH, TV, CP 3, G 3, CF, 2 st. £ BB £18–£23·50, DB £33–£39·50, DBB £26–£31, WB, ⊉, Bk £3, L £4·50, D £8, cc 1 3.

★Railway, *Prince's St, LA12 7NQ.* ✆ (0229) 52208. Closed Xmas. C. ⊷ 8 bedrs, 2 ba, Dgs. ✗ mc, LD 9. ⌂ CH, Dgs, CP 40, CF, 2 st. £ BB £15, DB £24, WB, ⊡, Bk £3, L £3, D £7·50, Dep a.
Bridgefield House, H, x, y (R), *Spark Bridge, LA12 8DA.* ✆ Lowick Bridge (022 985) 239. Closed Jan & Feb. C. ⊷ 6 bedrs, 3 bp, 2 ba, Dgs. ⌂ CH, ns, CP 10,

---

CF, 1 st. £ BB fr £11·50, DB fr £23, WT (b) fr £157·50, (c) fr £80·50, DT (b) fr £22·50, ⊉, D £11·25, cc 1 2 5.

UMBERLEIGH Devon. Maps 3B and 4C
Pop 138. South Molton 7, London 188, Barnstaple 7½, Bideford 14, Crediton 24, Holsworthy 22, Okehampton 20.
Golf Saunton 18h.

◼★★Rising Sun Inn, *EX37 9DU.* ✆ High Bickington (0769) 60447. Open Mar–Oct, RS winter, C 10. ⊷ 6 bedrs, 4 bp, 1 ba, Dgs. ✗ mc, at, LD 8.30. ⌂ CH, TV, Dgs, CP 12, G 2, pf, 3 st. £ BB £18–£20, DB £34–£38, DBB £25–£27, ⊉, Bk £2·50–£3, D £7·50–£8·50, cc 1 3.

UPCHURCH Kent. M. Area 10C
Pop 1,800. London 38, Rochester 7½, Canterbury 21, Maidstone 11, Margate 36.
EC Wed. **Golf** Gillingham 18h. **See** Beautiful and ancient Parish Church, Roman Diggings.

Rescue Service: Upchurch Garage Ltd, Horsham La. ✆ Medway (0634) 31684.

UPHOLLAND Lancs. Map 20C
Pop 7,780. M6 Motorway 1½, London 193, Ormskirk 7½, St Helens 7, Wigan 4½.
Golf Beacon Park 18h. **See** Church, Beacon Park.

◼★★Holland Hall, *6 Lafford La, Wigan, WN8 0QZ.* ✆ (0695) 624426. C. ⊷ 13 bedrs, 5 bp, 8 bps, TV. ✗ a l c, mc, at, LD 10. ⌂ N, CH, Ac, con 40, CF, 0 st. £ BB £24–£26, DB £31–£33, WT £203·50–£215·50, WT £42–£44, DBB £33·50–£35·50, WB, ⊉ 10%, Bk £3·95, L £8·50, D £9·50, cc 1 2 3 4 5 6, Dep b.

UPMINSTER Greater London (Essex).
Maps 7B and 17F
Pop 90,000. Romford 3½, London 19, Brentford 6½, Dartford Tunnel 6½, Rainham 5, Southend-on-Sea 22.
EC Thur. **Golf** Upminster 18h. **See** Windmill.

Rescue Service: Talbot, A E & Sons, Station Road Garage. ✆ (040 22) 20091.

UPPER LANGFORD Avon. M. Area 5A.
Pop 150. 4m NE of Axbridge. Bath 21, London 125, Bristol 14, Bridgwater 20, Wells 14, Weston-Super-Mare 10.
Golf Worlebury 18h.

Rescue Service: Avon Auto Centre, Bath Rd. ✆ Churchill (0934) 852573.

UPPER SLAUGHTER Gloucestershire.
Map 14E
See also LOWER SLAUGHTER.
Pop 167. Stow-on-the-Wold 3, London 87, Burford 11, Cheltenham 15, Cirencester 17, Evesham 18.
Golf Burford 18h. **See** Church, Bridge, Well nearby.

◼♣★★★Lords of the Manor, *GL54 2JD.* ✆ Cotswold (0451) 20243. Closed Jan 7–20. C 2. ⊷ 15 bedrs, 14 bp, 1 bps, 3 ba. ✗ mc, LD 9.30. ⌂ CH, TV, Dgs, CP 20, pf, CF, 0 st. £ BB £35, DB £47–£75, WB, ⊡, Bk £5, L £7·50, cc 1 2 3 5 6, Dep a.

UPPINGHAM Leicestershire. Maps 15A and 23E
Pop 3,492. Kettering 14, London 89, Huntingdon 34, Leicester 18, Market Harborough 12, Melton Mowbray 15, Peterborough 21, Stamford 12.

EC Thur. **MD** Fri, Sat. **Golf** South Luffenham 18h. **See** Uppingham School (apply to Porter), Church.

★★★Falcon, *High St East, LE15 9PY.* ✆ (0572) 823535. C. ⊷ 26 bedrs, 14 bp, 1 bps, 1 sh, 4 ba, TV, Dgs. ✗ a l c, mc, at, LD 10. ⌂ N, CH, Dgs, CP 25, G 3, Ac, con 50, CF, 3 BGf, 1 st, Dis. £ BB £23–£30, DB £32–£38, WB, ⊡, Bk £3·50, L £6·50, D £7·50, cc 1 2 3 5.

★★Marquess of Exeter, *52 Main St, Lyddington, Oakham, LE15 9LT.* ✆ (0572) 823887.

★Central (R), *High St West, LE15 9PY.* ✆ (0572) 822352. RS Wed. C. ⊷ 12 bedrs, 4 bp, 2 ba, TV, Dgs. ✗ a l c, mc, at, LD 9. ⌂ CH, TV, Ac, con 20, CF, 1 st. £ BB £16–£20·50, DB £25–£29·50, WB, ⊡, Bk £3, L £6·75, D £6·75, cc 1 3, Dep b.

UPTON-UPON-SEVERN Hereford & Worcester (Worcestershire). Map 13D
Pop 2,057. Tewkesbury 6, London 111, M50 Motorway 4, Bromyard 17, Evesham 13, Ledbury 10, Worcester 10.
EC Thur. **Golf** Malvern 18h. **See** Church (1879—built in 13th cent style), White Lion Inn, Bridge, old houses.

★★★White Lion, *High St, WR8 0HJ.* ✆ (068 46) 2551. C. ⊷ 10 bedrs, 8 bp, 2 ba, TV, Dgs. ✗ a l c, mc, at, LD 9. ⌂ CH, Dgs, CP 10, Ac, con 12, CF, 1 st. £ BB £27·30–£29·50, DB £36·75–£39·50, DBB £45·50–£51·50, WB, ⊉, Bk £5, L £7·95, D £7·95, cc 1 3, Dep a.

Rescue Service: Ryall Garage, Tewkesbury Rd. ✆ (068 46) 2271.

UPTON SNODSBURY Hereford & Worcester (Worcestershire). Map 14C
Pop 334. Stratford-upon-Avon 19, London 112, Droitwich 9, Worcester 7.
MD Mon. **Golf** Worcester G and CC 18h. **See** 13th cent Church, Old Bull cottages (half-timbered, formerly the old Bull Inn), old houses, old Smithy.

Rescue Service: Richards, H J, Woodview Garage. ✆ (090 560) 203.

URMSTON Greater Manchester (Lancashire). Map 20A
Pop 44,009. Altrincham 5, London 185, M63 Motorway 1, Manchester 5, Stockport 9, Walkden 6, Warrington 13.
EC Wed. **MD** Tue, Fri, Sat. **Golf** William Wroe, Urmston 18h, Davyhulme 18h. **See** 12th cent Church.

Specialist Body Repairer: Goddard & Staines Ltd, Higher Rd. ✆ 061-748 0321.

UTTOXETER Staffordshire. Map 22E
Pop 11,250. Burton-on-Trent 13, London 135, Ashbourne 12, Derby 18, Leek 19, Lichfield 17, Stafford 14, Stoke-on-Trent 15, Stone 13, Tamworth 24.
EC Thur. **MD** Wed, Sat. **Golf** Uttoxeter 9h. **See** Parish Church, Racecourse, Alton Towers 8 m N.

Repairers: Fryer, A J & Co, Derby Road Garage. ✆ (088 93) 2301.
Furbank, H W Ltd, Market Street Garage. ✆ (088 93) 2858.

UXBRIDGE Greater London. Map 7A
Pop 63,941. Ealing 8½, London 16, Denham 2, Harrow 8, Kingston upon Thames 15, Slough 6, Staines 11.

EC Wed. **MD** Fri, Sat. **Golf** Hillingdon 9h, Harefield Place 18h. **See** Market House, St Margaret's Church, old inns.

Repairer: Courtwood Car Services, Penfield Estate, Lancaster Rd. ✆ (0895) 36567.

VENTNOR Isle of Wight. Map 6F
Pop 5,810. Shanklin 3½, London (Fy) 86, Newport 9½, Yarmouth 20.
EC Wed. **Golf** Ventnor 9h. **See** Ventnor Botanic Garden, old Church at Bonchurch (grave of Swinburne), St Boniface Down.
🛈 34 High St. ✆ I.O.W. (0983) 853625.

◼★★★**Royal** (TH), *Belgrave Rd, PO38 1JJ.* ✆ Isle of Wight (0983) 852186. Closed Nov–Feb. C. ◖► 55 bedrs, 55 bp, TV, Dgs. ✕ a l c, mc, at, LD 9. 🅿 Lt, N, CH, Dgs, CP 56, Ac, sp, con 120, CF, 1 st. **£** BB £33·50, DB £52·50, WB, 🅣, cc 1 2 3 4 5 6.

★★★**Ventnor Towers**, *Madeira Rd, PO38 1QT.* ✆ Isle of Wight (0983) 852277. C. ◖► 30 bedrs, 17 bp, 4 bps, 4 ba, TV, Dgs. ✕ mc, at, LD 8.30. 🅿 N, CH, Dgs, CP 40, U 1, Ac, sp, gc, tc, pf, con 30, CF, 7 BGf, Dis. **£** BB £15·50–£19·50, DB £31–£39, WT £189–£220, DT £27–£32, DBB £20–£27, WB, 🅣, Bk £5, L £5, D £8, cc 1 2 3 5 6.▲

◖#★★**Winterbourne** (R), *Bonchurch, PO38 1RQ.* (1 m E). ✆ Isle of Wight (0983) 852535. Closed Dec–Jan. C 7. ◖► 20 bedrs, 18 bp, 2 bps, TV, Dgs. ✕ mc, at, LD 9.30. 🅿 N, CH, TV, Dgs, CP 30, sp, con 40, CF, 0 st. **£** BB £24–£28, DB £48–£56, WB, 🅣, D £10·75, cc 1 2 3 5 6, Dep a.

◖#★**Madeira Hall** (RI), *Trinity Rd, PO38 1NS.* ✆ Isle of Wight (0983) 852624. Open Mar–Oct. C. ◖► 12 bedrs, 3 bp, 1 bps, 3 ba, Dgs. ✕ mc, LD 7.30. 🅿 CH, TV, CP 12, sp, CF, 5 st. **£** BB £12–£14·25, DB £24–£28·50, DBB £15·40–£39·90, WB, 🅙, 5%, Bk £3, L £3·60, D £5·50, cc 1 2 3.

Ap. Lake (RI), *Bonchurch, PO38 1RF.* ✆ Isle of Wight (0983) 852613. Open Mar–Oct. C. ◖► 11 bedrs, 2 ba, Dgs. ✕ mc, at, LD 6. 🅿 TV, ns, CP 21, Ac, con 25, CF, 5 st. **£** BB £8·50–£13·25, DB £17–£26·50, WT £92·75–£106·75, DT £16·25–£18·25, DBB £11·30–£15·25, 🅙, Bk £2, L £3, D £4·50, Dep a.

Channel View, H, x (RI), *Hambrough Rd, PO38 1SQ.* ✆ Isle of Wight (0983) 852230.

Cliffview, H, z (R), *Hambrough Rd, PO38 1SQ.* ✆ Isle of Wight (0983) 852226. C. ◖► 18 bedrs, 2 sh, 3 ba, TV, Dgs. 🅿 CH, TV, Dgs, CF, 2 st. **£** BB £9·50–£12·50, DB £18–£22, WT (a) £85·50–£88·50, (b) £80–£85, (c) £60–£70, DT (a) £14·50–£16·90, (b) £12·50–£16, 🅙, Bk £2·60, D £3·50, cc 3.

Hillside, PH, y, *Mitchell Ave, PO38 1DR.* ✆ Isle of Wight (0983) 852271. Open Mar–Oct. C. ◖► 16 bedrs, 6 bp, 2 ba, TV, Dgs. 🅿 CH, TV, Dgs, CP 12, CF, 2 st. **£** BB £10·75–£13·75, DB £21·50–£27·50, WT (b) £99·75–£120·75, (c) £72·25–£96·25, DT (b) £14·25–£17·25, 🅣, Bk £2, D £3·50.

Horseshoe Bay, H, x (R), *Shore Rd, Bonchurch, PO38 1RN.* ✆ Isle of Wight (0983) 852487. Open Apr–Oct. C 8. ◖► 7 bedrs, 3 bp, 1 bps, 1 ba, Dgs. ✕ mc, CP 7, 1 BGf, 1 st, Dis. **£** BB £9–£11·50, DB £18–£27, DT (b) £13·50–£18, 🅙, L £3·30.

Kimberly, H, z (R), *Alpine Rd, PO38 1BT.* ✆ Isle of Wight (0983) 852148. Closed Nov. C. ◖► 16 bedrs, 4 bp, 2 bps, 3 ba. 🅿 CH, TV, CP 12, CF. **£** BB £9·79–£12·90,

DB £17·80–£23·82, WT (b) £76–£95, DT (b) £12·40–£15, 🅙, D £3·50.

Macrocarpa, H, y (R), *Mitchell Av, PO38 1DW.* ✆ Isle of Wight (0983) 852428. Open Apr–Oct. C. ◖► 20 bedrs, 6 bp, 5 bps, 3 ba, Dgs. 🅿 ch, TV, Dgs, CP 20, CF, 1 st. **£** BB £10·50–£13·50, DB £21–£27, WT (b) £85–£115, DT (b) £13·50–£16·50, 🅣, Bk £2, D £4·60.

Palmerston, H, z (RI), *Hambrough Rd, PO38 1SQ.* ✆ Isle of Wight (0983) 852713. Open May–Sep. C. ◖► 12 bedrs, 1 bps, 2 ba, TV, CF. **£** BB £7–£9, DB £14–£18, WT (b) £65–£77, DT (b) £9·50–£11, 🅣.

Picardie, PH, z (RI), *Esplanade, PO38 1JX.* ✆ Isle of Wight (0983) 852647.

Richmond, H, z (RI), *Esplanade, PO38 1JX.* ✆ Isle of Wight (0983) 852496. Open Apr–Oct. C. ◖► 12 bedrs, 6 bps, 2 ba, Dgs. 🅿 ch, TV, CP 6, CF, 1 st. **£** BB £8·50, DB £17, WT (b) £86·50–£90, DT (b) £12·50, 🅣, cc 3.

St Maur, H, y (RI) *Castle Rd.* ✆ Isle of Wight (0983) 852570. C. 3 ba. ◖► 16 bedrs, 5 bp, 5 bps, 4 ba. 🅿 CH, TV, CP 12, CF, 0 st. **£** BB £9·50–£12, DB £19–£28, WT (b) £88–£100, DT (b) £13·50–£16, 🅣, Bk £3, L £5·50, D £8·50, cc 1.

Under Rock, H, y (R), *Shore Rd, Bonchurch, PO38 1RF.* ✆ Isle of Wight (0983) 852714. Open Mar–Oct. C 10. ◖► 8 bedrs, 2 ba, TV. 🅿 CH, CP 12, 2 BGf, 2 st. **£** BB £14, DB £28, WT (b) £126, DT (b) £18, 🅙.

Wellington, H, x (RI), *Belgrave Rd, PO38 1SW.* ✆ Isle of Wight (0983) 852404.▲

Windsor-Carlton, PH, z (RI), *4 Alexandra Gdns, PO38 1EE.* ✆ (0983) 852543. Open Mar–Oct. C. ◖► 15 bedrs, 1 bp, 5 ba, Dgs. 🅿 TV, Dgs, CP 4, CF. **£** BB £8·63–£9·20, DB £17·26–£18·40, WT (b) £82–£91, DT (b) £12·40–£13·80, 🅣.

Rescue Service: Chale Service Station, High St, Chale. ✆ Isle of Wight (0983) 730466.

Danelaw Motor Services Ltd, Bonchurch Garage, Bonchurch Village Rd. ✆ Isle of Wight (0983) 854145.

Spracks Garage, Down La. ✆ Isle of Wight (0983) 853016.

VERWOOD Dorset. Map 6E
Pop 5,100. Ringwood 4½, London 97, Blandford Forum 17. Bournemouth 12, Dorchester 33, Salisbury 20, Shaftesbury 19, Wareham 19.
EC Wed. **Golf** Ferndown 18h. **See** Parish Church.

Rescue Service: Verwood Motors Ltd, Ringwood Rd. ✆ (0202) 822395.

VERYAN Cornwall. Map 2F
Pop 500. St Austell 12, London 245, Falmouth (Fy) 16, Newquay 20, Truro 12 (Fy 11).
Golf Truro 18h. **See** 15th cent Church, Carne Beacon (Ancient Burial Place).

★★★**Nare** (R), *TR2 5PF.* ✆ Truro (0872) 501279. C. ◖► 37 bedrs, 33 bp, 3 ba, TV. ✕ mc, at, LD 9.15. 🅿 CH, TV, CP 80, U 5, sp, sb, sol, gym, con, CF, 10 BGf, 0 st, Dis. **£** BB £13–£26·25, DB £26–£52·50, DBB £22–£35, 🅣, Bk £5, D £10·25, cc 1 2 3 5, Dep b.

◼★★**Elerkey House** (R), *TR2 5QA.* ✆ Truro (0872) 501261. Closed Dec 17–Mar 1. C 6. ◖► 9 bedrs, 3 bp, 3 sh, 1 ba, TV. ✕ mc, at, LD 8.30. 🅿 TV, CP 12, 1 BGf, 1

st. **£** BB £14–£17·50, DB £29–£36·50, DBB £20–£23·50, DBB £20–£23·50, WB, 🅣, D £6·50, cc 1 2 3, Dep.

Treverbyn House, G, x (R), *Pendower Rd, TR2 5QL.* ✆ Truro (0872) 501201. Closed Dec–Jan. C 7. ◖► 4 bedrs, 2 ba. 🅿 CH, TV, CP 9, 1 st. **£** BB £12·50, DB £25, WT (b) £136·50, DT (b) £20, 🅣, Bk £3·50, D £9.

WADEBRIDGE Cornwall. Map 2D
Pop 4,800. Camelford 11, London 238, Bodmin 7, Newquay 14, Truro 23.
EC Wed. **MD** Mon. **Golf** St Enodoc 18h. **See** Bridge (15th cent), Egloshayle Church (EE and Perp), St Breock's Church.
🛈 Town Hall. ✆ (020 881) 3725.

★★**Molesworth Arms**, *Molesworth St, PL27 7DP.* ✆ (020 881) 2055. RS Dec25. C (under 8 by arangement). ◖► 16 bedrs, 9 bp, 3 ba, TV, Dgs. ✕ a l c, mc, at, LD 9.30. 🅿 CH, TV, Dgs, CP 50, U 4, Ac, con 100, CF, 1 st. **£** BB £14–£15·50, DB £19–£21, DBB £19–£20·50, 🅣, Bk £3, D £6·50, cc 1 3.

◼★**Swan**, *Molesworth St, PL27 7DD.* ✆ (020 881) 2526.

Laurels, G, xy (RI), *The Whitecross, PL27 7JQ.* ✆ (020 881) 3341. Open Mar–Nov. C 14. ◖► 4 bedrs, 1 ba, ns, TV. 🅿 CH, CP 10. **£** BB £7·50–£8·50, DB £14–£16, WT (b) £52–£55, DT (b) £9·50–£10·50, 🅣.

White Lodge, PH, xy (RI), *Old Polzeath, PL27 6TJ.* ✆ Trebetherick (020 886) 2370.

Wyndhurst, G, z (Unl), *69 Molesworth St, PL27 7DS.* ✆ (020 881) 3435.

Rescue Service: Broad Meadows Filling Station, Padstow Rd. ✆ (020 881) 2046.
Brooklyn Garage. ✆ (020 881) 2758.
I. C. R. Fisher, Motor & Gen. Engineers, Polmoral Rd. ✆ (020 881) 2546.
Meadowhead Garage, Eddystone Rd. ✆ (020 881) 3281.
W. A. Hawkey & Sons Ltd, Egloshayle Rd. ✆ (020 881) 2121.

WAKEFIELD West Yorkshire. Map 25F and 33B
See also OSSETT.
Pop 76,296. Barnsley 9½, London 182, M1 Motorway 2½, Boroughbridge 34, Bradford 14, Doncaster 19, Halifax 17, Huddersfield 13, Leeds 9, Pontefract 9, Stockport 39.
EC Wed. **MD** Mon, Tue, Thur, Fri, Sat. **Golf** City of Wakefield 18h, Wakefield Woodthorpe 18h. **See** Cathedral, Ancient Bridge with Chantry Chapel, Museum, City Art Gallery, St Helen's Church, Waterton Chapel, remains of Sandal Castle, Heath Hall 1½ m E. Nostell Priory 5 m SE.
🛈 Town Hall, Wood St. ✆ Wakefield (0924) 370211.

★★★**Stoneleigh** (R), *Doncaster Rd, WF1 5HA.* ✆ (0924) 369461. C. ◖► 26 bedrs, 12 bp, 9 bps, 3 ba, TV. ✕ a l c, mc, at. **£** BB £20–£34, DB £30–£48, WB, 🅙, Bk £4, L £6·50, D £8·95, cc 1 3.

★★★**Swallow**, *Queen St, WF1 1JU.* ✆ (0924) 372111. C. ◖► 64 bedrs, 64 bp, TV, Dgs. ✕ a l c, mc, LD 9.30. 🅿 Lt, N, CH, Dgs, CP 50, Ac, con 120, CF, 1 st. **£** BB £30–£40, DB £40–£50, WB, 🅣, Bk £6, L £8, D £10, cc 1 2 3 5 6, Dep b.

★★★**Walton Hall**, *The Balk, Walton, WF2 6PW.* ✆ (0924) 257911.

Sandal Court, H, y, *108 Barnsley Rd, WF1 5NX.* ✆ (0924) 258725. C. ⊷ 12 bedrs, 2 ba. ✗ a l c. ⊡ CH TV, ns, CP 16, 4 st. £ BB fr £15, DB fr £23, ⑪, Bk £2·50, L £5·50, D £5·50, cc 1 5.

Repairer: Glanfield Lawrence (Wakefield) Ltd, 68 Ings Rd. ✆ (0924) 372812.
Rescue Service: Newton Hill Garage, 267 Leeds Rd, A61. ✆ (0924) 374182.

WALBERTON West Sussex. Map 7E
2 m N of Yapton. Pop 1,785. Pulborough 10, London 49, Arundel 3½, Bognor Regis 7, Chichester 7½, Littlehampton 6.
Golf Bognor Regis 18h. **See** Church with Saxon font, Nat Trust Woodland (walks).

⚑★★★Avisford Park, *Yapton La, BN18 0LS.* ✆ Yapton (0243) 551215.

WALFORD Hereford & Worcester (Hereford). Map 13E
M50 Motorway 3, Gloucester 17, London 121, Hereford 16, Monmouth 7, Ross-on-Wye 3.

▣⚑★★Walford House, *HR9 5RY* (on B4228). ✆ Ross-on-Wye (0989) 63829. C. ⊷ 10 bedrs, 9 bp, 1 bps, TV, Dgs. ✗ mc, at, LD 9.30. ⊡ CH, CP 100, CF, 1 BGf, 0 st, Dis. £ BB £20–£25, DB £34–£40, DBB £30–£35, WB, ⑪, Bk £3·50, D £10, cc 1 2 3 5.

WALKERINGHAM Nottinghamshire. Map 23A
Gainsborough 4, London 154, Doncaster 18, Grimsby 39, Humber Bridge 36, Rotherham 24, Thorne 20, Worksop 17.

Brickmakers Arms, H, x, *Fountain Hill Rd, DN10 4LT.* ✆ Gainsborough (0472) 890375. C. ⊷ 11 bedrs, 1 bp, 6 bps, 1 ba, ns, TV. ✗ a l c. ⊡ CH, TV, CP 40, U 1, G 1, CF, 2 BGf, 0 st. £ BB fr £20, DB fr £26·50, ⑪, Bk £3·50, L £5, D £8, cc 1 3 4 5.

WALL Northumberland. Map 31E
Pop 200. Hexham 3½, London 285, Alnwick 40, Bellingham 13, Hawick 49, Jedburgh 44.
Golf Hexham 18h & 9h. **See** Hadrian's Wall, Chester Fort.

★★The Hadrian Inn, *NE46 4EE.* ✆ Humshaugh (043 481) 232.

WALLASEY Merseyside. Map 19A
Pop 70,285. Birkenhead 3, London 201.
EC Wed. **MD** Daily (except Wed). **Golf** Warren Pk 18h. **See** Parish Church, Town Hall, River Mersey (shipping).
⊡ The Bathing Pool, Marine Par. ✆ 051-638 7144.

★Grove, *Grove Rd, L45 3HF.* ✆ 051-630 4558. C. ⊷ 14 bedrs, 5 ba, TV, Dgs. ✗ a l c, mc, LD 10. ⊡ N, CH, Dgs, CP 15, Ʌ◦, CF. £ BB £21 50 £23 65, DB £31·50–£34·65, WT £233·45–£256·79, DT £33·75–£36·68, DBB £27–£29·70, WB, ⑪, L £5·35, D £6·50, cc 1 2 3 5 6, Dep a.
Clifton, G, z (Unl), *293 Seabank Rd, L45 5AF.* ✆ 051-639 6505. Closed Xmas week. C. ⊷ 6 bedrs, 1 ba. ⊡ CH, TV, CF. £ BB fr £7·50, DB fr £15, ⑪.
Divonne, PH, z, *71 Wellington Rd, L45 2NE.* ✆ 051-639 4727. Closed Xmas & New Year. C. ⊷ 15 bedrs, 5 bps, 3 ba, TV, Dgs. ⊡ CH, TV, CP 6, CF, 5 BGf, 1 st, Dis. £ BB £9·50–£10·50, DB £18, WT (b) £105, DT £15, ⑪, Bk £2, D £4·50.
Sea Level, PH, z (Unl), *126 Victoria Rd, New Brighton, L45 9LD.* ✆ 051-639 3408.

Repairer: Recovery North West, 12 Rullerton Rd. ✆ 051-630 3636.

WALLINGFORD Oxfordshire. Maps 14F & 6B
See also NORTH STOKE.
Pop 6,500. Henley-on-Thames 11, London 46, Aylesbury 25, Basingstoke 28, High Wycombe 21, Newbury 18, Oxford 12, Reading 14, Wantage 14.
EC Wed. **MD** Fri. **Golf** Streatly 18h. **See** St Peter's Church, St Leonard's Church, St Mary-le-More Church, 17th cent open-sided Town Hall, Bridge, old houses and inns, Almshouses, Wallingford Castle (open to public), 16th cent Flint House (Museum), Wittenham Clumps.
⊡ Stone Hall, High St. ✆ Wallingford (0491) 35351 ext 249.

★★★George, *High St, OX10 0BS.* ✆ (0491) 36665. C. ⊷ 18 bedrs, 7 bp, 2 bps, 2 ba, TV, Dgs. ✗ a l c, mc, at, LD 10.30 (9.30 Sun). ⊡ CH, Dgs, CP 80, Ac, con 100, CF, 1 st. £ BB £27–£32, DB £38–£42, WB, ⑪, Bk £4·75, L £7·25, D £7·25, cc 1 3 4 5, Dep b.
★★★Shillingford Bridge, *Shillingford Rd, OX10 8LZ.* ✆ Warborough (086 732) 8567. C. ⊷ 32 bedrs, 31 bp, 1 ba, TV. ✗ a l c, mc, at, LD 10. ⊡ CH, Dgs, CP 100, Ac, sp, pf, sc, con 60, CF, 5 BGf, 0 st, Dis. £ BB fr £30, DB fr £40, ⑪, Bk £4, L £9, D £9, cc 1 3 4 5.
⚑★★★Springs, *Wallingford Rd, North Stoke, OX9 6BE.* ✆ (0491) 36687.

WALLINGTON Greater London (Surrey). Map 7A
Carshalton 1, London 12, Coulsdon 3, Croydon 3, Mitcham 3, Sutton 2.

Rescue Service: McKinnon Motors Ltd, 31 Stafford Rd. ✆ 01-669 5135.

WALLSEND Tyne & Wear. Maps 31F & 32D
Pop 41,604. Newcastle 3½, London 276, Durham 18, Tynemouth 5, Morpeth 16.
EC Wed. **MD** Sun. **Golf** Wallsend 18h.
See Holy Cross Church.

▣★★★Newcastle Moat House, *Coast Rd, NE28 9HP.* ✆ (0632) 628989. C. ⊷ 155 bedrs, 155 bp, ns, TV, Dgs. ✗ a l c, LD 9.45. ⊡ Lt, N, CH, CP 500, Ac, con 500, CF.

Rescue Service: Bewicke Service Station. Bewicke Rd, Willington Quay. ✆ (0632) 625809.
Truscott Engineering Ltd, Wallsend Test Centre, Berwicke Rd. ✆ (0632) 623885.

WALSALL West Midlands. Map 21E
Pop 265,000. Birmingham 8½, London 120, M6 Motorway 1, Kidderminster 17, Lichfield 9¼, Stafford 17, Sutton Coldfield 9, Tamworth 11, Wolverhampton 6½.
EC Thur. **MD** Tue, Fri, Sat. **Golf** Walsall 18h. **See** St Matthew's Parish Church, Art Gallery and Museum, Arboretum, Rushall Manor.

★★★Baron's Court, *Walsall Wood, WS9 9AH.* ✆ Brownhills (0543) 376543. C. ⊷ 76 bedrs, 76 bp, TV. ✗ a l c, mc, at, LD 9.45. ⊡ Lt, N, CH, CP 180, Ac, con 120, CF, 0 st. £ BB £30–£34, DB £38–£43, DBB £32, WB, ⑫, 5%, Bk £3·50, L £6·50, D £8, cc 1 2 3 4 5.
★★★M Crest Birmingham-Walsall, *Birmingham Rd, WS5 3AB.* ✆ (0922) 33555. C. ⊷ 100 bedrs, 100 bp, ns, TV,

Dgs. ✗ a l c, mc, at, LD 9.45. ⊡ Lt, N, CH, Dgs, CP 300, Ac, con, CF, 14 BGf, 1 st, Dis. £ B fr £40, BD fr £50, WB, ⑪, Bk £5·25, D £9·25, cc 1 2 3 4 5 6, Dep b.
★★County, *Birmingham Rd, WS1 2NG.* ✆ (0922) 32323. C. ⊷ 47 bedrs, 11 bp, 3 bps, 19 sh, 5 ba, TV, Dgs. ✗ a l c, mc, LD 9.45. ⊡ N, CH, Dgs, CP 35, Ac, con 40, CF, 4 st. £ BB £24–£32, DB £32–£37, DBB £26·50–£38, WB, ⑪, Bk £4·50, L £5·70, D £6·60, cc 1 2 3 5 6, Dep b.
★★Royal, *Ablewell St, WS1 2EL.* ✆ (0922) 24555. C. ⊷ 36 bedrs, 4 bp, 32 bps, 4 ba, TV. ✗ mc, at, LD 9.45. ⊡ Lt, N, CH, TV, CP 40, Ac, con 200, CF, 1 st. £ BB fr £23·50, DB fr £33, ⑪, Bk £3·75, D £5·45, cc 1 2 5, Dep b.

Repairer: Reginald Tildesley Ltd, Wolverhampton St. ✆ (0922) 21212.
MC Repairer: Motor Cycle Mart (Walsall) Ltd, 12 Ablewell St. ✆ (0922) 23363.
Sctr Repairer: Motor Cycle Mart (Walsall) Ltd, 12 Ablewell St. ✆ (0922) 23363.
Rescue Service: Hamstead Service Station Ltd, Day St. ✆ (0922) 613232 & (0922) 612555.
Palfrey Service Station, Wednesbury Rd. ✆ (0922) 24327.
Walsall Way Service Station, Wolverhampton Rd. ✆ (0922) 25372.

WALTHAM CROSS Hertfordshire. Map 15F
Enfield 3, London 15, M25 Motorway 1½, Cheshunt 1½, Epping 8, Hatfield 13.
See Waltham Abbey 2½ m E, Lee Valley Regional Pk.

Rescue Service: Instantworth Ltd, Waltham Cross Car Port, 206 High St. ✆ (0922) 26297.

WALTHAM-ON-THE-WOLDS
Leicestershire. Map 23E
Pop 591. Melton Mowbray 5, London 109, Grantham 10.
Golf Melton Mowbray 9h. **See** 14th cent Church.

Rescue Service: Regent Services (Waltham) Ltd, Main St. ✆ (066 478) 229.

WALTON Merseyside. Map 19A.
Liverpool 3, London 198, M62 Motorway 4, Bootle 2, Ormskirk 10, Runcorn 15, St Helens 10, Southport 17, Warrington 17.

Rescue Service: Maple Motors, 1a Lancaster St. ✆ 051-525 5099.

WALTON-ON-THAMES Surrey. Map 7A
Pop 49,501 (inc Weybridge). Kingston upon Thames 5½, London 14, Epsom 9, Leatherhead 8, Richmond-upon-Thames 9, Ripley 7½, Staines 5¾, Weybridge 2
EC Wed. **Golf** Burhill 18h, St George's Hill 18h and 9h. **See** Church (12th cent brasses, Scold's bridle), Manor House, Museum.

★★Ashley Park, *Ashley Park Rd, KT12 1JP.* ✆ (093 22) 20196.

Repairers: H W Motors, New Zealand Av. ✆ (0932) 220404.
Walchry Motors Ltd, 143 Hersham Rd. ✆ (093 22) 23761.

WALTON-ON-THE-NAZE Essex. Map 17A
Pop 5,664. Colchester 17, London 73, Clacton 7½, Harwich 14, Ipswich 25.

EC Wed. **MD** Thur. **Golf** Frinton 19h & 18h. **See** Naze tower.
⊤ Princess Esplanade. **ᘯ** Frinton-on-Sea (025 56) 5542.

Rescue Service: Hall Lane Garage, 23 Hall La. **ᘯ** Frinton-on-Sea (025 56) 5684. Sterling Cars, High St. **ᘯ** Frinton-on-Sea (025 56) 5768.

WANSFORD Cambridgeshire. Maps 15A and 23E
Pop 400. Alconbury 16, London 83, Kettering 22, Leicester 33, Peterborough 7½, Stamford 5.
EC Wed, Sat. **Golf** Burghley Park, Stamford 18h. **See** Old packhorse bridge, ancient Church.

★★**Haycock,** *London Rd, PE8 6JA.*
ᘯ Stamford (0780) 782223. RS Xmas. C. **⋈** 28 bedrs, 14 bp, 1 bps, 6 ba, TV, Dgs.
✗ a l c, mc, at, LD 10.15. ⊡ N, CH, CP 300, Ac, pf, con 150, CF, 1 st. **£** BB £24–£60, DB £38–£60, WB, ⊤, Bk £4·50, L £5, cc 1 3 4 5, Dep b.

★★**M Sibson House,** *PE8 6ND.*
ᘯ Stamford (0780) 782227. C. **⋈** 4 bedrs, 4 bp, TV, Dgs. ✗ a l c, mc, at, LD 10. ⊡ CH, TV, CP 50, Ac, sp, sb, sol, con 80, CF, 1 st.
£ BB £27, DB £38, DBB £35–£41, ⊤, Bk £4·50, L £4·95, D £8, cc 1 2 3 5, Dep b.

WANTAGE Oxfordshire. Maps 6A and 14F
Pop 9,071. Wallingford 14, London 60, M4 Motorway 10, Amesbury 37, Faringdon 9, Marlborough 23, Newbury 14, Oxford 15, Reading 23, Salisbury 42, Swindon 17.
EC Thur. **MD** Wed, Sat. **Golf** Frilford Heath 18h (2). **See** King Alfred's Statue, Parish Church, old Bear Hotel, Styles Almshouses. Kingstone Lisle Park, W.

★★**Bear,** *Market Place, OX12 8AB.*
ᘯ (023 57) 66366. C. **⋈** 25 bedrs, 25 bp, TV, Dgs. ✗ a l c, mc, at, LD 10. ⊡ Lt, CH, Ac, con 80, CF, 3 st. **£** BB £20·50–£32·50, DB £29·50–£46·50, WB, ②, Bk £3·50, L £5·50, cc 1 3 4 5.

Repairers: Mellors of Challow Ltd, Faringdon Rd. **ᘯ** (023 57) 2751. Segsbury Motors Ltd, 32 Newbury St. **ᘯ** (023 57) 3993.
Rescue Service: Erbsmails, Grove Street Garage. **ᘯ** (023 57) 3747.
G Finch-Recovery, Challow Station Garage, Challow Station, Faringdon. **ᘯ** (023 57) 2726.
Ridgeway Garages (Wantage) Ltd, Grove Rd. **ᘯ** (023 57) 65511.

WARBOYS Cambridgeshire. Map 15B
Pop 2,870. Huntingdon 7, London 69, Cambridge 20, Ely 20, Royston 27, Peterborough 16, Wisbech 26.
Golf Ramsey 18h. **See** Church, 13th cent spire, 17th cent Manor House.

Rescue Service: Clifford's Garage, 64 High St. **ᘯ** Ramsey (0487) 822424.

WARE Hertfordshire. Map 15F
Pop 14,203. Hoddesdon 4, London 24, Baldock 16, Bishop's Stortford 10, Hatfield 8½, Royston 17.
EC Thur. **MD** Tue. **Golf** Chadwell Spring 9h, East Herts 18h. **See** Parish Church, The Priory (now Council offices).

★★★**M Ware Moat House,** *Baldock St, SG12 9DR.* **ᘯ** (0920) 5011. C. **⋈** 50 bedrs, 44 bp, 6 bps, TV, Dgs. ✗ a l c, mc, at, LD 9.30. ⊡ Lt, N, CH, Dgs, CP 100, Ac, con

100, CF, 1 st. **£** BB £33–£36, DB £46–£47, WB, ⊤, Bk £3·85, L £7, D £7, cc 1 3 4 5.

Repairer: Charvill Bros Ltd, Baldock St.
ᘯ (0920) 2557 and (0920) 2862.

WAREHAM Dorset. Map 5F
Pop 6,261. Bournemouth 13, London 117, Blandford Forum 14, Dorchester 16, Ringwood 21, Weymouth 17.
EC Wed. **MD** Thur. **Golf** Wareham 9h, Lakey Hill 18h. **See** Parish Church, St Martin's Church (effigy of Lawrence of Arabia), John Streche Almshouses, Clouds Hill (NT) (Lawrence memorial cottage), 8 m NW, grave at Morton, Smedmore House 5½ m S, Royal Armoured Corps Museum (Bovington Camp), 6 m W, Corfe Castle, 4 m SE.

★★★**Priory** (R), *Church Green, BH20 4ND.* **ᘯ** 2772.

◩★★★**Springfield,** (R), *Grange Rd, BH20 5AL.* **ᘯ** (092 95) 2177. C 2. **⋈** 32 bedrs, 32 bp, TV, Dgs. ✗ a l c, mc, at, LD 9.30. ⊡ Lt, N, CH, Dgs, CP 50, sp, rf, con 100, CF, 9 BGf, 1 st, Dis. **£** WB, Bk £4·50, L £1·50, D £8, cc 1 4 5.

★★**Worgret Manor,** *Worgret, BH20 6AB.* **ᘯ** (092 95) 2957. RS Xmas. C. **⋈** 9 bedrs, 3 bps, 2 ba, TV, Dgs. ✗ a l c, mc, at, LD 9.15. ⊡ ch, TV, CP 40, Ac, con 20, CF, 1 BGf, 1 st, Dis. **£** BB £15–£21, DB £24–£36·50, WB, ⊤, Bk £3·50, L £4·95, D £6·85, cc 1 3 4 5.

★**Black Bear,** *South St, BH20 4LT.*
ᘯ (092 95) 3280. C. **⋈** 12 bedrs, 1 bp, 3 ba, TV. ✗ a l c, mc, at, LD 9.15. ⊡ CH, TV, Dgs, CP 4, Ac, con 50, CF, 1 st. **£** BB £14·50, DB £28·50–£30·50, WB, ②, Bk £2·75, L £3·25, D £5·25, cc 1 5 6.

Rescue Service: Auto-Maintenance (Wareham) Ltd, 3 Bonnets La. **ᘯ** (092 95) 2314.
Purbeck Motor Co Ltd, Stoborough. **ᘯ** (092 95) 2151.
Wareham Auto-Point, North St. **ᘯ** (092 95) 2823.

WARGRAVE Berkshire. Map 6B
Pop 3,000. Slough 12, London 32, Bagshot 15, Farnham 23, Henley-on-Thames 5, High Wycombe 12, Reading 6½.
EC Wed. **Golf** Henley 18h, Sonning 18h.
See Church, St George and Dragon Hotel, War Memorial, Crazies Hill with Village Well.

Repairer: Wargrave Motors Ltd, High St.
ᘯ (073 522) 2206.

WARLEY West Midlands. Map 14A
See CRADLEY HEATH, OLDBURY, ROWLEY REGIS, SMETHWICK.

WARMINSTER Wiltshire. Map 5D
Pop 16,000. Amesbury 19, London 99, Bath 16, Chippenham 20, Devizes 15, Frome 7, Salisbury 20, Shaftesbury 15, Wincanton 16.
EC Wed. **MD** Fri. **Golf** Warminster 18h.
See Church, Warminster School, old inns, old Meeting House at Horningsham, Longleat House 4 m W.
⊤ Old Bell Hotel, Market Pl. **ᘯ** Warminster (0985) 216611.

◩★★**Old Bell,** *Market Pl, BA12 9AN.*
ᘯ (0985) 216611. C. **⋈** 16 bedrs, 9 bp, 1 bps, 2 ba, TV, Dgs. ✗ a l c, mc, LD 10.30. ⊡ CH, Dgs, CP 20, Ac, con 75, CF, 2 st. **£** BB fr £19, DB fr £26, WB (Nov–Mar), ②, Bk £3, L £4, D £4, cc 1 3 4 5 6, Dep b.

Stoneleigh, G, z (RI), *7 Boreham Rd, BA12 9GP.* **ᘯ** (0985) 213419. C 2. **⋈** 6 bedrs, 3 ba. ✗ a l c. ⊡ CH, TV, CP 8, 1 BGf, 4 st. **£** BB £7·50–£8, DB £15–£16, WT £67–£75, ⊤, Bk £3, D £3·50.

Rescue Service: Zeals Garage Ltd, Zeals.
ᘯ Bourton (0747) 327.

WARMLEY Avon. M. Area 5B
Chippenham 16, London 108, Bath 9, Bristol 5½, Cheltenham 41, Chepstow 17, Gloucester 35, Radstock 14, Shepton Mallet 22, Tetbury 21, Wells 22.
Golf Warmley 9h. **See** Warmley House and Grounds.

Rescue Service: Bridgeyate Motor Co Ltd, London Rd. **ᘯ** Bristol (0272) 673447.
Parrot Vein Motor Co, 105 Bath Rd, North Common. **ᘯ** Bristol (0272) 670276.

WARRINGTON Cheshire. Map 20D
See also GRAPPENHALL.
Pop 175,000. M6 Motorway 4, London 183, M62 Motorway 2½, Altrincham 11, Bolton 17, Chester 20, Knutsford 11, Liverpool 17, Manchester 16, Northwich 11, St Helens 9½, Walkden 13, Wigan 12, Whitchurch 31.
MD Every day exc Thur & Sun. **Golf** Warrington 18h. **See** Parish Church, Holy Trinity Church, Museum and Library, old 'Barley Mow' Inn, Cromwell Statue, 18th cent Town Hall, Art Gallery.
⊤ 80 Sankey St. **ᘯ** Warrington (0925) 36501.

★★★**M Fir Grove,** *Knutsford Old Rd, Grappenhall, WA2 2LD.* **ᘯ** (0925) 67471. C. **⋈** 40 bedrs, 40 bp, TV, Dgs. ✗ a l c, mc, at, LD 10. ⊡ N, CH, TV, Dgs, CP 120, Ac, con 200, CF, 20 BGf, 1 st, Dis. **£** BB £28, DB £38, WT £250, DT £43, DBB £36, WB, ⊤, Bk £3·75, L £7, D £8, cc 1 2 3 4 5 6, Dep a.

★★★**Paddington House,** *514 Manchester Rd, WA1 3TZ.* **ᘯ** (0925) 816767. C. **⋈** 36 bedrs, 36 bp, TV. ✗ a l c, mc, at, LD 9.30. ⊡ Lt, N, CH, CP 200, Ac, con, CF, 6 BGf, 3 st. **£** cc 1 2 3 5 6, Dep b.▲

★★**Old Vicarage** (R), *Stretton Rd, Stretton, WA4 4NS.* (3½ m SE B5356).
ᘯ Norcott Brook (092 573) 238. Closed Bank Holidays & preceding evening. C. **⋈** 29 bedrs, 14 bp, 7 bps, a ba, TV, Dgs. ✗ mc, LD 8.30 (Sat 9, Sun 8). ⊡ Lt, CH, TV, CP 70, U 7, Ac, con 40, CF, 3 st. **£** BB fr £18·50, DB fr £31, DBB fr £27, WB, ⊤, Bk £4·50, L £6·50, D £8·50, cc 1 4 3.

◩★★**Patten Arms,** *Parker St, WA1 1LS.* **ᘯ** (0925) 36602. Closed Xmas. C. **⋈** 43 bedrs, 29 bp, 14 bps, TV, Dgs. ✗ a l c, mc, at, LD 9.30. ⊡ CH, Dgs, CP 20, G 5, Ac, con 25, CF, 1 st. **£** BB £50·60, WB, ⊤, Bk £3·30, L £4·50, D £5·50, cc 1 2 3 5 6, Dep b.

Birchdale, PH, z (RI), *Birchdale Rd, Appleton, WA4 5AW.* **ᘯ** (0925) 63662. Closed Xmas. C. **⋈** 22 bedrs, 4 ba, Dgs. ⊡ CH, TV, CP 30, CF, 2 st. **£** BB £16, DB £24, DT (b) £22, ⊤, Bk £3, L £4·50, D £6.

Specialist Body Repairer: A & A Motors, Holmsfield Rd, Howley. **ᘯ** (0925) 30464.
Repairer: Baldwins Garage (Warrington) Ltd, Winwick St. **ᘯ** (0925) 50011.
Rescue Service: A & A Motors Ltd, Holmsfield Rd. **ᘯ** (0925) 30464.
D R Edwards, Burtonwood Service Area Garage, Burtonwood. **ᘯ** (0925) 38829.

Fearnhead Cross Garage, T/As
Willowbrook Service Station, 168
Manchester Rd. ✆ (0925) 32144.
Howarth Motors Ltd, 101 Knutsford Rd.
✆ (0925) 65265.
Ilott & Sons, Wharf St. ✆ (0925) 39771.

WARTON Lancashire. Map Area 27C
Lancaster 8, London 246, Barrow in
Furness 36, Kendal 14, Windermere 22.

Rescue Service: Townend Garage, Sands
La. ✆ Carnforth (0524) 733837.

WARTON Lancashire. Map 27D
Pop 2,678. Preston 8, London 219,
Blackpool 10, Lancaster 27.
Golf Silverdale 9h. **See** Washington
House.

Rescue Service: Lytham Road Service
Station, 72 Lytham Rd, Freckleton.
✆ Freckleton (0772) 632480.

WARWICK Warwickshire. Map 14B
See also LEAMINGTON SPA.
Pop 22,000. Banbury 20, London 92,
Birmingham 21, Bromsgrove 23, Chipping
Norton 27, Coventry 10, Daventry 19,
Moreton-in-Marsh 22, Rugby 14,
Stratford-upon-Avon 8, Tamworth 27.
EC Thur. **MD** Sat. **Golf** Leamington and
County 18h. **See** Castle, St Mary's Church,
St Nicholas' Church, St John's House
(Museum), Old Market Hall and Museum,
Lord Leycester Hospital, Oken's House
(Dolls' Museum), Court House (Georgian
Ballroom), Guy's Cliffe (beauty spot),
Packwood House 8½ m NW.
🛈 Court House, 2 Jury St. ✆ Warwick
(0926) 492212.

★★★★M **Ladbroke,** *Longbridge, CV34
6RE.* ✆ (0926) 499555. C. 🛏 127 bedrs,
127 bp, TV, Dgs. ✗ mc, at, LD 10 (Sun
9.30). 🅿 Lt, N, CH, CP 200, Ac, sp, con
350, CF, 1 BGf, 1 st, Dis. £ BB £46, DB £63,
WB, 🔲, Bk £6, L £8, D £10·50,
cc 1 2 3 4 5 6, Dep b.
★★**Lord Leycester,** *Jury St, CV34 4EJ.*
✆ (0926) 491481. C. 🛏 48 bedrs, 39 bp, 9
bps, TV, Dgs. ✗ mc, at, LD 8.30. 🅿 N, CH,
Dgs, CP 50, con 100, CF, 3 st. £ BB £26,
DB £39–£42, WT £170, DT £27, DBB £23,
WB, 🔲, Bk £3·50, L £4·50, D £8·50,
cc 1 2 3 5 6, Dep b.
★★**Warwick Arms,** *High St, CV34 4AT.*
✆ (0926) 492759. RS Dec 25–Jan 1. C.
🛏 30 bedrs, 11 bp, 18 bps, 2 ba, TV, Dgs.
✗ a l c, mc, at, LD 10. 🅿 ch, Dgs, CP 30,
Ac, sb, sol, gym, con 130, CF, 2 st. £ BB
£23, DB £38, WT £211–£234, DT £27·50–
£33·50, DBB £24–£30, WB, 🔲, Bk £3·50, L
£4·50, D £7·50, cc 1 2 3 5 6, Dep b.
★★**Woolpack,** *Market Pl, CV34 4SD.*
✆ (0926) 496191.
Avon, G, z (Unl), *7 Emscote Rd, CV34
4PH.* ✆ (0926) 491367. Closed Xmas Day
C. 🛏 / bedrs, 2 ba. 🅿 CH, TV, CP 6, 1 st.
£ DB fr £16, DT fr £8, 🔲.
Guys Cross, PH, x (Rl), *122 Coventry Rd,
CV34 5HL.* ✆ (0926) 491208.
Westham, G, z (Rl), *76 Emscote Rd,
CV34 4PH.* ✆ (0926) 491756.

WASDALE HEAD Cumbria. Map 26F
Ravenglass 12, London 309, Broughton-
in-Furness 21, Eskdale 10, Nether
Wasdale 5½, Whitehaven 21.
Golf Seascale 18h. **See** Wastwater Lake,
Climbing Centre.

■★★**Wasdale Head Inn,** *Wasdale Head,
Gosforth, CA20 1EX.* ✆ (09406) 229. RS,

10 Nov–27 Dec incl. C. 🛏 10 bedrs, 8 bp,
2 bps, Dgs. ✗ a l c, mc, at, LD 8. 🅿 CH, CP
50, CF, 1 st. £ BB £16·25–£18·25, DB
£32·50–£36·50, WT £171·50, DT £24·50–
£26·50 (½ Board only) 🔲, Bk £4, L £4·60, D
£8·25, cc 1 5, Dep a.

WASHFORD Somerset. Map 4D
Pop 500. Taunton 16, London 159,
Bridgwater 18, Dunster 4½, Tiverton 23.
EC Wed. **MD** Mon. **Golf** Minehead and
West Somerset 18h. **See** Cleeve Abbey
remains. West Somerset Rly (Steam
Engines).
★★**Dragon House** (R), *Bilbrook, TA24
6HQ.* ✆ (0984) 40215. Closed Dec, Jan. C.
🛏 11 bedrs, 7 bp, 2 bps, 1 ba, TV, Dgs.
✗ a l c, mc, at, LD 9.15. 🅿 CH, CP 25, rf,
con 12, CF, 1 BGf, 0 st. £ BB £18·50–£29,
DB £30–£46, WB, 🔲, Bk £5, D £9·75,
cc 1 2 3 4 5 6.

WASHINGTON Tyne & Wear. Map 32D
Pop 50,000. Durham 11, London 271,
Newcastle upon Tyne 6, Sunderland 6½.
Golf Wearside 18h. **See** Washington Old
Hall, Holy Trinity Church, Waterfowl Park.
★★★M **Post House** (TH), *Emerson
District 5, NE37 1LB.* ✆ 091-416 2264. C.
🛏 145 bedrs, 145 bp, TV, Dgs. ✗ a l c, mc,
at, LD 10. 🅿 Lt, N, CH, Dgs, CP 198, U 3,
Ac, con 100, CF, 13 BGf, 0 st, Dis. £ BB
£39, DB £51·50, WB, 🔲, cc 1 2 3 4 5 6.

Rescue Service: Washington
Coachworks, Swan Rd. ✆ 091-416 3212.

WATCHET Somerset. Map 4D
Pop 3,050. Taunton 15, London 159,
Bridgwater 16, Dunster 6, Tiverton 24.
EC Wed. **Golf** Minehead and West
Somerset 18h. **See** St Decuman's Well
and Church, West Somerset Rly (Steam
Engines).
🛈 2 Market St. ✆ Watchet (0984) 31824.
★★**Downfield,** *St Decuman's Rd, TA23
0HR.* ✆ (0984) 31267. C. 🛏 6 bedrs, 2 bp,
4 bps, TV, Dgs. ✗ a l c, mc, at, LD 9.30.
🅿 CH, TV, Dgs, CP 25, Ac, con 25, CF, 1 st.
£ BB £24·15–£25, DB £35·65–£37, WT
£135–£140, DT £29·45–£30, 🔲, Bk £3·75,
L £3·95, D £8·50, cc 1 3 4 5 6, Dep a.

WATERMILLOCK Cumbria. Map 26D
Pop 677. Int 40 M6 Motorway 6¼, London
281, Ambleside 15, Kendal 26, Keswick
17, Penrith 7¼.
Golf Penrith 18h.

■▮★★**Leeming House** (R), *Ullswater,
CA11 0JJ.* ✆ Pooley Bridge (08536) 622.
Closed Jan, Feb. C 🛏 18 bedrs, 16 bp, 2
bps, annexe 7 bedrs, 6 bp, 1 bps. ✗ mc, at,
LD 8.45. 🅿 CH, TV, CP 40, Ac, pf, con 20, 2
BGf, 1 st, Dis. £ BB £25–£32, DB £50–£64,
WB, 15%, 🔲, Bk £6·50, L £b·75, D £16·75,
cc 1 3 4 5 6, Dep a.
■▮★★**Old Church** (R), *Penrith, CA11
0JN.* ✆ Pooley Bridge (085 36) 204.

WATFORD Hertfordshire. Map 15E
See also BUSHEY.
RAC Office, *130 St Albans Rd, Watford,
WD2 4AH.* ✆ (General) Watford (0923)
33543, (Rescue Service only) Watford
(0923) 33555.
Pop 75,500. Aylesbury 23, London 16, M1
Motorway 3, Barnet 10, Dunstable 18,
Harrow 7, Hatfield 13, Rickmansworth 3,
St Albans 7.
See Plan, p 366.

EC Wed. **MD** Tue, Fri, Sat. **P** See Plan.
Golf West Herts 18h. **See** St Mary's
Church, Bedford Almshouses, Cassiobury
Park and Whippendell Woods, Museum,
RC Church.

★★★M **Caledonian,** *St Albans Rd, WD1
1RN.* ✆ (0923) 29212. C. 🛏 86 bedrs, 86
bp, TV, Dgs. ✗ a l c, mc, at, LD 9.45. 🅿 Lt,
N, CH, Dgs, Ac, con 150, CF, 0 st. £ BB
£34–£36, DB £42–£43, DT £46–£48, DBB
£41·50–£43·50, WB, 🔲, Bk £4·75, L £5·50,
D £7·50, cc 1 2 3 5 6, Dep b.
The White House, H, z (R), *29 Upton Rd,
WD1 2EL.* ✆ (0923) 37316.

Repairer: Blackaby & Pearce (Watford)
Ltd, Sheepcot Service Station, North
Orbital Rd, Garston. ✆ Garston (092 73)
74166.
Rescue Service: Connoisseur Cars Ltd,
Pinner Rd. ✆ (0923) 33267 & (0923)
31107.▲
Darryl Motors Ltd, 175 Rickmansworth
Rd. ✆ (0923) 34034.
Jewell (Bushey Vale Garages) Ltd, 201
High St. ✆ (0923) 37211.
Move-a-Car & Commercial Ltd, Imperial
Way. ✆ (0923) 26634.

WATTON Norfolk. Map 16D
Pop 4,800. Newmarket 31, London 94,
East Dereham 10, Norwich 21, Scole 22,
Dereham 8½, Thetford 12.
EC Thur. **MD** Wed. **Golf** Dereham 9h. **See**
Wayland Wood 1 m S, the traditional site
of 'The Babes in the Wood'
(commemorative town sign in front of
Clock Tower in High St).

Rescue Service: Drome Garage Ltd,
Norwich Rd. ✆ (0953) 881343.

WATTON-AT-STONE Hertfordshire.
Map 15F
Pop 2,043. Hatfield 9½, London 30,
Baldock 11, Bishop's Stortford 9½,
Hoddesdon 9, Luton 18, Royston 15.
EC Wed, Sat. **See** Village lock up. **Golf**
East Herts 18h.

Rescue Service: Watton Service Station
Ltd, High St. ✆ Ware (0920) 830256.

WEARE Somerset. M. Area 5C
Pop 590. Wells 11, London 133,
Bridgwater 14, Bristol 19, Glastonbury 12,
Radstock 23, Weston-super-Mare 11.
Golf Berrow 18h. **See** St Gregory's
Church, Ambleside Water Gardens and
Aviaries.

Rescue Service: W P Counsell & Sons,
Weare Garage and Service Station.
✆ Axbridge (0934) 732248.

WEARHEAD Durham. Map 26A
Pop 200. Middleton-in-Teesdale 13,
London 271, Alston 11, Bellingham 37,
Durham 30, Hexham 22, Newcastle upon
Tyne 34, West Auckland 26.
Golf Bishop Auckland 18h. **See** Burnhope
Reservoir, Killhope Wheel.

Rescue Service: Hodgson's Garage
(Wearhead) Ltd. ✆ (095 63) 278.

WEDMORE Somerset. Map 5C
Pop 2,635. Wells 7½, London 129,
Bridgwater 14, Bristol 23, Glastonbury 8½,
Radstock 24, Weston-super-Mare 15.
Golf Burnham & Berrow 18h. **See** 13th
cent St Mary's Church, 15th cent Cross in
churchyard.

WATFORD

0 miles ¼ ½

N

RAC

To St. Albans 7 m.
To M1. Int.6
A412
To St. Albans 3 m.
To Crematorium 3 m.

RAC Northern Home
Counties Office
130 St Albans Road

Ministry
of Employment
& Productivity

Watford
Junction

Park Avenue

Mill Way

Golf
Course

Rec.
Ground

Park Avenue Greatham Road

R. Colne

Link Road

Radlett Road

Rec
Ground

Bushey Hall Road

Gladstone Rd.

Beechen Grove

High St.
Station

A411
To London 16½m.

Buses Only

Clifton St.

Woodford Rd.

Queens Rd.

Broadway

Eastcourt Rd.

Multi-storey
Car Park

Beechen Grove

Palace
Theatre

P.O. Market

Multi-storey
Car Park

Smith St.

Loates Lane

Church St.

Granville Rd.

Exchange Rd.

Lady's Close

Watford A.F.C.

Vicarage Rd.

Merton Rd.

Wiggenhall Rd.

Police
Station
& Law Court

St. John's Rd.

Clarendon Rd.

St. Albans Road

Stamford Rd.

Canterbury Rd.

Wellington Rd.

Albert Rd.

Beechen Grove

The Parade

Rosslyn Rd.

Town
Hall

Exchange Road

Multi-storey
Car Park

Market St.

Francis Rd.

Marlborough Road

Estcourt Rd.

Cassio Rd.

Whippendell Rd.

(Private) P

Harwoods Rd.

Queens Avenue

Hagden Lane

Church Rd.

Park Road

Nascot St.

Denmark St.

Alexandra Rd.

Essex Rd.

Milton Rd.

The Avenue

Langley Road

Proutens Road

Technical
College

Swimming
Baths

Library

Memorial
Hospital

Cassiobury Park

Hempstead Road

Rickmansworth Road

Sports
Ground

Park Avenue

Whippendell Road

Station
Station Approach

To Rickmansworth 4 m.
A412

A411
To Aylesbury 23 m.

Cassiobury Park Avenue

Shepherds Rd.

Parkside

Cassiobury

Proutens Drive

N.W. Proutens

Millard Rd.

Whippendell Road

P Car Park
C Public Conveniences
▨ Pedestrian precinct

*For abbreviations see inside back cover—***RAC**

MC Repairer: D G Ratcliffe, Wells Road Garage, Wells Rd. ✆ (0934) 712170.
Sctr Repairer: D G Ratcliffe, Wells Road Garage, Wells Rd. ✆ (0934) 712170.

WEDNESBURY West Midlands. Map 21E
Pop 34,511. Birmingham 7½, London 119, Bridgnorth 20, Bromsgrove 17, Kidderminster 14, Walsall 3, Wolverhampton 5.
EC Thur. **MD** Fri, Sat. **Golf** Sandwell Park 18h. **See** St Bartholomew's Church, Art Gallery and Museum.

Specialist Body Repairer: Rapid Auto Body Repairs Ltd, Bridge St. ✆ 021-556 0549 & 2193.

WEDNESFIELD West Midlands. Map 21E
Pop 33,048. Birmingham 12, London 123, Stafford 15, Walsall 4½, Wolverhampton 2.
EC Wed. **MD** Tue, Fri, Sat.

Rescue Service: J Kenyon & Son (Wednesfield) Ltd, Wednesfield Garage, Wolverhampton Rd. ✆ Wolverhampton (0902) 731372 and (0902) 732407.

WEEDON Northamptonshire. Map 14D
Pop 2,400. Towcester 8½, London 69, M1 Motorway 3, Daventry 4, Hinckley 26, Leicester 30, Market Harborough 21, Northampton 8½, Nuneaton 29, Rugby 13.
Golf Farthingstone 18h. **See** Parish Church.

★★★**M Crossroads,** *NN7 4PX.* ✆ (0327) 40354. Closed Dec 25–26. C. ⇔ 10 bedrs, 7 bp, 1 ba, TV. ✗ a l c, mc, at, LD 10.30. 🅑 CH, CP 100, Ac, con 30, CF, 1 BGf, 5 st. **£** BB £27·50–£34, DB £36–£45, WB, Ⓛ, Bk £3·95, L £10, D £10, cc 1 2 3 5, Dep b.

Rescue Service: Clarke Bros, Stowe Hill Garage. ✆ (0327) 40369.
Freeway Motors Ltd, Watling St. ✆ (0327) 40344.

WELLESBOURNE Warwickshire. Map 14D
¼ m SW of Wellesbourne Hastings. Pop 4,024. Banbury 15, London 87, Chipping Norton 21, Moreton-in-Marsh 16, Stratford-upon-Avon 5, Warwick 6½.
EC Mon, Wed or Thur. **Golf** Stratford-upon-Avon 14h. **See** Charlecote Park (Nat Trust), Shakespeare Country.

★★**King's Head,** *CV35 9LT.* ✆ Stratford-upon-Avon (0789) 840206. C. ⇔ 14 bedrs, 2 bp, 2 bps, 3 ba, Dgs. ✗ a l c, mc, LD 9. 🅑 CH, TV, CP 40, Ac, con 25, CF, 1 st. **£** BB £16–£24, DB £25–£34, WB, Ⓛ, Bk £3·95, L £5, D £6, cc 1 3 4 5 6.

Rescue Service: Wellesbourne Garage. ✆ Stratford-upon-Avon (0789) 840223.

WELLING Greater London (Kent). M. Area 7B
London 12, Bromley 7, Dartford 5, Sidcup 3½.
EC Wed, Thur.

Rescue Service: A G Chambers (Auto) Ltd, Anchor Service Station, 322 Bellegrove Rd. ✆ 01-854 6256.

WELLINGBOROUGH Northamptonshire. Map 15A
Pop 39,821. Bedford 17, London 67, Bletchley 22, Cambridge 37, Huntingdon 27, Kettering 7, Northampton 10, Peterborough 30.

EC Thur. **MD** Wed, Fri, Sat. **Golf** Wellingborough 18h. **See** Churches, Tithe Barn.

★★★**Hind,** *Sheep St, NN8 1BY.* ✆ (0933) 222827. C. ⇔ 32 bedrs, 32 bp, TV, Dgs. ✗ a l c, mc, at. 🅑 N, CH, CP 16, G 3, con 120, CF, 5 BGf, 1 st. **£** BB £32·20–£34·50, DB £41·40–£44·85, WB, Ⓛ, Bk £3·90, L £4·95, D £6·95, cc 1 2 3 4 5 6, Dep b.

■★**High View** (R), *156 Midland Rd, NN8 1NG.* ✆ (0933) 226060. C. ⇔ 16 bedrs, 9 bps, 3 ba, TV, Dgs. ✗ a l c, LD 7.30. 🅑 CH, TV, ns, CP 8, Ac, CF, 2 BGf, 2 st. **£** BB fr £14·50, DB fr £23, Ⓛ, Bk £3·50, L £4·20, D £4·20, cc 1 2 3 5.

Oak House, PH, z (Unl), *9 Broad Green, NN8 4LE.* ✆ (0933) 71133. Closed Xmas. C. ⇔ 6 bedrs, 5 bps, 1 sh, Dgs. 🅑 CH, TV, CP 6, CF. **£** BB £14·50, DB £25, WT (b) £133, DT (b) £19, ②.

Repairer: York, Ward & Rowlatt Ltd, Oxford St. ✆ (0933) 222403.

WELLINGTON Shropshire. Map 19F
See also TELFORD and DONNINGTON.
Pop 16,000. Wolverhampton 18, London 143, M54 Motorway 1, Atherstone 43, Bridgnorth 14, Lichfield 29, Newport 8, Shrewsbury 11, Tamworth 36, Whitchurch 21.
EC Wed. **MD** Mon, Tue, Thur, Sat. **Golf** Wrekin 18h. **See** Wrekin College, All Saints' Parish Church, old houses and inns, the Wrekin 1,335 ft.
🆈 9 Walker St. ✆ Telford (0952) 48295.

■✦✦✦**Buckatree Hall,** *The Wrekin, Telford TF6 5AL.* ✆ Telford (0952) 51821. C. ⇔ 37 bedrs, 37 bp, TV, Dgs. ✗ a l c, mc, at. 🅑 N, CH, Dgs, CP 110, Ac, con 40, CF, 12 BGf, 0 st, Dis. **£** BB £32·50–£39, DB £42–£48, WB, Ⓛ, Bk £3·70, L £6·85, D £6·85, cc 1 2 3 5.

★★**Charlton Arms,** *Church St, Telford TF1 1DG.* ✆ Telford (0952) 51351. C. ⇔ 27 bedrs, 22 bp, 3 ba, TV, Dgs. ✗ a l c, mc, at, LD 9.30. 🅑 N, CH, CP 100, Ac, con 180, CF, 0 st. **£** BB £23·50, DB £42, WB, ② 10%, Bk £3·50, L £5·50, D £7, cc 1 2 3 5 6, Dep b.

★★**Falcon,** *Holyhead Rd, TF1 2DD.* ✆ Telford (0952) 55011. Closed Xmas, RS Sun. C 2. ⇔ 13 bedrs, 2 bp, 3 bps, 3 ba, Dgs. ✗ a l c, mc, LD 8.30. 🅑 CH, TV, Dgs, CP 32. **£** BB £15·50–£19·50, DB £21–£28, WB, ②, Bk £2·50, L £2, D £6·50, cc 1.

Rescue Service: Furrows Ltd, Haygate Rd, Telford. ✆ Telford (0952) 42433.
G Ralphs, Lawley Garage. ✆ Telford (0952) 505010.
Reades Garage (Wellington) Ltd, Watling St. ✆ Telford (0952) 44162.

WELLINGTON Somerset. Map 4D
Pop 9,359. Taunton 6½, London 150, M5 Motorway 2, Dunster 22, Exeter 25, Honiton 20, Tiverton 14.
EC Thur. **Golf** Taunton and Vivary 18h. **See** 15th cent Parish Church, Wellington Monument, Wellington School.
🆈 6 South St. ✆ Wellington (082 347) 2716.

Blue Mantle, H, z (R), *2 Mantle St, TA21 8AW.* ✆ (082 347) 2000. C. ⇔ 9 bedrs, 2 ba, Dgs. ✗ a l c. 🅑 CH, TV, CF, 4 st. **£** BB £10, DB £19, WT (b) £85, DT (b) £13·50, Ⓛ, Bk £2, L £3·25, D £4·50, cc 1.

Repairer: Richardson's Garage (Wellington) Ltd, 9 and 44 High St. ✆ (082 347) 4181.
MC Repairer: M D Motorcycles, 14 North St. ✆ (082 347) 4076.
Rescue Service: Wellington Motors, Ivy Bank, 75 Waterloo Rd. ✆ (082 347) 2453.

WELLS Somerset. Map 5C
See also CHILCOMPTON and WORTH. Pop 8,374. Shepton Mallet 5½, London 122, Bath 19, Bristol 21, Glastonbury 5½, Radstock 12, Weston-super-Mare 19.
EC Wed. **Golf** Wells (Somerset) 9h, Mendip 18h.
See Cathedral, Bishop's Palace, Browne's Gate, Old Deanery, Almshouse, Town Hall, medieval Tithe Barn, Museum, St Cuthbert's Church, Vicar's Close (14th cent St) and Wookey Hole Caves 1½ m NW.
🆈 Town Hall, Market Pl. ✆ Wells (0749) 72552.

★★★**Swan,** *Sadler St, BA5 2RX.* ✆ (0749) 78877. C. ⇔ 26 bedrs, 21 bp, 5 bps, 1 ba, TV, Dgs. ✗ a l c, mc, at. 🅑 CH, Dgs, CP 30, con 50, CF. **£** BB fr £27·50, DB £38–£54, WB, Ⓛ, Bk £3·50, L £6·50, D £9·75, cc 1 3 4 5 6, Dep b.

★★**White Hart,** *19 Sadler St, BA5 2RR.* ✆ (0749) 72056. C 5. ⇔ 10 bedrs, 2 bp, 1 bps, 2 ba, annexe 5 bedrs, 5 bp, TV. ✗ a l c, mc. 🅑 ch, TV, CP 17, 0 st. **£** BB £19·50–£22·50, DB £28–£31·50, DBB £26·10–£28·10, Ⓛ, Bk £3·25, L £4, D £6·60, cc 1 2 3 5.

★**Worth House** (R), *BA5 1LW.* ✆ (0749) 72041. Open Mar–Nov & Xmas. C 3. ⇔ 8 bedrs, 2 bp, 1 bps, 1 ba. ✗ a l c, mc, at, LD 8. 🅑 CH, TV, CP 22, 2 st. **£** BB £15–£17, DB £26–£30, WT £163–£191, DT £26–£28, ②, Bk £4, L £6, D £6.

Bekynton, G, z (Unl), *7 St Thomas St, BA5 2UU.* ✆ (0749) 72222. C. ⇔ 10 bedrs, 2 bps, 3 ba, Dgs. 🅑 CH, TV, CP 6, 3 st. **£** BB £8·60–£9·25, DB £17·20–£19·50, WT (b) £90·50–£98, (c) £54·35–£60, DT (b) £13·80–£15, Ⓛ, D £5·50.

Tor, G, x (Unl), *20 Tor St, BA5 2US.* ✆ (0749) 72322. C. ⇔ 9 bedrs, 1 ba, Dgs. 🅑 ch, TV, Dgs, CP 10, CF. **£** BB £8·50–£9·25, DB £17–£18·50, WT (b) £91–£96·50, (c) £56·50–£61·50, DT (b) £13·50–£14·50, ②.

Repairer: F W Sampson & Sons Ltd, City Garage, Broad St. ✆ (0749) 72706.
Rescue Service: Gunnings of Wells, Priory Rd. ✆ (0749) 73809.
Harris Motors (Wells), Glastonbury Rd. ✆ (0749) 72626.
Provincial Garage (Wells) Ltd, Bath Rd. ✆ (0749) 72099.

WELLS-NEXT-THE-SEA Norfolk. Map 16C
Pop 2,389. Fakenham 10, London 123, Cromer 19, East Dereham 20, King's Lynn 27, Norwich 31.
EC Thur. **MD** Wed. **Golf** Fakenham 9h. **See** Holkham Hall 2 m W, Blakeney Point Bird Sanctuary 8 m E, Two Miniature Railways (1 longest in world).

■★**Crown,** *The Buttlands, NR23 1EX.* ✆ Fakenham (0328) 710209. Closed Dec 25. C. ⇔ 14 bedrs, 4 bp, 2 ba, TV, Dgs. ✗ a l c, mc, at, LD 9.30. 🅑 CH, Dgs, CP 10, CF, 0 st. **£** BB £12·50–£15, DB £25–£35, WT £178–£196, DT £25·50–£30·50, DBB

£21–£26, WB, ①, Bk £4·50, L £5·50, D £8·50, cc 2 3 5, Dep.

Rescue Service: Barker & Sons (Wells) Ltd, West End Garage, Freeman St. ✆ Fakenham (0328) 710315. G F Rose & Co, Polka Rd. ✆ (0328) 710213.

WELWYN Hertfordshire. Map 15F Pop 7,000. Hatfield 4½, London 25, A1(M) Motorway 1, Baldock 12, Bishop's Stortford 19, Hoddesdon 10, Luton 12. **EC** Wed. **Golf** Panshanger 18h. **See** Roman Villa and Bath House.

★★M Clock, *AL6 9XA.* ✆ (043871) 6911. C. ➡ 72 bedrs, 68 bp, 7 bps, TV, Dgs. ✗ a l c, mc, at, LD 10. ⓓ CH, CP 200, Ac, con 300, CF, 5 BGf, 3 st. £ BB £27·95, DB £34·95, DT £37, WB, ①, Bk £3·30, L £4·50, D £4·50, cc 1 3 4 5 6, Dep b.

WELWYN GARDEN CITY Hertfordshire. Map 15F Pop 47,000. Hatfield 2½, London 23, Baldock 14, Bishop's Stortford 18, Hoddesdon 10, Luton 12. **EC** Wed. **Golf** Panshanger 18h. **See** Arts and Crafts Gallery. ⓘ Campus, West. ✆ (07073) 31212.

◼★★★M Crest, Homestead Lane, *AL7 4LX.* ✆ (07073) 24336. RS Xmas. C. ➡ 58 bedrs, 58 bp, ns, TV, Dgs. ✗ a l c, mc, at, LD 9.30. ⓓ Lt, N, CH, Dgs, CP 50, Ac, con 80, CF, 0 st. £ B fr £42, BD fr £51, WB, ①, Bk £5·25, D £9·25, cc 1 2 3 4 5 6, Dep b.

WEMBLEY Greater London (Middx). Map 7A Pop 124,892. Denham 9, London 7, Ealing 3, Harrow 3½, Uxbridge 8½. **EC** Wed. **See** Empire Stadium, Empire Pool and Sports Arena.

★★★M Wembley International (late Crest), *Empire Way, HA9 8DS.* ✆ 01-902 8839. C. ➡ 323 bedrs, 323 bp, TV, Dgs. ✗ a l c, mc, at, LD 10·15. ⓓ Lt, N, CH, Dgs, CP 50, Ac, con 200, CF, 1 st. £ BBc fr £37·50, DBc fr £47·50, ①, Bk £3·25, L £6·25, D £6·25, cc 1 2 3 4 5 6, Dep b.

Rescue Service: J D Madden Garages Ltd, Unit 20, Block M, Watkin Rd. ✆ 01-903 0301. Wembley Autos, T/As John Candler Cars Ltd, 199 Ealing Rd. ✆ 01-920 9595.

WEMBURY Devon. Map 3E Pop 3,154. Ashburton 23, London 210, Dartmouth 26, Kingsbridge 19, Plymouth 6, Totnes 21. **Golf** Staddon Heights 18h. **See** Church, Wembury House N.T.

Rescue Service: Warren Bros (Plymstock) Ltd. T/As Down Thomas Garage, Down Thomas. ✆ Plymouth (0752) 862661.

WENDOVER Buckinghamshire. Map 15E Pop 6,391. Denham 19, London 36, Aylesbury 5, High Wycombe 10, Oxford 24, Hawksmoor th 16, St Albans 21, Slough 20, Wallingford 23. **EC** Wed. **Golf** Ellesborough 18h. **See** Restored Parish Church, old houses and inns.

Rescue Service: London Road Service Station, South St. ✆ (0296) 622017.

WEST BILNEY Norfolk. Map Area 16E Swaffham 8, London 104, Cromer 42, Downham Market 13, King's Lynn 7, Norwich 36.

Rescue Service: Queensway Service Station, A47. ✆ King's Lynn (0553) 840505.

WENTBRIDGE North Yorkshire. Map 25D Pop 150, Doncaster 11, London 176, A1(M) Motorway 6, Barnsley 6, Boroughbridge 35, Pontefract 4½, Selby 17, Tadcaster 18, Wakefield 12. **EC** Thur. **Golf** Pontefract 18h. **See** Old Houses.

⬛★★★★Wentbridge House, *WF8 3JJ.* ✆ Pontefract (0977) 620444. RS Dec 25 & 26. C. ➡ 17 bedrs, 10 bp, 7 bps, annexe 3 bedrs, 1 ba, TV. ✗ a l c, mc, LD 9.30. ⓓ CH, CP 120, G 3, con 120, CF, 4 BGf, 1 st, Dis. £ BB fr £23·50, DB fr £30, WB, ①, Bk £5, L £7·50, D £12·50, cc 1 2 3 5, Dep b.

WEOBLEY Hereford & Worcester (Herefordshire). Map 13C Pop 1,082. Hereford 12, London 144, Brecon 29, Builth Wells 29, Knighton 22, Leominster 9, Rhayader 34. **EC** Wed. **Golf** The Herefordshire, Wormsley 18h. **See** Parish Church, 'Black and White' houses, the Willow Gallery.

★★Red Lion, *HR4 8SE.* ✆ (054 45) 220.

WEST BAGBOROUGH Somerset. Map 4D Bridgwater 10, London 151, Minehead 17, Taunton 9, Wiveliscombe 7.

Higher House, G, x (Rt). *TA4 3EF.* ✆ Bishops Lydeard (0823) 432996. Open Feb–Nov. C. ➡ 5 bedrs, 1 ba, Dgs. ⓓ CH, TV, Dgs, ns, CP 12, CF, 3 st. £ BB £9–£10, DB £18–£20.

WEST BOLDON Tyne & Wear. Map 32D Pop 10,528 (inc Boldon Colliery). Sunderland 5, London 274, Durham 16, Newcastle upon Tyne 6½. **EC** Wed. **Golf** Boldon 18h. **See** Ancient Church, Boldon Mill.

Rescue Service: Bank Top Garage, Addison Rd. ✆ Boldon (0783) 362726.

WEST BRIDGFORD Nottinghamshire. Map 22D *See also* NOTTINGHAM. Pop 27,795. Leicester 24, London 121, Loughborough 13, Melton Mowbray 16, Nottingham 1½. **EC** Mon, Wed, Thur. **Golf** Wollaton Park, Nottingham 18h. **See** St Giles' Church, Holy Rood Church (Edwalton), County Hall, Notts Co Cricket Ground at Trent Bridge.

Rescue Service: B & K Thomas Ltd, 17 Loughborough Rd. ✆ Nottingham (0602) 862121.

WEST BROMWICH West Midlands. Map 21D Pop 166,000. Birmingham 4½, London 116, M5 Motorway 1½, Bridgnorth 20, Bromsgrove 14, Kidderminster 15, Walsall 5½, Wolverhampton 8. **EC** Wed. **MD** Mon, Fri, Sat. **Golf** Sandwell Park 18h. **See** Restored 12th cent Manor House, Bishop Asbury Cottage (founder of Methodist Church in USA), Oak House (Tudor).

★★★M West Bromwich Moat House, *Birmingham Rd, B70 6RS.* ✆ 021-553 6111. C. ➡ 181 bedrs, 181 bp, TV, Dgs. ✗ a l c, mc, LD 9.45. ⓓ Lt, N, CH, CP 200,

Ac, con 180, CF, 0 st. £ BB fr £36, DB fr £48, WB, ①, Bk £4, L £7·65, D £7·95, cc 1 2 3 4 5 6, Dep b.

Specialist Body Repairer Fred Smith & Sons (Motor Bodies) Ltd, Sams Lane. ✆ 021-553 4845.

Rescue Service: Skidmores Garage Ltd, 350 Spon La. ✆ 021-553 5681 and 021-552 5975.

WESTBURY Wiltshire. Map 5D Pop 8,000. Pewsey 22, London 98, Bath 15, Chippenham 15, Devizes 13, Frome 7, Warminster 3½. **EC** Wed. **Golf** West Wilts, Warminster 18h. **See** Parish Church, White Horse turf cutting on Downs. ⓘ Westbury Travel Ltd, Bratton Rd. ✆ Westbury (0373) 864811.

★Cedar, *114 Warminster Rd, BA13 3PG.* ✆ (0373) 822753. C. ➡ 11 bedrs, 6 bp, 1 bps, 1 ba, TV, Dgs. ✗ mc, at, LD 8.30. ⓓ CH, TV, Dgs, CP 35, Ac, CF, 4 st. £ BB £15–£18, DB £27·50, ②, cc 1 6.

WEST BYFLEET Surrey. Map 7A. Pop 4,928. Byfleet 1½, London 22, Kingston upon Thames 11, Epsom 12, Leatherhead 8½, Ripley 3½, Staines 7½, Weybridge 4, Woking 3. **EC** Wed. **Golf** West Byfleet 18h. **See** Manor House, Churches.

Rescue Service: W Carey Motor Engineers Ltd, rear of 1, 2, 3 Parvis Rd. ✆ Byfleet (093 23) 41073.

WEST CAMEL Somerset. M. Area 5C Pop 400. Wincanton 9½, London 118, Crewkerne 15, Frome 20, Glastonbury 14, Ilminster 16, Shepton Mallet 14, Sherborne 7, Taunton 25. **EC** Wed. **Golf** Yeovil 18h. **See** 15th cent Parish Church, ancient Tithe Barn and Dovecote.

Rescue Service: Camel Cross Motors. ✆ Marston Magna (0935) 318. Steart Road Garage. ✆ Marston Magna (0935) 343.

WEST CHILTINGTON West Sussex. Map 7C *See also* PULBOROUGH. 3 m E of Pulborough. Pop 2,070. Dorking 23, London 46, Arundel 11, Brighton 20, Haywards Heath 17, Horsham 14, Worthing 12. **Golf** West Sussex, Pulborough 18h. **See** Stocks and whipping post outside Church.

★★Roundabout, *Monkmead La, RH20 2PF* (1¾ m S). ✆ (079 83) 3838. Closed Jan. C. 3. ➡ 19 bedrs, 16 bp, 3 bps, annexe 2 bedrs, 2 bp, TV, Dgs. ✗ mc, at, LD 9. ⓓ CH, Dgs, CP 45, con 20, 3 BGf, 2 st. £ BB £27·75–£29·75, DB £45·50–£47·50, DBB £37–£39, WB, ①, Bk £4·50, L £7·20, D £9·25, cc 1 2 3 4 5 6, Dep a.

WESTCLIFF-ON-SEA Essex. Maps 10A and 17D *See also* SOUTHEND-ON-SEA. Romford 24, London 41, Brentwood 20, Chelmsford 20, Dartford Tunnel 20, Rainham 25, Southend-on-Sea 1. **EC** Wed. **Golf** Thorpe Hall 18h, Rochford Hundred 18h. **See** Beecroft Art Galleries.

⬛★Balmoral (R), *34 Valkyrie Rd, SS0 8BU.* ✆ Southend (0702) 342947. RS Dec 25–26. C. ➡ 19 bedrs, 14 bp, 5 bps, TV,

Dgs. ✗ mc, at, LD 7.30. ☎ CH, TV, Dgs, CP 16, Ac, con 25, CF, 0 st. £ BB £22, DB £35, DBB £27·50, WB, ⊡, Bk £2·50, D £5·50, cc 1 3.

Bridgemont, PH, z (Rl), *56 Crowstone Ave, 5SO 8HU.* ✆ Southend (0702) 48840. C. ✍ 8 bedrs, 2 sh, 1 ba, TV. ✗ a l c. ☎ CH, TV, CP 4, 2 st. £ BB £9, DB £16, WT (b) £78·50, DT £12·50, ⊡, cc 1 4 5.

Cobham Lodge, H, z (Rt), *2 Cobham Rd, SSO 8EA.* ✆ Southend (0702) 346438. C. ✍ 28 bedrs, 2 bp, 6 bps, 3 sh, 4 ba, TV, Dgs. ☎ CH, TV, CP, CF, 3 BGf, 9 st. £ BB £12·50–£15·50, DB fr £22, WT (b) £90–£95, DT £18–£18·50, ⊡, Bk £2·75, D £5·50, cc 1 5.

Marine View, G, z (Unl), *4 Trinity Av, SSO 7PU.* ✆ Southend (0702) 344104. Closed Xmas. C. ✍ 6 bedrs, 1 ba. ☎ CH, TV. £ BB £8–£8·50, DB £15–£16, WT £53–£56, ⊡.

Mayfair, G, z (Unl), *52 Crowstone Av, SSO 8HU.* ✆ Southend (0702) 340693. Closed Xmas. C. ✍ 6 bedrs, 1 ba. ☎ CH, TV, CP 4. £ BB £7–£7·50, DB £14–£15, WT (b) £58–£62, DT (b) £10–£10·50, ⊡.

Miramare, PH, z (Rl), *84 Station Rd, SSO 7RQ.* ✆ Southend (0702) 44022.

Pavilion, PH, z (Unl), *1 Trinity Av, SSO 7PU.* ✆ Southend (0702) 41007. C. ✍ 8 bedrs, 2 ba, Dgs. ☎ CH, TV, Dgs, CF, 2 st. £ BB fr £8·50, DB fr £16, WT (b) fr £70, (c) fr £50, DT (b) £11·50, ⊡.

Rose House, H, z (Rl), *21 Manor Rd, SSO 7SR.* ✆ Southend (0702) 341959. C. ✍ 20 bedrs, 2 bp, 4 bps, 2 sh, 3 ba, TV, Dgs. ✗ a l c. ☎ CH, TV, CP 10, CF, 1 BGf, 3 st. £ BB £10–£12, DB £20–£25, WT (b) £60–£70, DT (b) £15–£17, ⊡, Bk £2, L £3, D £5, cc 1 5.

West Park, H, z (R), *11 Park Rd, SSO 7PQ.* ✆ Southend (0702) 330729. C. ✍ 21 bedrs, 12 bp, 4 bps, 4 sh, 4 ba, Dgs. ✗ a l c. ☎ CH, TV, Dgs, CP 16, CF, 3 st. £ BB £18–£21, DB £34·50, DT £24, ⊡, Bk £3·50, L £3·50, D £6·25, cc 1 5.

WEST COKER Somerset. Map 5E
Pop 1,157. Yeovil 3, London 128, Crewkerne 5½, Dorchester 19, Frome 29, Glastonbury 19, Ilminster 12, Shepton Mallet 23, Wincanton 18.
Golf Yeovil 18h. **See** Montacute House 2½ m NW. Dec & Perp church.

★★**M Four Acres,** *High St, BA22 9AJ.* ✆ (093 586) 2555. C. ✍ 18 bedrs, 18 bp, 2 ba, TV, Dgs. ✗ a l c, mc, at, LD 9.30. ☎ CH, CP 100, G 5, con 60, CF, 5 BGf, 1 st, Dis. £ BB £30, DB £38·50, WB, ⊡, L £6, D £6, cc 1 3 4 5 6, Dep b.

Rescue Service: R H Neal, The Garage. ✆ (093 586) 2735.

WEST CORNFORTH Durham. M. Area 24E
Pop 3,392. Darlington 14, London 260, Alston 44, Durham 6½, Stockton-on-Tees 12.
EC Wed. **Golf** Durham City 18h.

Rescue Service: Slake Terrace Garage, Slake Ter. ✆ Ferryhill (0740) 54240.

WEST DIDSBURY Greater Manchester. Map 20B
M56 Motorway 2, London 180, Liverpool 36, Manchester 4, Stockport 4½.

Horizon, H, *69 Palatine Rd, M20 9LJ.* ✆ 061-445 4705. C. ✍ 12 bedrs, 7 bp, 7

---

bps, 5 sh, TV. ☎ CH, TV, CP 25, CF, 1 BGf, 0 st, Dis. £ BB £15·50, DB £19·50–£23, WT fr £75, DT (b) fr £19·50, ⊡, Bk £3·50, D £4, cc 1 3 4 5.

WEST DRAYTON Greater London (Middx). M. Area 7A
3½ m S of Uxbridge. Pop 23,723 (inc Yiewsley). Brentford and Chiswick 7, London 13, Ealing 7½, Harrow 9, Slough 6½.
EC Wed. **Golf** Hillingdon 9h.

Specialist Body Repairer Swan Motors, Trout Rd, Yiewsley. ✆ (089 54) 2514 and (089 54) 5277.
Rescue Service: Gardiner Bros, Ironbridge Rd. ✆ (089 54) 43381.
Martin Iver Ltd, 195 High St, Yiewsley. ✆ (089 54) 6361.

WESTERHAM Kent. Map 7B
Pop 5,000. Bromley 11, London 23, M25 Motorway 4½, Croydon 12, East Grinstead 13, Godstone 6½, Purley 10, Sevenoaks 6, Sidcup 13, Tonbridge 14, Uckfield 22.
EC Wed. **Golf** Limpsfield Common 18h. **See** General Wolfe's birthplace 1727, Quebec House (now museum), Wolfe's Statue, restored EE and Perp Church, Squerryes Court, Chartwell (home of Sir Winston Churchill) 1½ m SE, Statue of Sir Winston on Westerham Green.

★★★**King's Arms,** *Market Sq, TN16 1AN.* ✆ (0959) 62990. C. ✍ 12 bedrs, 12 bp, TV, Dgs. ✗ a l c, mc, at, LD 10·15. ☎ CH, CP 35, U 6, CF, 2 st. £ BB £35, DB £48, ⊡, Bk £3·50, L £8·90, D £8·90, cc 1 3 4 5 6.

WESTERHOPE Tyne & Wear. M. Area 32C
Pop 12,539. Newcastle upon Tyne 4½, London 278, Corbridge 14.
EC Wed. **Golf** Westerhope Municipal 18h.

Rescue Service: Westerhope Garage, Stamfordham Rd. ✆ Newcastle (0632) 869165.

WESTGATE-ON-SEA Kent. Map 10D
Pop 6,512. Rochester 40, London 67, Canterbury 13, Dover 21, Margate 2.
EC Wed. **Golf** Westgate and Birchington 18h.

★★**Ivyside,** *25 Sea Rd, CT8 8SB.* ✆ Thanet (0843) 31082. C. ✍ 55 bedrs, 25 bp, 30 bps, 3 ba, TV, Dgs. ✗ a l c, mc, at, LD 8.30. ☎ CH, TV, Dgs, CP 40, Ac, sp, sc, sb, sol, con 100, CF, 10 BGf, 0 st, Dis. £ BB £14–£20, DB £34–£40, WT £140–£170, DT £24–£27, WB, ⊡, Bk £2·90, L £5, D £7·50, cc 1 5, Dep.

All Seasons, PH, z (Rl), *65 St Mildred's Rd, CT8 8RL.* ✆ Thanet (0843) 31805. C. ✍ 10 bedrs, 2 ba, TV, Dgs. ☎ CH, TV, Dgs, ns, CF. £ BB £9–£9·50, DB £18–£19, WT £60–£65, DT £12–£13, ⊡, Bk £2·50, D £3·50.

WEST GRINSTEAD West Sussex. M. Area 7C
Pop 2,580. Horsham 6½, London 43, Brighton 16, Crawley 13, Haywards Heath 11, Petworth 15, Pulborough 12, Worthing 14.
Golf Manning Heath, Horsham 18h. **See** Old Church, RC Church & Shrine, Knepp Castle (ruin).

Rescue Service: Buck Barn Garage. ✆ Cowfold (040 386) 263.

WEST HAGLEY Hereford & Worcester (Worcestershire). M. Area 21F
Birmingham 11, London 122, Bridgnorth 15, Bromsgrove 7, Kidderminster 5½, Walsall 14, Wolverhampton 12, Worcester 18.
Golf Stourbridge 18h.

Rescue Service: Smith's Garage (Hagley) Ltd, 5 Worcester Rd. ✆ Hagley (0562) 883154.

WEST HYDE Herts. Map 15E
Denham 3, London 20, Amersham 7½, Beaconsfield 7, Ruislip 5, Slough 9, Watford 6½.

Rescue Service: Elm Lodge Garage Ltd, Old Uxbridge Rd. ✆ Rickmansworth (092 37) 70369.

WEST LULWORTH Dorset
See LULWORTH

WEST MALLING Kent. Map 10C
Pop 2,600. M20 Motorway 2, London 35, M26 Motorway 4, Maidstone 6, Sevenoaks 12, Tonbridge 10.
EC Wed. **Golf** West Malling G & CC 18h. **See** St Leonards Tower, Manor Country Park S on A228.

Callis Court, PH, xy (R), *London Rd.* ✆ (0732) 840174. C 5. ✍ 4 bedrs, 2 bp, 1 ba, Dgs. ☎ CH, TV, Dgs, CP 20, CF, 5 st. £ BB £20–£26, DB £30·50–£40, WT (c) £140–£165, DT (b) £30–£33, ⊡, Bk £3·25, L £5·50, D £9·50, cc 1 5.

WEST MEON Hampshire. M. Area 6D
Pop 750. Alston 11, London 59, Cosham 14, Fareham 13, Petersfield 8½, Winchester 13.
EC Thur. **Golf** Corhampton 18h. **See** Winchester Hill, Gothic Church.

Rescue Service: Meon Garages Ltd, Warnford Rd. ✆ (073 086) 219. Warr's Garage. ✆ (073 086) 288.

WEST MOORS Dorset. Maps 5F and 6E
Pop 6,573. Ringwood 5½, London 98, Blandford Forum 15, Bournemouth 8, Dorchester 27, Wareham 16.
EC Wed. **Golf** Ferndown 18h.

Rescue Service: Dear Bros (West Moors) Ltd, Station Rd. ✆ Ferndown (0202) 872261.
West Moors Garage, Ringwood Rd. ✆ Ferndown (0202) 877313.

WESTON Hertfordshire. M. Area 15D
Pop 985. Hatfield 15, London 30, Baldock 3, Bishop's Stortford 18, Hoddesdon 17, Luton 13.
EC Tue. **Golf** Letchworth 18h. **See** Church.

Rescue Service: Pugh & Field Ltd, Swan Garage. ✆ (046 279) 247.

WESTONBIRT Gloucestershire. Maps 5B and 13F
Pop 550 (inc Lasborough). Swindon 20, London 97, Bath 19, Bristol 22, Chepstow 28, Tetbury 3.
Golf Westonbirt 9h. **See** Arboretum (150 acres of forest trees and decorative shrubs).

★★★**Hare & Hounds,** *Tetbury, GL8 8QL.* ✆ (066 688) 233. C. ✍ 23 bedrs, 19 bp, 2 ba, TV, Dgs. ✗ a l c, mc, at. ☎ CH, CP 50, U 4, G 4, Ac, tc, sc, con 120, CF, 2 BGf, 1 st, Dis. £ BB £20–£34, DB £38–£47, DBB

£28–£37·50, WB, ①, Bk £4·50, L £6, D £9, cc 1 2 3 6.

WESTON-ON-THE-GREEN Oxfordshire. Map 14F
Pop 498. High Wycombe 30, London 60, Banbury 16, Bicester 5, Burford 23, Chipping Norton 16, Oxford 8, Towcester 24.
Golf Chesterton 18h. **See** Church, Inns, Stocks, Oxfordshire Way (footpath), Otmoor.

★★★★**Weston Manor**, OX6 8QW.
✆ Bletchington (0869) 50621. C. ⇔ 18 bedrs, 1 bp, annexe 6 bedrs, 6 bp, ns, TV. ✗ a l c, mc, LD 9.30. ⓓ CH, CP 100, Ac, sp, sc, con 100, CF, 1 BGf, 1st, Dis.
£ BB £35–£39·50, DB £45–£55, WB, ①, Bk £3·50, L £4·95, D £10, cc 1 2 3 5.

Rescue Service: Weston-on-the-Green Service Station, A43. ✆ Bletchington (0869) 50282.

WESTON-SUPER-MARE Avon. Map 5A
See also WORLE.
Pop 57,980. Bath 31, London 136, M5 Motorway 4, Bridgwater 18, Bristol 20, Glastonbury 24, Radstock 24, Wells 19.
EC Mon, Thur. **Golf** Weston-super-Mare 18h. **See** Floral Clock, Winter Gdns, Model Village, Museum, Model Rly, Rozel Music Gardens, Mini-Zoo and Aquarium, Worlebury Hill with ancient British encampment, old Church at Uphill, Brean Down Bird Sanctuary, Kewstoke Woods, ancient Church and St Kew Steps at Kewstoke, Steepholm and Flatholm Islands.
🛈 Beach Lawns. ✆ Weston-super-Mare (0934) 26838.

★★★**Grand Atlantic** (TH), Beach Rd, BS23 1BA. ✆ (0934) 26543. C. ⇔ 79 bedrs, 79 bp, TV, Dgs. ✗ a l c, mc, at, LD 9.30. ⓓ Lt, N, CH, Dgs, CP 150, Ac, sp, tc, con 350, CF, 9 st. £ BB £36·50, DB £58·50, WB, ①, cc 1 2 3 4 5 6, Dep (Xmas).
★★★**Royal Pier**, Birnbeck Rd, BS23 2EJ. ✆ (0934) 26644. C. ⇔ 42 bedrs, 29 bp, 7 ba, TV, Dgs. ✗ a l c, mc, at, LD 9.15. ⓓ Lt, N, CH, TV, CP 30, Ac, con 50, CF, 1 st. £ BB £19–£24, DB £38–£48, WB, ①, Bk £3, L £5, D £7·50, cc 1 3 5, Dep b.
★★**Albert**, Beach Rd, BS23 1AX.
✆ (0934) 21363. Closed Dec. C. ⇔ 74 bedrs, 21 bp, 11 ba, Dgs. ✗ mc, at, LD 7.30. ⓓ Lt, N, ch, TV, Dgs, CP 24, U 1, Ac, con, CF. £ BB £12·50–£17, DB £25–£31·50, WT £95·20–£105, DT £18·70–£21, WB, ②, Bk £3·50, L £5, D £6, cc 1 5.
◩★★**Berni Royal**, South Parade, BS23 1JN. ✆ (0934) 23601. C. ⇔ 37 bedrs, 35 bp, 2 bps, TV. ✗ mc, LD 10.30. ⓓ Lt, N, CH, Dgs, CP 86, Ac, con 200, CF, 2 st. £ BB fr £23, DB fr £41, WT fr £203, DT fr £29, DBB fr £26, WB, ②, Bk £2·50, L £5·25, D £7·25, cc 1 2 3 5, Dep b.
★★**Dauncey's** 33 Birnbeck Road, BS23 2EE. ✆ (0934) 21144. C. ⇔ 47 bedrs, 10 bp, 9 bps, 6 ba, Dgs. ✗ mc, at, LD 7. ⓓ Lt, ch, TV, Dgs, Ac, CF, 3 st. £ WB, Dep.
★★**Dorville**, Madeira Rd, BS23 2EX.
✆ (0934) 21522.
★★**Queenswood** (R), Victoria Park, BS23 2HZ. ✆ (0934) 21759. C. ⇔ 19 bedrs, 7 bp 6 bps, 2 ba, TV, Dgs. ✗ mc, at, LD 8. ⓓ CH, TV, CP 6, Ac, con 30, CF, 3 st. £ BB fr £12·50, DB fr £25, WT fr £125, DT

fr £22·50, WB, ②, Bk £3, L £4, D £7·50, cc 1 3 4 5, Dep a.
◩★★**Russell** (R), 15 Clevedon Rd, BS23 1DA. ✆ (0934) 20195.
★**Bay View**, Atlantic Road South, BS23 2DH. ✆ (0934) 24893. C. ⇔ 31 bedrs, 9 bp, 5 bps, 4 sh, 3 ba, TV, Dgs. ✗ mc, at, LD 8. ⓓ CH, TV, CP 16, Ac, con 100, CF, 5 BGf, 2 st. £ BB £11·50–£16, DB £23–£32, WT £91·50–£132·50, DT £17–£21, WB, ①, Bk £2, L £2·50, D £4, cc 1 5, Dep a.
Abingdon, G, z (Rl) 197 Locking Rd, BS23 3HE. ✆ (0934) 25840. C. ⇔ 5 bedrs, 2 ba, TV, Dgs. ⓓ CH, Dgs, CP 5, CF. £ BB £6·50–£7·50, DB £13–£15, WT b) £54–£60, DT (b) £8·50–£10, ①.
Ashford Villa, G, z (Unl), 48 Locking Rd, BS23 3DN. ✆ (0934) 26679. C. ⇔ 5 bedrs, 1 ba, Dgs. ⓓ CH, TV, Dgs, CP 4, CF. £ BB £6–£7·50, DB £12–£13·50, WT (b) £50–£60, DT £9–£10, ①, D £3.
Avonlea, PH, z (Unl), 24 Severn Rd, BS23 1DN. ✆ (0934) 413361. Closed Dec & Jan. C 2. ⇔ 10 bedrs, 2 ba. ⓓ CH, TV, CP 8, 2 st. £ BB £6·25–£7·25, DB £12·50–£14·50, WT (b) £65–£69·70, (c) £43–£50, DT (b) £9·35–£10, ①, Bk £2·25, D £4·25.
Baymead, H, z (Rl), Longton Grove Rd, BS23 1LS. ✆ (0934) 22951. Open Mar–Nov & Xmas. C. ⇔ 34 bedrs, 2 bp, 9 ba, Dgs. ⓓ Lt, CH, TV, CP 7, 7 BGf, 0 st, Dis. £ BB £10–£14, DB £20–£28, WT (b) £70–£90, DT (b) £12–£15, ①, Bk £2, L £3·50, D £3·50, cc 1 5.
Beachlands, H, x (R), 17 Uphill Rd North, BS23 4NG. ✆ (0934) 21401. Closed Xmas, Jan & Feb. C. ⇔ 19 bedrs, 7 bp, 4 bps, 2 ba, Dgs. ⓓ CH, TV, CP 14, G 3, CF, 2 BGf, 0 st, Dis. £ BB £10·95–£14·95, DB £21·90–£30·50, WT (b) £89·75–£104·75, DT (b) £15·95–£17·95, ①, Bk £2·50, D £5·75, cc 1 4.
Braeside, G (Rl), 2 Victoria Park, BS23 2HZ. ✆ (0934) 26642. C. ⇔ 8 bedrs, 1 bps, 2 ba, Dgs. ⓓ CH, TV, CF. £ BB £7·50–£9, DB £15–£20, WT (b) £59–£71, DT (b) £10–£12, ②, L £3·50, D £3·50.
Denewood, PH, z (Unl) 8 Madeira Rd, BS23 2EX. ✆ (0934) 20694. Open Apr–Oct. C 3. ⇔ 17 bedrs, 2 ba, Dgs. ⓓ CH, TV, Dgs, 2 st. £ BB £9, DB £18, WT (b) £70, DT (b) £10, ①, D £4.
Flora Glen, G, z (Unl), 130 Locking Rd, BS23 3HF. ✆ (0934) 20592.
Fourways, G, z (Unl), 2 Ashcombe Rd, BS23 3DY. ✆ (0934) 23827. Open Mar–Oct. C 10. ⇔ 9 bedrs, 1 ba. ⓓ ch, TV, CP 8, 2 st. £ BB £5·50–£7·50, DB £11–£15, ①.
Glascote, PH, z (Rl), 36 Upper Church Rd, BS23 2DX. ✆ (0934) 21086. C. ⇔ 12 bedrs, 4 sh, 2 ba, Dgs. ⓓ ch, TV, Dgs, CF, 1 BGf, 1 st, Dis. £ BB £8·50–£12·50, DB £16–£25, WT (b) £52–£70, DT (b) £11–£13, ①.
Glenelg, PH, y (Rl), 24 Ellenborough Park South, BS23 1XN. ✆ (0934) 20521. Open Apr–Oct. C. ⇔ 15 bedrs, 3 ba, Dgs. ⓓ CH, CP 15, CF, 1 BGf, 2 st. £ BB £9·50, DB £17–£19, WT (b) £65–£78, (c) £58–£70, ①.
Jonwyn, G, z (Unl), 129 Milton Rd, BS23 2UY. ✆ (0934) 23271. Closed Xmas. C. ⇔ 5 bedrs, 1 bp, 1 ba, Dgs. ⓓ ch, TV, CP 6, CF, 1 BGf, 1 st. £ BB £7·50, DB £13–£14, ①.
Keswick House, G, z (Unl), 195 Locking Rd, BS23 3HE. ✆ (0934) 28434.
Kinclaven, PH, z (Rl), 5 Park Pl, BS23 2BA. ✆ (0934) 21723. Open Mar–Oct. C 3.

⇔ 20 bedrs, 3 ba. ⓓ TV, CP 15. £ BB £8–£11, DB £15–£20, WT (b) £69–£80·50, DT (b) £11·50–£13·80, ①.
Kynance, G, z (Unl), 53 Walliscote Rd, BS23 1EE. ✆ (0934) 25439. C. ⇔ 8 bedrs, Dgs. ⓓ TV, Dgs, CF, BB fr £6, DB fr £12, WT fr £63, (c) fr £42, DT (b) fr £9, ①.
L'Arrivee, G, z (R), 75 Locking Rd, BS23 3DW. ✆ (0934) 25328. C. ⇔ 5 bedrs, 2 ba, TV. ⓓ Ch, TV, CF, 1 st. £ BB £7·50, DB £13, WT (b) £57·50–£70, DT (b) £10–£12, ①, Bk £2·25, L £3·50, D £4·75, ①.
Lydia, G, z (Rl), 78 Locking Rd, BS23 3ET. ✆ (0934) 25962. C. ⇔ 6 bedrs, 2 ba, Dgs. ⓓ CH, TV, Dgs, CP 5, CF. £ BB £7–£8·50, DB £14–£17, WT (b) £70–£80, DT (b) £10–£12, ①, Bk £2, L £2·50, D £3·50.
Milton Lodge, PH, z (Unl), 15 Milton Rd, BS23 2SH. ✆ (0934) 23161. C. ⇔ 6 bedrs, 3 bp, 3 bps, TV. ⓓ CH, TV, CP 5, 1 st. £ BB £9–£10, DB £18–£20, WT (b) £77–£84, DT (b) £13–£14, ②.
Newton House, PH, z (R), 79 Locking Rd, BS23 3DW. ✆ (0934) 29331. C. ⇔ 7 bedrs, 2 bp, 3 ba, TV. ✗ a l c. ⓓ CH, TV, CP 9, CF. £ BB £8–£10, DB £16–£22, WT (b) £68–£80, DT (b) £11–£13, ①.
Northcliff, G, x (Unl), Uphill Way, Uphill, BS23 4XP. ✆ (0934) 20784. C 3. ⇔ 5 bedrs, 1 ba, Dgs. ⓓ CH. £ BB fr £7·50, DB fr £14·50, WT fr £69·50, DT fr £11·25, ①.
St Vincent, PH, z (Unl), 9 Victoria Park, BS23 2HZ. ✆ (0934) 29584. Open Apr–Oct & Xmas. C. ⇔ 9 bedrs, 2 ba, Dgs. ⓓ CH, TV, ns, CP 7, CF. £ BB £7–£8, DB £13·50–£16, WT (b), £55–£65, DT (b) £10·50–£11·50, ②, £ £3·50.
Salopian, G, z (Rl), 191 Locking Rd, BS23 3HE. ✆ (0934) 20881. C. ⇔ 6 bedrs, 2 ba, ns, TV. ⓓ CH, TV, CP 6, CF, 1 st. £ BB £6–£7·50, DB £12–£15, WT (b) £54–£64, DT (b) £9–£10·50, ①, D £3.
Sandringham, H, z, 1 Victoria Sq, BS23 1AA. ✆ (0934) 24891. C. ⇔ 36 bedrs, 22 bp, 3 ba, TV, Dgs. ✗ a l c. ⓓ Lt, CH, TV, Dgs, CF, 1 st. £ BB £13·50–£15·50, DB £21–£31, ②, Bk £3, L £2·50, D £4·50, cc 1 5.
Sandy Lodge, PH, 11 Albert Quadrant, BS23 2QY. ✆ (0934) 22283.
Scottsdale, PH, z (Unl), 3 Ellenborough Park North, BS23 1XH. ✆ (0934) 26489. Open Mar–Nov. C 14. ⇔ 13 bedrs, 2 ba. ⓓ CH, TV, CP 13. £ BB £10, DB £20, WT (b) £75–£82, DT (b) £13, ①.
Shire Elms, G, z (Rl), 71 Locking Rd, BS23 3DQ. ✆ (0934) 28605.
Southmead, G, z (Unl), 435 Locking Rd, BS22 8QN. ✆ (0934) 29351. Closed Xmas. ⇔ 6 bedrs, 1 ba, Dgs. ⓓ CH, TV, CP 6, 2 st. £ BB £8–£9, DB £13–£14, WT (b) £75–£80, DT (b) £11–£11·50, ①.
Sunnydale, PH, z (Unl), 35a Severn Rd, BS23 1DP. ✆ (0934) 26353. Open April–Oct. C 3. ⇔ 10 bedrs, 3 ba, Dgs. ⓓ CH, TV, Dgs, CP 6, 2 st. £ BB £6–£8, DB £12–£16, WT (b) £55–£70, DT (b) £8·75–£11, ①.
Tra-Bon, PH, z (Unl), 4 Neva Rd, BS23 1YD. ✆ (0934) 29536.
Vaynor, G, z (Unl), 346 Locking Rd, BS22 8PD. ✆ (0934) 32332. C. ⇔ 4 bedrs, 1 ba, Dgs. ⓓ CH, TV, Dgs, CP 3, CF, 1 st. £ BB £6–£6·50, DB £12–£13, ①.
Willow, PH, z (Unl), 3 Clarence Rd East, BS23 4BT. ✆ (0934) 413736. Open Apr–Sept. C. ⇔ 9 bedrs, 1 bp, 3 bps, 1 ba. ⓓ CH, TV, CP 8, CF, 3 st. £ BB £7–£11, DB £14–£22, WT (c) £45–£58, ①.
Wychwood, PH, z (R), 148 Milton Rd, BS23 2UZ. ✆ (0934) 27793. C. ⇔ 10

bedrs, 3 ba, Dgs. 🏠 CH, TV, CP 10, CF. **£** BB fr £7·48, DB fr £14·96, WT (b) fr £74·75, DT (b) fr £11·50, [1], Bk £2·50, D £4·60.

Rescue Services: Sam Burdge Garage Ltd, Milton Rd. ☎ (0934) 26428.
Channel Service Station, 30 Locking Rd. ☎ (0934) 20921.
German, W L Ltd, 108 Milton Rd. ☎ (0934) 23856.
Passey & Porter Ltd, Locking Rd. ☎ (0934) 28291 and (0934) 22359.
Victoria Garage (Weston) Ltd, Alfred St. ☎ (0934) 21451.

WESTON TURVILLE Buckinghamshire. Map 15E.
Watford 21, London 38, Aylesbury 4, Denham 22, Dunstable 13, High Wycombe 15, St Albans 21.
EC Thur. **Golf** Weston Turville 18h. **See** Church.

▣★★**Five Bells,** *40 Main St, HP22 5RW.* ☎ Stoke Mandeville (029 661) 3131. RS Boxing Day–New Year inc. C. 🛏 17 bedrs, 1 bp, 16 bps, 1 ba, TV. ✕ a l c, mc, at, LD 10. 🏠 CH, CP 100, con 20, CF, 5 BGf, 1 st, Dis. **£** Bk £3·50, L £5·50, D £7·50, cc 1 5.

WESTON UNDER REDCASTLE Shropshire. Map 19F
8 m S of Whitchurch. Pop 241. Telford (Wellington) 15, London 158, Market Drayton 8½, Shrewsbury 11.
Golf Hawkstone Park 18h. **See** Church.

★★★**Hawkstone Park,** *SY4 5UY.* ☎ Lee Brockhurst (093 924) 611. C. 🛏 43 bedrs, 43 bp, annexe 16 bedrs, 16 bp, TV, Dgs. ✕ mc, at, LD 9.30. 🏠 N, CH, TV, CP 300, Ac, sp, gc, tc, pf, sb, sol, gym, con 200, CF, 2 BGf, st, Dis. **£** BB £25–£29·50, DB £38–£46, WT £254–£291, DT £37–£42·50, DBB £26·25–£30·25, WB, [1], Bk £4·75, L £5·25, D £7·25, cc 1 2 3 5, Dep b.▲

WEST QUANTOXHEAD Somerset. Map 4D
Pop 291. Taunton 14, London 160, Bridgwater 14, Dunster 8½, Tiverton 26.
Golf Minehead and West Somerset 18h. **See** St Ethelreda's Church, Quantock Hills.

Rescue Service: St Audries Garages Ltd. ☎ Williton (0984) 32437.

WEST RUNTON Norfolk. Map 16C
Pop 750. Cromer 2½, London 136, Fakenham 20.
EC Wed. **Golf** Sheringham 18h.

★★★**Links Country Park,** *NR27 9QH.* ☎ (026 375) 691. C. 🛏 22 bedrs, 20 bp, 14 bps, Dgs. ✕ a l c, mc, at, LD 6. 🏠 Lt, N, CH, Dgs, CP 120, Ac, gc, con 50, CF, 1 st. **£** BB £12·75–£16·75, WT £130–£178·50, [1], Bk £3·75, L £5·95, D £8·75, cc 1 3 4 5, Dep b.

WEST TIMPERLEY Gtr Manchester. M. Area 20B
Altrincham 1, London 181, Manchester 7, Wilmslow 7½.

Repairer: Jackson & Edwards Ltd, Eagle Garage, Manchester Rd, Broadheath. ☎ 061-973 3021.

WESTWARD HO! Devon. Map 4C
See also BIDEFORD.
Pop 1,500. Bideford 2½, London 204, Bude 26.
EC Wed. **Golf** Royal North Devon 18h. **See** Kipling Tors.

▣★★**Buckleigh Grange** (R), *Buckleigh Rd, EX39 3PU.* ☎ Bideford (023 72) 4468. Open Apr–Nov, Easter & Xmas. C 1. 🛏 12 bedrs, 2 bps, 7 sh, 2 ba, Dgs. ✕ mc, at, LD 6. 🏠 ch, TV, CP 20, Ac, tc, CF, 1 st. **£** BB £10·50–£11·50, DB £21–£23, WB, [1], Bk £2·85, D £6·30, Dep a.
Buckleigh Lodge, G, x (Rl), *Bay View Rd, EX39 1BJ.* ☎ Bideford (023 72) 75988. Open Mar–Oct. C. 🛏 6 bedrs, 1 bp, 2 ba. 🏠 CH, TV, CP 7, CF. **£** BB £7·50, DB £15–£18, WT (b) £75, DT (b) £11·50, [1].

Repairer: Twose, F C, Nelson Garage, Nelson Rd. ☎ Bideford (023 72) 4129.

WEST WICKHAM Greater London (Kent). M. Area 7B
2¼ m NW of Keston. Bromley 3, London 12, Croydon 4, Purley 6½, Sevenoaks 13, Sidcup 8½, Westerham 9½.
EC Wed. **Golf** Langley Park 18h.

Repairer: West Wickham (1954) Ltd, 203 High St. ☎ 01-777 2900.
Rescue Service: West Wickham Service Station, Wickham Court Rd. ☎ 01-777 1809.

WEST WITTON North Yorkshire. Map 26B.
Harrogate 35, London 239, Boroughbridge 30, Darlington 28, Hawes 12, Leyburn 4, Middleton in Teesdale 39, Northallerton 22, Skipton 30, Thirsk 28.

★★**Wensleydale Heifer** *DL8 4LS.* ☎ Wensleydale (0969) 22322. C. 🛏 17 bedrs, 7 bp, 7 bps, 2 ba, TV, Dgs. ✕ mc, LD 9. 🏠 CH, Dgs, ns, CP 30, Ac, CF, 2 BGf, 2 st. **£** BB £12–£25, DB £24–£36, WB, [2], Bk £4, L £4, D £10·50, cc 1 5.▲

WEST WOODBURN Northumberland. Map 31C
Pop 250. Corbridge 16, London 296, Alnwick 31, Bellingham 4, Hawick 41, Hexham 16, Jedburgh 36, Newcastle upon Tyne 29.
Golf Bellingham 9h. **See** Roman Fort, Pele Tower.

★**Fox & Hounds,** *NE48 2RA.* ☎ Bellingham (0660) 60210. C. 🛏 10 bedrs, 2 ba, Dgs. ✕ a l c, mc, LD 8.30. 🏠 CH, TV, Dgs, CP 30, Ac, CF, 2 st. **£** BB £10, DB £19·50, [2], Bk £2·20, L £2·95, D £4·20.
Bay Horse, I, x, *NE48 2RX.* ☎ Bellingham (0660) 60218. C. 🛏 4 bedrs, 1 ba, Dgs. ✕ a l c. 🏠 CH, TV, Dgs. ✕ a l c. 🏠 CH, TV, Dgs, CP 30, CF.

Rescue Service: West Woodburn Service Station Ltd. ☎ Bellingham (0660) 60241.

WETHERAL Cumbria. Map 26C
Pop 4,081. Penrith 17, London 293, M6 Motorway 3½, Brampton 6½, Carlisle 4½.
Golf Carlisle 18h. **See** Old Priory Gateway.

★★★**Crown,** *CA4 8ES.* ☎ (0228) 61888. C. 🛏 52 bedrs, 50 bp, 2 bps, TV, Dgs. ✕ a l c, mc, at, LD 9.30. 🏠 N, CH, CP 80, Ac, sc, sb, con 120, CF, 1 BGf, 1 st, Dis. **£** BB £37·50, DB £47·50, WB, [1], BB £3, L £5·50, D £7·95, cc 1 2 3 4 5, Dep b.▲

WETHERBY West Yorkshire. Map 25E
Pop 10,000. Doncaster 31, London 195, Boroughbridge 13, Harrogate 8½, Leeds 12, Pontefract 17, Skipton 29, Tadcaster 6½, York 12.
EC Wed. **MD** Mon, Thur. **Golf** Linton Road 18h. **See** Bridge, old inns, National Hunt Race Course, Branham Park 4 m S, Harewood House 6 m SW.
ℹ Council Offices, 24 Westgate. ☎ Wetherby (0937) 62706.

★★★M **Ladbroke,** *Leeds Rd, LS22 5HE.* ☎ (0937) 63881. C. 🛏 72 bedrs, 72 bp, TV, Dgs. ✕ a l c, mc, at, LD 9·45. 🏠 N, CH, CP 140, Ac, con 150, CF, 36 BGf, Dis. **£** B fr £38·50, BD fr £47, WB, [2], Bk £4, L £3, D £8·75, cc 1 3 4 5 6, Dep b.

Repairer: Trimoco Cars Wetherby, Deighton Rd. ☎ (0937) 65311.
Rescue Service: D & M Rowlands, Automobile Engineers, Deighton Rd. ☎ (0937) 65333.

WETTON Staffordshire. Map 22C
Ashbourne 8½, London 148, Buxton 14, Leek 9½, Matlock 16.

Hallows Grange Country House, *DE6 2AF.* ☎ Alstonefield (033 527) 346.

WEYBOURNE Norfolk. Map 16C
Pop 555. Fakenham 15, London 128, Cromer 7, East Dereham 21, Norwich 25.
EC Wed. **Golf** Sheringham 9h. **See** NNR Station.

★★**Maltings,** *The Street, NR25 7SY.* ☎ (026 370) 275. C. 🛏 22 bedrs, 14 bp, 2 bps, 6 sh, 3 ba, TV, Dgs. ✕ a l c, mc, at, LD 9. 🏠 CH, Dgs, CP 150, Ac, con 40, CF, 6 BGf, 1 st, Dis. **£** BB £20–£24, DB £38–£40, WT £238, DT £42, DBB £30·50–£34·50, WB, [1], Bk £3·50, L £6, D £10·50, cc 1 2 3 5, Dep b.

WEYBRIDGE Surrey. Map 7A
Pop 51,820 (inc Walton). Kingston upon Thames 8, London 18, Bagshot 11, Ealing 14, Epsom 12, Leatherhead 9½, Richmond-upon-Thames 10, Ripley 6½, Staines 6, Woking 7.
EC Wed. **Golf** St George's Hill 18h and 9h, Burhill 18h. **See** St James's Church (Chantrey Monument), Museum.

★★★**Oatlands Park,** *146 Oatlands Dr, KT13 9HB.* ☎ (0932) 47242. C. 🛏 144 bedrs, 98 bp, 15 ba, TV, Dgs. ✕ a l c, mc, at, LD 9.30. 🏠 Lt, N, CH, CP 100, Ac, sp, gc, tc, sc, con 200, CF, 5 BGf, 1 st, Dis. **£** WB, [1], Bk £3·50, L £7, D £8·50, cc 1 3 4 5 6, Dep.
★★★**Ship Thistle,** *Monument Green, KT13 8BQ.* ☎ (0932) 48364. C. 🛏 39 bedrs, 39 bp, 1 ba, ns, TV, Dgs. ✕ a l c, mc, LD 9.30. 🏠 N, CH, TV, Dgs, CP 65, Ac, con 140, CF. **£** £46·75–£52·75, DB £59·50–£64·50, WB, [2], Bk £4·75, L £8·50, D £8·50, cc 1 2 3 4 5 6, Dep b.

Repairer: Moores Weybridge Ltd, Monument Hill. ☎ (0932) 46231.

WEYMOUTH Dorset. Map 5F
See also PORTLAND.
Pop 45,000 (inc Melcombe Regis). Dorchester 8, London 130, Axminster 30, Lyme Regis 28, Wareham 17.
See Plan, p 372.
EC Wed. **MD** Thur. **P** See Plan. **Golf** Weymouth 18h. **See** St Mary's Church, King George III, Statue, Guildhall, Early 17th cent semi-detached houses in Trinity St (restored and furnished with 17th cent objects), Chesil Bank (11 m breakwater of graded pebbles), Butterfly Farm, Portland

WEYMOUTH

0 miles   ½

P Car Park
C Public Conveniences

To Dorchester 8 m.

A354

RAC

LODMOOR

To Wareham 19 m.

A353

Police Stat.

Coombe Av.

Cranford Av.

College

Hospital

Spa Rd.

Ullswater Dr.

Radipole Lane

River Wey

Radipole Lake

Radipole Park Drive

Alexandra Rd.

Dorchester Rd.

Carlton Rd. N.

Carlton Rd. S.

Greenhill

Esplanade

Lennox St.

Chafeys Lake

Golf Course

Hospital

Radipole Lane

Norfolk Rd.

Sussex Rd.

Kitchener Rd.

Franklin Rd.

Longcroft Rd.

Corporation Rd.

Westham Rd.

College

Railway Station

Park St.

King St.

Queen St.

St. Mary St.

St. Thomas St.

Crescent St.

Victoria St.

Esplanade

Pier Bandstand

Jubilee Clock

Pedestrian Precinct
10.30-17.30 Mon.-Sat.

Bus Station

Weymouth Bay

Pier

Pavilion Theatre
& Ballroom

Ferries to
Ch. Is. & France

Pleasure Pier

Abbotsbury Road

Newstead Rd.

Westwey Rd.

Crown Courts

Multi - storey
Level Crossing
(Railway)

G.P.O.

Commercial Rd.

Kings Statue

Alexandra Gdns.

Harbour

North Quay

Guildhall

St. Leonards Rd.

Municipal Offices

Rodwell Rd.

Hospital

Rodwell Av.

Bincleaves Rd.

Belleview Rd.

Portland Breakwater

To Abbotsbury 9 m.

B3157

Chickerell Rd.

Banville Rd.

Quibo La.

Crematorium Rd.

Shircroft Rd.

Dennis Rd.

Chickerell Rd.

Football Ground

Wyke Road

Cross Rd.

Rodwell Road

Lanehouse Rocks Rd.

Wyke Road

Buxton Road

Old Castle Rd.

High St. Portland

A354

To Portland 6m.

Portland Harbour

N

© The Royal Automobile Club, 1984

© Crown copyright reserved

Castle 6 m S, Abbotsbury Swannery 7 m NW.
🛈 Pavilion Complex. ✆ Weymouth (03057) 72444.

★★Central, *15 Maiden St, DT4 8BB.* ✆ (0305) 771411. Open Apr–Oct. C. ⇄ 29 bedrs, 6 bp, 3 bps, 7 ba, Dgs. ✗ LD 8. 🅿 Lt, N, CH, TV, CP 10, Ac, CF, 1 st. £ BB £9·75–£16·10, DB £19·50–£30, WT £78–£106, ②, Bk £1·75, L £3·50, D £3·80.

★★Crown, *51 St Thomas St, DT4 8EQ.* ✆ (0305) 785695. Closed Xmas. C. ⇄ 79 bedrs, 44 bp, 5 bps, 14 ba, Dgs. ✗ a l c, mc, LD 8. 🅿 Lt, N, CH, TV, G 9, Ac, con 150, CF. £ BB £15–£19, DB £24·50–£31·80, WB, ②, Bk £2, L £4·25, D £5·25, cc 1 5.

★★Glenburn (R), *42 Preston Rd, DT3 6PZ.* ✆ (0305) 832353. C 3. ⇄ 13 bedrs, 5 bp, 8 bps, TV. ✗ a l c, mc, LD 9.30. 🅿 CH, CP 20, con 50, CF, 6 BGf, 5 st. £ BB fr £18·50, DB fr £36·50, WB, ②, Bk £2·75, L £2·75, D £7·50, cc 1 3 5.

◼★★Hotel Rex (R), *29 The Esplanade, DT4 8DN.* ✆ (0305) 773485. Closed Xmas. C. ⇄ 21 bedrs, 14 bp, 7 bps, TV. ✗ a l c, LD 11. 🅿 Lt, N, CH, TV, G 7 CF, 5 st. £ BB £18·30–£21·50, DB £30–£39, WT £138–£150, WB, ②, £5, cc 1 5.

★★Old York (R), *55 The Esplanade, DT4 8DG.* ✆ (0305) 786558. Closed Xmas.C. ⇄ 10 bedrs, 10 bps, 1 ba, Dgs. ✗ a l c. 🅿 N, CH, TV, con 30, CF, 4 st. £ BB £17–£19·60, DB £27·50–£34·50, WT £101–£125, WB, ②, Bk £2, L £4·25, D £5.

◼★★Prince Regent, *139 The Esplanade, DT4 7NR.* ✆ (0305) 771313. Closed Xmas. C. ⇄ 50 bedrs, 25 bp, 10 ba, TV. ✗ a l c, mc, at, LD 8·30. 🅿 Lt, N, ch, TV, CP 2, Ac, con 200, CF, 6 st.£ WB, cc 1 2 3 5 6, Dep.

★★Rembrandt (R), *12 Dorchester Rd, DT4 7JU.* ✆ (0305) 786253.

★★Streamside, (R), *Preston Rd, DT3 6QB.* ✆ Preston (0305) 833121.

★Bay View (R), *35 The Esplanade, DT4 8DH.* ✆ (0305) 782083. Open June–Sept. C. ⇄ 10 bedrs, 6 bps, 4 sh, TV, Dgs. ✗ mc, at, LD 6.30. 🅿 CH, Dgs. £ BB £10–£18·50, DB £17–£20, ①, Bk £2, D £5, cc 1 3 5, Dep.

Bedford House, PH, z (Unl), *17 The Esplanade, DT4 8DT.* ✆ (0305) 786995. Open Apr–Oct. C 3. ⇄ 9 bedrs, 2 ba, Dgs. 🅿 TV, Dgs, 4 st. £ DB £13–£17, WT (b) £66–£75, DT (b) £10·50–£12, ①.

Beechcroft, PH, z (R), *128 The Esplanade, DT4 7EH.* ✆ (0305) 786608. Open April–Oct. C. ⇄ 29 bedrs, 2 bp, 8 bps, 10 sh, 6 ba, Dgs. 🅿 CH, TV, 2 BGf, 2 st. £ BB £11·04–£14·03, DB £22·08–£28·06, WT (b) £85·10–£90·85, (c) £67·85–£79·35, DT (b) £15·18–£15·87, ①, cc 1 5.

Birchfields, PH, z (RI), *22 Abbotsbury Rd, DT4 0AE.* ✆ (0305) 773255. C. ⇄ 10 bedrs, 3 ba, Dgs. 🅿 CH, TV, CP 4, U 1, CF. £ BB £7–£10, DB £14–£20, DT (b) fr £10·50, ①.

Cavendale, PH, z (Unl), *10 The Esplanade, DT4 8EB.* ✆ (0305) 786960. Closed Dec. C. ⇄ 9 bedrs, 1 ba, Dgs. 🅿 Ch, TV. £ BB £6–£8·50, DB £12–£17, WT £42–£56, DT £6–£8·50, ①, Bk £3, D £3·50.

Compton Lodge, H, z (R), *185 Dorchester Rd, DT4 7LF.* ✆ (0305) 782532. Closed Xmas. C. ⇄ 26 bedrs, 3 bps, 6 sh, 2 ba. 🅿 CH, TV, Dgs, CP 26, CF, 2 BGf, 4 st. £ BB £14·50–£19·50, DB

£21·50–£30, WT (b) £72–£98, DT (b) £20–£24, ①.

Concorde, PH, z (RI), *131 The Esplanade, DT4 7RY.* ✆ (0305) 76900.

Frensham, H, z (R) *70 Abbotsbury Rd, DT4 0BJ.* ✆ (0305) 786827. C. ⇄ 10 bedrs, 4 bps, 2 ba, TV, Dgs. ✗ a l c. 🅿 CH, TV, Dgs, CP 5, CF. 1 BGf. £ BB £9–£12, DB £18–£24, WT (b) £74–£87, DT (b) £12–£14, ①, Bk £3, D £3·50, cc 1 5.

Golden Lion, l, z, *19 St Edmund St, DT4 8AR.* ✆ (0305) 786778. Open May–Sep. C 5. ⇄ 19 bedrs, 1 bp, 8 ba. 🅿 CH, TV, Dgs.£ BB £10–£12, WT £70–£84, ①.

Greenhill, PH, z (R), *8 Greenhill, DT4 7SQ.* ✆ (0305) 786026. C. ⇄ 16 bedrs, 7 bps, 5 ba. ✗ a l c. 🅿 CH, TV, CP 15, CF, 1 st, 1 BGf, Dis. £ BB £11–£14, DB £21–£27, WT (b) £86–£96, DT (b) £14·50–£16, ②, cc 1 5.

Hazeldene, G, z (Rt), *16 Abbotsbury Rd, DT4 0AE.* ✆ (0305) 782579. C 5. ⇄ 7 bedrs, 3 ba. 🅿 CH, TV, CP 7, U1, 1 st. £ BB £7–£7·50, DB £14–£15, WT (b) £52–£65, (c) £42–£52, DT (b) £9–£9·50, ①.

Kenora, PH, z (RI), *5 Stavordale Rd, Westham, DT4 0AD.* ✆ (0305) 771215. Open Apr–Oct. C. ⇄ 18 bedrs, 3 bps, 3 ba. 🅿 CH, TV, CP 16, CF, 3 BGf, 1st.£ BB £8·57–£9·68, DB £17·14–£20·36, WT £72·34–£83·80, DT £12·13·13·18, ②, cc 1.

Kings Acre, H, z (RI), *140 The Esplanade, DT4 7NH.* ✆ (0305) 782534. Open Mar–Sept. C. ⇄ 14 bedrs, 4 sh, 3 ba. 🅿 CH, TV, CP 9, 5 st. £ BB £9–£11·50, DB £19–£23, DT (b) £13–£15, ①, cc 1 5.

Leam, PH, z (RI), *102 The Esplanade, DT4 7EB.* ✆ (0305) 784127. Open Mar–Oct. C 3. ⇄ 19 bedrs, 9 sh, 3 ba, Dgs. 🅿 TV, CF.£ cc 1.

Millmead, G, xy (R) *Goose Hill, Portesham, DT3 4HE.* ✆ Abbotsbury (030 587) 432. Open Feb–Nov. C 10. ⇄ 7 bedrs, 7 sh, 1 ba, TV, Dgs. 🅿 CH, TV, Dgs, CP 15, 3 BGf, Dis. £ BB £11·50, DB £23, WT (b) £115, (c) £72, DT (b) £18·50, ①, £7, cc 1 5.

Neptune, G, z (RI), *23 Avenue Rd, DT4 7JH.* ✆ (0305) 73721.

Redcliff, H, z (RI), *18 Brunswick Terr, DT4 7SE.* ✆ (0305) 784682. Closed Dec. C. ⇄ 12 bedrs, 3 ba. 🅿 ch, TV, CP 7, CF. £ BB £8·50–£9·50, DB £17–£19, WT (b) £82–£89, DT (b) £11·70–£12·70, ①.

Richmoor, H, z (RI), *146 The Esplanade.* ✆ (0305) 785087.

Sandcombe, z (RI), *8 The Esplanade, DT4 4EB.* ✆ (0305) 786833. Open Mar–Nov. C 5. ⇄ 9 bedrs, 2 ba. 🅿 CH, TV, Dgs, CP 2, 4 st. £ BB £7–£9, DB £14–£15, WT (b) £59·50–£73, DT (b) £10·50–£12, ①, Bk £2, D £3·50.

Sou'West Lodge, H, z (RI), *Rodwell Rd, DT4 8QT.* ✆ (0305) 783749.

Sunningdale, PH, y (RI), *52 Preston Rd, DT3 6QA.* ✆ Preston (0305) 832179. Open Mar–Nov. C. ⇄ 22 bedrs, 6 bp, 1 bps, 5 sh, 3 ba, Dgs. 🅿 ch, TV, Dgs, CP 22, CF, 2 BGf, 2 st. £ BB £11·75–£18, DB £23·50–£36, WT (b) £92–£113, DT £14·75–£17·75, ①, D £3·50.

Tamarisk, PH, z (RI), *12 Stavordale Rd, DT4 0AB.* ✆ (0305) 786514. Open April–Oct. C. ⇄ 17 bedrs, 2 bp, 4 bps, 3 ba, TV. 🅿 CH, TV, CP 19, CF, 2 BGf, 1 st, Dis. £ BB £8·50–£11·25, DB £17–£22·50, WT (b) £71–£83, DT (b) £11–£12·50, ①.

Treverbyn Court, PH, y (RI), *65 Dorchester Rd, DT4 7JX.* ✆ (0305) 786170. Closed Dec. C. ⇄ 14 bedrs, 3

bps, 1 sh, 2 ba, ns, TV, Dgs. 🅿 ch, TV, CP 14, CF, 1 st. £ BB £9–£14, DB £18–£33, WT (b) £70–£104, DT (b) £12·50–£17, ②, Bk £3·25, D £4, cc 5.

Turks Head, l, x, *East St, Chickerell, DT3 4PS.* ✆ (0305) 783093. Closed 23rd–28th Dec. C. ⇄ 4 bedrs, 4 bp, TV, Dgs. ✗ a l c. 🅿 CH, CP 12, CF, 1 st. £ BB £20–£24, DB £24–£30, WT (b) £115–£135, DT (b) £18·50–£22, ②, Bk £2·50, L £3·25, D £6·50, cc 1 5.

Repairer: Olds, Dorchester Rd. ✆ (0305) 786311.
Rescue Service: Lynch Lane Motor Engineers, 50B Lynch Lane. ✆ (0305) 781244.
Marsh Road Garage, Marsh Rd. ✆ (0305) 76116.
Olds, Bramden La, Portesham. ✆ Abbotsbury (030 587) 247.
Putton Lane Garage, Lower Putton La, Chickerell. ✆ (0305) 783255.
Westham Service Station, 114 Abbotsbury Rd. ✆ (0305) 783969.

WHEATLEY Oxfordshire. M. Area 14F Pop 4,000. High Wycombe 20, London 50, Aylesbury 16, Banbury 26, Bicester 14, Oxford 6.
Golf Headington, Oxford 18h. **See** Manor House, Old Buildings, Ancient Windmill.

Rescue Service: Collet's Garage, London Rd. ✆ (086 77) 2270.
H.M. Trinder, Car Sales & Service, Unit 5, Littleworth. ✆ (086 77) 4792.

WHEDDON CROSS Somerset. Map 4D Dunster 6½, London 172, Bampton 13, Ilfracombe 29, Minehead 9½.

Higherley, G, xy, (R), *TA24 7EL.* ✆ Timberscombe (064 384) 582. C. ⇄ 6 bedrs, 1 sh, 1 ba, TV, Dgs. ✗ a l c. 🅿 CH, TV, Dgs, CP 30, CF, 2 BGf. £ BB fr £8·25, DB fr £16·50, WT (b) fr £92 (c) fr £57, DT (b) fr £13·25, ①, Bk £2·10, L £3·50, D £6·25, cc 1 3.

WHICKHAM Tyne & Wear. Map 32C Pop 21,712. A1(M) Motorway 6, Gateshead 4, London 246, Consett 10, Corbridge 16, Newcastle upon Tyne 4½, Stanley 5½.
EC Wed. **Golf** Whickham 18h. **See** Gibside Chapel, Tanfield Railway.

Rescue Service: Leslie's Garage Ltd, Bank Top. ✆ (0632) 881788.

WHIDDON DOWN Devon. Maps 3B and 4E
Pop 100. Exeter 15, London 185, Ashburton 16, Crediton 11, Newton Abbot 18, Okehampton 7.
Golf Okehampton 18h.

Rescue Service: Whiddon Down Garage, Exeter Rd. ✆ (064 723) 222.

WHIMPLE Devon. Map 4F
Pop 1,100. Honiton 8, London 161, Exeter 9½, Lyme Regis 22, Tiverton 15.
Golf Exeter G and CC 18h. **See** Church.

Long Range, H, y (R), *Straightway Rd, EX5 2QT.* ✆ (0404) 822196. C. ⇄ 11 bedrs, 5 bp, TV, Dgs, CP 15, U 1, CF, 3 st. £ BB £11, DB £22, WT (b) fr £115, (c) fr £70, DT (b) fr £18, ①, Bk £3, D £7.

WHITBURN Tyne & Wear. Map 32D
Pop 5,900 (inc Whitburn Colliery)
Sunderland 3, London 272, Newcastle
upon Tyne 11.
EC Wed. **Golf** Whitburn 18h. **See** Church.

Rescue Service: Coast Road Garage, Mill
Lane Rd. ✆ (0783) 293240.

WHITBY North Yorkshire. Map 24B
Pop 13,403. Scarborough 19, London 232,
Middlesbrough 30, Pickering 20.
EC Wed. **MD** Sat. **Golf** Whitby 18h. **See**
Abbey ruins, St Mary's Church, Pannett
Park (with Aviary, Art Gallery and
Museum), Town Hall, Capt Cook's house
in Grape La, (monument in People's Park).
🛈 New Quay Rd. ✆ Whitby (0947)
602674.

★★**Royal,** *West Cliff, YO21 3HA.*
✆ (0947) 602234.
★★**Saxonville**, *Ladysmith Av, YO21*
3HX. ✆ (0947) 602631. Open May–Oct &
Easter. C 4. 🛏 22 bedrs, 2 bp, 4 bps, 4 ba.
✗ mc. 🅿 ch, CP 20, Ac, con, 6 st. £ BB
£13·25–£16, DB £26·50–£32, DBB
£18·50–£21·50, 🛈, Bk £2·50, L £3·10, D
£6·50, cc 1 2 3 5 6, Dep a.
∰★★**Sneaton Hall**, *Sneaton, YO22 5HP.*
(3 m S on the B1416). ✆ (0947) 605929.
RS Xmas. C. 🛏 8 bedrs, 3 bp, 3 bps, 3 sh, 1
ba, Dgs. ✗ a l c, mc, LD 8.30. 🅿 Ch, TV,
Dgs, CP 15, CF. £ BB £13·50, DB £25–£27,
2, Bk £3·50, D £4·50, D £6·50, cc 4.
★**Beach,** *The Parade, Sandsend, YO21*
3SZ. ✆ (0947) 83200.
★**Marvic** (R), *White Point Rd, YO21 3JR.*
✆ (0947) 602400.
Banchory, PH, x (R), *3 Crescent Ter,*
West Cliff, YO21 3EL. ✆ (0947) 603513.
Corner, G, z (RI), *3 Crescent Place,*
YO21 3HE. ✆ (0947) 602444. C. 🛏 6
bedrs, 1 ba. 🅿 CH, TV, CF. £ BB £7–£7·50,
DB £14–£15, WT (c) £75·25–£78·75 (c)
£49–£52·50, DT (b) £10·75–£11·25, 🛈.
Enfield House, PH, z (RI) *3 Church Sq,*
West Cliff, YO21 3EG. ✆ (0947) 602984.
Open April–Oct. C. 🛏 10 bedrs, 10 bps, 2
ba. 🅿 TV, CF. £ BB £7–£8, DB £14–£16,
WT £63–£69·50, DT (b) £10·50–£11·50, 🛈.
Esklet, G, x (Unl), *22 Crescent Av, YO21*
3ED. ✆ (0947) 605663. Open Feb–Oct &
Dec. C. 🛏 7 bedrs, 2 ba, ns, Dgs. 🅿 Ch, ns,
CF. £ BB fr £7, DB fr £14, WT (b) fr £65, DT
(b) fr £10, 🛈.
Europa, PH, z (Unl), *10 Hudson St, West*
Cliff, YO21 3EP. ✆ (0947) 602251. Open
Apr–Oct. C 2. 🛏 7 bedrs, 2 ba. 🅿 CH, TV, 2
st. £ BB £7·50, DB £14, WT (b) £62, DT (b)
£10, 🛈.
Hudsons, G, z (RI), *24 Hudson St,*
YO21 3EP. ✆ (0947) 605277. Closed
Xmas. C. 🛏 6 bedrs, 4 sh, 1 ba, TV, Dgs.
✗ a l c. 🅿 CH, TV, Dgs, ns, CF.
Prospect of Whitby, PH, z (RI), *12*
Esplanade. ✆ (0947) 603026.
Seacliffe, PH, z (R), *North Promenade,*
YO21 3JX. ✆ (0947) 603139. C. 🛏 20
bedrs, 4 ba, TV, Dgs. ✗ a l c, mc, LD 7. 🅿 CH, TV,
Dgs, CP 8, CF, 1 BGf, 2 st. £ BB £10·50–
£11, DB £21–£22, WT (b) £98, DT £15–
£15·50, 2, Bk £3, D £5.

Repairers: Arundale of Whitby Ltd,
Stokesby Garage, Castle Park. ✆ (0947)
602841.
Geo. Harrison (Whitby) Ltd, 6 Upgang La.
✆ (0947) 603321.
Rescue Service: Summerfield Garage,
Stainsacre. ✆ (0947) 602238.

WHITCHURCH Avon. Map 5A
Pop 930. Bath 9, London 103, Bristol 3½,
Radstock 13, Shepton Mallet 16, Wells 17,
Weston-super-Mare 22.
EC Wed. **Golf** Knowle 18h. **See** Norman
Church.

Rescue Service: Hursley Hill Garage, Wells
Rd. ✆ (0272) 832303.

WHITCHURCH Buckinghamshire. Map
15E
Pop 841. Aylesbury 5, London 45, Bicester
17, Bletchley 12, Buckingham 12,
Dunstable 17.
Golf. Halton 16h. **See** Church, The
Grange, Old Priory.

The Priory, H, x, *High St, HP22 4JS.*
✆ (0296) 641239. C 10. 🛏 10 bedrs, 2 bp,
1 bps, 3 sh, 2 ba, TV. ✗ a l c. 🅿 CH, TV,
Dgs, CP 13, 2 st. £ BB fr £24, DB fr £33·50,
🛈, Bk £3·60, D £6, cc 1 3 5.

WHITCHURCH Hampshire. Map 6D
Pop 3,700. Basingstoke 12, London 59,
Andover 8, Newbury 14, Winchester 13.
EC Wed. **MD** Fri. **Golf** Overton 9h. **See**
Hill Fort, Silk Mill, Church, Bere Mills.

★★**White Hart,** *Newbury St, RG28 7DN.*
✆ (025 682) 2900. C. 🛏 20 bedrs, 3 bp, 2
bps, 4 sh, 4 ba, Dgs. ✗ a l c, mc, at, LD 10.
🅿 ch, TV, Dgs, CP 24, G 8, Ac, con 24, CF.
£ BB £17–£22·50, DB fr £26, 🛈, Bk £2·75,
L £9·50, D £10, cc 1 3 4 5 6.

WHITCHURCH Hereford &
Worcestershire (Herefordshire). Map 13E
M50 Motorway 8, Ross-on-Wye 7,
London 128, Gloucester 20, Hereford 16,
Monmouth 20.
Golf Ross-on-Wye 18h.

Crown PH, x, *HR9 6DB.* ✆ Symonds Yat.
(0600) 890234. Closed Xmas. C. 🛏 5
bedrs, 2 ba, Dgs. ✗ a l c. 🅿 CH, TV, CP 40,
CF, 3 st. £ BB £10, DB £18, WT £90, DT (b)
£14, 🛈, L £3·50, D £4·50, cc 1 3 4 5.
Portland, G, x (RI), *HR9 6DB.*
✆ Symonds Yat (0600) 890757. C. 🛏 8
bedrs, 8 sh, 1 ba, TV, Dgs. ✗ a l c. 🅿 CH,
TV, Dgs, CP 6, CF, 1 st. £ BB £10–£11·50,
DB £18–£21, WT £95–£100, DT £14·50–
£16·25, 🛈.

Rescue Service: Border Service Station.
✆ Symonds Yat (0600) 890516.

WHITCHURCH Shropshire. Map 19D
Pop 7,246. Newport 21, London 163,
Chester 20, Nantwich 10, Northwich 24,
Shrewsbury 18, Stone 24, Warrington 31,
Wellington 21, Welshpool 34, Wrexham
15.
EC Wed. **MD** Fri. **Golf** Hill Valley 18h. **See**
Parish Church, Higginson's Almshouses,
Church. Sir Edward German born here—
1862.
🛈 Civic Centre, High St. ✆ Whitchurch
(0948) 4577.

∰★★★★**Terrick Hall,** *Terrick Rd, SY13*
4JZ. ✆ (0948) 3031. C. 🛏 10 bedrs, 10
bp, TV, Dgs. ✗ a l c, mc, at, LD 9. 🅿 CH, TV,
CP 50, Ac, gc, tc, sc, con 200, CH, 2 BGf, 2
st. £ BB £14·50–£20, DB £29, WT £150,
DBB £21·50, 🛈, Bk £3·50, L £5, D £7,
cc 1 2 3 5, Dep b.
∰★★**Dodington Lodge**, *Dodington,*
SY13 1EN. ✆ (0948) 2539. C. 🛏 9 bedrs,
3 bp, 2 ba, Dgs. ✗ mc, at, LD 9. 🅿 CH, TV,
CP 40, Ac, con 10, CF, 2 st. £ BB fr £12·50,
DB fr £23, 🛈, Bk £3, D £6·50, cc 1 3, Dep b.

★★**Redbrook Hunting Lodge,**
Wrexham Rd, SY13 3ET. ✆ Redbrook
Maelor 204.

Rescue Service: Victoria Garage
(Whitchurch) Ltd, Newport Rd. ✆ (0948)
2052.
Wrexham Road Garage Ltd, Wrexham Rd.
✆ (0948) 2257.

WHITEHAVEN Cumbria. Map 26F
Pop 26,714. Cockermouth 13, London
311, Egremont 5, Workington 7¼.
EC Wed. **MD** Thur, Sat. **P** Disc Parking is
in operation from 8.30 am to 6 pm
Mondays to Saturdays with the exception
of the Market Pl/James St area where the
scheme operates on Mon, Tue, Wed & Fri
only, and vehicles using the authorised
parking places within the zone must
display a disc set to indicate the time of
arrival. PARKING DISCS must be
displayed facing outwards at either the
front windscreen or the side window
nearest the kerb and are obtainable from
Town Hall, Police Station and Traffic
Wardens. PARKING MUST NOT TAKE
PLACE WHERE THERE ARE YELLOW
LINES ALONG THE ROAD. **Golf** St Bees
9h. **See** St Nicholas Church tower and
remains, Pottery Craft Centre, Museum in
19th cent Market Hall, St Bees Head,
Egremont Castle 5 m SE.
🛈 Market Pl. ✆ Whitehaven (0946) 5678.

★★**Chase,** *Corkickle, CA28 8AA.*
✆ (0946) 3656.

Rescue Service: County Garage Co
(Whitehaven) Ltd, Quay St. ✆ (0946)
2311.

WHITESTONE Devon. Map 4F
Pop 1,000. Exeter 4, London 173, Crediton
8, Moretonhampstead 13, Newton Abbot
18, Okehampton 19.
EC Tue. **Golf** Exeter G and CC 18h. **See**
13th cent St Catherine's Church.

Rowhorne House, F, xy (Unl),
Rowhorne, EX4 2LQ. ✆ Exeter (0392)
74675.

WHITESTONE Hereford & Worcester
(Herefordshire) M. Area 13C
Pop 697. Ledbury 11, London 129,
Bromyard 10, Hereford 4, Leominster 13,
Worcester 21.
EC Wed. **Golf** Wormsley 18h.

Rescue Service: Whitestone Service
Station. ✆ Hereford (0432) 850464.

WHITFORD Devon. M. Area 5E
Pop 588. Axminster 3½, London 150,
Honiton 8½, Lyme Regis 7½.
Golf Axe Cliff, Axmouth 18h.

Rescue Service: Chantry Garage & Guest
House. ✆ Colyton (0297) 52359.

WHITLEY BAY Tyne & Wear. Map 31F
and 32B
Pop 37,288. Tyne Tunnel 5, London 282,
Alnwick 34, Coldstream 52, Sunderland
14.
EC Wed. **MD** Sat. **Golf** Whitley Bay Ltd
18h. **See** Seaton Delaval Hall 4 m NW, St
Mary's Island, Lighthouse.
🛈 Promenade. ✆ Whitley Bay (0632)
524494.

★★**Ambassador,** *South Par, NE26 2RG.*
✆ (0632) 531218. C. 🛏 28 bedrs, 14 bp, 2
sh, 6 ba, TV, Dgs. ✗ a l c, mc, at, LD 9.45.
🅿 N, CH, TV, Dgs, CP 11, G 4, Ac, CF, 1 st.

£ BB £14·50–£26, DB £23·25–£31·50, WB, ☑, Bk £4·50, L £3·95, D £7·30, cc 1 4 5.

★Holmedale (R), *106 Park Av, NE26 1DN.* **☎** (0632) 513903. C. **⇔** 20 bedrs, 5 bp, 4 ba, TV, Dgs. **✗** a l c, LD 9. ⓓ TV, Dgs, CP 10, Ac, con 16, CF, 2 st. **£** BB fr £12·65, DB fr £18·40, WB, ☑, cc 1 3 4 5 6.

Croglin, PH, z (R), *35 South Par, NE26 2RF.* **☎** 091-253 4311. C. **⇔** 48 bedrs, 17 bp, 11 sh, 7 ba, TV, Dgs. **✗** a l c. ⓓ CH, Dgs, CP 16, U 1, CF, 1 st. **£** BB £14–£28, DB £18–£30, ☑, Bk £3, L £5, D £7·50, cc 1 3 4 5.

Downton, PH, z, *South Par, NE26 2AA.* **☎** (0632) 525941. C. **⇔** 22 bedrs, 7 bp, 4 ba, TV. **✗** a l c. ⓓ CH, TV, CF, 2 st. **£** cc 1 5.

York, *30 Park Parade, NE26 1DX.* **☎** (0632) 528313.

Rescue Service: Davidson, G & Sons Ltd, Ford House, Whitley Rd. **☎** (0632) 522225.
Foxhunters Garage Ltd, Foxhunters Rd. **☎** (0632) 528282.

WHITLEY BRIDGE N. Yorkshire. Map 25D
Pop 453. Doncaster 13, London 174, M62 Motorway ½, Pontefract 7½, Selby 7, Snaith 6.
Golf Selby 18h.

Rescue Service: L R Carroll & Son, Station Garage. **☎** (0977) 661256.

WHITMINSTER Gloucestershire. Map Area 13F
1 m North of Intersection 13 (M5), Stroud 6, London 106, Bristol 27, Cheltenham 17, Gloucester 8.

Rescue Service: White House Autos, Frombridge Garage, A38. **☎** Gloucester (0452) 740979.

WHITSTABLE Kent. Map 10D
Pop 26,000. Rochester 26, London 56, Ashford 20, Canterbury 7, Margate 16.
EC Wed. **MD** Thur. **Golf** Chestfield 18h. Seasalter 9h. **See** All Saints' Church, St Alphege's Church, The Castle.
ⓘ 1 Tankerton Rd. **☎** Whitstable (0227) 272233.

Rescue Service: Quinney's Auto Service, Swalecliffe Garage, 107 Herne Bay Rd, Swalecliffe. **☎** Chestfield (022 779) 2396.

WHITTINGTON Shropshire. Map 19E
Pop 1,200. Shrewsbury 18, London 172, Llangollen 12, Oswestry 3, Whitchurch 17, Wrexham 16.
EC Wed. **Golf** Oswestry 18h. **See** Remains of Norman castle.
ⓘ Babbinswood. **☎** Oswestry (0691) 4888.

★Ye Olde Boot Inn, *Castle St, SY11 4DF.* **☎** Oswestry (0091) 662250. C. **⇔** 8 bedrs, 2 ba, Dgs. **✗** a l c, LD 10. ⓓ CH, Dgs, CP 100, Ac, 1 st. **£** BB £10, DB £20, WB, ☑, Bk £3, L £4·50, D £5·50.

WHITTLE-LE-WOODS Lancashire. Map 27D
Pop 3,600. Chorley 3, London 206, Blackburn 8½, Preston 8.
EC Wed. **Golf** Shawhill 18h. **See** Churches, Lochs.

★★★Shawhill Golf & Country Club, *PR6 7PP.* **☎** Chorley (025 72) 69221. C. **⇔** 13 bedrs, 13 bp, TV, Dgs. **✗** a l c, mc, at, LD 9·45. ⓓ N, CH, TV, CP 200, Ac, gc, sb, sol, con 60, CF. **£** BB £38, DB £60, DT £53,

DBB £46, WB, ☑, Bk £5, L £7, D £8, cc 1 2 3 5.

WHITWELL-ON-THE-HILL North Yorkshire. Map 25C
Pop 135. York 12, London 205, Helmsley 17, Malton 6, Pickering 14.
Golf Malton 18h. **See** Kirkham Priory, Castle Howard House (open to public).

⬛★★★Whitwell Hall (R), *YO6 7JJ.* **☎** (065 381) 551. C 12. **⇔** 11 bedrs, 8 bp, 3 bps, annexe 9 bedrs, 6 bp, 3 bps, TV, Dgs. **✗** mc, at, LD 8.15. ⓓ CH, CP 40, G 4, Ac, sp, tc, sb, sol, con 70, CF, 4 BGf, 3 st. **£** BB £30–£34, DB £37–£59, WB, ☑, Bk £5, L £6, D £14, cc 1 3 4 5.

WHIXLEY Yorkshire. M. Area 25E
Pop 650. Wetherby 7½, London 202, Boroughbridge 8, Harrogate 9½, York 12.
EC Wed. **Golf** Knaresborough 18h. **See** Allerton Park, Whixley Hall.

Rescue Service: West View Garage. **☎** Green Hammerton (0901) 30260.

WICKEN Northamptonshire. Map 15C
Pop 321. Bletchley 10, Buckingham 5, Towcester 8, Northampton 17.
Golf Milton Keynes 18h. **See** Church.

⬛★★★Wicken Country, *Cross Tree Rd, Milton Keynes, MK19 6BX.* **☎** (090 857) 239. C. **⇔** 16 bedrs, 4 bp, 5 bps, TV, Dgs. **✗** a l c, mc, at, LD 9.30. ⓓ CH, Dgs, CP 40, U 4, Ac, sp, tc, con 25, CF, 1 BGf, 2 st. **£** BB £24·50–£27·50, DB £34–£40, ☑, Bk £3·50, L £7·50, D £7·50, cc 1 2 3.

WICKFORD Essex. Maps 10A and 17F
Pop 22,200. Romford 16, London 32, Brentwood 10, Chelmsford 10, Colchester 28, Dartford Tunnel 18, Southend-on-Sea 10.
EC Wed. **MD** Mon, Fri, Sat. **Golf** Basildon 18h. **See** Church.

Rescue Service: Good Companions Garage, Chelmsford Rd, Battlebridge. **☎** (037 44) 3034.
Swan Garages (Wickford) Ltd, The Broadway. **☎** (037 44) 2155.

WICKHAM MARKET Suffolk. Map 17A
Pop 2,154. Ipswich 13, London 87, Aldeburgh 11, Saxmundham 8, Scole 20, Stowmarket 19.
EC Wed. **MD** Mon. **Golf** Woodbridge 18h. **See** Church, water mill on R Deben still in use.

Repairer: C C Nesling Ltd, High St. **☎** (0728) 746161.

WICKWAR Avon. Maps 5B and 13F
Pop 913. Chippenham 18, London 109, Bath 17, Bristol 14, Cheltenham 28, Chepstow 16, Gloucester 22, Tetbury 13.
EC Sat. **Golf** Chipping Sodbury 18h. **See** Holy Trinity Church, Town Hall.

Rescue Service: A E Wilcox & Sons Ltd, High St. **☎** (045 424) 213.

WIDEMOUTH BAY Cornwall. Map 3A
Holsworthy 11, London 222, Bude 3½, Camelford 16, Launceston 16.
EC Wed. **Golf** Bude 18h.

⬛★Brocksmoor, *Poundstock, EX23 0DF.* **☎** (028 885) 207. Closed Jan & Feb. C. **⇔** 10 bedrs, 1 bp, 2 ba, Dgs. **✗** a l c, mc, at, LD 8.30. ⓓ CH, TV, CP 20, sp, gc, CF, 1 BGf, 6 st. **£** BB £9–£11, DB £18–£22, WT £65–£66, DT £20–£22, WB, ☑, Bk £2·30, L £3·75, D £5, Dep a.

⬛★Trelawny (R), *Marine Dr, Widemouth Bay, EX23 0AH.* **☎** (028 885) 328. C. **⇔** 10 bedrs, 2 bps, 2 ba. **✗** mc, at, LD 9. ⓓ CH, TV, CP 30, Ac, gc, CF. **£** BB £10–£15, DB £20–£30, WT £69–£97·70, WB, ☑, Bk £2·60, L £3, D £4·50, cc 1 5, Dep a.

Beach House, PH, y (R), *EX23 0AW.* **☎** (028 885) 256.

WIDNES Cheshire. Maps 19A & 20D
Pop 55,000. Northwich 12, London 185, Chester 16, Liverpool 12, Nantwich 24, St Helens 7, Warrington 7, Whitchurch 28.
EC Thur. **MD** Mon, Fri, Sat. **Golf** Widnes 18h. **See** Bridges, Museum.

★★Hillcrest, *Cronton La, WA8 9AR.* **☎** 051-424 1616.

WIGAN Greater Manchester (Lancashire). Map 20C
See also STANDISH and UPHOLLAND.
Pop 81,674. London 195, M6 Motorway 3, Bolton 10, Chorley 8, Manchester 19, Ormskirk 11, Preston 17, St Helens 8, Walkden 10, Warrington 12.
EC Wed. **MD** Daily exc Wed. **Golf** Haigh Hall Municipal 18h. **See** 14th cent All Saints' Church, ancient Mab's Cross, Haigh Hall, Tyldesley Monument (Civil War), Wigan 'Pier'.

★★★Brocket Arms, *Mesnes Rd, WN1 2DD.* **☎** (0942) 46283. C. **⇔** 27 bedrs, 25 bp, 2 bps, TV. **✗** a l c, LD 9.30. (Fri & Sat 10). ⓓ N, CH, CP 60, Ac, con 200, CF, 2 st. **£** BB £25, DB £36, ☑, Bk £4, L £4·50, D £7·50, cc 1 2 3 5 6.

★★Bel Air (R), *236 Wigan La, WN1 2RP.* **☎** (0942) 41410. RS Sun. **⇔** 11 bedrs, 10 bp, 1 bps, 1 ba, TV. **✗** a l c, LD 9. ⓓ CH, CP 10, con 20, 2 st. **£** BB fr £18·65, DB fr £24·85, ☑, Bk £3·50, L £5·50, D £7, cc 1 5.

★★Bellingham, *149 Wigan La, WN1 2NB.* **☎** (0942) 43893. C. **⇔** 17 bedrs, 1 bp, 9 bps, 1 sh, 3 ba, TV, Dgs. **✗** a l c, mc, LD 9. ⓓ CH, TV, Dgs, CP 30, Ac, con 20, CF, 1 st. **£** BB fr £17, DB fr £25, WB, ☑, Bk £2·50, L £4·95, D £4·95, cc 1 2 3 5.

⬛★★Grand, *Dorning St, WN1 1ND.* **☎** (0942) 43471. RS Sun. C. **⇔** 30 bedrs, 11 bp, 19 bps, TV, Dgs. **✗** a l c, mc, at, LD 9.30. ⓓ CH, CP 6, Ac, con 130, CF, 2 st. **£** BB £19, DB £28, WT fr £196, DT fr £27, WB, ☑, Bk £2·50, L £3·95, D £4·95, cc 1 3 4 5, Dep b.

Rescue Service: Mabs Cross Motors Ltd, Mesnes St. **☎** (0942) 43271.
Wilsons Garage, Rear of 258 Manchester Rd, Higher Ince. **☎** (0942) 492088.

WIGMORE Hereford and Worcester (Herefordshire). Map 13A
Pop 373. Leominster 9½, London 158, Hereford 20, Knighton 9½, Ludlow 10.
EC Wed. **Golf** Ludlow 18h. **See** St James's Church (11th cent), Abbey ruins.

Rescue Service: W A W Phillips, Castle Garage. **☎** 206.

WIGTON Cumbria. Map 26E
Pop 4,720. Penrith 22, London 298, Carlisle 11, Cockermouth 15, Keswick 20, Maryport 15.
EC Wed. **MD** Tue. **Golf** Silloth 18h. **See** Church of St Mary the Virgin.

★★Greenhill Lodge, *Red Dial, CA7 8LS.* **☎** (0965) 43304. C. **⇔** 8 bedrs, 1 bp, 2 ba. **✗** a l c, mc, at, LD 9.15. ⓓ CH, CP 120, Ac, con, CF, 3 st. **£** BB £18–£21, DB £30–£36,

WT £150, DT £28, DBB £23–£26, WB, ☐,
Bk £3, L £4·50, D £8·50, cc 1 2 3 5.
High Greenrigg, H, x, *Caldbeck (3¼
miles West B5299), CA7 8HD.* ✆ Caldbeck
(069 98) 430. Closed 10 dys Xmas & New
Year. C. ⌗ 8 bedrs, 1 bps, 2 ba, Dgs. ☐ CH,
TV, Dgs, CP 8, CF, 3 BGf, 1 st, Dis. £ BB
£10, DB £20, WT (b) fr £96 (½ board), ☐, D
£6.

Rescue Service: Huntington, J W & Son,
Southend Garage. ✆ (0965) 2670.

WILLAND Devon. Map 4F
Pop 1,435. Taunton 16, London 159,
Exeter 15, Honiton 11, Tiverton 6.
EC Wed. **MD** Wed. **Golf** Tiverton 18h.
See 14th cent Church.

Rescue Service: L J Spearing & Son, The
Garage. ✆ Tiverton (0884) 820224.

WILLENHALL West Midlands. Map 21E
Pop 45,000. Birmingham 10, London 121,
Bromsgrove 18, Kidderminster 19,
Stafford 17, Walsall 2½. Wolverhampton 3.
EC Thur. **MD** Wed, Sat. **Golf** Walsall 18h.
See Lock Museum.

Rescue Service: New Invention Motor
Services Ltd, Lichfield Rd. ✆ Bloxwich
(0922) 76484.

WILLINGTON Durham. Map 24E
Pop 7,500. A1(M) Motorway 10, Bishop
Auckland 6, London 257, Consett 15,
Darlington 16, Durham 7.
EC Wed. **Golf** Crook 18h. **See** Parish
Church.

Rescue Service: Bromley's Garage, South
St. ✆ (038 889) 6380.

WILLITON Somerset. Map 4D
Pop 2,463. Taunton 14, London 157,
Bridgwater 16, Dunster 6½, Tiverton 24.
EC Sat. **Golf** Minehead and W Somerset
18h. **See** Parish Church, Cleeve Abbey
ruins 2½ m W, Quantock Hills, Dunster
Castle 5½ m WNW, West Somerset Rly
(Steam Engines).

★★White House (R), *Long St, TA4 4QW.*
✆ (0984) 32306. Open May–Oct. ⌗ 8
bedrs, 2 bp, 2 ba, annexe 5 bedrs, 4 bp,
Dgs. ✗ LD 8.15. ☐ CH, TV, Dgs, CP 21, 4
BGf, 1 st, Dis. £ BB fr £19, DB fr £34, WB,
☐, Bk £5, D £13·50, Dep a.

WILMCOTE Warwickshire. Map 14C
Pop 1,044. Stratford-upon-Avon 4,
London 97, Birmingham 21, Bromsgrove
19, Droitwich 20, Evesham 14, Warwick
9½, Worcester 23.
EC Wed. **Golf** Stratford-upon-Avon 18h.
See Mary Arden's House (home of
Shakespeare's mother).

★★Swan House, *The Green, CV37 9XJ.*
✆ Stratford-upon-Avon (0789) 67030. RS
Sun evening. C. ⌗ 11 bedrs, 3 bp, 3 ba.
✗ a l c, mc, LD 9. ☐ CH, Dgs, CP 40, Ac,
con 20, 2 st. £ BB £17, DB £27–£30, WB, ☐
10%, Bk £2·50, L £1·25, D £8, cc 1 3 5,
Dep a.

WILMINGTON Devon. Map 4F
Pop 250. Ilminster 16, London 152,
Axminster 6, Honiton 4, Taunton 18.
Golf Honiton 18h. **See** Widworthy
Church and Manor.

★★Home Farm (R), *EX14 9JR.*
✆ (040 483) 278. Closed Jan & Feb. C.
⌗ 14 bedrs, 7 bp, 3 ba, Dgs. ✗ a l c, mc, at,
LD 9. ☐ CH, Dgs, CP 20, CF, 6 BGf, 2

st. £ BB £15–£21, DB £27–£35, WB, ☐, Bk
£4, L £5, D £9, cc 1 5, Dep a.

WILMSLOW Cheshire. Map 19B
Pop 30,055. Congleton 12, London 173,
Altrincham 7, Knutsford 6½, Macclesfield
7½, Manchester 12, Sandbach 16,
Stockport 7.
EC Wed. **MD** Fri. **Golf** Wilmslow 18h. **See**
St Bartholomew's Church, Handforth Hall,
Hawthorn Hall.

★★★Stanneylands (RI), *Stanneylands
Rd, SK9 4EY.* ✆ (0625) 525225. C. ⌗ 34
bedrs, 33 bp, 2 ba, TV. ✗ a l c, mc, at, LD
10. ☐ N, CH, CP 80, con 65, CF, 13 BGf, 1
st, Dis. £ BB £18–£38, DB £25–£50, WB, ☐,
Bk £4·50, L £7, D £12·50, cc 1 2 3 4 5 6,
Dep b.

★★★Valley Lodge, *Altrincham Rd, SK9
4LR.* ✆ (0625) 529201. C. ⌗ 87 bedrs, 74
bp, 13 bps, TV, Dgs. ✗ a l c, mc, at, LD
10.30. ☐ Lt, N, CH, CP 300, CF, 7 st. £ BB
fr £34·50, DB fr £46, DBB fr £41·50, WB, ☐,
Bk £4, L £6·25, D £7·25, cc 1 2 3 5, Dep.▲

Repairer: Moores & Newton Ltd, Water
La. ✆ (0625) 527311.

WILSTEAD (WILSHAMSTEAD)
Bedfordshire. Map 15C
Pop 1,750. Luton 15, London 48, Baldock
15, Bedford 4.

Old Manor House, H, x (R), *Cotton End
Rd, MK45 3BT.* ✆ Bedford (0234) 740262.
C. ⌗ 9 bedrs, 2 ba. ☐ CH, TV, CP 10, CF, 1
st. £ BB £13, DB £21, DT (b) fr £18, ☐.

WILTON Wiltshire. Map 6C
Pop 4,000. Salisbury 3, London 86,
Devizes 21, Shaftesbury 16, Warminster
17, Wincanton 25.
EC Wed. **MD** Thur. **Golf** Salisbury and S
Wilts 18h. **See** Wilton House, Wilton
Royal Carpet Factory, Great Fair (Sheep)
Sept.

★★Pembroke Arms, *SP2 0BH.*
✆ Salisbury (0722) 743127. C. ⌗ 8 bedrs,
2 bp, 2 ba, Dgs. ✗ a l c, mc, at, LD 9.45.
☐ ch, TV, Dgs, CP 40, Ac, CF, 0 st. £ BB
£15–£18, DB £29–£35, ☐, Bk £3, L £4, D
£10, cc 1 3.

Repairer: Marks, F W & Sons Ltd,
Shaftesbury Rd. ✆ (0722) 3237.
Specialist Body Repairer: Marks, F W &
Sons Ltd, Shaftesbury Rd. ✆ (0722) 3237.

WIMBORNE MINSTER Dorset. Map 5F
Pop 5,531. Ringwood 10, London 103,
Blandford Forum 9, Bournemouth 9,
Dorchester 22, Salisbury 26, Wareham 12.
EC Wed. **MD** Fri. **Golf** Broadstone
(Dorset) 18h. **See** Minster (11th cent
astronomical clock and chained Library),
St Margaret's Chapel and Hospital,
Priest's House Museum, Julians' Bridge,
Model of town (off West Row), Badbury
Rings 3 m NW.
🛈 Minster Grounds. ✆ Wimborne (0202)
886116.

★★★King's Head (TH), *The Square,
BH21 1JA.* ✆ (0202) 880101. C. ⌗ 28
bedrs, 12 bp, 10 ba, TV, Dgs. ✗ a l c, mc, at,
LD 9.15. ☐ Lt, CH, Dgs, CP 25, Ac, con 60,
CF, 1 st. £ BB £34–£36·50, DB £46·50–
£53·50, WB, ☐, cc 1 2 3 4 5 6, Dep (Xmas).

Repairers: Dibben's Garage, 19 West St.
✆ (0202) 882261.
English, F Ltd, Poole Rd. ✆ (0202)
886211.

Rescue Service: Hayes Garage, Wimborne
Rd West. ✆ (0202) 882421.
Three Cross Garage, Three Legged Cross.
✆ (0202) 825255.
Wimborne Ford Ltd, Poole Rd. ✆ (0202)
886211.

WINCANTON Somerset. Map 5D
Pop 3,800. Amesbury 30, London 110,
Frome 15, Glastonbury 23, Ilminster 25,
Salisbury 24, Shaftesbury 11, Shepton
Mallet 12, Sherborne 9, Taunton 33,
Warminster 16.
EC Thur. **MD** Tue. **Golf** Sherborne 18h.
See 'The Dogs' South St (assoc with Wm
of Orange), Stourhead (Nat Trust) 7 m NE.
🛈 The Library, 7 Carrington Way.
✆ Wincanton (0963) 32173.

★★Dolphin, *High St, BA9 9JF.* ✆ (0963)
32215. C. ⌗ 10 bedrs, 4 bp, 2 bps, 1 ba,
TV, Dgs. ✗ a l c, mc, at, LD 9.30. ☐ CH, TV,
Dgs, CP 20, G 2, Ac, con 50, CF, 0 st. £ BB
fr £16·50, DB fr £30, DBB fr £18·50, WB, ☐,
Bk £2·75, L £4·95, D £6, cc 1, Dep a.

▮★★★Holbrook House, *Holbrook, BA9
8BS.* ✆ (0963) 32377. C. ⌗ 20 bedrs, 14
bp, 5 ba, Dgs. ✗ a l c, mc, at, LD 8.30.
☐ CH, TV, Dgs, CP 30, U 6, sp, tc, sc, con
25, CF, 2 st. £ BB £16·50–£18·50, DB £33–
£37, WT £155, DT £30·50, DBB £23·50–
£25·50, WB, ☐, Bk £4, L £4·50, D £7·50,
cc 1 2 3.

MC Repairer: Light, W H & Co, Bayford
Garage. ✆ (0963) 32207.
Rescue Service: Southgate Garage,
Southgate. ✆ (0963) 33950.

WINCHCOMBE Gloucestershire. Map
14C
Pop 4,792. Stow-on-the-Wold 11, London
96, Cheltenham 7, Evesham 10, Stratford-
upon-Avon 22, Tewkesbury 11.
EC Thur. **Golf** Cleeve Hill 18h. **See** St
Peter's Church, George Inn, Hailes Abbey
ruins and Museum, Belas Knap (Neolithic
Long Barrow), Roman Villa sites at
Spoonley and Wadefield, Sudeley Castle.
🛈 Town Hall. ✆ Cheltenham (0242)
602925.

★★George, *High St, GL54 5LT.*
✆ Cheltenham (0242) 602321.

Rescue Service: Winchcombe Motors,
Broadway Rd. ✆ Cheltenham (0242)
603299.

WINCHESTER Hampshire. Map 6D
Pop 33,221. Basingstoke 18, London 65,
Alton 17, Andover 14, Fareham 19,
Newbury 24, Petersfield 19, Romsey 10,
Salisbury 23, Southampton 12.
See Plan p 377.
MD Mon, Wed, Fri, Sat. **P** See Plan. **Golf**
Royal Winchester 18h, Hockley 18h. **See**
Cathedral, Guildhall (with Art Gallery),
Winchester College (apply porter), St
Cross Hospital and Church (Wayfarer's
Dole), Great Hall of Winchester Castle
(legendary Round Table of King Arthur
and his Knights), West Gate (Museum),
King Alfred's Statue, City Museum, 14th
cent Kingsgate (City Gateway, with St
Swithin's Church built over), Hampshire
Regt Museum (Serle's House), Royal
Greenjackets Museum, The Weirs (City
Wall), Wolvesey Castle ruins, 15th cent
Chesil Rectory, 12th cent St John's
Church, City Mill, Avington Park 4 m NE.
🛈 Guildhall. ✆ Winchester (0962) 68166.

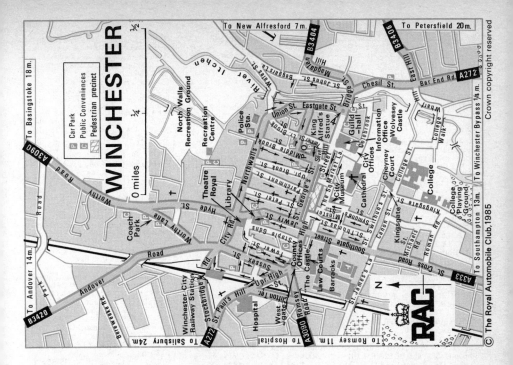

★★★★**Wessex** (TH), *Paternoster Row, SO23 9LQ.* ✆ (0962) 61611. C. ⇔ 94 bedrs, 91 bp, 3 bps, TV, Dgs. ✗ a l c, mc, at, LD 10. ⚙ Lt, N, CH, Dgs, CP 40, Ac, con 120, CF, 4 st. £ BB £47, DB £61, WB, ①, cc 1 2 3 4 5 6, Dep (Xmas).

⬟★★★★**Lainston House,** *Sparsholt (3 miles W on the A272), SO21 2LT.* ✆ (0962) 63588. C. ⇔ 34 bedrs, 34 bp, TV. ✗ a l c, mc, at, LD 10.30. ⚙ N, CH, Dgs, CP 150, Ac, tc, con 60, CF, 16 BGf, Dis. £ BB fr £41·50, DB fr £55·50, WB, ② 10%, Bk £3·50, L £10, D £15, cc 13 4 5 6.▲

Kings Head, I, x *Hursley Village SO21 2JW.* ✆ (0962) 75208. Closed Xmas Day. C. ⇔ 5 bedrs, 2 ba. ✗ a l c. ⚙ CH, TV, CP 30, 2 st. £ BB £11·50, DB £20, ②, D £5, cc 1 5.

WINCLECheshire. Map 22C
Leek 8, London 162, Buxton 9, Congleton 10, Macclesfield 6.

Fourways Diner Motel, x (Rt) *Cleulow Cross, SK11 0QL.* ✆ (026 07) 228. C. ⇔ 7 bedrs, 2 bp, 5 bps, TV, Dgs. ✗ a l c. ⚙ CH, CP 40, CF, 1 BGf, 2 ot. £ BB £14·18, DB £20—£24, WT (c) £120—£140, WB, ①, Bk £2·50, L £4·50, D £5·50, cc 1 3.

WINDERMERECumbria. Map 26D
Pop 8,065. M6 Motorway 16, London 264, Ambleside 5, Broughton-in-Furness 22, Kendal 8, Lancaster 28, Penrith 26, Ulverston 17.

EC Thur. **Golf** Windermere 18h. **See** Lake, Orrest Head (extensive views), St Martin's Church Townend (Troutbeck) 2 m N. ⓘ Victoria St. ✆ Windermere (096 62) 4561.

★★★★**Old England** (TH), *Bowness, LA23 3DF.* ✆ (096 62) 2444. C. ⇔ 82

bedrs, 82 bp, TV, Dgs. ✗ a l c, mc, at, LD 9.30. ⚙ Lt, N, CH, Dgs, CP 60, Ac, sp, con 325, CF, 7 BGf, 2 st. £ BB £44, DB £62·50, WB, ①, cc 1 2 3 4 5 6, Dep (Xmas).

◼★★★**Beech Hill,** *Newby Bridge Rd, LA23 3LR.* ✆ (096 62) 2137. C. ⇔ 47 bedrs, 47 bp, TV, Dgs. ✗ a l c, mc, at, LD 9. ⚙ N, CH, TV, Dgs, CP 50, Ac, sp, sb, sol, con 150, CF, 5 BGf, 2 st. £ BB £37—£40, DB £50—£56, WT £160—£200, WB, Bk £3·50, L £5·50, D £8, cc 1 3 4 5, Dep b.

★★★**Belsfield** (TH), *Kendal Rd, LA23 3EL.* ✆ (096 62) 2448. C. ⇔ 64 bedrs, 37 bp, 16 bps, 5 ba, TV, Dgs. ✗ a l c, mc, at, LD 9.15. ⚙ Lt, N, CH, Dgs, CP 80, Ac, sp, con 130, CF, 17 BGf, 1 st, Dis. £ BB £30·50—£39, DB £48—£56, WB, ①, cc 1 2 3 4 5 6.

◼★★★**M Burn How** (R), *Back Belsfield Rd, Bowness, LA23 3EW.* ✆ (096 62) 6226. Closed Jan. C. ⇔ 24 bedrs, 21 bp, 1 ba, TV. ✗ a l c, mc, LD 9.15. ⚙ CH, CP 30, Ac, con 24, CF, 5 BGf, 1 st, Dis. £ BB £25—£28, DB £35—£42, ①, Bk £3, L £1·50, D £8·50, cc 3 4.

⬟★★★★**Langdale Chase,** *LA23 1LW.* ✆ Ambleside (0966) 32201. C. ⇔ 28 bedrs, 17 bp, 7 bps, 4 sh, 3 ba, annexe 7 bedrs, 7 bp, TV, Dgs. ✗ mc, at, LD 8.45. ⚙ N, CH, TV, Dgs, CP 50, tc, con 25, CF, 2 BGf, 1 st, Dis. £ BB fr £26·50, DB fr £51, WB, ①, Bk £4·50, L £7·25, D £12·50, cc 1 3 4 5 6, Dep b.

◼★★★**Low Wood,** *LA23 1LP* (3½ m N A591). ✆ Ambleside (0966) 33338. C. ⇔ 130 bedrs, 81 bp, 17 bps, 12 ba, TV, Dgs. ✗ a l c, mc, LD 10. ⚙ N, CH, TV, Dgs, CP 200, Ac, pf, con, CF, 43 BGf, 2 st. £ BB £14·35—£23·25, DB £28·70—£46·50, DBB £22·20—£31·45, WB, ①, Bk £4, L £4, D £9·30, cc 1 2 3 5, Dep.

★★★**Priory,** *Rayrigg Rd, LA23 1EX.* ✆ (096 62) 4377. RS Dec—Feb. C. ⇔ 15 bedrs, 13 bp, 2 bps, TV, Dgs. ✗ mc, at, LD 8.45. ⚙ N, CH, TV, CP 50, Ac, con 50, 1 st. £ BB £22·50, DB £45, WB, ①, Bk £2·75, L £4·50, D £8·50, cc 13 4 5 6.

★★★**Royal,** *Bowness, LA23 3DB.* ✆ (096 62) 3045. C. ⇔ 29 bedrs, 25 bp, 4 bps, 5 ba, TV, Dgs. ✗ mc, at, LD 10. ⚙ CH, Dgs, CP 20, U 5, Ac, con, CF. £ BB £17·85—£23·35, DB £35·70—£46·70, WT £174—£214, DT £30·85—£36·50, DBB £26·60—£32·50, WB, ①, Bk £4, L £4, D £9·50, cc 1 2 3 4 5, Dep.

★★★**Wild Boar,** *Crook Rd, LA23 3NF.* (3½ m E B5284). ✆ (096 62) 5225. C. ⇔ 38 bedrs, 33 bp, 5 bps, 3 ba, TV, Dgs. ✗ a l c, mc, at, LD 8.45. ⚙ CH, Dgs, CP 60, U 2, con, CF, 2 st. £ BB £24·75—£27, DB £49·50—£54, DT £42·70—£45, DBB £36·35—£38·70, WB, ①, Bk £4·50, L £4, D £12·25, cc 1 2 3 5, Dep.

★★★**Windermere Hydro,** *Helm Rd, Bowness, LA23 3BA.* ✆ (096 62) 4455. C. ⇔ 96 bedrs, 86 bp, 10 bps, TV, Dgs. ✗ mc. ⚙ Lt, N, CH, CP 100, Ac, con 200, CF, 14 BGf, 1 st, Dis. £ BB fr £33, DB fr £50·60, WB (winter), ①, cc 1 2 3 5.

◼★★★**Applegarth,** *College Rd, LA23 3AE.* ✆ (096 62) 3206. Closed Jan—Feb. C. ⇔ 14 bedrs, 1 bp, 13 bps, TV, Dgs. ✗ a l c, mc, at, LD 7.45. ⚙ N, CH, CP 12, CF, 5 st. £ BB £19—£21, DB £36—£42, WT £168—£175, WB, ①, Bk £5, D £9, cc 1 3.▲

◼★★**Bordriggs** (R), *Longtail Hill, LA23 3JD.* ✆ (096 62) 3567. C. ⇔ 13 bedrs, 13 bp, 1 ba, TV. ✗ a l c, mc, at, LD 8. ⚙ CH, TV, CP 13, sp, con 24, CF, 2 BGf, 0 st, Dis. £ BB fr £15·50, DB fr £31, WT fr £140, WB, Bk £2·50, D £7·50.

◨★★**Burnside,** *Kendal Rd, Bowness,
LA23 3EP.* ✆ (096 62) 2211. C. ⋈ 31
bedrs, 8 bp, 23 bps, 3 ba, TV, Dgs. ✗ a l c,
mc, at, LD 8.30. ฿ CH, TV, Dgs, CP 50, Ac,
con 60, CF. £ BB £21–£25, DB £38–£46,
WT £150–£160, WB, ①, Bk £3·50, L £3·95,
D £9·50, cc 1 3 4 5.

◨★★**Ellerthwaite Lodge,** *New Rd,
LA23 2LA.* ✆ (096 62) 5115. Open Mar–
Nov. C. ⋈ 10 bedrs, 10 bp, TV, Dgs. ✗ LD
8.30. ฿ CH, CP 20, Ac, CF, 3 st.
£ cc 1 3 4 5 6, Dep.

◨★★**Grey Walls,** *Elleray Rd, LA23 1AG.*
✆ (096 62) 3741. Open Mar–Nov. C. ⋈ 17
bedrs, 4 bp, 10 bps, TV, Dgs. ✗ a l c, mc, at,
LD 7.45. ฿ CH, TV, CP 20, Ac, con
20, CF. £ BB £13·75–£16·50, DB £27·50–
£33, WT £145–£160, WB, ①, cc 1 3 4 6,
Dep a.

◨★★**Hideaway** (R), *Phoenix Way, LA23
1DB.* ✆ (096 62) 3070. C. ⋈ 13 bedrs, 7
bp, 4 bps, 1 sh, 1 ba, TV. ✗ mc, at, LD 7.30.
฿ CH, TV, CP 16, con 20, CF. £ BB £13–
£18, DB £26–£38, WT £110–£160, DBB
£16–£23, WB, ①, Bk £5, D £8, Dep a ▲.

◨★★**Holbeck Ghyll** (R), *Holbeck Lane,
LA23 1LU.* ✆ Ambleside 32375.

◨▲★★**Lindeth Fell** (R), *Bowness, LA23
3JP.* ✆ (096 62) 3286. Open Mar–Oct. C 5.
⋈ 13 bedrs, bp, 7 bps, TV, Dgs. ✗ mc,
LD 7. ฿ CH, TV, CP 14, tc, CF, 1 BGf, 0 st, Dis.
£ BB £19·95, DB £39·95, DBB £27·95, Bk
£5, D £9·50, cc 1 2 3 5, Dep a.

◨▲★★**Lindeth Howe** (Rl), *Longtail Hill,
Storrs Park, LA23 3JF.* ✆ (096 62) 5759.
Closed Xmas & New Year. C. ⋈ 12 bedrs,
4 bp, 8 bps, TV. ✗ mc, LD 8.15. ฿ CH, CP
30, con 12, CF, 1 st. £ BB £20–£32, DB
£33–£44, DBB £22·50–£28·50, WB, ①, Bk
£5, D £8·50, cc 1 3, Dep a.

◨▲★★**Linthwaite** (R), *Oaks Dr, LA23
3JA.* ✆ (096 62) 3688. Closed Nov–Dec.
C 8. ⋈ 11 bedrs, 11 bp, TV. ✗ mc, at,
LD 7. ฿ CH, ns, CP 25, pf, 1 st. £ BB £20–£22,
DB £40–£44, Bk £4, D £9, Dep a.

◨★★**Ravensworth** (R), *Ambleside Rd,
LA23 1BA.* ✆ (096 62) 3747. C. ⋈ 13
bedrs, 10 bp, 3 bps, TV, Dgs. ✗ mc, LD 7.
฿ CH, Dgs, ns, CP 13, CF, 3 st. £ BB
£13·50–£16·50, DB £21–£31, WB, ①, Bk
£2·50, L £2·50, D £8, cc 1 5 6.

◨★★**St Martin's,** *Lake Rd, LA23 3DE.*
✆ (096 62) 3731. Closed Dec–Jan. C.
⋈ 17 bedrs, 3 bp, 5 bps, 3 ba, Dgs. ✗ a l c,
mc, LD 9.30. ฿ CH, TV, CP 10, CF, 3 st.
£ BB £15·50–£18·50, DB £31–£36, DBB
£23–£27, ①, Bk £4, D £8·50, cc 1 2 3 5.

◨★★**Sun,** *Troutbeck Bridge, LA23 1HH.*
✆ (096 62) 3274.

◨★★**Cranleigh** (Rl), *Kendal Rd, Bowness,
LA23 3EW.* ✆ (096 62) 3293. Open Mar–
Oct. RS Mar. C 12. ⋈ 11 bedrs, 4 bp, 4 sh,
2 ba. ✗ LD 5.30. ฿ ch, TV, CP 11, 1 st.
£ BB £13·50–£14·50, DB £26–£35, WB, ①,
Bk £3·50, D £7·50, Dep a.

◨★**Elleray,** *Cross St, LA23 1AE.*
✆ (096 62) 3120. C. ⋈ 13 bedrs, 1 sh, 4
ba, TV, Dgs. ✗ a l c, mc, LD 9. ฿ CH, TV,
Dgs, 1 st. £ BB fr £11·50, DB fr £22, ②,
cc 1 6, Dep a.

◨★**Knoll** (R), *Lake Rd, Bowness, LA23
2JF.* ✆ (096 62) 3756. Open Mar–Oct. C 3.
⋈ 12 bedrs, 3 bp, 4 ba. ✗ mc, at, LD 7.
฿ CH, TV, CP 15, 2 st. £ BB £12, DB fr £24,
DBB fr £17, WB, ①, Bk £3·50, L £5·50, D
£6·50, Dep.

Boston House, G, x (Unl), *The Terrace,
LA23 1AT.* ✆ (096 62) 3654.

Braemount House, H, z (R), ✆ (096 62)
5967.

Cragg Brow Cottage, PH, y (R),
✆ (096 62) 4080.

Dunvegan, G, z (Unl), *Broad St, LA23
2AB.* ✆ (096 62) 2333. Open Mar–Oct. C.
⋈ 4 bedrs, 1 ba. ฿ CH, TV, CP 4, CF. £ BB
fr £8, DB fr £16, WT (b) fr £84, (c) fr £56,
DT (b) fr £12, ①.

Elim Bank, H, z (R), *Lake Rd, LA23 2JJ.*
✆ (096 62) 4810. C. ⋈ 7 bedrs, 2 ba, TV.
✗ a l c. ฿ CH, TV, CP 7, CF, 1 st. £ BD
£16–£20, WT (c) £56–£70, ②, Bk £1·10, D
£6·55, cc 1 3 5 ▲.

Glenville, PH, z (R), *Lake Rd, LA23 2EQ.*
✆ (096 62) 3371. C. ⋈ 9 bedrs, 1 bps, 2
ba. ฿ CH, TV, CP 12, CF. £ BB £10–
£10·50, DB £19–£24, WT (b) £119–£133,
DT (b) £16·50–£19, ①, Bk £2, D £7.

Hawksmoor, G, z (Rl), *Lake Rd, LA23
2EQ.* ✆ (096 62) 2110. Closed Dec, Jan. C.
⋈ 6 bedrs, 1 ba. ฿ TV, ns, CP 10. £ BB
£7·50–£11, DB £15–£21, WT (b) £81–£96,
(c) £55–£68, DT (b) £13–£16, ①.

Mylne Bridge, PH, z (R), *Brookside Lake
Rd, LA23 2BX.* ✆ (096 62) 3314. Open
Mar–Nov C. 7. ⋈ 12 bedrs, 5 bps, 2 ba.
✗ a l c. ฿ CH, TV, CP 12, 2 st. £ BB £9·75–
£11·75, DB £18·50–£21·50, WT (b) £100–
£115, DT (b) £15·25–£17, ②, Bk £3, D
£6·25.

Oakthorpe, PH, z (R), *High St, LA23
1AF.* ✆ (096 62) 3547. Closed Xmas &
First 2 wks Jan. C. ⋈ 21 bedrs, 7 sh, 5 ba,
TV, Dgs. ฿ ch, TV, Dgs, CP 18, CF, 6 st.
£ BB £11–£12·50, DB £22–£28, WT (b)
£123–£140, DT (b) £19–£22, ①, Bk £3, D
£8, cc 1 5 ▲.

Rockside, G, x (R), *Ambleside Rd, LA23
1AQ.* ✆ (096 62) 5343. Closed Dec 15–
Jan 3. C. ⋈ 14 bedrs, 1 sh, 2 ba. ✗ a l c.
฿ CH, TV, CP 12, CF, 1 st. £ BB £9·50–
£10, DB £17–£21, WT (c) £56–£65, ①, Bk
£3·25, cc 5.

Rosemount, PH, z (R), *Lake Rd, LA23
2EQ.* ✆ (096 62) 3739. C. ⋈ 8 bedrs, 2
bps, 1 sh, 3 ba, Dgs. ฿ CH, TV, CP 6, G 2,
CF, 3 st. £ BB £9–£11, DB £18–£22, WT
(b) £101–£112, DT (b) £15·50–£17.

St John's Lodge, PH, x (Rl), *Lake Rd.*
✆ (096 62) 3078. Closed Dec. C 2. ⋈ 10
bedrs, 7 bps, 1 sh, 1 ba, TV, Dgs. ✗ a l c.
฿ CH, TV, CP 10. £ BB £9·50–£10·50, DB
£20–£25, WT (b) £110–£125, (c) £75–£85,
DT (b) £16·50–£18·50, ①, Bk £3·50, D
£6·50 ▲.

Thornleigh, G, z (Rt), *Thornbarrow Rd,
LA23 2EW.* ✆ (096 62) 4203.

Waverley, H, x (R), *College Rd, LA23
1BX.* ✆ (096 62) 5026.

Westlake, G, z (Rl), *Lake Rd, LA23 2EQ.*
✆ (096 62) 3020. C. ⋈ 7 bedrs, 1 bps, 4
sh, 1 ba, TV. ฿ CH, TV, Dgs, CP 5, CF. £ BB
£8–£8·50, DB £16–£19, WT (b) £90–£100,
DT (b) £13·50–£16, ①.

Repairer: Smith, R (Windermere) Ltd, The
Garage, Main Rd. ✆ (096 62) 2451.
Rescue Service: Old Smithy Garage,
Lowside. ✆ (096 62) 3551.
Storrs Hall Garage, Storrs Hall Park.
✆ (096 62) 3195.

WINDSOR Berkshire. Map 7A
Pop 30,000. Brentford and Chiswick 14,
London 21, M4 Motorway 3, Bagshot 10,
Ealing 15, Henley-on-Thames 14, High
Wycombe 17, Reading 17, Slough 2,
Staines 6.
See Plan, p 379.
EC Wed. **MD** Sat. **P** See Plan. **Golf**
Maidenhead 18h. **See** Castle (State
Apartments, Albert Memorial Chapel, St

George's Chapel, Queen Mary's Doll's
House, etc), Royal Mausoleum (Frogmore,
Home Park), Guildhall, Nell Gwynne's
House (Church St), St John's Church,
Great Park and Savill Gdn, Safari Park
(Zoological Gardens) off Windsor–
Bracknell Rd, Eton College, Windsor
Forest, Virginia Water Valley Gardens.

◨▲★★★★**Oakley Court,** *Windsor Rd,
Water Oakley, SL4 5UR.* ✆ Maidenhead
(0628) 74141. C. ⋈ 90 bedrs, 90 bp, TV.
✗ a l c. ฿ N, CH, CP 120, gc, tc, pf, con 70,
CF, 2 st. £ BB £48, DB £60, WB, ①, Bk £5, L
£11·50, D £17, cc 1 3 4 5, Dep b.

★★★**Castle** (TH), *High St, SL4 1LJ.*
✆ (075 35) 51011. C. ⋈ 85 bedrs, 85 bp,
TV, Dgs. ✗ a l c, mc, at, LD 9.45. ฿ Lt, N,
CH, Dgs, CP 90, Ac, con 400, CF, 1 st. £ BB
£47·50, DB £61, WB, ①, cc 1 2 3 4 5 6,
Dep (Xmas).

★★★**Wrens Old House,** *Thames St, SL4
1PX.* ✆ (075 35) 61354. Closed 4 days
Xmas. C. ⋈ 40 bedrs, 26 bp, 11 bps, 2 ba,
TV, Dgs. ✗ a l c, mc, at, LD 9.30. ฿ N, CH,
Dgs, CP 65, Ac, pf, con 60, CF. £ BBc fr
£44, DBc fr £59, WB, ①, Bk £5,
cc 1 3 4 5 6, Dep b.

◨★★**Royal Adelaide,** *Kings Rd, SL4
2AG.* ✆ (075 35) 56665. C. ⋈ 34 bedrs, 8
bp, 16 bps, 3 ba, TV, Dgs. ✗ a l c, LD 9.
฿ CH, Dgs, CP 20, Ac, con 70, CF, 3 BGf, 5
st. £ BB fr £20·75, DB fr £30·75, WB, ①, Bk
£3·50, D £7·50, cc 1 3 4 5 6, Dep b.

◨★★**Ye Harte & Garter,** *High St, SL4
1LR.* ✆ (075 35) 63426. Closed Xmas. C.
⋈ 44 bedrs, 34 bp, 4 ba, TV. ✗ a l c, LD
10.30. ฿ Lt, N, CH, Ac, con 180, CF, 1 st.
£ BB £24·15–£31·40, DB £40·95–£50·20,
WB, ②, cc 1 3 4 5.

Clarence, PH, z (R), *Clarence Rd, SL4
5AR.* ✆ (075 35) 64436. C. ⋈ 20 bedrs,
13 bps, 3 ba, TV, Dgs. ✗ a l c. ฿ CH, TV,
CF, 3 st. £ BB fr £13·50, DB fr £21·50, WT
(c) fr £75·25, ①, Bk £2·50, cc 1 3 5 ▲.

Repairers: A A Clark Ltd, 72 Arthur Rd.
✆ (075 35) 56841.
Friary Motors Ltd, Straight Rd, Old
Windsor. ✆ (075 35) 61402.
Specialist Body Repairer: Rogers Service
Station, Dedworth Rd. ✆ (075 35) 69191.
Rescue Service: Rogers Service Station,
Dedworth Rd. ✆ (075 35) 69191
Stag Motors (Windsor) Ltd, 2 Elm Rd.
✆ (075 35) 64143.

WINFRITH NEWBURGH Dorset.
M. Area 5F
Pop 599. Wareham 8½, London 125,
Blandford Forum 16, Dorchester 8½,
Weymouth 10.
EC Sat. **Golf** Weymouth 18h, Lakey Hill
18h.

Rescue Service: Rainbow Garage
(Winfrith) Ltd, East Knighton.
✆ Warmwell (0305) 852823.

WINKFIELD Berkshire. Map 7A
Pop 8,345. Windsor 6, London 27,
Bagshot 6, Henley-on-Thames 15, High
Wycombe 16, Reading 13, Staines 10.
Golf Downshire 18h. **See** Old houses,
Church.

Rescue Service: Baileys Garage, Maidens
Green. ✆ Winkfield Row (034 47) 2511.

WINKHILL Staffordshire. M. Area 22C
Ashbourne 8½, London 147, Buxton 15,
Leek 5½, Stoke-on-Trent 14.
EC Wed.

WINDSOR

0 miles ¼ ½

RAC

N

To London Airport | A332

To Slough 2m. | B3022

To M4. Int. 6

To Maidenhead 6m. | A308

To Twyford 12m. | B3024

To Winkfield 5m. | B3022

To Ascot 6m. | A332

To Staines 6m. | A308

To Datchet 1m. | B470

River Thames

Golf Course (9 holes)

Victoria Br. (3 ton limit)

The Castle

Frogmore House

Mausoleum (Duchess of Kent)

Mausoleum (Queen Victoria & Prince Consort)

Shaw Farm

Queen Elizabeth's Walk

Queen Victoria's Walk

The Long Walk

The Home Park (Private)

Victoria Barracks

Albert Road

Hog Common

Kings Road

Public Recreation Ground

The Playing Fields

Datchet Lane

Eton College

Police Station

High Street

ETON

Keats Lane

South Meadow

The Council Offices

Windsor Br. (Closed)

The Brocas

Station

Thames St.

King Edward VII Avenue

Lime Avenue

Guildhall & Information Royal Mews

Buses only Sats 10am - 5 pm

Datchet Rd.

High St.

Sheet St.

Grove Rd.

Alexandra Rd.

Francis Rd.

St. Leonards Rd.

Osborne Rd.

Bolton Av.

King Edward VII Hospital

Bolton Rd.

Alexandra Gdns.

Coach Park

Park Station

Multi Storey

WARD ROYAL

Royal Free School

Barry Ave.

Arthur Road

Oxford Rd.

Vansittart Rd.

Clarence Rd.

Multi-storey Car Park

East Berks College

Police Station

Alma Rd.

Peas Road

York Av.

Stovell Rd.

Swimming Pool

Clewer Park

School

School

Post Office

Parsonage Lane

St. John's House

Chapel

Haileybury & I.S.C. Junior School

School

Hatch Lane

Combermere Barracks

Post Office

Municipal Offices

Post Office

Springfield Road

Imperial Road

B3173

Butler Rd.

St. Leonards Road

Cemetery

Industrial Estate

Post Office

Maidenhead Road

Vale Road

Kentons Lane

Dedworth Road

Clewer Lane

Smiths Lane

School

School

School

School

Winkfield Road

Post Office

Clewer Hill Road

Porter Av.

Wolf Lane

P.O.

Gallys Road

Longmead

St. Leonards Hill

Racecourse

Grand Stand

Safari Park

Etonwick Rd.

P Car Park
C Public Conveniences

RAC—For Explanatory Notes to Directory see page 116

379

Repairer: Boydon & Sons. ✆ Waterhouses (053 86) 255.

WINKLEIGH Devon. Maps 3B and 4E
Pop 1,065. Crediton 13, London 190, Barnstaple 18, Bideford 18, Holsworthy 19, Okehampton 9.
Golf Torrington 9h. **See** All Saints' Church.

Rescue Service: Bissett's Garage, Exeter Rd. ✆ (083 783) 246.

WINSFORD Cheshire. Map 19D
Pop 26,956. Middlewich 3½, London 169, Chester 16, Nantwich 9½, Northwich 5.
EC Wed. **MD** Thur, Sat. **Golf** Sandiway 18h. **See** St Chad's Church, Rock salt mines.

Rescue Service: Dickinson Bros (Winsford) Ltd, Over Sq. ✆ (060 65) 2241.

WINSFORD Somerset. Map 4D
Pop 340. Taunton 29, London 172, Dunster 9, Ilfracombe 29, Lynmouth 19, South Molton 20, Tiverton 18.
Golf Minehead and W Somerset 18h. **See** Devil's Punch Bowl.

▣★★**Royal Oak,** *TA24 7JE.* ✆ (064 385) 232. C. ⇔ 11 bedrs, 11 bp, 1 ba, TV, Dgs. ✖ a l c, mc, at, LD 9.30. ▣ CH, TV, Dgs, CP 20, G 3, pf, CF, 1 st. **£** BB fr £25, DB fr £50, WT fr £215·25, WB, ▣, Bk £2·50, L £5·95, D £9·50, cc 1 3 4 5 6, ▲

WINSLOW Buckinghamshire. Map 15C
Pop 3,500. Aylesbury 10, London 50, Bicester 14, Bletchley 9, Buckingham 5½, Dunstable 19, Northampton 22.
EC Thur. **MD** Mon/Tue. **Golf** Buckingham 18h. **See** 13th cent Parish Church of St Laurence, Keech's Primitive Baptist Chapel (1626), Claydon House 3 m SW.

Rescue Service: Alf Chapman (Motor Engineers), 14a Horn St. ✆ (029 671) 2782.

WINSTER Derbyshire. Map 22C
Matlock 4½, London 148, Ashbourne 11, Buxton 18, Chesterfield 13, Mansfield 22, Newcastle under Lyme 32.

Winster Hall, H (R), *DE4 2DE.* ✆ (062 988) 204. C. ⇔ 6 bedrs, 2 ba, TV, Dgs. ✖ a l c. ▣ CH, Dgs, ns, CP 20, CF. **£** BB £8·50–£9·50, DB £17–£19, WT (c) £56–£63, ▣.

WINTERBOURNE Avon. Map 5A
Chipping Sodbury 7, London 113, M4 Motorway (via M32) 2½, Bath 15, Bristol 7, Chepstow 16, Gloucester 29.

▣▲★★★★**Grange,** *Northwoods, BS17 1RP.* ✆ (0454) 777333. C. ⇔ 33 bedrs, 33 bp, TV, Dgs. ✖ mc, at, LD 11. ▣ CH, CP 70, con 30, CF, 16 BGf, 2 st. **£** BB £43·50, DB £58·50, WB, ▣, Bk £5, L £8·50, D £12, cc 1 2 3 5, Dep b.▲

WINTERBOURNE ABBAS Dorset. Map 5E
Pop 162. Dorchester 5, London 127, Lyme Regis 19, Wareham 21, Weymouth 10.
Golf Came Down 18h. **See** Church, 'Nine Stones'.

Rescue Service: Bride Valley Motors, Bridport Rd. ✆ Martinstown (030 588) 370.

WINTERBOURNE WHITECHURCH Dorset. Map 5F

Pop 574. Blandford Forum 5, London 111, Bournemouth 19, Dorchester 11, Ringwood 21, Wareham 11.
Golf Lakey Hill, Bere Regis 18h. **See** 13th cent Church.

Rescue Service: Forge Garage. ✆ Milton Abbas (0258) 271.

WINTERSLOW Wiltshire. Map 6C
Pop 1,500. Basingstoke 20, London 78, Andover 13, Amesbury 9½, Lyndhurst 20, Romsey 14, Salisbury 6½, Winchester 18.
Golf High Post, Salisbury 18h. **See** Church, 14th cent Barn, Roche Court by appt only.

★★**Pheasant,** *London Rd, SP5 1BN.* ✆ (0980) 862374. RS Xmas. C. ⇔ 10 bedrs, 2 bp, 2 ba, TV, Dgs. ✖ a l c, mc, at (summer), LD 9.30. ▣ CH, Dgs, CP 100, Ac, con 40, CF, 1 st. **£** BB £15, DB £30–£36, DBB £18–£31, WB, ▣, Bk £3·50, L £5·75, D £7, cc 1 3, Dep a.

WISBECH Cambridgeshire. Maps 16E and 23F
Pop 17,000. Ely 23, London 94, Boston 29, Huntingdon 33, King's Lynn 13, Peterborough 20, Spalding 20, Swaffham 26.
EC Wed. **MD** Thur, Sat. **Golf** Sutton Bridge 9h. **See** Church of SS Peter and Paul, North and South Brinks (Georgian), Peckover House, Wisbech and Fenland Museum, Monument to Thomas Clarkson.

★★**Rose & Crown,** *Market Pl, PE13 1DG.* ✆ (0945) 583187. C. ⇔ 20 bedrs, 16 bp, 2 ba, TV, Dgs. ✖ a l c, mc, LD 9.15. ▣ CH, TV, Dgs, CP 12, Ac, con, CF, 1 st. **£** BB £18·25–£26·75, DB £29·25–£38·75, WB, ▣, Bk £4, L £7, D £9, cc 1 2 3 5 6, Dep b.

★★**White Lion,** *South Brink, PE13 1JD.* ✆ (0945) 584813. C. ⇔ 18 bedrs, 8 bp, 3 bps, 3 ba, TV, Dgs. ✖ a l c, mc, at, LD 9.30. ▣ CH, Dgs, CP 25, Ac, con 100, CF, 1 st. **£** BB £18·50–£21·95, DB £29–£32·95, WB, ▣, Bk £3·75, L £5·75, D £5·75, cc 1 2 3 5 6, Dep.

Glendon, PH, y (R), *Sutton Rd, PE13 5DR.* ✆ (0945) 584812. Open Mar–Oct. C. ⇔ 18 bedrs, 1 bp, 3 ba, Dgs. ▣ ch, TV, Dgs, CP 60, CF. **£** BB fr £14, DB fr £23, ▣.

Rescue Service: Paragon Garage, Elm High Rd. ✆ (0945) 582471.
Young Motors Ltd, Elm Rd. ✆ (0945) 582681.

WITHAM Essex. Map 17F
Pop 25,681. Chelmsford 9, London 42, Braintree 7, Colchester 13, Southend-on-Sea 49.
EC Wed. **MD** Sat. **Golf** Braintree 18h. **See** St Nicholas' Church, 14th cent inns—Red Lion, Spread Eagle and White Hart, Model Village, Faulkbourne Hall 1½ m.

★★**M Rivenhall Motor Inn,** *Rivenhall End, CM8 3HB.* ✆ (0376) 516969. Closed Jan 26–31. C. ⇔ 43 bedrs, 41 bp, 1 ba, TV, Dgs. ✖ a l c, mc, at, LD 9.30. ▣ CH, Dgs, CP 100, Ac, sc, con 60, CF, 34 BGf, 3 st. **£** BB fr £22, DB £36, ▣, Bk £4·50, L £6·95, D £6·95, cc 1 2 3 5 6, Dep b.

★★**White Hart,** *Newland St, CM8 2AF.* ✆ (0376) 512245. C. ⇔ 13 bedrs, 13 bp, TV, Dgs. ✖ mc, at, LD 10. ▣ CH, CP 48, Ac, con 60, CF, 0 st. **£** BB £18·75, DB £28·25, DBB £24·25, WB, ▣, Bk £3, L £5·50, D £5·50, cc 1 2 3 5 6, Dep b.

Spread Eagle, *Newland St, CM8 2BD.* ✆ (0376) 512131.

Rescue Service: Glovers Motors Ltd, Newland St. ✆ (0376) 513373.

WITHERIDGE Devon. Maps 3B and 4F
Pop 700. Tiverton 10, London 173, South Molton 10.
EC Thur. **Golf** Chulmleigh 18h. **See** Church, thatched cots.

Rescue Service: Witheridge Garage, 20 Fore St. ✆ Tiverton (0884) 860771.

WITHLEIGH Devon. Maps 3B & 4F
Tiverton 3½, London 166, South Molton 17.

Rescue Service: Green Vale Garage. ✆ Tiverton (0884) 253357.

WITHYPOOL Somerset. Map 4D
Pop 232. Taunton 33, London 176, Dunster 14, Ilfracombe 26, Lynton 17, South Molton 11, Tiverton 20.

▣★**Westerclose** (RI), *TA24 7QR.* ✆ Exford (064 383) 302.

WITNEY Oxfordshire. Map 14F
Pop 14,500. Oxford 11, London 69, Bicester 18, Burford 7½, Chipping Norton 13, Faringdon 12, Wantage 17.
EC Tue. **MD** Thur, Sat. **Golf** Burford 18h. **See** Town noted for manufacture of blankets. Early 18th cent Blanket Hall with one-hand clock, 17th cent Butter Cross, Grammar School, Church.
▣ Town Hall, Market Sq. ✆ Witney (0993) 4379.

Rescue Services: M A Wilkins (Car Sales), 1A Bridge St. ✆ (0993) 3361.
Witney Motor Co Ltd, Station Rd. ✆ (0993) 73121.

WITTERING Cambridgeshire. Map Area 23E
Alconbury 21, London 88, Kettering 24, Leicester 33, Peterborough 10, Spalding 20, Stamford 4.

Rescue Service: Aero Service Station, A1 Great North Rd. ✆ Stamford (0780) 783373.

WITTERING West Sussex.
See EAST WITTERING.

WIVELISCOMBE Somerset. Map 4D
Pop 2,145. Taunton 9½, London 153, Dunster 14, South Molton 26, Tiverton 15.
Golf Vivary 18h. **See** Court House (carved façade), 15th cent Cross in churchyard.

Hurstone, G, F, xy (R), *Waterrow, TA4 2AT.* ✆ (0984) 23441. C. ⇔ 5 bedrs, 1 bp, 2 ba, Dgs. ▣ TV, Dgs, CP 8, CF. **£** BB £10·50–£12·50, DB £20–£27, WT (b) £85–£95, DT (b) £15·50–£17·50, ▣, Bk £2·50, L £3, D £5·75.

Rescue Service: Jones Automobile Engineers (Wiveliscombe) Ltd, West St. ✆ (0984) 23216.

WIX Essex. Map 17C
Pop 621. Colchester 12, London 68, Clacton 10, Harwich 6, Ipswich 14.
EC Wed. **Golf** Harwich and Dovercourt 9h. **See** Church Abbey, Carbonells Hall.

New Farm, F, xy (Unl), *Spinnels Lane, CO11 2UJ.* ✆ (025 587) 365. C. ⇔ 5 bedrs, 1 ba. ▣ CH, TV, CP 8, CF, 2 st. **£** BB £8·50–£9·50, DB £17–£19, WT (c) £84–£90, DT (b) £14–£15, ▣, Bk £2·50, D £5·50.

WOBURN Bedfordshire. Map 15C
Pop 828. Dunstable 9, London 43, M1
Motorway 4, Aylesbury 16, Baldock 22,
Bedford 13, Bletchley 5, Northampton 22.
Golf Millbrook 18h. **See** St Michael's
Church, Woburn Abbey, Park and Wild
Animal Kingdom (Safari drive-through
Game Reserve).

★★★★**Bedford Arms,** *George St, MK17
9PX.* ✆ (052 525) 441. C. ⋈ 55 bedrs, 55
bp, TV, Dgs. ✗ a l c, mc, at, LD 10.30. ⊞ N,
CH, Dgs, CP 85, G 1, Ac, con 60, CF, 2 BGf,
1 st, Dis. £ BB £25·60–£48, DB £30–£54,
WB, ⊡, Bk £4·50, L £7·95, D £8·95,
cc 1 3 4 5, Dep b.

WOBURN SANDS Buckinghamshire.
Map 15C
Pop 2,340. Dunstable 10, London 44, M1
Motorway 2½, Aylesbury 17, Baldock 24,
Bedford 12, Biggleswade 21, Bletchley 4,
Northampton 22.
EC Wed. **Golf** Bletchley 18h. Woburn
Sands 18h. **See** Church.

Rescue Service: R W Harris & Sons
(Woburn Sands) Ltd, Newport Rd.
✆ Milton Keynes (0908) 582252.
Milton Keynes Motor Co, Newport Rd.
✆ Milton Keynes (0908) 582398.

WOKING Surrey. Map 7A
Pop 21,073. Kingston upon Thames 14,
London 24, Bagshot 7½, Farnham 14,
Guildford 6½, Ripley 5, Staines 9,
Weybridge 7.
EC Wed. **MD** Tue, Fri, Sat. **Golf** Woking
18h. **See** Mosque, Church,
Commonwealth Memorial in Brookwood
Cemetery, Wisley Gardens.
⛭ Council Offices, Guildford Rd.
✆ Woking (048 62) 5931.

★★**Wheatsheaf,** *Chobham Rd, GU21
4AL.* ✆ (048 62) 73047.

Rescue Services: Goldsworth Service
Station, 131 Goldsworth Rd. ✆ (048 62)
63001.
Teagle Cars Ltd, Kingfield Service Station,
Kingfield Rd, Old Woking. ✆ (048 62)
68353.

WOKINGHAM Berkshire. Map 6B
Pop 27,000. Staines 15, London 32,
A329(M) Motorway 1½, Bagshot 8½,
Basingstoke 17, Farnham 16, Henley-on-
Thames 10, Reading 7, Windsor 10.
EC Wed. **MD** Tue, Thur, Fri, Sat. **Golf**
Downshire 18h. **See** 17th cent Lucas
Almshouses, restored Church.

⬣★★★★**St Annes Manor,** *London Rd,
RG11 1ST.* ✆ (0734) 784427. C. ⋈ 20
bedrs, 19 bp, 1 bps, TV, Dgs. ✗ a l c, mc, at,
LD 9·45. ⊞ N, CH, CP 100, G 2, Ac, con
100, CF, 1 st. £ BB £38–£48, DB £48–£58,
WT £339–£456, DT £48·42–£65·14, WB,
⬒, Bk £4, L £6, D £8·50, cc 1 2 3 4 5 6,
Dep b.

Rescue Services: A G K Motors
(Broadcode Ltd), Langborough Rd.
✆ (0734) 791332.
Changa Service Station, Forest Rd.
✆ Bracknell (0344) 24141.
Gowrings of Wokingham Ltd,
Finchampstead Rd. ✆ (0734) 780873.

WOLSINGHAM Durham. Map 26A
Pop 2,849. West Auckland 10, London
258, Alston 25, Corbridge 26, Durham 15,
Hexham 27, Middleton-in-Teesdale 18,
Newcastle upon Tyne 21.

Golf Crook 18h. **See** Father Duckett's
Cross.

Rescue Service: Hathaway Garage,
Industial Estate, Durham Rd. ✆ Bishop
Auckland (0388) 526084.
T S Middlemiss, Dobinsons Yard.
✆ (095 65) 7363.

WOLSTANTON Staffordshire. M. Area
19D
Pop 4,899. Newcastle-under-Lyme 1½,
London 151, Congleton 10, Nantwich 13,
Sandbach 10, Stoke-on-Trent 2.
EC Thur. **Golf** Wolstanton 18h. **See**
Church, Moreton House.

Rescue Service: Leeding Garages Ltd,
Knutton Rd. ✆ Newcastle (0782) 562796
and (0782) 562858.

WOLVERHAMPTON West Midlands.
Map 21E
Pop 255,400. Birmingham 13, London
124, M6 Motorway 5, Bridgnorth 14,
Bromsgrove 19, Kidderminster 15,
Lichfield 14, Newport 18, Stafford 15,
Walsall 6½, Wellington 18.
EC Thur. **MD** Mon, Fri, Sat. **Golf** Penn
18h. S Staffordshire 18h. **See** St Peter's
Collegiate Church, Museum and Art
Gallery, St John's Church, Bantock House,
Moseley Old Hall 3½ m N.

★★★**Connaught,** *Tettenhall Rd, WV1
4SW.* ✆ (0902) 24433. C. ⋈ 68 bedrs, 44
bp, 6 bps, 5 ba, TV. ✗ a l c, mc, at, LD 9.45.
⊞ Lt, N, CH, TV, CP 60, Ac, sb, sol, con
300, CF, 1 st. £ BB £19·50–£25·80, DB
£29·50–£35·50, ⊡, Bk £3·50, L £4·25, D
£6·50, cc 1 2 5, Deb b.

★★★**Goldthorn,** *Penn Rd, WV3 0ER.*
✆ (0902) 29216. Closed Xmas. C. ⋈ 70
bedrs, 62 bp, 1 bps, 5 sh, annexe 16 bedrs,
8 bp, 4 bps, 1 ba, TV, Dgs. ✗ a l c, mc, at,
LD 9.30. ⊞ N, CH, Dgs, CP 90, Ac, con
140, CF, 2 st. £ BB fr £21, DB fr £30·50, ⬒,
Bk £3·50, L £6·45, D £6·45, cc 1 3 5,
Deb b.

★★★**Mount,** *Mount Rd, Tettenhall Wood,
WV6 8HL.* (2½ m W off A454). ✆ (0902)
752055. C. ⋈ 62 bedrs, 45 bp, 6 ba, TV,
Dgs. ✗ a l c, mc, at, LD 9.30. ⊞ N, CH, Dgs,
CP 250, Ac, con 200, CF, 24 BGf, 1 st, Dis.
£ B fr £23, BD fr £33, ⊡, Bk £4·25, L £6·60,
D £7·70, cc 1 2 3 4 5 6, Dep b.

★★★**Park Hall,** *Park Dr, Goldthorn Park,
WV4 5AJ.* (Sedgley 3 m S A459).
✆ (0902) 331121. C. ⋈ 57 bedrs, 49 bp,
TV, Dgs. ✗ a l c, mc, at, LD 9·30. ⊞ Lt, CH,
Dgs, CP 500, Ac, CF, 1 st. £ B fr £22, BD fr
£33, WB, ⊡, Bk £4·25, L £6·75, D £6·75,
cc 1 2 3 4 5 6, Dep b.

◼★★**M Fox,** *118 School St, WV3 0NR.*
✆ (0902) 21680. C. ⋈ 29 bedrs, 29 bps,
TV, Dgs. ✗ a l c, mc, at, LD 9.30. ⊞ CH, TV,
Dgs, CP 25, Ac, con 30, CF, 2 st. £ BB fr
£22, DB fr £28, WB, ⊡, Bk £3, L £3, D
£4·85, cc 1 3, Dep b.

★★**York,** *138 Tettenhall Rd, WV6 0BQ.*
✆ (0902) 754743. Closed Dec 25 & 26. C.
⋈ 17 bedrs, 6 bp, 3 bps, 2 ba, TV, Dgs.
✗ a l c, mc, at, LD 9.30. ⊞ CH, Dgs, CP 40,
Ac, con 25, CF, 1 BGf, 3 st. £ BB fr £12·50–
£23·50, DB £25–£33, WB, ⊡, Bk £3, D
£6·50, cc 1 2 3 5 6.

Repairers: Bristol Street Motors
(Wolverhampton), 67 Bilston Rd.
✆ (0902) 52611.
Hewitts Garages Ltd, Stafford St.
✆ (0902) 29122.

Specialist Body Repairer: Bristol Street
Motors (Wolverhampton), 67 Bilston Rd.
✆ (0902) 52611.▲
Bushbury Motor Co Ltd, Bridge Works, 80
Stafford Rd. ✆ (0902) 28998.
Rescue Service: Bulls Head Garage Ltd,
Horseley Fields. ✆ (0902) 52838.
Compton Road Motors Ltd, 38 Compton
Rd. ✆ (0902) 23628.
Croft Service Station, Brewood Rd,
Coven. ✆ (0902) 790217 and (0902)
790491.
Nicholls & Co (Garages) Ltd, Pearson St.
✆ (0902) 22607.
Ring Road Garage (Wolverhampton) Ltd,
1 Jeddo St, Penn Rd. ✆ (0902) 29195.
Wolverhampton Motor Bodies, Ltd,
Woden Rd. ✆ (0902) 23334.
Wolverhampton Motor Services Ltd,
Cleveland Rd. ✆ (0902) 25691.

WOLVERTON Buckinghamshire. Map
15C
Pop 6,290. Bletchley 8½, London 54,
Aylesbury 19, Bedford 17, Buckingham
10, Kettering 27, Northampton 16,
Towcester 10.
EC Wed. **MD** Fri. **Golf** Abbey Hill 18h.
See Old Wolverton Church.

Rescue Service: Drivers Motors, Cosgrave
Lodge Park. ✆ Milton Keynes (0908)
566187.
Wolverton Motor Co Ltd, Stratford Rd.
✆ Milton Keynes (0908) 313117.

WOMENSWOLD Kent. Map 10D
Canterbury 7, London 65, Dover 10,
Folkestone 11, Margate 17, Ramsgate 17.
Golf Canterbury 18h. **See** Church.

Woodpeckers Country, H, y (Rt), *CT4
6HB.* ✆ Canterbury (0227) 831319.
Closed 23 Dec–1 Feb. C. ⋈ 15 bedrs, 5
bps, 3 ba, TV, Dgs. ⊞ CH, Dgs, CP 22, G 2,
CF, 1 BGf, 3 st (ramp), Dis. £ BB £14–£16,
DB £28–£32, WT (b) £117–£126, DT (b)
£19–£20, ⊡, Bk £3, D £7.▲

WOODBRIDGE Suffolk. Map 17A
Pop 7,224. Ipswich 7½, London 81,
Aldeburgh 17, Saxmundham 13, Scole 23,
Stowmarket 18.
EC Wed. **MD** Thur. **Golf** Woodbridge 18h.
See St Mary's Church, Shire Hall, old
houses and inns.

⬣★★★★**Seckford Hall,** *Gt Bealings, IP13
6NU.* ✆ (039 43) 5678. C. ⋈ 24 bedrs, 23
bp, 1 ba, TV, Dgs. ✗ a l c, mc, at, LD 9.30.
⊞ CH, Dgs, CP 100, U 3, pf, con 100, CF, 0
st. £ BB £34, DB £48, WB, ⊡, Bk £3·50, L
£6·50, D £12, cc 1 2 3 5 6, Deb b.

★★**Crown** (TH), *2 Thorofare, IP12 1AD.*
✆ (039 43) 4242. C. ⋈ 16 bedrs, 4 ba,
annexe 10 bedrs, 10 bp, TV, Dgs. ✗ a l c,
mc, at, LD 9. ⊞ CH, Dgs, CP 30, Ac, CF, 1
st. £ BB £33·50–£36, DB £41–£50·50, ⊡,
cc 1 2 3 4 5 6, Dep (Xmas).

WOODCHURCH Kent. Map 10E
Pop 1,700. Tenterden 3½, London 58,
Ashford 7½, Hythe 15, New Romney 11,
Rye 11.
EC Wed. **Golf** Tenterden 18h.

Rescue Service: Woodchurch Garage Ltd,
39 Front Rd. ✆ (023 386) 477.

WOODFORD Gloucestershire. M. Area
13F
Tetbury 15, London 111, Bath 23, Bristol
16, Chepstow 16, Gloucester 17.
EC Wed. **Golf** Stinchcombe Hill 18h.

Rescue Service: Taylers of Woodford Ltd,
Woodford, Berkeley. ✆ Falfield (0454)
260133.

WOODFORD BRIDGE Greater London
(Essex). Map 15F
London 11, Enfield 7½, Epping 8½, Rainham
11, Romford 8½.

★★★**Prince Regent,** *Manor Road,*
✆ 01-504 7635.

WOODFORD GREEN Greater London
(Essex). M. Area 15F
1½ m N of Woodford. London 11, Enfield 5,
Epping 7, Rainham 12, Romford 9½.
EC Thur. **Golf** Woodford 9h. **See** Statue
of Sir Winston Churchill.

★★★**M Woodford Moat House,** *Oak
Hill, IG8 9HY.* ✆ 01-505 4511 C. ⊨ 99
bedrs, 69 bp, 30 bps, 2 ba, TV, Dgs. ✗ a l c,
mc, at, LD 10.15. 🅿 Lt, N, CH, CP 120, Ac,
con 100, CF, 24 BGf, 0 st, Dis. £ BB £28–
£38·50, DB £37–£48, WB, ①, Bk £4·25, L
£8·35, D £8·35, cc 1 2 3 4 5 6, Dep b.
Torry-Glen (London Motorists), G, x
(Temp) *17 Broomhill Rd, IG8 9EZ.*
✆ 01-504 5742.

Repairer: Hill Automobiles (Woodford)
Ltd, 75 High Rd. ✆ 01-504 9511.

WOODHALL SPA Lincolnshire. Map
23C
Pop 2,445. Spalding 30, London 129,
Boston 14, Horncastle 6½, Lincoln 18,
Sleaford 17.
EC Wed. **Golf** Woodhall Spa 18h. **See**
Springs and Mineral Baths, Wellington
Monument, Tower on the Moor,
Tattershall Castle 3 m SE.
🅘 Jubilee Park, Stixwould Rd. ✆ Woodhall
Spa (0526) 52448.

★★★**Golf,** *The Broadway, LN10 6SG.*
✆ (0526) 53535. C. ⊨ 51 bedrs, 41 bp, 10
bps, 2 ba, TV, Dgs. ✗ mc, at, LD 9.15. 🅿 N,
CH, TV, CP 90, Ac, con 200, CF, 9 BGf, 2
st. £ BB £27, DB £36, ②, Bk £4, D £8,
cc 1 2 3 5.
★**Spa,** *LN10 6SR.* ✆ (0526) 52421.

WOODKIRK West Yorkshire. M. Area
25F and 33D
Pop 3,820. 1½ m SW of Tingley, Wakefield
5, London 188, Bradford 10, Halifax 14,
Huddersfield 12, Leeds 6.
Golf Middleton 9h. **See** Church.

Rescue Service: Heybeck Garage Ltd,
Leeds Rd. ✆ Batley (0924) 472660.

WOODSTOCK Oxfordshire. Map 14F
Pop 1,996. Oxford 8, London 64, Banbury
15, Bicester 11, Burford 15, Chipping
Norton 12.
EC Wed. **Golf** North Oxford 18h. **See**
Blenheim Palace and Garden Centre,
Grave of Sir Winston Churchill (Bladon
Church), Woodstock Leathercraft (on
application).
🅘 Hensington Rd Car Park. ✆ Woodstock
(0993) 811038.

★★★**Bear,** *Market Pl, OX7 1SZ.* ✆ (0993)
811511. C. ⊨ 44 bedrs, 35 bp, 1 bps, 4 ba,
TV, Dgs. ✗ a l c, mc, at, LD 10. 🅿 N, CH,
Dgs, CP 40, Ac, con 100, CF, 8 BGf fr £25,
WB, ①, Bk £6·50, L £8·95, D £9·50,
cc 1 2 3 5 6, Dep a.
★★**Kings Arms,** *19 Market Place, OX7
1TS.* ✆ (0993) 811412. C. ⊨ 9 bedrs, 2
bp, 2 bps, 1 ba, TV, Dgs. ✗ a l c, mc, at, LD
9.30. 🅿 ch, TV, Dgs, Ac, con, CF, 0 st. £ BB

£19–£21, DB £28–£38, WB, ①, Bk £4, L £5,
D £7, cc 1 2 3 5 6.
★★**Marlborough Arms,** *Oxford St, OX7
1TS.* ✆ (0993) 811227. Closed Dec 24–
27. C. ⊨ 15 bedrs, 6 bp, 3 ba, TV, Dgs.
✗ a l c, mc, at, LD 10 (summer). 🅿 CH,
Dgs, CP 20, Ac, con 20, CF, 0 st. £ BB £20,
DB £34–£40, WB, ①, Bk £4, L £5·60, D
£8·95, cc 1 2 3 5.

Repairer: Young's Garage (Woodstock)
Ltd, 1 Oxford St. ✆ (0993) 811286.

WOODY BAY Devon. Map 4C
Lynton 3, London 188, Barnstaple 15,
Ilfracombe 12, South Molton 18.

■🏩★★**Woody Bay,** *EX31 4QX.*
✆ Parracombe (05983) 264. C. ⊨ 14
bedrs, 9 bp, 1 bps, 2 ba, Dgs. ✗ a l c, mc,
at, LD 9.30. 🅿 CH, TV, Dgs, CP 24, con 20,
CF, 10 st. £ BB £16–£20·50, DB £32–£41,
WT £135–£145, WB, ①, Bk £3·50, D £7,
cc 1 3 4 5 6, Dep a.▲
The Red House, PH, y (RI), *EX31 4QX.*
✆ Parracombe (05983) 255. Open Apr–
Oct. C 4. ⊨ 6 bedrs, 3 bp, 1 ba, Dgs. 🅿 CH,
TV, CP 8, 10 st. £ BB £10·50–£11·50, DB
£17–£20·50, WT (b) £89–£99·75, DT (b)
£13·60–£14·10, ①.

WOOL Dorset. Map 5F
Pop 2,679. Wareham 5, London 122,
Dorchester 11, Weymouth 12.
EC Wed, Sat. **Golf** Wareham 9h, Lakey Hill
18h. **See** Church, Bindon Abbey ruins,
Woolbridge Manor (now hotel), Clouds
Hill (Lawrence Memorial Cottage) 4 m
NNW (grave at Moreton 3½ m NW), Royal
Armoured Corps Museum (Bovington
Camp).

Rescue Service: Wool & Bovington
Motors Ltd, Dorchester Rd. ✆ Bindon
Abbey (0929) 462248.

WOOLACOMBE Devon. Map 4C
See also MORTEHOE.
Pop 1,063. Dunster 38, London 203,
Barnstaple 13, Ilfracombe 5½, Lynmouth
20.
Golf Ilfracombe 18h. **See** Barricane Shell
Beach, Mortehoe Church, Morte Pointe.
🅘 Hall '70', Beach Rd. ✆ Woolacombe
(0271) 870553.

■★★★**Beach** (R), *The Esplanade,
EX34 7DJ.* ✆ (0271) 870449. Open Apr–
Oct. C. ⊨ 36 bedrs, 24 bp, 4 ba. ✗ mc, at,
LD 8.30. 🅿 ch, CP 31, U 2, Ac, sol, con
50, CF, 7 st. £ BB £12–£27, DB £24–£56,
WT £110–£190, DBB £16–£33, WB, ②, Bk
£2·75, L £4·50, D £5·75, Dep.
★★★**Narracott Grand,** *Beach Rd, EX34
7BS.* ✆ (0271) 870418. Closed Dec, Jan.
Open Xmas & New Year. C. ⊨ 99 bedrs,
93 bp, 6 bps, TV, Dgs. ✗ a l c, mc, at, LD
8·30. 🅿 Lt, N, CH, TV, Dgs, CP 60, G 60, sp,
sc, sb, sol, con, CF, 4 st. £ WT £138·50–
£246·50, WB, ②, Bk £4, D £7, cc 1 5, Dep a.
★★★**Watersmeet,** *EX34 7EB.* ✆ (0271)
870333. Open Apr–Oct. C. ⊨ 36 bedrs, 17
bp, 1 bps, 8 ba. ✗ mc, at, LD 8.30. 🅿 ch,
TV, CP 30, G 20, sp, tc, con 50, CF, 1 BGf, 1
st, Dis. £ BB £18·50–£24·50, DB £37–£49,
WT £155–£207, DT £25·50–£32·50, DBB
£22·50–£29·50, WB, ①, Bk £5·65, L £7·25,
D £8·50, cc 2 5, Dep a.▲
★★★**Woolacombe Bay,** *EX34 7BN.*
✆ (0271) 870388. C. ⊨ 48 bedrs, 48 bp,
TV. ✗ mc, at, LD 9.30. 🅿 Lt, N, CH, TV, CP
70, sp, gc, tc, sc, sb, sol, gym, con 100, CF,

1 st. £ DBB £34·80–£43·60, WB, ②, Bk £3,
D £8·50, cc 1 3.
■★★**Atlantic** (R), *Sunnyside Rd, EX34
7DG.* ✆ (0271) 870469. Open Apr–Sept.
C. ⊨ 14 bedrs, 9 bp, 1 bps, 2 sh, 2 ba.
✗ a l c, mc, at, LD 7.15. 🅿 CH, TV, CP 14,
CF, 2 st. £ BB £11·50–£19, DB £23–
£34·60, ①, Bk £2·50, L £2, D £6.
■★★**Little Beach** (R), *The Esplanade,
EX34 7DJ.* ✆ (0271) 870398. Open Apr–
Oct, Feb–Mar bookings only. C. ⊨ 10
bedrs, 4 bp, 4 bps, 1 ba, Dgs. ✗ mc, LD 8.
🅿 CH, TV, Dgs, CP 6, sb, sol, CF, 20 st.
£ BB £15·50–£23·50, DB £31–£35, DBB
£22–£25, WB, ①, Bk £4, D £9·25, cc 1 3 6,
Dep.
■★★**Sands** (R), *Bay View Rd, EX34 7DQ.*
✆ (0271) 870550. Open May–Sept. C.
⊨ 23 bedrs, 4 bp, 3 bps, 1 sh, 4 ba, Dgs.
✗ mc, at, LD 8.15. 🅿 ch, CP 18, CF. £ BB
£10–£17, DB £20–£34, ①, Bk £3, D £6,
Dep.
■★★**Waters Fall,** *Beach Rd, EX34 7AD.*
✆ (0271) 870365. Closed Nov & Jan–Feb.
C 5. ⊨ 17 bedrs, 15 bp, 1 ba, Dgs. ✗ mc,
at, LD 8. 🅿 CH, TV, CP 17, CF. £ BB £11–
£15, DB £22–£30, WB, Bk £3, L £4·50, D
£5·50, Dep.
■★★**Whin Bay** (R), *Bay View Rd, EX34
7DQ.* ✆ (0271) 870475. Open Mar–Oct. C.
⊨ 16 bedrs, 4 bp, 10 bps, 2 ba, Dgs. ✗ mc,
at, LD 8. 🅿 CH, TV, CP 16, sol, CF, 1 st.
£ BB £10–£16, DB £20–£30, DBB £14–
£18, WB, ①, D £6, cc 1 2 3 6, Dep a.
■★**Crossways** (RI), *The Esplanade,
EX34 7DJ.* ✆ (0271) 870395. Open Mar–
Sep. C. ⊨ 8 bedrs, 3 bps, 3 sh, 1 ba, Dgs.
✗ mc, LD 7. 🅿 ch, TV, CP 9, CF, 13 st.
£ BB £10–£13, DB £20–£29, DBB £13–
£17·50, ②, Dep a.
■★**Headlands** (R), *Beach Rd, EX34 7BT.*
✆ (0271) 870320. Closed Dec–Feb. C.
⊨ 11 bedrs, 1 bp, 2 bps, 2 ba, Dgs. ✗ mc,
at, LD 7. 🅿 ch, TV, CP 15, CF, 2 st. £ BB fr
£9, DB fr £18, DBB £14–£20, WB, ①, Bk £3,
L £4, D £5·50, cc 2, Dep a.
★**Sunnyside** (RI), *Sunnyside Rd, EX34
7DG.* ✆ (0271) 870267. Open Mid May–
Mid Sept. C. ⊨ 7 bedrs, 2 bp, 6 ba, Dgs.
✗ LD 7.15. 🅿 TV, CP 12, Ac, CF, 2 BGf, 1
st, Dis. £ BB £10–£13·50, DB £20–£54, ①,
D £5, Dep.
Barton House, PH, x (R), *Barton Rd,
EX34 7BA.* ✆ (0271) 870548. C. ⊨ 12
bedrs, 6 bp, 2 bps, 2 ba, Dgs. 🅿 CH, Dgs,
CP 12, CF, 1 st.
Combe Ridge, PH, x (Unl), *The
Esplanade, EX34 7DJ.* ✆ (0271) 870321.
Springside, PH, x (RI), *Mullacott Rd,
EX34 7HF.* ✆ (0271) 870452. Open Mar–
Oct. C. ⊨ 7 bedrs, 2 bp, 1 ba. 🅿 CH, TV,
CP 10, CF.
Sunnycliff, PH, xy (RI), *Mortehoe, EX34
7BY.* ✆ (0271) 870597. C 10. ⊨ 8 bedrs, 4
bp, 4 bps, 2 ba, ns, TV. 🅿 CH, CP 11, 1 BGf,
2 st. £ BB £14–£16, DB £28–£32, WT (b)
£120–£140, DT (b) £20–£22, ①.

Repairer: Cowlers Central Garage,
Arlington Rd. ✆ (0271) 870428.
Rescue Service: Cowlers Central Garage,
Arlington Rd. ✆ (0271) 870428.

WOOLER Northumberland. Map 31A
Pop 1,833. Newcastle upon Tyne 47,
London 321, Alnwick 16, Berwick-upon-
Tweed 17, Coldstream 13, Corbridge 38,
Hexham 37.
EC Thur. **MD** Mon, Wed, Sat. **Golf** Wooler
9h. **See** Ancient British Camps.

⊞ High St. Car Park. ℓ Wooler (0668) 81602.

◼★★Tankerville Arms, *Cottage Rd, NE71 6AD*. ℓ (0668) 81581. C. ⊯ 16 bedrs, 4 bp, 2 bps, 4 ba, annexe 1 bedr, 1 bp, Dgs. ✗ mc, LD 9.30. ⊡ CH, TV, CP 80, Ac, con 60, CF, 1 BGf, 0 st. £ WB, ⊡.

◼★Ryecroft, *NE71 6AB*. ℓ (0668) 81459. Closed Dec 24–Jan 3. C. ⊯ 11 bedrs, 2 ba, Dgs. ✗ mc, at, LD 8.30. ⊡ ch, TV, CP 20, CF, 2 st. £ BB £11–£14, DB £21–£27, WB, ⊡, Bk £3, D £9, Dep a.

Rescue Service: E R Laidler, 1a Cheviot St. ℓ (0668) 81591.

WOOLFARDISWORTHY Devon. Map 3A
Pop 782. Bideford 9, London 211, Bude 17.
Golf Royal North Devon 18h.

◼♨★★Manor House (R), *EX39 5QS*. ℓ Clovelly (023 73) 380.

WOOLSINGTON Tyne & Wear. Maps 32A & 31F
Pop 10,194. Newcastle 5½, London 278, Gosforth 3, Ponteland 3, Throckley 4½.
EC Wed. **Golf** Gosforth 18h.

Rescue Service: Autoport, Ponteland Rd. ℓ Newcastle (0632) 869146.

WOOTTON BASSETT Wiltshire. Maps 5B & 6A
Pop 9,305. Swindon 7, London 84, Avebury 10, Chippenham 13, Cricklade 8.
EC Thur. **MD** Wed. **Golf** Swindon 18h.
See 17 cent Town Hall (Museum).

Angel, l, z, *47 High St, SN4 7AQ*. ℓ Swindon (0793) 852314. C 12. ⊯ 6 bedrs, 1 ba, TV. ✗ a l c. ⊡ TV, CP 8, 2 st. £ BB £14, DB £25, ⊡, Bk £2·50, L £4·50, D £7, cc 1 3 4 5.

Rescue Service: Wootton Bassett Service Station, 92 High St. ℓ Swindon (0793) 852083.

WOOTTON COURTENAY Somerset. Map 4D
Pop 262. Dunster 3½, London 169, Lynmouth 15, Minehead 4, Tiverton 24.
EC Thur, Sat. **Golf** Minehead and West Somerset 18h.
See Ancient Church, Exmoor.

Rescue Service: Burnell's Garage. ℓ Timberscombe (064 384) 242.

WORCESTER Hereford & Worcester (Worcestershire). Maps 13D and 14C
Pop 74,790. Evesham 16, London 114, M5 Motorway 2½, Bromyard 14, Droitwich 6½, Hereford 25, Kidderminster 14, Ledbury 16, Stratford-upon-Avon 27, Tewkesbury 15.
EC Thur. **MD** Wed, Fri, Sat. **Golf** Worcester G and CC 18h. **See** Cathedral, Commandery, Guildhall, Museum and Art Gallery, Queen Elizabeth's House, Shire Hall, 15th cent Greyfriars, Worcester Royal Porcelain Works and Museum, Spetchley Park Gdns 3 m ESE, Elgar Museum at Broadheath.
⊞ Guildhall. ℓ Worcester (0905) 23471.

★★★Giffard (TH), *High St, WR1 2QR*. ℓ (0905) 27155. C. ⊯ 104 bedrs, 104 bp, TV, Dgs. ✗ a l c, mc, at, LD 9.45. ⊡ Lt, N, CH, Dgs, Ac, con 120, CF, 0 st. £ BB £43, DB £54·50, WB, ⊡, cc 1 2 3 4 5 6, Dep (Xmas).

★★Diglis, *Riverside, WR1 2NF*. ℓ (0905) 353518.

★★Star, *Foregate St, WR1 1EA*. ℓ (0905) 24308. C. ⊯ 38 bedrs, 20 bp, 1 bps, 15 sh, 7 ba, TV, Dgs. ✗ a l c, mc, at, LD 9·45. ⊡ Lt, N, CH, TV, Dgs, CP 80, Ac, con 150, CF, 0 st. £ BB fr £19, DB fr £30, WB, ⊡, Bk £3, L £4·95, D £5·75, cc 1 3, Dep b.

★★Ye Olde Talbot, *Friar St, WR1 2NA*. ℓ (0905) 23573. C. ⊯ 17 bedrs, 17 bp, TV. ✗ a l c, mc, LD 10. ⊡ CH, TV, Ac, 1 st. £ BB fr £33, DB fr £43, WB, £ Bk £4, L £5·25, D £7, cc 1 3 4 5.

★Park House (RI), *12 Droitwich Rd, WR3 7LJ*. ℓ (0905) 21816. RS Xmas. C. ⊯ 6 bedrs, 1 ba, Dgs. ✗ mc, LD 7.30. ⊡ CH, TV, Dgs, CP 8, 1 st. £ BB £10·50–£11·50, DB £18, WT £135–£140, DT £20·50–£21·50, DBB £16–£17, WB, ⊡, Bk £2·50, L £4·50, D £5.

★Talbot, *Barbourne Rd, WR1 1HT*. ℓ (0905) 21206. C. ⊯ 14 bedrs, 4 ba, Dgs. ✗ a l c, mc, LD 9.45. ⊡ ch, TV, Dgs, CP 40, Ac, con 20, 0 st. £ BB £11·50, DB £20, ⊡, Bk £2·70, L £4·70, D £5, Dep b.

Barbourne, PH, z (RI), *42 Barbourne Rd, WR1 1HU*. ℓ (0905) 27507. Closed Xmas. C. ⊯ 6 bedrs, 1 ba, TV, Dgs. ✗ a l c. ⊡ CH, TV, CP 3, U 1, G 2, CF, 5 st. BB £12·50–£15, DB £15–£19, WT £112, DT £18·50–£20, ⊡, Bk £1·50, L £2, D £3·50, cc 1 5.

Loch Ryan, H, z (RI), *119 London Rd, WR5 2DH*. ℓ (0905) 351143. C. ⊯ 18 bedrs, 2 bps, 3 ba. ⊡ CH, TV, CF, 2 BGf, 1 st, Dis. £ BB £10·50–£11·50, DB £21–£25, ⊡, Bk £2.

St Lawrence, PH, z (RI), *Bath Rd (A39), WR5*. ℓ (0905) 351383. Closed Jan & Feb. C. ⊯ 15 bedrs, 2 ba. ⊡ CH, TV, CP 17. £ BB £8–£9, DB £16–£18, WT (c) £45–£56, DT (b) £12–£14, ⊡.

Repairers: Mann Egerton & Co Ltd, Austin House, Castle St. ℓ (0905) 27100.
D R Tansell Repairs, 8 Diglis Rd. ℓ (0905) 353666.
Specialist Body Repairers: D R Tansell Repairs, 8 Diglis Rd. ℓ (0905) 353666.
Rescue Service: H A J Law Ltd, Newtown Trading Estate, Newtown Rd. ℓ (0905) 21366.
Holywell Motors Ltd, Comer Rd, St Johns. ℓ (0905) 421930.
Larkhill Service Station (Worcester) Ltd, London Rd. ℓ (0905) 22721.
Motor & Body Repairers (Worcester) Ltd, Weir La, Bromwich Road Industrial Estate. ℓ (0905) 423682.
D. Taylor Auto's, Padmore Garage, Blockhouse Close. ℓ (0905) 22918.
Warndon Service Station, Cranham Dr, Warndon Estate. ℓ (0905) 52970.

WORCESTER PARK Surrey. Map 7A
Mitcham 5, London 11, Croydon 8, Kingston-upon-Thames 4, Leatherhead 8, Reigate 11.

Rescue Service: Forge Garage (Milbank Motor Co), 177 Central Rd. ℓ 01-337 1866.

WORFIELD Shropshire. M. Area 13B
Pop 2,053. Bridgnorth 4, London 141, Birmingham 21, Bromsgrove 22, Wellington 12, Wolverhampton 10.
EC Thur. **Golf** Shifnal 18h. **See** St Peter's Church, remains of Roman earthworks at Chesterton.

♨★★Old Vicarage (R), *WV15 5JZ*. ℓ (074 64) 498. C. ⊯ 10 bedrs, 7 bp, 3 bps, TV, Dgs. ✗ a l c, mc, at, LD 9.45. ⊡ CH, ns, CP 20, con 20, CF, 1 st. £ BB £25·87, DB £35·07, WT £136·85, DT £30, WB, ⊡, Bk £2, L £6·95, D £7·95, cc 1 3 4 5, Dep a.

Rescue Service: Worfield Garages (Salop) Ltd, Bridgnorth Rd. ℓ (074 64) 203.

WORKINGTON Cumbria. Map 26E
Pop 29,600. Cockermouth 8½, London 306, Egremont 13, Maryport 5½.
EC Thur. **MD** Wed, Sat. **Golf** Workington 18h. **See** St Michael's Church, Helena Thompson Museum.

★★★Cumberland Arms, *Belle Isle St, CA14 2XQ*. ℓ (0900) 64401. Closed Xmas Day, C. ⊯ 29 bedrs, 27 bps, 2 sh, TV, Dgs. ✗ a l c, mc, LD 9.30. ⊡ ch, TV, CP 60, Ac. £ BB £16, DB £23, ⊡, Bk £3, L £3·50, D £7·50, cc 1 3 4 5 6, Dep.

★★Westland, *Branthwaite Rd, CA14 4SS*. ℓ (0900) 4544. C. ⊯ 51 bedrs, 46 bp, 3 ba, TV, Dgs. ✗ a l c, mc, at, LD 9.30. ⊡ N, CH, CP 200, Ac, con 200, CF, 15 BGf, 2 st. £ BB £18–£24, DB £24–£31, WB, ⊡ 10%, Bk £4, D £9, cc 1 3 4 5.

★★M Crossbarrow, *Little Clifton, CA14 1XS*. ℓ (0900) 61443. C. ⊯ 37 bedrs, 29 bp, 8 bps, TV, Dgs. ✗ a l c, mc, LD 9·30. ⊡ CH, Dgs, CP 50, CF, 3 BGf, 1 st, Dis. £ BB £19·54–£21·38, DB £30·23–£34·25, ⊡, Bk £2·75, L £3, D £5·50, cc 1 5. Dep a.

Morven, G (R), *Siddick Rd, CA14 1LE*. ℓ (0900) 2118.▲

Rescue Service: Belle Isle Street Garage, Unit 5, Solway Rd. ℓ (0900) 66655.
I M Potts, Motor Engineer, Belle Isle St. ℓ (0900) 64085 & (0900) 62507.

WORKSOP Nottinghamshire. Map 22B
Pop 36,900. Newark 25, London 151, Chesterfield 16, Doncaster 16, Gainsborough 19, Lincoln 28, Mansfield 13, Ollerton 9, Rotherham 14, Sheffield 18, Thorne 22.
EC Thur. **MD** Wed, Fri, Sat. **Golf** Worksop 18h. Lindrick 18h. Kilton Forest 18h, Serlby 9h. **See** Priory Church, 13th cent Lady Chapel, 14th cent Gatehouse, ancient Market Cross.
⊞ Queens Buildings, Potter St. ℓ Worksop (0909) 475531.

Rescue Service: Gregory's of Worksop, Turner Rd, off Carlton Rd. ℓ (0909) 474355.

WORLE Avon. Map 5A
Pop 4,300. Bristol 18, London 131, M5 Motorway 1½, Bath 30, Bridgwater 20, Weston-super-Mare 3.
Golf Worlebury 18h.

★★M Old Manor, *Queensway, Kewstoke*. ℓ (0934) 515143. RS Xmas Day. C. ⊯ 25 bedrs, 8 bp, 13 bps, 1 sh, 1 ba, TV, Dgs. ✗ a l c, mc, at, LD 10. ⊡ CH, TV, Dgs, CP 25, Ac, sb, sol, con, CF, 2 st. £ BB fr £20, DB fr £30, ⊡, Bk £2·50, L £9, D £9, cc 1 3 4 5, Dep a.▲

WORPLESDON Surrey. Map 7A
Pop 8,500. Woking 4, London 31, Bagshot 8, Guildford 4.
EC Wed. **Golf** Worplesdon 18h. **See** Parish Church, 17th cent Burpham Court.

★★Worplesdon Place, *Perry Hill, GU3 3RY*. ℓ (0483) 232407. C. ⊯ 14 bedrs, 9 bp, 2 ba, TV, Dgs. ✗ a l c, mc, at, LD 10. ⊡ CH, Dgs, CP 150, Ac, pf, con 100, CF, 1

st. **£** BB fr £19, DB fr £33, ②, 10%, L £6·30,
D £6·30, cc 1 2 3 5 6, Dep. ▲

WORSLEY Greater Manchester
(Lancashire). Map 20A
Pop 89,000. Altrincham 9½, London 189,
Manchester 6, St Helens 15, Walkden 1½,
Warrington 13, Wigan 11.
EC Wed. **Golf** Ellesmere 18h. **See** Old
Warke Dam, Packet House, The Delph,
Wardley Hall, St Mark's Church, Worsley
Old Hall, Pembroke Halls.

Rescue Service: Stableford Garage,
Barton Rd. **☎** 061-794 2851.

WORTHING West Sussex. Map 7E
Pop 92,600. Horsham 20, London 56,
Arundel 10, Brighton 11, Littlehampton 8½,
Pulborough 14.
EC Wed. **MD** Sat. **Golf** Worthing 18h (2),
Worthing Hill Barn 18h. **See** Museum and
Art Gallery, Salvington Mill, Cissbury Ring,
Sompting Church (Saxon) 1½ m,
Chanctonbury Ring 5 m N, Trans-Norman
Church at Broadwater, Tarring Cottages
and Parsonage Row Cottages at West
Tarring (late 15th cent).
🛈 Town Hall, Chapel Rd. **☎** Worthing
(0903) 39999 ext 132.

★★★**Berkeley,** *Marine Par, BN11 3QD.*
☎ (0903) 31122. C. ⊯ 76 bedrs, 36 bp, 4
bps, 12 ba, TV, Dgs. ✗ mc, at, LD 9. 🅱 Lt,
N, CH, TV, Dgs, CP 50, Ac, con 80, CF, 7
BGf, 8 st. **£** BB £16·50–£23·95, DB
£29·50–£43·95, DT £24·65–£34·95, DBB
£19·70–£28·50, WB, ①, Bk £3·50, L £4·95,
D £4·95, cc 1 2 3 5 6, Dep b.

★★★**Chatsworth,** *The Steyne, BN11
3DU.* **☎** (0903) 36103. C. ⊯ 93 bedrs, 76
bp, 3 bps, 2 ba, TV, Dgs. ✗ a l c, LD 8.30.
🅱 Lt, N, CH, Ac, con 140, CF, 5 st (ramp).
£ BB £22–£32, DB £40–£48, WT £231–
£250, DT £33–£37, WB, ②, Bk £3·50, L
£5·95, D £6·50, cc 1 5 6, Dep b.

★★★**Eardley,** *Marine Par, BN11 3PW.*
☎ (0903) 34444. C. ⊯ 83 bedrs, 53 bp, 4
bps, 4 ba, TV, Dgs. ✗ a l c, mc, at, LD 9.30.
🅱 Lt, N, CH, Dgs, CP 20, Ac, con 134, CF,
2 st. **£** BB £21–£28, DB £34–£50, WT
£160–£200, DT £27–£36, WB, ②, Bk £3, L
£5·75, D £6·50, cc 1 5, Dep b.

★★★**Warnes,** *Marine Par, BN11 3PR.*
☎ (0903) 35222. Closed Jan 1–6. C. ⊯ 62
bedrs, 49 bp, 7 bps, 7 ba, TV, Dgs. ✗ a l c,
mc, at, LD 8.45. 🅱 Lt, N, ch, TV, CP 30, U 2,
Ac, sol, con 300, CF, 7 BGf, 5 st. **£** BB £17–
£28, DB £33–£44, WT £192–£267, DT
£37·50–£40, DBB £24–£35, WB, ①, Bk £5,
L £6, D £7·50, cc 1 2 3 5.

★★**Ardington,** *Steyne Gdns, BN11 3DZ.*
☎ (0903) 30451. C. ⊯ 56 bedrs, 22 bp, 22
bps, 6 ba, TV, Dgs. ✗ a l c, mc, at, LD 8.15.
£ BB £16·50–£20, DB £30–£34, DBB £39–
£45, WB, ①, Bk £3·50, D £6·25,
cc 1 2 3 5 6, Dep a.

★★**Beechwood Hall,** *Park Crescent,
Wykeham Rd, BN11 4AH.* **☎** (0903)
32872. C. ⊯ 14 bedrs, 11 bp, 1 bps, 2 ba,
TV, Dgs. ✗ mc, at, LD 8. 🅱 CH, Dgs, CP 60,
con 20, CF, 2 BGf, 2 st. **£** BB £18, DB £32,
WB, ①, Bk £3·50, L £4, D £6·75, cc 1 3 5,
Dep b.

★★**Kingsway,** *Marine Par, BN11 3QQ.*
☎ (0903) 37542. C. ⊯ 32 bedrs, 21 bp, 4
bps, 3 ba, TV, Dgs. ✗ a l c, mc, at, LD 8.30.
🅱 Lt, CH, TV, Dgs, CP 25, U 2, con 25, CF, 1
st. **£** BB £17–£25, DB £28, WT £89–£175,
DT £16–£27·50, WB, ②, Bk £4·40, L £4·75,
D £6·95, cc 1 2 3 4 5, Dep.

★**Wansfell** (Rt), *49 Chesswood Rd,
BN11 2AA.* **☎** (0903) 30612. C 4. ⊯ 12
bedrs, 2 bp, 4 bps, 2 ba, TV. ✗ mc, at, LD
7.30. 🅱 CH, ns, CP 8, con 20, CF, 4 st. **£** BB
£11·50–£16·25, DB £23–£32·50, WB, ②,
Bk £3·25, L £4·50, D £5·75, Dep.

Blair House, G, z (Rl), *11 St. George's Rd,
BN11 2DS.* **☎** (0903) 34071. C. ⊯ 7
bedrs, 2 bp, 4 bps, 1 ba, Dgs. 🅱 CH, TV, CP
6, 3 st. **£** BB £9–£12·50, DB £18–£25, WT
(b) £91–£115, DT (b) £13–£14·50, ②, Bk
£2·50, D £4·75.

Bonchurch, G, z (Rt), *1 Winchester Rd,
BN11 4DJ.* **☎** (0903) 202492. C 4. ⊯ 7
bedrs, 1 sh, 1 ba. ✗ a l c. 🅱 CH, TV, CP 4.
£ BB £7·50–£8, DB £15–£16, WT (b) £63–
£75, DT £11–£11·50, ①, D £4·75.

Camelot House, G, z (Rl), *20 Gannon
Rd, BN11 2DT.* **☎** (0903) 204334. Closed
Xmas. C. ⊯ 6 bedrs, 1 bps, 2 ba, TV, Dgs.
🅱 CH, TV, Dgs, CP 3, CF. **£** BB £8·50–£10,
DB £17–£22, WT (b) £78–£85, DT (b)
£12·50–£14, ①.

Mayfair, H, z (R), *Heene Ter, BN11 3NS.*
☎ (0903) 201943. C. ⊯ 22 bedrs, 3 bps, 2
sh, 4 ba, TV. 🅱 ch, CF, 6 st. **£** BB £12–£15,
DB £24–£30, WT (b) £102–£120, DT £17–
£20, ②, Bk £3·25, L £4·25, D £5·25.

Meldrum House, G, z (Unl), *8 Windsor
Rd, BN11 2LX.* **☎** (0903) 33808. Closed
Dec. C 3. ⊯ 6 bedrs, 1 ba. 🅱 CH, 1 BGf, 0
st, Dis. **£** BB £7–£9·50, DB £14–£19, WT
(a) £46–£60, (b) £72–£85, DT (b) £10·50–
£13·50, ①.

Osborne, G, z (Rl), *175 Brighton Rd,
BN11 2EX.* **☎** (0903) 35771. C. ⊯ 7
bedrs, 1 bps, 1 ba, ns, TV, Dgs. ✗ a l c.
🅱 ch, TV, ns, CF, 1 BGf, 1 st, Dis. **£** BB £8–
£9, DB £16–£21, WT (b) £85–£92, DT (b)
£13–£14, ①, D £5, cc 1 5.

St Georges Lodge, PH, yz (Rl),
Chesswood Rd, BN11 2AG. **☎** (0903)
208926.

Village House, H, x, *The Square, Findon,
BN14 0TE.* **☎** Findon (090 671) 3350. C.
⊯ 9 bedrs, 3 ba, Dgs. ✗ a l c. 🅱 CH, TV,
Dgs, CP 12, CF, 1 st. **£** BB £12·50–£13·50,
DB £20–£22, ①, Bk £3, L £5·50, D £6·50,
cc 1 3 4 5.

Windsor House, H, z (R), *14 Windsor
Rd, BN11 2LX.* **☎** (0903) 39655. C. ⊯ 26
bedrs, 3 bp, 6 bps, 4 ba, TV, Dgs. ✗ a l c.
🅱 CH, CP 18, CF, 5 BGf, 1 st, Dis. **£** BB
£8·50–£12·50, DB £17–£32, WT (b)
£97·50–£105, DT (b) £13·50–£18, ②, Bk
£2·50, D £5.

Windsor Lodge, G, z (Unl) *3 Windsor
Rd, BN11 2LU.* **☎** (0903) 200056.

Repairers: Half Moon Lane Garage, Half
Moon La, Salvington. **☎** (0903) 61166 and
(0903) 61235.
Salvington Garages Ltd, Swandean
Garage, Arundel Rd. **☎** (0903) 64242.
Steele, H D & Son Ltd, Teville Rd.
☎ (0903) 37527.

Specialist Body Repairer: J S Arnold
(Coachbuilders) Ltd, 41 Park Rd.
☎ (0903) 35125.
A E Ledger (Coachworks) Ltd, Bashfords
La. **☎** (0903) 31606.
Rescue Service: Heath & Wiltshire
(Durrington) Ltd, The Boulevard. **☎** (0903)
43344.
Kenvad Engineering (1975) Ltd, 27
Lyndhurst Rd. **☎** (0903) 203089.
Jupps Garage, Queens Rd. **☎** (0903)
200997.
P D H Garages Ltd, Upper Brighton Rd.
☎ (0903) 37487.

West Sussex Motors, Ivy Arch Rd.
☎ (0903) 200272.

WORTWELL Norfolk. Map 16B.
Harleston 2½, London 106, Bungay 6, East
Dereham 29, Great Yarmouth 25,
Lowestoft 20, Norwich 21, Saxmundham
20, Thetford 29.

Rescue Service: Goodswens Garage, 60
High Rd. **☎** Homersfield (098 686) 212.

WOTTON-UNDER-EDGE
Gloucestershire. Map 13F
Pop 4,851. Tetbury 10, London 106, Bath
21, Bristol 17, Cheltenham 25, Chepstow
19, Chippenham 16, Gloucester 21.
EC Wed. **MD** Fri. **Golf** Cotswold Hill 18h.
See Tolsey Clock, Parish Church of St
Mary, Blue Coat School, Bradley Court,
Berkeley Castle 6 m NW.

★★**Swan,** *Market St, GL12 7AE.*
☎ Dursley (0453) 842439. C. ⊯ 28 bedrs,
20 bp, 1 bps, 2 ba, TV, Dgs. ✗ a l c, mc, at,
LD 10.15. 🅱 CH, Dgs, CP 8, Ac, con 20,
CF. **£** BB fr £25, DB fr £33, WB, ①, Bk
£4·50, L £5·50, D £6, cc 1 3 4 5 6.

Varley Farm, F, xy (Unl), *Talbots End,
Cromhall, GL12 8AJ.* **☎** Wickwar
(045 424) 292. Open Mar–Sept. C. ⊯ 3
bedrs, 2 ba. 🅱 CH, TV, CP 4, CF, 5 st. **£** BB
£9, DB £16·50, WT (c) £52·50, ①.

Rescue Service: Falfield Garage, A38,
Falfield. **☎** Falfield (0454) 260286.

WRAYSBURY Berkshire. M. Area 7A
3 m SW of Colnbrook. Pop 3,600. Staines
3, London 19, Bagshot 11, Ealing 14,
Harrow 15, Slough 5, Uxbridge 9½,
Windsor 4.
EC Wed. **Golf** Datchet 18h. **See**
Ankerwyke-Priory and old nunnery, King
John's House, 13th cent Church.

Rescue Service: Bell Weir Garage, Hythe
End. **☎** (078 481) 2393.

WREKENTON Tyne & Wear. Map 32C.
Pop 10,407. Birtley 2, London 270, A1 (M)
Motorway 2, Newcastle 4, Tyne Tunnel 7,
Washington 3.
EC Wed. **Golf** Ravensworth 18h. **See**
Bowes Railway, only rope hauled railway.

Rescue Service: Autocare J S Charlton
Tyres Ltd, High St. **☎** Low Fell (0632)
870241.

WRENTHAM Suffolk. Map 16B.
Pop 830. Saxmundham 15, London 109,
Beccles 8, Lowestoft 8, Southwold 5.

Rescue Service: W J Boast & Son Ltd,
London Road Garage. **☎** (050 275) 391 &
(050 275) 254.

WRIGHTINGTON Lancashire. Map 20C
Pop 3,144. M6 Motorway 2, London 201,
Ormskirk 11, Preston 12, St Helens 13,
Southport 17, Wigan 5.
EC Wed. **Golf** Beacon Park 18h. **See**
Harrock Hall, Boars Den Tumulus, Skull
House, Church.

MC Repairer: D Smith Motor Cycles, 2
Toogood La. **☎** Eccleston (0257) 451570.
Gibson's Car Hire, 275 Mossy Lea Rd.
☎ Standish (0257) 421668.

WRINEHILL Staffordshire. M. Area 19D.
Pop 961. Newcastle-under-Lyme 6½,
London 156, Crewe 7, M6 Motorway 10,
Nantwich 8½, Stoke-upon-Trent 8½.
Golf Onneley 9h. **See** Betley Court,
Museum, Betley Old Hall Farm.

Repairer: Wrinehill Garage Ltd (Gudian Group) Newcastle Rd. ✆ Crewe (0270) 820300 & (0270) 820673.

WRINGTON Avon. Map 5A
Pop 2,193. Bath 19, London 123, Bridgwater 22, Bristol 11, Radstock 17, Wells 14, Weston-super-Mare 11.
Golf Weston-super-Mare 18h.

Rescue Service: Richards Garage, Broad St. ✆ (0934) 862278.

WRITTLE Essex. Maps 10A and 17F
Pop 5,741. Brentwood 10, London 32, Bishop's Stortford 18, Chelmsford 2, Epping 15, Woodford 21.
Golf Chelmsford 18h. **See** 13th cent All Saints' Church, Highlands Park.

Rescue Service: W C Flegg & Sons, Oxney Garage, Ongar Rd. ✆ Chelmsford (0245) 420149.

WROTHAM HEATH Kent. Map 7B
Swanley 11, London 29, M26 Motorway 1½, Maidstone 8½, Sevenoaks 9.

★★★★**M Post House,** *London Rd, TN15 7RS.* ✆ Borough Green (0732) 883311. C. ✉ 119 bedrs, 118 bp, 1 bps, ns, TV, Dgs. ✗ a l c, mc, at, LD 11. ⓓ N, CH, CP 130, Ac, sp, sb, sol, gym, con 50, CF, 1 BGf, 0 st, Dis. £ BB £44–£50·50, DB £57–£63·35, WB, Ⅰ, Bk £5·25, L £9·70, D £11·85, cc 1 2 3 4 5 6, Dep b.

WROXHAM Norfolk. Map 16A
Pop1,300. Norwich 7, London 118, Cromer 18, Fakenham 29, Great Yarmouth 19.
EC Wed. **Golf** Norwich 18h. **See** The Broads, Church.

The Broads, PH, x (Rl), *Station Rd, NR12 8UR.* ✆ (060 53) 2869. C. ✉ 19 bedrs, 10 bp, 3 ba, Dgs. ✗ a l c. ⓓ CH, TV, Dgs, CP 18, CF, 2 st. £ BB £12·50–£14, DB £21·50–£23·50, WT (b) £112, DT (b) £18, Ⅰ, Bk £2·75, L £3·50, D £4·20,▲

WROXTON Oxfordshire. Map 14D
Pop 506. Banbury 3, London 75, Chipping Norton 14, Daventry 19, Evesham 28, Moreton-in-Marsh 18, Stratford-upon-Avon 17, Warwick 19.
Golf Tadmarton Heath 18h. **See** Church, Abbey.

★★**Wroxton House,** *OX15 6PZ.*
✆ Wroxton St Mary (029 573) 482. C. ✉ 12 bedrs, 3 bp, 3 bps, 3 ba, TV, Dgs. ✗ a l c, LD 9.30. ⓓ CH, TV, CP 60, Ac, con 30, CF, 6 st. £ BB £25·75–£42·90, WB, Ⅰ, L £5·95, D £7·25, cc 1 2 3 5 6.

WYCHBOLD Hereford & Worcester (Worcestershire). M. Areas 13B and 14A
2½ m NE of Droitwich. Pop 1,900. Stratford-upon-Avon 20, London 113, Droitwich 4, Kidderminster 9½.
Golf Droitwich 18h. **See** Hanbur Hall.

Rescue Service: Wychbold Garage, Worcester Rd. ✆ (052 786) 448.

WYE Kent. Map 10D
Pop 2,100. Ashford 4, London 59, Canterbury 10, Folkestone 14.
EC Wed. **Golf** Ashford (Kent) 18h. **See** Parish Church, Wye Downs Nature Reserve.

★**Kings Head,** *Church St, TN25 5BN.*
✆ (0233) 812418.
New Flying Horse, I, z, *Upper Bridge St.* ✆ (0233) 812297. C. ✉ 10 bedrs, 4 bp, 2

ba, TV, Dgs. ✗ a l c. ⓓ CH, CP 100, CF, 3 st. £ BB £18–£22, DB £26–£34, WT (b) £133–£170, DT (b) £22–£28·50, Ⅰ, Bk £4, L £7·90, D £7·90, cc 1 3 4 5.

WYLYE Wiltshire. Map 5D
Amesbury 10, London 89, Devizes 18, Salisbury 11, Warminster 10, Wincanton 20.

Rescue Service: White Heather Service Station, Deptford. ✆ (098 56) 206.

WYMONDHAM Norfolk. Map 16D
Pop 9,500. Thetford 19, London 101, East Dereham 11, Lowestoft 31, Norwich 9½, Scole 18.
EC Wed. **MD** Fri. **Golf** Eaton, Norwich 18h. **See** Abbey Church, Market Cross.

★★**Abbey** (Unl), *10 Church St, NR18 0PH.* ✆ (0953) 602148. C. ✉ 31 bedrs, 22 bp, 1 bps, 3 sh, 5 ba, TV, Dgs. ✗ mc, at, LD 8·30. ⓓ Lt, N, CH, CP 4, U 3, Ac, con 40, CF, 5 BGf, 1 st, Dis. £ BB fr £13·50, DB fr £23·50, DT £19·50, WB, Ⅰ, Bk £3, L £2·45, D £5, cc 1 2 3 5.

Sinclair, PH, x, *28 Market St, NR18 0BB.* ✆ (0953) 606721. C. ✉ 12 bedrs, 12 bp, 2 ba, TV, Dgs. ✗ a l c. ⓓ CH, TV, CP 6, U 3, G 6, CF. £ BB £24, DB £34, WT (c) £140–£180, DT (b) £29·50–£45, Ⅰ, Bk £3, L £3, D £5·50, cc 1 3 5.

Rescue Service: Wymondham Motor Co, London Rd. ✆ (0953) 602263

WYRE PIDDLE Hereford & Worcester (Worcestershire). Map 14C
Evesham 6, London 104, Birmingham 32, Cheltenham 18, Ross-on-Wye 32, Stratford upon Avon 18, Worcester 10.
Golf Evesham 18h. **See** Church.

★★**Avonside** (R), *Main Rd, NR10 2JB.* ✆ Pershore (0386) 552654. Open Mar-Oct. C 7. ✉ 7 bedrs, 6 bp, 1 bps, TV, Dgs. ✗ a l c, mc, at, LD 8.30. ⓓ CH, CP 8, sp, pf, 2 st. £ BB £28–£32, DB £34–£42, WB, ⅔, Bk £5·50, L £2·50, D £9·50.

YARCOMBE Devon. Map 5E
Pop 490. Ilminster 10, London 145, Axminster 11, Crewkerne 13, Honiton 7½, Taunton 11.
EC Wed. **Golf** Honiton 18h. **See** Church.

Rescue Service: Stringer Services, The Garage. ✆ Chard (046 06) 2676.

YARLET Staffordshire. M. Area 22E
2 m N of Marston, Stafford 3½, London 136, Stone 3½.

Rescue Service: Yarlet Bank Service Station. ✆ Sandon (088 97) 248.

YARMOUTH Isle of Wight. Map 6E
Pop 971. Newport 9½, London (Fy) 86, Cowes 12, Ventnor 20.
EC Wed. **Golf** Freshwater Bay 18h. **See** 17th cent St James's Church, old inns, 16th cent Yarmouth Castle.
ⓘ Quay Rd. ✆ Yarmouth (0983) 760015.

Repairer: Mill Road Garage (Yarmouth) Ltd. ✆ Isle of Wight (0983) 760436.

YARMOUTH, GREAT Norfolk. Map 16B
See also GORLESTON-ON-SEA
Pop 52,000. Lowestoft 10, London 127, Cromer 34, Norwich 18, Scole 34.
EC Thur. **MD** Wed, Sat. **Golf** Gt Yarmouth and Caister 18h, Gorleston 18h. **See** 'The Rows', Old Merchant's House (museum), Nelson Monument, St Nicholas Parish Church, restored medieval Tollhouse, 17th

cent Fisherman's Hospital, Caister Castle ruins (with Motor Museum adj).
ⓘ Marine Par. ✆ Great Yarmouth (0493) 2195.

■★★★**Carlton,** *Marine Parade South, NR30 3JE.* ✆ (0493) 855234. C. ✉ 94 bedrs, 60 bp, 10 sh, 5 ba, TV, Dgs. ✗ a l c, mc, at, LD 9.30. ⓓ Lt, N, CH, Dgs, CP 18, Ac, con 200, CF, 5 st. £ BB fr £32·45, DB fr £43·45, WB, Ⅰ, cc 1 2 3 5.▲

★★**Imperial** (R), *North Drive, NR30 1EQ.* ✆ (0493) 851113. C. ✉ 60 bedrs, 26 bp, 11 bps, 4 ba, TV, Dgs. ✗ a l c, mc, at, LD 10.30. ⓓ Lt, N, CH, TV, Dgs, CP 50, Ac, con 100, CF, 9 st. £ BB £25–£30, DBB £30–£40, WT £154–£175, DT £29–£35, DBB £26–£34, WB, Ⅰ, Bk £4·50, L £9·50, D £10·50, cc 1 2 3 5 6, Dep b.

★★**Sandringham,** *74 Marine Par, NR30 3JH.* ✆ (0493) 52427.
★★**Star,** *Hall Quay, NR30 1HG.* ✆ (0493) 842294. C. ✉ 42 bedrs, 39 bp, 1 bps, 3 ba, TV, Dgs. ✗ a l c, mc, at, LD 9.45. ⓓ Lt, N, CH, Dgs, Ac, con 80, CF, 0 st. £ BB £25–£31·50, DB £30–£44, WT £195, DT £43·50, DBB £37, WB, Ⅰ, Bk £3·75, L £5·50, D £6·50, cc 1 2 3 5 6, Dep b.

★★**Ambassador** (R), *64 Wellesby Dr, NR30 1EX.* ✆ (0493) 855120. C. ✉ 35 bedrs, 35 bps, 2 ba, TV. ✗ mc, at, LD 9. ⓓ Lt, CH, TV, CP 25, Ac, con 25, CF, 9 st. £ BB £19·50, DB £28, DT £25–£30·50, DBB £19–£24·50, WB, Ⅰ, Bk £3, L £4, D £5·50, Dep.

★**Burlington** (R), *North Drive, NR30 1EG.* ✆ (0493) 844568. Open Apr–Oct. C ✉ 32 bedrs, 18 bp, 9 bps, 2 ba, TV. ✗ mc, at, LD 8.30. ⓓ Lt, TV, CP 40, Ac, sp, con CF, 2 BGf, Dis. £ BB £18–£26, BD £28–£38, DT £21–£24, DBB £18–£24, WB, Ⅰ, Bk £3·50, L £5, D £7, cc 1 4.

★**Palm Court** (R), *North Drive, NR30 1EF.* ✆ (0493) 844568. Open Apr–Oct & Xmas. C. ✉ 45 bedrs, 10 bp, 24 bps, 6 ba, TV, Dgs. ✗ mc, at, LD 8. ⓓ Lt, CH, TV, CP 45, sp, sb, sol, con, CF, 0 st. £ BB £16–£26, DB £26–£39, WT £95–£145, DT £19–£26, DBB £17–£26, WB, Ⅰ, Bk £5, L £5, D £7, cc 1 3, Dep a.

Chequers, PH, z (Rl), *27 Nelson Rd South, NR30 3JA.* ✆ (0493) 53091.
Georgian House, PH, y (R), *16 North Dr, NR30 4EW.* ✆ (0493) 842623. C 5. ✉ 25 bedrs, 9 bp, 4 ba. ⓓ CH, TV, CP 24, 3 st. £ BB £12–£25, DB £18–£36, WT (c) £55–£90, Ⅰ.

Repairer: St John's (Yarmouth) Motors Ltd, 81 Southtown Rd. ✆ (0493) 56686.
Rescue Service: Trimoco Cars, Station Rd. ✆ (0493) 603677.

YARNTON Oxfordshire. M. Area 14F
Pop 2,468. Oxford 4½, London 61, Banbury 18, Bicester 13, Burford 17, Chipping Norton 16.
Golf North Oxford 18h. **See** 11th cent Parish Church.

Rescue Service: Blenheim Service Station, The Garth, Woodstock Rd. ✆ Kidlington (086 75) 2192.

YATELEY Hampshire. M. Area 6B
Pop 20,465. Bagshot 7, London 34, Basingstoke 14, Farnham 12, Guildford 15, Henley-on-Thames 16, Reading 12, Woking 12.
Golf East Berkshire, Crowthorne 18h. **See** Church with Lychgate.

Rescue Service: Yateley Motor Co, Reading Rd. ✆ (0252) 873323.

YATTENDON Berkshire. Map 6B
Pop 310. Reading 11, London 49, M4 Motorway 5½, Newbury 8.
Golf Streatley 18h. **See** Manor House, Grange and Rectory (all Queen Anne Period), 'The Miraculous Well'.

★★**Royal Oak**, *The Square, RG18 0UF.*
✆ (0635) 201325. C. ⊷ 5 bedrs, 5 bp, TV, Dgs. ✗ a l c, mc, at, LD 10.30. ⊡ CH, Ac, CF, 0 st. £ BB £32·50, DB £48, DBB £47·50, WB, ②, Bk £5, L £4·50, D £4·50, cc 1 2 3 5.

YATTON Avon. Map 5A
Pop 6,734. Bristol 13, London 126, M5 Motorway 4, Bath 28, Bridgwater 24, Shepton Mallet 25, Weston-Super-Mare 10.
Golf Clevedon 18h.

Firebox, H, *Station Approach.* ✆ (0934) 832119.

Rescue Service: Breakdown Services (Westonway) Ltd, Yatton Motors, High St. ✆ (0934) 833458 & (0934) 832152.

YEADON West Yorkshire. Map 25E
Pop 12,000. Leeds 7½, London 198, Bradford 5, Harrogate 12, Skipton 15, York 29.
EC Tue. **MD** Mon, Fri. **Golf** Rawdon G and LTC 9h, Horsforth Ltd 18h. **See** Church, Farnfield Park

Rescue Service: J C T 600 Ltd, Henshaw Garage, Apperley La. ✆ Rawdon (0532) 502231.

YELVERTON Devon. Map 3C
Pop 673. Exeter 33, London 204, Ashburton 18, Kingsbridge 22, Plymouth 9½, Saltash 10, Tavistock 5.
Golf Yelverton 18h. **See** Church, 13th cent Buckland Abbey (Drake Museum), Nat Trust 2¾ m SW.

♨★★★★**Moorland Links,** *PL20 6DA.*
✆ (0822) 852245. C. ⊷ 31 bedrs, 31 bp, TV, Dgs. ✗ a l c, mc, at, LD 10. ⊡ CH, Dgs, CP 120, Ac, sp, tc, con 200, CF, 6 BGf, 2 st. £ BB fr £29·50, DB fr £38, WB, ①, Bk £3, L £6, D £8·95, cc 1 2 3 5.

Burrator Inn, *Dousland, PL20 6NP.*
✆ (0822) 854370. Closed Xmas. C. ⊷ 9 bedrs, 2 bps, 4 ba, TV, Dgs. ✗ a l c. ⊡ CH, TV, Dgs, CP 60, CF, 1 st. £ BB £9·50–£10·50, DB £18–£25, WT (c) £57, DT (a) £20, DT (b) £15, ①.

Rescue Service: Crapstone Garage, 3 Lisbon Villas, Crapstone ✆ (0822) 2800. Roundabout & Moxham. ✆ (0822) 852931.

YEOVIL Somerset. Map 5C
See also WEST COKER.
Pop 27,265. Sherborne 5, London 125, Crewkerne 8½, Dorchester 18, Frome 25, Glastonbury 17, Ilminster 13, Shepton Mallet 20, Wincanton 14.
EC Thur. **MD** Mon, Fri. **Golf** Yeovil 18h. **See** Church, Wymondham (Hendford Manor Hall), Tithe Barn in Preston Rd (Private), Montacute House 4 m W, Tintinhull House 4 m NW, Fleet Air Arm Museum 4½ m N, East Lambrook Manor 7½ m SW, Brympton d'Evercy (Mansion House) 2 m W.

★★★**Manor Crest**, *Hendford, BA20 1TG.*
✆ (0935) 23116. C. ⊷ 42 bedrs, 40 bp, 2

bps, ns, TV, Dgs. ✗ a l c, mc, at, LD 10. ⊡ Lt, N, CH, CP 100, Ac, con 60, CF, 10 BGf, 2 st. £ B fr £40, BD fr £50, WB, ①, Bk £5·25, D £9·25, cc 1 2 3 4 5 6, Dep b.

◪★★**Mermaid**, *High St, BA20 1RE.*
✆ (0935) 75558. Closed Xmas. C. ⊷ 15 bedrs, 3 bp, 3 bps, 5 ba. ✗ a l c, mc, at, LD 9.30. ⊡ CH, TV, Dgs, CP 12, G 3, Ac, con 40, CF, 2 st. £ BB £22·50–£23·50, DB £33–£35, WB, ②, Bk £3·50, cc 1 3 5 6.

◪★★**Three Choughs**, *Hendford, BA20 1TW.* ✆ (0935) 74886. C. ⊷ 41 bedrs, 9 bp, 17 sh, 5 ba, TV, Dgs. ✗ a l c, mc, at, LD 9.15. ⊡ ch, TV, Dgs, Ac, con 40, CF, 3 st. £ BB £22–£30, DB £35–£42, DT £33–£40, DBB £28–£40, WB, ①, Bk £2, L £2·95, D £6·50, cc 1 2 3 5 6.

Highlands, PH, xy (R), *175 West Coker Rd, BA20 2HE.* ✆ West Coker (093 586) 2318. C 5. ⊷ 12 bedrs, 2 bp, 10 bps, 2 ba. ✗ a l c. ⊡ CH, TV, CP 50, U 1, G, 1, BGf, 1 st, Dis. £ BB £10·50–£17·50. DB £21–£25, WT (c) £68, ①, Bk £1·75, L £2·50, D £6.

Wyndham, G (RI), *142 Sherborne Rd, BA21 4HQ.* ✆ (0935) 21468. ⊷ 6 bedrs, 1 ba, Dgs. ⊡ ch, TV, Dgs, CP 6, CF, 0 st. £ BB £7, DB £14, WT (b) £77, DT (b) £11, ①.

Repairer: Douglas Seaton Ltd, Clarence St. ✆ (0935) 5131.
Specialist Body Repairer: Douglas Seaton Ltd, West Hendford. ✆ (0935) 27421.
Rescue Service: A M Motors, Unit 7, Enterprise Mews, 17 Lynx Trading Estate. ✆ (0935) 73574.
Hinder, A W & Sons, Marlclose Garage, Ilchester Rd. ✆ (0935) 6512.
Loder V.A.G. Vale Rd, Penn Mill Trading Estate. ✆ (0935) 22158.
Norman, J H & Sons, West Coker Rd. ✆ (0935) 6527.
Douglas Seaton Ltd, West Hendford. ✆ (0935) 27421.
Somerset Motors Ltd, Sherborne Rd. ✆ (0935) 23581.

YORK North Yorkshire. Map 25C
See also HAXBY.
Pop 97,240. Selby 13, London 193, Boroughbridge 17, Bridlington 41, Harrogate 22, Helmsley 24, Leeds 24, Malton 17, Market Weighton 19, Pontefract 25, Thirsk 23.
See Plan, p. 387.
EC Wed. **MD** Daily. **P** See Plan. **Golf** Fulford (York) 18h. **See** Minster, Walls and Gates, St Mary's Abbey ruins, Clifford's Tower, All Saints' Church (North St), Holy Trinity Church, Guildhall, Mansion House (by apptm), The Shambles, City of York Art Gallery, St William's College, St Anthony's Hall (Borthwick Institute of Historical Research), Merchant Taylors' Hall, Treasurer's House, Castle Museum, Merchant Adventurers' Hall, 14th cent Old Starre Inn, Railway Museum, Viking Centre, Wax Museum, Fairfax House, Benningborough Hall 7 m NW.
⑦ De Grey Rooms, Exhibition Sq. ✆ York (0904) 21756.

♨★★★★★**Middlethorpe Hall,**
Bishopthorpe Rd, YO2 1QP. ✆ (0904) 641241. C 8. ⊷ 12 bedrs, 12 bp, TV, Dgs. ✗ a l c, mc, at, LD 9.45. ⊡ Lt, N, CH, CP 40, con 50, CF. £ B £50, BD £60–£70, ①, Bk £4·50, L £10–£12, D £13·50, cc 1 2 3 5, Dep b.

★★★★**Royal York** (late **Royal Station**), *Station Rd, YO2 2AA.* ✆ (0904) 53681. C.

⊷ 130 bedrs, 88 bp, 24 bps, 6 ba, TV, Dgs. ✗ mc, at, LD 9.15 (8.45 Sun). ⊡ Lt, N, CH, Dgs, CP 110, Ac, gym, con 180, CF, 6 st. £ WB, Bk £4·50, L £6·50, D £9, cc 1 2 3 4 5 6, Dep b.

★★★★**Viking**, *North St, YO1 1JF.*
✆ (0904) 59822. C. ⊷ 187 bedrs, 187 bp, TV, Dgs. ✗ mc, at, LD 9.45. ⊡ Lt, N, CH, Dgs, CP 5, G 100, Ac, con 350, CF. £ BB £45–£48·50, DB £62·50–£67, WB, ①, Bkc £3·50, D £6·50, cc 1 2 3 5 6, Dep b.

★★★**Chase**, *Tadcaster Rd, Dringhouses, YO2 2QQ.* ✆ (0904) 707171. Closed Dec 25 & 26. C. ⊷ 80 bedrs, 59 bp, 16 bps, 6 sh, 4 ba, TV. ✗ a l c, mc, at, LD 8.45. ⊡ Lt, N, CH, TV, CP 100, U 12, Ac, con 120, CF, 0 st. £ BB £28–£30, DB £50, WT £210, WB, ①, L £5, D £9·50, cc 1 2 3 5 6, Dep b.

★★★**Dean Court**, *Duncombe Pl, YO1 2EF.* ✆ (0904) 25082. C. ⊷ 36 bedrs, 34 bp, 2 bps, TV. ✗ mc, at, LD 8.50. ⊡ Lt, N, CH, CP 12, con 12, CF. £ BB £35, DB £65, WT £227·50, DBB £45, WB, ①, Bk £5, L £7·50, D £11·50, cc 1 2 3 4 5 6, Dep b.

★★★**Disraelis**, *140 Acomb Rd, YO2 4HA.* ✆ (0904) 781181. Closed Xmas week. C. ⊷ 10 bedrs, 7 bp, 1 ba, TV. ✗ a l c, mc, at, LD 10. ⊡ CH, TV, CP 40, Ac, con 30, CF, 2 st. £ BB £18–£25, DB £30–£38, DBB £22–£26, WB, ②, Bk £2·50, L 4·25, D £7·95, cc 1 2 3 5 6, Dep.▲

♨★★★**Fairfield Manor**, *Shipton Rd, Skelton, YO3 6XW.* ✆ (0904) 25621. Closed 1st week Jan. C 5. ⊷ 25 bedrs, 22 bp, 3 bps, TV. ✗ a l c, mc, at, LD 9.15. ⊡ CH, ns, CP 50, Ac, con 60, 5 BGf, 0 st. £ BB £35–£48–£50, WB, ②, 10%, Bk £4, L £5·75, D £7·75, cc 1 2 3 5.▲

★★★**Ladbroke Abbey Park**, *The Mount, YO2 2BN.* ✆ (0904) 58301. C. ⊷ 84 bedrs, 77 bp, 3 ba, TV, Dgs. ✗ mc, at, LD 8.30. ⊡ Lt, N, CH, TV, CP 35, Ac, con 100, CF, 3 st. £ BB £31·50–£36·50, DB £40–£50, WB, ②, Bk £5·25, L £6·50, D £8·50, cc 1 2 3 4 5 6, Dep b.

★★★**M Post House** (TH), *Tadcaster Rd, YO2 2QF.* ✆ (0904) 707921. C. ⊷ 147 bedrs, 147 bp, TV, Dgs. ✗ a l c, mc, LD 10. ⊡ Lt, N, CH, Dgs, Ac, con 90, CF, 19 BGf, 0 st, Dis. £ BB £44, DB £58·50, WB, ①, cc 1 2 3 4 5 6, Dep (Xmas).

★★**Abbots Mews** (R), *Marygate Lane, Bootham, YO3 7DE.* ✆ (0904) 34866. C. ⊷ 15 bedrs, 1 bp, 14 bps, 1 ba, annexe 11 bedrs, 3 bp, 8 bps, TV, Dgs. ✗ a l c, LD 9.30. ⊡ CH, Dgs, CP 20, Ac, sol, con 50, CF, 10 BGf, Dis. £ BB £22–£35, DB £34–£50, DBB £22–£35, WB, ①, Bk £3·50, L £2, D £10, cc 1 2 3 5, Dep a.▲

★★**Ashcroft**, *294 Bishopthorpe Rd, YO2 1LH.* ✆ (0904) 59286. Closed Xmas & New Year. C. ⊷ 11 bedrs, 10 bp, 1 bps, annexe 4 bedrs, 3 bp, 1 bps, TV, Dgs. ✗ mc, at, LD 7.30. ⊡ CH, TV, Dgs, CP 40, Ac, con 40, CF, 4 BGf, 4 st. £ BB fr £17, DB fr £34, DBB fr £23, WB, ②, Bk £3·50, L £4·25, D £6, cc 1 2 3 5, Dep a.

★★**Beechwood Close** (R), *19 Shipton Rd, YO3 6RE.* ✆ (0904) 58378. Closed Xmas. C. ⊷ 12 bedrs, 1 bp, 3 bps, 2 sh, 3 ba, TV. ✗ mc, at, LD 9 (9.30 Sat). ⊡ CH, TV, ns, CP 36, Ac, gc, CF, 2 BGf, 3 st. £ BB £15·50–£18·50, DB £31–£35, DBB £17·45–£23·50, WB, ②, Bk £2·75, L £3·25, D £6, cc 1 3.

★★**Kilima**, *129 Holgate Rd, YO2 4DE.*
✆ (0904) 58844. C. ⊷ 15 bedrs, 15 bp, TV. ✗ a l c, LD 9.30. ⊡ CH, CP 20, CF, 2 BGf, 0 st. £ BB £20–£26, DB £36–£40, WB, ②, Bk £3·50, L £7, D £7, cc 1 2 3 5 6.

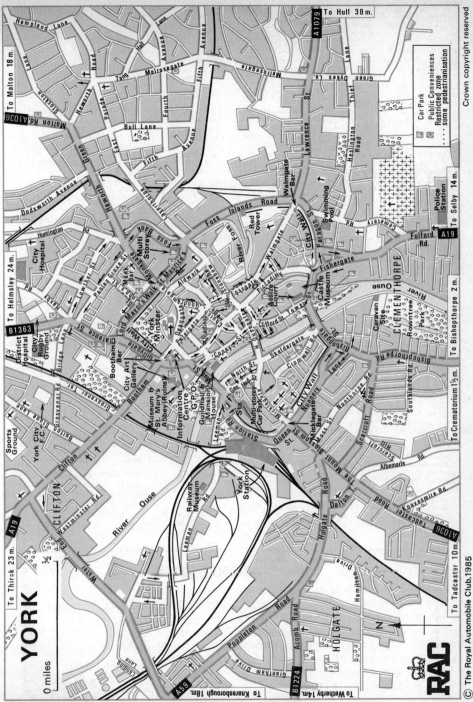

YORK

	Car Park
C	Public Conveniences
	Restricted zone
....	some pedestrianisation

To Thirsk 23 m.

To Malton 18 m.

Hempland Lane

Malton Rd. A1036

To Hull 38 m.

A1079

To Helmsley 24 m.

B1363

To Selby 14 m.

A19

Fulford Rd.

To Bishopthorpe 2 m.

River Ouse

CLEMENTHORPE

Police Station

To Crematorium 1½ m.

To Tadcaster 10 m.

A1036

To Wetherby 14 m.

B1224

To Knaresborough 18 m.

A59

HOLGATE

City Wall

York Minster

City Hospital

District Hospital

York City F.C.

Sports Ground

0 miles

★★Newington (R), *Mount Vale, YO2 2DJ.* ✆ (0904) 25173. C. ➡ 33 bedrs, 3 bp, 7 bps, 15 sh, 1 ba, annexe 16 bedrs, 1 bp, 10 bps, 4 sh, 1 ba, TV, Dgs. ✗ a l c, mc, at, LD 8.45. ⓓ Lt, CH, TV, Dgs, CP 32, Ac, sp, sb, sol, con 30, CF, 7 st. £ BB £15·35–£21·75, DB £27·20–£38·70, WT £168·35–£184.45, DT £24·05–£26·35, DBB £20·10–£26·30, WB, ②, Bk £2·50, L £3·95, D £6·50, cc 1 2 3 5 6.

★★Sheppard (R), *63 Blossom St, YO2 2BD.* ✆ (0904) 20500. Closed Xmas. C. ➡ 19 bedrs, 15 bp, 4 sh, 2 ba, ns, TV, Dgs. ✗ a l c, mc, at, LD 9.30. ⓓ N, CH, Dgs, ns, CP 10, U 3, G 1, Ac, con 20, CF, 10 st. £ BB £17–£25, DB £25–£40, WT £157–£210, DBB £18·50–£26, WB, ①, Bk £2·50, L £4·50, D £6·50, cc 1 3, Dep a.▲

★★Town House (R), *100 Holgate Rd, YO2 4BB.* ✆ (0904) 36171. Closed Dec 24–Jan 1. C. ➡ 23 bedrs, 11 bp, 6 bps, 2 sh, 1 ba, TV, Dgs. ✗ a l c, mc, at, LD 9.30. ⓓ CH, CP 21, Ac, CF, 1 st. £ BB £15–£22·75, DB £28–£35, WB, ②, Bk £3·50, L £5·50, D £6·50, cc 1 2 3 5 6.▲

Alcuin Lodge, G, z (R), *15 Sycamore Place, YO3 7DW.* ✆ (0904) 32222.

Alhambra Court, PH, z (RI), *31 St Marys, Bootham, YO3 7DD.* ✆ (0904) 28474. C. ➡ 22 bedrs, 20 bp, 2 bps, ns, TV. ⓓ CH, TV, CP 20.£ BB £11–£17, DB £20–£29, WT £66·50–£96, DT £16–£20·50, ②, Bk £2, D £6, cc 1 3.

Amblesyde, G, z (Unl), *62 Bootham Cres, YO3 7AH.* ✆ (0904) 37165.

Ascot, G, z (Unl), *94 Bishopthorpe Rd, YO2 1JS.* ✆ (0904) 24506.▲

Ascot House, PH, x (Unl), *80 East Parade, YO3 7YH.* ✆ (0904) 25782. C. ➡ 9 bedrs, 3 bp, 6 bps, 1 ba, TV, Dgs. ⓓ CH, TV, CP 10, CF, 2 st. £ BB £13, DB £20–£22, WT (c) £70, ①.

Beech House, G, z (RI), *6 Longfield Ter, YO3 7DJ.* ✆ (0904) 34581. Closed Xmas & New Year. C 5. ➡ 7 bedrs, 2 bps, 2 ba, TV. ⓓ CH, TV, ns, CP 5. £ BB £7·50–£9·50, DB £14–£25, ①.

Cavalier, PH, z (RI), *39 Monkgate, YO3 7PB.* ✆ (0904) 36615. C. ➡ 10 bedrs, 2 bp, 2 bps, 3 ba, TV, Dgs. ⓓ CH, TV, Dgs, 3 st. £ BB £9–£10·50, DB £18–£24, WT (c) £63–£70, DT (b) £13·50–£16, ①.

Clifton View, G, z (Unl), *118 Clifton, YO3 6BQ.* ✆ (0904) 25047. C. ➡ 10 bedrs, 9 sh, 2 ba, TV. ⓓ CH, TV. £ BB £6·50–£8·50, DB £15–£17, ①.

Crescent, G, z (Unl), *77 Bootham, YO3 7DQ.* ✆ (0904) 23216. Closed Nov & Dec. C 10. ➡ 8 bedrs, 2 ba. ⓓ CH, TV, ns, 12 st. £ BB £8·50–£9·50, DB £15–£17, WT (c) £52·50–£56, ①.

Croft, PH, z (Unl), *103 The Mount, YO2 2AX.* ✆ (0904) 22747. Closed Jan & Xmas. C 2. ➡ 10 bedrs, 2 sh, 3 ba. ⓓ CH, TV, Dgs, 3 st. £ BB £10–£12, DB £20–£24, WT (b) £100–£114, DT (b) £16–£18, ①, cc 1 3.

Derwent Hill Country House, PH, z (RI), *Stamford Bridge YO4 1DO.* ✆ (0759) 72027. Closed Xmas. C. ➡ 7 bedrs, 6 bp, 1 sh, Dgs. ⓓ CH, TV, Dgs, CP 10, CF, 10 st. £ BB £13, DB £22, WT (c) £70, DT (b) £16, ①.

Fairmount, PH, z (RI), *230 Tadcaster Rd, YO2 2ES.* ✆ (0904) 38298. C. ➡ 8 bedrs, 4 bps, 2 ba. TV. ⓓ CH, TV, CP 7, U 2, CF, 5 st. £ BB £12·65, DB £25·30–£26·50, WT (c) £185·50, ①, cc 1 2 3 5.

Field House, H, z (RI), *2 St George's Place, YO2 2DR.* ✆ (0904) 39572.

Fleece, I, x, *Bishop Wilton, YO4 1RU.* ✆ Bishop Wilton (075 96) 251. C 10. ➡ 4 bedrs, 2 ba. ✗ a l c. ⓓ CH, TV, Dgs, CP 20, 1 st. £ BB £9·50, DB £18, ②, Bk £3, L £3, D £6·50.

Grasmead House, H, z (RI), *1 Scarcroft Hill, YO2 1DF.* ✆ (0904) 29996. C 5. ➡ 6 bedrs, 6 bp, ns, TV, Dgs. ⓓ CH, TV, Dgs, ns. £ DB £32–£36, WT (c) £106–£120, ①, cc 3.

Green View, G, z (Unl), *5 Clifton Green, YO3 6LH.* ✆ (0904) 21964.▲

Hazelwood, G, z (Unl), *24/25 Portland St, YO3 7EH.* ✆ (0904) 26548. Open Feb–Nov. C. ➡ 15 bedrs, 2 bp, 3 bps, 2 ba, TV. ⓓ CH, TV, CP 6, CF. £ BB £7·50–£9, DB £15–£21, WT (c) £49·90–£69·90, ②.

Heworth, G, z (R), *126 East Par, YO3 7YG.* ✆ (0904) 426384. C. ➡ 7 bedrs, 1 ba, Dgs. ⓓ CH, TV, Dgs, CP 1, CF, 2 st. £ BB £7–£9·50, DB £14–£17, WT (b) £70–£90, (c) £45–£65, DT (b) £11–£13·50, ①.

Inglewood, G, z (Unl), *7 Clifton Green, Clifton, YO3 6LH.* ✆ (0904) 53523. C. ➡ 7 bedrs, 2 bps, 1 ba, TV. ⓓ CH, TV, G 1. £ BB £9·50–£10, DB £16–£27, ①.

Linden Lodge, PH, z (Rt), *6 Nunthorpe Av, Seacroft Rd, YO2 1PF.* ✆ (0904) 20107.

Marina, G, x (RI), *Naburn, YO1 4RL.* ✆ (0904) 27365. Closed Dec. C. ➡ 6 bedrs, 1 bp, 5 sh. ⓓ CH, TV, CP 12, 1 BGf. £ BB £10·50–£11·50, DB £19–£24, WT (b) £108·50–£112, DT (b) £15·50–£16, ①.

Mayfield, PH, z (RI), *75 Scarcroft Rd, YO2 1DB.* ✆ (0904) 54834. C. ➡ 7 bedrs, 2 bp, 5 bps, ns, TV. ✗ a l c. ⓓ CH, CF, 4 st. £ BB £17·50, DB (b) £136·50, DT (b) £24, ①, Bk £2·50, L £2, D £6·50, cc 1 2 3.

Minster View, G, z (Unl), *2 Grosvenor Ter, Bootham, YO3 7AG.* ✆ (0904) 55034.

Closed Xmas. C. ➡ 7 bedrs, 3 bp, 2 ba, Dgs. ⓓ CH, TV, CP 6, CF, 1 BGf, 1 st. £ BB £6·50–£8·50, WT (b) £77–£91, DT (b) £11–£13, ①.

Old Vic, G, z (Rt), *2 Wenlock Ter, YO1 4DU.* ✆ (0904) 37888.

Orchard Court, PH, z (RI), *4 St Peters Grove, Bootham, YO3 6AQ.* ✆ (0904) 53964. Closed Xmas & New Year. C. ➡ 10 bedrs, 1 bp, 4 bps, 2 sh, 1 ba, TV, Dgs. ⓓ ch, TV, ns, CP 10, CH, 1 BGf, 3 st, Dis. £ BB £9–£17, DB £18–£32, WT (b) £98–£146, DT (b) £15–£22, ②, Bk £3·50, D £6, cc 1 3.

Priory, PH, z (Unl), *126 Fulford Rd, YO1 4BE.* ✆ (0904) 25280. Closed Xmas. C. ➡ 20 bedrs, 3 bps, 4 ba. ⓓ CH, TV, CP 25, 5 st. £ BB £11–£14, DB £20–£26, ①, cc 1 2 3 5.▲

St Denys, PH, z (RI), *St Denys Rd, YO1 1QD.* ✆ (0904) 22207. Closed Xmas. C. ➡ 10 bedrs, 7 bp, 2 ba, TV, Dgs. ⓓ CH, TV, Dgs, CP 7, CF, 2 st. £ BB £12·50–£16, DB £25–£28, ①.

St. Raphael, G, z (Unl), *44 Queen Anne's Rd, Bootham, YO3 7AF.* ✆ (0904) 54187. C 10. ➡ 7 bedrs, 2 ba. ⓓ CH, TV, 1 ba. £ BB £8·50–£9·50, DB £17–£19, ①.

Repairers: Forsselius Ltd, Blossom St. ✆ (0904) 55885.
Foxton's Garage Ltd, Station Garage, Leeman Rd. ✆ (0904) 59241.
Leedhams (York) Ltd, Lendal Bridge. ✆ (0904) 25448.

Rescue Service: Allisons & Knowles, York Road Garage, Wilberfoss. ✆ Wilberfoss (075 95) 232.
Clifton Garage, Clifton. ✆ (0904) 58647.
Elmfield Garage, Malton Rd. ✆ (0904) 23360.
Haw's Garage, Lowther St. ✆ (0904) 22064.
Huntingdon Garage, 67 North Moor Rd, Huntingdon. ✆ (0904) 768808.
Russell's Garage (York) Ltd, The Stonebow. ✆ (0904) 55118.
Stables Garage, The Crescent, Blossom St. ✆ (0904) 51808.
Till & Elliot Ltd, Murton Garage, Hull Rd. ✆ (0904) 23740.
Wa'side Garage, Malton Rd. ✆ (0904) 55427.

YOULGRAVE Derbyshire. Map 22C
Pop 1,215. Matlock 9, London 153, Ashbourne 13, Bakewell 4½, Buxton 12.
Golf Buxton & Bakewell 18h.

Rescue Service: Peter Prince (Automobile & Electrical Engineers) Ltd, The Garage. ✆ (062 986) 206.

RAC NATIONAL MAPS

Going on a long journey?
These are the maps you need to plan it. *RAC National Maps* clearly illustrate the entire motorway system.
Bold use of colours distinguishes primary routes, main and secondary routes for easy reference. (See pages 37-8)
England and Wales: 10 miles to 1 inch
Scotland: 8 miles to 1 inch
Ireland: 8 miles to 1 inch

RAC

Directory– Scotland

Directory of appointed hotels, small hotels, guest hotels, etc., repairers and agents in Scotland. See separate sections for England, Wales, The Channel Islands and Northern Ireland.

National Tourist Board:
Scottish Tourist Board
23 Ravelston Terrace, Edinburgh EH4 3EU
☎ 031-332 2433

For explanatory notes to Directory see page 116
For abbreviations see inside back cover

ABERDEEN Grampian (Aberdeenshire).
Map 41D
Pop 203,927. Stonehaven 14, London
491, Banff 46, Braemar 58, Edinburgh 117,
Fraserburgh 42, Glasgow 136, Huntly 38,
Peterhead 32.
See Plan, p. 391.
EC Wed. MD Fri. P See Plan. Golf Royal
Aberdeen 18h (2) and 9h, Bon-Accord
18h, etc. See Cathedral of St Machar, St
Andrew's Episcopal Cathedral, St Mary's
RC Cathedral, University (Marischal and
King's Colleges), 17th cent Mercat Cross,
Art Gallery and Regional Museum, Provost
Ross's House (museum), Town House
(incorp part of the Old Tolbooth), Brig o'
Balgownie, Brig o' Dee, Fish Market,
Girdleness Lighthouse, Granite Quarry,
Drum Castle 10 m SW.
ℹ St Nicholas House, Broad St.
✆ Aberdeen (0224) 632727.

★★★★M Holiday Inn, Old Meldrum Rd,
Bucksburn, AB2 9LN. ✆ (0224) 713911.
RS Xmas. C. ⊯ 98 bedrs, 98 bp, ns, TV,
Dgs. ✗ a l c, mc, at, LD 10.30. ⌂ CP 80,
Ac, sp, gym, con 180, CF, 23 BGf, 0 st.
£ BB fr £52·25, DB fr £60·56, WB, ② Bk
£4·50, L £9·50, D £9·50, cc 1 2 3 4 5 6,
Dep.
★★★Caledonian Thistle, Union Ter,
AB9 1HE. ✆ (0224) 640233. C. ⊯ 81
bedrs, 71 bp, 10 bps, 2 ba, ns, TV, Dgs.
✗ a l c, mc, at, LD 9.30. ⌂ Lt, N, CH, Dgs,
CP 35, Ac, con 30, CF, 10 st. £ BB £45·75–
£52·75, DB £54·50–£64·50, WB, ②, Bk
£4·75, L £6·95, D £8·95, cc 1 2 3 4 5 6,
Dep b.
★★★M Skean Dhu, Dyce Airport, AB2
0DW. ✆ (0224) 725252. C. ⊯ 148 bedrs,
148 bp, 2 ba, TV, Dgs. ✗ a l c, mc, at, LD
10.45. ⌂ N, CH, CP 300, Ac, sp, con 300,
CF, 75 BGf, 0 st, Dis. £ BB £45·45, DB
£53·95, WT £410·20, DT £58·60, DBB
£53·70, WB, ②, Bk £3·50, L £5, D £8·25,
cc 1 2 3 4 5 6, Dep b.
★★★Stakis Tree Tops, 161 Springfield
Rd, AB9 2QH. ✆ (0224) 33377. C. ⊯ 92
bedrs, 92 bp, 1 ba, ns, TV, dgs. ✗ a l c, mc,
at, LD 10. ⌂ Lt, N, CH, TV, Dgs, CP 300,
Ac, sp, sb, con 500, CF, 17 BGf, 0 st, Dis.
£ BB £44·50, DB £50, WB, ②, Bk £2·50, L
£5·50, D £8·95, cc 1 2 3 4 5 6, Dep b.
■★★Gloucester, 102 Union St, AB9
1FT. ✆ (0224) 641095. C. ⊯ 71 bedrs, 71
bp, TV, Dgs. ✗ a l c, mc, at, LD 8.30. ⌂ Lt,
N, CH, Ac, con 60, CF, 2 st. £ BB £35, DB
£48·50, WB, ②, Bk £4, L £2·50, D £9,
cc 1 2 3 4 5 6.
★★Imperial, Stirling St, AB9 2JY.
✆ (0224) 589101. C. ⊯ 109 bedrs, 10 bp,
9 bps, 90 sh, TV, Dgs. ✗ a l c, mc, at, LD
9·45. ⌂ Lt, N, CH, Dgs, Ac, con 50, CF, 2 st.
£ BB £35, DB £46, WB, ①, Bk £5·50, L
£5·50, D £6·50, cc 1 2 3 4 5 6, Dep b.
★★Northern, 1 Great Northern Rd,
AB9 2UL. ✆ (0224) 43342. C. ⊯ 57 bedrs,
27 bp, 27 bps, 9 ba, TV, Dgs. ✗ a l c, mc, at,
LD 10·50. ⌂ Lt, N, CH, Dgs, con 180, CF,
2 st. £ BB fr £21·50, DB fr £36, WB, ①, Bk
£5·20, L £5·30, D £10·50, cc 1 2 3 4 5 6.
★Ferryhill House, Bon Accord St, AB1
2UA. ✆ (0224) 590867. C. ⊯ 10 bedrs,
2 bp, 4 bps, 2 ba, TV, Dgs. ✗ a l c, mc, LD
7.30. ⌂ N, ch, TV, Dgs. ✗ a l c, mc,
£16–£24, DB £34–£38, ② 10%, Bk £4, L £3,
cc 3 5, Dep b.
Craig Rossie, G, z (Unl), 293 Gt Western
Rd, AB1 6PP. ✆ (0224) 581548. Closed
Dec. C. ⊯ 6 bedrs, 2 ba, TV, Dgs. ⌂ CH,

Dgs. £ BB £8–£10, DB £16–£18, WT (c)
£55, ①.
Dunromin, G, z (Unl), 75 Constitution St,
AB2 1ET. ✆ (0224) 647995. C. ⊯ 6 bedrs,
2 ba, ns, Dgs. ⌂ CH, TV, CF. £ BB £10, DB
£16–£20, WT (c) £70, ①.
Klibreck, G, z (Unl), 410 Gt. Western Rd,
AB1 6NR. ✆ (0224) 36115. Closed Xmas
& New Year. C. ⊯ 6 bedrs, 2 ba. ⌂ CH, TV,
ns, CP 3, 3 BGf, 2 st. £ BB £10–£10·50, DB
£18–£19, DT £14–£15, ②.
Tower, H, z, 36 Fonthill Rd, AB1 2UJ.
✆ (0224) 24050.
Western, G, z (Unl), 193 Gt Western Rd,
AB1 6PS. ✆ (0224) 596919. Closed Xmas
& New Year. C. ⊯ 6 bedrs, 1 ba. ⌂ CH,
TV, CP 6, 3 st. £ BB £9–£10, DB £16–£17,
WT £60–£65, ①.

Repairers: Aberdeen Motors Ltd, 19
Justice Mill La. ✆ (0224) 56151.
Callanders Engineering (Aberdeen) Ltd,
366 King St. ✆ (0224) 634211.
Cordiner's Garage Ltd, Menzies Rd.
✆ (0224) 52206.
Rescue Service: City Garage, Loch St.
✆ (0224) 21317.
Harper Motor Co Ltd, 43 Holburn St.
✆ (0224) 29022.

ABERDOUR Fife. Map 36D
Pop 1,200. South Queensferry 7½, London
392, Dunfermline 7½, Edinburgh 17,
Glasgow 45, Kincardine 17, Kinross 13,
Kirkcaldy 8, Lanark 37.
EC Wed. Golf Aberdour 18h. See Old
Church of St Fillan, Castle (gardens,
dovecote), St Bridget's Church (ruins), at
Dalgety, 1½ m S lies small island of
Inchcolm with ruins of Abbey of St
Columba (1123) and 13th cent Church
(boats during season).
★★Woodside, High St, KY3 0SW.
✆ (0383) 860328. RS Xmas & New Year.
C. ⊯ 12 bedrs, 2 bp, 4 bps, 3 ba, TV, Dgs.
✗ a l c, mc, at, LD 8.45. ⌂ ch, TV, Dgs, CP
36, Ac, con 30, CF, 0 st. £ Bk £3·50,
L £7·50, D £7·50, cc 1 2 3 5 6.
Rescue Service: Woodside Garage, High
St. ✆ (0383) 860337.

ABERFELDY Tayside (Perthshire). Map
36B
Pop 1,500, Crieff 22, London 438,
Blairgowrie 29, Crainlarich 37, Dundee 46,
Edinburgh 68, Glasgow 90, Lochearnhead
30, Perth 31, Pitlochry 14.
EC Wed. Golf Aberfeldy 9h. See Black
Watch Monument, Gen. Wade's Bridge
(1733), The Birks—Nature Trail.
ℹ 8 Dunkeld St. ✆ Aberfeldy (0887)
20276.
★★Palace, Breadalbane Ter, PH15 2AG.
✆ (0887) 20359. Open Apr–Oct. C. ⊯ 18
bedrs, 1 bp, 2 bps, 6 ba, Dgs. ✗ a l c, mc,
at, LD 8.30. ⌂ CH, TV, ns, CP 30, Ac, CF, 4
st. £ BB £10–£13·50, DB £20–£27, ①, Bk
£3, L £3·80, D £7.
★★Weem, Weem, PH15 2LD. ✆ (0887)
20381.
Balnearn, PH, y (Unl), Crieff Rd, PH15
2BJ. ✆ (0887) 20431. C. ⊯ 13 bedrs, 4 ba,
Dgs. ⌂ ch, TV, CP 15, G 2, CF, 0 st.
£ BB £10·35, DB £20·70, WT £104·65, DT
£14·95, ②.
Crossroads, G, z (Unl), 4 Kenmore Street,
PH15 2BL. ✆ (0887) 20293.
Guinach, H, y (R), Urlar Rd, PH15 2ET.
✆ (0887) 20251. Open Mar–Oct. C under
1 & over 8. ⊯ 7 bedrs, 3 ba, Dgs. ⌂ CH,

TV, ns, CP 12, G 2, CF, 1 st, Dis. £ BB
£11–£12·50, DB £22–£25, WT (b) £110–
£126, WT (c) £70–£80, DT (b) £17·50–
£20, ①, Bk £4·50, L fr £2, D £6·50–£7·50.
Nessbank, PH, x (RI), Crieff Road, PH15
2BJ. ✆ (0887) 20214. Open Mar–Oct. C.
⊯ 7 bedrs, 2 ba, Dgs. ⌂ TV, ns, CP 7, CF, 1
st. £ BB £11·50, DB £23, WT (b) £110, DT
(b) £18·50, ②, Bk £4·50, D £8.
Tom-an-Droighne, G, PH15 2JS.
✆ (0887) 20489.

Repairer: King & Sons, Central Station
Garage. ✆ (0887) 20254.
Rescue Service: McDougall, T, Weem
Garage, Weem. ✆ (0887) 20499.
Scottish Co-operative Wholesale Society
Ltd, The Garage, 48 Dunkeld St. ✆ (0887)
20325.

ABERFOYLE Central (Perthshire). Map
36C
Pop 793. M9 Motorway 17, Stirling 19,
London 414, Edinburgh 54, Glasgow 27,
Lochearnhead 23.
Golf Aberfoyle 9h. See The Trossachs,
Assoc with 'Rob Roy' and 'The Lady of the
Lake', Queen Elizabeth National Forest
Park.
ℹ Main St. ✆ Aberfoyle (087 72) 352.
Rescue Service: A. N. Johnston–Aberfoyle
Motors Ltd. ✆ (087 72) 341.

ABERLADY Lothian (East Lothian). Map
37E
Pop 1,214. Haddington 5, London 374,
Edinburgh 15, Glasgow 60, Peebles 32.
Golf Gullane 18h (3). See Parish Church
(monument by Canova), Mercat Cross,
Nature Reserve.
★★Kilspindie House, Main St, EH32
0RE. ✆ (08757) 319. C. ⊯ 12 bedrs, 8 bp,
3 bps, TV, Dgs. ✗ mc, LD 9.30. ⌂ CH, TV,
CP 30, U 3, con 20, CF, 1 st. £ BB £10–
£18·50, DB £20–£28, DBB £17–£20·80,
WB, ①, Bk £3·50, L £3·50, D £6·80, cc 1 3,
Dep b.

ABERLOUR Grampian (Banffshire). Map
40B
Pop 800. Tomintoul 20, London 513,
Braemar 53, Craigallachie 2, Edinburgh
138, Glasgow 155, Grantown-on-Spey 20.
EC Wed. Golf Dufftown 18h. See
Drostan's Well (relic of ancient church),
Waterfalls on Aberlour Burn.
★★Aberlour, High St, AB3 9QB.
✆ (03405) 287. C. ⊯ 18 bedrs, 14 bp, 1
bps, 3 sh, 4 ba, Dgs. ✗ a l c, mc, at, LD 9.
⌂ CH, TV, Dgs, CP 20, U 3, G 3, Ac, CF, 0
st. £ BB £13·25–£15·75, DB £24·90–
£26·10, ②, Bk £2·95, L £1·80, D £4·90.
Rescue Service: Frank Ogg & Son, 19 High
St. ✆ (03405) 505.

ABERNETHY Tayside (Perthshire). Map
36D
Kinross 12, London 411, Dundee 21,
Edinburgh 39, Glasgow 58, Kirkcaldy 23,
Perth 8½, St Andrews 24, Stirling 34.
Rescue Service: Tower Garage, Main Rd.
✆ (073 885) 285.

ABINGTON Strathclyde (Lanarkshire).
Map 29B
Pop 196. Beattock 18, London 351, Ayr
45, Dumbarton 35, Edinburgh 40,
Glasgow 36, Kilmarnock 43, Lanark 7½,
Paisley 43, Peebles 30, Thornhill 22.

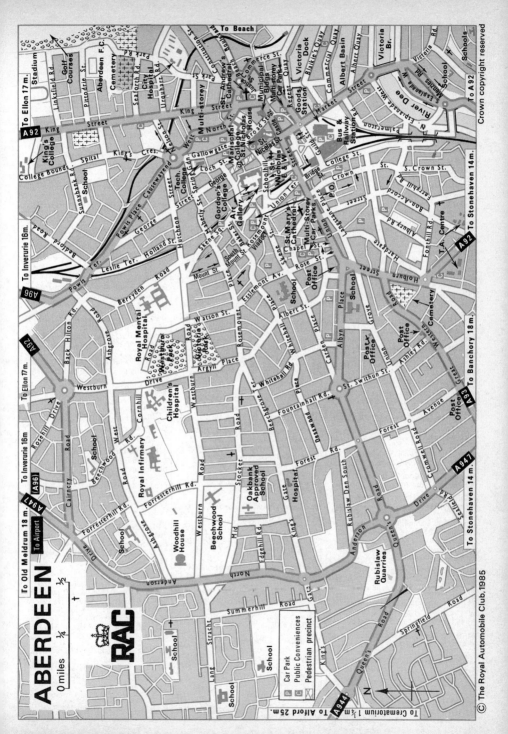

ABERDEEN

RAC

To Old Meldrum 18 m.

To Airport

0 miles ¼ ½

EC Wed. **Golf** Leadhills 9h, Biggar 18h.
See Iron Age Fort.
🛈 'Little Chef', ✆ Crawford (086 42) 436.

★★**Abington,** *Carlisle Rd, ML12 6SD.*
✆ (086 42) 467. 🛏 26 bedrs, 8 bp, 8 ba,
ns, TV, Dgs. ✖ mc, at, LD 10. 🅲 CH, TV, ns,
CP 20, G 14, Ac, CF, 3 st. £ BB £16–
£17·50, DB £27–£30, WT £119–£140, DT
£20, DBB £17–£19, WB, 🄑, Bk £3·50, L
£3·95, D £7·50, cc 1 3, Dep b.

Rescue Service: James Harvie & Sons,
Carlisle Rd. ✆ Crawford (086 42) 375.

ABOYNE Grampian (Aberdeenshire).
Map 41C
Pop 2,500. Fettercairn 22, London 485,
Aberdeen 30, Braemar 27, Craigellachie
48, Edinburgh 111, Glasgow 130,
Grantown-on-Spey 45, Huntly 38,
Stonehaven 28.
EC Thur. **Golf** Aboyne 18h. **See** Winter
Sports centre, St Machar's Cross, Church
of St Thomas, Aboyne Games in Sept,
Glentaner Deer Forest, Craigievar Castle
7 m NE.

🏩★★**Balnacoil House,** *AB3 5JD.*
✆ (0339) 2252. C. 🛏 13 bedrs, 3 bp, 1
bps, 3 ba, Dgs. ✖ mc, at, LD 9. 🅲 CH, TV,
Dgs, CP, U 2, CF, 1 st. £ BB £16·50–
£17·50, DB £30–£32, WT £150, DT £32,
DBB £24·50–£26·50, WB, 🄑, Bk £2·75, L
£4·25, D £8, cc 5, Dep a.

🏩★★**Birse Lodge,** *Charleston Rd, AB3
5EL.* ✆ (0339) 2253. Open Mar–Oct, RS
Nov–Feb. C. 🛏 12 bedrs, 11 bp, 1 bps, 1
ba, annexe 4 bedrs, 4 bp, Dgs. ✖ mc, at, LD
8. 🅲 CH, TV, CP 30, CF, 5 BGf, 1 st, Dis.
£ BB £19, DB £38, WT £196, DT £28, DBB
£25, 🄑, Bk £6, L £10, cc 2 5, Dep.
★**Charleston,** *Ballater Rd, AB3 5HY.*
✆ (0339) 2475.

ACHARACLE Highland (Argyll). Map
38F
Pop 500. Ballachulish 56 (Fy 29), London
531 (Fy 505), Edinburgh 174 (Fy 148),
Fort William 44 (Fy 33), Glasgow 144 (Fy
111), Mallaig 34.
EC Sat. **Golf** Fort William 18h. **See**
Lighthouse, 14th cent Castle.

Rescue Service: Loch Sheil Garage.
✆ Salen (096 785) 246.

ACHNASHEEN Highland (Ross &
Cromarty). Map 39A
Pop 30. Garve 16, London 568, Beauly 31,
Dingwall 30, Edinburgh 193, Gairloch 29,
Glasgow 207, Kyle of Lochalsh (Fy) 39,
Ullapool 48.
EC Wed. **Golf** Gairloch 9h. **See** Cottage
Pottery, Craft Centre.

🏩★★**Ledgowan Lodge,** *IV22 2EJ.*
✆ (044 588) 252. Open Apr–Oct. C. 🛏 18
bedrs, 10 bp, 3 ba, Dgs. ✖ a l c, mc, at, LD
8.30. 🅲 CH, TV, Dgs, CP 25, Ac, CF, 1 BGf,
2 st. £ BB £17·45–£21·50, DB £30–£42,
WT £144–£200, DBB £24–£32, WB, 🄑, Bk
£3·95, L £1·50, D £9, cc 1 2 3 4 5 6.

AIRDRIE Strathclyde (Lanarkshire). Map
48A
Pop 37,528. M8 Motorway 3½, Lanark 17,
London 385, Edinburgh 33, Glasgow 11,
Kincardine 21, Peebles 40, Stirling 19.
EC Wed. **MD** Tue, Fri. **Golf** Airdrie 18h.
See Museum Arts Centre.

★★**Tudor,** *Alexandra St, ML6 0BA.*
✆ (023 64) 64144. C. 🛏 21 bedrs, 10 bp,
4 ba, TV, Dgs. ✖ a l c, mc, at, LD 9.30. 🅲 N,

ch, TV, CP 100, Ac, con 180, CF, 2 st. £ BB
£22·50–£26·95, DB £31·35–£39·60, WB,
🄑, Bk £3, L £7·60, D £7·60, cc 1 2 5.

Repairer: Watson Bros, High St.
✆ (023 64) 62401.
Specialist Spring Repairer: Jonas
Woodhead & Sons (Scotland) Ltd,
Chapelhall Industrial Estate, Chapelhall.
✆ (023 64) 62481.

ALNESS Highland (Ross-shire). Map 43E
Inverness 23, London 552, Bonar Bridge
18, Dingwall 10, Edinburgh 152, Glasgow
163.
EC Wed. **Golf** Alness 9h.

Rescue Service: Car Tuning & Servicing
Centre, Alness Industrial Estate, Alness,
Inverness. ✆ (0349) 882818.

ANNAN Dumfries & Galloway
(Dumfriesshire). Map 30 E
Pop 8,952. Eastriggs 3½, London 311,
Beattock 24, Brampton 23, Carlisle 17,
Dumfries 15, Edinburgh 76, Glasgow 79,
Langholm 18.
EC Wed. **MD** Fri, Sat. **Golf** Powfoot 18h.
See Town Hall (housing 14th cent Brus
Stone), Moat House, 18th cent Annan Old
Church.

★**Corner House,** *78 High St, DG12 6DL.*
✆ (046 12) 122754. C. 🛏 31 bedrs, 1 bps,
7 ba, Dgs. ✖ mc, at, LD 8. 🅲 CH, TV, Dgs, CP
60, Ac, con 250, CF, 22 st. £ BB £13·75,
DB £20·35, 🄑, cc 1 3.
Ravenswood, PH, *z* (RI), *St John's Rd,
DG12 6AW.* ✆ (046 12) 2158. C. 🛏 8
bedrs, 2 ba. ✖ a l c. 🅲 CH, TV, CF, 2 st.
£ BB £10·50–£11, DB £20–£21, DT (b)
£15·50–£16·50, 🄑.

Rescue Service: M & M Services, Annan
Rd, Eastriggs. ✆ Eastriggs (046 14) 444.

ANSTRUTHER Fife. Map 37C
Pop 2,814. Largo 10, London 422,
Edinburgh 48, Glasgow 76, Kinross 32,
Kirkcaldy 22, Perth 38, St Andrews 9.
EC Wed. **Golf** Anstruther 9h. **See** The
Auld Kirk Manse (Melville's Watch
Tower), Chalmers House.
🛈 Scottish Fisheries Museum, St Ayles.
✆ Anstruther (0333) 310628.

★★★**Craw's Nest,** *Bankwell Rd, KY10
3DA.* ✆ (0333) 691. C. 🛏 31 bedrs, 31 bp,
TV. ✖ a l c, mc, at, LD 8.45. 🅲 N, CH, CP
150, Ac, sb, sol, con 300, CF, 0 st. £ BB
£21, DB £40–£44, WT £177–£190, DBB
£27–£29, 🄑 10%, Bk £3·50, L £5·50, D
£8·50, cc 1 2 3 5 6, Dep a.

🏩★★**Smugglers Inn,** *High St East, KY10
3DQ.* ✆ (0333) 310506. C. 🛏 9 bedrs, 1
bp, 5 bps, 3 sh, 2 ba, Dgs. ✖ a l c, mc, LD
9.30. 🅲 CH, TV, Dgs, CP 20, CF, 1 st. £ BB
£15–£17, DB £30–£34, 🄑, cc 1 2 3 5.

Rescue Service: W Band & Son, Crail Rd.
✆ (0333) 310502.

APPIN Strathclyde (Argyll). Map 35A
Pop 250. Connel 20, London 492,
Ballachulish 10, Crianlarich 44, Dalmally
37, Edinburgh 133, Fort William 40,
Glasgow 104, Inveraray 49, Oban 25.
EC Wed. **See** Stalker Castle, Culloden
Stone, Appin Pottery.

Rescue Service: Gunn's Garage, Tynribbie.
✆ (063 173) 279.

ARBROATH Tayside (Angus). Map 37B
Pop 24,093. Dundee 16, London 445,
Brechin 12, Edinburgh 71, Forfar 15,
Glasgow 95, Montrose 13.
EC Wed. **Golf** Arbroath 18h. **See** Abbey
ruins, St Vigean's Church and Museum,
Patrick Allan–Fraser Chapel, Water Tower
(view), Cliffs and Caves.
🛈 105 High St. ✆ Arbroath (0241) 72609.

★★**Seaforth,** *Dundee Rd, DD11 1QF.*
✆ (0241) 72232. C. 🛏 20 bedrs, 11 bp, 3
ba, ns, TV, Dgs. ✖ mc, at, LD 9. 🅲 CH, TV,
Dgs, CP 100, U 6, Ac, con 150, CF, 3 st.
£ BB £16·50–£23, DB £30–£34·50, WT
£140, DT £28, DBB £22–£32·50, WB, 🄑,
Bk £3·60, L £3·75, D £6·50, cc 1 2 3 5 6.
Kingsley House, G, *z* (RI), *29 Market
Gate, DD11 1AU.* ✆ (0241) 73933. C.
🛏 15 bedrs, 3 ba, TV, Dgs. 🅲 CH, TV, CF.
£ BB £7–£8, DB £13–£15, WT £50–£66,
DT £10·50, 🄑.

Rescue Service: Carlaw-Lamb's Ltd, 1
Burnside Dr. ✆ 72921.
Brothock Coachworks, 12 Convent St.
✆ (0271) 72532.

ARDEN Strathclyde (Dunbartonshire).
Map 35D
Glasgow 21, London 409, Arrochar 15,
Crianlarich 30, Dumbarton 7, Edinburgh
63, Stirling 33.

🏩★★★**Lomond Castle,** *Alexandria, G83
8RA.* ✆ (038 985) 681. C. 🛏 21 bedrs, 17
bp, 4 bps, TV, Dgs. ✖ a l c, mc, at, LD 9.30.
🅲 N, CH, CP 100, Ac, sp, tc, sb, sol, gym,
con 150, CF, 1 st. £ BB £35–£45, DB £45–
£50, DT £50–£60, DBB £44–£54, WB, 🄑,
Bk £4·50, L £6, D £9, cc 1 2 3 5 6.

ARDENTINNY Strathclyde (Argyll). Map
35C
Pop 100. Arrochar 32, London 455 (Fy
423), Dunoon 11, Edinburgh 109 (Fy 80),
Glasgow 67 (Fy 35), Inveraray 32.
Golf Blairmore 9h. **See** Loch Long, Argyll
National Park.

🏩★★**Ardentinny,** *PA23 8TR.*
✆ (036 981) 209. Open Mar–Oct. C. 🛏 11
bedrs, 6 bp, 5 bps, TV, Dgs. ✖ LD 8.15.
🅲 CH, TV, CP 30, pf, CF, 0 st. £ BB
£18·50–£19·50, DB £29·50–£34, WT
£182–£208, DT £27–£31. DBB £25·50–
£29·50, WB, 🄑, Bk £6, D £12·50,
cc 1 2 3 5, Dep a.

ARDEONAIG Central (Perthshire). Map
36A
Lochearnhead 14, London 441, Aberfeldy
16, Crianlarich 20, Edinburgh 77, Glasgow
61.
Golf Killin 18h.

★★**Ardeonaig,** ✆ Killin (056 72) 400.
Open Apr–Oct. RS Nov–Mar. C. 🛏 14
bedrs, 10 bp, 4 bps, Dgs. ✖ mc, at, LD
8.45. 🅲 CH, TV, CP 40, pf, con 28, CF, 4
BGf, 0 st, Dis. £ BB £17·50–£19, DB £35–
£38, DBB £28–£30, WB, 🄑, Bk £3·25, D
£10·75.

ARDGAY Highland (Ross & Cromarty).
Map 42F
Inverness 38, London 567, Bonar Bridge 1,
Dingwall 25, Edinburgh 167, Glasgow
178.
Golf Bonar Bridge 12h.

Rescue Service: R M Lang, T/As The
Garage. ✆ (086 32) 231 & (086 32) 258.

ARDLUI Strathclyde (Dunbartonshire).
Map 35D
Pop 32. Glasgow 42, London 429,
Arrochar 9½, Crianlarich 8½, Dunbarton 28,
Edinburgh 86.
Golf Helensburgh 18h, Killin 9h. **See** Rob
Roy's Cave, Pulpit Rock.

■★★**Ardlui,** *G83 7EB.* ↳ Inveroglas
(030 14) 243. C. ⇥ 11 bedrs, 2 bp, 3 ba,
TV, Dgs. ✗ a l c, mc, at, LD 8.30. 🅿 CH, TV,
Dgs, CP 60, pf, CF, 1 st. £ BB £15.52–
£17.70, DB £26.45–£34.15, WB, ②, Bk
£3.75, L £5.50, D £8, cc 2 3.

ARDVASAR Highland (Isle of Skye).
Map 38D
Armadale (Fy to Mallaig) ½, London (Fy)
533, Edinburgh (Fy) 176, Glasgow (Fy)
146, Kyleakin (Fy to Kyle of Lochalsh) 22.

★★**Ardvasar,** *IV48 8RS.* ↳ (047 14) 223.
Not open Xmas & 1 & 2 Jan. ⇥ 12 bedrs, 4
bp, 4 ba. ✗ a l c, mc, LD 8.45. 🅿 CH, CP
30, CF, 1 st. £ BB £12–£17, DB £20–£30,
DBB £20–£23, ①, Bk £3.50, L £2.50, D
£8.50, cc 3, Dep a.

ARINAGOUR Isle of Coll, Strathclyde
(Argyll). Map 38E (Ferry to Oban),
Dalmally 22, London 479, Ballachulish 37,
Edinburgh 121, Fort William 48, Glasgow
90, Inveraray 38, Lochgilphead 36.
EC Thur.

★**Coll,** *Isle of Coll, PA78 6SZ.* ↳ (087 93)
334. C. ⇥ 9 bedrs, 2 ba, TV, Dgs. ✗ mc, at,
LD 9. 🅿 ch, TV, Dgs, CP 30, sb, sol, con 12,
CF, 2 st. £ BB £14–£17.50, DB £24–£30,
WT £200–£225, DT £29.25–£32.25, DBB
£21.25–£24.25, ②, Bk £4, L £8, D £9.25,
cc 1 5 6.
Tigh-na-Mara, G, x (RI), *PA78 6SY.*
↳ (087 93) 354. Open Mar–Oct. C. ⇥ 8
bedrs, 3 ba, Dgs. ✗ a l c. 🅿 CH, TV, CP 10.
£ BB £8.50–£9, DB £17–£18, WT (b)
£105–£112, DT (b) £16–£17, ①, Bk £2.50,
L £2.80, D £7.50.

ARISAIG Highland (Inverness-shire).
Map 38F
Fort William 35, London 524, Edinburgh
167, Glasgow 137, Mallaig 9.
Golf Fort William 18h. **See** "Bonnie Prince
Charlie" Country.

■**★★★★Arisaig House** (R), *Beasdale,*
PH39 4NR. ↳ (068 75) 622. Open Apr–
Oct. C 10. ⇥ 14 bedrs, 15 bp, 2 ba, TV.
✗ mc, at, LD 8.30. 🅿 CH, CP 15, 0 st. £ BB
£26.50, DB £55, DBB £45, ②, D £17.50,
cc 1 2 3.

ARMADALE Lothian (Midlothian), Map
36F
Pop 9,530. Biggar 23, London 386,
Bathgate 2½, Edinburgh 21, Glasgow 23,
Lanark 17, Whitburn 2½.
EC Wed. **MD** Sat. **Golf** Bathgate 18h.

Rescue Service: H Mackenzie, Mayfield
Garage, 42a Mayfield Drive. ↳ (0501)
31469.

ARNOL Isle of Lewis, Western Isles. Map
Area 45A
Stornoway 15 (Fy to Ullapool), London
599, Edinburgh 224, Glasgow 228.

Rescue Service: Arnol Motors (K
Maclennan), The Garage, Arnol.
↳ Shawbost (085 171) 248.

ARROCHAR Strathclyde
(Dunbartonshire). Map 35D

Pop 989 (inc Tarbet). Glasgow 36,
London 423, Crianlarich 18, Dumbarton
23, Dunoon 39, Edinburgh 77, Inveraray
22, Stirling 51.
EC Wed (win). **Golf** Helensburgh 18h.
See "Rest and Be Thankful" Hill, Glen
Croe, Loch Lomond, Loch Sloy hydro-
electric works to the N, Ben Arthur 2,891
ft to NW.

Rescue Service: Mactavish's Garage.
↳ (030 12) 244.

AUCHENCAIRN Dumfries & Galloway
(Kirkcudbrightshire). Map 29E
Pop 170. Dalbeattie 7, London 348,
Edinburgh 91, Dumfries 21, Gatehouse of
Fleet 19, Glasgow 90, New Galloway 22.
EC Wed. **Golf** Kirkcudbright 18h. **See**
Orchardton Tower, Hestan Island
Smugglers Cave.

■**★★★Balcary Bay,** *DG7 1QZ.*
↳ (055 664) 217. C. ⇥ 11 bedrs, 4 bp, 1
bps, 7 ba, TV, Dgs. ✗ a l c, mc, at, LD 9.30.
🅿 CH, TV, Dgs, CP 50, con 20, CF, 0 st.
£ BB £17–£22, DB £24–£44, WB, ①, Bk
£3.50, L £5, D £7.50, cc 1 2 3 4 5 6.▲

AUCHTERARDER Tayside (Perthshire).
Map 36D
Pop 3,000. Dunfermline 23, London 414,
Crieff 9, Edinburgh 39, Glasgow 45,
Kincardine 24, Kinross 19, Perth 14,
Stirling 20.
EC Wed. **Golf** Auchterarder 18h,
Gleneagles Hotel Courses: King's 18h,
Queen's 18h, Prince's 18h, Glendevon 18h.
See Aircraft Museum.
🅸 Crown Wynd, High St. ↳ Auchterarder
(076 46) 3450.

★★★★★**Gleneagles,** *PH3 1NF.*
↳ (076 46) 2231. C. ⇥ 254 bedrs, 254 bp,
TV, Dgs. ✗ a l c, mc, at, LD 9. 🅿 Lt, N, CH, CP,
Ac, sp, gc, tc, pf, sc, sb, sol, gym, con 400,
CF, 1 BGf, 0 st, Dis. £ BB £52.25–£67.25,
DB £89.50–£114.50, WB, ①, Bk £7.25, L
£13.50, D £17.50, cc 1 2 3 4 5 6, Dep.

AULTBEA Highland (Ross & Cromarty).
Map 42E
Pop 150. Dundonnell 20, London 602,
Beauly 68, Edinburgh 228, Gairloch 12,
Glasgow 238, Ullapool 50.
EC Wed. **Golf** Gairloch 9h. **See** Inverewe
Gardens 4 m S, viewpoints at Tournaig
and Drumbreac.

■**★★Drumchork Lodge,** *IV22 2HU.*
↳ (044 582) 242. RS Nov–Feb. C. ⇥ 15
bedrs, 4 bp, 3 sh, 3 ba, Dgs. ✗ mc, at, LD 8.
🅿 ch, TV, Dgs, CP 50, Ac, sb, sol, CF. £ BB
£14.85–£19.60, DB £28.60–£36, DBB
£23.65–£27.40, ②, Bk £4, L £2, D £9,
cc 1 2 3 5.
★★**Aultbea,** *IV22 2HX.* ↳ (044 582) 201.
Open Apr–Oct. C. ⇥ 9 bedrs, 1 bp, 3 ba,
Dgs. ✗ mc, at, LD 8. 🅿 CH, TV, Dgs, CP 30,
CF, 0 st. £ BB fr £15, DB fr £30, DBB £23,
②, Bk £3, L £3.50, D £8, cc 1 3.

Rescue Service: A Forbes & Sons.
↳ (044 582) 200.

AVIEMORE Highland (Inverness-shire).
Map 40C
Pop 1,570. Kingussie 11, London 499,
Carrbridge 7, Edinburgh 124, Glasgow
135, Grantown-on-Spey 14.

EC Wed. **Golf** Boat of Garten 18h. **See**
Centre for ski-ing and exploration of the
Cairngorms, Ben Macdhui 4,296 ft, Rock

of Craigellachie, Loch-an-Eilean, 3¾ m S,
Wildlife Park 7 m, Larig Ghru Pass 7½ m SE.
🅸 Main Rd. ↳ Aviemore (0479) 810363.

★★★ **M Badenoch,** *Centre, PH22 1PH.*
↳ (0479) 810261. C. ⇥ 78 bedrs, 60 bp, 8
ba, TV, Dgs. ✗ mc, at, LD 9.30. 🅿 Lt, N,
CH, TV, Dgs, CP 100, Ac, sb, sol, gym, con
1500, CF, 0 st. £ BB £14.70–£28.70, DB
£24.60–£39.70, WT £150–£157.50, DT
£20.60–£28.70, DBB £16.10–£24, WB, ①,
Bk £3, L £4.50, D £8, cc 1 2 3 4 5 6, Dep b.
★★★**M Stakis Coylumbridge,** *PH22*
1QN. ↳ (0479) 810661. C. ⇥ 173 bedrs,
173 bp, TV, Dgs. ✗ a l c, mc, at. 🅿 N, CH,
Dgs, CP 200, Ac, sp, tc, sb, sol, gym, con
700, CF, 48 BGf, 1 st, Dis. £ WB, Bk £4.50,
L £4.50, D £8.50, cc 1 2 3 5 6, Dep b.
★★★**M Post House** (TH), *Centre, PH22*
1PJ. ↳ (0479) 810771. C. ⇥ 103 bedrs,
103 bp, TV, Dgs. ✗ a l c, mc, at, LD 9.30.
🅿 Lt, N, Dgs, CP 140, Ac, con 100, CF, 29
BGf, 1 st. £ BB £35.50, DB £54.50, WB, ①,
cc 1 2 3 4 5 6, Dep (Xmas).
■**★★Cairngorm,** *Grampian Rd, PH22*
1PE. ↳ (0479) 810233. C. ⇥ 23 bedrs, 13
bp, 5 bps, 3 ba, Dgs. ✗ a l c, mc, at, LD 9.
🅿 N, ch, TV, CP 25, U 3, Ac, con 50, CF, 0
st. £ BB £15.50–£17.50, DB £29–£33,
DBB £24–£26, WB, ①, Bk £4, D £8.50,
cc 1 2 3 4 5 6, Dep.
■**★★Lynwilg,** *PH22 1PZ.* ↳ (0479)
810207.

Rescue Service: Four Seasons Service
Station, 115 Grampian Rd. ↳ (0479)
810232.
Grants Service Station, Main St. ↳ (0479)
810205.

AYR Strathclyde (Ayrshire). Map 28B
See also PRESTWICK.
Pop 49,481. Dalmellington 14, London
381, Abington 45, Edinburgh 71, Girvan
21, Glasgow 33, Kilmarnock 12, Lanark
43, Largs 31, Thornhill 44.
EC Wed. **MD** Tue, Fri. **Golf** Ayr, Belleisle
and Seafield Municipal Courses 18h (2).
See Burns' Cottage, Monument, Statue
House and gardens (Alloway), The Twa
Brigs, Tam o' Shanter Inn (museum), Burns
Statue, Ayr Academy, Auld Kirk, Auld Brig,
St John's Church Tower, Wallace Tower,
Loudoun Hall, Birthplace (plaque) of
Macadam in Wellington Sq (road making
fame), Alloway Auld Kirk, RC Cathedral.
🅸 30 Miller Rd. ↳ Ayr (0292) 68077.

■**★★★★Belleisle House,** *Doonfoot, KA7*
4DU. ↳ (0292) 42331 C. ⇥ 16 bedrs, 14
bp, 2 bps, 1 ba, TV, Dgs. ✗ a l c, mc, at.
🅿 N, CH, Dgs, CP 50, gc, con, CF, 2 BGf.
£ BB £25–£27.50, DB £30.50–£37.50,
DBB £22.50–£32.50, ②, Bk £2.70, D £8.95,
cc 1 2 3 5.
★★★**Caledonian,** *Dalblair Rd, KA7 1UG.*
↳ (0292) 269331. C. ⇥ 110 bedrs, 118
bp, TV. ✗ a l c, mc, at, LD 10. 🅿 Lt, N, CH,
CP 50, Ac, con 600, CF, 1 st. £ BB £33.50,
DB £52, WB, ②, Bk £4, L £2.50, D £9,
cc 1 2 3 4 5 6.
★★★**Marine Court,** *12 Fairfield Rd, KA7*
2AS. ↳ (0292) 267461. C. ⇥ 28 bedrs, 28
bp, 3 ba, TV, Dgs. ✗ a l c, mc, at. 🅿 N, CH,
TV, Dgs, CP 100, Ac, sp, sb, sol, gym, con
350, CF, 13 BGf, 1 st, Dis. £ BB £32, DB
£44, WT £240, DT £39, DBB £35, WB, ②,
Bk £3.50, L £4.50, D £9, cc 1 2 3 5 6.
★★★**Pickwick,** *19 Racecourse Rd, KA7*
2TD. ↳ (0292) 260111. C. ⇥ 15 bedrs, 10
bp, 5 bps, 4 ba, TV. ✗ a l c, LD 9.30. 🅿 N,
CH, CP 100, con 30, CF, 3 st. £ BB £25, DB

£40, DBB £49–£52, ⓶, Bk £5, D £9, cc 3, Dep b.

★★★Savoy Park, *16 Racecourse Rd, KA7 2UT.* ✆ (0292) 266112. C. ✉ 17 bedrs, 14 bp, 3 bps, 2 ba, TV, Dgs. ✖ a l c, mc, at, LD 8.30. ⓓ N, CH, ns, CP 90, Ac, con 90, CF, 4 st. £ BB £22·50, DB £40, DBB £32·50, WB, ⓶, Bk £4·50, L £4·50, D £10, cc 1 2 3, Dep.

★★★Stakis Station, *Burns Statue Sq, KA7 4SF.* ✆ (0292) 263268. RS Oct–Mar. C. ✉ 74 bedrs, 74 bp, 4 ba, TV, Dgs. ✖ a l c, mc, at, LD 8.30. ⓓ Lt, N, CH, TV, CP 40, Ac, con 410, CF, 0 st. £ WB, Bk £3·50, L £5·50, D £7·50, cc 1 2 3 5 6.

■**★★Annfield,** *49 Maybole Rd, KA7 4SF.* ✆ (0292) 41986. RS Xmas and New Year. C. ✉ 9 bedrs, 1 bp, 2 ba, TV, Dgs. ✖ a l c, LD 8.45. ⓓ CH, TV, CP 50, Ac, CF, 5 st. £ BB £8·50–£10, DB £16–£24, ⓵, Bk £3·50, L £4, D £6·50, Dep.

■**★★Ayrshire and Galloway,** *1 Killoch Place, KA7 2AE.* ✆ (0292) 262626. RS Xmas and New Year. C. ✉ 25 bedrs, 8 bp, 5 ba, TV, Dgs. ✖ a l c, LD 8.45. ⓓ CH, TV, CP 20, Ac, CF, 1 st. £ BB £12–£20, DB £22–£30, ⓵, Bk £3·50, L £4, D £6·50, Dep.

★★Balgath, *8 Drumire Rd, Doonfoot, Alloway, KA7 4HR.* ✆ (0292) 42441. C. ✉ 15 bedrs, 4 bp, 7 bps, 2 ba, TV, Dgs. ✖ a l c, mc, at, LD 9.30. ⓓ CH, TV, Dgs, CP 100, Ac, CF, 3 st. £ BB £14–£18, DB £26–£32, DBB £21–£25, ⓶, Bk £3, L £4·60, D £9·50, cc 1 2 3 5, Dep.

■**★★Burns Monument,** *Monument Rd, Alloway, KA7 4PQ.* ✆ (0292) 42466. RS Xmas and New Year. C. ✉ 9 bedrs, 9 bp, 2 bps, 1 ba, Dgs. ✖ a l c, mc, LD 9.45. ⓓ CH, TV, CP 12, Ac, pf, con 180, CF, 2 st. £ BB £12–£18, DB £12–£14, DBB £7·50–£25·50, ⓶, Bk £4, L £3, D £7·50, Dep.

★★Chestnuts, *52 Racecourse Rd, KA7 2UZ.* ✆ (0292) 264393. C. ✉ 14 bedrs, 4 bp, 4 bps, 2 sh, 3 ba, TV, Dgs. ✖ mc, LD 9.45. ⓓ CH, TV, Dgs, CP 45, con 26, CF, 3 st. £ BB £13–£19, DB £26–£34, WT £120–£160, DBB £17·50–£23·50, WB, ⓶, Bk £4, D £6·95, cc 1 2 3 5 6.

★★Gartferry, *44 Racecourse Rd, KA7 2UY.* ✆ (0292) 262768. C. ✉ 13 bedrs, 2 bp, 5 bps, 1 ba, TV, Dgs. ✖ LD 10. ⓓ CH, TV, CP 100, Ac, con 200, CF, 6 BGf, 10 st. £ cc 1 2 3 5 6.

■**★★Monkwood,** *33 Carrick Rd, KA7 2RD.* ✆ (0292) 260952. C. ✉ 11 bedrs, 2 bp, 2 bps, 7 sh, 2 ba, TV, Dgs. ✖ a l c, mc, at, LD 9.30. ⓓ N, CH, TV, Dgs, CP 35, Ac, con 60, CF, 5 st. £ BB £12·50–£18, DB £20–£21, DBB £17·50–£22, WB, ⓵, Bk £2·50, L £2·40, D £6·40, Dep b.

★★Old Racecourse. *2 Victoria Park, KT7 1HT.* ✆ (0292) 262873. C. ✉ 10 bedrs, 3 ba, Dgs. ✖ mc, at, LD 9.30. ⓓ TV, CP 30, Ac, sol, CF, 2 st. £ BB £12–£14, DB £24–£28, WT £106–£120, DT £19–£21, DBB £16–£18, WB, ⓵, Bk £3, L £3, D £7·50, cc 1 2 3 5 6, Dep a.

Clifton, H, y (RI), *19 Miller Rd, KA7 2AX.* ✆ (0292) 264521. C. ✉ 11 bedrs, 5 bps, 2 ba, TV. ⓓ ch, TV, ns, CP 16, CF, 2 BGf, 3 st. £ BB £10–£14, DB £18–£24, WT £90–£109, DT £16–£20, ⓶, Bk £3, L £3·50, D £6·50, cc 2 3.

Windsor, PH, z (Unl), *6 Alloway Place, KA7 2AA.* ✆ (0292) 264689.

Specialist Body Repairer: Archd Jeffrey Ltd, 13 York St. ✆ (0292) 67142. *Repairer:* Appleyard of Ayrshire, 18 Holmston Rd. ✆ (0292) 266944.

BAILLIESTON Strathclyde (Lanarkshire). M. Area 48D M73 Motorway 1½, Hamilton 7, London 383, Edinburgh 40, Glasgow 5½, Motherwell 9, Stirling 23.

Rescue Service: Swinton Garage, 218 Swinton Rd. ✆ 041-771 4368.

BALLACHULISH Highland (Argyll). Map 39E *See also* DUROR. Pop 1,254. Crianlarich 39, London 475, Dalmally 38, Edinburgh 118, Fort William 14, Glasgow 85, Mallaig (Fy) 57, Oban 37. **EC** Wed. **Golf** Fort William 18h. ⓘ Interpretive Centre. ✆ Ballachulish (085 52) 296.

■**★★Ballachulish,** *PA34 4JY.* ✆ (085 52) 239. C. ✉ 36 bedrs, 18 bp, 9 bps, 7 ba, TV, Dgs. ✖ a l c, mc, at, LD 8.30. ⓓ N, CH, Dgs, CP 60, con 100, CF, 5 st. £ BB £11·50–£18·90, DB £28·50–£37·90, WB, ⓶, Bk £3·50, L £3·50, D £4, cc 1 2 3 4 5 6, Dep a.

★Loch Leven, *North Ballachulish, PH33 6SA.* ✆ Onich (085 53) 236. C. ✉ 10 bedrs, 3 ba, Dgs. ✖ mc, at, LD 8.30. ⓓ ch, TV, Dgs, CP 100, CF, 0 st. £ BB £10–£15, DB £20–£30, WT £124–£159, DT £19–£24, DBB £16–£21, WB, ⓶, Bk £2·50, D £6, cc 1 3, Dep a.

Lyn Leven, G, *West Laroch.* ✆ (085 52) 392.

Rescue Service: Ballachulish Hotel Garage. ✆ (085 52) 215. Chisholms of Ballachulish. ✆ (085 52) 431.

BALLATER Grampian (Aberdeenshire). Map 41 C Pop 1,100. Braemar 16, London 479, Aberdeen 41, Craigellachie 45, Edinburgh 104, Glasgow 120, Grantown-on-Spey 37, Huntly 40, Stonehaven 38. **EC** Thur. **Golf** Ballater 18h. **See** Falls of Muick, Lochnagar 3,786 ft, Loch Kinord 4 m NE, Balmoral Castle grounds and Crathie Church 8 m W, Highland Games 3rd Thur in Aug. ⓘ Station Sq. ✆ Ballater (0338) 55306.

♨**★★Darroch Learg** (R), *Braemar Rd, AB3 5UX.* ✆ (0338) 55443. Open Feb–Oct. C. ✉ 15 bedrs, 13 bp, 2 bps, 2 ba, TV, Dgs. ✖ mc, at, LD 8.30. ⓓ CH, TV, CP 25, con 40, 1 BGf, 2 st. £ BB £10·50–£17, DB £21–£34, WT £150–£189, DT £23–£29, DBB £17–£25, ⓵, Bk £4·50, L £3·50, D £8.▲

Deeside, H, x, *Braemar Rd, AB3 5RQ.* ✆ (0338) 55420. C. ✉ 5 bedrs, 1 bp, 2 ba, TV. ✖ a l c. ⓓ ch, TV, CP 15, CF, 2 st. £ BB £13·50–£15, DB £23–£26, WT (b) £126, DT (b) £20, ⓵, Bk £4, L £4, D £8·50, cc 3.

Moorside, G, x (RI), *Braemar Rd, AB3 5RL.* ✆ (0338) 55492. Open May–Oct. C. ✉ 8 bedrs, 1 bp, 3 bps, 2 ba, Dgs. ⓓ CH, TV, CP 10, CF, 3 st. £ BB £11–£13, DB £18–£20, WT (b) £84, DT (b) £13, ⓶.

Morvada, G, x (RI), *Braemar Rd, AB3 5RL.* ✆ (0338) 55501. Open Apr–Oct. C. ✉ 6 bedrs, 2 bps, 2 ba, Dgs. ⓓ CH, TV, CP 6, CF. £ DB £18–£22, ⓵.

Rescue Service: Riverside Garage, Tullick Rd. ✆ (0338) 55323.

BALLINLUIG Tayside (Perthshire). Map 36B

Pop 250. Perth 22, London 439, Aberfeldy 9, Blairgowrie 18, Crieff 28, Edinburgh 66, Glasgow 76, Pitlochry 4. **EC** Thur. **Golf** Pitlochry 18h.

■**★★Ballinluig Inn,** *PH9 0LG.* ✆ (079 682) 242.

BALLOCH Strathclyde (Dunbartonshire). Map 35D Pop 1,740. Glasgow 18, London 406, Arrochar 18, Crianlarich 33, Dumbarton 5, Edinburgh 60, Lochearnhead 41, Stirling 29. **EC** Wed. **Golf** Vale of Leven, Bonhill 18h. **See** Loch Lomond, Cameron Estate Gardens, Wildlife & Leisure Park. ⓘ Car Park. ✆ Alexandria (0389) 53533.

★★Balloch, *G83 8LQ.* ✆ (0389) 52579. C. ✉ 13 bedrs, 6 bp, 3 ba, Dgs. ✖ a l c, mc, at, LD 8. ⓓ CH, TV, CP 30, Ac, con 80, CF, 0 st. £ BB £16·50–£21·25, DB £26·67–£32·75, WB, ⓶, Bk £3, HT £3·40, cc 1 2 3 5.

BALMACARA Highland (Ross & Cromarty). Map 38D Pop 300. Invergarry 45, London 559, Achnasheen (Fy) 34, Edinburgh 193, Glasgow 172, Invermoriston 51, Kyle of Lochalsh 5½.

■**★★ Balmacara,** *IV40 8DH.* ✆ (059 986) 283. Open Mar–Nov. C. ✉ 30 bedrs, 25 bp, 5 bps, 3 ba, Dgs. ✖ mc, at, LD 8.45. ⓓ CH, TV, Dgs, CP 30, Ac, con 50, CF, 5 BGf, 0 st, Dis. £ BB £12·50–£19·50, DB £25–£32, WB, ⓵, Bk £3, L £3·50, D £8·75, cc 1 3, Dep a.

BANAVIE Highland (Inverness-shire). Map 39E. Pop 150. Fort William 3½, London 493, Edinburgh 136, Fort Angus 50, Glasgow 102, Mallaig 40, Newtonmore 44, Oban 50. **Golf** Fort William 18h. **See** Neptune's Staircase.

■**★★Moorings** (RI), *PH3 7LY.* ✆ (039 77) 550. Open Mar–Nov. C 11. ✉ 14 bedrs, 4 bp, 1 bps, 4 sh, 3 ba. ✖ a l c, mc, at, LD 8.30. ⓓ CH, TV, Dgs, CP 25, con 30, 1 BGf, 2 st. £ BB £12–£26, DB £24–£36, DBB £22–£36, ⓵, Bk £4, L £5·50, D £9·75, cc 3.

BANCHORY Grampian (Kincardineshire). Map 41C Pop 7,000. Fettercairn 17, London 480, Aberdeen 18, Braemar 40, Craigellachie 55, Edinburgh 105, Glasgow 124, Grantown-on-Spey 61, Huntly 42, Stonehaven 16. **EC** Thur. **Golf** Banchory 18h. **See** Bridge of Feugh, Crathes Castle 2 m E, Deeside Agricultural Society show and sports last Sat in July. ⓘ Dee Street Car Park. ✆ Banchory (033 02) 2000.

♨**★★★Banchory Lodge,** *Dee St, AB3 3HS.* ✆ (033 02) 2625. Closed Dec–Jan. C. ✉ 25 bedrs, 22 bp, 1 bps, 2 ba, TV, Dgs. ✖ mc, at, LD 9.15. ⓓ CH, TV, CP 50, sb, con 40, CF, 1 BGf, 3 st. £ BB £28·75–£34, DB £46–£57·50, WT £265·65–£305·90, DT £37·95–£43·70, DBB £33·35–£39·10, ⓵, Bk £4, L £4·95, D £10·95, cc 1 2 3 4 5 6, Dep b.

♨**★★★Raemoir,** *AB3 4ED.* ✆ (033 02) 2622. C. ✉ 18 bedrs, 14 bp, 2 ba, ns, TV, Dgs. ✖ mc, at, LD 9.15. ⓓ CH, TV, Dgs, ns, CP 200, U 3, G 7, con 60, CF, 3 BGf, 0 st,

Dis. **£** BB £25–£28, DB £45–£48, WT £217–£238, DT £31–£34, WB, ☑ 10%, Bk £5·25, D £12·50, cc 1 2 3 5 6.

■**★★★Tor-na-Coille,** *Inchmarlo Rd, AB3 4AB.* ✆ (033 02) 2242. Closed Xmas. C. ⊯ 25 bedrs, 15 bp, 10 bps, 2 ba, TV, Dgs. ✘ mc, at, LD 10. ⯁ Lt, ch, TV, CP 60, Ac, pf, sc, con 60, CF, 2 st. **£** BB £28, DB £40, WT £250, WB, ①, Bk £3·50, L £2·00, D £10, cc 1 2 3 4 5 6.

★★**Burnett Arms,** *Main St, AB3 3TD.* ✆ (033 02) 2545. C. ⊯ 17 bedrs, 4 bp, 6 bps, 1 sh, 2 ba, ns, Dgs. ✘ mc, at, LD 8.45. ⯁ CH, TV, Dgs, CP 40, Ac, con 100, CF, 1 st. **£** BB £18–£19, DB £28–£30, WT £151·25, DB £30·25, DBB £25·50–£26·50, WB, ①, Bk £3, L £4·75, D £7·50, cc 2 3 5.

Rescue Services: Cumming & Dempster, North Deeside Rd. ✆ (033 02) 2255.

BANFF Grampian (Banffshire). Map 41A Pop 4,234. Huntly 20, London 532, Aberdeen 46, Craigellachie 36, Edinburgh 157, Elgin 33, Fraserburgh 23, Glasgow 174, Peterhead 35.
EC Wed. **Golf** Duff House Royal 18h. **See** Biggar Fountain, Mercat Cross, Duff House, Town House with Steeple, Museum.
⊡ Collie Lodge. ✆ Banff (026 12) 2419.

■**★★★Banff Springs,** *Golden Knowes Rd, AB4 2JE.* ✆ (026 12) 2881. RS Xmas, New Year and Easter. C. ⊯ 30 bedrs, 25 bp, 5 bps, TV. ✘ mc, at, LD 9·30. ⯁ N, CH, CP 120, con, CF, 3 st. **£** WB, Bk £4, L £3·50, D £8·50, cc 1 2 3 5 6.

★★**County** (R), *High St, AB4 1AE.* ✆ (026 12) 5353. Open Feb–Dec & New Year, RS Xmas & New Year. C 10. ⊯ 6 bedrs, 6 bp, TV, Dgs. ✘ mc, at, LD 9.30. ⯁ CH, ns, CP 10, 5 st. **£** BB £28–£30, DB £44–£46, WT £238–£329, DT £38–£47, DBB £29–£44, ①, Bk £5·50, L £7·00, D £14·50, cc 1 3, Dep a.

★★**Fife Lodge,** *Sandyhill Rd, AB4 1BE.* ✆ (026 12) 2436. C. ⊯ 6 bedrs, 3 bp, 3 bps, TV, Dgs. ✘ a l c. ⯁ ch, Dgs, Ac, CF, 2 st. **£** BB £18–£22, DB £28–£32, DBB £25–£29, ②, Bk £3·50, L £4, D £7, cc 3.
Carmelite House, PH, z (R), *Low St, AB4 1AY.* ✆ (026 12) 2152. C. ⊯ 9 bedrs, 1 sh, 2 ba, Dgs. ⯁ ch, TV, CP 8, CF, 5 st. **£** BB £8·95,–£11·75, DB £17·90–£23·50, WT (b) £81–£104, DT (b) £12·90–£16·50, ①, Bk £2·75.

BANNOCKBURN Central (Stirlingshire). Map 36D.
M9 motorway 1½, Falkirk 8, London 402, Dunblane 6, Dunfermline 20, Edinburgh 33, Glasgow 24, Perth 35, Stirling 2.
See Battlefield (assoc Robert I).

Rescue Service: Stirlingshire Auto Services, Newmarket. ✆ (0786) 813433.

BARR Strathclyde (Ayrshire). Map 28D Pop 155. Pinwherry 7, London 394, Ayr 24, Dalmellington 21, Edinburgh 93, Gatehouse of Fleet 46, Girvan 8, Glasgow 52, Stranraer 31.
EC Wed. **Golf** Girvan Burgh 18h. **See** Church.

Rescue Service: Gunnings Motors (Barr) Ltd, Gladneuk Garage. ✆ (046 586) 271.

BARRHEAD Strathclyde (Renfrewshire). Maps 48F, 35F & 36E Pop 20,000. East Kilbride 10, London 393, Edinburgh 53, Glasgow 8, Irvine 18, Paisley 4.

EC Tue. **Golf** Fereneze 18h.

★★**Dalmeny Park,** *Lochlibo Rd, G78 1LE.* ✆ 041-881 9211. C. ⊯ 18 bedrs, 10 bps, 4 ba, TV, Dgs. ✘ a l c, mc, LD 9.30. ⯁ CH, CP 100, Ac, con 160, CF, 2 st. **£** cc 1 2 3 5.

Rescue Service: Carlibar Motors, 113a Carlibar Rd. ✆ 041-880 5280.

BATHGATE Lothian (West Lothian). Map 36E
Pop 14,388. Lanark 19, London 387, M8 Motorway 2½, Edinburgh 18, Glasgow 25, Kincardine 15, Peebles 38, Stirling 22.
EC Wed. **MD** Fri. **Golf** Bathgate 18h. **See** Highland Games (May), Beecraigs Country Park (Fish Farm).

★★★**Golden Circle,** *Blackburn Rd, EH48 2EL.* ✆ (0506) 53771. C. ⊯ 75 bedrs, 56 bp, 19 bps, 2 ba, TV, Dgs. ✘ a l c, mc, at, LD 9.30. ⯁ Lt, N, CH, Dgs, CP 250, Ac, con 200, CF, 20 BGf, 1 st, Dis. **£** BB £33, DB £44, WB, ①, Bk £5·50, L £4·95, D £7·95, cc 1 2 3 5 6, Dep b.

■**★★Dreadnought,** *17 Whitburn Rd, EH48 1HE.* ✆ (0506) 630791.

BEATTOCK Dumfries & Galloway (Dumfriesshire). Maps 29D and 30C
Carlisle 39, London 333, Abington 19, Brampton 44, Dumfries 19, Edinburgh 52, Glasgow 55, Hawick 45, Langholm 32, Peebles 36, Selkirk 36.
EC Wed. **Golf** Moffat 18h.

⬥★★**Beattock House,** *DG10 9QB.* ✆ (068 33) 403/2. C. ⊯ 7 bedrs, 2 bps, 2 ba, Dgs. ✘ a l c, mc, at, LD 9. ⯁ CH, TV, Dgs, CP 25, Ac, pf, sc, rf, con 20, CF, 8 st. **£** BB fr £14·50, DB fr £27·90, DT fr £25, DBB fr £22, ②, Bk £3·75, L £4·95, D £7·50, Dep a.

Rescue Service: Millars Garage, Main St. ✆ (068 33) 338.

BEAULY Highland (Inverness-shire). Maps 39B and 40A
Pop 3,650. Inverness 11, London 539, Achnasheen 31, Dingwall 8½, Edinburgh 164, Glasgow 162, Invermoriston 26, Ullapool 48.
EC Wed. **Golf** Muir of Ord 18h. **See** Priory remains (Valliscaulian Order).

■**★★Priory,** *The Square, IV4 7BX.* ✆ (0463) 782309. C. ⊯ 12 bedrs, 6 bp, 3 ba, TV. ✘ a l c, mc, at, LD 9. ⯁ CH, TV, Dgs, Ac, con 100, CF, 1 st. **£** BB £10–£17·75, DB £18–£28, WT £90–£130, DT £18·50–£24·50, DBB £15·50–£24·50, WB, ①, Bk £2·75, L £1·50, D £4·50, cc 1 2 3 5 6.
Heathmount, G, x (RI), *Station Rd, IV4 7EQ.* ✆ (0463) 782411. Closed Dec. C. ⊯ 5 bedrs, 2 ba, Dgs. ✘ CH, TV, Dgs, CP 5, CF, 2 st. **£** BB £7–£8, DB £14–£16, WT (b) **£** 77–£90, DT (b) £11–£13, ①.

BEESWING Dumfries and Galloway (Dumfriesshire). Map 29F
Pop 150. Dumfries 7, London 334, Edinburgh 78, Gatehouse of Fleet 26, New Galloway 21, Glasgow 80, Thornhill 14.
Golf Southerness 18h.

Garloff, F, y (Unl), *Lochanhead Rd, DG2 8JE.* ✆ Lochfoot (038 773) 225. C. ⊯ 6 bedrs, 2 ba, Dgs. ⯁ CH, TV, CP 6, CF, 3 st. **£** BB £7·48, DB £14·96, WT (b) £84, DT (b) £13·80, ①.

BELLSHILL Strathclyde (Lanarkshire). Map 48B

Pop 21,570. Abington 29, London 380, M 74 Motorway 1½, Edinburgh 35, Glasgow 9½, Kincardine 26, Lanark 16, Peebles 40, Stirling 23.
EC Wed. **Golf** Bellshill 18h. **See** Church.

Repairers: Gopal Motors (Bellshill), New Edinburgh Rd. ✆ (0698) 747995. Taggarts (Bellshill) Ltd, 5 North Rd. ✆ (0698) 748516.
Specialist Body Repairer: Taggarts (Bellshill) Ltd, 5 North Rd. ✆ (0698) 748516.
Rescue Service: Gopal Motors (Bellshill), New Edinburgh Rd. ✆ (0698) 747995. Robb & Allan Motors Ltd, Gasworks Rd. ✆ (0698) 747317.

BIGGAR Strathclyde (Lanarkshire). Map 30A
Pop 1,931. Abington 12, London 363, Ayr 53, Edinburgh 28, Glasgow 36, Haddington 40, Kincardine 37, Lanark 13, Peebles 17, Stirling 43.
EC Wed. **MD** Sat. **Golf** Biggar 18h. **See** Boghall Castle ruins, Old Church (1545), Cadger's Bridge, Gladstone Court Museum, Biggar Motte 12th cent.
⊡ Main St. ✆ Biggar (0899) 20348.

⬥★★**Hartree,** *ML12 6JJ.* ✆ (0899) 20215. C. ⊯ 32 bedrs, 8 bp, 1 sh, 5 ba, TV, Dgs. ✘ a l c, mc, at, LD 10. ⯁ CH, TV, Dgs, CP 60, Ac, pf, con 55, CF, 5 st. **£** BB £17–£18·50, DB £32–£34, WB, ②, Bk £3·75, L £4, D £10, cc 1 2 5 6.

⬥★★**Toftcombs,** *ML12 6QX.* ✆ (0899) 20142. C. ⊯ 8 bedrs, 2 ba, Dgs. ✘ a l c, mc, at, LD 9. ⯁ CH, TV, Dgs, CP 100, con 200, CF, 1 st. **£** BB £12·50, DB £25, WB £160, DT £23, DBB £18·50, WB, ①, Bk £4, L £4·70, D £7, cc 1 2 3 5 6.

Rescue Service: J & J Campsie Ltd, Station Garage. ✆ (0899) 20089. James Stephen & Sons, Central Garage. ✆ (0899) 20030.

BISHOPBRIGGS Strathclyde (Lanarkshire). Map 48C
Pop 24,000. Glasgow 3, London 380, Edinburgh 48, Kincardine 26, Stirling 24.
EC Wed. **Golf** Bishopbriggs 18h, Pittlehill Public Course 18h. **See** Antonine's Wall, Castle Hall (site of Roman Fort), Cadder Parish Church.

Repairer: Ashfield For Ford, 27 Colston Rd. ✆ 041-772 6161.

BLACKBURN Lothian (West Lothian). Map 36F
Pop 5,768. Lanark 17, London 385, Abington 30, Edinburgh 18, Glasgow 26, Kincardine 16, Peebles 30.
EC Wed. **Golf** Bathgate 18h.

Rescue Service: Ian Young Coachworks, Toll Garage, Whitburn Rd. ✆ Bathgate (0506) 56843.

BLACKFORD Tayside (Perthshire). Map 36D
Pop 600. Dunblane 9½, London 411, Crieff 12, Dunfermline 23, Edinburgh 39, Glasgow 41, Kincardine 23, Kinross 18, Perth 19, Stirling 16.
EC Wed. **Golf** Gleneagles Hotel courses 18h (2) and 9h. **See** Tullibardine Castle.

★**Blackford,** *Moray St, PH4 1QF.* ✆ (076 482) 246. C. ⊯ 5 bedrs, 2 bp, 3 ba, TV. ✘ a l c, mc, LD 9·45. ⯁ CH, TV, Dgs,

1 st. **£** BB £12–£13, DB £22·50–£25, ①, Bk £3, L £4·50, D £5.

BLAIR ATHOLL Tayside (Perthshire). Map 40E
Pop 300. Killiecrankie 3, London 450, Dalwhinnie 24, Edinburgh 75, Glasgow 87, Pitlochry 6½.
EC Thur. **Golf** Blair Atholl 9h. **See** Blair Castle, Falls of Garry (salmon leap) and Bruar, Pass of Killiecrankie, St Bride's Church (grave of 'Bonnie Dundee'), Old Blair 1 m N.

Rescue Service: Blair Atholl Garage.
☎ (079 681) 221.

BLAIRGOWRIE Tayside (Perthshire). Map 36B
Pop 5,760. Perth 15, London 431, Aberfeldy 29, Braemar 34, Brechin 29, Dundee 18, Edinburgh 56, Forfar 20, Glasgow 72, Pitlochry 23.
EC Thur. **Golf** Rosemount 18h (2) & 9h.
See Ardblair Castle, Clunie Castle on island in Clunie Loch (not open to public) Newton Castle, Craighall Mansion, Fish Pass near Bridge (Donald Cargill's Leap ½ m above bridge), Beech Hedge of Meikleour (approx 85 ft high), 4 m S.
ⅰ Wellmeadow. **☎** Blairgowrie (0250) 2960.

⬥★★Altamount House (R), *Coupar Angus Rd, PH10 6JN.* **☎** (0250) 3512.
■★★Angus, *Wellmeadow, PH10 6NH.*
☎ (0250) 2838.
Glenshieling, G, y (RI) *Hatton Rd, PH10 7HZ.* **☎** (0250) 4605. C. **⊷** 6 bedrs, 2 ba.
⬚ CH, TV, CP 18, CF, 1 st. **£** BB £8–£9, DB £16–£18, WT £86–£95, DT £13–£14, ①.

BLANTYRE Strathclyde (Lanarkshire). Map 48D
Pop 19,875. M 74 Motorway 2½, Hamilton 2½, London 379, Abington 29, Dalmellington 46, Edinburgh 38, Glasgow 8½, Kilmarnock 21, Kincardine 29, Lanark 16, Largs 37, Peebles 42, Stirling 27.
EC Wed. **Golf** Strathclyde 9h. **See** Birthplace of David Livingstone 1813, adjacent cottage and houses restored as national memorial and museum, Monument to Mining disaster 1877. Hamilton Country Park nearby.

Rescue Service: J Mackie Ltd, 42 Main St, High Blantyre. **☎** (0698) 822166.

BOAT OF GARTEN Highland (Inverness-shire). Map 40D
Pop 350. Aviemore 6, London 504, Carrbridge 4½, Edinburgh 129, Glasgow 141, Grantown-on-Spey 9, Kingussie 18.
EC Thur. **Golf** Boat of Garten 18h. **See** Loch Garten (home of the Osprey).

★★★The Boat, *PH24 3BH.* **☎** (047 983) 258. Open Dec–Oct. RS Nov. C. **⊷** 36 bedrs, 22 bp, 9 bps, 3 ba, TV, Dgs. **✗** mc, at, LD 9. **⬚** CH, TV, CP 40, Ac, CF, 3 st. **£** BB £17·50–£22, DB £35–£44, WT £175–£189, BT £29–£31, DBB £24·50–£28, WB, ①, Bk £4, L £5, D £10, cc 1 2 3 5.
■★★Craigard, *Kinchurdy Rd, PH24 3BP.* **☎** (047 983) 206. C. **⊷** 20 bedrs, 7 bp, 1 bps, 4 ba. **✗** mc, LD 8. **⬚** ch, TV, Dgs, CP 30, U 4, con 50, CF, 1 st. **£** BB £14–£15, DB £28–£33, DBB £22·50–£23·50, ②, Bk £3·75, L £4, D £8, cc 1 2 3 5 6.
Granlea, G, y, (Unl), *Deshar Rd, PH24 3BN.* **☎** (047 983) 601. Open Jan–Oct, Dec 26–31. C. **⊷** 5 bedrs, 1 ba, Dgs. **⬚** CH, TV, Dgs, CP 6, CF, 1 BGf, 3 st. **£** BB

£7–£8, DB £14–£16, WT (b) £75–£80, DT (b) £11–£12, ①.
Moorfield House, PH, x (RI), *Deshar Rd, PH24 3BN.* **☎** (047 983) 646. Open Jan–Oct & Xmas. C. **⊷** 6 bedrs, 1 sh, 1 ba, Dgs. **⬚** CH, TV, ns, CP 12, CF, 2 st. **£** BB £9–£10, DB £18–£20, WT (b) £95–£102, DT (b) £14·50–£15·50, ②, D £6·50.

BONAR BRIDGE Highland (Sutherland). Map 43E
Pop 600. Alness 18, London 566, Edinburgh 191, Glasgow 198, Helmsdale 38, Lairg 10, Ullapool 47.
EC Wed. **Golf** Bonar Bridge and Ardgay 12h. **See** Stone Age Burial Cairns.
ⅰ **☎** Ardgay (086 32) 333.

■★★Bridge, *IV24 3EB.* **☎** (086 32) 204. C. **⊷** 16 bedrs, 5 bp, 5 bps, 5 ba, TV, Dgs. **✗** a l c, mc, at, LD 9. **⬚** ch, CP 20, Ac, con 40, CF, 0 st. **£** BB £16·50–£21·50, DB £29–£38, WT £165, DT £28, DBB £25–£27·50, WB, ②, Bk £3, D £7·50, cc 1 2 3 5 6.

BO'NESS Central (West Lothian). Map 36F
Pop 14,641. Abington 43, London 394, Dunfermline 17, Edinburgh 19, Glasgow 13, Kincardine 11, Kirkcaldy 25, Stirling 18.
EC Wed. **Golf** West Lothian 18h. **See** Kinneil House, Railway Museum.

Rescue Service: Douglas Haston & Son Ltd, 20 Corbiehall. **☎** (0506) 822357.

BONNYBRIDGE Central (Stirlingshire). Map 48A
Pop 5,390. Cumbernauld 5, London 396, Edinburgh 29, Glasgow 11, Kincardine 11, Lanark 28, Stirling 10.
EC Wed. **Golf** Bonnybridge 9h. **See** Roman Trail & Fort.

Rescue Service: Mill Garage, 19 Bridge St. **☎** (032 481) 2539.

BORGUE Dumfries & Galloway (Kirkcudbrightshire). Map 29E
Kirkcudbright 6, London 360, Dumfries 31, Edinburgh 103, Glasgow 94, New Galloway 24.
Golf Kirkcudbright 18h.

⬥★★Senwick House, *Brighouse Bay, DG6 4TP.* **☎** (055 77) 236. C. **⊷** 9 bedrs, 4 bp, 1 bps, 4 sh, 2 ba, TV, Dgs. **✗** mc, at, LD 9. **⬚** CH, TV, Dgs, CP 25, tc, CF, 2 st. **£** BB £13·50–£16·50, DB £27–£33, DT £21·50–£23, DBB £23–£24·50, WB, ②, Bk £2·50, D £8, cc 5, Dep a.

BOTHWELL Strathclyde (Lanarkshire). Map 36E
Pop 5,713. M74 Motorway ½, Hamilton 2, London 380, East Kilbride 6½, Edinburgh 35, Glasgow 10.
MD Wed. **Golf** Bothwell Castle 18h. **See** 14th cent Church & Castle.

★★Silvertrees, *Silverwells Cres, G71 8DP.* **☎** (0698) 852311. C. **⊷** 24 bedrs, 24 bp, annexe 17, 17 bp, TV, Dgs. **✗** a l c, mc, LD 9. **⬚** CH, TV, Dgs, CP 100, U 3, con 200, CF, 6 BGf, 4 st. **£** BB £32, DB £38, WT £322, DT £46, DBB £39·50, ②, Bk £4·50, L £6·50, D £7·50, cc 1 2 3 5 6, Dep b.

BOWMORE Isle of Islay, Strathclyde (Argyll). Map 34E
Port Askaig 11, (Steamer Service to Loch Tarbert), London 491, Edinburgh 144, Glasgow 103.
ⅰ **☎** Bowmore (049 681) 254.

■★★Lochside, *Shore St, PA43 7LB.* **☎** (049 681) 244. C. **⊷** 7 bedrs, 2 bp, 5 bps, 2 ba, TV, Dgs. **✗** a l c, mc, at, LD 7.30. **⬚** CH, Dgs, Ac, CF, 0 st. **£** BB £19–£23, DB £36–£42, DBB £26–£30, ①, Bk £3, L £3, D £7, cc 1 2 3 6.

BRAEMAR Grampian (Aberdeenshire). Map 40F
Pop 400. Perth 47, London 463, Aberdeen 58, Blairgowrie 34, Craigellachie 55, Edinburgh 88, Glasgow 104, Grantown-on-Spey 46, Huntley 57, Pitlochry 41, Stonehaven 56.
EC Thur. **Golf** Braemar 18h. **See** Mountain chairlift at Devil's Elbow, Castle, Mountains and Falls, Linn of Dee, Royal Braemar Gathering 1st Sat in Sept, Balmoral Castle grounds 7 m NE, Crathie Church 7 m ENE, Braemar Castle.
ⅰ **☎** Braemar (033 83) 600.

★★★Invercauld Arms, *AB3 5YR.* **☎** (033 83) 605.
Braemar Lodge, PH, y (RI) *Glenshee Rd, AB3 5YQ.* **☎** (033 83) 617.
Callater Lodge, PH, x (RI), *9 Glenshee Rd, AB3 5YQ.* **☎** (033 83) 275. Closed mid Oct–Boxing Day. C. **⊷** 9 bedrs, 3 ba, Dgs. **⬚** CH, TV, Dgs, CP 20, CF, 1 BGf, 3 st. **£** BB £11·00, DB £22·20, WT (b) £124·50, DT (b) £18·60, ①, D £7.50.

Repairer: Grant & Co, Castleton Garage.
☎ (033 83) 210.

BRECHIN Tayside (Angus). Map 41E
Pop 7,674. Forfar 11, London 453, Blairgowrie 29, Edinburgh 79, Glasgow 98, Montrose 8½, Stonehaven 25.
EC Wed. **Golf** Brechin 18h. **See** Ancient Cathedral, 10th–11th cent Round Tower, 13th cent Maison Dieu Chapel ruins, Edzell Castle and Gardens 5½ m N. Water mill.

Repairer: A Simpson & Son (Motors) Ltd, Clerk St. **☎** (035 62) 2146.

BRIDGE OF ALLAN Central (Stirlingshire). Map 36D
Pop 4,314. M9 Motorway 2, Stirling 3, London 398, Crieff 19, Dunfermline 21, Edinburgh 37, Glasgow 29, Kincardine 12, Kinross 22, Lochearnhead 26, Perth 31, St Andrews 50.
EC Wed. **Golf** Bridge of Allan 9h. **See** Wallace Monument.

■★★★Royal, *Henderson St, FK9 4HL.* **☎** (0786) 832284. C. **⊷** 34 bedrs, 17 bp, 6 ba, TV, Dgs. **✗** mc, at, LD 9. **⬚** Lt, N, CH, CP 60, Ac, con 30, CF, 7 st. **£** BB £16·50–£28·50, DB £29–£44, WB, ①, Bk £4·25, L £1, D £8·50, cc 1 2 3 5, Dep b.

BRIDGE OF CALLY Tayside (Perthshire). Map 36B
Pop 202. Blairgowrie 5½, London 437, Braemar 29, Edinburgh 62, Glasgow 77, Pitlochry 18.
EC Thur. **Golf** Blairgowrie 18h (2) & 9h.

★★Bridge of Cally, *PH10 7JJ.* **☎** (025 086) 231. C. **⊷** 9 bedrs, 3 bp, 3 bps, 2 ba, Dgs. **✗** mc, at. **⬚** CH, TV, CP 50, pf, CF, 0 st. **£** BB £15–£16·50, DB £25–£29, WT £160–£170, DT £24–£25·50, DBB £21·50–£23·50, WB, ①, Bk £2·75, L £3·05, D £9·45, cc 1 3 5.

BRIDGE OF EARN Tayside (Perthshire). Map 36D
Pop 1,753. London 412, M 90 (Int 9) Motorway ½, Edinburgh 38, Glasgow 56,

Kincardine 30, Kinross 13, Perth 4, St Andrews 28, Stirling 34.
EC Wed. **See** Elcho Castle, Pitkeathly Wells.

★★Moncreiffe Arms, *Main St, PH2 9PJ.*
((073 881) 2931.

BROADFORD Isle of Skye, Highland (Inverness-shire). Map 38D.
Pop 800. Armadale (Fy to Mallaig) 16, London (Fy) 549, Dunvegan 42, Edinburgh (Fy) 192, Glasgow (Fy) 162, Kyleakin (Fy to Kyle of Lochalsh) 8, Portree 28.
Golf Sconser 9h. **See** Ben na Caillich (2,403 ft) 2½ m W.
🛈 (Broadford (047 12) 361.

◼★★**Broadford,** *IV49 9AB.* ((047 12) 204. Open Apr–Oct. C. ⇔ 20 bedrs, 3 bp, 6 bps, Dgs. ✕ mc, at, LD 9. 🖿 ch, TV, CP 30, Ac, pf, con, CF, 0 st. **£** BB £17·50–£22·50, DB £33–£39, WB, 🛈, cc 1 3.

BRODICK Isle of Arran, Strathclyde (Bute). Map 28B
Pop 816. London (Fy to Ardrossan) 398, Ayr 18, Edinburgh 74, Glasgow 29, Kilmarnock 14, Largs 11, Paisley 22.
EC Wed. **MD** Thur. **Golf** Brodick 18h. **See** Brodick Castle 1 m N, Goatfell Mt 2866 ft, Nature Centre, Museum.
🛈 The Pier. (Brodick (0770) 2140.

◼Ap. Glenartney (RI), *KA27 8BX.*
((0770) 2220.

BRORA Highland (Sutherland). Map 43C
Pop 1,800. Golspie 5, London 592, Bona Bridge 27, Edinburgh 217, Glasgow 224, Helmsdale 11, Lairg 24.
EC Wed. **Golf** Brora 18h. **See** Wool Mills.

★★Royal Marine, *KW9 6QS.* ((0408) 21252. Closed 1st week Jan. RS Nov–Mar & Easter. C. ⇔ 11 bedrs, 4 bps, 5 ba, Dgs. ✕ mc, at, LD 7.45. 🖿 CH, TV, Dgs, CP 40, U 8, Ac, gc, con 20, CF. **£** BB £12–£16·50, DB £20–£28, DBB £19·50–£24, WB, ②, Bk £3, L £2, D £7·50, cc 1 5, Dep a.

Rescue Service: Rapsons Garage, Victoria Rd. ((040 82) 245.

BROUGHTON Borders (Peebles-shire). Map 30A
Pop 300. Tweedsmuir 8, London 358, Abington 17, Ayr 58, Beattock 25, Edinburgh 27, Glasgow 40, Lanark 18, Haddington 38, Kincardine 42, Peebles 12, Stirling 49.
Golf West Linton 18h. **See** Ruined Church, Churchyard.

★★Green Mantle, *ML12 6HQ.*
((089 94) 302. Closed Jan 10–Feb 21. ⇔ 6 bedrs, 1 bp, 2 bps, 3 ba, TV, Dgs. ✕ a l c, mc, at, LD 9. 🖿 CH, TV, Dgs, CP 120, Ac, CF, 2 st. **£** BB £20–£24, DB £25–£35, WB, 🛈, Bk £3, L £3·50, D £8·95, cc 1 2 3 5.

BRUICHLADDICH Isle of Islay, Strathclyde (Argyll). Map 34E
Port Askaig 13 (Steamer Service to Loch Tarbert), London 494, Edinburgh 148, Glasgow 106.

Bruichladdich, H, xy, *PA49 7UN.* (Port Charlotte (049 685) 305. C. ⇔ 6 bedrs, 2 ba, Dgs. 🖿 CH, TV, Dgs, CP, 2 st. **£** BB £11–£15, DB £20–£24, WT (b) £115, DT (b) £18·50–£19·50, ②, Bk £3, D £8·50.

Rescue Service: Bruichladdich Engineering, Bruichladdich Pier. (Port Charlotte (049 685) 291.

BUCKIE Grampian (Banffshire). Map 41A
Pop 7,950. Keith 12, London 534, Banff 19, Craigellachie 18, Edinburgh 159, Elgin 16, Glasgow 176, Huntly 22.
EC Wed. **Golf** Strathlene 18h. **See** Church.

★★Cluny, *2 High St, AB5 1AL.* ((0542) 32922.
★★St Andrews, *St Andrews Sq, AB5 1BT.* ((0542) 31227. RS winter. C. ⇔ 15 bedrs, 3 bp, 5 ba, TV, Dgs. ✕ mc, at, LD 8. 🖿 CH, TV, Dgs, G 9, Ac, con 280, CF 1 st. **£** BB £14–£16·50, DB £22–£25, WT £146, DT £24·35, DBB £21·50–£24, WB, 🛈, Bk £2, L £3·15, D £7·50, cc 1 3 6.

CALLANDER Central (Perthshire). Map 36C
Pop 1,768. M9 Motorway 11, Doune 7½, London 413, Arrochar 46, Crieff 28, Dumbarton 32, Dunfermline 34, Edinburgh 50, Glasgow 33, Kincardine 26, Kinross 36, Lochearnhead 13, Perth 34, St Andrews 64, Stirling 16.
EC Wed. **Golf** Callander Municipal 9h.
See The Trossachs, Falls of Bracklinn, Falls of Leny, Loch Vennachar, Brig o' Turk, St Kessog's Church, Ben Ledi (2,875 ft), War Memorial.
🛈 Leny Rd. (Callander (0877) 30342.

♨▲★★★★**Roman Camp,** *Main St, FK17 8BG.* ((0877) 30003. Open Feb–Nov. RS Feb, Mar, Oct, Nov. C. ⇔ 11 bedrs, 9 bp, 2 bps, 2 ba, TV, Dgs. ✕ LD 8.30. 🖿 CH, ns, CP 24, pf, con 12, CF, 4 BGf, 2 st. **£** BB £32–£48, DB £42–£60, WB, 🛈, Bk £4·50, L £9·50, D £15.
♨**Pinewood,** *Leny Rd, FK17 8AP.* ((0877) 30111. C. ⇔ 16 bedrs, 2 bp, 3 ba, Dgs. ✕ mc, at, LD 8.30. 🖿 CH, TV, Dgs, ns, CP 30, Ac, CF, 1 st. **£** BB £9–£10, DB £18–£20, WT £110–£119, DBB £15–£18, 🛈, Bk £3, L £0·70, D £6, cc 1 3, Dep a.
★**Waverley,** *Main St, FK17 8BD.*
((0877) 30245. C. ⇔ 10 bedrs, 4 ba, Dgs. ✕ a l c, mc, at, LD 9. 🖿 TV, Dgs, CF. **£** BB £8·50, DB £17, WT £115, DBB £16, WB, Bk £2·50, L £4, D £7, cc 1 3.
Annfield House, G, y (Unl), *18 North Church St, FK17 8EG.* ((0877) 30204. Open Mar–Oct. C. ⇔ 8 bedrs, 2 ba, Dgs. 🖿 ch, TV, Dgs, CP 8, 2 st. **£** BB £6·50, DB £13, WT (c) £45·50, 🛈.
Arden House, G, x (Unl), *Bracklinn Rd, FK17 8EQ.* ((0877) 30235. C. ⇔ 10 bedrs, 2 ba, Dgs. 🖿 CH, TV, ns, CP 12, CF. **£** BB £7·50–£8·50, DB £15–£17, WT (b) £80–£92, DT (b) £12·50–£14·50, ②, D £6.
Kinnell House, G, z (Unl), *24 Main St, FK17 8RR.* ((0877) 30181. C. ⇔ 8 bedrs, 2 ba, Dgs. 🖿 CH, TV, CP 7, CF. **£** BB £7–£8, DB £14–£16, WT £72–£79, DT £11–£12, ②.
Lubnaig, H, y (R), *Leny Feus, FK17 8AS.* ((0877) 30376.
Riverview House, PH, z (RI), *Leny Rd, FK17 8AL.* ((0877) 30635. Open Mar–Oct. C. ⇔ 6 bedrs, 2 bp, 1 ba, Dgs. 🖿 CH, TV, Dgs, CP 8, CF, 2 st. **£** BB £8–£9, DB £16–£18, WT (b) £91, DT (b) fr £13, 🛈.
Rock Villa, G, x (Unl), *1 Bracklinn Rd, FK17 8EH.* ((0877) 30331. Open Apr–Sep. C. ⇔ 7 bedrs, 1 ba. 🖿 CH, CP 7, CF. **£** BB £7–£7·50, DB £14–£15, WT £47–£50, ②.

CAMBUSLANG Strathclyde (Lanarkshire). Map 48D
Pop 14,607. London 382, Abington 32, Edinburgh 40, Glasgow 4, Kincardine 28, Kilmarnock 22, Lanark 20, Paisley 7½, Stirling 27.
EC Wed. **Golf** Cambuslang 9h.

Repairer: Andrew W L Munro, 260 Hamilton Rd. (041-641 3121.

CAMPBELTOWN Strathclyde (Argyll). Map 28A
Pop 5,500. Tarbert 26, London 517, Edinburgh 171, Glasgow 130, Lochgilphead 51.
EC Wed. **MD** Mon. **Golf** Machrihanish 18h. **See** Celtic Cross, Davaar Island (Crucifixion Cave picture), Lighthouse.
🛈 (Campbeltown (0586) 2056.

★★★Royal, *Main St, PA28 6AG.*
((0586) 52017. C. ⇔ 16 bedrs, 8 bp, 4 bps, 2 ba, TV, Dgs. ✕ mc, at, LD 8.30. 🖿 Lt, N, CH, TV, Dgs, ns, CP 8, G 4, Ac, con 120, CF, 0 st. **£** BB £13·50–£16, DB £25–£28·50, WT £113·50, DT £24·25, DBB £22·25–£24·75, WB, 🛈, Bk £3·50, L £3·50, D £6, cc 1 2 3 5 6.
◼★**Ardshiel,** *Kilkerran Rd, PA28 6JL.*
((0582) 52133. C. ⇔ 12 bedrs, 2 ba, TV, Dgs. ✕ mc, at, LD 9. 🖿 CH, TV, Dgs, CP 12, con 40, CF, 6 st. **£** BB £14, DB £27, WT £157, DBB £22, WB, ②, Bk £3·50, L £4·50, D £8, cc 1 2 3 5.

CANNICH Highland (Inverness-shire). Map 39A
Pop 400. Drumnadrochit 12, London 550, Beauly 17, Edinburgh 185, Glasgow 160, Invermoriston 25, Inverness 27.
Golf Muir of Ord 18h. **See** Glen Cannich, Glen Affric, Plodda Falls 5 m, Corrimony Chambered Cairn 5 m.

◼★★**Glen Affric,** *IV4 7LW.* ((045 65) 214. Open Apr–Oct. C. ⇔ 23 bedrs, 5 bp, 5 ba, Dgs. ✕ mc, at, LD 8. 🖿 CH, TV, Dgs, CP 40, Ac, pf, CF, 1 st. **£** BB £10–£11, DB £20–£22, WT £115, DT £18, DBB £16–£17, 🛈, Bk £3·50, D £5·50.

CANONBIE Dumfries & Galloway (Dumfriesshire). Map 30F
Pop 1,350. Carlisle 14, London 308, Edinburgh 76, Glasgow 88, Dumfries 30, Langholm 6.
Golf Carlisle 18h.

◼★★**Cross Keys,** *DG14 0SY.* ((054 15) 382.

CARFRAEMILL Borders (Berwickshire). Map 37E
Lauder 4, London 352, Berwick-upon-Tweed 35, Coldstream 25, Edinburgh 23, Glasgow 65, Haddington 17, Kelso 21.
Golf Lauder 9h.

◼★★**Carfraemill,** *by Lauder, TD2 6RA.*
((057 85) 200. C. ⇔ 9 bedrs, 2 bp, 2 bps, 4 ba, TV, Dgs. ✕ mc, at, LD 9. 🖿 CH, TV, Dgs, CP 60, Ac, con 18, CF, 3 st. **£** BB DBB £30–£36, 🛈, Bk £3·50, L £5·50, D £8, cc 3.

CARNOUSTIE Tayside (Angus). Map 37A
Pop 9,217. Dundee 11, London 439, Brechin 20, Edinburgh 65, Forfar 14, Glasgow 88, Montrose 21.
EC Tue. **Golf** Carnoustie 18h. **See** Ancient Camp, Buddon Ness with High and Low Lighthouse, Waterwheel Mill.

⑦ 24 High St. ✆ Carnoustie (0241) 52258.

★★**Earlston,** *24 Church St, DD7 6DE.*
✆ (0241) 52352.
★★**Glencoe,** *Links Parade, DD7 7JF.*
✆ (0241) 53273. RS New Year. C. ⊷ 10
bedrs, 2 bp, 5 bps, 3 ba, TV, Dgs. ✗ mc, at,
LD 9. ⊡ CH, TV, Dgs, CP 10, CF, 5 st. £ BB
£13·75, DB £29·70, DBB £19·80–£21, ⛶,
Bk £2·75, D £6·50, cc 1 2 3 5 6, Dep b.

CARRBRIDGE Highland (Inverness-
shire). Map 40C
Pop 400. Aviemore 7, London 506,
Edinburgh 131, Elgin 41, Glasgow 142,
Grantown-on-Spey 10, Inverness 24,
Kingussie 19.
EC Wed. **Golf** Carrbridge 9h. **See**
Landmark Auditorium, Nature Trail,
Sluggan Bridge 2¼ m.
⑦ ✆ Carrbridge (047 984) 630.

Dalrachney Lodge, PH, y (RI), *PH23
3AT.* ✆ (047 984) 252.
Old Manse, PH, xy (R), *Duthill, PH3
3ND.* ✆ (047 984) 278. Closed Nov. C.
⊷ 8 bedrs, 2 ba, Dgs. ⊡ CH, TV, CP 6, CF,
3 st. £ BB £8, DB £16, WT (b) £84, DT £13,
⛶, D £5·50.

Rescue Service: Macdonald, Ron M, Old
Bridge Garage. ✆ (047 984) 254.
Mackenzie, P, The Garage. ✆ (047 984)
213.

CASTLE DOUGLAS Dumfries &
Galloway (Kirkcudbrightshire). Map 29E
Pop 3,500. Crocketford 8½, London 344,
Dumfries 18, Edinburgh 89, Gatehouse-of-
Fleet 14, Glasgow 82, New Galloway 14.
EC Thur. **MD** Tue. **Golf** Castle Douglas
9h. **See** 13th cent Threave Castle ruins 1½
m W, Threave Estate Gardens 1½ m SW,
Carlingwark Loch (Wild Bird Sanctuary).
⑦ Markethill. ✆ Castle Douglas (0556)
2611.

◼★★★**Douglas Arms,** *King St, DG7
1DB.* ✆ (0556) 2232. C. ⊷ 26 bedrs, 12
bp, 5 ba, TV, Dgs. ✗ mc, at, LD 9. ⊡ CH,
TV, Dgs, ns, CP 29, Ac, con 50, CF, 1 st.
£ BB £13–£21, DB £22–£34, DBB £19–
£28·50, WB, ⛶, Bk £4·50, L £3·50, D £7·50,
cc 1 2 3 5.
◼⚑★★**Ernespie House,** *DG7 3JG.*
✆ (0556) 2188. C. ⊷ 16 bedrs, 4 bp, 1
bps, 1 sh, 4 ba, Dgs. ✗ a l c, mc, at, LD 9.
⊡ CH, TV, CP 30, Ac, con 250, CF. £ BB
£10–£14, DB £20–£27, WT £100–£108, DT
£18–£20·75, DBB £16–£21, WB, ⛶, Bk
£1·30, L £2·65, D £6, cc 1 2 3.
★★**Imperial,** *King St, DG7 1AA.* ✆ (0556)
2086. C. ⊷ 14 bedrs, 4 bps, 3 ba, ns, Dgs.
✗ a l c, mc, at, LD 7. ⊡ CH, TV, Dgs, CP 15,
G 9, Ac, con 45, CF, 1 st. £ BB £12·50–£18,
DB £24–£33, WT £127–£160, DT £20–
£25·50, WB, ⛶, Bk £2·75, L £2·15, HT
£3·50, cc 1 3 6.
★★**Kings Arms,** *St Andrews St, DG7
1EL.* ✆ (0556) 2626. RS New Year. C.
⊷ 15 bedrs, 4 bp, 2 bps, 3 ba, Dgs. ✗ mc,
LD 8. ⊡ TV, Dgs, CP 17. £ BB £14–£19,
DB £28–£38, WT £156–£167, DT £32·50–
£35, DBB £23·50–£29·50, WB, ⛶, Bk £4, L
£5, D £10·50, cc 1 2 3 5 6.
◼★**Merrick** (R), *King St, DG7 1DZ.*
✆ (0556) 2173. RS in winter. C. ⊷ 6
bedrs, 3 sh, 1 ba, Dgs. ✗ a l c, LD 8. ⊡ TV,
Dgs, CP 6, CF, 16 st. £ BB £8·50–£9·50,
DB £16–£18, WT £98–£110, DT £16–£17,
DBB £12·50–£17, ⛶, Bk £2·50, L £3·50, D
£4.

Rescue Service: J Haugh & Co, Crown
Garage, King St. ✆ (0556) 2038.

CASTLETOWN Highland (Caithness).
Map 43B
Pop 1,000. Thurso 5, London 658 (Fy
657), Edinburgh 283 (Fy 285), Glasgow
294 (Fy 289), Helmsdale 49, Wick 15.
EC Thur.

Rescue Service: D M Motors, Murrayfield.
✆ (084 782) 634.
Mackay's Garage, Main St. ✆ (084 782)
230.

CHAPELHALL Strathclyde
(Lanarkshire). Map 48B
Pop 4,619. Wishaw 6, London 382,
Edinburgh 32, Glasgow 13, Newmains 4½,
Stirling 20.
EC Wed. **Golf** Bellshill 18h.

Rescue Service: L F Hood Ltd, Bo-ness
Rd. ✆ Holytown (0698) 733388.

CHIRNSIDE Borders (Berwickshire).
Map 37F
Pop 1,240. Berwick-upon-Tweed 9,
London 343, Coldstream 12, Edinburgh
44, Galashiels 32, Glasgow 89,
Haddington 30, Kelso 17, Lauder 25,
Selkirk 35.
EC Wed. **Golf** Duns 9h. **See** Grave of
racing driver Jim Clark (Memorial Room
and Trophy Collection in Burgh Chambers,
Duns, 7 m).

◼⚑★★**Chirnside Countryhouse** (R).
TD11 3LD. ✆ (089 081) 219. Closed
Xmas. C. ⊷ 15 bedrs, 4 ba, Dgs. ✗ mc, at,
LD 8.45. ⊡ Lt, ch, TV, Dgs, CP 20, Ac, CF,
3 st. £ BB £13, DB £26, DBB £21·50, WB,
⛶, Bk £3, L £5, D £8·50, cc 1 2 3 5 6.

CLARKSTON Strathclyde
(Renfrewshire). Map 48D
Pop 18,200. East Kilbride 5, London 338,
Glasgow 5, Edinburgh 49, Paisley 7½,
Kilmarnock 17.
EC Tue. **Golf** Cathcart Castle 18h.

Rescue Service: King's Auto Point, 14
Busby Rd. ✆ 041-638 1136.
Strathclyde Road Rally Performance Ltd,
4 Strawhill Rd ✆ 041-644 4683.

CLELAND Strathclyde (Lanarkshire).
Map 48B
Pop 3,528. M74 Motorway 5, Wishaw 2½,
London 379, Ayr 43, Dunfermline 34,
Edinburgh 32, Glasgow 15, Kilmarnock
29, Kincardine 27, Kirkcaldy 43, Lanark
12, Peebles 36, Stirling 25.
EC Wed. **Golf** Wishaw 18h. **See** Castle.

Rescue Service: Bellside Service Station,
Carlisle Rd. ✆ Cleland (0698) 860451.

COATBRIDGE Strathclyde
(Lanarkshire). Map 48B
Pop 48,301. M73 Motorway 2½,
Motherwell 6, London 384, Edinburgh 35,
Glasgow 9½, Kincardine 22, Lanark 19,
Peebles 43, Stirling 20.
EC Wed. **Golf** Drumpellier 18h. **See**
Churches, War Memorial.

★★★**Coatbridge,** *Glasgow Rd, ML5 1EL.*
✆ (0236) 24392.
Rescue Service: Central Garage,
Summerlee Industrial Estate, West Canal
St. ✆ (0236) 21365.

COLDSTREAM Borders (Berwickshire).
Map 31A

Pop 1,429. Newcastle upon Tyne 60,
London 334, Alnwick 32, Berwick-upon-
Tweed 14, Edinburgh 48, Glasgow 91,
Haddington 34, Kelso 9, Lauder 22.
EC Thur. **Golf** Coldstream 9h. **See** Old
Marriage-house, Lennel Church ruins,
Museum, Wild Fowl Sanctuary on Hirsel
Estate. 18th cent Bridge, Coldstream
Guards Memorial, Flodden Field 4 m SE.
⑦ Henderson Park. ✆ Coldstream (0890)
2607.

Rescue Service: Coldstream Garage, High
St. ✆ (0890) 2159.

COMRIE Tayside (Perthshire). Map 36B
Pop 1,406. Dunblane 17, London 418,
Crieff 6½, Edinburgh 53, Glasgow 58,
Lochearnhead 12, Stirling 23.
EC Wed. **Golf** Comrie 9h. **See** Deil's
(Devil's) Cauldron on River Lednock,
Melville's Monument, Tartan's Museum.

★**Comrie,** *Drummond St, PH6 2DY.*
✆ (0764) 70239.

Rescue Service: Comrie Garage,
Drummond St. ✆ (0764) 70494.

CONDORRAT Strathclyde
(Dunbartonshire). Map 48A
Pop 7,700. Airdrie 5, London 389,
Arrochar 45, Dumbarton 24, Edinburgh 35,
Glasgow 10, Kincardine 17, Lanark 22,
Peebles 47, Stirling 15.
EC Wed. **Golf** Dullatur 18h.

Rescue Service: R J McKenna Motors,
143 Main St. ✆ Cumbernauld (023 67)
22447.

CONNEL Strathclyde (Argyll). Map 35A
Pop 250. Taynuilt 6½, London 473,
Ballachulish 33, Dalmally 19, Edinburgh
114, Fort William (Fy) 43, Glasgow 85,
Inveraray 33, Mallaig (Fy) 87, Oban 5.
EC Wed. **Golf** Glencruitten 18h. **See** Falls.
Bridge.

★★**Falls of Lora,** *PA37 1PB.* ✆ (063 171)
483. RS Xmas & New Year. C. ⊷ 30 bedrs,
23 bp, 3 ba, Dgs. ✗ a l c, mc, at, LD 9.30.
⊡ N, ch, TV, CP 40, con 30, CF, 4 BGf, 0 st,
Dis. £ BB £10·50–£28·50, DB £17–£59, DT
£18·50–£24·50, DBB £14·50–£35·50, ⛶,
Bk £4·25, L £6·50, D £8·25, cc 1 2 3 5 6.▲

CONNEL NORTH Strathclyde (Argyll).
Map 35A
Pop 320. Taynuilt 8, London 474,
Ballachulish 33, Dalmally 19, Edinburgh
115, Fort William (Fy) 43, Glasgow 86,
Inveraray 33, Mallaig (Fy) 87, Oban 5.
EC Wed. **Golf** Glencruitten 18h.

◼★★**Ossian's,** *PA37 1RB.* ✆ Connel
(063 171) 322. Open Apr–Sep. C. ⊷ 14
bedrs, 6 bp, 4 ba. ✗ at, LD 8.15. ⊡ Lt, N,
Dgs, ns, CP 50, pf, CF, 6 BGf, 0 st. £ BB
£13·59–£14·68, DB £27·18–£31·36, DBB
£18·76–£24·18, WB, ⛶, Bk £3, D £8·50,
cc 2 3, Dep a.

CONON BRIDGE Highland (Ross &
Cromarty). Maps 39B and 40A
Pop 600. Muir of Ord 3½, London 547 (Fy
540), Beauly 6½, Dingwall 2½, Edinburgh
171 (Fy 168), Glasgow 183 (Fy 172),
Inverness (Fy) 11.
EC Thur. **Golf** Muir of Ord 18h.

Rescue Service: Riverford Service Station.
✆ Dingwall (0349) 61361.

CONTIN Highland (Ross & Cromarty).
Map 39B

Pop 1,129. Muir of Ord 6, London 546,
Achnasheen 22, Beauly 9, Dingwall 7½,
Edinburgh 171, Glasgow 175, Ullapool 40.
EC Thur. **Golf** Strathpeffer 18h. **See** Falls
of Rogie, Shell Shop, Forest Walk, Church.

◼★**Achilty,** *IV14 9EG.* ⬗ Strathpeffer
(099 72) 355.
Coul House, H, xy, *IV14 9ED.*
⬗ Strathpeffer (099 72) 487.

Rescue Service: Smith's Garage, High St.
⬗ Strathpeffer (099 72) 472.

COUPAR ANGUS Tayside (Perthshire).
Map 37A
Pop 2,026. Perth 12, London 428,
Aberfeldy 32, Blairgowrie 4½, Dundee 14,
Edinburgh 53, Forfar 17, Glasgow 70,
Pitlochry 27.
EC Wed. **Golf** Rosemount, Blairgowrie
18h (2) & 9h. **See** Cistercian Abbey ruins.

Repairer: Lamb & Gardiner, The Grange,
Union St. ⬗ (082 82) 271.

COVE Strathclyde (Dunbartonshire).
Map 35C
Pop 876, Helensburgh 17, London 426,
Arrochar 17, Dumbarton 23, Edinburgh 82,
Glasgow 39.
EC Thur. **Golf** Helensburgh 18h. **See**
Church.

★★**Knockderry,** *G84 0NX.* ⬗ Kilcreggan
(043 684) 2283.

COYLTON Strathclyde (Ayrshire). Map
29A
Pop 1,800. Coalhall 2, London 379,
Abington 40, Ayr 6, Dalmellington 11,
Edinburgh 69, Girvan 22, Glasgow 36,
Kilmarnock 14, Lanark 42, Largs 33,
Thornhill 38.
EC Wed. **Golf** Ayr 18h.

Rescue Service: Hillhead Garage. ⬗ Joppa
(029 257) 247.

CRAIGELLACHIE Grampian (Banffshire).
Map 40B
Pop 450. Aberlour 2, London 515, Banff
36, Braemar 55, Edinburgh 140, Elgin 13,
Glasgow 157, Grantown-on-Spey 24,
Huntly 18, Stonehaven 71.
EC Thur. **Golf** Dufftown 9h. **See** Telford's
Bridge.

◼★★★**Craigellachie,** *AB3 9SS.*
⬗ (034 04) 204. C. ⬬ 28 bedrs, 20 bp, 2
bps, 6 sh, 3 ba, Dgs. ✗ a l c, mc, at, LD
9.30. ⌂ TV, CP 70, Ac, pf, con 20, CF, 6
BGf, 3 st. **£** BB £18–£19·50, DB £34–£37,
DT £31·50, DBB £26·50–£28, WB, ⬚, Bk
£3·50, L £3·50, D £8·50, cc 1 3, Dep b.

CRAIGHOUSE Isle of Jura, Strathclyde
(Argyll). Map 34F
Pop 200. Feolin 8½ Steamer Service to
West Tarbert. London 488, Edinburgh
142, Glasgow 101, Lochgilphead 14.

◼★★**Jura,** *PA60 7XU.* ⬗ (049 682) 243.
C. ⬬ 18 bedrs, 4 bp, 5 ba, Dgs. ✗ a l c, mc,
at, LD 9.15. ⌂ CH, TV, Dgs, CP 10, G 6, Ac,
pf, con 12, 2 st. **£** BB £16·50–£18, DB
£33–£36, WT £164, DT £26·85, DBB £25–
£26·50, ⬚, Bk £3·50, D £8·50, cc 1 2 3 5,
Dep a.

CRAIGNURE Isle of Mull, Strathclyde
(Argyll). Map 34B
Pop 50. Fy to Oban. London 478,
Edinburgh 121, Glasgow 90.
EC Wed. **Golf** Tobermory 9h. **See** Church.

◼★★★**Isle of Mull,** *PA65 6BB.*
⬗ (068 02) 351. Open Apr–Oct. RS Nov–
Mar. C. ⬬ 60 bedrs, 60 bp, Dgs. ✗ mc, at,
LD 8.30. ⌂ N, ch, TV, CP 50, Ac, con 30,
CF, 14 BGf, 0 st, Dis. **£** BB £28, DB £46,
DBB £23–£37, WB, ⬚, Bk £4, L £3, D £9,
cc 1 2 3 5 6.

CRAIL Fife. Map 27C
Pop 968. Largo 14, London 426,
Edinburgh 51, Glasgow 78, Kinross 36,
Kirkcaldy 26, Perth 39, St Andrews 10.
EC Wed. **Golf** Balcomie Links 18h. **See**
Old Town House with Dutch tower,
Mercat Cross, 16th cent Tolbooth, Parish
Church, Balcomie Castle ruins.

★**Croma,** *33 Nethergate Rd, KY10 3TU.*
⬗ (0333) 50239. Open Mar–Oct. C. ⬬ 9
bedrs, 2 bp, 4 ba, Dgs. ✗ at, LD 10.
⌂ CH, TV, Dgs, ns, CP 10, Ac, CF, 1 st.
£ BB £8·50–£11, DB £17–£22, WT £85–
£100, DT £17·50–£19·50, DBB £15–
£17·50, WB, ⬚, Bk £4, L £2, D £6·75, Dep a.
★**Marine,** *54 Kirkgate, KY10 3TZ.*
⬗ (0333) 50239.
Caiplie, G, x *(RI), 53 High St, KY10 3RA.*
⬗ (0333) 50564. Open Feb–Nov. C. ⬬ 7
bedrs, 2 ba, Dgs. ⌂ ch, TV, CF, 2 st. **£** BB
£7·50–£10·50, DB £15–£21, WT (b) £77–
£98, DT (b) £14·50–£16·50, ⬭, Bk £3·50, D
£6·50.

Rescue Service: Thomas Richardson, 7 St
Andrews Rd. ⬗ (0333) 363.

CRAWFORD Strathclyde (Lanarkshire).
Map 29B
Pop 328. Beattock 15, London 348,
Abington 4, Edinburgh 44, Glasgow 40.
EC Wed. **Golf** Leadhills 9h. **See** Crawford
Castle, Roman Forts & Cairns.

◼★**Crawford Arms,** *117 Carlisle Rd,
ML12 6TP.* ⬗ (086 42) 267.
Field End, G, xy *(Unl), "The Loaming",
ML12 6TN.* ⬗ (086 42) 276. Closed Xmas
& New Year. C. ⬬ 5 bedrs, 1 bps, 1 sh, 1
ba, TV. ⌂ CH, TV, ns, CP 6, CF, 2 st. **£** BB
£7·50–£13, DB £15–£18, WT (b) £73, (c)
£45, ⬚, Bk £2, L £2·50, D £4·50.

Specialist Body Repairer: South Scotland
Coachworks, 110 Carlisle Rd. ⬗ (086 42)
236.
Rescue Service: South Scotland
Coachworks, 110 Carlisle Rd. ⬗ (086 42)
236.

CREETOWN Dumfries & Galloway
(Kirkcudbrightshire). Map 29G
Gatehouse of Fleet 12, London 375,
Edinburgh 111, Girvan 86, Glasgow 91,
New Galloway 25, Stranraer 32.

◼★★**Ellangowan,** *DG8 7JF.*
⬗ (067 182) 201.

CRIEFF Tayside (Perthshire). Map 36B
Pop 5,100. Dunblane 15, London 416,
Aberfeldy 23, Dunfermline 30, Edinburgh
47, Glasgow 47, Kinross 26, Kincardine
30, Lochearnhead 19, Perth 18, Pitlochry
35, Stirling 21.
EC Wed. **MD** Fri. **Golf** Crieff 18h. **See**
10th cent Market Cross, Old Stocks, 17th
cent Drummond Cross, Glass Works,
Pottery, Highland gathering 3rd Sat in
Aug. Oldest Public Library in Scotland
(founded 1691) at Innerpeffray 2 m ESE,
Drummond Castle Gardens 2½ m SW.
ⓘ James Sq. ⬗ Crieff (0764) 2578.

★★**George,** *King St, PH7 3HB.* ⬗ (0764)
2089.

★★**Murray Park,** *Connaught Ter, PH7
3DJ.* ⬗ (0764) 3731. C. ⬬ 15 bedrs, 10
bp, 3 ba, TV, Dgs. ✗ mc, at, LD 9.30. ⌂ ch,
TV, Dgs, CP 50, con 20, CF, 1 BGf, 3 st.
£ BB £16–£20, DB £32–£40, DBB £25–
£29, ⬚, Bk £6, L £8, D £12·50, cc 5.
★**Gwydyr House** (R), *Comrie Road, PH7
4BP.* ⬗ (0764) 3277. Open Apr-Oct. C.
⬬ 10 bedrs, 3 ba, Dgs. ✗ mc, LD 8. ⌂ ch,
TV, CP 15, Ac, CF, 1 BGf, 5 st. **£** BB £9·25–
£10·50, DB £18·50–£21, DBB £15·85–
£17·10, ⬚, Bk £3·60, L £4·20, D £6·60.
★**Star,** *45 East High St, PH7 3JA.*
⬗ (0764) 2632. C. ⬬ 13 bedrs, 6 bp, 5 ba,
TV, Dgs. ✗ a l c, mc, at, LD 9. ⌂ CH, TV,
Dgs, CP 100, U 3, Ac, sb, con 200, CF, 1 st.
£ BB £10, DB £18–£20, WT £98, WB, ⬚, Bk
£2·50, L £1·50, D £5, cc 1 2 5, Dep.
Ap. Kingarth (Unl), *Perth Rd, PH7 3EQ.*
⬗ (0764) 2060.
Leven Lodge, H, x (RI), *Comrie Rd, PH7
4BA.* ⬗ (0764) 2529. C. ⬬ 9 bedrs, 3 ba,
Dgs. ⌂ ch, TV, Dgs, CP 4, U 3, CF. **£** BB
£8–£9, DB £16–£18, WT (b) £90–£100, DT
(b) £13–£14·50, ⬚, Bk £3, D £5·50.
Lockes Acre, H, xy, *Comrie Rd, PH7
4BP.* ⬗ (0764) 4736. C. ⬬ 7 bedrs, 2 ba,
TV. ⌂ CH, TV, CP 40, CF, 1 st. **£** BB £9–
£10·50, DB £18–£21, DT £14·50–£31, ⬚,
cc 1 3.
Sydney Villa, G, x (Rt), *57 Burrell St,
PH7 4DG.* ⬗ (0764) 2757. C. ⬬ 4 bedrs, 2
ba, TV, Dgs. ⌂ CH, TV, Dgs, CP 4. **£** BB £7,
DB £14, WT £77, DT £11, ⬚.

Repairer: West End Garage, Comrie Rd.
⬗ (0764) 2125.
Rescue Service: J Duff & Sons, Central
Garage. ⬗ (0764) 2147.

CRINAN Strathclyde (Argyll). Map 34D
Pop 70. Lochgilphead 6½, London 475,
Edinburgh 128, Glasgow 87, Tarbert 20,
Inveraray 31, Oban 34.
EC Sat. **Golf** Lochgilphead 9h. **See**
Dunadd Hill.

★★★**Crinan,** *PA31 8SR.* ⬗ (054 683)
235. Open mid Mar-Oct. RS Nov–Feb. C.
⬬ 22 bedrs, 20 bp, 2 bps. ✗ mc, at, LD 9.
⌂ Lt, CH, TV, CP 30, Ac, CF, 0 st. **£** BB
£28·50–£31·65, DB £45–£63·80, ⬭, Bk
£5·95, D £14·50, cc 1 2 3 5 6, Dep.

CROCKETFORD Dumfries & Galloway
(Kirkcudbrightshire). Map 29C
Pop 100. Dumfries 9, London 336,
Edinburgh 80, Gatehouse of Fleet 23,
Glasgow 82, New Galloway 15.
EC Thur. **Golf** Castle Douglas 9h.

★★**Galloway Arms,** *Stranraer Rd, DG2
8RA.* ⬗ (055 669) 240. Open Dec–Oct. RS
Nov. C. ⬬ 13 bedrs, 8 bp, 5 bps, 2 ba, TV,
Dgs. ✗ a l c, mc, at, LD 10. ⌂ CH, TV, CP
30, Ac, con 50, CF. 1 st. **£** BB £15–£20, DB
£26–£34, WT £150–£170, DT £25–£30,
DBB £20–£26, WB, ⬚, Bk £3·50, L £5·50, D
£8·50, cc 1 3 5, Dep a.

CROSSHOUSE Strathclyde (Ayrshire).
Map 29A
Pop 2,498. Kilmarnock 2½, London 386,
Ayr 13, Edinburgh 63, Glasgow 22, Irvine
5, Largs 24.
See Andrew Fisher Memorial Gardens.

★**Laurieland,** *82 Irvine Rd, KA2 0HE.*
⬗ Kilmarnock (0563) 35182.

CROSSMICHAEL Dumfries & Galloway
(Kirkcudbrightshire) Map 29E

Pop 440. Crocketford 9, London 345,
Dumfries 19, Edinburgh 89, Gatehouse of
Fleet 18, Glasgow 78, New Galloway 10.
Golf Castle Douglas 9h.

■**♨★★Culgruff House,** *DG7 3BB.*
℡ (055 667) 230. C. **⊷** 16 bedrs, 1 bp, 4
ba, Dgs. **✗** a l c, mc, at, LD 10. **🅿** CH, TV,
ns, CP 50, U 8, Ac, con 80, CF, 5 st. **£** BB
£12·65, DB £23–£27·60, WT fr £115, DT fr
£21·62, DBB £19·55–£21·85, **②**, Bk £2·30,
D £8, cc 1 2 3 6.

CULLEN Grampian (Banffshire). Map 41A
Pop 1,300. Keith 12, London 534, Banff
13, Craigellachie 28, Edinburgh 159, Elgin
21, Glasgow 177, Huntly 23.
EC Wed. **Golf** Cullen 18h. **See** Mercat
Cross, 13th cent Church, Deskford
Church 3 m S.
ℹ 20 Seafield St. **℡** Cullen (0542) 40757.

★★★**Seafield Arms,** *Seafield St. AB5
2SG.* **℡** (0542) 40791. C. **⊷** 24 bedrs, 17
bp, 1 sh, 2 ba, TV, Dgs. **✗** a l c, mc, at, LD
9.30. **🅿** N, TV, Dgs, CP 30, Ac, con 30, CF,
0 st. **£** BB £18–£21·70, DB £33·60–£40,
DBB £153·30–£178, WB, **②** 10%, Bk £3·80,
L £4·60, D £7·90, cc 1 2 3 5 6.
★★**Cullen Bay,** *AB5 2XA.* **℡** (0542)
40432. Open Feb–Dec. C. **⊷** 14 bedrs, 4
bp, 6 sh, 3 ba, TV, Dgs. **✗** mc, LD 9. **🅿** ch,
TV, CP 150, U 3, Ac, con 200, CF, 1 BGf, 1
st, Dis. **£** BB £15–£16, DB £28–£32, DT
£21, DBB £18–£24, WB, **②**, Bk £3·50, L £4,
D £4·50, cc 3 5, Dep a.

CUMBERNAULD Strathclyde
(Dunbartonshire). Map 48A
Pop 48,000. Lanark 23, London 392,
Dumbarton 26, Edinburgh 35, Glasgow
13, Kincardine 15, Peebles 47, Stirling 13.
EC Wed. **Golf** Palacerigg 18h. **See**
Country Park.

Rescue Service: Watson Bros (Airdrie)
Ltd, Carbrain Ring Rd, South Carbrain.
℡ (023 67) 25574.

CUMMERTREES Dumfries & Galloway
(Dumfriesshire). Map 29F
M6 Motorway 19, Annan 4, London 314,
Beattock 25, Dumfries 13, Edinburgh 80,
Glasgow 82.
Golf Powfoot 18h.

Richmond, PH, x (Rl) *DG12 5QF.*
℡ (046 17) 255. C. **⊷** 4 bedrs, 1 ba, Dgs.
🅿 TV, CP 6. **£** BB £5·50, DB £11, WT (b)
£56, DT (b) £8, **①**, Bk £2, L £2, D £3.

CUMNOCK Strathclyde (Ayrshire). Map
29A
Pop 9,616. New Cumnock 6, London 370,
Abington 30, Ayr 15, Dalmellington 13,
Edinburgh 59, Glasgow 33, Kilmarnock
15, Lanark 31, Sanquhar 14, Thornhill 29.
EC Wed. **MD** Fri. **Golf** Ballochmyle,
Mauchline 18h. **See** Mercat Cross (1703),
Peden Monument, Dumfries House, Baird
Institute.
ℹ Glaisnock St. **℡** Cumnock (0290)
23058.

★★**Dumfries Arms,** *KA18 1BY.*
℡ (0290) 20282. C. **⊷** 7 bedrs, 2 bps, 2 ba,
Dgs. **✗** a l c, mc, at, LD 8. **🅿** CH, TV, Dgs,
CP 50, Ac, CF, 0 st. **£** BB £12·65–£15·18,
DB £21·50–£25·30, **①**, Bk £2·50, L £4·95,
D £5·50.
★★**Royal,** *1 Glaisnock St, KA18 1BP.*
℡ (0290) 20822. C. **⊷** 12 bedrs, 3 ba, TV,
Dgs. **✗** a l c, mc, at, LD 9. **🅿** CH, TV, Dgs,

CP 8, U 2, Ac, CF. **£** BB £14–£15, DB £27–
£28, **②** 10%, Bk £3·50, L £4, D £6·50, cc 1.

Rescue Service: Skerrington Garage,
Dumfries Rd (A76). **℡** (0290) 20050.

CUPAR Fife. Map 37C
Pop 6,559. M90 Motorway 16, Kirkcaldy
17, London 417, Dundee 12, Dunfermline
29, Edinburgh 42, Glasgow 55, Kinross 19,
Perth 22, St Andrews 10, Stirling 41.
EC Thur. **MD** Tue. **Golf** Cupar 9h. **See**
Parish Church, County Hall, Town Hall,
Mercat Cross, Scotstarvit Tower, Hill of
Tarvit House 1½ m S.

Specialist Body Repairer: Glenvarigill Co
Ltd, James Place, Ceres Rd. **℡** (0334)
53346.

Rescue Service: J B W Smith Ltd, 97A
Bonnygate, **℡** (0334) 52334.

DAILLY Strathclyde (Ayrshire). Map 28D
Pop 1,093. Dalmellington 15, London 382,
Ayr 17, Edinburgh 86, Girvan 6, Glasgow
48.
EC Wed, **MD** Tue, Fri. **Golf** Turnberry 18h
(2). **See** Dalquharran Castle.

Rescue Service: Coleman Bros, The
Garage, Sturgeons Brae. **℡** (046 581) 235.

DALBEATTIE Dumfries & Galloway
(Kirkcudbrightshire). Map 29E
Pop 3,890. Beeswing 7, London 341,
Dumfries 13, Edinburgh 84, Gatehouse of
Fleet 22, Glasgow 88, New Galloway 21.
EC Thur. **Golf** Dalbeattie 9h. **See** RC
Church, Craignair Church, Town Hall,
Orchardton Tower 4 m S.
🅿 Car Park. **℡** Dalbeattie (0556) 610117.

Galla, G, y (Rl) *Haugh of Urr Rd, DG5
4LP.* **℡** (0556) 610425.

DALKEITH Lothian (Midlothian). Map
37E
Pop 8,669. Lauder 20, London 368,
Abington 40, Beattock 41, Coldstream 41,
Edinburgh 7, Galashiels 26, Glasgow 50,
Haddington 14, Lanark 37, Peebles 23.
EC Tue. **MD** Mon. **Golf** Newbattle 18h.
See St Nicholas Church, King's Park,
Dalkeith Palace, Newbattle Abbey.

Repairer: Adam Young & Son Ltd,
Eskbank Toll. **℡** 031-663 2172.
Wm Stewart (Motors) Ltd, Newmills Rd.
℡ 031-663 3156.

DALRY Dumfries & Galloway
(Kirkcudbrightshire). Map 29C
Pop 6,400. Crocketford 16, London 352,
Dalmellington 19, Dumfries 26, Edinburgh
81, Glasgow 66, New Galloway 3,
Thornhill 20.
EC Wed. **Golf** Kilbirnie 18h. **See** St John's
Stone, Covenanters' Graves in
Churchyard, Blair Castle.

■★★**Lochinvar,** *DG7 3UP.* **℡** (064 43)
210. RS Oct 31–Mar 30. C. **⊷** 15 bedrs, 3
bp, 5 ba, Dgs. **✗** mc, LD 8. **🅿** ch, ns, CP
40, U 4, con 24, CF, 3 st. **£** BB £11·95, DB
£23·90–£28·90, WT £119·50, DBB
£18·95–£21·45, **①**, Bk £3·50, L £4, D £7,
Dep.
■**♨★★Milton Park,** *DG7 3SR.*
℡ (064 43) 286. Open Apr–3rd week in
Oct. C. **⊷** 17 bedrs, 4 ba, Dgs. **✗** mc, at,
LD 7·30. **🅿** ch, TV, ns, CP 20, Ac, tc,,pf, con
50, CF, 2 st. **£** BB £13, DB £26, DBB fr £22,
②, Bk £5, D £9, Dep a.

Rescue Service: William Bone, The
Garage. **℡** (064 43) 208.

DAVIOT Highland (Inverness-shire). Map
39
Carrbridge 20, London 527, Aviemore 27,
Edinburgh 156, Elgin 35, Glasgow 165,
Grantown-on-Spey 29, Inverness 5½.

♨★★Meallmore Lodge, *IV1 2XG.*
℡ (046 385) 206. C. **⊷** 11 bedrs, 3 bp, 2
ba. **✗** a l c, mc, at, LD 9·30. **🅿** CH, TV, Dgs,
CP 80, G 3, pf, con 100, CF, 3 st. **£** BB £13–
£15, DB £26–£34, WT £166·50–£173·50,
DT £25·45–£27·45, DBB £20·95–£24·95,
WB, **②** 10%, Bk £3, L £4·50, D £7·95,
cc 1 3 5.

DINGWALL Highland (Ross & Cromarty).
Maps 39B and 40A
Conon Bridge 2½, London 540,
Achnasheen 30, Beauly 8½, Bonar Bridge
27, Edinburgh 167, Glasgow 178,
Inverness 15, Ullapool 47.
EC Thur. **MD** Wed. **Golf** Strathpeffer 18h.
See Museum. Highland Games (July).

★★**Royal,** *High Street, IV15 9HL.*
℡ (0349) 62130**▲**.

DINNET Grampian (Aberdeenshire). Map
41C
Ballater 7, London 486, Aberdeen 34,
Grantown-on-Spey 43, Huntley 34.

Rescue Service: Dinnet Service Station.
℡ (033 985) 261.

DIRLETON Lothian (East Lothian). Map
37C
Pop 593. Haddington 7½, London 377,
Berwick-upon-Tweed 42, Edinburgh 20,
Glasgow 64.
Golf North Berwick 18h. **See** 13th cent
Dirleton Castle.

★★★**Open Arms,** *EH39 5EG.* **℡** (0620)
85241. C. **⊷** 7 bedrs, 6 bp, 1 bps, TV, Dgs.
✗ mc, at, LD 9.30. **🅿** CH, CP 25, Ac, CF, 1
st. **£** BB £15–£37·50, DB £30–£50, DBB
£25·50–£46, **②** 10%, Bk £3, D £11·75,
cc 1 2 3 5.

DOLLAR Central (Clackmannanshire).
Map 36D
Pop 2,500. Dunfermline 12, London 402,
Crieff 22, Edinburgh 27, Glasgow 35,
Kincardine 7½, Kinross 12, Lochearnhead
38, Perth 21, Stirling 11.
EC Thur. **Golf** Dollar 18h. **See** Castle
Campbell ruins, Dollar Academy,
Conservation Area.

Rescue Service: Stewart Bros, The
Garage, 30 Bridge St. **℡** (025 94) 2233.

DORNIE Highland (Ross & Cromarty).
Map 38D
Pop 500. Invergarry 39, London 552 (Fy
530), Edinburgh 187, Glasgow 166 (Fy
171), Invermoriston 46, Kyle of Lochalsh
10, Strome Ferry 9½.
Golf Kyle of Lochalsh 9h. **See** Eilean
Donan Castle.

■★★**Dornie,** *Francis St. IV40 8DT.*
℡ (059 985) 205. Open Apr-Oct, RS Nov-
Apr. C. **⊷** 13 bedrs, 4 ba, Dgs. **✗** mc, at,
LD 8. **🅿** TV, Dgs, CP 30. **£** BB £15, DB £30,
WT £185, DT £26·50, DBB £24, WB, **①**, Bk
£4, L £5, D £9, cc 3.

DORNOCH Highland (Sutherland). Map
43E
Pop 1,100. Bonar Bridge 13, London 576,
Edinburgh 204, Glasgow 211, Helmsdale
28, Lairg 21.

EC Thur. **Golf** Royal Dornoch 18h and 9h.
See Restored Cathedral, Skelbo Castle
ruins, Dornoch Castle (now hotel).
🛈 The Square. ✆ Dornoch (086 281) 400.

◼︎★★★**Royal Golf,** *Grange Rd, IV25
3LG.* ✆ (0862) 810283. Open Apr–Oct, RS
Nov–Mar. C. 🛏 36 bedrs, 30 bp, 2 ba, TV,
Dgs. ✖ mc, at, LD 9.30. 🅿 N, CH, TV, Dgs,
CP 25, gc, con 60, CF, 6 BGf. **£** WB, L
£3·50, D £13·50, cc 1 2 3 5, Dep a.
★★**Burghfield House,** *IV25 3HW.*
✆ (0862) 810212. Open Apr-Oct, RS Nov–
Mar. C. 🛏 16 bedrs, 4 bp, 4 ba, TV, Dgs.
✖ mc, LD 9. 🅿 N, ch, TV, Dgs, CP 100, pf,
con 86, CF, 2 BGf, 3 st. **£** BB £17·50–
£19·80, DB £35–£39·60, WT £184, DT
£26·30, DBB £24–£26·30, WB, 🛈, L £6·50,
D £11·50, cc 1 2 3 5.
★★**Dornoch Castle,** *Castle St, IV25 3SD.*
✆ (0862) 810216. Open Apr-Oct. C. 🛏 20
bedrs, 11 bp, 1 sh, 2 ba, Dgs. ✖ mc, at, LD
8.15. 🅿 Lt, CH, TV, ns, CP 20, sol, gym, con
30, CF, 4 BGf, 3 st. **£** BB £14–£30·50, DB
£20–£33·50, DBB £23–£40·50, WB, 🛈, Bk
£3, L £3·50, D £9·75, cc 1 3, Dep a.▲

Rescue Service: G A Mackenzie, Dornoch
& Evelix Service Station. ✆ (0862) 341
and (0862) 255.

DOUNE Central (Perthshire). Map 36C
Pop 741. M9 Motorway 3, Bridge of Allan
5, London 406, Crieff 19, Dunfermline 26,
Edinburgh 42, Glasgow 32, Kincardine 18,
Kinross 28, Lochearnhead 21, Perth 31,
Stirling 8.
EC Wed. **Golf** Dunblane 18h. **See** 15th
cent Doune Castle and Doune Park
Gardens, also Doune Motor Museum,
Bridge (16th cent), Market Cross (17th
cent), Scotland's African Safari Park (at
Blair Drummond–A84 (Doune–Stirling
Rd).

◼︎★★**Woodside,** *Stirling Rd, FK16 6AB.*
✆ (0786) 841237. C. 🛏 14 bedrs, 6 bp, 3
ba, Dgs. ✖ LD 9. 🅿 CH, TV, Dgs, CP 80,
con 20, 0 st. **£** BB £17–£20·50, DB £28–
£33·50, WT £165–£190, DT £30–£32, DBB
£26–£30, WB, 🄯, cc 1.

DRUMMORE Dumfries & Galloway
(Wigtownshire). Map 28F
Pop 390. Glenluce 16, London 398,
Edinburgh 135, Gatehouse of Fleet 52,
Glasgow 97, New Galloway 51, Stranraer
17.
EC Wed. **Golf** Dunskey 18h & 9h. **See**
Mull of Galloway (Lighthouse), 18th cent
Church, St Medan Chapel ruins.

★**Queen's,** *Mill St, DG9 9PS.* ✆ (077 684)
300. C. 🛏 10 bedrs, 3 ba, Dgs. ✖ a l c, mc,
at, LD 9. 🅿 ch, TV, Dgs, Ac, 1 st. **£** BB £10–
£11, DB £20–£22, BDD £16·50–£18·50,
WB, 🛈, Bk £2, L £2·50, D £8·50, Dep a.

DRUMNADROCHIT Highland
(Inverness-shire). Maps 39B and 40C
Invermoriston 12, London 539, Beauly 14,
Edinburgh 173, Glasgow 148, Inverness
14.
EC Thur. **Golf** Inverness 18h. **See**
Urquhart Castle ruins, Stone Circle at
Corrimony, Cobb Memorial, Loch Ness.

Rescue Service: J A Menzies & Sons Ltd,
Lewiston Garage. ✆ (045 62) 212.

DRYMEN Central (Stirlingshire). Maps
35D and 36C
Pop 659. Bearsden 12, London 410,
Arrochar 30, Crianlarich 44, Dumbarton

12, Edinburgh 54, Glasgow 17,
Lochearnhead 32, Stirling 22.
EC Wed. **Golf** Buchanan Castle 18h. **See**
18th cent restored Drymen Bridge,
Mountain and lake scenery of Loch
Lomond, Salmon Leap at the Potts of
Gartness.

★★★**Buchanan Arms,** *Main St, G63
0BP.* ✆ (0360) 60588. C. 🛏 35 bedrs, 35
bp, 2 ba, TV, Dgs. ✖ a l c, mc, at, LD 9.30.
🅿 N, CH, CP 120, Ac, con 120, CF, 3 BGf, 0
st, Dis. **£** BB £17–£34, DB £31–£52, DBB
£23–£44, WB, 🛈, Bk £4, L £6·50, D £10·25,
cc 1 2 3 5 6.

DULNAIN BRIDGE Highland (Moray).
Map 40D
Pop 350. Aviemore 11, London 510,
Carrbridge 6½, Edinburgh 135, Glasgow
146, Grantown-on-Spey 3.
EC Wed. **Golf** Carrbridge 9h. **See** Castle.

◼︎★★**Skye of Curr,** *PH26 3AP.*
✆ (047 985) 345. C. 🛏 8 bedrs, 4 ba, Dgs.
✖ mc, LD 8. 🅿 CH, TV, Dgs, CP 25, CF, 2
st. **£** BB £11–£13·50, DB £22–£27, DBB
£20–£22, 🛈, L £2·75, D £8·75, cc 1 2 3 5.

Rescue Service: John Ross & Co, Main St.
✆ (047 985) 377.

DUMBARTON Strathclyde
(Dunbartonshire). Maps 35F and 36E
Pop 26,335. M898 Motorway 5, Glasgow
14, London 402, Arrochar 23, Crianlarich
37, Edinburgh 59, Kincardine 38, Gourock
33 (Fy 21), Lochearnhead 46, Paisley 16
(Fy 11), Stirling 34.
EC Wed. **MD** Fri. **Golf** Dumbarton 18h.
See Castle.

★★**Dumbuck,** *Glasgow Rd, G82 1EG.*
✆ (0389) 63818.

Repairer: Strathford Motor Co,
Dumbarton Rd. (A82), Milton. ✆ (0389)
65131.

DUMFRIES Dumfries & Galloway
(Dumfriesshire). Map 30E
Pop 31,000. Annan 16, Brampton 39,
Carlisle 33, London 327, Beattock 19,
Dalmellington 41, Edinburgh 71,
Gatehouse of Fleet 35, Glasgow 73,
Langholm 28, New Galloway 23, Thornhill
14.
EC Thur. **MD** Wed. **Golf** Dumfries and
Galloway 18h, Dumfries and County 18h.
See Burns House, Burns Mausoleum,
Burns Statue, Burgh Museum, The Auld
Bridge, Greyfriars Church, St Michael's
Church, Globe Inn, Lincluden Abbey 2 m
NW, Sweetheart Abbey 6 m S,
Caerlaverock Castle ruins and Wildfowl
centre 7 m SE.
🛈 Whitesands. ✆ Dumfries (0387) 53862.

★★★**Cairndale,** *English St, DG1 2DF.*
✆ (0387) 54111. C. 🛏 45 bedrs, 29 bp, 4
ba, TV, Dgs. ✖ a l c, mc, at, LD 9. 🅿 Lt,
N, CH, TV, CP 60, Ac, con 60, CF, 2 BGf, 2
st. **£** BB £19–£26, DB £30–£38, DBB
£27·25–£34·25, WB, 🛈, Bk £3, L £5, D
£8·25, cc 1 2 3 5.

🏨★★★**Rockhall,** *Collin, DG1 4J10.*
✆ (038 775) 427. C. 🛏 9 bedrs, 5 bp, 4
bps, 1 sh, 5 ba, TV, Dgs. ✖ mc, a, LD 11.
🅿 CH, TV, Dgs, CP 200, Ac, con 120, CF, 1
st. **£** BB £18–£25, DB £32–£38, WB, 🛈, Bk
£3, L £1·95, D £6·50, cc 1 2 3 5 6.
★★★**Station,** *Lovers Walk, DG1 1LT.*
✆ (0387) 54316. C. 🛏 30 bedrs, 17 bp, 13
bps, 1 ba, TV, Dgs. ✖ mc, LD 9.30. 🅿 Lt, N,

CH, TV, CP 60, Ac, con 60, CF, 0 st. **£** BB
£15–£27, DB £25–£33, DBB £16·50–£32,
WB, 🄯, Bk £3·75, L £4·25, D £7·25,
cc 1 2 3 5 6, Dep b.

★★**Cargenholm,** *New Abbey Rd, DG2
8ER.* ✆ (0387) 54988. C. 🛏 12 bedrs, 2
bp, 3 ba, Dgs. ✖ a l c, mc, LD 9. 🅿 CH, TV,
Dgs, CP 120, Ac, CF, 2 st. **£** BB £13·50–
£16·50, DB £19·50–£22·50, WT £129·50,
DT £18·50, DBB £14·75–£16·25, 🛈, Bk
£2·75, L £4·25, D £7·75.
★★**Skyline,** *123 Irish St, DG1 2NP.*
✆ (0387) 62416.
◼︎★**Edenbank,** *Laurie Knowe, DG2 7HA.*
✆ (0387) 52759.
★**Moreig,** *67 Annan Rd, DG1 3EG.*
✆ (0387) 55524.▲
◼︎★**Nithsdale,** *St Mary St, DG1 1HA.*
✆ (0387) 53452. C. 🛏 14 bedrs, 3 ba.
✖ LD 7·30. 🅿 TV, CF, 0 st. **£** BB £9·50, DB
£18·80, 🛈, Bk £2·50, D £3·50, Dep a.
◼︎★**Winston,** *Rae St, DG1 1JD.* ✆ (0387)
54433. Closed Dec 24–Jan 3. C. 🛏 14
bedrs, 7 sh, 3 ba, Dgs. ✖ mc, LD 7·30.
🅿 CH, TV, Dgs, CP 6, Ac, CF, 3 st. **£** BB
£10·35–£11·50, DB £20·70–£23, WT £95–
£100, DT £16·80–£19, DBB £13·80–£16,
🄯, Bk £3, L £2·50, D £3·50.
Embassy, H, y, *Newbridge, DG2 2EG.*
✆ (0387) 233. C. 🛏 5 bedrs, 2 ba, TV, Dgs.
✖ a l c, 🅿 ch, TV, Dgs, CP 50, CF, 4 st.
£ BB £12–£17, DB £24–£34, 🛈, Bk £2·50,
L £4·50, D £5.
Fulwood, PH, z (Unl), *30 Lovers Walk,
DG1 1LX.* ✆ (0387) 52262. C. 🛏 5 bedrs,
1 ba. 🅿 CH, TV, U 1, 4 st. **£** BB £7·50–£8,
DB £14, WT £98, 🛈.

Repairer: Thomas Corrie Ltd, Morris
House, Buccleuch St. ✆ (0387) 54301.
Specialist Body Repairer: J B Stevenson &
Jeffrey Ltd, Rosefield Mills. ✆ (0387)
54481.
MC Repairer: Grierson & Graham Ltd, 36
Church Cres. ✆ (0387) 53405.
Rescue Service: A G Dickson, Cumberland
St. ✆ (0387) 69292.
Border Cars, 244 Heathhall Industrial
Estate. ✆ (0387) 67835.

DUNBAR Lothian (East Lothian). Map
37F
Pop 5,614. Cockburnspath 8½, London
365, Berwick-upon-Tweed 29,
Coldstream 32, Edinburgh 29, Galashiels
42, Glasgow 74, Haddington 11, Kelso 38,
Lauder 32, Selkirk 48.
EC Wed. **Golf** Dunbar 18h, Winterfield
Municipal 18h. **See** Castle ruins, 17th cent
Town House, 16th cent dovecote, Parish
Church
🛈 Town House, High St. ✆ Dunbar (0368)
63353.

◼︎★★**Bayswell,** *Bayswell Park, EH42
1AE.* ✆ (0368) 62225. C. 🛏 12 bedrs, 11
bp, 1 bps, TV, Dgs. ✖ mc, LD 9.30. 🅿 CH,
CP 20, con 20, CF, 2 st. **£** BB £24–£39, DB
£36–£42, 🛈, Bk £5, L £5, D £9, cc 1 2 3
Cruachan, G (Unl), *East Links Rd.*
✆ (0368) 63595. Closed Xmas & New
Year. C. 🛏 4 bedrs, 2 ba, Dgs. 🅿 CH, TV,
CP 3, CF, 1 st. **£** BB fr £8, DB fr £16, WT (b)
£91, DBB £13, 🛈, Bk £2, D £5.
Marine, G, x (Unl), *7 Marine Rd, EH42
1AR.* ✆ (0368) 63315. C. 🛏 9 bedrs, 2 ba,
Dgs. 🅿 CH, TV, Dgs, ns, CF, 5 st. **£** BB
£7·50–£8·50, D £15–£16, 🛈.
St Beys, G, *2 Bayswell Rd, EH42 1AB.*
✆ (0368) 63571.

Springfield, G, x (RI), *42 Belhaven Rd,
EH42 1NH.* ✆ (0368) 2502. Open Feb–
Oct. C. 🛏 7 bedrs, 3 ba, TV, Dgs. 🅙 CH, CP
9, CF. £ BB £18–£18·50, DB £20–£21, WT
(b) £107–£113, ②, Bk £4, D £7, cc 1 3.

Rescue Service: D M Conversions,
Edinburgh Rd, West Barnes. ✆ (0368)
62604.

DUNDEE Tayside (Angus). Map 37A
Pop 192,000. Glenrothes 24, London 429,
Aberfeldy 46, Blairgowrie 18, Edinburgh
55, Forfar 14, Glasgow 78, Kinross 30,
Kirkcaldy 29, Montrose 30, Perth 21,
Pitlochry 41, St Andrews 12.
EC Wed. **MD** Tue. **Golf** Monifieth 18h (2).
See Tay Road Bridge, Museum and Art
Gallery, St Andrew's Church (1772), Law
Hill (viewpoint), Claypotts Castle,
Broughty Castle, Camperdown Park
(Zoo), The Old Steeple, War Memorial,
modernised Town Cross, Caird Hall,
Episcopal and RC Cathedrals, Dudhope
Park and Castle, Albert Institute and
Public Library, The Howff (quaint
gravestones).
🛈 16 City Sq. ✆ Dundee (0382) 27723.

■★★★**Angus Thistle,** *101 Marketgait,
DD1 1QU.* ✆ (0382) 26874. C. 🛏 58
bedrs, 43 bp, 15 bps, ns, TV, Dgs. ✗ a l c,
mc, at, LD 9.30. 🅙 Lt, N, CH, Dgs, CP 18,
con 400, CF, 0 st. £ BB £36·75–£44·75, DB
£49·50–£61·50, WB, ②, Bk £4·75, L £4·50,
D £8·50, cc 1 2 3 4 5 6, Dep b.

★★★**Invercarse,** *371 Perth Rd, DD2
1PG.* ✆ (0382) 69231. RS New Year. C.
🛏 27 bedrs, 6 bp, 21 bps, ns, TV, Dgs.
✗ a l c, mc, at, LD 9.45. 🅙 N, CH, CP 200,
Ac, con 200, CF, 1 st. £ BB £17–£35·95,
DB £27–£43·90, WB, ①, Bk £3·95, L £4·55,
D £8·30, cc 1 2 3 5, Dep b.

★★★**Swallow,** *Kingsway West, DD2
5JT.* ✆ (0382) 641122. C. 🛏 69 bedrs, 69
bp, TV, Dgs. ✗ a l c, mc, at, LD 9·45. 🅙 N,
CH, CP 100, Ac, sp, sb, sol, gym, con, CF, 4
BGf, 0 st. £ BB £40·50, DB £50·25, WB, ①,
Bk £5, L £4·50, D £9, cc 1 2 3 5 6, Dep b.

★★**Queen's,** *Nethergate, DD1 4DU.*
✆ (0382) 22515. C. 🛏 60 bedrs, 11 bp, 1
bps, 9 ba, TV. ✗ a l c, mc, at, LD 9.30. 🅙 Lt,
N, CH, CP 40, Ac, con 120, CF, 0 st. £ BB
£15–£34·20, DB £30–£48·40, DBB £20–
£41·70, WT, ②, Bk £2·75, L £4, D £7·50,
cc 1 2 3 4 5 6, Dep.

■★★**Tay,** *Whitehall Cres, DD1 4AY.*
✆ (0382) 21641.

Specialist Radiator Repairer: Serck
Radiator Services Ltd, 30 Stirling St.
✆ (0382) 22551.
Rescue Service: Scott Fyfe (Motors) Ltd,
East Kingsway Service Station. ✆ (0382)
81715.
T G Simpson, Ninewells Garage, 570 Perth
Rd. ✆ (0382) 68384.

DUNDONNELL Highland (Ross &
Cromarty) Map 42E
Pop 70. Garve 31, London 583,
Achnasheen 47, Beauly 44, Dingwall 43,
Edinburgh 208, Gairloch 33, Glasgow 212,
Inverness (Fy) 53, Ullapool 24.
Golf Gairloch 9h. **See** An Teallach
Mountain (3,483ft).

■★★**Dundonnell,** *IV23 2QS.*
✆ (085 483) 204. Open Apr–Oct. C. 🛏 24
bedrs, 23 bp, 1 bps, TV, Dgs. ✗ a l c, mc, at,
LD 8.15. 🅙 CH, Dgs, CP 60, pf, con 25, CF,
1 st. £ BB £18–£21, DB £30–£37, WT

£125–£175, DBB £27–£31, WB, Bk £4, L
£2·50, D £8·50, cc 1 3.

DUNFERMLINE Fife. Map 36D
Pop 52,000. Queensferry 7, London 391,
A823(M) Motorway 2½, Crieff 30, Dundee
40, Edinburgh 16, Glasgow 38, Kincardine
10, Kinross 12, Kirkcaldy 12, Lanark 36,
Lochearnhead 48, St Andrews 39, Stirling
22.
EC Wed. **Golf** Dunfermline 18h, Canmore
18h, Pitreavie 18h. **See** Royal Palace ruins,
Abbey Church (Bruce's Tomb, St
Margaret's Shrine), Andrew Carnegie
Birthplace Memorial (Moodie St), Forth
Rail and Road Bridges, Pittencrieff Glen,
Pittencrieff House (museum), City
Chambers, 16th cent Abbot's House, St
Margaret's Cave (Bruce St), Culross
Palace 6½ m W, The Study.
🅿 Glen Bridge Car Park. ✆ Dunfermline
(0383) 720999.

★★★**Keavil House,** *Crossford,
KY12 8QW.* ✆ (0383) 736258. C. 🛏 32
bedrs, 28 bp, 4 bps, TV. ✗ mc, at, LD 9.
🅙 CH, TV, CP 80, Ac, tc, con, CF, 10 BGf, 0
st, Dis. £ BB £26, DB £26–£36, DBB
£33·50–£36, WB, ②, Bk £4, L £4, D £7·30,
cc 1 2 3 5.

★★★**King Malcolm Thistle,** *Wester
Pitcorthie, KY11 5DS.* ✆ (0383) 722611.
C. 🛏 48 bedrs, 48 bp, ns, TV, Dgs. ✗ a l c,
mc, at, LD 9.30. 🅙 N, CH, TV, Dgs, CP 60, Ac,
con 150, CF, 20 BGf, 5 st. £ BB £38·75–
£46·75, DB £47·50–£52·50, WB, ②, Bk
£4·75, L £5·25, D £8·50, cc 1 2 3 4 5 6,
Dep b.

★★★**Pitferrane Arms,** *Main St,
Crossford, KY12 8NJ.* ✆ (0383) 736132.
C. 🛏 31 bedrs, 20 bp, 11 bps, TV. ✗ a l c,
mc, at, LD 9.30. 🅙 N, CH, Dgs, CP 50, Ac,
con 80, CF, 7 BGf, 0 st, Dis. £ BB £22–£25,
DB £32–£36, DBB fr £30, WB, ①, Bk £4·50,
L £6·50, D £8, cc 1 2 3 6, Deb b.

★★**Brucefield,** *Woodmill Rd, KY11 4AD.*
✆ (0383) 722199. 🛏 9 bedrs, 6 bp, 1 ba,
TV, Dgs. ✗ mc, LD 8. 🅙 CH, TV, CP 100,
Ac, con 100, CF, 5 st. £ BB £13·50–£18·50,
DB £23·50–£30, DT £25, DBB £20·50–
£25·50, ②, Bk £3·50, L £4·50, D £7, cc 1.

DUNKELD Tayside (Perthshire). Map
36B
Pop 600. Bankfoot 6, London 432,
Blairgowrie 11, Crieff 21, Dundee 28,
Edinburgh 57, Glasgow 69, Perth 15,
Pitlochry 13.
EC Thur. **Golf** Dunkeld and Birnam 9h.
See Cathedral (14th cent), Scottish
Horse Regiment Museum, Falls.
🅿 The Cross. ✆ Dunkeld (035 02) 688.

■★★**Atholl Arms,** *Bridge St, PH8 0AQ.*
✆ (035 02) 219. RS Xmas. C. 🛏 20 bedrs,
4 bp, 5 ba, Dgs. ✗ a l c, mc, at, LD 9. 🅙 ch,
TV, Dgs, CP 16, U 2, Ac, CF, 6 st. £ BB
£13–£30, DB £26–£36, DBB £42–£54, WB,
②, Bk £2·75, D £8, cc 1 2 3 5.

Ap. Taybank, *Tay Ter, PH8 0AQ.*
✆ (038 02) 340. C. 🛏 6 bedrs, 2 ba, Dgs.
✗ mc, LD 8.30. 🅙 ch, TV, Dgs, CP 24, 2 st.
£ BB £11–£24, DB £24, DT £21–£50, DBB
£18–£36, ①, Bk £3, L £3·50, D £7·50.

Rescue Service: Dunkeld Garage, Atholl
St. ✆ (035 02) 212.
Young's Garage, Birnam. ✆ (035 02) 276.

DUNNET Highland (Caithness). Maps
43B and 46E

Castletown 3, London 652, Edinburgh
277, Glasgow 284, Helmsdale 52, Thurso
8, Wick 18.
EC Thur. **See** 14th cent Church, Dunnet
Head and Lighthouse.

■★★**Northern Sands,** *KW14 8XD.*
✆ (084 785) 270. C. 🛏 14 bedrs, 2 bp, 1
bps, 3 ba, Dgs. ✗ a l c, mc, at, LD 8.30.
🅙 ch, TV, Dgs, CP 60, Ac, pf, CF, 2 st. £ BB
£11–£12, DB £22–£24, ①, Bk £4·50, cc 3.

DUNNING Tayside (Perthshire). Map
36D
Pop 641. Dunfermline 20, London 411,
Crieff 14, Edinburgh 37, Glasgow 48,
Kincardine 21, Kinross 17, Perth 9½, St
Andrews 36, Stirling 23.
EC Thur. **Golf** Dunning 9h. **See** St Serf's
Church with massive Norman Tower.

Rescue Service: Robert Nicol & Son,
Burnside Garage, Muckhart Rd.
✆ (076 484) 203.

DUNOON Strathclyde (Argyle). Map 35E
Pop 8,759. Arrochar 39, London 466 (Fy
412), Edinburgh 118 (Fy 69), Glasgow 76
(Fy 24), Inveraray 39.
EC Wed. **Golf** Cowal 18h. **See** Statue of
Burns' 'Highland Mary', Argyll National
Park, Kilmun Arboretum 6 m N, Younger
Botanical Gardens 7 m NW, Cowal
Highland Gathering last Fri, Sat in Aug.
🅿 Pier Esplanade. ✆ Dunoon (0369) 3785.

■★★**Abbeyhill,** *Dhalling Rd, PA23 8EA.*
✆ (0369) 2204. C. 🛏 14 bedrs, 7 bp, 7
bps, TV, Dgs. ✗ mc, at, LD 8.30. 🅙 CH,
Dgs, CP 40, CF, 3 st. £ BB £22, DB £35, ①,
Bk £4·50, D £8, cc 3.

★★**Argyll,** *Argyll St, PA23 7NE.* ✆ (0369)
2059.

★★**Queen's,** *Marine Par, PA23 8HE.*
✆ (0369) 4224. C. 🛏 22 bedrs, 6 ba, TV,
Dgs. ✗ a l c, mc, at, LD 8.30. 🅙 CH, TV,
Dgs, CP 30, Ac, con 60, CF, 7 st. £ BB £15,
DB £30, WT £150, DBB £20–£30, WB, ②,
Bk £1·50, L £3, D £7·50, cc 1 3 5 6.

■★★**Royal Marine,** *Hunters Quay,
PA23 8HJ* (2 m N A815). ✆ (0369) 3001.
Esplanade, H, x (RI), *Victoria Par, PA23
7HU.* ✆ (0369) 4070. Open Apr–mid Oct.
C. 🛏 53 bedrs, 15 bp, 1 bps, 13 ba, TV,
Dgs. 🅙 Lt, CH, TV, CP 14, U 6, CF, 2 st.
£ BB £10·50–£13·50, DB £21–£27, WT
£85–£95, DT £15–£18, ②, Bk £2·50, L
£3·25, D £5.
Rosscairn, PH, x (Unl), *51 Hunter St,
Kirn, PA23 8JR.* ✆ (0369) 4344. C. 3.
🛏 10 bedrs, 10 bps, 1 ba. 🅙 CH, TV, ns,
CP 8. £ BB £19·70–£21, WT (b) £85–£94,
DT (b) £12·85–£14·50, ①, D £4·50,
cc 1 3 6.

Repairers: Wilson's Garage Co (Argyll)
Ltd, East Bay Promenade. ✆ (0369) 3094.
Rescue Service: Pearce & McKechnie, 22
Jane St. ✆ (0369) 5320.

DUNSCORE Dumfries & Galloway
(Dumfriesshire). Map 29D
Pop 160. Dumfries 8½, London 336,
Dalmellington 33, Edinburgh 73, Glasgow
70, New Galloway 21, Thornhill 10.
Golf County & Galloway 18h. **See**
"Bloody Lags Grave", Well Towers.

Rescue Service: Dunscore Garage Co Ltd,
Kirkgate. ✆ (038 782) 252.

DUNTOCHER Strathclyde
(Dunbartonshire). Map 48E, 35F and 36E

Pop 3,032. Glasgow 8½, London 396,
Arrochar 28, Crianlarich 43, Dumbarton
6½, Edinburgh 53, Greenock (Fy) 14,
Kincardine 32, Paisley (Fy) 6½.
EC Wed. **See** Roman wall.

★★Maltings, *Dumbarton Rd, G81 6DP.*
✆ (0389) 75371. C. ✉ 28 bedrs, 28 bp, TV,
Dgs. ✗ a l c, mc, at, LD 8.30. 🅰 N, CH, TV,
Dgs, CP 250, Ac, con 16, CF, 12 BGf, 3 st.
£ BB £25–£28, DB £36–£40, DT £38·25–
£41·75, WB, ☑, Bk £3, L £5, D £6·50,
cc 1 2 3 4 5 6, Dep b.

DURNESS Highland (Sutherland). Map
42B
Pop 200. Lairg 56, London 649 (Fy 636).
Bettyhill 36, Edinburgh 267, Glasgow 278,
Ullapool 65.
See Cave of Smoo (1 m E).
🆑 ✆ Durness (097 181) 259.

Rescue Service: Campbell & Morrison,
West End. ✆ (097 181) 366.

DUROR Highland (Inverness-shire).
Maps 35A & 39E
Pop 225. Appin 5, London 497, Edinburgh
138, Glasgow 110, Glencoe 9, Oban 30.
Golf Fort William 18h. **See** James Glen,
Ancient Cemetery.

■★★Stewart, *PA38 4BW.* ✆ (063 174)
268. Open Apr–Oct, RS Nov–Mar. C. ✉ 26
bedrs, 26 bp, 2 ba, TV, Dgs. ✗ mc, at, LD
8.30. 🅰 CH, TV, ns, CP 50, Ac, pf, sb, sol,
gym, con 25, CF, 6 BGf, 10 st. **£** BB
£19·50–£27, DB £31–£38, WT £150–£175,
DBB £30–£37, WB, ☑, Bk £5, D £11·50,
cc 1 2 3 5, Dep a.

DYCE Grampian (Aberdeenshire). Map
41D
Pop 7,195. Aberdeen 5½, London 497,
Banff 40, Edinburgh 122, Fraserburgh 41,
Glasgow 141, Huntly 34, Peterhead 31.
Golf Auchmill 9h. **See** Aberdeen Airport.

★★★★M Holiday Inn, *Aberdeen Airport,
Riverview Dr, Farburn, AB2 0AZ.* ✆ (0224)
770011. C. ✉ 154 bedrs, 154 bp, TV, Dgs.
✗ a l c, mc, at, LD 11. 🅰 N, CH, CP 200,
Ac, sp, sb, sol, gym, con 250, CF, 1 BGf, 1
st, Dis. **£** BB £60·85, DB £75·70, WB, ☑, Bk
£5·65, L £10·50, D £9·90, cc 1 2 3 4 5 6,
Dep b.

EAST KILBRIDE Strathclyde
(Lanarkshire). Map 48D
Pop 76,000. Hamilton 6½, London 383,
Abington 31, Dalmellington 44, Edinburgh
41, Glasgow 8, Kilmarnock 18, Kincardine
33, Lanark 20, Largs 33, Paisley 12,
Peebles 46, Stirling 31.
EC Wed. **Golf** East Kilbride 18h. **See**
Church with crown tower, Olympic-length
Swimming Pool, Sports Centre, Mains
Castle, Museum.

★★★Bruce, *Cornwall St, G74 1AF.*
✆ (035 52) 29771. C. ✉ 84 bedrs, 37 bp,
47 bps, TV, Dgs. ✗ a l c, mc, at, LD 9.45.
🅰 Lt, N, CH, Dgs, G 20, Ac, con 50, CF, 1
st. **£** WB, Bk £5·10, L £5·50, D £9·25,
cc 1 2 3 5 6.

■★★★★Crutherland County, *Strathaven
Rd, G75 0Q2.* ✆ (035 52) 34633. RS Jan
1 & 2. C. ✉ 21 bedrs, 7 bp, 11 bps, 2 sh, TV.
✗ a l c, LD 10.30. 🅰 N, CH, CP 50, pf, con
40, CF, 5 BGf. **£** BB £28, DB £30, ☑, Bk £2,
L £4, D £6, cc 1 2 3.

★★★Stuart Thistle, *Cornwall Way, G74
1JS.* ✆ (035 52) 21161. C. ✉ 30 bedrs, 26
bp, 4 bps, ns, TV. ✗ a l c, LD 9.30. 🅰 Lt, N,

CH, TV, Ac, con 160, CF, 2 st. **£** BB
£34·75–£39·75, DB £41·50–£47·50, WB,
☑, Bk £4·75, cc 1 2 3 4 5 6, Dep b.

★★Torrance, *Main St, G74 4LN.*
✆ (035 52) 25241. RS Jan. C. ✉ 27 bedrs,
8 bp, 3 ba, TV. ✗ a l c, at, LD 10.15. 🅰 N,
ch, Ac, con 85, CF. **£** BB £22–£27·50, DB
£33–£36, WB, ☑, Bk £2, cc 1 2 3 5, Dep b.

Rescue Service: Kingsway Service
Station, Kingsway. ✆ (035 52) 20311.

EAST LINTON Lothian (East Lothian).
Map 37E
Pop 1,394. Cockburnspath 13, London
367, Berwick-upon-Tweed 34,
Coldstream 34, Edinburgh 23, Glasgow
68, Haddington 5½, Kelso 40.
EC Wed. **Golf** Dunbar 18h. **See** Church,
Hailes Castle, Preston Mill and Phantassie
Dovecote (Nat Trust). John Rennie,
engineer and bridge builder, born here—
memorial.

■★★The Harvesters, *EH40 3DP.*
✆ (0620) 860395. Open Feb–Dec, Closed
Xmas. C. ✉ 3 bedrs, 2 bp, 1 bps, annexe 7
bedrs, 4 bp, 2 ba, Dgs. 🅰 ch, TV, CP 40, CF,
£ BB £20–£30, DB £40–£50, ☑, L £4,
cc 1 2 3 5, Dep a.

Rescue Service: Horsburgh's Garages,
Haddington Rd. ✆ (0620) 223.

EASTRIGGS Dumfries & Galloway
(Dumfriesshire). Map 30E
Gretna 4½, London 307, Beattock 28,
Brampton 20, Carlisle 14, Dumfries 19,
Edinburgh 80, Glasgow 83, Langholm 18.
EC Wed. **Golf** Powfoot 18h.

Rescue Service: Grieve's Garage, Annan
Rd. ✆ (046 14) 203.

EAST SALTOUN Lothian (East Lothian).
Map 37E
Pop 540. Lauder 17, London 364,
Berwick-upon-Tweed 38, Coldstream 38,
Edinburgh 16, Galashiels 27, Glasgow 60,
Haddington 6, Kelso 34, Peebles 30.
Golf Gifford 9h. **See** Parish Church.

Rescue Service: Fiddes Bros, East Saltoun
Service Station, Main St. ✆ Pencaitland
(0875) 340316.

EAST WEMYSS Fife. Map 37C
Pop 1,810. Kirkcaldy 5, London 405,
Dundee 26, Edinburgh 30, Glasgow 55,
Kinross 20, Perth 27, St Andrews 18.
EC Wed. **Golf** Leven 18h. **See** McDuff
Castle, ruins, historic Caves.

Rescue Service: Lamberts Garage.
✆ Buckhaven (0592) 713405.

ECCLEFECHAN Dumfries & Galloway
(Dumfriesshire). Map 30E
Pop 800. Gretna Green 9½, London 313,
Beattock 20, Brampton 23, Carlisle 19,
Dumfries 15, Edinburgh 72, Glasgow 75,
Langholm 14.
EC Thur. **Golf** Lockerbie 9h. **See** Carlyle's
birthplace, Thomas Carlyle Monument.

MC Repairer: John Cook, Templand Acre
Garage. ✆ (057 63) 230.
Rescue Service: John Cook, Templand
Acre Garage. ✆ (057 63) 230.

EDINBURGH Lothian (Midlothian). Map
37E
See also MUSSELBURGH
RAC Office, *17 Rutland Sq, Edinburgh,
EH1 2BQ.* ✆ 031-229 3555.
Pop 444,741. Dalkeith 7, London 375,
Abington 42, Ayr 73, Beattock 54,

Coldstream 48, Dunfermline 16, Galashiels
32, Glasgow 45, Haddington 15, Kelso 43,
Kilmarnock 63, Kincardine 26, Kinross 26,
Kirkcaldy 25, Lanark 33, Lauder 26,
Peebles 23, Stirling 36.
See Plan, p. 404.
P See Plan. **Golf** Six Corporation courses
and numerous others. **See** Castle and War
Memorial, Palace of Holyroodhouse, St
Giles' Cathedral, National Museum of
Antiquities, Royal Scottish Museum, 17th
cent White Horse Close, Outlook Tower,
Parliament House, John Knox's House
(Museum), National Gallery, 17th cent
Gladstone's Land, Royal Botanic Gdn,
Lady Stair's House (Literary Museum),
Episcopal and RC Cathedrals, Museum of
Childhood, Huntly House Museum,
University, 17th cent Greyfriars Kirk,
Royal Scottish Academy, Canongate
Tolbooth, Zoo, International Festival and
Tattoo Aug/Sept, Craigmillar Castle 2½ m
SE, Lauriston Castle 4 m NW.
🆑 5 Waverley Bridge. ✆ 031-332 2433.

★★★★Caledonian, *Princes St, EH1 2AB.*
✆ 031-225 2433. C. ✉ 254 bedrs, 219 bp,
35 bps, ns, TV. ✗ a l c, mc, at, LD 10. 🅰 Lt,
N, CH, CP 185, Ac, con 300, CF, 2 st. **£** BB
£47–£62, DB £75–£100, WB, ☑, Bk £7, L
£9, D £10·50, cc 1 2 3 4 5 6, Dep b.

■★★★★George, *George St, EH2 2PB.*
✆ 031-225 1251. C. ✉ 196 bedrs, 196 bp,
TV, Dgs. ✗ a l c, mc, at, LD 9. 🅰 Lt, N, CH,
TV, Dgs, CP 30, Ac, con 160, CF. **£** BB
£43–£53·60, DB £58–£91·60, WT
£415·45–£443·45, DT £69·10–£73·10,
DBB £59·35–£73·10, WB, ☑, Bk £6·60, L
£9·75, D £9·75, cc 1 2 3 4 5 6, Dep.

★★★★Ladbroke Dragonara, *Bells Mills,
Belford Rd, EH4 3DG.* ✆ 031-332 2545. C.
✉ 146 bedrs, 146 bp, TV. ✗ mc, LD 10.30.
🅰 Lt, N, CH, CP 90, G 28, Ac, con 400, CF,
21 BGf, 0 st, Dis. **£** BB £60·50–£66, DB
£82·50–£91, DBB £56–£74, WB, ☑, Bk
£5·75, L £7·50, D £10·50, cc 1 2 3 4 5 6.

★★★★M Royal Scot, *111 Glasgow Rd,
EH12 8NF.* ✆ 031-334 9191. C. ✉ 252
bedrs, 252 bp, TV, Dgs. ✗ a l c, mc, at, LD
10.30. 🅰 Lt, N, CH, Dgs, CP 350, Ac, sp, sb,
sol, gym, con, CF, 33 BGf, 0 st, Dis. **£** BB
£42·50–£45, DB £52–£56, WB, ☑, Bk
£5·50, L £9·50, D £9·50, cc 1 2 3 5 6,
Dep b.

★★★Albany, *39 Albany St, EH1 3QY.*
✆ 031-556 0397. RS Dec. C. ✉ 22 bedrs,
16 bp, 6 bps, TV, Dgs. ✗ a l c, mc, LD 10.
🅰 N, CH, TV, Dgs, Ac, con 30, CF, 4 BGf, 6
st. **£** BB £34–£49, DB £48–£68, WB, ☑, Bk
£3·75, L £7·50, D £10·50, cc 1 2 3 5.

★★★Barnton Thistle, *562 Queensferry
Rd, EH4 6AS.* ✆ 031-339 1144. C. ✉ 50
bedrs, 27 bp, 23 bps, ns, TV, Dgs. ✗ a l c,
mc, LD 9.30. 🅰 Lt, N, CH, TV, Dgs, CP 150, Ac,
con 120, CF, 2 st. **£** BB £40·75–£49·75, DB
£52·50–£04·50, WD, ☑, Dk £4·75, L £6·50,
D £8·50, cc 1 2 3 4 5 6, Dep b.

★★★Braid Hills, *134 Braid Rd, EH10
6JD* (2½ m S of A702). ✆ 031-447 8888. C.
✉ 68 bedrs, 68 bp, 2 ba, TV, Dgs. ✗ a l c,
mc, at, LD 8.45. 🅰 N, CH, TV, CP 30, Ac,
con 30, CF, 1 st. **£** BB £26–£35, DB £39–
£55, DBB £26, WB, ☑, cc 1 2 3 5 6, Dep b.

★★★Carlton, *North Bridge, EH1 1SD.*
✆ 031-556 7277. C. ✉ 220 bedrs, 220 bp,
TV, Dgs. ✗ a l c, mc, at, LD 10.30. 🅰 Lt, N,
CH, Ac, sp, sc, sb, sol, gym, con, CF. **£** BB
£37–£44, DB £54–£60, DBB £27–£53, WB,
☑, Bk £4·85, L £6·85, D £8·75,
cc 1 2 3 4 5 6, Dep b.

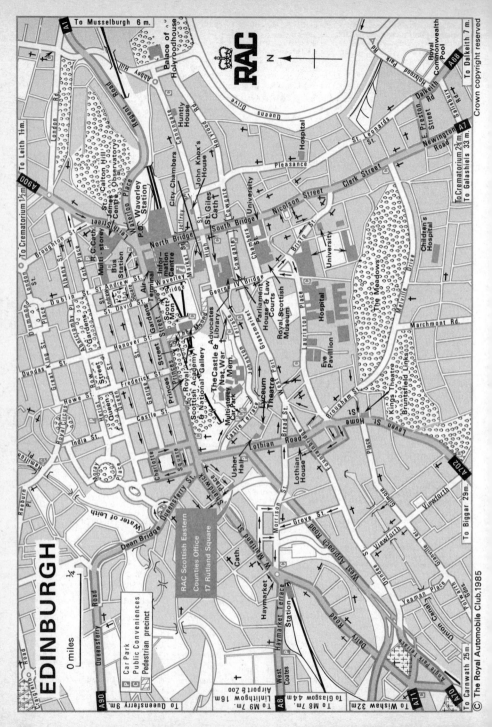

EDINBURGH

0 miles   ¼

P Car Park
C Public Conveniences
   Pedestrian precinct

RAC Scottish Eastern
Counties Office
17 Rutland Square

RAC

N

To Musselburgh 6 m.

Crown copyright reserved

© The Royal Automobile Club.1985

★★★M Crest, *Queensferry Rd, EH4 3HL.* ✆ 031-332 2442. C. ⋈ 120 bedrs, 120 bp, ns, TV, Dgs. ✖ a l c, mc, at, LD 9.45. 🅰 Lt, N, CH, Dgs, CP 120, Ac, con 170, CF, 3 st. £ BB fr £48·50, DB fr £68, WB, 🔟, Bk £5·50, D £9·25, cc 1 2 3 4 5 6, Dep b.

★★★Ellersly House, *Ellersly Rd, EH12 6HZ.* ✆ 031-337 6888. C. ⋈ 50 bedrs, 50 bp, TV, Dgs. ✖ a l c, mc, at, LD 8.30. 🅰 Lt, N, ch, CP 50, Ac, con 40, CF, 6 BGf, 2 st. £ BB £37, DB £54, WB, 🔢, Bk £4, D £9, cc 1 2 3 4 5 6.

★★★King James Thistle, *St James Centre, EH1 3SW.* ✆ 031-556 0111. C. ⋈ 162 bedrs, 117 bp, 45 bps, ns, TV, Dgs. ✖ a l c, LD 9.30. 🅰 Lt, N, CH, TV, Dgs, CP 15, Ac, con 250, CF, 1 st. £ BB £49·75–£56·75, DB £69·50–£79·50, WB, 🔢, Bk £4·75, cc 1 2 3 4 5 6, Dep b.▲

★★★Mount Royal, *53 Princes St, EH2 2DG.* ✆ 031-225 7161. C. ⋈ 153 bedrs, 145 bp, 4 ba, TV, Dgs. ✖ a l c, mc, at, LD 9. 🅰 Lt, N, CH, TV, Ac, con 120, CF, 6 st. £ BBc fr £35, DBc fr £51, WB, cc 1 2 3 4 5 6.

▤★★★Old Waverley, *43 Princes St, EH2 2DB.* ✆ 031-556 4648. C. ⋈ 66 bedrs, 57 bp, 9 bps, 4 ba, TV. ✖ a l c, at, LD 9. 🅰 Lt, N, CH, Dgs, Ac, con 24, CF, 21 st. £ BB £38, DB £56, DBB £27–£47, WB, 🔟, Bk £4·50, L £5·50, D £9·50, cc 1 2 3 4 5 6, Dep a.

★★★M Post House (TH), *Corstorphine Rd, EH12 6UA.* ✆ 031-334 8221. C. ⋈ 208 bedrs, 208 bp, TV, Dgs. ✖ a l c, mc, at, LD 10.15. 🅰 Lt, N, CH, Dgs, CP 158, Ac, con 150, CF, 1 st. £ BB fr £44, DB fr £58·50, WB, 🔟, cc 1 2 3 4 5 6.

★★★Roxburghe, *38 Charlotte Sq, EH2 4HG.* ✆ 031-225 3921. C. ⋈ 76 bedrs, 61 bp, 15 bps, TV, Dgs. ✖ a l c, mc, at, LD 9.45. 🅰 Lt, N, CH, Ac, con 200, CF, 2 BGf, 2 st. £ BBc £40·50–£55, DBc £52·50–£90, WT, 🔟, Bk £3, L £4·50, D £9·50, cc 1 2 3 4 5 6, Dep.

★★Clarendon, *18 Grosvenor St, EH12 5EG.* ✆ 031-337 7033. C. ⋈ 55 bedrs. 53 bp, 2 ba, TV, Dgs. ✖ mc, LD 9.30. 🅰 Lt, N, ch, Ac, con 25, CF, 3 st. £ BB £30, DB £50, DBB £25–£39, WB, 🔟, Bk £3·50, D £7·50, cc 1 2 3 4 5 6, Dep.

★★Hailes, *2 Wester Hailes Centre, EH14 2SW.* ✆ 031-442 3382.

★★Harp, *St John's Rd, EH12 8AX.* (Corstorphine) (3¼ m W A8). ✆ 031-334 4750. C. ⋈ 25 bedrs, 10 bp, 15 bps, TV, Dgs. ✖ a l c, mc, LD 9. 🅰 N, CH, Dgs, CP 50, Ac, con 120, CF, 4 BGf, 1 st, Dis. £ BB £21·20–£30·50, DB £32·80–£41, WT £175–£227·50, DT £25–£42·50, DBB £21–£38·50, WB, 🔟, Bk £3·25, L £4, D £8, cc 1 2 3 5, Dep.

★★Iona, *17 Strathearn Pl, EH9 2AL.* ✆ 031-447 6264. RS New Year. C. ⋈ 17 bedrs, 2 bp, 2 bps, 9 sh, 4 ba, Dgs. ✖ mc, LD 9. 🅰 Cll, TV, Dgs, CP 20, CF, 4 BGf, 2 st. £ BB £19–£20, DB £35–£39, WB, 🔢, Bk £3·50, L £4·50, D £8, cc 1 3.

▤★★Murrayfield, *18 Corstorphine Rd, EH12 6HN.* ✆ 031-337 1844. C. ⋈ 22 bedrs, 7 bp, 6 ba, TV, Dgs. ✖ a l c, mc, at, LD 9.30. 🅰 N, ch, TV, Dgs, CP 40, Ac, con 40, CF, 6 BGf, 2 st. £ BB £22–£25·50, DB £33–£36·50, 🔟, Bk £3, L £3·95, D £4·50, cc 1 2 3 5 6.

North British. *Being Refurbished.*

Amaragua, G, z (Unl), *10 Kilmaurs Ter, EH16 5DR.* ✆ 031-667 6775. C. ⋈ 6 bedrs, 2 ba, Dgs. 🅰 CH, TV, ns. £ BB £9–£11, DB £17–£20, 🔟.

Arden, H, z, *18 Royal Ter, EH7 5AQ.* ✆ 031-556 8688.

Buchan, G, z (Unl), *3 Coates Gdns, EH12 5LG.* ✆ 031-337 1045. C. ⋈ 9 bedrs, 3 ba, TV, Dgs. 🅰 ch, TV, CF. £ BB £10–£10·50, DB £18–£19, WT (b) £101·50–£122·30, WT (c) £70, DT £14·50–£17·50, 🔟, Bk £3.

Cumberland, PH, y (Unl), *1 West Coates, EH12 5JQ.* ✆ 031-337 1198. C. ⋈ 7 bedrs, 2 bp, 5 bps, 2 ba, TV, Dgs. 🅰 CH, TV, CP 25, 0 st. £ BB £18·50, DB £37, 🔟.

Dorstan, PH, z (Unl), *7 Priestfield Rd, EH16 5HJ.* ✆ 031-667 6721. Closed Xmas & New Year. C. ⋈ 14 bedrs, 3 bp, 1 bps, 2 sh, 3 ba, Dgs. 🅰 CH, TV, CP 9, CF, 2 BGf, 2 st. £ BB £9·75–£10·75, DB £19·50–£26, 🔟.

Galloway, G, z (Unl), *22 Dean Park Cres, EH4 1PH.* ✆ 031-332 3672. C. ⋈ 10 bedrs, 1 bp, 1 bps, 3 ba, Dgs. 🅰 CH, TV, Dgs, CF. £ BB £9–£12, DB £18–£30, WT (c) £54–£72, DT (b) £13–£16, 🔟, Bk £2, D £4.

Glendale, PH, x (Unl), *5 Lady Rd, EH16 5PA.* ✆ 031-667 6588.

Glenisla, PH, z (Unl), *12 Lygon Rd, EH16 5QB.* ✆ 031-667 4098. Closed 2-3 weeks winter. C. ⋈ 9 bedrs, 2 ba, Dgs. 🅰 CH, TV, Dgs, CP 5, CF, 2 st. £ BB £10·50–£12, DB £19–£20, DT (b) £15–£17·50, 🔟.

Golf View, PH, z (Unl), *2 Marchhall Rd, EH16 5HR.* ✆ 031-667 4812. Open Apr–Oct. C. ⋈ 11 bedrs, 3 bp, 3 bps, 4 ba, Dgs. 🅰 CH, TV, CP 11, CF, 5 BGf, 1 st, Dis. £ BB £11·50–£15, DB £18·40–£27·60, 🔟.

Hillview, G, z (Unl), *92 Dalkeith Rd, EH16 5AF.* ✆ 031-667 1523. C. ⋈ 8 bedrs, 1 bp, 2 ba, Dgs. 🅰 CH, TV, CP 3, 3 st. £ BB £8·50–£10, DB £17–£23, DT (b) £14–£16, 🔟, Bk £2, D £5·50.

Kariba, PH, z (Unl), *10 Granville Ter, EH10 4PQ.* ✆ 031-229 3773. C. ⋈ 7 bedrs, 1 bps, 4 sh, 2 ba, TV. 🅰 CH, TV, ns, CP 3. £ BB £12–£18, DB £18–£25.

Kildonan Lodge, H, z (R), *27 Craigmillar Park, EH16 5PE.* ✆ 031-667 2793. Closed Jan. C. ⋈ 9 bedrs, 3 ba, TV, Dgs. 🅰 CH, CP 20, CF, 4 st. £ BB £9·50–£12·50, DB £17–£23, WT (b) £90–£108, 🔟, D £9·50, cc 2.

Lygon, PH, z (Unl), *4 Lygon Rd, EH16 5QE.* ✆ 031-667 1374. C. ⋈ 6 bedrs, 2 ba, Dgs. 🅰 CH, TV, Dgs, CF, 3 st. £ BB £9·50–£10, DB £17–£18, DT (b) £14–£14·50, 🔟, Bk £2·50, D £4·50.

Manor House, H, z, *Hailes Av, EH13 0LZ.* ✆ 031-441 1176.

Marchhall, H, z, *14 Marchhall Cres, EH16 5HL.* ✆ 031-667 2743. C. ⋈ 11 bedrs, 5 sh, 3 ba, ns, TV, Dgs. 🅰 CH, TV, CF. £ BB £10–£14, DB £22–£26, WT (c) £75–£95, DT (b) £15–£19, 🔟.

Marvin, G, z (Unl), *46 Pilrig St, EH6 5AL.* ✆ 031-554 6605. Closed Xmas. C. ⋈ 7 bedrs, 1 bp, 1 sh, 2 ba, TV, Dgs. 🅰 CH, TV, Dgs, ns, CP 6, CF, 5 st. £ BB £9·50, DB £16–£25, WT (c) £50–£78·75, 🔟, Bk £2·50.

Newington, G, z (Unl), *18 Newington Rd, EH9 1QS.* ✆ 031-667 3356. C. ⋈ 8 bedrs, 2 sh, 3 ba, Dgs. 🅰 CH, TV, Dgs, CP 3, CF, 2 BGf, 2 st. £ BB £12–£13, DB £20–£21, WT (c) £50, 🔟, Bk £4.

Roselea, G, (Unl), *11 Mayfield Rd, EH9 2NG.* ✆ 031-667 6115. C. ⋈ 6 bedrs, 2 ba, Dgs. 🅰 TV, ns, CP 3, CF. £ BB £9–£11, DB £17–£20, WT £57·50–£72, DT £12·50–£15, 🔟, D £4·50.

Salisbury, PH, z (RI), *45 Salisbury Rd, EH16 5AA.* ✆ 031-667 1264. C. ⋈ 14 bedrs, 2 bps, 5 ba, Dgs. 🅰 CH, TV, ns, CP

12, CF, 2 BGf, 10 st. £ BB £8–£11, DB £16–£22, WT £48–£66, 🔟, Bk £2.

Salisbury View, G, z (Unl), *64 Dalkeith Rd, EH16 5AE.* ✆ 031-667 1138. C. ⋈ 6 bedrs, 2 ba. 🅰 CH, TV, CP 6, 2 BGf, 2 st. £ BB £7·50–£9·50, DB £15–£18, 🔟.

Shamilar, G, z, *20 Newington Rd, EH9 1QS.* ✆ 031-667 2827. C. ⋈ 9 bedrs, 3 bps, 1 sh, 3 ba. 🅰 ch, TV, CP 2. £ BB £8·50–£10, DB £17–£20, WT (c) £50–£63, 🔟, Bk £2·50.▲

Sharon, G, z (Unl), *1 Kilmaurs Ter, EH16 5BZ.* ✆ 031-667 2002. Closed Xmas & New Year. C 5. ⋈ 9 bedrs, 3 ba. 🅰 CH, TV, ns, CP 5. £ BB £8–£10, DB £15–£18, 🔟.

Sherwood, G, z (Unl), *42 Minto St, EH9 2BR.* ✆ 031-667 1200. Open Feb–Nov. C. ⋈ 6 bedrs, 1 ba, Dgs. 🅰 CH, TV, Dgs, CP 4, 7 st. £ BB £9–£10, DB £16–£18, 🔟.

Southdown, G, (Unl), *20 Craigmillar Park, EH16 5PS.* ✆ 031-667 2410. C. ⋈ 9 bedrs, 7 sh, 3 ba, TV, Dgs. 🅰 CH, TV, ns, CP 8, CF. £ BB £8–£9·50, DB £15–£19, WT £52·50–£67·50, 🔟.

Stewart House, H, z, *17 Merchiston Av, EH10 4PJ.* ✆ 031-229 5289. C. ⋈ 8 bedrs, 1 bp, 7 bps. 🅰 CH, TV, Dgs, ns, CF. £ BB £20–£26, DB £28–£40, 🔟, Bk £5, cc 2 3.

Thirty Nine Steps, G, z (Unl), *62 South Trinity Rd, EH5 3NX.* ✆ 031-552 1349.

Thrums, PH, z (RI), *14 Minto St, EH9 1RQ.* ✆ 031-667 5545. C. ⋈ 8 bedrs, 1 bp, 1 bps, 2 ba, TV, Dgs. ✖ a l c. 🅰 CH, TV, CP 7, CF, 2 BGf, 1 st. £ BB £7·50–£9·50, DB £15–£18, WT (b) £70, WT (c) £42, DT (b) £12–£13·50, 🔟.▲

Villa San Monique, G, z (Unl), *4 Wilton Rd, EH16 5NY.* ✆ 031-667 1403. C 2. ⋈ 5 bedrs, 2 ba, ns. 🅰 CH, TV, ns, CP 8, 2 BGf, 1 st. £ DB £14–£17, 🔟.

Repairers: Alexanders of Edinburgh Ltd, Semple St. ✆ 031-229 3331.
Scotrad Ltd, 477 Gorgie Rd. ✆ 031-443 4597.
Sloan, J M & Co Ltd, 454 Gorgie Rd. ✆ 031-346 1661.
Rescue Service: Cochrane's Garage (Edinburgh) Ltd, 12 West Mayfield. ✆ 031-667 4475.
David Waddell & Son Ltd, Colinton Motor Garage, Spylaw St, Colinton. ✆ 031-441 1551.
Howden Motor Repairs, 198 Glasgow Rd. ✆ 031-334 8060.
J & T Motors, Auto Engineers, 131 Newbigging, Musselburgh. ✆ 031-665 2788.
Leith Walk Tyre & Accessories Ltd, Leith Walk Service Station, 37 Haddington Pl. ✆ 031-356 2195.
J & D McNeill (Motors), 3 St Albans Rd. ✆ 031-667 9333.
New Town Garage, 17 Circus La. ✆ 031-556 4187.
Renault Ltd, Gorgie Rd. ✆ 031-444 1673.
Restalrig Service Station, 126 Restalrig Rd. ✆ 031-554 3175.
Richmond Garage, 31 Rankeillor St. ✆ 031-667 1155.
Scott, J B & Son, Kingsknowe Garage, Lanark Rd. Slateford. ✆ 031-443 2936.
Stirling & Wilson, Plewlands Garage, Morningside Dr. ✆ 031-447 6237.

EDZELL Tayside (Angus). Map 41E
Pop 751. Brechin 6, London 459, Edinburgh 85, Glasgow 104, Montrose 12, Stonehaven 22.

EC Thur. **Golf** Edzell 18h. **See** Castle and Gardens, The Retreat (Glen Esk), Folk Museum 8½ m NW.

★★★**Glenesk,** *High St, DD9 7TF.*
✆ (035 64) 319. C. ⊨ 25 bedrs, 19 bp, 3 ba, TV, Dgs. ✖ a l c, mc, at, LD 9.45. ⓓ CH, TV, Dgs, CP 150, U 8, pf, con 150, CF, 3 st. £ BB £21–£24, DB £38–£44, WT £185·50, DBB £25·50–£28·50, ⓣ, cc 2 5.

★★**Panmure Arms,** *High St, DD9 7TA.*
✆ (035 64) 420. C. ⊨ 16 bedrs, 5 bp, 11 bps, TV, Dgs. ✖ mc, at, LD 9. ⓓ CH, Dgs, CP 30, Ac, sp, pf, sc, sb, sol, con 150, CF, 1 st. £ BB fr £23, DB fr £36, WT £183, DT £34, DBB £31, WB, ⓣ, Bk £3, L £3·75, D £8, cc 1 2 3 5.

EILEAN IARMAIN Isle of Skye, Highland (Inverness-shire). Map 38D
Pop 200. Armadale (Fy to Mallaig) 8, London 541, Dumbarton 6, Edinburgh 174, Glasgow 154, Kyleakin (Fy to Kyle of Lochalsh) 14.

◼★**Eilean Iarmain,** *Camus Croise, Isle Ornsay, Isle of Skye, IV43 8QR.*
✆ (047 13) 332. C. ⊨ 7 bedrs, 3 ba, Dgs. ✖ mc, at, LD 8.30. ⓓ CH, CP 10, pf, con 25. £ BB £9–£14, DB £18–£28, WT £154– £189, DBB £18–£24, WB, ② 10%, Bk £4, L £5, D £9, cc 1 3.

ELGIN Grampian (Moray). Map 40B
Pop 19,245. Rothes 9½, London 527, Banff 33, Craigellachie 13, Carrbridge 41, Edinburgh 152, Glasgow 170, Grantown-on-Spey 34, Huntly 27, Inverness 39.
EC Wed. **Golf** Hard Hillock 18h. **See** Ruins of Cathedral (13th cent), St Giles Church, Muckle Cross, Museum, Covesea Caves, Duffus Castle remains 3 m NW.
ⓣ 17 High St. ✆ Elgin (0343) 3388.

★★★**Eight Acres,** *Sheriff Mill, IV30 3UL.*
✆ (0343) 3077. ⊨ 58 bedrs, 33 bp, 21 bps, 4 sh, 2 ba, TV, Dgs. ✖ a l c, mc, at, LD 9. ⓓ N, CH, TV, Dgs, CP 200, Ac, sp, sc, sb, sol, gym, con 100, CF, 8 st. £ BB £26·50, DB £40·50, DBB £34·50, WB, ⓣ, Bk £4·50, L £5·50, D £8, cc 1 2 3 4 5 6.

★★**St Leonards,** *Duffy Av, IV30 1QS.*
✆ (0343) 7350. C. ⊨ 17 bedrs, 8 bp, 3 ba, TV, Dgs. ✖ mc, LD 8. ⓓ ch, TV, Dgs, CP 60, Ac, con 150, CF, 6 st. £ BB £15–£18, DB £26–£30, DT £25, WB, ②, Bk £3·50, L £4, D £8, cc 1 3.

Rescue Service: Alex D Scott, Sher-Morr Garages, Sheriff Mill. ✆ (0343) 7121.

ELIE Fife. Map 37C
Pop 802. Largo 5, London 417, Edinburgh 43, Glasgow 70, Kirkcaldy 18, Kinross 27, Leven 8.
EC Wed. **Golf** Elie 18h & 9h. **See** 17th cent Church, Chapel ruins, Castle.

Elms, G, x (Rl), *Park Pl, KY9 1DH.*
✆ (0333) 330404. C. ⊨ 7 bedrs, 1 bps, 2 ba. ⓓ CH, TV, CF, 1 BGf, 1 st. £ BB £7·50– £8, DB £15–£20, WT (b) £80–£100, WT (c) £50–£60, DT (b) £12–£13, ⓣ, Bk £2·50, D £4·50.

ELLON Grampian (Aberdeenshire). Map 41D
Pop 5,830. Aberdeen 16, London 508, Banff 38, Edinburgh 133, Fraserburgh 26, Glasgow 152, Peterhead 17.
EC Wed. **MD** Mon. **Golf** Macdonald 18h. **See** Haddo House 6 m NW, Castle ruins, Old Bridge, Toll House.

ⓣ Market St Car Park. ✆ Ellon (0358) 20730.

◼★★★**M Ladbroke,** *South Rd, AB4 9NP.*
✆ (0358) 20666. C. ⊨ 40 bedrs, 40 bp, TV, Dgs. ✖ mc, at, LD 9·30. ⓓ N, CH, CP 200, Ac, con, CF, 3 BGf, 1 st, Dis. £ WB, Bk £3·75, D £8·50, cc 1 2 3 5 6.

★**New Inn,** *Market St, AB4 9JD.*
✆ (0358) 20425.

Rescue Service: County Garage, 99 Station Rd. ✆ (0358) 20206.
Neil Ross (Motors) Ltd, 41 Bridge St. ✆ (0358) 20311.

ERSKINE Strathclyde (Renfrewshire). Maps 48E, 35F and 36E.
Pop 8,977. Glasgow 10, London 397, M8 Motorway ½, Dumbarton 6, Edinburgh 55, Largs 24, Paisley 6.
EC Wed. **Golf** Erskine 18h.

★★★**M Crest,** *PA8 6AN.* ✆ 041-812 0123. C. ⊨ 200 bedrs, 200 bp, ns, TV, Dgs. ✖ a l c, mc, at, LD 10. ⓓ Lt, N, CH, TV, Dgs, CP 350, Ac, con 1000, CF. £ BB fr £48·25, DB fr £62·50, WB, ⓣ, Bk £5·25, D £9·95, cc 1 2 3 4 5 6, Dep b.

ETTRICK BRIDGE Borders (Selkirkshire). Map 30B
Pop 60. Langholm 35, London 348, Edinburgh 44, Glasgow 76, Selkirk 6.
EC Thur. **Golf** Selkirk 9h.

◼★★★**Ettrickshaws,** *TD7 5HW.* ✆ (0750) 52229. Closed mid Dec–mid Feb. C 9. ⊨ 6 bedrs, 5 bp, TV, Dgs. ✖ mc, at, LD 8.30. ⓓ CH, ns, CP 8, pf, 1 st. £ BB £22–£28, DB £23–£30, WB, DBB £23–£30, ②, D £11, cc 1 2 3 4 5 6.

FALKIRK Central (Stirlingshire). Map 36F
See also POLMONT
Pop 36,881. Amadale 7½, London 394, M9 Motorway 2, Abington 43, Arrochar 56, Dumbarton 35, Edinburgh 25, Glasgow 23, Kincardine 7, Lanark 28, Peebles 41, Stirling 11.
EC Wed. **Golf** Falkirk 18h. **See** Falkirk Town Steeple, Old Parish Church, Mausoleum (Callendar Park), Roman remains (Antonine Wall, presumed site of city at Camelon, etc).

★★★**Stakis Park,** *Camelon Rd, Arnothill, FK1 5RY.* ✆ (0324) 28331. C. ⊨ 55 bedrs, 55 bp, TV, Dgs. ✖ a l c, mc, at, LD 9.45. ⓓ Lt, N, CH, Dgs, CP 100, Ac, con 250, CF, 1 st. £ WB, Bk £2·50, L £2, D £4·40, cc 1 2 3 5, Dep b.

Repairer: A Crawford & Son Ltd, East End Garage, Callendar Rd. ✆ (0324) 24204.
Specialist Body Repairer: J B Stevenson Ltd, High Station Rd. ✆ (0324) 37601.

FEARN Highland (Ross & Cromarty). Map 43E
Alness 14, London 562, Bonar Bridge 15, Dingwall 26, Edinburgh 187, Glasgow 194.
EC Wed. **Golf** Tain 18h. **See** Abbey Ruins.

Rescue Service: Fearn Service Station, Mounteagle Pl, Hill of Fearn. ✆ (086 283) 2216.

FEARNAN Tayside (Perthshire). Map 36A.
Pop 200. Killin 14, London 449, Edinburgh 78, Glasgow 68, Kenmore 4, Lochearnhead 20, Perth 40.
EC Wed. **Golf** Taymouth Castle 18h.

◼★**Tigh-an-Loan,** *PH15 2PF.*
✆ Kenmore (08873) 249. C. ⊨ 10 bedrs, 2 ba, Dgs. ✖ mc, at, LD 7.30. ⓓ ch, TV, Dgs, CP 25, pf, CF, 2 st. £ Bk £2·50, L £2·50, D £6·50.

FIONNPHORT Isle of Mull. Map 34A
Craignure 35, London (Fy) 514, Edinburgh (Fy) 257, Glasgow (Fy) 128, Salen 38.

Rescue Service: Alistair McDougall, Corrie-Glen. ✆ (068 17) 294.

FOCHABERS Grampian (Moray). Map 40B
Pop 1,550. Keith 7½, London 529, Banff 24, Craigellachie 13, Edinburgh 154, Elgin 99, Glasgow 172.
EC Wed. **Golf** Spey Bay 18h. **See** Church.

★★**Gordon Arms,** *80 High Street, IV32 7DH.* ✆ (0343) 820508. C. ⊨ 13 bedrs, 7 bp, 1 bps, 3 ba, TV, Dgs. ✖ mc, at, LD 8.30. ⓓ CH, Dgs, CP 50, Ac, CP 100, CF, 2 BGf, 0 st, Dis. £ BB £18–£28, DB £30–£40, WT £140–£200, DT £27–£30, DBB £25–£29, WB, ⓣ, Bk £3, L £3·50, D £7, cc 1 2 3 5.

★**Grant Arms,** *42 High St, IV32 7DX.*
✆ (0343) 820202.

FORFAR Tayside (Angus). Map 37A
Pop 12,742. Glenrothes 37, London 442, Blairgowrie 20, Brechin 11, Dundee 14, Edinburgh 67, Glasgow 87, Montrose 17, Perth 30.
EC Thur. **Golf** Forfar 18h. **See** Forfar Old Parish Church Steeple and the Bell, Meffan Institute Museum, Parks, Balmashanner War Memorial (Balmashanner Hill), Restenneth Priory ruins 1½ m NE, Glamis Castle 5½ m SW, Kirkwynd Cottages (Angus Folk Museum) at Glamis 5½ m SW.

★★**Royal,** *Castle St, DD8 3AE.* ✆ (0307) 62691.

FORRES Grampian (Moray). Map 40B
Pop 7,440, Grantown-on-Spey 21, London 527, Carrbridge 26, Craigellachie 23, Edinburgh 152, Elgin 12, Glasgow 169, Inverness 27.
EC Wed. **Golf** Muiryshade 18h. **See** Market Cross, Falconer Museum, Witches Stone, Nelson Tower (fine view), Sueno's Stone 1 m NE.
ⓣ Falconer Museum. ✆ Forres (0309) 72938.

◼★★**Park,** *Victoria Rd, IV36 0BN.*
✆ (0309) 72328.
◼★★**Ramnee,** *Victoria Rd, IV36 0BN.*
✆ (0309) 72410. Open Feb–Dec. C. ⊨ 20 bedrs, 9 bp, 4 bps, 3 ba, TV. ✖ mc, LD 9. ⓓ CH, TV, Dgs, CP 50, U 1, con 80, CF, 2 st. £ BB fr £18·50, DB fr £28·75, DBB fr £28·75, ②, Bk £4, L £5, D £9·20, cc 1 2 3 6, Dep a.

Regency, G, z (Unl), *66 High St, IV36 0PQ.* ✆ (0309) 72558.

Rescue Service: Dickson Motors (Forres) Ltd, Tytler St. ✆ (0309) 72122.
P S Nicholson (Forres) Ltd, Bogton Pl. ✆ (0309) 72142.

FORSINARD Highland (Sutherland). Map 43A
Helmsdale 24, London 627, Edinburgh 252, Glasgow 259, Melvich 15, Thurso 28.
Golf Reay 18h.

★★**Forsinard,** *KW13 6YT.*
✆ (064 17) 221. Open Apr–Oct, RS Easter. C. ⊨ 10 bedrs, 6 bp, 2 bps, 1 ba, Dgs.

✗ mc, at, LD 9. 🅿 CH, TV, Dgs, ns, CP 30, pf, CF, 1 BGf, 1 st, Dis. **£** BB £13–£13·50, DB £24–£29, DBB £21·50–£24, 🄶, Bk £5, L £5, D £8·50, cc 1 3, Dep a.

FORT AUGUSTUS Highland (Inverness). Map 39C
Pop 1,000. Fort William 31, London 521 (Fy 524), Carrbridge 49, Edinburgh 155, Glasgow 130, Invergarry 7, Invermoriston 6.
EC Wed. **Golf** Inverness 18h. **See** St Benedict's Abbey, Inchnacardoch Forest, General Wade's Road over Corrieyarrick Pass, Loch Ness, Caledonian Canal.
🄸 Car Park. **** Fort Augustus (0320) 6367.

★★Lovat, Main Rd, PH32 4BE. **** (0320) 6706. Open Dec–Oct. C. **🚗** 24 bedrs, 2 bp, 1 sh, 6 ba, Dgs. **✗** mc, at, LD 8. 🅿 ch, TV, Dgs. CP 50, Ac, con 40, CF, 0 st. **£** BB £13–£16·50, DB £26–£33, WT £120–£160, DT £20–£25, DBB £21–£24·50, WB, 🄸, Bk £3, L £4·90, D £8.

Rescue Service: West End Garage, Main St. **** (0320) 6247.

FORT WILLIAM Highland (Inverness-shire). Map 39E
Pop 4,270. Ballachulish 14, London 490, Crianlarich 51, Dalmally 64, Dalwhinnie 46, Edinburgh 132, Glasgow 99, Invergarry 25, Kingussie 47, Mallaig 44, Oban 48.
EC Wed (win). **Golf** Fort William 18h. **See** Ben Nevis (highest mountain in Gt Britain, 4,418 ft, annual foot race to summit and back 1st Sat in Sept), West Highland Museum, Inverlochy Castle ruins 2 m NW.
🄸 Travel Centre. **** Fort William (0397) 3581.

🄼**★★★M Ladbroke,** PH33 6TG. **** (0397) 3117. RS Winter. C. **🚗** 61 bedrs, 61 bp, 2 ba, TV, Dgs. **✗** mc, at, LD 9.30. 🅿 N, CH, CP 70, Ac, sb, con 70, CF, 12 BGf, 4 st. **£** BB £25–£35, DB £48–£54, WT £131–£181, DBB £41–£43, WB, 🄸, Bk £5·50, L £2·95, D £9, cc 1 2 3 5 6, Dep b.

★★M Croit Anna, Druimarbin, PH33 6RR. **** (0397) 2268. C. **🚗** 96 bedrs, 40 bp, 22 bps, 34 sh, 20 ba, Dgs. **✗** mc, at, LD 8·30. 🅿 N, ch, TV, Dgs, CP 70, Ac, con 100, CF, 2 BGf, 0 st, Dis. **£** BB £17·50–£19·50, DB £33–£39, WB, 🄶, Bk £4, L £6, D £8, cc 1 3 6.

★★Grand, Gordon Sq. PH33 6DX. **** (0397) 2928. C. **🚗** 30 bedrs, 24 bp, 6 bps, TV, Dgs. **✗** a l c, mc, at, LD 8.30. 🅿 N, CH, CP 20, Ac, con 120, CF, 8 st. **£** BB £12·50–£18·50, DB £24–£33, WT fr £135, DT fr £21, DBB £19, WB, 🄶, Bk £3·25, L £2·50, D £7, cc 1 2 3 5 6, Dep b.

🄼**★★Highland,** Union Rd, PH33 6QY. **** (0397) 2291. C. **🚗** 58 bedrs, 26 bp, 12 bps, 6 ba, TV, Dgs. **✗** mc, at, LD 9.30. 🅿 Lt, N, CII, Dgs, CP 00, Ac, con 120, CF, 3 st. **£** BB £15–£19, DB £30–£38, WT £149–£189, DT £25–£29, DBB £23–£27, WB, 🄶, 10%, Bk £3·50, L £4, D £8, cc 1 2 3 4 5 6, Dep a.

★★Milton, PH33 6TG. **** (0397) 2331. Open May–Oct. C. **🚗** 61 bedrs, 35 bp, 6 ba, Dgs. **✗** mc, at, LD 8·30. 🅿 N, CH, TV, Dgs, CP 200, con 250, CF, 3 BGf, 1 st, Dis. **£** BB £15·50–£21·20, DB £27–£38, WT £127–£166, DT £24·50–£28·50, DBB £21·50–£27·50, WB, 🄸, Bk £3·25, L £3, D £8·10, cc 1 2 3 6, Dep a.

🄼**★★Nevis Bank,** Belford Rd, PH33 6BY. **** (0397) 2595. C. **🚗** 24 bedrs, 6 bp, 4 ba,

---

Dgs. **✗** a l c, mc, at, LD 8.30. 🅿 CH, TV, Dgs, CP 17, Ac, con 40, CF, 1 st. **£** BB £13·50, DB £24–£28, WT £125, DT £19·50, DBB £17·50–£19·50, WB, 🄶, Bk £3·50, L £3·25, D £6·50, cc 1 2 3 6, Dep.▲

Rescue Service: Colin MacMillan's Garage, Heathercroft. **** (0397) 3877. Wm Gilbert, Ness Motors Ltd, North Rd. **** (0397) 4913.

FRASERBURGH Grampian (Aberdeenshire). Map 41B
Pop 12,900. Mintlaw 13, London 534, Aberdeen 42, Banff 23, Edinburgh 160, Glasgow 179, Huntly 39, Peterhead 17.
EC Wed. **Golf** Fraserburgh 18h. **See** Lighthouse, 16th cent Wine Tower (old house), 18th cent Cross.
🄸 Saltoun Sq. **** Fraserburgh (034 62) 2315.

★★Alexandra, High St, AB4 5HE. **** (0346) 28249. C. **🚗** 36 bedrs, 22 bp, 2 sh, 3 ba, TV, Dgs. **✗** a l c, mc, at, LD 9. 🅿 Lt, N, CH, TV, Dgs, CP 30, U 6, sb, con 100, CF, 1 st. **£** BB £15–£17, DB £26–£32, WT £90, DT £25·50, DBB £21–£23, 🄸, Bk 2·50, L £3, D £5·50, cc 1 2 3 5 6.

Rescue Service: W J Ironside, 94 Commerce St. **** (034 62) 28514.

FREUCHIE Fife. Map 37C
Pop 869. Glenrothes 4, London 409, Cupar 8, Dundee 20, Edinburgh 34, Glasgow 59, Kirkcaldy 9½, Perth 19.
Golf Falkland 9h.

★★Lomond Hills, High St, KY7 7EY. **** Falkland (0337) 57329. C. **🚗** 17 bedrs, 9 bp, 1 bps, 4 sh, 3 ba, TV, Dgs. **✗** a l c, mc, at, LD 9.15. 🅿 CH, TV, Dgs, CP 60, sb, sol, con 120, CF, 0 st. **£** BB £14–£20, DB £24–£31, WT £300–£325, DT £26–£28, DBB £21–£27, 🄸, Bk £2·50, L £5·25, D £7, cc 1 2 3 4 5 6.

FRIOCKHEIM Tayside (Angus). Map 27A
Pop 827. Glenrothes 41, London 446, Dundee 19, Edinburgh 71, Forfar 9, Glasgow 95, Montrose 11, Stonehaven 33.
EC Thur. **Golf** Arbroath 18h.

Rescue Service: Blair's Garage, Guthrie. **** (024 12) 219.

GAIRLOCH Highland (Ross & Cromarty). Map 42E
Pop 250. Achnasheen 28, London 596, Edinburgh 221, Glasgow 225, Ullapool 57.
EC Wed. **Golf** Gairloch 9h. **See** Loch Maree, View indicator and vantage points at Gairloch, Crask and Red Point, Slattadale Forest Walk and Victoria Falls, Inverewe Gardens 5 m NE.
🄸 Achtercairn. **** Gairloch (0445) 2130.

🄼**★★★Gairloch,** IV21 2BL. **** (0445) 2001. Open Apr–Sep. C. **🚗** 50 bedrs, 36 bp, 10 bps, 4 ba, Dgs. **✗** mc, at, LD 9. 🅿 Lt, N, ch, TV, Dgs, CP 50, tc, pf, CF, 4 BGf, 0 st, Dis. **£** BB £25–£28, DB £40–£46, DBB £20–£37, WB, 🄸, Bk £4, L £3, D £9, cc 1 2 3 5 6, Dep.

Rescue Service: John Bain & Son, North Erradale. **** North Erradale (044 585) 213. Mackenzie & Maclennan, The Garage. **** (0445) 2255.

GALASHIELS Borders (Selkirkshire). Map 30B

Pop 13,000. Melrose 4, London 344, Edinburgh 31, Glasgow 67, Haddington 32, Jedburgh 17, Kelso 18, Lauder 13, Peebles 18, Selkirk 6½.
EC Wed. **Golf** Ladhope 18h. **See** War Memorial, 17th cent Mercat Cross, Old Gala House, Home of Sir Walter Scott at Abbotsford 2 m SE, Dryburgh Abbey 7 m SE.
🄸 Bank St. **** Galashiels (0896) 55551.

🏨**★★★Kingsknowes,** Selkirk Rd, TD1 3HY, **** (0896) 3478. C. **🚗** 10 bedrs, 7 bp, 1 ba, TV, Dgs. **✗** a l c, mc, LD 8.45. 🅿 CH, CP 50, tc, CF, 5 st. **£** BB £23–£26, DB £36–£40, DT £38, DBB £30·50–£33·50, WB, 🄶, Bk £3·50, L £7·50, D £7·50, cc 1 2 3 5 6, Dep b.

🏨**★★★Woodlands House,** Windyknowe Rd, TD1 1RQ. **** (0896) 4722.
🄼**★Royal,** Channel St, TD1 1BA. **** (0896) 2918.
Buckholmburn, G, x (R), Edinburgh Rd, TD1 2EY. **** (0896) 2697. C. **🚗** 8 bedrs, 4 sh, 2 ba, Dgs. 🅿 CH, TV, Dgs, ns, CP 20, CF, 1 st. **£** BB £11, DB £22, 🄸, Bk £3, L £3, D £5, cc 1 3 5.

Rescue Service: John Robertson (Motor Engineer), Gala Lane, Market St. **** (0896) 56005.

GARVE Highland (Ross & Cromarty). Map 39B
Pop 149. Contin 6, London 555 (Fy 553), Achnasheen 16, Beauly 15, Dingwall 13, Edinburgh 184 (Fy 182), Glasgow 191 (Fy 182), Inverness 26 (Fy 22), Ullapool 33.
EC Tue. **Golf** Strathpeffer 18h. **See** Loch Garve, General Wade's Bridge.

🄼**★★Garve,** IV23 2PR. **** (099 75) 205.
🄼**★Inchbae Lodge,** Inchbae, IV23 2PH. **** (099 75) 269. C. **🚗** 6 bedrs, 3 bp, 2 ba, annexe 6 bedrs, 6 bps, Dgs. **✗** a l c, mc, at, LD 9.30. 🅿 CH, Dgs, CP 20, con 25, CF, 6 BGf, 1 st, Dis. **£** BB £12·75–£18, DB £25·50–£32, DBB £22·25–£27·25, WB, 🄸, Bk £3·50, L £3·50, D £9·50–£10.
🄼**★Aultguish Inn,** IV23 2PQ. (10 m NW A835). **** Aultguish (099 75) 254.

GATEHOUSE OF FLEET Dumfries & Galloway (Kirkcudbrightshire). Map 29E
Pop 890. Castle Douglas 14, London 358, Dumfries 35, Edinburgh 102, Girvan 47, Glasgow 89, New Galloway 19, Stranraer 44.
EC Thur. **Golf** Gatehouse of Fleet 9h. **See** Cardoness Castle ruins, Anwoth Churchyard, Rutherford's Monument.
🄸 Car Park. **** Gatehouse (055 74) 212.

🏨**★★★★Cally Palace,** DG7 2DL. **** (055 74) 341. C. **🚗** 60 bedrs, 58 bp, 2 bps, TV, Dgs. **✗** a l c, mc, at, LD 9.30. 🅿 Lt, N, CH, CP 100, sp, tc, pf, sb, sol, con 116, CF, 4 BGf, 0 st, Dis. **£** BB £29–£55, DB £38–£57, WT £206·50–£232·75, DT £29·50–£39, DBB £25·50–£35, WB, 🄸, Bk £3·50, L £4·50, D £8·25.▲
🄼**★★★Murray Arms,** Main St, DG7 2HY. **** Gatehouse (055 74) 207. C. **🚗** 14 bedrs, 11 bp, 1 bps, 2 ba, annexe 5 bedrs, 3 bp, 1 ba, TV, Dgs. **✗** mc, at, LD 8·45. 🅿 N, CH, TV, CP 20, Ac, tc, pf, con 30, CF, 1 BGf, 1 st, Dis. **£** BB £17·50–£22, DB £39–£44, DBB £27–£31, WB, 🄸, Bk £3, L £2·50, D £9·25, cc 1 2 3 5 6.
🄼**★★★Murray Arms,** Main St, DG7 2HY. **** Gatehouse (055 74) 204. C. **🚗** 7 bedrs, 2 ba, Dgs. **✗** a l c, mc, LD 8.45. 🅿 CH, TV, Dgs, CP 8, CF. **£** BB £9·50, DB £19, 🄶, Bk £2·50.▲

Bank o'Fleet, H, z, *47 High St, DG7 2HR.*
☎ Gatehouse (055 74) 302. C. ⌘ 6 bedrs,
6 sh, Dgs. ✗ a l c. 🅿 ch, TV, Dgs, ns, CF, 1
st.

Rescue Service: W & A Cambell, Anworth
Garage, Fleet St. ☎ Gatehouse (055 74)
227.

GIFFNOCK Strathclyde (Renfrewshire).
Map 48D
Pop 13,381. Strathaven 13, London 387,
Edinburgh 50, Glasgow 4½, Kilmarnock 17,
Lanark 27, Paisley 6½.
EC Tue. **Golf** Whitecraigs 18h.

★★★**MacDonald Thistle,** *Mains Ave,
G46 6RA.* ☎ 041-638 2225. C. ⌘ 58
bedrs, 50 bp, 8 bps, ns, TV, Dgs. ✗ a l c, at,
LD, 9.30. 🅿 Lt, N, CH, TV, Dgs, CP 250, Ac,
sb, sol, gym, con, CF, 0 st. £ BB £39.75–
£46.75, DB £51.50–£57.50, WB, 🄯, Bk
£4.75, L £6.25, D £9.50, cc 1 2 3 4 5 6,
Dep b.▲

Repairer: Armour Motors (Glasgow) Ltd,
34 Fenwick Rd. ☎ 041-637 7161.

GIFFORD Lothian (East Lothian). Map
37E
Pop 883. Chirnside 25, London 368,
Berwick-upon-Tweed 33, Coldstream 33,
Edinburgh 20, Galashiels 29, Glasgow 64,
Haddington 4½, Kelso 37, Lauder 20,
Peebles 34.
EC Wed. **Golf** Gifford 9h. **See** 18th cent
Church, Yester House, ruins of Yester
Castle, Mercat Cross. Village is good
example of 18th cent planning and of
historic and architectural interest.

★**Goblin Ha',** *Main St, EH41 4QH.*
☎ (062 081) 244.

GIRVAN Strathclyde (Ayrshire). Map
28D
Pop 7,698. Pinwherry 8, London 395, Ayr
21, Dalmellington 22, Edinburgh 91,
Gatehouse of Fleet 47, Glasgow 53,
Stranraer 30.
EC Wed. **Golf** Girvan Burgh 18h,
Turnberry Hotel courses, 18h (2). **See**
Stumpy Tower (ancient Tolbooth), Ailsa
Craig Bird Sanctuary 10 m W.
🄸 Bridge St. ☎ Girvan (0465) 2056.

★★**Hamilton Arms,** *12 Bridge St, KA26
9HH.* ☎ (0465) 2182.
■★**Westcliffe,** *Louisa Dr, KA26 9AH.*
☎ (0465) 2128.

Repairer: Lawson's Garage, 19 Vicarton
St. ☎ (0465) 2230.
Rescue Service: North End Motors, 2
Maxwell St. ☎ (0465) 3375.

GLASGOW Strathclyde (Lanarkshire).
Maps 36E and 48C and D
See also BARRHEAD, GIFFNOCK,
MILNGAVIE, PAISLEY and
RUTHERGLEN.
RAC Office, *200 Finnieston Street,
Glasgow, G3 8HH.* ☎ (General) 041-248
4444. (Rescue Service only) 041-248
5474.
Pop 755,429. Hamilton 11, London 388,
M8 Motorway 1, Abington 37, Arrochar
37, Crianlarich 52, Dumbarton 15,
Edinburgh 45, Gourock 25, Kilmarnock 20,
Kincardine 28, Lanark 25, Lochearnhead
51, Paisley 6½, Peebles 50, Stirling 26.
See Plan, pp. 410 and 411.
P See Plan. **Golf** Eight public courses and
numerous others. **See** Glasgow Cathedral,
University, Art Gallery and Museum

(Kelvingrove Park), Old Glasgow
Museum, Transport Museum, Tolbooth
Steeple, Iron Steeple, St Andrew's Church,
Episcopal and RC Cathedrals, Strathclyde
University, Pollok House, Botanic
Gardens, Kelvin Hall, Zoo, Parks,
Crookston Castle 4 m SE, Bothwell Castle
ruins 7 m SE.
🄸 George Sq. ☎ 041-221 7371.

■★★★★**Albany** (TH), *Bothwell St, G2
7EN.* ☎ 041-248 2656. C. ⌘ 251 bedrs,
251 bp, TV, Dgs. ✗ a l c, mc, LD 10.45.
🅿 Lt, N, CH, Dgs, CP 25, Ac, con 750, CF,
0 st. £ BB £50.50, DB £68.50, WB, 🄯,
cc 1 2 3 4 5 6.

★★★★**Stakis Grosvenor,** *Great Western
Rd, G12 0TA.* ☎ 041-339 8811. C. ⌘ 93
bedrs, 93 bp, TV, Dgs. ✗ a l c, mc, at, LD
10. 🅿 Lt, N, CH, TV, Dgs, CP 60, Ac, con,
CF, 6 st. £ WB, Bk £3.75, L £4.40, D £4.40,
cc 1 2 3 5 6, Dep b.

■★★★★**M Holiday Inn,** *Argyle St, G3
8RR.* ☎ 041-226 5577. C. ⌘ 296 bedrs,
296 bp, TV, Dgs. ✗ a l c, mc, at, LD 11.
🅿 Lt, N, CH, Dgs, CP 200, sp, sc, sb, sol,
gym, con 300, CF, 0 st. £ BB £58.55, DB
£71.10, DBB £68.55, WB, 🄯, Bk £5.65, L
£9.95, D £9.95, cc 1 2 3 4 5 6.

★★★**Bellahouston,** *517 Paisley Rd
West, G51 1RN.* ☎ 041-427 3146. C.
⌘ 122 bedrs, 122 bp, TV, Dgs. ✗ a l c, mc,
at. 🅿 Lt, N, CH, Dgs, CP 150, Ac, con 325,
CF, 0 st. £ BB £28–£42, DB £35.50–£50,
WB, 🄯, Bk £5.50, D £9, cc 1 2 3 5 6.

★★★**M Crest,** *Argyle St, G2 8LL.*
☎ 041-248 2355. C. ⌘ 123 bedrs, 123 bp,
ns, TV, Dgs. ✗ a l c, mc, at, LD 9.45. 🅿 Lt,
N, CH, Dgs, Ac, con, CF, 0 st. £ BB fr
£42.75, DB fr £57, WB, 🄯, Bk £5.25, D
£8.95, cc 1 2 3 4 5 6, Dep b.

★★★**North British,** *50 George Sq, G2
1DS.* ☎ 041-332 6711.

★★★**Tinto Firs,** *470 Kilmarnock Rd, G43
2BB.* ☎ 041-637 2353. C. ⌘ 26 bedrs, 23
bp, ns, TV. ✗ a l c, mc, LD 9.30. 🅿 N, CH,
CP 45, con 200, CF, 1 BGf, 0 st. £ BB
£43.75–£46.75, DB £49.50–£53.50, WB,
🄯, Bk £4.75, L £5.50, D £9.50,
cc 1 2 3 4 5 6, Dep b.

■★★**Blythswood,** *320 Argyle St, G2
8LY.* ☎ 041-221 4133. C. ⌘ 65 bedrs, 3
bp, 1 bps, 16 ba. ✗ a l c, mc, at, LD 8.30.
🅿 Lt, N, CH, TV, Ac, con 60, CF, 35 st. £ BB
£18.15, DB £30.25, 🄯.

★★**Ewington** (R), *132 Queen's Dr, G42
8QW.* ☎ 041-423 1152. C. ⌘ 47 bedrs, 4
bp, 12 bps, 9 ba, TV, Dgs. ✗ mc, at, LD 8.
🅿 Lt, N, CH, TV, Dgs, CF 12, Ac, con 35,
CF, 12 BGf, 8 st. £ BB £14–£18, DB £26–
£30, WB, 🄯, Bk £2.75, L £2.75, D £3.50,
cc 1 2 3 5.

★★**Newlands,** *290 Kilmarnock Rd, G43
2XS.* ☎ 041-632 9171. C. ⌘ 17 bedrs, 15
bp, 1 ba, TV. ✗ a l c, mc, at, LD 11. 🅿 N,
CH, ns, CF, 0 st. £ BB £22, DB £42, WB, 🄯,
Bk £3, L £2.75, HT £3.50, cc 1 2 3 5.

★★**Sherbrooke,** *11 Sherbrooke Av, G41
4PG.* ☎ 041-427 4227.▲
■★**Cavendish** (R), *1 Devonshire Gdns,
G12 0UX.* ☎ 041-339 2001.
★**Dunkeld** (RI), *10 Queen's Dr, G42 8BS.*
☎ 041-424 0160. RS Xmas. C. ⌘ 22
bedrs, 1 bps, 5 ba, TV, Dgs. ✗ mc, at, LD 8.
🅿 N, CH, TV, Dgs, CP 8, Ac, con 80, CF, 11
BGf, 5 st. £ BB £13.50, DB £23.95–£30, DT
fr £24, DBB fr £18.75, 🄯, Bk £2.30, L
£5.25, D £5. Dep b.
★**Queen's Park** (Unl), *10 Balvicar Dr,
G42 8QT.* ☎ 041-423 1123. RS Xmas &

New Year. C. ⌘ 30 bedrs, 6 bps, 7 ba, Dgs.
✗ mc, at, LD 7.30. 🅿 N, CH, TV, con 15, 3
BGf, 1 st. £ BB £11.90, DB £22.50–£29.20,
🄯, Bk £2.75, L £2.75, D £4.50, Dep.
Chez Nous, G, z (RI), *33 Hillhead St, G12
8PX.* ☎ 041-334 2977. C. ⌘ 17 bedrs, 4
ba, Dgs. 🅿 ch, TV, Dgs, CP 9, 4 BGf, 4 st.
£ BB £9–£10, DB £16–£17, 🄯, Bk £2.50.
Linwood, PH, y (RI), *356 Albert Dr, G41
5PJ.* ☎ 041-427 1642.
Marie Stuart, H, z (RI), *48 Queen Mary
Av, G42 8DT.* ☎ 041-423 6363. C. ⌘ 31
bedrs, 8 bp, 1 bps, 4 ba, TV, Dgs. 🅿 ch, TV,
Dgs, CP 30, CF, 2 st. £ BB £13.10–£23.25,
DB £26.30–£31.30, 🄸, Bk £2.45, L £3.50,
D £4.50.
Smith's, PH, z (Unl), *963 Sauchiehall St,
Kelvingrove, G3 7TH.* ☎ 041-339 7674. C.
⌘ 13 bedrs, 4 bps, 5 ba, Dgs. 🅿 Lt, N, CH, TV,
ns, CP 4, CF. £ BB £8–£8.50, DB £16–£30,
🄸
⌘ 26 bedrs, 5 ba. 🅿 CH, TV, 5 st. £ BB
£9.20–£12.65, DB £17.25–£18.40, 🄸, Bk
£1.75.
Wilkie's, G, z (RI), *14 Hillhead St, G12
8PY.* ☎ 041-339 6898. Closed Jan & Dec.
C. ⌘ 13 bedrs, 4 bps, 5 ba, Dgs. 🅿 Lt, ch,
TV, ns, CP 4, CF. £ BB £8–£8.50, DB £16–
£30, 🄸.

Repairers: Ashfield Motors, 41 Ashfield
St. ☎ 041-336 3211-4.
Callander's Garages Ltd, 15 Julian Av.
☎ 041-339 8711.
Callenders Engineering Co Ltd, 47 Kirklee
Rd. ☎ 041-334 8155.
Carlaw (Cars) Ltd, 222 Nether Auldhouse
Rd. ☎ 041-649 4585.
Park Automobile Co Ltd, 69 Dumbreck
Rd. ☎ 041-427 2206.
Prosser, H & Sons Ltd, 470 Royston Rd.
☎ 041-552 4713.
Skelly's (Glasgow) Ltd, 694 Cumbernauld
Rd. ☎ 041-770 4242.
Specialist Body Repairers: Ashfield
Motors, 41 Ashfield St.
☎ 041-336 3211-4.
Beattie Bros Autos, 219 Govan Rd.
☎ 041-427 0818.
James B Stevenson Ltd, 27 Napiershall St.
☎ 041-339 1264.
Rescue Service: Ashfield Motors, 41
Ashfield St. ☎ 041-336 3211-4.
Blairhall Motors, 70 Stanley St, Kinning
Park. ☎ 041-429 1121.
G. A. Crichton (Motor Engineers), 20
Havelock St. ☎ 041-334 4282.
John Rennie & Sons Ltd, 324 Battlefield
Rd. ☎ 041-632 5160.
P Currie of Shettleston (Garages) Ltd, 85
Amulree St. ☎ 041-778 4377.
U Save Autos, 2 Old Dumbarton Rd.
☎ 041-339 8057.

GLASGOW AIRPORT (Abbotsinch),
Strathclyde (Renfrewshire). Map 48E
See RENFREW.

GLENBORRODALE Highland (Argyll).
Map 38F
Ballachulish 66 (Fy 34), London 544 (Fy
509), Edinburgh 186 (Fy 152), Fort
William 54 (Fy 37), Glasgow 153 (Fy 115),
Mallaig 44.
■★★**Clan Morrison,** *Acharacle,
PH36 4JP.* ☎ (097 24) 232. Open Mar–
Oct. C. ⌘ 6 bedrs, 6 bp, 2 ba, Dgs. ✗ a l c,
mc, at, LD 8.15. 🅿 CH, TV, Dgs, CP 40, 6
BGf, 1 st, Dis. £ BB £15.18–£17.70, DB
£30.36–£35.40, WB, 🄸, Dep.

■⚒★★**Glenborrodale Castle** (TH), *Ardnamurchan, Acharacle, PH36 4JP.* ✆ (097 24) 266. Open Mar–Oct & Xmas. C. 🚗 23 bedrs, 2 bp, 7 ba, TV, Dgs. ✖ mc, at, LD 9.30. 🏠 N, ch, Dgs, CP 40, Ac, sp, CF, 4 BGf, 3 st. £ DBB £35, WB, ①, cc 1 2 3 4 5 6, Dep (Xmas).

GLENCAPLE Dumfries & Galloway (Dumfriesshire). Maps 29D and 30E Pop 270. Cummertrees 10, London 325, Brampton 37, Carlisle 31, Dumfries 5, Edinburgh 76, Glasgow 78, Langholm 31. **Golf** Dumfries 18h. **See** ruins of Caerlaverock Castle.

■★★**Nith,** *DG1 4RE.* ✆ (038 777) 213. RS New Year. C. 🚗 10 bedrs, 2 bp, 2 bps, 2 sh, 3 ba, TV, Dgs. ✖ mc, LD 8.30. 🏠 ch, CP 20, Ac, sb, con, CF, 2 st. £ Bk £3, L £3·10, D £7·50, cc 1.

GLENCARSE Tayside (Perthshire). Map 37A Pop 43. Bridge of Earn 7, London 421, Dundee 15, Edinburgh 46, Glasgow 63, Perth 6. **EC** Wed, Sat. **Golf** Perth 18h. **See** Pitfour Castle.

★**Newton House,** *PH2 7LX.* ✆ (073 886) 250. C. 🚗 5 bedrs, 3 bp, 2 bps, 2 ba, TV, Dgs. ✖ a l c, mc, LD 9.45. 🏠 CH, TV, Dgs, CP 40, con 25. £ BB £25–£30, DB £32–£40, WB, ①, Bk £3·50, L £2, D £10, cc 1 3 5.

GLENCOE Highland (Argyll). Map 39E Pop 357. Crianlarich 35, London 472, M85 Motorway 4, Dalmally 36, Edinburgh 115, Fort William 28 (Fy 16), Glasgow 85, Oban 39. **Golf** Fort William 18h. **See** MacDonald Memorial, Signal Rock.

■★★**King's House,** *PA39 4HY* (12 m SE A82). ✆ Kingshouse (085 56) 259. Open Feb-Oct. C. 🚗 21 bedrs, 12 bp, 4 ba, Dgs. ✖ a l c, mc, at, LD 8·15. 🏠 ch, TV, CP 60, pf, CF, 5 BGf, 2 st. £ BB £12–£17, DB £24–£37, DBB £21–£28, WB, ①, Bk £3·50, L £3·50, D £9·50, cc 1 2.

Scorry Breac, G, y (Unl), *Hospital Dr, PA39 4HT.* ✆ Ballachulish (085 52) 354. Open Feb–Oct. C. 🚗 5 bedrs, 2 ba. 🏠 CH, TV, CP 8. £ BB £9·50–£10·50, DB £15–£17, WT (b) £80·50–£94·50, DT (b) £11·50–£13·50, ①.

GLENEAGLES Tayside (Perthshire) *See* AUCHTERARDER.

GLENFARG Tayside (Perthshire). Map 36D Pop 319. Queensferry 23, London 406, M90 Motorway 3, Dundee 27, Edinburgh 32, Glasgow 52, Kinross 6½, Perth 11, St Andrews 28. **EC** Sat. **Golf** Milnathort 9h. **See** Scott's View.

★★**Bein Inn,** *PH2 9PY.* ✆ (057 73) 216. Closed Xmas. C. 🚗 14 bedrs, 12 bp, 2 ba, TV. ✖ a l c, mc, at, LD 9.30. 🏠 CH, CP 70, CF, 4 BGf, 2 st. £ BB fr £16·50, DB fr £23, WT fr £127, DBB fr £26, WB, ②, Bk £3·25, L £2·50, D £10, cc 1 3 6, Dep a ▲.

GLENFINNAN Highland (Inverness-shire). Map 38F Pop 50. Fort William 17, London 507, Corran 14, Edinburgh 149, Glasgow 120, Lochailort 9, Spean Bridge 24.

Golf Fort William 18h. **See** Jacobite Monument, St Marys & Finnan Church.

■★★**Stage House Inn,** *PH37 4LT.* ✆ Kinlocheil (039 783) 246. Open Mar–Oct. C. 🚗 9 bedrs, 3 bp, 6 bps, Dgs. ✖ a l c, mc, at, LD 8. 🏠 CH, CP 25, pf, CF, 5 st. £ BB £13·50–£14·50, DB £27–£29, WT £145–£152, DBB £22·50, ②, Bk £3·50, L £3, D £8, cc 1 3 6.

GLENLIVET Grampian (Banffshire). Map 40D Tomintoul 11, London 504, Aberdeen 76, Dufftown 15, Edinburgh 129, Glasgow 146, Grantown-on-Spey 18. **See** Distillery

■⚒★★**Blairfindy Lodge,** *AB3 9DJ.* ✆ (080 73) 376.

GLENROTHES Fife. Map 37C Pop 36,200. M90 Motorway 13, Queensferry 21, London 405, Dundee 23, Dunfermline 17, Edinburgh 30, Glasgow 55, Kinross 13, Kirkcaldy 6, Perth 22, St Andrews 21. **EC** Tue. **Golf** Glenrothes 18h. **See** St Columba's Church, St Paul's RC Church, Leslie House, Balbirnie House, 'Ex Terra'—sculpture by Benno Schosz (Town Centre).

⚒★★★★**Balgeddie House,** *Leslie Rd, KY6 3ET.* ✆ (0592) 742511. Closed Xmas & Jan 1 & 2. C. 🚗 18 bedrs, 16 bp, 2 bps, 2 ba, TV. ✖ mc, at, LD 9.30. 🏠 CH, TV, Dgs, CP, con 12, CF, 1 BGf, 2 st. £ BB £23–£31, DB £46, DBB £33–£41, WB, ② 10%, Bk £4, L £9, D £10, cc 1 2 3 6.

GOLSPIE Highland (Sutherland). Map 43E Pop 1,400. Bonar Bridge 21, London 587, Edinburgh 212, Glasgow 219, Helmsdale 17, Lairg 18. **EC** Wed. **Golf** Golspie 18h. **See** Dunrobin Castle and family Museum, St Andrew's Kirk and Burial Ground. 🅣 ✆ Golspie (040 83) 3835.

■★★**Golf Links,** *KW10 6TT.* ✆ (040 83) 3408. C. 🚗 9 bedrs, 5 bp, 2 ba, Dgs. ✖ mc, at, LD 8. 🏠 CH, TV, Dgs, CP 18, CF, 1 st. £ BB £13·50–£16·50, DB £27–£33, DBB £21·50–£24·50, ②, Bk £3·75, D £8, cc 1 3 5 6.

■★★**Sutherland Arms,** *Main St, KW10 6SA.* ✆ (040 83) 3234. C. 🚗 11 bedrs, 9 bp, 2 ba, Dgs. ✖ mc, at, LD 8·30. 🏠 CH, TV, CP 30, Ac, con 100, 1 st. £ BB £10·50–£12·50, DB £20–£25, WT £140, DT £22, DBB £19·50–£21·50, ②, Bk £3·80, L £5·50, D £8·50, cc 5.

Rescue Service: Central Garage, Golspie, South Argo Ter. ✆ (040 83) 3471. Golspie Motors Ltd, Station Rd. ✆ (040 83) 3205.

GOUROCK Strathclyde (Renfrewshire). Map 35F Pop 11,071. Glasgow 24, London 411, Dumbarton 33 (Fy 21), Edinburgh 69, Glasgow 24, Kilmarnock 34, Largs 14, Paisley 19. **EC** Wed. **Golf** Gourock 18h. **See** 'Granny Kempock' Stone, Levanne Castle ruins. 🅣 Municipal Buildings. ✆ Gourock (0475) 31126.

★★★**M Stakis Gantock,** *Cloch Rd, PA19 1AR.* ✆ (0475) 34671. C. 🚗 63 bedrs, 63 bp, TV, Dgs. ✖ a l c, mc, at, LD 9.30. 🏠 N. CH, Dgs, CP 65, Ac, con, CF, 4 st. £ WB, Bk

£3·50, L £4·40, D £4·40, cc 1 2 3 5 6, Dep b.

Claremont, G, z (Unl), *34 Victoria Rd, PA19 1DF.* ✆ (0475) 31687. C. 🚗 6 bedrs, 1 ba, TV, Dgs. 🏠 CH, TV, CP 4, 1 st. £ BB £9, DB £18, WT (c) £56, ①, Bk £1·75.

GRANGEMOUTH Central (Stirlingshire). Map 36F Pop 21,599. Falkirk 2½, London 397, Abington 45, Arrochar 60, Dumbarton 37, Edinburgh 25, Glasgow 26, Kincardine 6, Lanark 28, Stirling 12. **EC** Wed. **Golf** Polmonthill 18h.

Rescue Service: Inch Service Station, Bo'ness Rd. ✆ (0324) 484833. Middle Street Lane Garage, Middle Street La. ✆ (0324) 484838.

GRANTOWN-ON-SPEY Highland (Moray). Map 40D Pop 1,880. Tomintoul 13, London 508, Aberdeen 78, Braemar 46, Carrbridge 10, Craigellachie 24, Edinburgh 131, Elgin 34, Glasgow 147, Kingussie 26, Stonehaven 75. **EC** Thur. **Golf** Grantown 18h. **See** Parish Church, Bridge, Granite Buildings. 🅣 54 High St. ✆ Grantown-on-Spey (0479) 2773.

■★★**Garth,** *Castle Rd, PH26 3HN.* ✆ (0479) 2836.Closed Nov. C. 🚗 14 bedrs, 7 bp, 2 bps, ns, TV, Dgs. ✖ mc, at, LD 8.30. 🏠 CH, TV, ns, CP 10, U 1, tc, CF, 5 st. £ BB £13–£17, DB £25–£29, WT £128–£131, DT £21–£23, DBB £29–£33, WB, ②, Bk £3·20, L £3, D £8·25, cc 3 4.

■★★**Rosehall,** *The Square, PH26 3JU.* ✆ (0479) 2721.

■★★**Seafield Lodge,** *Woodside Av, PH26 3JN.* ✆ (0470) 2152. Open Apr–Oct, RS Jan, Feb, Mar. C. 🚗 14 bedrs, 3 bp, 6 bps, 2 ba, Dgs, CP 40, con 25, CF. £ BB £13·80, DB £27·60–£32·60, DBB £20·70–£24·15, WB, ①, Bk £3·50, D £9, cc 1 2 5, Dep a.

■★**Dunvegan,** *Heathfield Rd, PH26 3HX.* ✆ (0479) 2301. Closed Xmas. C. 🚗 9 bedrs, 2 ba, Dgs. ✖ mc, at, LD 7·30. 🏠 CH, TV, Dgs, CP 9, G 1, CF, 3 st. £ BB £8·75–£10·95, DB £17·50–£21·90, WB, ①, Bk £4·60, D £5·80.

Braemoray, PH, x (RI), *Woodlands Ter, PH26 3PU.* ✆ (0479) 2303. **Dunachton, G, y** (RI), *off Grant Rd, PH26 3LD.* ✆ (0479) 2098. C. 🚗 8 bedrs, 1 bp, 1 ba, Dgs. 🏠 CH, Dgs, CP 12, CF. £ BB £7·25, DB £14·50–£15·50, DT (b) £11·60, ①, D £4·35.

Ravenscourt, G, y (Unl), *Seafield Av, PH26 3JG.* ✆ (0479) 2286. Closed Nov & Dec. C. 🚗 6 bedrs, 2 ba, Dgs. 🏠 CH, TV, CP 15, CF, 2 st. £ BB £6·50–£7·25, DB £13–£14·50, WT (b) £63–£75, DT (b) £10–£11·50, ①, Bk £1·75, D £4·25.

GREENLAW Borders (Berwickshire). Maps 31A and 37F Pop 600. Kelso 9, London 343, Berwick-upon-Tweed 20, Coldstream 10, Edinburgh 37, Galashiels 18, Glasgow 37, Lauder 12, Selkirk 22. **Golf** Duns 9h. **See** Polwarth Tower.

■⚒★★**Purves Hall** (RI), *TD10 6UJ.* ✆ Leitholm (089 084) 558. C 5. 🚗 8 bedrs, 3 bp, 5 bps, Dgs. ✖ mc, at, LD 8.45. 🏠 CH, CP 7, Dgs, Ac, CF. £ BB £22–£24, DB £36–£40, DBB £32·50–£34·50, WB, ②, Bk £4·25, L £1·50, D £10·50, Dep a.

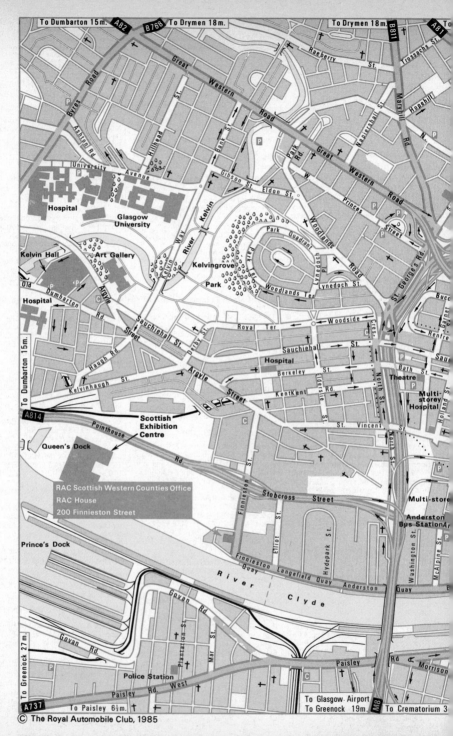

For abbreviations see inside back cover—

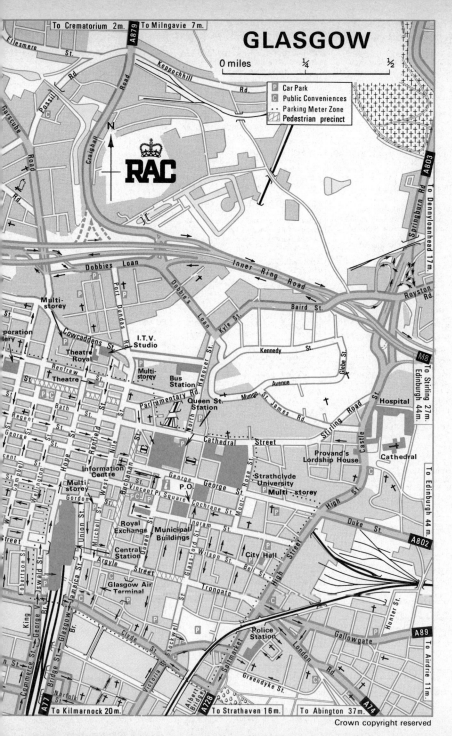

GLASGOW

0 miles   ¼   ½

P Car Park
C Public Conveniences
· · Parking Meter Zone
Pedestrian precinct

To Crematorium 2m.   To Milngavie 7m.

Ellesmere St.

Keppochhill   Rd.

Rd.

Garscube   Road

Craighall   Road

Pinkston   Road

Possil   Rd

N

RAC

A879

A803

To Dennyloanhead 17m.
Springburn Rd

M8

To Stirling 27m.
Edinburgh 44m.

To Edinburgh 44 m.

A802

To Airdrie 11m.

Dobbies   Loan

Inner   Ring   Road

Port   Dundas   Rd.

Dobbie's   Loan

Baird   St.

Royston Rd.

Multi-storey

Cowcaddens   St.

Corporation Gallery

Theatre Royal

I.T.V. Studio

Kyle St.

Hanover St.

Kennedy   St.

Glebe St.

Hospital

Renfrew St.

Theatre

Bath   St.

Renfield   St.

Multi-storey

Bus Station

Parliamentary   Rd.

North   Hanover   St.

Queen St. Station

Mungo   St.

Avenue

St. James'   Rd.

Stirling   Road

Castle   St.

Cathedral

Regent   St.

Hope   St.

Nile   St.

Cathedral   Street

Rose   St.

Provand's Lordship House

George   St.

Information Centre

Multi storey

Buchanan   St.

West   Nile   St.

George   St.

P.O.

George   Square

Strathclyde University

Multi - storey

High   St.

Gordon   St.

Mitchell   St.

St. Vincent Pl.

Cochrane   St.

Ingram   St.

Mont-rose St.

Union   St.

Royal Exchange

Municipal Buildings

Wilson   St.

Bell   St.

City Hall

Duke   St.

A802

Central Station

Argyle   Street

Glassford   St.

Trongate

High   Street

Hunter   St.

Glasgow Air Terminal

Robertson   St.

Oswald   St.

George V Br.

Jamaica   St.

Glasgow   Br.

Clyde   Br.

Stockwell   St.

Saltmarket

Police Station

London   Rd.

Gallowgate

A89

Bridge   St.

Victoria   Br.

Albert   Bridge

Greendyke   St.

Commerce   St.

King   St.

Norfolk   St.

A77

A728

A74

To Kilmarnock 20m.   To Strathaven 16m.   To Abington 37m.

-For Explanatory Notes to Directory see page 116

411

GREENOCK Strathclyde (Renfrewshire).
Map 35F
Pop 56,194. Glasgow 21, London 408,
Dumbarton 30 (Fy 17), Edinburgh 66,
Glasgow 21, Gourock 3½, Kilmarnock 31,
Largs 14, Paisley 16.
EC Wed. **Golf** Greenock 18h and 9h,
Whinhill 18h. **See** Museum, Art Gallery,
Free French Memorial, Custom House,
Lyle Hill, Newark Castle 3½ m E.
⟦ℹ⟧ Municipal Buildings. ✆ Greenock
(0475) 24400.

★★★Tontine (RI), *6 Ardgowan Sq, PA16
8MG.* ✆ (0475) 23316. C. ➡ 32 bedrs, 23
bp, 3 ba, TV, Dgs. ✖ a l c, mc, at, LD 9. ⟦P⟧ N,
CH, Dgs, CP 12, G 12, Ac, con 175, CF, 2
BGf, 4 st. £ BB £27·50–£33, DB £38–£42,
WB, ⟦1⟧, Bk £3·50, L £5·50, D £7·50,
cc 1 2 3 5 6, Dep b.

Repairer: J K Millar, West Renfrew
Garage, 26 Brougham St. ✆ (0475) 83336.
Rescue Service: Clydeview Motors, 37
Cartsburn St. ✆ (0475) 26040.
Wellpark Garage, Drumfrochar Rd.
✆ (0475) 22031.

GRETNA Dumfries & Galloway
(Dumfriesshire). Map 30F
Pop 2,200. Carlisle 9, London 303,
Beattock 30, Brampton 15, Dumfries 24,
Edinburgh 82, Glasgow 85, Langholm 15.
EC Wed. **Golf** Powfoot, Annan 18h. **See**
Lochmaben Stone, Marriage Smithy and
Museum at Gretna Green.
⟦ℹ⟧ Annan Rd. ✆ Gretna (046 13) 834.

★★Gretna Chase, *CA6 5JB.* ✆ (046 13)
517. C. ➡ 8 bedrs, 3 bp, 2 bps, 2 ba.
✖ a l c, mc, LD 9.30. ⟦P⟧ CH, TV, CP 40, Ac,
con 30, CF, 1 st. £ BB £18–£21, DB £30–
£40, ⟦2⟧, Bk £2·50, L £7, D £9, cc 1 2 3 5,
Dep a.

★★M Royal Stewart, *Glasgow Rd, CA6
5DT.* ✆ (046 13) 210.
⟦■⟧**★★Solway Lodge,** *CA6 5DN.*
✆ (046 13) 266. C. ➡ 3 bedrs, 3 sh,
annexe 7 bedrs, 7 bp, TV, Dgs. ✖ mc, at,
LD 9. ⟦P⟧ CH, TV, CP 40, CF, 7 BGf, 1 st, Dis.
£ BB £13·50, DB £25, ⟦2⟧, Bk £3, L £2·50, D
£6, cc 1 2 3 5 6, Dep a.
⟦■⟧**★Surrone House** (R), *Annan Rd, CA6
5DL.* ✆ (046 13) 621. C. ➡ 6 bedrs, 4 bp, 2
bps, 2 ba, TV, Dgs. ✖ at, LD 8.30. ⟦P⟧ CH,
TV, Dgs, CP 20, CF, 1 BGf, 1 st, Dis. £ BB
£11–£13·80, DB £22, WT £110, DT £21,
DBB £16, ⟦1⟧, Bk £3, L £6, D £6.▲

GULLANE Lothian (East Lothian). Map
37C
Pop 2,254. Haddington 7½, London 377,
Berwick-upon-Tweed 45, Edinburgh 18,
Glasgow 62, Peebles 35.
EC Wed. **Golf** Gullane 18h (3) and 9h.
See St Andrew's Church ruins, slight
remains of Saltcoats Castle.

⟦⚑⟧**★★★Greywalls,** *Muirfield, EH31 2EG.*
✆ (0620) 842144.
⟦■⟧**★★Bissets,** *Main St, EH31 0NR.*
✆ (0620) 842230. Closed Nov. C. ➡ 26
bedrs, 6 ba, Dgs. ✖ mc, at, LD 9. TV, CP
24, U 2, Ac, CF, 1st. £ BB £11–£14, DB
£20–£25, DBB £18–£21, WB, ⟦1⟧, Bk £3·50,
L £2, D £7·50, cc 2 3 5.
★★Queen's, *Main St, EH31 2AS.*
✆ (0620) 842275.

HADDINGTON Lothian (East Lothian).
Map 37E
Pop 6,526. Lauder 22, London 369,
Berwick-upon-Tweed 39, Coldstream 37,

Edinburgh 17, Galashiels 30, Glasgow 62,
Kelso 38, Peebles 31.
EC Thur. **Golf** Haddington 18h. **See** 12th
cent ruins of St Martin's Church, St Mary's
Church, Town House, Lennoxlowe House,
Hailes Castle 4 m NE.

Rescue Service: Ideal Garages
(Edinburgh) Ltd, Ideal Garage, Hardgate.
✆ (062 082) 3287.

HAMILTON Strathclyde (Lanarkshire).
Map 48B
See also BOTHWELL.
Pop 51,614. Larkhall 4, London 376, M74
Motorway 1, Abington 26, Dalmellington
44, Edinburgh 36, Glasgow 11,
Kilmarnock 24, Kincardine 29, Lanark 14,
Largs 40, Paisley 18, Peebles 39, Stirling
27.
EC Wed. **MD** Wed. **Golf** Strathclyde 18h.
See 18th cent Parish Church, Celtic
Cross, Burgh Museum (inc Cameronian
Regimental Museum), Chatelherault
Lodge, Cadzow Castle, ruins, Mausoleum,
Country Park.

★★Royal, *119 Quarry St.* ✆ (0698)
285926.

Specialist Radiator Repairer: Serck
Radiator Services Ltd, 175 Almada St.
✆ (0698) 282115.

HARDGATE Strathclyde
(Dunbartonshire). Map 48E
Glasgow 8, London 396, Dumbarton 7,
Edinburgh 53, Paisley 9.

★★Cameron House, *Main St, G81 5PJ.*
✆ (0389) 73535. C. ➡ 16 bedrs, 4 bp, 12
bps, TV. ✖ mc, at, LD 9.30. ⟦P⟧ Lt, N, CH, TV,
CP 60, G 8, con 100, CF, 5 st. £ BB £22, DB
£34, WT £217, DT £31, DBB £29, ⟦1⟧, Bk
£3·30, L £2·20, D £6·84, Dep a.

HARTHILL Strathclyde (Lanarkshire).
Map 36F
Pop 3,390. Lanark 16, London 385,
Abington 33, Dunfermline 25, Edinburgh
24, Glasgow 21, Kilmarnock 38,
Kincardine 19, Kinross 35, Kirkcaldy 34,
Peebles 36, Stirling 23.
EC Wed. **Golf** Eastfield 18h.

Rescue Service: James Brodie, Mill Road
Garage. ✆ (050 15) 214.

HAWICK Borders (Roxburghshire). Map
30D
Pop 16,584. Corbridge 50, London 330,
Bellingham 38, Brampton 37, Edinburgh
48, Glasgow 80, Hexham 53, Jedburgh 15,
Kelso 21, Langholm 23, Lauder 27,
Newcastle upon Tyne 62, Selkirk 12.
EC Tue. **Golf** Hawick 18h. **See** St Mary's
Parish Church, Goidielands Peel Tower,
Branxholm, Wilton Lodge Park, Museum
and Art Gallery, Hawick Mote (mound of
Norman Castle), "Common Riding" (old
custom) early June, Hermitage Castle
11½ m S.
⟦ℹ⟧ Common Haugh Car Park. ✆ Hawick
(0450) 2547.

★★Kirklands, *West Stewart Pl, TD9 8BH.*
✆ (0450) 72263. Closed Xmas. C. ➡ 6
bedrs, 2 bp, 1 bps, 1 ba, TV, Dgs. ✖ a l c,
mc. ⟦P⟧ CH, CP 20, CF. £ BB £19·50–
£22·50, DB £32–£34, WB, ⟦2⟧, Bk £3·50, L
£3, D £8.
⟦⚑⟧**★★Mansfield House,** *Weensland Rd,
TD9 9EL.* ✆ (0450) 3988.

Repairers: A & J Guthrie, 61 High St.
✆ (0450) 2287.
Milligan & Bell Ltd, 7 Bridge St. ✆ (0450)
2179.

HELENSBURGH Strathclyde
(Dunbartonshire). Map 35D
Pop 14,751. Dumbarton 8, London 410,
Arrochar 17, Crianlarich 34, Edinburgh 65,
Glasgow 22, Lochearnhead 49, Stirling
38.
Golf Helensburgh 18h. **See** Birthplace of
J L Baird (television pioneer), Henry Bell
Obelisk, St Andrew's Church, Loch
Lomond 5 m.
⟦ℹ⟧ Pier Head Car Park. ✆ Helensburgh
(0436) 2642.

★★★M Commodore, *112 West Clyde St,
G84 8ES.* ✆ (0436) 6924. C. ➡ 45 bedrs,
45 bp, TV, Dgs. ✖ a l c, mc, at, LD 9.30.
⟦P⟧ Lt, N, CH, Dgs, CP 150, Ac, con 100, CF,
12 BGf, 2 st. £ BB fr £25, DB fr £38, DBB fr
£33, WB, ⟦1⟧, Bk £3·75, L £5·50, D £8·50,
cc 1 2 3 5 6, Dep b.

Repairer: A & D Fraser Ltd, 135 East
Clyde St. ✆ (0436) 3344.

HELMSDALE Highland (Sutherland).
Map 43D
Pop 1,000. Golspie 16, London 603,
Bettyhill 44, Bonar Bridge 39, Edinburgh
228, Glasgow 235, Lairg 36, Melvich 39,
Thurso 45, Wick 38.
EC Wed. **Golf** Helmsdale 9h.
⟦ℹ⟧ ✆ Helmsdale (043 12) 640.

⟦■⟧**★Belgrave Arms,** *Dunrobin St, KW8
6JX.* ✆ (043 12) 242. C. ➡ 10 bedrs, Dgs.
✖ mc, LD 8. ⟦P⟧ TV, Dgs, CP 11, CF. £ BB
£9·50, DB £19, WT £100, DT £17, DBB
£6·50, ⟦2⟧ 10%, Bk £2·50, L £1·50, D £5,
cc 3.

Rescue Service: E M & T Rapson, Shore
Garage. ✆ (043 12) 613.

HOLLYBUSH Strathclyde (Ayrshire).
Map 29A
Pop 103. Patna 3½, London 376, Abington
45, Ayr 6½, Dalmellington 9, Edinburgh 73,
Girvan 20, Glasgow 39, Lanark 47.
EC Wed. **Golf** Ayr Belleisle 18h, Patna 9h.

⟦⚑⟧**★★★Hollybush House,** *KA6 7EA.*
✆ Dalrymple (029 256) 214. RS Dec 24–
Mar 31. C. ➡ 12 bedrs, 6 bp, 1 bps, 2 ba.
✖ a l c, mc, LD 9.30. ⟦P⟧ CH, TV, Dgs, CP
40, G 6, pf, con 70, CF, 1 st. £ BB £15–£25,
DB £20–£40, WB, ⟦2⟧, Bk £4·50, L £11·50, D
£11·50, cc 1 2 3 6, Dep a.

HUNTLY Grampian (Aberdeenshire).
Map 41A
Pop 4,250. Kildrummy 15, London 512,
Aberdeen 38, Banff 21, Braemar 57,
Craigellachie 18, Edinburgh 137,
Fraserburgh 39, Glasgow 154, Peterhead
47, Stonehaven 51.
EC Thur. **MD** Wed. **Golf** Huntly 18h. **See**
Castle ruins, Leith Hall at Kennethmont
9½ m S.
⟦ℹ⟧ The Square. ✆ Huntly (0466) 2255.

⟦⚑⟧**★★Castle,** *AB5 4SH.* ✆ (0466) 2696. C.
➡ 24 bedrs, 7 bp, 2 bps, 4 sh, 3 ba, Dgs.
✖ mc, at, LD 9.30. ⟦P⟧ CH, TV, CP 20, U 3,
Ac, pf, con 45, CF, 2 BGf, 2 st. £ BB £15–
£18, DB £28–£33·50, WT £126–£141, DT
£25·50–£30, DBB £23–£27·50, WB, ⟦1⟧, Bk
£3·50, L £3·80, D £8, cc 3 5.

Rescue Service: Argyll Garage, Chapel St.
✆ (0466) 2501.

INCHNADAMPH Highland
(Sutherland). Map 42D.
Ledmore 6, London 607, Bonar Bridge 36,
Durness (Fy) 46, Edinburgh 232, Glasgow
236, Lairg 33, Ullapool 24.
See 16th cent Ardvreck Castle ruins, Allt-
Nan-Uamh Caves, Loch Assynt.

★★**Inchnadamph,** *IV27 4HN.* ✆ Assynt
(057 12) 202. Open Mar–Oct. C. ⊷ 28
bedrs, 7 bp, 7 ba, Dgs. ✖ mc, at, LD 7.45.
🅰 CP 30, G 2, pf, CF, 2 BGf, 2 st. £ BB
£12·75–£15·75, DB £25·50–£32·50, WT
£135·75–£143·25, DBB £18·75–£22·15,
⊡, Bk £3·50, L £4·50, D £6·50, cc 1 3 5.

INNELLAN Strathclyde (Argyll). Map
35E
Pop 1,306. Dunoon 5½, London 467 (Fy
417), Edinburgh 121 (Fy 74), Glasgow 79
(Fy 35).
EC Wed. **Golf** Innellan 9h, Cowal, Dunoon
18h.

Braemar, PH, xy (Unl), *30 Shore Rd,
PA23 7SP.* ✆ (036 983) 203. Open Apr–
Oct. C. ⊷ 20 bedrs, 8 ba, ns. ✖ a l c. 🅰 ch,
TV, Dgs, ns, CP 20, CF, 3 BGf, 2 st. £ BB
£12·65–£13·80, DB £25·30–£27·60, WT
(b) £104·65–£112·70, DT (b) £14·95–
£16·10, ⊡, Bk £3·45, L £4·02, D £6·90,
cc 2 3.

INNERLEITHEN Borders (Peeblesshire).
Map 30B
Pop 2,500. Selkirk 15, London 356,
Edinburgh 28, Galashiels 11, Glasgow 56,
Moffat 24, Peebles 6½.
EC Tue. **Golf** Innerleithen 9h. **See** St
Ronan's Well.

Rescue Service: Innerleithen Garage,
Peebles Rd. ✆ (0896) 830241.

INVERARAY Strathclyde (Argyll). Map
35C
Pop 450. Arrochar 21, London 444,
Dalmally 15, Dunoon 39, Edinburgh 99,
Glasgow 57, Lochgilphead 24, Oban 38.
EC Wed. **Golf** Lochgilphead 9h. **See**
Inveraray Castle, The Bell Tower (fine
view from roof), Crarae Gdns 9½ m SW.
🆔 ✆ Inveraray (0499) 2063.

Rescue Service: W D Semple, Shore St.
✆ (0499) 2150.

INVERGARRY Highland (Inverness-
shire). Map 39C
Pop 150. Spean Bridge 15, London 513.
Dalwhinnie 57, Edinburgh 148, Fort
William 25, Glasgow 124, Invermoriston
14, Kingussie 55, Kyle of Lochalsh 54.
Golf Fort Augustus 9h. **See** Castle ruins,
Curious monument (Well of the Seven
Heads).

⚹★★**Glengarry Castle** (R), *PH35 4HW.*
✆ (080 93) 254. Open Apr–Oct. C. ⊷ 29
bedrs, 19 bp, 4 ba, Dgs. ✖ mc, at, LD 8.15.
🅰 CH, TV, Dgs, CP 45, G 2, tc, pf, CF, 3 st.
£ BB £15–£21, DB £27–£35, ⊡, Bk £4, L
£4·50, D £7·75, cc 1 3, Dep a.
★★**Inn on the Garry,** *PH35 4HG.*
✆ (080 93) 206.
Ardgarry, F, x (Unl), *Faichem, PH35
4HG.* ✆ (080 93) 226. C. ⊷ 4 bedrs, 2 ba.
🅰 CH, TV, Dgs, ns, CP 10, CF, 3 st. £ DB
£16, WT (b) £84, DT (b) £12, ⊡.
Lundie View, G, x (Rl), *PH35 4HN.*
✆ (080 93) 291. Closed Xmas & New Year.
C. ⊷ 6 bedrs, 2 sh, 2 ba, Dgs. 🅰 CH, TV,
Dgs, CP 6, CF, 6 BGf, 0 st, Dis. £ BB £7–

£7·50, DB £14–£15, WT (b) £75–£77, DT
(b) £11–£11·50, ⊡.

INVERGOWRIE Tayside (Perthshire).
Map 37A
Pop 1,500. Glencarse 12, London 432,
Aberfeldy 46, Blairgowrie 16, Dundee 3½,
Edinburgh 57, Glasgow 75, Perth 17,
Pitlochry 41.
EC Wed. **Golf** Caird Park, Dundee 18h
and 9h.

Rescue Service: Invergowrie Motors,
Mylnefield Rd. ✆ (082 67) 204.

INVERINATE Highland (Ross &
Cromarty). Map 38D
Invergarry 36, London 480, Edinburgh
135, Glasgow 93, Kyle of Lochalsh 12.
See Eilean Donan Castle, Loch Duich,
Glen Shiel 6 m SE.

Rescue Service: Inverinate Service
Station. ✆ Glenshiel (059 981) 330.

INVERKEITHING Fife. Map 36D
Pop 5,000. Queensferry 4½, London 388,
M90 Motorway 1, Dunfermline 4,
Edinburgh 13, Glasgow 40, Kincardine 14,
Kinross 13, Kirkcaldy 13, Lanark 34.
EC Wed. **Golf** Aberdour 18h. **See** Market
Cross, St Peter's Church, old Tolbooth,
Hospitium of the Grey Friars (Museum),
16th cent Fordell Lodging, Lammas Fair in
August.

★**Queen's,** *Church St, KY11 1LJ.*
✆ (0383) 413075. C. ⊷ 13 bedrs, 4 ba,
Dgs. ✖ mc, at, LD 9. 🅰 ch, TV, CP 40, CF, 3
st. £ BB £14, DB £24, DBB £20, ⊡, Bk £4, L
£1·95, D £7, cc 1 2.

INVERKIP Strathclyde (Ayrshire).
Map 35E
Pop 884. Greenock 6, London 414,
Edinburgh 72, Glasgow 27, Largs 9,
Skelmorlie 3.
EC Wed. **Golf** Gourlock 18h.

★★**Langhouse,** *Langhouse Rd, PA16
ODE.* ✆ Wemyss Bay (0475) 521211.

INVERMORISTON Highland (Inverness-
shire). Map 39D
Pop 400. Fort Augustus 6, London 526
(Fy 531), Beauly 26, Edinburgh 161,
Glasgow 136, Invergarry 14, Inverness 28,
Kyle of Lochalsh 56.
EC Thur. **Golf** Torvean 18h. **See** Parish
Church, St Columba's Well, Hydro-Electric
Works, Loch Ness, Glen Moriston
footprints.

◼★★**Glenmoriston Arms,**
Glenmoriston, IV3 6YB. ✆ Glenmoriston
(0320) 51206. Open Apr–Nov. C. ⊷ 8
bedrs, 6 bp, 1 ba, Dgs. ✖ a l c, mc, at,
LD 8.30. 🅰 ch, TV, CP 24, pf, CF, 2 st.
£ BBc £14–£20, DBc £26–£30, ⊡, Bk
£4·50, L £3·50, D £7, cc 1 2 3 6.

INVERNESS Highland (Inverness-shire).
Maps 39B and 40A
Pop 41,000. Carrbridge 23, London 529,
Achnasheen (Fy) 41, Beauly 12, Dingwall
(Fy) 13, Edinburgh 154, Elgin 39, Glasgow
165, Invermoriston 28, Ullapool (Fy) 54.
EC Wed. **MD** Mon, Tue. **Golf** Inverness
18h. **See** Episcopal Cathedral, Castle,
Town House, Town Steeple, Abertarff
House, Museum and Art Gallery, Castle
Stewart (restored 1625), 17th cent
Dunbar's Hospital, 'Stone of Tubs',
Highland Folk Museum, Highland Games
3rd week in July, Culloden Battlefield,

Regimental Museum and 18th cent Fort at
Fort George 10 m NE, Caledonian Canal.
🆔 23 Church St. ✆ Inverness (0463)
234353.

★★★**M Caledonian,** *33 Church St, IV1
1DX.* ✆ (0463) 235181. C. ⊷ 120 bedrs,
120 bp, TV, Dgs. ✖ a l c, mc, at, LD 8.30.
🅰 Lt, N, CH, CP 30, Ac, con 600, CF, 1 st.
£ BB £28, DB £46, WB, ⊡, Bk £4, L £2·50,
D £11, cc 1 2 3 4 5 6.
★★★**M Drumossie,** *Perth Rd, IV1 2BE.*
✆ (0463) 236451. C. ⊷ 73 bedrs, 49 bp,
22 bps, 3 ba, ns, TV, Dgs. ✖ mc, LD 8.30.
🅰 N, CH, CP 120, Ac, con 150, CF, 4 st.
£ BB £22–£25, DB £32–£46, DBB £21·50–
£29·50, WB, ⊡, Bk £3·50, L £4·80, D £9,
cc 1 2 3 5 6.
★★★**Kingsmills,** *Culcabock Rd, IV2 3LP.*
✆ (0463) 237166. C. ⊷ 54 bedrs, 54 bp, 1
ba, TV, Dgs. ✖ a l c, mc, at, LD 9.45. 🅰 N,
CH, TV, CP 100, Ac, sc, con 50, CF, 7 BGf,
1 st, Dis. £ BB £35·75–£51·50, DB £50·50–
£64, WB, ⊡, Bk £4·50, L £3·50, D £9·95,
cc 1 2 3 4 5 6, Dep.▲
◼★★★**M Ladbroke,** *Nairn Rd, IV2 3TE.*
✆ (0463) 239666. C. ⊷ 108 bedrs, 108
bp, TV, Dgs. ✖ a l c, mc, at, LD 10. 🅰 Lt, N,
CH, CP 150, Ac, con 250, CF, 0 st. £ BB
£36·50–£42·50, DB £53–£62·70, WB, ⊡,
Bk £5·50, L £6·50, D £9, cc 1 2 3 5, Dep b.
◼★★★**Station,** *Academy St, IV1 1LG.*
✆ (0463) 231926. Closed Xmas & New
Year. C. ⊷ 63 bedrs, 44 bp, 8 sh, TV, Dgs.
✖ a l c, mc, at, LD 9. 🅰 N, CH, CP 10,
Ac, con 100, CF, 2 st. £ BB £16–£36·50,
DB £32–£56, WB, ⊡, Bk £4·95, L £2·50, D
£9·50, cc 1 2 3 4 5 6, Dep a.
◼★★**Craigmonie,** *9 Annfield Rd, IV2
3HX.* ✆ (0463) 231649. C. ⊷ 30 bedrs, 30
bp, 1 ba, TV, Dgs. ✖ a l c, mc, at, LD 9.30.
🅰 Lt, N, CH, Dgs, CP 60, Ac, sb, sol, con
130, CF. £ BB £16–£23, DB £30–£38, WT
£160–£195, DBB £23–£27·50, WB, ⊡, Bk
£3·75, L £4·95, D £8·50, cc 1 2 3 5, Dep a.
★★**Cumming's,** *Church St, IV1 1EW.*
✆ (0463) 232531. C. ⊷ 38 bedrs, 6 bp, 4
bps, 1 sh, 10 ba, Dgs. ✖ mc, LD 8. 🅰 Lt, N,
CH, TV, CP 25, Ac, con 150, CF, 0 st. £ BB
£16–£22, DB £28–£38, DT £25–£28, DBB
£21–£26, WB, ⊡, Bk £3·50, L £3·50, D
£6·50.
◼⚹★★**Dunain Park** (R), *By Inverness,
IV3 6JN.* ✆ (0463) 230512. C. ⊷ 6 bedrs,
4 bp, 1 ba, Dgs. ✖ mc, at, LD 9 (Sun 8).
🅰 CH, TV, Dgs, CP 30, U 1, CF, 0 st. £ DB
£40–£66, ⊡, Bk £6, L £6, D £17.
◼★★**M Muirtown,** *11 Clachnaharry Rd,
IV3 8LT.* ✆ (0463) 234800. C. ⊷ 8 bedrs,
4 bp, 4 bps, TV, Dgs. ✖ a l c, mc, at, LD 9.
🅰 ch, Dgs, CP 100, Ac, con 130, CF, 1 st.
£ BB £19·80, DB £26·40, WT £196·30, DT
£29·15, ⊡, Bk £3·30, L £3·85, D £6·50,
cc 1 2 3 5 6.
◼★★**Palace,** *Ness Walk, IV3 5NE.*
✆ (0463) 223243. C. ⊷ 84 bedrs, 84 bp,
TV, Dgs. ✖ mc, at, LD 8.45. 🅰 Lt, N, CH,
Dgs, CP 50, CF, 0 st. £ BB £19·50–£24·40,
DB £35–£43, WT £135–£199, DT £29–£33,
DBB £26–£30, WB, ⊡, Bk £3·25, L £3, D
£8·50, cc 1 2 3 5 6, Dep.▲
Brae Ness, PH, z (Unl), *Ness Bank, IV2
4SF.* ✆ (0463) 231732. Open Apr–Nov. C.

⇔ 15 bedrs, 3 ba, Dgs. 🏠 CH, TV, ns, CP 8, CF, 1 BGf. £ BB £11·50–£23, DB £19–£25, WT (b) £90–£102·50, DT (b) £14·75–£16·25, ⊞, Bk £2·50, D £5·75.
Four Winds, G, x (Unl), *42 Old Edinburgh Rd, IV2 3PG.* **☎** (0463) 230397.
Leinster Lodge, G, y, *27 Southside Rd, IV2 4XA.* **☎** (0463) 233311. C. **⇔** 5 bedrs, 2 ba, Dgs. 🏠 ch, TV, Dgs, CP 7. £ BB £7·50, DB £15, ⊞.
St Ann's House, PH (Unl), *37 Harrowden Rd, IV3 5QN.* **☎** (0463) 236157. Open Apr–Oct. C 7. **⇔** 6 bedrs, 1 bp, 4 bps, 1 ba, TV, Dgs. 🏠 CH, TV, ns, CP 3. £ BB £8·50–£9·50, DB £17–£22·50, WT (b) £90–£110, DT (b) £14–£16·75, ⊞, D £5·50.

Rescue Service: Commercial Garage, Carsgate Rd North. **☎** (0463) 238120.
Corrie Motors Ltd, 52 Harbour Rd. **☎** (0463) 226000.
Hamilton Bros (Northern) Ltd, Harbour Rd, Longman. **☎** (0463) 230777.
T P McHardy, Blackpark Filling Station, Clachnaharry Rd. **☎** (0463) 233632.

INVERSHIN Highland (Sutherland). Map 42F
Pop 40. Bonar Bridge 7½, London 573, Edinburgh 198, Glasgow 205, Lairg 7½, Ullapool 44.
Golf Bonar Bridge and Ardgay 9h. **See** Falls of Shin and Salmon Leap 2¼ m N.

★★Invershin, *IV27 4ET.* **☎** (054 982) 202. Closed last week Jan. C. **⇔** 12 bedrs, 8 bp, 3 ba, annexe 12 bedrs, 8 bp, 3 ba, TV, Dgs. ✗ mc, at, LD 9.30 (winter 8.30). 🏠 CH, Dgs, CP 40, Ac, pf, rf, CF, 4 BGf, 1 st, Dis. £ BB £13–£14, DB £26–£28, WT £80, DBB £20–£22, ⊞, Bk £4, L £4, D £6, cc 1 3 5 6.

INVERURIE Grampian (Aberdeenshire). Map 41C
Pop 6,150. Kintore 4, London 500, Aberdeen 15, Edinburgh 125, Glasgow 145, Huntly 22, Peterhead 32, Perth 85.
EC Wed. **MD** Thur. **Golf** Inverurie 18h. **See** The Bass, Carnegie Museum.
ⓘ Town Hall, The Square. **☎** Inverurie (0467) 20600.

★Gordon Arms, *Market Pl, AB5 9SA.* **☎** (0467) 20314. C. **⇔** 11 bedrs, 6 bps, 2 ba, Dgs. ✗ mc, LD 8. 🏠 CH, TV, Dgs, con 220, CF, 1 st. £ BB £13·75–£16·75, DB £20·50–£23·50, WB, ⊞, Bk £2·50, L £3·50, D £4·50, cc 1 2 3 5.

IRVINE Strathclyde (Ayrshire). Map 28B
Pop 53,200. Kilmarnock 7, London 390, Ayr 11, Edinburgh 68, Glasgow 26, Largs 18, Paisley 21.
EC Wed. **Golf** Irvine 18h, Ravenspark 18h. **See** Burns Memorial, Town House, Mercat Cross, Seagate Castle ruins, Burns Museum, Eglinton Castle ruins and Gardens.

★★★★Hospitality Inn, *Roseholme, Anniek Water, KA11 4LD.* **☎** (0294) 74272.▲
★★Redburn, *65 Kilwinning Rd, KA12 8SU.* **☎** (0294) 76792. C. **⇔** 17 bedrs, 3 bp, 6 ba, Dgs. ✗ a l c, mc, at, LD 10. 🏠 N, TV, CP 100, Ac, con 300, CF, 1 st. £ BB £15–£20, DB £30–£35, WB, ②, Bk £3, L £4·50, D £6·75, cc 1 2 3 5 6, Dep b.

Rescue Service: Springbank Service Station, Ayr Rd. **☎** (0294) 78362.

ISLE OF ARRAN Strathclyde (Argyll)
See BRODICK, KILMORY, LAMLASH, WHITING BAY.

ISLE OF BUTE Strathclyde (Bute)
See ROTHESAY.

ISLE OF COLL Strathclyde (Argyll)
See ARINAGOUR.

ISLE OF CUMBRAE Strathclyde (Bute)
See MILLPORT.

ISLE OF HARRIS Western Islands (Ross & Cromarty)
See TARBERT.

ISLE OF ISLAY Strathclyde (Argyll)
See BOWMORE, BRUICHLADDICH, PORT ASKAIG.

ISLE OF JURA Strathclyde (Argyll)
See CRAIGHOUSE.

ISLE OF LEWIS Western Islands (Ross & Cromarty)
See STORNOWAY.

ISLE OF MULL Strathclyde (Argyll)
See CRAIGNURE, FIONNPHORT, SALEN, TOBERMORY.

ISLE OF SOUTH UIST Western Islands (Inverness-shire)
See LOCHBOISDALE.

ISLE OF SKYE Highland (Inverness-shire)
See ARDVASAR, BROADFORD, EILEAN IARMAIN, KYLEAKIN, PORTREE, SKEABOST BRIDGE, TEANGUE, UIG.

ISLE OF WHITHORN Dumfries & Galloway
See WHITHORN.

JEDBURGH Borders (Roxburghshire). Map 30B
Pop 4,134. Corbridge 46, London 327, Bellingham 33, Edinburgh 47, Galashiels 17, Glasgow 81, Hawick 15, Hexham 47, Kelso 11, Lauder 26, Newcastle upon Tyne 57, Selkirk 16.
EC Thur. **Golf** Jedburgh 9h, Minto 18h. **See** Abbey, Queen Mary's House, Jedburgh Castle (Jail Museum).
ⓘ Murray's Green. **☎** Jedburgh (083 56) 3435.

⬛★★ Jedforest, *TD8 6PJ.* **☎** Camptown (083 54) 274. Closed Xmas. C. **⇔** 7 bedrs, 3 ba, TV, Dgs. ✗ a l c. 🏠 ch, TV, Dgs, CP 50, Ac, pf, CF, 0 st. £ BB £16·95–£22·50, DB £25·50–£28·50, WB, ⊞, Bk £3·75, L £3·50, D £6·95, Dep a.
Ferniehirst Mill Lodge, PH, xy (R), *TD8 6PQ.* **☎** (0835) 63279. Closed Nov. C. **⇔** 11 bedrs, 5 bp, 3 bps, 2 ba, Dgs. 🏠 CH, CP 16, 2 BGf, 2 st. £ BB £12·65–£13·80, DB £23·30–£27·60, WT (b) £150·65–£165, DT (b) £22·65–£24·80, ②, D £11.
Kenmore Bank, G, y (R), *Oxnam Rd, TD8 6JJ.* **☎** (0835) 62369. C. **⇔** 6 bedrs, 2 ba. 🏠 CH, TV, CP 6, 0 st. £ BB £8, DB £16, ⊞.

Repairer: Butler & Oliver, Station Garage. **☎** (0835) 3473.
MC Repairer: Butler & Oliver, Station Garage. **☎** (0835) 3473.
Rescue Service: G D Williamson & Son, Jed Service Station, 27 Newbongate. **☎** (0835) 2262.

JOHN O'GROATS Highland (Caithness). Maps 43B and 46E
Pop 600. Wick 17, London 655, Edinburgh 280, Glasgow 287, Thurso 20.

See Duncansby Head Lighthouse, Stacks of Duncansby, most Northerly inhabited place on British mainland.
ⓘ **☎** John O'Groats (095 581) 373.

⬛★★John O'Groats House, *KW1 4YR.* **☎** (095 581) 203. Open Apr–Oct. C. **⇔** 17 bedrs, 7 sh, 5 ba, TV, Dgs. ✗ a l c, mc, at, LD 8.45. 🏠 ch, TV, Dgs, CP 50, G 5, Ac, pf, con 70, CF, 1 st. £ BB £10–£14, DB £20–£28, ⊞, Bk £2·50, L £2, D £5, cc 1 3 5.
⬛★Sea View, *KW1 4YR.* **☎** (095 581) 220. Open Apr–Oct. C. **⇔** 9 bedrs, 1 bp, 1 bps, 2 ba, Dgs. ✗ mc, at, LD 8. 🏠 CH, TV, Dgs, CP 24, U 2, Ac, CF, 1 st. £ BB £8–£10·50, DB £16–£21, WT £112–£122, DBB £98–£120, ⊞, Bk £2, L £4·50, D £6, Dep a.

JOHNSTONE Strathclyde (Renfrewshire). Map 48F
Pop 22,947. Paisley 3½, London 396, Edinburgh 56, Glasgow 11, Gourock 17, Kilmarnock 20, Largs 20.
EC Tue. **Golf** Cochrane Castle 18h. **See** Castle.

Rescue Service: County Motor Garage Co, Thornhill. **☎** (0505) 20157.

JOHNSTONE BRIDGE Dumfries & Galloway (Dumfriesshire). Maps 29D and 30C
Lockerbie 7, London 325, Beattock 7½, Brampton 37, Carlisle 31, Dumfries 15, Edinburgh 59, Glasgow 62, Langholm 24.
Golf Lockerbie 9h, Moffat 18h.

★★Dinwoodie Lodge, *Main Rd, DG11 2SL.* **☎** (057 64) 289. C. **⇔** 8 bedrs, 2 bps, 2 ba, TV, Dgs. ✗ a l c, mc, at, LD 9.30. 🏠 CH, TV, Dgs, CP 100, Ac, con 15, CF, 3 BGf, 0 st, Dis. £ BB £16–£25, DB £27–£40, ⊞, Bk £3·50, L £4, D £5·50, cc 1 2 3 5, Dep b.

KEITH Grampian (Banffshire). Map 41A
Pop 4,460. Huntly 10, London 522, Banff 21, Craigellachie 15, Edinburgh 147, Elgin 16, Glasgow 164.
EC Wed. **Golf** Keith 18h. **See** Milton Tower ruins, 17th cent bridge.
ⓘ Church Rd. **☎** Keith (045 22) 2634.

★★Royal, *Church Rd, AB5 3BR.* **☎** (054 22) 2528. C. **⇔** 13 bedrs, 3 bp, 3 ba. ✗ a l c, mc, at, LD 8.30. 🏠 ch, TV, Dgs, CP 20, G 4, Ac, con 150, CF, 3 st. £ BB £12–£19, DB £20–£30, WT £130–£140, DT £23–£25, DBB £19·50–£26, ②, Bk £4, L £4·50, D £7·50, cc 1 5 6.
Tarnash House, G, xy (Unl), *AB5 3PB.* **☎** (054 22) 2728. Open May–Oct. C. **⇔** 4 bedrs, 2 ba, Dgs. 🏠 CH, TV, CP 10, G 1, CF. £ BB £6·50–£7, DB £13–£14, ⊞.

Rescue Services: D C George 91–93 Regent St. **☎** (054 22) 2735.
Keith Garage, 147 Moss St. **☎** (054 22) 2501.
Mutch, H, 65 Regent St. **☎** (054 22) 2167.

KELSO Borders (Roxburghshire). Map 31A
Pop 5,213. Jedburgh 11, London 338, Coldstream 9, Edinburgh 44, Galashiels 18, Glasgow 84, Haddington 38, Hawick 21, Lauder 18, Selkirk 19.
EC Wed. **Golf** Kelso 18h. **See** 12th cent Abbey remains, Bridge, Roxburgh Castle ruins, Floors Castle, Mellerstain (at Gordon).
ⓘ 66 Woodmarket. **☎** Kelso (0573) 23464.

◼★★★Cross Keys, *36 The Square, TD5 7HL.* ✆ (0573) 23303. C. ⊷ 26 bedrs, 16 bp, 4 bps, 6 ba, TV, Dgs. ✗ mc, at, LD 9. ⌂ Lt, N, CH, TV, Dgs, Ac, con 300, CF, 2 st. **£** BB £16–£23, DB £26–£34, WB, ①, Bk £4, L £4·90, HT £3·90, cc 1 2 3 5, Dep a ▲

◼★★★Ednam House, *Bridge St, TD5 7HT.* ✆ (0573) 24168.

Bellevue, G, z (RI), *Bowmont St, TD5 7DZ.* ✆ (0573) 24588. C. ⊷ 8 bedrs, 2 bps, 2 ba. ⌂ CH, TV, CP 8, 1 BGf. **£** BB £8·50–£9, DB £16–£18, DT (b) £11·50–£12·50, ①.

Maxmill Park, G, x (Unl), *Maxmill Park, TD5 8DQ.* ✆ (0573) 24468. C. ⊷ 10 bedrs, 4 bp, 6 bps, TV. ⌂ CH, TV, Dgs, CP 20, G 3, CF, 5 BGf, 0 st, Dis. **£** BB £7·75–£8·25, DB £15·50–£16·50, WT (c) £54·25–£57·75, ①, Bk £2.

Repairer: Croall Bryson & Co Ltd, Roxburghshire Works. ✆ (0573) 24345.
Rescue Service: Fish Rodger & Son Ltd, 31/35 Sheddon Park Rd. ✆ (0573) 24488.

KENMORE Tayside (Perthshire). Map 36B
Pop 150. Aberfeldy 5½, London 444, Crianlarich 31, Edinburgh 74, Glasgow 74, Lochearnhead 25.
EC Wed. **Golf** Taymouth Castle 18h. **See** Parish Church (rebuilt 1780), Bridge (1774).

◼★★★Kenmore, *Village Sq, PH15 2NA.* ✆ (088 73) 205. C. ⊷ 25 bedrs, 23 bp, 2 bps, 3 ba, TV. ✗ mc, at, LD 9. ⌂ Lt, CH, TV, CP 100, U 1, gc, pf, con 30, CF, 0 st. **£** BB £19·50–£22·50, DB £39–£44·50, DDB £28–£31, ②, Bk £4·50, L £3·50, D £10·50, cc 1 2 3 6.

KILCHRENAN Strathclyde (Argyll). Map 35A
Dalmally 18, London 473, Edinburgh 115, Glasgow 85, Inveraray 32, Oban 19.

⚑★★★Ardanaiseig, *Taynuilt, PA35 1HE.* ✆ (086 63) 333. Open Apr–Oct. C. 8 ⊷ 14 bedrs, 14 bp, TV. ✗ mc, at, LD 8.45. ⌂ CH, CP 12, tc, pf. **£** DBB £48·50–£63, ①, Bk £5·50, D £20, cc 1 2 3 5 6, Dep a.

⚑★★★Taychreggan, *Lochaweside by Taynuilt, PA35 1HQ.* ✆ (086 63) 211. Open Apr 1st–Oct 14th. C. ⊷ 17 bedrs, 14 bp, 1 ba, Dgs. ✗ mc, at, LD 9. ⌂ ch, TV, Dgs, CP 35, pf, CF, 0 st. **£** BB £20–£30, DB £40–£60, DBB £31–£41, ②, Bk £3, L £6, D £11, cc 1 2 3 5 6.

KILCREGGAN Strathclyde (Dunbartonshire). Map 35C
Pop 1,698 (inc Cove). Helensburgh 16, London 425, Arrochar 16, Crianlarich 32, Dumbarton 22, Edinburgh 81, Glasgow 38.
EC Wed. **Golf** Helensburgh 18h.

★★Kilcreggan, *Argyll Rd, G84 0JP.* ✆ (043 684) 2243. C. ⊷ 8 bedrs, 3 bp, 5 bps, TV, Dgs. ✗ a l c, mc, at, LD 9. ⌂ CH, TV, Dgs, CP 40, Ac, CF, 1 BGf, 0 st, Dis. **£** BB £14·50–£15·50, DB £29–£31, DBB £19–£21, WB, ①, Bk £3·75, L £4·50, D £7·50, cc 1 3 5.

KILDRUMMY Grampian (Aberdeenshire). Map 41C
Pop 220. Glenkindie 3½, London 497, Aberdeen 33, Braemar 34, Edinburgh 122, Elgin 38, Glasgow 139.

Golf Aboyne 18h.

⚑★★★Kildrummy Castle, *AB3 8RA.* ✆ (033 65) 288. Open Mar–Dec. C. ⊷ 17 bedrs, 16 bp, 1 bps, TV, Dgs. ✗ a l c, mc, at, LD 9. ⌂ CH, CP 30, Ac, pf, con 30, CF, 18 st. **£** BB £21–£26, DB £36–£46, WT £161–£203, DT £28–£40, DBB £23–£36, WB, ②, Bk £4, L £7·50, D £12, cc 1 2 3 4 6.

KILLEARN Central (Stirlingshire). Maps 35D and 36C
Pop 1,086. Glasgow 16, London 405, Dumbarton 15, Edinburgh 49, Stirling 21.
EC Wed. **Golf** Buchanan Castle, Drymen 18h.

★★Black Bull, *2 The Square, G63 9NG.* ✆ (0360) 50215. C. ⊷ 12 bedrs, 5 bp, 2 ba, Dgs. ✗ a l c, mc, at, LD 8.30. ⌂ CH, TV, CP 60, Ac, con, CF, 1 st. **£** BB £16·50–£20·35, DB £26·68–£32·45, WB, ②, Bk £3, HT £3·20, cc 1 2 5.

KILLIECRANKIE Tayside (Perthshire). Map 40F
Pop 100. Pitlochry 4, London 448, Aberfeldy 16, Blair Atholl 4, Dalwhinnie 27, Edinburgh 72, Glasgow 84.
Golf Pitlochry 18h.

★★Killiecrankie, *PH16 5LG.* ✆ (0796) 3220. Open Mar–Oct. C. ⊷ 12 bedrs, 10 bp, 2 ba, Dgs. ✗ mc, at, LD 8.30. ⌂ CH, TV, Dgs, CP 30, G 2, CF, 4 BGf, 2 st. **£** BB £13·80–£19·25, DB £27·60–£38·50, DBB £22·25–£29·80, ②, Bk £3·50, L £2, D £10.

Dalnasgadh House, G, xy (Unl), *PH16 5LN.* ✆ (0796) 3237. C 5. ⊷ 6 bedrs, 2 ba. ⌂ CH, TV, CP 10, 3 st. **£** BB £8·50–£9, DB £15–£16, WT (c) £105–£112, ①, Bk £2·50.

KILLIN Central (Perthshire). Maps 35B and 36A
Pop 600. Lochearnhead 8, London 435, Aberfeldy 22, Crianlarich 14, Edinburgh 71, Glasgow 55.
Golf Killin 9h. **See** Church, Finlarig Castle ruins, Healing Stones of St Fillan in The Old Mill, Falls of Dochart, Loch Tay, Burial ground of the chiefs of the Clan MacNab, Ben Lawers, 3,984 ft.
⊞ Main St. ✆ Killin (056 72) 254.

★★Bridge of Lochay, *Bridge of Lochay, FK21 8TS.* ✆ (056 72) 272. Closed Jan. C. ⊷ 17 bedrs, 4 bp, 3 bps, 4 ba, Dgs. ✗ mc, LD 9. ⌂ ch, TV, Dgs, CP 35, Ac, pf, CF, 0 st. **£** BB £12·25–£12·75, DB £23·50–£29·50, DBB £19·50–£23, WB, ②, Bk £3·75, L £4·95, D £7·75.

★★Killin, *FK21 8TP.* ✆ (056 72) 296. C. ⊷ 30 bedrs, 10 bp, 3 bps, 4 ba, Dgs. ✗ a l c, mc, at, LD 9.30. ⌂ Lt, CH, TV, Dgs, CP 50, U 4, G 4, Ac, pf, CF, 1 st. **£** BB £23–£33, DB £36–£40, DBB £28–£40, WB, ②, Bk £5, L £5, D £9, cc 1 2 3 5 6, Dep.

Rescue Service: Hamish MacGregor, Main St. ✆ (056 72) 319.
Lix Toll Garage. ✆ (056 72) 280.

KILMARNOCK Strathclyde (Ayrshire). Map 29A
Pop 46,000. Mauchlin 8, London 383, Ayr 12, Edinburgh 61, Glasgow 21, Lanark 31, Largs 26, Paisley 20, Thornhill 48.
EC Wed. **MD** Wed, Thur, Fri, Sat. **Golf** Annanhill 18h. **See** Burns Monument and Museum (Kay Park), Laigh Kirk, Dick Institute and Museum, remains of Dean Castle, 15th cent Church.

★★★Howard Park, *136 Glasgow Rd, KA3 1UT.* ✆ (0563) 31211. C. ⊷ 46 bedrs, 46 bp, TV, Dgs. ✗ a l c, mc, at, LD 9.30.

⌂ Lt, N, CH, Dgs, CP 200, Ac, con 150, CF, 0 st. **£** BB £31·50, DB £42·50, WB, ①, Bk £5·50, L £5·50, D £7·50, cc 1 2 3 5 6.

Old Rome Farmhouse, *Gatehead, KA2 9AJ.* (2 miles W on A759). ✆ Drybridge (0563) 850265.

Repairer: J & W Scott, West End Garage, 40 Grange St. ✆ (0563) 25281.
Specialist Radiator Repairer: Serck Radiator Services Ltd, Moorfield Estate. ✆ (0563) 23168.
Rescue Service: Maconochies of Kilmarnock Ltd, 26 Campbell St. ✆ (0563) 22681.
Moorfield Garage. ✆ (0563) 22789.

KILMAURS Strathclyde (Ayrshire). Map 29A
Kilmarnock 3, London 386, Ayr 15, Edinburgh 60, Glasgow 20, Irvine 6½.
See Burns Monument and Museum at Kilmarnock 3 m.
Rescue Service: Tourhill Commercials, 35 Crosshouse Rd. ✆ Kilmarnock (0563) 43386.

KILMORY Isle of Arran, Strathclyde (Bute). Map 28B
Pop 4,100. Brodick 16 (Steamer to Ardrossan), London 414, Edinburgh 90, Glasgow 45.
EC Wed. **Golf** Blackwaterfoot 12h. **See** Torrylin Cairn.

◼★★Lagg, *KA27 8PQ.* ✆ Sliddery (077 087) 255. Open Mar–Oct. C. ⊷ 16 bedrs, 7 bp, 3 ba, Dgs. ✗ a l c, mc, at, LD 9. ⌂ CH, TV, Dgs, CP 50, pf, con 120, CF, 0 st. **£** BB £15–£16, DB £30–£32, WT £170, DT £28, DBB £26–£27, ②, Bk £3, L £3·50, D £10·50.

KILSYTH Strathclyde (Stirlingshire). Map 48C
Pop 10,500. Airdrie 9, London 394, Dumbarton 23, Edinburgh 37, Glasgow 12, Kincardine 16, Lanark 26, Peebles 50, Stirling 14.
EC Wed. **Golf** Kilsyth 9h. **See** Colzium-Lennox House, Castle.
Rescue Service: Kilsyth Service Station, Kingston Rd. ✆ (0236) 822277.

KILWINNING Strathclyde (Ayrshire). Map 28B
Pop 15,000. Irvine 3, London 393, Ayr 14, Edinburgh 69, Glasgow 24, Kilmarnock 9, Largs 16.
EC Wed. **Golf** Irvine Ravenspark 18h. **See** 12th cent Abbey, Eglinton Castle and grounds.

⚑★★★Mountgreenan Mansion House, *Mountgreenan Estate.* ✆ (0294) 57733.
Rescue Service: Howie's Garage, 4 Stevenston Rd. ✆ (0294) 52687.

KINCARDINE Fife. Map 36D
Pop 2,500. M9 Motorway 3½, Queensferry 16, London 400, Crieff 30, Dunfermline 10, Edinburgh 26, Glasgow 28, Kinross 17, Stirling 12.
EC Tue. **Golf** Tulliallan 18h. **See** 17th cent Mercat Cross, Tulliallan Castle, Swing Bridge, Culross Palace 4½ m E.
Rescue Service: Kincardine Motors, Fere-Galt. ✆ (0259) 30230.

KINCLAVEN Tayside (Perthshire). Map 36B

Perth 12, London 428, Aberfeldy 25, Blairgowie 5, Dundee 17, Edinburgh 53, Forfar 21, Glasgow 69, Pitlochry 20.
Golf Perth 18h (3). **See** Kinclaven Bridge.

⚑★★★Ballathie House, *Kinclaven by Stanley, PH1 4QN.* **☎** Meikleour (025 083) 268.

KINGHOLM QUAY Dumfries & Galloway (Dumfriesshire). Maps 29D and 30E
Dumfries 1½, London 329.
Golf Dumfries 18h. **See** Castledykes Park, Caer Taverock Castle Ruins and Nature Reserve, 6 m SE.

★Swan at Kingholm, *DG1 4SU.* **☎** Dumfries (0387) 53756. C. **⊷** 10 bedrs, 3 ba, Dgs. ✖ mc, LD 7.30. ☎ ch, Dgs, CP 40, CF, 1 st. **£** BB £11·50, DB £20, WB, ☐, Bk £2·50, L £3, D £4, cc 1.

KINGSEAT Fife. Map 36D
M90 Motorway 1½, Rosyth 6½, London 394, Cowdenbeath 2½, Dunfermline 2½, Edinburgh 18, Glasgow 40, Perth 24.

Rescue Service: Clarwood Motors, Henderson St. **☎** Dunfermline (0383) 34459.

KINGUSSIE Highland (Inverness-shire) Maps 39D and 40C
Pop 1,190. Newtonmore 3, London 488, Carrbridge 19, Dalwhinnie 13, Edinburgh 112, Grantown-on-Spey 26, Fort William 47, Glasgow 124, Invergarry 55.
EC Wed. **Golf** Kingussie 18h. **See** Highland Folk Museum, China Studios, Wildlife Park (5 m).
🛈 Caledonia Buildings, King St. **☎** Kingussie (054 02) 297.

▣★★Duke of Gordon, *Newtonmore Rd, PH21 1HE.* **☎** (054 02) 302. Open Jan–Oct. C. **⊷** 55 bedrs, 5bp, 5 bps, TV, Dgs. ✖ mc, at, LD 9. ☎ Lt, TV, Dgs, CP 80, Ac, pf, con 120, CF, 6 BGf, 2 st. **£** BB £16·50, DB £32, DBB £23·50, ☐, Bk £2·75, L £3·25, D 7·50, cc 1 2 3 5 6.

Rescue Service: West End Garage, Newtonmore Rd. **☎** (054 02) 478.

KINLOCHBERVIE Highland (Sutherland). Map 42B
Pop 423. Lairg 46, London 623, Durness 18, Edinburgh 248, Glasgow 255.
Golf Royal Dornoch 18h and 9h.

★★★Kinlochbervie, *IV27 4RP.* **☎** (097 182) 275. RS Nov–Mar. C. **⊷** 14 bedrs, 14 bp, TV, Dgs. ✖ mc, at, LD 8. ☎ CH, CP 40, CF. **£** BB £18–£38, DB £32–£60, DBB £48–£86, WB, ☐, Bk £6·50, L £5·60, D £13·95, Dep.

KINLOCHLEVEN Highland (Argyll). Map 39E
Pop 1,620. Glencoe 6, London 478, Ballachulish 6, Edinburgh 121, Fort William 21, Glasgow 91.
EC Wed. **Golf** Fort William 18h. **See** 'Devil's Staircase'.

Rescue Service: Wades Road Garage, Wades Rd. **☎** (085 54) 249.

KINLOCH RANNOCH Tayside (Perthshire). Maps 39F and 40E
Pop 300. Tummel Bridge 6½, London 457, Aberfeldy 20, Dalwhinnie 31, Edinburgh 88, Glasgow 88, Lochearnhead 40, Pitlochry 20.
EC Wed. **Golf** Strathtay 9h. **See** The Barracks, Rannoch Moor.

★★Dunalastair, *The Square, PH16 5PW.* **☎** (088 22) 323. RS Oct–May. C. **⊷** 24 bedrs, 10 bp, 10 sh, 4 ba, Dgs. ✖ mc, at, LD 8.30. ☎ CH, TV, Dgs, ns, CP 25, U 4, G 3, Ac, pf, con 45, CF, 6 BGf, 0 st, Dis. **£** BB £10·95–£13·95, DB £21·90–£27·90, WT £124·65, DT £22·85, DBB £18·90–£21·90, WB, ☒, Bk £3·95, L £5·45, D £7·95, cc 1 3, Dep a.

★★Loch Rannoch, *PH16 5PS.* **☎** (088 22) 201. C. **⊷** 13 bedrs, 13 bp, TV, Dgs. ✖ a l c, mc, at, LD 10. ☎ N, CH, Dgs. CP 40, sp, tc, pf, sc, sb, sol, gym, con 40, CF, 1 st. **£** £22–£25, DB £40–£50, DBB £28–£34·50, WB, ☐, Bk £3·75, L £4·50, D £9·75, cc 1 2 3 5.

Rescue Service: J & P Brown, The Garage. **☎** (088 22) 331.

KINROSS Tayside (Kinross-shire). Map 36D
Pop 4,700. S. Queensferry 17, London 401, M90 Motorway 1, Dundee 30, Dunfermline 12, Edinburgh 27, Glasgow 45, Kincardine 17, Kirkcaldy 16, Perth 16, St Andrews 35, Stirling 33.
EC Thur. **Golf** Kinross 18h. **See** Loch Leven, Loch Leven Castle, Priory ruins on St Serf's Island.
🛈 Kinross Service Area, M90 off Junc 6. **☎** Kinross (0577) 63680.

★★★Green, *KY13 7AS.* **☎** (0577) 63467. C. **⊷** 45 bedrs, 40 bp, 5 bps, TV, Dgs. ✖ a l c, mc, at, LD 9.30. ☎ N, CH, Dgs, CP 60, sp, gc, pf, sc, sb, sol, con 100, CF. **£** BB £30–£35, DB £40–£45, WB, ☒, Bk £4·50, L £5·50, D £8·50, cc 1 2 3 5 6, Dep b.

★★Bridgend, *High St, KY13 7DL.* **☎** (0577) 63413.

Rescue Service: Kirklands Garage (Kinross) Ltd, High St. **☎** (0577) 62244.

KIPPEN Central (Stirlingshire). Map 36C
Pop 529. M9 Motorway 12, Stirling 9½, London 405, Dumbarton 28, Dunblane 11, Edinburgh 44, Glasgow 24, Lochearnhead 22, Perth 36.
EC Wed. **Golf** Aberfoyle 9h. **See** Church, Dovecote.

Rescue Service: Glen Gyle Garage Ltd, Fintry Rd. **☎** (078 687) 254.

KIRK BEAN Dumfries & Galloway (Dumfriesshire). Map 29F
New Abbey 5, London 338, Dalbeattie 12, Edinburgh 82, Glasgow 84.

Cavens, G, x (RI), *DG2 8AA.* **☎** (038 788) 234. Closed Xmas & New Year. C. **⊷** 6 bedrs, 4 bp, 2 bps, Dgs. ☎ TV, Dgs, CP 12, CF, 2 BGf, 0 st. **£** BB £12, DB £24, WT £136·50, DT £19·50, ☐.

KIRKCALDY Fife. Map 37C
Pop 49,820. M90 Motorway 9, S. Queensferry 16, London 400, Dundee 29, Dunfermline 12, Edinburgh 25, Glasgow 51, Kinross 16, Perth 28, St Andrews 23.
EC Wed. **Golf** Dunnikier Municipal 18h. **See** Sailor's Walk (Nat Trust Scot), Ravenscraig Castle ruins, Beveridge, Dunnikier and Ravenscraig Parks, Art Gallery and Museum, Royal Palace of Falkland 9½ m NW.
🛈 Esplanade. **☎** Kirkcaldy (0592) 267775.

★★★Dean Park, *Chapel Level.* **☎** (0592) 261635.

★★★Parkway, *Abbotshall Rd, KY2 5DG.* **☎** (0592) 262143. C. **⊷** 32 bedrs, 32 bp, TV, Dgs. ✖ a l c, mc, at, LD 10·45. ☎ N,

CH, CP 90, Ac, sb, sol, con 300, CF, 4 BGf, 1 st, Dis. **£** BB £20–£30, DB £30–£40, DBB £19–£37, WB, ☒, Bk £3·50, L £6, D £9, cc 1 2 3 5 6, Dep b.

Rescue Service: W J Taylor, 4 Park Rd. **☎** (0592) 51200.

KIRKCONNEL Dumfries & Galloway (Dumfriesshire). Map 29A
Pop 2,640. Sanquhar 3, London 357, Abington 19, Ayr 28, Dalmellington 17, Edinburgh 57, Glasgow 48, Thornhill 15.
EC Thur. **Golf** Sanquhar 9h. **See** St Connel's Church (ruin).

Rescue Service: Hammonds Garage, 42 Main St. **☎** (065 93) 282.

KIRKCOWAN Dumfries & Galloway. Map 28F
Newton Stewart 6, London 375, Edinburgh 109, Glasgow 87, Girvan 30, Stranraer 18, Wigtown 8.

Rescue Service: Kirkcowan Service Station, 9 Main St. **☎** (067 183) 229.

KIRKCUDBRIGHT Dumfries & Galloway (Kirkcudbrightshire). Map 29E
Pop 3,400. Dalbeattie 13, London 354, Dumfries 25, Edinburgh 97, Glasgow 88, New Galloway 18.
EC Thur. **Golf** Kirkcudbright 18h. **See** Tolbooth, Market Cross, Museum, Broughton House, McLellans Castle ruins, Dundrennan Abbey ruins 7 m SE, Cardonness Castle 6½ m NW.
🛈 Harbour Sq. **☎** Kirkcudbright (0557) 30494.

★★★Mayfield, *DG6 4ET.* **☎** (0557) 30523. Open Mar–Oct. C. **⊷** 19 bedrs, 6 ba, ns, Dgs. ✖ a l c, mc, LD 8. ☎ CH, TV, Dgs, CP 25, G 5, Ac, CF. **£** BB £10, DB £20, WT £119, DT £19, DBB £17, WB, ☐, Bk £3, L £4·20, D £7.

★★Royal, *St Cuthbert St, DG6 4DY.* **☎** (0557) 30551.

★★Selkirk Arms, *Old High St, DG6 4JG.* **☎** (0557) 30402. C. **⊷** 16 bedrs, 2 bp, 4 ba. ✖ a l c, mc, at, LD 8. ☎ ch, TV, CP 4, G 16, CF, 4 BGf, 0 st, Dis. **£** BB £13·65–£15, DB £27·30–£34·95, WT £158–£175, DBB £21·65–£25·95, WB, ☒, Bk £3·25, L £4·25, D £8·50, cc 1 3 5.▲

Rescue Service: James McMurray & Son, Royal Garage, Mew Lac. **☎** (0557) 30412.

KIRKINTILLOCH Strathclyde (Dunbartonshire). Map 48C
Pop 36,000. M73 Motorway 5½, Hamilton 15, London 400, Edinburgh 41, Glasgow 8, Stirling 19.
EC Wed. **Golf** Kirkintilloch 18h. **See** 17th cent Parish Church with museum, Peel Park (site of Roman Fort).

Rescue Service: Robert H Turner Ltd, Oxgang Garage, Waterside Rd. **☎** 041-776 7771.

KIRKMICHAEL Tayside (Perthshire). Map 40F
Pop 150. Blairgowrie 12, London 443, Edinburgh 68, Glasgow 84, Pitlochry 12.
EC Thur. **Golf** Pitlochry 18h.

★★Log Cabin, *PH10 7NB.* **☎** Strathardle (025 081) 288. C. **⊷** 13 bedrs, 7 bp, 6 bps, TV, Dgs. ✖ mc, at, LD 9. ☎ CH, TV, Dgs, ns, CP 60, Ac, CF, con 40, CF, 4 BGf, 0 st, Dis. **£** BB £15–£30, DB £30–£42, WT £175–£215, DT £29·50–£36·50, DBB £26–

£33, WB, ⬛, Bk £4, L £3·50, D £12,
cc 1 2 3 5 6, Dep a.

■★**Aldchlappie,** *PH10 7NS.*
☎ Strathardle (025 081) 224. C 5. ➭ 6
bedrs, 5 bp, 1 ba, Dgs. ✘ mc, LD 9.30.
⬛ TV, CP 25, G 4, pf, 2 st. £ BB £12·50–
£20·50, DB £25–£31, DT £35, DBB
£31·50–£37·50, ⬛, Bk £3·50, L £2·50, D
£7·50.

■★**Strathlene,** *PH10 7NT.*
☎ Strathardle (025 081) 347. C. ➭ 7
bedrs, 2 bp, 2 ba, Dgs. ✘ a l c, mc, at, LD
9.30. ⬛ CH, TV, Dgs, CP 3, Ac, CF, 0 st.
£ BB £10·50–£13, DB £18–£21·50, WT
£114–£120, DT £18·50–£19·50, DBB
£15·50–£18, WB, ⬛, Bk £2·50, L £3·50, D
£6·50, cc 1 2 3 5, Dep b.

Rescue Service: Kirkmichael Garage, Main
St. ☎ Strathardle (025 081) 272.

KIRKPATRICK-FLEMING Dumfries &
Galloway (Dumfriesshire). Map 30F
Gretna 4, London 307, Annan 6½,
Ecclefechan 6, Edinburgh 85, Glasgow 81,
Langholm 14.
EC Wed. **Golf** Lockerbie 9h. **See** Gretna
Green nearby.

Rescue Service: G & T Moffat & Co Ltd,
The Garage, Lockerbie. ☎ (046 18) 233.

KYLEAKIN Isle of Skye, Highland
(Inverness-shire). Map 38D
Pop 300. Fy to Kyle of Lochalsh. London
580, Broadford 8, Edinburgh 207,
Glasgow 193, Mallaig (Fy) 22.

★★**Marine,** *IV41 8PL.* ☎ Kyle (088 54)
4585.

KYLE OF LOCHALSH Highland (Ross &
Cromarty). Map 38D
Pop 900. Invergarry 48, London 561 (Fy
570), Achnasheen 35, Broadford 8 (Fy to
Kyleakin), Edinburgh 196, Glasgow 174,
Invermoriston 56.
EC Thur. **Golf** Kyle 9h. **See** Eilean Donan
Castle, Castle Moil across Kyle Akin on
Isle of Skye, Balmacara House (4 m E),
Loch Alsh.
🆔 ☎ Kyle (0599) 4276.

Retreat, G, x (Unl), *Main St, IV40 8BY.*
☎ Kyle (0599) 4308. Open Apr–Oct. C 3.
➭ 14 bedrs, 14 sh, 3 ba, Dgs. ⬛ CH, TV,
CP 10, G 2, 5 BGf, 1 st, Dis. £ BB £8·50, DB
£17, ⬛.

Rescue Service: Clan Garage. ☎ Kyle
(0599) 4328.
Central Garage Kyle, Main St. ☎ (0599)
4329.
F & F Motors. ☎ (0599) 4728.

LAGGAN Highland (Inverness-shire).
Maps 39D & 40E
Pop 140. Dalwhinnie 7, London 481,
Aviemore 22, Edinburgh 106, Fort William
33, Glasgow 118.
EC Thur. **Golf** Newtonmore 18h.

Monadhliath, H, xy, *Laggan Bridge,
PH20 1BT.* ☎ (052 84) 273. C. ➭ 8 bedrs,
3 ba, Dgs. ⬛ CH, CP 40, CF. £ BB £9·50–
£11·75, DB £19–£20, WT (b) £80–£99·50,
DT (b) £15–£18·75, ⬛, Bk £3·95, L £2·95,
D £6·50, cc 1 3.

LAIRG Highland (Sutherland). Map 42D
Pop 950. Bonar Bridge 11, London 577,
Bettyhill 46, Durness 56, Edinburgh 202,
Glasgow 209, Helmsdale 50, Ullapool 44.

EC Wed. **Golf** Royal Dornoch 18h and 9h.
See Falls of Shin and Salmon Leap, Hut
Circles and other ancient relics.
🆔 ☎ Lairg (0549) 2160.

■★★★**Sutherland Arms,** *Main Rd, IV27
4AT.* ☎ (0549) 2219. Open Apr–Oct. C.
➭ 24 bedrs, 17 bp, 1 bps, 6 ba, Dgs. ✘ mc,
at, LD 8·30. ⬛ ch, TV, CP 30, pf, CF, 5 BGf,
0 st, Dis. £ BB £25–£28, DB £40–£46, DBB
£20–£37, WB, ⬛, Bk £4, L £3, D £9,
cc 1 2 3 5 6.

Repairer: Sutherland Transport & Trading
Co Ltd. ☎ (0549) 2465.
Rescue Service: James Paterson & Son,
West End Garage, Lochside. ☎ (0549)
2213.

LAMLASH Isle of Arran, Strathclyde
(Bute). Map 28B
Pop 4,100. Brodick 4 (Steamer to
Ardrossan 1), London 402, Edinburgh 78,
Glasgow 33.
EC Wed. **Golf** Lamlash 18h. **See** Holy
Island.

Rescue Service: Automarine Engineers,
Lamlash Garage. ☎ (077 06) 209.

LANARK Strathclyde (Lanarkshire).
Maps 29B and 36F
Pop 9,778. Abington 18, London 369, Ayr
40, Edinburgh 33, Glasgow 26,
Kilmarnock 30, Peebles 27, Stirling 34.
EC Thur. **MD** Mon. **Golf** Lanark 18h & 9h.
See Parish Church of St Nicholas, Tower
and William Wallace Statue, ruins of 12th
cent St Kentigern's Church, Cora Castle
ruins, Craignethan Castle ruins 4½ m NW,
18th cent Tolbooth.

🏩★★**Cartland Bridge,** *ML11 9UF.*
☎ (0555) 4426. RS New Year's Day. C.
➭ 15 bedrs, 4 ba, Dgs. ✘ a l c, mc, at, LD
9.30. ⬛ CH, TV, Dgs, CP 300, pf, con 200,
CF, 3 st. £ BB fr £17·50, DB fr £35, WT fr
£221·50, DT fr £31·50, DBB fr £26, WB, ⬛,
Bk £2·10, L £5·50, D £8·50, cc 1 2 3 5.

Repairer: W H Cox (Lanark) Ltd,
Clydesdale Garage and Motor Works.
☎ (0555) 2371.
Rescue Service: A G Barr–Vehicle Repair
Service, Caldwellside Industrial Estate.
☎ (0555) 4815.

LANGBANK Strathclyde
(Renfrewshire). Map 35F
Pop 804. Glasgow 14, London 402, M8
Motorway 1½, Dumbarton (via toll bridge)
10, Edinburgh 59, Glasgow 14, Greenock
7, Paisley 9½.
EC Wed. **Golf** Erskine 18h.

🏩★★★★**Gleddoch House,** *PA14 6YE.*
☎ (047 554) 711. Closed Xmas & Jan 1st
& 2nd. C. ➭ 20 bedrs, 18 bp, 2 bps, 1 ba,
TV, Dgs. ✘ a l c, LD 9. ⬛ N, CH, CP 100,
ap, gc, pf, sc, rf, sb, con 30, CF, 3 st. £ BB
£48–£55, DB £65–£85, WB, ⬛, Bk £5, L
£7·50, D £15, cc 1 2 3 4 5 6, Dep b.

LANGHOLM Dumfries & Galloway
(Dumfriesshire). Map 30D
Pop 2,500. Carlisle 20, London 314,
Beattock 32, Brampton 20, Dumfries 28,
Edinburgh 71, Glasgow 86, Hawick 23.
EC Wed. **Golf** Langholm 9h. **See** Remains
of Castle, Old Custom Common Riding,
last Fri in July, Gilnockie Tower 4 m N.
🆔 High St. ☎ Langholm (0541) 80581.

★★**Eskdale,** *Market Pl, DG13 0JH.*
☎ (0541) 80357. C. ➭ 14 bedrs, 3 bps, 3

ba, TV, Dgs. ✘ a l c, mc, LD 9. ⬛ CH, TV,
CP 12, Ac, con 100, CF, 1 st. £ BB £12·25–
£13·75, DB £21·50–£24·50, WT fr £110,
DT fr £17·25, DBB fr £14·75, WB, ⬛, Bk
£3·50, L £3·75, D £6, cc 1 3, Dep b.

★★**Holmwood House,** *Holmwood Drive,
DG13 0PR.* ☎ (0541) 80211. C. ➭ 7
bedrs, 1 bp, 1 bps, 1 sh, 1 ba, Dgs. ✘ mc,
at, LD 9. ⬛ CH, TV, Dgs, CP 25, Ac, CF, 2
st. £ BB £11–£12·50, DB £20–£23, DBB
£17–£18·50, ⬛, Bk £2·50, L £3·50, D £5·50,
Dep a.

■★**Crown,** *High St, DG13 0JH.* ☎ (0541)
80247. Open Apr–Sep. C. ➭ 8 bedrs, 2 ba,
Dgs. ✘ mc, LD 8. ⬛ CH, TV, CP 4, Ac, CF,
1 st. £ BB £10, DB £19, DBB £15–£16·50,
⬛, Bk £2·50, L £3, D £6.

LARBERT Central (Stirlingshire). Map
36D
Pop 19,771. Falkirk 3½, London 397,
Dumbarton 33, Edinburgh 28, Glasgow
22, Kincardine 7, Lanark 26, Stirling 8½.
EC Wed. **Golf** Falkirk Tryst 18h.

Rescue Service: Alexander Hardie,
Muirhall Garage, 167 Main St. ☎ (0324)
2799.

LARGO Fife. Map 37C
Pop 3,000. Lundin Links 1½, London 412,
Dundee 20, Edinburgh 38, Glasgow 65,
Kinross 22, Kirkcaldy 12, St Andrews 10.
EC Thur. **Golf** Lundin Links 18h. **See**
Parish Church and Celtic Cross, Statue of
Alexander Selkirk—Defoe's 'Robinson
Crusoe'—whose birthplace was in Lower
Largo.

Rescue Service: Purves Motors, Main St,
Upper Largo. ☎ Upper Largo (033 36)
217.

LARGS Strathclyde (Ayrshire). Map 35E
Pop 10,830. Irvine 17, London 408, Ayr 31,
Edinburgh 74, Glasgow 29, Gourock 14,
Kilmarnock 26, Paisley 23.
EC Wed. **Golf** Largs 18h, Routenburn 18h.
See St Columba's Parish Church,
Skelmorlie Aisle in old Churchyard, Round
Tower.
🆔 Pier Head. ☎ Largs (0475) 673765.

★★**Elderslie,** *Broomfields, KA30 8DR.*
☎ (0475) 686460. Closed Xmas. C. ➭ 25
bedrs, 9 bp, 4 bps, 4 ba, Dgs. ✘ mc, LD
8.30. ⬛ CH, TV, Dgs, CP 40, Ac, con 40,
CF, 4 BGf, 0 st, Dis. £ BB £14–£16, DB
£28–£32, DBB £21–£23, ⬛, Bk £3·25, L
£4·70, D £7, cc 1 2 3 5.▲

■★★**Glen Eldon,** *2 Barr Cres, KA30
8PX.* ☎ (0475) 673381. Closed Mar. C.
➭ 9 bedrs, 3 bp, 6 bps, 2 ba, TV. ✘ LD
7.45. ⬛ CH, TV, ns, CP 18, Ac, con 20, CF,
5 st. £ BB £15, DB £30, DBB £22, WB, ⬛,
Bk £2·50, L £2, D £6·50, Dep.

★★**Mackerston** (RI), *3 Mackerston Pl,
KA30 8BZ.* ☎ (0475) 673264. C. ➭ 44
bedrs, 10 bp, 15 ba, Dgs. ✘ a l c, mc, at, LD
7.45. ⬛ Lt, CH, TV, Dgs, CP 35, con 25, CF,
2 st. £ BB £12·50–£15·50, DB £25–£35,
WT £150–£175, DT £23–£25, DBB
£19·50–£24·75, WB, ⬛, Bk £2·75, L £3·50,
D £7, cc 1 2 3.

★★**Queen's,** *North Promenade, KA30
8QW.* ☎ (0475) 673253. C 3. ➭ 14 bedrs,
2 bp, 4 ba, Dgs. ✘ a l c, mc, at, LD 8. ⬛ CH,
TV, CP 80, Ac, 3 st. £ BB £10·50–£15, DB
£30–£40, ⬛, Bk £3·50, L £3·50, D £7·50,
cc 1 2 3 4 5 6.▲

★★**Springfield,** *North Bay, KA30 8QL.*
☎ (0475) 673119. C. ➭ 41 bedrs, 2 bp, 12
bps, 10 ba. ✘ mc, LD 8. ⬛ Lt, CH, TV, CP

84, Ac, con, CF, 8 BGf, 0 st, Dis. **£** BB £15–
£18, DB £26–£32, WT £145, DT £24·50,
DBB £19·75–£22·75, ⬜, Bk £3, L £4·75, D
£6·75, cc 1 2 3 5 6.
Aubery, G, x (Unl), *22 Aubery Cres,*
KA30 8PR. ✆ (0475) 672330.
Holmesdale, G, z (Unl), *75 Moorburn*
Rd, KA30 9DE. ✆ (0475) 674793. Closed
Oct & Xmas & New Year. C. 🚪 8 bedrs, 2
ba. ⬟ CH, TV, CP 4, 2 BGf, 0 st, Dis. **£** BB
£7·50, DB £15, WT (b) £75, WT (c) £51, DT
(b) £11, ②.
Sunbury, G, z (Unl), *12 Aubery Cres,*
KA30 8PR. ✆ (0475) 673086. Open Mar–
Nov. C. 🚪 6 bedrs, 2 ba, Dgs. ⬟ ch, TV, ns,
CP 6, CF, 3 st. **£** BB £7·50, DB £15, WT (b)
£75, WT (c) £50, DT (b) £11.50, ⬜.

LAUDER Borders (Berwickshire). Maps
30B and 37E
Pop 810. Jedburgh 21, London 348,
Berwick-upon-Tweed 32, Coldstream 22,
Edinburgh 27, Galashiels 13, Glasgow 69,
Haddington 21, Kelso 18, Peebles 26.
EC Thur. **Golf** Lauder 9h. **See** 17th cent
Tolbooth, 17th cent Church.

Rescue Service: Lauderdale Garage,
Edinburgh Rd. ✆ (057 82) 228.

LENNOXTOWN Strathclyde
(Dumbartonshire). Map 33C
Glasgow 8, London 396, Dumbarton 19,
Edinburgh 46, Lochearnhead 36, Stirling
21.

Glazertbank, PH, yz, *Main St, G65 7DJ.*
✆ (0360) 310790. C. 🚪 5 bedrs, 5 bp, Dgs.
✖ a l c, ⬟ CH, TV, Dgs, CP 40, CF, 5 BGf, 0
st, Dis. **£** BB £13·50, DB £20, ②, L £2·95, D
£3·70, cc 1 2.

LERWICK
See SHETLAND ISLANDS.

LESLIE Fife. Map 37C
Pop 3,760. M90 Motorway 13, London
403, Glenrothes 3, Edinburgh 28, Glasgow
53, Kinross 11, Kirkcaldy 8, Perth 20.
EC Wed. **Golf** Leslie 18h. **See**
Strathendry Castle, Falkland Palace
4 m N, Loch Leven (W).

Rescobie, H, yz (Rt) *Valley Dr, KY6 3BQ.*
✆ Glenrothes (0592) 742143. C. 🚪 8
bedrs, 3 bp, 2 ba, TV, Dgs. ✖ a l c. ⬟ CH,
CP 10, 2 st. **£** BB £21–£24, DB £38·50–
£43, WT (b) £203, DT (b) £29, ②, Bk £4, L
£4, D £8, cc 1 2 3.

LETHAM Fife. Map 37C
Pop 170. Glenrothes 9, London 414,
Dundee 15, Dunfermline 25, Edinburgh 40,
Glasgow 59, Kinross 16, Kirkcaldy 14,
Perth 21, St Andrews 15, Stirling 37.
Golf Ladybank 18h.

⬟★★★★Fernie Castle, *Ladybank, KY7*
7RU. ✆ (033 781) 209.

LEUCHARS Fife. Map 37A
Cupar 6, London 423, Edinburgh 51,
Glasgow 72, Dundee 8, Perth 35, St
Andrews 6.

Rescue Service: Leuchars Garage, 2
Meadow Rd. ✆ (033 483) 440.

LEVEN Fife. Map 37C
Pop 9,430. East Wemyss 4, London 409,
Dundee 22, Edinburgh 34, Glasgow 60,
Kinross 19, Kirkcaldy 8½, Perth 27, St
Andrews 14.
EC Thur. **Golf** Leven Links 18h, Leven
Municipal 18h. **See** Letham Glen.
⅃ South St. ✆ Leven (0333) 29464.

★★Caledonian, *High St, KY8 4NG.*
✆ (0333) 24101.

Rescue Service: James J Anderson,
Lundin Links Service Station, Largo Rd.
✆ Lundin Links (0333) 320380.

LINWOOD Strathclyde (Renfrewshire).
Map 48F
Pop 13,697. Paisley 3, London 396,
Edinburgh 56, Glasgow 11, Gourock 17,
Kilmarnock 21, Largs 21.
EC Tue. **Golf** Elderslie 18h.

⬛★★Golden Pheasant, *Moss Rd, PA3*
3HP. ✆ Johnstone (0505) 21266. C. 🚪 12
bedrs, 12 bp, TV, Dgs. ✖ a l c, mc, at, LD
8.30. ⬟ CH, CP 100, Ac, con 80, CF, 1 st.
£ BB £20·35, DB £32·75, Bk £3, D £6·50,
cc 1 2 3 5.

LOCH AWE Strathclyde (Argyll). Map
35A
Pop 100. Dalmally 3, London 458,
Edinburgh 101, Glasgow 70, Inveraray 16,
Oban 22.
EC Wed. **Golf** Glencruitten 18h. **See**
Kilchurn Castle ruins, Loch Awe, Ben
Cruachan (3,689 ft).

⬛★★Carraig-Thura, *PA33 1AF.*
✆ Dalmally (083 82) 210. Open Apr–Nov.
C. 🚪 20 bedrs, 11 bp, 5 bps, 4 ba, Dgs.
✖ mc, at, LD 8. ⬟ CH, TV, CP 25, pf, con
25, CF, 3 st. **£** WB ② 10%, Bk £3·50, L
£2·50, D £10, cc 1 2 3 5 6, Dep.

LOCHBOISDALE Isle of South Uist,
Western Islands, (Inverness-shire). Map
44C
Pop 697. Steamer service to Oban,
London 477, Edinburgh 121, Glasgow 90.
EC Wed. **Golf** Askernish 9h.
⅃ ✆ Lochboisdale (087 84) 286.

★Lochboisdale, *PA81 5TH.*
✆ (087 84) 332.

LOCHCARRON Highland (Ross &
Cromarty). Map 38B
Pop 350. Invergarry 59, London 572,
Achnasheen 22, Edinburgh 223 (Fy 207),
Glasgow 232 (Fy 186), Invermoriston (Fy)
59, Kyle of Lochalsh (Fy) 18.
EC Thur. **Golf** Lochcarron 9h. **See** Strome
Castle.

⬛★Lochcarron, *IV54 8YS.* ✆ (052 02)
226. Open Jan–Nov, RS Xmas & New Year.
C. 🚪 7 bedrs, 4 bp, 3 ba, Dgs. ✖ mc, at, LD
8.30. ⬟ TV, CP 30, 3 st. **£** BB £12–£17, DB
£22–£32, DBB £18–£24, ②, Bk £3·25, L
£2·50, D £7·95, cc 1 3.

Rescue Service: Lochcarron Garage, Main
St. ✆ (052 02) 205.

LOCHGAIR Strathclyde (Argyll). Map
35C
Pop 60. Inveraray 16, London 461,
Edinburgh 115, Glasgow 73,
Lochgilphead 7½.
Golf Lochgilphead 9h. **See** Crarae
Gardens 6 m NE.

⬛★★Lochgair, *PA31 8SA.* ✆ (054 682)
233.

LOCHGILPHEAD Strathclyde (Argyll).
Map 35C
Pop 1,900. Inveraray 23, London 468,
Edinburgh 122, Glasgow 80, Oban 36.
EC Tue. **Golf** Lochgilphead 9h. **See** St
Mary's Church.
⅃ Lochnell St. ✆ Lochgilphead (0546)
2344.

⬛★★Stag, *Argyll St, PA31 8NE.*
✆ (0546) 2496.

Rescue Service: Fyneside Service Station,
Paterson St. ✆ (0546) 2229.
McDonald & MacLellan, Stag Garage,
Lorne St. ✆ (0546) 2100.

LOCHINVER Highland (Sutherland).
Map 42C
Pop 350. Inchnadamph 13, London 620,
Dingwall 74, Durness 52, Edinburgh 245,
Glasgow 249, Lairg 44, Ullapool 34.
EC Tue. **MD** Fri. **See** Castle, Caves, Falls
(Highest in Britain).
⅃ ✆ Lochinver (057 14) 330.

⬛★★★Culag, *IV27 4LQ.* ✆ (057 14) 209.
Open Apr–Oct. C. 🚪 43 bedrs, 19 bp, 9 ba,
Dgs. ✖ mc, at, LD 8.45. ⬟ Lt, N, CH, TV,
Dgs, CP 35, pf, CF, 1 st. **£** BB £22–£30, DB
£42–£47, ⬜, Bk £3·50, L £3, D £9·50,
cc 1 2 3 5 6.

LOCH MAREE Highland (Ross &
Cromarty). Map 42E
Achnasheen 19, London 587, Edinburgh
212, Gairloch 9, Glasgow 216.
Golf Gairloch 9h.

★★Loch Maree, *IV22 2HN.* ✆ (044 589)
200

LOCHWINNOCH Strathclyde
(Renfrewshire). Maps 35F and 36E
Pop 2,327. Paisley 10, London 403, Ayr
27, Edinburgh 63, Glasgow 18, Gourock
17, Kilmarnock 17, Largs 13.
EC Wed. **Golf** Lochwinnoch 18h. **See**
Clochoderick Stone, ruins of Barr Castle,
Regent Moray Bridge, Renfrewshire
Regional Park.

Repairer: Wm Struthers & Sons Ltd,
Newton-of-Barr. ✆ (0505) 843314.

LOCKERBIE Dumfries & Galloway
(Dumfriesshire). Map 30C
Pop 3,000. Carlisle 24, London 318,
Beattock 14, Brampton 30, Dumfries 12,
Edinburgh 66, Glasgow 69, Langholm 18.
EC Tue. **MD** Tue. **Golf** Lockerbie 18h.
9h. **See** Old Tower, Roman Camp.

⬟★★Dryfesdale, *DG11 2SF.* ✆ (057 62)
2427. C. 🚪 10 bedrs, 8 bp, 3 ba, TV, Dgs.
✖ a l c, mc, at, LD 9. ⬟ CH, TV, Dgs, CP 50,
con 50, CF, 1 BGf, 1 st, Dis. **£** BB £16–
£22·50, DB £24–£38, WT ⬜, Bk £3·50, L
£5·50, D £9·50, cc 1 2 3 5 6.

⬟★★Lockerbie House, *DG11 2RD.*
✆ (057 62) 2610. Closed Xmas. C. 🚪 30
bedrs, 23 bp, 1 bps, 4 ba, Dgs. ✖ a l c, mc,
LD 9. ⬟ CH, TV, Dgs, CP 100, Ac, sb, sol,
con 50, CF. **£** WB, Bk £4, L £6, D £6,
cc 1 2 3 5 6.▲

★★Queen's, *Annan Rd, DG11 2RB.*
✆ (057 62) 2415. C. 🚪 16 bedrs, 1 bp, 7
bps, 8 sh, 2 ba, TV, Dgs. ✖ a l c, mc, at, LD
8.30. ⬟ CH, TV, CP 100, G 2, rf, con 100,
CF, 0 st. **£** BB £13·75–£16·75, DB £27·50–
£33·50, WT £240–£260, DT £35–£38, DBB
£23·50–£26·50, WB, ⬜, Bk £3·15, L £5·75,
D £8·50, cc 1 3 6.

★★Somerton House, *Carlisle Rd, DG11*
2DR. ✆ (057 62) 2583.▲
★Blue Bell, *High St, DG11 2ES.*
✆ (057 62) 2309. C. 🚪 6 bedrs, 2 ba, Dgs.
✖ mc, LD 9. ⬟ CH, TV, Dgs, CP 8, Ac, 2 st.
£ BB £20, DB £18, ⬜, Bk £2·25, D £7·50.

Rescue Service: Johnstone Bridge
Service Station. ✆ Johnstone Bridge
(057 62) 213.

Victoria Garage, 1 Victoria Rd. ☎ (057 62) 2418.

LOSSIEMOUTH Grampian (Moray). Maps 40B and 43F
Pop 6,100. Elgin 5½, London 532, Banff 38, Edinburgh 175, Glasgow 175, Huntly 32.
EC Thur. **Golf** Moray 18h (2). **See** Ramsay Macdonald's birthplace, Mercat Cross.

Rescue Service: Ian Watt, The Square.
☎ (034 381) 2064.

LUNAN BAY Tayside (Angus). Map 37B
Pop 25. Arbroath 8, London 453, Dundee 24, Edinburgh 79, Forfar 16, Glasgow 102, Montrose 5.
Golf Montrose 18h. **See** Redcastle (ruins).

⚹★★Lunan Bay, *Inverkeilor by Arbroath Angus, DD11 5ST.* ☎ (024 13) 265. C.
➡ 11 bedrs, 6 bp, 2 sh, 2 ba, TV, Dgs.
✗ a l c. ₪ CH, TV, Dgs, CP 150, CF, 1 st.
£ BB £26–£28, DB £36–£38, WT £196–£287, DT £39–£41, ② Bk £5, L £1·95, D £10·95, cc 1 2 3 5.▲

MACDUFF Grampian (Banffshire). Map 41A
Pop 3,975. Huntly 21, London 533, Aberdeen 47, Banff 1, Edinburgh 158, Fraserburgh 22, Glasgow 175, Peterhead 35.
EC Wed. **Golf** Royal Tarlair 18h. **See** War Memorial with 70 ft tower.

★★Deveron House, *Union Rd, AB4 1UD.*
☎ (0261) 32309. C. ➡ 17 bedrs, 15 bp, 2 ba, TV, Dgs. ✗ a l c, mc, at, LD 9.30. ₪ CH, TV, CP 12, Ac, con 100, CF, 0 st. **£** BB £16–£22, DB £25–£39, WT £120–£150, DT £24–£30, DBB £19–£26, WB, ①, B £3, L £4.30, D £8, cc 1 2 3 5, Dep.

★★Fife Arms, *Shore St, AB4 1UB.*
☎ (0261) 32408. C. ➡ 13 bedrs, 4 bp, 4 bps, 4 sh, ba, Dgs. ✗ mc, at, LD 9. ₪ CH, TV, Dgs, CP 12, G 4, Ac, con 80, CF, 0 st.
£ BB £13–£16, DB £22·50–£26, DT £24, DBB £20–£21, WB, ①, Bk £2, L £2, D £7, cc 1 3 5 6.

MALLAIG Highland (Inverness-shire). Map 38D
Pop 1,050. Fort William 43, London 533 (Fy 535), Edinburgh 176 (Fy 174), Glasgow 146 (Fy 146).
EC Wed. **Golf** Traig, Arisaig 9h. **See** Harbour, Loch Nevis, Loch Morar.
ⓘ Station Buildings. ☎ Mallaig (0687) 2170.

■★★Marine, *Station Rd, PH41 4PY.*
☎ (0687) 2217. Closed Xmas & New Year.
C. ➡ 21 bedrs, 6 bp, 4 ba, ns, Dgs. ✗ mc, LD 8. ₪ ch, TV, CP 10, Ac, CF, 3 BGf, 2 st.
£ BB £12–£18, DB £20–£28, WT £99, DT £18·50, DBB £18·50–£21·50, WB, ①, Bk £2·50, L £2·60, D £6·50, oo 2, Dep a.

★★West Highland, *PH41 4QZ.*
☎ (0687) 2210. Open Apr–Oct. C. ➡ 26 bedrs, 11 bp, 6 ba, Dgs. ✗ mc, at, LD 8.30. ₪ CH, TV, Dgs, CP 30, Ac, con 80, CF, 6 st.
£ BB £14–£18, DB £24–£27, DT £26, DBB £21–£22·50, WB, ②, Bk £4, L £5, D £8, cc 1 2 3 4 5 6, Dep a.
Rescue Service: Morar Motors Ltd.
☎ (0687) 2118.

MEIGLE Tayside (Perthshire). Map 37A
Pop 357. Coupar Angus 5½, London 433, Blairgowrie 8, Dundee 13, Edinburgh 58, Forfar 12, Glasgow 75, Perth 18.

EC Thur. **Golf** Alyth 18h. **See** Museum, Font in Church.

⚹★★King of Kinloch, *PH12 8QX.*
☎ (082 84) 273. Closed Jan. C. ➡ 7 bedrs, 1 bp, 2 ba. ✗ mc, at, LD 8.45. ₪ ch, CP 45, G 2, con 20, CF, 11 st. **£** BB £16·50–£19·50, DB £29–£31, DBB £25·50–£28·50, ② 12·5%, Bk £4, L £5·50, D £9, cc 1, Dep a.

MELROSE Borders (Roxburghshire). Map 30B
Pop 2,000. St Boswells 2½, London 340, Edinburgh 35, Galashiels 4, Glasgow 71, Hawick 14, Jedburgh 12, Lauder 11, Kelso 13, Selkirk 6½.
EC Thur. **Golf** Melrose 9h. **See** Abbey ruins, Abbey Museum, 15th cent Darnick Tower, 17th cent Cross, Timontium (site of Roman camp), Dryburgh Abbey ruins 4 m SE, Abbotsford (home of Sir Walter Scott) 2 m W.
ⓘ Priorwood, nr Abbey. ☎ Melrose (089 682) 2555.

★★Burt's, *Market Sq, TD6 9PN.*
☎ (089 682) 2285. C. ➡ 22 bedrs, 6 bp, 3 ba, TV, Dgs. ✗ a l c, mc, LD 9.30. ₪ CH, TV, Dgs, CP 36, CF, 0 st. **£** BB £14·50–£17, BB £28–£32, DBB £23–£25·50, ①, Bk £3·50, L £6, D £8·75, cc 1 2 3 5 6.

■★★George & Abbotsford, *High St, TD6 9PD.* ☎ (089 682) 2308. C. ➡ 42 bedrs, 14 bp, 15 bps, 11 ba, TV, Dgs.
✗ a l c, mc, at, LD 10.30. ₪ CH, TV, Dgs, CP 180, G 5, Ac, con 230, CF, 9 st. **£** BB £14–£17·60, DB £25–£30·80, WT £175·50–£193·05, DT £27–£29, DBB £20·50–£24·75, WB, ①, Bk £3·50, L £4·50, D £8·50, cc 1 2 3 5, Dep b.

Repairer: Croall, Bryson & Co Ltd, Palma Pl. ☎ (089 682) 2048.

MILLPORT Isle of Cumbrae, Strathclyde (Bute). Map 35E
Pop 1,400. (Ferry to Largs). Irvine 17, London 408, Ayr 31, Edinburgh 74, Glasgow 29, Gourock 14, Kilmarnock 26, Paisley 23.
Golf Millport 18h. **See** Lighthouse, Museums, Research Station, Episcopal Cathedral (smallest in Britain).

Westbourne, H, z *West Bay, KA28 0HA.* ☎ (047 553) 423.

MILNATHORT Tayside (Kinross-shire). Map 36D
Pop 2,500. Kinross 1½, London 402, M90 Motorway 1, Crieff 27, Dundee 28, Edinburgh 28, Glasgow 46, Kirkcaldy 15, Perth 15, St Andrews 28, Stirling 24.
EC Thur. **Golf** Milnathort 9h. **See** Castle, Nature Reserve (RSPB), Loch Leven.

Rescue Service: Stewart & Smart, Stirling Rd. ☎ Kinross (0577) 62423.

MILNGAVIE Strathclyde (Dunbartonshire). Map 48E
Pop 12,000. Glasgow 7, London 395, Dumbarton 11, Edinburgh 49, Gourock 28 (Fy 26), Kincardine 29, Lochearnhead 43, Paisley 10 (Fy 9½), Stirling 27.
EC Tue. **Golf** Milngavie 18h. **See** Milngavie Mill, Lillie Art Gallery, Tannoch Loch, Drumclog moor.

★★★Black Bull Thistle, *Main St, G62 6BH.* ☎ 041-956 2291. C. ➡ 27 bedrs, 24 bp, 3 bps, ns, TV, Dgs. ✗ a l c, mc, LD 9. ₪ N, CH, TV, Dgs, CP 70, Ac, con 120, CF, 2 st. **£** BB £37·30–£41·30, DB £44·30–

£50·30, WB, ②, Bk £4·75, cc 1 2 3 4 5 6, Dep b.

Rescue Service: Strathclyde Motor Co Ltd, 112 Main St. ☎ 041-942 2385.

MILTON Strathclyde (Dunbartonshire) Map 48E
Glasgow 13, London 401, Dumbarton 2, Edinburgh 57, Paisley 14.

Rescue Service: Strathford Motor Co Ltd, Dumbarton Rd. ☎ Dumbarton (0389) 65131.

MOFFAT Dumfries & Galloway (Dumfriesshire). Maps 29D and 30C
Pop 2,200. Beattock 2, London 335, Abington 18, Ayr 62, Dalmellington 51, Edinburgh 51, Glasgow 53, Hawick 44, Peebles 33, Selkirk 34, Thornhill 31.
EC Wed. **Golf** Coateshill 18h. **See** Colvin Fountain, J L Macadam's grave (old churchyard), Devil's Beef Tub 5 m N, Grey Mare's Tail, 200 ft fall, 10 m NE.
ⓘ Church Gate. ☎ Moffat (0683) 20620.

■★★★M Ladbroke, *DG10 9ET.*
☎ (0683) 20464. C. ➡ 51 bedrs, 44 bp, 4 bps, 2 ba, TV, Dgs. ✗ a l c, mc, at, LD 9.30. ₪ N, CH, TV, CP 70, Ac, con 50, CF, 21 BGf, 4 st. **£** BB £25–£35, DB £42–£57, WT £135–£190, WB, ②, Bk £5, L £3, D £9, cc 1 2 3 4 5 6, Dep b.

★★Annandale, *High St, DG10 9HF.*
☎ (0683) 20013. Open Apr–Nov. C. ➡ 19 bedrs, 2 sh, 6 ba, annexe 5 bedrs, 5 bp, TV, Dgs. ✗ mc, LD 8·15. ₪ CH, TV, Dgs, CP 50, Ac, CF, 5 BGf, 8 st. **£** BB £13–£18, DB £26–£32, DBB £18–£19, ②, Bk £4, D £6·75, cc 1 2 3 5 6.

★★Balmoral, *High St, DG10 9HQ.*
☎ (0683) 20288. C. ➡ 15 bedrs, 2 bp, 3 ba, Dgs. ✗ a l c, mc, at, LD 9. ₪ ch, TV, Dgs, CP 72, G 4, Ac, CF, 1 st. **£** BB £14–£16, DB £24–£28, WT £165–£175, DT £24–£26, DBB £21–£23, WB, ②, Bk £3·50, L £4·20, D £7·70, cc 1 2 3 4 5 6, Dep b.

★★Moffat House, *High St, DG10 9HL.*
☎ (0683) 20039. Open Mar–Nov. C. ➡ 8 bedrs, 3 bp, 5 bps, Dgs. ✗ mc, at, LD 8·45. ₪ ch, TV, Dgs, CP 25, G 6, Ac, con 40, CF, 2 BGf, 0 st, Dis. **£** BB £18–£21, DB £29–£35, WT £180–£200, DT £31–£33, DBB £23·50–£26·80, WB, ①, Bk £3·75, L £5·75, D £9, cc 2 3 5.

■★Buccleuch Arms, *High St, DG10 9ET.* ☎ (0683) 20003.

Arden House, G, x (Unl), *High St, DG10 9HG.* ☎ (0683) 20220. Open Mar–Oct. C. ➡ 8 bedrs, 4 bps, 4 sh, 2 ba, Dgs. ₪ CH, TV, CP 9, CF. **£** BB £8·50–£9·50, DB £15–£19, WT (c) £53–£60, DT (b) £12–£13·50, ①

Bridge, G, x (Unl), *Well Rd, DG10 9JT.*
☎ (0683) 20383. Open Mar–Nov. C. ➡ 6 bedrs, 2 ba, Dgs. ₪ CH, TV, Dgs, CP 10, CF. **£** BB £8–£9, DB £14–£16, DT (b) £11–£12.

Hartfell House, G, xy (Rl), *Hartfell Cres, DG10 9AL.* ☎ (0683) 20153. Open Mar–Dec & New Year. C. ➡ 9 bedrs, 4 ba, Dgs. ₪ CH, TV, CP 10, CF. **£** BB £9·10, DB £18·20, WT (b) £102, DT (b) £15·08, ①, Bk £2·80, D £6·50.

Rockhill, G, x (Unl), *14 Beechgrove, DG10 9RS.* ☎ (0683) 20283. Open Mar–Oct. C. ➡ 10 bedrs, 2 ba, Dgs. ₪ CH, TV, CP 6, CF, 2 BGf, 1 st. **£** BB £7·50–£8·50, DB £15–£17, WT (b) £81–£89·50, DT (b) £12·50–£13·50, ②

St Olaf, G, z (Unl), *Eastgate, DG10 9AE.*
☎ (0683) 20001. Open Apr–Sep. C. ⊭ 7 bedrs, 1 ba, Dgs. 🅿 CH, Dgs, G 4, CF.

MONIAIVE Dumfries & Galloway (Dumfriesshire). Map 29C
Pop 430. Dunscore 7, London 343, Dalmellington 25, Dumfries 16, Edinburgh 69, Glasgow 67, New Galloway 14, Thornhill 8½.
EC Thur. **Golf** Thornhill 18h. **See** Fort, Mote, Old Cross.

🅵⛟★★**Woodlea,** *DG3 4EN.* ☎ (084 82) 209. Open Mar–Oct. C. ⊭ 14 bedrs, 7 bp, 2 ba, TV, Dgs. ✗ mc, at, LD 8.30. 🅿 ch, TV, CP 20, Ac, sp, tc, pf, sb, sol, gym, CF, 1 st.
£ BB £13·80–£20·30, DB £27·60–£46·40, DBB £22–£30, WB, ②, Bk £2·70, D £6·80.
★**Craigdarroch Arms,** *High St, DG3 4HN.* ☎ (084 82) 205. C. ⊭ 9 bedrs, 2 ba, Dgs. ✗ a l c, mc, at, LD 9. 🅿 CH, TV, Dgs, CP 6, Ac, CF, 0 st. £ BB £8, DB £16, DT £18, DBB £13, Bk £2·50, L £5, D £7, Dep a.

Rescue Service: McCulloch & Irving, High St. ☎ (084 82) 313.
Riverside Garage, Dunreggan St.
☎ (084 82) 238.

MONKTON Strathclyde (Ayrshire). Map 28B
Pop 968. New Cumnock 21, London 385, Ayr 4, Edinburgh 69, Glasgow 29, Irvine 8, Kilmarnock 8, Troon 3.
EC Wed.

⛟★★★**Adamton House,** *Baird Rd, KA9 2SQ.* ☎ (0292) 70678. C. ⊭ 28 bedrs, 2 bp, TV, Dgs. ✗ a l c, mc, at, LD 9.30. 🅿 N, CH, TV, Dgs, CP 50, Ac, con 100, CF, 4 st.
£ BB £28·50, DB £44·50, WT £175, DT £40, DBB £36, WB, ①, Bk £3, L £4, D £8·50, cc 1 2 3 4 5 6.

MONTROSE Tayside (Angus). Maps 37B and 41E
Pop 12,286. Arbroath 14, London 458, Brechin 8½, Dundee 30, Edinburgh 87, Forfar 17, Glasgow 105, Stonehaven 23.
EC Wed. **Golf** Montrose 18h, Broomfield Course 18h. **See** 18th cent Church, Statue of Sir Robert Peel, Museum, William Lamb Memorial Studio, 18th cent Town Buildings, Melville Gardens.
🅸 212 High St. ☎ Montrose (0674) 2000.

Linksgate, G (Unl), *11 Dorward Rd, DD10 8SB.* ☎ (0674) 72273. C. ⊭ 7 bedrs, 2 ba, Dgs. 🅿 CH, TV, Dgs, CP 8, CF, 3 st. £ BB £6·50–£9·50, DB £17–£19, WT (b) £83–£93, DBB £12·50–£13·50, ①.

MONYMUSK Grampian (Aberdeenshire). Map 41C
Pop 278. Torphins 10, London 498, Aberdeen 19, Banff 34, Braemar 45, Craigellachie 39, Edinburgh 123, Forfar 56, Fraserburgh 42, Glasgow 142, Grantown-on-Spey 57, Huntly 23, Peterhead 39, Montrose 44, Stonehaven 32.
EC Wed. **Golf** Kemnay 9h.

★**Grant Arms,** *AB3 7HJ.* ☎ (046 77) 226. C. ⊭ 10 bedrs, 1 bp, 7 ba, Dgs. ✗ at, LD 9. 🅿 CH, TV, CP 20, Ac, pf, CF, 1 BGf, 1 st, Dis. £ BB £20·75–£23·30, DB £34·95–£46·55, WT £221·90, ①, Bk £3·30, D £10, cc 5, Dep a.

MORAR Highland (Inverness-shire). Map 38D

Fort William 39, London 528 (Fy 532), Edinburgh 171, Fort Augustus 67, Glasgow 141, Mallaig 3, Spean Bridge 45.
See Loch Morar (deepest in Europe).

★★**Morar,** *PH40 4PA.* ☎ Mallaig (0687) 2346. Open Apr–Oct. C. ⊭ 28 bedrs, 10 bp, 6 ba, Dgs. ✗ mc, at, LD 8·30. 🅿 CH, TV, Dgs, CP 50, Ac, pf, CF, 1 st. £ BB £12–£21, DB £26–£35, WT £170, DT £25–£31, DBB £20–£26, WB, ②, Bk £4, L £5, D £8, Dep.

MOTHERWELL Strathclyde (Lanarkshire). Map 48B
See also WISHAW.
Pop 32,500 (inc Wishaw). Abington 27, London 378, M74 Motorway 1½, Dalmellington 46, Edinburgh 35, Glasgow 13, Kilmarnock 27, Kincardine 28, Lanark 14, Largs 43, Peebles 38, Stirling 26.
EC Wed. **Golf** Colville Park 18h. **See** Dalzell House with 15th cent tower, RC Cathedral.

★★★**Garrion,** *73 Merry St, ML1 1JN.* ☎ (0698) 64561. C. ⊭ 29 bedrs, 14 bp, 5 ba, TV, Dgs. ✗ a l c, mc, at, LD 9.30. 🅿 Lt, N, CH, Dgs, CP 60, Ac, sb, gym, con 200, CF, 1 st. £ BB £21·50–£28·50, DB £31–£36, WT £256·90, DT £36·70, DBB £27·45–£32·45, WB, ①, Bk £3, L £4·25, D £5·95, cc 1 2 3 5 6.

Repairer: Taggarts (Motherwell) Ltd, Knowetop Garage. ☎ (0698) 66133.

MOY Highland (Inverness-shire). Map 40A
Aviemore 20, London 519, Carrbridge 12, Inverness 12, Nairn 22.

Invermoy House, G, x (RI), *IV13 7YE.* ☎ Tomatin (080 82) 271. Closed Nov. C. ⊭ 7 bedrs, 1 bps, 2 ba, Dgs. 🅿 CH, TV, CP 10, CF, 7 BGf, 0 st, Dis. £ BB £8–£9·75, DB £16–£19·50, WT (b) £80·90, ①.

MUIRHEAD Strathclyde (Lanarkshire). Map 48C
Pop 6,000. M73 Motorway 2, Hamilton 11, London 377, Edinburgh 40, Glasgow 7, Kincardine 20.
EC Wed. **Golf** Muirhead 18h.

★★**Crow Wood House,** *Cumbernauld Rd, G69 9BS.* ☎ 041-779 3861.

MUIRKIRK Strathclyde (Ayrshire). Map 29A
Pop 2,334. Douglas 10, London 372, Abington 21, Ayr 24, Dalmellington 22, Edinburgh 49, Glasgow 27, Kilmarnock 22, Lanark 22, Paisley 33, Thornhill 38.
EC Wed. **Golf** Ballochmyle Mauchline 18h. **See** Cameron's Stone (memorial), John Brown's Stone, Tibbie's Brig (assns with Robert Burns).

Rescue Service: Enterprise Workshop, Glasgow Rd. ☎ (029 06) 357.

MUIR OF ORD Highland (Ross & Cromarty). Maps 39B and 40A
Pop 1,000. Inverness 12, London 540, Achnasheen 29, Beauly 2½, Dingwall 6, Edinburgh 165, Glasgow 164, Ullapool 45.
EC Thur. **Golf** Muir of Ord 18h.

★★**Ord Arms,** *Gt North Rd, IV6 7XR.* ☎ (0463) 870286. RS Sunday night. C. ⊭ 12 bedrs, 3 bp, 3 bps, 3 ba, TV, Dgs. ✗ a l c, mc, at, LD 8.30. 🅿 Lt, CH, CP 100, Ac, con 60, CF, 3 BGf, 3 st. £ BB £13, DB £22·77–£25·30, DBB £15, WB, ①, Bk £2·50, HT £3·95, cc 1.

MUSSELBURGH Lothian (Midlothian). Map 37E
Pop 17,133. Lauder 21, London 369, Edinburgh 6, Galashiels 28, Glasgow 51, Haddington 11, Peebles 24.
EC Thur. **Golf** Monktonhall 18h. **See** Tolbooth, Mercat Cross, Inveresk Church, Old Bridge, French Ambassador's House, Harbour.
🅸 Brunton Hall. ☎ 031-665 6597.

🅵★★**M Drummore,** *North Berwick Rd, EH21 8JT.* ☎ 031-665 2302. Open Apr–Dec. C. ⊭ 47 bedrs, 47 bps, TV, Dgs. ✗ mc, at, LD 10. 🅿 N, CH, Dgs, CP 150, Ac, con 150, CF, 47 BGf, 1 st, Dis. £ BB £20, DB £38, WT £175, DT £26, DBB £22, WB, ①, Bk £3·50, L £3·75, D £3·75, cc 1 2 3 5 6, Dep.

Rescue Service: J & T Motors, 131 Newbigging. ☎ 031-665 2788.

NAIRN Highland (Nairnshire). Map 40A
Pop 9,997. Grantown-on-Spey 23, London 529, Carrbridge 24, Edinburgh 154, Elgin 21, Glasgow 171, Inverness 15.
EC Wed. **Golf** Nairn 18h and 9h, Nairn Dunbar 18h. **See** Highland Games in Aug, Ardclach Bell Tower 8 m SE. Cawdor Castle 5 m SW.
🅸 King St. ☎ Nairn (0667) 52753.

★★★**Golf View,** *Seabank Rd, IV12 4HD.* ☎ (0667) 52301. C. ⊭ 55 bedrs, 45 bp, 10 bps, 3 ba, TV, Dgs. ✗ a l c, mc, at, LD 9.30. 🅿 Lt, N, ch, TV, CP 30, sp, tc, sb, con 80, CF, 2 st. £ BB £30–£35, DB £48–£60, WT £196–£231, DBB £40–£45, WB, ②, Bk £3·95, L £5·75, D £10·50, cc 1 2 3 5.

★★★**Newton,** *Inverness Rd, IV12 4RX.* ☎ (0667) 53144. C. ⊭ 44 bedrs, 44 bp, TV, Dgs. 🅿 Lt, CH, TV, Dgs, CP 50, CF, 1 BGf, 8 st. £ BB £28, DB £46–£48, WT £224–£231, DT £32–£33, ①, Bk £3·50, L £4·75, D £11, cc 1 2 3 5.

🅵★★★**Royal Marine,** *Marine Rd, IV12 4EB.* ☎ (0667) 53381. RS Jan, Feb, Nov, Dec. C. ⊭ 43 bedrs, 37 bp, 6 sh, TV, Dgs. ✗ a l c, mc, at, LD 8.30. 🅿 Lt, CH, TV, Dgs, CP 37, Ac, con 80, CF, 0 st. £ BB £12–£13·50, DB £24–£27, WT £170–£175, DT £25–£30, DBB £23·50–£29, WB, ①, Bk £3, L £3, D £9, cc 2 3 5 6.

★★★**Windsor,** *Albert St, IV12 4HP.* ☎ (0667) 53108. C. ⊭ 60 bedrs, 30 bp, 24 bps, 6 ba, TV, Dgs. ✗ a l c, mc, at, LD 9.30. 🅿 Lt, N, CH, TV, Dgs, CP 40, Ac, rf, con 140, CF, 8 BGf, 3 st. £ BB £18·10–£22·90, DB £33–£42·35, WT £192·20–£211·55, DT £26·60–£30·10, DBB £26·60–£32·90, WB, ②, Bk £3·50, L £4, D £9·50, cc 1 2 3 5 6. ▲

★★**Alton Burn,** *Alton Burn Rd, IV12 5ND.* ☎ (0667) 52051. C. ⊭ 19 bedrs, 17 bp, 4 ba, Dgs. ✗ mc, at, LD 8. 🅿 ch, TV, CP 50, Ac, sp, tc, con 50, CF, 2 BGf, 1 st, Dis. £ BB £15–£17, DB £28–£32, WB, ①, Bk £3·50, L £4·25, D £8·25, cc 1 3, Dep a.
Ardgour, PH, y (Unl), *Seafield St, IV12 4HN.* ☎ (0667) 54230. Open Mar–Oct. C. ⊭ 10 bedrs, 2 ba, Dgs. 🅿 ch, TV, CP 8, CF. £ BB £7·50, DB £15, WT (b) £80, DT (b) £12, ①.

NETHY BRIDGE Highland (Inverness-shire). Map 40D
Pop 450. Blair Atholl 59, London 509, Braemar 24, Carrbridge 8½, Edinburgh 134, Glasgow 146, Grantown-on-Spey 5, Kingussie 22.
EC Thur. **Golf** Nethybridge 9h. **See** Coire Cas Ski Grounds.

■★★★**Nethybridge,** *PH25 3DP.*
✆ (047 982) 203. Closed Nov. C. ⇥ 62
bedrs, 62 bp, 1 bps, 5 ba, TV, Dgs. ✗ mc,
LD 9. ⌂ Lt, N, ch, TV, CP 50, Ac, con 100,
CF, 5 BGf, 1 st, Dis. £ BB £17–£19, DB
£34–£38, ☲ 10%, Bk £2·50, L £2, D £2·50,
cc 1 2 3 5 6.

NEW ABBEY Dumfries & Galloway
(Kirkcudbrightshire). Maps 29F and 30E
Pop 400. Dumfries 6½, London 333,
Edinburgh 77, Gatehouse of Fleet 33,
Glasgow 79, New Galloway 27.
Golf Southerness 18h. **See** Sweetheart
Abbey, beautiful 13th cent monastic
remains, St Mary's RC Church, Kirkconnel
Tower, Waterloo Monument, Corn Mill.

■★**Abbey Arms,** *DG2 8BU.* ✆ (038 785)
215.

NEWARTHILL Strathclyde
(Lanarkshire). Map 48B
Pop 6,210. Wishaw 1½, London 380,
Edinburgh 32, Glasgow 14, Kilmarnock
30, Kincardine 25, Lanark 13, Peebles 38,
Stirling 23.
EC Wed. **Golf** Motherwell 18h. **See**
Roman Catholic Grotto.

★★**Silverburn,** *Loanhead Rd, ML1 5BA.*
✆ (0698) 732503. Closed New Year. C.
⇥ 8 bedrs, 6 bp, 2 bps, 1 ba, TV, Dgs.
✗ a l c, mc, at, LD 9.30. ⌂ N, CH, TV, Dgs;
CP 80, G 1, Ac, con 80, 1 st. £ BB,£16–£19,
DB £33, WB, ☲, Bk £2·75, L £2, D £5·50,
cc 1 2 3 6, Dep b.

NEWBRIDGE Lothian (Midlothian). Map
36F
Edinburgh 8, London 380, M8/M9
Motorway ½, Dunfermline 11, Glasgow 37,
Lanark 27, Stirling 27.

Rescue Service: Dougie Miller (Motors),
8a Bridge St. ✆ 031-333 3372.

NEWBURGH Grampian
(Aberdeenshire). Map 41D
Aberdeen 13, London 504, Ellon 5,
Edinburgh 130, Glasgow 149, Inverurie
16, Peterhead 20.

★★**Udny Arms,** *AB4 0BL.* ✆ (035 86)
444. C. ⇥ 25 bedrs, 15 bp, 10 bps, TV.
✗ mc, at, LD 9.30. ⌂ N, CH, Dgs, CP 57,
con 120, CF, 15 st. £ BB £31, DB £41, DBB
£43·50, WB, ☲, Bk £3·50, D £13·50,
cc 1 2 3 6.

NEWCASTLETON Borders
(Roxburghshire). Map 30D
Pop 943. Canonbie 10, London 318,
Bellingham 31, Carlisle 24, Edinburgh 68,
Glasgow 95, Hawick 22, Jedburgh 28,
Langholm 15.
EC Thurs. **Golf** Newcastleton 9h. **See**
Hermitage Castle.

Grapes. H. ✗, *Douglas Square, TD9 0QU.*
✆ Liddesdale (054 121) 245. C. ⇥ 4
bedrs, 1 sh, 1 ba. ✗ a l c, ⌂ mc, TV, Dgs, CP
4, CF, 1 st. £ Bk £1·75, D £6.

NEW CUMNOCK Strathclyde
(Ayrshire). Map 29A
Pop 4,479. Kirkconnel 8, London 364,
Abington 28, Ayr 21, Dalmellington 10,
Edinburgh 64, Glasgow 38, Kilmarnock
21, Lanark 37, Thornhill 23.
EC Wed. **Golf** New Cumnock 9h. **See**
Afton Reservoir.
ℹ Town Hall. ✆ New Cumnock (029 04)
581.

Rescue Service: Andrew McGarva, Afton
Service Station, Castle St. ✆ (029 04)
217.

NEW GALLOWAY Dumfries & Galloway
(Kirkcudbrightshire). Map 29C
Pop 300. Crocketford 13, London 349,
Dalmellington 21, Dumfries 23, Edinburgh
83, Gatehouse of Fleet 19, Glasgow 69,
Stranraer 44, Thornhill 22.
EC Thur. **Golf** New Galloway 9h. **See**
Kells Church, Kenmure Castle.

■★★**Kenmure Arms,** *High St, DG7 3RL.*
✆ (064 42) 360.

■★**Crosskeys,** *High St, DG7 3RN.*
✆ (064 42) 218. RS Jan–Feb, Nov–Dec. C.
⇥ 8 bedrs, 2 ba, Dgs. ✗ a l c, mc, at, LD 8.
⌂ ch, TV, Dgs, CP 8, U 2, CF, 2 st. £ BB
£13·20–£14·30, DB £26·40–£28·60, WT
£126·50–£132, DT £27·50–£28·60, DBB
£19·80–£20·90, ☲, Bk £2·50, L £3–£5, D
£6·60.

■★**Ken Bridge,** *DG7 3PR.* ✆ (064 42)
211.

NEWMAINS Strathclyde (Lanarkshire).
Maps 48B & 36F
Pop 6,880. Lanark 9, London 378,
Edinburgh 31, Glasgow 17, M8 Motorway
4½, M74 Motorway 6, Motherwell 5.
EC Wed. **Golf** Wishaw 18h.

Rescue Service: Mains Service Station,
111 Westwood Rd. ✆ Wishaw (069 83)
63499.

NEWMILL-ON-TEVIOT Borders
(Roxburghshire). Map Area 30D
Langholm 19, London 323, Edinburgh 52,
Glasgow 84, Hawick 4.

Rescue Service: Armstrong's Garage, (W
H & A Armstrong). ✆ Hawick (0450)
85204.

NEWTONMORE Highland (Inverness-
shire). Maps 39D and 40C
Pop 935. Blair Atholl 34, London 485,
Dalwhinnie 10, Edinburgh 109, Fort
William 45, Glasgow 121, Invergarry 57,
Kingussie 2¼.
EC Wed. **Golf** Newtonmore 18h. **See** Clan
Macpherson Museum, Cluny Castle 6 m.
ℹ ✆ Newtonmore (054 03) 253.

■★★**Mains,** *Main St, PH20 1DF.*
✆ (054 03) 206. C. ⇥ 30 bedrs, 5 bp, 10
bps, 3 ba. ✗ mc, at, LD 8.30. ⌂ ch, TV,
Dgs, CP 50, U 6, Ac, CF. £ BB £10–£12·50,
DB £19–£21, DBB £10·50–£16·50, ☲, Bk
£3·25, L £1·70, D £6·50, cc 1 2 3 5.

Alvey House, PH, xy (RI), *Golf Course
Rd, PH20 1AT.* ✆ (054 03) 260. C. ⇥ 7
bedrs, 3 bps, 1 ba. ⌂ CH, TV, CP 10, CF, 2
st. £ BB £20, DB £20–£24, WT (b)
£98, DT (b) £15, ☲, Bk £3, D £3·50.

Ard Na Coille, PH, xy (RI), *Kingussie Rd,
PH20 1AY.* ✆ (054 03) 214.

NEW TON STEWART Dumfries &
Galloway (Wigtownshire). Map 29E
Pop 2,000. New Galloway 17, London
367, Edinburgh 101, Gatehouse of Fleet
18, Girvan 30, Glasgow 82, Stranraer 22.
EC Wed. **MD** Thur. **Golf** Wigtown 9h. **See**
Church, War Memorial, Bridge (Earl of
Galloway Monument).
ℹ Dashwood Sq. ✆ Newton Stewart
(0671) 2431.

■★★★**Bruce,** *Queen St, DG8 6JL.*
✆ (0671) 2294. Open Feb–Nov. C. ⇥ 17
bedrs, 17 bp, 1 ba, TV, Dgs. ✗ mc, at, LD 8.30.
⌂ CH, TV, CP 20, G 4, sol, CF, 0 st. £ BB

£21–£22·50, DB £36–£38, WT £189–£217,
DT £34–£35·50, DBB £31–£32·50, WB, ☲,
Bk £3, L £3, D £10, cc 1 2 3 5 6.

■♨★★★**Kirroughtree,** *DG8 6AN.*
✆ (0671) 2141. Open Mar–Nov. C 10.
⇥ 22 bedrs, 21 bp, 1 bps, TV. ✗ a l c, mc,
at, LD 9.30. ⌂ CH, ns, CP 60, gc, tc, con
40, 10 st. £ BB £24–£28, DB £48–£56, WT
£217–£254, DBB £41–£45, WB, ☲, L
£8·50, cc 1 2 3 5 6.▲

■♨★★**Creebridge House,** *DG8 6NP.*
✆ (0671) 2121. RS Jan 1st–5th & Dec
28th–31st. C 8. ⇥ 18 bedrs, 11 bp, 1 bps,
2 ba, TV, Dgs. ✗ mc, at, LD 8.30. ⌂ CH, CP
40, con 30, CF, 1 BGf, 1 st, Dis. £ BB
£14·50–£20·50, DB £29–£41, DBB £24–
£31·50, WB, ☲, Bk £3·50, L £2·50, D £9·50,
cc 1 3 6.

■★★**Crown,** *Queen St, DG8 6JW.*
✆ (0671) 2107. ⇥ 9 bedrs, 4 bp, 2 sh, 3
ba, Dgs. ✗ mc, at, LD 8.30. ⌂ CH, TV, Dgs,
CP 25, Ac, pf, con 80, CF, 0 st. £ BB
£12·50–£18, DB £25–£29, WT £152–£164,
DT £22·50–£24·50, DBB £20·50–£22·50,
WB, ☲, Bk £3·50, L £4·30, D £8,
cc 1 2 3 5 6.

★★**Galloway Arms,** *Victoria St, DG8
6DB.* ✆ (0671) 2282.

■★**Cairnsmore,** *Victoria St, DG8 6BT.*
✆ (0671) 2162.

Rescue Service: Thomas Corrie Ltd, 100
Queen St. ✆ (0671) 2467.

NEWTON WAMPHRAY Dumfries &
Galloway (Dumfries-shire). Map 29D, 30C
Lockerbie 9, London 327, Moffat 7,
Edinburgh 60, Glasgow 62.
Golf Moffat 18h.

■★★**Red House,** *DG10 9NF.* ✆ (057 64)
214. Open Easter–Nov 15th. C. ⇥ 6 bedrs,
2 ba, Dgs. ✗ mc, LD 7.30. ⌂ CH, TV, Dgs,
ns, CP 20, 2 st. £ BB £13·50, DB £27, WT
£140·50, DBB £20·25, ☲, Bk £3·40, L
£4·50, D £6·75, cc 5.

NORTH BALLACHULISH Highland
(Argyll).
See BALLACHULISH.

NORTH BERWICK Lothian (East
Lothian). Map 37C
Pop 5,229. East Linton 6, London 377,
Berwick-upon-Tweed 41, Edinburgh 22,
Glasgow 67, Haddington 11.
EC Thur. **Golf** West Links 18h, East Links
18h. **See** Ruins of Pre-Reformation
Church Burgh Museum, 12th cent St
Andrew's Kirk, The Law (613 ft), Dirleton
Castle 2½ m W, Tantallon Castle 3 m E,
Hailes Castle (E Linton), Bass Rock (Bird
Sanctuary), 17th cent Tower House.
ℹ 18 Quality St. ✆ North Berwick (0620)
2197.

■★★★**Marine** (TH), *Cromwell Rd, EH39
4LZ.* ✆ (0620) 2406. C. ⇥ 85 bedrs, 75
bp, 10 bps, TV, Dgs. ✗ a l c, mc, at, LD
9.30. ⌂ Lt, N, CH, Dgs, CP 200, Ac, sp, tc,
sc, sb, con 250, CF, 6 BGf, 0 st, Dis. £ BB
£34·50, DB £54, WB, ☲, cc 1 2 3 4 5 6,
Dep (Xmas).

★★**Blenheim House,** *Westgate, EH39
4AF.* ✆ (0620) 2385. C. ⇥ 11 bedrs, 5 bp,
1 bps, 5 sh, 2 ba, TV, Dgs. ✗ mc, LD 9.
⌂ ch, CP 20, CF, 3 BGf, 1 st, Dis. £ BB
£14–£16, DB £28–£34, WT £130–£140,
DBB £22–£26, ☲, Bk £4, L £5·50, D £8.

★★**Nether Abbey,** *Dirtleton Av, EH39
4BQ.* ✆ (0620) 2802. C. ⇥ 17 bedrs, 3 bp,
9 bps, 4 ba, Dgs. ✗ mc, LD 8.30. ⌂ CH, TV,
Dgs, CP 60, CF, 2 BGf, 1 st, Dis. £ BB

£14·50–£18, DB £29–£32·50, ②, Bk £3·50, L £3·50, D £8, cc 1 3.

★★Point Garry, *West Bay Rd, EH39 4AW.* ✆ (0620) 2380. Open Apr–Oct. C. ⊨ 15 bedrs, 2 bp, 6 bps, 2 ba, Dgs. ✗ mc, at, LD 9. ⓓ CH, TV, CP 10, CF, 1 BGf, 1 st, Dis. £ BB £16·50–£18·50, DB £30–£34, DBB £22–£24, WB, ② 10%, Bk £4·50, D £7.

OBAN Strathclyde (Argyll). Map 35A
Pop 7,000. Dalmally 23, London 477, Ballachulish 37, Edinburgh 121, Fort William 48, Glasgow 90, Inveraray 38, Lochgilphead 36.
EC Thur. **Golf** Glencruitten 18h. **See** RC Cathedral, McCaig Tower, St John's Episcopal Cathedral, Museum, Highland Gathering last week in Aug.
ⓘ Argyll Sq. ✆ Oban (0631) 63122.

◼★★★**Alexandra,** *Corran Esplanade, PA34 5AA.* ✆ (0631) 62381. Open Apr–Oct. C. ⊨ 57 bedrs, 40 bp, 2 bps, 8 ba, Dgs. ✗ mc, LD 8.30. ⓓ Lt, N, ch, TV, CP 40, Ac, CF, 1 BGf, 3 st. £ BB £25–£28, DB £40–£46, DBB £20–£37, WB, ①, Bk £4, L £3, D £9, cc 1 2 3 5 6, Dep.

★★★Caledonian, *Station Sq, PA34 5RT.* ✆ (0631) 63133. Open Apr–Oct. C. ⊨ 72 bedrs, 72 bp, Dgs. ✗ mc, at, LD 8.30. ⓓ Lt, N, CH, TV, Dgs, CP 10, CF, 1 st. £ BB £19–£23·90, DB £34–£42, WT £135–£199, DT £28·50–£32·50, DBB £25·50–£29·50, WB, ②, Bk £3·25, L £3, D £8·50, cc 1 2 3 5 6, Dep a.

★★★Great Western, *The Esplanade, PA34 5PP.* ✆ (0631) 63101. Open Apr–Oct. C. ⊨ 74 bedrs, 63 bp, 3 bps, 6 ba, Dgs. ✗ mc, at, LD 8.30. ⓓ Lt, N, TV, CP 25, Ac, con 120, CF, 4 st. £ BB £25–£28, DB £40–£46, DBB £20–£37, WB, ①, Bk £4, L £3, D £9, cc 1 2 3 5 6, Dep.

◼★★★**Regent,** *Esplanade, PA34 5PZ.* ✆ (0631) 62341.

★★Lancaster, *Corran Esplanade, PA34 5AD.* ✆ (0631) 62587. Closed Xmas & New Year. C. ⊨ 28 bedrs, 3 bp, 2 bps, 5 ba. ✗ a l c, mc, LD 8. ⓓ ch, TV, CP 20, sp, sb, sol, CF, 6 st. £ BB £15, DB £30–£34, DBB £21–£23, ①, Bk £3, L £3·75, D £7.

★★Park, *Esplanade, PA34 5PR.* ✆ (0631) 63621. C. ⊨ 81 bedrs, 22 bp, 29 bps, 8 ba, TV, Dgs. ✗ mc, LD 8.30. ⓓ Lt, N, CH, TV, CP 20, con 80, CF, 0 st. £ BB £17–£25, DB £32–£46, DBB £21·50–£29·50, WB, ②, Bk £3·50, L £4·80, D £9, cc 1 2 3 6.

★★Rowan Tree, *George St, PA34 5NX.* ✆ (0631) 62954.

◼★**King's Knoll,** *Dunollie Rd, PA34 5JH.* ✆ (0631) 62536. C. ⊨ 18 bedrs, 5 ba, Dgs. ✗ a l c, mc, LD 7.30. ⓓ CH, TV, Dgs, CP 9, CF, 6 BGf. £ BB £9–£11, DB £18–£22, DBB £14·50–£16·50, WB, ①, Bk £2·50, L £3·50, D £6, Dep.

Ardblair, G, y (Unl), *Dalriach Rd, PA34 5JB.* ✆ (0631) 62668. Open May–Sept. C. ⊨ 22 bedrs, 7 ba. ⓓ CH, TV, CP 12, CF. £ BB £6–£7, DB £12–£14, DT £10·50–£11·50, ①.

Craigvarran House, G, x (Unl), *Ardconnel Rd, PA34 5DJ.* ✆ (0631) 62686.

Foxholes, H, x (RI), *PA34 4SE.* ✆ (0631) 64982. Open Apr–Oct & Xmas & New Year. C. ⊨ 6 bedrs, 2 ba, TV, Dgs. ✗ a l c. ⓓ CH, Dgs, CP 10, CF, 2 BGf, 1 st. £ BB £17·50–£22·50, DB £25–£34, WT (b) £210–£245, DT (b) £15–£17·50, ①, D £6.

Glenburnie, PH, z (Unl), *Esplanade, PA34 5AQ.* ✆ (0631) 62089. Open Apr–Oct. C 3. ⊨ 15 bedrs, 4 bps, 3 ba, Dgs.

ⓓ ch, TV, ns, CP 12, U 1, 2 BGf, 5 st. £ BB fr £8·22, DB fr £16·44, ② 5%.

Heatherfield, PH, y (Unl), *Albert Rd, PA34 5EJ.* ✆ (0631) 62681. C. ⊨ 10 bedrs, 3 ba, Dgs. ⓓ TV, CP 15, CF, 2 BGf, 2 st. £ BB £7–£9, DB £14–£18, WT (b) £77–£90, DT £11–£13·50, ①, Bk £2·50, D £4·50.

Kenmore, G, z (Unl), *Soroba Rd, PA34 4JF.* ✆ (0631) 63592. C. ⊨ 6 bedrs, 6 sh, 1 ba, Dgs. ⓓ ch, TV, CP 12, 2 BGf, 4 st. £ BB £7·50–£8·50, DB £15–£17, ①.

Roseneath, G, z (Unl), *Dalriach Rd, PA34 5EQ.* ✆ (0631) 64262. Closed Xmas & New Year. C. ⊨ 10 bedrs, 2 ba, Dgs. ⓓ CH, TV, CP 10, CF, 1 st. £ BB £6·75–£9, DB £13·50–£18, WT £64–£81, DT £10·75–£13·50, ①.

Sgeir-Mhaol, G, z (Unl), *Soroba Rd, PA34 4JF.* ✆ (0631) 62650. C. ⊨ 6 bedrs, 1 ba. ⓓ CH, TV, CP 10. £ BB £7, DB £14, DT £10·50, ①.

Rescue Service: West Highland Coachworks, Unit 5, Soroba Rd. ✆ (0631) 63840.
John A. Cook, Lochavullin Industrial Estate. ✆ (0631) 64463.
Struthers of Oban, Breadalbane Pl. ✆ (0631) 63066.
Wilson's Garage Co (Argyll) Ltd, Airds Pl. ✆ (0631) 63173.

OLD MELDRUM Grampian (Aberdeenshire). Map 41D
Pop 1,085. Inverurie 5, London 505, Aberdeen 17, Banff 37, Braemar 62, Edinburgh 150, Fraserburgh 30, Glasgow 130, Huntly 23, Peterhead 28.
Golf Oldmeldrum 9h. **See** 17th cent Church, Mounie Castle, Barra Castle, Meldrum House (now hotel).

Rescue Service: Meldrum Motors, 3 Market Sq. ✆ (065 12) 2247.

OLD RAYNE Grampian (Aberdeenshire). Map 41C
Inverurie 8½, London 508, Aberdeen 25, Edinburgh 133, Glasgow 153, Huntly 14, Insch 4, Peterhead 37.

★**Lodge,** *AB5 6RY.* ✆ (046 45) 205.

ONICH Highland (Inverness-shire). Map 39E
Pop 280. Ballachulish 4, London 478, Crianlarich 53, Edinburgh 121, Fort William 10, Glasgow 89, Oban 48.
EC Thur. **Golf** Fort William 9h. **See** 'The Sleeping Chancellor' (viewpoint), Glenrigh waterfall, Mausoleum at Callart.

◼★★**Creag Dhu,** *PH33 6RY.* ✆ (085 53) 238. Open Apr–Oct. C. ⊨ 20 bedrs, 12 bp, 5 bps, 2 ba. ✗ a l c, mc, at, LD 8.30. ⓓ CH, TV, Dgs, ns, CP 30, CF, 2 st. £ BB £15·50–£19·50, DB £31–£39, DBB £24–£28, ②, Bk £3·50, L £4, D £8·50, cc 1 2 3 5 6.

◼★★**Onich,** *PH33 6RY.* ✆ (085 53) 214. C. ⊨ 24 bedrs, 6 bp, 1 bps, 4 ba, TV, Dgs. ✗ a l c, mc, at, LD 10.30. ⓓ CH, TV, Dgs, CP 50, Ac, sol, gym, con 25, CF, 2 st. £ BB £12–£17, DB £24–£34, DBB £20–£25, WB, ①, Bk £3·75, L £3, D £8, cc 1 2 3 6, Dep a.

Tigh-a-Righ, PH, x (RI), *PH33 6SE.* ✆ (085 53) 255.

Rescue Service: Camerons Garage, Main Rd. ✆ (085 53) 224.

ORKNEY ISLANDS Map 46
An archipelago of 50 islands, about 30 inhabited.

See Antiquities (Skara Brae, Earl's Palace, etc), cliff scenery. In Kirkwall, St Magnus Cathedral, Bishop's Palace, Earl Patrick's Palace, 18th cent Tankerness House, Scapa Flow 'Royal Oak' memorial.
ⓘ Broad St. ✆ Kirkwall (0856) 2856.

STROMNESS
Pop 1,500. London via Scrabster 655, Kirkwall 15.
EC Thur. **MD** Wed. **Golf** Ness 18h.
ⓘ Pierhead. ✆ Stromness (0856) 850716.

★★Stromness, *15 Victoria St, KW16 3AA.* ✆ (0856) 850298.

OUTER HEBRIDES
See LOCHBOISDALE and STORNOWAY.

PAISLEY Strathclyde (Renfrewshire). Map 48F
See also LINWOOD.
Pop 85,855. Strathaven 19, London 393, M8 Motorway 1, Abington 43, Dumbarton 16 (Fy 11), Edinburgh 52, Glasgow 7, Gourock 19, Kilmarnock 20, Largs 23.
EC Tue. **MD** Mon. **Golf** Barshaw Municipal 18h. **See** 12th cent Abbey Church Palace of Paisley (adj to Abbey), Museum, Art Gallery, Observatory, Thomas Coats Memorial Church, RC Cathedral, Weaver's Cottage (Museum).

◼★★**Ardgowan,** *Blackhall St, PA1 1TN.* ✆ 041-889 2196. C. ⊨ 17 bedrs, 17 bp, TV, Dgs. ✗ a l c, mc, LD 9.30. ⓓ Lt, N, CH, TV, Dgs, CP 50, Ac, sb, con 100, CF, 2 st. £ BB £21, DB £30, DT £28·50, DBB £25·50, ②, Bk £2·50, L £3·50, D £4·50, cc 1 3.

◼★★**Rockfield,** *125 Renfrew Rd, PA3 4EA.* ✆ 041-889 6182. C. ⊨ 20 bedrs, 20 bp, TV, Dgs. ✗ mc, at, LD 8·30. ⓓ CH, Dgs, CP 100, Ac, con 40, CF, 6 st. £ BB £28·88, DB £34·34, WB, ②, Bk £3, cc 1 2 3 5.

Repairer: Greenlaw Garage, 4 Greenlaw Dr. ✆ 041-887 9020.
Specialist Body Repairer B C R Coachworks, 30 St James St. ✆ 041-889 8006.

PATHHEAD FORD Lothian (Midlothian). Map 37E
Pop 1,500. Lauder 15, London 367, Berwick-upon-Tweed 49, Coldstream 37, Edinburgh 12, Galashiels 23, Glasgow 54, Haddington 11, Kelso 32, Peebles 21.
EC Wed. **Golf** Newbattle 18h. **See** Crichton Castle.

★★Stair Arms, *EH37 5TX.* ✆ Ford (0875) 320277.

PATNA Strathclyde (Ayrshire). Map 29A
Pop 2,467. Dalmellington 5, London 372, Ayr 10, Edinburgh 72, Girvan 19, Glasgow 42, Lanark 45.
EC Wed. **Golf** Patna 9h.

Rescue Service: Bridgend Garage, 14 Ayr Rd. ✆ (029 253) 208.

PEEBLES Borders (Peeblesshire). Map 30A
Pop 6,000. Walkerburn 8½, London 361, Abington 30, Beattock 36, Edinburgh 22, Galashiels 18, Glasgow 49, Haddington 31, Lanark 27, Langholm 50, Lauder 26, Selkirk 21.
EC Wed. **MD** Fri. **Golf** Peebles Municipal 18h. **See** Old Parish Church, Neidpath Castle, ruins of 12th cent Church, Mercat Cross, St Andrew's Church Tower (ruins), War Memorial, Chambers Institute,

Traquair House 6 m SE, Dawyck Gardens
8 m SW.
ⓘ High St. ☎ Peebles (0721) 20138.

★★★**Park,** *Innerleithen Rd, EH45 8BA.*
☎ (0721) 20451. C. 🚪 27 bedrs, 22 bp, 3
bps, 2 ba, TV, Dgs. ✗ mc, at, LD 9. ⓝ N, CH,
CP 30, Ac, con 30, CF, 1 st. £ BB £21·60–
£29·50, DB £34·25–£44·50, WT £182–
£200, DT £37, DBB £25–£35, WB, ①, Bk
£5·50, D £8·50, cc 1 2 3 5 6, Dep b.

■★★★**Tontine,** *High St, EH45 8AJ.*
☎ (0721) 20892. C. 🚪 37 bedrs, 36 bp, 1
bps, TV, Dgs. ✗ mc, at, LD 9·30. ⓝ N, CH,
Dgs, CP 30, Ac, CF, 5 st. £ BB £34, DB
£49·50, WB, ①, cc 1 2 3 4 5 6, Dep (Xmas).

⁌★★**Cringletie House,** *EH45 8PL.*
☎ (072 13) 233. Open Mar–Dec. C. 🚪 16
bedrs, 10 bp, 1 bps, 1 ba, Dgs. ✗ mc, at,
LD 8·30. ⓝ Lt, CH, TV, Dgs. ✗ a l c, mc, at, LD
£ BB £18·50–£20·50, DB £37–£43, DBB
£32·50–£33·50, ②, Bk £4, D £13.

■**⁌**★★**Venlaw Castle,** *Edinburgh Rd,
EH45 8QG.* ☎ (0721) 20384. Open Apr–
Oct, RS Oct. C. 🚪 12 bedrs, 2 bp, 4 bps, 3
ba, Dgs. ✗ mc, LD 8. ⓝ CH, TV, CP 20, U 2,
CF. £ BB £13–£14, DB £27–£31, WT
£140–£150, DBB £21–£25, WB, ①, Bk £4,
L £3, D £8·50, cc 1 2 4 5 6.

★**Riverside,** *Glasgow Rd, EH45 8JE.*
☎ (0721) 20776. C. 🚪 8 bedrs, 2 ba, TV,
Dgs. ✗ mc, LD 8·20. ⓝ ch, TV, Dgs, CP 40,
U 1, Ac, pf, CF, 2 st. £ BB £9·50–£10, DB
£19–£20, DT £18–£19, DBB £15–£16, WB,
①, Bk £2·50, L £3·20, D £13.

Lindores, G, x (Unl), *60 Old Town, EH45
8JE.* ☎ (0721) 20441. Closed Nov. C. 🚪 5
bedrs, 2 ba. ⓝ CH, TV, CP 3, CF, 2 st. £ DB
£14·50–£15, WT (c) £101·50–£105, ①.

Rescue Service: Tweeddale Motor Co
Ltd, Innerleithen Rd. ☎ (0721) 20627.

PENICUIK Lothian (Midlothian). Map
37E
Peebles 13, London 374, Edinburgh 11,
Glasgow 52.

Rescue Service: Hays of Penicuik, Unit 1,
Eastfield, Industrial Estate, Eastfield Drive.
☎ (0968) 72003.

PERTH Tayside (Perthshire). Map 36B
See also GLENFARG
Pop 41,654. Bridge of Earn 4, London 416,
M90 (Int 10) Motorway 2, Aberfeldy 31,
Blairgowrie 15, Crieff 18, Dundee 21,
Edinburgh 41, Forfar 30, Glasgow 57,
Kirkcaldy 29, Pitlochry 26, St Andrews 32,
Stirling 33.
EC Wed. **MD** Mon, Fri. **Golf** King James
VI 18h. North Inch Municipal 18h. **See** St
John's Kirk, St Ninian's Cathedral, Fair
Maid of Perth's House, Black Watch
Museum, Art Gallery and Museum, Bridge,
Greyfriars Churchyard, Scone Palace
2 m N, Abernethy Round Tower, 6 m SE.
ⓘ The Round House, Marshall Pl. ☎ Perth
(0738) 22900.

★★★**Isle of Skye,** *Dundee Rd, PH2 7AS.*
☎ (0738) 24471. C. 🚪 44 bedrs, 27 bp, 17
bps, 1 ba, TV, Dgs. ✗ mc, at, LD 9. ⓝ N,
CH, Dgs, CP 60, Ac, con 200, CF, 7 BGf, 2
st, Dis. £ BB £30, DB £43, DBB £16–
£21·50, WB, ②, Bk £3·50, L £5, D £9,
cc 1 2 3 4 5, Dep.

★★★**Lovat,** *90 Glasgow Rd, PH2 0LT.*
☎ (0738) 36555. C. 🚪 25 bedrs, 13 bp, 2
bps, 2 ba, TV. ✗ a l c, mc, LD 9.30. ⓝ N,
CH, CP 60, con 300, CF, 6 st. £ BB £15–
£26, DB £24–£32, WB, ②, Bk £3·50, L
£4·75, D £3·50, cc 1 2 3 5, Dep b.▲

★★★**Royal George** (TH), *Tay St, PH1
5LD.* ☎ (0738) 24455. C. 🚪 43 bedrs, 43
bp, TV, Dgs. ✗ a l c, LD 10. ⓝ N, CH, Dgs,
CP 20, G 12, Ac, con 100, CF. £ BB £34,
DB £53, WB, ①, cc 1 2 3 4 5 6,
Dep (Xmas).

■★★★**Salutation,** *South St, PH2 8PH.*
☎ (0738) 22166. C. 🚪 62 bedrs, 55 bp, 6
ba, TV, Dgs. ✗ a l c, mc, at, LD 8·30. ⓝ N,
CH, U 2, Ac, con 300, CF, 0 st. £ BB £14–
£16·50, DB £29–£33, WB, ②, Bk £3·50, L
£2·50, D £8, cc 1 2 3 4 5 6.

■★★★**Stakis City Mills,** *West Mill St,
PH1 5QP.* ☎ (0738) 28281. C. 🚪 78
bedrs, 78 bp, TV, Dgs. ✗ a l c, mc, at, LD
10.30. ⓝ N, CH, CP 60, Ac, con 200, CF, 0
st. £ WB, Bk £3·50, L £2, D £8·50,
cc 1 2 3 5 6, Dep b.

★★**County,** *26 County Pl, PH2 8EE.*
☎ (0738) 23355. C. 🚪 23 bedrs, 4 bp, 8
bps, 3 ba, ns, TV, Dgs. ✗ a l c, mc, at, LD
10. ⓝ N, CH, TV, Dgs, CP 10, Ac, con 70,
CF, 0 st. £ BB £11·50–£14·50, DB £25–
£28, WT £140, DT £25, DBB £21, WB, ①,
Bk £2·50, L £1·35, D £7, £ cc 1 2 3 4 5 6.

★★**Queen's,** *Leonard St, PH2 8HB.*
☎ (0783) 25471. C. 🚪 55 bedrs, 27 bp, 10
ba, TV. ✗ a l c, mc, at, LD 8·30. ⓝ Lt, N,
CH, TV, CP 40, Ac, con 80, CF, 0 st. £ BB
£14–£22, DB £26–£34, WB, ②, Bk £3·50, L
£3·75, D £5·25, cc 1 2 3 5.

Clark Kimberley, G, z (Unl), *57 Dunkeld
Rd, PH1 5RP.* ☎ (0783) 37406.

Clunie, G, z (Unl), *12 Pitcullen Cres, PH2
7HT.* ☎ (0738) 23625. Closed Xmas. C.
🚪 7 bedrs, 1 bp, 1 bps, 1 sh, 2 ba. ⓝ CH,
TV, ns, CP 7, CF, 1 st. £ BB £10, DB £18–
£19, WT (b) £94·50, WT (c) £63, DT
£13·50. ①

Darroch, G, z (Unl), *9 Pitcullen Cres, PH2
7HT.* ☎ (0738) 36893. C. 🚪 6 bedrs, 2 ba,
TV. ⓝ CH, TV, CP 10. £ BB £8·50, DB £17,
①.

Pitcullen, G, z (Unl), *17 Pitcullen Cres,
PH2 7HT.* ☎ (0738) 26506. C. 🚪 6 bedrs,
2 ba, Dgs. ⓝ CH, TV, CP 6, CF, 2 st. £ BB
£7·50–£8, DB £15–£16, ①.

Tatra, G, z (Unl), *1 Pitcullen Cres, PH2
7HT.* ☎ (0738) 25951. C. 🚪 4 bedrs, 2 ba,
Dgs. ⓝ CH, TV, Dgs, CP 7, CF, 1 st. £ BB
£7·50, DB £15, ①.

Tigh Mhorag, G, z (Unl), *69 Dunkeld Rd,
PH1 5RP.* ☎ (0738) 22902.

Rescue Services: Heron Rossleigh,
Glenearn Rd. ☎ (0738) 20811.
G Mutch Mechanical Services, Shore Rd.
☎ (0738) 26688.
Strathmore Motors Ltd, Arran Rd, North
Muirton. ☎ (0738) 22156.
Repairer: Heron Rossleigh, Glenearn Rd.
☎ (0738) 20811.

PETERCULTER Grampian
(Aberdeenshire). Map 41D
Pop 12,295. Stonehaven 11, London 489,
Aberdeen 7, Braemar 51, Craigellachie 56,
Edinburgh 115, Glasgow 134, Grantown-
on-Spey 71, Huntly 38.
Golf Hazehead, 18h(2) and 9h. **See** Rob
Roy Statue, Normandykes earthworks.

Rescue Service: Aitken's Garage, 279
North Deeside Rd, Culter. ☎ Aberdeen
(0224) 733260.

PETERHEAD Grampian (Aberdeenshire).
Map 41B
Pop 16,850. Aberdeen 31, London 523,
Banff 35, Aberdeen 148, Fraserburgh 17,
Glasgow 167, Huntly 47.

EC Wed. **Golf** Craigenian 18h. **See**
Museum and Art Gallery. 12th cent St
Peter's Kirk, Harbour.

Rescue Service: Bayview Garage Ltd,
South Rd. ☎ (0779) 3418.
Finnie Motors, 36 Ugie St. ☎ (0779) 5801.

PHILPSTOUN Lothian (West Lothian).
Map Area 36F
Edinburgh 15, London 390, Glasgow 34,
Lanark 28, Stirling 22.

Rescue Service: Crawford Johnston
Contracts Ltd, Burnside Garage,
Threemiletown. ☎ (050 683) 4930.

PINWHERRY Strathclyde (Ayrshire).
Map 28D
Pop 500. Newton-Stewart 20, London
387, Dalmellington 28, Edinburgh 99,
Gatehouse of Fleet 39, Girvan 8½, Glasgow
61, New Galloway 39, Stranraer 26.
EC Wed. **Golf** Girvan 18h.

Rescue Service: Pinwherry Garage, Main
St. ☎ (046 584) 221.

PITLOCHRY Tayside (Perthshire). Maps
36B and 40F
Pop 2,500. Dunkeld 12, London 444,
Aberfeldy 14, Blairgowrie 23, Braemar 41,
Dalwhinnie 31, Edinburgh 69, Glasgow
80, Perth 26.
EC Thur (win). **Golf** Pitlochry 18h. **See**
Loch Faskally and Dam ('Fish Ladder' and
Observation Chamber for salmon passing
upstream—open to visitors). Festival
Theatre, Highland Games, Sept, Black
Spout (waterfall), Blair Castle 6½ m NW.
ⓘ 22 Atholl Rd. ☎ Pitlochry (0796) 2215.

★★★★**Atholl Palace** (TH), *Atholl Rd,
PH16 5LY.* ☎ (0796) 2400. C. 🚪 92 bedrs,
77 bp, 15 bps, TV, Dgs. ✗ a l c, mc, at, LD
9. ⓝ Lt, N, CH, Dgs, CP 150, Ac, sp, sb, con
450, CF, £ BB £34·50, DB £56·50, WB, ①,
cc 1 2 3 4 5 6, Dep Xmas.

★★★**Fisher's,** *Atholl Rd, PH16 5BN.*
☎ (0796) 2000. C. 🚪 77 bedrs, 46 bp, 5
bps, 15 bp, TV. ✗ mc, at, LD 8.30. ⓝ Lt, N,
CH, TV, CP 60, U 5, G 5, Ac, con 50, CF, 0
st. £ BB fr £14·25, DB fr £28·50, DBB fr
£20·50, WB, ②, Bk £3·50, D £8·50,
cc 1 2 3 5 6.

■**⁌**★★★**Green Park,** *Clunie Bridge Rd,
PH16 5JY.* ☎ (0796) 2537. Open Mar–Oct.
C. 🚪 39 bedrs, 30 bp, 4 bps, 4 ba, TV.
✗ mc, at, LD 8. ⓝ ch, TV, CP 50, U 4, Ac,
pf, con 70, CF, 10 BGf, 2 st. £ BB £18–
£20·50, DB £36–£41, DBB £26–£33, WB,
①, Bk £3·50, D £9, Dep a.

■★★★**Pitlochry Hydro,** *Knockard Rd,
PH16 5JH.* ☎ (0796) 2666. C. 🚪 63 bedrs,
59 bp, 4 ba, TV, Dgs. ✗ mc, LD 8.30. ⓝ Lt,
N, CH, TV, Dgs, CP 62, U 3, Ac, gc, tc, sol,
con 90, CF, 3 BGf, 1 st, Dis. £ BB £30, DB
£44–£50, DBB £22–£39, WB, ①, Bk £3·75,
L £4, D £8·70, cc 1 2 3 4 5 6.

■★★★**Scotland's,** *Bonnethill Rd, PH16
5BT.* ☎ (0796) 2292. C. 🚪 51 bedrs, 21
bp, 25 bps, 3 ba. ✗ a l c, mc, LD 9.30.
ⓝ Lt, N, ch, TV, CP 45, Ac, con 70, CF, 1 st.
£ BB £18·40–£27·90, DB £30·80–£49·80,
WB, ①, L £6.30, D £8·90, cc 1 2 3 5 6.

■★★**Acarsaid** (RI), *8 Athol Rd,
PH16 5EA.* ☎ (0796) 2389. C. 🚪 18
bedrs, 15 bp, 3 bps, 3 ba. ✗ a l c, mc, at, LD
8. ⓝ ch, TV, CP 20, Ac, CF, 1 st. £ BB
£14·50–£15·35, DB £29–£30·70, ②, Bk
£4·50, L £5, D £9, cc 1 2 3.

★★**Birchwood** (R), *2 East Moulin Rd,
PH16 5DW.* ☎ (0796) 2477. C. 🚪 11

bedrs, 6 bp, 2 bps, 1 ba, annexe 5 bedrs, 5 bps. ✕ mc, at, LD 7.30. 🅰 CH, TV, ns, CP 25, Ac, CF, 5 BGf, 2 st. £ BB £15–£17·75, DB £24·50–£30·50, DBB £18·75–£21, WB, ⬜, Bk £3·25, L £3·25, D £7·25.

◪★★**Burnside** (Rt), *West Moulin Rd, PH16 5EA.* ☎ (0796) 2203. Open Mar–Oct. C. ⋈ 17 bedrs, 12 bp, 5 bps, annexe 6 bedrs, 1 bp, 1 bps, 4 sh, 2 ba, TV. ✕ a l c, mc, at, LD 8.30. 🅰 CH, CP 30, Ac, con 40, CF, 1 BGf, 0 st, Dis. £ BB £17·12–£19·24, DB £29·30–£35·10, ⬜, L £4, D £8·35, cc 2 3 5, Dep a.

◪★★**Castlebeigh,** *Knockard Rd, PH16 5HJ.* ☎ (0796) 2925. Open Apr–Oct. C 14. ⋈ 18 bedrs, 18 bp, TV, Dgs. ✕ LD 8. 🅰 CH, TV, Dgs, CP 30. £ BB £12·50–£14·50, DB £25–£29, DBB £18·50–£22·50, WB, ⬜, Bk £4·50, L £6, D £10.

◪★★**Claymore,** *162 Atholl Rd, PH16 5AR.* ☎ (0796) 2888. C 5. ⋈ 7 bedrs, 5 bp, 1 ba, TV, Dgs. ✕ LD 8.30. 🅰 TV, CP 25, CF, 2 st. £ BB £14·50–£16·50, DB £28–£32, DBB £23·50–£25·50, WB, ☒, Bk £3·75, L £4·75, D £8·50, Dep a.

◪★★**Craigvrack,** *West Moulin Rd, PH16 5EQ.* ☎ (0796) 2399. Open Apr–Oct. C. ⋈ 19 bedrs, 7 bp, 2 bps, 4 ba, Dgs. ✕ mc, at, LD 8.30. 🅰 CH, TV, Dgs, CP 21, con 36, CF, 2 BGf, 2 st. £ BB £11–£17, DB £22–£34, WT £120–£132, DT £21–£23·50, DBB £19–£25, WB, ⬜, Bk £3·50, L £2·80, D £7·50, cc 1 3 6.

◪★★**Dundarach,** *Perth Rd, PH16 5DJ.* ☎ (0796) 2862. C. ⋈ 27 bedrs, 20 bp, 7 bps, 2 ba, TV, Dgs. ✕ mc, at, LD 8.30. 🅰 ch, TV, Dgs, CP 24, Ac, con, CF, 3 BGf, 2 st. £ BB £14–£16, DB £14–£15·50, DBB £19–£22, ⬜, Bk £3, L £4·75, D £7·50.

◪★★**Wellwood,** *West Moulin Rd, PH16 5EA.* ☎ (0796) 2879.

◪★**Airdaniar,** *160 Atholl Rd, PH16 5QL.* ☎ (0796) 2266. Open Apr–Oct. C. ⋈ 10 bedrs, 1 bp, 3 bps, 2 ba, TV, Dgs. ✕ mc, at, LD 8. 🅰 CH, ns, CP 15, Ac, pf, CF, 3 BGf, 1 st, Dis. £ BB £12·75–£13·75, DB £25·50–£31·50, WT £131·25–£138·25, DBB £19·75–£22·75, WB, ⬜, Bk £4, L £4, D £8.
Fasganeoin, PH, y *Perth Rd, PH16 5PJ.* ☎ (0796) 2387. Open Apr–Oct. C. ⋈ 9 bedrs, 2 ba. 🅰 ch, CP 20, CF, 2 st. £ BB £10–£11·50, DB £20–£23, WT £108–£118, DT (b) £16–£17·50, ⬜, Bk £3·50, D £7, cc 3.

POLMONT Central (Stirlingshire). Map 36F
Pop 17,648. Armadale 7, London 394, M9 Motorway 1, Edinburgh 23, Glasgow 26, Kincardine 7, Lanark 24, Stirling 14.
EC Wed. **Golf** Polmont 9h. Polmonthill 18h. **See** Antonine Wall.

★★★**Inchyra Grange,** *Grange Rd, FK2 0YB.* ☎ (0324) 711911. C. ⋈ 30 bedrs, 30 bp, TV, Dgs. ✕ a l c, mc, LD 9.30. 🅰 N, CH, Dgs, CP 150, Ac, con 120, CF, 16 BGf, 1 st, Dis. £ BB £31, DB £45, DBB £39·50, WB, ⬜, Bk £4, L £6·50, D £8·50, cc 1 2 3 5.

POOLEWE Highland (Ross & Cromarty). Map 42E
Pop 299. Gairloch 6, London 602, Edinburgh 227, Glasgow 231, Ullapool 52.
EC Thur. **Golf** Gairloch 9h. **See** Inverewe Gardens, Loch Maree.

Rescue Service: Loch Ewe Service Station. ☎ (044 586) 239.

PORT APPIN Strathclyde (Argyll). Map 35A

Pop 70. Connel 20, London 492, Ballachulish 18, Dalmally 39, Edinburgh 134, Fort William (Fy) 28, Glasgow 105. Inveraray 52, Mallaig (Fy) 71, Oban 24.
EC Thur. **Golf** Oban 18h. **See** Castle Stalker, Clach Thoull (natural arch).

◪★★**Airds,** *PA38 4DF.* ☎ Appin (063 173) 236.

PORT ASKAIG Isle of Islay. Strathclyde (Argyll). Map 34F.
(Steamer Service to Loch Tarbert.)
London 480, Edinburgh 134, Glasgow 92.
EC Tue. **Golf** Islay, Machrie 18h. **See** Round Church (Bowmore), Kildalton and Kilchoman Celtic Crosses, Loch Gruinart.

◪★★**Port Askaig,** *PA46 7RD.* ☎ (049 684) 245. C 6. ⋈ 9 bedrs, 2 bp, 2 bps, 3 ba, TV, Dgs. ✕ mc, at, LD 9. 🅰 CH, TV, Dgs, CP 10, G 6, 1 BGf, 1 st. £ BB £14·50–£18, DB £27–£33, WT £140–£160, DBB £22–£28, WB, ⬜, Bk £3·50, L £4·50, D £8·50, Dep a.

PORT GLASGOW Strathclyde (Renfrewshire). Maps 35F & 36E
Paisley 13, London 405, Glasgow 19, Edinburgh 63, Erskine Bridge 9, Greenock 3½.

Rescue Service: Bouverie Motors, Lower Bouverie St. ☎ (0475) 45953.

PORTPATRICK Dumfries & Galloway (Wigtownshire). Map 28F
Glenluce 13, London 395, Edinburgh 126, Gatehouse of Fleet 47, Glasgow 89½, New Galloway 47, Stranraer 7½.
EC Thur. **Golf** Dunskey 18h and 9h. **See** Dunskey Castle ruins. 17th cent Parish Church.

◪★★★**Fernhill,** *Heugh Rd, DG9 8TD.* ☎ (077.681) 220. C. ⋈ 15 bedrs, 12 bp, 3 bps, 3 ba, TV, Dgs. ✕ mc, at, LD 9.30. 🅰 ch, TV, Dgs, CP 40, Ac, con 25, CF, 1 st. £ BB £16·50–£21, DB £31–£36, DBB £23–£24, WB, ☒, Bk £3·50, L £2·50, D £9, cc 1 3 5 6.

★★★**Portpatrick,** *DG8 8TQ.* ☎ (077 681) 333. Open Apr–Oct. C. ⋈ 59 bedrs, 26 bp, 1 bps, 8 ba, Dgs. ✕ mc, at, LD 9. 🅰 Lt, N, ch, TV, Dgs, CP 100, Ac, sp, tc, con 100, CF, 6 BGf, 1 st, Dis. £ BB £24·20, DB £48·40, ⬜, cc 1 2 3 5.

◪★★**Braefield House** (RI), *Braefield Rd, DG9 8TA.* ☎ (077 681) 255. Open Apr–Oct. C. ⋈ 7 bedrs, 3 bps, 1 ba. ✕ a l c, LD 8. 🅰 CH, TV, CP 15, CF, 2 st. £ BB £11·50–£13, DB £22–£27, WB, ⬜, Bk £3·50, L £3·95, D £7·50, Dep a.

◪★★**Mount Stewart,** *South Crescent, DG9 8LE.* ☎ (077 681) 291.

PORTREE Isle of Skye, Highland (Inverness-shire). Map 38A
Pop 1,800. Broadford 26, London (Fy) 573, Dunvegan 21, Edinburgh (Fy) 216, Glasgow (Fy) 186.
EC Wed. **Golf** Portree 9h. **See** Flora Macdonald Monument, Parish Church, Skye Wool Mills, Dunvegan Castle 15 m W.
☒ Meall House. ☎ Portree (0478) 2137.

◪★★**Rosedale,** *Quay Brae, IV51 9DB.* ☎ (0478) 2531. C. ⋈ 18 bedrs, 9 bp, 7 bps, 2 ba, annexe 3 bedrs, 3 bp, Dgs. ✕ mc, at, LD 8. 🅰 CH, TV, CP 12, CF. £ BB £18–£19·50, DB £29–£36, DBB £23–£28, ☒, Bk £3, D £8·50.

★★**Royal,** *Bank St, IV51 9BU.* ☎ (0478) 2525. C. ⋈ 28 bedrs, 17 bp, 5 ba, Dgs. ✕ mc, at, LD 8. 🅰 N, CH, TV, CP 20, G 8, Ac, CF, 0 st. £ BB £15–£18, DB £24–£36, DT £25–£28, DBB £21–£25, WB, ⬜, Bk £3·50, L £4, D £6·50.
Isles, H, z (RI), *Somerled Sq, IV51 9EH.* ☎ (0478) 2129.

Repairer: Ewen MacRae & Co, West End Garage. ☎ (0478) 2554.
Rescue Service: Neil Beaton (Portree) Ltd, Dunvegan Rd. ☎ (0478) 2002.

PORTSOY Grampian (Banff). Map 41A.
Pop 1,780. Huntly 18, London 530, Banff 6, Edinburgh 157, Glasgow 171, Elgin 27.
EC Wed. **Golf** Cullen 18h. **See** ruins of Boyne Castle 2 m E, Findlater Castle ruins 3 m W.

Rescue Service: Portsoy Motors, Seafield Ter. ☎ (026 14) 318.

PORT WILLIAM Dumfries & Galloway (Wigtownshire). Map 28F
Pop 528. Wigtown 10, London 384, Edinburgh 118, Gatehouse of Fleet 35, Girvan 47, Glasgow 98, New Galloway 35, Stranraer 23.
EC Thur. **Golf** Monreith 9h.

◪★★★**Corsemalzie House,** *DG8 9RL.* ☎ (098 886) 254. Closed Feb. C. ⋈ 15 bedrs, 10 bp, 5 bps, 1 ba, TV, Dgs. ✕ mc, at, LD 9.15. 🅰 CH, CP 30, U 1, pf, CF, 0 st. £ BB £19–£25, DB £32–£42, WT £154–£182, DBB £28·75–£29·75, WB, ☒, Bk £4·25, L £6·30, D £9·40, cc 1 2 3 5, Dep a.

★★**Greenmantle,** *Mochrum, DG8 9LY.* ☎ (098 87) 357. C. ⋈ 7 bedrs, 6 bps, 1 ba, Dgs. ✕ mc, at, LD 9.30. 🅰 CH, TV, CP 20, CF, 3 st. £ BB £9·50–£13·50, DB £19–£27, DBB £17–£20, WB, ⬜, Bk £2·50, L £4·50, D £7.

★★**Monreith Arms,** *The Square, DG8 9SE.* ☎ (098 87) 232. C. ⋈ 13 bedrs, 1 bp, 5 ba, Dgs. ✕ mc, at, LD 8. 🅰 ch, TV, Dgs, CP 8, Ac, CF, 5 st. £ BB £11·30, DB £22·60–£24·10, WT £138·60, DT £19·80, DBB £17·20–£18·70, WB, ⬜, Bk £3, L £4, D £6.

PRESTWICK Strathclyde (Ayrshire). Map 28B
Pop 13,532. Ayr 2½, London 384, Edinburgh 70, Glasgow 30, Kilmarnock 9, Largs 28.
EC Wed. **Golf** Prestwick 18h, Prestwick St Cuthbert 18h, Prestwick St Nicholas 18h. **See** St Cuthbert's Church, Mercat Cross, Airport (Spectator Enclosure), St Nicholas Church (ruins).
☒ 2 The Cross, Station Rd. ☎ Prestwick (0292) 79234.

★★**Carlton,** *187 Ayr Rd, KA9 1TP.* ☎ (0292) 76811. C. ⋈ 37 bedrs, 37 bp, TV, Dgs. ✕ a l c, mc, at, LD 11 (12 Fri & Sat). 🅰 N, CH, TV, Dgs, CP 250, Ac, con 70, CF, 15 BGf, 1 st, Dis. £ BB £21·50–£23, DB £37–£40, DT £30–£34, DBB £29–£30·50, WB, ☒, Bk £3·50, L £3·75, D £7·50, cc 1 2 3 5 6.

★★**Links,** *22 Links Rd, KA9 1QJ.* ☎ (0292) 77792.

◪★★**St Nicholas,** *41 Ayr Rd, KA9 1SY.* ☎ (0292) 79568. C. ⋈ 16 bedrs, 6 bps, 1 sh, 3 ba, TV. ✕ mc, LD 8.30. 🅰 CH, TV, Dgs, CP 50, Ac, sp, tc, con 120, CF, 2 BGf, 1 st, Dis. £ BB £14, DB £26–£28, DBB £18–£19, ⬜, Bk £1·50, L £2·50, HT £2·80, cc 1 2 3 5.

■★**Auchencoyle,** *13 Links Rd, KA9 1QG.* ✆ (0292) 78316. C. ◪ 6 bedrs, 3 bps, 1 ba, Dgs. ✘ a l c, mc, at, LD 8.30. 🅘 CH, TV, Dgs, CP 16, CF, 1 st. £ BB £9·25–£11·25, DBB £18·50–£27·50, WT £110·75, DT £16·75, DBB £14·25–£16·25, ⊞, Bk £2, L £2·50, D £5.

■★**Golden Eagle,** *Main St, KA9 1PB.* ✆ (0292) 77566.

★**Moreland's,** *45 Marina Rd, KA9 1QZ.* ✆ (0292) 77590.

■★**North Beach,** *Links Rd, KA9 1QG.* ✆ (0292) 79069.

Braemar, PH, z (Rt), *113 Ayr Rd, KA9 1TN.* ✆ (0292) 75820. C. ◪ 6 bedrs, 1 ba, TV, Dgs. ✘ a l c. 🅘 CH, Dgs, CP 10, CF, 3 st. £ BB £7–£7·50, DB £14–£15, DT £11·75, ⊞, Bk £1·50, L £1·75, D £3·50–£6·25.

Kincraig, PH, z (Rl), *39 Ayr Rd, KA9 1SY.* ✆ (0292) 79480. C 3. ◪ 6 bedrs, 3 ba. 🅘 CH, TV, CP 8. £ BB £8·50, DB £15, ⊞.

RATTRAY Tayside (Perthshire). Map 36B
Perth 17, London 432, Aberfeldy 30, Braemar 34, Brechin 28, Dundee 18, Edinburgh 57, Forfar 20, Glasgow 73, Pitlochry 23.

Rescue Service: Woodford Garage, High St. ✆ Blairgowrie (0250) 3369.

RENFREW Strathclyde (Renfrewshire). Map 48E
Pop 21,759. Glasgow 5½, London 393, M8 Motorway 1, Dumbarton 9½, Edinburgh 50, Gourock 18, Paisley 2½.
EC Wed. **Golf** Renfrew 18h. **See** Parish Church, Glasgow Airport 2 m SW.

■★★★★★**M Excelsior** (TH), *Abbotsinch, Paisley, PA3 2TR.* ✆ 041-887 1212. C. ◪ 316 bedrs, 316 bp, TV, Dgs. ✘ a l c, mc, at, LD 10. 🅘 Lt, N, CH, Dgs, CP 35, Ac, con 650, CF, 1 st. £ BB £48·50, DB £64·50, WB, ⊞, cc 1 2 3 4 5 6.

★★★**M Dean Park,** *Glasgow Rd, PA4 8YB.* ✆ 041-886 3771. C. ◪ 120 bedrs, 120 bp, 1 ba, TV, Dgs. ✘ mc, at, LD 9·45. 🅘 N, CH, CP 200, Ac, con, 2 st. £ BB £34–£36, DB £40–£42, DT £47·50–£49·50, DBB £41·50–£43·50, WB, ⊞, Bk £5, L £5, D £7·50, cc 1 2 3 5 6, Dep b.

★★★**M Stakis Normandy,** *Inchinnan Rd, PA4 9EJ.* ✆ 041-886 4100. C. ◪ 142 bedrs, 142 bp, TV, Dgs. ✘ a l c, mc, at, LD 10.15. 🅘 Lt, N, CH, CP 400, Ac, con, CF, 4 st. £ WB, Bk £2, L £1·20, D £4·40, cc 1 2 3 5 6, Dep b.

Rescue Services: D W & H Ferguson, Porterfield Rd. ✆ 041-886 2777
J & D Harvey (Motors), Porterfield Rd. ✆ 041-886 4009.
Glebe Coachworks, Glebe St. ✆ 041-885 1818.

RHU Strathclyde (Dunbartonshire). Map 35D
Pop 2,186. Helensburgh 2, London 412, Arrochar 15, Edinburgh 67, Glasgow 24, Stirling 39.
EC Wed. **Golf** Helensburgh 18h.

★★★**Rosslea Hall,** *Shore Rd, G84 8NF.* ✆ (0436 820) 684. C. ◪ 16 bedrs, 16 bp, ✆ (0292) 77566.

■★**Ardecaple,** *Shore Rd, G84 8LS.* ✆ (0436 820) 200. C. ◪ 10 bedrs, 4 bp, 2

ba, TV, Dgs. ✘ a l c, mc, at, LD 9. 🅘 ch, TV, Dgs, CP 100, Ac, con 130, CF, 2 st. £ BB £17·60–£21·45, DB £27·78–£33·82, WB, ⊞, Bk £3, HT £3·25, cc 1 2 3 5.

ROCKCLIFFE Dumfries & Galloway (Kirkcudbrightshire). Map 30E
Pop 100. Dalbeattie 6, London 347, Dumfries 20, Edinburgh 90, Gatehouse of Fleet 28, Glasgow 94, New Galloway 27.
Golf Colvend 9h. **See** 7th cent Excavations.

■♨★★★★**Baron's Craig,** *DG5 4QF.* ✆ (055 663) 225. Open Apr–Oct. C. ◪ 27 bedrs, 20 bp, 3 ba, TV, Dgs. ✘ mc, at, LD 9. 🅘 ch, CP 50, con 30, CF, 5 BGf, 1 st, Dis. £ BB £23·25–£35·25, DB £40·70–£64·70, DBB £30·35–£44·50, ⊞, Bk £3, L £2·70, D £11.

■★★**Clonyard House,** *Colvend, DG5 4QW.* ✆ (055 663) 372. C. ◪ 11 bedrs, 6 bp, 1 bps, 1 ba, Dgs. ✘ a l c, mc, at, LD 9. 🅘 ch, TV, CP 30, Ac, con 50, CF, 1 BGf, 2 st. £ BB £14–£17, BB £25–£30, DBB £19·50–£22, WB, ⊞, Bk £3, L £3·50, D £7, Dep a.

ROSEBANK Strathclyde (Lanarkshire). Map 48B
Pop 100. Abington 22, London 373, M74 Motorway 4, Ayr 39, Dalmellington 46, Edinburgh 36, Glasgow 17, Kilmarnock 29, Kincardine 33, Lanark 7, Stirling 31.
EC Wed. **Golf** Larkhall 9h. **See** Popinjay Inn.

★★★**Popinjay,** *ML8 5QB.* ✆ Crossford (055 586) 441. C. ◪ 38 bedrs, 38 bp, TV, Dgs. ✘ a l c, mc, LD 10. 🅘 N, CH, CP 200, Ac, pf, con 100, CF, 1 st. £ BB £24·50, DB £35, WB, ⊞, Bk £3, L £4·50, D £7, cc 1 2 3 5 6, Dep b.

ROSEMARKIE Highland (Ross & Cromarty). Maps 39B and 40A
Pop 1,080. Fortrose 1, London 542, Achnasheen 41, Beauly 17, Dingwall 17, Edinburgh 167, Glasgow 179, Inverness 14, Ullapool 58.
EC Thur. **Golf** Fortrose and Rosemarkie 18h. **See** Fairy Glen, Museum, Cathedral ruins at Fortrose.

★★**Marine,** *11 Marine Ter, IV10 8WL.* ✆ Fortrose (0381) 20253. Open Apr–Sep. RS Apr. C. ◪ 9 bedrs, 9 bp, 5 bps, 8 ba, Dgs. ✘ mc, LD 8.30. 🅘 ch, TV, CP 50, U 10, con 30, CF, 7 BGf, 2 st. £ BB £9·50–£12, DB £19–£27, WT £100–£124, WB, ⊞, 5%, Bk £3, L £4·50, D £6·75.

ROSLIN Lothian (Midlothian). Map 37E
Pop 2,000. Galashiels 30, London 374, Dalkeith 6½, Edinburgh 7½, Glasgow 51, Penicuik 3½.
EC Wed. **Golf** Glencorse 18h. **See** 14th cent Castle, Roslin Glen.

Rescue Service: Rosslyn Garage, 22a Penicuik Rd. ✆ 031-440 1363.

ROTHES Grampian (Moray). Map 40B
Pop 1,445. Craigellachie 3½, London 518, Banff 31, Dundee 143, Elgin 10, Glasgow 161.
EC Wed. **Golf** Dufftown 18h.

■♨★★★★**Rothes Glen,** *IV33 7AH.* ✆ (034 03) 254. Open Mar 1–mid Nov. C. ◪ 16 bedrs, 13 bp, 3 ba, Dgs. ✘ a l c, mc, LD 8.45. 🅘 ch, TV, Dgs, CP 40, CF, 2 st. £ BB £24·50–£29·50, DB £44·50–£50, WT £280, DBB £38·50–£43·15, ⊞ 10%, Bk £5·50, L £6·50, D £14·00, cc 2 3 5.

ROTHESAY Strathclyde (Bute). Map 35E
Pop 5,000. Ferry Service to Wemyss Bay, Largs 6, London 415, Arrochar 52 via Colintraive Ferry, Edinburgh 80, Glasgow 29, Gourock 8, Inveraray 51 via Colintraive Ferry.
EC Wed. **Golf** Rothesay 18h. **See** Remains of 13th cent Castle, Bute Museum of Natural History, Parish Church (ruins of old church nearby), 17th cent Mansion House, Gardens.
🅣 The Pier. ✆ Rothesay (0700) 2151.

St Ebba, PH, x (Rl) *37 Mount Stuart Rd, Craigmore, PA20 9EB.* ✆ (0700) 2683. C. ◪ 16 bedrs, 8 bps, 2 ba, TV, Dgs. 🅘 TV, CP 6, CF, 0 st. £ BB £13–£16, DB £26–£32, WT (b) £99–£120, DT (b) £15–£18, ⊞, Bk £3, D £6·50.

Rescue Service: McKirdy & McMillan Ltd, East Princess St. ✆ (0700) 2317.

ROY BRIDGE Highland (Inverness-shire). Map 39E
Pop 200. Spean Bridge 3, London 502 (Fy 504), Edinburgh 130, Dalwhinnie 32, Fort William 12, Glasgow 115 (Fy 116), Invergarry 19, Kingussie 35.
Golf Spean Bridge 9h. **See** Glen Roy Parallel Roads, Monessie Gorge.

■★★**Glenspean Lodge,** *PH31 4AW.* ✆ Spean Bridge (039 781) 224.

RUTHERGLEN Strathclyde (Lanarkshire). Map 48D
Pop 24,732. M74 Motorway 6, Hamilton 11, London 381, Abington 35, Edinburgh 44, Glasgow 2½, Kilmarnock 21, Lanark 23
EC Tue. **Golf** Cambuslang 9h. **See** Church of St Mary the Virgin (12th cent steeple), Mercat Cross.

★★**King's Park,** *Mill St, G73 2AP.* ✆ 041-647 5491. C. ◪ 24 bedrs, 12 bp, TV, Dgs. ✘ a l c, mc, at, LD 10. 🅘 N, CH, TV, CP 100, Ac, con 250, CF, 7 st. £ BB £22–£25, DB £34, WB, ⊞, Bk £4·95, L £4·50, D £7·50, cc 1 2 3 5, Dep b.

ST ANDREWS Fife. Map 37C
Pop 13,490. M90 Motorway 27, Kirkcaldy 24, London 424, Dundee 12, Dunfermline 39, Edinburgh 49, Glasgow 75, Kinross 35, Perth 32.
EC Thur. **Golf** Four 18h courses—Old, New, Eden and Jubilee, and 5 putting greens, open to visitors, St Andrews GC and New GC admit visitors as temp members, visitors to Royal and Ancient must be guests of members. **See** Cathedral ruins, Chapter House and Museum, St Rule's Church (Tower), Holy Trinity Church, University, Byre Theatre, Botanic Gdns, Castle ruins, The Pends, West Port, Sessions House, Queen Mary's House, Dutch Village (Craigtown Park), Lammas Fair, Aug.
🅣 South St. ✆ St Andrews (0334) 72021.

★★★★**Rusack's Marine,** *KY16 9JQ.* ✆ (0334) 74321.▲

★★★**Rufflets,** *KY16 9TX.* ✆ (0334) 72594. C. ◪ 18 bedrs, 16 bp, 2 bps, annexe 3 bedrs, 3 bp, TV. ✘ a l c, mc, LD 9. 🅘 CH, CP 50, U 4, Ac, con 40, CF, 3 BGf, 1 st, Dis. £ BB £50, DB £46–£50, WT £196–£266, DT £28–£43, DBB £23–£39, WB, ⊞, Bk £4·50, L £5·50, D £10·50, cc 1 2 3 5 6, Dep a.

■★★★**Scores,** *The Scores, KY16 9BB.* ✆ (0334) 72575. C. ◪ 30 bedrs, 30 bp, 3

ba, TV, Dgs. ✗ a l c, LD 9. 🄿 Lt, N, ch, TV, Ac, con, CF, 2 st. £ BB £22–£29, DB £39–£49·50, DBB £32–£39, WB, 🄾 8%, Bk £6, D £10, cc 1 2 3 5 6.

★★Ardgowan, *2 Playfair Ter, KY16 9HX.* ✆ (0334) 72970.

Argyle, PH, z (Rl), *127 North St, KY16 9AG.* ✆ (0334) 73387.

Arran House, G, z (Unl), *5 Murray Park, KY16 9AW.* ✆ (0334) 74724. C. ✎ 13 bedrs, 3 bp, 4 ba, ns, Dgs. 🄿 CH, TV, Dgs, ns, CF, 2 BGf, 2 st. £ BB £8–£12, DB £14–£21, WT (b) £82–£93, DT (b) £12–£14·50, 🄾, Bk £3, D £5·50.

Beachway House, PH, z (Unl), *4 Murray Park, KY16 9AW.* ✆ (0334) 73319. Closed Nov & Dec. C. ✎ 18 bedrs, 7 ba, Dgs. 🄿 CH, TV, CF, 2 BGf, 2 st. £ BB £8·50–£12, DB £15–£22, WT (b) £87–£96, DT (b) £14–£16, 🄾, Bk £1·50, D £5·50.

Cleveden House, G, z (Unl), *3 Murray Pl, KY16 9AP.* ✆ (0334) 74212. C. ✎ 6 bedrs, 2 ba. 🄿 CH, TV, CP 12, CF, 3 st. £ BB £8·50–£9, DB £17–£18, 🄾.

Lorimer House, G, z *19 Murray Park, KY16 9AW.* ✆ (0334) 76599. C 3. ✎ 4 bedrs, 2 sh, 2 ba. 🄿 CH, TV, CF. £ BB £7·50–£10·50, DB £15, 🄾.

Number Ten, G, z (Unl) *10 Hope St, KY16 9HT.* ✆ (0334) 74601. Closed Dec. C. ✎ 10 bedrs, 2 sh, 3 ba, Dgs. 🄿 CH, TV, Dgs, CF, 3 BGf, 2 st. £ BB £9–£11, DB £17–£23, WT (b) £92–£98·50, DT (b) £14·50–£15·50, 🄾.

West Park, G, z (Rt), *5 St Mary's Pl, KY16 9UY.* ✆ (0334) 75933. Closed Dec. C. ✎ 6 bedrs, 3 ba. 🄿 CH, TV, CF, 2 BGf, 2 st. £ BB £7·50–£10, DB £15–£20, WT (b) £80–£95, DT (b) £12·50–£15, 🄾, Bk £2, L £2·50, D £6.

Yorkston House, PH, z (Rt), *70 Argyle St, KY16 9BV.* ✆ (0334) 72019. C. ✎ 12 bedrs, 3 ba. 🄿 CH, TV, CF. £ BB £10, DB £18·50, WT (b) £98·70, DT £14·85, 🄾.

Rescue Service: Bob Clark's (St Andrews) Motor Services Ltd, 15 Alexandra Pl. ✆ (0334) 73040 & (0334) 72566. Central Motors (St Andrews) Ltd, 106 South St. ✆ (0334) 75055.

ST BOSWELLS Borders (Roxburghshire). Map 30B
Pop 2,140. Jedburgh 10, London 337, Edinburgh 37, Galashiels 7½, Glasgow 74, Hawick 14, Kelso 10, Lauder 13, Selkirk 9.
EC Wed. **MD** Mon, Thur. **Golf** St Boswells 9h. **See** Bemersyde Heights (Scott's View), Lessudden House (1680), Dryburgh Abbey 3 m E, Wallace Monument near Dryburgh, 12th cent Church 2 m W at Bowden.

■🄕■★★★★**Dryburgh Abbey,** *TD6 0RQ.* ✆ (0835) 22261. C. ✎ 29 bedrs, 23 bp, 6 ba, TV, Dgs. ✗ mc, at, LD 8.30. 🄿 CH, TV, Dgs, CP 290, pf, con 200, CF, 4 BGf, 3 st. £ BB £19·80–£22·80, DB £35–£48·80, WB, 🄾, L £3, D £11, cc 1 2 3 4 5 6, Dep b▲.

Rescue Service: Lawrie's Garage Ltd, The Green. ✆ (0835) 22241.

ST FILLANS Tayside (Perthshire). Map 36A
Pop 120. Comrie 5, London 423, Crieff 12, Edinburgh 58, Glasgow 54, Lochearnhead 6½, Stirling 27.
Golf St Fillans 9h. **See** Power Station built in rock.

★★★**Four Seasons,** *PH6 2NF.* ✆ (076 485) 333. C. ✎ 12 bedrs, 12 bp,

annexe 12 bedrs, 12 bp, TV, Dgs. ✗ mc, at, LD 9.45. 🄿 CH, CP 50, G 2, con 20, CF, 6 BGf, 1 st, Dis. £ BB £27–£32, DB £44–£54, WT £287–£322, DT £41–£46, DBB £35·50–£40·50, 🄾, Bk £5, L £7·50, D £11, cc 1 2 6.

■★★**Drummond Arms,** *PH6 2NF.* ✆ (076 485) 212.

SALEN Isle of Mull, Strathclyde (Argyll). Map 34B
Pop 100, Craignure 11 (Steamer Service to Oban), London 493, Edinburgh 133, Glasgow 104.
EC Wed. **Golf** Western Isles, Tobermory 9h.

Rescue Service: Kennedy's Garage. ✆ Aros (068 03) 396.

SANQUHAR Dumfries & Galloway (Dumfriesshire). Map 29A
Pop 2,070. Thornhill 12, London 353, Abington 16, Ayr 32, Dalmellington 21, Edinburgh 56, Glasgow 46, Kilmarnock 36, Lanark 29.
EC Thur. **Golf** Sanquhar 9h. **See** 15th–16th cent Castle Ruins: motte-hill, 18th cent Council House, 'Riding of the Marches' ceremony in Aug, Eliock House was birthplace of 'the Admirable Crichton', Post Office (1763).

■★★**Mennockfoot Lodge,** *DG4 6HS.* ✆ (065 92) 477. C. ✎ 4 bedrs, 2 bp, annexe 8 bedrs, 2 bp, 3 ba. ✗ a l c, at, LD 8.30. 🄿 CH, TV, CP 25, con 18, CF, 2 BGf, 1 st, Dis. £ BB £14–£15, DB £22–£24, 🄾, Bk £4, L £3·70, D £8▲.

★**Nithsdale,** *High St, DG4 6DJ.* ✆ (065 92) 506. C. ✎ 6 bedrs, 1 sh, 1 ba, TV, Dgs. ✗ a l c, mc, LD 8. 🄿 CH, TV, Dgs, Ac, con 20, CF, 1 st. £ BB £10, DB £20, WB, 🄾, Bk £3·50, L £3·50, D £5·50, cc 1 2 3 6.

Rescue Service: J & J Leith Ltd, Nithsdale Garage, High St. ✆ (065 92) 322.

SCOURIE Highland (Sutherland). Map 42B
Pop 289. Lairg 43, London 620, Edinburgh 245, Glasgow 252, Tongue 59, Ullapool 43.
Golf Dornoch 18h. **See** Bird Sanctuary on Handa Island (boat trips during summer).

■★★**Scourie,** *IV27 4SX.* ✆ (0971) 2396. Open Apr–Oct. C. ✎ 20 bedrs, 14 bp, 2 ba, Dgs. ✗ mc, at, LD 8.30. 🄿 ch, TV, Dgs, CP 30, pf, CF, 2 st. £ BB £15–£20·20, DB £30–£37, WT £150–£180, DT £21·85–£25, DBB £21·40–£27·20, 🄾, Bk £4, L £1·80, D £7·50, cc 1 3 5 6.

SEAMILL Strathclyde (Ayrshire). Map 35E
Pop 4,960, Irvine 11, London 401, Ayr 23, Edinburgh 75, Glasgow 30, Kilmarnock 18, Largs 7½, Paisley 23.
EC Wed. **Golf** West Kilbride 18h.

Rescue Service: Gordon Diack & Co, Seamill Garage. ✆ West Kilbride (0294) 822129.

SHETLAND ISLANDS Map 47
An Archipelago of 100 islands, about 20 inhabited. Noted for woollen industry, fishing, coast scenery and birdlife.

BRAE Mainland. Map 47C
Lerwick 23, London (via Aberdeen) 515, Edinburgh (Fy) 140, Glasgow 153.

■🄕■★★★★**Busta House** (R), *Busta, ZE2 9QN.* ✆ (080 622) 506. Closed mid Dec–mid Jan. C 12. ✎ 21 bedrs, 13 bp, 8 bps, ns, TV, Dgs. ✗ mc, at, LD 9.30. 🄿 CH, ns, CP 30, con 20, CF, 18 st. £ BB £20–£48, DB £30–£56, DT £36–£69, DBB £28·50–£61·50, WB, 🄾, Bk £4·50, L £7·50, D £13·50.

LERWICK Mainland. Map 47F
Pop 6,195. London (via Aberdeen) 492, Edinburgh (Fy) 117, Glasgow (Fy) 130.
EC Wed. **Golf** Dale 18h. **See** Noss Island Bird Sanctuary, Town Hall, Fort Charlotte, Clickimin Broch.
🄸 Market Cross. ✆ Lerwick (0595) 3434.

Shetland, *under construction,* Holmsgarth Rd. ✆ (0595) 5515.

Repairer: Bolt's Motor Garage Ltd, North Rd. ✆ (0595) 2855.

VIRKIE Mainland. Map 47E
Lerwick 23, London (via Aberdeen) 514, Edinburgh (Fy) 140, Glasgow (Fy) 159.

Meadowvale, H, xy. ✆ Sumburgh (0950) 60240.

SKEABOST BRIDGE Isle of Skye, Highland (Inverness-shire). Map 38A
Broadford 32, London 580, Dunvegan 16, Edinburgh 223, Glasgow 193, Portree 6.

🄕★★★**Skeabost House,** *IV51 9NR.* ✆ (047 032) 202. Open Apr–Oct. C. ✎ 20 bedrs, 15 bp, 3 ba, Dgs. ✗ mc, at, LD 8. 🄿 N, ch, TV, CP 40, G 2, gc, pf, CF, 5 BGf, 3 st. £ BB £16·50–£22, DB £31–£44, DBB £26–£31·50, 🄾, Bk £4·50, L £3·70, D £9·50.

SKELMORLIE Strathclyde (Ayrshire). Map 35E
Pop 1,620. Greenock 9, London 417, Edinburgh 75, Glasgow 30, Gourock 8, Largs 5, Paisley 25.
EC Wed. **Golf** Skelmorlie 12h. **See** Skelmorlie Castle, Wemyss Castle, The measured mile over which Clyde ships undergo their speed trials is off Skelmorlie.

🄕★★★**Manor Park.** ✆ (0475) 520832. Closed Jan 3–mid Feb. C. ✎ 7 bedrs, 5 bp, 1 bps, 1 sh, 1 ba, TV. ✗ a l c, mc, at, LD 9. 🄿 CH, CP 150, Ac, con 50, CF, 9 st. £ BB £27·50, DB £50, WB, 🄾 10%, D £10.

SOUTH BALLACHULISH Highland (Argyll).
See BALLACHULISH.

SOUTHEND Strathclyde (Argyll). Map 28A
Pop 300. Campbeltown 5½, London 527, Edinburgh 181, Glasgow 139, Lochgilphead 60.
EC Wed. **Golf** Dunaverty 18h. **See** Rock Footprints, traditionally marking St Columba's arrival in Scotland, annual Conventicle on site, Mull of Kintyre headland and lighthouse.

★★**Keil,** *Campeltown, PA28 6RT.* ✆ (058 683) 253.

SOUTH QUEENSFERRY Lothian (West Lothian). Map 36F
Pop 5,000. Edinburgh 9½, London 384, M9 Motorway 2, Dunfermline 7½, Glasgow 39, Kincardine 14, Kinross 17, Kirkcaldy 15.
EC Wed. **Golf** Dundas 9h. **See** Hopetoun House, Parish Church, Forth Road and Rail Bridges.

■★★★**M Forth Bridges Moat House,** *Forth Bridge Road, EH30 9SF.* ✆ 031 331

1199. C. 🛏 108 bedrs, 108 bp, TV, Dgs.
✗ a l c, mc, at, LD 9.45. 🅟 N, CH, Dgs, CP
200, Ac, sp, sc, sb, sol, gym, con 140, CF,
20 BGf, 2 st. £ BB £38·75, DB £48·75, DT
£63·70, DBB £56·75, WB, 🆃, Bk £4·25, L
£6·95, D £8, cc 1 2 3 4 5 6, Dep b.
★★**Hawes Inn,** *Newhalls Rd, EH30 9TA.*
✆ 031 331 1990.

SPEAN BRIDGE Highland (Inverness-
shire). Map 39E
Pop 135. Fort William 9½, London 499 (Fy
501), Dalwhinnie 35, Edinburgh 133,
Glasgow 112 (Fy 113), Invergarry 16,
Kingussie 38.
EC Thur. **Golf** Spean Bridge 9h. **See**
Commando Memorial 1¼ NW, Glen Roy
Parallel Roads.

■★★**Letterfinlay Lodge,** *Letterfinlay,*
PH34 4DZ (7½ m N of Spean Bridge on
A82). ✆ Invergloy (039 784) 222. Open
Mar–Oct. C. 🛏 15 bedrs, 2 bp, 3 bps, 4 ba,
Dgs. ✗ mc, at, LD 8.30. 🅟 CH, TV, Dgs, CP
100, pf, con 50, CF, 3 st. £ BB £11–£16, DB
£22–£32, 🆃, Bk £3·50, L £5, D £8,
cc 1 2 3 5 6.

■★★**Spean Bridge,** *PH34 4ES.*
✆ (039 781) 250.

Rescue Service: A D J Stevenson, The
Garage. ✆ (039 781) 257.
Westco Motors, Spean Bridge Filling
Station. ✆ (039 781) 296.

STEPPS Strathclyde (Lanarkshire). Map
48C
Pop 4,400. M73 Motorway 4, Hamilton 10,
London 377, Edinburgh 42, Glasgow 4½,
Kincardine 23, Stirling 54.
EC Wed. **Golf** Crow-Wood 18h. **See**
Wallaces Well & Monument.

★★★**Garfield House,** *Cumbernauld Rd,*
G33 6HW. ✆ 041 779 2111. C. 🛏 21
bedrs, 21 bp, TV, Dgs. ✗ a l c, mc, LD 9.30.
🅟 N, CH, CP 60, con 160, CF, 20 st. £ BB
£27·95, DB £34·95, DBB £34·70, WB, 🆃,
Bk £3, L £2, D £6·75, cc 1 2 3 5 6, Dep b.

STEVENSTON Strathclyde (Ayrshire).
Maps 29A and 35F
Pop 11,550. Irvine 5, London 395, Ayr 17,
Edinburgh 72, Glasgow 27, Kilmarnock
12, Largs 13, Paisley 21.
EC Wed. **Golf** Ardeer 18h. **See** Parish
Church.

Rescue Service: Beach Service Station,
32 Caledonian Rd. ✆ (0294) 62487.
Steel's Garage, Portland Pl. ✆ (0294)
63268.

STIRLING Central (Stirlingshire). Map
36D
Pop 29,776. Falkirk 10, London 395, M9
Motorway 2½, Arrochar 51, Crieff 21,
Dumbarton 34, Dunfermline 22, Edinburgh
35, Glasgow 26, Kincardine 12, Kinross
23, Lanark 34, Lochearnhead 30, Perth 33.
EC Wed. **MD** Thur. **Golf** King Park 18h.
See Castle, Parliament Hall, Chapel Royal,
S African War Memorial, Museum and Art
Gallery, Tolbooth (1701), Mercat Cross,
Darnley's House, Argyll's Lodging, old
Bridge, Church of Holy Rude, Mar's Work,
Guildhall, Bruce's Statue, Abbey Craig
with Wallace Monument 2 m NNE, Field
of Bannockburn (Memorial),
Cambuskenneth Abbey ruins 1 m E,
Doune Castle and Doune Park Gardens,
also Doune Motor Museum 6½ m NW,

Scotland's African Safari Park (at Blair
Drummond—A84 Stirling/Doune Rd).
🆃 Dumbarton Rd. ✆ Stirling (0786) 5019.

★★★**Golden Lion,** *8 King St, FK8 1BD.*
✆ (0786) 5351.
★★**King Robert,** *Glasgow Rd, Whins of*
Milton, FK7 0LJ. ✆ (0786) 811666.

Rescue Service: Schaffer Motors, Site 5,
Back O'Hill Estate. ✆ (0786) 4440.

STONEHAVEN Grampian
(Kincardineshire). Map 41F
Pop 9,000. Brechin 24, London 478,
Aberdeen 15, Braemar 56, Edinburgh 103,
Glasgow 122, Montrose 23.
EC Wed. **Golf** Stonehaven 18h. **See**
Restored 16th cent Tolbooth, Mercat
Cross, Fireball Ceremony at Hogmanay,
Dunnottar Castle ruins 1½ m S, Muchalls
Castle 4½ m NE.
🆃 The Square. ✆ Stonehaven (0569)
62806.

■★★★**M Commodore,** *Cowie Park, AB3*
2PZ. ✆ (0569) 62936. C. 🛏 40 bedrs, 40
bp, 5 ba, TV, Dgs. ✗ mc, at, LD 10. 🅟 N,
CH, TV, Dgs, CP 250, Ac, con 400, CF, 0 st.
£ WB, Bk £2·75, L £5, D £8·50, cc 1 2 3 5.
★★**St Leonards,** *Bath St, AB3 2DE.*
✆ (0569) 62044.

STORNOWAY Isle of Lewis. Western
Islands (Ross & Cromarty). Map 45D
Pop 5,957. Fy to Ullapool, London 584,
Edinburgh 209, Glasgow 213 (181).
EC Wed. **MD** Mon. **Golf** Stornoway 18h.
See Lewis Castle, Chapel of Eye,
Callanish Stones, Dun Carloway Pictish
tower, Butt of Lewis Lighthouse.
🆃 South Beach St. ✆ Stornoway (0851)
3088

★★**Royal,** *Cromwell St, PA87 2DG.*
✆ (0851) 2109. C. 🛏 20 bedrs, 6 ba, Dgs.
✗ mc, at, LD 9. 🅟 CH, TV, Dgs, Ac, CF, 2
st. £ BB £12·75, DB £25·50, WT £120, DT
£21, DBB £18·50, WB, 🆃, Bk £2·75, L
£1·50, D £8, cc 1 2 3 5 6, Dep b.

Rescue Service: Alexander's Lewis Motor
Garage Ltd, Bells Rd. ✆ (0851) 2303.

STRACHUR Strathclyde (Argyll). Map
35C
Pop 750. Arrochar 21, London 444 (Fy
434), Dunoon 19, Edinburgh 98 (Fy 89),
Glasgow 56 (Fy 44), Inveraray 21.
See Old Church.

★★★**Creggans Inn,** *PA27 8BX.*
✆ (036 986) 279. C. 🛏 22 bedrs, 17 bp, 2
bps, 4 ba, TV. ✗ a l c, mc, at, LD 9.30.
🅟 CH, TV, Dgs, CP 80, Ac, pf, con 25, CF, 2
BGf, 1 st, Dis. £ BB £25·50–£35, DB £37–
£55, WB, 🆃, cc 1 2 3 5 6, Dep a.

STRANRAER Dumfries & Galloway
(Wigtownshire). Map 28F
Pop 10,000. Glenluce 9½, London 391,
Edinburgh 120, Gatehouse of Fleet 44,
Girvan 30, Glasgow 82, New Galloway 44.
EC Wed. **Golf** Creachmore 18h. **See** Peel
Tower (known as 'Stranraer Castle'), Old
Town Hall, Lochinch and Castle, Kennedy
Gdns 3 m E, Glenluce Abbey 7½ m E,
Logan Botanic Garden 10 m S.
🆃 Port Rodie. ✆ Stranraer (0776) 2595.

★★★**George,** *George St, DG9 7RJ.*
✆ (0776) 2487. C. 🛏 28 bedrs, 12 bp, 6
sh, 7 ba, TV, Dgs. ✗ a l c, mc, at, LD 9.30.
Ac, gym, con 20, CF, 1 st. £ BB £16·50–
£22, DB £27·50–£36, WT £135–£155, DBB

£20–£24, WB, 🆃, Bk £3·50, L £3·50, D
£9·50, cc 1 2 3 5.

★★★**North West Castle,** *Cairnryan Rd,*
DG9 8EH. ✆ (0776) 4413. C. 🛏 75 bedrs,
75 bp, 2 ba, TV, Dgs. ✗ mc, at, LD 9.30.
🅟 Lt, N, CH, CP 100, sp, sb, sol, con 60, CF,
0 st. £ BB £20–£25, DB £37·50–£42, WB,
🆃, Bk £3·50, L £4, D £7·75.
■★**Buck's Head,** *Hanover St, DG9 7RP.*
✆ (0776) 2064.
■★**Craig Nelder,** *Cairnryan Rd, DG9*
8HA. ✆ (0776) 3281. C. 🛏 11 bedrs, 2 bp,
1 sh, 2 ba, Dgs. ✗ mc, at, LD 9. 🅟 CH, TV,
CP 14, Ac, CF, 1 st. £ BB £12–£17, DB
£22–£28, 🞲, Bk £2·50, L £1·40, D £3·50,
Dep a.

Rescue Service: Burgess Motor Services,
Bellevilla Rd. ✆ (0776) 2451.

STRATHAVEN Strathclyde
(Lanarkshire) Map 29A
Pop 10,000. Kirkmuirhill 6½, London 374,
Abington 19, Ayr 29, Edinburgh 44,
Glasgow 15, Kilmarnock 20, Lanark 13,
Paisley 19.
EC Wed. **Golf** Strathaven 18h. **See** 15th
cent Castle ruins.

Rescue Service: James Watson, Town
Park Garage, Commercial Rd. ✆ (0357)
20262.

STRATHBLANE Central (Stirlingshire).
Map 48E
Pop 835. Glasgow 11, London 398,
Arrochar 33, Crainlarich 48, Dumbarton
20, Edinburgh 47, Lochearnhead 49,
Stirling 27.
EC Wed. **Golf** Strathendrick 9h. **See**
Duntreath Castle 2 m NW.

★★**Kirkhouse Inn,** *G63 9AA.* ✆ (0360)
70621. C. 🛏 17 bedrs, 10 bp, 3 ba, TV,
Dgs. ✗ a l c, mc, at, LD 9.30. 🅟 N, CH, TV,
CP 250, Ac, pf, rf, con 30, CF, 1 st. £ BB
£20–£23, DB £26–£31, DT £34–£39, DBB
£29–£32, WB, 🆃, Bk £3·50, L £5·25, D
£9·25, cc 1 2 3 5, Dep b.▲

STRATHDON Grampian
(Aberdeenshire). Map 41C.
Braemar 24, London 489, Aberdeen 45,
Edinburgh 122, Glasgow 135, Inverness
63.

★**Colquhonnie,** *AB3 8UN.* ✆ (097 52)
210. C. 🛏 10 bedrs, 3 ba, Dgs. ✗ mc, at,
LD 7.30. 🅟 CH, CP 20, U 4, Ac, pf, con 20,
CF, 1 st. £ BB £9, DB £16, 🆃.

Rescue Service: Massie's Garage, Rough
Park. ✆ (097 52) 215.

STRATHPEFFER Highland (Ross &
Cromarty). Maps 39B and 40A
Pop 700. Contin 2½, London 548,
Achnasheen 23, Beauly 11, Dingwall 4½,
Edinburgh 173, Glasgow 177, Ullapool 40.
EC 1 hr. **Golf** Strathpeffer 18h. **See** Eagle
Stone, Ben Wyvis (3,429 ft), Vitrified Fort
(Knockfarrel), Falls of Rogie 5 m W,
Ancient Spa.
🆃 Visitors Centre. ✆ Strathpeffer (099 72)
415.

★★**Highland,** *IV14 9AN.* ✆ (099 72) 457.
■★**Holly Lodge,** *IV14 9AR.* ✆ (099 72)
21254. Open Mar–Oct. C. 🛏 7 bedrs, 2 bp,
3 bps, 1 ba, Dgs. ✗ mc, at, LD 8. 🅟 CH, TV,
Dgs, CP 12, 1 BGf, 3 st. £ BB £15–£16, DB
£32–£36, DBB £21–£25, 🞲, D £10.

STRATHTUMMEL Tayside (Perthshire).
Map 40E

Pitlochry 9½, London 453, Braemar 44, Dundee 54, Edinburgh 78, Fort William 73, Glasgow 90, Perth 35, Tummel Bridge 3. **Golf** Pitlochry 18h.

◨★★**Loch Tummel,** *PH16 5RP.* ✆ Tummel Bridge (088 24) 272. Closed Xmas. C. ⋈ 7 bedrs, 2 bp, 3 ba, Dgs. ✗ a l c, mc, at, LD 9. ◨ CH, TV, Dgs, CP 40, pf, CF, 1 BGf, 1 st. £ BB £12–£14, DB £20–£28, WB, ▣, Bk £3, L £3, D £7·50, cc 1 2 3, Dep.
♨★★**Port-an-Eilean,** *PH16 5RX.* ✆ Tummel Bridge (088 24) 233.

STRICHEN Grampian (Aberdeenshire). Map 41B
Pop 910. Mintlaw 6½, London 528, Aberdeen 34, Banff 19, Edinburgh 154, Fraserburgh 8½, Glasgow 173, Huntly 26, Peterhead 14.
EC Wed. **Golf** Fraserburgh 18h. **See** 'White Horse' on side of Mormond Hill.

Ap. Freemasons, *High St, AB4 4SQ.* ✆ (077 15) 218.

STROMNESS
See ORKNEY ISLANDS

STRONTIAN Highland (Argyll). Map 38F
Pop 250. Loch Aline 20 (Fy to Oban), London 533 (Fy 497), Edinburgh 176 (Fy 140), Fort William 44, Glasgow 133 (Fy 110), Ballachulish (Fy 20).
EC Wed, Thur. **See** Lead Mines.

◨♨★★**Kilcamb Lodge,** *PH36 4HY.* ✆ (0967) 2257. C. ⋈ 11 bedrs, 3 bps, 3 ba, Dgs. ✗ mc, LD 9. ◨ ch, TV, CP 50, pf, CF, 1 st. £ BB £10·90–£12·90, DB £21·80–£25·80, ▣, Bk £3·50, L £1·60, D £9·50.

SWINTON Borders (Berwickshire). Map 37F
Coldstream 6½, London 340, Berwick upon Tweed 12, Edinburgh 45, Glasgow 88.

Rescue Service: Greenview Garage, Main St. ✆ (089 086) 236.

SYMINGTON Strathclyde (Lanarkshire). Maps 29B and 30A
Pop 1,192. Abington 9, London 360, Ayr 50, Edinburgh 32, Glasgow 34, Kincardine 41, Lanark 10, Peebles 21.
EC Wed. **Golf** Biggar 18h. **See** 12th cent Church, 18th cent Inn.

◨★★**Wyndales House,** *ML12 6JU* (2 m SW A73). ✆ Tinto (089 93) 207.

Rescue Service: Tinto Garage Co Ltd, 61 Biggar Rd. ✆ Tinto (089 93) 200.

TAIN Highland (Ross & Cromarty). Map 43E
Pop 2,200. Alness 14, London 562, Bonar Bridge 14, Dingwall 25, Edinburgh 187, Glasgow 194.
EC Thur. **Golf** Tain 18h. **See** Mercat Cross, 15th cent Church, Gothic Memorial, Museum, Old Tower, Curfew bell rung nightly.

★★**Mansfield,** *Scotsburn Rd, IV19 1PR.* ✆ (0862) 2052. Closed Jan 1 & 2. C. ⋈ 19 bedrs, 13 bp, 2 bps, 1 ba. ✗ mc, at, LD 8.45. ◨ N, CH, TV, Dgs, CP 50, con 20, 3 st. £ Bk £2·25, L £2·25, D £7, cc 1 3, Dep b.
★★**Royal,** *High St, IV19 1AB.* ✆ (0862) 2013. C. ⋈ 25 bedrs, 15 bp, 7 bps, 2 ba. ✗ a l c, mc, at, LD 9. ◨ N, ch, TV, Dgs, CP 40, U 8, con 50, CF. £ BB £16–£21, DB

£35, ▣ 10%, Bk £3·75, L £4, D £12, cc 1 2 3 5 6 , Dep a.

TARBERT Isle of Harris, Western Isles (Inverness-shire). Map 45E
Pop 904. Fy to Uig, London 607, Edinburgh (Fy) 246, Glasgow (Fy) 218, Kyleakin (Fy) 46, Mallaig (Fy) 56, Stornoway 34.
EC Thur.
ⓘ ✆ Harris (0859) 2011.

★★**Harris,** *PA85 3DL.* ✆ Harris (0859) 2154. Open Apr–Oct. C. ⋈ 26 bedrs, 12 bp, 2 bps, 3 ba, Dgs. ✗ mc, at, LD 8.30. ◨ ch, CP 26, con 60, CF, 4 st.

TARBERT Strathclyde (Argyll). Map 35E
Pop 226. Ardrishaig 11, London 481, Edinburgh 135, Glasgow 93, Lochgilphead 13, Whitehouse 8.
EC Wed. **Golf** Helensburgh 18h. **See** Ruins 13th cent Castle.
ⓘ ✆ Tarbert (088 02) 429.

◨♨★★★**Stonefield Castle,** *PA29 6YJ.* ✆ (088 02) 207. Open Apr–Oct. C. ⋈ 31 bedrs, 31 bp, 1 ba, ns, Dgs. ✗ a l c, mc, at, LD 9. ◨ Lt, CH, TV, Dgs, CP 50, G 3, Ac, sp, tc, rf, sb, sol, con 120, CF, 12 BGf, 4 st. £ BB £30, DB £54, ▣, Bk £4·50, L £2, D £14·50, cc 1 2 3 4 5, Dep a.
★★**Bruce,** *PA29 4YJ.* ✆ (088 02) 577. Open Mar–Dec. C. ⋈ 11 bedrs, 2 bp, 9 bps, 1 ba, Dgs. ✗ mc, at, LD 9. ◨ CH, TV, Dgs, con 20, CF, 4 st. £ BB £13·50–£14·50, DB £25–£27, WT £115·50–£127, ▣, Bk £3, L £3, D £7·50, cc 1 3 6, Dep a.▲

TARLAND Grampian (Aberdeenshire). Map 41C
Pop 410. Aboyne 5, London 490, Aberdeen 31, Braemar 26, Craigellachie 43, Edinburgh 116, Glasgow 135, Grantown-on-Spey 40, Huntly 33, Stonehaven 33.
EC Wed. **Golf** Tarland 9h. **See** Craigievar Castle, Earth House, 2 m NE, Stone Circle ¾ m SE.

Repairer: Hamish D Paterson. ✆ (033 981) 232.

TAYNUILT Strathclyde (Argyll). Map 35A
Pop 400. Dalmally 11, London 466, Ballachulish 40, Edinburgh 109, Fort William (Fy) 50, Glasgow 79, Inveraray 26, Oban 12.
EC Wed. **Golf** Glencruitten, Oban 18h. **See** Nelson Monument, Old Blast Furnace where cannon balls for the 'Victory' were made.

◨★★**Netherlorn,** *PA35 1HT.* ✆ (086 62) 243.
◨★★**Polfearn,** *PA35 1JQ.* ✆ (086 62) 251. Open Mar–Oct. C 3. ⋈ 16 bedrs, 2 bp, 8 bps, 2 ba, Dgs. ✗ a l c, mc, at, LD 9. ◨ ch, TV, Dgs, CP 30, con 30, 1 BGf, 0 st, Dis. £ BB £13–£17, DB £22–£30, DBB £18·50–£22·50, ▣, Bk £3, L £3, D £8·50, cc 1 2 3 4 5 6.

TEANGUE Highland, Isle of Skye (Inverness-shire). Map 38D
Pop 50. Armadale (Fy to Mallaig) 4½, London (Fy) 537, Edinburgh (Fy) 180, Glasgow (Fy) 150, Kyleakin (Fy to Kyle of Lochalsh) 17.

★★**Toravaig** (RI), *IV44 8RJ.* ✆ (047 13) 231. Open Mar–Oct. C. ⋈ 9 bedrs, 2 bps, 1 ba, Dgs. ✗ mc, at, LD 8. ◨ ch, TV, CP 20, pf, CF, 2 st. £ BB £13–£16, DB £26–

£36, WT £158–£172, DT £27–£30, DBB £21·50–£26·50, ▣, Bk £4, L £5, D £8·50, cc 2 3 5.

THORNHILL Dumfries & Galloway (Dumfriesshire). Map 29D
Pop 1,450. Dumfries 14, London 341, Abington 22, Ayr 44, Dalmellington 24, Edinburgh 62, Glasgow 59, Kilmarnock 48, Moffat 31, New Galloway 22.
EC Thur. **Golf** Thornhill 9h. **See** 18th cent pillared Cross, Thomson Monument, ancient cross near Nith Bridge (½ m), Dalveen Pass, Drumlanrig Castle.

★★**Buccleuch & Queensberry,** *South Drumlanrig St, DG3 5LU.* ✆ (0848) 30215. C. ⋈ 11 bedrs, 4 bp, 1 bps, 2 ba, Dgs. ✗ a l c, mc, at, LD 8. ◨ ch, TV, Dgs, CP 50, U 4, CF, 1 st. £ BB £10–£16, DB £20–£27, DT £22·25, DBB £19·75–£23·75, ▣, Bk £3·25, L £3, D £7·75, cc 1 3 6.
♨★★**Trigony House,** *Closeburn, DG3 5EZ.* ✆ (084 84) 211. C. ⋈ 6 bedrs, 1 bp, 2 bps, 2 ba, Dgs. ✗ a l c, mc, LD 8.45. ◨ CH, TV, CP 20, G 3, Ac, CF, 1 st. £ BB £17·50–£20·50, DB £24–£33, DBB £24–£37, WB, ▣, Bk £3·50, L £6, D £7.

THURSO Highland (Caithness). Maps 43B and 46E
Pop 8,000. Helmsdale 41, London 644, Edinburgh 269, Glasgow 276, Melvich 16, Wick 20.
EC Thur. **MD** Tue. **Golf** Thurso 18h. **See** Ruins of 13th cent Bishop's Palace, St Peter's Church, Harold's Tower, House and collection of Robt Dick (botanist), Castle of Mey gardens (occasionally in Summer) 11 m NE, Atomic Energy Reactor at Dounreay 8 m W.
ⓘ Car Park, Riverside. ✆ Thurso (0847) 2371.

★★**Pentland,** *Princes St, KW14 7AA.* ✆ (0847) 63202. C. ⋈ 57 bedrs, 18 bp, 8 bps, 31 sh, Dgs. ✗ a l c, mc, at, LD 8.30. ◨ N, CH, TV, Ac, con, CF. £ BB £12–£25, DB £24–£35, ▣, Bk £3·50, L £2·50, D £5·50.
★★**Royal,** *Traill St, KW14 8EH.* ✆ (0847) 63191. Open Feb–Nov & Xmas. C. ⋈ 100 bedrs, 12 bp, 48 bps, 12 ba, Dgs. ✗ a l c, mc, at, LD 8.30. ◨ N, ch, TV, CP 50, Ac, con 250, CF, 11 BGf, 0 st, Dis. £ BB £12·90–£16·90, DB £25·80–£33·80, WT £167·30, DT £23·90, DBB £20·40–£24·40, WB, ▣, Bk L £4·50, D £7·50, Dep a.
★★**St Clair,** *Sinclair St, KW14 7AJ.* ✆ (0847) 63730. C. ⋈ 27 bedrs, 2 bp, 4 bps, 6 ba, Dgs. ✗ mc, at, LD 9. ◨ N, CH, TV, Dgs, U 6, Ac, pf, sc, con 20, CF, 4 BGf, 1 st. £ BB £12–£15, DB £21–£25, WT £140·60, DT £21·80, DBB £18·50–£20·50, ▣, Bk £3·30, L £3·30, D £6·50.

Rescue Service: Ness Motors, Bridgend. ✆ (0847) 3161.

TIGHNABRUAICH Strathclyde (Argyll). Map 35E
Pop 1,800. Arrochar 43, London 465 (Fy 461), Dunoon 46, Edinburgh 119 (Fy 117), Glasgow 78 (Fy 72), Inveraray 48.
EC Wed. **Golf** Kyles of Bute, Kames 9h, Tighnabruaich 9h.

Rescue Service: Andrews Garage, Village Brae. ✆ (070 081) 386.

TOBERMORY Isle of Mull, Strathclyde (Argyll). Maps 34B and 38E

Pop 800. Craignure 21 (Fy to Oban),
London 498, Edinburgh 141, Glasgow
111.
EC Wed. **Golf** Western Isles 9h. **See** Ben
More (highest point on island), 3,169 ft.
🛈 48 Main St. 📞 Tobermory (0688) 2182.

■★★★**Western Isles,** *PA75 6PW.*
📞 (0688) 2012. Open Mar–Oct & New
Year. C. 🛏 29 bedrs, 15 bp, 5 ba, TV, Dgs.
✕ mc, at, LD 8.45. 🅿 N, ch, TV, CP 20, G 6,
Ac, gc, con 30, CF, 1 st. £ WB, Bk £4, L £2,
D £9, cc 1 2 3 5, Dep a.
■★**Mishnish,** *PA75 6NU.* 📞 (0688)
2009. C. 🛏 14 bedrs, 5 bp, 1 bps, 5 ba,
Dgs. ✕ a l c, mc, at, LD 9. 🅿 CH, TV, Dgs,
Ac, pf, con 25, CF, 1 st. £ BB £10–£15, DB
£20–£30, DBB £18–£23, WB, 🛈, Bk £2·50,
D £8·50.

Rescue Service: MacGlip's Garage,
Ledaig. 📞 (0688) 2103.

TOMINTOUL Grampian (Banffshire).
Map 40D
Pop 300. Braemar 300, London 493,
Aberdeen 65, Craigellachie 21, Edinburgh
118, Glasgow 135, Grantown-on-Spey 13,
Huntly 28.
EC Wed. **Golf** Dufftown 9h. **See** Loftiest
village in the Highlands and ski-ing centre,
Church of Scotland, RC Church, Glen
Avon.
🛈 📞 Tomintoul (080 74) 285.

★★**Richmond Arms,** *Main Rd, AB3 9ET.*
📞 (080 74) 209.

Rescue Service: J Grant & Son, 57 Main
St. 📞 (080 74) 249.

TONGUE Highland (Sutherland). Map
43A
Pop 150. Lairg 36, London 613, Bettyhill
13, Durness 37, Edinburgh 238, Glasgow
245.
Golf Reay 18h. **See** Massive ruins of
Castle Varrich Round Tower, Tongue
House, Ben Loyal 2,504 ft.

■★★**Ben Loyal,** *IV27 4XE.* 📞 (084 755)
216. RS Nov–Mar. C. 🛏 13 bedrs, 2 bp, 3
bps, 4 ba, ns, Dgs. ✕ mc, at. 🅿 ch, TV, CP
18, CF, 0 st. £ BB £12·75–£14·75, DB £20–
£33·50, DBB £17–£23·75, WB, 2, Bk
£3·25, L £3, D £7·50, cc 1 3 6, Dep a.
■★★**Tongue,** *IV27 4XF.* 📞 (080 05) 206.
Open Mar–Oct, Xmas & New Year. C.
🛏 21 bedrs, 15 bp, 4 ba, ns, TV, Dgs.
✕ mc, at, LD 8.45. 🅿 CH, TV, ns, CP 60, pf,
con, CF, 7 BGf, 0 st, Dis. £ BB £16·95–
£24·95, DB £23·90–£48·95, WT £182–
£216·65, DBB £20·95–£28·95, WB, 2, Bk
£3·95, L £4·25, D £8·95, cc 1 2 3 5 6,
Dep a.

TORRIDON Highland (Ross & Cromarty).
Map 38B
Achnasheen 20, London 591, Edinburgh
220 (Fy 218), Gairloch 30, Glasgow 227,
Loch Carron 23.
Golf Lochcarron 9h.
🛈 Junction of A896 and Diabeg Rd.
📞 (044 587) 221.

♨★★**Loch Torridon,** *IV22 2EX.*
📞 (044 587) 242.

TROON Strathclyde (Ayrshire). Map 28B
Pop 14,254. Monkton 4, London 389, Ayr
7, Edinburgh 69, Glasgow 29, Kilmarnock
9, Largs 24, Paisley 27.
EC Wed. **Golf** Troon 18h (2), Troon
Municipal 18h (3). **See** Lady Isle Bird
Sanctuary.

🛈 Municipal Buildings, South Beach.
📞 Troon (0292) 315131.

★★★★**Marine,** *8 Crosbie Rd, KA10 6HG.*
📞 (0292) 314444. C. 🛏 70 bedrs, 70 bp, 1
ba, TV, Dgs. ✕ a l c, mc, at, LD 9.30. 🅿 Lt,
N, CH, TV, CP 150, U 5, Ac, pf, con 150, CF,
9 st. £ BB £30–£37, DB £50–£58, DBB
£29–£47, WB, 🛈, Bk £5, L £6·50, D £11,
cc 1 2 3 4 5 6, Dep a.
★★★**Sun Court,** *19 Crosbie Rd, KA10
6HF.* 📞 (0292) 312727. Closed Xmas. C.
🛏 20 bedrs, 18 bp, 1 ba, TV, Dgs. ✕ a l c,
mc, LD 9.30. 🅿 CH, TV, CP 70, tc, sc, con
30, CF, 5 BGf, 2 st. £ BB £29–£31, DB £44–
£50, WT £220, WB, 🛈, Bk £2·50, L £7·50, D
£11·50, cc 1 2 5.
■★★**Ardneil,** *51 St Meddans St, KA10
6NU.* 📞 (0292) 311611. C. 🛏 7 bedrs, 3
bp, 2 ba, TV. ✕ a l c, mc, at, LD 8.30. 🅿 ch,
TV, Dgs, CP 45, Ac, con 60, CF, 4 st. £ BB
£13–£16·50, DB £22–£28, WB, 🛈, Bk £3, L
£4·50, D £8, cc 1 2.
★★**Craiglea,** *80 South Beach, KA10 6EG.*
📞 (0292) 311366. C. 🛏 22 bedrs, 11 bp, 1
bps, 4 ba, Dgs. ✕ a l c, mc, at, LD 8.45.
🅿 CH, TV, CP 14, Ac, con, CF, 1 BGf, 2 st.
£ BB £19·50–£23, DB £32–£38, WT £200–
£250, DT £32–£36·50, DBB £27–£31, 2,
Bk £2, L £6·50, D £8·50, cc 1 2 3 5, Dep a.
■★★**South Beach,** *73 South Beach,
KA10 6EG.* 📞 (0292) 312033. C. 🛏 28
bedrs, 7 bp, 9 bps, 1 sh, 4 ba, TV, Dgs.
✕ mc, at, LD 8. 🅿 CH, TV, Dgs, CP 40, Ac,
con 50, CF, 2 st. £ BB £12–£17·50, DB
£24–£31, WT £140, DT £21–£26, DBB
£15·50–£23, WB, 2, Bk £3, L £3·25, D £6,
cc 1 2 3, Dep a.
Glenside, G, z (Unl), *2 Darley Pl, KA10
6JQ.* 📞 (0292) 313677. C. 🛏 5 bedrs, 2
ba, Dgs. 🅿 CH, TV, CP 5, CF. £ DB £15, 🛈

Repairer: Appleyard (Ayrshire) Ltd,
Dundonald Rd. 📞 (0292) 314141.
MC Repairer: Cooper Bros, 117
Templehill. 📞 (0292) 313616.
Sctr Repairer: Cooper Bros, 117
Templehill. 📞 (0292) 313616.

TUMMEL BRIDGE Tayside (Perthshire).
Map 40E
Aberfeldy 13, London 458, Edinburgh 81,
Glasgow 83, Dalwhinnie 32, Pitlochry 12.

♨★★★**Port-an-Eilean,** *Strathtummel,
PH16 5RX.* 📞 (088 24) 233. Open Apr–
Oct. C. 🛏 11 bedrs, 6 bp, 3 ba, Dgs. ✕ mc,
at, LD 8.45. 🅿 CH, CP 20, G 2, pf, CF, 2 st.
£ BB £14–£17, DB £28–£33, DBB £22–
£24·50, 2, Bk £3·50, D £8.

TURNBERRY Strathclyde (Ayrshire).
Map 28D
Pop 164. Maybole 7, London 386, Ayr 15,
Dalmellington 20, Edinburgh 85, Girvan 5,
Glasgow 47.
EC Wed. **Golf** Turnberry 18h (2). **See**
Remains of castle assoc with King Robert
the Bruce.

★★★★**Turnberry,** *Maidens Rd, KA26
9LT.* 📞 (065 53) 202. C. 🛏 124 bedrs, 124
bp, TV, Dgs. ✕ a l c, mc, at, LD 9.30. 🅿 Lt,
N, CH, TV, ns, CP 200, sp, gc, tc, sb, sol,
gym, con, CF, 10 BGf, 1 st, Dis. £ BB £35–
£75, DB £55–£110, WB, 🛈, Bk £7, L £9·50,
D £17, cc 1 2 3 4 5, Dep.

TWEEDSMUIR Borders (Peeblesshire).
Map 30A
Pop 60. Moffat 15, London 350, Abington
22, Beattock 16, Edinburgh 35, Glasgow
48, Lanark 25, Peebles 17.

Golf West Linton 18h. **See** Church.

■★★**Crook Inn,** *ML12 6QN.* 📞 (089 97)
272. C. 🛏 8 bedrs, 5 bp, 1 bps, 2 sh, 1 ba,
Dgs. ✕ a l c, mc, at, LD 8.45. 🅿 CH, TV, CP
60, G 3, pf, CF, 1 st. £ BB £19–£23, DB
£32–£40, WT £149–£163, DBB £25–£29,
WB, 2, Bk £4·25, L £4·25, D £9·50.

UDDINGSTON Strathclyde
(Lanarkshire) Map 48D
Pop 5,000. Bothwell 1½, London 382,
Coatbridge 5, East Kilbride 6½, Edinburgh
38, Glasgow 8, M73 1½, M74 1½.
EC Wed. **Golf** Hamilton 9h. **See** Castle
Ruins, Roman roads.

Rescue Service: Park Autos (Viewpark),
754a Old Edinburgh Rd, Viewpark,
Uddingston, Glasgow. 📞 Bellshill (0698)
747531.
S R Coachworks, Old Mill Rd. 📞 (0698)
818101.

UIG Isle of Skye. Highland (Inverness-
shire). Maps 38A and 45F
Pop 200. Portree 16, London (Fy) 590,
Dunvegan 26, Edinburgh (Fy) 233,
Glasgow (Fy) 203.
Golf Portree 9h.

★★**Uig** (R), *IV51 9YE.* 📞 (047 042) 205.
Open mid Apr–Oct. RS mid Apr–May 1. C
12. 🛏 12 bedrs, 6 bp, 6 bps. ✕ mc, at, LD
8. 🅿 CH, CP 20, Ac, con 15, 1 BGf, 1 st,
Dis. £ BB £15·50–£26, DB £31–£52, WT
£175–£210, DBB £23·50–£36, WB, 2, Bk
£4, D £8, cc 1 2 3 5 6, Dep a.
■★**Ferry Inn,** *IV51 9XP.* 📞 (047 042)
242. RS Dec, Jan, Feb, Mar. C. 🛏 6 bedrs,
1 bp, 2 ba, Dgs. ✕ a l c, mc, LD 8.30. 🅿 CH,
TV, Dgs, CP 19, CF, 1 st. £ BB £18, DB
£22–£26, DBB £18–£20, 2 10%, Bk £3, L
£5, D £6·50, Dep a.

ULLAPOOL Highland (Ross & Cromarty).
Map 42E
Pop 800. Garve 32, London 584,
Achnasheen 48, Beauly 48, Bonar Bridge
47, Dingwall 47, Durness 69, Edinburgh
209, Gairloch 57, Glasgow 213, Lairg 44.
EC Tue. **Golf** Gairloch 9h. **See** Loch
Broom, Falls of Measach 11m SSE, boat
trips during summer to the Summer Isles.
🛈 📞 Ullapool (0854) 2135.

■★★★**M Ladbroke,** *North Rd, IV26 2TG.*
📞 (0854) 2314. Open Apr–Oct. C. 🛏 60
bedrs, 60 bp, TV, Dgs. ✕ mc, LD 9. 🅿 N,
CH, TV, CP 80, Ac, sb, CF, 30 BGf, 0 st, Dis.
£ BB £27·50–£31·50, DB £42–£48, DBB
£37–£41, WB, 🛈, Bk £5, D £9·50,
cc 1 2 3 4 5 6, Dep b.
■★★★**Royal,** *Garve St, IV26 2SY.*
📞 (0854) 2181. Closed Dec 24–Jan 5. C.
🛏 60 bedrs, 45 bp, 3 bps, 8 ba, Dgs.
✕ a l c, mc, at, LD 9.30. 🅿 N, CH, TV, Dgs,
CP 200, Ac, pf, con 75, CF, 7 BGf, 1 st, Dis.
£ BB £13–£18·50, DB £28–£43, WT £160–
£190, DBB £22·50–£31·50, WB, 2, Bk
£3·50, L £3·50, D £10·25, cc 1 2 3 4 5,
Dep a.
■★★**M Harbour Lights,** *Garve Rd, IV26
2SX.* 📞 (0854) 2222. Open Apr–Oct. C.
🛏 22 bedrs, 9 bp, 6 bps, 3 ba, TV, Dgs.
✕ mc, at, LD 9. 🅿 N, CH, TV, Dgs, CP 30, CF, 4 BGf,
2 st. £ BB £14·50–£17·50, DB £21–£29, 🛈,
Bk £3·75, L £1·80, D £5·90, cc 1 5, Dep a.

VIRKIE
See SHETLAND ISLANDS.

WALKERBURN Borders (Peeblesshire).
Map 30B

Pop 1,000. Galasheils 9, London 352, Edinburgh 29, Glasgow 58, Peebles 8, Selkirk 12.
EC Tue. **Golf** Innerleithen 9h. **See** Tweed Mill and Museum.

◼♨★★**Tweed Valley,** *Galashields Rd, EH43 6AA.* ☎ (089 687) 220. C. ⊨ 15 bedrs, 8 bp, 7 bps, 2 ba, TV, Dgs. ✗ a l c, mc, at, LD 9.30. 🅿 CH, TV, Dgs, CP 35, Ac, pf, sb, sol, gym, con 30, CF, 3 st. £ BB £13–£27, DB £26–£45, DT £25–£41, DBB £21·50–£26·50, WB, ▯, Bk £3·75, L £3·50, D £8·50, cc 1 2 3 5 6.

WEST CALDER Lothian (Midlothian). Map 36F
Pop 2,203. Biggar 20, London 384, Abington 34, Dunfermline 23, Edinburgh 17, Glasgow 29, Kincardine 24, Kirkcaldy 33, Lanark 16, Peebles 35, Stirling 29.
EC Wed. **Golf** Harburn 18h.

Rescue Service: Bryce's Garage, 41 West End. ☎ (0506) 388.

WEST KILBRIDE Strathclyde (Ayrshire). Map 35E
Pop 4,960. Ardrossan 5, London 405, Ayr 23, Edinburgh 75, Glasgow 30, Kilmarnock 18, Paisley 23.
EC Wed. **Golf** West Kilbride 18h. **See** Castle Ruins, Ancient Building.

Rescue Service: M. Pisani, Station Garage, Cumbrieshaw St. ☎ (0294) 823217.

WEST LINTON Borders (Peeblesshire). Maps 30A and 36F
Pop 1,000. Broughton 12, London 370, Abington 23, Beattock 37, Edinburgh 17, Glasgow 43, Lanark 21, Peebles 13.
EC Thur. **Golf** West Linton 18h. **See** 12th cent Parish Church, 17th cent Lady Gifford's Well.

Rescue Service: Fleming, John & Son, Smithy Garage, Deanfoot Rd. ☎ (096 86) 261.
Gordon Arms Garage, Townhead.
☎ (096 86) 313.

WHITBURN Lothian (West Lothian). Map 36F

Lanark 16, London 384, M8 Motorway 2, Edinburgh 22, Glasgow 24, Kincardine 18, Peebles 33, Stirling 25.

Rescue Service: J & A Browning Ltd, 11 East Main St. ☎ (0501) 40536.

WHITEBRIDGE Highland (Inverness-shire). Map 40C
Pop 620. Fort Augustus 9, London 530 (Fy 533), Carrbridge 41, Edinburgh 164, Glasgow 143 (Fy 144), Invergarry 17, Invermoriston 16, Inverness 28.
Golf Fort Augustus 9h.

◼★★**Whitebridge,** *IV1 2UN.*
☎ Gorthleck (045 63) 226. Closed Jan, Feb. C. ⊨ 12 bedrs, 3 bp, 5 bps, 2 ba, TV, Dgs. ✗ mc, at. 🅿 ch, CP 30, U 2, pf, CF, 1 st. £ BB £12·25–£14·75, DB £24·50–£32, DBB £20–£24, ▯, Bk £3, L £5·50, D £7·75, cc 1 2 3 5 6, Dep a.

WHITHORN Dumfries & Galloway (Wigtownshire). Map 29E
Pop 1,000. Wigtown 10, London 384, Edinburgh 118, Gatehouse of Fleet 36, Girvan 48, Glasgow 106, New Galloway 35, Stranraer 32.
EC Wed. **Golf** St Medan, Port William 9h. **See** 12th–15th cent Priory Church, Museum.

★★**Queen's Arms,** *Isle of Whithorn, DG8 8LF.* ☎ (098 85) 369. C. ⊨ 10 bedrs, 4 bp, 2 ba, TV, Dgs. ✗ a l c, mc, at, LD 10. 🅿 N, ch, TV, Dgs, CP 12, CF, 0 st. £ BB £12·50, DB £25–£30, WT £143·50, DT £22, DBB £21–£23·50, WB, ▯, Bk £2·50, L £2·50, D £8·50, cc 1 2 3 5, Dep a.

WICK Highland (Caithness). Map 43B
Pop 7,000. Helmsdale 35, London 638, London 425, Edinburgh 51, Glasgow 71, Kinross 25, Kirkcaldy 26, St Andrews 11.
EC Wed. **MD** Thur. **Golf** Reiss 18h. **See** Parish Church, Town Hall, Glass Factory, ruins of Sinclair and Girnigoe castles, Noss Head, "Castle of Auld Wick" 1 m SSE.
🅸 Whitechapel Rd off High St. ☎ Wick (0955) 2596.

◼★★★**M Ladbroke,** *Riverside, KW1 4NL.* ☎ (0955) 3344. Closed Xmas & New Year. C. ⊨ 48 bedrs, 48 bp, TV, Dgs. ✗ mc,

at, LD 8.45. 🅿 N, CH, CP 20, Ac, con 150, CF, 17 BGf, 3 st. £ BB £36, DB £53·50, WB, ▨, Bk £5, L £1·95, D £9·75, cc 1 2 3 5 6, Dep b.

★★**Station,** *2 Bridge St, KW1 4NH.*
☎ (0955) 4545. Open Apr–Oct. C. ⊨ 33 bedrs, 19 bp, 4 sh, 7 ba, TV, Dgs. ✗ a l c, mc, at, LD 9.30. 🅿 Lt, N, ch, TV, ns, CP 30, Ac, CF, 2 st. £ BB £18–£25, DB £26–£35, WT £150, DT £31·50, DBB £27–£34, WB, ▯, Bk £4, L £4·50, D £9.

Ap. Rosebank, *Thurso St, KW1 5LF.*
☎ (0955) 3244. Closed Xmas. C. ⊨ 26 bedrs, 10 bps, 3 ba, TV. ✗ a l c, mc, LD 10. 🅿 ch, TV, CP 14, U 1, Ac, CF, 1 st. £ BB £12·50–£16, DB £25–£32, WT £161–£195, DT £23–£27, DBB £19–£23, WB, ▯, Bk £4, L £4·50, D £7, cc 1 2 3 4 5 6.

Rescue Service: Mowatt's Garage, George St. ☎ (0955) 2322.

WISHAW Strathclyde (Lanarkshire). Map 48B
Pop 30,540. Abington 26, London 377, M74 Motorway 4½, Ayr 40, Edinburgh 33, Glasgow 15, Kilmarnock 8, Lanark 10, Peebles 33.
EC Wed. **Golf** Wishaw 18h, Colville Park 18h. **See** Dalzell House with 15th cent tower.

◼★★**Coltness,** *Coltness Rd, ML2 7EX.*
☎ (0698) 381616. C. ⊨ 12 bedrs, 4 ba, Dgs. ✗ a l c, mc, at, LD 9. 🅿 CH, TV, Dgs, CP 120, Ac, con 80, CF, 2 st. £ BB £16·50, DB £26·68, WB, ▨, Bk £3, L £2·25, D £4·25, cc 1 2 3 5.

WORMIT Fife. Map 37A
M90 Motorway 24, Glenrothes 20, London 425, Edinburgh 51, Glasgow 71, Kinross 25, Kirkcaldy 26, St Andrews 11.

♨★★**Sandford Hill,** *DD6 8RG.*
☎ Newport-on-Tay (0382) 541802. Closed Jan 1 & 2. C. ⊨ 15 bedrs, 13 bp, 1 ba, TV, Dgs. ✗ a l c, mc, at, LD 9.30. 🅿 CH, TV, CP 50, tc, con 30, CF, 6 st. £ BB £21–£25, DB £32–£38, WT £150–£180, DT £25·70–£30·20, DBB £21–£30·50, WB, ▨, Bk £3·50, L £6·50, D £9·20, cc 1 2 3 5 6.

GOING PLACES SERIES

The *RAC Going Places* series offers a unique compilation of motor and walking tours. Each book is written by an author who is on 'home ground'. These modestly priced guides describe the topography, history, flora and fauna of each area, together with details of places of interest and motor tours and relevant maps.
(See pages 37-8)

RAC

Directory–Wales

Directory of appointed hotels, small hotels, guest houses, etc., repairers and agents in Wales.
See separate sections for England, Scotland, The Channel Islands and Northern Ireland.

National Tourist Board:
Wales Tourist Board
Brunel House,
2 Fitzalen Road, Cardiff CF2 1UY
☎ Cardiff (0222) 499909
Tourist Information Centre:
3 Castle Street, Cardiff CF1 2RE
☎ Cardiff (0222) 27281

For explanatory notes to Directory see page 116
For abbreviations see inside back cover

More Wales per gallon

To travel in Wales is to enjoy magnificent scenery, bustling market towns, quiet villages, cosmopolitan cities - all in a relatively small area so your gallon goes a long way. It's easy to decide where to go and what to see in Wales. There are four publications to help you make the right choices - the 'Going Places' touring guide, 'Where to Stay' Serviced and Self Catering and our free 132 page 'Wales Guide'.

Work out your route, decide on your accommodation and away you go. 'Going Places' has 72 pages packed with information - details of scenic routes and tourist attractions, maps and helpful motoring information. The 'Where to Stay' guides list thousands of holiday addresses and makes choosing a inn, hotel, guesthouse, caravan, flat, cottage or farm an enjoyable task.

All these publications are available from leading newsagents and booksellers or just fill in the form below:-

432

ABERDARE Mid Glamorgan. Map 12F
Pop 38,250. Newport 28, London 165,
Caerphilly 17, Hirwaun 3½, Merthyr Tydfil
6½, Pontypool 23, Pontypridd 11.
EC Thur. **MD** Sat. **Golf** Aberdare 18h. **See**
12th cent Parish Church of St John,
Brecon Beacons National Park.

★★**Ysguborwen**, CF44 0AX. ✆ 872606.

Rescue Service: Golden Acres Garage,
Park View Ter, Abercwmboi. ✆ Mountain
Ash (0443) 472380.
Morgans Garage, Tramway, Roberts-
town Industrial Estate. ✆ (0685) 876181.
Tinney Motors Ltd, 27A Cardiff St.
✆ (0685) 872108

ABERDARON Gwynedd. Map 18E
Pop 375. Pwllheli 14, London 256,
Caenarfon 33.
EC Wed. **Golf** Nefyn 18h, Abersoch 9h.
See St Mary's Wishing Well, Whistling
Sands, Hell's Mouth, Bardsey Island.

★★**Ty Newydd**, LL53 8BE. ✆ (0758)
207. Open Mar–Oct. ➤ 14 bedrs, 8 bp, 1
bps, 3 ba. ✗ mc, LD 9, ⊡ CH, TV, CP 8, G 2,
CF, 0 st. £ BB £18–18, DB £30–£32, DBB £23–
£24, ①, Bk £5, L £4, D £8-25.

ABERDYFI Gwynedd. Map 12A
Pop 1,200. Newtown 39, London 215,
Aberystwyth 28, Bala 39, Dolgellau 24,
Rhayader 49, Welshpool 48.
EC Wed. **Golf** Aberdyfi 18h. **See** Happy
Valley ("Bearded Lake"), Bird Rock 9 m,
Dolgoch Falls 9 m, Cader Idris (2,927 ft).
ⓘ Snowdonia National Park Centre, The
Wharf. ✆ Aberdyfi (065 472) 321.

★★★**Trefeddian**, LL35 0SB.
✆ (065 472) 213. Open Mar–Dec, C. ➤ 44
bedrs, 41 bp, 3 bps, Dgs. ✗ mc, at, LD
8.30. ⊡ Lt, ch, TV, CP 28, G 16, sp, tc, sol,
CF, 1 st. £ BB £11–£22, DB £22–£44, WT
£168–£182, DT £29–£31, DBB £27–£29,
WB, ①, Bk £2-50, L £7, D £7-70, cc 1.
★★**Penhelig Arms**, LL35 0LT.
✆ (065 472) 215. C 10. ➤ 11 bedrs, 4 bp,
7 bps, TV. ✗ mc, at, LD 9.30. ⊡ CH, CP 12.
£ BB £13–£18, DB £26–£36, WT £125–
£159, DBB £18-95–£23-95, WB, ①, Bk
£3-95, D £5-95, cc 1 2 3 5 6, Dep b.
Bodfor, H, x, Bodfor Ter, LL35 0EA.
✆ (065 472) 475.
Cartref, G, x (Unl), LL35 0NR.
✆ (065 472) 273

Rescue Service: Gray, Jones & Sons, The
Garage, A493. ✆ (065 472) 208.

ABERGAVENNY Gwent. Map 13E
Pop 12,000. Ross 22, London 143, Builth
Wells 32, Brecon 20, Chepstow 29,
Hereford 23, Monmouth 15, Newport 18,
Pontypool 10, Tredegar 11.
EC Thur. **MD** Tue, Fri. **Golf**
Monmouthshire 18h. **See** Castle grounds
and Museum, St Mary's Church, Sugar
Loaf Mountain 4 m NW, Llanvihangel
Court 4½ m NW, Raglan Castle 8½ m SE,
Grosmont Castle 9 m NE, Skenfrith Castle
10½ m E, White Castle 5½ m E.
ⓘ 2 Lower Monk St. ✆ Abergavenny
(0873) 3254.

★★**Angel** (TH), Cross St, NP7 5EN.
✆ (0873) 7121. C. ➤ 29 bedrs. 29 bp, Dgs,
TV. ⊡ CH, Dgs, CP 27, Ac, con 200, CF, 2
st. £ BB fr £36-50, DB fr £50-50, WB, ①,
cc 1 2 3 4 5 6, Dep (Xmas).
★★**Llanwenarth Arms**, Brecon Rd,
NP7 7RB. ✆ (0873) 810550.

Ambleside, G, z (Unl), 8 Monmouth Rd,
NP7 5HH. ✆ (0873) 3823. C. ➤ 5 bedrs, 1
ba. ⊡ ch, TV, CP. £ BB fr £7.
Park, G, z (Rl), 36 Hereford Rd, NP7 5RA.
✆ (0873) 3715. C. ➤ 8 bedrs, 2 ba, Dgs.
⊡ CH, TV, Dgs, ns, CP 8, 1 BGf, 2 st. £ BB
£8-50–£9, DB £17–£18, WT (b) £85–£90,
DT (b) £13–£13-50, ①, Bk £2-50, D £4-75.

Rescue Service: Blorenge Motors,
Merthyr Rd, Llanfoist. ✆ (0873) 7213.
Keith Price, T/As Merthyr Road Garage,
Merthyr Rd. ✆ (0873) 5414 & (0873)
2612.
Whittal-Williams Ltd, Park Rd. ✆ (0873)
5916.

ABERGELE Clwyd. Map 18B
Pop 12,315. Mold 24, London 215,
Chester 34, Colwyn Bay 7, Denbigh 8,
Rhyl 5, Queensferry 26.
EC Thur. **MD** Mon. **Golf** Abergele 18h.
See St Michael's Church 1 m W, Gwrych
Castle.

★★**Kinmel Manor**, St Georges Rd, LL22
9AS. ✆ (0745) 822014. C. ➤ 22 bedrs, 19
bp, 1 bps, 1 sh, 1 ba, TV, Dgs. ✗ a l c, mc,
at, LD 10. ⊡ CH, TV, Dgs, CP 100, Ac, sp,
sb, sol, con 250, CF. £ BB £21–£24, DB
£34–£38, WT £203, DT £29, DBB £24–£26,
WB, ①, Bk £3-50, L £5, D £7,
cc 1 2 3 4 5 6

Rescue Service: Belgrano Services,
Belgrano House, Towyn Rd, Belgrano.
✆ (0745) 823225.▲

ABERGYNOLWYN Gwynedd. Map 18F
Newtown 41, London 218, Aberdyfi 11,
Aberystwyth 30, Dolgellau 12.

Dolgoch Falls, H, x (R), Tywyn, LL36
9UW. ✆ (065 477) 258. Open Feb–Nov. C
5. ➤ 6 bedrs, 1 ba, Dgs. ✗ a l c, mc. ⊡ CH, TV,
Dgs, CP 200, 1 st. £ BB £10-25, DB
£20-50, WT (b) £92-75, DT (b) fr £14-75,
①, Bk 4, D £5-75, cc 5.

ABERPORTH Dyfed. Map 11D
Pop 800. Lampeter 27, London 230,
Aberystwyth 33, Cardigan 6½, Carmarthen
26.
EC Wed. **Golf** Cardigan 18h.

★★★**Penrallt**, SA43 2BS. ✆ (0239)
810227. RS Dec 24–Jan 1. C. ➤ 17 bedrs,
13 bp, 4 bps, TV, Dgs. ✗ mc, at, LD 9.
⊡ CH, TV, Dgs, CP 100, CF, 3 st. £ BB £25,
DB £36, WB, ①, Bk £3, cc 1 3 5 6
★★**Highcliffe**, SA43 2DA. ✆ (0239)
810534. RS Oct–Mar. C. ➤ 12 bedrs, 6 bp,
annexe 6 bedrs, 6 bp, TV, Dgs. ✗ mc, at,
LD 9. ⊡ CH, CP 16, CF. £ BB £18,
£32, WT £157–£166, DT £19, DBB £24,
WB, ①, Bk £4-50, L £6, D £6, cc 1 3
★★**M Morlan** (R), SA43 2EN. ✆ (0239)
810611. Open Mar–Oct. C. ➤ 38 bedrs,
14 bp, 24 bps, TV, Dgs. ✗ a l c, mc, at, LD
9. ⊡ CH, CP 46, G 6, Ac, con 40, CF, 13
BGf, 1 st. £ BB £16-20–£17, DB
£26-40–£28, DBB £18-75–£20, WB, ②, Bk
£3-20, L £6, cc 1 2 3 5 6

ABERSOCH Gwynedd. Map 18E
Pop 1,050. Pwllheli 6½, London 247,
Aberdaron 10.
EC Wed. **Golf** Abersoch 9h.

★★★**Abersoch**, LL53 7HR. ✆ (075 881)
2406. C. ➤ 9 bedrs, 5 bp, 2 bps, 1 ba,
annexe 5 bedrs, 3 bp, 2 bps, TV, Dgs.
✗ a l c, mc, at, LD 9.30. ⊡ CH, CP 50, Ac,
con 60, 6 st. £ BB £20–£23-50, DB £40–

£47, DBB £28–£34, WB, ②, Bk £4, L £2-50,
D £11-50, cc 1 2 3 5, Dep a.
♨★★★**Porth Tocyn** (R), Bwlch Tocyn,
LL53 7BU. ✆ (075 881) 2966. Open Mar–
Oct, Xmas, New Year. C 7. ➤ 18 bedrs, 18
bp. ✗ mc, at, LD 9.30. ⊡ CH, TV, CP, sp, tc,
con 30, CF, 3 BGf, 1 st, Dis. £ BB £22–£28,
DB £36–£53, DBB £27-20–£40, WB, ①, Bk
£5, L £6, D £9-20, cc 1 2.
★★★**Riverside** (R), LL53 7HW.
✆ (075 881) 2419. Open Mar–Oct. C.
➤ 12 bedrs, 10 bp, 2 sh, 2 ba, TV. ✗ a l c,
mc, at, LD 8.30. ⊡ CH, TV, CP 25, sp, CF.
£ BB £16-50–£22, DB £33–£44, DBB
£27-50–£33, WB, ②, Bk £4-50, D £11-50,
cc 3 6.
▣♨★★**Deucoch**, LL53 7LD.
✆ (075 881) 2680. C. ➤ 10 bedrs, 3 bp, 6
bps, 2 ba, TV, Dgs. ✗ a l c, mc. ⊡ CH, CP 50,
CF, 1 st. £ BB £14-50–£23, DB £29–£36,
WT £129-50–£157-50, DBB £21–£25, WT,
②, Bk £3, D £7-50, cc 1 2 3 5.
★★**Neigwl** (R), Sarn Rd, LL53 7DY.
✆ (075 881) 2363. C. ➤ 11 bedrs, 2 bp, 1
bps, 2 ba, TV. ✗ mc, at, LD 10. ⊡ CH, TV,
CP 30, U 2, G 1, Ac, CF, 4 BGf, Dis. £ BB
£16-18, DB £24–£36, DBB £20–£26, ②,
Bk £4, L £4, D £8-50, cc 1 2 3, Dep a.
★★**White House**, LL53 7AG.
✆ (075 881) 2136. Open Mar–Oct. C.
➤ 16 bedrs, 9 bp, 3 ba, TV, Dgs. ✗ mc, LD
9.30. ⊡ ch, TV, Dgs, CP 200, CF, 3 st. £ BB
£12-50–£18, DB £31–£36, ①, Bk £4, L £2,
D £7-50, cc 1 2 3 4 5. Dep a.
Llysfor, G, xy (Rl), LL53 7AL.
✆ (075 881) 2248. Open April–Oct. C.
➤ 8 bedrs, 1 bp, 2 ba, Dgs. ⊡ CH, TV, CP
12, CF. £ BB £9–£10, DB £18–£22, WT (b)
£94–£100, (c) £63–£70, DT (b) £13-50–
£15, ①, Bk £2-50, D £5, cc 5.

ABERTILLERY Gwent. Map 12F
Pop 20,000. Pontypool 9, London 152,
Abergavenny 13, Brecon 22, Caerphilly 14,
Newport 16, Pontypridd 18, Tredegar 9.
EC Wed. **MD** Thur, Sat. **Golf** West
Monmouthshire 18h. **See** St Illtyd's
Church, Castel Taliorum (ancient mound).

Rescue Service: Park Garage, Llwynon
Rd, Six Bells. ✆ (0495) 213232.

ABERYSTWYTH Dyfed. Map 12A
Pop 15,300. Rhayader 34, London 211,
Aberdyfi 28, Bala 47, Cardigan 38,
Dolgellau 33, Lampeter 24, Newtown 43.
EC Wed. **MD** Mon. **Golf** Aberystwyth
18h. **See** Castle ruins and Gorsedd Circle,
National Library of Wales, University
College of Wales, Plant Breeding Station,
Vale of Rheidol Narrow Gauge Rly to
Devil's Bridge, Nanteds Mansion.
ⓘ Eastgate. ✆ Aberystwyth (0970)
612125.

♨★★★**Conrah** (R), Chancery, Llanfarian,
SY23 4DF. ✆ (0970) 617041. Closed Dec
24–Jan 2, C5. ➤ 13 bedrs, 10 bp, 2 ba, TV.
✗ mc, at, LD 9. ⊡ Lt, CH, CP 60, sp, sb,
con 50, 2 st. £ BB £26–£32, DB £40–£52,
DBB £189, WT, ②, Bk £4, L £6-50, D £9,
cc 1 2 3 5 6.
★★**Belle Vue Royal**, Marine Ter, SY23
2BA. ✆ (0970) 617558. C. ➤ 42 bedrs, 11
bp, 10 ba, TV, Dgs. ✗ a l c, mc, LD 9. ⊡ N,
CH, TV, Dgs, CP 7, G 9, Ac, con, CF, 1 BGf,
4 st. £ BB £16-10–£21-85, DB £29-90–
£35-65, WT £152-95–£175-09, DBB
£19-55–£25-01, WB, ②, Bk £3, L £5-25, D
£7-75, cc 1 2 3 5.
★★**Groves** (R), North Par, SY23 2NF.
✆ (0970) 617623. Closed Xmas & New

Year. C 3. ⊯ 12 bedrs, 5 bp, 7 bps, TV.
✗ mc, LD 8.30. 🅿 CH, CP 8, 1 st. £ BB
£18, DB £28·50, WB, ⊉, Bk £3·50, D £5·75,
cc 1 2 3.

■★★**Marine,** *Marine Ter, SY23 2DA.*
☎ (0970) 612444.

★★**Sea Bank,** *Victoria Ter, SY23 2DH.*
☎ (0970) 617617. C. ⊯ 28 bedrs, 12 bp, 4
bps, 3 ba, TV, Dgs. ✗ mc, at, LD 8. 🅿 Lt,
CH, Dgs, U 1, G 1, Ac, CF. £ BB £14–£18,
DB £23–£28, WT £143–£145, DBB £20–
£24, ⊉, Bk £2·75, L £4·60, D £6,
cc 1 2 3 5 6.

★**Cambrian,** *Alexandra Rd, SY23 1LG.*
☎ (0970) 612446. C. ⊯ 15 bedrs, 2 bp, 5
bps, 3 ba, TV, Dgs. ✗ a l c, mc, LD 9. 🅿 CH,
Dgs, con 20, CF, 3 st. £ BB £12–£14, DB
£22–£26, WT £140–£160, DT £20–£25,
DBB £16·75–£18·75, WB, ⊉, Bk £2·50, L
£4·25, D £4·75, cc 1 3, Dep.

★**Four Seasons** (R), *50 Portland St, SY23
2DX.* ☎ (0970) 612120. Closed 24 Dec–3
Jan. C. ⊯ 16 bedrs, 6 bp, 3 ba. ✗ mc, at,
LD 8.30. 🅿 CH, TV, CP 12, Ac, 2 st. £ BB
£14–£18·50, DB £24–£31, WB, ⊉, Bk £3, L
£5·75, D £6·75, cc 1 3.

Glyn Garth, G, z (R), *South Rd, SY23
1JS.* ☎ (0970) 615050. Closed 2 weeks
Xmas. C 7. ⊯ 10 bedrs, 4 bp, 2 bps, 1 ba.
🅿 CH, TV. £ BB £8·50–£10, DB £17–£30,
WT (c) £50–£100, DT (b) £14–£22, ⊡, Bk
£3·50, D £6·50.

Savannah, G, z, *27 Queen's Rd,
SY23 2HN.* ☎ (0970) 615377. Closed
Xmas Day. C. ⊯ 5 bedrs, 2 ba. 🅿 CH, TV,
Dgs, 6 st. £ BB £7, DB £14, WT (b) £73·50,
DT (b) £10·50, ⊡.

Swn-y-Don, G, z (Rl), *40 North Par,
SY23 2NF.* ☎ (0970) 612647. C. ⊯ 25
bedrs, 25 bps, 4 ba. 🅿 CH, TV, Dgs,
ns, CP 7, 2 st. £ BB £11·50–£12·50, DB
£23–£25, WT (b) £109–£112·70, ⊡.

Windsor, PH, z (Unl), *41 Queen's Rd,
SY23 2HN.* ☎ (0970) 612134. C. ⊯ 10
bedrs, 3 sh, 2 ba. 🅿 CH, TV. £ BB £7–£8,
DB £14–£16, WT (b) £70–£77, DT (b) fr
£10·75, ⊡.

Rescue Service: Evans Bros, Royal Oak
Garage, Llanfarian. ☎ (0970) 612311.

AMLWCH Gwynedd. Map 18A
Pop 4,000. Bangor 19, London 256,
Caernarfon 25, Holyhead 20.
EC Wed. **MD** Fri. **Golf** Bull Bay 18h. **See**
Harbour cut out of solid rock, Church of
Our Lady, fine cliffs.

★★**Trecastell,** *Bull Bay, LL68 9SA.*
☎ (0407) 830651. C. ⊯ 12 bedrs, 8 bp, 2
bps, 2 ba, Dgs. ✗ mc, LD 8. 🅿 CH, TV, CP
60, Ac, gc, CF, 3 st. £ BB £14–£16, DB
£24–£28, ⊡, Bk £3·50, D £6·50, cc 1 2 3.

AMMANFORD Dyfed. Map 12E
Pop 5,795. Neath 15, London 198,
Carmarthen 17, Lampeter 20, Llandovery
20, Llanelli 13, Swansea 16.
EC Thur. **MD** Fri. **Golf** Glynhir (Llandeilo)
18h.

★★**The Mill at Glynhir** (R), *Llandybie,
SA18 2TE.* ☎ Llandybie (0269) 850672. C
11. ⊯ 7 bedrs, 4 bp, 3 bps, annexe 2 bedrs,
1 bp, 1 bps, TV, Dgs. ✗ a l c, mc, at, LD 9.
🅿 CH, CP 20, sp, gc, pf, con 17. £ BB £21,
DB £42, WT £131–£175, WB, ⊉, Bk £4, L
£6·50, D £9·50, Dep a.

Rescue Service: Brooklands Garage, 209
Cwmamman Rd, Garnant. ☎ Amman Valley
(0269) 825246.

BALA Gwynedd. Map 18D
Pop 1,850. Shrewsbury 44, London 199,
Aberdyfi 29, Betws-y-Coed 23,
Caernarfon 46, Corwen 11, Dolgellau 18,
Porthmadog 29, Welshpool 33.
EC Wed. **MD** Thur. **Golf** Bala Lakeside 9h.
See Bala Lake, Gorsedd Circle on Bala
Green.
🎫 Snowdonia Nat. Park, High St. ☎ Bala
(0678) 520367.

★★★**White Lion Royal,** *High St, LL23
7AE.* ☎ (0678) 520314. C. ⊯ 22 bedrs, 22
bp, TV, Dgs. ✗ mc, at, LD 8.30. 🅿 ch, TV,
Dgs, CP 40, Ac, con 60, CF, 1 st. £ BB fr
£22, DB fr £30, WB, ⊉ 10%, Bk £3·30, L
£4·50, D £6·60, cc 1 3 4 5 6.

★★**M Bala Lake** (R), *LL23 7BS.* ☎ (0678)
520344. C. ⊯ 13 bedrs, 1 bp, 12 bps, TV,
Dgs. ✗ mc, at, LD 8.30. 🅿 CH, TV, 40, G
10, sp, gc, CF, 6 BGf, 1 st, Dis. £ BB
£18·50–£20, DB £28·50–£32·50, DBB
£25–£26·50, ⊡, Bk £3·50, L £6, D £6·50,
cc 1 3, Dep a.

★★**Plas Coch,** *High St, LL23 7AB.*
☎ (0678) 520309. Closed Xmas. C. ⊯ 10
bedrs, 2 bp, 6 sh, 3 ba, Dgs. ✗ a l c, mc, LD
9. 🅿 CH, TV, CP 20, CF, 0 st. £ BB £14–
£17·50, DB £23–£29·20, WT £104–£113,
DBB £17·45–£20·55, WB, ⊡, Bk £3, L
£3·50, D £5·95, cc 1 2 3 5, Dep.

Fronderw, PH, y (R), *Stryd y Fron,
LL23 7YD.* ☎ (0678) 520301. Closed
Xmas. C. ⊯ 8 bedrs, 1 bp, 1 bps, 2 sh, 2 ba.
✗ a l c. 🅿 ch, TV, CP 10, CF, 1 BGf, 1 st.
£ BB fr £9·50, DB fr £19, WT (b) fr
£104·65, (c) fr £66·15, DT (b) fr £15, ⊡, D
£5·50, cc 1 4.

Plas Teg, G, x (Rl), *45 Tegid St,
LL23 7EN.* ☎ (0678) 520268. C. ⊯ 8
bedrs, 2 ba. 🅿 CH, TV, ns, CP 12, CF, 1 st.
£ BB £8·25, DB £16·50, WT (c) £85, DT fr
£8·25, ⊡, Bk £3·50, D £5·95.

Rescue Service: Williams, E & Sons, The
Garage. ☎ (0678) 520777.

BANGOR Gwynedd. Map 18C
Pop 14,558. Betws-y-Coed 20, London
237, Caernarfon 9, Colwyn Bay 20,
Holyhead 23, Llandudno 20.
EC Wed. **MD** Fri, Sat. **Golf** St Deiniol,
Bangor 18h. **See** Cathedral, University
College of N Wales, Art Gallery, Museum,
Menai Suspension Bridge, Penrhyn Castle
1 m E.
🎫 Garth Rd. ☎ Bangor (0248) 52786.

★★★**British,** *High St, LL57 1NP.*
☎ (0248) 4911. C. ⊯ 53 bedrs, 53 bp, 4
ba, TV. ✗ a l c, mc, LD 9. 🅿 Lt, N, CH, TV,
CP 50, U 2, Ac, con 150, CF, 0 st. £ BB £15,
DB £30, DT £23, DBB £20, WB, ⊡, Bk
£2·50, L £3·50, D £5, cc 1 6.

★★**Castle,** *High St, LL57 1NV.* ☎ (0248)
353441. C. ⊯ 43 bedrs, 2 bp, 7 bps, 5 sh, 6
ba, TV, Dgs. ✗ a l c, mc, at, LD 9. 🅿 Lt, N,
CH, TV, Dgs, CP 30, Ac, sb, sol, con 50, CF,
1 st. £ BB £12·50–£18·50, DB £25–£32·50,
WT £145, DT £21, DBB £17·50–£23·50,
WB, ⊉, Bk £3, L £3·50, D £5, cc 1 2 3 5 6.

★★**Telford** (R), *Holyhead Rd.* ☎ (0248)
52543.

★★**Ty Uchaf,** *Talybont, LL57 3UR.*
☎ (0248) 352219. C 10. ⊯ 10 bedrs, 7 bp,
3 bps, TV. ✗ a l c, mc, at, LD 9. 🅿 CH, TV,
CP 40, Ac, 1 st. £ BB £15–£16, DB £26, DT
£25, DBB £21, WB, ⊉, Bk £3, L £4, D £6,
cc 1 3 6, Dep b.

Rescue Service: City Motorcycles, Cyttir
La. ☎ (0248) 52085.

Elias Garage Ltd, 347 High St. ☎ (0248)
364452.
Pandy Motors, Tregarth. ☎ Bethesda
(0248) 600619.

BARGOED Mid Glamorgan. Map 12F.
Pop 9,687. Newport 16, London 153,
Caerphilly 9, Merthyr Tydfil 12, Pontypool
13, Pontypridd 11.
EC Wed. **MD** Thur. **Golf** Bargoed 18h.
See Crystal Factory.

Rescue Service: C Price Motor Engineers,
Station Garage, Station Rd. ☎ (0443)
832067 & (0443) 836468.

BARMOUTH Gwynedd. Map 18E
Pop 2,200. Dolgellau 10, London 216,
Betws-y-Coed 35, Caernarfon 37,
Porthmadog 20.
EC Wed. **MD** Thur. **Golf** Royal St David's
18h. **See** St John's Church, Guild of St
George Cottages, Dinas Oleu, Llanaber
Church (1¾ m), Bontddu Gold Mines.
🎫 Old Library. ☎ Barmouth (0341)
280787.

★★**Cors-y-Gedol,** *LL42 1DP.* ☎ (0341)
280402. C. ⊯ 30 bedrs, 11 bp, 5 ba, ns, TV,
Dgs. ✗ a l c, mc, at, LD 9. 🅿 Lt, CH, TV,
Dgs, CP 20, Ac, sb, sol, con 70, CF, 1 st.
£ BB £17–£26, DB £31–£42·50, WT £172–
£179, DT £31–£35·50, DBB £24·50–£35,
WB, ⊡, Bk £4·74, L £6·50, D £9,
cc 1 2 3 5 6.

■★★**Royal,** *King Edward St, LL42 1AB.*
☎ (0341) 280383. Open Apr–Oct. C. ⊯ 16
bedrs, 2 bp, 14 bps, 1 ba, TV. ✗ a l c, mc, at,
LD 8.30. 🅿 ch, TV, CP 22, Ac, con 35, CF, 0
st. £ BB £17·50–£18·50, DB £25–£33·50,
DBB £33–£38·50, WB, ⊉, Bk £2·75, L
£4·75, D £8, cc 1 3, Dep a.

★**Bryn Melyn** (R), *Panorama Rd,
LL42 1DQ.* ☎ (0341) 280556. Open Mar–
Nov. C. ⊯ 9 bedrs, 8 bps. ✗ mc,
LD 8.30. 🅿 CH, TV, CP 7, CF, 3 st. £ BB
£15, DB £24, WT £103–£115, DBB £18·50,
WB, ⊡, Bk £2·50, L £4·50, D £6·50, cc 1,
Dep a.

★**Marwyn** (R), *21 Marine Par, LL42 1NA.*
☎ (0341) 280185. Open Feb–Nov. RS
Feb–Mar & Oct–Nov. C 7. ⊯ 7 bedrs, 3 bp,
4 bps, TV. ✗ a l c, mc, at, LD 9. 🅿 CH, TV,
ns, U 2, 0 st. £ BB £13·50–£14·50, DB £41–
£47, DBB £133–£154, WB, ⊡, Bk £3·50, L
£4·50, D £7·50, cc 1 3.

★**Min-y-Mor,** *Promenade, LL42 1HW.*
☎ (0341) 280555. Open Apr–Oct. C. ⊯ 50
bedrs, 6 bp, 5 bps, 8 ba. ✗ mc, at, LD 7.30.
🅿 ch, TV, CP, Ac, con, CF, 9 BGf, 0 st, Dis.
£ BB £10·50, DB £21–£25, WT £105·50,
DBB £15·50–£17·50, ⊡, Bk £2·50, L £4, D
£5, cc 1 3.

★**Ty'r Craig Castle** (R), *Llanaber Rd,
LL42 1YN.* ☎ (0341) 280470. Open Mar–
Oct. C. ⊯ 12 bedrs, 2 bp, 6 bps, 1 sh, 2 ba,
TV. ✗ a l c, mc, at, LD 8. 🅿 CH, CP 15, CF,
1 st. £ DB £24–£29, WT £124, DBB
£18·50–£21, WB, ⊉, Bk £2·50, L £6·50, D
£6·50, Dep a.

Morwendon, G, xy (R), *Llanaber, LL42
1RR.* ☎ (0341) 280566. C 5. ⊯ 7 bedrs, 3
sh, 1 ba. 🅿 CH, TV, CP 10, BB £8–£9·25, DB
£16–£18·50, WT (b) £87·50–£95, DT £13–
£14, ⊡, Bk £2·50, D £5·50.

Repairers: Birmingham Garage. ☎ (0341)
280644.
Bradbury's Garage, Park Rd. ☎ (0341)
280448.

BARRY South Glamorgan. Map 4B
Pop 44,671. Cardiff 9½, London 159,
Bridgend 17.
EC Wed. **Golf** Brynhill 18h. **See** Castle
ruins, largest dry dock in Wales, Zoo.
🛈 Barry Island. ✆ Barry (0446) 747171.

★★★**M International,** *Port Rd, Rhoose,*
CF6 9BT. ✆ (0446) 710787. C. ⇆ 32
bedrs, 32 bp, TV, Dgs. ✗ a l c, mc, at, LD
10.30. 🅿 N, CH, TV, CP 200, Ac, con 120,
CF, 12 BGf, 0 st, Dis. **£** BB £26·95–£27·95,
DB £33·95–£34·95, WB, 🛈, Bk £3·50, L
£2·50, D £9, cc 1 2 3 5 6, Dep b.
★★★**Mount Sorrel,** *Porthkerry Rd, CF6*
8XY. ✆ (0446) 740069. C. ⇆ 33 bedrs, 16
bp, 17 bps, annexe 4 bedrs, 4 bp, TV, Dgs.
✗ a l c, mc, LD 10. 🅿 N, CH, TV, Dgs, CP
17, Ac, con 50, CF, 6 BGf, 4 st. **£** BB £24–
£26, DB £32–£35, WT £168–£188, DT
£28–£32, DBB £24–£28, WB, 🗷, Bk £3·50,
L £3·80, D £7·50, cc 1 2 3 4 5 6, Dep b.
Aberthaw House, H (R), *Porthkerry Rd,*
CF6 8AX. ✆ (0446) 737314. Closed
Xmas. C. ⇆ 9 bedrs, 5 sh, 2 ba, TV, Dgs.
✗ a l c. 🅿 CH, CF. **£** BB fr £15·50, DB fr
£25, WB 🗷 10%, Bk £1·75, D £4·50.
May Tree, G, z (Rt), *9 The Parade, CF6*
8SD. ✆ (0446) 734075. Closed Xmas
week. C. ⇆ 15 bedrs, 2 bps, 4 ba, Dgs.
🅿 CH, TV, Dgs, ns, CP 4, 1 BGf, 3 st. **£** BB
£10·35–£12·25, DB £17·25–£21·27, WT
(c) £72–£75, 🛈.
Sheridan, G, z (Unl), *11 The Parade, CF6*
8SD. ✆ (0446) 738488.
Windsor Lodge, G, z (Rl), *1 Windsor Rd,*
CF6 8SD. ✆ (0446) 736915.

Rescue Service: Griff's Garage, Robbins
La, Cadoxton. ✆ (0446) 734459.
Hind's Garages Ltd, Dock View Rd.
✆ (0446) 732699.
Redrup Motors (Barry) Ltd, Cardiff Rd,
Cadoxton. ✆ (0446) 735340.
Tanner Electrics, 59 Broad St. ✆ (0446)
732138 & 730548.

BEAUFORT Gwent. Map Area 12F
Abergavenny 9, London 152, Ebbw Vale 2,
Merthyr Tydfil 9.

Rescue Service: Carno Garage, Reservoir
Rd. ✆ Ebbw Vale (0495) 301366.

BEAUMARIS Gwynedd. Map 18A
Pop 2,500. Bangor 7, London 244,
Caernarfon 12, Holyhead 22.
EC Wed. **Golf** Baron Hill 18h. **See** 13th
cent Castle ruins, 14th cent Church, 17th
cent Old Bull's Head, 17th cent Town Hall,
The Old Gaol and Courthouse.

★★★**Bulkeley Arms,** *Castle St, LL58*
8AW. ✆ (0248) 810415. C. ⇆ 43 bedrs,
19 bp, 7 ba, TV, Dgs. ✗ mc, at, LD 9. 🅿 Lt,
CH, Dgs, CP 21, Ac, con 150, CF, 3 st. **£** BB
£12–£29, DB £44–£55, WT £180–£260, DT
£27·50–£38·50, DBB £21·50–£32·50, WB,
🗷, Bk £3·50, L £6, D £8·50, cc 1 2 3 5 6.
★★**Bishopsgate** (Rl), *Castle St, LL58*
8AB. ✆ (0248) 810302. Open Apr–Oct.
C 5. ⇆ 11 bedrs, 6 bps, 1 sh, 2 ba, TV, Dgs.
✗ a l c, mc, LD 9. 🅿 CP 10, 2 st. **£** BB
£13·50–£14·50, DB £27–£32, 🗷, Bk £3·50,
L £4·95, D £7·50, cc 1 3 6.
Sea View, G, x (Unl), *West End, LL58*
8BG. ✆ (0248) 810384. Closed Xmas.
C 10. ⇆ 5 bedrs, 1 ba. 🅿 ch, TV, CP 5.
£ BB £9–£10, DB £16, DT (b) £13, 🛈.

BEDDGELERT Gwynedd. Map 18C
Pop 320. Bala 30, London 230, Betws-y-
Coed 17, Caernarfon 12, Dolgellau 27,
Porthmadog 8, Pwllheli 19.
EC Wed. **Golf** Porthmadog 18h. **See** 6th
cent Priory Church, "Gelert's Grave",
Aberglaslyn Pass, Gwynant Valley,
Snowdon, Gwynant and Dinas Lakes.

★★★**Royal Goat,** *LL55 4YE.*
✆ Porthmadog (0766) 224.
★**Tanronen,** *LL55 4YB.* ✆ (076 686)
3471. C. ⇆ 9 bedrs, 2 ba, TV. ✗ a l c, mc,
at, LD 9. 🅿 CH, TV, CP 12, U 3, CF, 1 st.
£ BB £11·50, DB £23, WT £106·50, DBB
£17·75, WB, 🛈, L £3·75, D £6·75, cc 1 3.
Sygun Fawr Country House, PH, xy
(R), *LL55 4NE.* ✆ (076 686) 258.

BEDWAS Gwent. Map Area 4B
Newport 10, London 147, Cardiff 10,
Merthyr Tydfil 17, Pontypool 17, Swansea
44.
Rescue Service: John Paul Motors Ltd, 31
Newport Rd. ✆ Caerphilly (0222) 885205.

BELGRANO Clwyd.
See ABERGELE.

BENLLECH BAY Gwynedd. Map 18A
Pop 3,500. Bangor 10, London 248,
Caernarfon 16, Holyhead 20.
EC Thur. **Golf** Bull Bay 18h. **See** Roman
Village.

★★**Bay Court,** *Beach Rd, LL74 8SW.*
✆ Tynygongl (0248) 852573. C. ⇆ 18
bedrs, 2 bp, 3 ba, annexe 5 bedrs, 5 bp,
Dgs. ✗ a l c, mc, at, LD 9.30. 🅿 N, CH, TV,
CP 65, Ac, CF, 5 BGf, 2 st. **£** BB £12–£15,
DB £24–£30, WB, 🛈, Bk £3·50, L £3·50, D
£5·50, cc 1 2 3, Dep.
★★**Glanrafon,** *LL74 8TF.* ✆ Tynygongl
(0248) 852364. Open Apr–Oct. RS Xmas
& New Year. C. ⇆ 19 bedrs, 12 bp, 2 ba.
✗ mc, LD 9. 🅿 CH, TV, Dgs, CP 100, Ac,
con 100, CF. **£** BB £11·50–£17·50, DB
£23–£29, WT £110–£133, DBB £16·50–
£20, WB, 🛈, Bk £3, D £7, cc 1 3.

BETWS-Y-COED Gwynedd. Map 18D
Pop 7,000. Corwen 22, London 216, Bala
22, Bangor 20, Caernarfon 23, Conway Bay
17, Denbigh 23, Dolgellau 32, Llandudno
17, Porthmadog 23, Rhyl 25, Ruthin 25.
EC Thur. **Golf** Betws-y-Coed 9h. **See** Old
Church, Pont-y-Pair Bridge, Conwy Falls,
Swallow Falls, Dolwyddelan Castle 5 m
SW, Railway Museum.
🛈 ✆ Betws-y-Coed (069 02) 426.

🏕★★★**Plas Hall** (R), *Pont-y-Coed, LL25*
0PJ. ✆ (069 06) 206. C. ⇆ 16 bedrs, 15
bp, 1 bps, TV. ✗ mc, at, LD 9. 🅿 CH, CP 50,
Ac, pf, con 25, CF, 4 BGf, 0 st, Dis. **£** BB
£17–£25, DB £29–£42, WB, 🛈, Bk £3, L
£5·50, D £7·50, cc 1 2 3 5 6.
🏕★★★**Royal Oak,** *LL24 0AY.*
✆ (009 02) 219. C. ⇆ 29 bedrs, 21 bp, 1
ba, TV. ✗ a l c, mc, at, LD 9. 🅿 CH, CP 200,
Ac, con 20, CF, 0 st. **£** BB £25–£30, DB
£36–£40, WT £160–£240, DBB £25–£28,
🗷, Bk £3, L £4·50, D £7, cc 1 2 3 5 6,
Dep a.
★★★**M Waterloo,** *LL24 0AR.*
✆ (069 02) 411.
🏕★★★**Craig-y-Dderwen** (R), *LL24 0AS.*
✆ (069 02) 293. Closed Xmas. C. ⇆ 22
bedrs, 11 bp, 6 bps, 3 ba, TV, Dgs. ✗ a l c,
mc, at, LD 8.30. 🅿 CH, CP 50, pf, con, CF, 1
BGf, 4 st. **£** BB £13·50–£19·50, DB £26–
£39, WT £160, WB, 🗷, Bk £3, L £5·50, D
£7·50, cc 1 2 3 4 5 6, Dep a.

★★**Gwydyr,** *LL24 0AB.* ✆ (069 02) 217.
★**Park Hill** (R), *Llanrwst Rd, LL24 0HD.*
✆ (069 02) 540. Closed Jan & 2 weeks
Oct. C 6. ⇆ 11 bedrs, 6 bp, 2 bps, 1 sh, 1
ba, Dgs. ✗ mc, at, LD 7.30. 🅿 CH, TV, CP
12, sp, sb. **£** BB £14–£15, DB £30–£32,
DBB £20·50–£22·50, WB, 🗷, Bk £3·50, L
£3, D £7, cc 1 2 3.
★**Fairy Glen** (R), *Fairy Glen, LL24 0SH.*
✆ (069 02) 269. Closed Xmas. C. ⇆ 10
bedrs, 5 bp, 3 ba, Dgs. ✗ mc, at, LD 7.30.
🅿 CP 13, CF, 1 st. **£** BB £12–£16·50, DB
£24–£33, WT £125–£135, DT £21–£23,
DBB £18–£22, WB, 🛈, Bk £3, L £3·50, D
£6·50, cc 2 ▲.
Bod Hyfryd, G, x (Unl), *Holyhead Rd,*
LL24 0BN. ✆ (069 02) 220. C. ⇆ 7 bedrs,
2 ba, Dgs. 🅿 CH, TV, Dgs, ns, CP 4, CF, 6 st.
£ BB £6·50–£8, DB £13–£14, WT £42–£52,
DT £9·50–£12·50, 🛈.
Hafan, G, xy (Rl), *LL24 0BL.* ✆ (069 02)
233. Closed Xmas. C 3. ⇆ 7 bedrs, 1 bp, 4
bps, 2 sh, 2 ba, TV, Dgs. 🅿 ch, TV, CP 10.
£ DB fr £20, 🛈.
Mount Garmon, PH, x (Rl) *Mount*
Garmon, LL24 0AN. ✆ (069 02) 335.
Closed Dec. C 5. ⇆ 5 bedrs, 3 bps, 1 ba.
🅿 CH, TV, CP 5, 5 st. **£** BB £12–£17·50, DB
£18–£25, WT £100–£125, DT £15–£18·50,
🛈, Bk £3·50, D £6.

Rescue Service: Betws-y-Coed Motors,
Service Garage. ✆ (069 02) 303.

BIRCHGROVE West Glamorgan. Map
Area 12E
Neath 3½, London 188, Carmarthen 28,
Swansea 5.

Rescue Service: Birchgrove MOT Centre
Ltd, Birchgrove Rd. ✆ Swansea (0792)
812359.

BLACKWOOD Gwent. Map 12F
Pop 7,000. Newport 13, London 150,
Caerphilly 8, Hirwaun 19, Merthyr Tydfil
15, Pontypool 9, Pontypridd 12, Tredegar
8½.
EC Thur. **MD** Fri, Sat. **Golf** Blackwood 9h.
See St Margaret's Church.

★★★**Maes Manor,** *Maesruddud La, NP2*
0AG. ✆ (0495) 224551. C. ⇆ 10 bedrs, 7
bp, 2 ba, annexe 13 bedrs, 10 bp, 3 sh, 1 ba,
TV, Dgs. ✗ a l c, mc, at, LD 9. 🅿 N, CH, TV,
Dgs, CP 150, Ac, con 250, CF, 5 BGf, 0 st,
Dis. **£** BB £25–£27, DB £40–£42, WT £299,
DT £39·50, DBB £32·50, WB, 🛈, Bk £3, L
£7, D £7·50, cc 1 2 3 5 6, Dep b.

BLAENAU FFESTINIOG Gwynedd. Map
18D
Pop 5,700. Bala 21, London 220, Betws-y-
Coed 11, Caernarfon 26, Denbigh 33,
Dolgellau 21, Porthmadog 12, Ruthin 36.
EC Thur. **Golf** Ffestiniog 9h. **See**
Llechwedd Slate Caverns, Cymerau Falls
and Old Bridge 2 m SW, Tanygrisiau Hydro
Electric Power Stn, Stwlan Dam, Rhaeadr-
y-Cwm, 300 ft fall and viewpoint,
Ffestiniog Railway.
🛈 Snowdonia National Park, High St.
✆ Blaenau Ffestiniog (076 681) 360.

Rescue Service: Cambrian Motor Co.
✆ (076 681) 211.
Gwynedd A Evans, Gwylfa Garage.
✆ (076 681) 588.

BODEDERN Gwynedd Map 18A
Bangor 20, London 257, Caernarfon 26,
Holyhead 7.

Crown, I, x. ☎ Valley (0407) 740734. C. ☛ 5 bedrs, 1 ba, Dgs. 🅿 CH, Dgs, CP 80, 1 st. £ BB £7, DB £14, WT (c) £49, Ⅰ

BONTDDU Gwynedd. Map 18F
Pop 200. Dolgellau 5, London 212, Betws-y-Coed 34, Caernarfon 42, Porthmadog 25.
EC Sat. **Golf** Royal St David's, Harlech 18h. **See** Old Gold-mine, Waterfalls.

★★★★Bontddu Hall, *LL40 2UF.* ☎ (034 149) 661. Open Apr–Oct. C 3. ☛ 16 bedrs, 12 bp, 4 bps, annexe 8 bedrs, 8 bp, TV, Dgs. ✗ mc, a, LD 9.15. 🅿 ch, CP 50, con 30, CF, 1 BGf, 1 st, Dis. £ BB £23·50–£36·50, DB £47–£53, WT £290–£315, DT £41–£45, DBB £36·50–£39·50, ②. Bk £3·50, L £4·75, D £12·95, cc 1 2 3 5 6.

BONTNEWYDD Gwynedd. Map 18C
Porthmadog 17, London 245, Betws-y-Coed 23, Caernarfon 2, Pwllheli 19.
Golf Caernarfon 18h.

Dwynfa, PH, xy (Unl), *LL54 7YH.* ☎ Llanwnda (0286) 830414.

BRECON Powys. Map 12D
See also LIBANUS
Pop 7,000. Abergavenny 20, London 163, Builth Wells 16, Hereford 36, Hirwaun 19, Leominster 37, Llandovery 21, Llanelli 47, Merthyr Tydfil 18, Neath 34, Swansea 39, Tredegar 19.
EC Wed. **MD** Tue, Fri. **Golf** Brecon 9h & 18h. **See** Cathedral (orig Priory Church), Norman castle remains, County Museum, Regimental Museum, Siddons Arms (birthplace of Sarah Siddons), Shire Hall, RC Church, 13th cent Church, Christ College, Brecon Beacons.
🅸 Brecon Beacons National Park. ☎ Brecon (0874) 4437.

★★Castle of Brecon, *The Avenue, LD3 9DB.* ☎ (0874) 2551. C. ☛ 20 bedrs, 7 bp, 2 sh, 4 ba, annexe 12 bedrs, 12 bps, TV. ✗ mc, LD 8.45. 🅿 N, ch, TV, ns, CP 70, Ac, con 200, CF, 6 BGf, 0 st, Dis. £ BB £15·50–£18·50, DB £28·50–£34·50, WB, ②. Bk £3, L £4·50, D £6·95, cc 1 2 3 5 6, Dep a.▲

★★Nant Ddu Lodge, *Cantref Cwm Taf, Storey Arms, CF48 2HY.* ☎ (0685) 7911. C. ☛ 8 bedrs, 3 bp, 5 bps, TV, Dgs. ✗ a l c, mc, at, LD 9. 🅿 N, CH, TV, Dgs, CP 50, Ac, con 100, CF, 0 st. £ BB £22–£30, DB £27–£36, WT £110–£150, WB, Ⅰ. Bk £2·50, L £2·50, D £2·50, cc 1 3 4 6.

★★Nythfa House, *LD3 7NG.* ☎ (0874) 4287. C. ☛ 8 bedrs, 8 bp, annexe 9 bedrs, 9 bp, TV, Dgs. ✗ mc, at, LD 9.30. 🅿 N, ch, TV, CP 60, sc, CF, 2 BGf, 2 st. £ BB £19–£22, DB £29–£34, WT £201·50–£219·50, DT £31·50–£34·50, DBB £26–£29, Ⅰ, Bk £2·50, L £4, D £7·50, cc 1 3.

Rescue Service: Bronllys Motors, Bronllys. ☎ Talgarth (0874) 711268.

BRIDGEND Mid Glamorgan. Map 4B
Pop 28,000. Cardiff 19, London 169, Hirwaun 25, Neath 17, Pontypridd 17, Swansea 20.
EC Wed. **Golf** Southerndown 18h. **See** 15th cent cottages (once hospice of Knights of St John of Jerusalem), Ewenny Priory 1½ m S, Old Bridge, Norman Gateway, Coity Castle ruins 2 m.

Rescue Service: Cambrian Car Care Ltd, Australian Terrace, off Cemetery Rd. ☎ (0656) 57191.

Glazing Services (Cabs) Ltd, North Rd, Industrial Estate. ☎ (0656) 56735.
Valeford Motor Co Ltd, Cowbridge Rd. ☎ (0656) 4281.

BROAD HAVEN Dyfed. Map 11E
Pop 600. Haverfordwest 7, London 250, Pembroke 13, St David's 6.
EC Mon. **Golf** Haverfordwest 9h, Milford Haven 18h.
🅸 Pembrokeshire Coast Nat. Park. ☎ Broad Haven (043 783) 412.

Broadhaven, H, x, *SA62 3JN.* ☎ (043 783) 366. Open Feb–Nov. C. ☛ 38 bedrs, 3 bp, 3 bps, 1 ba, TV, Dgs. 🅿 ch, TV, Dgs, CP 100, CF, 0 st. £ BB £9–£14, DB £20–£28, WT (b) £98–£127, DT (b) £16–£21, Ⅰ, Bk £2·85, D £6, cc 1 5.

BRONANT Dyfed. Map 12A
Rhayader 28, London 202, Aberystwyth 11, Lampeter 15.

Rescue Service: Bronant Service Station. ☎ (097 421) 221.

BUILTH WELLS Powys. Map 12D
Pop 1,500. Ross-on-Wye 49, London 171, Abergavenny 33, Brecon 16, Hereford 40, Knighton 23, Leominster 34, Llandovery 24, Ludlow 37, Newtown 34, Rhayader 13, Tredegar 34.
EC Wed. **MD** Mon. **Golf** Builth Wells 9h. **See** 12th cent Cistercian Abbey, Telford's iron bridge, Wyeside Arts Centre Complex.
🅸 Groe Car Park. ☎ Builth Wells (0982) 553307.

★★Lion, *2 Broad St, LD2 3DT.* ☎ (0982) 553670. C. ☛ 16 bedrs, 8 bp, 2 bps, 2 sh, 4 ba, TV, Dgs. ✗ a l c, mc, at, LD 9. 🅿 CH, TV, Dgs, CP 14, U 3, G 3, Ac, con 60, CF, 0 st. £ BB £10·50–£15, DB £27–£30, WT £110–£135, DT £24–£30, DBB £18–£22, WB, Bk £3, L £6, D £6·50, cc 1 3, Dep b.▲

★★Pencerrig, *LD2 9XX.* ☎ (0982) 553226. C. ☛ 27 bedrs, 10 bp, 5 ba, TV, Dgs. ✗ a l c, mc, at, LD 9.30. 🅿 ch, TV, Dgs, CP 40, Ac, con 80, CF, 5 BGf, 0 st, Dis. £ BB £16–£18, DB £26–£30, WT £173·60, DT £27·50, DBB £22·75–£24·75, WB, Ⅰ, Bk £3, L £4·75, D £6·75, cc 1 2 3 5.

★Llanlwedd Arms, *Station Rd, LD2 3SR.* ☎ (0982) 553282.
Rhydfelin Farm, G, x (Rl), *Cwmbach, LD2 3RW.* ☎ (0982) 553678.

Rescue Service: Smithfield Garage (Wear & Probert), Brecon Rd. ☎ (0982) 552639.
Weale Bros, Hay Road Garage. ☎ (0982) 553647.

BURRY PORT Dyfed. Map 12E
Pop 5,000. Llanelli 4, London 205, Carmarthen 15.
EC Tue. **Golf** Ashburnham 18h. **See** Pembrey Parish Church, St Mary's Church.

Rescue Service: Ace Garage, Gwscwm Rd. ☎ (055 46) 2396.

BURTON Dyfed. Map 11E
Pop 500. Pembroke Dock 2½, London 247, Haverfordwest 8½, Milford Haven 6½.
Golf Haverfordwest 9h.

★★Beggar's Reach, *SA73 1PD.* ☎ Neyland (0646) 600700. C. ☛ 10 bedrs, 10 bp, Dgs. ✗ mc, at, LD 9.30. 🅿 CH, TV, Dgs, CP 30, con 20, CF, 0 st. £ BB £16·50, DB £21, WT £102, DBB £14·60, WB, ②, Bk £2, L £1·25, D £5, cc 1.

CAERLEON Gwent. Maps 5A and 13E
Pop 6,270. Chepstow 14, London 137, M4 Motorway 2, Abergavenny 16, Monmouth 20, Newport 3, Pontypool 8.
Golf Caerleon 9h. **See** Roman Amphitheatre, Roman relics in Museum, Church of St Cadoc Priory.

Rescue Service: Argosy Coachworks Ltd, Ponthir Rd. ☎ (0633) 420666.

CAERNARFON Gwynedd. Map 18C
See also LLANWNDA
Pop 9,260. Betws-y-Coed 23, London 240, Aberdaron 33, Bangor 9, Dolgellau 39, Holyhead 29, Porthmadog 19, Pwllheli 20.
EC Thur. **MD** Sat. **Golf** Caernarfon 18h. **See** Medieval Castle, Town Walls, foundations of Segontium Roman Fort (Museum), Twthill (viewpoint), Statues of Earl Lloyd George and Sir Hugh Owen, St Peblin Church, St Mary's Chantry, Bryn Bras Castle 4½ m E, Hafodty Gardens.
🅸 The Square. ☎ Caernarfon (0286) 2232.

★★★Royal, *LL55 1AR.* ☎ (0286) 3184. Closed Dec 24th–Jan 2nd. C. ☛ 58 bedrs, 54 bp, 4 bps, TV, Dgs. ✗ a l c, mc, at, LD 9. 🅿 Lt, N, CH, TV, CP 200, Ac, con 150, CF, 0 st. £ cc 1 2 3 4 5 6, Dep.

★★Prince of Wales, *Bangor St, LL55 1AR.* ☎ (0286) 3367. Open Apr–Sep. C. ☛ 22 bedrs, 6 ba, TV, Dgs. ✗ a l c, mc, at, LD 9. 🅿 CH, Dgs, CP 9, Ac, con 50, CF. £ BB £11–£16, DB £22–£32, WT £124, DT £20–£22, DBB £18, WB, ②, Bk £3, L £4, cc 1 2 3 5 6, Dep a.▲

★Menai Bank (R), *North Rd, LL55 1BD.* ☎ (0286) 3297.
Cae Garw, G, z (Unl), *Llanberis Rd, LL55 2DF.* ☎ (0286) 3196. C. ☛ 4 bedrs, 2 ba. 🅿 CH, TV, CP 6, CF, 2 BGf, 3 st. £ BB £7·50–£8, DB £14, WT (c) £44–£51, DT (b) £10–£11, Ⅰ.

Menai View, PH, z (Unl), *North Rd, LL55 1BD.* ☎ (0286) 4602. Open Mar–Oct. C. ☛ 4 bedrs, 1 ba. 🅿 CH, TV, CF. £ BB £8·25, DB £16·50, WT (b) £103·25, DT (b) £14·75, Ⅰ, Bk £2·80, L £3·50, D a l c, cc 1 5.

Tal Menai, G, y (Unl), *Ffordd Bangor, LL55 1TP.* ☎ (0286) 2160. Closed Dec, Jan & Easter. C. ☛ 5 bedrs, 1 ba. 🅿 CH, TV, ns, CP 5, CF. £ BB £8·50–£9·50, DB £15, WT (b) fr £66·50, DT (b) £11·50–£12, Ⅰ.

Wallasea, G, z (Unl), *21 Segentium Tce, LL55 2PH.* ☎ (0286) 3564. Closed Dec. C. ☛ 4 bedrs, 4 sh, 1 ba. 🅿 CH, TV, Dgs, CF. £ BB £8–£9, DB £14–£15, WT (c) £52·50–£56, Ⅰ.

Repairer: Caernarfon Motors Ltd, Red Garage, Bangor St. ☎ (0286) 2475.
Rescue Service: Gwalia Garage, Caeathraw. ☎ (0286) 3096.

CAERPHILLY Mid Glamorgan. Maps 4B and 12F
Pop 28,992. Newport 11, London 148, Bridgend 19, Cardiff 7, Hirwaun 20, Merthyr Tydfil 16, Pontypool 15, Pontypridd 7½, Tredegar 16.
EC Wed. **MD** Daily. **Golf** Caerphilly 18h. **See** Very large 13th cent moated Castle with leaning Tower, ruins of Van House.
🅸 Twyn Car Park. ☎ Caerphilly (0222) 863378.

Rescue Service: Caerphilly Garages Ltd, Nantgarw Rd. ☎ (0222) 861287.

CAERSWS Powys. Map 12B
Pop 900. Newtown 6, London 183,
Aberdyfi 32, Aberystwyth 37, Bala 48,
Dolgellau 34, Lampeter 53, Rhayader 20.
Golf Newtown 18h. **See** Roman and
British Camps.

⬛★★★**Maesmawr Hall,** *SY17 5SF.*
✆ (068 684) 255. C. ➥ 13 bedrs, 5 bp, 4
bps, 2 ba, annexe 6 bedrs, 4 bp, 1 bps, TV,
Dgs. ✗ a l c, mc, at, LD 9. ⬛ CH, TV, Dgs,
CP 100, U 2, Ac, pf, con 100, CF, 4 BGf, 2
st. £ BB £20·25–£26·25, DB £33·50–
£42·50, WT £171–£191, DT £34–£38, DBB
£27·25–£34, WB, ⬛, Bk £4·50, L £7·50, D
£8, cc 1 2 3 5 6, Dep a.▲

CAPEL CURIG Gwynedd. Map 18D
Pop 400. Betws-y-Coed 5½, London 222,
Bangor 15, Caernarfon 18, Porthmadog
19, Pwllheli 31.
EC Wed. **Golf** Betws-y-Coed 9h. **See**
Old Parish Church of St Julitta, St Curig
Church (mosaic altar dome), The Ugly
House.

★★**Cobdens,** *LL24 0EE.* ✆ (069 04) 243.
★★**Tyn-y-Coed,** *LL24 0EE.* ✆ (069 04)
231. C. ➥ 13 bedrs, 13 bp, TV, Dgs. ✗ mc,
at, LD 9. ⬛ CH, TV, CP 80, Ac, pf, rf, con
120, CF, 0 st. £ BB £14·50, DB £25, WB, ⬛,
Bk £3, L £5, D £7, cc 1 2 3.

CARDIFF South Glamorgan. Map 4B
See also ST MELLONS
RAC Office, *202 Newport Rd, Cardiff,
CF2 1YR.*
✆ (General) Cardiff (0222) 490959,
(Rescue Service only) Cardiff (0222)
493030.
Pop 281,300. Newport 12, London 149,
M4 Motorway 4½, Bridgend 19, Caerphilly
7½, Hirwaun 25, Merthyr Tydfil 23,
Pontypridd 11.
See Plan, p 438.
EC Wed. **P** See Plan. **Golf** Cardiff 18h.
Llanishen 18h, Radyr 18h. **See** Castle
(Medieval, Victorian additions with lavish
rooms), Cathays Park (Civic Centre), St
Fagan's Castle (Welsh Folk Museum),
National Museum of Wales, University,
City Hall, St John's Church, RC Cathedral,
National Sport Centre, Parks, Llandaff
Cathedral 2 m NW (massive modern
sculpture in nave), Castell Coch 6 m NW.
ℹ 3 Castle St. ✆ Cardiff (0222) 27281.

★★★★**Inn on the Avenue,** *Circle Way
East, Llanedeyrn, CF3 7XF.* ✆ (0222)
732520. C. ➥ 150 bedrs, 150 bp, ns, TV.
✗ a l c, mc, at, LD 10·30. ⬛ Lt, N, CH, TV,
CP 300, Ac, sp, sol, gym, con 250, CF,
26 BGf, 0 st, Dis. £ BB £38, DB £49·50,
WB, ⬛, Bk £4·75, L £8, D £9·50,
cc 1 2 3 4 5 6.▲
★★★**M Crest,** *Westgate St, CF1 1JB.*
✆ (0222) 388681. C. ➥ 160 bedrs, 160
bp, ns, TV, Dgs. ✗ a l c, mc, at, LD 9.45.
⬛ Lt, N, CH, Dgs, CP 75, Ac, con 300, CF,
1 st. £ BB fr £46·25, DB fr £62·50, WB, ⬛,
Bk £5·25, D £9·25, cc 1 2 3 4 5 6, Dep b.
★★★**M Ladbroke Wentloog Castle,**
Newport Rd, Castleton, CF3 8UQ.
✆ Castleton (0633) 680591. C. ➥ 54
bedrs, 34 bp, 20 bps, ns, TV, Dgs. ✗ a l c,
mc, at, LD 10·30. ⬛ N, CH, ns, CP 150, Ac,
sb, con 110, CF, 25 BGf, 1 st, Dis. £ BB
£6·40–£33, DB £30·80–£38·50, WT £160–
£200, DBB £28·16–£35·20, WB, ⬛, Bk
£4·60, L £4·50, D £6·50, cc 1 2 3 5, Dep b.
★★★**Park,** *Park Pl, CF1 3UD.* ✆ (0222)
23471. C. ➥ 108 bedrs, 108 bp, TV, Dgs.

✗ a l c, mc, at, LD 11. ⬛ Lt, N, CH, TV, CP
80, Ac, con 300, CF, 4 st. £ BB fr £43·45,
DB fr £54·45, WB, ⬛, cc 1 2 3 4 5.
★★★**M Post House** (TH), *Church Rd,
Pentwyn, CF3 7XA.* ✆ (0222) 731212. C.
➥ 150 bedrs, 150 bp, TV, Dgs. ✗ a l c, mc,
at, LD 10.15. ⬛ Lt, N, CH, Dgs, CP 210, Ac,
con 140, CF, 38 BGf, Dis. £ BB fr £39·50,
DB fr £52, WB, ⬛, cc 1 2 3 4 5 6.
★★★**Royal,** *St Mary St, CF1 1LL.*
✆ (0222) 383321. C. ➥ 67 bedrs, 42 bp, 4
bps, 9 ba, TV, Dgs. ✗ a l c, mc, at, LD 10.
⬛ Lt, N, CH, Ac, con 350, CF, 6 st. £ BB
£23–£34, BD £35–£36, WB, ⬛, Bk £4·25, L
£6·70, D £6·70, cc 1 2 3 4 5 6.
⬛★★**Beverley,** *75 Cathedral Rd, CF1
9OG.* ✆ (0222) 43443. RS winter
weekends. C. ➥ 18 bedrs, 18 bp, TV, Dgs.
✗ mc, at, LD 9. ⬛ CH, TV, Dgs, CP 20, Ac,
con 30, CF, 4 st. £ BB £28, DB £35, WB, ⬛,
Bk £3·50, L £4·50, D £6·50, cc 1 3.
⬛★★**Sandringham,** *21 St Mary St, CF1
2PL.* ✆ (0222) 32161.
Ap. Pen-y-Lan (R), *Penylan Rd, CF2
5HX.* ✆ (0222) 496444.
Ambassador, PH, z (R), *4 Oakfield St,
Roath, CF2 3RD.* ✆ (0222) 491988.
Closed Xmas. C. ➥ 16 bedrs, 4 ba. ⬛ CH,
TV, CP 10, 3 BGf, 4 st. £ ⬛.
Auden, H, z (RI), *77 Romilly Rd, CF5 1FL.*
✆ (0222) 31999.
Balkan, PH, z (Unl), *144 Newport Rd,
CF2 1DT.* ✆ (0222) 463673. C. ➥ 13
bedrs, 1 bp, 4 sh, 3 ba, TV. ⬛ CH, TV, CP
15, 3 BGf, 1 st, Dis. £ BB £9·20–£12, DB
£16·10–£23, ⬛.
Cheriton, PH, z (R), *98 Fidlas Rd,
Llanishen, CF4 5NE.* ✆ (0222) 759730.
Clayton, PH, z (RI), *65 Stacey Rd. CF2
1DS.* ✆ (0222) 492345.
Imperial, PH, z (R), *132 Newport Rd,
CF2 1DJ.* ✆ (0222) 490032. C. ➥ 25
bedrs, 4 sh, 4 ba, TV, Dgs. ✗ a l c. ⬛ CH,
TV, Dgs, CP 15, G 4, CF, 5 BGf, 2 st. £ BB
£11·50, DB £20, DT fr £15·50, ⬛, Bk £2·50,
D £4, cc 5.
Tane's, PH, z (Unl), *148 Newport Rd,
Roath, CF2 1AJ.* ✆ (0222) 491755. C. ➥ 9
bedrs, 2 ba. ⬛ CH, TV, ns, CP 9, CF. £ BB fr
£9·20, DB fr £16·10, WT fr £64·40, ⬛.

Repairers: Dutton-Forshaw West,
Penarth Rd. ✆ (0222) 398241.
Godfrey Motor Co Ltd, 505 Newport Rd.
✆ (0222) 490511.
Howells Garages (Cardiff) Ltd, 501
Newport Rd. ✆ (0222) 495591.
Smart, Cliff Ltd, Rhiwbina Motor Garage,
Heol-y-Deri St, Rhiwbina. ✆ (0222)
63232.
UBM Ford, 505 Newport Rd. ✆ (0222)
490511.
MC Repairer: Car Distributors (Cardiff)
Ltd, 134 City Rd. ✆ (0222) 30022.
Sctr Repairer: Car Distributors (Cardiff)
Ltd, 134 City Rd. ✆ (0222) 30022.
Rescue Service: A1 Auto Repairs, 32
Norbury Rd. ✆ (0222) 568864.
Brooks & Williams Ltd, Curran
Embankment, Penarth Rd. ✆ (0222)
394752.
Clee Bros Ltd, Woodville Garage, Cathays
Ter. ✆ (0222) 21226 and (0222) 25577.
Dyer & Son Ltd, 14 Wellfield Pl. ✆ (0222)
496502.
Heath Motor Co, Llanishen St. ✆ (0222)
27959.
John Dugdale (Motor Engineers) Ltd, The
Garage, Merthyr Rd, Whitchurch.
✆ (0222) 63004.

Mark Hocking & Co, Milton St, City Rd.
✆ (0222) 494384.
R C Motors, Grosvenor Garages, Tintern
St. ✆ (0222) 28766.
St Peters Garage, 59a Inverness Pl.
✆ (0222) 486906.
S C Powell, T/As Crossways Service
Station, 225 Cowbridge Rd West, Ely.
✆ (0222) 592127.
Smiths Garage, R/O 77, Harriet St,
Cathays. ✆ (0222) 32603.

CARDIGAN Dyfed. Map 11D
Pop 4,290. Lampeter 29, London 234,
Aberystwyth 38, Carmarthen 25,
Fishguard 17, Haverfordwest 26,
Pembroke 37, Tenby 32.
EC Wed. **MD** Mon, Sat. **Golf** Cardigan
18h. **See** Castle ruins, St Mary's Church,
Old Bridge, St Dogmael's Abbey ruins 1 m
W, Cilgerran Castle ruins 2 m SE, Wildlife
Park.
ℹ 3 Heathfield, Pendre. ✆ Cardigan
(0239) 613230.

⬛★**Angel,** *36 St Mary St, SA43 1ET.*
✆ (0239) 612656. Closed Xmas. C. ➥ 10
bedrs, 3 ba, Dgs. ✗ a l c, LD 7.30. ⬛ TV,
Dgs, CP 8, G 4, CF, 1 st. £ BB fr £10, DB fr
£18, ⬛, Bk £3, D £4.

Rescue Service: T M Daniel, Tivy Garage,
Priory St. ✆ (0239) 612089.

CARMARTHEN Dyfed. Maps 11F and
12E
Pop 12,471. Llandovery 28, London 212,
Cardigan 25, Haverfordwest 30, Lampeter
23, Llanelli 16, Neath 31, Pembroke 32,
Swansea 27, Tenby 27.
EC Thur. **MD** Mon, Tue, Wed, Fri, Sat. **Golf**
Carmarthen 18h. **See** St Peter's Church,
County Museum, 14th cent Gatehouse,
Kidwelly Castle 8 m S. Roman
Amphitheatre.
ℹ Lammas St. ✆ Carmarthen (0267)
31557.

★★★**Ivy Bush Royal** (TH), *Spilman St,
SA31 1LG.* ✆ (0267) 235111. C. ➥ 88
bedrs, 78 bp, 10 bps, TV, Dgs. ✗ a l c, mc,
at, LD 9. ⬛ N, CH, Dgs, CP 75, U 3, Ac,
con 250, CF, 18 BGf, Dis. £ BB fr £32·50,
DB fr £46, WB, ⬛, cc 1 2 3 4 5 6, Dep a,
Xmas.
★★**Boar's Head,** *Lammas St, SA31 3AE.*
✆ (0267) 236043.
★**Falcon** (R), *Lammas St, SA31 3AP.*
✆ (0267) 237152. Closed Xmas. C. ➥ 15
bedrs, 3 bp, 4 bps, 2 ba, TV, Dgs. ✗ a l c,
mc, LD 9.30. ⬛ ch, Dgs, CP 100, Ac, con
100, CF. £ BB £16·50–£19·75, DB £26–
£29·50, ⬛, Bk £2·50, L £1·25, D £4,
cc 1 2 3, Dep a.

CHEPSTOW Gwent. Map 13E
Pop 10,000. Chippenham 32, London 123,
M4 Motorway 2, Abergavenny 29, Bath
25, Bristol 16, Gloucester 28, Monmouth
16, Newport 15, Pontypool 21, Ross-on-
Wye 24, Swindon 48, Tetbury 29.
EC Wed. **Golf** St Pierre 18h. **See** Castle
ruins, St Mary's Church, 13th cent Tintern
Abbey ruins 4 m N, Caldicote Castle 4½ m
SW.
ℹ The Gatehouse, High St. ✆ Chepstow
(029 12) 3772.

★★★**M Two Rivers,** *Newport Rd, NP6
5PR.* ✆ (029 12) 5151. C. ➥ 31 bedrs, 28
bp, TV, Dgs. ✗ a l c, mc, LD 9·30.
⬛ Lt, N, CH, TV, Dgs, CP 200, Ac, con 200,
CF, 9 BGf, 0 st, Dis. £ BB £29·50, DB £40,

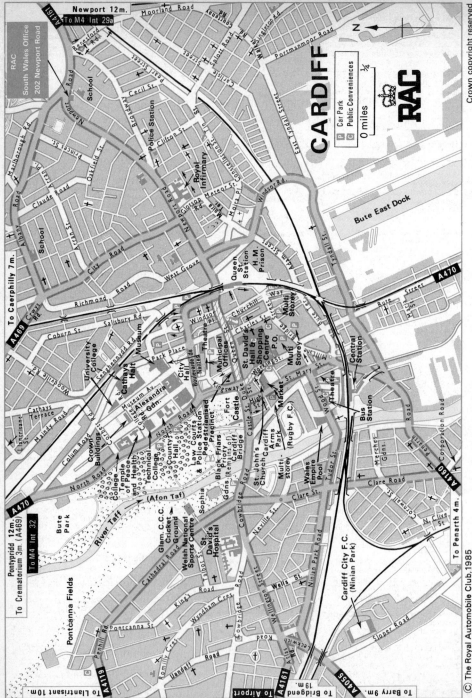

CARDIFF

Symbol	Meaning
P	Car Park
C	Public Conveniences

0 miles ¼

RAC

Newport 12m.
To M4 Int 29a
A4161

RAC South Wales Office 202 Newport Road

To Caerphilly 7m.

A469

A470

Pontypridd 12m. (A469)
To Crematorium 3m. (A469)

To M4 Int 32

Pontcanna Fields

To Llantrisant 10m.

A4119

To Barry 9m.
A4055

To Airport
A4161

To Bridgend 4m.

To Penarth 4m.
A4160

A470

Bute East Dock

*For abbreviations see inside back cover—*RAC

DBB £34·50–£50, ②, Bk £3·25, L £5·55, D £6·95, cc 1 2 3 5 6, Dep b.

★★**Beaufort,** *Beaufort Sq, NP6 5EP.*
✆ (029 12) 5074. C. ⋈ 12 bedrs, 2 bp, 1 sh, 3 ba, Dgs. ✗ a l c, at, LD 9.30. ⓓ CH, TV, Dgs, CP 12, con 12, CF. £ BB £20–£28, DB £30–£38, DBB £27–£35, WB, ②, Bk £3·50, L £5·95, D £6·95, cc 1 2 3 5, Dep b.

★★**Castle View,** *16 Bridge St, NP6 5PZ.*
✆ (029 12) 70349. C. ⋈ 8 bedrs, 7 bp, 1 bps, TV, Dgs. ✗ a l c, mc, LD 9. ⓓ CH, Dgs, ns, CF, 2 st. £ BB £23–£25, DB £36–£39, DBB £24–£26, WB, ①, Bk £3·45, L £8·50, D £8·50, cc 1 2 3.

★★**George** (TH), *Moor St, NP6 5DB.*
✆ (029 12) 5363. C. ⋈ 20 bedrs, 5 bp, 1 bps, 3 ba, TV, Dgs. ✗ a l c, mc, LD 9.30. ⓓ CH, CP 29, Ac, con 30, CF, 3 st. £ BB fr £31·50, DB fr £41·50, WB, ①, cc 1 2 3 4 5 6, Dep (Xmas).

★★**Old Ferry,** *Beachley Peninsula, NP6 7HH.* ✆ (029 12) 2474.▲
First Hurdle, H, z, *9 Upper Church St, NP6 5EX.* ✆ (029 12) 2189. Closed Xmas. C. ⋈ 10 bedrs, 1 bps, 4 ba, Dgs. ✗ a l c. ⓓ CH, TV, Dgs, CF, 2 BGf, 1 st, Dis. £ BB £14–£18, DB £22–£28, WT (b) fr £120, DT (b) fr £18, ②, Bk £2·50, L £3, D £3·50, cc 1 3 5.

Rescue Service: Larkfield of Chepstow Ltd, Newport Rd. ✆ (029 12) 2861.

CHIRK Clwyd. Map 19C
Pop 3,564. Shrewsbury 22, London 177, Llangollen 6½, Newport 38, Welshpool 21, Whitchurch 20, Wrexham 10.
Golf Llangollen and District 18h. **See** 14th cent Castle.

■★★**Hand,** *Church St, LL14 5EY.*
✆ (0691) 772479. C. ⋈ 12 bedrs, 2 bps, 4 ba. ✗ a l c, mc, at, LD 11. ⓓ CH, TV, CP 100, U 3, con 100, CF, 2 st. £ BB £17·75–£19·75, DB £25·50–£29, WT £147, DT £23, DBB £20–£22, WB, ①, Bk £3, L £5·50, D £7·50, cc 1 2 3 5 6.

Rescue Service: Hughes, A V, The Garage, Holyhead Rd. ✆ (0691) 772467.
Terrys Auto Repairs, Unit 3, Acorn Industrial Estate, Holyhead Rd. ✆ (0691) 777286.

CHURCHSTOKE Powys. Maps 12B and 13A
Pop 600. Ludlow 22, London 165, Bridgnorth 33, Newtown 12, Shrewsbury 26.
See Chirbury Gorge, glacial overflow.

♨★★**Mellington Hall,** *SY15 6HN.*
✆ (058 85) 456.

CILGERRAN Dyfed. Map 11D
Pop 350. Newcastle Emlyn 9, London 232, Cardigan 3, Newport 11, Aberaeron 24.
EC Wed. **Golf** Gwbert-on-Sea 18h. **See** 13th cent Castle (open to public).

Rescue Service: Terry & Everton, Pendre Garage, High St. ✆ Cardigan (0239) 614205.

COEDKERNEW Gwent. Map 5A
Pop 158, Newport 5, London 142, Caerphilly 9½, Cardiff 9, Tredegar 23.
Golf Tredegar 18h.

Rescue Service: Coedkernew Garage, Cardiff Rd. ✆ Castleton (0633) 680232.

COEDPOETH Clwyd. Map 19C
Pop 4,240. Wrexham 3½, London 183, Chester 14, Corwen 16, Llangollen 12,

---

Mold 10, Queensferry 12, Ruthin 13, Welshpool 32.
Golf Wrexham 18h. **See** Offa's Dyke, Bersham Forge.

Rescue Service: T C Jones & Son, Premier Garage. ✆ Wrexham (0978) 757238.

COLWYN BAY Clwyd. Map 18B
See also OLD COLWYN.
Pop 25,500. Mold 30, London 222, Bangor 20, Betws-y-Coed 17, Chester 42, Denbigh 19, Llandudno 5½, Queensferry 34, Rhyl 11.
EC Wed. **Golf** Old Colwyn 9h, Rhos-on-Sea 18h. **See** Welsh Mountain Zoo, Harlequin Puppet Theatre, Bodnant Gardens 5 m SW.
ℹ Prince of Wales Theatre. ✆ Colwyn Bay (0492) 30478.

★★★★**M Hotel 70°,** *Penmaenhead, LL29 9LD.* ✆ (0492) 516555. RS Dec 24–Jan 1. C. ⋈ 43 bedrs, 43 bp, TV, Dgs. ✗ a l c, mc, at, LD 9.30. ⓓ N, CH, Dgs, CP 200, Ac, con 120, CF, 21 BGf, 5 st. £ BB £31–£38, DB £42–£54, WB, ①, Bk £4·50, L £8·35, D £10·75, cc 1 2 3 4 5 6, Dep.▲

★★★**Hopeside,** *63 Princes Dr, LL29 8PW.* ✆ (0492) 33244. C 6. ⋈ 18 bedrs, 13 bp, 5 bps, TV, Dgs. ✗ mc, at, LD 9. ⓓ CH, ns, CP 20, con 30, CF, 2 st. £ BB £15–£20·50, DB £30–£38, DT £30, WB, Bk £3, L £5, D £7, cc 1 2 3 5, Dep a.

★★★**Norfolk House,** *Princes Dr, LL29 8PF.* ✆ (0492) 31757. RS Xmas & New Year. C. ⋈ 28 bedrs, 13 bp, 5 bps, TV, Dgs. ✗ mc, at, LD 9. ⓓ N, CH, CP 40, Ac, con 20, CF, 7 st. £ BB £25·50–£26·50, DB £38–£39, DBB £33·75, WB, ①, Bk £3·25, D £8·25, cc 1 2 3 5 6.

★★★**Rhos Abbey,** *111 Rhos Promenade, Rhos-on-Sea, LL28 4NG.* ✆ (0492) 46601. C. ⋈ 32 bedrs, 19 bp, 13 bps, TV, Dgs. ✗ a l c, mc, at, LD 9. ⓓ L t, N, CH, Dgs, CP 70, Ac, con 140, CF, 8 st. £ BB £26·50, DB £42, WT £165, DT £34·50, DBB £30·50, WB, ②, Bk £3, L £4, D £6·95, cc 1 2 3 5 6, Dep a.▲

★★**Ashmount** (R), *College Av, Rhos-on-Sea, LL28 4NT.* ✆ (0492) 45479. C. ⋈ 18 bedrs, 5 bp, 13 bps, TV, Dgs. ✗ a l c, mc, at, LD 8. ⓓ CH, CP 10, Ac, CF, 3 BGf, 0 st, Dis. £ BB £12–£14, DB £24, DBB £16·50–£17·50, WB, ①, Bk £2·75, L £2, D £5·50, cc 1 3 5, Dep b.

★★**St Enoch's** (R), *Marine Rd, LL28 4BL.* ✆ (0492) 2031. C. ⋈ 21 bedrs, 7 bp, 1 bps, 2 sh, 3 ba, TV, Dgs. ✗ mc, at, LD 7·30. ⓓ ch, TV, CP 4, Ac, CF, 1 BGf. £ BB £12–£16, DB £22–£30, WT £115–£120, DT £23–£25, WB, ①, Bk £3, L £4·50, D £6·50, cc 1 3, Dep a.

■★**Marine** (RI), *West Promenade, LL28 4BP.* ✆ (0492) 30295. Open Apr–Sept. C. ⋈ 15 bedrs 7 bps 3 ba. ✗ mc, at, LD 7.30. ⓓ ch, TV, CP 12, Ac, CF, 1 st. £ BB £11–£12·50, DB £20–£24, DBB £13·60–£16, WB, Bk £2·50, L £2, D £4·50, cc 2 5.

★**Melfort** (RI), *Llanerch Rd East, Rhos-on-Sea, LL28 4DF.* ✆ (0492) 44390. Closed Dec. C. ⋈ 17 bedrs, 2 bps, 3 ba, Dgs. ✗ mc, at, LD 6·45. ⓓ ch, TV, CP 18, Ac, CF, 1 BGf, 2 st. £ BB £10, DB £20, WT £94·50, DT £15, DBB £13·50, WB, ②, Bk £2, L £2·50, D £5·50, Dep a.

★**West Point** (R), *102 Conwy Rd, LL29 7LE.* ✆ (0492) 30331. Closed Nov. C. ⋈ 14 bedrs, 7 bp, 3 ba, Dgs. ✗ a l c, mc, LD 7·30. ⓓ CH, TV, Dgs, ns, CP 12, rf, con 12, CF, 2 st. £ BB £10·75–£13,

---

DB £20–£24, WB, ①, Bk £3, L £3·75, D £5·75, cc 1 2 3 5 6, Dep a.

■★**Whitehall** (R), *Cayley Promenade, Rhos-on-Sea, LL28 4EP.* ✆ (0492) 47296. Open Apr–Oct. C 3. ⋈ 14 bedrs, 6 bps, 4 ba. TV, Dgs. ✗ LD 7. ⓓ ch, TV, CP 6, 9 st. £ BB £10–£11, DB £20–£25·50, DBB £15·50–£18·75, ②, Bk £2·50, L £3, D £6·50, Dep a.

Cabin Hill, PH, z (RI), *College Av, Rhos-on-Sea.* ✆ (0492) 44568. Open Mar–Oct. C. ⋈ 10 bedrs, 3 bps, 2 ba. ⓓ CH, TV, CP 6, CF. £ BB £9·50–£11·50, DB £18–£24, WT (b) £77–£96, DT (b) £11–£15, ①, Bk £3, D £5.

Clevedon, PH, z (R). *Hawarden Rd, LL29 8NA.* ✆ (0492) 2368.

Grosvenor, H, z (R), *106 Abergele Rd, LL29 7PS.* ✆ (0492) 30798.▲

Idaho, PH, z (R), *19 Wynnstay Rd, LL29 8NB.* ✆ (0492) 30730.

Southlea, PH, z (RI). *4 Upper Promenade, LL28 4BS.* ✆ (0492) 2004. C. ⋈ 9 bedrs, 3 ba, Dgs. ✗ a l c. ⓓ CH, TV, Dgs, CF. £ BB £8·75–£9·50, DB £17·50–£19, WT (b) £75–£80, DT (b) £11·75–£13, ①

Sunny Downs, PH, (Rt), *66 Abbey Rd, Rhos-on-Sea, LL28 4NU.* ✆ (0492) 44256. C 3. ⋈ 17 bedrs, 4 bps, 3 ba, Dgs. ✗ a l c. ⓓ CH, TV, CP 12, CF, 5 st. £ BB LD 10·45–£11·95, DB £20·90–£23·90, WT (c) £73·15–£83·65, DT £13·95–£15·55, ②, Bk £4, D £6·50.▲

CONNAHS QUAY Clwyd. Map 19C
Pop 14,700. Queensferry 1½, London 191, Colwyn Bay 31, Mold 6½, Rhyl 22.
EC Wed. **MD** Thur. **Golf** Hawarden 9h. **See** Heritage Trail, Hawarden Castle.

Rescue Service: Golftyn Service Station, Church St. ✆ Deeside (0244) 812200.

CONWY Gwynedd. Map 18B
See also RO-WEN
Pop 13,000. Conwy Bay 5½, London 227, Bangor 16, Betws-y-Coed 14, Llandudno 4.
EC Wed. **MD** Tue, Sat. **Golf** Caernarfonshire 18h. **See** Castle (1284), St Mary's Church, Elizabethan Mansion (Plas Mawr), on quay—'smallest house in Britain', Telford's suspension Bridge, Bodnant Gardens, Tal-y-Cafn 4 m S, Sychnant Pass 3 m W.
ℹ Snowdonia Nat. Park Centre, Castle St. ✆ Conwy (049 263) 2248.

★★**Castle** (TH), *High St, LL32 8DB.*
✆ (049 263) 2324. C. ⋈ 25 bedrs, 25 bp, TV, Dgs. ✗ a l c, mc, LD 9.15. ⓓ CH, Dgs, CP 30, Ac, con 25, CF, 2 st. £ BB fr £34, DB fr £50·50, WB, ①, cc 1 2 3 4 5 6, Dep (Xmas).

★★**Castle Bank** (R), *Mount Pleasant, LL32 8NY.* ✆ (0492) 3888. Closed Jan–Mar. C. ⋈ 9 bedrs, 8 bps, 2 ba, TV. ✗ LD 8. ⓓ CH, TV, CP 12, CF, 4 st. £ BB £13–£15, DB £26–£30, WT £120–£130, DBB £20, WB, ②, Bk £3·50, L £4·75, D £7·50, Dep a.▲

★★**M Lodge** (R), *Tal-y-Bont, LL32 8YX.*
✆ (049 269) 766. Closed Xmas & New Year. C. ⋈ 10 bedrs, 10 bp, TV, Dgs. ✗ a l c, mc, at, LD 9.30. ⓓ CH, CP 30, CF, 6 BGf, 1 st, Dis. £ BB £22–£25, DB £32–£35, DBB £23–£25, WB, ②, Bk £3·50, L £5, D £9·50, cc 1 2 3 5.

Llys Gwilym, G, x (R), *3 Mountain Rd, LL32 8PU.* ✆ (0492) 2351. C 2. ⋈ 6 bedrs, 1 sh, 2 ba. ⓓ CH, TV, CP 3, CF, 2 st.

£ BB fr £7·50, DB fr £14, WT fr £66·50, DT fr £10·50, ⊡, Bk £2·50, L £3·50, D £4.
Sunnybanks, G, y (Unl), *Woodlands, LL32 8LT.* ☎ (049 263) 3845. Open Apr–Oct. C. 🛏 7 bedrs, 2 ba, Dgs. 🏠 CH, TV, CP 6, 1 st. £ BB fr £7, DB fr £14, WT (b) fr £60, (c) fr £49, DT (b) fr £10·50, ⊡, D £4.

CORRIS Powys. Map 18F
Machynlleth 5¾, London 211, Aberdyfi 14, Aberystwyth 22, Dolgellau 9¼, Welshpool 41.

★**Braich Goch,** *nr Machynlleth, SY20 9RD.* ☎ (065 473) 229. RS Xmas. C. 🛏 6 bedrs, 2 bps, 2 ba, Dgs. ✕ a l c, mc, at, LD 10. 🏠 ch, TV, Dgs, CP 20, CF, 2 st. £ BB £10–£11, DB £20–£26, WT £133–£142·50, DT £20–£21·50, DBB £15–£18, WB, ⊡, Bk £3, L £5·50, D £5·75, cc 1.

CORWEN Clwyd. Map 19C
Pop 2,164. Llangollen 10, London 194, Bala 11, Betws-y-Coed 22, Chester 28, Mold 21, Queensferry 26, Ruthin 12, Wrexham 20.
Golf Llangollen 18h. **See** 13th cent Church, Dee Valley, Berwyn Mountains, Pen-y-Pigyn 800 ft (viewpoint), Caer Drewyn 1 m.

COSHESTON Dyfed. Map 11E.
Kilgetty 9, London 242, Fishguard 33, Cardigan 36, Haverfordwest 12, Pembroke Dock 3.

★**Hill House,** *SA72 4UH.* ☎ Pembroke (064 63) 4352.

COWBRIDGE South Glamorgan. Map 4B
Pop 1,199. Cardiff 12, London 162, Bridgend 6½, Caerphilly 16, Pontypridd 12.
EC Wed. **MD** Tue. **Golf** Southerndown 18h. **See** Grammar School (17th cent foundation), medieval Southgate, EE and Perp Church.

▣★★**Bear,** *High St, CF7 7AF.* ☎ (044 63) 4814. RS Xmas. C. 🛏 21 bedrs, 18 bp, 3 bps, 2 ba, TV, Dgs. ✕ a l c, mc, at, LD 10. 🏠 CH, Dgs, CP 150, Ac, con 150, CF, 5 BGf, 0 st, Dis. £ BB £19·50–£23, DB £32, DT £35, DBB £30, WB, ⊡2, Bk £2·30, L £4·50, D 7, cc 1 2 3 6, Dep b.

Rescue Service: Ace Autos, Unit 2, Llandow Industrial Estate. ☎ (044 63) 4866.
Bear Lane Auto Repairs, Bridge Garage, High St. ☎ (044 63) 2784.
High Street Garage (Cowbridge) Ltd, 60 High St. ☎ (044 63) 2599.
Tudor Garage (Ystrad Owen) Ltd. ☎ (044 63) 2422.

CRICCIETH Gwynedd. Map 18C
Pop 1,530. Porthmadog 5, London 232, Caernarfon 17, Pwllheli 8½.
EC Wed. **Golf** Criccieth 18h. **See** Castle ruins at Llanystumdwy 1½ m W, Lloyd George Museum, Brynawelon (home of late Earl Lloyd George), Grave of David Lloyd George, 8th cent St Catherine's Parish Church, St Cybi's Well 4 m W.

🏛★★★**Bron Eifion** (R), *LL52 0SA.* ☎ (076 671) 2385. C 3. 🛏 19 bedrs, 13 bp, 6 bps, 1 ba, TV, Dgs. ✕ mc, at, LD 9. 🏠 N, CH, TV, CP 100, pf, con 30, CF, 1 BGf, 2 st. £ WT £215–£250, DT £36–£43, DBB £31–£36, WB, ⊡, Bk £4, L £6·50, D £11, cc 1.
★★**George IV, High St,** *LL52 0BS.* ☎ (076 671) 2168.
★★**Lion,** *Y Maes, LL52 0AA.* ☎ (076 671) 2460. C. 🛏 41 bedrs, 12 bp, 1 bps, 7 ba, TV. ✕ a l c, mc, at, LD 8.15. 🏠 Lt, ch, TV, Dgs, CP 20, G 12, Ac, CF, 2 BGf, 0 st, Dis. £ BB £12·50–£17, DB £23–£32, WT £145·60–£170·10, DT £20·80–£24·30, DBB £18–£23·50, WB, ⊡, Bk £3·25, L £2·80, D £6·75, cc 1 2 3 5.
▣🏛★★**Parciau Mawr** (Rl), *LL52 0RP.* ☎ (076 671) 2368. Open Mar–Sept. C 5. 🛏 7 bedrs, 2 bp, 2 ba, annexe 6 bedrs, 6 bps, TV. ✕ LD 8. 🏠 CH, CP 60, 3 BGf, 1 st, Dis. £ BB £15–£20·50, DB £30–£36·50, DBB £21·50–£27·50, WB, ⊡2, Bk £2·75, D £6·50, cc 1 3 4, Dep.
★★**Plasgwyn** (R), *Pentrefelin, LL52 0PT.* ☎ (076 671) 2559. C. 🛏 16 bedrs, 7 bps, 9 sh, 2 ba, TV, Dgs. ✕ a l c, mc, at, LD 9. 🏠 CH, TV, Dgs, CP 50, U 4, Ac, con 80, CF, 1 st. £ BB £14–£15, DB £28–£30, WT £170–£185, DT £24–£26, DBB £19–£21, ⊡2, Bk £2·50, L £4, D £6·50, cc 1 3 5, Dep a.
★★**Plas Isa** (R), *Portmadoc Rd, LL52 0HP.* ☎ (076 671) 2024. C. 🛏 12 bedrs, 12 bp, ns, TV. ✕ a l c, mc, LD 9.30. 🏠 N, CH, CP 15, CF, 0 st.
★**Abereistedd** (Rl), *West Par, LL52 0EN.* ☎ (076 671) 2710. Open Mar–Nov. C 3. 🛏 14 bedrs, 5 bps, 3 ba, Dgs. ✕ mc, at, LD 7.30. 🏠 CH, TV, CP 8, U 2, 1 st. £ BB £10–£11, DB £20–£30, DBB £14–£18, ⊡, Bk £2·50, L £2, D £6, Dep a.
★**Caerwylan,** *Beach Bank, LL52 0HW.* ☎ (076 671) 2547. Open Apr–Oct. C. 🛏 31 bedrs, 6 bp, 7 ba, Dgs. ✕ mc, at, LD 7.30. 🏠 Lt, CP 9, U 8, G 6, CF, 1 st. £ BB £8·50, DB £17·60–£23, WT £100, DT £13·50, DBB £12·50, ⊡, Bk £2·40, L £3·85, D £5.
▣★**Henfaes** (R), *Portmadoc Rd, LL52 0HP.* ☎ (076 671) 2396. Open Apr–Oct. C. 🛏 11 bedrs, 9 bp, 2 ba, TV. ✕ mc, at, LD 7.30. 🏠 CH, TV, CP 11, G 4, CF, 4 st. £ BB £13·80, DB £27·60, WT £115, DBB £16·10, ⊡.
Bron Rhiw, PH, x (Rl), *Caernarfon Rd, LL52 0PH.* ☎ (076 671) 2257. Open Mar–Oct. C. 🛏 14 bedrs, 4 ba, Dgs. 🏠 ch, TV, Dgs, CP 12, CF, 1 st. £ BB £7·50–£8, DB £15–£16, WT (b) fr £70, DT (b) fr £11, ⊡.
Glyn-y-Coed, PH, x (Rl), *Portmadoc Rd, LL52 0HL.* ☎ (076 671) 2870. Closed Dec. C. 🛏 10 bedrs, 3 ba, Dgs. 🏠 ch, TV, CP 12, CF, 4 st. £ BB fr £10, DB fr £20, WT (b) fr £100, DT (b) fr £15, ⊡, Bk £2, L £3, D £5.▲
Min-y-Gaer, PH, z (Rl), *Portmadoc Rd, LL52 0HP.* ☎ (076 671) 2151. Open Apr–Oct. C. 🛏 10 bedrs, 2 ba, TV, Dgs. 🏠 ch, TV, CP 12, CF, 7 st. £ BB £8·50–£9·50, DB £17–£19, WT £83–£89, DT £12·50–£13·50, ⊡, cc 1 5.
Moorings, G, *20 Min-y-mor, LL52 0EF.* ☎ (076 671) 2794.
Mor Heli, H, x (R), *Marine Ter, LL52 0EF.* ☎ (076 671) 2794.
Mynydd Ednyfed, PH, xy (R), *Caernarfon Rd, LL52 0PH.* ☎ (076 671) 2200. C. 🛏 10 bedrs, 2 sh, 2 ba, Dgs. ✕ a l c. 🏠 CH, TV, CP 12, CF. £ BB £13–£14, DB £26–£31, WT (b) £120–£130, (c) £70–£80, DT (b) £20–£21, ⊡2, Bk £3·75, L £4·50, D £7·25.
Neptune, H, z (Rl), *Marine Ter, LL52 0EF.* ☎ (076 671) 2794. C. 🛏 12 bedrs, 3 ba, ns, Dgs. 🏠 ch, TV, Dgs, CP 20, CF. £ BB fr £9, DB fr £18, WT fr £80, DT fr £12, ⊡, Bk £3, D £3·50.

CRICKHOWELL Powys. Map 12F
Pop 2,000. Abergavenny 6½, London 150, Brecon 14, Builth Wells 27, Tredegar 10.
EC Wed. **MD** Thur. **Golf** Old Rectory, Llangattock 9h. **See** Vale of Usk, Church, 17th cent Bridge, 13th cent Castle ruins.

★**Bear,** *High St, NP8 1BW.* ☎ (0873) 810408.
Dragon Country House, PH, x (R), *High St.* ☎ (0873) 810362. C. 🛏 15 bedrs, 6 bp, 2 ba, TV. ✕ a l c. 🏠 CH, TV, Dgs, CP 18, CF, 2 BGF, 1 st, Dis. £ BB £9·50–£15·50, DB £19–£25, WT (b) £89·50–£103·50, DT (b) £14·75–£15·50, ⊡2, Bk £2·25, D £5.

CROESGOCH Dyfed. Map 11C
Haverfordwest 14, London 257, Fishguard 10, St David's 15.
Golf St Davids 9h.

Torbant, F, xy (R), *SA62 5JN.* ☎ (034 83) 276.

CRUGYBAR Dyfed. Map 12C
Pop 35. Llandovery 10, London 194, Carmarthen 22, Lampeter 10, Llanelli 29, Neath 35, Swansea 34.
EC Thur. **Golf** Lampeter. 18h. **See** Roman Gold Mines.

🏛★★**Glanrannell Park,** *SA19 8SA.* ☎ Talley (055 83) 230. Open April–Oct. C. 🛏 8 bedrs, 5 bp, 1 ba, Dgs. ✕ mc, at, LD 8. 🏠 CH, TV, Dgs, CP 40, U 1, G 3, pf, CF, 1 st. £ BB £14–£15·50, DB £28–£31, WT £175, DT £26·50, DBB £20·50–£23, ⊡2, Bk £1·50, L £1·50, D £7.

Rescue Service: New Mill Garage. ☎ Pumpsaint (055 85) 352.

CWMBRAN Gwent. Map 13E
Pop 47,013. Chepstow 19, London 141, M4 Motorway 4, Newport 5, Pontypool 4½.
EC Wed. **MD** Fri and Sat. **Golf** Pontnewydd 9h.
ⓘ 42 Gwent Sq. ☎ Cwmbran (063 33) 67411.

★★★**M Commodore,** *Mill Lane, Llanyrafon, NP4 2SH.* ☎ (063 33) 4091. C. 🛏 60 bedrs, 47 bp, 11 bps, 2 sh, 1 ba, TV, Dgs. ✕ mc, at, LD 10. 🏠 Lt, N, CH, TV, Dgs, CP 250, G 8, Ac, con 200, CF, 6 BGf, 0st, Dis. £ BB £19·60–£29, DB £27–£37, WT £142·45, DT £23·35, DBB £20·35, WB, ⊡, Bk £3, L £3·25, D £ 7·25, cc 1 2 3 5 6, Dep b.

Rescue Service: Cwmbran Exhaust & Steering Centre Ltd, No 2 Court Rd, Industrial Estate. ☎ (063 33) 72572.
Mon Motors (Cwmbran) Ltd, Avondale Rd. ☎ (063 33) 5255.

DEGANWY Gwynedd. Map 18B
See also LLANDUDNO
Colwyn Bay 5½, London 227, Bangor 17, Betws-y-Coed 16, Llandudno 2½.
Golf Caernarfon 9h.

★★**Bryn Cregin Garden,** *Ty Mawr Rd, LL31 9UR.* ☎ (0492) 83402.
★★**Deganwy Castle,** *Deganwy Rd, LL31 9DA.* ☎ (0492) 83358. C. 🛏 29 bedrs, 12 bp, 5 ba, Dgs. ✕ mc, at, LD 9.15. 🏠 CH, TV, Dgs, CP 70, Ac, con 100, CF, 1 st. £ BB £15·50–£20, DB £30–£38, DBB £20·50–£22·50, WB, ⊡, Bk £3·50, L £5·25, D £7·50, cc 1 2 3 5, Dep.

DENBIGH Clwyd. Map 18D
Pop 9,000. Ruthin 7½, London 204, Betws-y-Coed 23, Colwyn Bay 19, Mold 16, Rhyl 11.
EC Thur. **Golf** Denbigh 9h. **See** Castle ruins, St Hilary's Tower, Bull Inn, ruins of Leicester's 'Cathedral' Church, Burgess

Gate, Old Town Walls, Hawk and Buckle Inn, Abbey ruins.

★★**Bull**, *Hall Sq, LL16 3NU.* ✆ (074 571) 2072. C. ⊯ 14 bedrs, 3 bp, 4 ba, Dgs. ✗ a l c, mc, at, LD 9.30. ⓓ CH, TV, Dgs, CP 12, Ac, con 90, CF, 2 st. £ BB £14·75–£15·75, DB £28·50–£29·50, WB, ①, L £3·50, D £4·50, cc 1 3 5, Dep b.

DINAS MAWDDWY Gwynedd. Map 18F
Pop 350. Welshpool 28, London 198, Aberdyfi 23, Aberystwyth 31, Bala 24, Dolgellau 10, Newtown 30, Rhayader 40. **EC** Thur. **Golf** Dolgellau 9h.
🅣 Meirion Mill. ✆ Dinas Mawddwy (065 04) 311.

Rescue Service: R Evans & Sons, The Garage. ✆ (065 04) 204.

DOLGELLAU Gwynedd. Map 18F
See also BONTDDU.
Pop 2,500. Welshpool 37, London 207, Aberdyfi 24, Aberystwyth 33, Bala 18, Betws-y-Coed 32, Caernarfon 39, Newtown 40, Porthmadog 24, Rhayader 50.
EC Wed. **MD** Fri. **Golf** Dolgellau 9h. **See** Torrent and Precipice Walks, Bridge (1638), ruins of Cymmer Abbey, Ty'n-y-Coed Estate 5½ m SW, Church 13c. 🅣 Snowdonia Nat. Park, The Bridge. ✆ Dolgellau (0341) 422888.

★★**Dolserau Hall**, *LL40 2AG.* ✆ (0341) 422522. C. ⊯ 12 bedrs, 9 bp, 3 bps, 1 ba, Dgs. ✗ a l c, mc, LD 9. ⓓ Lt, ch, TV, CP 80, Ac, con 50, CF, 2 st. £ BB £10–£12, DB £20–£22, WT £100–£120, DBB £17–£20, ①, Bk £3·50, L £3·50, D £7, cc 1 2 3 4 5 6, Dep b.

◼★★**George III**, *Penmaenpool, LL40 1YD.* ✆ (0341) 422525.

★★**Golden Lion Royal**, *Lion St, LL40 1DN.* ✆ (0341) 422579. C. ⊯ 22 bedrs, 11 bp, 5 ba, annexe 4 bedrs, 4 bp, TV, Dgs. ✗ a l c, mc, at, LD 9.30. ⓓ ch, TV, Dgs, CP 25, Ac, sb, sol, con 200, CF, 2 BGf, 0 st, Dis. £ BB £12–£18, DB £24–£31, WT £130–£150, DT £23–£24, DBB £20·50–£24, WB, ①, Bk £1·75, L £2·50, D £7·50, cc 1 2 3 5 6.

★★**Royal Ship**, *Queens Sq, LL40 1AR.* ✆ (0341) 422209. C. ⊯ 23 bedrs, 8 bp 1 bps, 6 ba, TV. ✗ a l c, mc, at. ⓓ Lt, CH, TV, CP 8, U 3, Ac, CF, 1 st. £ BB £12–£16, DB £24–£32, WT £115–£136, DBB £19·25–£22·75, WB, ①, L £4·50, D £7·75, cc 1 3.

Clifton, PH, z (Unl). *Smithfield Sq, LL40 1ES.* ✆ (0341) 422554. C. ⊯ 6 bedrs, 1 ba, TV. ✗ a l c, ⓓ CH, TV, Dgs, CP 3, 1 st. £ BB £10–£11, DB £17–£18, WT (b) £84–£91, DT £13–£14, ①.

DOLWYDDELAN Gwynedd. Map 18D
Pop 500. Corwen 26, London 221, Bala 27, Betws-y-Coed 6, Denbigh 28, Dolgellau 27, Porthmadog 17, Rhyl 31, Ruthin 30.
EC Thur. **Golf** Betws-y-Coed 9h. **See** Restored 12th cent Keep of Castle, modernised Perp Church.

★★**Elen's Castle** (R), *LL25 0EJ.* ✆ (069 06) 207. Open Apr–Sep. C. ⊯ 10 bedrs, 2 bp, 2 bps, 1 ba, ns, TV, Dgs. ✗ mc, at, LD 8. ⓓ CH, Dgs, ns, CP 40, U 3, CF, 0 st. £ BB £12·70–£17·70, DB £32·80–£39, WT £102–£109, DBB £16·40–£19·50, ②, Bk £3·60, L £1·20, D £6·40, Dep a.

DYFFRYN ARDUDWY Gwynedd. Map 18E

Pop 957. Barmouth 5, London 221, Harlech 5.
EC Wed. **MD** Fri. **Golf** Harlech 18h. **See** Shell Island.

Rescue Service: J H & E J Roberts & Sons. Smithy Garage. ✆ Dyffryn (034 17) 279.

EGLWYSFACH Dyfed (Powys). Map 12A
Pop 120. Machynlleth 5, London 110, Aberystwyth 13.
Golf Ynyslas 18h. **See** Bird Sanctuary.

⊯★★★★**Ynyshir Hall** (RI), *SY20 8TA.* ✆ Glandyfi (065 474) 209. Closed 1st 2 weeks Jan. C. ⊯ 11 bedrs, 6 bp, 1 bps, 3 sh, 1 ba, Dgs. ✗ a l c, mc, at, LD 9. ⓓ CH, TV, ns, CP 20, con 20, CF, 1 BGf, 3 st. £ BB £20–£30, DB £40–£60, DBB £28·50–£36·50, WB, ② 10%, Bk £5, L £8·50, D £14·95, cc 1 2 3 4 5 6, Dep.

EWLOE Clwyd. M. area 19C
Pop 1,700. Hawarden 2, London 190, Chester 8½, Colwyn Bay 33, Queensferry 2, Wrexham 12.
EC Mon. **Golf** Connahs Quay 18h. **See** Ewloe Castle, Hawarden Castle 1 m.

Rescue Service: B & H Motor Services, Holywell Rd. ✆ Hawarden (0244) 536117.

FAIRBOURNE Gwynedd. Map 18E
Pop 250. Dolgellau 8½, London 216, Aberdyfi 16.
EC Sat. **Golf** Aberdyfi 18h. **See** Excellent sands, Miniature Railway, Waterfalls at Panteinion.

★★**Brackenhurst** (R), *LL38 2HX.* ✆ (0341) 250226. Open May–Oct. C. ⊯ 10 bedrs, 1 bp, 1 bps, 2 ba, Dgs. ✗ mc, at. ⓓ CH, TV, Dgs, CP 15, con 20, CF, 1 BGf, 0 st, Dis. £ BB £12, DB £24–£25·50, DBB £14–£16·50, ①, Bk £2·50, L £3·50, D £6·50, cc 1 3, Dep a.

★★**Springfield**, *Beach Rd, LL38 2PX.* ✆ (0341) 250378.

Einion, G, x (R), *Friog, LL38 2NX.* ✆ (0341) 250644.

Llety Heulog, G, x (R), *2 Alyn Rd, LL38 2LZ.* ✆ (0341) 250228.

FFESTINIOG Gwynedd. Map 18D
Pop 6,350. Bala 19, London 218, Betws-y-Coed 14, Caernarfon 25, Denbigh 31, Dolgellau 19, Porthmadog 10, Ruthin 34.
EC Thur. **See** Narrow Gauge Rly, Cynfae Falls, Rhaiadr Cwm.

Newborough House, PH, x, (R), *Church Sq, LL41 4LL.* ✆ (076 676) 2682. C4, ⊯ 6 bedrs, 2 ba, Dgs, ⓓ CH, TV, CP 6, CF, 0 st. £ BB £10–£11, DB £17–£18, WT (b) £95–£140, DT (b) £15·50–£21·50, ②, Bk £3, L £4, D £6.

Rescue Service: E Lloyd Jones, The Garage, Sun St. ✆ (076 676) 2594.

FISHGUARD Dyfed. Map 11C
Pop 4,980 (inc Goodwick). Lampeter 44, London 248, Cardigan 17, Haverfordwest 15, St David's 17.
EC Wed. **MD** Thur. **Golf** Newport 9h. **See** Strumble Head 3 m NW.
🅣 Town Hall. ✆ Fishguard (0348) 873484.

★★★**Fishguard Bay**, *Quay Rd, Goodwick, SA64 0BT.* ✆ (0348) 873571. C. ⊯ 62 bedrs, 27 bp, 6 sh, 12 ba, Dgs. ✗ mc, at, LD 9.30. ⓓ Lt, N, CH, TV, Dgs, CP 50, Ac, sp, con 300, CF, 3 BGf, 0 st, Dis. £ BB £21–£23, DB £32–£34, WT fr £180,

DT fr £29·50, DBB fr £23, WB, ①, Bk £4·50, L £6, D £7, cc 1 2 3 5 6, Dep.

★★**Cartref** (R), *High St, SA65 9AW.* ✆ (0348) 872430. C. 7. ⊯ 14 bedrs, 3 bp, 3 bps, 2 ba, ✗ mc, at, LD 8. ⓓ CH, TV, CP 3, 2 st. £ BB £13–£14, DB £23–£24, WT £160, DT £24, DBB £20–£23, WB, ②, Bk £3·50, L £4, D £6·50, cc 1 3.

★**Manor House** (R), *11 Main St, SA65 9HG.* ✆ (0348) 873260. C. ⊯ 8 bedrs, 2 ba, Dgs. ✗ a l c, mc, at, LD 10. ⓓ ch, TV, Ac, con 50, CF, 2 st. £ BB £9·50, DB £19, WT £95, DT £17, DBB £75, WB, ①, Bk £3·50, L £4·50, D £6·50, cc 1 2 3 6.

Rescue Service: Fishguard Motors Ltd, Midlands Garages, West St. ✆ (0348) 872253.

Seafront Garage, Parrog. ✆ (0348) 873400.

FLINT Clwyd. Map 19C
Pop 12,900. Queensferry 5½, London 195, Colwyn Bay 27, Denbigh 16, Mold 6½, Rhyl 18.
EC Thur. **MD** Fri. **Golf** Flint 9h. **See** Ruins of Castle (13th cent), Cornist Hall and Parkland.

Rescue Service: Jones Motors Services, Chester Rd. ✆ (035 26) 3292.

FOUR MILE BRIDGE Gwynedd. Map 18A
Pop 600. Bangor 21, London 258, Holyhead 4.
EC Thur. **Golf** Holyhead 18h.

★★★**Anchorage**, *LL65 2EZ.* ✆ Valley (0407) 740168. C. ⊯ 18 bedrs, 8 bp, 6 bps, 2 ba, TV. ✗ a l c, mc, LD 9.30. ⓓ CH, TV, CP 100, CF, 2 BGf, 2 st. £ BB £19–£21, DB £29–£31, WB, ②, Bk £3·50, L £2·50, D £8, cc 1 3, Dep a.

FURNACE Dyfed (Powys). M. Area 12A. Machynlleth 6, London 111, Aberystwyth 12. **See** Ynyshir Reserve (R.S.P.B.).

Rescue Service: Artists Valley Garage. ✆ Glandyfi (065 474) 275.

GANLLWYD Gwynedd Map 18F
Dolgellau 5½, London 213, Ffestiniog 13, Bala 23, Barmouth 23

★**Tyn-y-Groes**, *LL40 2HN.* C. ⊯ 10 bedrs, 1 bp, 2 ba, TV, Dgs. ✗ a l c, mc, at, LD 9. ⓓ CH, TV, Dgs, CP 30, G 1, Ac, pf, CF, 1 st. £ BB fr £13, DB fr £23, WT fr £125, DT fr £21, WB, ①, , Bk £3, L £3·50, D £5·50, cc 1 2 3.

GARN DOLBENMAEN Gwynedd. Map 18C
Pop 280, Porthmadog 7, London 236, Caernarfon 13, Pwllheli 11.
EC Wed. **Golf** Criccieth 16h. **See** Pennant Valley.

Rescue Service: Pennant Motors, Bryncir. ✆ (076 675) 685.

GARTH Powys. Map 12D
Pop 320. Builth Wells 6, London 177, Aberystwyth 37, Llandovery 17.
Golf Builth Wells 9h.

Rescue Service: Prynne's Service Station. ✆ Llangammarch Wells (059 12) 287.

GILFACH GOCH Mid Glamorgan. Map 12F
Pop 3,554. Pontypridd 8½, London 164, Bridgend 10, Cardiff 18.
EC Thur. **Golf** Llantrisant and Pontyclun 18h.

Rescue Service: Cresta Service Station, Hendreforgan. ☎ Tonyrefail (0443) 672271.

GLASBURY-ON-WYE Powys. Map 12D
Pop 373. Ross-on-Wye 35, London 156, Abergavenny 23, Brecon 12, Builth Wells 15, Hereford 25, Leominster 27, Tredegar 24.
See St Peter's Church, Glasbury House.

★★**Llwynau Bach Lodge,** *HR3 5PT.*
☎ (049 74) 473. C 10. ⊭ 6 bedrs, 6 bp, TV, Dgs. ✗ mc, at, LD 9.30. ❆ CH, CP 25, sp, pf, 1 st. £ BB £20·50, DB £36, DBB £26, ☷, Bk £3·50, L £3·75, D £9·75, cc 1 2 3.

GLYN CEIRIOG Clwyd. Map 19C
Pop 821. Oswestry 8, London 181, Chester 28, Llangollen 4, Shrewsbury 28, Wrexham 16.
Golf Oswestry 18h. **See** 10th cent Church.

◼★★**Plas Owen,** *LL20 7DA.*
☎ (069 172) 707. C. ⊭ 13 bedrs, 13 bp, TV, Dgs. ✗ a l c, mc, LD 7.30. ❆ CH, TV, Dgs, CP 120, Ac, con 180, CF, 1 st. £ BB £16·50–£18·50, DB £30–£35, WT £175–£190, DT £25–£27·50, DBB £20–£25, ☷, Bk £4, L £7·50, D £7·50, Dep a.
★**Glyn Valley,** *LL20 7EU.* ☎ (069 172) 210. C. ⊭ 9 bedrs, 5 bps, 2 ba, TV, Dgs. ✗ a l c, mc, at, LD 10. ❆ ch, TV, Dgs, CP 40, Ac, pf, con 100, CF, 2 st. £ BB £14–£16, DB £27–£29, WT £118–£149, DT £23, DBB £21–£22, WB, ☷, Bk £2·75, L £6, D £6·50.

GLYNGARTH Gwynedd. Map 18A
Menai Bridge 2, London 242, Bangor 4½, Caernarfon 10, Holyhead 23.

★★**Gazelle,** *LL59 5PD.* ☎ (0248) 713364. C. ⊭ 10 bedrs, 3 ba, annexe 3 bedrs, 1 bp, TV. ✗ a l c, mc, at, LD 9.30. ❆ CH, TV, CP 50, con 20, CF, 1 st. £ BB £16–£21, DB £28–£33, WB, ☷, cc 1 2 3.▲

GROES Clwyd. Map 18D
Pop 268. Denbigh 3, London 207, Bala 24, Betws-y-Coed 19, Colwyn Bay 20, Rhyl 13.
EC Thur. **MD** Tue. **Golf** Denbigh 18h. **See** Castle.
Rescue Service: Pentre Engineering, Pentre Cwm. ☎ Nantglyn (074 570) 247.

GROESLON Gwynedd. Map Area 18C
Penygroes 2, London 245, Caernarfon 5, Nefyn 16, Pwllheli 11.
Golf Caernarfon 18h.
Rescue Service: Dolydd Garage, Groeslon. ☎ Llanrwng (0286) 830562.

GRONANT Clwyd. Map Area 19A
Pop 1,250. Queensferry 16, London 212, Holywell 9, Prestatyn 1½.
Golf Prestatyn 18h. **See** Talacre Abbey ½ m.
Rescue Service: Abbey Service Station, Llanasa Rd, Upper Gronant. ☎ Prestatyn (074 56) 4729.

GWALCHMAI Gwynedd. Map 18A
Bangor 13, London 250, Amlwch 13, Caernarfon 19, Holyhead 11, Rhosneigr 6.
Rescue Service: Horseshoe Garage.
☎ (0407) 720353.

GWBERT-ON-SEA Dyfed. Map 11D
Pop 150. Cardigan 3, London 237.
Golf Cardigan 18h.

★★★**Cliff,** *SA43 1PP.* ☎ (0239) 613241. C. ⊭ 70 bedrs, 56 bp, 14 bps, 6 ba, TV, Dgs. ✗ a l c, mc, at, LD 10. ❆ N, CH, TV, CP 150, Ac, sp, gc, pf, sc, con 120, CF, 5 BGf, 1 st, Dis. £ BB £20–£28, DB £40–£56, WT £240–£295, DT £34·50–£42·50, DBB £28–£36, WB, ☷, Bk £3, L £3, D £8·25, cc 1 2 3 5 6, Dep b.

HARLECH Gwynedd. Map 18E
Pop 1,200. Dolgellau 20, London 226, Bala 31, Betws-y-Coed 25, Caernarfon 27, Porthmadog 9½.
🆔 Snowdonia Nat. Park, High St. ☎ Harlech (0766) 658.
EC Wed. **Golf** Royal St David's 18h. **See** Castle, Pottery.

Castle Cottage, G, (R) *LL46 2YL.*
☎ (0766) 780479. C. ⊭ 5 bedrs, 1 ba, Dgs. ✗ a l c. ❆ ch, TV, Dgs, CF, 2 st. £ BB £9·85, DB £19·70, WT (c) £59·10, ☷, Bk £3, cc 1 5.

Rescue Service: Roberts, L, Morfa Garage, Morfa Rd. ☎ (0766) 780288.

HAVERFORDWEST Dyfed. Map 11E
Pop 9,200. Carmarthen 30, London 243, Cardigan 26, Fishguard 15, Pembroke 11, St David's 15, Tenby 20.
EC Thur. **MD** Tue, Sat. **Golf** Haverfordwest 9h. **See** Norman castle remains (adj old gaol now County Museum and Records Office), 13th cent St Mary's Church, 12th cent St Martin's Church, Augustinian Priory ruins.
🆔 40 High St. ☎ Haverfordwest (0437) 3110.

★★**Hotel Mariners,** *Mariners Sq, SA61 2DU.* ☎ (0437) 3353. Closed Xmas. ⊭ 29 bedrs, 15 bp, 3 bps, 4 ba, TV, Dgs. ✗ mc, at, LD 9.30. ❆ N, CH, CP 30, CF, 0 st. £ BB £17·50–£25·50, DB £29–£37.

★★★**Pembroke House** (R), *6 Spring Gdns, SA61 2EJ.* ☎ (0437) 3652. Closed Xmas. C. ⊭ 25 bedrs, 15 bp, 5 bps, 2 ba, TV, Dgs. ✗ mc, at, LD 10. ❆ N, CH, TV, ns, CP 30, Ac, CF, 6 st. £ BB £16·80–£19·80, DB £23–£26, DBB £20–£23, WB, ☷, Bk £2·75, L £3·50, D £6·75, cc 1 2 3 4 5 6.▲
Alandale, G, x, (Unl), *43 Nun St, St Davids, SA62 6NU.* ☎ (0437) 720333. C. ⊭ 6 bedrs, 1 ba. ❆ CH, TV, Dgs, CF. £ BB £7·75–£8, DB £15·50–£16, WT £80–£85, ☷
Cuckoo Grove, F, xy (Unl), *Cuckoo Grove, SA61 2UY.* ☎ (0437) 2429. Open April–Oct, C, NS, ⊭ 5 bedrs, 2 ba, ns, ❆ CH, TV, ns, CP, CF. £ BB £7·50, DB £15, WT (c) £50, ☷.
Elliotts Hill, H, xy, (R), *Crowhill Rd, SA62 6HT.* ☎ (0437) 4720.
Trearched, F, xy (Unl), *Croes Goch, SA62 5JP.* ☎ (034 83) 310. C, ⊭ 7 bedrs, 2 ba, Dgs, ❆ CH, CP 20, CF, £ BB £8–£10, DB £16–£20, WT (b) £84–£100, (c) £56–£70, DT (d) £12·50–£15, ☷.

MC Repairer: Mason Motor Cycles, Fountain Row Barn St. ☎ (0437) 3574.
Rescue Service: Bland, J & G (Motors) Ltd, 36 Bridgend Sq. ☎ (0437) 2717.
Dreen Hill Motors, Dale Rd. ☎ (0437) 2121.
James Lewis Williams, New Road Service Station, Freystrop. ☎ Johnston (0437) 890376.
Parry & Blockwell, Merlins Bridge. ☎ (0437) 3129.

Pelcomb Motor Services, St David's Rd. ☎ Camrose (043 784) 362.
R & J Cobb Ltd, Roundabout Garage, Merlins Bridge. ☎ (0437) 66470.
W H Baker (Haverfordwest) Ltd, Dew St. ☎ (0437) 3772.
Repairer: Greens Motors Ltd. Salutation Sq., ☎ (0437) 4511.

HAY-ON-WYE Powys. Map 13C
Pop 1,300. Ross-on-Wye 30, London 151, Abergavenny 29, Brecon 16, Builth Wells 19, Hereford 21, Knighton 27, Leominster 22, Monmouth 33, Tredegar 27.
EC Tue. **MD** Mon, Thur. **Golf** Brecon 18h, Builth Wells 9h. **See** Castle, 13th cent St Mary's Church, St John's Chapel, remains of Town Walls.
🆔 Chamber of Trade Information Centre, Car Park.

★**Crown,** *Broad St, HR3 5DB.* ☎ (0497) 820435. C. ⊭ 14 bedrs, 2 bp, 3 ba. ✗ mc, LD 8. ❆ ch, TV, CP 30, U 2, Ac, pf, con, 3 st. £ BB £12–£12·50, DB £21·50–£25, WT £146–£150, DT £22–£23, DBB £18–£22, ☷, Bk £3·50, D £6, cc 3, Dep a.

HENDY Dyfed (West Glamorgan). Map 12E
Pop 2,500. M4 Motorway ¼, Pontardulais 1, London 199, Ammanford 7½, Carmarthen 18, Llanelli 6, Neath 15, Swansea 15.
EC Thur.
Rescue Service: Hendy Service Station, Iscoed Rd. ☎ Pontardulais (0792) 882679 and (0792) 882248.

HOLYHEAD Gwynedd. Map 18A
See also TREARDDUR BAY
Pop 12,000. Bangor 23, London 261, Caernarfon 29.
EC Tue. **MD** Fri, Sat. **Golf** Trearddur Bay 18h. **See** Harbour, Holyhead Mountain (Roman remains), South Stack Lighthouse, St Cybi's Church.
🆔 Marine Sq, Salt Island Approach. ☎ Holyhead (0407) 2622.

Marine, PH, x (R). *Marine Sq, LL65 1DG.* ☎ (0407) 3512.

HOLYWELL Clwyd. Map 19A
Pop 9,000. Mold 9, London 200, Betws-y-Coed 35, Colwyn Bay 23, Denbigh 14, Queensferry 10, Rhyl 13, Ruthin 9.
EC Wed. **MD** Thur, Fri, Sat. **Golf** Holywell 9h. **See** St Winefride's Well and Church, St James's Church.
🆔 Little Chef Services, A55, Halkyn. ☎ Holywell (0352) 780144.

Miners Arms, I, x, *Rhes-y-Cae, CH8 8JG.* ☎ Halkyn (0352) 780567. C, ⊭ 8 bedrs, 2 ba. ✗ a l c. ❆ CH, TV, CP 150, CF, 2 st. £ BB £13·50, DB £25, WT (c) £110, DT (b) £17·50, ☷, Bk £3·50, L £2, D £5.

Repairers: Hillcrest Motor Co (Holywell) Ltd, Halkyn Rd. ☎ (0352) 711711. Holway Garage, Holway Rd. ☎ (0352) 710888.

JOHNSTON Dyfed. Map 11E
Pop 750. Haverfordwest 4, London 247, Pembroke 8, Tenby 16.
Golf Milford Haven 18h.

Redstock, G, xy (R), *SA62 3HW.* ☎ (0437) 890287.

KIDWELLY Dyfed. Map 12E
Pop 3,100. Llanelli 7½, London 208, Carmarthen 9, Llandovery 32.

EC Tue. **Golf** Ashburnham, Burry Port 18h. **See** Kidwelly Castle Church, old bridge.

Rescue Service: Pinged Hill Garage Ltd, Pinged Hill. ✆ (0554) 890436.

KILGETTY Dyfed. Map 11F
Pop 500. Carmarthen 21, London 233, Cardigan 28, Fishguard 25, Haverfordwest 15, Pembroke 10, Tenby 5. **EC** Wed. **MD** Fri. **Golf** Tenby 18h. **See** Carew Castle 6 m SW.
🛈 Kingsmoor Common. ✆ Saundersfoot (0834) 813672.

Rescue Service: R G Thomas & Son, Kingsmoor Garage, Kingsmoor Rd. ✆ Saundersfoot (0834) 812433.

KNIGHTON Powys. Map 13A
Pop 2,190. Leominster 18, London 157, Builth Wells 23, Ludlow 15, Newtown 26, Rhayader 23, Shrewsbury 34, Welshpool 34.
EC Wed. **MD** Thur. **Golf** Knighton 9h. **See** Church, Offa's Dyke.
🛈 The Old School. ✆ Knighton (0547) 528573.

Rescue Service: R Naughton & Son, Garth Garage, Garth Rd. ✆ (0547) 528419.

LAMPETER Dyfed. Map 12C
Pop 2,700. Llandovery 19, London 203, Aberystwyth 23, Cardigan 29, Carmarthen 23, Newtown 53, Swansea 45.
EC Wed. **MD** Alt Tue. **Golf** Llangybi 9h. **See** St David's College.
🛈 Town Hall. ✆ Lampeter (0570) 422426.

♨★★★Falcondale, *SA48 7RX.* ✆ (0570) 422910. RS Sunday evening. C. 🗪 20 bedrs, 5 bp, 13 bps, 1 ba, TV. ✗ a l c, mc, at, LD 9.30. 🏰 Lt, CH, TV, CP 60, Ac, tc, pf, con 150, CF, 3 st. £ BB £14–£22, DB £24–£32, WT £100–£135, DBB £18–£22.50, WB, 🚶, Bk £3.75, L £6.50, D £6.50, cc 1 3 6, Dep a

★★Black Lion Royal, *High St, SA48 7BG.* ✆ (0570) 422172. C. 🗪 17 bedrs, 6 bp, 1 bps, 3 ba, TV, Dgs. ✗ mc, LD 9. 🏰 CH, TV, Dgs, CP 50, Ac, con, CF, O st. £ BB £13.50–£17, DB £22–£28, WB, 🚶, cc 1 2 3 6.

LANGLAND BAY West Glamorgan.
Maps 12E and 4A
Swansea 5, London 193, Llanelli 16.
EC Wed. **Golf** Langland Bay 18h.

★★★Osborne, *Rotherslade Rd, SA3 4QL.* ✆ (0792) 06274. C. 🗪 41 bedrs, 21 bp, 6 ba, TV, Dgs. ✗ a l c, mc, at, LD 8.45. 🏰 Lt, N, ch, TV, CP 41, con 35, CF, O st. £ BB £24–£33, DB £33.75–£40, WB, 🚶, Bk £4.25, D £6.75, cc 1 2 3 4 5 6, Dep b.

★★Brynfield (R), *Brynfield Rd, SA3 4SX.* ✆ (0792) 66208. C. 🗪 12 bedrs, 9 bp, TV. ✗ a l c, mc, at. 🏰 CH, TV, CP 30, Ac, con 40, CF, O st. £ BB £19.80–£23, DB £30–£35, WT £120–£145, DBB £26–£42, WB, 🚶, 5%, L £6.30, D £7.50, cc 1 2 6.

★Ael-y-Don (R), *Langland Bay Rd, SA3 4QP.* ✆ (0792) 66466. Open Apr–Oct. C 5. 🗪 17 bedrs, 1 bp, 5 bps, 2 ba. ✗ mc, LD 7.30. 🏰 CH, TV, ns, CP 13, G 3, Ac, con 25, CF, 12 st. £ BB £12.25–£14.25, DB

£24.50–£28.50, DBB £16.95–£18.95, WB, 🚶, Bk £3.75, D £4.95, Dep a.

Brynteg, PH, z (RI), *1 Higher La, SA3 4NS.* ✆ Swansea (0792) 66820. Closed Dec. C. 🗪 10 bedrs, 2 bp, 2 ba, Dgs. 🏰 CH, TV, Dgs, CP 9, CF. £ BB £10.30–£10.95, DB £18.40–£21.85, WT (b) £73.60–£86.25, DT (b) £13.80–£14.95, 🚶.
Wittenberg, PH, x (RI), *2 Rotherslade Rd, SA3 4QN.* ✆ Swansea (0792) 69696. Closed Xmas. C 3. 🗪 12 bedrs, 9 bps, 2 ba, ns. 🏰 CH, TV, CP 12, 2 st. £ BB £12–£15.50, DB £20–£25, WT (b) £75–£110, DT (b) £15.50–£18, 🚶.

LETTERSTON Dyfed. Map 11C
Pop 850. Haverfordwest 10, London 253, Fishguard 6, Mathry 4½, Milford Haven 18, St Davids 14.
EC Wed. **Golf** Haverfordwest 9h.

■★★M Brynawelon, *SA62 5UD.* ✆ (0348) 840307. Closed Xmas. C. 🗪 25 bedrs, 22 bp, 3 bps, TV. ✗ mc, LD 9. 🏰 N, CH, CP 100, Ac, con 25, CF, 10 BGf, 0 st. Dis. £ WB.

LIBANUS Powys. Map 12D
Pop 150. Merthyr Tydfil 15, London 177, Hirwaun 14, Brecon 4, Sennybridge 3½.
Golf Brecon 9h.

★★M Mountains, *LD3 8EN.* ✆ Brecon (0874) 4242.

LISVANE South Glamorgan. M. Area 4B
Newport 10, London 147, Bridgend 20, Cardiff 6, Pontypridd 12.
Rescue Service: Lisvane Garage, Lisvane Rd. ✆ (0222) 751474.

LITTLE HAVEN Dyfed. Map 11E
Pop 200. Haverfordwest 7, London 257, Pembroke 13, St David's 14, Tenby (Fy) 21.
Golf Haverfordwest 9h. Milford Haven 18h.

★★Little Haven, *Strawberry Hill, SA62 3UT.* ✆ (043 783) 422. C. 🗪 14 bedrs, 8 bp, 1 ba, TV, Dgs. ✗ mc, LD 10.30. 🏰 CH, TV, CP 20, Ac, CF, 0 st. £ WB, D £6.50.
Pendyffryn, PH, x (Rt), *SA62 3LA.* ✆ Broad Haven (043 783) 337. Open Apr–Oct. C 4. 🗪 7 bedrs, 2 ba, TV. 🏰 CH, TV, ns, CP 6.

LLANARMON-DYFFRYN-CEIRIOG Clwyd. Map 19E
Pop 161. Shrewsbury 26, London 183, Bala 23, Dolgellau 44, Llangollen 17, Welshpool 22, Whitchurch 28.
Golf Oswestry 18h. **See** Ceiriog Falls, Church.

★★★Hand, *LL20 7LD.* ✆ (069 176) 666. C. 🗪 14 bedrs, 9 bp, 2 ba, Dgs. ✗ mc, at, LD 9. 🏰 CH, TV, Dgs, CP 30, tc, pf, con 30, CF, 4 BGf, 0 st, Dis. £ BB £23–£25, DB £37–£40, WT £105, Bk £3.50, L £7.50, D £9.50, cc 1 3.
★★West Arms, *LL20 7LD.* ✆ (069 176) 665. C. 🗪 13 bedrs, 5 bp, 1 bps, 3 ba, Dgs. ✗ mc, at. 🏰 CH, TV, CP 35, Ac, pf, con 20, CF, 4 BGf, 1 st, Dis. £ BB £18–£22, DB £36–£40, DBB £30–£40, WB, 🚶, Bk £3.50, L £7.50, D £8.50, cc 1 2 3 5, Dep a.

LLANBEDR Gwynedd. Map 18E
Pop 550. Dolgellau 16, London 219, Bala 35, Betws-y-Coed 28, Caernarfon 28, Porthmadog 12.
Golf Royal St David's 18h. **See** Cwm Bychan Lake and Roman Steps, Shell Island, Harlech Castle 3 m N.

♨★★Cae Nest Hall (R). *LL45 2NL.* ✆ (034 123) 349. Open Mar–Oct. C. 🗪 9 bedrs, 2 bp, 2 sh, 2 ba, TV, Dgs. ✗ a l c, LD 9. 🏰 CH, TV, CP 15, CF. £ BB £11.50–£15.50, DB £23–£31, WT £150–£165, DT £24.75–£26.75, DBB £20.25–£24.25, 🚶, 10%, Bk £4, L £4.50, D £8.75, cc 3.
★★Ty Mawr, *LL45 2PX.* ✆ (034 123) 440. C. 🗪 10 bedrs, 2 bp, 4 bps, 1 ba, TV, Dgs. ✗ a l c, mc, at, LD 8.45. 🏰 CH, TV, Dgs, CP 20, CF, 4 st. £ BB £13–£16, DB £26–£32, WT £182, DT £26, DBB £18–£21, 🚶, Bk £3, L £5, D £5, Dep a.▲

LLANBEDROG Gwynedd. Map 18E
Pop 775. Pwllheli 4, London 246, Aberdaron 11.
EC Wed. **Golf** Abersoch 18h. **See** Old Church.

★★Bryn Derwen (R), *LL53 7UA.* ✆ (0758) 740257. C. 🗪 10 bedrs, 10 bp, 2 ba, TV. ✗ mc, at, LD 8. 🏰 TV, CP 25, Ac, con 50, CF, 4 BGf, 0 st, Dis. £ BB £13–£25, DB £26–£50, DBB £15–£30, WB, 🚶, Bk £5, D £7.50, cc 1 3, Dep.
Glyn Garth, H, x (R), *LL53 7UB.* ✆ (0758) 720268. C. 🗪 10 bedrs, 3 bps, 2 ba, Dgs. ✗ a l c. 🏰 CH, TV, CP 15, CF, 6 st. £ BB £11–£18, DB £22–£28, WT (b) £108–£126, (c) £70–£90, DT (b) £17–£20, 🚶, Bk £2.50, L £2.50, D £6, cc 1 5.▲

Rescue Service: Glyn-y-Weddw Arms Service Station. ✆ (0758) 740523.

LLANBERIS Gwynedd. Map 18C
Pop 3,500. Betws-y-Coed 16, London 232, Bangor 10, Caernarfon 7, Dolgellau 40, Porthmadog 23.
Golf Caernarfon 18h. **See** Snowdon (Rack Rly to summit), Dolbardarn Castle, Ceunant Mawr, 60 ft Waterfall, Lake Padarn (railway along north shore), Bryn Bras Castle 3½ m NW.
🛈 Snowdonia Nat. Park. ✆ Llanberis (0286) 870765.

Lake View, PH, x (R), *Tan-y-Pant.* ✆ (0286) 870422. C. 🗪 7 bedrs, 2 bp, 2 ba, TV. ✗ a l c. 🏰 CH, TV, CP 12, CF. £ BB fr £11, DB fr £19, 🚶, Bk £2.75, L £4.75, D £5.75.

Rescue Service: Davies, W, Snowdon Garage. ✆ (0286) 870225.

LLANBRYNMAIR Powys. Map 18F
Newton 18, London 193, Aberystwyth 29, Dolgellau 22, Rhayader 30.

Rescue Service: John Davies & Sons, Dolgoch Garage. ✆ (065 03) 224.

LLANDEILO Dyfed. Map 12E
Pop 2,000. Llandovery 12, London 197, Carmarthen 14, Lampeter 20, Llanelli 18, Swansea 22.
EC Thur. **MD** Fri, Mon. **Golf** Glynhir 18h. **See** Rebuilt 13th cent Church, 19th cent Bridge (views), Dynevor Castle ruins 1 m W, Carreg Cennan Castle ruins 3 m SE, Talley Abbey and lakes 7 m N.

★★★Cawdor Arms, *Rhosmaen St, SA19 6EN.* ✆ (0558) 823500. RS Nov–Mar. C. 🗪 18 bedrs, 14 bp, 4 bps, TV, Dgs. ✗ mc, at, LD 9.30. 🏰 CH, Dgs, CP 8, sb, con 25, CF, 2 st. £ BB £27–£28, DB £39–£45, DBB £27–£30, WB, 🚶, Bk £5, L £6, D £13.50, cc 1 2 3 5 6.

Repairer: Howells (Llandeilo) Ltd, Central Garages, Rhosmaen St. ✆ (0558) 823221.

LLANDOGO Gwent. Map 13E
Pop 350. Chepstow 8, London 131,
Abergavenny 21, Gloucester 26,
Monmouth 7, Pontypool 21.
Golf Monmouth 9h.
Brown's PH, x (Rt), *NP5 4TW.* ✆ Dean
(0594) 530262. Closed Dec & Jan. C. ➤ 8
bedrs, 1 ba, Dgs. ✗ a l c. 🅳 CH, TV, Dgs,
CP 24, 1 st. £ BB £9·50, DB £17, 🗓, Bk £3,
L £3·95, D £4·50.

LLANDOVERY Dyfed. Map 12C
Pop 2,100. Brecon 21, London 184, Builth
Wells 24, Carmarthen 28, Lampeter 19,
Llanelli 29, Merthr Tydfil 31, Swansea 35.
EC Thur. **MD** Fri. **Golf** Lampeter 18h. **See**
Remains of 12th cent castle, Parish
Church with 15th cent tower, College
(apply to Warden), Usk Reservoir 5 m SE,
Brecon Beacons National Park.
🛈 Central Car Park, Broad St.
✆ Llandovery (0550) 20693.

★**Castle,** *Kings Rd, SA20 0AP.* ✆ (0550)
20343.
Llwyncelyn, G, xy (R), *Chain Bridge,
SA20 0EP.* ✆ (0550) 20566. Open Feb–
Nov. C. ➤ 6 bedrs, 2 ba. ✗ a l c. 🅳 CH, TV,
CP 12, CF. £ BB £9·90–£11, DB £19·80–
£22, WT (b) £105–£111·65, (c) £58·90–
£65·45, DT (b) £16·50–£17·60, 🗓, Bk
£3·30, L £3·50, D £6·60.

Rescue Service: Morris Isaac, Service
Garage. ✆ (0550) 20213.

LLANDRINDOD WELLS Powys. Map
12D
Pop 4,200. Hereford 41, London 171,
Builth Wells 7, Knighton 18, Llandovery
27, Leominster 33, Newtown 24,
Rhayader 10.
EC Wed. **MD** Fri. **Golf** Llandrindod Wells
18h. **See** Modern Spa, Castell Collen
(Roman Camp), Elan Valley Reservoirs.
🛈 Rock Park Spa. ✆ Llandrindod Wells
(0597) 2600.

★★★**Metropole,** *Temple St, LD1 5DY.*
✆ (0597) 2881. C. ➤ 122 bedrs, 122 bp.
TV, Dgs. ✗ a l c, mc, at, LD 8.30. 🅳 Lt, N,
CH, TV, Dgs, CP 150, Ac, sp, con 400, CF, 2
st. £ BB £23·50–£26·50, DB £40–£43, WT
£176–£201·50, DT £25·75–£27·75, DBB
£19·75–£21·75, WB, 🗓, Bk £4·75, L £6, D
£8, cc 1 2 3 5 6.
★★**Glen Usk,** *South Crescent LD1 5DH.*
✆ (0597) 2085. Open Apr–Oct & Xmas. C.
➤ 67 bedrs, 6 bp, Dgs. ✗ a l c, mc, at, LD
8.30. 🅳 Lt, CH, TV, Dgs, CP 12, Ac, con
150, CF, 6 st. £ BB fr £24·75, DB fr £35,
WB, 🗓, cc 1 3 4 5.
★★**M Park,** (R) *Rhayader Rd, Crossgates,
LD1 6RF.* ✆ Penybont (059 787) 201. C.
➤ 7 bedrs, 7 bps, TV, Dgs. ✗ a l c, mc, at,
LD 10. 🅳 CH, Dgs, CP 30, sp, CF, 7 BGf, 0
st. £ BB £9·40–£13·80, DB £18·80–£23·60,
DBB £15·20–£17·60, WB, 🗓, Bk £2·50, L
£3·50, D £5.
Clifton, G, z (R) *Wellington Rd, LD1
5NB.* ✆ (0597) 2527.
Griffin Lodge, PH, z (R), *Temple St, LD1
5HF.* ✆ (0597) 2432. C 5. ➤ 8 bedrs, 3
bps, 1 sh, ns, Dgs. ✗ a l c, mc, at, LD
8, 2 st. £ BB fr £10·50, WT (b) fr £112, DT
(b) fr £17, 🗓, Bk £3, L £3·50, D £6·50.
Three Wells, F, x (R), *Howey, LD1 5PB.*
✆ (0597) 2484. Closed Dec. C. ➤ 8 bedrs,
4 bps, 2 ba. 🅳 CH, TV, ns, CP 20, CF. £ BB
£7–£8, DB £14–£16, WT (b) £70–£84, DT
(b) £10·50–£12, 🗓.

Rescue Service: Brook House Garage,
Dolau, ✆ Penybont (059 787) 249.
M Burgins & Son, Mountain Garage, Dolau.
✆ Llangunllo (054 781) 6371.

LLANDUDNO Gwynedd. Map 18B
See also DEGANWY.
Pop 20,000. Colwyn Bay 4½, London 227,
Bangor 19, Betws-y-Coed 19.
EC Wed. **Golf** North Wales 18h,
Llandudno (Maesdu) 18h, Rhos-on-Sea
18h. **See** Gt Ormes Head and 12th cent
Church of St Tudno, Rapallo House
Museum, Marine Drive and Lighthouse,
Haulfre Gardens, Happy Valley 2 m S,
Conwy Castle 4 m S, Bodnant Gardens
8½ m S.
🛈 Chapel St. ✆ Llandudno (0492) 76413.

★★★★**St George's,** *St. George's Place,
LL30 2LG.* ✆ (0492) 77544. C. ➤ 90
bedrs, 36 bp, 51 bps, TV, Dgs. ✗ mc, at, LD
8.45. 🅳 Lt, N, CH, TV, Dgs, CP 30, Ac, sb,
sol, con 150, CF, 8 st. £ BB £18·50–£26,
DB £37–£52, DBB £23–£35, WB, 🗓, Bk £5,
L £7, D £9·50, cc 1 2 3 5, Dep b.▲
🔳★★★**Bodysgallen Hall,** *LL30 0DS.*
✆ (0492) 84466. C 8. ➤ 19 bedrs, 19 bp,
TV. ✗ a l c, mc, at, LD 9. 🅳 N, CH, CP 70,
tc, rf, con 40, 1 BGf, 3 st. £ BB £30–£55,
DB £53–£68, WT £329·50–£429·50, DBB
£43·50–£68·50, WB, 🗓, 10%, Bk £5, L
£8·30, D £13·50, cc 1 2 3 5 6, Dep b.
★★★**Empire,** *Church Walks, LL30 2HE.*
✆ (0492) 79955. Closed 2 weeks Xmas
and New Year. C. ➤ 56 bedrs, 56 bp, TV,
Dgs. ✗ a l c, mc, at, LD 9. 🅳 N, CH, CP
35, sp, sb, sol, con 40, CF, 3 st. £ BB
£22·50–£29, DB £30–£48, DBB £21–£31,
WB, 🗓, Bk £3·75, L £7, D £9·75,
cc 1 2 3 4 5 6, Dep.
★★★**Gogarth Abbey,** *West Shore, LL30
1QY.* ✆ (0492) 76211. C. ➤ 42 bedrs, 27
bp, 4 bps, 5 ba, TV, Dgs. ✗ mc, at, LD 8.30.
🅳 CH, TV, CP 50, Ac, sp, sb, sol, con 20,
CF. £ BB £15–£20, DB £28–£40, DBB
£20–£30, WB, 🗓, Bk £3·50, L £4, D £8,
cc 1 2 3, Dep.
★★★**Imperial,** *Vaughan St, LL30 1AP.*
✆ (0492) 77466. C. ➤ 142 bedrs, 81 bp, 1
bps, 24 ba, TV, Dgs. ✗ mc, at, LD 8.30.
🅳 Lt, N, CH, TV, Dgs, CP 50, Ac, sb, sol,
gym, con, CF. £ BB £17–£19, DB £34–£38,
WT £206·95, DT £28·85, DBB £22–£24,
WB, 🗓, Bk £3·50, L £4·50, D £7·35,
cc 1 2 3 5, Dep.▲
★★★**Marine,** (TH), *Vaughan St, LL30
1AN.* ✆ (0492) 77521. C. ➤ 79 bedrs, 54
bp, 5 ba, TV, Dgs. ✗ a l c, mc, at, LD 9.
🅳 Lt, N, CH, Dgs, CP 28, con 40, CF, 2 BGf,
6 st. £ BB fr £26, DB fr £39·50, WB, 🗓,
cc 1 2 3 4 5 6, Dep (Xmas).
🔳★★★**St Tudno,** *North Parade, LL30
2LP.* ✆ (0492) 74411. Closed Xmas and
Jan. C. ➤ 21 bedrs, 18 bp, 3 bps, ns, TV,
Dgs. ✗ mc, at. 🅳 Lt, CH, Dgs, ns, CP 5, sp,
con 20, CF. £ BB £17·50–£30, DB £30–
£50, DBB £24·50–£35, WB, 🗓, Bk £3·95, L
£6·25, D £10·50, cc 1 2 3 5.
★★**Clarence,** *Gloddaeth St, LL30 2DS.*
✆ (0492) 76485. Open Apr–Sep. C. ➤ 84
bedrs, 42 ba, Dgs. ✗ mc, at, LD 8. 🅳 Lt, N,
CH, TV, Dgs, Ac, CF, 0 st. £ BB £11–£16,
DB £22–£32, WT £124, DT £20–£22, DBB
£18, WB, 🗓, Bk £3, L £4, D £4·75,
cc 1 2 3 5 6, Dep a.
★★**Dunoon (R),** *Gloddaeth St, LL30
2DW.* ✆ (0492) 77078. Open Mar–Oct. C.
➤ 59 bedrs, 40 bp, 4 ba, TV, Dgs. ✗ mc, at,
LD 8. 🅳 Lt, N, CH, TV, Dgs, CP 24, Ac, sol, CF,
1 BGf, 1 st, Dis. £ BB £10–£16·50, DB £19–

£33, WT £100–£155, DT £15–£24, DBB
£14–£23, 🗓, Bk £3, L £4·50, D £6, Dep b.
★★**Four Oaks** (R), *Promenade,
LL30 1AY.* ✆ (0492) 76506. Open Mar–
Oct. C. ➤ 58 bedrs, 19 bp, 6 bps, 7 ba,
Dgs. ✗ mc, at, LD 8. 🅳 Lt, ch, TV, Dgs, ns,
CP 10, Ac, con 50, CF, 1 st. £ BB £9–£15,
DB £18–£30, WT £100–£150, DT £16·50–
£23·50, DBB £15–£20, WB, 🗓, Bk £3, L
£6.
🔳★★**Headlands** (R), *Hill Ter, LL30 2LS.*
✆ (0492) 77485. C. ➤ 17 bedrs, 12 bp, 3
bps, 2 ba, TV, Dgs. ✗ a l c, mc, at, LD 10.
🅳 Lt, CH, TV, CP 7, CF, 8 st. £ BB £13–
£16·50, DB £26–£33, DBB £21–£24·50,
WB, 🗓, Bk £3, L £3, D £8, cc 1 3, Dep.
★★**Ormescliffe,** *Promenade, LL30 1BE.*
✆ (0492) 77191. C. ➤ 65 bedrs, 22 bp, 13
bps, 7 ba, Dgs. ✗ mc, at, LD 8. 🅳 LT, TV,
CP 15, con 120, CF, 2 BGf, 6 ST. £ BB
£12·50–£17·05, DB £25–£34·10, WT
£140–£155, DT £20·10–£26, DBB £18·75–
£25·05, WB, 🗓, Bk £3, L £3·50, D £6·50,
cc 1 3 5, Dep.
★★**Risboro,** *Clement Av, LL30 2ED.*
✆ (0492) 76343. C. ➤ 71 bedrs, 52 bp, 19
bps, TV, Dgs. ✗ mc, at. 🅳 Lt, N, CH, ns, CP
34. Ac, sp, sb, sol, con 150, CF. £ BB £17–
£20, DB £30–£36, WT £161–£182, WB, 🗓,
Bk £3, L £4, D £6·50, cc 1 3, Dep.▲
🔳★★**Royal,** *Church Walks, LL30 2HW.*
✆ (0492) 76476. Open Mar–Oct. C. ➤ 35
bedrs, 7 bp, 3 bps, 25 sh, 5 ba, Dgs. ✗ mc,
at, LD 7.15. 🅳 Lt, CH, TV, Dgs, CP 25, con,
CF, 2 BGf, 0 st, Dis. £ BB £8·50–£11, DB
£17–£22, WB, 🗓, Bk £4·25, D £5·75, Dep a.
★★**Somerset** (R), *Central Promenade,
LL30 2LF.* ✆ (0492) 76540. Open Mar–
Oct. C. ➤ 37 bedrs, 29 bp, 8 bps, 1 ba, TV,
Dgs. ✗ mc, at, LD 7.30. 🅳 Lt, CH, ns, CP
18, G 3, Ac, CF, 8 st. £ BB £12·50–£14·50,
DB £25–£29, WT £126–£168, DT £18–£24,
WB, 🗓, Bk £3·50, L £4·50, D £6·50,
cc 1 2 3 4 5 6, Dep b.
★**Bedford** (R), *Craig-y-Don Par, LL30
1BN.* ✆ (0492) 76647. C. ➤ 30 bedrs, 2
bp, 3 bps, 5 ba, Dgs. ✗ a l c, mc, at, LD
8.30. 🅳 ch, TV, Dgs, CP 30, Ac, con 40, CF,
2 BGf, 3 st. £ BB £7–£9·50, DB £15–£20,
WT £92–£120, WB, 🗓, Bk £3, L £4·50, D
£7·50, Dep a.
🔳★**Branksome** (R), *62 Lloyd St,
LL30 2YP.* ✆ (0492) 75989.
★**Bron Orme** (Rl), *Church Walks, LL30
2HL.* ✆ (0492) 76735. Open Apr–Oct. C
10. ➤ 9 bedrs, 2 ba. ✗ mc, at, LD 7.30.
🅳 ch, TV, ns. £ BB £7·50–£8, DB £14–£15,
DBB £21·50–£22·50, 🗓, Bk £2·50, L £3·75,
D £4·75, Dep.
★**Clontarf** (Rl), *West Shore, LL30 2AS.*
✆ (0492) 77621. Open Feb–Nov. C 7.
➤ 10 bedrs, 1 bp, 3 bps, 2 ba, Dgs. ✗ a l c,
mc, at, LD 7. 🅳 CH, TV, CP 10, 3 st. BB
£11·50, DB £20·50–£23·50, DBB £15·50–
£17, 🗓, Bk £4, D £7, cc 3, Dep.
★**Cranleigh** (Rl), *Gt Ormes Rd, LL30
2AR.* ✆ (0492) 77688. Open Mar–Oct. C 2.
➤ 13 bedrs, 4 bps, 4 ba, Dgs. ✗ mc, at, LD
7.30. 🅳 CH, TV, Dgs, ns, CP 13, CF, 1 BGf,
4 st. £ BB £9·50–£12·50, DB £19–£28·50,
DT £19–£20·75, DBB £14·50–£18, 🗓, L
£4·50, D £6·50, Dep a.
★**Esplanade,** *Llandudno Prom, LL30
2LL.* ✆ (0492) 76687. C. ➤ 60 bedrs, 38
bp, 4 bps, 3 ba, TV, Dgs. ✗ mc, at, LD 7.30.
🅳 Lt, N, CH, TV, Dgs, CP 30, Ac, con, CF, 0
st. £ BB £12–£19·50, DB £24–£39, DT fr
£21, DBB £18–£21, WB, 🗓, Bk £3, L £5, D
£7·50, cc 1 2 3,▲

▣★Fairhaven (R), *Craig-y-Don Prom,
LL30 1BG.* Open Apr–Sep. C 6. ⚲ 11
bedrs, 6 bp, 4 bps, 1 ba, TV, Dgs. ✖ mc, LD
7. ⌂ CH, TV, Dgs, CP 6, Ac, 3 BGf, 3 st.
£ BB £13·50–£16, DB £27–£32, WT £160–
£180, DT £24–£28, DBB £21–£25, ①, Bk
£4·50, L £3, D £6, Dep.

▣★Hilbre Court (R), *Gt Orme's Rd, LL30
2AR.* ✆ (0492) 76632. Open Mar–Oct. C 3.
⚲ 10 bedrs, 3 bp, 2 bps, 3 ba, TV, Dgs.
✖ a l c, mc, at, LD 7.30. ⌂ ch, TV, Dgs, CP
5, CF, 1 BGf, 0 st, Dis. **£** BB £10·65–
£11·75, DB £21·30–£26·40, DBB £14·25–
£17·25, WB, ①, Bk £4, L £3, D £8, cc 1 3.

▣★Leamore (R), *40 Lloyd St, LL30 2YG.*
✆ (0492) 75552. C. ⚲ 11 bedrs, 1 bp, 6
bps, 2 ba, TV, Dgs. ✖ mc, at, LD 7. ⌂ CH,
TV, Dgs, CP 4, CF, 0 st. **£** BB £9–£13, DB
£18–£26, DBB £12–£16, WB, ①, Bk £3, L
£2, D £4, Dep a.

★Marlborough (R), *Deganwy Ave, LL30
2LN.* ✆ (0492) 75846. Open Mar–Oct. C.
⚲ 41 bedrs, 16 bp, 3 bps, 5 ba, TV. ✖ a l c,
mc, at, LD 7.30. ⌂ Lt, TV, CP 3, Ac, CF, 1
BGf, 0 st, Dis. **£** BB £11·15–£13·90, DB
£20·58–£27·85, DBB £13·40–£16·90, WB,
①, Bk £2, D £3·50, Dep.

★Min-y-Don (R), *North Par, LL30 2LP.*
✆ (0492) 76511. Open Apr–Oct & Xmas.
C. ⚲ 20 bedrs, 2 bp, 1 bps, 3 ba. ✖ mc, at,
LD 8.30. ⌂ TV, CP 6, Ac, CF. **£** BB £9·50–
£9·75, DB £19–£21, WT £106–£106·95,
DT £13·50–£14·50, DBB £12·50–£14·95,
WB, ①, Bk £2, L £2·95, D £4·70, cc 6,
Dep a.

★Oak Alyn (R), *Deganwy Ave, LL30 2YB.*
✆ (0492) 76497. RS Feb. C. ⚲ 14 bedrs, 2
bp, 6 bps, 2 ba, ns, TV, Dgs. ✖ mc, LD 6.
⌂ CH, Dgs, ns, CP 14, Ac, 1 st. **£** BB £8·50,
DB £17–£19, DBB £12·50–£13·50, WB, ①,
Bk £2, L fr £1, D £4·50, cc 1 3, Dep a.

★Ravenhurst (R), *West Shore, LL30 2BB.*
✆ (0492) 75525. Open Feb–Oct & Xmas.
C. ⚲ 22 bedrs, 9 bp, 4 bps, 2 ba, TV, Dgs.
✖ a l c, mc, at, LD 7.45. ⌂ ch, TV, Dgs, ns,
CP 15, Ac, CF, 5 BGf, 0 st, Dis. **£** BB
£11·50–£14·50, DB £23–£29, WT £116–
£135, DT £17–£21, DBB £16·50–£20·50,
WB, ①, Bk £3, L £3·50, D £7·50, cc 3.

★Richmond (R), *St George's Pl, LL30
2NR.* ✆ (0492) 76347. Open Mar–Oct. C.
⚲ 26 bedrs, 17 bp, 5 bps, 5 ba, TV. ✖ at,
LD 7.30. ⌂ Lt, ch, TV, Ac, CF, 1 BGf, 8 st.
£ BB £9·50–£10·90, DB £19–£21·80, DBB
£14·50–£15·90, WB, ②, Bk £3·75, L £1·50,
D £5·75, Dep.

★Rothesay (R), *83 Church Walks, LL30
2HD.* ✆ (0492) 76844. Open Easter &
May–Oct. C. ⚲ 22 bedrs, 1 bps, 4 ba, Dgs.
✖ mc, at, LD 7.30. ⌂ TV, Dgs, Ac, CF, 1
BGf, 8 st. **£** BB £10·25, DB £20·50, DBB
£14·50, ①, Bk £3, L £2, D £4·50.

★Sandringham, *West Par, LL30 2BD.*
✆ (0492) 76513. C. ⚲ 18 bedrs, 6 bp, 3
ba, TV. ✖ a l c, mc, LD 8. ⌂ CH, TV, CP 10,
Ac, con 60, CF, 4 st. **£** BB £11–£14, DB
£22–£28, WT £105–£120, DBB £15·50–
£19·50, ①, Bk £3·50, L £4·50, D £7, Dep.

★Sunnymede (R), *West Par, LL30 2BD.*
✆ (0492) 77130. Open Mar–Nov. C. ⚲ 18
bedrs, 6 bp, 2 bps, 3 ba, TV. ✖ a l c, mc, at,
LD 7. ⌂ ch, TV, CP 18, Ac, CF, 6 BGf, 1 st,
Dis. **£** BB £9–£15, DB £18–£30, DBB £14–
£20, ②, Bk £4, L £2·50, D £5, Dep.

★Tan Lan (R), *Great Orme's Rd, West
Shore, LL30 2AR.* ✆ (0492) 75981. Open
Mar 1–Oct 31. C. ⚲ 19 bedrs, 3 bp, 7 bps,
4 ba, ns, TV, Dgs. ✖ a l c. ⌂ CH, TV, N,
CH, Dgs, CP 10, con 12, CF, 7 BGf, 1 st,
Dis. **£** BB £11·50–£15, DB £23–£30, WT

£110–£120, DT £17–£18·80, DBB £16–
£20, WB, ②, Bk £3, L £4, D £7▲.

Bella Vista, PH, z (RI), *72 Church Walks,
LL30 2HG.* ✆ (0492) 76855.

Braemar, G, z (Unl), *5 St David's Rd,
LL30 2UL.* ✆ (0492) 76257. C 7. ⚲ 6
bedrs, 1 ba, ns, Dgs. ⌂ CH, TV, ns. **£** BB
£6·50–£7·50, DB £13–£14, WT (b) £65–
£70, DT (b) £9·50–£10·50, ①.

Brannock, PH, z (RI), *36 St David's Rd,
LL30 2UH.* ✆ (0492) 77483. C. ⚲ 6 bedrs,
1 ba. ⌂ CH, TV, CP 5, CF. **£** BB £6·95–
£7·50, DB £13·90–£15, WT (c) £48–£50,
①.

Brigstock, PH, z (RI), *1 St David's Pl,
LL30 2UG.* ✆ (0492) 76416. Open Apr–
Oct. C. ⚲ 10 bedrs, 2 ba, Dgs. ⌂ ch, TV,
CP 7, CF, 1 st. **£** BB £8–£9, DB £16–£18,
WT (b) £75–£82·50, DT (b) £11·50–
£12·50, ①, Bk £3, D £4·50.

Britannia, PH, z (RI), *15 Craig-y-Don
Par, LL30 1BG.* ✆ (0492) 77185. C. ⚲ 9
bedrs, 2 bps, 2 ba, TV, Dgs. ✖ a l c, mc, at,
CF, 1 BGf, 3 st. **£** BB fr £7·50, DB fr £15, ①.

Buile Hill, PH, z (RI), *St Mary's Rd, LL30
2UE.* ✆ (0492) 76972. Open Apr–Oct. C.
⚲ 11 bedrs, 3 bps, 2 ba. ⌂ CH, TV, Dgs,
CP 6, CF. **£** BB £9·75–£15, DB £19·50–
£30, WT (b) £88·20–£115·50, DT (b) £14–
£16, ②.

Carmel, PH, x (Unl), *17 Craig-y-Don Par
Promenade, LL30 1BG.* ✆ (0492) 77643.
Open Mar–Oct. C 4. ⚲ 10 bedrs, 5 bps, 1
ba, TV, Dgs. ⌂ CH, TV, CP 7, 1 BGf, 4 st.
£ BB fr £9·50, DB £14·50–£19, WT (b) fr
£77, (c) fr £52·50, DT (b) £10·25–£11, ①.

Carmen, H, z (R), *4 Carmen Sylva Rd,
LL30 1LZ.* ✆ (0492) 76361. C. ⚲ 16
bedrs, 1 bps, 3 ba, TV, Dgs. ⌂ CH, TV, Dgs,
CF, 2 st. **£** BB £7·99–£10·45, DB £15·98–
£21·90, WT (c) £54·65–£62·95, DT (b)
£11·45–£12·50, ①, Bk £1·75, L £4, D £4·50.

Causeway, PH (RI), *Lloyd St, LL30 2YP.*
✆ (0492) 75466. Open Mar–Oct. C. ⚲ 7
bedrs, 2 bps, 1 ba, Dgs. ✖ a l c. ⌂ ch, TV,
CP 6, U 1, CF, Dis. **£** BB £9–£13, DB £20–
£26, WT (b) £70–£80, DT £12–£14, ①, Bk
£2, D £5.

Cleave Court, PH, z (Unl), *1 St Seiriols
Rd, LL30 2YY.* ✆ Colwyn Bay (0492)
77849.

Cliffbury, PH, z (Unl), *34 St David's Rd,
LL30 2UH.* ✆ (0492) 77224. Open Apr–
Oct. C 6. ⚲ 6 bedrs, 1 ba. ⌂ ch, TV, CP 4.
£ BB £6–£6·50, DB £12–£13, WT £59–£62,
DT £8·50–£9, ①.

Concord, PH, z (RI), *35 Abbey Rd, LL30
2EH.* ✆ (0492) 75504. Open Feb–Nov. C.
⚲ 13 bedrs, 1 bp, 1 ba. ⌂ ch, TV, CP 8, CF,
1 BGf, 3 st. **£** BB £7·50–£8, DB £15–£18,
WT (b) £79–£84, DT (b) £11·30–£12, ①,
Bk £2·50, D £3·50.

Cornerways, PH, z (Unl), *2 St David's
Place, LL30 2UG.* ✆ (0492) 77334. Open
Mar–Oct. C 7. ⚲ 10 bedrs, 2 bp, 2 bps, 2
ba, TV, CH, TV, ns, CP 5. **£** BB £8·50–
£12·50, DB £17–£21, WT (b) £80·50–
£87·50, DT (b) £11·50–£12·50, ①, Bk £3, D
£4.

Craig-Ard, PH, z (Unl), *3 Arvon Av, LL30
2DY.* ✆ (0492) 77318. C. ⚲ 18 bedrs, 4
ba, ns, Dgs. ⌂ CH, TV, Dgs, CP 12, CF.
£ BB £7–£8·50, DB £20–£26, WT (b) £70–
£80·50, DT (b) £9–£11·50, ①, cc 5.

Cumberland, PH, z (R), *North Par, LL30
2LP.* ✆ (0492) 76379. C. ⚲ 14 bedrs, 1
bps, 1 sh, 3 ba, TV, Dgs. ✖ a l c. ⌂ CH, TV,
CP 4, CF, 2 BGf, 7 st. **£** BB £7–£9, DB £14–
£18, WT (b) £70–£77, DT (b) £10–£11, ①,
Bk £1·50, L £2·50, D £3.

Glenthorne, PH, z (RI), *2 York Rd, LL30
2EF.* ✆ (0492) 79591. Open Mar–Oct. C 4.
⚲ 9 bedrs, 1 bp, 2 ba, Dgs. ⌂ ch, TV, Dgs,
CP 6, CF, 1 BGf, 3 st. **£** BB £7–£7·50, DB
£14–£18, WT (b) £62–£64, DT (b) £9–
£9·25, ①, Bk £2, D £3.

Grafton, H, z (RI), *13 Craig-y-Don Par,
Promenade, LL30 1BG.* ✆ (0492) 76814.
Open Feb-Nov. C. ⚲ 20 bedrs, 4 bp, 14
bps, 1 ba, TV. ⌂ CH, CP 15, CF, 4 Bgf, Dis.
£ BB £14·50, DB £23–£29, WT (b) £110–
£130, DT (b) £15·50–£18·50, ①, Bk £2·50,
L £2·50, D £4, cc 1 5.

Hatfield House, PH, z (Unl), *12 St
David's Rd, LL30 2UL.* ✆ (0492) 76518.
Open Mar–Oct. C. ⚲ 10 bedrs, 2 ba.
⌂ CH, TV, CF, 1 st. **£** BB £7–£8, DB £14–
£16, WT (b) £66·50–£70, DT (b) £9·50–
£10, ①.

Llys Madoc, PH, z (RI), *14 Charlton St,
LL30 2AA.* ✆ (0492) 77430. Open Mar–
Oct. C. ⚲ 12 bedrs, 4 ba, Dgs. ⌂ ch, TV,
CF, 6 st. **£** BB £7–£8·50, DB £14–£17, WT
(b) £65–£75, DT (b) £9·50–£11, ①, L
£2·50, D £4.

Lynwood, PH, z (RI), *Clonmel St, LL30
2LE.* ✆ (0492) 76613. C. ⚲ 13 bedrs, 4 ba,
Dgs. ⌂ ch, TV, Dgs, CF, 2 BGf, 6 st. **£** BB
£8–£10, DB £15–£18, WT (b) £68–£75, DT
(b) £10–£11, ①.

Mayfair, PH, z (Rt) *4 Abbey Rd, LL30
2EA.* ✆ (0492) 76170. Open Mar–Sept. C.
⚲ 13 bedrs, 4 bp, 2 ba, Dgs. ⌂ CH, TV, CP
2, CF, 3 st. **£** BB £8–£9·50, DB £16–£21,
WT (c) £55–£65, DT (b) £80–£95, ①, cc 6.

Mayfield, PH, z (Unl), *19 Curzon Rd,
LL30 1TB.* ✆ (0492) 77427.

Minion, PH, x (RI), *21 Carmen Sylva Rd,
LL30 1EQ.* ✆ (0492) 77740. Open Mar–
Oct. C. ⚲ 16 bedrs, 4 bps, 4 ba, Dgs. ⌂ ch,
TV, Dgs, CP 8, CF, 1 BGf, 1 st, Dis. **£** BB
£5·75–£6, DB £11·50–£14, WT £66·50–
£73·50, DT (b) £9·50–£10·50, ②.

Montclare, PH, z (R), *North Par, LL30
2LP.* ✆ (0492) 77061.

Moorfield, PH, *15 Chapel Rd, LL30 2SY.*
✆ (0492) 76147.

Nant-y-Glyn, PH, z (Unl), *59 Church
Walks, LL30 2HL.* ✆ (0492) 75915. Open
Apr–Oct. C 5. ⚲ 10 bedrs, 2 ba. ⌂ CH, TV.
£ BB £7–£8, DB £14–£16, WT (b) £66·50–
£73·50, DT (b) £10–£11, ①.

Oakwood, G, z (Unl), *21 St David's Rd,
LL30 2UH.* ✆ (0492) 79208. Open May–
Sept. C. ⚲ 7 bedrs, 1 bp, 1 ba. ⌂ CH, TV,
CF, 1 st.

Orotava, PH, y, *105 Glan-y-Mor Rd,
Penrhyn Bay, LL30 3PH.* ✆ (0492) 49780.
Open Apr–Oct. C 6. ⚲ 6 bedrs, 1 ba. ⌂ ch,
TV, CP 6, 1 st. **£** BB £8·75, DB £17·50, WT
(b) £96·25, DT (b) £13·75, ②, Bk £2·50, L
£5.

Plas Madoc, PH, z (RI), *60 Church
Walks, LL30 2HL.* ✆ (0492) 76514. Open
Mar–Oct. C 5. ⚲ 6 bedrs, 1 ba. ⌂ ch, TV,
CP 5, 12 st. **£** BB £7·50–£8, DB £13–£14, WT (b)
£14·50, WT £67–£69, DT £9·75–£10, ①.

Puffin Lodge, PH, z (RI), *Central
Promenade, LL30 1AT.* ✆ (0492) 77713.
Open Mar–Oct. C. ⚲ 12 bedrs, 2 bp, 1 bps,
3 ba. ⌂ TV, CP 16, CF, 6 st. **£** BB £9·20–
£10·50, DB £18·40–£21, WT (b) £82–£85,
DT £55–£60, ①, Bk £3, D £5.

Queensway, PH, z (RI), *Grand
Promenade, LL30 1BB.* ✆ (0492) 77728.
Open Mar–Oct. C. ⚲ 21 bedrs, 2 bp, 3 ba,
Dgs. ⌂ ch, TV, Dgs, CF, 1 BGf, 5 st. **£** BB
£10·35–£10·50, DB £20·70–£22, DT (b) fr
£15, ①, Bk £2, D £3·50.

Rosaire, PH, z (RI), *2 St Seiriols Rd, LL30 2YY.* ✆ (0492) 77677. Open May–Sept. C. ⇔ 12 bedrs, 2 ba. ⓕ ch, TV, CP 6, 1 st. £ BB £6·50–£7·50, DB £12·50–£14·50, WT (b) £63–£65, DT (b) £9·75, ⊞, cc 1 2 3 4 5 6.

St David's, G, z (RI) *32 Clifton Rd, LL30 2YH.* ✆ (0492) 79216. C. ⇔ 6 bedrs, 1 ba. ⓕ CH, TV, CF, 1 st. £ BB £8, DB £16, WT (b) fr £70, DT (b) fr £10, ⊞.

St Hilary, PH, z (Unl), *16 Promenade, Craig-y-Don, LL30 1BG.* ✆ (0492) 75551. C. ⇔ 11 bedrs, 1 bps, 3 ba, TV, Dgs. ⓕ CH, TV, Dgs, CF, 3 BGf, 3 st. £ BB fr £7·50, DB fr £15, ⊞.

Spindrift, G, z (Unl) *24 St David's Rd, LL30 2UL.* ✆ (0492) 76490. C. ⇔ 7 bedrs, 1 bps, 1 ba. ⓕ CH, TV, CF, 1 BGf. £ BB £7–£8, DB £14–£16, WT (b) £60–£65, DT (b) £9–£10, ⊞, cc 1 2 3 4 5 6.

Tilstone, PH, x (R), *Carmen Sylva Rd, Craig-y-Don.* ✆ (0492) 75588. ⇔ 7 bedrs, 2 ba. ⓕ CH, TV. £ BB £8, DB £16, WT (b) fr £85, (c) fr £53, DT (b) fr £12·50, ⊡.

Warwick, PH, y (R), *56 Church Walks.* ✆ (0492) 76823.

Westdale, PH (RI), *37 Abbey Rd, LL30 2EH.* ✆ (0492) 77996. Open Mar–Oct. C. ⇔ 13 bedrs, 1 bp, 2 ba, Dgs. ⓕ ch, TV, CP 5, G 1, 1 BGf, 3 st. £ BB £6·50–£8·50, DB £13–£20, WT (b) £63–£77, DT (b) £9–£11, ⊞.

White Court, PH, z (RI), *2 North Parade, LL30 2LP.* ✆ (0492) 76719. Open Apr–Oct & Xmas. C. ⇔ 16 bedrs, 4 bps, 1 ba, TV, Dgs. ⓕ CH, TV, CF. £ BB £8·50–£10, DB £17–£23, WT (c) £75–£85, (b) £58–£67, DT (b) £11–£12·50, ⊡, Bk £1·75, D £2·95.

Wilton, H, z, *South Parade, LL30 2LN.* ✆ (0492) 76086. Open Feb–Oct. C. ⇔ 16 bedrs, 1 bp, 1 ba, TV, Dgs. ⓕ Dgs, CF. £ BB £8–£11, DB £16–£24, WT (b) £70–£85, (c) £56–£70, DT (b) £10–£15, ⊞, D £4.

Specialist Body Repairer: Biltons Accident Repairs Specialists, Builder St West. ✆ (0492) 75870 & (0492) 75401.
Rescue Service: L.S.P. Motors Ltd, Mostyn Broadway. ✆ (0492) 78217. Windsor Garage, Court St. ✆ (0492) 75953.

LLANDUDNO JUNCTION Gwynedd. Map 18B
Colwyn Bay 4, London 227, Bangor 16, Betws-y-Coed 16, Llandudno 3½.
EC Wed. **Golf** Caernarfon 18h, Conwy 18h. **See** Felin Isa watermill Llansantffraid Glan Conwy, Bodnant Gardens (NT).

◨★★**Station,** *Conway Rd, LL31 9NE.* ✆ Deganwy (0492) 81259.

LLANDYSSUL Dyfed. Maps 11D and 12C
Pop 1,100. Lampeter 12, London 217, Aberystwyth 31, Cardigan 17, Carmarthen 16.
EC Wed. **MD** Alt Tue. **Golf** Carmarthen 18h. **See** EE Church with later additions.

Glan Dŵr, G, F, xy (R), *Pontsian, SA44 4UA.* ✆ Pontshaen (054 555) 255.

Rescue Service: Lloyd Jones, D & Sons, Bargoed Garage, Llangeler. ✆ Velindre (0559) 370335.
Valley Services (Llandyssul) Ltd, Pencader Rd. ✆ (055 932) 2288.

LLANELLI Dyfed. Map 12E
Pop 30,000. Neath 16, London 201, M4 Motorway 5, Carmarthen 16, Brecon 47, Llandovery 29, Swansea 11.
EC Tue. **MD** Thur. **Golf** Ashburnham 18h.
See Parc Howard Mansion (Museum Art Gallery Gardens, recreational facilities), Swiss Valley (reservoirs, walks).

★★★**Stradey Park** (TH), *Furnace, SA15 4HA.* ✆ (055 42) 58171. C. ⇔ 77 bedrs, 77 bp, TV, dgs. ✗ a l c, mc, at, LD 9.30. ⓕ Lt, N, CH, Dgs, CP 120, Ac, con 450, CF, 20 BGf, dis. £ BB fr £32·50, DB fr £46, WB, ⊞, cc 1 2 3 4 5 6, Dep (Xmas).

★★**Diplomat,** *Ael-y-Bryn, Felin-Foel, SA15 3PJ.* ✆ (055 42) 58321. C. ⇔ 12 bedrs, 8 bp, 1 bps, 3 sh, 3 ba, TV, Dgs. ✗ a l c, mc, at, LD 9.45. ⓕ Lt, CH, Dgs, CP 200, Ac, con 100. £ BB £20·50–£27, DB £27·50–£35·50, ⊡, Bk £4, L £6·95, D £9·50, cc 1 2 3 5 6.▲

Rescue Service: Manton Motors, Yspitty Service Station, Bynea. ✆ (055 42) 54450.

LLANFAETHLU Gwynedd. Map 18A
Bangor 25, London 263, Amlwch 10, Caernarfon 31, Holyhead 10.
See Windmills.

Rescue Service: Moduron Maethlu Motors Ltd, The Garage. ✆ (040 788) 759.

LLANFAIR CAEREINION Powys. Map 19E
Welshpool 8, London 178, Bala 33, Dolgellau 28, Newtown 12.

Rescue Service: Terry Evans, Banwy Garage. ✆ (0938) 554.

LLANFAIRPWLLGWYNGYLL Gwynedd. Map 18C
Pop 2,840. Menai Bridge 2, London 242, Bangor 4, Caernarfon 7½, Holyhead 15.
EC Thur. **Golf** Bangor. **See** Marquis of Anglesey's Column, Britannia Bridge, Model Railway, Railway sign of Britain's longest place name Llanfairpwllgwyngyllgogerychwyrndrobwll-llandysyliogogoch.

◨★★★**Carreg Bran,** *Church La.* ✆ Llanfairpwll (0248) 714224. C. ⇔ 10 bedrs, 10 bp, 1 ba, ns, TV, Dgs. ✗ a l c, mc, at, LD 10. ⓕ N, CH, CP 60, Ac, con 80, CF, 2 st. £ BB £23·95, DB £38·50, WT £225, DT £35, WB, ⊞, Bk £4·75, L £5·25, D £8·95, cc 1 2 3 5 6.

Repairer: The Automobile Palace (Anglesey) Ltd, Holyhead Rd. ✆ (0248) 714355.

LLANFARIAN Dyfed
See ABERYSTWYTH.

LLANFERRES Clwyd, Map 19C.
Mold 4½, London 196, Chester 16, Denbigh 13, Llangollen 15, Rhyl 24, Ruthin 5¾, Wrexham 14.

Druid Inn, I, x, *Ruthin Rd, Nr Mold, CH7 5SN.* ✆ (035 285) 225.

LLANFYLLIN Powys. Map 19E
Pop 1,252. Welshpool 11, London 181, Bala 21, Dolgellau 31, Shrewsbury 26.
Golf Welshpool 18h.

◨★★★**Bodfach Hall,** *Y-Parc, SY22 5HS.* ✆ (069 184) 272. Open Mar–Dec. C. ⇔ 9 bedrs, 6 bp, 1 bps, 1 ba, TV, Dgs. ✗ a l c, mc, at, LD 8.45. ⓕ ch, CP 25, pf, con 20, CF, 4 st. £ BB £17·50, DB £35, WT £136·50, ⊡, L £5·50, D £7·50, cc 5.

◨★★**Cain Valley,** *High St, SY22 5AQ.* ✆ (069 184) 366. C. ⇔ 13 bedrs, 8 bp, 5 bps, TV, Dgs. ⓕ CH, TV, Dgs, CP 24, G 3, Ac, con 40, CF, 1 st. £ BB £14, DB £28, WT £90–£125, DBB £15–£19, WB, ⊞, Bk £2·70, L £4·50, D £6·80, Dep a.

Rescue Service: Tom Morris, The Garage. ✆ (069 184) 257.

LLANFYNYDD Dyfed. Map 12C
Pop 250. Llandovery 16, London 200, Carmarthen 12, Lampeter 18, Llanelli 20.
Golf Llandybie 18h.

Pen-y-Bont, I, x, *SA32 7TG.* ✆ Dryslwyn (055 84) 292.

LLANGAMMARCH WELLS Powys. Map 12D
Pop 300. Builth Wells 8, London 179, Brecon 17, Llandovery 15, Newtown 38, Rhayader 18.
EC Wed. **Golf** Builth Wells 9h. **See** Cefn Brith Farm.

◨★★★**Lake,** *LD4 4BS.* ✆ (059 12) 202. C. ⇔ 25 bedrs, 12 bp, 4 bps, 5 ba, TV, Dgs. ✗ a l c, mc, at, LD 9. ⓕ CH, Dgs, CP 70, G 3, gc, tc, pf, con 30, CF, 2 BGf, 4 st. £ BB £13·75–£21, DB £25–£39, WT £145–£149, WB, ⊞, Bk £4·75, L £5·50, D £9·50, cc 1 3, Dep.

LLANGOED Gwynedd. Map 18A
Beaumaris 2½, London 246, Bangor 9, Caernarfon 10, Holyhead 27.

Rescue Service: Gorddinog Garage. ✆ (024 878) 661 & (024 878) 524.

LLANGOLLEN Clwyd. Map 19C
Pop 3,117. Shrewsbury 29, London 184, Corwen 10, Mold 19, Ruthin 15, Welshpool 28, Whitchurch 23, Wrexham 11.
EC Thur. **Golf** Llangollen 18h. **See** Vale of Llangollen, Parish Church of St Collen, 14th cent bridge, Plas Newydd (home of "Ladies of Llangollen", house, ground and glen), Pontcysyllte Aqueduct (by Telford), Dinas Bran Castle ruins, Valle Crucis Abbey ruins, 2 m Horseshoe Pass, International Musical Eisteddfod in July. ⓘ Town Hall. ✆ Llangollen (0978) 860828.

♨★★★★**Bryn Howel,** *LL20 7UW* (2¾ m E A539). ✆ (0978) 860331.

★★★**Hand,** *Bridge St, LL20 8PL.* ✆ (0978) 860303. C. ⇔ 58 bedrs, 50 bp, 8 bps, TV, Dgs. ✗ a l c, mc, at, LD 8·30. ⓕ N, CH, Dgs, CP 50, Ac, con 140, CF. £ BB fr £27·50, DB fr £41·25, WB, ⊞, cc 1 3 4 5.

★★★**Royal** (TH), *Bridge St, LL20 8PG.* ✆ (0978) 860202. C. ⇔ 33 bedrs, 33 bp, TV, Dgs. ✗ a l c, mc, at, LD 9. ⓕ CH, Dgs, CP 23, G 2, Ac, con 80, CF. £ BB fr £34, DB fr £50·50, WB, ⊞, cc 1 2 3 4 5 6, Dep (Xmas).

★★**Chain Bridge,** *LL20 8BS.* ✆ (0978) 860215. C. ⇔ 36 bedrs, 17 bp, 6 bps, 8 sh, 3 ba, Dgs. ✗ mc, at, LD 9. ⓕ TV, CP 100, Ac, con 100, CF, 0 st. £ BB £13–£22, DB £25–£40, WB, ⊞, Bk £3, L £5·50, D £6, cc 1 2 3 5 6, Dep a.

◨★★**Ty'n-y-Wern,** *A5 Shrewsbury Rd, LL20 8PG.* ✆ (0978) 860252. C. ⇔ 10 bedrs, 2 bp, 2 sh, 2 ba, TV, Dgs. ✗ mc, at, LD 9. ⓕ ch, Dgs, CP 100, Ac, 1 st. £ BB £15–£17, DB £28–£32, DBB £40–£44, WB, ⊞, Bk £3·50, L £3·50, D £6·95, cc 3.

Four Poster, PH, x (RI), *Mill St Sq, LL20 8RY.* ✆ (0978) 861062.

Rescue Service: Regent Garage, Market St. ✆ (0978) 860779.

LLANGORSE Powys. Map 12D
Pop 400. Abergavenny 16, London 159, Brecon 6, Talgarth 4½, Tredegar 15.
Golf Brecon 9h & 18h. **See** Llangorse Lake 5 m E.

★**Red Lion,** *LD3 7TY.* ✆ (087 484) 238.

LLANGRANOG Dyfed. Map 11D
Pop 150. Lampeter 19, London 222, Aberystwyth 29, Cardigan 12, Carmarthen 25, New Quay 7.
EC Wed. **Golf** Cardigan 18h.

Pentre Arms, H, x, *Llangranog, Llandyssul, SA44 6SW.* ✆ (023 978) 229.

LLANGURIG Powys. Map 12B
Pop 500. Rhayader 9½, London 186, Aberdyfi 42, Aberystwyth 25, Dolgellau 44, Lampeter 40, Newtown 18.
Golf Llanidloes 9h. **See** Ancient Church of St Curig.

★★**Glansevern Arms,** *Pant Mawr, SY18 6SY.* ✆ (055 15) 240. Closed Xmas. C. ⊯ 7 bedrs, 5 bp, 2 bps, 2 ba, TV, Dgs. ✗ mc, at, LD 8. ⊡ CH, Dgs, CP 20, pf, con 15, CF, 2 st. **£** BB £10·90, DB £15·50, DB £25, DBB £25·50, WB, ⏢, Bk £5, L £7·50, D £10.

Blue Bell, I, x, *Nr Llanidloes, SY18 6SG.* ✆ (055 15) 254. C. ⊯ 10 bedrs, 1 bp, 2 ba, Dgs. ✗ a l c. ⊡ CH, Dgs, CP 40, CF, 1 st. **£** BB £10·90, DB £21·80–£23·80, WT (c) £70–£80, DT (b) £10·90–£12·90, ⏢, Bk £3·50, L £5, D £7·60, cc 1 5.

Old Vicarage, G, x (R), *SY18 6RN.* ✆ (055 15) 280. C. ⊯ 4 bedrs, 2 ba, Dgs. ✗ a l c. ⊡ CH, TV, Dgs, CP 6, CF, 3 st. **£** BB £10·50–£11·50, DB £17–£19, WT £99–£105, DT £17·50–£18·50, ⏢, Bk £2·50, L £3·50, D £7.

LLANGYNOG Powys (Shropshire). Map 18F
Penybontfawr 3, London 186, Bala 13, Llanwddyn 9, Oswestry 17, Shrewsbury 32.
See Churches.

★**New Inn,** *SY10 0EX.* ✆ Pennant (067 174) 229. C. ⊯ 8 bedrs, 3 bp, 2 ba, Dgs. ✗ a l c. ⊡ CH, TV, Dgs, CP 100, Ac, pf, con 100, CF, 1 st. **£** BB £11·50, DB £22–£26, WB, ⏢, Bk £2·80, L £3·75, D £5, Dep.

LLANHARAN Mid Glamorgan. Map 4B
Pop 5,774. Caerphilly 12, London 160, Bridgend 7½, Cardiff 13, Hirwaun 24, Pontypridd 10.
Golf Llantrisant and Pontyclun 18h.

Rescue Service: J David Ltd, The Garage, Bridgend Rd and at Llantrisant Rd. ✆ Llantrisant (0443) 226218.
Pyne Bros, Brynna Rd. ✆ Llantrisant (0443) 226377.

LLANIDLOES Powys. Map 12B
Pop 2,381. Newtown 14, London 205, Aberdyfi 37, Aberystwyth 30, Dolgellau 39, Lampeter 45, Rhayader 12.
Golf St Idloes 9h. **See** Market Hall and Museum, Wesley's Preaching Stone, ancient Church of St Idloes (with 13th cent Arcade, orig part of Cwmhir Abbey), Llyn Clywedog Reservoir.
⏢ Great Oak St. ✆ Llanidloes (055 12) 2605.

■★**Red Lion,** *Longbridge St, SY18 6EE.* ✆ (055 12) 2270. Closed Xmas. C. ⊯ 6 bedrs, 3 sh, 3 ba. ✗ a l c, mc, at, LD 9.30. ⊡ TV, CP 8, Ac, CF, 0 st. **£** BB £8·50–£10, DB £17–£18, ⏢, Bk £2·25, L £4·95, D £4·95, Dep a.

Rescue Service: Minerva Garage, Longbridge St. ✆ (055 12) 2201.

LLANLLWNI Dyfed. M. Area 12C
Pop 616. 9½ m W of Lampeter, London 213, Aberystwyth 31, Cardigan 24, Carmarthen 15, Fishguard 39.
Golf Lampeter 18h. **See** Church, Castell Pyr.

Rescue Service: Tegfan Garage. ✆ Maesycrugiau (055 935) 235.

LLANON Dyfed. Map 12A
Pop 700. Lampeter 15, London 217, Aberystwyth 11, Cardigan 27.
EC Wed. **Golf** Aberystwyth 18h.

Rescue Service: Dragon Service Station, Ceredigion. ✆ (097 48) 462.

LLANRHAEADR Clwyd. M. Area 18D
Pop 662. 3½ m SE of Denbigh, Ruthin 5, London 201.
Golf Oswestry 18h. **See** Highest Waterfall in Wales (240 ft), Church.

★★★**Bryn Morfydd** *nr Denbigh, LL16 4NP.* ✆ Llannynys (074 578) 313. C. ⊯ 17 bedrs, 14 bp, 3 bps, TV, Dgs. ✗ a l c, mc, at, LD 10. ⊡ N, CH, TV, Dgs, CP 100, Ac, sb, sol, con, CF, 5 BGf, 0 st. **£** BB £15–£25, DB £25–£35, DBB £30–£35, WB, ⏢, Bk £5, L £5, D £8·50, cc 1 2 3 5, Dep b.

LLANRWST Gwynedd. Map 18D
Pop 3,000. Corwen 23, London 218, Bala 24, Betws-y-Coed 4, Colwyn Bay 14, Denbigh 20, Llandudno 15, Rhyl 22, Ruthin 27.
EC Thur. **MD** Tue. **Golf** Betws-y-Coed 9h. **See** 17th cent bridge, 15th cent Tu Hwnt i'r Bont (now restaurant), 15th cent Parish Church of St Crwst and Gwydir Chapel, Gwydir Park, Gwydir Castle and Gardens.

▟★★★★**Maenan Abbey,** *Maenan, LL26 0UL.* ✆ Dolgarrog (049 269) 247. C. ⊯ 12 bedrs, 9 bp, 3 bps, TV, Dgs. ✗ a l c, mc, at, LD 9.45. ⊡ CH, TV, CP 60, pf, con, CF, 4 st. **£** BB £13·80–£18, DB £23–£30, WB, ⏢, Bk £3·95, L £4·95, D £9·50, cc 1 2 3 5 6, Dep b.▲

★★★**Plas Maenan,** *Maenan, LL26 0YR.* ✆ Dolgarrog (049 269) 232. C. ⊯ 15 bedrs, 15 bp, TV. ✗ a l c, LD 10. ⊡ N, CH, CP 100, Ac, con 100, CF, 8 st. **£** BB £19·25–£24, DB £31–£37·50, WT £152·50–£177·65, DT £23·95–£28·95, DBB £20–£25, WB, ⏢, Bk £3, L £3·95, D £8, cc 1 2 3 5 6, Dep a.

★★**Eagles** *Ancaster Sq, LL26 0LG.* ✆ (0492) 640454. C. ⊯ 14 bedrs, 10 bp, 1 bps, 1 ba, TV, Dgs. ✗ mc, LD 8.30. ⊡ ch, TV, Dgs, CP 70, Ac, con 150, CF, 2 st. **£** BB £12·50–£14·50, DB £27–£28·50, WT £153–£168, DBB £19–£23, WB, ⏢, Bk £3·75, L £4·50, D £7, cc 1 3.

■★★**Meadowsweet** (R), *Station Rd, LL26 0DS.* ✆ (0492) 640732. RS Nov– Easter (except Xmas), C. ⊯ 10 bedrs, 10 bps, 2 ba, TV, Dgs. ✗ a l c, mc, LD 9.30. ⊡ CH, Dgs, ns, CP 10, Ac, CF, 1 st. **£** BB £17·50–£21·50, DB £27–£36, WB, ⏢, Bk £5, L £5·95, D £8, cc 1 2 3, Dep a.

Rescue Service: Central Garage, The Square. ✆ (0492) 640445.

LLANSANTFFRAID-YM-MECHAIN Powys.
Map 19E. Shrewsbury 19, London 173, Oswestry 9, Welshpool 11.

Rescue Service: Brian Foulkes, Meifod Road Garage. ✆ (069 181) 740.

LLANTES Dyfed. Map Area 11F
St Clears 8, London 229, Haverfordwest 18, Pembroke 15, Tenby 9.

Rescue Service: H & G Motor Services, A477. ✆ (069 181) 647.

LLANTRISANT Mid Glamorgan. Map 4B
Pop 6,034 (inc Talbot Green). Caerphilly 9, London 157, Bridgend 10, Cardiff 10, Pontypridd 7.
MD Sat. **Golf** Llantrisant and Pontyclun 18h. **See** Perp Church, 13th cent Castle ruins.

Rescue Service: Llantrisant Motors (1934) Ltd, Talbot Garage. ✆ (0443) 223324.

LLANTWIT MAJOR South Glamorgan. Map 4B
Pop 8,776. Cardiff 15, London 164, Bridgend 9½, Caerphilly 21, Pontypridd 19.
EC Wed. **Golf** Southerndown 18h. **See** St Illtyd's Church, 15th cent Town Hall, Dovecote and 13th cent Gatehouse, old Swan Inn.

Repairer: Williams Garage Ltd, Collhugh St. ✆ (044 65) 3466.

LLANVETHERINE Gwent. Map 13E
Pop 100. Ross-on-Wye 17, London 138, Abergavenny 5½, Hereford 22, Monmouth 12.
Golf Llanfuist 18h. **See** 14th cent Church, 13th cent White Castle ruins 1 m SE, Offa's Dyke Path.

Rescue Service: W G Lane & Sons, Forge Garage. ✆ Cross Ash (087 386) 388.

LLANWNDA Gwynedd. Map 18C
Caernarfon 3½, London 244, Betws-y-Coed 27, Holyhead 33, Porthmadog 17, Pwllheli 17.
Golf Caernarfon 18h. **See** Caernarfon Bay.

★★★**M Stables** (R), *LL54 5SD.* ✆ (0286) 830711. C. ⊯ 12 bedrs, 12 bp, TV, Dgs. ✗ a l c, mc, at, LD 9.45. ⊡ N, CH, CP 60, Ac, sp, sol, con 50, CF, 12 BGf, 1 st, Dis. **£** BB £24–£26·40, DB £35–£38·50, WB, ⏢, Bk £4·75, L £5·75, D £8·50, cc 1 2 3, Dep a.

LLANWRTYD WELLS Powys. Map 12D
Pop 500. Builth Wells 13, London 185, Brecon 24, Llandovery 11, Knighton 36, Newtown 44, Rhayader 21.
EC Wed. **Golf** Builth Wells 9h. **See** Mountain scenery, Abernant Lake, Spa.

▟★★★**Abernant Lake,** *Station Rd, LD5 4RR.* ✆ (059 13) 250. Closed Jan. C. ⊯ 56 bedrs, 31 bp, 9 ba, Dgs. ✗ mc, at, LD 8.45. ⊡ Lt, CH, TV, Dgs, CP 100, Ac, sp, tc, pf, con 100, CF, **£** BB fr £24·20, DB fr £48·40, WB (winter only), ⏢, cc 1 3 4 5.

★**Neuadd Arms,** *LD5 4RB.* ✆ (059 13) 236. C. ⊯ 18 bedrs, 1 bp, 5 ba, Dgs. ✗ mc, LD 8.30. ⊡ CH, TV, Dgs, CP 10, Ac, rf, CF, 1 st. **£** BB £11–£13, DB £22–£23, WT £110–£120, DT £18, DBB £17–£18·50, WB, ⏢, Bk £2, L £5, D £6, cc 1 4.

Rescue Service: W R Powell & Sons, The Garage, Beulah Rd. ✆ (059 13) 259.

LLWYNGWRIL Gwynedd. Map 18E
Dolgellau 11, London 218, Aberdyfi 13,
Newtown 47
Rescue Service: Edwards & Thomas,
Llwyngwril Garage. ✆ Fairbourne (0341)
250629.

LLYSWEN Powys. Map 12D
Pop 150. Brecon 9, London 159,
Abergavenny 21, Builth Wells 12, Hereford
29, Leominster 30.
Golf Brecon 9h, Cradoc 18h. **See** Church.

◼★**Griffin Inn,** *LD3 0UR.* ✆ (087 485)
241. C. ⇔ 6 bedrs, 4 bp, 2 bps, TV, Dgs.
✗ mc, LD 9. ⓓ CH, Dgs, CP 18, G 2, CF.
£ BB £12·50, DB £20, DBB £18·50, ⬜,
cc 1 2 3 5 6, Dep a.

LOUGHOR West Glamorgan. Map 12E
Neath 13, London 198, M4 Motorway 4,
Carmarthen 24, Brecon 41, Llandovery 33,
Swansea 7.

Rescue Service: Castle Garages
(Loughor) Ltd, 1–5 Castle St. ✆ Swansea
(0792) 892242.

LOWER REDBROOK Gwent. M. Area
13E.
Gloucester 21, London 125, Chepstow 14,
Monmouth 3.
See Wye Valley.
Rescue Service: Startime Services.
✆ Monmouth (0600) 3208.

MACHYNLLETH Powys. Maps 12A and
18F
See also EGLWYSFACH and PENNAL.
Pop 1,904. Newtown 28, London 205,
Aberdyfi 10, Aberystwyth 17, Dolgellau
15, Welshpool 38.
EC Thur. **MD** Wed. **Golf** Machynlleth 9h.
See Owain Glyndwr Institute, Plas
Machynlleth, Castleragh Memorial
Clock.
🄸 Canolfan Owain Glyndwr.
✆ Machynlleth (0654) 2401.

★★**Wynnstay** (TH), *Maengwyn St, SY20
8AE.* ✆ (0654) 2003. C. ⇔ 31 bedrs, 9 bp,
1 bps, 5 ba, TV, Dgs. ✗ a l c, mc, at, LD 8.
ⓓ CH, Dgs, CP 42, Ac, con 30, CF. £ BB fr
£31, DB fr £41, WB, ⬜, cc 1 2 3 4 5 6,
Dep (Xmas).

Rescue Service: Gareth Humphreys, The
Service Garage, Cemmaes Rd.
✆ Cemmaes Rd. (065 02) 356.

MALLWYD Gwynedd. Map 18F
Pop 200. Welshpool 26, London 198,
Aberdyfi 21, Aberystwyth 29, Bala 18,
Dolgellau 10, Newtown 28, Rhayader 43.
EC Thur.

★**Brigands Inn** (R), *SY20 9HY.* ✆ Dinas
Mawddwy (065 04) 208. Closed Nov. C.
⇔ 14 bedrs, 3 bp, 1 sh, 4 ba, Dgs. ✗ a l c,
mc, at, LD 9.15. ⓓ ch, TV, CP 50, U 2, pf,
CF, 1 st. £ BB £12·95–£14·95, DB £25·90–
£29·90, WT £125, DBB £19·45–£21·45,
WB, ⬜, Bk £3·25, L £3·75, D £6·50,
cc 1 3 6.

MANORBIER Dyfed. Map 11F
Pop 350. Tenby 5, London 244, Pembroke
6.
Golf Tenby 18h. **See** 12th cent Castle,
12th cent Parish Church.

★★**Castle Mead** (RI), *SA70 7TA.*
✆ (083 482) 358. Open Mar–Sept. C. ⇔ 8
bedrs, 6 bp, 2 bps, 1 ba, annexe 3 bedrs, 3
bp. ✗ mc, LD 8. ⓓ CH, TV, CP 20, CF. £ BB

£14–£16, DB £40–£44, WT £129–£140, ⬜,
Bk £2·50, L 85p, D £7, cc 3.

Rescue Service: The Garage. ✆ (083 482)
485.

MENAI BRIDGE Gwynedd. Map 18C
Pop 2,300. Bangor 2½, London 240,
Caernarfon 8, Holyhead 21.
EC Wed. **MD** Mon. **Golf** Baron Hill,
Beaumaris 9h. **See** Suspension Bridge
(built by Telford), Museum of Childhood,
St Tysilio Church.
🄸 Coed Cyrnol. ✆ Menai Bridge (0248)
712626.

★★**Anglesey Arms,** *LL59 5EA.* ✆ (0248)
712305. C. ⇔ 17 bedrs, 16 bp, 1 sh, 1 ba,
Dgs. ✗ mc, at, LD 9. ⓓ CH, TV, Dgs, CP 30,
Ac, CF, 1 st. £ BB £16–£18, DB £36, WT
£170, DT £29, DBB £23–£25, WB, ⬜, Bk
£3, L £4·50, D £7, cc 1 3, Dep.

MERTHYR TYDFIL Mid Glamorgan.
Map 12F
Pop 61,500. Tredegar 7½, London 162,
Brecon 18, Caerphilly 16, Hirwaun 6,
Llandovery 31, Newport 26, Pontypridd
12.
EC Thur. **MD** Tue, Sat. **Golf** Cilsanws 9h.
See Cyfarthfa Castle, now museum and
art gallery, Morlais Castle (ruins).
🄸 Cyfarthfa Park. ✆ Merthyr Tydfil (0685)
71491.

★★**Castle,** *Castle St, CF47 8BG.*
✆ (0685) 2327. C. ⇔ 47 bedrs, 47 bp, TV,
Dgs. ✗ mc, LD 9. ⓓ Lt, N, CH, Ac, CF, 1 st.
£ BB £23, DB £29, WB, ⬜, Bk £3, D £5·75,
cc 1 2 3 5, Dep b.

Rescue Service: P & S Motors, 29–33
Brecon Rd. ✆ (0685) 71872.
Thomas & Davis (Merthyr Tydfil) Ltd,
Pentrebach Rd. ✆ (0685) 2773.

MILFORD HAVEN Dyfed. Map 11E
Pop 13,750. Haverfordwest 7, London
250, Pembroke 8, Tenby 17.
EC Thur. **MD** Fri. **Golf** Milford Haven 18h.
See St Katharine's Church, St Thomas à
Becket Chapel, Harbour, Oil refinery
tanker terminals, Cliff walks and gardens,
fine scenery.

★★**Lord Nelson,** *Hamilton Ter, SA73
3AW.* ✆ (064 62) 5341. C. ⇔ 26 bedrs, 27
bp, 1 ba, TV, Dgs. ✗ a l c, mc, at, LD 9. ⓓ N,
CH, Dgs, CP 40, con 80, CF, 3 st. £ BB £25,
DB £35, WB, ⬜, cc 1 2 3 5 6.
Belhaven House, PH, z (R), *29 Hamilton
Ter, SA73 3JJ.* ✆ (064 62) 5983. C. ⇔ 12
bedrs, 7 sh, 4 ba, guide Dgs only. ✗ a l c.
ⓓ CH, TV, CF, 2 st. £ BB £12·30–£17·30,
DB £24·60–£26·60, WT (c) £61·50–
£73·80, DT £13·50–£14·50, ⬜, Bk £2·30, D
£3, cc 1 2 3 5.

MILTON Dyfed. Map 11F
Pop 250. Carmarthen 28, London 240,
Pembroke 4, Haverfordwest 13.
Golf Tenby 18h. **See** 13th cent Norman
Church, Market Cross.

★★**Milton Manor** (R), *SA70 8PG.*
✆ Carew (064 67) 398. C. ⇔ 26 bedrs, 14
bp, 7 bps, 5 sh, 5 ba, TV, Dgs. ✗ a l c, mc,
at, LD 9.30. ⓓ CH, TV, Dgs, CP 40, gc, rf,
sol, con 12, CF, 6 BGf, 0 st, Dis. £ BB
£13·35–£17·35, DB £26·70–£34·70, DBB
£18·15–£22·15, WB, ⬜, Bk £2, L £2, D
£6·25.

MINERA Clwyd.
Pop 1,395. 5 m W of Wrexham. London
183, Chester 14, Ruthin 12, Shrewsbury
33.
See Lead Mines.

Rescue Service: H K Motors, Wern Rd.
✆ Wrexham (0978) 757843.

MOLD Clwyd. Map 19C
Pop 8,860. Wrexham 11, London 191,
Chester 11, Colwyn Bay 30, Corwen 21,
Denbigh 16, Llangollen 19, Queensferry
6½, Rhyl 22, Ruthin 10.
EC Thur. **MD** Wed, Sat. **Golf** Mold 18h.
See 15th cent Church, Norman Castle at
Bailey Hill.
🄸 Town Hall, Earl St. ✆ Mold (0352)
59331.

★★**Bryn Awel,** *Denbigh Rd, CH7 1BL.*
✆ (0352) 58622. Closed Dec 24–Jan 2. C.
7 bedrs, 3 bp, 1 ba, TV. ✗ a l c, mc, at, LD
10.15. ⓓ CH, CP 60, G 6, Ac, con, CF, 2 st.
£ BB £14·50–£22, DB £22·75–£30, WB, ⬜,
Bk £3, L £1·95, D £8, cc 1 3 5 6, Dep b.

Repairer: Slaters of Mold Ltd, Bro Alun,
King St. ✆ (0352) 3715.

MONMOUTH Gwent. Map 13E
Pop 7,350. Gloucester 24, London 129,
Abergavenny 15, Chepstow 16, Hay-on-
Wye 33, Hereford 17, Newport 22,
Pontypool 20, Ross-on-Wye 10.
EC Thur. **MD** Mon, Sat. **Golf** Monmouth
9h. **See** Castle ruins (birthplace of Henry
V), Statue of Henry V, Statue of the Hon.
C S Rolls (one of the founders of Rolls-
Royce Ltd and a pioneer of flying), St
Mary's Church, St Thomas's Church,
Nelson Museum and Local History Centre,
Monnow Bridge and 13th cent
Gatehouse, 17th cent Wye Bridge, Great
Castle House, several old inns, Naval
Temple on Kymin Hill 2 m, Pembridge
(13th cent moated border Castle) 4 m
NW.
🄸 Nelson Museum. ✆ Monmouth (0600)
3899.

★★★**King's Head,** *Agincourt Sq, NP5
3DY.* ✆ (0600) 2177. C. ⇔ 25 bedrs, 19
bp, 4 bps, 2 sh, 2 ba, TV, Dgs. ✗ a l c, mc,
LD 9 (Sat 10). ⓓ N, CH, TV, Dgs, CP 20,
Ac, con 200, CF, 0 st. £ BB £37·50, DB
£49, WB, ⬛, Bk £4·50, L £8, D £10,
cc 1 2 3 5 6, Dep b.

★★**Beaufort Arms,** *Agincourt Sq, NP5
3BT.* ✆ (0600) 2411. C. ⇔ 25 bedrs, 3 bp,
4 ba, Dgs. ✗ a l c, mc, LD 10. ⓓ CH, TV,
Dgs, CP 50, Ac, con 120, CF, 1 st. £ BB
£12–£17, DB £24–£28, WT £129·50, DT
£21·25, DBB £18·50–£23·50, WB, Bk £3, L
£2·75, D £8·50, cc 1 2 3 5.
Leasbrook Country, *Dixton, NP5 5SN.*
✆ (0600) 2831.
Queens Head, I, z, *St James St.* ✆ (0600)
2767. C. ⇔ 6 bedrs, 1 bp, 5 bps, TV, Dgs.
✗ a l c. ⓓ CH, TV, Dgs, CP 6, CF. £ BB
£10·90–£12, DB £20·80–£24, WT £75–
£85, D £15–£17, ⬜, Bk £2·50, L £3, D £3,
cc 1 5.

Repairer: E B Manns, St James Garage, St
James Sq. ✆ (0600) 2773.

MORFA NEFYN Gwynedd. Map 18C
Pop 850. Porthmadog 19, London 247,
Aberdaron 12, Caernarfon 21, Pwllheli 7.
EC Wed. **Golf** Morfa Nefyn 18h. **See** Ty
Coch Inn 200 yrs old.

★★Linksway (R), *LL53 6BG*. ✆ Nefyn
(0758) 720258. C. ⊷ 25 bedrs, 22 bp, 2
ba, Dgs. ✗ a l c, mc, at, LD 9.30. 🏰 CH, TV,
CP 100, U 5, Ac, con 40, CF, 4 BGf, 1 st,
Dis. £ WB, Bk £1·95, L £3·95, D £6·95,
Dep a.
★★Woodlands Hall, *Edern, LL53 6JB*.
✆ Nefyn (0758) 720425.

Rescue Service: Claremont Garage.
✆ Nefyn (0758) 720209.

MOUNTAIN ASH Mid Glamorgan. Map
12F
Pop 28,000. Newport 23, London 161,
Caerphilly 13, Hirwaun 7½, Merthyr Tydfil
10, Pontypool 19, Pontypridd 7½, Tredegar
18.
EC Thur. **Golf** Cefnpennar 18h. **See**
Llanwonno Church, Clydach Valley,
Dyffryn Woods and Gorsedd Circle.

Rescue Service: Cardiff Rd Garage.
✆ (0443) 472259.

MUMBLES West Glamorgan. Map 12E
Pop 13,712. Swansea 3½, London 193,
Carmarthen 29, Llanelli 13.
EC Wed. **Golf** Langland Bay 18h. **See**
Oystermouth Castle ruins, Lighthouse on
Mumbles Head, cliff scenery of Gower
Peninsula.

★St Anne's (R), *Weston La, SA3 4EY*.
✆ Swansea (0792) 69147. Closed Xmas.
C. ⊷ 25 bedrs, 17 bp, 2 bps, 3 ba, TV.
✗ mc, at, LD 6·30. 🏰 CH, TV, CP 40, CF, 7
BGf, 3 st. £ BB £13·80–£16·68, DB
£20·70–£23, DB £18·40–£19·28, 🏰, Bk
£2·30, D £4·60.
Carlton, PH, z (R), *654 Mumbles Rd,
SA3 4EA*. ✆ Swansea (0792) 60450.
Harbour Winds, PH, x (Unl), *18 Over-
land Rd, SA3 4LP*. ✆ Swansea (0792)
69298. Open Apr–Sept. C. ⊷ 8 bedrs, 1 bp,
1 bps, 2 ba, Dgs. 🏰 CH, TV, ns, CP 16, CF.
£ BB £10–£13, DB £20–£26, WT (b) £102–
£110, DT (b) £15·50–£16·50, 🏰.
Shoreline, PH, z (Rl), *648 Mumbles Rd,
Southend, SA3 4EA*. ✆ Swansea (0792)
66322. C. ⊷ 13 bedrs, 1 bp, 4 bps, 2 ba,
TV. 🏰 CH, TV, 2 st. £ BB £10–£16, DB
£16–£23, WT (b) £122·50, (c) £59·50, DT
(b) £14·50–£20·50, 🏰, cc 1 5.
Southend, PH, x (Rl), *724 Mumbles Rd,
SA3 4EL*. ✆ Swansea (0792) 66329. C.
⊷ 11 bedrs, 2 ba, TV, Dgs. ✗ a l c. 🏰 ch,
TV, CP 2, CF, 4 st. £ BB £9–£10, DB £16–
£18, DT (b) £13–£16, 🏰, Bk £3, L £3·50, D
£3·50, cc 1 3 5.

NARBERTH Dyfed. Map 11F
Pop 1,000. Carmarthen 20, London 233;
Cardigan 22, Fishguard 19,
Haverfordwest 10, Pembroke 13, Tenby
10.
EC Wed. **MD** Thur. **Golf** Tenby 18h. **See**
St Andrew's Church, Llawhaden Castle 3
m NW, Blackaldern Gardens.

Blaenmarlais, H, xy (Rl), *Redstone Rd,
SA67 7ES*. ✆ (0834) 860326.

MC Repairer: J Bowen & Sons
(Llawhaden) Ltd. ✆ Llawhaden (099 14)
206.
Sctr Repairer: J Bowen & Sons
(Llawhaden) Ltd. ✆ Llawhaden (099 14)
206.
Rescue Service: Commercial Garage Ltd,
Spring Gardens. ✆ (0834) 860429.
Rushacre Garage, Redstone Rd. ✆ (0834)
860573.

NEATH West Glamorgan. Map 12E
Pop 15,125. Hirwaun 16, London 184, M4
Motorway 3¼, Bridgend 17, Llandovery 16,
Llanelli 16, Swansea 7½.
EC Thur. **MD** Wed. **Golf** Neath 18h. **See**
St Thomas' Church, Abbey ruins, Castle
ruins, remains of Roman Fort, Wild Life
Park.

★★Cimla Court, *77 Cimla Rd, SA11 3TT*.
✆ (0639) 3771. Closed Xmas. C. ⊷ 25
bedrs, 19 bp, 3 bps, 3 sh, 1 ba, TV, Dgs.
✗ a l c, mc, at, LD 10.30. 🏰 Lt, N, CH, TV,
CP 100, Ac, con 200, CF, 25 BGf, 2 st.
£ BB £22·50, DB £45, 🏰, Bk £2·75, L
£5, HT £7·25, cc 1 2 3 5 6.▲

NEFYN Gwynedd. Map 18C
Pop 1,150. Porthmadog 17, London 247,
Aberdaron 13, Caernarfon 19, Pwllheli 6½.
EC Wed. **Golf** Morfa Nefyn 18h. **See** St
Mary's Church, now Maritime Museum.

⚘★★Plas Pistyll (R), *LL53 6LU*.
✆ (0758) 720372. Open Apr–Sept & Xmas.
C. ⊷ 24 bedrs, 6 ba, Dgs. ✗ mc, at, LD
8.30. 🏰 CH, TV, Dgs, CP 40, pf, CF, 1 BGf,
3 st. £ WB, Dep a.
★Caeau Capel (R), *LL53 6EB*. ✆ (0758)
720240. Open May–Sept & Easter. RS
Easter–Spring Bank Hol. C. ⊷ 23 bedrs, 4
bp, 4 ba, Dgs. ✗ mc, at, LD 7.30. 🏰 ch, TV,
Dgs, CP 30, Ac, tc, CF, 1 BGf, 1 st, Dis.
£ WB, 🏰, c 1 3.

Rescue Service: Trenholme Blue Motors
Garage, Church St. ✆ (0758) 720206.

NELSON Mid Glamorgan. Map 12F
Pop 4,324. Newport 17, London 154,
Bridgend 22, Caerphilly 7, Hirwaun 13,
Merthyr Tydfil 10, Pontypool 12,
Pontypridd 5½, Tredegar 14.
EC Thur. **MD** Mon. **Golf** Bargoed 18h.

Rescue Service: J L Richards, Dynevor
Garage. ✆ (0443) 450202.

NEWBRIDGE-ON-WYE Powys. Map
12D
Pop 297. Hereford 45, London 175, Builth
Wells 6½, Knighton 22, Leominster 37,
Llandovery 23, Rhayader 7½.
EC Thur. **Golf** Llandrindod Wells 18h. **See**
All Saints' Church, River Wye.

★New Inn, *LD1 6HY*. ✆ (059 789) 211.
Closed Xmas. C. ⊷ 10 bedrs, 1 bp, 2 ba,
Dgs. ✗ a l c, mc, at, LD 9. 🏰 ch, TV, Dgs, CP
100, Ac, CF, 0 st. £ BB £11·50, DB £23–
£26, WB, 🏰, Bk £3·50, L £3, D £6, cc 1.

Rescue Service: John A Powell, Great
House Garage. ✆ (059 789) 235.

NEWCASTLE EMLYN Dyfed. Map 11D
Pop 547. Lampeter 19, London 223,
Aberystwyth 28, Cardigan 10, Carmarthen
17, Fishguard 23, Haverfordwest 30,
Tenby 36.
EC Wed. **MD** Fri. **Golf** Cardigan 18h. **See**
Castle ruins, Teifi Falls, Cenarth Falls 2½ m
W, Henllan Falls 3 m.

★★Emlyn Arms (R), *Bridge St, SA38
9DU*. ✆ (0239) 710317. C. ⊷ 18 bedrs, 9
bp, 3 ba, annexe 20 bedrs, 20 bp, TV, Dgs.
✗ a l c, mc, at, LD 8.45. 🏰 CH, TV, CP 120,
Ac, pf, con 50, CF, 10 BGf, 1 st. £ BB
£12·50–£21·50, DB £23–£32, DT £22·40–
£31·40, DBB £18·45–£27·45, WB, 🏰, Bk
£3·50, L £3·95, D £5·95, cc 1 2 3 5 6.

NEW CROSS Dyfed. Map 12A
Ponterwyd 10, London 204, Aberystwyth
5, Capel Bangor 3, Ystrad Meurig 8.

Golf Aberystwyth 18h.

Rescue Service: Gifford & Evans, Hillcrest
Garage, nr Aberystwyth. ✆ Llanilar
(097 47) 228.

NEWPORT Dyfed. Map 11D
Pop 800. Newcastle Emlyn 17, London
240, Cardigan 10, Fishguard 7½.
EC Wed. **Golf** Newport 9h. **See** Church,
Norman Castle, Hill Fort.
🏰 Nat. Park Centre, East St. ✆ Newport
(0239) 820912.

Rescue Service: Pioneer Garage, West St.
✆ (0239) 820217.

NEWPORT Gwent. Map 13E and 5A
Pop 133,698. Chepstow 15, London 137,
M4 Motorway 1, Abergavenny 18,
Caerphilly 11, Cardiff 12, Merthyr Tydfil
26, Monmouth 22, Pontypool 9, Tredegar
20.
EC Thur. **MD** Weekdays. **Golf** Tredegar
Park 18h. **See** Norman Castle ruins (13th
cent), St Woolos Cathedral, Museum and
Art Gallery, Murals at Civic Centre,
Transporter Bridge, Double View
(Ridgeway).
🏰 John Frost Sq. ✆ Newport (0633)
842962.

★★★★Celtic Manor, *The Coldra, NP6
2YA*. ✆ (0633) 413000. C. ⊷ 17 bedrs, 17
bp, TV. ✗ a l c, mc, at, LD 10.30. 🏰 N, CH,
TV, CP 150, U 1, Ac, con 120, CF, 0 st.
£ BB £38–£53, DB £45–£70, 🏰, Bk 5·75, L
£9, D £8, cc 1 2 3 5 6, Dep b.
▣★★★M Ladbroke, *The Coldra, NP6
2YG*. ✆ (0633) 412777. C. ⊷ 120 bedrs,
120 bp, TV, Dgs. ✗ mc, at, LD 9.45. 🏰 N,
CH, CP 400, Ac, con 500, CF, 72 BGf, 1 st,
Dis. £ BB £42, DB £57, WB, 🏰, Bk £4·25, L
£4, D £9·25, cc 1 2 3 5 6, Dep b.
★★Queen's, *Bridge St, NP4 4RN*.
✆ (0633) 62992. C. ⊷ 43 bedrs, 29 bp, 4
ba, TV, dgs. ✗ a l c, mc, at, LD 10. 🏰 N, CH,
Ac, con 60, CF, 0 st. £ BB £22·50–£32, DB
£34–£39, WB, 🏰, Bk £4·50, L £8·65, D
£8·65, cc 1 2 3 5, Dep b.
★★Westgate, *Commercial St, NP1 1TT*.
✆ (0633) 66244. C. ⊷ 70 bedrs, 30 bp, 15
ba, TV, Dgs. ✗ a l c, mc, at, LD 10. 🏰 Lt, N,
CH, TV, Dgs, CP 20, Ac, con 200, CF, 5 st.
£ BB £25–£35, DB £30–£40, WT £170, DT
£40, DBB £36–£45, WB, 🏰, Bk £3·25, L
£3·75, D £6, cc 1 2 3 4 5 6, Dep.
St Etienne, G, z (Unl), *162 Stow Hill,
NP4 4FZ*. ✆ (0633) 62341. C. ⊷ 6 bedrs,
6 sh, Dgs. 🏰 CH, TV, CF. £ BB £10–£12,
DB £20, WT (c) £40, 🏰.

Repairer: Lex Mead, Morris Hse,
Shaftesbury St. ✆ (0633) 858451.
Rescue Service: Automotive Services,
Newcastle Engine Works, 26 Coomassie
St. ✆ (0633) 51504.
County Motor Services, 248 Conway Rd.
✆ (0633) 275120.
Newport Vehicle Service Centre, 10A
Junction Rd. ✆ (0633) 58633.
Precision Tuning Auto Repairs (Maindee)
Ltd, 55a Archibald St, Maindee. ✆ (0633)
841521.

NEW QUAY Dyfed. Maps 12C and 11B
Pop 800. Lampeter 15, London 219,
Aberystwyth 22, Cardigan 19.
EC Wed. **Golf** Lampeter 9h.

Rescue Service: Adams Garage, George
St. ✆ (0545) 560263.

NEW RADNOR Powys. Map 12D
Pop 293. Hereford 25, London 157, Builth
Wells 14, Knighton 10, Rhayader 19.
EC Wed. **Golf** Llandrindod Wells 18h.

Rescue Service: Radnor Autos (Nant
Melan) Ltd, Melan Service Station,
Llanfihangel-Nant-Melan. ✆ (054 421)
249.

NEWTOWN Powys. Map 12B
Pop 5,517. Ludlow 32, London 175,
Aberystwyth 43, Builth Wells 34,
Rhayader 32, Welshpool 13.
EC Thur. **MD** Tue. **Golf** St Giles 9h. **See**
Robt Owen's grave, Owen Memorial
Museum, Textile Museum, Davies Art
Gallery.
🄿 Central Car Park. ✆ Newtown (0686)
25580.

★★★**Bear**, *Broad St, SY16 2LU.* ✆ (0686)
26964. C. ⬱ 36 bedrs, 28 bp, 5 bps, 3 sh, 2
ba, TV, Dgs. ✘ a l c, mc, at, LD 9.30. 🄰 N,
CH, Dgs, CP 60, Ac, con 40, CF, 1 st. £ BB
£19–£25, DB £27–£35, WT £150–£160,
DBB £20–£23, WB, 🄸, Bk £3, L £6·75, D
£6·75, cc 1 2 3 5.

Repairer: Meirion Motors, Pool Rd.
✆ (0686) 25942.
Smithfield Service Station. ✆ (0686)
26854.

NEYLAND Dyfed. Map 11E
Carmarthen 34, London 246, Fishguard
23, Haverfordwest 8½, St David's 23,
Tenby 13.

Rescue Service: Cleddau Bridge Garages
Ltd, Honeyborough Roundabout.
✆ (0646) 600858.

NORTHOP Clwyd. Map 19C
Pop 2,600. Mold 3, London 194, Chester
12, Colwyn Bay 29, Queensferry 5, Rhyl
19.
Golf Mold 18h. **See** Parish Church.

⚑★★★★**Chequers**, *Chester Rd,
Northophall, CH7 6JH.* ✆ Deeside (0244)
816181. C. ⬱ 30 bedrs, 28 bp, 2 bps, ns,
TV, Dgs. ✘ a l c, mc, at, LD 9.45. 🄰 CH,
Dgs, CP 200, U 2, con 100, CF, 1 BGf, 2 st.
£ BB £20–£27, DB £45–£50, WT £175–
£195, DT £30–£32, DBB £25–£27, WB, 🄸,
Bk £4·25, L £6, D £8, cc 1 2 3 5.

OLD COLWYN Clwyd. Map 18B
Mold 29, London 221, Colwyn Bay 1,
Denbigh 18, Queenferry 33, Rhyl 10.

★★**Lyndale**, *410 Abergele Rd, LL 29 9AB.*
✆ Colwyn Bay (0492) 515429. C. ⬱ 14
bedrs, 6 bp, 8 bps, TV, Dgs. ✘ a l c, mc, at,
LD 9. 🄰 CH, TV, Dgs, CP, at, Ac, CF, 5 st. £ BB £16,
DB fr £28, DT fr £23·50, WB, 🄸, Bk £3·50, L
£3·95, D £5·50, cc 1 3 4.

OVERTON-ON-DEE Clwyd. Map 19C
Whitchurch 12, London 175, Chester 19,
Llangollen 11, Shrewsbury 22, Wrexham
7.

Rescue Service: C H Wason & Son,
Overton Garage. ✆ (097 873) 240 and
711.

PEMBROKE Dyfed. Map 11E
Pop 5,500. Carmarthen 32, London 244,
Cardigan 37, Haverfordwest 19 (Fy 10),
Tenby 10.
EC Wed. **Golf** South Pembrokeshire 9h.
See Well preserved 12th-13th cent
Castle, Monkton Priory, Church, remains
of Lamphrey Palace 2 m E.

🄳 Drill Hall, Main St. ✆ Pembroke
(064 63) 2148.

★★★**Court**, *Lamphey, SA71 5NY.*
✆ (0646) 672273. C. ⬱ 22 bedrs, 22 bp,
TV. ✘ a l c, mc, at, LD 9.45. 🄰 CH, CP 100,
Ac, sp, sb, sol, gym, con 40, CF, 3 BGf, 4 st.
£ BB £16–£23, DB £32–£46, DBB £21–
£28, WB, 🄸, Bk £4·50, L £5·95, D £9·50,
cc 1 2 3 5 6, Dep.

★★**Lion**, *High St, SA71 4JS.* ✆ (0646)
4501. C. ⬱ 11 bedrs, 2 ba, ns, TV, Dgs.
✘ a l c, mc, at. 🄰 TV, Dgs, CP 10, Ac, con
90, CF, 3 st. £ BB £13·75, DB £25, WT
£117·25–£126·35, DT £20·75–£22·35,
DBB £16·75–£18·05, 🄸, Bk £2, L £4·50, D
£4·50, cc 1 2 3.

⚑★★**Underdown Country House** (R),
Grove Hill, SA71 5PT. ✆ (0646) 683350.
C. ⬱ 6 bedrs, 6 bp, 1 ba, TV, Dgs. ✘ a l c,
mc, at, LD 10. 🄰 N, CH, TV, CP 20, 1 Ac,
con 40, CF. £ BB fr £18·50, DB fr £28·50,
WT £175, DT £30, WB, 🄸, 10%, Bk £4·95, L
£9·30, D £9·30, cc 1 3, Dep a.

★★**Wheeler's Old King's Arms**, *Main
St, SA71 4UQ.* ✆ (0646) 683611.

★**Coach House Inn**, *116 Main St, SA71
4HN.* ✆ (0646) 684602. C. ⬱ 14 bedrs, 13
bp, 1 bps, TV. ✘ a l c, mc, at, LD 10. 🄰 CH,
Ac, sol, con 30, CF, 5 BGf, 1 st, Dis. £ BB
£19–£20, DB £29–£30, WT £133–£150, DT
£29–£30, DBB £24·25–£25, WB, 🄶, Bk £3,
L £5·25, D £5·25, cc 1 2 3 5.

Rescue Service: W L Silcox & Son Ltd, 15
Water St, Pembroke Dock. ✆ (0646)
683143.

PEMBROKE DOCK Dyfed. Map 11E
Pop 8,200. Pembroke 2, London 246,
Haverfordwest 11, Milford Haven 7, Tenby
11.
EC Wed. **MD** Fri. **Golf** Sth Pembroke 9h.

★★★**M Cleddau Bridge**, *Essex Rd,
SA72 6UT.* ✆ Pembroke (0646) 685961.
C. ⬱ 24 bedrs, 24 bps, 4 ba, TV, Dgs.
✘ a l c, mc, at, LD 9.30. 🄰 N, CH, TV, CP
150, Ac, sp, con 180, CF, 24 BGf, 0 st, Dis.
£ BB £15–£27·50, DB £30–£37·50, WB, 🄸,
B £3·50, cc 1 2 3 5 6, Dep b.

Rescue Service: Mel Neale Commercial
Repairs, Pater Workshop, Dock Yard.
✆ Pembroke (0646) 684599.

PENARTH South Glamorgan. Map 4B
Pop 23,551. Cardiff 4, London 153,
Bridgend 22.
EC Wed. **Golf** Glamorganshire 18h. **See**
Turner House Art Gallery, St Peter's
Church, Penarth Head, Penarth Holiday
Festival (July).
🄳 West House. ✆ Penarth (0222) 707201.

★★**Glendale**, *10 Plymouth Rd, CF6 2DH.*
✆ (0222) 706701. Closed Xmas. C. ⬱ 18
bedrs, 8 bp, 3 bps, 3 ba, TV, Dgs. ✘ a l c,
mc, at, LD 9.30. 🄰 CH, TV, Dgs, Ac, con 50,
CF, 1 BGf, 2 st. £ BB £15·50–£17·50, DB
£24–£27·50, WT £157·50, DT £24·50, DBB
£20·50–£22·50, WB, 🄸, L £4, D £6,
cc 1 2 3, Dep a.▲

★**Walton House** (R), *37 Victoria Rd, CF6
2HY.* ✆ (0222) 707782. Closed Xmas. RS
weekends Oct–Mar. C. ⬱ 13 bedrs, 4 bp,
1 bps, 2 ba, TV, Dgs. ✘ mc, LD 8. 🄰 CH,
CP 16, con 40, 2 st. £ BB £15–£17, DB
£26–£32, DT £27, DBB £22·50–£24, WB,
🄸, Bk £4·50, L £5, D £7·50, cc 1 3.

PENMAENMAWR Gwynedd. Map 18B
Pop 4,050. Colwyn Bay 10, London 232,
Bangor 10, Betws-y-Coed 19, Caernarfon
19, Llandudno 9.
EC Wed. **Golf** Penmaenmawr 9h.

Rescue Service: Glyn Percin Garage,
Conway Old Rd. Dwygfylchi. ✆ (0492)
622737.

PENNAL Gwynedd (Powys). Map 18F
Pop 180. Machynlleth 4, London 209,
Dolgellau 18.
EC Wed. **MD** Wed. **Golf** Aberdovey 18h.
See Roman Fort.

⚑★★**Llugwy Hall Country House**,
SY20 9JX. ✆ (065 475) 228. C. ⬱ 11
bedrs, 7 bp, 2 bps, TV, Dgs. ✘ mc, at, LD 9.
🄰 CH, Dgs, CP 40, Ac, con 25, CF, 0 st.
£ BB £19·50–£22·50, DB £28–£31·50, WT
£185–£195, DT £28–£37, DBB £26–£35,
WB, 🄶, Bk £3·50, L £2, D £6·50,
cc 1 2 3 5 6, Dep b.

PENPERGWM Gwent. Map 13E
Pop 300. Chepstow 21, London 144,
Abergavenny 3, Monmouth 13, Pontypool
9, Tredegar 14.
Golf Abergavenny 18h.

Rescue Service: Bryn Engineering Ltd,
✆ Gobion (087 385) 287.

PENRHYNDEUDRAETH Gwynedd.
Map 18C
Pop 1,820. Bala 25, London 224, Betws-y-
Coed 20, Caernarfon 20, Denbigh 37,
Dolgellau 22, Pwllheli 16, Ruthin 40.
EC Thur. **Golf** Royal St David's 18h. **See**
Portmeirion, Snowdonia National Park.

Repairers: S Pierce & Sons, The Garage.
✆ (0766) 770300.

PENYBONT Powys. Map 12B.
New Radnor 9, London 166, Builth Wells
12, Hereford 34, Rhayader 10.
Golf Llandrindod Wells 18h. **See** Pottery.

★★**Severn Arms**, *LD1 5UA.* ✆ (059 787)
224. Closed Xmas week. C. ⬱ 10 bedrs,
10 bp, 10 ba, Dgs. ✘ mc, LD 9.30. 🄰 CH,
TV, Dgs, CP 40, pf, CF, 1 st. £ BB £12, DB
£22, DBB £r £19·95, 🄸, Bk £3·50, D £6·95,
cc 1 3.

PENYGROES Gwynedd. Map 18C
Pop 3,000. Bala 43, London 243,
Aberdaron 28, Betws-y-Coed 28,
Caernarfon 6½, Dolgellau 38, Porthmadog
18, Pwllheli 15.
Golf Caernarfon 9h. **See** Snowdon 3,560
ft (Mtn Rly to summit).

Repairer: J T Jones & Sons, Cardigan
Garage. ✆ (0286) 880218.
Rescue Service: J B Services, County Rd.
✆ (0286) 881864.

PONTFAEN Dyfed. Map 11D
Lampeter 42, London 246, Cardigan 18,
Carmarthen 34, Fishguard 5,
Haverfordwest 16.

Tregynon, F, xy (R), *SA65 9TU.*
✆ Newport (0239) 820531. Closed Xmas.
C. ⬱ 5 bedrs, 2 ba, ns. ✘ a l c. 🄰 CH, TV,
CP, CF, 2 BGf, Dis. £ BB £8·60, DB £17·20,
WT (b) £95, DT (b) £13·80, 🄸.

PONTLLANFRAITH Gwent. Map 12F
Pop 8,500. Newport 20, London 149,
Bridgend 26, Caerphilly 7, Hirwaun 18,
Merthyr Tydfil 14, Pontypool 8,
Pontypridd 11, Tredegar 10.

EC Thur. **Golf** Blackwood 9h. **See** Penllwyn Hotel (former Tudor Manor House), St Tudor's Church, Gelligroes Mill (working watermill).

Repairer: Gibbs Bros Garages (Pontllanfraith) Ltd, Commercial St. ℄ Blackwood (0495) 223294.

PONTYCLUN Mid Glam. Map 4B
Pop 2,418. M4 Motorway 2½, Llantrisant 1½, London 158, Bridgend 11, Cardiff 10, Pontypridd 9.
Golf Llantrisant & Pontyclun 18h. **See** Miskin Manor, Church.

Rescue Service: Ace Tyres & Auto Joinery Works. ℄ Llantrisant (0443) 228997. Windsor Garage, rear of Windsor Hotel, Llantrisant Rd. ℄ Llantrisant (0443) 225120.

PONTYPOOL Gwent. Map 13E
Pop 36,815. Chepstow 20, London 143, Abergavenny 11, Caerphilly 14, Monmouth 20, Newport 8½, Pontypridd 19, Tredegar 17.
EC Thur. **MD** Daily. **Golf** Pontypool 18h. **See** Grotto, Pontypool Park.

Rescue Service: Auto Service (Pontypool) Ltd, Pontymoel. ℄ (049 55) 57111. Thomas B Rice & Son, Stable Garage, Clarence St. ℄ (049 55) 2920.

PONTYPRIDD Mid Glamorgan. Maps 12F and 4B
Pop 34,050. Caerphilly 7, London 155, Bridgend 17, Cardiff 11, Hirwaun 14, Merthyr Tydfil 11, Pontypool 19, Tredegar 19.
EC Thur. **MD** Wed, Sat. **Golf** Pontypridd 18h. **See** Pontypridd Old Bridge, St Catherine's Church, Library.

Rescue Service: Harold Lewis, Pontypridd Motors, Merthyr Rd. ℄ (0443) 402115. Laser Tuning, Old Station Yard, Treforest. ℄ (0443) 406133 & (0443) 407870. YNYS Garage, Glyndwr Av. ℄ (0443) 403049.

PORTHCAWL Mid Glamorgan. Map 4B
Pop 15,300. Bridgend 5½, London 174, Neath 16, Swansea 18.
EC Wed. **Golf** Royal Porthcawl 18h, Pyle and Kenfig 18h. **See** 13th cent St John's Church (Newton).
🛈 Old Police Station, John St. ℄ Porthcawl (065 671) 6639.

★★★**Sea Bank,** *The Promenade, CF36 3LU.* ℄ (065 671) 2261. C. ⊷ 64 bedrs, 42 bp, 10 ba, TV. ✗ a l c, mc, at, LD 10. 🅿 Lt, N, CH, Dgs, CP 100, Ac, sb, sol, gym, con 100, CF, 0 st. £ BB £27·50–£33, DB £38–£47·50, WB, ⬛, Bk £4, L £6, D £8, cc 1 2 3 5, Dep.

★★**Brentwood,** *Mary St, CF36 37N.* ℄ (065 671) 2725. C. ⊷ 27 bedrs, 17 bp, 2 bps, 1 sh, 3 ba, TV, Dgs. ✗ a l c, mc, at, LD 10.30. 🅿 CH, TV, CP 15, Ac, con 60, CF, 2 st. £ BB £14–£17, DB £22–£28, WB, ⬛, Bk £3, L £3, D £5·25, cc 1 2 3 6, Dep a.

★★**Fairways,** *West Drive, CF36 3LS.* ℄ (065 671) 2085. C. ⊷ 27 bedrs, 5 bp, 9 bps, 3 ba, TV. ✗ a l c, mc, at, LD 9.45. 🅿 Lt, CH, TV, CP 20, Ac, con 60, CF. £ BB £16–£28, DB £25–£40, WT £180–£210, DT £27·50–£33, DBB £26–£35, WB, ⬛, Bk £2·50, L £4·35, D £6·50, cc 1 2 3.

★★**Glenuab,** *50 St Mary St, CF36 3IY.* ℄ (065 671) 8242.

★★**Maid of Sker,** *West Rd, Nottage, CF36 3SN.* ℄ (065 671) 2172. C. ⊷ 10 bedrs, 10 bp, TV, Dgs. ✗ mc, at, LD 10. 🅿 CH, CP 100, Ac, con 120, CF, 4 BGf, 0 st, Dis. £ BB fr £25, DB fr £35, WT fr £165, DT fr £26, WB, ⬛, Bk £3, L £3·90, D £5·25, cc 1 2 3.

★★**Seaways,** *Mary St, CF36 3TA.* ℄ (065 671) 3510. C. 3. ⊷ 16 bedrs, 2 bp, 4 bps, 3 ba, TV, Dgs. ✗ a l c, LD 9.30. 🅿 ch, TV, CF, 3 st. £ BB £13·60–£20, DB £24–£31, WT £115, DT £21·50, DBB £18·70–£24·75, WB, ⬛, L £2·50, D £4·95, cc 1 2 3 5.

Collingwood, PH, z (R), *40 Mary St, CF36 3YA.* ℄ (065 671) 2899. C. ⊷ 8 bedrs, 1 ba, Dgs. 🅿 CH, TV, Dgs, CF. £ BB fr £7·50, DB fr £14, WT fr £69·50, (c) fr £47, DT (b) fr £11, ⬛, D £3·50.

Oakdale, PH, z (Unl), *46 Mary St, CF36 3YA.* ℄ (065 671) 3643. C. ⊷ 8 bedrs, 1 ba. 🅿 CH, TV, CP 2, CF. £ BB fr £7, DB fr £14, WT (b) fr £70, DT (b) fr £10, ⬛.

Penoyre, G, z (Unl), *29 Mary St, CF36 27N.* ℄ (065 671) 4550. Closed Xmas. C. ⊷ 4 bedrs, 1 ba, Dgs. 🅿 CH, TV, Dgs, CF. £ BB £7·50–£8, DB £15–£16, WT (c) £50–£53·50, DT (b) £11–£11·50, ⬛.

Rescue Service: Globe Garage Ltd, 1 Bridgend Rd. ℄ (065 671) 2067. Thomas Motors (Porthcawl) Ltd, Suffolk Pl. ℄ (065 671) 6221.

PORTHMADOG Gwynedd. Map 18C
Pop 2,000. Bala 29, London 228, Betws-y-Coed 23, Caernarfon 19, Dolgellau 20, Pwllheli 13.
EC Wed. **MD** Fri. **Golf** Porthmadog and Borth-y-Gest 18h. **See** Terminus of Ffestiniog Narrow Gauge Rly, Black Rock Sands.
🛈 High St. ℄ Porthmadog (0766) 2981.

★★**Royal Sportsman** (TH), *High St, LL49 9HA.* ℄ (0766) 2015. C. ⊷ 21 bedrs, 5 bp, 5 ba, TV, Dgs. ✗ a l c, mc, at, LD 9. 🅿 ch, Dgs, CP 28, Ac, con 40, CF, 4 BGf, 1 st, Dis. £ BB fr £31·50, DB fr £41·50, WB, ⬛, L £2 3 4 5 6, Dep (Xmas).

★★**Tyddyn Llwyn,** *Black Rock Rd, LL49 9UR.* ℄ (0766) 2205. C. 2. ⊷ 10 bedrs, 1 sh, 2 ba. ✗ LD 9. 🅿 CH, TV, Dgs, CP 50, Ac, con 80, CF, 1 st. £ BB £13–£15·50, DB £26–£31, DBB £18–£20·50, WB, ⬛, Bk £3, D £6, cc 1 3.

Rescue Service: Glan Aber Garage, Borth-y-Gest. ℄ (0766) 2364.

PORT TALBOT West Glamorgan. Maps 4A and 12E
Pop 40,143. Bridgend 12, London 180, M4 Motorway 2, Neath 5½, Swansea 8.
EC Wed. **MD** Tue, Sat. **Golf** Maesteg 9h. **See** Margam Abbey, Parish Church.

★★★**M Aberafan,** *Aberavon Sea Front, SA12 6QP.* ℄ (0639) 884949. C. ⊷ 67 bedrs, 67 bp, TV, Dgs. ✗ mc, at, LD 10.30. 🅿 Lt, N, CH, Dgs, CP 150, Ac, con 500, CF, 1 st. £ BB £26·50–£28, DB £33–£35, WT £172–£182, DT £39·20–£41·60, DBB £33·75–£35·75, WB, ⬛, Bk £3, L £5·85, D £7·75, cc 1 2 3 6.

★★**Twelve Knights,** *Margam Rd, SA13 2DB.* ℄ (0639) 882381. C. ⊷ 10 bedrs, 10 bp, TV, Dgs. ✗ a l c, mc, at, LD 10. 🅿 CH, ns, CP 120, Ac, con 180, CF. £ BB £25·20–£31·50, DB £33·60–£42, WB, ⬛, Bk £5, L £6·50, D £6·50, cc 1 2 3 5, Dep b.

MC *Repairer:* Mount Motorcycles (Port Talbot) Ltd, 57 Commercial St, Taibach. ℄ (0639) 883936.

Rescue Service: A & E Lawrence, Gas Works Estate, Victoria Rd, Aberavon. ℄ (0639) 897157.

PRESTATYN Clwyd. Map 18B
Pop 15,000. Queensferry 18, London 214, Denbigh 13, Rhyl 4.
EC Thur. **MD** Tue & Fri. **Golf** Prestatyn 18h. **See** Offa's Dyke Path.
🛈 Council Offices, Nant Hall Road. ℄ Prestatyn (074 56) 2484.

Hawarden House, *13–15 Victoria Rd, LL19 7SW.* ℄ (074 56) 4226.

Rescue Service: Allitts Motors, Marine Garage, Marine Rd. ℄ (074 56) 2128. V Smith Ltd, County Garage, Meliden Rd. ℄ (074 56) 2424.

PRESTEIGNE Powys. Map 13A
Pop 1,330. Leominster 12, London 151, Builth Wells 21, Hereford 23, Knighton 6, Ludlow 16, Rhayader 26.
EC Thur. **Golf** Knighton 9h. **See** Church (Norman origin), Old houses and Inns, Packhorse Bridge.

★★**Radnorshire Arms** (TH), *High St, LD8 2BE.* ℄ (0544) 267406. C. ⊷ 6 bedrs, 6 bp, annexe 10 bedrs, 10 bp, TV, Dgs. ✗ mc, at, LD 8.15. 🅿 Dgs, CP 20, G 6, Ac, CF, 6 st. £ BB fr £36·50, DB fr £51, WB, ⬛, cc 1 2 3 4 5 6, Dep (Xmas).

PWLLHELI Gwynedd. Map 18C
Pop 4,000. Porthmadog 13, London 242, Aberdaron 14, Caernarfon 19.
EC Thur. **MD** Mon, Wed. **Golf** Pwllheli 18h. **See** Gimblet Rock.
🛈 Y Maes. ℄ Pwllheli (0758) 3000.

Rescue Service: Geraint Hughes, Bridge Garage, Abererch Rd. ℄ (0758) 2022.

RAGLAN Gwent. Map 13E
Pop 1,800. Chepstow 13, London 136, Abergavenny 9, Monmouth 8, Newport 16, Pontypool 12.
Golf Monmouth 9h. **See** Ruins of 15th cent Castle, 14th-15th cent Church.

Rescue Service: Raglan Motors (Gwent) Ltd, Usk Rd. ℄ (0291) 690058.

RED WHARF BAY Gwynedd. Map 18A
Pop 1,080. Bangor 10, London 246, Caernarfon 15, Holyhead 22.
EC Thur. **Golf** Baron Hill 9h.

★**Min-y-Don,** *LL75 8RJ.* ℄ Tynygongl (0248) 852596. Open Apr–Sep. RS winter. C. ⊷ 18 bedrs, 3 bp, 3 ba, Dgs. ✗ mc, at, LD 10.30. 🅿 CH, TV, Dgs, CP 50, 3 st. £ Bk £4, L £1·65, D £6, cc 1 3, Dep a.

RHAYADER Powys. Map 12B
Pop 1,190. Hereford 47, London 174, Aberystwyth 34, Knighton 23, Leominster 38, Llandovery 31, Newtown 32.
EC Thur. **MD** Wed. **Golf** Llandrindod Wells 18h. **See** St Clement's Church, St Bride's Church, Elan Valley Reservoirs.
🛈 Old Swan, West St. ℄ Rhayader (0597) 810591.

★★**Elan Valley,** *Elan Valley, LD6 5HN.* (2½ m SW B4518). ℄ (0597) 810448. Closed Xmas. C. ⊷ 11 bedrs, 3 bp, 2 bps, 2 ba, Dgs. ✗ mc, at, LD 8. 🅿 CH, TV, Dgs, CP 50, U 6, Ac, con 100, CF, 2 st. £ BB £15–£16, DB £26–£28, WT £110–£127, DT £25·50–£28·50, DBB £19·50–£22·50, WB, ⬛, Bk £3·50, L £6, D £6·50, cc 2.▲

★**Lion Royal,** *West St, LD6 5AB.*
✆ (0597) 810202. RS Nov 1-Mar 31. C.
🚗 20 bedrs, 5 ba, Dgs. ✗ mc, at, LD 8.
🅿 TV, Dgs, CP 20, G 20, Ac, pf, rf, con 120,
0 st. **£** BB £12, DB £24, WT £140, DT £22,
DBB £17, ⬜, Bk £4, L £5·50, D £6.

RHOOSE South Glamorgan.
See BARRY.

RHOSNEIGR Gwynedd. Map 18A
Pop 1,569. Bangor 19, London 257,
Caernarfon 25, Holyhead 12.
EC Wed. **Golf** Holyhead 18h.

★★**Bay,** *LL64 5QW.* ✆ (0407) 810332. C.
🚗 26 bedrs, 6 bp, 5 ba, Dgs. ✗ mc, at, LD
8.15. 🅿 Dgs, CP 60, U 8, tc, CF. **£** BB
£11·50–£12·65, DB £23–£25·30, WT £126,
DT £25, ②, Bk £3, L £3, D £6·50.

Rescue Service: Premier Motor & Marine
Co, Premier Garage. ✆ (0407) 810449.

RHOS-ON-SEA Clwyd. Map 18B
See COLWYN BAY.

RHOSSILI West Glamorgan. Map 12E
Pop 333. Knelston 5, London 204,
Carmarthen 48, Cardiff 73, Llanelli 25,
Loughor 20, Pontardulais 24, Swansea 16.
Golf Pennard 18h. **See** St Mary's Church,
Rhossili Bay.

★★**Worms Head,** *SA3 1PJ.* ✆ Gower
(0792) 390512. Closed Xmas. C. 🚗 21
bedrs, 2 bp, 3 bps, 3 ba. ✗ a l c, mc, LD 8.
🅿 CH, TV, CP 20, Ac, con 36, CF, 5 BGf, 3
st. **£** BB £12·50, DB £25–£27, DBB
£17·50–£18·50, WB, ⬜, Bk £3·75, L £3, D
£6, Dep.

RHUDDLAN Clwyd. Map 18B
Pop 3,175. Queensferry 21, London 211,
Colwyn Bay 12, Denbigh 8½, Mold 19, Rhyl
12.
EC Thur. **Golf** Rhuddlan 18h. **See**
Rhuddlan Castle ruins, Bodrhyddan Hall,
Vale of Clwyd Church.

Rescue Service: D E Jones & Son Ltd,
Central Garage, Rhyl Rd. ✆ (0745)
590328.

RHYL Clwyd. Map 18B
Pop 23,000. Queensferry 22, London 212,
Colwyn Bay 11, Denbigh 11, Mold 22.
EC Thur. **MD** Wed, Sat. **Golf** Rhyl 9h. **See**
Royal Floral Hall, T'yn Rhyl—17th cent
house, The Marine Lake Leisure Park,
Rhuddlan Castle ruins 2½ m SE,
Bodrhyddan Hall 3 m SE.
ℹ Promenade. ✆ Rhyl (0745) 55068.

★★★**Westminster,** *East Parade, LL18
3AH.* ✆ (0745) 2241. C. 🚗 57 bedrs, 46
bp, 10 ba, TV, Dgs. ✗ a l c, mc, at, LD 10.
🅿 Lt, N, CH, TV, Dgs, CP 26, Ac, sb, sol,
gym, con 200, CF, 6 st. **£** BB £16·50–£18,
DB £24–£28, WT £133, WB, ②, 10%, Bk £3,
L £5·85, D £5·85, cc 1 2 3 5 6, Dep b.

★**Grange,** *East Promenade LL18 3AW.*
✆ (0745) 53174. C. 🚗 28 bedrs, 23 bp, 2
sh, 3 ba, TV, Dgs. ✗ a l c. 🅿 CH, TV, Dgs,
CP 17, CF, 6 BGf, 2 st. **£** BB fr £12·50, DB
fr £25, WT (b) fr £95, DT (b) fr £16·50, ⬜,
Bk £2·70, L £3, D £5·25, cc 1 3 5.

Arncliffe, G, z (Unl), *100 Crescent Rd,
LL18 1LY.* ✆ (0745) 53634. Closed Dec.
C. 🚗 6 bedrs, 1 ba. 🅿 ch, TV, Dgs, CP.
£ BB £6–£7, DB £12–£14, WT (b) £58–
£60, DT (b) £8·50–£9, ⬜, Bk £2·50, L
£3·50, D £3·50.

Bryn-Mawr, PH, z (R), *17 East Parade,
LL18 3AG.* ✆ (0745) 2821. Open Feb–

Nov. C. 🚗 13 bedrs, 3 ba. 🅿 CH, TV, CP 4,
CF 8 st. **£** BB fr £12, DB fr £21, WT (b) fr
£60, DT (b) fr £14, ⬜, Bk £3, D £4.

Harbour, H, x, *Foryd Rd, LL18 5AT.*
✆ (0745) 4206. C. 🚗 13 bedrs, 13 bp, TV,
Dgs. ✗ a l c. 🅿 CH, TV, Dgs, CP 50, CF.
£ BB £12–£12·50, DB £24–£25, WT (b)
£98–£105, DT £15–£17, ②, Bk £2, L £2·95,
D £4·50, cc 1 5.

Sandringham, H, z, *47 West Parade,
LL18 1HH.* ✆ (0745) 53986.
Toomargoed, PH, z (Rl), *31 John St,
LL18 1PP.* ✆ (0745) 4103.
Wroxeter, G, z, (Rl), *29 Warren Rd, LL18
1DR.* ✆ (0745) 53904. C. 🚗 7 bedrs, 2 ba,
TV. 🅿 CH, TV, CF.

Rescue Service: John W Foulds, Clifton
Service Station, 21 Grange Rd. ✆ (0745)
50226.
West End Garage, Ffynnongroew Rd.
✆ (0745) 2149.

ROSSETT Clwyd. Map 19c
Whitchurch 18, London 181, Chester 7,
Mold 11, Nantwich 21, Wrexham 5½

Rossett Court (R), *Chester Rd,
LL12 0HN.* ✆ Chester (0244) 570518. C.
🚗 5 bedrs, 1 ba. ✗ a l c. 🅿 CH, TV, CP 15,
CF. **£** BB £10, DB £16–£20, DT (b) £16, ②,
Bk £2, D £6.

RO-WEN Gwynedd. Map 18E
Betwys-y-Coed 12, London 228, Bangor
22, Caernarfon 28, Colwyn Bay 9½,
Conway 5.

🍴★★**Tir-y-Coed** (R), *LL32 8TP.* ✆ Tyn-y-
Groes (049 267) 219. Open Mar–Oct. C. 5.
🚗 7 bedrs, 5 bp, 1 bps, 1 sh, TV, Dgs.
✗ mc, at, LD 7.30. 🅿 ch, TV, CP 10, CF, 6
st. **£** BB £13·50–£16·50, DB £27–£30,
DBB £19·50–£21·50, ②, Bk £3, D £6·75.

RUABON Clwyd. Map 19C
Pop 5,500. Shrewsbury 27, London 181,
Wrexham 5, Oswestry 10, Llangollen 6.
EC Sat. **Golf** Llangollen 18h. **See** Church,
Belan Tower, Offa's Dyke.

★★**Wynnstay Arms,** *LL14 6BL.*
✆ (0978) 822187. C. 🚗 9 bedrs, 2 bp, 1
ba, TV, Dgs. ✗ a l c, mc, LD 9.45. 🅿 CH,
CP 80, U 1, Ac, con 120, CF, 2 st. **£** BB
£17·50–£20, DB £28–£32, DBB £22·50–
£30, WB, ⬜, Bk £2·50, L £4·50, D £6,
cc 1 2 3 6.

RUTHIN Clwyd. Map 19C
Pop 4,338. Wrexham 18, London 196,
Betws-y-Coed 25, Corwen 12, Denbigh
7½, Llangollen 15, Mold 10.
EC Thur. **MD** Tue, Thur, Fri. **Golf** Ruthin-
Pwllglas 18h. **See** St Peter's Church
(black oak roof of 500 panels), old
houses, Maen Huail, Ruthin Castle.
ℹ Town Hall. ✆ Ruthin (082 42) 3992.

★★★**Castle,** *St Peter's Sq, LL15 1AA.*
✆ (082 42) 617074. C. 🚗 20 bedrs, 20 bp,
TV, Dgs. ✗ a l c, mc, at, LD 8.45. 🅿 CH,
Dgs, CP 50, Ac, con 75, CF, 2 BGf, 0 st,
Dis. **£** BB fr £22, DB fr £34, DBB fr £22·50,
WB ⬜, Bk £3·50, L £4, D £6·95,
cc 1 2 3 5 6, Dep a.

★★★**Ruthin Castle,** *Corwen Rd, LL15
2NU.* ✆ (082 42) 2664. C. 🚗 60 bedrs, 60
bp, Dgs. ✗ a l c, mc, at, LD 9. 🅿 Lt, N, CH,
TV, CP 200, Ac, pf, con 120, CF, 14 BGf.
£ BB £27, DB £44·50, WB, ⬜, Bk £4·25, L
£5·75, D £8·90, cc 1 2 3 5.

Rescue Service: Slaters of Ruthin Ltd,
Well St. ✆ (082 42) 2645.

ST ASAPH Clwyd. Map 18B.
Pop 2,780. Mold 16, London 207, Betws-
y-Coed 26, Colwyn Bay 11, Denbigh 5½,
Rhyl 5½.
EC Thur. **MD** Thur. **Golf** Rhuddlan 18h.
See Small 15th cent Cathedral, Parish
Church of St Kentigern, Bodelwyddan
Marble Church.

★★★**Oriel House,** *Upper Denbigh Rd,
LL17 0LW.* ✆ (0745) 582716. C. 🚗 19
bedrs, 12 bp, 7 bps, TV, Dgs. ✗ a l c, mc,
LD 9.30. 🅿 CH, CP 150, Ac, con 200, CF,
4 BGf, 0 st, Dis. **£** BB £24·50–£25, DB
£40–£42, DBB £31·50–£32, WB, ②, Bk
£3·50, L £5·50, D £9·50, cc 1 2 3 5 6.

★★**Plas Elwy,** *The Roe, LL17 0LT.*
✆ (0745) 582263. C. 🚗 7 bedrs, 7 bps, 1
ba, TV. ✗ LD 10.30. 🅿 CH, CP 20, sp, CF,
2 st. **£** BB £16·50–£18, DB £25–£27·50,
WT £180–£198, DT £25–£27·50, DBB
£22–£24·50, ⬜, Bk £4, L £3·95, D £6,
cc 1 2 3 5, Dep b.

ST ATHAN South Glamorgan. Map Area
4B
Cardiff 15, London 165, Bridgend 13.
Rescue Service: Vincents (Garages) Ltd.
✆ St Athan (0446) 750418.

ST CLEARS Dyfed. Map 11F
Pop 1,170. Carmarthen 9, London 221,
Cardigan 23, Haverfordwest 21,
Pembroke 23, Tenby 17.
EC Wed. **MD** Tue. **Golf** Tenby 18h. **See**
12th cent Church, Castle mound, Castle
House, Gothic Villa.

Black Lion, H, X, ✆ (0994) 230700. C.
🚗 11 bedrs, 3 ba, TV, Dgs. ✗ a l c. 🅿 CH,
TV, Dgs, CP 25, CF, 1 st. **£** BB £8·50–
£9·50, DB £17–£19, WT (c) £56–£63, ⬜,
Bk £2·50, L £5, D £7.▲

ST DAVID'S Dyfed. Map 11C
Pop 1,520. Haverfordwest 15, London
259, Fishguard 17.
Golf St David's 9h. **See** Cathedral,
Bishop's Palace ruins.
ℹ Nat. Park Centre, City Hall. ✆ St David's
(0437) 720392.

🍴★★★**Warpool Court,** *Goat St, SA62
6BN.* ✆ (0437) 720300.
🍴🎦★★**Whitesands Bay,** *SA62 6PT.*
✆ (0437) 720403. C. 🚗 15 bedrs, 6 bp, 6
bps, 2 ba, TV, Dgs. ✗ mc, at, LD 9. 🅿 ch,
TV, ns, CP 30, Ac, sp, sb, sol, con 45, CF.
£ BB £13–£21, DB £16–£25, DBB £22–
£30, WB, ⬜, Bk £3·50, D £8·95, cc 1 3 6,
Dep a.▲

★★**Old Cross,** *Cross Square, SA62 6SP.*
✆ (0437) 720387. Open Mar–Oct. C.
🚗 17 bedrs, 17 bp. ✗ a l c mc, at, LD
8.30. 🅿 CH, TV, Dgs, CP 25, CF, 0 st. **£** BB
£12·50–£21, DB £25–£37, WT £130–
£180, DT £21–£26, DBB £20–£24, WB, ②,
Bk £2·50, D £6·80.

★★**St Non's,** *Catherine St, SA62 6RJ.*
✆ (0437) 720239. RS Jan–Feb. C. 🚗 20
bedrs, 20 bp, TV, Dgs. ✗ mc, at, LD 9.
🅿 CH, Dgs, CP 50, Ac, CF, 5 BGf, 1 st, Dis.
£ BB £14–£17·70, DB £28–£35·40, WT
£142·50–£176, DBB £21·75–£26·85, WB,
②, Bk £3·15, L £3, D £9·15, cc 1 2 3 5,
Dep a.

Belmont House, G, z, (Rl), *12 Cross Sq,
SA62 6SE.* ✆ (0437) 720264. C. NS. 🚗 8
bedrs, 2 ba, ns. 🅿 CH, TV, CP 8, CF, 1 st.
£ DB £17–£18, WT (b) £85–£95, DT (b)
£13–£14.

Pen-y-Daith, G, x (Rl), *12 Millard Park,
SA62 6QH.* ✆ (0437) 720720. Open Mar–

Oct. C. ⊨ 8 bedrs, 4 ba. 🅐 CH, TV, CP 8, CF, 4 BGf, 1 st, Dis. £ BB fr £8, DB fr £16, WT (b) fr £85, DT (b) fr £13, 🆃.

Ramsey, G, x (Unl), *Lower Moor, SA62 6RP.* ☎ (0437) 720321. C. ⊨ 7 bedrs, 2 ba, Dgs. 🅐 ch, TV, Dgs, CP 10, CF. £ BB £7, DB £14, WT (b) £80, DT (b) fr £12, 🆃.
Y Glennydd, G, z (RI), *51 Nun St, SA62 6NU.* ☎ (0437) 720576. Closed Dec. C. ⊨ 10 bedrs, 3 ba. 🅐 CH, TV, CF. £ BB fr £7·50, DB fr £15, WT fr £75, DT fr £12·50, 🆃.

ST MELLONS South Glamorgan. Map 5A
Pop 1,239. Newport 7, London 144, Caerphilly 7, Cardiff 4.
EC Wed. **Golf** St Mellons 18h.

★★★**St Mellons County Club,** *CF3 8XR.* ☎ Castleton (0633) 680355. C. ⊨ 11 bedrs, 11 bp. ✗ mc, at. 🅐 CH, TV, CP 200, Ac, sp, tc, sc, sb, sol, gym, con 200, CF, 20 BGf, 1st, Dis. £ BB £25–£30, DB £36–£48, 🆃, Bk £4, L £5·50, D £7·50, cc 1 2 3 5 6.

SAUNDERSFOOT Dyfed. Map 11F
Pop 2,500. Carmarthen 23, London 235, Cardigan 29, Fishguard 27, Haverfordwest 7, Pembroke 11, Tenby 3.
EC Wed. **Golf** Tenby 18h. **See** St Issell's Church, Harbour, Wisemans Bridge, Monkstone Point.

★★★**St Brides,** *St Brides Hill, SA69 9NH.* ☎ (0834) 812304. C. ⊨ 49 bedrs, 32 bp, 17 bps, TV, Dgs. ✗ a l c, mc, at, LD 9. 🅐 N, CH, CP 70, Ac, sp, sb, sol, con 120, CF, 5 BGf. £ BB £26·50–£30·50, DB £43–£51, DBB £28–£32·50, WB, 🆃, Bk £5, L £6·25, D £8·65, cc 1 2 3 5 6, Dep.
★★**Glen Beach,** *Swallow Tree Woods, SA69 9DE.* ☎ (0834) 813430. C. ⊨ 10 bedrs, 1 bp, 9 bps, 1 ba, Dgs. ✗ a l c, mc, LD 10. 🅐 N, CH, CP 50, Ac, con 30, CF, 6 st. £ BB £17–£19, DB £32–£38, WT £160–£180, DBB £26–£28, WB, ②, Bk £3·75, L £4, D £9, cc 1 2 3, Dep.
★★**Rhodewood House,** *St Brides Hill, SA69 9NU.* ☎ (0834) 812200. C. ⊨ 34 bedrs, 17 bp, 2 bps, 5 ba, TV, Dgs. ✗ a l c, mc, at, LD 9.30. 🅐 ch, TV, Dgs, CP 50, Ac, sol, con 120, CF, 5 BGf, 0 st, Dis. £ BB £13–£19, DB £24–£36, WT £125–£163, DT £21·50–£26·50, DBB £19·50–£25·50, WB, ②, Bk £3, L £1·75, D £6·50, cc 1 2 3 5, Dep.▲

Bay View, PH, x (R), *Pleasant Valley.* ☎ (0834) 813417. Open Apr–Oct. C. ⊨ 12 bedrs, 3 ba. 🅐 CH, TV, CP 16, CF, 1 st. £ BB £8–£11, DB £16–£22, WT (b) £80–£96, DT (b) £11·50–£13·75, 🆃.
Claremont, PH, z (RI), *St Brides Hill, SA69 9NP.* ☎ (0834) 813231. Open Apr–Sept & Xmas. C. ⊨ 21 bedrs, 4 bps, 7 ba, TV. 🅐 CH, TV, CP 15, CF, 4 BGf, 3 st. £ BB £10–£12, DB £20–£27, WT (b) £80–£98, DT (b) £13 £16, 🆃, cc 5.▲
Harbour Light, PH, x (R), *2 High St. SA69 9LT.* ☎ (0834) 813496. Closed Dec. C. ⊨ 11 bedrs, 3 ba, ns, TV. ✗ a l c. 🅐 CH, TV, CP 8, CF, 2 st. £ BB £7–£10, DB £14–£20, WT £70–£95, DT £10–£14, 🆃, cc 1 3 5.
Malin House, PH, xy (RI), *St Brides Hill, SA69 9NP.* ☎ (0834) 812344. Open April–Oct. C. ⊨ 11 bedrs, 4 bp, 7 bps, 1 ba, TV. 🅐 CH, TV, CP 20, CF, 2 BGf, 3 st. £ BB £10–£11, DB £20–£22, WT (b) £105–£112, DT (b) £15–£16, 🆃, D £7.▲
Merlewood, H, y (R), *St Brides Hill, SA69 9NP.* ☎ (0834) 812421.▲

SENNYBRIDGE Powys. Map 12D
Pop 300. Brecon 8½, London 171, Builth Wells 23, Llandovery 12, Llanelli 39, Merthyr Tydfil 19, Swansea 30, Tredegar 25.
EC Thur. **MD** Wed & Fri. **Golf** Brecon 9h.
See Brecon Beacons National Park, 14th cent Keep.

Rescue Service: Sennybridge Service Station, Castle Ter. ☎ (087 482) 557.

SKEWEN West Glamorgan. Map 12E
Pop 6,508. Neath 1½, London 185, Carmarthen 27, Llanelli 14, Swansea 6.
EC Thur. **Golf** Swansea Bay 18h. **See** Ruins of Neath Abbey.

Rescue Service: Stadium Garage, Dynevor Pl. ☎ (0792) 812495.

SLEBECH Dyfed. M. Area 11F
5 m E of Haverfordwest. Carmarthen 25, London 238, Tenby 13.

Rescue Service: Green Bower Garages Ltd. ☎ Rhos (043 786) 251.

SWANSEA West Glamorgan. Map 12E
See also LANGLAND BAY and MUMBLES.
Pop 173,150. Neath 7½, London 188, M4 Motorway 4½, Bridgend 20, Brecon 39, Carmarthen 27, Lampeter 45, Llandovery 35, Llanelli 11.
See Plan, p. 454.
EC Thur. **MD** Sat. **P** See Plan. **Golf** Swansea Bay 18h, Clyne 18h. **See** Civic Centre, Royal Institute of S Wales (Museum), Guildhall, Law Courts, Brangwyn Hall (the British Empire Panels by Frank Brangwyn for House of Lords), Glynn Vivian Art Gallery, University, St Mary's Church, All Saints' Church, Southend Fishing Village, Lifeboat Stn and Lighthouse, Clyne Castle Gardens. 🅸 Oystermouth Sq, The Mumbles. ☎ Swansea (0792) 61302.

★★★★**M Dragon** (TH), *39 Kingsway Circle, SA1 5LS.* ☎ (0792) 51074. C. ⊨ 118 bedrs, 118 bp, TV, Dgs. ✗ a l c, mc, at, LD 9.30. 🅐 Lt, N, CH, Dgs, CP 40, Ac, con 300, CF. £ BB fr £45·50, DB fr £60·50, WB, 🆃, cc 1 2 3 4 5 6, Dep (Xmas).
★★★**M Dolphin,** *Whitewalls, SA1 3AB.* ☎ (0792) 50011. C. ⊨ 65 bedrs, 65 bp, TV, Dgs. ✗ a l c, mc, at, LD 9.15. 🅐 Lt, N, CH, ns, Ac, con 300, CF, 1 st. £ BB £19–£28·50, DB £29·50–£39·50, WB, 🆃, Bk £4·50, L £4·75, D £6·75, cc 1 2 3 5 6, Dep b.
★★★**M Fforest,** *Pontardulais Rd, Fforestfach, SA5 4BA.* ☎ (0792) 588711. Closed Xmas. C. ⊨ 19 bedrs, 18 bp, TV. ✗ a l c, mc, at, LD 10.30. 🅐 N, CH, TV, CP 180, Ac, con 360, CF, 5 BGf, 0 st, Dis. £ BB £16–£38·85, DB £32–£50·70, DBB £21·85–£45·90, WB, 🆃, Bk £3·85, L £3·50, D £4, cc 1 2 3 5.
★★✗**Beaumont** (Rt), *72 Walter Rd, SA1 4QA.* ☎ (0792) 43044. RS Xmas. C. ⊨ 14 bedrs, 2 bp, 6 bps, 2 ba, TV, Dgs. ✗ LD 8.30. 🅐 CH, TV, CP 12, CF, 1 st. £ BB £18–£23, DB £26–£30, WB, 🆃, Bk £3·50, L £4·75, D £7·95, cc 1 3 5, Dep b.
★★**Llwyn Helyg** (R), *Ffynone Rd, SA1 6BT.* ☎ (0792) 465735. C. ⊨ 11 bedrs, 11 bp, TV, Dgs. ✗ a l c, LD 10. 🅐 CH, TV, CP 15, CF, 5 st. £ BB £19, DB £28, WT £192, DBB £25·50, 🆃, L £4·75, D £6·50, cc 1 2 3 4 5 6.
★★**Windsor Lodge** (R), *Mount Pleasant, SA1 6EG.* ☎ (0792) 42158. Closed Xmas.

C. ⊨ 18 bedrs, 11 bp, 3 bps, 3 ba, TV, Dgs. ✗ mc, at, LD 8.30. 🅐 CH, Dgs, CP 20, sb, con 24, CF, 1 st. £ BB £20–£25, DB £30–£35, WT £200–£250, DT £32–£40, DBB £28·50–£33·50, WB, ②, Bk £3·50, L £3·50, D £8·50, cc 1 2 3.
Alexander, PH, z (RI), *3 Sketty Lane, Uplands, SA2 0EU.* ☎ (0792) 470045. C. ⊨ 7 bedrs, 4 bp, 2 bps, 1 sh, 1 ba, TV. ✗ a l c. 🅐 CH, TV, CF, 2 st. £ BB £11–£15, DB £24, WT (c) £74–£80, DT (b) £95–£115, 🆃, cc 1 3 5.
Beachway, G, z (Unl), *8 Bryn Rd, Brynmill, SA2 0AR.* ☎ (0792) 466557.
Coynant Farm, F, xy (Unl), *Felindre, SA5 7PU.* ☎ Ammanford (0269) 2064. C. ⊨ 5 bedrs, 3 bps, 2 ba, TV. 🅐 CH, TV, ns, CP 10, CF. £ DB £16–£17, WT (b) £73·50–£83·50, DT (b) £11–£12, 🆃.
Crescent, G, z (Unl), *132 Eaton Cres, Uplands, SA1 4QR.* ☎ (0792) 466814. Closed Xmas & New Year. C. ⊨ 8 bedrs, 1 bps, 2 sh, 1 ba, Dgs. 🅐 CH, TV, CP 4, CF, 4 st. £ cc 1 5.
Tregare, H, z (RI), *9 Sketty Rd, Uplands, SA2 0EU.* ☎ (0792) 470608. C 12. ⊨ 11 bedrs, 3 bp, 5 bps, 1 sh, 2 ba, TV, Dgs. 🅐 CH, TV, Dgs, CP 5. £ BB £10, DB £18, WT (b) £98, DT (b) £15, 🆃, cc 1 5.
Uplands Court, G, z (RI), *134 Eaton Court, Uplands, SA1 4QS.* ☎ (0792) 473046. C. ⊨ 8 bedrs, 3 sh, 3 ba, TV, Dgs. 🅐 CH, TV, CF. £ BB £9–£12, DB £17–£19, WT (b) fr £83, DT (b) £14–£17, 🆃.
Westlands, G, z (RI), *34 Bryn Rd, SA2 0AR.* ☎ (0792) 466689. C. ⊨ 6 bedrs, 1 ba. ✗ a l c. 🅐 CH, TV, CF. £ BB £6·50–£7·50, DB £13–£15, WT (b) £69·50–£76·50, (c) £45–£52, DT (b) £10–£11, 🆃.
Winston, PH, x (RI), *11 Church La, Bishopston, SA3 3JT.* ☎ Bishopston (044 128) 2074. Closed Xmas. ⊨ 19 bedrs, 4 bp, 4 bps, 8 sh, 2 ba, TV, Dgs. 🅐 CH, TV, CP 20, CF. £ BB fr £10, DB fr £20, WT fr £70, DT fr £16, 🆃.▲
Wittenberg, PH, x (RI), *2 Rotherslade Rd, SA3 4QN.* ☎ (0792) 69696.

Rescue Services: Gors Service Station Ltd, 65 Heol-y-Gars, Cockett. ☎ (0792) 582048.
McFarlane Motors, Cwmfelin Industrial Estate, off Heol-y-Gars Rd, Cwmbwrla. ☎ (0792) 43289 & (0792) 461960.
Siloh Motors (Swansea) Ltd, Millbrook Industrial Estate, Landore. ☎ (0792) 43732 & (0792) 461777.
Repairer: Fletchers (Swansea) Ltd, 511 Carmarthen Rd, Cwmdu. ☎ (0792) 588141.

TALSARNAU Gwynedd. Map 18C
Pop 500. Bala 25, London 224, Betws-y-Coed 20, Dolgellau 21, Porthmadog 5½.
EC Wed. **Golf** Royal St David's, Harlech 18h.

Repairer: R J Williams & Sons, The Garage. ☎ Penrhyndeudraeth (0766) 770286.

TAL-Y-LLYN Gwynedd. Map 18F
Pop 300. Newtown 38, London 215, Aberdyfi 13, Aberystwyth 27, Dolgellau 9.
EC Wed. **Golf** Aberdyfi 18h. **See** Talyllyn Lake, path to summit of Cader Idris, St Mary's Church, Narrow Gauge Rly (Tywyn to Abergynolwyn).

★★**Tynycornel,** *LL36 9AJ.* ☎ Abergynolwyn (065 477) 282. Open Easter–Oct. RS Nov–Easter. C. ⊨ 4 bedrs,

SWANSEA

0 miles ½

To Neath 8 m.

To Merthyr Tydfil 30m.

To Crematorium 2m

To Carmarthen 27 m.

FOXHOLE

N

Crown copyright reserved

P Car Park
G Public Conveniences
..... Parking Zone
Pedestrian precinct

Wern Ter.
Wern Fawr Road
Dany Graig Rd.
Vigol St.
Fabian St.
Port Tennant Road
Mackworth St.
Delhi St.
Fabian Way
Morris Lane
Pentre Guinea Rd.
Foxhole Rd.
R. Tawe
Neath Road
Strand
Llangyfelach Rd.
Carmarthen Road
Wauh Wen Rd.
Martin Rd.
Townhill Rd.
Gors Avenue
Townhill Rd.
Pen-y-Craig Rd.
Dyfnallt Avenue
Gwent Rd.
Powys Avenue
Kings Dock
Dry Dock
Prince of Wales Dock
West Pier
Dry Dock
Channel
Entrance
Pleasure Steamers
Swansea Bay
Marina
Maritime & trawler Rd
Industrial Museum
Museum
Adelaide
Cambrian Pl.
Somerset Pl.
Burrows Rd.
P.P.O.
Quay Parade
High Street Station
Cut Road
Multi-Storey
Police Sta.
Swansea Castle
Castle St.
High St.
New Orchard St.
Wind St.
York St.
Victoria Rd.
Sutland
Albert Row
Princess Way
Ferrara Quay
Leisure Centre
Multi-storey
Bathurst St.
West Glamorgan County Council
Swansea City A.F.C. Ground
Art Gallery
Technical College
Library
North Hill Rd.
Dyfatty St.
De la Beche St.
Alexandra Rd.
Grove Pl.
Mount Pleasant
Mount Pleasant Hospital
Terrace Rd.
Cromwell St.
Multi-storey Car Park
Fire Station
Multi-storey Car Park
Picton Arc.
Belle Vue Way
The Kingsway
Oxford St.
St. Helen's Rd.
Singleton St.
Wellington St.
Bus Station
Grand Theatre
Nelson St.
West Way
Orchard St.
Page St.
Maisel Street
Mansel Street
Park St.
Dillwyn St.
Union St.
Plymouth St.
Glamorgan St.
Oystermouth Rd.
Constitution Hill
Brooklands Terrace
Hanover St.
Rose Hill
Brynmill Rd.
Brynymor Rd.
Walter Rd.
Western St.
St. Helen's Avenue
Vincent St.
Beach St.
Bond St.
Argyle St.
Brunswick St.
King Edward's Rd.
Bryn Rd.
Mumbles Rd.
Victoria Rd.
Guildhall & Brangwyn Hall
Law Courts
Victoria Park
Swimming Baths

To Port Eynon 16M
To Airport
To Mumbles 5 m.

A483
A4067
A4118
A4067

© The Royal Automobile Club, 1985

For abbreviations see inside back cover—RAC

2 bp, 1 ba, Dgs. ✖ a l c, mc, at, LD 8.30.
🅐 CH, Dgs, CP 60, G 2, pf, sb, sol, con 30,
CF, 3 BGf, 3 st. £ cc 1 3 5, Dep.
▣★**Minffordd** (R), *LL36 9AJ.* ✆ Corris
(065 473) 665. Open Apr–Oct & Xmas.
Closed Jan & Feb. RS Mar, Nov, Dec. C 3.
🚑 7 bedrs, 3 bp, 2 bps, 2 sh. ✖ mc, LD
8.30. 🅐 CH, CP 12, 2 BGf, 1 st. £ BB £17–
£23·40, DB £28–£40·80, DBB £22–£29·90,
WB, 🄳, Bk £·20, D £9·50, cc 1 3 5.

TAN-Y-GROES Dyfed. Map 11D
Lampeter 25, London 228, Aberporth 2½,
Aberystwyth 31, Cardigan 7½, Carmarthen
24.
Golf Cardigan 18h.

Rescue Service: Gary Povey, Gogerddan
Garage. ✆ Aberporth (0239) 810414.

TENBY Dyfed. Map 11F
See also SAUNDERSFOOT.
Pop 4,950. Carmarthen 27, London 239,
Cardigan 32, Haverfordwest 20,
Pembroke 10.
EC Wed. **Golf** Tenby 18h. **See** Ruined
Castle, ancient Town Walls, Parish
Church, Tudor Merchants House, 15th
cent Plantagenet House, Museum, Caldy
Island and Monastery (adm to
Monastery—men only), Old Custom: St
Margaret's Fair—3rd week July.
🄸 Guildhall. The Norton. ✆ Tenby (0834)
2402.

★★★**Imperial,** *Esplanade, SA70 7HR.*
✆ (0834) 3737. C. 🚑 46 bedrs, 38 bp, 8
bps, TV, Dgs. ✖ mc, at, LD 9.30 🅐 Lt, N,
ch, Dgs, CP 16, G 16, Ac, tc, con, CF, 4 BGf,
0 st. £ BB £20–£35, DB £40–£70, DBB
£26–£40, WB, 🄳, Bk £4·25, D £8·95,
cc 1 2 3 4 5 6, Dep b.
★★**Atlantic,** *Esplanade, SA70 7DU.*
✆ (0834) 2881. C. 🚑 33 bedrs, 23 bp, 6
bps, 3 ba, TV, Dgs. ✖ mc, at, LD 9.30.
🅐 CH, TV, Dgs, CP 28, Ac, pf, con, CF, 2
BGf, 2 st. £ BB £16·50–£18·50, DB
£30·50–£32·50, WT £115·50–£129·50, DT
£26–£28, DBB £22–£24, 🄳, Bk £3, L £4·95,
D £7·50, cc 1 3, Dep b.
★★**Fourcroft,** *The Croft, SA70 8AP.*
✆ (0834) 2516. Open Apr–Oct. C. 🚑 38
bedrs, 34 bp, 4 bps, 1 ba, TV. ✖ mc, at, LD
8. 🅐 Lt, CH, TV, Ac, sp, CF, 5 st. £ BB £14–
£18·50, DB £25–£34, WT £133–£145, DBB
£19–£23, WB, 🄳, Bk £3·50, L £3·50, D
£7·50, cc 1 3 6, Dep a.
★★**Royal Gate House,** *North Beach,
SA70 7ET.* ✆ (0834) 2255.▲
★★**Royal Lion,** *High St, SA70 7EX.*
✆ (0834) 2127. Open Mar–Dec. C. 🚑 36
bedrs, 14 bp, 16 bps, 5 ba, TV, Dgs. ✖ a l c,
LD 10.30. 🅐 Lt, CH, TV, CP 4, Ac, CF, 2 st.
£ BB £14–£20, DB £28–£43, DT £19–£26,
DBB £19–£27·50, WB, 🄳, Bk £4, D £7,
cc 1 3, Dep a.
★**Buckingham** (R), *Esplanade, SA70
6DQ.* ✆ (0834) 2622
▣★**Croft** (R), *Sea Front, SA70 8AP.*
✆ (0834) 2576. Open Apr–Oct. C. 🚑 20
bedrs, 10 bp, 2 ba, TV, Dgs. ✖ mc, at. 🅐 ch,
TV, CP 5, Ac, sp. CF 1 st. £ BB £10–£14·35,
DB £20–£25, 🄳, D £6·50, cc 1 2 3, Dep a.
★**Harbour Heights** (Rl) *The Croft, SA70
8AP.* ✆ (0834) 2132. Open Feb–Nov. C.
🚑 10 bedrs, 7 bp, 2 ba, TV. ✖ mc, at, LD
7.30. 🅐 ch, TV, CP 4, Ac, sp, CF, 10 BGf, 1
st. Dis. £ BB £26–£27, DB £52–£54, DBB
£16·75, DB £18–£30, WT £98–£120, DT
£17–£23, DBB £15–£21, WB, 🄳, Bk £2, L
£2·50, cc 1 2 3.
Belvedere, PH, y (R), *Serpentine Rd,
SA70 8DD.* ✆ (0834) 2549. Open Apr–

Oct. C. 🚑 14 bedrs, 1 bp, 4 ba, Dgs.
✖ a l c. 🅐 CH, TV, Dgs, CP 20, CF, 4 BGf, 1
st. £ BB £9–£12, DB £18–£27, WT (b)
£91–£110, DT (b) £13–£16, 🄳, Bk £3, D
£4·50.
Heywood Lodge, PH, xy (Rl) *Heywood
La, SA70 8BN.* ✆ (0834) 2684. Open Apr–
Oct. C. 🚑 14 bedrs, 4 bps, 7 bps, 3 ba, Dgs.
✖ a l c. 🅐 CH, TV, Dgs, CP 20, CF. £ BB
£9·75–£14·50, DB £18·55–£27, WT (b)
£98·90–£103·50, DT £14·50–£16·50, 🄳,
Bk £2·50, L £2·50, D £6·75.
Myrtle House, PH, z (Rl), *St Mary's St,
SA70 7HW.* ✆ (0834) 2508. Open Feb–
Nov & Xmas. C. 🚑 9 bedrs, 2 ba, Dgs.
🅐 CH, TV, Dgs, CF, 1 st. £ BB £9–£11, DB
£18–£22, WT (b) £80–£90, (c) £58–£70,
DT (b) £13–£15, cc 1 5.
Pembroke, H, z (R), *Warren St, SA70
7JX.* ✆ (0834) 3670.
Richmond, H, *The Croft.* ✆ (0834) 2533.
Open Apr–Oct. C. 🚑 18 bedrs, 2 bp, 2 sh, 3
ba. 🅐 ch, TV, CF, 6 st. £ BB £10–£12, DB
£20–£24, 🄳, cc 1 3 5.
Ripley St. Mary's, H, x (Rl), *St. Mary's
St, SA70 7HN.* ✆ (0834) 2837. Open Feb–
Nov. C. 🚑 14 bedrs, 6 bp, 3 ba, Dgs. 🅐 ch,
TV, Dgs, CF, 4 st. £ BB £9–£12·50, DB
£16–£24, WT (b) £90–£110, DT (b) £12–
£16, 🄳, cc 1 5.
St Oswalds, G, z (Unl), *Picton Terr,
SA70 7DR.* ✆ (0834) 2130. Open Apr–
Oct. C. 🚑 13 bedrs, 3 bp, 2 ba, TV, Dgs.
🅐 CH, TV, CP 9, CF, 1 BGf, 4 st. £ BB
£8·50–£10, DB £17–£23, WT (b) £75–
£110, (c) £55–£75, DT (b) £12·50–£15, 🄳,
Bk £2·50, L £3, D £4.
Sea Breezes, PH, z (Rl), *18 The Norton,
SA70 8AA.* ✆ (0834) 2753. Open Mar–
Oct. C. 🚑 26 bedrs, 6 bp, 5 ba, ns, TV.
🅐 ch, TV, CF. £ BB £9–£16, DB £18–£31,
WT (b) £75–£95, DT £12–£17·50, 🄳, Bk
£3·50, L £3·50, D £4·50.
Southbourne, H, z, *Southcliff Gdns,
SA70 7DS.* ✆ (0834) 2186.

THREE COCKS Powys. Map 12D
Pop 400. Ross-on-Wye 34, London 156,
Abergavenny 21, Brecon 10, Builth Wells
15, Hereford 25, Leominster 27.
Golf Brecon 9h. **See** St Peter's Church,
old Gwernyfed (Elizabethan Manor
House).

★**Three Cocks,** *LD3 0SL.* ✆ Glasbury
(049 74) 215. Closed Jan. C. 🚑 7 bedrs, 3
ba, Dgs. ✖ LD 7.30. 🅐 CH, TV, CP 40, CF,
6 st. £ BB £15·50, DB £31, DBB £28·25,
WB, 🄳, Bk £4·50, D £12·75, cc 1 2 3 5 6.

TINTERN Gwent. Map 13E
Pop 250. Monmouth 9½, London 138,
Chepstow 6.
Golf Chepstow 9h & 18h. **See** Abbey
ruins (12th cent), The Wyndcliffe.
🄸 Tintern Abbey. ✆ Tintern (029 18) 431.

★★**Beaufort,** *NP6 6SF.* ✆ (029 18) 202.
C. 🚑 25 bedrs, 15 bp, 10 bps, TV, Dgs.
✖ a l c, mc, at, LD 9. 🅐 CH, Dgs, CP 100,
Ac, pf, con 150, CF, 1 st. £ BB £28, DB £44,
WB, 🄳, Bk £4·25, L £3, D £7·50,
cc 1 2 3 4 5 6, Dep b.
★★**Royal George, z** (Unl), *NP6 6SP.* ✆ (029 18)
205. C. 🚑 5 bedrs, 1 bp, 1 bps, 1 ba,
annexe 14 bedrs, 14 bp, TV, Dgs. ✖ mc, at,
LD 9.15. 🅐 CH, TV, CP 36, pf, rf, CF, 10 BGf, 1
st, Dis. £ BB £26–£27, DB £52–£54, DBB
£29–£30, 🄳, Bk £4·50, L £6·50, D £7·95,
cc 1 2 3.
★**Wye Valley,** *NP6 6SP.* ✆ (029 18) 441.

Fountain, I, x, *Trelleck Grange, NP6
6QW.* ✆ (029 18) 303. RS Dec–Feb. C.
🚑 4 bedrs, 1 ba, TV, Dgs. ✖ a l c. 🅐 CH,
Dgs, CP 40, CF. £ BB £14·50, DB £19·50,
DT £14, 🄳, L £4·80, D £4·80.
Parva Farmhouse, G, x (Rl), *NP6 6SQ.*
✆ (029 18) 411. C. 🚑 7 bedrs, 4 ba, Dgs.
✖ a l c. 🅐 CH, TV, CP 10, CF, 1 BGf, 3 st.
£ BB £12·50–£14, DB £19–£21, WT (b)
£95–£105, DT (b) £15–£17.

TONYREFAIL Mid Glamorgan. Maps 4B
and 12F
Pop 10,870. Pontypridd 5½, London 161,
Bridgend 9½, Cardiff 14, Hirwaun 16,
Neath 29, Swansea 31.
EC Thur. **MD** Tue. **Golf** Llantrisant and
Pontyclun 18h.

Repairer: Tonyrefail Motors Ltd,
Penrhiwfer Rd. ✆ (0443) 670377.

TRAWSFYNYDD Gwynedd. Map 18D
Pop 1,100. Bala 18, London 217, Betws-y-
Coed 16, Dolgellau 12, Porthmadog 11.
Golf Royal St David's, Harlech 18h. **See**
Tomen y Mur (old Welsh Fort), Nuclear
Power Station, Pistyll-y-Cain waterfall.

Rescue Service: J M Hughes & Sons,
Cambrian Garage. ✆ (076 687) 233.

TREARDDUR BAY Gwynedd. Map 18A
Pop 1,347. Bangor 22, London 259,
Caernarfon 28, Holyhead 2.
EC Wed. **Golf** Holyhead 18h. **See** Ancient
Monuments.

▣★★★**Beach,** *Lon St Ffraid, LL65 2YT.*
✆ (0407) 860332. C. 🚑 26 bedrs, 23 bp, 3
bps, Dgs. ✖ a l c, mc, at, LD 10. 🅐 CH, TV,
Dgs, CP 200, sc, sb, sol, con 100, CF, 6 st.
£ BB £22·95–£25·95, DB £35·90–£38·90,
DBB £23·95–£26·95, WB, 🄳, Bk £3·95, L
£3·50, D £6, cc 1 2 3 5 6.
▣★★★**Trearddur Bay,** *Lon Isallt, LL65
2UW.* ✆ (0407) 860301. C. 🚑 28 bedrs,
18 bp, 5 ba, TV, Dgs. ✖ a l c, mc, at, LD
9.30. 🅐 N, CH, TV, Dgs, CP 200, sp, con
100, CF, 3 st. £ BB £17·50–£28, DB £32–
£52, 🄳, Bk £4, L £5, D £7·50, cc 1 2 3 5.
★★**Seacroft,** *Ravensport Rd, LL65 2YU.*
✆ (0407) 860348.
Moranedd, G, z (Unl), *Trearddur Rd.*
✆ (0407) 860324. Open May–Sept. C.
🚑 7 bedrs, 2 ba, Dgs. 🅐 CH, TV, Dgs, CP 8,
CF. £ BB £6, DB £12, WT (b) £63, (c) £42,
DT (b) £9, 🄳.

TREDEGAR Gwent. Map 12F.
Pop 14,200. Abergavenny 11, London
155, Brecon 19, Caerphilly 16, Merthyr
Tydfil 7½, Newport 20, Pontypool 17.
EC Thur. **MD** Wed. **Golf** Nantyglo 18h.
See Town Clock, Bedwellty Park,
Rocking Stone (Pochin).

Rescue Service: W J A Cosh (Tredegar)
Ltd, Crown Garage, Merthyr Rd.
✆ (049 525) 2555.
D B Lewis, Gelli Garage, Gelli La.
✆ (049 525) 2541.

TREGARON Dyfed. Map 12C
Pop 950. Rhayader 25, London 200,
Aberystwyth 17, Lampeter 10, Newtown
42.
EC Thur. **MD** Alt. Tue. **Golf** Lampeter 9h.
See Strata Florida Abbey 6 m NE.
🄸 The Square. ✆ Tregaron (097 44) 415.

★**Talbot,** *The Square, SY25 6JL.*
✆ (097 44) 288.
Aberdwr, G, y (Unl), *Abergwesyn Rd,*
✆ (097 44) 255. Open Mar–Nov. C. 🚑 3

bedrs, 2 ba, Dgs. 🄿 TV, ns, CP 12, CF, 1 st.
£ BB £8–£9, DB £16–£18, WT (b) fr £91,
DT (b) £13, 🄸.
Brynawel, G, x (Unl), *Station Rd, SY25
6HX.* ✆ (097 44) 310. Closed Xmas week
& New Year. C. 🛏 4 bedrs, 1 ba, Dgs.
🄿 CP 4, CF. £ BB fr £7, DB fr £14, WT (b)
fr £68·50, DT (b) fr £11·50, 🄶.

Rescue Service: Glanteify Garage.
✆ Pontrhydfendigaid (097 45) 205.

TREMADOG Gwynedd. Map 18C
See also PORTHMADOG
Pop 950. Porthmadog 1, London 229,
Betws-y-Coed 22, Caernarfon 18, Pwllheli
13.
EC Wed. **Golf** Porthmadog 18h. **See**
Birthplace of Lawrence of Arabia.

★★Madoc *Market Sq, LL49 9RB.*
✆ Porthmadog (0766) 2021. C. 🛏 22
bedrs, 2 bps, 6 ba, Dgs. ✗ a l c, mc, at, LD
8.30. 🄿 TV, Dgs, CP 14, U 4, Ac, CF, 1 st.
£ BB £15·95, DB £29·75, WB, 🄶, Bk £2·50,
L £3·50, D £5·50, cc 1 3.

TREORCHY Mid Glamorgan. Map 12F
Pop 6,398. Pontypridd 9½, London 165,
Bridgend 15, Hirwaun 10, Neath 22,
Swansea 25.
EC Thur. **MD** Thur. **Golf** Penrhys 18h. **See**
Site of "Gorsedd" (venue of Druids
ceremony).

Rescue Service: Wynne's Garages
(Rhondda) Ltd, Ynysowen Rd. ✆ (0443)
772277.

TRETOWER Powys. M.Area 12F
3 m NW of Crickhowell. Pop 650.
Abergavenny 9, London 152, Brecon 11,
Brynmawr 10, Talgarth 9.
Golf Abergavenny 18h. **See** Tretower
Court.

Tretower Court, l, x, *NP8 1RF.* ✆ Bwlch
(0874) 730204.

TY NANT Clwyd. Map 18D
Pop 190. Bala 10, London 200, Betws-y-
Coed 15, Colwyn Bay 30, Denbigh 17,
Llandudno 33, Ruthin 14.
EC Thur. **Golf** Corwen 18h

Rescue Service: Jet Filling Station A5.
✆ Maerdy (049 081) 307.

TYWYN Gwynedd. Map 18E
Pop 2,800. Aberdyfi 4½, London 220,
Dolgellau 19.
EC Wed. **Golf** Aberdyfi 18h. **See** St
Cadfan's Church containing St Cadfan's
Stone, Railway Museum, Narrow Gauge
Rly to Abergynolwyn, Dogloch Falls 5 m
NE, Castell-y-Bere off A 4405.
🄸 ✆ Tywyn (0654) 710070.

★★Corbett Arms *Corbett Sq LL36 9DG.*
✆ (0654) 710264. C. 🛏 21 bedrs, 10 bp, 9
bps, 6 ba, TV, Dgs. ✗ mc, LD 8.45. 🄿 CH,
TV, Dgs. CP 45, U 3, G 6, Ac, sp, con 50, CF,
0 st. £ BB £15–£17·50, DB £30–£35, WT

£165–£174, DT £25–£25·30, DBB £21·25–
£25·75, WB, 🄸, Bk £4·25, L £4·50, D £7·35,
cc 1 2 3 5 6, Dep a.
★Greenfield (R), *High St, LL36 9AD.*
✆ (0654) 710354. Open Jan–Oct. C. 🛏 14
bedrs, 4 ba. ✗ mc, LD 8.30. 🄿 CH, TV, Ac,
CF, 0 st. £ BB £9·75–£10·25, DB £19·50–
£20·50, DBB £13·25–£13·75, WB, 🄶, Bk
£2·75, L £3·25, D £3·75.

Rescue Service: W D Pugh & Sons
(Tywyn) Ltd, Beacon Garage. ✆ (0654)
710319.

USK Gwent. Map 13E
Pop 2,000. Chepstow 14, London 136, M4
Motorway 9½, Abergavenny 11,
Monmouth 13, Newport 11, Pontypool 7.
EC Wed. **Golf** Abergavenny 9h. **See**
Castle ruins, Priory Church of St Mary,
13th cent Priory Gatehouse, Remains of
large Roman Encampment, Raglan Castle
5 m NE.

★★Three Salmons, *Bridge St, NP5 1BQ.*
✆ (029 13) 2133.
Stardust, H, y, *Llanbadoc, NP5 1TG.*
✆ (029 13) 2223.

Repairer: Woodside Garage & Implement
Co Ltd, ✆ (029 13) 2136.
Rescue Service: G C Clench, Castle
Parade Garage. ✆ (029 13) 2014.

WELSHPOOL Powys. Map 19E
Pop 5,000. Shrewsbury 18, London 172,
Bala 33, Dolgellau 37, Knighton 34,
Llangollen 28, Ludlow 32, Newtown 13,
Whitchurch 34, Wrexham 31.
EC Thur. **MD** Mon. **Golf** Welshpool 18h.
See Powis Castle, St Mary's Church,
Powysland Museum, Old Inns, Narrow
gauge railway to Llanfair.
🄸 Vicarage Garden Car Park. ✆ Welshpool
(0938) 2043.

★★Royal Oak, *The Cross, SY21 7DG.*
✆ (0938) 2217. C. 🛏 25 bedrs, 12 bp, 6
bps, 2 ba, TV, Dgs. ✗ a l c, mc, at, LD 9.
🄿 N, CH, TV, CP 80, U 2, Ac, con 200, CF, 0
st. £ BB fr £14·50, DB fr £29, DBB fr £20,
WB, 🄸, Bk £4, L £5·25, D £6, cc 1 2 3 5 6,
Dep.
Garth Derwen (R), *Buttington, SY21
8SU.* ✆ Trewern (093 874) 238. Open mid
Jan–mid Dec. C. 🛏 8 bedrs, 5 bps, 2 ba,
TV, Dgs. ✗ a l c, mc, at, LD 7.45. 🄿 CH, TV,
Dgs, CP 20, CF, 0 st. £ BB £13·50–£19, DB
£21–£30, WT £105–£135, DBB £15·95–
£20·45, WB, 🄶, Bk £2·75, L £2·20, D £5·45,
cc 1, Dep a.▲
Tynllwyn, F, x (Unl), *SY21 9BW.*
✆ (0938) 3175. C. 🛏 6 bedrs, 2 ba. 🄿 CH,
TV, Dgs, CP 8. £ BB £8–£8·50, DB £16–£17,
WT (b) fr £85, DT fr £13, 🄸.

WHITEBROOK Gwent. Map 13E
Chepstow 10, London 133, Abergavenny
20, Gloucester 24, Monmouth 5,
Pontypool 23.

★★Crown at Whitebrook, *Monmouth,
NP5 4TX.* ✆ Monmouth (0600) 860254.
Closed Jan 1–20. C. 🛏 8 bedrs, 6 bp, 2
bps, Dgs. ✗ a l c, mc, at, LD 10. 🄿 CH,
Dgs, CP 40, CF, 1 BGf, 3 st. £ BB £20, DB
£38–£40, DBB £32, WB, 🄸, L £9·25, D
£17·50, cc 1 2 3 5 6.

WOLFSCASTLE Dyfed. Map 11C
Pop 300. Haverfordwest 7, London 250,
Fishguard 7, St Davids 15.
Golf Haverfordwest 9h.

★★Wolfscastle Country (Cl),
SA62 5LZ. ✆ Treffgarne (043 787) 225.
Closed 5 days Xmas. C. 🛏 13 bedrs, 7 bp,
4 ba, TV, Dgs. ✗ a l c, mc, at, LD 9.30.
🄿 ch, TV, Dgs, CP 50, Ac, tc, sc, con 12,
CF. £ BB £16·45, DB £27·90–£29·90, WT
£154·04, DT £30·45, DBB £24·45–£34·45,
🄶, 10%, Bk £3·75, L £3·50, D £8·90, cc 1 3.

WREXHAM Clwyd. Map 19C
Pop 40,479. Whitchurch 15, London 178,
Chester 11, Llangollen 11, Mold 11,
Nantwich 18, Queensferry 12, Ruthin 17,
Shrewsbury 29, Welshpool 31.
EC Wed. **MD** Mon. **Golf** Wrexham 18h.
See Church of St Giles (tomb of Elihu
Yale, founder of Yale University USA) in
churchyard, RC Cathedral.
🄸 Guildhall Car Park, Town Centre.
✆ Wrexham (0978) 357845.

★★★M Crest, *High St, LL13 8HP.*
✆ (0978) 353431. C. 🛏 80 bedrs, 80 bp,
ns, TV, Dgs. ✗ a l c, mc, at, LD 9.30. 🄿 Lt,
N, CH, Dgs, CP 85, G 24, Ac, con 40, CF, 3
st. £ B fr £36, BD fr £46, WB, 🄸, Bk £5·25,
D £8·95, cc 1 2 3 4 5 6, Dep.

Repairer: Anchor Motor Co Ltd, High
Town Rd. ✆ (0978) 364151.
Rescue Service: Kirbys (Wrexham) Ltd,
67 Regent St. ✆ (0978) 351001..

YSTRADGYNLAIS Powys. Map 12E
Pop 8,400. Brecon 24, London 190,
Llanelli 20, Neath 10, Swansea 13.
EC Thur. **MD** Fri. **Golf** Palleg 9h. **See** Dan
yr Ogof Caves at Penycae, Scwd Henrhyd
Falls at Colbren.

Rescue Service: Cross Garage
(Ystradgynlais) Ltd, Brecon Rd.
✆ Glantawe (0639) 843179.

YSTRAD MYNACH Mid Glamorgan.
Map 12F
Pop 6,276. Newport 14, London 152,
Caerphilly 4½, Hirwaun 15, Merthyr Tydfil
11, Newport 14, Pontypool 10, Pontypridd
7½, Tredegar 11.
EC Thur. **Golf** Bargoed 18h. **See** Old Mill
Forge.

Repairer: Gwynn's Garage (Ystrad
Mynach) Ltd, Central Garage. ✆ Hengoed
(0443) 813121.

Directory–The Channel Islands Northern Ireland & Reference Listings

Directory of appointed hotels, small hotels, guest houses, etc., repairers and agents in The Channel Islands.

Directory of appointed hotels, repairers and agents in Northern Ireland.
See separate sections for England, Scotland and Wales.

Reference Listings
Modern Hotels, Motels and Motor Hotels. See page 463.
Country House Hotels. See page 466.
Appointed Hotels within Five Miles of a Motorway. See page 472.
RAC Appointed Caravan Sites. See page 476.

For explanatory notes to Directory see page 116
For abbreviations see inside back cover

ALDERNEY Channel Islands. Map 2A
Pop 1,900. Guernsey 21, Jersey 36.
EC Wed. **Golf** Longy Rd 9h. **See** Church
of St Anne, Island Hall, Court Houses, Old
Forts, Museum, Quesnard Lighthouse,
Gannet colony on L'Etacs, Island of
Burhou, Bird Sanctuary, Railway, cliff
walks.
🛈 States Office, New St. ✆ Alderney
(048 182) 2994.

★★**Chez André,** *Victoria St.* ✆ (048 182)
2777.

GUERNSEY Channel Islands. Map 2A
RAC Port Office, *St Julian's Pier, St Peter
Port.* ✆ Guernsey (0481) 20822.
Pop 53,313. Weymouth 75, Jersey 25.
EC Thur. **MD** Mon, Sat. **P** Car Parks are
indicated by "P" signs. Before using these
parks, motorists **must** obtain parking
"clocks" from the Police Station. Cars
must not be parked on a public highway
(except on a car park) other than for
loading or unloading. Except with the
permission of the Chief Officer of Police,
vehicles may not be driven, ridden or
parked on the beaches between 11 am
and 7 pm between Whit Sunday and the
15th Sept. **Golf** Royal Guernsey
L'Ancresse 18h. **See** Castle Cornet Beau
Sejour, Royal courts, Yacht Marina and
Dehus Dolmen at Fort Doyle, Sausmarez
Park, Le Vauxbelets (Little Chapel),
Occupation Museum at Forest, Vale
Castle, Victor Hugo's House, Aquarium,
Moulin Huet Pottery, Herm Island.
🛈 States of Guernsey Tourist Committee,
PO Box 23, St Peter Port. ✆ Guernsey
(0481) 23555.

★★★★**Old Government House,** *Ann's
Pl, St Peter Port.* ✆ (0481) 24921. C. ⊯ 73
bedrs, 73 bp, TV, Dgs. ✖ a l c, mc, at, LD
9.15. 🅟 Lt, N, CH, TV, CP 30, Ac, sp, con
200, CF, 8 st. £ WB, Bk £2·50, L £5, D
£6·50, cc 1 2 3 4 5 6, Dep.

★★★★**St Pierre Park,** *St Peter Port.*
✆ (0481) 28282.
⊯★★★**Green Acres,** *St Martin's.*
✆ (0481) 35711. C. ⊯ 48 bedrs, 44 bp, 4
bps, TV. ✖ mc, at, LD 8.30. 🅟 CH, CP 75,
sp, sol, CF, 2 BGf, 2 st. £ Dep.

★★★**L'Atlantique,** *Perelle Bay, St
Saviours.* ✆ (0481) 64056. C 8. ⊯ 21
bedrs, 21 bp, 1 ba, TV. ✖ a l c, mc, LD 10.
🅟 CH, Dgs, CP 70, sp, con 40, 1 st. £ BB
£12–£48, DB £24–£48, DBB £18–£60, WB,
🛈, Bk £2·50, L £4, D £7, cc 1 2 3 4 5 6,
Dep.

★★★**Ronnie Ronalde's,** *St Martin's.*
✆ (0481) 35644. C. ⊯ 51 bedrs, 51 bp, 2
ba, TV. ✖ a l c, mc, at, LD 9. 🅟 Lt, N, CH,
CP 200, U 3, Ac, sp, gc, tc, con 50, CF, 1 st.
£ BB £21–£28·50, DB £42–£57, DBB £23–
£31·50, WT, 🛈, Bk £3, L £4·50, D £6·25,
cc 1 2 3 5 6, Dep a.

★★★**Royal,** *Esplanade, St Peter Port.*
✆ (0481) 23921. C. ⊯ 79 bedrs, 73 bp, 1
sh, 6 ba, TV, Dgs. ✖ a l c, mc, at, LD 9.
🅟 Lt, N, CH, Dgs, CP 125, Ac, sp, con 200,
CF, 3 st. £ BB £11·50–£20, DB £23–£52,
WT £133–£199·50, DT £19–£38·50, DBB
£16–£30, WB, 🛈, Bk £3, L £4·50, D £5·50,
cc 1 2 3 4 5, Dep.

★★★**St Margaret's Lodge,** *St Martin's.*
✆ (0481) 35757. C. ⊯ 43 bedrs, 43 bp, 1
ba, TV, Dgs. ✖ a l c, mc, at, LD 9.45. 🅟 Lt,
N, CH, TV, CP 100, sp, con 80, CF, 0 st.
£ BB £11–£19·50, DB £22–£39, DBB

£15·50–£26·50, WB, 🛈, Bk £1·75, L £4·25,
D £6·75, cc 1 2 3 5, Dep b.
★★**De Havelet,** *Havelet, St Peter Port.*
✆ (0481) 22199. C. ⊯ 32 bedrs, 32 bp, TV,
Dgs. ✖ a l c, mc, LD 9.30. 🅟 CH, TV, CP
45, con 40, CF. £ BB £14·50–£20·50, DB
£23–£39, WT £129·50–£185·50, DT
£19·50–£27·50, DBB £14·50–£24·50, WB,
🛈, Bk £2·50, L fr £3·50, D fr £5,
cc 1 2 3 4 5.
★★**Grange Lodge,** *The Grange, St Peter
Port.* ✆ (0481) 25161. Open Feb–Nov. C.
⊯ 33 bedrs, 26 bp, 5 ba, TV, Dgs. ✖ mc, at,
LD 7.30. 🅟 ch, TV, Dgs, CP 30, sp, CF, 4
BGf, 2 st. £ BB £12–£14·50, DB £24–£29,
DBB £14–£18, 🛈, Bk £1·55, L £3·50,
cc 1 3 6, Dep a.▲
★★**Hougue du Pommier,** *Catel.*
✆ (0481) 56531. C. ⊯ 40 bedrs, 39 bp, 1
sh, TV. ✖ a l c, mc, at, LD 9.30. 🅟 CH, TV,
CP 90, Ac, sp, gc, con 30, CF, 12 BGf, 1 st.
Dis. £ BB £10·50–£20, DB £21–£40, WT
£112–£164·50, DBB £14–£23·50, WB, 🛈,
Bk £2·15, L £2·75, D £4·85, cc 1 3 6,
Dep a.▲
★★**La Favorita,** *Fermain Bay.* ✆ (0481)
35666. Open Mar–Dec. C. ⊯ 31 bedrs, 28
bp, 3 bps, TV. ✖ mc, at, LD 8.30. 🅟 CH, ns,
CP 25, Ac, con 40, CF, 1 BGf. £ BB £13–
£20, DB £26–£40, DBB £16–£23·50, WB,
🛈, L £4·50, D £5, cc 3, Dep a.
★★**Le Chalet,** *Fermain Bay.* ✆ (0481)
35716. Open Apr–Oct. C. ⊯ 46 bedrs, 42
bp, 4 bps, TV, Dgs. ✖ a l c, mc, at, LD 9.30.
🅟 ch, CP 30, con 40, CF. £ BB £16·75–
£19·50, DB £26·60–£36·60, WT £140·70–
£175·70, DT £20·10–£20·10, DBB £16·75–
£21·75, WB, 🛈, Bk £2·50, L £3·50, D £5,
cc 1 2 3 4 5 6.
★★**Moore's,** *Pollet, St Peter Port.*
✆ (0481) 24452. C. ⊯ 35 bedrs, 19 bps,
10 sh, 13 ba, TV, Dgs. ✖ a l c, mc, at, LD
8.30. 🅟 Lt, N, CH, Dgs, con 30, CF. £ BB
£13·50–£20, DB £22–£36·50, WT £119–
£115·75, DT £17–£22·25, DBB £14–
£21·50, WB, 🛈, L £3, D £5, cc 1 2 3 5 6.
★**Manor,** *Petit Bot, St Martins.* ✆ (0481)
37788. C. ⊯ 59 bedrs, 20 bp, 4 bps, 13 ba,
Dgs. ✖ a l c, mc, at, LD 8. 🅟 Lt, CP 40, CF,
CF. £ BB £11–£16, DB £20–£24, WT £98,
DT £16, DBB £14–£15, 🛈, Bk £2, L £2·50,
D £4.

Ann-Dawn, PH, x (RI) *Route des
Capelles, St Sampsons.* ✆ (0481) 25606.
Open Mar–Oct. C 5. ⊯ 15 bedrs, 1 bp, 6
bps, 1 sh, 3 ba, TV. 🅟 CH, CP 12, 1 BGf, 2
st. £ BB £9·50–£10·50, DB £19–£24, WT
£87·50–£98, DT £11·50–£14·50, 🛈, Bk
£1·95, D £3·50.
Baltimore House, H, z (R), *Les Gravees,
St Peter Port.* ✆ (0481) 23641. Open Mar–
Oct. C. ⊯ 12 bedrs, 1 bp, 4 bps, 3 sh, 2 ba,
Dgs. 🅟 ch, TV, CP 7, CF, 4 st. £ BB £7·50–
£12·75, DB £15–£25·50, WT (b) £66·50–
£103·25, DT (b) £9·50–£14·75, 🛈, Bk
£2·75, D £3·75, cc 1 2 3 5.
Changi Lodge, PH, xy (RI), *Les
Baissieres.* ✆ (0481) 56446. Open Apr–
Oct. C. ⊯ 14 bedrs, 2 bp, 3 ba. 🅟 CH, TV,
CP 15, CF. £ BB £9·50–£13, DB £18–£27,
DT (b) £11·50–£15·50, 🛈, cc 3.
Le Galaad, PH, x (RI) *Rue des Francais,
Castel.* ✆ (0481) 57233. Open Mar–Oct. C
4. ⊯ 11 bedrs, 1 bp, 6 bps, 1 ba, TV. 🅟 CH,
CP 15, 4 BGf, 1 st, Dis. £ BB £8–£14, DB
£16–£28, WT (b) £84–£105, DT (b) £12–
£15.
La Girouette Country House, PH, xy
(R), *La Girouette, St Saviour's.* ✆ (0481)
63269. Open Feb–Oct & Dec. C 3. ⊯ 14

---

bedrs, 2 bp, 8 bps, 2 ba, TV. 🅟 CH, ns, CP
14, 2 st. £ BB £11–£15, DB £22–£30, WT
£105–£138·60, DT £15–£19·80, 🛈, Bk
£2·50, L £4, D £4·50, cc 1 2 3.▲
Lynton, PH, xy (RI), *Hacse Lane,
L'Ancresse.* ✆ (0481) 45418. C. ⊯ 14
bedrs, 3 bp, 7 bps, 1 ba. 🅟 CH, TV, CP 15.
£ BB £9·50–£12·50, DB £19–£25, DT £26–
£31, 🛈.
Midhurst House, PH, z (Rt), *Candie Rd,
St Peter Port.* ✆ (0481) 24391. Open Mar–
Oct & Xmas. C 5. ⊯ 7 bedrs, 1 bp, 6 bps, 2
ba. 🅟 CH, TV, CP 7. £ BB £13–£15, DB £22–£26,
DT (b) £105–£119, 🛈.
Willows, PH, z (RI), *Nocq Rd, St
Sampsons.* ✆ (0481) 47064. Closed Xmas
& New Year. C. ⊯ 12 bedrs, 7 bps, 1 ba.
🅟 CH, TV, CP 12, CF, 3 BGf, 3 st. £ BB £9–
£13, DB £18–£26, WT (b) £77–£98, (c)
£63–£84, DT (b) £11–£14, 🛈.

MC Repairer: Millard & Co Ltd, Victoria
Rd, St Peter Port. ✆ (0481) 20777.
Rescue Service: Bougourd Bros Ltd, PO
Box 168, Les Banques. ✆ (0481) 24774.

RAC Office, *27 The Parade, St Helier.*
✆ Jersey (0534) 23813.
Pop 71,000. Guernsey 25, Weymouth 103.
EC Thur. **P** Car Parks are indicated by "P"
signs. Disc Park Areas: Parking Discs are
obtained at 15p each, and areas are
indicated by "Parking Disc Only" signs.
Group Meter Parking Zones in St Helier.
Public car parks (no time limit) in St Helier,
including a multi-storey in Green St.
Speed limit 40 mph on the island. **Golf** St
Brelade's Bay 18h, Royal Jersey 18h, La
Moye 18h. **See** Elizabethan Castle, Mount
Orgueil Castle, Potteries Museums,
Government building, Fort Regent, Gorey
Castle, underground installations dating
from German occupation (inc. hospital),
Corbiere Lighthouse, Shell House, Motor
Museum, Zoo, St Helier pro-Cathedral, St
Brelade's Bay and Church, annual "Battle
of Flowers".
🛈 States of Jersey Tourist Information
Bureau. Weighbridge, St Helier ✆ Jersey
(0534) 31958.

★★★★**Atlantic,** *La Moye, St Brelade's
Bay.* ✆ (0534) 44101. Closed Jan & Feb. C.
⊯ 46 bedrs, 46 bp, TV. ✖ a l c, mc, at, LD
9.15. 🅟 Lt, N, CH, CP 50, sp, tc, con, 4 BGf,
1 st, Dis. £ DB £45–£63, WT £253·75–
£313·25, DT £36·25–£44·75, DBB £30·75–
£39·25, 🛈, L £6, D £9·75, cc 1 2 3 4 5 6,
Dep b.
★★★★**Grand,** *Esplanade, St Helier.*
✆ (0534) 22301. C. ⊯ 118 bedrs, 118 bp,
2 ba, TV, dgs. ✖ a l c, mc, at, LD 9. 🅟 Lt, N,
CH, CP 40, G 24, Ac, sp, sol, gym, con
200, CF, 8 BGf, 5 st. £ BB £24–£41, DB
£48–£68, WT £213·50–£273, DBB
£30·50–£39, 🛈, Bk £3·50, D £6·50,
cc 1 2 3 5 6, Dep a.
★★★★**Hotel de la Plage,** *Havre des Pas,
St Helier.* ✆ (0534) 23474. C. ⊯ 96 bedrs,
96 bp, 1 ba, TV. ✖ a l c, mc, at, LD 9. 🅟 Lt,
N, ch, CP 80, G 8, con 15, CF, 3 st. £ BB
£16·50–£23·50, DB £30–£53, DT £22·50–
£33·50, DBB £19–£30, 🛈, Bk £3, L £5·25,
D £6·75, cc 1 2 3 4 5 6, Dep a.▲
★★★★**L'Horizon,** *St Brelade's Bay.*
✆ (0534) 43101. C. ⊯ 104 bedrs, 104 bp,
1 ba, TV. ✖ a l c, mc, at, LD 9.45. 🅟 Lt, N,
CH, CP 110, sp, sb, sol, con 70, CF. £ BB
£27·50–£33, DB £55–£88, DT £46·75–

£52·25, DBB £38·50–£44, ①, Bk £3·50, L £9, D £13·75, cc 1 2 3 4 5, Dep.▲
★★★★**Longueville Manor,** *St Saviour's.* ✆ (0534) 25501. C 7. ⊷ 33 bedrs, 33 bp, TV, dgs. ✗ a l c, mc, at, LD 9·30. ① Lt, N, CH, CP 30, sp, rf, con 15. £ BB £39–£42·50, DB £70–£77, WB, ①, Bk £4·50, L fr £10, D fr £12·50, cc 1 2 3 4 5 6, Dep a.
★★★★**Mermaid,** *St Peter.* ✆ (0534) 41255. C. ⊷ 68 bedrs, 68 bp, 2 ba, TV. ✗ a l c, mc, at, LD 9. ① N, CH, CP 150, Ac, sp, con 120, CF, 28 BGf, 7 st. £ BB £15– £22, DB £30–£44, DT £22–£29, DBB £19– £26, ②, Bk £3·50, L £5·50, D £6·50, cc 1 2 3 5 6.
★★★**Ambassadeur,** *St Clements Bay, St Clement.* ✆ (0534) 24455. Open Mar–Dec. C. ⊷ 41 bedrs, 41 bp, 1 ba, TV, Dgs. ✗ a l c, mc, at, LD 9·45. ① Lt, N, CH, CP 50, Ac, sp, CF, 3 st. £ BB £10–£24·50, DB £20–£49, WT £112–£229·25, DT £16– £32·75, DBB £13–£28·25, ①, L £4·40, D £5·50, cc 1 2 3 5 6, Dep b.
★★★**Apollo,** *St Saviour's Rd, St Helier.* ✆ (0534) 25441. C. ⊷ 53 bedrs, 53 bp, 1 ba, TV. ✗ a l c, mc, at, LD 8·30. ① Lt, N, CH, TV, CP 50, con 40, CF, 0 st. £ BB £18– £28·50, DB £29·50–£42, DT £29·50– £36·50, DBB £24·50–£31·50, WB, ①, Bk £3·50, L £5, D £6·50, cc 1 2 3 4 5 6, Dep b.
★★★**Beaufort,** *Green St, St Helier.* ✆ (0534) 32471. C. ⊷ 54 bedrs, 54 bp, 1 ba, TV. ✗ a l c, mc, at, LD 8. ① Lt, N, CH, TV, CP 30, Ac, cc 1 2 3 4.
★★★**Chateau de la Valeuse,** *St Brelade's Bay.* ✆ (0534) 43476. Open Mar–Oct. C 5. ⊷ 24 bedrs, 18 bp, 5 bps, 2 sh, 1 ba, ✗ a l c, mc, at, LD 9·15. ① N, CH, TV, CP 50, sp, 8 st. £ BB £16·50–£22·50, DB £33–£45, WT £150·50–£206·50, DT £21·50–£29·50, DBB £19·50–£29·50, ①, cc 1 2 3 6, Dep a.
★★★**Le Couperon de Rozel,** *Rozel Bay.* ✆ (0534) 62190. Open Apr–Oct. C. ⊷ 25

bedrs, 25 bp. ✗ a l c, mc, at, LD 9·45. ① N, ch, TV, CP 30, sp, con 30, CF, 7 BGf, 2 st. £ BB £13–£26, DB £26–£52, DT £20–£32, DBB £16–£30, ①, Bk £4, L £6, D £8, cc 1 2 3 4 5 6, Dep.
★★★**Little Grove,** *Rue de Haut, St Lawrence.* ✆ (0534) 25321. C. ⊷ 14 bedrs, 11 bp, 3 bps, 1 ba, TV, Dgs. ✗ a l c, mc, at, LD 10. ① N, CH, CP 24, sp, con 20, CF, 2 BGf, 3 st. £ BB £22–£24·50, DB £44– £49, DT £37, DBB £29·50–£32·50, WB, ①, Bk £2, L £4·50, D £8·50, cc 1 2 3 5, Dep a.
★★★**Old Court House,** *Gorey.* ✆ (0534) 54444. Open Mar–Oct. C. ⊷ 58 bedrs, 58 bp, 3 ba, TV. ✗ a l c, mc, at, LD 8·30. ① Lt, N, CH, CP 40, sp, sb, sol, CF, 9 BGf, 0 st. Dis. £ Bk £3, L £4·50, D £7·50, cc 1 2 3 5.
★★★**Ommaroo,** *Havre des Pas, St Helier.* ✆ (0534) 23493. C. ⊷ 85 bedrs, 51 bp, 23 bps, 8 ba, ns, TV, Dgs. ✗ a l c, mc, at, LD 8·30. ① Lt, N, CH, TV, Dgs, CP 60, Ac, con 100, CF, 3 st. £ BB £14–£27, DB £28–£44, WT £126–£182, WB, ①, Bk £2·50, L £4, D £6, cc 2 3 4 5, Dep.
★★★**Pomme D'Or,** *The Weighbridge, St Helier.* ✆ (0534) 78644. C. ⊷ 151 bedrs, 151 bp, TV, Dgs. ✗ a l c, mc, at, LD 8·30. ① Lt, N, CH, Ac, con 200, CF, 2 st. £ BB £22– £26, DB £34–£42, WT £196–£203, DT £28–£29, DBB £23–£24, WB ①, Bk £3·02, L £5·50, D £7·70, cc 1 2 3 5 6, Dep. ▲
★★★**Savoy** (R), *Rouge Bouillon, St Helier.* ✆ (0534) 30012. Open Mar–Nov. C. ⊷ 61 bedrs, 53 bp, 8 bps, 1 ba, TV. ✗ a l c, mc, at, LD 8·30. ① Lt, N, CH, CP 50, Ac, sp, con 140, CF, 12 BGf, 3 st. £ BB £12–£18, DB £24–£36, WT £140–£182, DT £20–£26, DBB £16–£22, ①, Bk £3, L £4, D £6, Dep.
★★**Dolphin,** *Gorey Pier. Gorey.* ✆ (0534) 53370. C. ⊷ 17 bedrs, 14 bps, 3 ba, Dgs. ✗ a l c, mc, at, LD 10. ① N, CH, TV, Ac, CF, 1 st. £ BB £14·50–£18, DB £29–£36, DBB £22·50–£25·50, DBB £18·50–£22, ①, L £4·50, D £8·50, cc 1 2 3 4 6, Dep a.
★★**Les Arches,** *Archirondel Bay, Gorey.* ✆ (0534) 53839. C. ⊷ 54 bdrs, 35 bp, 19

bps, 1 ba, TV, Dgs. ✗ mc, at. ① N, CH, TV, CP 120, sp, con 80, 6 st. £ BB £15·50– £22·25, DB £31–£44·50, DT £22·50– £32·50, DBB £19·50–£27·50, WB, ①, Bk £2·50, L £2·50, D £7, cc 1 3 4 6, Dep.
★★**L'Hermitage** (R), *Beaumont.* ✆ (0534) 3314. Open Mar–Oct. C. 14. ⊷ 109 bedrs, 96 bp, 13 bps, TV. ✗ mc, at, LD 8. ① N, CH, CP 100, Ac, sp, sb, 52 BGf, 3 st. £ BB £11·85–£17·80, DB £23·70– £35·60, WT £82·95–£141·05, DT £13·20– £20·15, DBB £12–£18·95, ①, Bk £2, L £3, D £4, cc 6, Dep.▲
★★**Mont Millais,** *St Helier.* ✆ (0534) 30281.
★★**Mount View** (R) *St John's Rd, St Helier.* ✆ (0534) 78887. Closed Jan–Feb & Xmas. C. ⊷ 36 bedrs, 11 bp, 20 bps, 2 ba, TV, Dgs. ✗ mc, at, LD 8. ① Lt, N, CP 12, Ac, CF, 4 st. £ BB £16–£23·50, DB £28– £41, WT £136·50–£175, DT £19·50–£25, DBB £16·50–£22, ①, Bk £2·50, L £3·50, D £5·50, cc 1 3, Dep.
★★**Royal Yacht,** *Weighbridge, St Helier.* ✆ (0534) 20511. C. ⊷ 45 bedrs, 18 bp, 27 bps, 1 ba, TV, Dgs. ✗ a l c, mc, at, LD 8·30. ① Lt, N, CH, TV, Ac, con 30, CF, 0 st. £ BB £16·50–£19, DB £33–£38, WT £175–£203, DT £23–£29, DBB £20·75–£24, ①, Bk £4, L £4·95, D £7·50, cc 1 3 4 6, Dep.
★★**Shakespeare** (R), *Samares Coast Rd, St Clements Bay.* ✆ (0534) 51915. Closed Jan & Feb. C. ⊷ 26 bedrs, 23 bp, 3 bps 2 ba, TV, Dgs. ✗ a l c, mc, at, LD 10. ① N, CH, CP 40, con 50, CF, 2 st. £ BB £12–£18, DB £24–£38, DBB £17·50–£27, ①, Bk £3·50, L £3·50, D £6, cc 1 2 3 5, Dep a.
Midvale, G, x (RI), *St Peter's Valley.* ✆ (0534) 42498. Open Apr–Oct. C 1. ⊷ 20 bedrs, 5 bp, 4 sh, 2 ba. ① ch, TV, CP 15, CF. £ DT (b) £12·25–£14·25, ①.
Willows, G, y, (RI). *Grand Vaux.* ✆ (0534) 37267.

Repairer: Tony Perchard Ltd, 13 Stopford Rd, St Helier. ✆ (0534) 71555.

AGHANLOO Co. Londonderry. Map 50B
Limavady 5, Belfast 75, Dungiven 14, Londonderry 21.
Rescue Service: T A Kerr, 88 Dowland Rd. ✆ Limavady (050 472) 4903.

BALLYCASTLE Co. Antrim. Map 51A
Pop 4,000. Ballymena 26, Belfast 54, Ballymoney 16, Bushmills 13, Cushendun 13.
EC Wed. **MD** Tue. **Golf** Ballycastle 18h. **See** Rathin Island, Knocklayd mountain (1,695 ft), Dunaneanie Castle, Holy Trinity Church 1756, Bunamargy Friary.
⑦ 61 Castle St. ✆ Ballycastle (026 57) 62024.
Rescue Service: Sheskburn Garage, Mary St. ✆ (026 57) 62478.

BALLYGALLY Co. Antrim. Map 51D
Pop 2,245. Larne 3, Belfast 22, Antrim 22, Ballymena 18, Coleraine 40.
Golf Cairndhu 18h. **See** Ballygally Castle (now Hotel), Sallagh Braes, Ballygally Head, Cairncastle Parish Church.

★★★**Ballygally Castle,** *274 Coast Rd, Larne, BT40 2QZ.* ✆ (057 483) 212. C. ⊷ 29 bedrs, 29 bp, TV, Dgs. ✗ a l c, mc, at, LD 9·30. ① N, CH, TV, Dgs, CP 50, tc, con, CF. £ BB £23·50, DB £36·50, cc 1 2 3 5.
★★**Halfway,** *Coast Rd, BT40 2RA.* ✆ (057 483) 265.

BALLYMONEY Co. Antrim. Map 51A
Pop 6,000. Ballymena 18, Belfast 46, Ballycastle 16, Coleraine 8.
EC Mon. **MD** Thur, Fri. **Golf** Portrush 18h. **See** Safari Park (5 m N).

Rescue Service: W J McCaw & Sons, 246 Moyarget Rd, Mosside. ✆ Dervock (026 57) 223.
J A Roddy, John St. ✆ (026 56) 63191.

BANGOR Co. Down. Map 51F
Pop 38,282. Belfast 12, Newtownards 4.
MD Wed. **Golf** Bangor 18h, Carnalea 18h, Clandeboys 18h (2). **See** Ward Park, Castle Park, Marine Gardens, Abbey.
⑦ Town Hall, The Castle. ✆ Bangor (0247) 54371.

★★★**Royal,** *Sea Front, BT20 5EB.* ✆ (0247) 473866. Closed Xmas. C. ⊷ 32 bedrs, 31 bp, 1 bps, TV, Dgs. ✗ a l c, mc, at, LD 9·15. ① Lt, N, CH, Ac, sol, con 70, CF, 0 st. £ BB £24, DB £24–£30, WB, ②, Bk £3, L £3, D £6·50, cc 1 2 3 5 6, Dep b.
★★★**Ballyholme** (Unl), *262 Seacliffe Rd, BT20 5HT.* ✆ (0247) 472807. C. ⊷ 36 bedrs, 7 bps, 6 ba. ✗ mc, at, LD 8. ① CH, TV, Dgs, CP 12, U 1, Ac, con 50, CF, 1 st. £ BB £14–£17, DB £22·50–£34, WT £126·50–£143·50, DT £22–£24, DBB £21– £24, WB, ①, Bk £3, L £4·50, D £6·50.

Rescue Service: Bangor Auto, 32A Belfast Rd. ✆ (0247) 51428.
Charles Hurst Motors (Bangor) Ltd, 71 Newtownards Rd. ✆ (0247) 4312.
S C Taylor Ltd, 2A Ballyholme Rd. ✆ (0247) 65307.

BELFAST Co. Antrim and Co. Down. Map 51F
See also NEWTOWN ABBEY.
RAC Office, *79 Chichester Street, Belfast, BT1 4JR.* ✆ (General) Belfast (0232) 240261. (Rescue Service only) Belfast (0232) 223333.
Pop 297,862. Antrim 14, Coleraine 4, Larne 19, Londonderry 74, Newry 33.
See Plan, pp 401.
MD Mon, Tue, Fri. **Golf** Royal Belfast (Craigavad) 18h, Balmoral 18h, Cliftonville 9h, Fortwilliam 18h, Belvoir Park 18h, Shandon Park 18h, The Knock 18h, Mahee Island 9h, Ormeau 9h. **See** Maysfield Leisure Centre, University, Botanical Gardens, Museums, Cathedrals (St Anne's Protestant, St Peter's RC), Ormeau Park, City Hall, Art Gallery, *Titanic* Memorial, "Giants' Ring" one of the largest prehistoric earthworks in Ireland, Farrell's Fort, Belfast Castle, Cave Hill (1,182 ft), with McArt's fort on summit, Albert Memorial (tilted 5ft out of plumb).
⑦ 52 High St. ✆ Belfast (0232) 246609.

★★★★M Forum (late **Belfast Europa**), *Great Victoria St. BT2 7AP*. ☎ (0232) 230091. C. ⊷ 200 bedrs, 200 bp, TV, Dgs. ✗ a l c, mc, at, LD 11.30. ⌂ Lt, N, CH, CP 40, Ac, con 400, CF, 1 st. £ B £44·50, BD £58, WB, ①, Bk £4·50, L £9·25, D £9·25, cc 1 2 3 5 6, Dep.

Repairer: J E Coulter Ltd, 58 Antrim Rd. ☎ (0232) 744744.
Rescue Service: Hills Engineering Works Ltd, 220 Holywood Rd. ☎ (0232) 656241. Peter Catling, 53 Knocklofty Park. ☎ (0232) 653965. W H Connolly Ltd, 357 Albertbridge Rd. ☎ (0232) 57575 & (0232) 57766.

CALEDON Co. Tyrone. Map 54B
Pop 500. Armagh 6, Belfast 46, Dungannon 12, Monaghan 10, Newry 31.
EC Wed. **Golf** Armagh 18h.

Rescue Service: Donnelly Bros (Motor Engineers) Ltd, 201 Killylea Rd. ☎ (086 156) 235.

CARNLOUGH Co. Antrim. Map 51C
Pop 2,280. Larne 12, Belfast 31, Ballymena 14, Coleraine 34.
Golf Cairndhu 18h. **See** Glenarm Castle, Cranny Falls, Little Trosk mountains, "Cairn Lake".
ℹ Post Office, Harbour Rd. ☎ Carnlough (0574) 85210.

★★Londonderry Arms, *BT44 0EU.*
☎ (0574) 85255. C 12. ⊷ 12 bedrs, 12 bp, TV. ✗ mc, at, LD 8.45 (7.45 Sun). ⌂ CH, TV, CP 16, con 30, 1 st. £ BB £15, DB £28, DBB £23·50, WB, ①, L £6·50, D £8·95, cc 1 2 3 5 6.

CARRICKFERGUS Co. Antrim. Map 51D
Pop 20,000. Belfast 10, Antrim 17, Ballymena 23, Larne 14.
EC Wed. **MD** Thur. **Golf** Carrickfergus 18h, Bentra Municipal 9h, Greenisland 9h, Whitehead 18h. **See** Castle, St Nicholas Church, Market sq, site of birthplace of Andrew Jackson (American President) at Boneybefore, Birthplace of Louis MacNeice (poet), Ruins of Dean Swift's first church at Kilroot.
ℹ Castle Green. ☎ Carrickfergus (096 03) 63604.

★★Coast Road, *BT38 7DP.* ☎ (096 03) 61021.▲
★Dobbins Inn, *BT38 7AF.* ☎ (096 03) 63905. Closed Xmas. C. ⊷ 13 bedrs, 2 bp, 3 sh, 4 ba, TV, Dgs. ✗ mc, at, LD 9.15. ⌂ N, CH, TV, Dgs, Ac, con 60, CF, 1 st. £ BB £14–£18·50, DB £27–£33·50, WB, ①, Bk £3, L £2, cc 1 3 5 6.

Rescue Service: Downshire Service Station, Larne Rd. ☎ (096 03) 63516.

CARRYDUFF Co. Down. Map 51F
Pop 3,800. Castlereagh 4, Belfast 6, Banbridge 21, Lisburn 6, Newtownards 11.
EC Wed. **Golf** Belvoir 18h, Shandon Park 18h.

Rescue Service: Jamison Bros, 636 Saintfield Rd. ☎ (0232) 812204.

CLOUGHEY Co. Down. Maps 51F & 55B
Kirkcubbin 5½, Belfast 26, Newtownards 16, Portaferry 5.

★★Roadhouse, 204 Main Rd, *BT22 1JA.*
☎ (024 77) 71500. Closed Xmas. C. ⊷ 9 bedrs, 4 bp, 5 bps. ✗ a l c, mc, LD 9.30.

⌂ CH, TV, CP 30, Ac, CF, 1 st. £ BB £15, DB £26, DBB £20, ①, Bk £3, L £4, D £5, cc 1 3, Dep b.

COLERAINE Co. Londonderry. Map 50B
Pop 18,000. Ballymena 23, Belfast 47, Larne 41, Londonderry 26, Portrush 5.
EC Thur. **MD** Mon, Tue, Wed, Fri. **Golf** Portstewart 18h, Portrush 18h, Castlerock 18h. **See** Mussenden Temple, Down Hill, Safari Park, Trim Trail, Mountsandel Fort—ancient fortress dominating River Bann, Bally hackell View Point, Daffodil gardens, University.
Repairer: Stuart & Co (Motors) Ltd, Hanover Pl. ☎ (0265) 2386.
Rescue Service: MacFarlane Motors Ltd, Ring Rd. ☎ (0265) 3153.

COMBER Co. Down. Map 51F
Pop 7,700. Dundonald 4, Belfast 10, Bangor 10, Downpatrick 18, Newtownards 4.
EC Wed. **Golf** Scrabo 18h, Mahee Island 9h. **See** Nendrun Castle, Sketrick Castle, Scrabo Hill, White Rock, Comber Square.

Rescue Service: J Middleton, North Down Garage, Belfast Rd. ☎ (0247) 872244.

COOKSTOWN Co. Tyrone. Map 50F
Pop 8,400. M22 Motorway 22, Moneymore 5, Belfast 45, Dungannon 10.
EC Wed. **MD** Fri, Sat. **Golf** Killymoon 18h. **See** Beaghmore Stone Circle, Sperrin Mountains, Springhill House, Moneymore, Lough Neagh, Wellbrook Beetling Mill, Salter's Castle, Ballybriest Cairns, Tullyhogue Fort, Arboe Cross.
ℹ Town Hall, Burn Rd. ☎ Cookstown (064 87) 63359.

Rescue Service: Bradford Bros, 2 Lissan Rd. ☎ (064 87) 63667.

CRAWFORDSBURN Co. Down. Map 51F
Pop 2,904. Holywood 7, Belfast 11, Bangor 2, Newtownards 6.
EC Thur. **Golf** Holywood 18h. **See** Ulster Folk Museum, Country Park.

★★★Old Inn, *Main St, BT19 1JH.*
☎ Helen's Bay (0247) 853255.

CUSHENDALL Co. Antrim. Map 51A
Pop 1,100. Larne 24, Belfast 43, Ballymena 19, Coleraine 33.
EC Tue. **Golf** Cushendall.

★★Thornlea, *6 Coast Rd, BT44 0RU.*
☎ (026 67) 71223. C. ⊷ 14 bedrs, 1 bp, 8 bps, 5 sh, 1 ba. ✗ mc, at, LD 9.15. ⌂ CH, TV, CP 30, G 1, Ac, con, CF, 1 st. £ BB £12·50, DB £24, WB, ①, Bk £3, L £5·50, cc 1 2 3 4 5, Dep a.▲

DERVOCK Co. Antrim. Map 51A
Pop 800. Ballymoney 5, Belfast 51, Ballycastle 10, Coleraine 9.
Golf Portrush 18h.

Rescue Service: A Chestnutt & Sons, 209 Knock Rd. ☎ (026 57) 41387.

DUNADRY Co. Antrim. Map 51C
Pop 204. Belfast 12, M2 Motorway ½, Antrim 3, Ballymena 10, Larne 16.
EC Wed. **Golf** Massereene 18h.

★★★★Dunadry Inn, 2 Islandreagh Dr, Muckamore, *BT41 2HA.* ☎ Templepatrick (084 94) 32474. Closed Dec 25–28. C. ⊷ 75 bedrs, 55 bp, 20 bps, TV. ✗ mc, at, LD 9.45. ⌂ N, CH, CP 350, Ac, pf, con 350, CF, 30 BGf, 2 st. £ BB £40, DB £50,

---

DBB £55, WB, ①, Bk £5, L £6·50, D £10, cc 1 2 3 4 5 6.

DUNDRUM Co. Down. Map 55B
Pop 1,800. Ballynahinch 11, Belfast 25, Banbridge 20, Downpatrick 8, Newry 23.
EC Thur. **Golf** Newcastle 18h. **See** Murlough Nature Reserve, Castle

Rescue Service: W Graham. Regent Service Station, Main St. ☎ (039 675) 250.

DUNGANNON Co. Tyrone. Map 50F
Pop 9,000. M1 Motorway 4, Belfast 42, Armagh 12, Cookstown 10, Monaghan 21, Portadown 16.
EC Wed. **MD** Tue, Thur. **Golf** Dungannon 18h.

★★★Inn on the Park, *Moy Rd, BT71 6BU.* ☎ (086 87) 25151. C. ⊷ 15 bedrs, 15 bp, 2 ba, TV. ✗ mc, at, LD 10. ⌂ Lt, N, CH, Dgs, CP 300, tc, con 300, CF, 4 BGf, Dis. £ BB £16, DB £28, WT £158, DT £25, DBB £25, WB, ①, Bk £3·75, L £5·95, D £6·95, cc 1 3 5.

DUNMURRY Co. Antrim. Map 51E
Pop 3,638. Belfast 5, M1 Motorway 2½, Antrim 20, Lisburn 3.
EC Wed. **Golf** Dunmurry 18h.

★★★★Conway (TH), *BT17 9ES.*
☎ Belfast (0232) 612101. C. ⊷ 78 bedrs, 78 bp, TV, Dgs. ✗ a l c, mc, at, LD 10. ⌂ Lt, N, CH, Dgs, CP 250, Ac, sp, sc, con 450, CF, 23 BGf, 0 st, Dis. £ BB £44·50, DB £52·50, ①, cc 1 2 3 4 5 6.

EGLINTON Co. Londonderry. Map 50D.
Limavady 9, Belfast 79, Dungiven 19, Londonderry 8.

★★★Glen House, 9 Main St, *BT47 3AA.* ☎ (0504) 810527.

ENNISKILLEN Co. Fermanagh. Map 54A
Pop 12,536. Dungannon 37, Belfast 74, Donegal 31, Omagh 22, Sligo 34.
EC Wed. **MD** Thur. **Golf** Enniskillen 9h. **See** Castle, Lakes, Castle Coole (NT).
ℹ Lakeland Visitor Centre, Shore Rd. ☎ Enniskillen (0365) 3110.

★Railway, *BT74 6AJ.* ☎ (0365) 22084.

Rescue Service: Lochside Garages Ltd, Tempo Rd. ☎ (0365) 4366.

FINAGHY Co Antrim. Map Area 51E
Belfast 4, M1 Motorway 1½, Antrim 21, Lisburn 4.

Rescue Service: Finaghy Garage Ltd, 87–89 Upper Lisburn Rd. ☎ Belfast (0232) 626711.

HOLYWOOD Co. Down. Map 51F
Pop 8,573. Belfast 5, Bangor 7, Newtownards 7.
EC Thur. **Golf** Holywood 18h, Royal Belfast 18h. **See** Holywood Priory remains.

★★★★Culloden, *Bangor Rd, Craigavad, BT18 0EX.* ☎ (023 17) 5223. C. ⊷ 72 bedrs, 72 bp, TV, Dgs. ✗ a l c, mc, at, LD 9.30. ⌂ Lt, N, CH, Dgs, CP 350, Ac, tc, sx, gym, con 400, CF. £ BB £49, DB £60, WB, ②, Bk £4·50, L £9, D £9, cc 1 2 3 5 6, Dep b.

IRVINESTOWN Co. Fermanagh. Map 50E
Pop 3,100. Dungannon 34, Belfast 71, Donegal 23, Omagh 15.
EC Thur. **MD** Wed. **Golf** Enniskillen 9h.

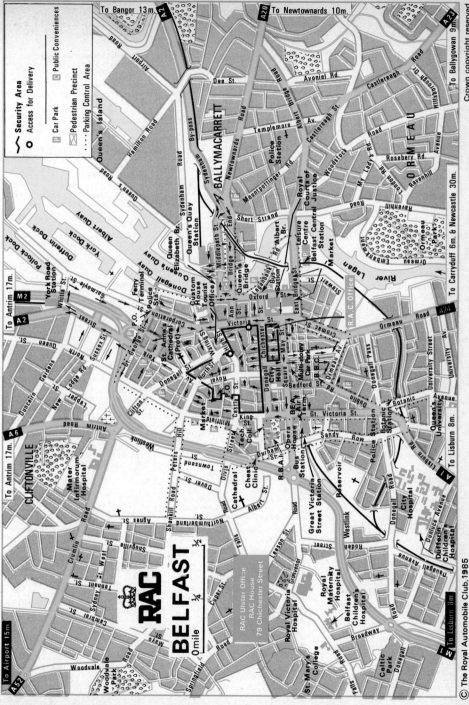

Map legend

Security Area

- ⌐ Access for Delivery
- P Car Park
- Pedestrian Precinct
- C Public Conveniences
- Parking Control Area

To Bangor 13 m. A2

To Newtownards 10 m. A20

To Ballygowan 9 m. A23

Crown copyright reserved

To Antrim 17 m. M2

To Antrim 17 m. A2

To Airport 15 m. A52

To Carryduff 6 m. & Newcastle 30 m.

To Lisburn 8 m. A1

To Lisburn 3 m. M1

RAC Ulster Office
RAC House
79 Chichester Street

RAC

BELFAST

0 mile ¼ ½

BALLYMACARRETT

ORMEAU

CLIFTONVILLE

★★**Mahons,** *Enniskillen Rd, BT74 9XX.*
℃ (036 56) 21656. RS Xmas. C. ⊷ 17
bedrs, 5 bp, 1 bps, 1 sh, 3 ba, TV. ✗ a l c,
mc, at, LD 9. ⓓ CH, TV, Dgs, CP 20, G 20,
Ac, con 50, CF, 2 st. £ BB £11–£11·50, DB
£23, DBB £18, WB, ②, Bk £3, L £4·50, D
£6·50, cc 1 3, Dep a.

KESH Co. Fermanagh. Map 50E
Pop 2,500. Omagh 16, Belfast 74,
Ballyshannon 19, Donegal 18, Enniskillen
13.
EC Thur. **Golf** Enniskillen 9h. **See** Boa
Island.

★★**Lough Erne,** *Main St.* ℃ (036 56)
31275. Closed Xmas. C. ⊷ 14 bedrs, 3
bps, 1 sh, 2 ba, Dgs. ✗ mc, at, LD 9. ⓓ CH,
TV, Dgs, CP 100, Ac, pf, con 250, CF, 1 st.
£ BB £9·50–£10·50, DB £19–£21, DBB
£16·50–£17·50, WB, ②, Bk £3, L £4·50
(£5·90 Sun), D £7, Dep a.

KILKEEL Co. Down. Map 55D
Pop 5,000. Newry 16, Belfast 49,
Downpatrick 22, Dundalk 27.
EC Thur. **MD** Wed. **Golf** Mourne Park,
Kilkeel 9h.
ⓘ Town Hall, Newry St. ℃ Kilkeel
(069 37) 63092.

★★**Kilmorey Arms.** ℃ (069 37) 62220.

Rescue Service: David McAtee & Sons
Ltd, 17 Greencastle St. ℃ (069 37) 62217.

LARNE Co. Antrim. Map 51 D
Pop 18,552. Belfast 19, Antrim 19,
Ballymena 18, Coleraine 42.
EC Tue, **MD** Wed, Fri. **Golf** Cairndhu 18h.
See Olderfleet Castle ruins, St. Cedma's
Parish Church, the Chaine Memorial
Tower, Old world villages of Glynn &
Glenco, Historical Centre & Market, Parks.
ⓘ Council Offices, Victoria Rd. ℃ Larne
(0574) 2313.

Rescue Service: Harbour Motor & Eng Co
Ltd, Curran Rd. ℃ (0574) 2071.
Larne Motor Co Ltd, Point Garage, Point
St. ℃ (0574) 2091.

LISBURN Co. Antrim. Map 51E
Pop 57,000. Belfast 6, M1 Motorway 1,
Antrim 17, Downpatrick 18, Dungannon
26.
EC Wed. **MD** Tue. **Golf** Lisburn 18h. **See**
Christ Church Cathedral, Castle Gardens,
Parks, Museum.

★★★**Woodlands,** *Belfast Rd BT27 4AP.*
℃ (084 62) 2741.

Repairer: Stevenson Bros (Lisburn) Ltd,
Seymour St. ℃ (084 62) 2214.
Rescue Service: Lisburn 24 Hour
Recovery, 292 Comber Rd. ℃ Baillies Mills
(084 663) 459.
Plantation Motors, Plantation Rd.
℃ (084 62) 75385.
Samual Ellis, 3 Old Rd, Ballinderry Upper.
℃ Aghalee (0846) 651388.

LONDONDERRY Co. Londonderry. Map
50C
Pop 90,400. Dungiven 19, Belfast 70,
Coleraine 30, Limavady 17, Strabane 14.
EC Thur. **MD** Wed, Thur. **Golf** City of
Derry 18h. **See** Cathedrals, Guildhall, City
Walls, Art Gallery.
ⓘ Foyle St. ℃ Londonderry (0504) 69501.

Rescue Service: Desmond Motors Ltd,
173 Strand Rd. ℃ (0504) 67613.

LURGAN Co. Armagh. Map 51E
Pop 24,000. Antrim 25, Lisburn 13, Belfast
22, Banbridge 10, Dungannon 20,
Portadown 6.
EC Wed. **MD** Tue. **Golf** Lurgan 18h. **See**
Brownlow House and park.

Rescue Service: H Wilson & Sons,
Portadown Rd. ℃ (076 22) 22278.

MAGHERAMORNE Co. Antrim. Map
51D
Pop 300. Carrickfergus 10, Belfast 21,
Antrim 28, Ballymena 24, Larne 4.
Golf Cairndhu 18h. **See** Nature Reserve
(R.S.P.B.).

⊞★★★★**Magheramorne House,** *BT
40 3HW.* ℃ Larne (0574) 79444. C. ⊷ 23
bedrs, 23 bp, 1 ba, TV, Dgs. ✗ a l c, mc, at,
LD 9.30. ⓓ Lt, N, CH, TV, Dgs, CP 50, Ac,
gc, con 100, CF, 3 BGf, 0 st, Dis. £ BB £24,
DB £38, WB, ①, Bk £4, L £5·25,
cc 1 2 3 5 6.

MILLIGANS CROSS Co. Down. M. Area
51F
Belfast 3½, Ballygowan 4½.

Rescue Service: Todd's Garage, Comber
Rd. ℃ Castlereagh (023 123) 576.

NEWCASTLE Co. Down. Map 55B
Pop 4,647. Belfast 26, Armagh 32,
Downpatrick 11, Newry 20.
EC Thur. **MD** Tue, Fri. **Golf** Royal County
Down 18h (2).
ⓘ Newcastle Centre, Central Promenade.
℃ Newcastle (039 67) 22222.

★★★**Slieve Donard,** *Downs Rd,
BT33 0AG.* ℃ (039 67) 23681. C. ⊷ 110
bedrs, 110 bps, TV, Dgs. ✗ a l c, mc, at, LD
9.30. ⓓ Lt, N, CH, TV, Dgs, ns, Ac, sp, gc, tc,
sb, con, CF. £ BB £23·50, DB £36·50, WB,
①, cc 1 2 3 5.

⊞★★**Enniskeen,** *Bryansford Rd, BT33
0LF.* ℃ (039 67) 22392. Open Mar–Oct. C.
⊷ 12 bedrs, 6 bp, 2 ba, TV. ✗ mc, at, LD 8.
ⓓ CH, TV, CP 45, Ac, con 50, CF, 1 st. £ BB
£14·50–£19·25, DB £26–£31·50, WT
£152–£184, DT £25–£27·25, DBB £20–
£26·60, WB, ①, Bk £3·25, L £5, D £7·25,
cc 1 3, Dep b.

NEWRY Co. Down. Map 55A
Pop 28,000. Banbridge 13, Belfast 36,
Armagh 18, Dundalk 13, Newcastle 20.
EC Wed. **MD** Thur, Sat. **Golf** Newry 18h.
ⓘ Arts Centre, Bank Par. ℃ Newry (0693)
66232. **See** RC Cathedral.

Repairer: Rowland & Harris Ltd, Railway
Av. ℃ (0693) 2201.

NEWTOWNABBEY Co. Antrim. Map
51F
Pop 71,917. Belfast 4, M2 Motorway 2,
Antrim 13, Carrickfergus 5, Larne 15.
EC Wed. **MD** Mon. **Golf** Fortwilliam,
Belfast 18h, Ballyclare 18h. **See** Valley
Leisure Centre, Multi-sports Complex.

★★★**M Chimney Corner,** *630 Antrim
Rd, BT36 8RH.* ℃ Glengormley (023 13)
44925.

Ap Abbeylands (Unl), *BT37 9SE.*
℃ Whiteabbey (0231) 64552.

NEWTOWNARDS Co. Down. Map 51F
Pop 23,000. Belfast 10, Bangor 4, Comber
4.

EC Thur. **MD** Sat. **Golf** Scrabo 18h. **See**
Movilla Abbey, Scrabo Tower, Market
Cross, Priory.

Rescue Service: Drumhirk Cars &
Commercial (J S Hardy), 183 Donaghadee
Rd. ℃ (0247) 818594.

OMAGH Co. Tyrone. Map 50E
Pop 20,000. Dungannon 23, Belfast 60,
Enniskillen 22, Strabane 17.
EC Wed. **MD** Mon. **Golf** Omagh 18h,
Newtownstewart 18h. **See**
Ulster American Folk Park, Gortin Glen
Forest.

★★**Royal Arms,** *51 High St, BT78 1BA.*
℃ (0662) 3262. RS Xmas. C. ⊷ 21 bedrs,
6 bp, 13 bps, 1 ba, TV. ✗ mc, at, LD 9.30
(8.30 Sun). ⓓ N, CH, TV, Dgs, CP 200, Ac,
pf, con 300, CF, 1 st. £ BB £11·50–£12·50,
DB £21–£23, DBB £16·50–£17·50, WB, ②,
Bk £3·50, L £4·75, cc 1 2 3 5.

PORTADOWN Co Armagh. Maps 51E &
55A
Pop 24,000. M12 Motorway 3, Lurgan 6,
Belfast 26, Armagh 10, Dungannon 16,
Newry 18.
EC Thur. **MD** Fri, Sat. **Golf** Portadown
18h.

★★★**Seagoe,** *Upper Church Lane,
BT63 5JE.* ℃ (0762) 333076. C. ⊷ 38
bedrs, 38 bp, TV. ✗ mc, at, LD 9.45. ⓓ N,
CH, TV, CP 200, Ac, con 400, CF, 7 BGf, 0
st, Dis. £ BB £21, DB £27, DT £35, DBB
£29·50, WB, ①, Bk £3·50, L £5, D £8,
cc 1 2 3 5.

Specialist Body Repairer: Thomas
Chapman, 47 Dobbin Rd, Drumnasoo.
℃ (0762) 32918.

PORTBALLINTRAE Co. Antrim. Map
51A
Pop 600. Ballymoney 11, Belfast 51,
Coleraine 6, Larne 44.
EC Thur. **Golf** Bushfoot 9h. **See** Giants
Causeway, Dunseverick Castle.
ⓘ 93 Ballyaghmore Rd. ℃ Bushmills
(026 57) 31672.

★★**Beach,** *BT57 8RT.* ℃ Bushmills
(026 57) 31214. C. ⊷ 28 bedrs, 14 bp, 5
ba, TV. ✗ mc, at, LD 8·45. ⓓ N, CH, TV, CP
30, Ac, con 150, CF, 1 st. £ WB, cc 1 3.

PORTRUSH Co. Antrim. Map 50B
Pop 5,750. Coleraine 5, Belfast 58,
Ballycastle 18, Ballymoney 12,
Bushmills 5.
EC Wed. **Golf** Royal Portrush 18h. **See**
Dunluce Castle, White Rocks.
ⓘ Town Hall. ℃ Portrush (0265) 823333.

Rescue Service: B Boyd, Glenvale Garage,
Coleraine Rd. ℃ (0265) 823702.

PORTSTEWART Co. Londonderry. Map
50B
Pop 6.500. Coleraine 4, Belfast 45, Larne
45, Londonderry 30.
EC Thur. **Golf** Portstewart 18h. **See** St
Patrick Well.
ⓘ Town Hall, The Crescent. ℃ Portstewart
(026 583) 2286.

★**Windsor** (Unl), *The Promenade, BT55
7AD.* ℃ (026 583) 2523. Open Apr–Sept.
C. ⊷ 28 bedrs, 5 bp, 4 ba. ✗ a l c, LD 7.30.
ⓓ CH, TV, Ac, con 40, CF, 2 st. £ Dep.

Modern Hotels, Motels and Motor Hotels

Modern Hotels generally designed to appeal more to the travelling motorist on a passing visit than to longer staying guests. The bedrooms are likely to be better, with a higher proportion of private bathrooms, and the meal hours longer than in hotels of similar classification without "M", but lounge accommodation and services may be more restricted. Additionally, each establishment is shown in the Directory under the appropriate place-name.

England

Avon
ALVESTON
★★★ M Post House (A38)
BRISTOL
★★★★ M Holiday Inn
★★★ M Crest Hotel (Hambrook)
FAILAND
★★★ M Redwood Lodge & Country Club (5 miles W of Bristol)
REDHILL
★★ M Paradise (A38) Cowslip Green
WORLE
★★ M Old Manor

Bedfordshire
LUTON
★★★ M Chiltern Hotel (on A505 1 mile from M1 Junction, 15 mins drive from Airport)
★★★ M Luton Crest Hotel

Berkshire
BRACKNELL
★★★★ M Ladbroke Hotel
MAIDENHEAD
★★★ M Crest Hotel
READING
★★★★ M Ramada
★★★ M Post House
SLOUGH
★★★★ M Holiday Inn, Langley

Buckinghamshire
BEACONSFIELD
★★★ M Bell House
HIGH WYCOMBE
★★★ M Crest
NEWPORT PAGNELL
★★★ M Travel Lodge (Service Area 3, M1)

Cambridgeshire
BRAMPTON
★★★ M Brampton, A1 Roundabout
CAMBRIDGE
★★★★ Cambridge Post House
NORMAN CROSS
★★★ M Crest Hotel (A1/A15)
ST. IVES
★★ M St. Ives
WANSFORD
★★ M Sibson House

Cheshire
BEESTON, Nr Tarporley
★★★ M Wild Boar Inn (10 miles SE of Chester on A44)
BUCKLOW HILL, Nr Knutsford
★★★ M Swan Motel, M6 exit 19 (on A556 10 miles SW of Manchester, 6 miles from Ringway Airport)
CHESTER
★★★ M Abbots Well Motor Inn, (on A41 200 yds from Chester By-pass Roundabout) at Christleton
★★★ M Post House
★★★ M Ladbroke Hotel (3½ miles N of Chester) at Backford Cross

HALE
★★★ M Ashley
NORTHWICH
★★★ M Hartford Hall
RUNCORN
★★★ M Crest Hotel, Beechwood
SANDBACH
★★★ M Saxon Cross (M6 exit 17)
WARRINGTON
★★★ M Fir Grove Motor Inn (Junction of A41 and A5117)

Cleveland
GUISBOROUGH
★ M Moor Cock, West End Road
MIDDLESBROUGH
★★★★ M Ladbroke Dragonara
★★★ M Blue Bell Motor Inn (Acklam)
★★★ M Marton Way Hotel
THORNABY-ON-TEES
★★★ M Post House (A19/A1044)

Cornwall
LOSTWITHIEL
★★ M Carotel Motel (A390)
REDRUTH
★★ M Crossroads Motel
ST. MELLION
★★★ M St. Mellion Golf and Country Club, Saltash

Cumbria
AMBLESIDE
★★★★ M Pillar
CARLISLE
★★★ M Crest Hotel, M6 Interchange No. 44 at Kingstown
PENRITH
★★ M Clifton Hill (2¾ miles S on A6)
TEBAY
★★★ M Tebay Mountain Lodge
WINDERMERE
★★★ M Burn How (Bowness)
WORKINGTON
★★ M Crossbarrow Motel (Little Clifton)

Derbyshire
DERBY
★★★ M Crest Hotel (Littleover)
LONG EATON
★★★ M Novotel
SANDIACRE
★★★ M Post House (M1 exit 25 on A52)
SOUTH NORMANTON
★★★★ M Swallow
SUDBURY
★ M Boars Head

Devonshire
ASHBURTON
★★ M Dartmoor (on A38/A384)
BARNSTAPLE
★★★ M Barnstaple
★★★ M North Devon (A361)
COMBE MARTIN
★★ M White Gates Motel
LEWDOWN
★★ M Coach House

EXETER
★★★ M Devon
Exeter By-Pass, Matford
★★★ M Exeter Arms
★★★ M Ladbroke Hotel, Kennford
★★ M Exeter Moat House (A30)
KINGSBRIDGE
★ M Crabshell Motor Inn
★ M Kingsbridge
PAIGNTON
★★ M Torbay Motel (A385 2 miles W of Paignton)
PLYMOUTH
★★★ M Novotel
TIVERTON
★★★ M Tiverton

Dorset
BOURNEMOUTH
★★★ M Crest Hotel
POOLE
★★★★ M Hospitality Inn
SHERBORNE
★★★ M Post House (A30—¼ mile W of Sherborne)

Durham
DARLINGTON
★★★★ M Blackwell Grange
DURHAM
★★★ M Bridge Hotel
Croxdale 3¾ m S on A167

East Sussex
BURWASH
★★ M Burwash Motel
EASTBOURNE
★★★ M Eastbourne
FOREST ROW
★★ M Brambletye
HALLAND
★★★ M Halland Forge (A22 3 miles S of Uckfield)
SEAFORD
★★ M Ladbroke (A259)

Essex
BASILDON
★★★ M Crest
BRENTWOOD
★★★ M Post House
BULPHAN
★★ M Ye Olde Plough House (A128)
CHELMSFORD
★★★ M Miami
EPPING
★★★ M Post House (A11)
HARLOW
★★★ M Green Man, Mulberry Green, Old Harlow
★★★ M Saxon Inn
NORTH STIFFORD
★★★ M Stifford Moat House (B186 off A13)
SOUTHEND-ON-SEA
★★★ M Airport Moat House, Aviation Way
WITHAM
★★ M Rivenhall Motor Inn
WOODFORD GREEN
★★★ M Woodford Moat House

Gloucestershire
BOURTON-ON-THE-WATER
★★ M Chester House
CHELTENHAM
★★★★ M Golden Valley Thistle
COLEFORD
★★ M Bells
GLOUCESTER
★★★ M Crest, Barnwood
NEWPORT
★★ M Newport Towers, Berkeley

Greater London
LONDON NW1
★★★ M Kennedy
LONDON NW3
★★★★ M Ladbroke Clive,
Hampstead
★★★ M Post House, Haverstock Hill
LONDON NW7
★★★ M Travelodge, Scratchwood
Service Area
LONDON SW5
★★★★ M London International,
Cromwell Road
LONDON W1
★★★★ M Regent Crest
LONDON W5
★★★ M Carnarvon, Ealing Common
HILLINGDON
★★★ M Master Brewer
HORNCHURCH
★★★ M Ladbroke Hotel
HOUNSLOW
★★★ M Master Robert
LONDON AIRPORT
★★★★ M Excelsior, Bath Road, West
Drayton
★★★★ M Holiday Inn, Stockley Road,
West Drayton
★★★ M Ariel, Bath Road, Hayes
★★★ M Heathrow Crest, Bath Road,
West Drayton
★★★ M Post House, Sipson Road,
West Drayton
★★★ M Skyway Hotel, Bath Road,
Hayes
WEMBLEY
★★★ M Wembley International,
Empire Way

Greater Manchester
ALTRINCHAM
★★ M Old Pelican
BOLTON
★★★ M Crest Hotel
★★★ M Last Drop Village
(Bromley Cross)
CHEADLE HULME
★★ M Ravenoak
LEIGH
★★★ M Greyhound Motor Hotel
(A580)
MANCHESTER
★★★M Post House (Northenden)
STANDISH
★★★ M Cassinellis Almond Brook
(Wigan)

Hampshire
BASINGSTOKE
★★★ M Crest Hotel
★★★ M Ladbroke Hotel (Northern
Ringway, Aldermaston Roundabout)
BROCKENHURST
★★★ M Carey's Manor
EASTLEIGH
★★★ M Crest
FARNBOROUGH
★★★ M Queen's

HAYLING ISLAND
★★★★ M Post House
OWER
★★★ M New Forest Moat House
(A31/36)
PORTSMOUTH
★★★★ M Holiday Inn
SHEDFIELD
★★★ M Meon Valley Golf & Country
Club
SOUTHAMPTON
★★★ M Post House

Hereford and Worcester
HEREFORD
★★★ M Hereford Moat House

Hertfordshire
BOREHAM WOOD
★★★ M Elstree Moat House, Barnet
By-pass
BUSHEY
★★★★ M Ladbroke Hotel
(Elton Way, Watford By-pass)
★★ M Spider's Web
HEMEL HEMPSTEAD
★★★ M Post House, M1, exit 8
HERTFORD
★★★ M White Horse Inn.
Hertingfordbury
MARKYATE
★★★ M Hertfordshire Moat House
REDBOURN
★★★ M Aubrey Park (B487) (Hemel
Hempstead)
ST. ALBANS
★★★ M Noke Thistle
SOUTH MIMMS
★★★ M Crest Hotel (Barnet By-pass,
Potters Bar)
STEVENAGE
★★★ M Roebuck (1 mile from A1(M)
on B197)
WARE
★★★ M Ware Moat House
WATFORD
★★★ M Caledonian
WELWYN
★★ M Clock
WELWYN GARDEN CITY
★★★ M Crest Hotel

Humberside
CLEETHORPES
★★ M Wellow
GRIMSBY
★★★★ M Humber Royal Crest
★★★ M Crest Hotel
HULL
★★★ M Crest Hotel, North Ferriby
POCKLINGTON
★★ M Feathers

Kent
BEXLEY
★★★ M Crest
CHATHAM
★★★ M Crest
DOVER
★★★★ M Holiday Inn
Townwall Street
★★★ M Dover Motel, Whitfield
GRAVESEND
★★ M Tollgate Moat House (A2[M])
NEWINGREEN
★★ M Royal Oak (A20)
WROTHAM HEATH
★★★★ M Post House

Lancashire
BLACKBURN
★★★ M Blackburn Moat House

BURNLEY
★★★ M Keirby
CHARNOCK RICHARD
★★★ M Travel Lodge, M6 Motorway
★★ M Hunters Lodge
LEYLAND
★★★★ M Ladbroke Hotel (Junction 28
M6)
PRESTON
★★★ M Crest Hotel
★★★ M Tickled Trout
★★★ M Trafalgar, Preston New Road,
Samlesbury

Leicestershire
LEICESTER
★★★★ M Holiday Inn
★★★ M Leicester Forest Moat House
(M1/A47)
★★★ M Leicester International
★★★ M Post House
LUTTERWORTH
★★ M Moorbarns, A5 Trunk Road
MARKET HARBOROUGH
★★ M Grove Motel
MEASHAM
★★ M Measham Inn

Lincolnshire
LINCOLN
★★★ M Eastgate Posthouse
★★ M Four Seasons

Merseyside
BIRKENHEAD
★★★ M Bowler Hat
HAYDOCK
★★★★ M Post House (Newton-le-
Willows)
KNOWSLEY
★★★ M Crest Hotel (A580
4 miles E of Liverpool)
LIVERPOOL
★★★★ M Atlantic Tower Thistle
★★★★ M Holiday Inn

Norfolk
NORWICH
★★★ M Hotel Nelson
★★★ M Hotel Norwich
★★★ M Post House

Northamptonshire
RUGBY
★★★★ M Post House (M1 Motorway)
SYWELL
★ M Sywell (Sywell Airport off A43
and A54)
WEEDON
★★★ M Crossroads

North Yorkshire
BEDALE
★★★ M Leeming (A1)
BURNT YATES
★★ M Bay Horse Inn
YORK
★★★ M Post House (A64)

Nottinghamshire
Nottingham
★★★★ M Victoria

Oxfordshire
ABINGDON
★★ M Upper Reaches
OXFORD
★★★ M Oxford Moat House (A43/34)
★★★ M TraveLodge, Peartree
Roundabout (A43/A34)

Somerset
FROME
★★★ M Mendip Lodge (A361)
ILMINSTER
★★★ M Horton Cross (on A303)
WEST COKER
★★ M Four Acres

South Yorkshire
ROTHERHAM
★★★★ M Carlton Park

Staffordshire
NEWCASTLE-UNDER-LYME
★★★ M Crest Hotel, Crossheath
★★★ M Post House (M6 exit 15)

Suffolk
BROME
★★ M Grange Motel
IPSWICH
★★★ M Ipswich Moat House
★★★ M Post House
MILDENHALL
★★ M Smoke House Inn
OULTON BROAD
★★ M Oulton Broad

Surrey
BURGH HEATH
★★ M Pickard
DORKING
★★★ M Punch Bowl (A25)
EAST HORSLEY
★★★ M Thatchers, Epsom Road
HORLEY
★★★★ M Gatwick Moat House
★★★★ M Gatwick Penta, Povey Cross
Road
★★★ M Chequers Thistle (A23)
★★★ M Post House, Povey Cross
Road
REDHILL
★★ M Mill House, Salfords (A23)
REIGATE
★★★ M Bridge House (A217)

Tyne & Wear
NEWCASTLE UPON TYNE
★★★★ M Holiday Inn, Seaton Burn
★★★ M Stakis Airport
WASHINGTON
★★★ M Post House (Emerson District
5)

Warwickshire
ALCESTER
★★ M Cherrytrees (A422)
WARWICK
★★★★ M Ladbrooke Hotel,
Longbridge

West Midlands
BIRMINGHAM
★★★★ M Holiday Inn
★★★★ M Strathallan Thistle
★★★ M Apollo
★★★ M Post House
★★ M Robin Hood Motel
CASTLE BROMWICH
★★ M Bradford Arms, Chester Road
COVENTRY
★★★ M Chace Crest Hotel
(Willenhall)
★★★ M Crest Hotel (Walsgrave)
(A45)
★★★ M Novotel (Longford)
★★★ M Post House (Allesley)
WALSALL
★★★ M Crest Hotel

WEST BROMWICH
★★★ M West Bromwich Moat House
WOLVERHAMPTON
★★ M Fox

West Sussex
COPTHORNE
★★★★ M Copthorne
CRAWLEY
★★★ M Crest Gatwick Airport,
Langley Drive, Tushmore Roundabout
★★★ M Goffs Park
★★★ M Gatwick Concord, Lowfield
Heath

West Yorkshire
BARNSDALE BAR
★★★ M TraveLodge (A1
7 miles S of Pontefract)
BRADFORD
★★★ M Novotel
BRAMHOPE
★★★ M Post House (A660)
HUDDERSFIELD
★★★ M Ladbroke Hotel, Ainley Top
LEEDS
★★★ M Ladbroke Hotel (A63 at
Garforth Roundabout)
★★★ M Stakis Windmill, Ring Road,
Seacroft
OSSETT
★★★ M Post House
OULTON
★★★ M Crest Hotel (5 miles S
of Leeds on A639)
WETHERBY
★★★ M Ladbroke Hotel, Leeds Road

Wiltshire
CHIPPENHAM
★★ M Angel (A4)
CORSHAM
★★ M Stagecoach (Pickwick)
SWINDON
★★★ M Crest Hotel, Stratton St.
Margarets
★★★ M Goddard Arms
★★★ M Post House (Marlborough
Road, Coate)

Scotland

Dumfries & Galloway
GRETNA
★★ M Royal Stewart (A74)
★★ M Solway Lodge
MOFFAT
★★★ M Ladbroke Hotel Motor Inn

Grampian
ABERDEEN
★★★★ M Holiday Inn
★★★ M Skean Dhu
DYCE
★★★★ M Holiday Inn
ELLON
★★★ M Ladbroke Hotel Motor Inn
STONEHAVEN
★★★ M Commodore, Cowie Park

Highland
AVIEMORE
★★★ M Badenoch
★★★ M Coylumbridge
★★★ M Post House
FORT WILLIAM
★★★ M Ladbroke Hotel Motor Inn
(A82)
★★ M Croit Anna, Druimarbin

INVERNESS
★★★ M Caledonian
★★★ M Drumossie
★★★ M Ladbroke Mercury
★★ M Muirtown (A9)
ULLAPOOL
★★★ M Ladbroke Hotel
★★ M Harbour Lights
WICK
★★★ M Ladbroke Hotel, Riverside

Lothian
EDINBURGH
★★★★ M Royal Scot
★★★ M Crest Hotel
★★★ M Post House
MUSSELBURGH
★★ M Drummore, Wallyford
Roundabout (A1)
SOUTH QUEENSFERRY
★★★ M Forth Bridges (off A90
7 miles N of Edinburgh)

Strathclyde
ERSKINE
★★★ M Crest Hotel
GLASGOW
★★★★ M Holiday Inn
★★★ M Glasgow Centre
GOUROCK
★★★ M Gantock
RENFREW
★★★ M Dean Park
★★★ M Normandy

Wales

Clwyd
COLWYN BAY
★★★★ M 70'
WREXHAM
★★★ M Crest Hotel

Dyfed
ABERPORTH
★★ M Morlan
LETTERSTON
★★ M Brynawelon, 9 m N of
Haverfordwest
PEMBROKE DOCK
★★★ M Cleddau Bridge

Gwent
CHEPSTOW
★★★ M Two Rivers
CWMBRAN
★★★ M Commodore (Llanyrafon)
LLANDOGO
★★ M Old Farmhouse
NEWPORT
★★★ M Ladbroke Hotel, The Coldra

Gwynedd
BALA
★★ M Bala Lake
BETWS-Y-COED
★★★ M Waterloo Motor Hotel
CAERNARFON
★★★ M Stables (Llanwnda)
CONWY
★★ M Lodge, Tal-y-Bont

Powys
**CROSSGATES, LLANDRINDOD
WELLS**
★★ M Park
LIBANUS
★★ M Mountains

South Glamorgan
BARRY
★★★ M International (nr Cardiff Airport)
CARDIFF
★★★ M Cardiff Centre
★★★ M Ladbroke Wentloog Castle
★★★ M Post House (Pentwyn)

West Glamorgan
PORT TALBOT
★★★ M Aberafan, Aberavon, Seafront
SWANSEA
★★★★ M Dragon (Kingsway Circle)
★★★ M Fforest Motel

NORTHERN IRELAND

Co. Antrim
BELFAST
★★★★ M Belfast Europa, Gt. Victoria Street
NEWTOWNABBEY
★★★ M Chimney Corner

Country House Hotels

Country House type hotels, all of which are shown in the Directory under the appropriate heading, and indicated by the symbol 🏚

England
Avon
FALFIELD
★★Park
Just off A381 1 m S of Falfield
LIMPLEY STOKE
★★★Cliffe
½ m off B3108—5½ m SE of Bath
RANGEWORTHY
★★Rangeworthy Court
THORNBURY
★★★Thornbury Castle
WINTERBOURNE
★★★Grange
6 m NE of Bristol on B4058

Bedfordshire
BEDFORD
★★★Woodlands Manor
Green Lane, Clapham, 2 m N on A6

Berkshire
MAIDENHEAD
★★Taplow House
1½ m E of Maidenhead—½ m N of the A4
WINDSOR
★★★★Oakley Court
Windsor Road, Water Oakley—2½ m S of Bray
WOKINGHAM
★★★St Annes Manor
7 m SE of Reading

Cleveland
SALTBURN-BY-THE-SEA
★★★Grinkle Park
2 m S of Easington on E side of unclassified road between A171 and A174

Cornwall
BODMIN
★★★Tredethy Country
Helland Bridge—3 m N of Bodmin
BUDOCK VEAN
★★★Budock Vean
Off A394—1½ m W of Falmouth
FALMOUTH
★★★Meudon
Mawnan Smith, 4 m S of Falmouth on Coast Road
★★★Penmere Manor
1½ m W of Falmouth off B3291
LAMORNA COVE
★★★Lamorna Cove
Off B3315—5 m SW of Penzance

LOOE
★★★Talland Bay
Talland-by-Looe, 1 m off A387—2 m W of Looe
★★Klymiarven
Barbican Hill
PORTSCATHO
★★★Rosevine
Porthcurnick Beach, just off A3078—3 m NE of St Mawes
★★Roseland House
Rose Vine, just off A3078—2½ m NE of St Mawes
RUAN HIGH LANES
★★Polsue Manor
7 m NE of St Mawes off A3078
ST AGNES
★★Rose-in-Vale
Mithian, just off B3285—2 m W of St Agnes
ST AUSTELL
★★Boscundle Manor
Tregrehan—2½ m NE of St Austell
ST IVES
★★★Tregenna Castle
½ m S of St Ives—W of A3074 direction signs
ST MAWGAN
★Dalswinton
3 m NW of St Columb Major—6 m from Newquay
ST WENN
★Wenn Manor
Bodmin, 4 m ENE of St Columb Major, just off B3274

Cumbria
ALSTON
★★Lovelady Shield
2½ m E of Alston off the B6294
AMBLESIDE
★★Kirkstone Foot
Kirkstone Pass Rd—½ m NE of Ambleside
★★Nanny Brow
Clappersgate—1 m W of Ambleside
BASSENTHWAITE
★★Overwater Hall
Ireby—4 m NNE of Bassenthwaite off B5299.
BRAMPTON
★Farlam Hall
2 m SE on A689
ELTERWATER
★★Eltermere
3 m W of Ambleside
GRANGE OVER SANDS
★★Graythwaite Manor
Fernhill Rd

HAWKSHEAD
★★★Tarn Hows
On B5285—1½ m NW of Hawkshead
★★Ees Wyke
5 m SSW of Ambleside
KESWICK
★★★Underscar
2 m N of Keswick
★★Red House
At Skiddaw, on A591—2½ m NW of Keswick
LEVENS
★★Heaves
Just off A6—4½ m S of Kendal
LONGTOWN
★Marchbank
3 m N of Longtown on W side of A7
POOLEY BRIDGE
★★★Sharrow Bay
Sharrow Bay, 4 m SE of Pooley Bridge—S of Lake Ullswater
TALKIN
★★Tarn End
½ m S of Brampton
THORNTHWAITE
★★Woodend
Woodend—nr Keswick
WATERMILLOCK
★★★Leeming House
Ullswater, on A592—8 m SW of Penrith
★★Old Church
7 m SW of Penrith
WIGTON
★★Green Hill Lodge
WINDERMERE
★★★Langdale Chase
Off W side of A591—2½ m NW of Windermere
★★Lindeth Fell
1 m S of Bowness off B5284
★★Lindeth Howe
Longtail Hill, Storrs Park
★★Linthwaite
Almost ¼ m E of Junction A5074 & B5284 on Kendal Rd & ¾ m S of Bowness

Derbyshire
DERBY
★★★Breadsall Priory
Moor Road, Morley—4 m NE of Derby
HASSOP
★★★Hassop Hall
1 m N of Bakewell

Devon
ASHBURTON
★★Holne Chase
Off A384—2½ m NW of Ashburton

AXMINSTER
★★Woodbury Park
Woodbury Cross—¼ m off
A35—1½ m E of Axminster
BARNSTAPLE
★★Roborough House
½ m off A39—1 m N of
Barnstaple
BERRYNARBOR
★★Sandy Cove
2½ m E of Ilfracombe
BIDEFORD
★★★Portledge
Fairy Cross, just off A39—4 m
SW of Bideford
★★Yeoldon House
Durrant Lane—1½ m NW of
Northam—just S of A386
BOVEY TRACEY
★★Edgemoor
Haytor Rd off B3344 2 m W of
Bovey Tracey
★★Prestbury
Brimley Lane—2¼ m SW of
Bovey Tracey on Ilsington Rd
BUCKFASTLEIGH
★★Bossell House
BUCKLAND-IN-THE-MOOR
★Buckland Hall
on U/C Rd 1 m SE of Buckland-
in-the-Moor, Ashburton
BURRINGTON
★★★Northcote Manor
Burrington Umberleigh
CHAGFORD
★★★Great Tree
2 m S of Whiddon Down on
A382
★★★Mill End
Sandy Park, 3 m S of Whiddon
Down (A30) on A382
★★★Teignworthy
Frenchbeer, 3 m SW off A382
★★Easton Court
1½ m E of Chagford on A382
CHILLINGTON
★★Oddicombe House
4½ m E of Kingsbridge on A379
CLAWTON
★Court Barn
4 m S of Holsworthy, just W of
Clawton
COMBE MARTIN
★★Coulsworthy House
Off A399 2½ m E of Combe
Martin
HAWKCHURCH
★★★Fairwater Head
3½ m E of Axminster off B3165
on Hawkchurch Rd
HAYTOR
★★Bel Alp
3 m W of Bovey Tracey on
Haytor Rd
★★Haytor
¼ m W of Ilsington on Haytor
Vale Rd—7 m NW of Newton
Abbot
HOLBETON
★★★Alston Hall
2½ m SW of Holbeton—1¾ m SE
of B3186
HONITON
★★★Deer Park
Weston, 2 m WNW of Honiton
on Buckerell Rd off A30
KINGSBRIDGE
★★★Buckland-Tout-Saints
Goveton—off A381—10 m S
of Totnes

LEE
★★Lee Manor
7¾ m S of Ilfracombe
LYDFORD
★★Lydford House
6¾ m N of Tavistock, 8½ m SW
of Okehampton
LYNMOUTH
★★Beacon
Countisbury Hill—¼ m E of
Lynmouth on A39
LYNTON
★★Combe Park
Hillsford Bridge—2 m SE of
Lynmouth on A39
MARTINHOE
★★Heddon's Gate
6 m W of Lynton, 1 m SW of
Martinhoe at Heddons Mouth
★Old Rectory
Parracombe—5½ m WSW of
Lynton
MARY TAVY
★★Moorland Hall
4 m NE of Tavistock
NEWTON ABBOT
★★Netherton House
3 m E at Combe-in-Teignhead
NEWTON FERRERS
★★Court House
Newton Ferrers—B3816, 6 m
SE of Plymouth
NORTH HUISH
★★Brookdale
7 m SW of Totnes, at South
Brent
OTTERY ST MARY
★★★Salston
¼ m off B3180—2 m E of Ottery
St Mary
PARKHAM
★★Foxdown Manor
6 m SW of Bideford
PLYMOUTH
★★Langdon Court
At Down Thomas on A379
PLYMPTON
★★Elfordleigh
2½ m N of railway line on
Shaugh Prior Rd
SIDMOUTH
★★Brownlands
¾ m NE of Sidmouth on Lyme
Regis Rd
SOUTH BRENT
★★Glazebrook House
1 m SW of South Brent on Ash/
Glazebrook Rd
STOKE GABRIEL
★★★Gabriel Court
Stoke Hill—4 m SE of Totnes
TEIGNMOUTH
★★Venn Farm
Higher Exeter Rd
WOODY BAY
★★Woody Bay
On Toll Road 3 m W of Lynton
WOOLFARDISWORTHY
★★Manor House
9 m W of Bideford—1¾ m S of
the A39
YELVERTON
★★Moorland Links
Just W of the A386

Dorset
MILTON ABBAS
★★Milton Manor
6 m SW of Blandford Forum

MILTON ON STOUR
★★★Milton Lodge
On B3092, off A303, 3 m SW of
Mere
STUDLAND
★★★Knoll House
On B3351—3 m S of
Sandbanks Ferry
★★Manor House
Manor Lane—3½ m S of
Sandbanks Ferry

East Sussex
HASTINGS
★★★Beauport Park
Beauport Park—On A2100—
3 m SE of Battle
PEVENSEY
★★★Glyndley Manor
Hailsham Road, Stone Cross—
2 m W of Pevensey

Essex
CHELMSFORD
★★★Pontlands Park
2 m SE of Chelmsford
DEDHAM
★★★Dedham Vale
Gun Hill Dedham off A12
★★★Maison Talbooth
Stratford Road

Gloucestershire
CIRENCESTER
★★★Stratton House
1 m NW of Cirencester on the
A417
LOWER SLAUGHTER
★★★Manor
1 m NW of Bourton-on-the-
Water
STINCHCOMBE
★★★Stinchcombe Manor
2 m W of Dursley
STROUD
★Burleigh Court
3 m SE of Stroud off A419 at
Brimscombe
★★★Stonehouse Court
On A419 2 m W of Stroud
UPPER SLAUGHTER
★★★Lords of the Manor
1½ m NW of Bourton-on-the-
Water

Greater London
HADLEY WOOD
★★★★West Lodge Park
Cockfosters Road (A111)/
Ferryhill Road
Greater Manchester
BOLTON
★★★Egerton House
Blackburn Road, Bromley
Cross—3 m N of Bolton on
A666

Hampshire
ASHURST
★★Busketts Lawn
174 Woodlands Rd,
Woodlands
★★Woodlands Lodge
Bartley Rd, Woodlands, 6 m W
of Southampton
AVON
**★★Tyrrells Ford Country
House**
4 m N by W Christchurch
BOTLEY
★★★Botleigh Grange
Grange Road, Hedge End

BRAMSHAW
★★**Bramble Hill**
½ m W of Bramshaw B3079
BROCKENHURST
★★**New Park Manor**
½ m off the A337, Lyndhurst
Road
BURLEY
★★★**Burley Manor**
2 m S of A31—3 m E of
Ringwood
★★**Moorhill House**
2 m S of A31—2 m E of
Ringwood
FLEET
★★★**Lismoyne**
Church Road, Fleet off B3013
LYMINGTON
★★★**Passford House**
Mount Pleasant Lane—2 m NE
of Lymington off A337
MIDDLE WALLOP
★★★**Fifehead Manor**
5 m NW of Stockbridge, off
A30
NEW MILTON
★★★★**Chewton Glen**
Off A337—1 m E of New
Milton
SPARSHOLT
★★★**Lainston House**
2½ m NW of Winchester

Hereford and Worcester
ABBERLEY
★★★**Elms**
12 m NW of Worcester on the
A443
BROADWAY
★★★**Dormy House**
Willersley Hill
★★**Collin House**
Collin Lane
DROITWICH
Ap. St Andrew's House
Worcester Road—Droitwich
EVESHAM
★★**Salford Hall**
Abbots Salford 4 m NW of
Evesham on A439
MALVERN
★★**Holdfast Cottage, Welland**
Malvern—3 m WSW of Upton-
on-Severn
PENCRAIG
★★**Pencraig Court**
4 m SW of Ross-on-Wye on
A40
ROSS-ON-WYE
★★★**Pengethley**
4 m W of Ross on A49
★★★**Wye**
Weston-under-Penyard—3 m
SE of Ross-on-Wye on A40
★★**Chasedale**
Walford Road
STONE
★★★★**Stone Manor**
2 m SE of Kidderminster
SYMONDS YAT
★★**Royal**
4 m NE of Monmouth
★★**Wye Rapids**
1 m off A40—7 m SW of Ross-
on-Wye
WALFORD
★★**Walford House**
3 m S of Ross-on-Wye on
B4228

Hertfordshire
ST ALBANS
★★★**Sopwell House**
Cottonmill Lane
STANSTEAD ABBOTS
★★★★**Briggens House**
3 m SE of Ware

Humberside
BEVERLEY
★★★**Tickton Grange**
3 m NE of Beverley on the
A1035
DRIFFIELD
★★**Wold House**
. Nafferton—1 m NE of Gt
Driffield
FLAMBOROUGH
★★**Timoneer Country Manor**
South Landing
HULL
★★★**Rowley Manor**
8 m NW, 1 m S of Little
Weighton

Isle of Wight
BEMBRIDGE
★**Elms Country**
Swaines Road
FRESHWATER
★★★**Farringford**
Bedbury Lane—Just outside
Freshwater
ST LAWRENCE
★★**Rocklands**
1¼ m W of Ventnor
SANDOWN
★★★**Broadway Park**
Melville Street, Sandown—½ m
NW of Centre
VENTNOR
★★**Winterbourne**
Bonchurch—1 m E of Ventnor
★**Madeira Hall**
Trinity Road

Kent
ASHFORD
★★★★**Eastwell Manor**
Eastwell Park—3 m N of
Ashford
CRANBROOK
★★**Kennel Holt**
4 m N of Hawkhurst off A229
SITTINGBOURNE
★★**Newington Manor**
3 m W of Sittingbourne
TUNBRIDGE WELLS
★★**Beacon**
Tea Garden Lane

Lancashire
PADIHAM
★★**Higher Trapp**
Simonstone—1 m off A671—2
m E of Padiham

Leicestershire
ROTHLEY
★★★**Rothley Court**
6 m N of Leicester on the
B5328

Lincolnshire
LINCOLN
★★**Washingborough Hall**
3 m E of Lincoln
MARKET RASEN
★★★**Limes**
Just off A46—½ m W of Market
Rasen

Norfolk
BUNWELL
★★**Bunwell Manor**
4 m E of Attleborough, just N
of Bunwell Street
GREAT WITCHINGHAM
★★**Lenwade House**
On A1067—Norwich–
Fakenham Rd
GRIMSTON
★★**Congham Hall**
HETHERSETT
★★**Park Farm**
6½ m SW of Norwich
HORNING
★★**Petersfield House**
¼ m E of Horning off B1354
ORMESBY ST MARGARET
★★**Ormesby Lodge**
Decoy Road—4 m N of Great
Yarmouth

Northamptonshire
WICKEN
★★**Wicken Country**
Cross Tree Rd—3 m SW of
Stony Stratford

Northumberland
CORNHILL-ON-TWEED
★★★**Tillmouth Park**
2 m NNW of Cornhill-on-
Tweed on A698
LONGHORSLEY
★★★★**Linden Hall**
6 m NW of Morpeth
POWBURN
★★★**Breamish House**
A697—9 m W of Alnwick

North Yorkshire
APPLETON LE MOORS
★★★**Dweldapilton Hall**
5 m N of Pickering
AUSTWICK
★**Traddock**
5 m NW of Settle
BOROUGHBRIDGE
★★★**Three Arrows**
Horsefair, just S of
Boroughbridge on Old Road
BURNSALL
★★**Fell**
¼ m S on B6160—7 m NE of
Skipton
GOATHLAND
★★**Goathland Hydro**
8 m SW of Whitby off A169
GREAT AYTON
★★★**Ayton Hall**
3 m NE of Stokesley
HARROGATE
★★★**Hob Green**
7 m N of Harrogate—2 m W of
A61
HAWES
★★**Simonstone Hall**
1½ m N of Hawes
HUNMANBY
★★**Wrangham House**
Stonegate, Hunmanby
KNARESBOROUGH
★★★**Dower House**
Bond End—3 m NE of
Harrogate
★★**Mitre**
3½ m NE of Harrogate
LASTINGHAM
★★★**Lastingham Grange**
3 m NE of Kirkby Moorside
MONK FRYSTON
★★★**Monk Fryston Hall**
Selby Rd (A63)

NORTHALLERTON
★★★Solberge Hall
5 m S of Northallerton off
A167
PATELEY BRIDGE
★★Harefield Hall
14 m NW of Harrogate
RAVENSCAR
★★★Raven Hall
½ m N of Ravenscar—11 m
NNW of Scarborough
SCARBOROUGH
★★★★Holbeck Hall
Seacliff Road, South Cliff
SCALBY
★★Wrea Head
WHITBY
★★Sneaton Hall
2 m S of Whitby
WHITWELL-ON-THE-HILL
★★★Whitwell Hall
6 m SW of Malton
YORK
★★★★Middlethorpe Hall
S of York–Bishopthorpe Road
★★★Fairfield Manor
Shipton Road—4 m NW

Oxfordshire
HORTON CUM STUDLEY
★★★Studley Priory
2 m N of B4027—7½ m NE of
Oxford
NORTH STOKE
★★★Springs
Wallingford Road—2 m S of
Wallingford
WESTON ON THE GREEN
★★★Weston Manor
On A43—9 m N of Oxford

Shropshire
BRIDGNORTH
★★Old Vicarage
Worfield, 3 m NE of Bridgnorth
CHURCH STRETTON
★★★Stretton Hall
All Stretton—1½ m N
ELLESMERE
★★Grange
½ m N of Ellesmere on A528
LUDLOW
★★Overton Grange
By A49
MARKET DRAYTON
★★Tern Hill Hall
Tern Hill—3 m SW of Market
Drayton on A53
OSWESTRY
★★Sweeney Hall Hotel
SHREWSBURY
★★Shelton Hall
2 m NW of Shrewsbury
WELLINGTON
★★★Buckatree Hall
Wrekin, Telford—1 m off A5—
2 m W of Wellington
**WESTON-UNDER-
REDCASTLE**
★★★Hawkstone Park
3½ m E of Wem
WHITCHURCH
★★★Terrick Hall
Terrick Road

Somerset
DULVERTON
★★Ashwick House
3 m NW of Dulverton
★★Three Acres Captain's
Country
¼ m off B3222—1½ m S of
Dulverton

EVERCREECH
★★Glen
¼ m off B3081—2 m SE of
Shepton Mallet
HOLFORD
★★★Alfoxton Park
15 m E of Minehead on A39
★★Combe House
¼ m S of Holford off A39
SHAPWICK
★★Shapwick House
On the A39 nr Street
WINCANTON
★★Holbrook House
Holbrook—1½ m NW of
Wincanton on A371
WITHYPOOL
★Westerclose
6½ m NW of Dulverton, nr
B3223, nr Minehead

Staffordshire
BURTON-ON-TRENT
★★★Newton Park
Newton Solney—3 m SE of
Burton-on-Trent on B3008
PATSHULL PARK
★★★Lakeside Lodge
Burnhill Green—7½ m WNW of
Wolverhampton
STONE
★★★Stone House
7 m N of Stafford

Suffolk
IPSWICH
★★★Belstead Brook
3 m SW of A12 at Belstead
NEWMARKET
★★Bedford Lodge
Bury Road
SHOTTISHAM
★★Wood Hall
Wood Hall Drive, 4 m SE of
Woodbridge (nr B1083)
SIX MILE BOTTOM
★★★Swynford Paddocks
Nr A11, 6 m SW of Newmarket
WOODBRIDGE
★★★Seckford Hall
Great Bealings—just off A12—
1 m WSW of Woodbridge

Surrey
BAGSHOT
★★★★Pennyhill Park
College Ride
CROYDON
★★★★Selsdon Park
Addington Rd—3½ m SE of
Croydon
FARNHAM
★★Trevena House
Alton Road
GODSTONE
★Wonham House
Eastbourne Rd—S Godstone
WEYBRIDGE
★★★Oatlands Park
Oatlands Drive

Warwickshire
BILLESLEY
★★★Billesley Manor
4 m W of Stratford-upon-Avon
off A422
EATHORPE
★★Eathorpe Park
Fosse Way—5 m NE of
Leamington

RUGBY
★★★Clifton Court
Clifton-on-Dunsmore—½ m off
B5414
STRATFORD UPON AVON
★★★★Welcombe
Just outside town on Warwick
Rd (A46)

West Sussex
CLIMPING
★★★Bailiffscourt
1½ m NW of Littlehampton
CUCKFIELD
★★★Ockenden Manor
Off A272—½ m SW of
Cuckfield
★★Hilton Park
Off A272—½ m SE of Cuckfield
EAST GRINSTEAD
★★★Gravetye Manor
Sharpthorne—4 m SW of East
Grinstead off B2110
STORRINGTON
★★★Little Thakeham
Merrywood Lane,
Storrington—6½ m NE of
Arundel
WALBERTON
★★★Avisford Park
Yapton Lane, 3 m WSW of
Arundel

West Yorkshire
HALIFAX
★★★Holdsworth House
Holdsworth Road—2½ m N of
Halifax
KILDWICK
★★★Kildwick Hall
4½ m S of Skipton
WENTBRIDGE
★★★Wentbridge House
1 m off A1—4 m N of Barnsdale
Bar

Wiltshire
CASTLE COMBE
★★★Manor House
½ m off B4039—6 m NW of
Chippenham
MALMESBURY
★★★Whatley Manor
Easton Grey—2½ m W on
B4040
MELKSHAM
★★★Beechfield House
Beanacre—1½ m N of
Melksham

Scotland

Borders
CHIRNSIDE
★★Chirnside Countryhouse
Chirnside Duns—½ m off
B6355—4 m S of Ayton
ETTRICK BRIDGE
★★Ettrickshaws
On Ettrick Water—7 m SW of
Selkirk
GALASHIELS
★★★Kingsknowes
Selkirk Road
★★Woodlands House
Windyknowe Road
GREENLAW
★★Purves Hall
3½ m E of Greenlaw
HAWICK
★★Mansfield House
Weensland Rd

JEDBURGH
★★Jedforest
3½ m S of Jedburgh on A68
PEEBLES
★★Cringletie House
Off A703—3 m N of Peebles
★★Venlaw Castle
Off A703—½ m N of Peebles
ST BOSWELLS
★★★Dryburgh Abbey
Dryburgh—On A68—2 m N of
St Boswells
WALKERBURN
★★Tweed Valley
Galashiels Rd

Central
CALLANDER
★★★Roman Camp
Main Street (A84)

Dumfries & Galloway
AUCHENCAIRN
★★★Balcary Bay
2½ m SW nr A711
BEATTOCK
★★Beattock House
½ m N on A74
BORGUE
★★Senwick House
4½ m SW of Kirkcudbright—S
of the B727
CASTLE DOUGLAS
★★Ernespie House
Just off A75
CROSSMICHAEL
★★Culgruff House
Off A713—4 m NNW of Castle
Douglas
DALRY
★★Milton Park
On A713—1½ m N of Dalry
DUMFRIES
★★★Rockhall
Collin—5½ m SE from Dumfries
on A75
GATEHOUSE OF FLEET
★★★★Cally Palace
1¼ m S of Gatehouse of Fleet
off A75
LOCKERBIE
★★Dryfesdale House
200 yds off A74
★★Lockerbie House
Dryfe Rd—1 m N of Lockerbie
MONIAIVE
★★Woodlea
3½ m SW on A702
NEWTON STEWART
★★★Kirroughtree
1 m E of Newton Stewart on
A172
★★Creebridge House
Newton Stewart
NEWTON WAMPHRAY
★Red House
Wamphray—Just E off A74—
3 m S of Beattock
PORT WILLIAM
★★★Corsemalzie
Off B7005—6 m W of Wigtown
ROCKCLIFFE
★★★Baron's Craig
Off A710—7 m S of Dalbeattie
THORNHILL
★★Trigony House
Closeburn—11½ m NW of
Dumfries

Fife
GLENROTHES
★★★Balgeddie House
1½ m W of Glenrothes on A911
LETHAM
★★★Fernie Castle
Ladybank—1 m N of Letham
on A914
WORMIT
★★Sandford Hill
3 m S of Tay Bridge on B946

Grampian
ABOYNE
★★Balnacoil House
1 m W of Aboyne on A93
BALLATER
★★Darroch Learg
Braemar Road
BANCHORY
★★★Banchory Lodge
Dee St
★★★Raemoir
2 m N of Banchory on B979
★★Blairfindy Lodge
5¾ m SE of Ballindalloch
HUNTLY
★★Castle
4 m N of Huntly
KILDRUMMY
★★★Kildrummy Castle
7 m W of Alford, 1 m SW of
church
ROTHES
★★★Rothes Glen
2½ m N on A941

Highland
ARISAIG
★★★Arisaig House
DAVIOT
★★Meallmore Lodge
Daviot—6½ m SE of Inverness
GLENBORRODALE
★★Glenborrodale Castle
(Ardnamurchan) On N shore of
Lock Sunart. 7 m SW of Solen
INVERGARRY
★★Glengarry Castle
1 m S of Invergarry off A82
INVERNESS
★★Dunain Park
3 m SW on A82
**SKEABOST BRIDGE, ISLE
OF SKYE**
★★★Skeabost House
6 m NW of Portree on A850
STRONTIAN
★★Kilcamb Lodge
by Loch Sunart—24 m SW of
Fort William—on A861
TORRIDON
★★Loch Torridon
Achnasheen

Lothian
GULLANE
★★★Greywalls
Muirfield—Off A198—¾ m ENE
of Gullane

Shetland
BRAE
★★★Busta House

Strathclyde
ARDEN
★★★Lomond Castle
W of Loch Lomond
AYR
★★★Belleisle House
Doonfoot—2 m S of Ayr

BIGGAR
★★Hartree
On A702—1 m NE of Biggar
E. KILBRIDE
★★★Crutherland
Strathaven Rd (A726), 2½ m S
of E Kilbride
HOLLYBUSH
★★★Hollybush House
On A713—6½ m SE of Ayr
KILCHRENAN
★★★Ardanaiseig
Kilchrenan—7 m SE of Taynuilt
★★Taychreggan
Lochaweside—6 m SE of
Taynuilt on B895
KILWINNING
★★★Mountgreenan
4 m N of Irvine
LANARK
★★Cartland Bridge
On A73—1½ m NW of Lanark
LANGBANK
★★★Gleddoch House
4½ m E of Port Glasgow, on S
side of River Clyde
MONKTON
★★★Adamton House
1 m N of Prestwick
SKELMORLIE
★★★Manor Park
St. Phillans—off A78—2 m S of
Skelmorlie
TARBERT
★★★Stonefield Castle
2 m N of Tarbert on A83

Tayside
KINCLAVEN
★★★Ballathie House
4 m NE of Stanley off B9099
LUNAN BAY
★★Lunan Bay
Inverkeilor—8 m NE of
Arbroath off A92
MEIGLE
★★Kings of Kinloch
1½ m W of Meigle on
Aberdeen—Perth Rd
PITLOCHRY
★★★Green Park
Clunie Bridge Road—½ m N of
Pitlochry on A9
TUMMEL BRIDGE
★★Port-An-Eilean
Strathtummel—7 m E of
Kinloch Rannoch, 9 m SW of
Pitlochry

Wales

Clwyd
LLANGOLLEN
★★★Bryn Howel
Trevor—3 m E of Llangollen on
A539
NORTHOP
★★★Chequers
Northop Hall—2 m E of
Northop on A55

Dyfed
ABERYSTWYTH
★★★Conrah
Chancery Llanfarian—4 m S of
Aberystwyth on A487
CRUG-Y-BAR
★★Glanrannell Park
2 m SW of A482—6 m NW of
Llanwrda

LAMPETER
★★★**Falcondale**
28½ m S of Aberystwyth
PEMBROKE
★★**Underdown Country House**
Grove Hill
ST DAVID'S
★★★**Warpool Court**
Goat Street—½ m SW of St David's
★★★**Whitesands Bay**
1½ m NW of St David's

Gwynedd
ABERSOCH
★★★**Porth Tocyn**
¾ m off Bwlch Tocyn Rd—1½ m S of Abersoch
★★**Deucoch**
6 m SW of Pwllheli
BETWS-Y-COED
★★**Plas Hall**
3 m SW of Betws-y-Coed via Roman track called Sam Helen
★★**Craig-y-Dderwen**
Just off A5 on River Conway
BONTDDU
★★★**Bontddu Hall**
5 m NW of Dolgellau
CRICCIETH
★★★**Bron Eifion**
1 m W of Criccieth on A497
★★**Parciau Mawr**
Overlooks Criccieth Castle
LLANBEDR
★★**Cae Nest Hall**
3 m S of Harlech on A496

LLANDUDNO
★★★**Bodysgallen Hall**
1½ m off B5115
LLANFAIR-PWLLGWYNGYLL
★★★**Carreg Bran**
Church Lane
LLANRWST
★★★**Maenan Abbey**
Maenan—3 m N of Llanrwst
NEFYN
★★**Plas Pistyll**
Pistyll—2 m NE of Nefyn on B4417
PENNAL
★★**Llugwy**
3 m W of Machynlleth
RO-WEN
★**Tir-y-Coed**
4 m S of Conwy

Powys
BRECON
★★**Nythfa House**
Just N of Brecon town centre—Off the B4602
CAERSWS
★★★**Maesmawr Hall**
6 m W of Newtown on A942
CHURCHSTOKE
★★**Mellington Hall**
3 m SE of Montgomery
EGLWYSFACH
★★★**Ynyshir Hall**
6 m SW of Machynlleth on A487

LLANFYLLIN
★★**Bodfach Hall**
Y-Parc—¼ m W of Llanfyllin on A490
LLANGAMMARCH WELLS
★★★**Lake**
1 m W of B4519—¾ m SE of Garth
LLANWRTYD WELLS
★★★**Abernant Lake**
½ m off A483 at Llanwrtyd Wells

Channel Islands

Guernsey
ST MARTIN'S
★★★**Green Acres**
1½ m SW of St Peter Port

Jersey
ST SAVIOUR'S
★★★★**Longueville Manor**
Off A3—2 m E of St Helier

Northern Ireland

Co Antrim
MAGHERAMORNE
★★★**Magheramorne**
3½ m SE of Larne

Co Down
NEWCASTLE
★★**Enniskeen**
Bryansford Rd

Appointed Hotels within Five Miles of a Motorway

This list may be helpful to members travelling on the major motorways who wish to stop at hotels or motels within easy distance.

The intersection numbers indicate the slip roads by which the motorways should be left in order to reach the hotels. (Intersection numbers are shown on motorway advance direction signs.)

M1 Motorway

Intersection No.	Hotels
2–4	London NW7
	★★★M TraveLodge, Scratchwood (on Motorway)
4	Boreham Wood
	★★★M Elstree Moat House
	★Grosvenor
	Bushey
	★★★★M Ladbroke
	★★M Spider's Web
4–5	Harrow Weald
	★★★Grimsdyke
5	Radlett
	★★Red Lion
5–6	Watford
	★★★M Caledonian
6	St Albans
	★★★M Noke Thistle
	★★★St Michael's Manor
	♨★★★Sopwell House
8	Hemel Hempstead
	★★★M Post House
9	Markyate
	★★★M Hertfordshire Moat House
	Redbourn
	★★★M Aubrey Park
	Harpenden
	★★★★Harpenden Moat House
	★★★Glen Eagle
10	Luton
	★★★M Chiltern, Dunstable Rd
	★★★M Luton Crest
	★★★Strathmore Thistle
	★★Leaside
11	Dunstable
	★★Highwayman
13	Woburn
	★★★★Bedford Arms
14	Milton Keynes
	★★Cock
	Newport Pagnell
	★★Swan Revived
14–15	Newport Pagnell
	★★★M TraveLodge (on Motorway)
15	Northampton
	★★★Grand
	★★★Saxon Inn
	★★★Moat House
	★★Angel
16	Weedon
	★★★M Crossroads
18	Crick
	★★★M Post House
18	Rugby
	♨★★★Clifton Court, Clifton

Intersection No.	Hotels
	★★★Three Horse Shoes
20	Lutterworth
	★★M Moorbarns
21	Leicester
	★★★★Grand
	★★★★M Holiday Inn
	★★★M Leicester International
	★★★Eaton Bray
	★★★M Leicester Forest Moat House
	★★★Leicestershire Moat House
	★★★M Post House
	★★Belmont
	Narborough
	★★Charnwood
22	Groby
	★★Brant Inn
22	Newtown Lindford
	★★Johnscliffe
23	Loughborough
	★★★King's Head
	★★Great Central
24	Castle Donington
	★★Donington Manor
24	Kegworth
	★★Yew Lodge
25	Long Eaton
	★★★M Novotel Nottingham/ Derby
	★Europa
25	Sandiacre
	★★★M Post House
	Nottingham
	★★★★Albany
	★★★George
	★★★Savoy
	★★★Strathdon Thistle
	★★Edwalton Hall (Edwalton)
	★★Sherwood
25–26	Nottingham
	★★★★M Victoria
26	Nottingham
	See above
	Eastwood
	★Sun Inn
27	Eastwood
	★Sun Inn
28	South Normanton
	★★★M Swallow
29	Chesterfield
	★★★Station
	★★Portland
30	Renishaw
	★★★Sitwell Arms
	Sheffield
	★★★★Grosvenor House
	★★★★Hallam Tower Post House
	★★★★St George
	★★Roslyn Court
	★★Rutland
	★★St Andrews
33	Sheffield
	See above
	Rotherham
	See below
34	Sheffield
	See above
	Rotherham
	★★★★M Carlton Park

Intersection No.	Hotels
	★★Brentwood
	★★Elton
35	Rotherham
	★★Brentwood
	★★Elton
37	Barnsley
	★★Queens
	★Royal
39	Wakefield
	★★★Stoneleigh
	★★★Swallow
40	Ossett
	★★★M Post House
	Wakefield
	★★★Stoneleigh
	★★★Swallow
43	Oulton
	★★★M Crest
	Leeds
	★★★★Ladbroke Dragonara
	★★★★Queens
	★★★M Ladbroke
	★★★Merrion
	★★★Metropole
	★★★M Stakis Windmill (Seacroft)
	★★★Golden Lion
	★★Wellesley
	★Hartrigg

M4 Motorway

Intersection No.	Hotels
4	London Airport
	★★★★M Excelsior (West Drayton)
	★★★★M Holiday Inn (West Drayton)
	★★★M Ariel (Hayes)
	★★★Berkeley Arms (Cranford)
	★★★M Heathrow Crest (West Drayton)
	★★★M Post House (West Drayton)
	★★★M Skyway (Hayes)
5	Slough
	★★★★M Holiday Inn
6	Windsor
	♨★★★★Oakley Court
	★★★Castle
	★★★Wrens Old House
	★★Ye Harte & Garter
	★★Royal Adelaide
8–9	Maidenhead
	★★★M Crest
	★★Thames
	★★Bear
	♨★★Taplow House
10	(A329 (M))
	Sonning-on-Thames
	★★★White Hart
	Wokingham
	♨★★★St Annes Manor
11–12	Reading
	★★★★M Ramada
	★★★M Post House

★★Ship
12 Pangbourne
  ★★★Copper Inn
13 Newbury
  ★★★Chequers
Yattendon
  ★★Royal Oak
14 Hungerford
  ★★★Bear
15 Swindon
  ★★★★Blunsdon House
    (Blunsdon)
  ★★★M Crest Hotel
    (Stratton St.
    Margarets)
  ★★★M Goddard Arms
  ★★★M Post House
    (Coate)
  ★★★Wiltshire
16 Swindon
    See above
17 Castle Combe
  ⚑★★★Manor House
Chippenham
  ★★M Angel
  ★Bear
Malmesbury
  ⚑★★★Whatley Manor
    (Easton Grey—2½
    m W on B4040)
  ★★★Old Bell
18 Old Sodbury
  ★★Cross Hands
Petty France
  ★★★Petty France
Tormarton
  ★★Compass Inn
19 Bristol
  ★★★★Grand
  ★★★★M Holiday Inn
  ★★★★Ladbroke
    Dragonara
  ★★★Avon Gorge
  ★★★M Crest Hotel
    (Hambrook)
  ★★★St. Vincent's
    Rocks
  ★★Hawthorns
  ★★Seeley's
Winterbourne
  ★★★Grange (M32 Int 1)
21 Alveston
  ★★★M Post House
  ★★Alveston House
22 Chepstow
  ★★★M Two Rivers
  ★★Beaufort
  ★★Castle View
  ★★George
  ★★Old Ferry
24 Newport
  ★★★★Celtic Manor
  ★★★M Ladbroke
  ★★Queen's
  ΛΛWestgate
25 Newport
    See above
26 Cwmbràn
  ★★★M Commodore
    Llanyrafon
29 (A48(M))
St. Mellons
  ★★★St. Mellons
    County Club
29 (A48(M)) & 32
Cardiff
  ★★★★Inn on the Avenue,
    LLanedeyrn
  ★★★M Crest

★★★M Ladbroke
    Wentloog Castle,
    Castleton
  ★★★Park
  ★★★M Post House
    Pentwyn
  ★★★Royal
  ★★Beverley
  ★★Sandringham
  Ap. Pen-y-Lan
37 Porthcawl
  ★★★Sea Bank
  ★★Maid of Sker
  ★★Brentwood
  ★★Fairways
  ★★Seaways
39–42 Port Talbot
  ★★★M Aberafan,
    Aberavon
  ★★Twelve Knights
42 & 44 Neath
  ★★★Cimla Court Motel
42, 44–47 Swansea
  ★★★★M Dragon
  ★★★M Dolphin
    (Whitewalls)
  ★★Llwyn Helyg
  ★★Windsor Lodge
47 Swansea
  ★★★M Fforest Motel
48 Llanelli
  ★★★Stradey Park
  ★★Diplomat

M5 Motorway

1 Birmingham
  ★★★Barr
  ★★★M Post House
West Bromwich
  ★★★M West
    Bromwich Moat
    House
2 Birmingham
  ★★★★Albany
  ★★★★M Holiday Inn
  ★★★★Midland
  ★★★★Plough & Harrow
  ★★★★M Strathallan
    Thistle
  ★★★M Apollo
  ★★★Crest
  ★★★Grand
  ★★★Royal Angus
    Thistle
  ★★Annabelle
  ★★Bailey House
  ★★Cobden
  ★★Norfolk
Dudley
  ★★Station
  ★Ward Arms
3 Birmingham
    As above
4 Bromsgrove
  ★★★Perry Hall

5 Bromsgrove
  ★★★Perry Hall
Droitwich
  ★★★★Chateau Impney
  ★★★Raven
  ⚑Ap.St. Andrew's
    House
6 Worcester
  ★★★Giffard
  ★★Star
  ★★Ye Olde Talbot
  ★Park House
  ★Talbot
7 Worcester
    See above
Pershore
  ★★Angel Inn
  ★★Manor House
8 Upton-on-Severn
  ★★★White Lion
9 Tewkesbury
  ★★★Bell
  ★★★Tewkesbury Park
  ★★★Royal Hop Pole
  ★Tudor House
10 Cheltenham
  ★★★★M Golden Valley
    Thistle
  ★★★★Queen's
  ★★★Carlton
  ★★George
  ★Park Place
  ★★Savoy
  ★Royal Ascot
  ★Wellesley Court
11 Cheltenham
    See above
Gloucester
  ★★★Bowden Hall
    (Upton St.
    Leonards)
  ★★★M Crest,
    Barnwood
  ★★★Tara
  ★★Fleece
  ★★New County
12 Gloucester
    See above
13 Stroud
  ★★★Bear of
    Rodborough
  ★★★Stonehouse Court
  ★★Alpine Lodge
  ⚑★★Burleigh Court
  ★★London
  ★★Imperial
14 & 16 Thornbury
  ⚑★★★Thornbury Castle
14 Falfield
  ⚑★★Park
Newport
  ★★M Newport
    Towers
Berkeley
  ★★Prince of Wales
Wotton-under-Edge
  ★★Swan
14–15 Alveston
  ★★★M Post House
  ★★Alveston House
16 Alveston
    See above
Bristol
  ★★★★Grand
  ★★★★M Holiday Inn
  ★★★★Ladbroke
    Dragonara
15 ★★★M Crest Hotel,
    Hambrook

Intersection No. via M4 (M32)	Hotels
	★★★Avon Gorge
	★★★St Vincent's Rocks
	★★Hawthorns
	★★Seeley's
17	Bristol
	See above
18	Bristol
	See above
19	Bristol
	See above
20	Clevedon
	★★★Walton Park
21	Weston-super-Mare
	★★★Grand Atlantic
	★★★Royal Pier
	★★Albert
	★★Dauncey's
	★★Dorville
	★★Queenswood
	★★Russell
	★Bay View
	Worle
	★★M Old Manor
22	Burnham-on-Sea
	★★Dunstan House
	★★Royal Clarence
	★Pine Grange
	★Richmond
	Highbridge
	★★Sundowner
	Lympsham
	★★Batch Farm
24	North Petherton
	★★Walnut Tree
25	Taunton
	★★★★Castle
	★★★County
	★★Corner House
	★★Falcon
	★★St Quintin
26	Blagdon
	★★★Mendip
27	Wellington
	★★Beam Bridge, Sampford Arundel
30	Exeter
	★★★Buckerell Lodge
	★★★M Exeter Arms
	★★★Gipsy Hill, Pinhoe
	★★★Imperial
	★★★Rougemont
	★★★Royal Clarence
	★★★White Hart
	★★Bystock
	★★Edgerton Park
	★★M Exeter Moat House
	★★Great Western
	★Windsor
31	Exeter
	★★★M Devon
	★★★M Ladbroke, Kennford
	★★St Andrews

M6 Motorway

Intersection No.	Hotels
1	Rugby
	♨★★★Clifton Court, Clifton

Intersection No.	Hotels
	★★★Three Horse Shoes
2	Coventry
	★★★★De Vere
	★★★★Leofric
	★★★Brandon Hall, Brandon
	★★★M Chace Crest, Willenhall
	★★★M Crest, Walsgrave
	★★★M Novotel (Longford)
	★★★M Post House (Allesley)
	★★Allesley
	★★Beechwood
3	Coventry
	See above
	Nuneaton
	★★M Longshoot Motel
4	**Birmingham National Exhibition Centre**
	★★Arden, Bickenhill (Solihull)
	Birmingham Airport
	★★★★Excelsior
	Coleshill
	★★★Coleshill
	Meriden
	★★★Manor
5	Sutton Coldfield
	★★★★Belfry
	★★★★Penns Hall
	★★★Moor Hall
	★★Sutton Court
6	Birmingham
	★★★★Albany
	★★★★M Holiday Inn
	★★★★Midland
	★★★Grand
	★★★M Post House— Great Barr
	★★★Royal Angus Thistle
	★★★Barr—Great Barr
	★★M Robin Hood Motel—Hall Green
	Sutton Coldfield
	See previous column
7	Birmingham
	★★★Barr
	★★★M Post House
	West Bromwich
	★★★M West Bromwich Moat House
8	West Bromwich
	See above
9	Walsall
	★★★Baron's Court (Walsall Wood)
	★★★M Crest
	★★County
	★★Royal
10	Walsall
	See above
	Wolverhampton
	★★★Connaught
	★★★Goldthorn
	★★★Mount
	★★★Park Hall
	★★M Fox
	★★York
11	Wolverhampton
	See above

Intersection No.	Hotels
11–12	Cannock
	★★Hollies
13	Stafford
	★★★Tillington Hall
	★★Garth
	★★Swan
	★Vine
14	Stafford
	See above
	Stone
	♨★★★Brooms
	★★★Crown
15	Newcastle-under-Lyme
	★★★Clayton Lodge
	★★★M Crest
	★★★M Post House
	★★Borough Arms
	★Deansfield House
	Stoke-on-Trent
	★★★★North Stafford
	Hanley
	★★★Stakis Grand
	Burslem
	★★George
17	Sandbach
	★★★Chimney House (Sandbach Heath)
	★★★M Saxon Cross
	★★Old Hall
19	Knutsford
	★Rose & Crown
	Bucklow Hill
	★★★M Swan
20	Grappenhall
	★★★M Fir Grove Inn
	★Rockfield
	Lymm
	★★★Lymm
	Daresbury
	★★★Lord Daresbury
	Warrington
	★★★Paddington House
	★★Old Vicarage— Stretton
	★★Patten Arms
21	Warrington
	★★★Paddington House
	★★Patten Arms
	★★Rockfield
22	Warrington
	See above
23	Haydock
	★★★★M Post House
23, 24 & 25	St Helens
	★★★Fleece
25	Wigan
	★★★Brocket Arms
	★★Bellingham
	★★Bel Air
	★★Grand
26	See above
27	Parbold
	★★Lindley
	Standish
	★★★M Cassinellis Almond Brook
27–28	Charnock Richard
	★★★M TraveLodge (on Motorway)
	★★M Hunters Lodge
28	Clayton-le-Woods
	★★★Pines
	Leyland
	★★★★M Ladbroke
	Whittle-le-Woods
	★★★Shawhill Golf & Country Club

Intersection No.	Hotels
31	Preston
	★★★M Crest Hotel
	★★★M Tickled Trout, Samlesbury
	★★★M Trafalgar, Samlesbury
32	Broughton
	★★★Broughton Park
	Preston
	★★★Barton Grange
34	Lancaster
	★★★★M Post House
36	Crooklands
	★★★Crooklands
	Heversham
	★★★Blue Bell at Heversham
	Levens
	⚑★★Heaves
	Beetham
	★Wheatsheaf
37	Kendal
	★★★County Thistle
	★★★Woolpack
	★★Gateway
	★★Shenstone Country
38	Tebay
	★★★M Tebay Mountain Lodge
39	Shap
	★★Shap Wells
40	Penrith
	★★★George
	★★Abbotsford
	★★M Clifton Hill
	★★Glen Cottage
	★★Strickland
	★★Station
	Edenhall
	★★Edenhall
42	Carlisle
	★★★M Crest
	★★★Crown & Mitre
	★★★Cumbrian Thistle
	★★★Hilltop
	★★★String of Horses, Faugh
	★★Carrow House
	★★Central
	★★Cumbria Park
	★★Pinegrove
	★Vallum House
	Wetheral
	★★★Crown
43	Carlisle
	See above
	Wetheral
	★★★Crown
44	Carlisle
	See above

M8 Motorway

Intersection No.	Hotels
4	Bathgate
	★★★Golden Circle
	★★Dreadnought

Intersection No.	Hotels
6	Airdrie
	★★Tudor
	Newarthill
	★★Silverburn
	Bellshill
	★Hattonrigg
8	Coatbridge
	★★★Coatbridge
	Stepps
	★★★Garfield
15	Rutherglen
	★★Kings Park
16, 19	Glasgow
	★★★★M Holiday Inn
	★★★M Crest
	★★★Tinto Firs
	★★Blythswood
	★★Newlands
17	Glasgow
	★★★★Stakis Grosvenor
	★Cavendish
18, 19	Glasgow
	★★★★Albany
20, 21	Glasgow
	★★Ewington
	★★Queen's Park
20, 21, 22	Glasgow
	★★★Bellahouston
21, 22, 23	Glasgow
	★★Sherbrooke
26, 27	Renfrew
	★★★★M Excelsior
	★★★Dean Park
	★★★M Stakis Normandy
27, 29	Paisley
	★★Ardgowan
	★★Rockfield
29	Linwood
	★★Golden Pheasant
29–30	Erskine
	★★★M Crest

M50 Motorway

Intersection No.	Hotels
1	Tewkesbury
	★★★Bell
	★★★Tewkesbury Park
	★★Royal Hop Pole
	★Tudor House
2	Ledbury
	★★Feathers
4	Ross-on-Wye
	★★★Chase
	⚑★★★Pengethley
	★★★Royal
	⚑★★★Wye
	⚑★★Chasedale
	★Brookfield House
	★Rosswyn
	★Wilton Court
	Kerne Bridge
	★Castle View
	Pencraig
	⚑★★Pencraig Court

M62 Motorway

Intersection No.	Hotels
4	Liverpool
	★★★★M Atlantic Tower Thistle
	★★★★M Holiday Inn
	★★★★St George's
	★★★Blundellsands
	★★★Crest
	★★★Park
	★★★Royal
	★★Green Park
	★★Lord Nelson
	★★Shaftesbury
	★Solna
7	Rainhill
	★Rockland
	St Helens
	★★★Fleece
8	Widnes
	★★Hillcrest
9	Warrington
	★★★Paddington House
	★★Patten Arms
12	Salford
	★★Racecourse
	★★Beaucliffe
17–19	Bury
	★Woolfield
19–21	Oldham
	★★★Belgrade
	Rochdale
	★★Midway
21	Littleborough
	★Sun
22	Rishworth
	★★Royal
23 & 24 & 25	Huddersfield
	★★★George
	★★★M Ladbroke
24 & 25	Halifax
	★★★Princess
26	Bradford
	★★★★Stakis Norfolk Gardens
	★★★M Novotel
	★★★Victoria
28	Ossett
	★★★M Post House
28, 29 & 30	Wakefield
	★★★Stoneleigh
	★★★Swallow
30	Oulton
	★★★M Crest
33	Monk Fryston
	⚑★★★Monk Fryston Hall
	Wentbridge
	⚑★★★Wentbridge House
35 via M18	Thorne
	★★Belmont
37	Howden
	★★★Bowmans

RAC Appointed Caravan Sites

England

Avon
BATH
Newbridge Caravan Park
Brassmill Lane. T Bath 28778
Newton Mill Touring Centre
Newton St Loe. T Bath 333909
SEVERN BEACH, Nr BRISTOL
Villa Caravan Park
T Pilning 2540
WESTON-SUPER-MARE, Nr
Oak Tree and West End Caravan &
Camping Parks
Locking. T Banwell 822529

Cambridgeshire
CAMBRIDGE, Nr
Highfield Farm
(B. H. Chapman), Comberton.
T Comberton 2308
Great Shelford Camping Club Site
behind 212 Cambridge Road, Great
Shelford. T Cambridge 841185
HUNTINGDON, Nr
'Anchor Cottage' Riverside Caravan &
Camping Site
Church Lane, Hartford. T Huntingdon
55642.
Quiet Waters Caravan Park
Hemingford Abbots. T Huntingdon 63405
Old Manor Caravan Park
Grafham. T Huntingdon 810264

Cornwall
Boswinger, Nr St Austell
Sea View International Caravan and
Camping Park
Boswinger, Gorran Haven. T Mevagissey
843425.
BUDE
East Thorne Caravan & Camping Park
Kilkhampton. T Kilkhampton 235
BUDE, Nr
Atlantic Leisure Park
Sandymouth Bay. T Bude 2563
Budemeadows Touring Holiday Park
T Widemouth Bay 646
Keywood Caravan Park
Whitstone. T Week St Mary 338.
Wooda Caravan & Camping Park
Wooda Farm, Poughill. T Bude 2069
CAMBORNE
Magor Farm Caravan Site
Tehidy. T Camborne 713367
CRANTOCK, Nr NEWQUAY
Treago Farm Caravan Site
Crantock. T Crantock 830277
Trevella Caravan & Camping Park
Crantock. T Crantock 830308
FALMOUTH
Maen Valley Caravan Park
T Falmouth 312190
FOWEY
Penhale Caravan & Camping Park
T Fowey 3425
GOONHAVERN
Silverbow Park
(Postal Nr Truro). T Perranporth 2347
HELSTON
Retanna Country Park
Edgcumbe. T Falmouth 40643.
HOLYWELL BAY, Nr NEWQUAY
Trevornick Camping & Caravan Park
Holywell Bay. T Crantock 830531

LAUNCESTON, Nr
Chapmanswell Caravan Park
St Giles-on-the-Heath. T Ashwater 382
LOOE
Camping Caradon
T Polperro 72388
Great Tree Holiday Park
St Martins. T Looe 3737
Treble B Holiday Centre Ltd
Polperro Road. T Looe 2425
Trelawne Holiday Estate
Pelynt. T Polperro 72151
LOSTWITHIEL
Powderham Castle Caravan & Tourist
Park
Lanlivery. T Bodmin 872277
MAWGAN PORTH, Nr NEWQUAY
Gluvian Caravan & Camping Park
Mawgan Porth. T St Mawgan 373
MULLION, Nr HELSTON
Mullion Holiday Park
Penhale Cross, Ruan Minor. T Mullion
240428
NEWQUAY
Hendra Touring Caravan & Camping
Park Ltd
T Newquay 5778
Newquay Tourist Park
T Newquay 71111
Rosecliston Park
Trevemper. T Crantock 830326
Treloy Farm Tourist Park
T Newquay 2063
Trevarrian Holiday Park
Trevarrian. T Mawgan Porth 381
NEWQUAY, Nr
Porth Beach Tourist Park
Porth. T Newquay 6531
Trevelgue Caravan Park
Porth. T Newquay 3475 or 5905
Trekenning Manor Tourist Park
T St Columb 880462
The White Acres Holiday Park, White
Cross
T St Austell 860220.
PADSTOW
Music Water Touring Site
Rumford. T Rumford 257
PENTEWAN, Nr St Austell
Pengrugla Caravan & Camping Site
St Ewe. T Mevagissey 843485
Penhaven Tourist Park
T Mevagissey 843687
Pentewan Sands Ltd, Pentewan
T Mevagissey 843485
'Sun Valley' Caravan Park, Pentewan
Road
T Mevagissey 843266
POLPERRO
Killigarth Manor Caravan & Camping
Site
T Polperro 72216
PORTHTOWAN
Rose Hill Touring Park
T Porthtowan 890802
REJERRAH, Nr NEWQUAY
Monkey Tree Farm Tourist Park
T Perranporth 2032
Newperran Tourist Site
Rejerrah. T Perranporth 2407
RUAN MINOR, Nr HELSTON
Sea Acres Caravan Park
Kennack Sands. T The Lizard 290665
St AGNES
Trevarth Park
Blackwater (Postal) Nr Truro. T Truro
560266

St AUSTELL
Trencreek Farm Caravan, Chalet and
Camping Park
Hewaswater. T St Austell 882540
St BURYAN, Nr PENZANCE
Tower Farm Camping & Caravan Park
T St Buryan 286
St IVES
Ayr Holiday Park
Higher Ayr. T Penzance 795855
St MABYN, Nr BODMIN
St Mabyn Holiday Park
T St Mabyn 236
St MAWES, Nr
Trethem Mill Tourist Caravan Park
St Just-in-Roseland. T Portscatho 504
SALTASH, Nr
Dolbeare Caravan Park ·
St Ive Road. T Landrake 332
Notter Bridge Caravan & Camping
Park
Notter Bridge. T Saltash 2318
TRURO
Leverton Place Caravan & Camping
Park
Green Bottom. T Truro 560462
TRURO, Nr
Ringwell Holiday Park
Bissoe Road, Carnon Downs. T Devoran
862 194
WADEBRIDGE
St Minver House Holiday Estate
St Minver. T Trebetherick 2305

Cumbria
AMBLESIDE
Skelwith Fold Caravan Park
T Ambleside 32277
APPLEBY, Nr
Wild Rose Caravan Park
Ormside. T Appleby 51077
ARNSIDE
Holgates Caravan Park
Cove Road, Silverdale. T Silverdale 701508
CARLISLE, Nr
Dandy Dinmont Caravan & Camping
Site
Blackford. T Rockcliffe 611
CARLISLE
Orton Grange Caravan & Camping
Site
Wigton Road. T (0228) 710252
COCKERMOUTH
Violet Bank Caravan Park
T Cockermouth 822169
Wyndham Hall Caravan Park
Main Keswick Road. T Cockermouth
822571
GRANGE-OVER-SANDS, Nr
Lakeland Holiday Park
Moor Lane, Flookburgh.
T Flookburgh 235
Old Park Wood Caravan Site
Cark-in-Cartmel. T Flookburgh 266
MEALSGATE
The Larches Caravan Park
T Low Ireby 379
MILNTHORPE
Fell End Caravan Park
Slackhead Road, Nr Hale. T Milnthorpe
2122
NEWBY BRIDGE
Bigland Hall Caravan Park
Haverthwaite. T Newby Bridge 31702
PENRITH, Nr
Lowther Caravan Park
Eamont Bridge. T Penrith 63631

SILLOTH
Solway Lido Holiday Centre
T Silloth 31236
Stanwix Park Holiday Centre
T Silloth 31671
TEBAY
Tebay Caravan Park
T Orton 482
ULLSWATER
The Quiet Caravan & Camping Site
(Postal) Watermillock, Nr Penrith.
T Pooley Bridge 337
WINDERMERE
Falbarrow Caravan Park.
T Windermere 4428
Hill of Oak Caravan Site
T Newby Bridge 31417
Limefitt Park
T Ambleside 32300
Park Cliffe Caravan & Camping Site
Birks Road, Tower Wood. T Newby Bridge
31344
White Cross Bay Caravan Park
T Windermere 3937
WINDERMERE, Nr
Ashes Lane Camping & Caravan Park
T Staveley 821119

Derbyshire
ASHBOURNE
Sandybrook Hall Holiday Centre
T Ashbourne 42679
BAKEWELL
Greenhills Caravan Park
Crow Hill Lane, Ashford-in-the-Water.
T Bakewell 3467 or 3052
NEWHAVEN, Nr BUXTON
**Newhaven Caravan & Camping
Holiday Park**
T Hartington 300

Devon
BAMPTON, Nr
Zeacombe Caravan and Camping Park
Blackerton Cross, East Anstey. T Anstey
Mills 279
BRAUNTON
**Lobb Fields Caravan and Camping
Park**
Saunton Road. T Braunton 812090
BUDLEIGH SALTERTON, Nr
Ladram Bay Caravan Site
Otterton. T Colaton Raleigh 68398
CHAWLEIGH, Nr
Yeatheridge Farm Caravan Park
East Worlington, Crediton. T Tiverton
860330
CHUDLEIGH
Holmans Wood Tourist Park
T Chudleigh 853785
CROYDE BAY
Croyde Bay Holidays
T Braunton 890351
Ruda Holiday Park
T Croyde 890671
CULLOMPTON
**Forest Glade Caravan and Camping
Park**
Kentisbeare. T Broadhembury 381
DARTMOUTH
Deer Park Holiday Estate
Stoke Fleming. T Stoke Fleming 253
DAWLISH
Cofton Farm
Starcross. T Starcross 890358
DUNSFORD, Nr
Clifford Bridge Caravan Park
T Cheriton Bishop 226
EXETER, Nr
Castle Brake Caravan Park
Woodbury. T Woodbury 32431

Kennford International Caravan Park
Kennford. T Exeter 833046
Pathfinder Village
Tedburn St Mary. T Tedburn St Mary 239
HOLSWORTHY
Hedley Wood Caravan Park
T Bridgerule 404
ILFRACOMBE
Mullacott Cross Caravan Park
T Ilfracombe 62212
Sandaway Holiday Park
Berrynarbor. T Combe Martin 3155
ILFRACOMBE, Nr
Watermouth Cove
Berrynarbor. T Ilfracombe 62504
LYNTON
Sunny Lyn Caravan and Camping Site
Lynbridge. T Lynton 3384
MODBURY
Broad Park Touring Caravan Site
Higher Eastleigh Farm. T Modbury
830256
NEWTON ABBOT
Stover International Caravan Park
Lower Stapel Hill. T Bickington 446
OKEHAMPTON
Moorcroft Caravan Park
Belstone Corner. T North Tawton 293
OKEHAMPTON, Nr
Olditch Caravan Park
T Sticklepath 734
PAIGNTON
Beverley Park Holiday Centre
Goodrington Road. T Churston 843887
Paignton International Camping Site
Totnes Road. T Paignton 521684
PLYMOUTH
Riverside Caravan Park
Longbridge Road. T Plymouth 334122
ROUSDON, Nr LYME REGIS
Shrubbery Caravan Park
T Lyme Regis 2227 or 2046
SIDMOUTH
Oakdown Touring Caravan Park
Weston. T Sidmouth 3731
TAVISTOCK
Higher Longford Caravan Park
Moorshop. T Tavistock 3360
TAVISTOCK, Nr
Woodovis House Caravan Park
Gulworthy. T Tavistock 832968
WOOLACOMBE
**Golden Coast Holiday Village &
Tourist Park.**
T Woolacombe 870343

Dorset
BRIDPORT, Nr
Freshwater Caravan Park
Burton Bradstock. T Burton Bradstock
897317
Highlands End Farm Caravan Park Ltd
Eype. T Bridport 22139
CHRISTCHURCH
Hoburne Caravan Park
Hoburne Lane, Highcliffe, Christchurch.
T Highcliffe 3379
OWERMOIGNE, Nr DORCHESTER
Sandyholme Caravan Park
Moreton Road. T Warmwell 852677
St LEONARDS
Oakdene Holiday Park
T Ferndown 875422
Redcote Holiday Park
Boundary Lane T Ferndown 872742
WAREHAM, Nr
Sandford Park Caravans Ltd
Holton Heath, (Postal) Nr Poole.
T Lytchett Minster 622513
WARMWELL, Nr DORCHESTER
Warmwell Holiday Village
T Warmwell 852313

WIMBORNE MINSTER
Merley Court Touring Park
T Wimbourne 881488
Wilksworth Farm Caravan Park
Cranborne Road. T Wimborne 885467 or
883769

Essex
COLCHESTER
Colchester Caravan Club Site
Cymbeline Way, Lexden. T Colchester
45551

Gloucestershire
CHELTENHAM
Cheltenham Racecourse
Prestbury Park, Prestbury
CIRENCESTER, Nr
Cotswold Caravan Park
Broadway Lane. T Cirencester 860216
FOREST OF DEAN
Forestry Commission
Forest Park Camp, Christchurch. T Dean
33376
LYDNEY, Nr
Clanna Caravan & Camping Park
Alvington. T Netherend 214
SLIMBRIDGE
Tudor Arms Caravan & Camping Park
Shepherds Patch. T Cambridge (Glos)
483
STROUD
**Rodborough Fort Holiday Caravan
and Camping Centre**
T Stroud 3478
WOTTON-UNDER-EDGE
Cotswold Gate Caravan Park
Cannonscourt Farm, Bradley. T Dursley
843128

Greater London
LONDON
Sewardstone Caravan Park
Sewardstone Road, Chingford.
T 01-529 5689

Hampshire
LYMINGTON
Shorefield Caravan Park
Shorefield Road, Downton. T Milford-on-
Sea 2513
NEW MILTON
Bashley Park Ltd
Sway Road. T New Milton 612340

Hereford & Worcester
BROMYARD
Bromyard Caravan Park
Petty Bridge, Worcester Road.
T Bromyard 82267
ORLETON
Orleton Rise Caravan Park
Green Lane, Orleton. T Richards Castle
617

Humberside
BRIDLINGTON
Shirley Caravan Park
Jewison Lane, Marton. T Bridlington
76442
South Cliff Caravan Park
T Bridlington 71051
KINGSTON-UPON-HULL, Nr
Burton Constable Caravan park
Old Lodges, Sproatley. T Skirlaugh 62508

Isle-of-Wight
SANDOWN
Sandown Caravan Park
Morton Road. T Sandown 402206
SHANKLIN
Lower Hyde Leisure Park
T Shanklin 866131

VENTNOR
Appuldurcombe Garden Caravan &
Camping Park
Appuldurcombe Road, Wroxall. T Ventnor
852597
YARMOUTH
The Orchards Holiday Caravan Park
Newbridge. T Calbourne 331

Kent
DOVER, Nr
Hawthorn Farm Caravan & Camping
Site
Martin Hill. T Dover 852658
FOLKESTONE, Nr
Blue Channel Caravan Park
New Dover Road, Capel-le-Ferne.
T Folkestone 53564
TENTERDEN
Woodlands Caravan and Camping
Park
Tenterden Road, Biddenden. T Biddenden
291216
THANET
Manston Caravan & Camping Park
Manston Court Road. T Manston 442

Lancashire
BLACKPOOL
Marton Mere Caravan Park
Mythop Road. T Blackpool 64280
BLACKPOOL, Nr
Kneps Farm Caravan Park
River Road, Thornton Cleveleys.
T Cleveleys 823632
CARNFORTH
Detron Gate Caravan Site
Bolton-le-Sands. T Carnforth 732842
CHORLEY, Nr
Royal Umpire Caravan Park
T Croston 600257
CLITHEROE, Nr
Three Rivers Woodland Park
Eaves Hall Lane, West Bradford.
T Clitheroe 23523
GARSTANG
Robinson's Caravan Site,
Claylands Fm, Cabus. T Forton 791242
Six Arches Holiday Caravan Park
Scorton. T Forton 791683
LONGRIDGE
Beacon Fell View Caravan Park
T Longridge 5434
LYTHAM St ANNES
Eastham Hall Caravan Park
Salcoates Road. T Lytham 737907
MORECAMBE
Regent Caravan Park
Westgate. T Morecambe 413940 or
416786
Venture Caravan Park
Westgate. T Morecambe 412986

Lincolnshire
FOLKINGHAM
Low Farm Touring Park,
Spring Lane. T Sleaford 322
MABLETHORPE
Golden Sands Estates
Quebec Road. T Mablethorpe 7871
NORTH SOMERCOTES
Lakeside Holiday Park
Nr Louth. T North Somercotes 315
SKEGNESS
Richmond Drive Carapark
T Skegness 2097
SPALDING, Nr
Lake Ross Caravan Park
Dozens Bank, West Pinchbeck. T Spalding
61690
STAMFORD
Casterton Caravan Park
Casterton Hill. T Stamford 52441

TATTERSHALL
Castle Leisure Park
T Coningsby 43193
WOODHALL SPA
Bainland Park
Horncastle Road. T Woodhall Spa 52903

Norfolk
ACLE
Clippesby Holidays
Clippesby. T Fleggburgh 367
BACTON
Cable Gap Caravan Park
Coast Road. T Walcott 650667
CAISTER
The Old Hall Caravan Park
T Gt Yarmouth 720400
Scratby Hall Caravan Park
Scratby. T Gt Yarmouth 730283
CROMER
Forest Park Caravan Site
Northrepps Road. T Cromer 513290
DISS, Nr
Osier's Caravan & Camping Park
Old Bury Rd, Stuston. T Diss 740335
DOWNHAM MARKET
Woodlakes Caravan & Camping Park
Holme Road, Stowbridge. T Kings Lynn
810414
GREAT YARMOUTH
Vauxhall Holiday Park
Acle New Road. T Great Yarmouth 57231
Wild Duck Caravan and Camping Park
Belton. T Gt Yarmouth 780268
GREAT YARMOUTH, Nr
Blue Sky Caravan Park
Burgh Road, Bradwell. T Great Yarmouth
780571
Burgh Castle Caravan Harbour &
Marina
Burgh Castle. T Great Yarmouth 780331
Cherry Tree Holiday Park
Mill Road, Burgh Castle. T Great Yarmouth
780229
HADDISCOE
Pampas Lodge
The Street, T Aldeby 265
HEACHAM
Heacham Beach Caravan Park
T Heacham 70270
NORWICH, Nr
Haveringland Hall Caravan Site
Cawston. T Norwich 871302

Northumberland
BAMBURGH
Glororum Caravan Park
T Bamburgh 205 or 272
BERWICK-ON-TWEED
Ord House Caravan Park
East Ord. T Berwick-upon-Tweed 305288
EMBLETON
Dunstan Hill Camping & Caravanning
Club site
Craster. T Embleton 310
HALTWHISTLE
Burnfoot Camp-Site
National Trust. T Haltwhistle 20106
ROTHBURY, Nr MORPETH
Coquetdale Caravan Park
Whitton. T Rothbury 20549
WOOLER
Bridgend Caravan Park
T Wooler 81447

Nottinghamshire
MANSFIELD, Nr
Sherwood Forest Caravan Park
Clipstone Park Estate, Old Clipstone.
T Mansfield 823132

Oxfordshire
STANDLAKE
Standlake Caravans
Lincoln Farm, High Street. T Standlake
239

Shropshire
OSWESTRY, Nr
Cranberry Moss Camping and
Caravan Park
Kinnerley. T Nesscliffe 444 or Knockin
296
WEM
Lower Lacon Caravan Park
T Wem 32376

Somerset
BLUE ANCHOR BAY, Nr
MINEHEAD
The Beeches Holiday Park
Blue Anchor. T Washford 40391
Blue Anchor Bay Caravan Park
Blue Anchor Bay. T Dunster 821360
CHEDDAR
Broadway House Caravan & Camping
Park
Axbridge Road. T Cheddar 742610
CHEDDAR, Nr
Bucklegrove Caravan Park
Rodney Stoke. T Wells 870261
TAUNTON
St Quintin Hotel Caravan & Camping
Park
Bridgwater Road, Bathpool. T Taunton
73016
WATCHET Nr
Warren Bay Caravan Park
T Watchet 31460
WELLS
The Homestead Caravan & Camping
Park
Wookey Hole. T Wells 73022
WELLS, Nr
Mendip Heights Camping and
Caravan Park
T Wells 870241

Suffolk
EAST BERGHOLT, Nr IPSWICH
The Grange Caravan Park
East End. T Colchester 298567
LOWESTOFT
Denes Family Holiday Village
Kessingland Beach. T Lowestoft 740636
SAXMUNDHAM
Cakes & Ale Caravan & Camping Park
Abbey Lane, Leiston. T Leiston 831655
WOODBRIDGE, Nr
The Moon & Sixpence
Waldringfield. T Waldringfield 650

Sussex–East
HASTINGS
Shearbarn Touring Park
Barley Lane. T Hastings 423583

Wiltshire
DEVIZES
'Lakeside'
Rowde. T Devizes 2767
Potterne Wick Caravan Park
Potterne. T Devizes 3277
SALISBURY
Coombe Nurseries Touring Caravan
Park
Race Plain, Netherhampton. T Salisbury
28451

Yorkshire–North
AYSGARTH
Westholme Caravan & Camping Site
T Aysgarth 268

BOROUGHBRIDGE
Ponderosa Caravan Park
Wetherby Road. T Boroughbridge 3190 or 2709
FILEY
Filey Brigg Touring Caravan Site and Country Park
T Scarborough 366212
HARROGATE
High Moor Farm Park
Skipton Road. T Harrogate 63637
Rudding Caravan Park
Follifoot. T Harrogate 870439
Shaws Trailer Park
Knaresborough Road. T Harrogate 884432
HARROGATE, Nr
Ripley Caravan Park
Knaresborough Road. T Harrogate 770050
HELMSLEY
Foxholme Touring Caravan Park
Harome. T Helmsley 70416 or 71696
KNARESBOROUGH
The Lido
Wetherby Road
LEYBURN
Akebar Park
Wensleydale. T Bedale 50201
LEYBURN, Nr
Constable Burton Hall Caravan Site
T Bedale 50428
MALTON, Nr
Castle Howard Caravan and Camping Site
Coneysthorpe. T Coneysthorpe 366
PICKERING, Nr
Rosedale Caravan and Camping Site
Rosedale Abbey. T Lastingham 272
Spiers House Caravan & Campsite
(Forestry Commission). T Lastingham 591
RICHMOND
Brompton-on-Swale Caravan Park
T Richmond 4629
RIPON
Sleningford Watermill Caravan & Camping Park
T Ripon 85201
Woodhouse Farm Caravan and Camping Park
Winksley. T Kirkby Malzeard 309
SCARBOROUGH
Burniston Road Touring Caravan Site
Field Lane. T Scarborough 366212
Scalby Manor Touring Caravan & Camping Site
Burniston Road. T Scarborough 366212
SCOTCH CORNER
Scotch Corner Caravan Park
T Richmond 2530 or 2961 or 4424
SKIPTON
Overdale Trailer Park
Harrogate Road. T Skipton 3480
THIRSK
Thirsk Racecourse
Station Road. T Thirsk 23720
WHITBY
Burnt House Caravan Site
Ugthorpe. T Whitby 840448
YORK
Rawcliffe Manor Caravan Site
Manor Lane. T York 24422
Weir Caravan Park
T Stamford Bridge 71377
Chestnut Farms Caravans
Acaster Malbis. T York 706371

Yorkshire–South
WORSBROUGH, Nr BARNSLEY
Greensprings Holiday Park
Rockley Lane. T Barnsley 88298

Wales
Clwyd
CORWEN
Hendwr Caravan Park
Llandrillo. T Llandrillo 210 or 252
Llawr Bettws Farm
T Maerdy 224
RHYL
Marine Caravan Park
Cefyndy Rd. T Rhyl 4461
RHYL, Nr
Happy Days Caravan Park
Towyn Road. T Rhyl 50924
WREXHAM, Nr
The Plassey Touring Caravan Park
Eyton. T Bangor-on-Dee 780277

Dyfed
ABERPORTH
Caerfelin Caravan Park
T Aberporth 810540
Llety Caravan Park
Tresaith. T Aberporth 810354 or 810274
ABERPORTH, Nr
Pilbach Caravan Park
Bettws Evan, Rhydlewis. T Rhydlewis 434
ABERYSTWYTH
Aberystwyth Holiday Village
Penparcau Road. T Aberystwyth 4211
ABERYSTWYTH, Nr
Glan-y-Mor Leisure Park
Clarach Bay. T Aberystwyth 828900
HAVERFORDWEST, Nr
Broad Haven Caravan Park
Broad Haven. T Broad Haven 277
Hasguard Cross Caravan Park
Hasguard. T Broad Haven 443
Redlands Touring Caravan Park
Little Haven. T Broad Haven 301
KILGETTY, Nr
The Croft Caravan Park
Reynalton. T Narberth 860315
LLANGRANOG
Gilfach Caravan Park
Blaencelyn, Llangranog, Llandyssul.
T Llangranog 250
LLANGRANOG, Nr
Cefn-Hwnt Caravan Park
Plwmp (Postal) Llandyssul. T Llangranog 333
LLANRHYSTYD
Pengarreg Camping & Caravan Centre
T Llanon 247
MAENCLOCHOG
Rosebush Caravan & Camping Site
Belle Vue House, Rosebush.
T Maenclochog 206
NEWPORT
Llwyngwair Manor Holiday Park
T Newport (Dyfed) 820498
St DAVID'S
Caerfai Bay Caravan and Tent Park
T St David's 720274
Hendre Eynon Caravan Site
T St David's 474
St DAVID'S, Nr
Torbant Caravan Park
Croesgoch (Postal) Nr Haverfordwest.
T Croesgoch 261
TAVERNSPITE, Nr WHITLAND
South Carvan Caravan Park
T Llanteg 651
TENBY
Crackwell Holiday Park
Penally. T Tenby 2688
Kiln Park
Marsh Road. T Tenby 4121
Rumbleway Caravan Park
New Hedges. T Tenby 3719 or 2739
Well Park
New Hedges. T Tenby 2179

Wood Park Caravans & Country Club
New Hedges. T Tenby 3414

Glamorgan–South
BARRY, Nr
Fontygary Bay Caravan Park
Rhoose. T Rhoose 710386

Glamorgan–West
GOWER
Blackhills Caravan & Camping Park
Fairwood Common. T Swansea 207065

Gwynedd
BARMOUTH
Islawrffordd Caravan & Camping Site
Tal-y-Bont. T Dyffryn 269
BETHESDA
Ogwen Bank Caravan Park & Country Club
Ogwen Bank. T Bethesda 600486
BRYNSIENCYN, ANGLESEY
Fron Farm
T Brynsiencyn 310
BRYNTEG, ANGLESEY
Ad Astra Caravan Park
T Tynygongl 853283
Nant Newydd Caravan Park
T Tynygongl 852842
CAERNARFON
Cadnant Valley Camping Park
Llanberis Road. T Caernarfon 3196
CAERNARFON, Nr
Bryn Gloch Farm Caravan & Camping Park
Betws Garmon. T Waunfawr 216
Bryn Teg Caravan Park
Llanrug. T Llanberis 871374
Dinlle Caravan Park
Dinas Dinlle. T Llanwnda 830 324
Morfa Lodge Caravan Site
Dinas Dinlle. T Llanwnda 830 205
between 9am and 5pm
LLANFAIRPWLLGWYNGYLL, ANGLESEY
Plas Coch Caravan and Leisure Park
Llanedwen. T Llanfairpwll 714272
LLANRWST, Nr
Maenan Abbey Caravan Park
Maenan. T Dolgarrog 630
LLIGWY BAY, ANGLESEY
Capel Elen Caravan Park
Lligwy, Dulas. T Moelfre 524
Home Farm Caravan Site
Marianglas. T Moelfre 237
Melin Rhos Farm Camping & Caravan Site
T Moelfre 213 or 345
Tyddyn Isaf Caravan Park
T Moelfre 203
Tyn Rhos Caravan & Camping Site
Moelfre. T Moelfre 497
PENMAENMAWR
The Gardens Caravan Park
Glanyrafon Road. T Penmaenmawr 622334
PENTRAETH
Rhos Caravan Park
T Pentraeth 214
PORTHMADOG
Garreg Goch Caravan Park
Morfa Bychan. T Porthmadog 2659 or 2210
Greenacres Caravan Park
Morfa Bychan. T Porthmadog 2781
PWLLHELI, Nr
Gimblet Rock Caravan Park
South Beach. T Abersoch 2045 or 2047.

TYWYN, Nr
Woodlands Holiday Park
Bryncrug. T Tywyn 710471

Powys
BRONLLYS
Anchorage Caravan Park
T Talgarth 711 246
CRICKHOWELL, Nr
Cwmdu Caravan & Camping Site
Cwmdu. T Bwich 730441
LLANGORSE
Lakeside Caravan & Camping Park.
T Llangorse 226
MONTGOMERY, Nr
Ye Olde Smithy Caravan Park
Abermule. T Abermule 657
SENNYBRIDGE, Nr
Dan-yr-Ogof Show Caves Caravan &
Tenting Park
Abercraf. T Abercrave 730284 or 730693
WELSHPOOL, Nr
Valley View Caravan Park
Pentrebeirdd. T Meifod 265 or 545

Scotland

Borders
ETTRICK
Angecroft Caravan Park
T Ettrick Valley 251 or 221
HAWICK, Nr
Hawick Riverside Caravan Park
Hornshole Bridge. T Hawick 73785
JEDBURGH
Lilliardsedge Park
T Ancrum 271
KELSO
Springwood Caravan Park
Springwood Estate. T Kelso 24596
PEEBLES
Rosetta Caravan & Camping Park
T Peebles 20770

Central
BRIDGE OF ALLAN
Allanwater Caravan Site
Blairforkie Drive. T Bridge of Allan
83 2254

Dumfries and Galloway
CREETOWN
Cassencarie Holiday Park
T Creetown 264
CROCKETFORD, Nr DUMFRIES
Brandedleys Carafarm
T Crocketford 250
ECCLEFECHAN, Nr
Hoddom Castle Caravan Park
Hoddom, Lockerbie. T Ecclefechan 251
GLENLUCE
Glenluce Caravan & Camping Site
T Glenluce 412
KIRKCOWAN
Three Lochs Caravan Park
Balminnoch. T Kirkcowan 304
KIRKCUDBRIGHT
Brighouse Bay Holiday Park &
Outdoor Activity Centre
Borgue. T Borgue 267
Seaward Caravan Park
T Borgue 267 or Kirkcudbright 31079
NEWTON STEWART
Creebridge Caravan Park
T Newton Stewart 2432 or 2324
SOUTHERNESS
Southerness Holiday Village
Southerness. T Kirkbean 278 or 281

STRANRAER
Aird Donald Caravan Park
T Stranraer 2025
Cairnryan Caravan & Chalet Park
T Cairnryan 231
Drumlochart Caravan Park
Lochnaw. T Leswalt 232
Wig Bay Holiday Park
Loch Ryan. T Kirkcolm 233

Fife
CUPAR
Clayton Caravan Park
T Balmullo 870242 or 870630
KINGHORN
Pettycur Bay Caravan Park
T Kinghorn 890321
KIRKCALDY
Dunnikier Caravan Site
Dunnikier Way. T Kirkcaldy 267563
LEVEN
Letham Feus Caravan Park
Letham Feus. T Kennoway 350323
PITTENWEEM
Grangemuir Caravan Site
T Anstruther 311213
St ANDREWS
Craigtoun Meadows Holiday Park
Mount Melville. T St Andrews 75959

Grampian
ABOYNE
Aboyne Loch Caravan Park
T Aboyne 2244
ALFORD
Haughton House Caravan and
Camping Site
T Alford 2107
BANCHORY
Silver Ladies Caravan Park
Strachan. T Banchory 2800
CULLEN
Logie Caravan Site
T Cullen 40766
ELGIN
North Alves Caravan Park
Alves. T Alves 223
FOCHABERS
Burnside Caravan & Camping Site
T Fochabers 820362
FORRES
Old Mill Caravan Park
Brodie. T Brodie 244
PETERCULTER
Lower Deeside Caravan Park
Maryculter. T Aberdeen 733860

Highland
AVIEMORE
Aviemore Centre Caravan Park
T Aviemore 810751
Glenmore Forest Park (Forestry
Commission) Camp Site
Glenmore. T Cairngorm 271
AVIEMORE, Nr
Campgrounds of Scotland Ltd
Caravan & Camping Park
T Boat of Garten 652
BEAULY
Cruivend Caravan & Camping Site
T Beauly 782367
DAVIOT
Auchnahillin Caravan Park
T Daviot 223
DORNOCH, Nr
Grannie's Heilan Hame
Embo. T Dornoch 810383 or 810260
FORT WILLIAM
Glen Nevis Caravan & Camping Park
Glen Nevis. T Fort William 2191

Lochy Caravan and Camping Park
Camaghael. T Fort William 3446
FORT WILLIAM, Nr
Linnhe Caravan Park Ltd
Annat, Corpach. T Corpach 376
GAIRLOCH
Sands Holiday Centre
T Gairloch 2152
NAIRN
Nairn East Beach Caravan Park
T Nairn 53764
TAIN
Meikle Ferry Caravan Park
Meikle Ferry. T Tain 2292

Lothian
EDINBURGH
Mortonhall Caravan Park
30 Frogston Road East, Liberton.
T Edinburgh 664 1533
HADDINGTON
Monksmuir Caravan Park
T East Linton 860340
MUSSELBURGH
Drum Mohr Caravan Park
Levenhall. T Edinburgh 665 6867

Strathclyde
AYR
Sundrum Castle Holiday Park
T Ayr 261464 or 287564
BALLOCH
Tullichewan Caravan Park
Old Luss Rd. T Alexandria 59475
CULZEAN CASTLE
Glenside Camping & Caravanning
Club Site
Culzean Castle. T Kirkoswald 627
DUNOON, Nr
Stratheck International Caravan Park
Inverchapel, Loch Eck. T Kilmun 472
INVERARAY
Battlefield Caravan Park
T Inveraray 2285
STRATHAVEN
Gallowhill Caravan Park
Lesmahagow Road. T Strathaven 21267

TAYINLOAN
Point Sands Caravan Park
T Tayinloan 263 or 275
WEMYSS BAY
Wemyss Bay Holiday Park
T Wemyss Bay 520813

Tayside
BLAIR ATHOLL
Blair Castle Caravan Site
T Blair Atholl 263
CARNOUSTIE
Woodlands Municipal Caravan Site
Newtown Road. T Carnoustie 52258 or
54430
COMRIE
Twenty Shilling Wood Caravan Site
T Comrie 70411
CRIEFF
Crieff Holiday Village
Turret Bank. T Crieff 3513
DUNKELD
Erigmore House Caravan Park
Birnam. T Dunkeld 236
KENMORE
Kenmore Caravan and Camping Park
T Kenmore 226
KIRRIEMUIR, Nr
Drumshademuir Caravan Park
Roundyhill. T Kirriemuir 73284
TUMMEL BRIDGE, Nr PITLOCHRY
Tummel Valley Holiday Park
T Tummel Bridge 221

Hotels, Guest Houses and Farmhouses

Ireland is closer by B+I

The only car ferry from Liverpool to Dublin

B+I's big, modern car ferries sail nightly from Liverpool (just at the end of the motorway) direct to Dublin.

Both ships have cabin accommodation for more than 500 people, and the finest, modern facilities throughout the vessel.

The only car ferry from Holyhead to Dublin

Only B+I sails from Holyhead direct to the heart of Dublin, daily in under four hours.

The only car ferry from Pembroke to Rosslare

B+I car ferries also sail from Pembroke to Rosslare, our short sea route, day and night.

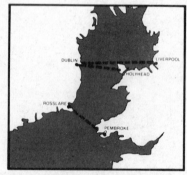

The best choice of routes and services on the Irish Sea

B+I is the Irish ferry company, with a unique brand of the best modern facilities and the best of friendly Irish service.

Book through RAC or B+I Line: London 01-734 4681 or 01-734 7512, Liverpool 051-227-3131 + 3551, Birmingham 021-236 5552, Manchester 061-834 1332, Leeds 0532 445527.

Ireland by B+I LINE

Liverpool-Dublin, Holyhead-Dublin, Pembroke-Rosslare.

482

Alnmouth (Northumberland)

Marine House Private Hotel

Alnmouth, Northumberland)
Telephone Alnmouth (0665) 830349

Relax in the friendly atmosphere of the
200-year-old recently modernised granary of
considerable charm overlooking the golf links
and beautiful beaches. 8 comfortable bedrooms,
some with shower and toilet. Traditional home
cooking, cocktail bar and games room. Ideal
centre for visiting the Castles or Roman Wall.
Perfect for Family or Golfing Holidays.
S.a.e. please for colour brochure/tariff.

Ambleside (Cumbria)

EES WYKE COUNTRY HOUSE
Nr. Sawrey, Ambleside, Cumbria LA22 0JZ

Telephone: Hawkshead (09666) 393

Ees Wyke is a charming Georgian
Country House set in its own grounds
overlooking the peaceful and beautiful
Esthwaite Water.

Ees Wyke has just six comfortable spacious
bedrooms each with bathroom en suite,
colour T.V. and tea-making facilities and
all bedrooms have breathtaking views of
Lake and Mountains.

Ambleside (Cumbria)

FIRE CERTIFICATE/RESIDENTIAL LICENCE

THE GABLES PRIVATE HOTEL
COMPSTON ROAD, AMBLESIDE, CUMBRIA
LA22 9DJ   R.A.C. & A.A. Listed

Situated in quiet open position, overlooking the Park and Tennis
Courts, etc, and Loughrigg Fell. Within three minutes of the Bus
Station. Ideally situated for Touring or a starting point for walks.
Two comfortable Lounges and Dining Rooms. Hot and cold
water in all Bedrooms. Television. Our aim is to give you
satisfaction and comfort. A Deposit of £5.00 per head required
upon confirmation of room reservation. Home Cooking and
Personal Attention. FREE CAR PARK. *Proprietors:* Mr & Mrs K.
Robinson. *Telephone:* Ambleside 3272 (STD Code 096-63).

Ashurst (Hampshire)

Axminster (Devonshire)

Bamburgh (Northumberland)

Barnstaple (Devon)

Barnstaple (Devonshire)

Bathampton (Avon)

The Tasburgh Bath

Telephone Bath
(0225)
25096

The Tasburgh Bath is situated just 1 mile from Bath City Centre, on the A36. A beautiful Victorian house set in very pleasant gardens with breathtaking views across the city and Avon Valley.
Licensed bar and evening meal on request.
Single room £12; double room £24; twin room £24; family room £10 adults/£8 under 14. All prices include breakfast and VAT. A service charge is not included.
You can book anytime, it's open all year, and no restrictions to the length of stay you want. Or, you can simply drop-in for a casual night or two without advance booking, whenever you wish, depending upon high season availability. Family rooms are available. Children are welcome.
Proprietors: Anne & Jim Bosworth.

Bedford (Bedfordshire)

Hurst House Hotel

178 HURST GROVE, BEDFORD, MK40 4DS
Tel: BEDFORD (0234) 40791

We offer comfortable accommodation in a friendly atmosphere. All bedrooms have washbasins, colour televisions, telephones and tea and coffee making facilities. There is an additional colour television in the guest lounge on the ground floor. We pride ourselves on our personal service and good home cooking. We also have a residential licence.

Access, Visa, Diners, American Express.

Brochure with pleasure from:
Paul and Lynne Godden.

Beeston (Nottinghamshire)

Brackley House Hotel and Hildegard's German Restaurant and Wine Bar

31 Elm Avenue, Beeston, Nottingham NG9 1BU
Tel: (Reservations) 0602 251787
(Guests) 0602 256739

Close to Notts. C.C., the hotel stands in extensive grounds. 14 bedrooms all with TV and hot & cold water. Lounge with colour TV; bar. A variety of entertainments can be enjoyed in a Continental atmosphere.

RAC MOTORISTS' DIARY

The motoring diary that is better by miles.
(See pages 37-8)

RAC

Birmingham (West Midlands)

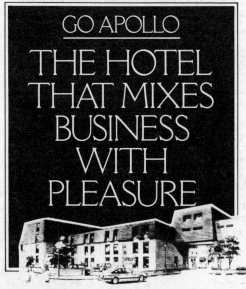

GO APOLLO

THE HOTEL THAT MIXES BUSINESS WITH PLEASURE

And that's no idle boast.

Just look at all we have to offer. 130 luxury bedrooms, each with private bathroom, colour TV, radio, direct dial phone, tea and coffee-making facilities; 4 executive suites; a choice of top-class bars and restaurants; conference facilities, with audio visual equipment readily available; free parking; and a perfect location, within easy walking distance of leading night clubs and casinos, just 5 minutes from Birmingham city centre and the M5, and close to the National Exhibition Centre.

What's more, the Apollo is a privately-owned hotel with its own ideas about personal service and the flexibility to look after your every need.

So, for business or pleasure, go Apollo.

For reservations or more information, ring 021-455 0271-6 today.

APOLLO HOTEL
Hagley Road,
Edgbaston,
Birmingham. B16 9RA.
Telex: 336759

Go Apollo!

AA *** RAC ***

Bolton Abbey (N Yorkshire)

The Devonshire Arms Hotel
Bolton Abbey, Skipton, North Yorkshire
Telephone: (075671) 441   Telex 51218

At Junction of B6160 and A59 Harrogate to Skipton road. A comfortable hotel in the Yorkshire Dales National Park recently restored and enlarged under the supervision of the Duchess of Devonshire, all 38 bedrooms have private bathrooms, television, radio, individually controlled central heating, direct dial telephones, tea and coffee tray and ample writing space.

Boughton Monchelsea (Kent)

Tanyard is a small medieval country house hotel in a truly rural setting tastefully furnished throughout with antiques. All bedrooms have private bath/shower room. The area is an ideal touring centre, Leeds Castle being only 6 miles away. Gatwick Airport, Dover and Folkestone are all approximately 45 minutes drive.
Tel: Maidstone 44705

"Tanyard" **Wierton Hill, Boughton Monchelsea, Nr. Maidstone, Kent**

Bournemouth (Dorsetshire)

Burley Court Hotel
✳ ✳ ✳
Bath Road, Bournemouth
Telephone: (0202) 22824 & 26704

The Burley Court Hotel is a privately-owned 3 star hotel having been the same family business for over 30 years, with continuing high standards in both food and service.

It is situated in the East Cliff district of Bournemouth, central for sea, shops and theatres. 41 bedrooms, with tea/coffee making facilities, telephone, radio, colour TV. Most rooms with private bathroom en suite. Licensed. Large car park. Central heating. Night Porter. Heated swimming pool (in season). Mid-week bookings accepted. Open throughout the year. Christmas Programme. Bargain Weekends.

Bournemouth (Dorsetshire)

Bournemouth (Dorset)

Bournemouth (Dorsetshire)

Bournemouth (Dorsetshire)

Bournemouth (Dorsetshire)

FOR YOUR SUPER HOLIDAY

SEAWAY

RAC Listed

(Street Plan: 9H)

22 WESTBY ROAD, BOSCOMBE, BOURNEMOUTH BH5 1HD

This well furnished and comfortable Guest House has an excellent position, minutes to sea and pier, buses, coaches, and main shopping centre.

★ A warm welcome awaits you ★ Children welcome (reduced rates when sharing parents' room)
★ Excellent cuisine and service ★ Separate tables ★ Free baby-sitting
★ Relax in our colour television lounge ★ Forecourt parking
Rates for '83—max. £59 plus VAT. No service charge. Open all year. Licensed.
Personal attention by Resident Proprietors: **Lyn and Dave Herbert**
Telephone: Bournemouth (0202) 35002, *or write for Brochure to* **Mrs. Herbert.** *SAE for reply.*

Bournemouth (Dorsetshire)

SIMPLY THE BEST VALUE IN

BOURNEMOUTH

SUPER SAVERS

★SO MUCH MORE FOR ALL THE FAMILY★

 SPLASH

 CHILD'S PLAY

 SWING

 SAIL

 CHEERS

 BRONZE

★VERY SPECIAL COMMERCIAL TERMS★

YOUR FREE COLOUR BROCHURE IS ONLY
A PHONE CALL AWAY

0202 26246 TRALEE HOTEL WEST HILL ROAD BOURNEMOUTH

RAC MOTORISTS' DIARY

The motoring diary that is better by miles.
(See pages 37-8)

Bournemouth (Dorsetshire)

WHITE HERMITAGE HOTEL Exeter Road, Bournemouth BH2 5AH

85 Bedrooms, most with private bath ● 5 Ground floor bedrooms with facilities for invalids ● Central heating throughout ● Children catered for. Dogs permitted ● Conference facilities up to 150 ● Car park for 60 cars.

Telephone: 0202 27363

Bournemouth (Dorset)

Woodside Private Hotel

29 SOUTHERN ROAD, SOUTHBOURNE, BOURNEMOUTH, BH6 3SR   Telephone Bournemouth 427213

Woodside Private Hotel is a highly recommended select family managed hotel which has acquired a high reputation for its warm and friendly atmosphere and for the high standard of furnishings, cleanliness and hygiene.

Situated in one of the most pleasant parts of Southbourne being only 3 minutes walk from all the amenities you require to ensure an enjoyable holiday, cliffs, paths to beaches, cliff lift, putting green, Fisherman's Walk, shops and buses. The Hotel has a reputation for excellent home cooking and varied menu served in the charming Dining Room at separate tables. Guests can relax in the comfortable Residents Lounge which has colour television or in the comfortable Reading Lounge or enjoy a drink in the comfortable Bar Lounge.

The Bedrooms are all tastefully decorated and furnished all have shaver points some with own shower.

● **Central heating** ● **Special Christmas programme** ● **Open all the year** ● **Licensed**

Braintree (Essex)

BENSON'S FAMOUS HOTEL AND RESTAURANT

Rayne Road, Braintree, Essex CM7 8RD. *Tel: (0376) 26251*

Enjoy the delights of countryside, whilst relaxing in our warm, friendly atmosphere. Excellent cuisine, restaurant and bar open to non-residents.

Braithwaite (Cumbria)

Tel: (059 682) 338

Braithwaite, Keswick, Cumbria CA12 5SY

IVY HOUSE HOTEL

Gleaming silver, oak beams, log fires, central heating, an elegant restaurant, traditional French and English dishes.
Small but beautiful on the edge of the fells.

Braunton (Devonshire)

DENHAM FARM HOLIDAYS

Denham Farm, North Buckland, Braunton. Tel: Croyde 890297 (STD 0271).

We are a mixed farm of 160 acres, set in a lovely country situation, yet only 2 miles from Croyde. Family owned and run, the atmosphere is friendly, free and happy, and we specialise in food that is both good and plentiful, with lots of farm cream.
Comfortable visitors' lounge with colour television and lounge bar for guests and their friends.

Braunton (Devonshire)

Brent Knoll (Somerset)

Brighton (SE Sussex)

Broadway (Worcestershire)

The Old Rectory

Willersey near Broadway   Tel: (0386) 853729

High class bed and breakfast, delightful accommodation, every facility, ideal for touring Cotswolds.
Free Brochure on request.   John and Helen Jones

Bristol (Avon)

2 miles from the motorway
7 miles from Bristol city centre
Miles apart from ordinary hotels

The Grange

Restaurant & Hotel

The Grange,
Northwoods, Winterbourne,
Bristol BS17 1RP
Tel: Winterbourne (0454) 777333

1

GOING PLACES SERIES

The *RAC Going Places* series offers a unique compilation of motor
and walking tours. Each book is written by an author who is on 'home
ground'. These modestly priced guides describe the topography,
history, flora and fauna of each area, together with details of places
of interest and motor tours and relevant maps.
(See pages 37-8)

RAC

RAC NAVIGATOR SERIES

The *RAC Navigator* series offers you more than just another road atlas. Each book is a unique guide to town and country combining regional and local 4 colour maps. Regional leisure maps highlight castles and ancient monuments, zoos and wildlife parks, steam railways and military museums, gardens and countryside of outstanding natural beauty, historic houses, art galleries and much more besides. The main local maps, at a scale of 1.6 miles to the inch, and town plans give a wealth of detail to anyone interested in exploring. (See pages 37-8)

1. South, Southeast, Thames and Chilterns, London.
2. The West Country, South Wales, Bristol and Cardiff.
3. East and West Midlands
4. Northern England.

Burnham-on-Sea (Somerset)

AA ** RAC   **THE DUNSTAN HOUSE HOTEL**   Les Routiers

Love Lane, Burnham-on-Sea, Somerset.   Tel: Burnham (0278) 784343 & 784300

A delightful Georgian period family run hotel/restaurant, ideal touring centre 2 miles M5, own gardens, noted for good a la carte and bar snack menus.

Resident Proprietors: Mr. & Mrs. J. Harrison

Burnley (Lancashire)

The Rosehill House Hotel is located in Burnley, in the heart of East Lancashire and ideally situated for business people as a convenient base from which to visit all the major towns and cities throughout Lancashire.

All bedrooms are centrally heated and have their own bath or shower, colour TV, radio, telephone and tea/coffee making facilities.

Rosehill House Hotel For further details
or reservations please telephone BURNLEY 53931
RHH Rosehill Avenue, Burnley BB11 2PW RAC**

Bury St Edmunds (Suffolk)

Ripley House Hotel
2 NORTHGATE AVENUE, BURY ST EDMUNDS, SUFFOLK
Tel: (0284) 4257
Restaurant – Bars – Parties & Weddings catered for

Buxton (Derbyshire)

Buckingham Hotel

1 Burlington Road, Buxton, Derbyshire SK17 9AS
Telephone: 0298-79414

Set on a broad, tree-lined avenue and over-looking the Pavilion Gardens, **The Buckingham,** a long established, personally run, two star hotel, offers excellent cuisine along with peace and comfort. All rooms with radio and room call, most with colour television and bathroom en suite. Games room and full size billiards table. Lift. Licensed. Full central heating.

Cambridge (Cambridgeshire)

Hamilton Guest House

88 CHESTERTON ROAD, CAMBRIDGE   Tel: 314866

Member Cambridge PHGH Association

Family run Guest House offering a high standard of comfort. 15 minutes walk from City Centre, close to river and parks. All rooms have central heating, h/c water, shaver points, colour TV, tea making facilities, radio, intercom and early call system. Most rooms have shower en suite. Public shower and bathroom. Private parking. English Breakfast

AA, RAC Listed

B&B from £9.00 per person per night

Cambridge (Cambridgeshire)

THE LENSFIELD HOTEL

AA & RAC Listed

Proprietors: Mr. and Mrs A. Paschalis

53 LENSFIELD ROAD, CAMBRIDGE
Tel: 355017/312905

Centrally situated, residentially run family hotel.
32 bedrooms – most have showers, WC, radio and televisions.
Central Heating. Ample parking.

RAC MOTORISTS' DIARY

The motoring diary that is better by miles.
(See pages 37-8)

Canterbury (Kent)

Canterbury's four star premier hotel first licensed in 1692. In the centre of the City and close to the Cathedral.
Seventy-four bedrooms, some with four poster beds, with private bathroom, telephone and colour television. The Hotel features modern facilities with the charm of an old timbered building. The ideal base to explore Canterbury. Private car park. Gourmet restaurant. Coffee shop. Full room service.

****

County Hotel Canterbury

High Street, Canterbury, Kent CT1 2RX
Telephone: **Canterbury (0227) 66266** *Telex:* **965076**

Canterbury (Kent)

ERSHAM LODGE HOTEL
Canterbury, Kent
Telephone: (0227) 463174

Ideally located on the A2 (Dover-London) close to the city centre. Comfortable, cosy rooms with bath or shower, GPO telephone, Colour TV, electronic radio-clock, new elegant lounge and dining room, patio. German, French, Italian spoken.

"To care for the comfort of our guests as long as they are staying under our roof, that's how we feel about hospitality." Fam. Pellay – Man. Prop.

Canterbury (Kent)

The Woodpeckers Country Hotel Ltd.
WOMENSWOLD, NR. CANTERBURY, KENT.
Tel: Canterbury (0227) 831319

Charming Victorian hotel, set in 2½ acres including lawns, flower beds and vegetable garden, with a happy atmosphere and good service. 16 comfortable rooms all with H/C water and tea/coffee making facilities. Warm air central heating, TV lounge and quiet lounge.

- Four-poster, Georgian, brass bedstead, bridal bedrooms all en suite and with colour TV.
- Farm Holiday Guide diploma winner for accommodation and food 3 years running 1979/80/81 (consecutively).
- Highly recommended for traditional country home baking.
- Heated swimming pool, water slide & diving board.

Horse riding, fishing, golf and tennis nearby. A wealth of historical places to visit just a short car ride away.

Carlisle (Cumbria)

THE CROWN HOTEL, Wetheral, Nr. Carlisle, Cumbria CA4 8ES
Tel: 0228 61888

The Crown Hotel is situated in the fashionable village of Wetheral adjacent to the River Eden, recently refurnished and extended. This original eighteenth century farmhouse now offers 52 de-luxe bedrooms. All rooms offer private bath/shower, colour television, video, direct dial telephone, radio alarm, coffee/tea making facilities, trouser press and hairdryer. The showpiece is the new Conservatory Restaurant situated in the garden, offers both a la carte and speciality menus. The village bar serves traditional real ales and bar snacks. Other facilities include three squash courts, full size snooker table, sauna and table squash. Flexible size conference facilities also available.

Carlisle (Cumbria)

VALLUM HOUSE HOTEL
Burgh Road, Carlisle CA2 7NB
Tel – Reception: 21860   Guests: 31939

- 11 Bedrooms – all with H&C
- TV, Radio and Intercom
- Tea and Coffee Making Facilities
- Lounge Bar (meals available)
- Restaurant with Table d'hote and A la Carte menu
- Delightful Gardens ● Relaxing Atmosphere
- RAC and AA Recommended

Chagford (Devon)

THREE CROWNS HOTEL

CHAGFORD   Tel: 06473 3444

Just off eastern edge of Dartmoor, one of the most popular and friendliest villages in Devon and in very beautiful country. Make this warm friendly 13th century hostelry of character your centre for walking, ****RAC**   riding, fishing and golfing holiday. Excellent cuisine. Four Poster Beds   **AA****

Chester-le-Street (Durham)

13th Century

 *Lumley Castle Hotel* ★★★

Stay in a genuine Castle

- •Close to A1M, Newcastle 20 minutes, Durham 10 minutes
- •Excellent Black Knight Restaurant   •Famed Elizabethan Banquet

Recommended by Egon Ronay, Michelin, BTA, NTB, AA, RAC

Chester-le-Street, Co. Durham. **Tel: 0385 891111**

Chipping Norton (Oxfordshire)

The Crown & Cushion Hotel

High Street,
Chipping Norton.

AA ** RAC
15th Century family-run
Coaching Inn.
Ideally located for visiting
Sir Winston Churchill's
birthplace, Blenheim Palace;
the Cotswolds,
Stratford-upon-Avon etc.

Telephone: (0608) 2533
Telex: 837955 IPSEG

Excellent modern facilities,
some rooms with telephone.
Open log fires, good cuisine and
real ales.
Ashley Courtenay, Egon Ronay
and Relais Routier
recommended.

MIDWEEK/WEEKEND BARGAIN BREAKS from £21.00

(Price includes En-Suite Bedroom, English Breakfast and Dinner for one person. VAT inclusive. Service discretionary)

Church Stretton (Shropshire)

Mynd House Hotel

CHURCH STRETTON
SHROPSHIRE, SY6 6RB
TEL: (0694) 722212

* AA/RAC Listed Hotel. Licensed
* Sensibly priced tariff
* Excellent varied menu
* Decor & Furnishings of a high standard
* Centrally heated throughout
* All guest rooms H & C and Shaver points, tea making facilities (some with private bath/toilet)
* Lounge with CTV
* Free Car Parking (Private)
* Bargain Breaks (November-March)

Situated in beautiful, unspoilt, varied countryside midway between Shrewsbury and Ludlow (A49), in midst of Shropshire hills.
Please send SAEB for brochure and tariff.

Church Stretton (Shropshire)

SANDFORD HOTEL

Watling Street, Church Stretton SY6 7BG
(Tel: 0694 722131)

Fully licensed family-run hotel in superb walking country and close to medieval towns. Many bedrooms en suite, comfortable lounge, bar and television room. Excellent reputation for food, with table d'hote and a la carte menus. Full central heating.

Prices: 2 nights, Dinner, Bed & Breakfast £33.60–£36.60.
7 nights, Dinner, Bed & Breakfast £110–£120.50.

Open all year.

Cliftonville (Kent)

Galleon Lights Hotel

OVERLOOKING THE ENGLISH CHANNEL.
MODERN, COMFORTABLE BEDROOMS MANY WITH PRIVATE BATH OR SHOWER AND COLOUR T.V.
SHORT OR LONG STAYS.
RESIDENTIAL LICENSED BAR.

12-14 FORT CRESCENT, CLIFTONVILLE, KENT.   Tel: (0843) 291703

Cranbrook (Kent)

The
WILLESLEY HOTEL
& RESTAURANT

This delightful hotel is situated in the heart of the Weald of Kent, offers bedrooms with private bath and colour television, and excellent cuisine. Close to many National Trust Properties.

Cranbrook, Kent   **Telephone: 0580 713555-6**

Cromer (Norfolk)

CLIFTONVILLE HOTEL

R.A.C. **   ### CROMER   A.A. **

On the West Cliff – Facing Sea – 40 rooms with sea view – Lift to all floors

FULLY LICENSED

Radio and G.P.O. Telephones in most rooms. Wing with private suites. Specially reduced terms for children sharing rooms with parents, also out of season periods October to May.

OPEN ALL YEAR   **SPECIAL 2 & 4 DAY "LET'S GO" BREAKS AVAILABLE**

Brochure and Terms available on request.

Tel: CROMER 512543/4   *Under personal supervision of Proprietor:* **T. A. Bolton**

When visiting London or Croydon, try-

NEW LEISURE COMPLEX OPENS SPRING 1985

somewhere different and very special

One of the loveliest country houses in England. Good food, fine wines and friendly service. Situated in 200 acres of beautiful parkland. All bedrooms with bathroom & colour TV. Amenities include: 18-hole golf course, tennis courts, swimming pool, riding, sauna, children's adventure playground, etc. Write, telephone or telex H. R. Aust for details.

SELSDON PARK HOTEL ★★★★

Sanderstead,
South Croydon, Surrey.
Telephone: 01-657 8811
Telex: 945003

Only half an hour from London.

Best Western

Britain's Largest Proprietor-Owned Hotel.

Crudwell (Wiltshire)

Mayfield House Hotel

Crudwell, Malmesbury
Wiltshire SN16 9EW
Tel: (06667) 409

21 bedroomed country house hotel. Olde Worlde restaurant, bar, TV lounge, walled garden and ample parking. Ideal tourist centre to visit places of historic interest.

Derby (Derbyshire)

ASTON COURT HOTEL
Midland Road, opposite Railway Station, Derby DE1 2SL
Tel: 0332 42716 – 45024   Car park
80 bedrooms most with private facilities, well furbished, privately owned hotel, restaurant 150. 3 conference rooms.
Competitive tariff. Special weekend and long term rates.

Dover (Kent)

East Cliff, Dover, Tel: 0304/211001-206000
STOPPING IN DOVER?
Visit our elegant Regency Hotel in Dover's most convenient position on the historic seafront opposite the Car Ferry entrance. Spacious modern single, double and family rooms - all with radio/colour TV.
The RENDEZVOUS RESTAURANT on the first floor serves a discerning clientele and offers magnificent seaviews.
SPECIAL PACKAGE OFFER - all the year round - ANY TWO NIGHTS with Dinner, Bed & Breakfast and a FREE DAY TRIP to FRANCE from £42 inclusive. Please ask for details.
ALSO CONFERENCE AND GROUP Facilities.
A Hotel in the Bressingham Holdings Ltd Group

Eastbourne (Sussex)

CHATSWORTH HOTEL Grand Parade, Eastbourne. *Tel: 0323 30327*
Situated right on the sea front. First class comfort, cuisine and service. All bedrooms have private facilities. Cosy residents' lounge bar. Partial central heating. Bargain breaks welcome. Small conferences up to 25. Bridge weekends.

For brochure and terms, write or phone: **V. W. Benzmann, Director**

RAC CONTINENTAL MOTORING GUIDE

Taking the car abroad?
Find out about driving regulations, motorways, speed limits, accident or breakdown routines, and insurance requirements in the *RAC Continental Motoring Guide*. At £2.95 (for members) an indispensable companion for motoring in 22 countries.
Contains a directory of RAC appointed Continental hotels. (See pages 37-8)

RAC

Ewen (Gloucestershire)

The Wild Duck Inn

AD 1563

Ewen, near Cirencester, Gloucestershire
Telephone: Kemble (028577) 310 or 364

AA ★★★   RAC ★★★   British Tourist Authority Commended   Egon Ronay

Exeter (Devon)

The Kings Arms Inn and Hotel
Tedburn St Mary, Exeter, Devon EX6 6EG

Accommodation, freehouse. Historic interest. Luncheons, dinners and bar meals. South coast resort easily reached, and the open beauty of Dartmoor is near at hand.

Exeter (Devon)

RADNOR HOTEL
79 St Davids Hill, Exeter, Devon EX4 4DW   Tel: 0392 72004

Situated just minutes walk from train stations and the city centre, this very comfortable hotel has full central heating. Most bedrooms have showers en suite and colour TV. Car park. Prices: singles £8.50; doubles £15-£18. Evening dinner by request at £4.50.

Exmouth (Devon)

AA ★★★   **DEVONCOURT HOTEL**   RAC ★★★

DOUGLAS AVENUE, EXMOUTH, DEVON. Tel: (0395) 272277/8/9

The Devoncourt Hotel stands in 4 acres of beautiful sub-tropical gardens facing the sea. Recommended by Ashley Courtenay, Egon Ronay, Michelin English Tourist and BHCA.

● All bedrooms with private bathroom and toilet en suite ● Heated Outdoor Swimming Pool ● Heated Indoor Swimming Pool ● Tennis Court ● 18 Hole Putting Green ● Exercise Room ● Croquet Lawn ● Games Room ● Golf and Fishing nearby ● Jaccuzi ● Sauna ● Solarium ● A la Carte Restaurant ● Private Beach Huts ● Colour TV, Radio, Telephone in all bedrooms ● Tea/Coffee Makers in all bedrooms ● Children Welcome ● Central Heating ● 2 Lifts to all floors ● Cocktail Bar ● Car Park ● Pets Welcome ● Baby Listening Service ● Christmas Entertainment Programme ● Winter Bargain Breaks available

Falmouth (Cornwall)

GOING PLACES SERIES

The *RAC Going Places* series offers a unique compilation of motor
and walking tours. Each book is written by an author who is on 'home
ground'. These modestly priced guides describe the topography,
history, flora and fauna of each area, together with details of places
of interest and motor tours and relevant maps. (See pages 37-8)

1. Southeast England
2. Scotland
3. West Country
4. Southwest England
5. Northwest England
6. Southern England

7. Home Counties
8. East Anglia and Essex
9. Central England
10. East Midlands
11. Wales
12. Northeast England

Meudon Hotel

Nr. Falmouth, Cornwall TR11 5HT

Experience a traditional English Country House holiday in a luxury hotel set amidst exotic flowering shrubs, in 8½ acres of superb sub-tropical gardens, originally laid out in the 18th century by 'Capability' Brown.

Owned and run by a family who care deeply about hospitality, good food, wine and service, Meudon offers English cuisine at its best, with the emphasis strongly on fresh sea food.

Service is unobtrusive, individual and attentive, with first class facilities, including 3 lounges, a cocktail bar and a glass terraced restaurant.

Telephone or write now for our colour brochure 0326 250541.

Felixstowe (Suffolk)

Grasmere (Cumbria)

Grasmere (Cumbria)

THE GRASMERE HOTEL
AA ★★ & RAC ★★
BRITISH HOTELS RESTAURANTS & CATERERS ASSOC. MEMBER

**GRASMERE,
near AMBLESIDE,
CUMBRIA, LA22 9TA**

Telephone: Reception 09665 277

A small privately-owned licensed hotel set in the midst of beautiful mountain scenery on the edge of the village in its own grounds with garden leading down to the River Rothay. There are 12 bedrooms (two ground floor), majority with private facilities, a lounge with colour television and a separate bar with log fire. The restaurant has unsurpassable views of the surrounding hills and garden. Vegetarians especially catered for. There is also ample car parking space.
Colour Brochure on request.
Resident Proprietors: Ian and Annette Mansie

Great Yarmouth (Norfolk)

Carlton Hotel

Marine Parade
Great Yarmouth
Norfolk NR30 3JE
Tel: 0493 55234

A Mount Charlotte Hotel

Gt. Yarmouth's premier hotel, overlooking sea. Luxury suites, 100 bedrooms with colour TV, Radio, telephone, 24 hour room service, Windsor restaurant, Bars, Lounges.

RAC MOTORISTS' DIARY
The motoring diary that is better by miles.
(See pages 37-8)

Gwithian (Cornwall)

RAC ** **GLENCOE HOUSE HOTEL** ** AA

Gwithian (St. Ives Bay), Nr. Hayle, Cornwall TR27 5BX

Tel: (0736) 752216

Small hotel, 11 bedrooms all with bathroom/WC or Shower/WC, Colour TV and Tea/Coffee maker en suite. Full central heating. Heated indoor swimming pool. Four-Poster Bed. Recommended licensed hotel facing rolling open countryside with access to scenic cliff walks, Gwithian Beach and sand dunes from the rear of hotel. National Trust and two 18-hole Golf Courses nearby. Good food with extensive menu. Relaxed informal atmosphere for a few guests only.

SPRING into SUMMER Bargain Breaks

Tariff includes:

Bedroom with en suite facilities		
Colour TV & Tea/Coffee maker	ANY 2 DAYS ..	**£46.00**
Choice of Dinner from extensive menu	ANY 5 DAYS ..	**£110.00**
Full English Breakfast		
VAT at 15%	ANY 7 DAYS ..	**£147.00**

Harlow (Essex)

Motorway from the North and South

The Harlow Moat House is situated on the A414 one mile from junction 7 of the M11 motorway.

M11–M25 links with the dual carriageway to the M1 North

M11–M25 via Dartford Tunnel South

120 bedrooms – Restaurant and Bar – Residents' Bar
Meeting Rooms for 200 delegates
Parking for 200 vehicles

HARLOW MOAT HOUSE

THE SIGN OF COURTESY

Southern Way, Harlow, Essex
Tel: 0279 22441   Telex: 81658

515

Harrogate (North Yorkshire)

Cheltenham Lodge Hotel

Cheltenham Parade, Harrogate, North Yorkshire HG1 1DB
Telephone (0423) 55041

A Warm Welcome Assured at our Family Run Hotel

- All rooms Colour TV & Radio
- 'En Suite' Rooms available
- Bargain Breaks

- Tea/Coffee making facilities
- 'A La Carte' Licensed Restaurant
- Major Credit Cards accepted

PRODUCE THIS ADVERTISEMENT FOR 5% DISCOUNT

Harrogate (North Yorkshire)

"GILLMORE"
98 KING'S ROAD,
HARROGATE,
NORTH YORKSHIRE HG1 5HH
Tel: 503699 and 57122
Proprietors: Mr. & Mrs. Gill

20 Bedroomed, Centrally Heated Family Run Hotel. Convenient Town/Conference Centre. Colour Television Lounge. Bar seats 50. Car Park. Enjoy hospitality of Giovanna and Norman.

Harrogate (Yorkshire)

SCOTIA HOUSE HOTEL

66 Kings Road, Harrogate, Yorks.   Tel: (0423) 504361

Small fully licensed Guest House. Centrally heated. Majority of rooms with private shower and colour TV. Pleasing decor. Conveniently placed for the busy conference/exhibition attender opposite new Conference Centre. Prices from £9 per person nightly.

Hastings (Sussex)

Eagle House Hotel

12 PEVENSEY ROAD, ST. LEONARDS,
HASTINGS, EAST SUSSEX, TN38 0JZ.
Telephone: (0424) 430535

Licensed hotel in own grounds. Car Park. Near sea front. Rooms with private toilets and showers. TV in all bedrooms. Teamaking facilities. Open all year.

CAR DRIVING FOR BEGINNERS

Is someone in your family learning to drive?
Car Driving For Beginners is written for novice drivers. In plain and non-technical English, this handy-sized paperback helps the learner to acquire that indefinable skill known as 'road sense'.
(See pages 37-8)

RAC

Hawkhurst (Kent)

Helmsley (North Yorkshire)

Hereford (Herefordshire)

Hereford (Herefordshire)

The Pilgrim Hotel

Much Birch, Hereford HR2 8HJ
Golden Valley (0981) 540742
- Country House in 4 acres of parkland
- All bedrooms ensuite with country views
- Weekend Breaks from £26.50 Dinner, Bed & Breakfast
  - RAC *** AA, Egon Ronay, Ashley Courtenay

High Wycombe (Buckinghamshire)

Clifton Lodge Hotel
210 West Wycombe Road,
High Wycombe, Bucks.
Tel: 0494 40095 or 29062

Ideally located for the Chilterns, Oxford, Cotswolds and Heathrow Airport. Approx. 1 mile from A40 London-Oxford motorway.
Family run hotel, licensed, T.V. in every room plus large car park and gardens. Also dining room and snacks served on request. *AA and RAC Listed.*

High Wycombe (Buckinghamshire)

Drake Court Hotel
141 London Road
High Wycombe
Bucks HP11 1BT
Telephone: 0494 23639

This friendly commercial hotel is on the A40, 'twixt Oxford and London, convenient for the M40, M4, Heathrow, Windsor and the Thames Valley and Chiltern Hills.

Ilford (Essex)

THE CRANBROOK HOTEL

24 COVENTRY ROAD, ILFORD, ESSEX   Telephone: 01-554 6544 or 554 4765

Licensed Restaurant. Most rooms with bathrooms, telephones and Colour TVs. 2 mins to Shopping Centre. 20 mins. by train to London.

Enquiries concerning advertisements in the 1986 edition should be sent to:

kingslea press limited

International Publishers' Representatives
Official Advertisement Representatives to The Royal Automobile Club
18/19 Ludgate Hill, Birmingham B3 1DW.
Tel: 021-236 8112. Telex: 338024 Bircom-G Kingslea
RAC Guide and Handbook
RAC Continental Motoring Guide

Ilfracombe (Devonshire)

Sandy Cove Hotel

THE SEA FOOD HOTEL

Combe Martin Bay, Berrynarbor, Nr. Ilfracombe, Devon. Tel: (0271-88) 2243

RAC** An Interplan Hotel

How would you like to arrive for a week's holiday at a hotel overlooking a beautiful bay, the sea and Exmoor? The first thing you would notice would be the acres of gardens and woods running down to the cliff edge, and the heated swimming pool set in its midst. A warm bath then dinner in the restaurant, a la carte including Caribbean and lobster dishes, a speciality is extra but the table d'hote is excellent. The hot carvery and Swedish Smorgasbord on a Saturday will wet your lips and the barbecues and country and western cabaret – first class (in the height of the season). Dance on a Saturday night until midnight, use the heated outdoor pool, putting green, games room, fitness room with gymnasium equipment, sauna and sun bed to your likes. Or relax in the 'Crows Nest' secluded cliff-top Summer House overlooking the bay and the sea. CHILDREN ARE VERY WELCOME AND AT CERTAIN TIMES OF THE YEAR THEY HAVE ABSOLUTELY **FREE** ACCOMMODATION PROVIDING THEY SHARE THEIR PARENTS' ROOM – YOU JUST PAY FOR THEIR MEALS. We are also happy if you bring your pets with you. Baby sitting can be arranged. Invalids catered for. Open all the year – Christmas and mini weekend breaks a speciality. Some 4 poster bedrooms for romantic honeymoons.

33 bedrooms, 17 Private Bathrooms. Fully Licensed. Combe Martin 1 mile, Ilfracombe 4 miles.
Please write or ring for free colour brochure to:
Dawn & Richard Gilson, Dept. (19), Sandy Cove Hotel, Combe Martin Bay, Berrynarbor, Nr. Ilfracombe, N. Devon

Ilkley (Yorkshire)

GREYSTONES HOTEL

1 Ben Rhydding Road, Ilkley, Yorkshire.   Tel: Ilkley 607408
10 bedrooms, 5 private bathroom. 3 private shower room. 1 general bathroom. Dogs allowed. Private car park 15. BB from £17. DB from £22. BK £3.50. Dinner £8.00 LD 8.45 p.m. WB alc mc Tourist Centre CC 1235.

Isles of Scilly

THE COMPLETE LEARNER DRIVER

You may be learning the rudiments of the knack of driving. Perhaps you have been behind the wheel since before the DoT test came into being. Or are you the average motorist?
Improve your driving skills by reading *The Complete Learner Driver*. (See pages 37-8)

RAC

Sandown (Isle of Wight)

Chester Lodge Private Hotel
BEACHFIELD ROAD, SANDOWN, I.W.   Telephone: 0983 402773

A detached residence situated in an ideal position in the best part of Sandown, just minutes to shops and sea, facing sea and level elevation, within easy reach to all parts, five minutes to Shanklin, easy access to Cliff Walk and the delightful Ferncliff Gardens.
The Hotel is tastefully furnished and decorated with large attractive lounge facing sea with part sun lounge. Also Television & Bar Lounge. Comfort is first consideration, equipped with modern furniture, all beds have spring interior mattresses and hot and cold water is installed in every room. Shaving plugs in bedrooms. Fitted carpets. Heating throughout. Car parking for 15 cars.
Separate tables and pleasant dining room which overlooks sea and gardens. Terms from £72.45 inc VAT at 15%.
The Service and Cuisine is personally executed to ensure satisfaction by the proprietors, Mr & Mrs Hayward.

Shanklin (Isle of Wight)

Totland Bay (Isle of Wight)

Ventnor (Isle of Wight)

Ventnor (Isle of Wight)

Kenilworth (Warwickshire)

Nightingales Hotel & Restaurant
95 Warwick Road, Kenilworth, Warwickshire CV8 1MP
A modest hotel managed by the owners, specialising in "Home Cooked" food. Rooms from £12.00.
Dinner from £6.50.

Kidderminster (Worcestershire)

RAC★★★★ **Stone Manor Hotel** ★★★★AA

KIDDERMINSTER   .   WORCESTERSHIRE
Tel: Chaddesley Corbett (056283) 555/6/7. Telex No. 335661

Stone Manor stands in its own 25 acres of well appointed gardens, with tennis court and outdoor swimming pool, offering a high standard of service and accommodation. 23 luxurious bedrooms all with bathroom, shower, hairdryer, tea making facilities, colour TV, radio and telephone.

The French Restaurant is fully air conditioned and offers a full à la carte menu with many specialities cooked at your table.

The banqueting facilities comprise 3 suites having seating capacity for dinner dances of 250/150/90 respectively plus small rooms for private dinner parties or meetings.

Car parking facilities for over 400 cars.   Stone Manor is privately owned.

Kingston-on-Thames (Surrey)

Self Catering Holiday Flats
Licensed Restaurant open
to Non-Residents
Caterers for Functions
Suites with private bathrooms
Free parking

HOTEL **ANTOINETTE**
OF KINGSTON

26 Beaufort Road, Kingston upon Thames, Surrey KT1 2TQ
Telephone: Reception: 01-546 1044
Telex: 928180

Lee (Devonshire)

WE ARE OPEN ALL YEAR ROUND

Lee Bay Hotel

Lee, Nr. Ilfracombe, North Devon EX34 8LP
Resident Proprietors: Paul & Sheila Prankerd

Just write or telephone Telephone: 0271 63503

This superbly situated 50 bedroomed Hotel, bordering on to the sea, surrounded by National Trust Land, must be one of the most luxurious, comfortable, and friendly Hotels in the West Country. All bedrooms have en suite bathroom facilities. Cuisine is beyond reproach. The Hotel is set in 35 acres of ground and offers Golf, Shooting-clays and game, Fishing, Riding, Windsurfing, Sauna, Solarium, Jacuzzi, Croquet lawn, Putting green, Childrens adventure playground, Outdoor heated swimming pool, Table tennis, Snooker/billiards, Childrens club, Laundry facilities,

Leeming Bar (Yorkshire)

AA*   **The White Rose Hotel**   RAC*
Leeming Bar, Northallerton, N. Yorkshire. Tel: 0677/22707/22097
Situated on A684 in village, ½ mile from A1 Motorway
FULLY LICENSED RESTAURANT – CAR PARKING
12 Bedrooms · Full Central Heating · En Suite Facilities
Colour TV · Radio/Roomcall

523

London E18

London N4

London NW2

London NW6

London NW11

London NW11

Lynton (N Devon)

Valley House Hotel
Lynbridge Road
Lynton, N Devon
Telephone Lynton
(05985) 2285
Visitors 3549

Early Victorian Country House Hotel in own grounds, situated off the B3234 in the West Lyn Valley, superb sea and Exmoor views. Full breakfast, mouth watering dinners, TV lounge, cosy well stocked bar.
Open all the year, off season breaks. French and German spoken.
Resident Proprietors: Brenda, Dennis and Peter Spiers
Visa card

Melksham (Wiltshire)

CONIGRE FARM HOTEL

Semington Road Melksham Wilts
tel (0225) 702229

Beautifully Restored Farmhouse
Privately Owned . Highly Personalised.

- Nine bedrooms with 5 en-suite and honeymoon suite.

- All rooms have colour TV, telephone and beverage facilities.

- Own grounds — private car park.

- Full mini-conference and seminar facilities.

- Features Mr. Bumble's Restaurant (open to non-residents).

Mevagissey (Cornwall)

VALLEY PARK PRIVATE HOTEL

Valley Park, Mevagissey, Cornwall PL26 6RS   Tel: 0726 842347
We are a small clean friendly family run, licensed hotel with ample public rooms. Car park. Gardens. 1 min level walk to harbour. Ideal centre for touring Cornwall.

Middleton-in-Teesdale (Durham)

THE TEESDALE HOTEL
Middleton-in-Teesdale DL12 0QG
Telephone: (STD 0833) 40264
Proprietors: Mr. & Mrs. D. Streit, FCFA

To our minds, Middleton-in-Teesdale has a receptive feeling of isolation. It is an attractive place, situated in the narrowing valley of Teesdale, which cannot seem to choose whether it wants to be a town or a village. At the head of the main street, jut before it divides and beings to climb more steeply, stands the stone-built mullion-windowed Teesdale Hotel. A coaching inn in former years, it has recently become a comfortable hotel under the ownership of Mr. & Mrs. D. P. J. Streit, whose daughter, Benita, acts as resident manager. Drive through the narrow archway and park, open the door into the hall and you will immediately feel the warmth and light of this tastefully modernised inn. Though it was early June there was a nip in the air and the coal fire, in a long low stone fireplace, was very welcoming. So, too, was our lunch of home-made soup and fish. We soon began to feel on top of the world — but then in Middleton you very nearly are! The hotel must make a perfect base for exploring the moors, hills and dales of Durham and North Yorkshire, and so as to entreat you to linger it offers a number of modernly appointed bedrooms, each tailor-made for comfort. As we left we made a mental note. 'We must go back to Teesdale'.

Morecambe (Lancashire)

MIDLAND HOTEL
Marine Road West, Morecambe LA4 4BZ.   Tel: 0524 417180
The outstanding 3 star Hotel with its unique position on the promenade has all the facilities to make your stay a memorable one. All the 46 bedrooms are equipped with private facilities, radio, telephone, colour television, and tea and coffee making equipment.

Newquay (Cornwall)

ATLANTIC HOTEL

RAC   AA   NHA

★

**CORNWALL'S
LEADING
HOTEL**

★

Telephone:
2244/5 (2 lines) Management.
3092 Visitors.

Magnificently situated on the Headland, 80 rooms, most with private bath and all with phone, radio, intercom, and baby listening service. The Hotel is fully centrally heated in public rooms and bedrooms. Sea views from every window. Excellent surfing and bathing from Hotel. Heated indoor and outdoor swimming pools, sauna baths and solarium. New Spa Bath and Fitness Room. SQUASH COURTS. Fully licensed Cocktail Bar and Lounge. Dancing nightly in season. Excellent Cuisine. Children's Play Corner. Nearby 18-hole Golf Course. Every modern comfort. Colour Television and billiards room. Lift. Garages, including lock-ups. SUN LOUNGE. Open Easter to September inclusive. Special early and late season terms.

Resident Props: Mr & Mrs W.J. Pascoe.

Newquay (Cornwall)

AA
★★★

RAC
★★★

BARROWFIELD HOTEL

**Hilgrove Road, Newquay, Cornwall TR7 2QY
Tel: Newquay 06373 2560 or 71434**

A warm welcome awaits you at the Barrowfield Hotel, where you will be afforded every comfort.

Relax in the comfort of our Cocktail Bar or Reception Lounds, or enjoy an evening's entertainment in the luxuriously furnished ballroom with top star cabaret.

For the energetically minded there is a fully equipped games room including full size pool table, table tennis and keep fit equipment. Afterwards, relax in our heated 90deg thermal spa bath, or make use of one of two saunas or four solarium.

All rooms have colour TV, tea making, hair dryer, radio/intercom and luxury bathroom en suite.

Superb outdoor heated pool, floodlit at night and Coffee Bar, open most of the day. Roof garden and gymnasium.

Resident Proprietors: Tony & Josie Cobley

* Ashley Courtenary & Michelin recommended

Norwich (Norfolk)

Grey Gables

**NORWICH ROAD, CAWSTON,
NORWICH NR10 4EY Tel: 0603 871259**
*Country House-Restaurant and accommodation, 10
miles north of Norwich. Former Rectory in pleasant
rural setting, convenient for Norwich, Broads and
coast. Comfortably furnished whilst retaining its
character. Excellent licensed dining room with
traditionally prepared food, fresh fruit and vegetables.
Good wine cellar. Gourmet menu available. Bedrooms
with private bathroom and colour TV. Full central
heating and open log fires.*
Children under 10 sharing parents room
accommodated free of charge, excluding July and
August. Free use of bicycles.

Oxford (Oxfordshire)

The Belfry

**Milton Common
OXFORD
Tel: Great Milton 08446 381
Telex: 837968**

42 bedrooms (36 with bath), all with colour TV, radio, telephone, tea/coffee maker.
Parking 200 cars. 45 minutes' London and Heathrow.
Privately-owned hotel situated at exit 7 of M40, specialising in conferences, weekend
holidays, good food, comfort.

RAC MOTORISTS' DIARY

The motoring diary that is better by miles.
(See pages 37-8)

Oxford (Oxfordshire)

TILBURY LODGE

TEL. (0865) 862138

*Tilbury Lodge is situated in a quiet country
lane just two miles west of the city centre, one
mile from the railway station and two miles
from Farmoor reservoir with its trout fishing
and sailing opportunities.
Good bus service available.
Botley shopping centre is a few minutes walk
away with restaurants, shops, launderette,
banks, etc.*

Central heating
Some rooms en suite
Ample parking
Children made welcome
Tea and coffee made free on request

TILBURY LODGE, 5 TILBURY LANE,
EYNSHAM ROAD, BOTLEY,
OXFORD OX2 9NB

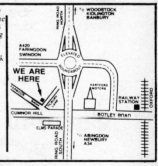

Oxford (Oxfordshire)

Westgate
Private Hotel

Traditional English breakfast. Car park at rear. Credit cards accepted.

1 Botley Road, Oxford OX2 0AA
Tel: 0865 726721
Ideally located for City Centre and University areas,
minutes away from coaches and railway. Colour TV
and radio in every room. Tea/coffee making facilities.

Oxford (Oxfordshire)

Westwood Hotel
Hinksey Hill, Oxford

Mr and Mrs Parker wish to provide a warm welcome, and comfortable accommodation with excellent food awaits the discerning visitor. The lounge and Restaurant and residential licensed bar and Restaurant opens out into 3½ acres of beautiful gardens and woodlands. Ideal for honeymooners and all demanding a peaceful rest.

All 17 bedrooms have private facilities along with radio-intercom Colour TV and Tea and Coffee facilities. Whilst our delux and honeymoon rooms also have a hairdryer and trouser press. During the Summer months, weather permitting, a BBQ is held usually on Tuesdays and Thursdays. Lunches are available to residents if required. Evening meals are available from 7–8pm Monday to Saturday and 6.30–7.00pm on Sundays (Winter only). BBQs are at 6.30pm.

Amenities close at hand include golf, horse riding and boating. Brochure available on request with further details. Tel: Oxford (0865) 735408.

At second roundabout arriving from town centre take the second exit marked FARRINGDON or WOOTON, then at top of hill bear left. Hotel is 100 yards on right. From the A34 North, turn off at the MAIDENHEAD sign A423. From the A34 South turn off at the first sign for Oxford then the first exit off of roundabout up Hinksey Hill.
Proprietors: Mrs & Mrs Parker

Padstow (Cornwall)

Green Waves Hotel
(W. R. Chellew, W. B. G. Chellew)

Trevone Bay, Padstow
Cornwall PL28 8RD

A.A. & R.A.C.
LISTED
Telephone :
Visitors
Padstow 520568
Management
Padstow 520114

Beach 100 yards; 23 bedrooms some ensuite; all with H&C; Separate tables; Residential licence; Colour TV; Lock up garages and car space; SAE for Brochure
Terms: *Dinner, Bed & Breakfast from £66 (excluding VAT)*
Under supervision of resident proprietors: Brian and Margaret Chellow
TEL: Padstow (0841) 520114
Ashley Courtenay Recommended

Padstow (Cornwall)

The Old Custom House Inn

South Quay, Padstow, Cornwall
Telephone: Padstow 532359

14 Bedrooms all with private bathrooms, sea and harbour views, central heating, colour television, tea and coffee making facilities. Restaurant, open to non-residents. Breakfast, bar meals & dinner available.

531

532

533

Rotherham (South Yorkshire)

THE CARLTON PARK HOTEL

Moorgate Road, Rotherham, South Yorkshire S60 2BG.   Tel: (0709) 64902

Modern 62 bedroom hotel with conference facilities, restaurant and theme bar. Situated in a residential area yet close to the M1.

St Agnes (Cornwall)

Penkerris Penwinnick Rd (B3277) St. Agnes, Cornwall
Tel: (087-255) 2262

Attractive detached house on outskirts of village (fields round garden). Bedrooms have TV and electric kettles. 2 bathrooms and public shower room. Convenient for beaches of Chapel Porth (National Trust) and Trevaunance Cove. Glorious cliff walks. Good touring centre.

Scarborough (Yorkshire)

HOLBECK HALL HOTEL

Magnificent country house hotel in superb clifftop position, first class cuisine served in our seaview restaurant. All rooms have private bathroom, colour TV, radio and telephone many with panoramic sea views. Conference and party bookings welcome. *FREE* car parking for over 50 cars.

Manager: Peter Temple, M.B.I.M.
Telephone: 0723 374374

Scarborough (Yorkshire)

SOUTHLANDS HOTEL

West Street, Scarborough, North Yorkshire YO11 2QW. Tel: (0723) 61461

Situate on the South Cliff ● Rooms have Private Facilities, Colour TV,
Tea-Making Tray ● Close Proximity to Sea, Golf, Tennis, Swimming,
Town ● Private Car Park

Seahouses (Northumberland)

Bamburgh Castle Hotel

Seahouses, Northumberland
Telephone: Seahouses 720283

FULLY LICENSED RESIDENTIAL HOTEL   OPEN TO NON-RESIDENTS AND FOR PRIVATE FUNCTIONS
The Hotel is beautifully situated above the harbour, with uninterrupted views of the Farne Islands.
Near shops, bus route, glorious stretches of sand and golf course.
All bedrooms H & C. Central heating.

Settle (Yorkshire)

Close House

Giggleswick, Settle,
Yorkshire BD24 0EA
Tel: Settle (07292) 3540

Charming farmhouse dating from 1676. 230 acre farm. Beautifully furnished antiques. High standard of cooking. Residential and table licence. BTA commendations. No children or dogs.

Bessie T. Hargreaves

Sevenoaks (Kent)

EMMA HOTEL

LONDON ROAD, SEVENOAKS, KENT
Tel: (0732) 73681

* 40 rooms all en-suite – central heating – colour TV – telephone – radio
* 2 VIP & Bridal Suites – fully licensed bars – full restaurant facilities
* Large car park
* Specialists in weddings – conferences – banqueting all with private bar
* Competitive prices
* Close to M25-A21
* Sister Emma Hotel, Boxley Road, Maidstone (0622) 677523 (ditto facilities)

Good value – competitively priced

Shrewsbury (Shropshire)

Take a break in the heart of England

Situated deep in the Heart of England, in the beautiful town of Shrewsbury, the Radbrook Hall Hotel and Leisure Centre offers the visitors a superb combination of business and leisure facilities.
Radbrook Hall is now one of Shropshire's leading hotels renowned for its excellent service and friendly atmosphere. Set in its own beautifully cultivated gardens the Hotel has 48 bedrooms all of which have either a private bathroom, or shower, and WC en suite. Each room has its own colour TV, radio and television.
Fully licensed, there are three banqueting halls seating 350, 140 and 50 persons for dinner. A dinner dance is held every Saturday.
Our extensive leisure facilities include:
● 6 International Squash Courts ● Indoor & Crown Green Bowling ● Games Room, Table Tennis, Pool, Billiards ● Aerobics ● Sauna, Jacuzzi-style Spa ● Sunbeds ● Horse Riding, Shooting and Golf nearby. ● Ample Car Parking.
JUST OFF THE A5 ON THE A488.

Radbrook Hall Hotel
& LEISURE CENTRE

RAC ★★★   AA ★★★
Radbrook Road Shrewsbury Shropshire
Tel (0743) 4861 or 241591/2/3

535

Sidmouth (Devon)

Sidmouth (Devonshire)

Sidmouth (Devonshire)

THE VICTORIA HOTEL

A luxury hotel
set in 5 acres overlooking glorious Sidmouth Bay

The unspoilt beauty of South Devon's most exclusive resort can be enjoyed to the full at the Victoria. Enchanting elevated gardens command inspiring views of the sands and superb coastline. Luxurious surroundings reflect a long tradition of excellence in cuisine and personal service. All the amenities that you would expect of one of England's finest hotels are at your disposal - including superb **indoor pool, sauna, solarium, hairdressing, games room, heated outdoor pool, lido and bar, private beach terrace, tennis, putting etc.. Private bath and colour T.V. with video link in every room.** Full entertainment programme. Excellent golf, fishing and riding nearby. For details of exceptional value low season breaks and reduced weekly tariff for families please contact - **R.G.Smith, Victoria Hotel RAC★★★★, Sidmouth, Devon EX10 8RY Telephone (03955) 2651.**

SIDMOUTH

Southampton (Hampshire)

Claremont

Open all year
Near the city centre
* Bed–Breakfast
* Central heating
* Colour TV lounge
* Car parking
**33-35 The Polygon,
Southampton**
Telephone: 23112 or 225334
Proprietress: Mrs. J. Jenkins

Southsea (Hampshire)

Stafford (Staffordshire)

Steyning (Sussex)

Stonehouse (Gloucestershire)

Torquay (Devon)

THE DEVONSHIRE HOTEL

Park Hill Road, Torquay, South Devon TQ1 2DY   RAC★★★
Tel: (STD 0803) 24850
Telex: 42712

Privately owned and situated in quiet garden setting of great charm – 'away from it all' – yet close to the harbour, beaches walk, entertainment and shopping centre. The ideal all seasons holiday hotel. Outdoor swimming pool (heated May-October). Spacious restaurant. Dancing in high season, excellent cuisine and extensive wine list. Large free car park. Own hard tennis court and games room. 69 well-equipped bedrooms (including 12 in a new annexe within the hotel grounds), majority with bathroom en suite, all with colour TV, radio and intercom, some on ground floor. Licensed lounge bar, colour TV lounge. Central heating throughout. Friendly service, midweek bookings accepted. Colour brochure and tariff on request.

THE PRINCES HOTEL

Park Hill Road, Torquay, South Devon TQ1 2DU   RAC★★★
Tel: (STD 0803) 25678
Telex: 42712

The Hotel enjoys a fine and secluded central position looking directly out over the sparkling blue waters of Torbay.
The former resident of the Earl of Cork and Orrery, carefully modernised and extended within private grounds.
● Outdoor heated swimming pool (heated May-October ● Delightful sun terrace with beautiful views of Torbay ● Majority of rooms with sea views ● Entertainment for all ages in season ● Ample free car parking ● Mid-week bookings ● Radio and intercom child listening service ● Colour television lounge ● Cocktail bar overlooking the bay ● 60 bedrooms, many with private bath en suite, well equipped.
Colour Brochure and Tariff from Resident Manager

Torquay (Devonshire)

The GRAND Hotel

RAC ★★★★

Sea Front, TORQUAY, South Devon.
Tel: (0803) 25234 Telex: 42891.

Enjoying one of the finest positions being just a few yards from the sea, **The Grand Hotel** provides a holiday for people with taste. Traditional elegance with high class standards of food and service. Comfortable & relaxing luxury, swimming pool, sauna, beauty salon, entertainment and leisure facilities. Everything you would expect from a premier 4-Star Hotel.

★ Free accommodation for children sharing with parents.

★ Conferences and Banquets specially catered for.

★ Low priced 'off-season' short stay packages.

★ OPEN ALL YEAR ROUND.

magnificent coastal view from the Hotel.

RAC CONTINENTAL MOTORING GUIDE

Taking the car abroad?
Find out about driving regulations, motorways, speed limits, accident or breakdown routines, and insurance requirements in the *RAC Continental Motoring Guide*. At £2.95 (for members) an indispensable companion for motoring in 22 countries. Contains a directory of RAC appointed Continental hotels. (See pages 37-8)

RAC

Torquay (Devon)

MAPLETON HOTEL

**St Luke's Road North
Torquay TQ2 5PD**

Nine bedroomed, friendly family hotel set in quiet tree-lined area, private parking, minutes from beach and shops. Excellent cuisine, licensed, fire certificate held.

Resident Proprietors: Brian and Muriel Varley

Tel: 0803 22389

Torquay (Devon)

AA RAC RSAC
★ ★ ★

Ashley Courtenay
Recommended

T.H.A.
RECOMMENDED

Hotel

Croft Road, Torquay, Devon
TQ2 5UD, England.
Tel: (0803) 28457/8 *or* 22745

In Torquay's finest position, central for everywhere. South facing with panoramic views across Torbay.

All bedrooms with private Bathroom/Shower and Toilet, Colour Television, Radio and Tea/Coffee facilities. Some with private balconies.

Completely modernised to offer an exceptionally high standard of luxurious living throughout the year.

Bars, Snooker, Billiards, Games Room and all-weather Tennis Courts, also a superb "FLOODLIT HEATED INDOOR SWIMMING POOL".

Two hundred-and-fifty yards from the Sea Front and only five minutes walk to Town Centre.

"If you care to choose,
We choose to care."

Brochure and Tariff forwarded with pleasure on request.

Torquay (Devonshire)

★ ★ RAC   ★ ★ AA

Complementing the delightful position of the hotel is the spacious and beautifully decorated and furnished interior. A modern, extremely comfortable hotel with a fine reputation for hospitality, impeccable service and appetising food.

Local facilities include golf, tennis, bowling, theatres, cinemas, gardens and the shopping centre of Torquay.

Tel: Torquay 38456.
Guests Torquay 38023

MAGNIFICENT SEA VIEWS....

Norcliffe Hotel
SEA FRONT BABBACOMBE DOWNS

Torquay (Devonshire)

Torquay (Devon)

Torquay (Devonshire)

WOODHAYE HOTEL

R A C

Old Torwood Road, Torquay, TQ1 1PP. Tel: Reception (0803) 26046 Guests (0803) 23982

Situated near Inner Harbour and town centre. Own secluded gardens. Forty modern bedrooms. Full central heating. Excellent food and attractive menus. Superb lounges, Sun terrace, restaurant, QE2 bar, Rooms en-suite. All rooms have tea-making facilities with ingredients supplied. Live Entertainment. Colour TV. Car park.

Colour Brochure with pleasure from: Roy and Rhona Foley

Tuxford (Nottinghamshire)

Newcastle Arms Hotel
Market Place
Tuxford
Notts NG22 0LA
Tuxford (0777) 870208

Situated in rural Nottinghamshire yet less than 2 minutes from the A1. This charming 17th century coachouse offers splendid accommodation for the businessman & tourist, with easy access to local tourist areas.

*• Conference & Board room facilities • fully licensed with 2 a la carte restaurants • AA/RAC * * • Egon Ronay used • spacious car parking.*

Ulverston (Cumbria)

Lonsdale House Hotel (Ulverston) Ltd.
Daltongate, Ulverston
23 bedrooms all with TV video playback machine, and most rooms with private bath or shower. Special rates for weekends. For further information please telephone 0229 52598.

𝕻addington 𝕳ouse 𝕳otel

MANCHESTER ROAD, WARRINGTON
Nearest Hotel to M6 – Junction 21.
Famous for Fresh and Finest Food.

BATCH FARM
COUNTRY HOTEL
Lympsham, Nr. Weston-super-Mare, Avon
Tel: Edingworth (093-472) 371
Proprietors: Mr. and Mrs. D. J. Brown

MEMBER OF

LICENSED BAR

● Charming old Country House open Easter to October ● Situated midway between resorts of Weston and Burnham-on-Sea. 3 miles sea and sands. Ideal centre for touring ● Guests have freedom of 150-acre working farm and good coarse fishing in River Axe running through our own grounds ● Carefully modernised accommodation. All bedrooms have H & C and shaver points. Some bedrooms en suite. Fitted carpets throughout ● Dining room, separate tables. Large lounge with colour TV, also lounge bar ● Large games room with table tennis etc for children ● Excellent home cooking, dinner, room and breakfast ● Please enclose stamp for coloured brochure and terms.

Weston-Super-Mare (Avon)

Weston-super-Mare (Avon)

Wilmslow (Cheshire)

Wilmslow (Cheshire)

Windsor (Berkshire)

Winsford (Somersetshire)

Woody Bay (Devonshire)

Woolacombe (Devonshire)

Workington (Cumbria)

York (Yorkshire)

Disraelis Hotel & Restaurant
140 ACOMB ROAD, YORK

RAC ***   Tel: 0904 781181   AA **

10 Bedroom luxury hotel set in beautiful grounds. All rooms with tea/coffee making facilities, television, telephone, most with en suite facilities. Ample car parking. Extensive a-la-carte restaurant. Bar snacks served lunch and evening. Ideally situated for businessman and tourist.

York (Yorkshire)

FAIRFIELD MANOR HOTEL
Shipton Road, Skelton, York YO3 6XW.
Tel: York 25621

An early Georgian mansion, fully restored to its former beauty. Original carved oak panelling, marble fireplaces and moulded ceilings with crystal chandeliers; all discreetly combined in the centrally heated comfort of modern hotelcraft. Superb cuisine, elegant relaxation, country walks in the private parkland, the thoroughbred tradition of northern hospitality.
There are 24 bedrooms, all with private bathrooms or shower-rooms, colour television, radio, telephone and tea-making facilities.

York (Yorkshire)

GREEN VIEW GUEST HOUSE
5 Clifton Green, York, North Yorkshire. Tel: 21964
Small family run guest house. TV all rooms. Close to City centre. Fully central heated. Ample car parking. Full Fire Certificate.
Personal attention of Maureen Bond.

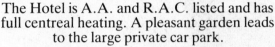

Connel (Argyll)

Dingwall (Ross-shire)

Dornoch (Sutherland)

Dumfries (Dumfriesshire)

Fort William (Scotland)

Few hotels in the Highlands are custom built but those built at the end of the last century contain their own unique and unforgettable atmosphere. Built in 1898 on a position enjoying panoramic views over Fort William and Loch Linnhe, the Highland Hotel is the ideal base from which to explore this area known as 'The Best of the Highlands'.

Send for colour brochure and details of our Ben Nevis Gold and Silver Holidays.

Fort William Highland Hotel THE BEST OF THE HIGHLANDS

Fort William PH33 6QY Tel: (0397) 2291

Fort William (Inverness-shire)

** AA **NEVIS BANK HOTEL** ** RAC

Belford Road, Fort William

Tel: (0397) 2595

Nevis Bank Hotel is a privately owned hotel situated on the eastern side of the town 10 minutes walk from the Main Street & Travel Centre and at the foot of the access road to Ben Nevis, Britain's highest mountain. The hotel is famous for its home cooking and comfortable surroundings. Cabaret in Ceilidh Bar most weekends throughout the year.

RAC MOTORISTS' DIARY

The motoring diary that is better by miles.
(See pages 37-8)

Gatehouse of Fleet (Kirkcudbrightshire)

LUNCHES
EVENING MEALS
UNTIL 8.45 pm
CHILDREN WELCOME

ANGEL HOTEL
GATEHOUSE OF FLEET
Props: Norie & Irene Moir
Phone: (055 74) 204

FULLY LICENSED
RESIDENTIAL

Gatehouse-of-Fleet (Dumfries & Galloway)

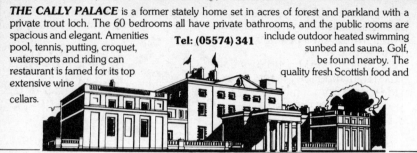

THE CALLY PALACE is a former stately home set in acres of forest and parkland with a private trout loch. The 60 bedrooms all have private bathrooms, and the public rooms are spacious and elegant. Amenities **Tel: (05574) 341** include outdoor heated swimming pool, tennis, putting, croquet, sunbed and sauna. Golf, watersports and riding can be found nearby. The restaurant is famed for its top quality fresh Scottish food and extensive wine cellars.

RAC NAVIGATOR SERIES

The *RAC Navigator* series offers you more than just another road atlas. Each book is a unique guide to town and country combining regional and local 4 colour maps. Regional leisure maps highlight castles and ancient monuments, zoos and wildlife parks, steam railways and military museums, gardens and countryside of outstanding natural beauty, historic houses, art galleries and much more besides. The main local maps, at a scale of 1.6 miles to the inch, and town plans give a wealth of detail to anyone interested in exploring. (See pages 37-8)

1. South, Southeast, Thames and Chilterns, London.
2. The West Country, South Wales, Bristol and Cardiff.
3. East and West Midlands
4. Northern England.

Glasgow (Lanarkshire)

The Macdonald Thistle Hotel

Eastwood Toll, Giffnock, Renfrewshire G46 6RA. Tel: 041-638 2225 Telex: 779138 ***

One of the Thistle Hotel group's well-located Scottish hotels, just a few miles from the centre of Glasgow and yet convenient for Kilmarnock, Paisley and Prestwick. Facilities include 58 tastefully decorated bedrooms with private bathroom, an excellent restaurant and a choice of bars, as well as conference and meeting facilities for up to 220 people.

For Reservations at Thistle Hotels throughout Britain telephone: 01-937 8033

THISTLE HOTELS

Gretna (Dumfrieshire)

Annan Road Gretna	**SURRONE HOUSE**	Tel: 046 13 341

Open all year for Farmhouse Bed and Breakfast and Evening Meal.
All rooms with TV/Radio and private Bathroom. TV Lounge.
Fully centrally heated.

Inverness (Inverness-shire)

Kingsmills Hotel

INVERNESS ★ ★ ★
the hotel you always look for
but seldom find . . .

. . . a superb country hotel in town!

Set in four acres of woodland gardens one mile south of the centre of Inverness, adjacent to the Golf Course. Private Squash Courts and parking for 100 cars. 54 beautifully appointed bedrooms all have private bathrooms (many with showers), colour T.V., and direct dial telephone. Six two-bedroomed service suites just a few steps from the main building are ideal for families.

We offer rare comfort, fine food and wines, convivial company and friendly, personal attention. Privately owned and cared for by Angus and Lilian Macleod, who with their staff look forward to the pleasure of welcoming you.

Please write for brochure and tariff to:—

Kingsmills Hotel, Culcabock Road, Inverness.
Telephone: (0463) 237166   Telex: 75566

Irvine (Ayrshire)

ROSEHOLM, ANNICK WATER, IRVINE AYRSHIRE, SCOTLAND.
Telephone: 0294 74272   Telex: 777097

(Formerly the Skean Dhu Hotel)

The hotel complex is easily reached from Prestwick Airport (15 minutes), Glasgow Airport (25 minutes) or Glasgow Central Station by a short train journey through Ayrshire Countryside. The Hotel offers guests a wide selection of accommodation all to the highest standard, including suites, with lounge, two double beds and direct access to lagoon. Studio rooms, with two single beds overlooking the Hotel's nine-hole Golf Course. All rooms have both bath and shower en-suite, colour television, coffee/tea making facilities, electric alarm, telephone, writing desk and full central heating. The design of the Hotel affords a concept of spacious luxury throughout. Banquet and conference facilities within the Hotel make the Irvine Skean Dhu an ideal venue for executive functions, while at the Hawiian Lagoon a braunch and an American Style menu are served throughout the day, late into the evening.
Irvine is located on the Ayrshire coast and within the immediate vicinity boasts some eight golf courses, including Troon. Sailing windsurfing, fishing, curling, a large sports complex, theatre and covered shopping mall all are close to hand.

Kelso (Roxburghshire)

Cross Keys Hotel
36-37 The Square, Kelso, Roxburghshire TD5 7HL
Tel: (0573) 23303–23304–24152

The hotel majestically overlooks the unique French style square of Kelso. The hotel is one of Scotland's oldest coaching inns _ now completely and tastefully modernised.
● Restaurant   ● Whipmans Bar
● Cocktail Bar   ● Coffee Mill

Kirkcudbright (Dumfries & Galloway)

Selkirk Arms Hotel *Kirkcudbright, Galloway*
Telephone: (0557) 30402

Where Robert Burns wrote *The Selkirk Grace*
David and Esther Armstrong, newly resident proprietors, extend a specially warm welcome to visitors. The Hotel is situated in the beautiful artist's town or Kirkcudbright in the heart of spectacular Galloway and just five minutes   walk from the harbour.
Ideal for family touring holidays as well as for activities including golf, sailing, riding and bird watching. Sea angling, fishing and shooting available during season.
26 bedrooms – Large secluded garden.
Morning coffee, luncheons and dinners provided daily. Hot bar meals and sandwiches available at lunch time in both bars. Regular garden barbeques.
Access, Visa, American Express and Diners Club credit cards welcome. *Please write for your free colour leaflet or for further information and reservations telephone Kirkcudbright (0557) 30402.*
AA** RAC** Ashley Courtenay recommended.

Largs (Ayrshire)

Lockerbie (Dumfriesshire)

SCOTLAND

Lockerbie (Dumfriesshire)

TAKE A BREAK:

GOING NORTH?
GOING SOUTH?
* IDEAL OVERNIGHT STOP
*300 YARDS FROM A74
Under the personal supervision of the proprietors:
Alex & Margaret Janes

Somerton House Hotel

● Bar
● Restaurant
● Lounge

Carlisle Road, Lockerbie, Dumfries-shire DG11 2DR

RAC** Telephone: Lockerbie (057 62) 2583 AA**

Nairn (Nairnshire)

AA★★★ RAC★★★

The Windsor Hotel

Albert Street, Nairn, Scotland
Telephone: Nairn 53108. *Visitors* 53315
Modernised 3 Star, Family Hotel, 60 bedrooms, all containing bathroom or shower suite, and all with colour T.V., intercom, baby listening service, radio, private phone and video.
Emphasis on good food and personal attention!
New air conditioned restaurant with extensive A la Carte menu including tender steaks and outstanding seafood specialities.
Five course Table d'hote Dinner, Steak Suppers — High Teas — Bar Lunches — Lunches — Afternoon Teas.
Weekend special Breaks — family rooms. Sandy beach, Golf, Bowling, Fishing etc.
Special Christmas & Hogmanay Programme!
Come along to the Windsor Hotel for that well deserved break at one of the better hotels in the North of Scotland.
Brochures on Request *Tel; NAIRN 53108 for further information*

Newton Stewart (Galloway)

KIRROUGHTREE HOTEL

**Newton Stewart
Galloway, SW Scotland
Tel: 0671-2141
AA***RAC
AA Rosette**

Luxury and Finest Cuisine – Plus Free Golf at Two Courses

Kirroughtree Hotel has been completely refurbished and is now one of Britain's most luxurious Country House Hotels. Bedrooms are exquisitely furnished in every detail, with coloured bathroom suites, colour TV etc., including the 4 honeymoon/wedding anniversary suites. Two beautiful dining rooms, one for non-smokers and elegant public rooms with period furnishings. **OUR NEW CHEF WAS, UNTIL HE JOINED US, HEAD CHEF AT INVERLOCHY CASTLE FOR 6 YEARS. HE WAS RECENTLY MADE A MASTER CHEF OF GREAT BRITAIN BY THE MASTER CHEFS INSTITUTE, AND YOU WILL EXPERIENCE MEMORABLE DINNER EVENINGS.** Eight acres of landscaped gardens with beautiful views and Putting, Bowling, Tennis, etc. One of the mildest climates in Britain because of the Gulf Stream. You will be accorded attentive service in a very friendly and relaxing atmosphere. Please send for colour brochure.

565

Stonehaven (Kincardineshire)

Strathblane (Stirlingshire)

Tarbert (Argyll)

Abersoch (Gwynedd)

Glyn Garth Hotel

Mini Weekends
or Mid Week Breaks

SMALL FAMILY RUN HOTEL WITH FIRST CLASS RESTAURANT

LLANBEDROG
Nr. ABERSOCH,
GWYNEDD
Tel: 740 268 (STD 0758)

North Wales
Tourism Council
Cyngor Croeso'r
Gogledd
Member

MINOTEL

Betws-y-Coed (Gwynedd)

Fairy Glen Hotel
AA RAC *

Dolgellau Road, Betws-y-Coed, Gwynedd.
Telephone: (06902) 269 or (0492) 641 463

The 300 year old hotel is peacefully situated in a
wooded valley overlooking the River Conway. Ten
bedrooms all with central heating, Tea/Coffee
facilities (most with private bath).

Personal attention; renowned cuisine, licensed;
open all year. Mini Breaks.

Ideal situation for touring North Wales by car or
by foot; golf, fishing, pony riding, etc. all available
locally.

Brecon (Powys)

The hotel incorporated within the castle.
The Castle Hotel will appeal to you whatever
your reason to visit Brecon.
Privately owned, with views across the Usk
Valley and the Brecon Beacons. Comfortable
lounges and bars, superb restaurant. 32
bedrooms most en-suite. Open all year.
RAC 2 Star.

Castle of Brecon Hotel

The Avenue, Brecon, Powys. Tel: 0874 5004/2551

Builth Wells (Powys)

LION HOTEL

2 Broad Street, Builth Wells, Powys
Tel: 0982 55 3670

*Overlooking River Wye, 16 letting rooms 12
with private bath or shower. TV Lounge,
Dining Room seating 135. Terms: min Bed
and Breakfast from £12 per person per night
+ VAT. Dinner Bed and Breakfast from
£18.00. Car park space for 14 cars.*

Conwy (Gwynedd)

Castle Bank Hotel

MOUNT PLEASANT, CONWY LL32 8NY

AA ** RAC
Ashley Courtenay
Recommended

Delightfully situated overlooking Conwy and surrounding countryside. Nine bedrooms all with shower and toilet, tea-making facilities, colour T.V. and a hair-dryer. Ample parking.

Write of phone for brochure – CONWY 3888

Criccieth (Gwynedd)

The Glyn-y-Coed Hotel
RAC & AA Listed

Family run hotel overlooking esplanade and facing due south. Cosy bar, separate tables in dining room, home cooking. Moderate terms with good reductions for children sharing family rooms. Bedrooms have hot/cold, tea/coffee making facilities, shaver points.

Private parking, fire certificate issued. Member of Wales Tourist Board, Criccieth Tourist Board, North Wales Tourism Council.

Fishing, riding, golf all available locally.

Brochure with pleasure SAE please to
Mrs. Ann Reynolds
Glyn-y-Coed Hotel,
Portmadoc Rd.,
Criccieth, Gwynedd.
Tel: 2870

Glyn Garth (Anglesey, Gwynedd)

THE GAZELLE HOTEL
** * RAC**
Glyn Garth, Menai Bridge, Anglesey
Your Hosts: Kenneth and Barbara Moulton

13 comfortable bedrooms each with TV and tea/coffee making facilities. Weddings and parties catered for. Ample car parking. **Tel: (0248) 713364**

Haverfordwest (Dyfed)

Pembroke House Hotel
** ** HAVERFORDWEST, WALES

● Private bathrooms ● Colour TV
● Telephone ● Car Park
● Cuisine du Gourmet
● Special 2 days break £38 per person
● Holiday Studios for Families

TELEPHONE: 0437 3652

CHEZ GILBERT RESTAURANT

Llanbedr (Gwynedd)

TŶ MAWR HOTEL
LLANBEDR, GWYNEDD
034 123 440

Tŷ Mawr is a fully licensed country house situated in Snowdonia National Park near the mountains and sea. We have ten bedrooms, most with bathrooms en-suite, tea and coffee making facilities and colour TV. Tastefully furnished and set in a lovely garden. Real Ale and excellent food served in the Bar or Restaurant, with open fires and central heating to ensure a warm and friendly stay.

Llandudno (Gwynedd)

ESPLANDADE HOTEL

**Glan-y-Mor Parade,
Promenade, Llandudno**
Telephone: (0492) 74343 (5 lines)

Premier seafront position. Ideally located for town and leisure facilities. Brochure and tariff on request from resident manager.
60 comfortable rooms. Fully Licensed. Most rooms with bathroom and toilet en-suite, direct dial telephones, tea and coffee making facilities. All bedrooms with colour TV, radio, intercom, and baby listening service. Central heating in Public Rooms and bedrooms. Car Park at rear. Colour TV Lounge. Two resident lounges, lift. Cocktail bar and small ballroom for special occasions. Golf facilities available to residents. Open all year. Xmas and New Year inclusive terms available – conferences – parties. Spring and Autumn breaks.

Llandudno (Gwynedd)

***

IMPERIAL
Hotel
LLANDUDNO

Brochure with pleasure from:
MR. G. R. LOFTHOUSE.

This imposing Victorian style hotel having recently undergone extensive refurbishment, occupies a central promenade position, and is within 2 mins walking distance of the town centre. Each of its 140 bedrooms is equipped with radio, telephone, tea/coffee making facilities and colour T.V., the majority are en suite. Centrally heated with lifts to all floors. Private parking. Entertainment most evenings in season. Three bars and disco. Sauna, Solarium and exercise room. Resident beauty therapist. Excellent cuisine, excellent value, friendly service.

IMPERIAL HOTEL, THE PROMENADE, LLANDUDNO, GWYNEDD.   Tel: (0492) 77466   Telex: 61606

GOING PLACES — WALES

How well do you know Wales?
You will find plenty of new ideas about days out, places of interest to visit and motor tours in Wales in *'Going Places' Wales.*
This guide is one of a series of twelve, each written by an author who is an acknowledged authority on his area.
(See pages 37-8)

Llandudno (Gwynedd)

★ ★

Clement Avenue, Llandudno
Gwynedd, LL30 2ED

Detached Hotel of Character in central situation, 71 bedrooms all with Bath/Shower, WC, Colour TV, Tea/Coffee Making Facilities, Radio/Intercom etc. Full Central Heating, Ballroom, Games Room, Heated Indoor SWIMMING POOL with Sauna, Jacuzzi, Solarium. Parking. Fully Licensed.
Mini and Maxi Breaks October to April. Open all the year.
FULL 4 day Xmas Programme.

Full information and colour brochure, please ring or write:
'Risboro Hotel', Llandudno. Tel. STD 0492 76343. *Proprietors:* L. M. & B. Irving.

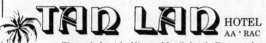

Neath (Glamorganshire)

Cimla Court Motel

AA ★ ★   RAC ★ ★

Member: Wales Tourist Board and B.H.R.A.

**Upper Cimla Road, Neath, West Glamorgan SA11 3TT
Telephone: 3771 and 2639**

Full à la Carte and Table d'Hote Menus · Luncheons and
Dinners served daily · All bedrooms with Radio/Intercom
and private bath facilities, all with Colour TV · Dance
every Saturday night · Private Car Park (100 cars) · Golf
Courses within 1 mile · Fishing (fresh water and sea)
within easy reach · Public Swimming Baths · Buildings of
Historic interest · Motel is ideally situated for easy
access to coast and countryside · Bird Gardens 1 mile

Penarth (South Glamorgan)

Glendale Hotel

10 PLYMOUTH ROAD, PENARTH CF6 2DH. Tel: (0222) 706701/708302

Fully Licensed. Weddings and Parties catered for.   **AA ** RAC**

Overlooking Alexandra Park, near beach and cliffs. 20 bedrooms, en-
suite with colour TV and video line. Cocktail Bar, Dining Room, 2
Lounges, Conference Room. Centrally Heated. Parking Facilities.

RAC MOTORISTS' DIARY

The motoring diary that is better by miles.
(See pages 37-8)

RAC

Rhayader (Powys)

ELAN VALLEY HOTEL

Nr Rhayader, Powys, Mid Wales. Tel: 0597 810448
Country Hotel near Elan Valley Lakes. Open all year. Special Winter Breaks. Visited by
H. M. Queen Elizabeth II. Free Trout Fishing for Residents.
Ashley Courtenay recommended

Rhos on Sea (Clwyd)

**66 Abbey Road, Rhos-on-Sea,
Colwyn Bay (Tel: 44256)**
Proprietors: Mr. & Mrs. W. H. Hanson

SUNNY DOWNS *PRIVATE HOTEL*

AA &
RAC Listed

● Bed & Breakfast & Evening Meal ● Bed & Breakfast
● Party Bookings ● Free Parking ● Fire Certificate
● Open All Year

Centrally situated in a quiet area between Colwyn Bay and
Llandudno, this attractive family run hotel is renowned for its
comfort, cleanliness and cuisine. There are a selection of single,
double and family rooms with some having their own facilities.
The hotel is fully central heated throughout, and has a fully
licensed restaurant, a comfortable lounge with colour TV and an
attractive bar lounge. Free car parking is provided for guests. 3
minutes stroll on level ground to the marine drive and the sea. The
Sunny Downs offers complete relaxation at a highly recommended
hotel. Tea making facilities in all rooms. For a brochure please
telephone or write to us.

St Clears (Dyfed)

BLACK LION HOTEL

St Clears, Dyfed.   *Telephone:* St Clears 230700

Small friendly hotel situated in quiet market town. Gateway to West Wales. Alongside A40 to
Fishguard and Pembroke. Easy access to many beaches and countryside.

St. Davids (Dyfed)

THE WHITESANDS BAY HOTEL

RAC *** AA

Above magnificent Whitesand Bay,
Nr. St. David's, Dyfed.
Tel: 0437 720403

The most Westerly hotel in Wales — situated quite on its own some two miles west of St. Davids on the headland overlooking magnificent Whitesand Bay and St. Davids Head.
The restaurant and most of the bedrooms afford panoramic views of the sea and offshore islands. Two clifftop houses provide additional accommodation in an idyllic setting.
A good reputation established over twenty years for cuisine, comfort, service and peace.
Heated outdoor pool, sauna, solarium, coffee shop. Fully licensed.
Adjacent to golf course and coastal path. Nearby sailing, riding, fishing and boat trips.
A choice of accommodation at varying price. Comprehensive colour brochure available on request.

Saundersfoot (Dyfed)

CLAREMONT HOTEL

St. Brides Hill, Saundersfoot, Nr. Tenby,
South West Wales, SA69 9NP.

Tel: (0834) 813231   Res: (0834) 812385
(South Wales Tour Council)

A private family-run hotel. AA & RAC listed. Residential licence. Excellent standard of accommodation, food, wine and service. Choice of menu. Use of heated swimming pool. Plus entertainment in season. Separate dining tables. Full Central heating. Colour TV lounge and bar lounge. Children welcome with large reductions. Sorry no pets. Ample free parking. Two minutes to beach and shops. All bedrooms with radios, bedlights, shaver points, wash basins, baby listening and Teasmades. Some rooms with private shower/WC, some with colour TV's available. Special Easter and Mini Holidays available.

For full details in illustrated colour brochure, phone or write to resident proprietors: Pauline and Brian Hooper.

Saundersfoot (Dyfed)

Saundersfoot (Dyfed)

Beaumont (Jersey, Channel Islands)

HOTEL L'HERMITAGE

BEAUMONT, JERSEY. C.I.
Tel: Office 33314; Visitors 22723 (STD 0534)

Ideally situated in extensive grounds, and only 3 minutes walk from the beach. The Hotel is centrally heated throughout, and all bedrooms have bathrooms en suite, radio and colour television, also tea and coffee making facilities. There is a heated swimming pool plus a new heated indoor swimming pool and sauna baths, and the large car park can accommodate 100 cars.

Dancing and Cabaret plus other entertainment 4 nights weekly.

St. Brelades Bay (Jersey, Channel Islands)

THERE ARE FEW HOTELS LIKE L'HORIZON IN THE WORLD. LET ALONE JERSEY.

Hotel L'Horizon is one of Britain's most prestigious hotels.

It is perfectly positioned, right at the water's edge of beautiful St. Brelade's Bay. Our rooms are luxurious by any standard, most with sun and sea facing balconies; all with TV, video, radio and direct dial telephone facility.

Our restaurant with resident orchestra is popular throughout the Island (no small boast in Jersey where people know and enjoy their food). We have three bars, the Star Grill, an indoor pool, a sauna, beauty parlour – the list is longer than we can print here. And the really nice part is, you can stay here whenever you like, Spring, Summer, Autumn, Winter. Send for our brochure.

Hotel L'Horizon
ONE OF BRITAIN'S PRESTIGE HOTELS

St. Brelade's Bay, Jersey CI.
Tel: (0534) 43101 (10 lines). Telex: 4192281

St. Peter Port (Guernsey, Channel Islands)

GRANGE LODGE HOTEL
THE GRANGE, ST. PETER PORT, GUERNSEY.   Tel: 25161

Open mid-Jan to 1st December ● Licensed Bar ● T.V. Lounge ● Large Garden
5 minutes to Centre of Town ● Ample Parking

St. Saviours (Guernsey, Channel Islands)

LA GIROUETTE
COUNTRY HOUSE HOTEL
(Licenced)
ST. SAVIOURS, GUERNSEY

One of Guernsey's leading small hotels with a
reputation for the high quality of its fare and
accommodation. Sheltered wooded gardens,
yet only a few minutes walk to the sea. An
ideal base for you to stay in Guernsey. Open
for most of the year round.

Write or Telephone (0481) 63269

Castel (Guernsey, Channel Islands)

Hotel Hougue du Pommier
CASTEL, GUERNSEY. Tel: 56531/2 53904 (0481)

This 1712 Farmhouse now transformed into an elegant 3 star Hotel, which stands in its own 10 acres of ground, with a solar heated swimming pool, 18 hole putting green, 18 hole pitch and putt golf course offers pleasure and relaxation. Enjoy our famous Carvery luncheons in our Tudor Bar or superb Dining Room. An à la Carte candlelit dinner in this renowned Farm House Restaurant with its extensive wine menu is a must. We are looking forward to welcoming you here in Guernsey.

Carrickfergus (Co. Antrim) — *Northern Ireland*

COAST ROAD HOTEL
28 Scotch Quarter, Carrickfergus.   Tel: 09603 61021

Comfortable hotel with 20 bedrooms, all with teasmade and telephones, some with private bathroom & colour TV. Golf, fishing, boating, leisure/sports centre and Carrickfergus Castle all nearby. New restaurant overlooking Belfast Lock.

Cushendall (Co. Antrim) — *Northern Ireland*

AA   RAC
THORNLEA HOTEL
Cushendall, Co. Antrim, N.I.   'Phone: 71223/71403

Situated in the heart of the beautiful Glens of Antrim and within convenient distance of boats and planes.

Fully Licensed   *Write for Brochure*

Caravan and Camping Sites

FUN AND FREEDOM HOLIDAYS FOR <u>ALL</u> THE FAMILY

Whatever your age or interests, there's a whole world of action and relaxation in a Village Holiday, with facilities that include:-

- Children's Adventure Playground and entertainments. BMX track.
- Licensed Clubhouse, Teen's Disco.
- 2 heated pools, indoor and outdoor.
- Solarium, sauna, gym, crazy golf.
- Launderette, General Store and Barbecue, Cafeteria and Takeaway.
- Horse riding, Pony Trekking, stables, bike hire, plus fishing nearby.

(Some facilities available only at peak times).

The ideal, all-weather, all-year-round holiday for mum, dad and the kids! The Village comprises a 55 acre, well equipped caravan/camping site in beautiful forest surroundings only 8 miles from Bournemouth.

- Pre-bookable touring and tent pitches.
- 'Super Plots' with plug-in mains electricity and water.
- Static holiday homes for sale.
- 6 and 8 berth luxury caravans for hire.

FANTASTIC OFF-PEAK BARGAINS Ask for details!

Village Holidays

£50 FREE entertainment voucher is available only on static holiday bookings.

I enclose S.A.E. for full details ☐
'Off-Peak' Bargains ☐ Please Tick

Name _____

Address _____

_____

Village Holidays at Oakdene Holiday Park, Dept. St. Leonards, Ringwood, Hants BH24 2RZ.
24 hr Tele-brochure service: **0202 875422.**

Village Holidays
nr. Bournemouth

Approved by AA, RAC, Camping Club of Gt. Britain.

Abersystwyth (Dyfed) _____ *Wales*

CARDIGAN BAY

ABERYSTWYTH HOLIDAY VILLAGE LTD
Penparcau Road, Aberystwyth, Dyfed.   Tel: (0970) 4211

Camping and Caravanning at its best. Set in 6 acres of the beautiful Rheidol Valley, conveniently situated for touring 10 minutes from ABERYSTWYTH centre, offering all necessary amenities, including free hot and cold showers. Outdoor heated swimming pool, night club, snack bar, shop, laundry, sauna on site. Children's amusements. *Send SAE for colour brochure.*

★ AA   RAC ★

PENGARREG CAMPING AND CARAVANNING CENTRE
LLANRHYSTUD NEAR ABERYSTWYTH.   Tel: (09748) 247

Camping and Caravanning at its very best. Caravan – 4-8 berth – for hire. Superb facilities. Situated on the sea front. Coastal road A487. *Send SAE for colour brochure.*

Appleby (Cumbria) _____

RAC Appointed   ## WILD ROSE PARK   A A

ORMSIDE, APPLEBY-IN-WESTMORLAND, CUMBRIA (Appleby (0930) 51077)

AA TRAIL – Northern Campsite of the Year 1981 and 1984. Highest possible AA Quality Awards. Member of 'Best of British' Caravan & Camping Parks Association.

Midway between English Lakes and Yorkshire Dales in the glorious unspoilt Eden Valley, this SPOTLESSLY CLEAN, FAMILY PARK offers a VERY WARM WELCOME to tourers and campers. Heated swimming pool and paddling pool, play areas, mains electricity, fly fishing. Beautiful unspoilt country 3 miles off A66; 12 miles off M6 (J38).
All main statics for sale. No letting. Brochure with pleasure.

586

Chudleigh (Devonshire)

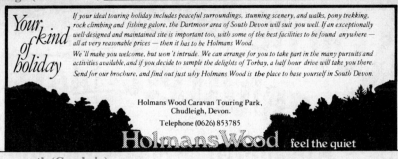
Cockermouth (Cumbria)

Croyde (N. Devon)

Devizes (Wiltshire)

POTTERNE CARAVAN PARK

POTTERNE, DEVIZES
telephone Devizes 3277

- Off A360. South of Devizes
- Excellent Touring Centre
- Picturesque 30 Pitch Site
- Full Range of Services Including Food Shop

Dinas Dinlle (Caernarfon)

Wales

COASTAL SNOWDONIA

A Tourist Board 'DRAGON' Award Park for High Standard of Accommodation

AA 4 Pennant, RAC, CC, ACSI
By Sea and Mountains

Only 300 yds. from long Sandy Beach
- New Luxury 6/8 berth caravans for hire (some 3 Bedrooms). All with shower, toilet, fridge, colour TV, continental quilts
- Licenced Club House
- Tourers & Campers on level grassland
- Electrical Hook-ups available
- Basket Meals ● Flush Toilets ● Take away food
- Razor Points ● Supermarket
- Childrens play area ● Pets welcome
- Launderette ● Childrens Entertainment Room
Excellent beach for swimming, surfing, canoeing, sailing and fishing. Riding, climbing, golf and many other sporting activities nearby.

For colour brochure – write or telephone: **Rob & Lorna Minors, Dinlle Caravan Park, Dinas Dinlle, Caernarfon. (Tel. 0286 830324)**

Dornoch (Sutherland)

Scotland

Grannie's Heilan Hame, Embo, Sutherland

A most attractive Caravan Park right on the beach. Ideal Highland touring centre in lowest Scottish rainfall area.
COCKTAIL AND LOUNGE BARS **International Rating**
Fully serviced Caravans to let. Golf, playground, entertainment, café, children's television room. Fish and Chicken bar, showers, launderette, site shop, gas, petrol, electric points for tourers.
RAC CARAVAN CLUB 3 STAR CAMPING CLUB
Directors: JOHN and NOEL MACKINTOSH
'Far away in the heilans there stands a wee house . . . by grannie's heilan' hame.'
by kind permission of **Mrs T. M. MacFarlane and Messrs. Mozart Allen.**
AA
Telephone: **Dornoch 810383**
Scottish Tourist Board Thistle Award Park

FOREST CAMPING LEAVES EVERYTHING ELSE IN THE SHADE

Camping in the forest is excitingly different–a whole new outdoor experience! There's so much to do, so much to see. The magic of the forest, fascinating wildlife, nature trails, fishing, pony trekking, birdwatching and lots more.

Forestry Commission camping/caravan sites are located close to major tourist areas, from the West Highlands to the New Forest.

Many are fully equipped with every modern facility–all are maintained to the highest standards.

Phone for full details on 031-334 0303 (or 2576) during office hours.	*For FREE colour brochure and 24 hour ansaphone ring 031-334 0066*

or write to: Forest Holidays (Dept. R.A.C.) 231 Corstorphine Road, EDINBURGH EH12 7AT.

Forestry Commission

MORTONHALL CARAVAN SITE
IN THE BEAUTIFUL CITY OF EDINBURGH

The Caravan Park, by repute one of the best in the UK, is situated within the beautiful parkland of a large private estate only 20 minutes by car from the centre of Edinburgh. The site has every amenity including a well-stocked licensed mini-market, top-class bar with meal service, games room, TV lounge and large well-equipped laundry, and is an ideal base for those wishing to see the historic capital of Scotland, or those on their way north or south.

Write now for free colour brochure and 1985 tariffs to: MORTONHALL CARAVAN PARK, Frogston Road East, Edinburgh EH16 6TJ.

Tel: 031-664 1533

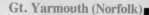

Ilfracombe (Devon)

SUN, SEA AND SAND AT SANDAWAY — DEVON'S LOVELIEST HOLIDAY PARK

Superb coastal scenery, the splendour of Exmoor National Park close by, a private beach and first class amenities — picturesque Combe Martin only ¼ mile away. Ilfracombe a mere ten minutes drive and the whole North Devon coast within easy reach. Our amenities include a licensed Club, Food Bar and occasional live entertainment, Mini-Supermarket, Launderette, Colour TV Lounge, Children's Playroom and fenced Play area. Public Telephone, Heated Swimming Pool. **CARAVANS, CHALETS & CAMPING.**

AA **B** APPOINTMENT **Rose award park**

S.a.e. to Y.H. Taylor,
Sandaway Holiday
Park, Combe Martin Bay,
Berrynarbor, Ilfracombe, Devon.
Tel: Combe Martin 3155

Kirkcowan (Wigtownshire) ——————————————— *Scotland*

THREE LOCHS CARAVAN PARK

Balminnoch, Kirkcowan, Newton Steward, Wigtownshire DG8 0EP   Tel. 067 183 304

We have lochs for: Sailing, Windsurfing, Canoeing. Stocked coarse fishing, river fishing. Children's play areas. Plenty of tranquility for relaxing. Luxury letting caravans, fridge, shower.

Lockerbie (Dumfriesshire) ——————————————— *Scotland*

HODDOM CASTLE CARAVAN PARK

HODDOM CASTLE, LOCKERBIE, DUMFRIESSHIRE.
Telephone: Ecclefechan (05763) 251

Ideal base for touring. Excellent on-site facilities, plus salmon and trout fishing, golf, woodlands, nature trails, and pleasant countryside for those who enjoy walking.

RAC NATIONAL MAPS

Going on a long journey?
These are the maps you need to plan it. *RAC National Maps* clearly illustrate the entire motorway system.
Bold use of colours distinguishes primary routes, main and secondary routes for easy reference. (See pages 37-8)
England and Wales: 10 miles to 1 inch
Scotland: 8 miles to 1 inch
Ireland: 8 miles to 1 inch

RAC

Looe (Cornwall) ———————————————

HISTORIC TRELAWNE ESTATE
Looe, Cornwall

You are assured of a friendly welcome and personal attention at our spacious, top quality Holiday Estate set in the magnificent parkland of a 14th century manor.
We believe we have the largest private well heated pool in SE Cornwall, an extensively equipped kiddies play area, and 5 acres of recreation fields and woodland. We have indoor games rooms and film shows, and during main season we organise sports, swimming galas, football, etc., for the youngsters. Children are welcome with their parents in the ballroom to enjoy live entertainment, cabaret, talent shows, fancy dress etc., all this at no extra charge.
We have comfortable bars, a large shop, also restaurant, cafe and takeaway, coin-op laundry, excellent showers, toilets and washbasins with abundant hot water.
This is an area of outstanding natural beauty, ideal for touring, and we are only 1½ miles from the sea.
Tourer pitches are level, well protected and spacious. Our reasonable charges are "all in" with no extras, regret no tents or dogs. We also have fully serviced caravans and flats for hire.
Free Brochure from Trelawne Holiday Estate, Looe, Cornwall (Dept RAC). Tel: 0503 72151

Looe (Cornwall)

Tel:- Looe (05036) 2425

LOOE, CORNWALL

For all self-catering holidays. Camping, Caravanning, Flats and Chalets. Write or 'phone for free brochure. Tel. LOOE (05036) 2425
Set in lovely countryside on the main A387, midway between Looe and Polperro. Ideally suited either as a touring centre for the South West, or for spending your holiday on the site.
We have all the facilities your family requires for real holiday enjoyment.

☆☆☆☆☆ FIVE STAR FREE FACILITIES FOR EVERYONE ☆☆☆☆☆

- ✿ FREE heated swimming and paddling pools, deck chairs and sun loungers.
- ✿ FREE membership of the TREBLE B Club; live groups in the Ballroom and the BEE HIVE Disco.
- ✿ FREE entry to three colour television lounges.
- ✿ FREE use of barbecue pit and tables, childrens' play areas and large field for games.
- ✿ FREE hot water at sinks and washbasins.

☆ PLUS ☆

All these other facilities are available ON SITE:
★ Late closing self-service store and off licence, ★ Ladies and Gents' hairdressing salon ★ Games Room with Amusement Arcade and Table Tennis ★ Restaurant and Take-Away ★ Launderette and Dryers—open 24 hours a day ★ Battery charging and ice pack service ★ ★ Public Telephones ★ Tarmac roads with street lighting ★ Separate dog exercise areas ★ Electric Hook-Ups for Tourers ★ ★ Crazy Golf – 18 holes.
TRY AN EARLY OR LATE HOLIDAY, (MAY, JUNE OR SEPTEMBER). IT'S MUCH CHEAPER AND QUIETER EVERYWHERE.
★ REMEMBER ★ THE TREBLE B HOLIDAY CENTRE IS SOUTH EAST CORNWALL'S ONLY AA RATED 5 PENNANT SITE.
Rallies are always welcome.   Please contact us for particulars regarding our very attractive rates.
Luxury Farm Cottages also available.   All enquiries to Dept. 21.

Lydney (Gloucestershire)

Clanna Caravan & Camping Park

Alvington, Nr Lydney, Gloucestershire

Open all year. Grassy woodland setting near Wye Valley and Royal Forest of Dean. Licensed bar. Country walks, Modern toilet blocks.
Tel: 059-452 214 *for bookings*

Lymington (Hampshire)

SHOREFIELD HOLIDAY VILLAGE

Shorefield Road, Downton, Lymington, Hants. SO4 0LH.
Telephone: 059 069 2513

Chalets, luxury caravans and touring pitches to let. Site 800 yards beach, heated outdoor pool, club with ballroom and restaurant. 5 miles from the New Forest.

Mablethorpe (Lincolnshire)

GOLDEN SANDS ESTATES LTD.

QUEBEC ROAD, MABLETHORPE, LINCOLNSHIRE.

Self catering holidays in De-Luxe Holiday Homes and Caravans with Mains Services, Free Club Membership, International Cabaret, Swimming Pools, Amusements, Playdrome, Riding, Restaurant and Supermarkets.

Mevagissey (Cornwall)

THE SEA VIEW INTERNATIONAL

Boswinger, Gorran Haven, Mevagissey, Cornwall. Tel: **0726 843425**

1984 "Site of the Year" and English Tourist Board Rose Award.

Level pitches, hookups, swimming pools, sandy beach ½ mile. 4/6 berth caravans for hire.

594

Trekenning Manor Tourist Park
Newquay, Cornwall
A picturesque small park with all the facilities of a large site including swimming pool, licensed bar, electric hook ups, etc. 10 minutes drive Newquay and North Cornwall beaches. Accommodation also available in Manor House. *Write or phone for colour brochure to Mrs J. Tarrant. Tel: St. Columb 0637 880462.*

TRELOY TOURIST PARK

A family run Caravan/Camping Park with heated swimming pool, licensed Club/family room, cafeteria, shop, launderette. Children free May — June.

R. A. Paull, Treloy Tourist Park, Newquay, Cornwall   Tel: 06373 2063

Designed and built by Caravanners for Caravanners

AA – 4 Pennant

RAC – Approved and Recommended

ANWB (Holland) – Recommended

ADAC (Germany) – Listed Site

Camping and Caravanning Club – Recommended

STOVER International Caravan Park

Lower Staple Hill, Newton Abbot, Near Torquay. Tel: (062-682) 446

In the heart of Glorious Devon

Reputed to be one of the most beautiful and luxuriously equipped caravan parks in the UK. Three luxury toilet blocks – fully tiled walls and floors, and heated in the early and late season. H & C to all washbasins. H & C showers – razor points – hair dryers. Two luxury bathrooms complete with bath, shower, washbasin and WC. Three chemical disposal points and facilities for emptying American RVs. Three enclosed rooms with stainless steel sinks and H & C for pots, pans also separate SS sinks and spin dryers for hand washing clothes. Auto. Launderette and ironing facilities, drying room. Emergency accommodation for tenters. Children's adventure playground. 150 electric hook-up points. Facilities for disabled. Bar/lounge. Games room, shop, cafe and take-away. Freezer pack service. Battery charging – dogs admitted but on leash. Caravans – motorhomes – trailer tents – tents all catered for – no caravans or chalets for hire.

Coloured brochure—SAE please

This caravan park has been completely redeveloped during the last three years – it has to be seen to be believed – It's beautiful! Open March to November.

Rosedale Caravan & Camping Park
Rosedale Abbey, Pickering, North Yorkshire YO18 8SA. Tel: 075 15 272

A quiet sprawling site delightfully situated on the edge of the village in the beautiful valley of Rosedale on the banks of the River Severn. Hot and cold showers, flush toilets, laundry room. Well stocked shop and children's play area are available for touring caravans, tents and caravanettes.

Trout fishing is on site, pony trekking, horse riding and mini golf are nearby and we are perfectly situated for a peaceful holiday amidst beautiful countryside, yet an ideal touring centre and only 17 miles from the coast. Open 1st March – 31st October. Enquires welcome. Please send SAE.

GO MOTORING WITH RAC TOURING AIDS

Advance warning triangle, obligatory in most European countries and useful in Britain.
Headlamp beam convertors, a necessity when driving a British car on the Continent.
First aid kit, required by law in parts of Europe.
Plus a variety of other useful extras including tow belts, travellers' adaptors, key rings, sunsitive sunglasses and clip-ons and PVC suit covers.
Available from any RAC Office or by mail order from the Publications Department at Croydon. (See pages 37-8.)

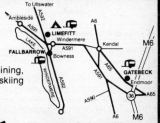

Woodhall Spa (Lincolnshire)

Yarmouth (Isle of Wight)

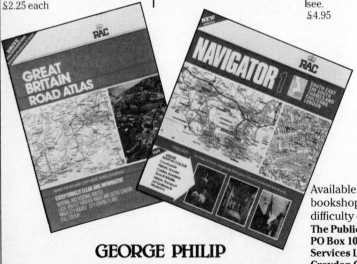

THE MAGIC OF ALTON TOWERS

It's a lot nearer than Disneyland!

Alton Towers is one of the world's great leisure parks.

A world of fun, fantasy and excitement woven into one of the most magnificent settings in England — the former estate of the Earls of Shrewsbury.

There's a stunning array of superb attractions for the whole family, including such famous names as the Corkscrew Rollercoaster, Black Hole, Log Flume, 1001 Nights and International Circus.

More than 70 rides and shows, plus the wonderful gardens, all for the one price.

This is the magic of Alton Towers

M6 signposted from J15, M1 J25, A52 to Ashbourne then signposted. Open every day Easter to October. For details ring (0538) 702200. Alton Towers, Alton, North Staffordshire, ST10 4DB.

Berkeley (Gloucestershire)

BERKELEY 🛡 CASTLE

ENGLAND'S MOST HISTORIC HOME

Built in 1153, the castle stands in a state of perfect preservation. This, the oldest inhabited castle in England, has everything one expects to find in such an historic building.

Here is the massive Norman Keep, Dungeon, Great Hall and Kitchen, and the cell which was the SCENE OF THE MURDER OF KING EDWARD II.

The State Apartments contain a magnificent collection of furniture, rare paintings and tapestries. Part of the world-famous Berkeley silver is also on display. The lovely Elizabethan Terraced Gardens, with an ancient bowling alley, overlook the water-meadows, the Kennels of the Berkeley Hounds and, beyond, the Deer Park with its Red and Fallow Deer. Picnic area adjacent to coach and car parks.

The WILDFOWL TRUST is on the Estate 5 miles from the Castle.

The Castle and Gardens are open to the public: April—Daily (except Mondays) 2-5. May to August—Weekdays (except Mondays) 11-5; Sundays 2-5. September—Daily (except Mondays) 2-5. October—Sundays only 2-4.30. Also Bank Holidays 11-5.

Refreshments and afternoon teas available. Luncheons, to order only, for parties of 20 or more persons. Free Coach and Car Park. Dogs not allowed.

Charge for admission £1.80, OAPs £1.60, Children 90p. Reductions for pre-arranged parties of 25 or over. Special times arranged for organised parties.

For further information apply to the Custodian, Berkeley Castle, Glos. (stamped addressed envelope please). Telephone 0453 810332.

Blackpool (Lancashire)

IT'S FUN ALL THE WAY THROUGH!

Blackpool's your number one holiday high-spot where the fun just goes on and on...

The savings go on with a wealth of superb accommodation at low, low prices.

The stars shine on, night after night, in a host of international entertainment and top-name spectaculars.

The illuminations and Lasers glow on, mile after mile, throughout late summer, in 'The Greatest Free Show on Earth.'

The thrills go on at Blackpool's famous Pleasure Beach with 40 action-packed acres of 'white knuckle' excitement, including the amazing new Ranger and Space Invader.

The family fun goes on with hundreds of attractions like Splashland – a safe, exciting aqua-adventure for children.

And the relaxation goes on with sightseeing, shopping, restaurants, the Zoo, the Tower and Circus, the exciting new fun pubs, fabulous discos and lots, lots more. Blackpool. Where else is so much fun always going on?

Miles of smiles for everyone.

Chester (Cheshire)

SEE CANDLES IN THE MAKING

ENJOY A DAY OUT IN THE HEART OF THE BEAUTIFUL CHESHIRE COUNTRYSIDE

In an area steeped in History, lies Cheshire Workshops, one of the largest manufacturers of hand sculptured candles in Europe. Come along and see for yourself just how this ancient craft has been revived and developed by Cheshire Workshops.

You will be completely absorbed and fascinated watching our craftsmen achieve such intricate detail with their hand carving, hand crafted glass and the making of rustic wood signs. Each item is an individual work of art.

We make every effort to ensure that your visit is enjoyable and memorable.

* HAYLOFT RESTAURANT * CRAFTSHOP
* CHILDRENS PLAY AREA * DEMONSTRATIONS
* FREE ADMISSION * FREE PARKING

COACHES WELCOME - PLEASE BOOK

OPENING HOURS:
WORKSHOPS & CRAFTSHOPS — Every Day including Sunday. 10am - 5pm. Evening Coach Parties by prior booking.
HAYLOFT RESTAURANT DAILY — (inc. Saturday & Sunday). 10am - 4.30pm

For further details on how to find us, please telephone Burwardsley, Near Chester CH3 9PF.
Tel: Tattenhall (0829) 70401

Cheshire Workshops

RURAL ENGLISH EXPERIENCE

Chichester (W Sussex)

CHICHESTER DISTRICT MUSEUM

29 Little London
Chichester
West Sussex PO19 1PB
Tel: Chichester (0243) 784683
Local history, archaeology and geology.
Temporary exhibitions. Museum shop.
Admission free

PALLANT HOUSE GALLERY

9 North Pallant
Chichester
West Sussex PO19 1YA
Tel. Chichester (0243) 774557
Queen Anne residence with restored period rooms, Edwardian Kitchen, collections of paintings, Bow Porcelain and glass.
Admission 50p adults; 30p OAPs, students; 10p accompanied children.

Opening Times: Tuesday - Saturday 10.00-5.30

Chichester (West Sussex)

WEALD & DOWNLAND

OPEN AIR MUSEUM
SINGLETON, NR. CHICHESTER, WEST SUSSEX.

A fascinating collection of rescued buildings from SE England, including Medieval Houses, Farm Buildings, Rural Craft Workshops, a Village School and a working Watermill, reconstructed in a beautiful Downland setting.

OPEN: April 1 – October 31, daily 11 a.m. – 5 p.m.
November 1 – March 31, Weds & Suns only, 11 a.m. – 4 p.m.

Light refreshments available April – October

Tel: Singleton 348

615

London SE1

Macclesfield (Cheshire)

District Of Newark
Past and Present for
Leisure & Pleasure

HISTORIC BUILDINGS
SHERWOOD FOREST
RIVERSIDE WALK

Appletongate Museum

Millgate Folk Museum

Tourist Information Office

Newark 702358

Newark 79403

Newark 78962

617

See the Crystal Glass Makers at

EDINBURGH CRYSTAL

Edinburgh Crystal invites you to their Visitors Centre at Penicuik. Factory Tours are available from 9.00 – 11.15 am and 1.00 – 3.30 pm Monday to Friday (Holidays excepted). Audio visual presentations are also available 9.30 – 11.30 am and 1.00 – 4.00 pm Mondays to

Glasscutting

Glassblowing

Saturdays and evenings on request for booked parties only. There is a small charge for the Factory Tour, while the audio visual presentation is free. It is regretted that children under the age of 10 cannot take the Factory Tour. Our Factory Shop is open to all visitors and provides an opportunity to buy giftware and tableware which is slightly below the normal Edinburgh Crystal quality, while our spacious cafeteria offers a comprehensive selection of light meals and refreshments in a relaxing atmosphere.

Where to find us

PENICUIK

← PEEBLES   A701   EDINBURGH →

EASTFIELD IND. ESTATE

VISITORS CENTRE
EDINBURGH CRYSTAL

EDINBURGH CRYSTAL

For full details of conditions, please contact:-

The Tours Organiser, Edinburgh Crystal, Eastfield, Penicuik, EH26 8HB. Tel: (STD 0968) 75128

GOING PLACES SERIES

The *RAC Going Places* series offers a unique compilation of motor and walking tours. Each book is written by an author who is on 'home ground'. These modestly priced guides describe the topography, history, flora and fauna of each area, together with details of places of interest and motor tours and relevant maps.
(See pages 37-8)

RAC

Wilton House
Nr. SALISBURY, WILTSHIRE

THE HOME OF THE EARL OF PEMBROKE

When you visit Wilton House, the home of the Pembroke family for over 400 years, you will be enchanted by its tranquil splendour and delightful grounds.

The "Pembroke Palace" doll's house, model railway and adventure playground are fun for all the family. Eight superb state rooms, including the magnificent Double Cube Room, in which many of our Kings and Queens have been entertained.

Egon Ronay recommended, fully licensed self service restaurant, open for coffee, lunches and teas, offering excellent value in home made cooking.

Be sure to visit our garden centre, just one minute by car.

619

Visitors-are-welcome
at BNFL Sellafield's Public
Exhibition Centre which is
just off the A595 as it passes
through Calderbridge. Information
Services-staff-are-available-to-answer
your questions on the nuclear industry
and about Sellafield in particular.

The Exhibition Centre is open from 10 am till
4 pm seven days a week from April to September
and during the rest of the year from Monday to
Friday. For further information please ring Seascale
(0940) 27735.

BNFL

British Nuclear Fuels plc

Sellafield Seascale Cumbria CA20 1PG

...Come
& take a stroll
down
memory lane...

YORK Castle
Museum is open
every day from
9.30am - 6.30pm
(Sunday 10.00am -
6.30pm).
October - March
closes at 5.00pm.
Last admission
one hour before
close.

York Castle Museum

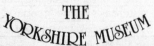

THE
YORKSHIRE MUSEUM

YORKSHIRE MUSEUM

YORKSHIRE MUSEUM GARDENS. YORK (NORTH YORKSHIRE MUSEUM)
Telephone: 0904 29745

Anglo Saxon and Viking life galleries, dinosaurs, Yorkshire Geology, Natural History, Yorkshire Pottery and medieval architectural sculptures.
Special Exhibition (European Award Winner 1983). New Roman life displays planned for Summer 1985.
Museum Shop. Toilets. Access for disabled.
Mary Gate Car Park, York Minster, railway station nearby.
Extensive botanical gardens contain Roman multangular tower and ruins of St. Mary's Abbey. Hospitium and astronomical observatory.
Monday to Saturday 10-5. Sunday 1-5.
Admission charge to Museum as advertised. Gardens free.

Garages and
Service Depots

GO MOTORING WITH RAC TOURING AIDS

Advance warning triangle, obligatory in most European countries and useful in Britain.
Headlamp beam convertors, a necessity when driving a British car on the Continent.
First aid kit, required by law in parts of Europe.
Plus a variety of other useful extras including tow belts, travellers' adaptors, key rings, sunsitive sunglasses and clip-ons and PVC suit covers.
Available from any RAC Office or by mail order from the Publications Department at Croydon. (See pages 37-8.)

Abergele (Clwyd)

Cannock (Staffordshire)

Cheltenham (Gloucestershire)

Croydon (Surrey)

Derby (Derbyshire)

RAINBOW MOTOR SERVICES

Goodsmoor Road, Sinfin. Tel: 766644
and Mount Street, Derby. Tel: 363595

Derby's Premier Service Garage
WHERE THE ACCENT IS ON SERVICE

We are pleased to offer: A comprehensive, fast service and repair facility on all British and Foreign Cars, from a short service to a major overhaul.

CRYPTON TUNING

Body Renovation and Accident Repairs undertaken.
24 Hour Breakdown and Recovery Service.

AN MoT SECOND TO NONE

Come and watch your car MoT'd in our modern workshop, if it should fail we won't charge for a re-test within one week.

Hours: 8.30-6.30 Mon-Fri. 8.30-12.00 Sat. 9.30-12.30 Sun.

Rainbow Motor Services is a family vehicle repair business established in 1971. We offer a first class standard of service and reliability together with competitive rates on commercial and private vehicles.

We are RAC and AA appointed and have a mechanic on call 24 hours a day. Our Goodsmoor Road and Mount Street Garages are open 7 days a week and offer the following services: MoT testing (charged only once), Mechanical repairs and servicing from minor adjustments to major overhauls, 24 hr. recovery, crypton tuning, body repairs, spray painting and windscreen fitting.

We have recently installed £2,500 worth of the most modern paint mixing equipment available, enabling us to mix and match any colour to manufacturers' specifications from basic solid colours through the new base coat and lacquer systems.

We operate a scheme whereby customers prepare their own cars and we will spray them for as little as £50.00.

Our customers are invited to visit our workshops, view work in progress or remain in our reception area where coffee is available.

RAC CONTINENTAL MOTORING GUIDE

Taking the car abroad?
Find out about driving regulations, motorways, speed limits, accident or breakdown routines, and insurance requirements in the *RAC Continental Motoring Guide*. At £2.95 (for members) an indispensable companion for motoring in 22 countries. Contains a directory of RAC appointed Continental hotels. (See pages 37-8)

RAC MOTORISTS' DIARY

The motoring diary that is better by miles.
(See pages 37-8)

Erith (Kent)

MAIN DEALERS

(DARTFORD) LTD.

RENT-A-CAR
RENT-A-VAN

SERVICE & BODYSHOP DIVISION

* 24 hour emergency recovery service
  Tel DARTFORD 25001 or 334999 anytime
* Full range of mechanical and body repairs on all makes of cars and vans with guaranteed repairs.
* Self drive Car, Van & Truck specialists.

Branches at:

Dartford	**Erith**
KT House, The Brent,	Erith Road, North Heath,
Dartford, Kent.	Erith, Kent.
Tel: Dartford (0322) 22171	Tel: Dartford (0322) 338191

CAR DRIVING FOR BEGINNERS

Is someone in your family learning to drive?
Car Driving For Beginners is written for novice drivers. In plain and non-technical English, this handy-sized paperback helps the learner to acquire that indefinable skill known as 'road sense'.
(See pages 37-8)

Halifax (West Yorkshire)

MAYFIELD

MAYFIELD GARAGE (HALIFAX) LTD.

QUEENS ROAD, HALIFAX, WEST YORKSHIRE. Tel: (0422) 67711

ALL MAJOR SERVICES CARRIED OUT ON ANY MAKE OF VEHICLE. LARGE BODY AND PAINT DEPARTMENT. 24 HOUR ACCIDENT RECOVERY SERVICE. TELEPHONE: HALIFAX 56569

Hartley Wintney (Hampshire)

RESCUE
SERVICE

RAVENSCROFT MOTORS

M3 FLEET SERVICE AREA, HARTLEY, WINTNEY, HANTS.
Tel: (Day) Fleet 29661 & 23031, (Night) Fleet 6566
24 HOUR BREAKDOWN AND RECOVERY SERVICE
ALL THE MOTORIST'S NEEDS

RECOVERY

Hayes (Middlesex)

FLYING FROM HEATHROW?

WHY NOT STORE YOUR CAR WITH US AND LET US
CARRY OUT YOUR SERVICING OR REPAIR WHILE
YOU ARE AWAY?

SERVICE SPECIALISTS FOR ALL MAKES. PETROL,
DIESEL, WASH & VALET FACILITIES – ALL
AVAILABLE ON THE PREMISES.

24 HOUR MINI-COACH SERVICE TO AND FROM
HEATHROW TERMINALS.

SEND FOR BROCHURE:

AIRWAYS GARAGE LTD.

242 BATH ROAD, HAYES, MIDDLESEX.
Telephone: 01-759 9661

Enquiries concerning advertisements in the 1986 edition should be sent to:

kingslea press limited

International Publishers' Representatives
Official Advertisement Representatives to The Royal Automobile Club
18/19 Ludgate Hill, Birmingham B3 1DW.
Tel: 021-236 8112. Telex: 338024 Bircom-G Kingslea
RAC Guide and Handbook
RAC Continental Motoring Guide

Helston (Cornwall)

AA

FLORA MOTORS LTD.
Lakeside Garage, Helston,
Cornwall TR13 8OR

Day: Helston 2337/62309
Night: Praze 831485

24 Hour Breakdown Recovery
service and Repairs to all makes of
vehicles. *MOTs*
Tyres and Exhaust Specialists.
Petrol and Diesel. Mobil.
Renault Service Point.

RAC

RAC MOTORISTS' DIARY
The motoring diary that is better by miles.
(See pages 37-8)

Kettering (Northamptonshire)

MEMBERS OF THE
MOTOR AGENTS
ASSOCIATION

OPEN 24 HOURS
FOR ALL SERVICES

PETROL – REPAIRS – ACCIDENT RECOVERY
Cartransporters – any distance

Contact: **CHRYSLER GARAGES (K) LTD**
(Incorporating Kettering Recovery Services)

Bayes Street
Kettering, Northants
Phone: (0536) 512738

RAC MOTORISTS' DIARY

The motoring diary that is better by miles.
(See pages 37-8)

Leeds (West Yorkshire)

THE DRIVING
FORCE
IN YORKSHIRE

RAC approved. Accident and Repair Centre
Paint Shop. Unipart Centre.
The Driving Force in Leeds for
AUSTIN ROVER JAGUAR Daimler

ROLLS ROYCE

Roseville Road, Leeds LS8 5QP. Tel: (0532) 432731

Liverpool (Merseyside)

INTER-CITY RECOVERY
24 HOUR BREAKDOWN SERVICE
Telephone: 051-263 2222

Radio Controlled Vehicles, Roadside and Motorway Assistance, Repairs,
Storage for Accident Damage Vehicles.

M.O.T. Test Centre: Durning Road, Edge Hill,
Liverpool L7 5NB

London SE1

Manchester (Greater Manchester)

Murton (Co. Durham)

Newton Abbot (Devonshire)

Rickmansworth (Hertfordshire)

GOING PLACES SERIES

The *RAC Going Places* series offers a unique compilation of motor and walking tours. Each book is written by an author who is on 'home ground'. These modestly priced guides describe the topography, history, flora and fauna of each area, together with details of places of interest and motor tours and relevant maps. (See pages 37-8)

1. Southeast England
2. Scotland
3. West Country
4. Southwest England
5. Northwest England
6. Southern England

7. Home Counties
8. East Anglia and Essex
9. Central England
10. East Midlands
11. Wales
12. Northeast England

Index